THE WEATHER ALMANAC

THE WEATHER ALMANAC

Edited by

James A. Ruffner

and

Frank E. Bair

SECOND EDITION

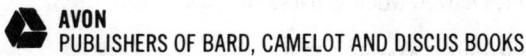

AVON
PUBLISHERS OF BARD, CAMELOT AND DISCUS BOOKS

AVON BOOKS
A division of
The Hearst Corporation
959 Eighth Avenue
New York, New York 10019

Published by arrangement with Gale Research Company.
Library of Congress Catalog Card Number: 73-9342
ISBN: 0-380-43000-2

First Avon Printing, March, 1979

Printed in the U.S.A.

CONTENTS

INTRODUCTION

The person who would be weather wise has information needs that extend from life- and property-saving knowledge of how to prepare for and cope with extreme conditions of storm, temperature, and the like, to mere curiosity about the magnitude of record breaking conditions of the past. More routinely, weather information is needed to help plan daily activities, business or vacation travel, relocation for health or retirement purposes, and countless other actions. Hence *Weather Almanac* provides a wide range of maps, charts, and safety rules based upon past records and experience to inform you (as far as possible in a single volume) of what may be expected from the restless atmosphere. Explanatory narratives of many of the basic processes involved enhance the significance of the various bits of information. *Weather Almanac* is a handy and comprehensive complement to the usual sources of day-to-day weather information in newspaper, radio, and television reports.

In the section on tornadoes, for example, *Weather Almanac* tells you what actions the U.S. Weather Service urges you to take immedately to protect yourself from this most violent of storms. Weather Service scientists also tell you exactly what a tornado is, where and when tornadoes occur most often, their typical duration and distance of travel. This *Weather Almanac* feature also provides tornado statistics and lets you follow selected tornado paths on U.S. maps.

The section on tornadoes is but one of a series of such sections in *Weather Almanac,* edited from official Weather Service pamphlets, to serve as a popular basic reference for severe weather and other extreme conditions. Similar facts are given for hurricanes, blizzards, heat waves, earthquakes, thunderstorms, lightning, floods, and tidal waves. Official records and statistics are included wherever they are useful and available.

Take the time to read the full text portraying each of these severe conditions. It will help you to better adapt yourself and your activities to the weather and let you prepare for a weather emergency at the best time: *before* it is upon you. Even if you must postpone full reading, do try to familiarize yourself with the *scope* of the information and *where* things are located. Then you can return to the book for quick, precise references again and again.

Of course, reference on storms and weather extremes is only one aspect of this book. Helping you to anticipate and understand day-in, day-out weather has been a main purpose in compiling it. *Weather Almanac* offers you a great storehouse of that kind of data, assembled and presented in a form to let you look up detailed facts as you need them.

This information begins with weather and climate data for the country as a whole. It is contained mostly in charts which present the monthly and yearly averages. The charts individually tell key aspects of the weather story for a given observation point, such as Denver, or Mobile, but are brought together on U.S. maps to provide a picture of the entire nation's weather quickly. The charts-on-a-map form lets you compare the range of monthly temperatures in one area against the range in another area. Temperature ranges for each of the twelve months are presented on separate maps. Similar gatherings of charts depict the nation's sunshine picture in area-by-area detail. Other charts tell the precipitation story. To serve the farmer and gardener, a table and maps combine to present freeze data and growing season lengths for various points in the U.S. The table lists the last date for spring frosts in the areas and for first frosts in the fall.

With these nationwide studies providing a background, *Weather Almanac* then gets very specific about the weather in individual cities of the country. Very detailed weather statistics for each city typically include 40 years or more of weather history. An accompanying narrative describes the climate there as a native might tell you about it if the native happened to be a meteorologist, too.

Air quality, while not an aspect of weather, is so weather-related that it belongs in a definitive weather book. *Weather Almanac* therefore includes a section on air pollution. Maps delineate the air quality control regions into which the country has been divided, and the federal "scorecard" on air quality is given for each region.

Weather Almanac also takes you around the world. One compact section gives you facts on temperature, precipitation, etc., for over 550 key cities in every part of the world.

In addition to these major features, sections are provided on weather and health (tips on choosing a retirement climate), obtaining and interpreting marine weather advisories, how to forecast the weather for yourself, and a potpourri of other weather information items.

Sources

Much of the data in this book is quoted directly from reports and records prepared by various U.S. Government departments, agencies and services which share parts of the country's great weather sciences efforts. For example, you will find several sets of safety rules for responding to harsh or unusual weather. These rules have been transcribed word-for-word from National Oceanic and Atmospheric Administration (NOAA) publications. This means the rules were developed by the nation's best informed, most responsible storm analysts, drawing on thousands of observations of damage and injury. Such authoritative suggestions have helped dramatically in minimizing the impact of severe weather, and they merit your fullest confidence.

The city-by-city weather records have the same confidence-worthiness, for they come directly from the cumulative records developed by the U.S. Weather Service observers around the country, and have been coordinated by people of the National Climate Center. The climate narratives were written by the climatologists located in the individual area, so come from first-hand experience as well as carefully-kept records.

New material for second edition

The second edition of *The Weather Almanac* has been made as up to date as possible as a source of statistical weather information and safety rules. The weather records of the 108 selected U.S. cities have been revised to incorporate the *Climatological Normals* for the period 1941-1970 which have become available since preparing the first edition. Weather extremes are current through 1975. Other statistical tables and the safety rules reflect the latest information available in mid 1976. Data on the NOAA Weather Radio Warning Network is also current through mid 1976.

Two aids to planning hot weather activities have been added. Degree day statistics now include *Cooling Degree Days* as well as *Heating Degree Days.* A section on the *Temperature Humidity Index* and its adaption to animals in the *Livestock Safety Index* has also been added.

A major new section on weather principles has been added and the cloud atlas has been revised. A weather glossary is now included. And since many users of *The Weather Almanac* commonly travel by jet aircraft, a section treating the subject of jet-lag or time-zone travel fatigue, with time-zone travel tips, has been prepared.

The section on air pollution has been largely rewritten and now includes an elementary treatment of the weather principles of air pollution episodes along with new information on the progress in the nation's air quality control regions toward meeting the primary, or health related, national ambient air quality standards.

Earthquakes are not a manifestation of the weather, of course, but the need of the general public to be informed about them and the precautions to be taken when and where they occur, and indeed before they occur, warranted a special section in the first edition as a complement to the various weather related hazards and associated safety rules. The earthquake statistics have been brought up to date and their history has been extended significantly.

With the long awaited Alaskan pipeline now a reality, many readers will be interested in the new feature detailing the climatology of the pipeline zone.

The editors hope that this new revised edition will be increasingly useful as a source of basic information about the vagaries of our canopy of air and a variety of environmental hazards.

James A. Ruffner
Frank E. Bair

U.S. WEATHER
IN
ATLAS FORMAT

NORMAL DAILY MAXIMUM, AVERAGE, MINIMUM,

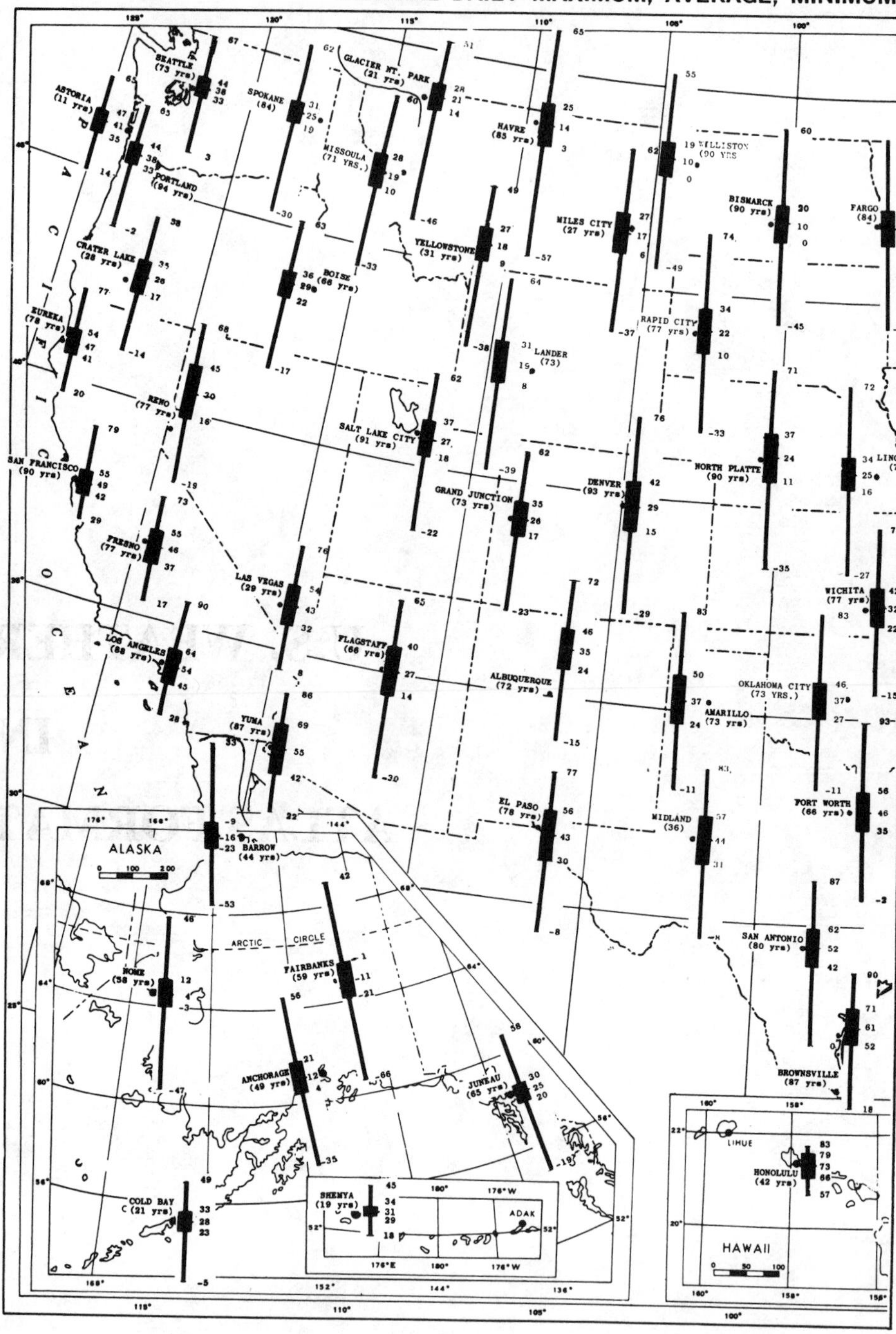

AND EXTREME TEMPERATURES (°F), JANUARY

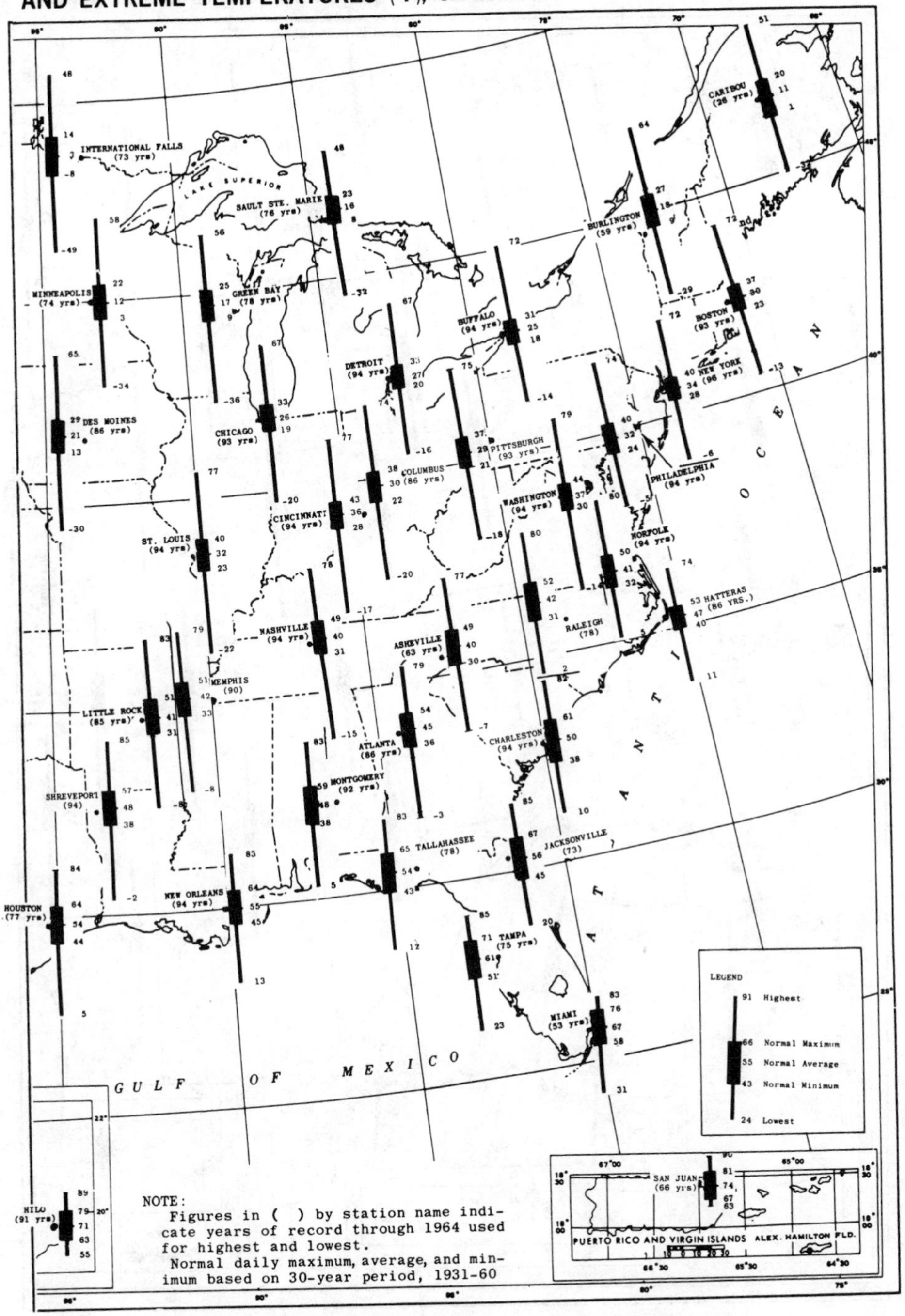

See tables beginning on page 329 for any adjustments indicated by 1941-1970 updates of normals, means, and extremes data.

NORMAL DAILY MAXIMUM, AVERAGE, MINIMUM,

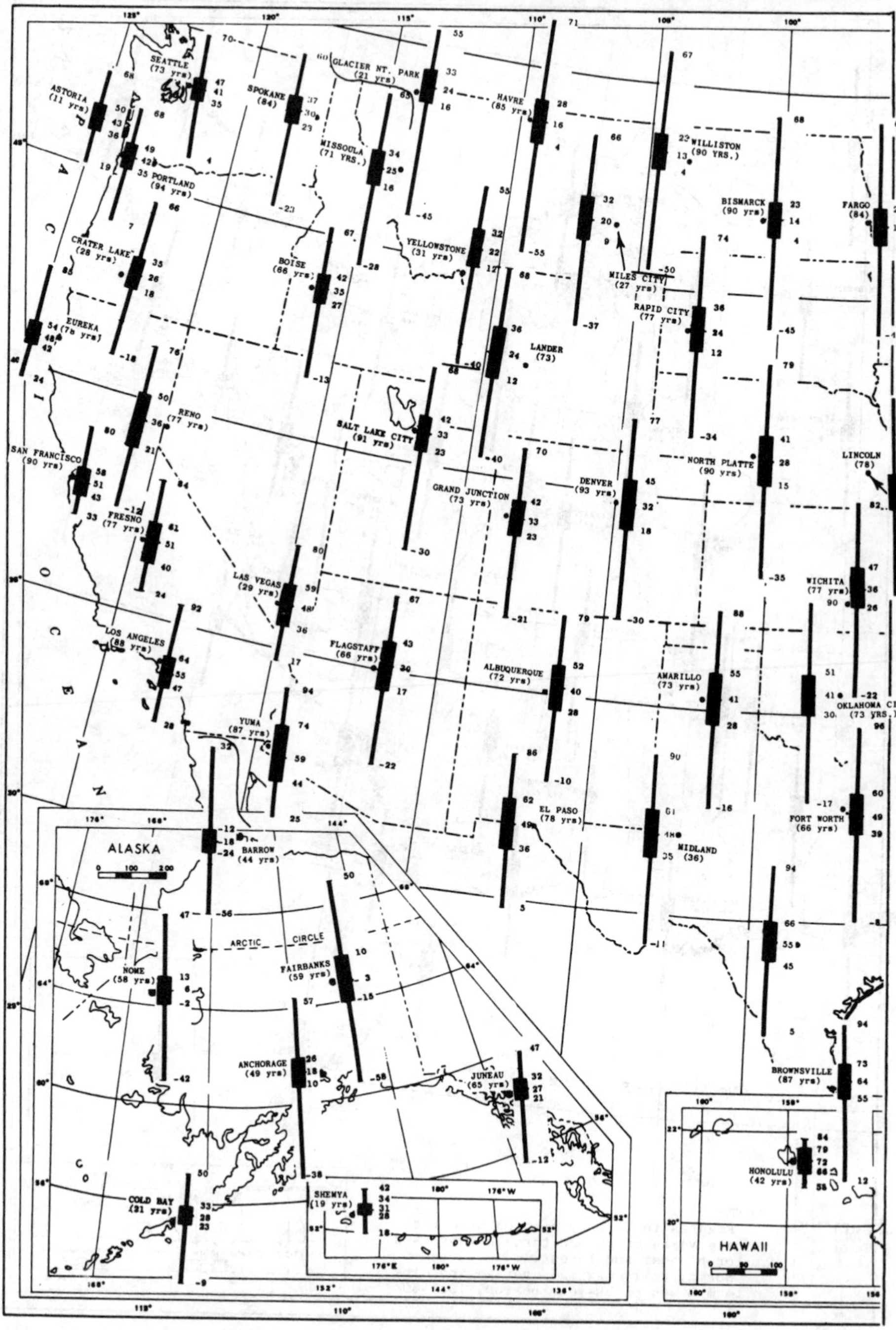

See table beginning on page 97 for any adjustments indicated by 1965-1975 updates of normals, means, and extremes data.

AND EXTREME TEMPERATURES (°F), FEBRUARY

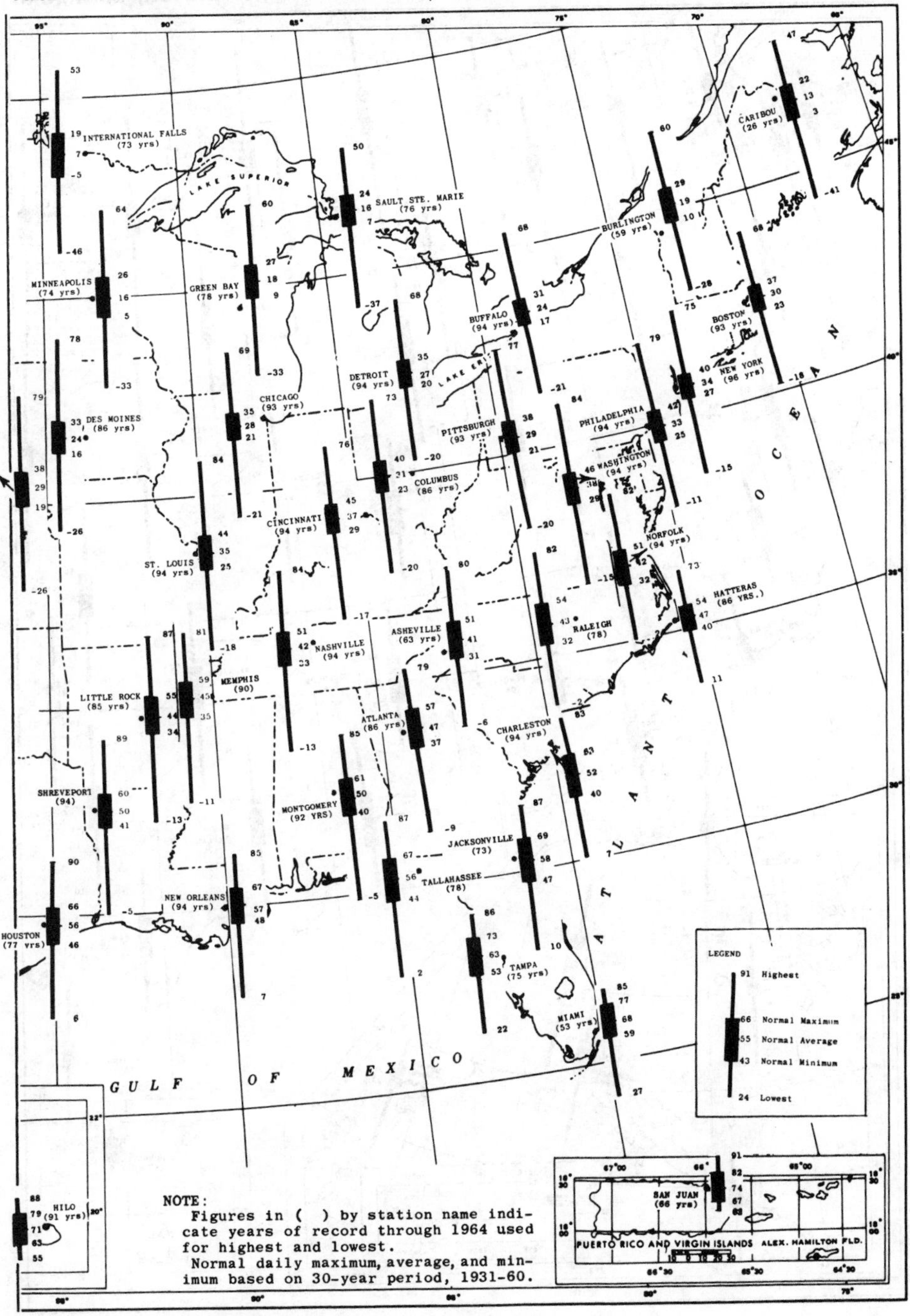

See tables beginning on page 329 for any adjustments indicated by 1941-1970 updates of normals, means, and extremes data.

NORMAL DAILY MAXIMUM, AVERAGE, MINIMUM,

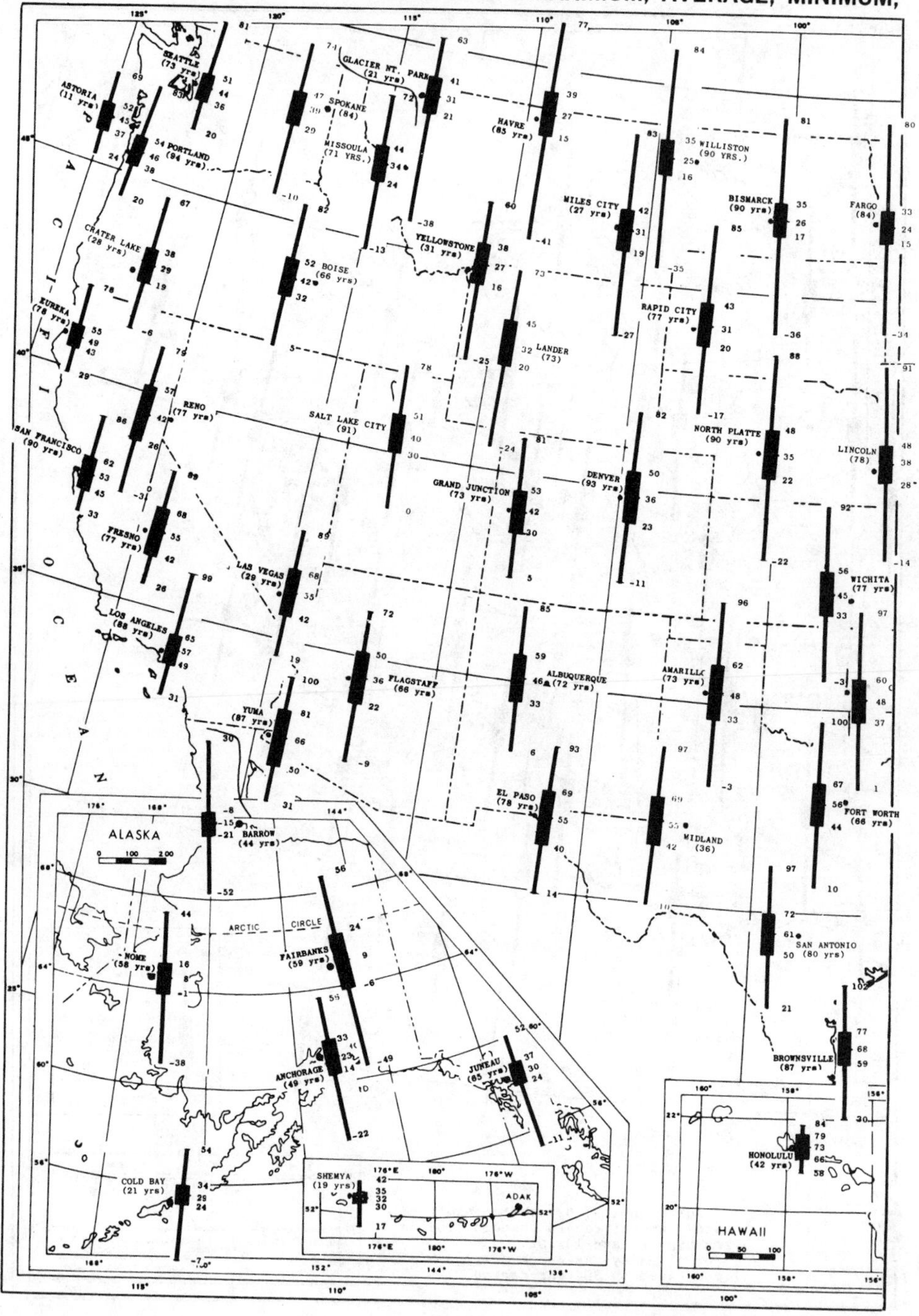

AND EXTREME TEMPERATURES (°F), MARCH

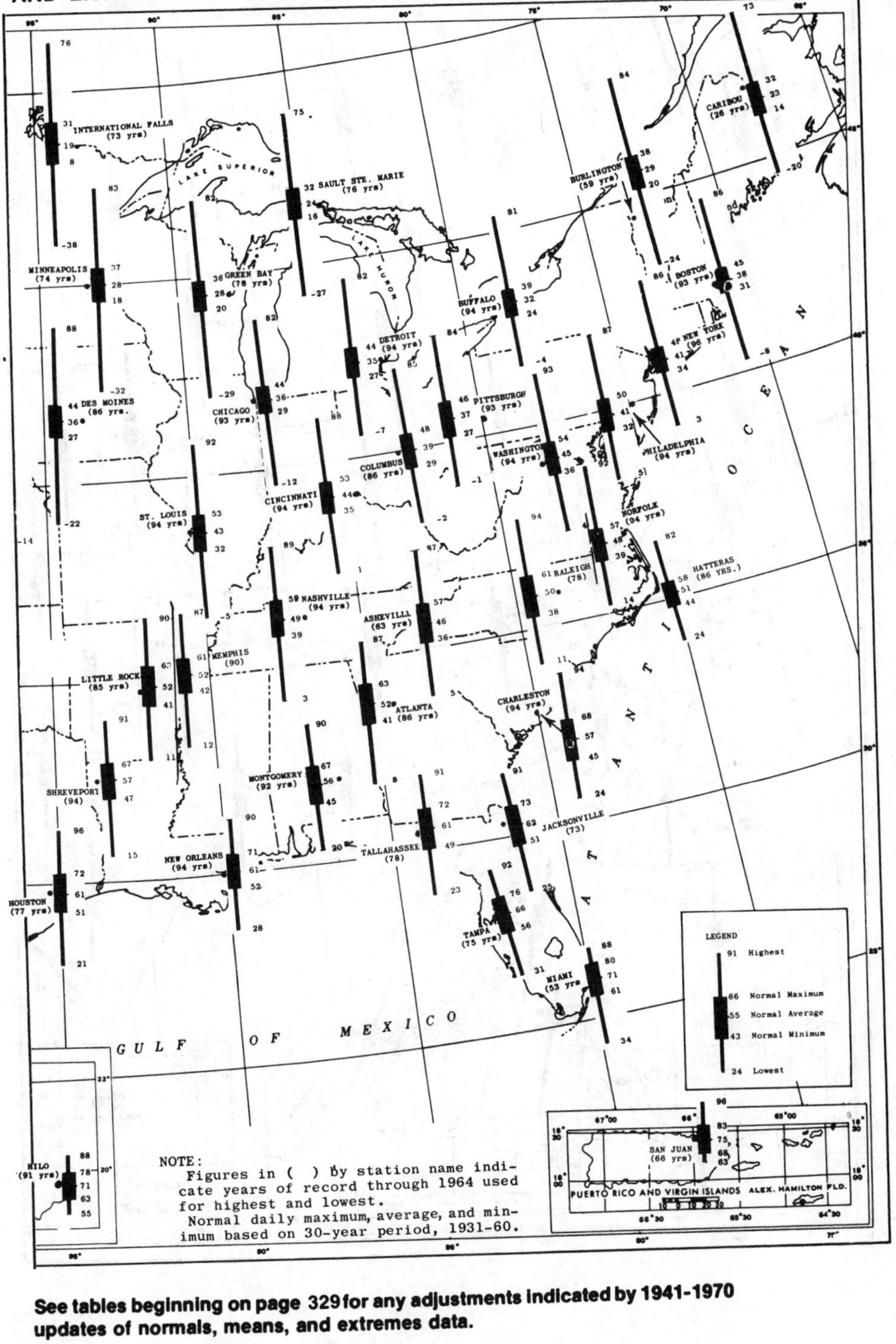

NOTE:
Figures in ( ) by station name indicate years of record through 1964 used for highest and lowest.
Normal daily maximum, average, and minimum based on 30-year period, 1931-60.

See tables beginning on page 329 for any adjustments indicated by 1941-1970 updates of normals, means, and extremes data.

NORMAL DAILY MAXIMUM, AVERAGE, MINIMUM.

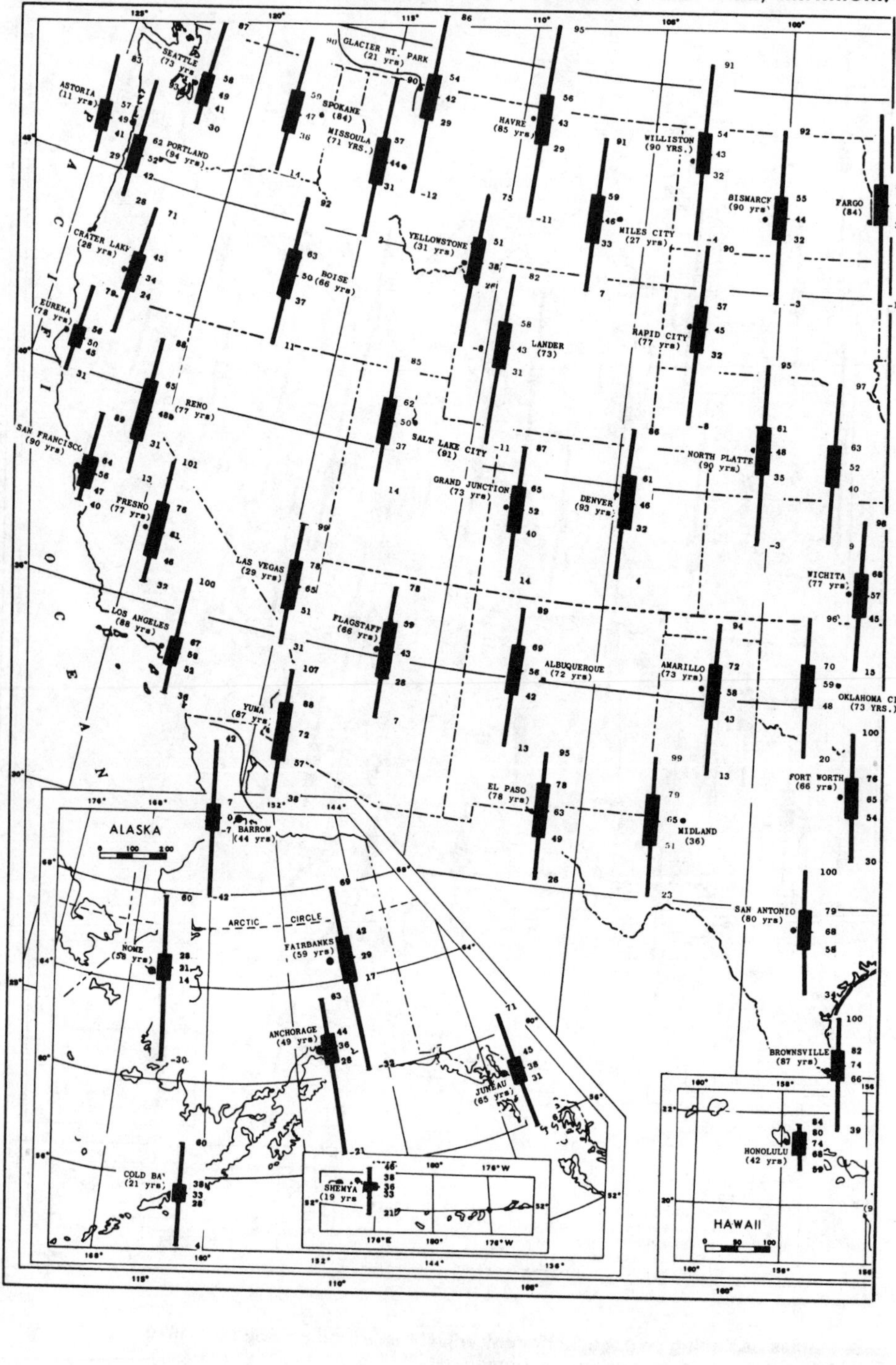

AND EXTREME TEMPERATURES (°F), APRIL

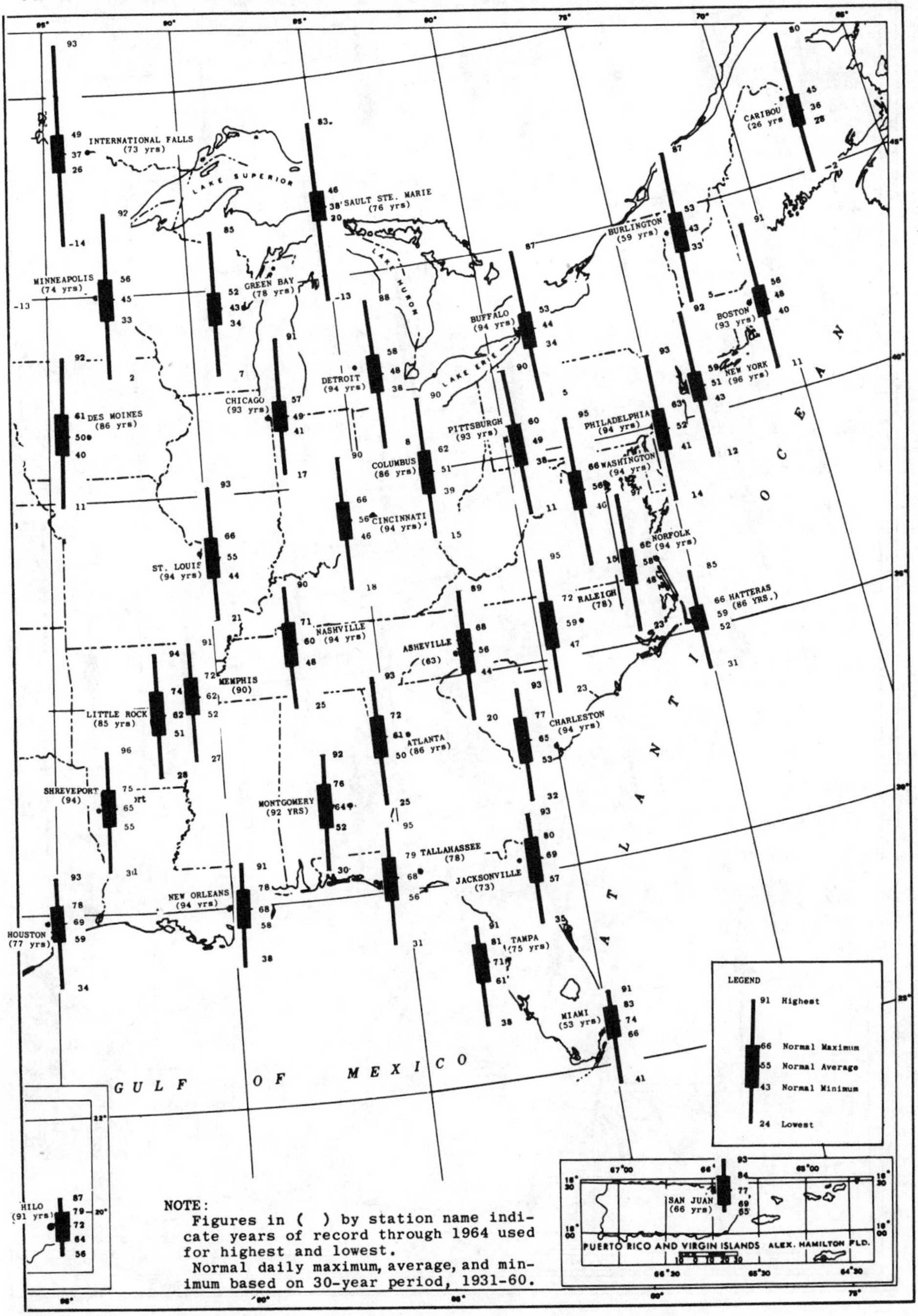

See tables beginning on page 329 for any adjustments indicated by 1941-1970 updates of normals, means, and extremes data.

NORMAL DAILY MAXIMUM, AVERAGE, MINIMUM,

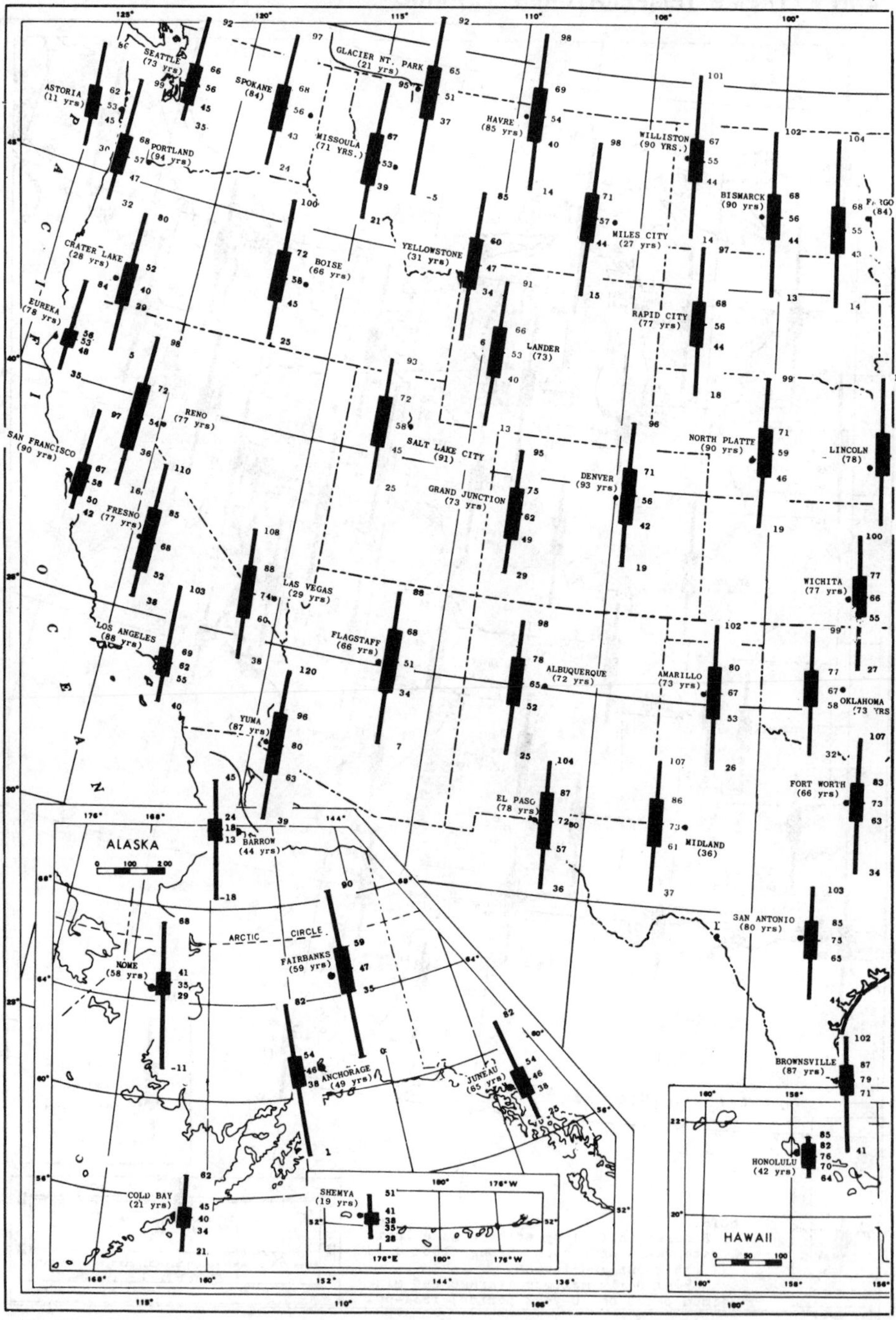

AND EXTREME TEMPERATURES (°F), MAY

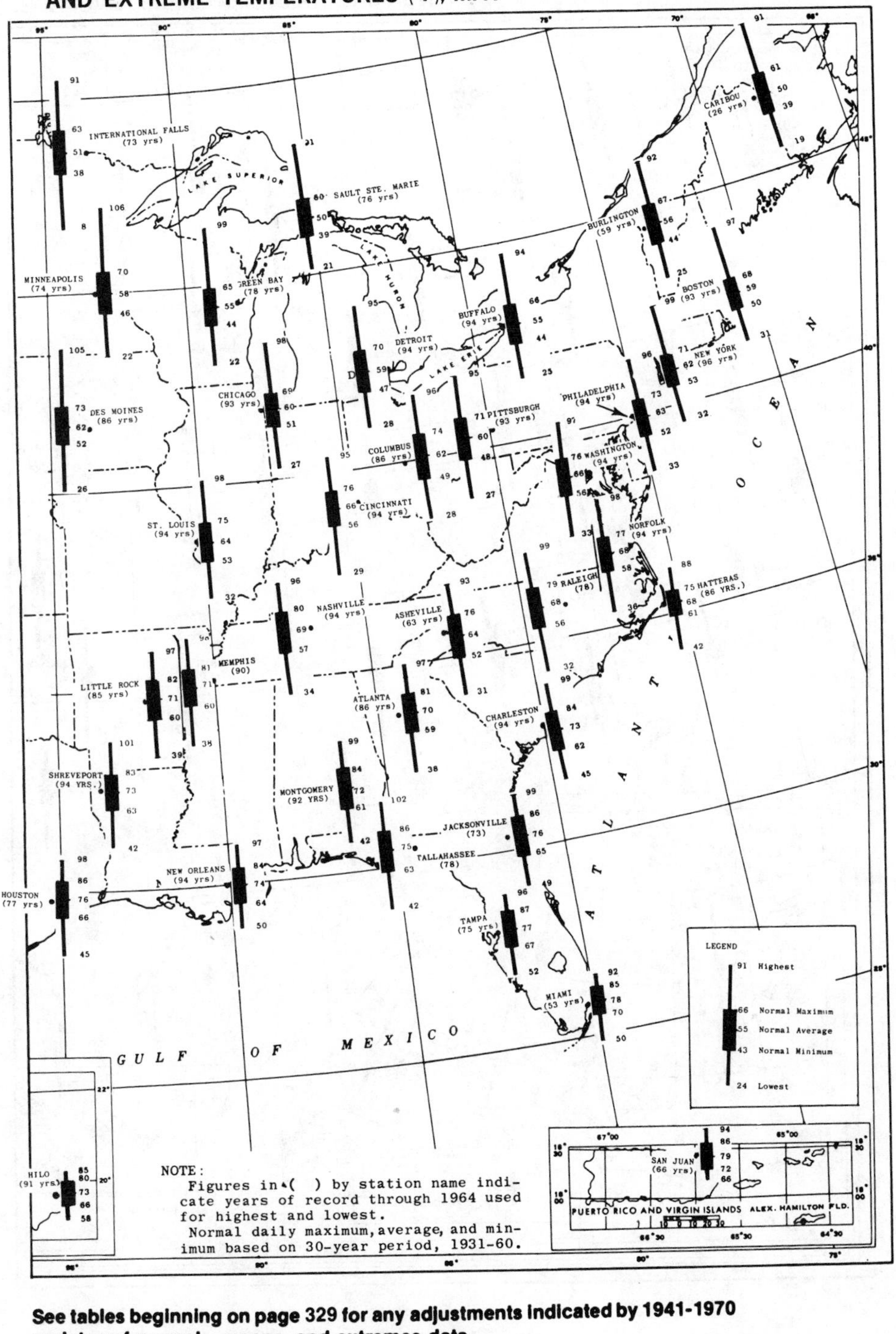

See tables beginning on page 329 for any adjustments indicated by 1941-1970 updates of normals, means, and extremes data.

NORMAL DAILY MAXIMUM, AVERAGE,

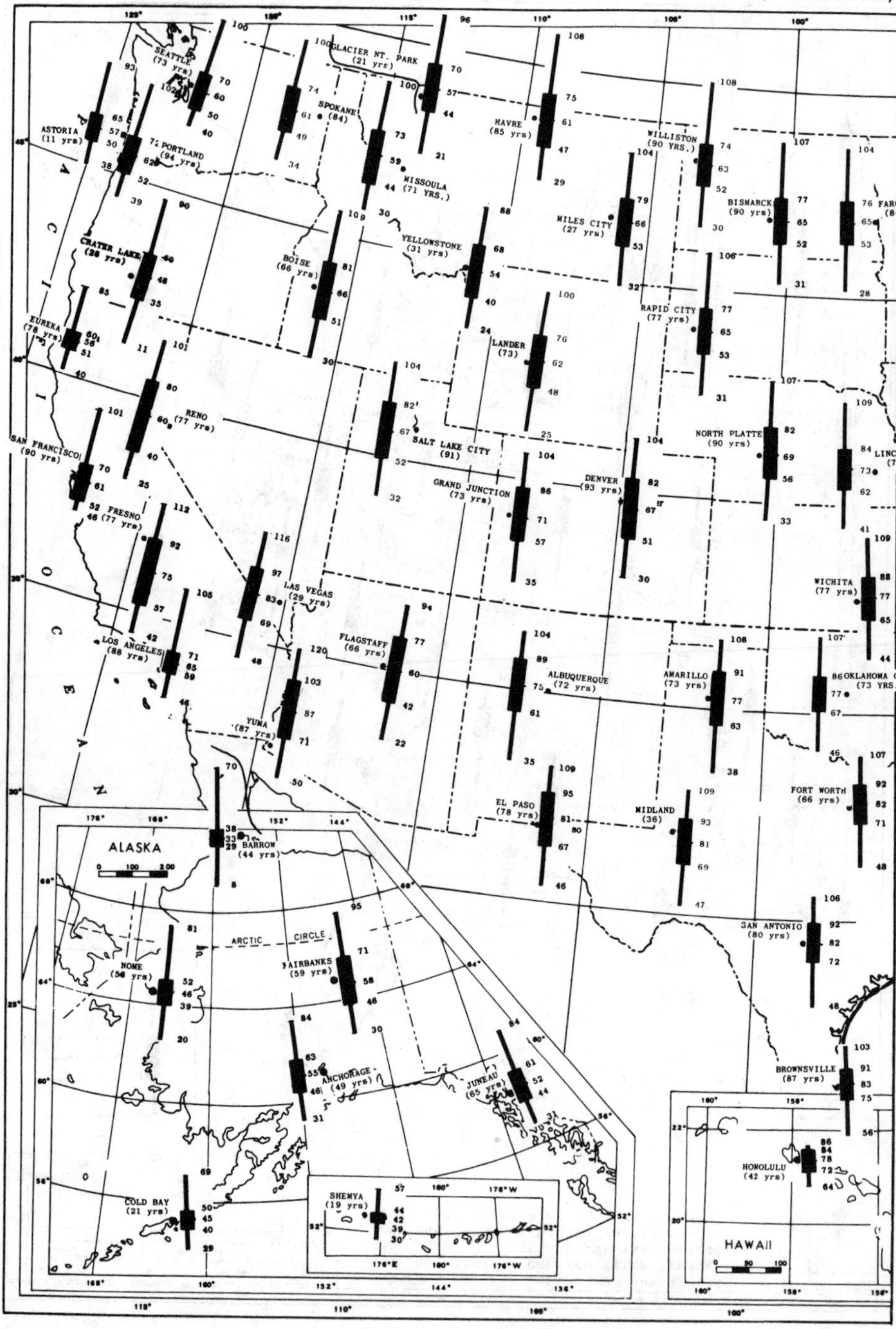

MINIMUM, AND EXTREME TEMPERATURES (°F), JUNE

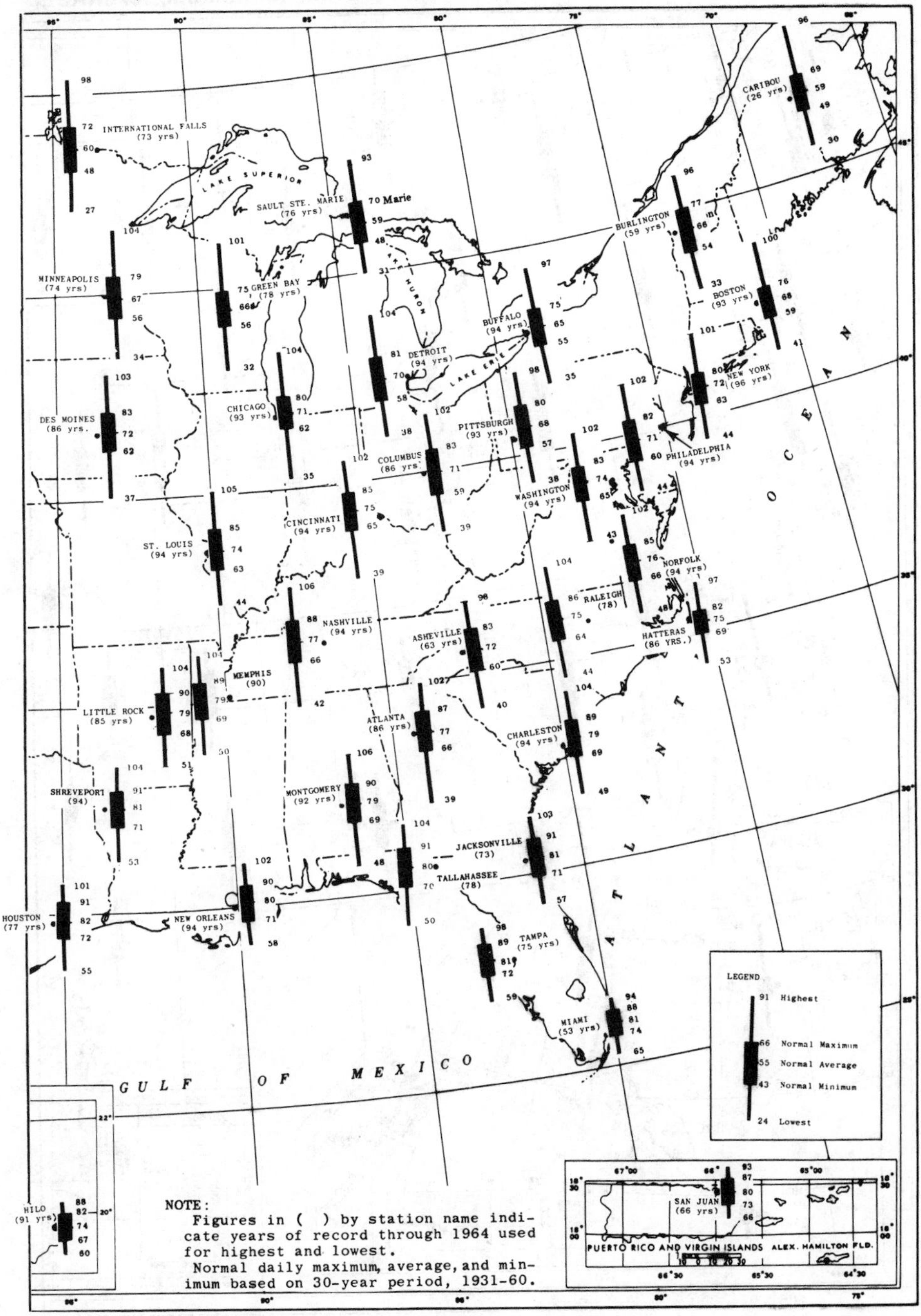

See tables beginning on page 329 for any adjustments indicated by 1941-1970 updates of normals, means, and extremes data.

NORMAL DAILY MAXIMUM, AVERAGE,

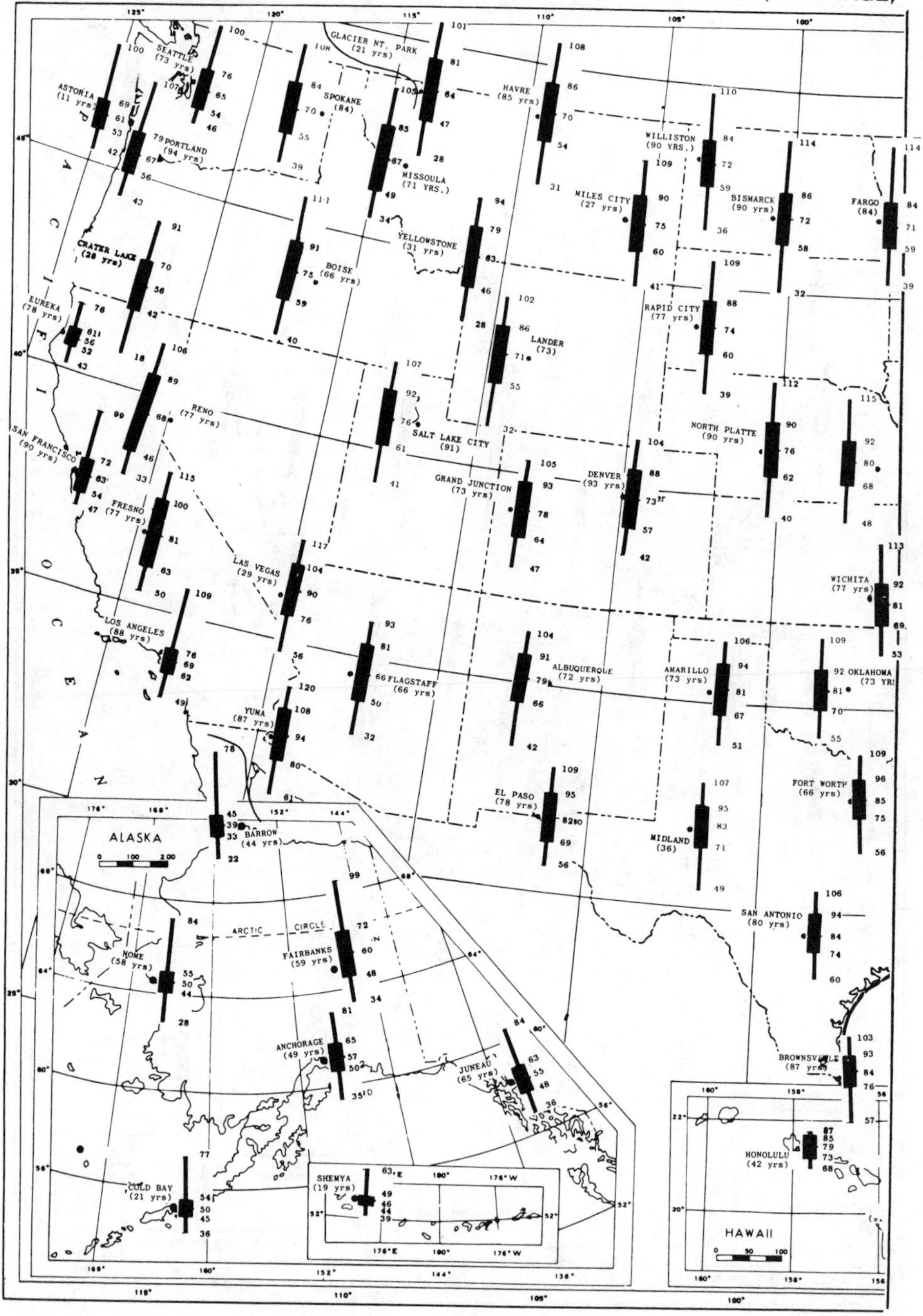

MINIMUM, AND EXTREME TEMPERATURES (°F), JULY

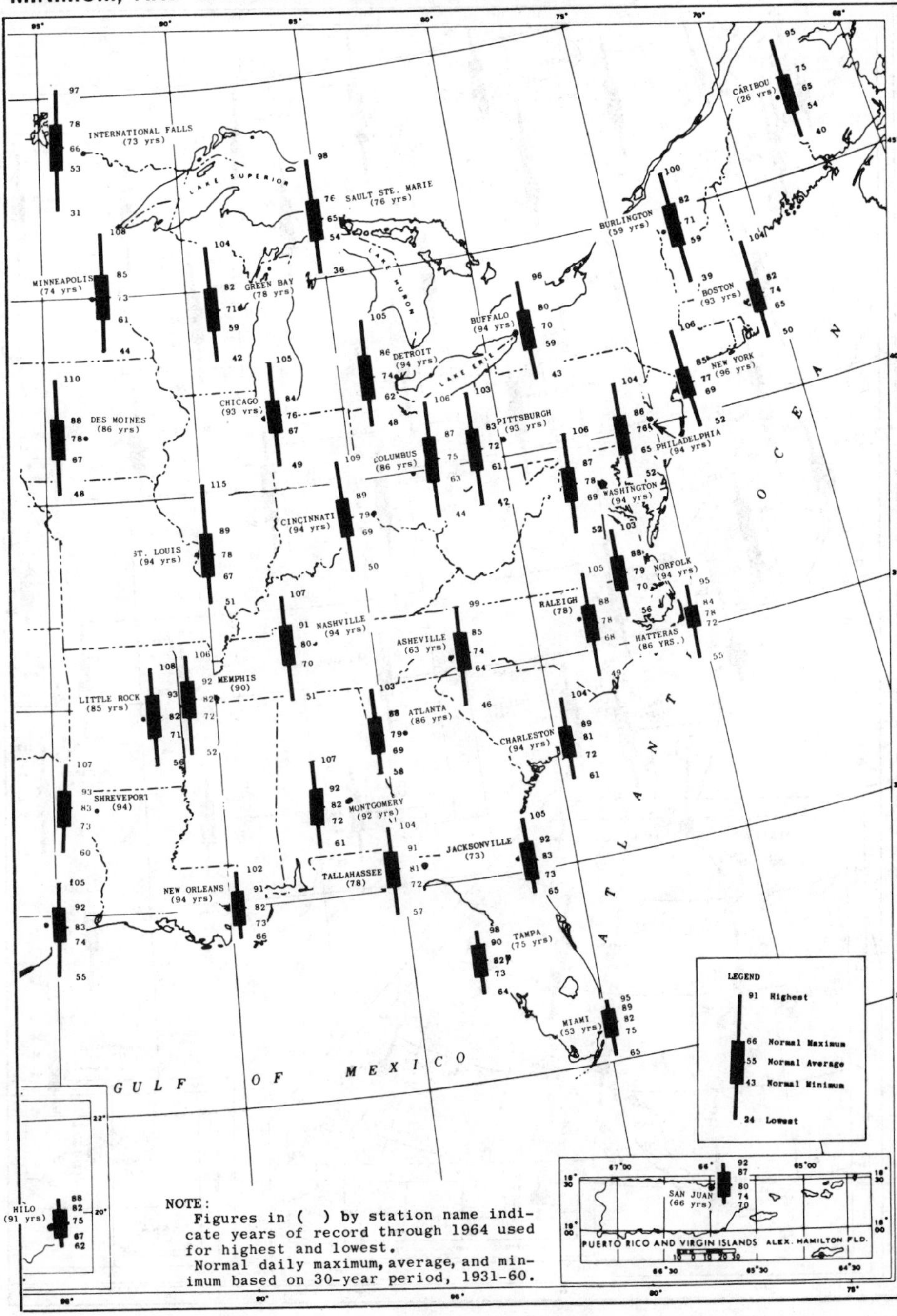

See tables beginning on page 329 for any adjustments indicated by 1941-1970 updates of normals, means, and extremes data.

NORMAL DAILY MAXIMUM, AVERAGE, MINIMUM,

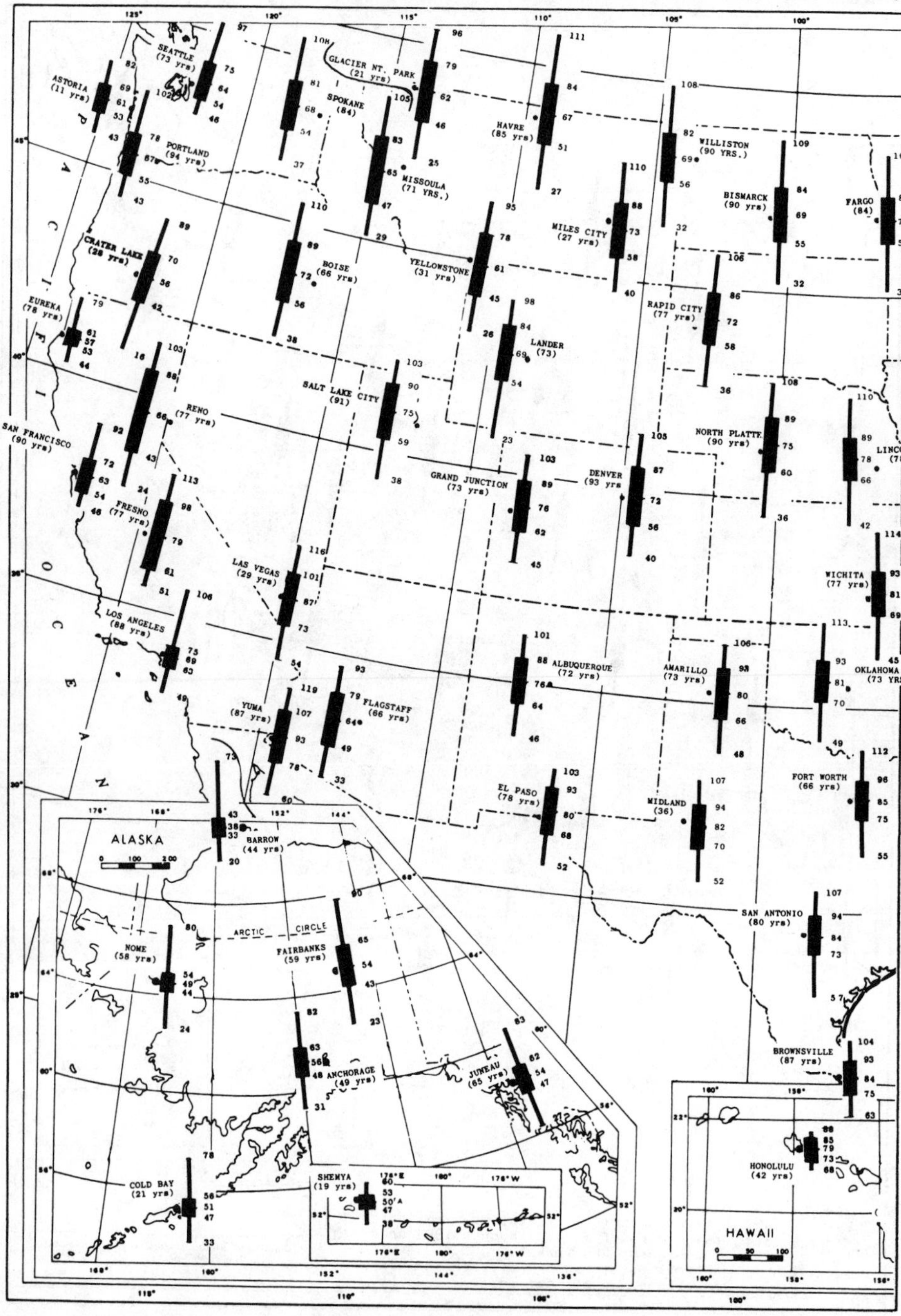

AND EXTREME TEMPERATURES (°F), AUGUST

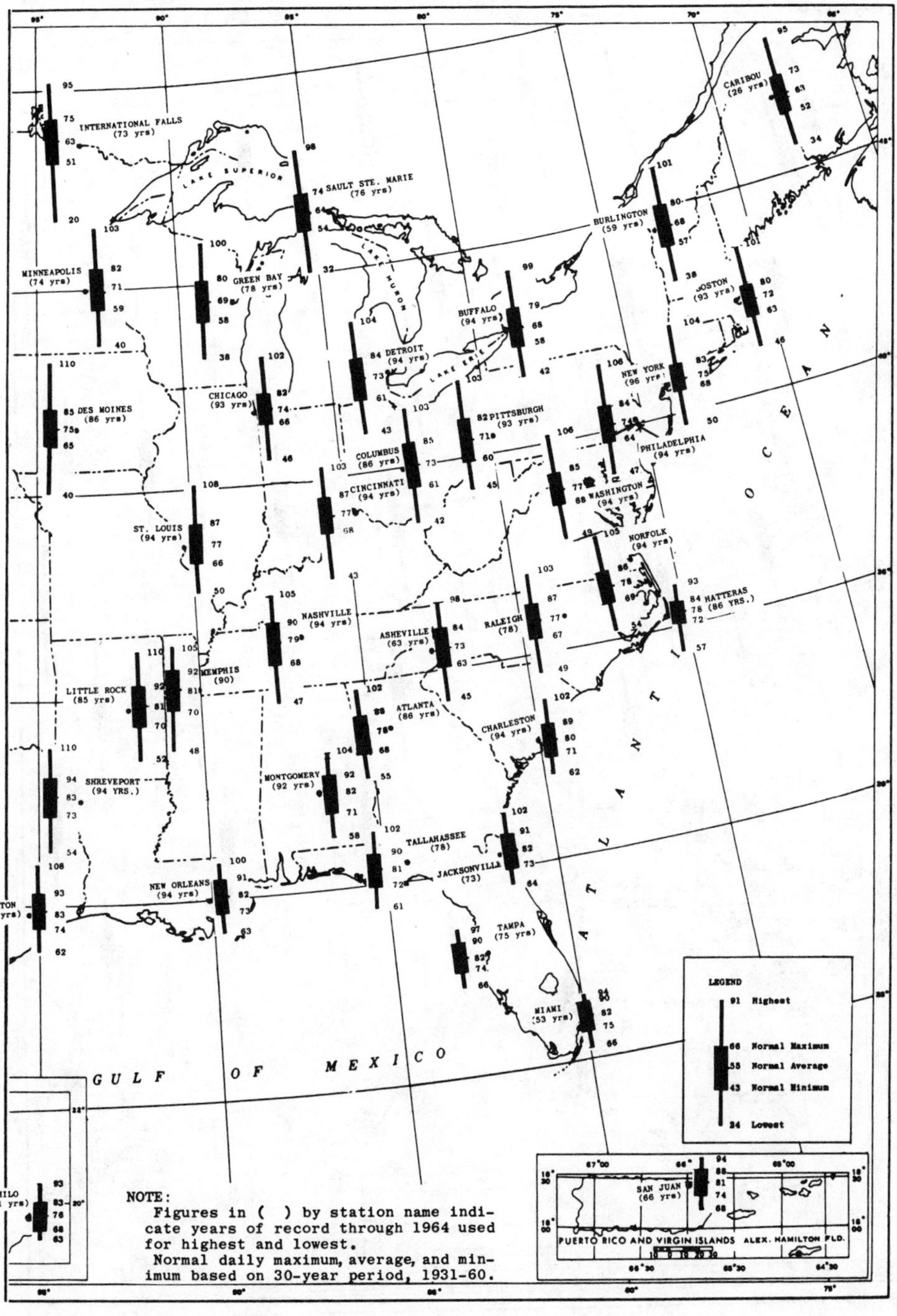

See tables beginning on page 329 for any adjustments indicated by 1941-1970 updates of normals, means, and extremes data.

NORMAL DAILY MAXIMUM, AVERAGE, MINIMUM,

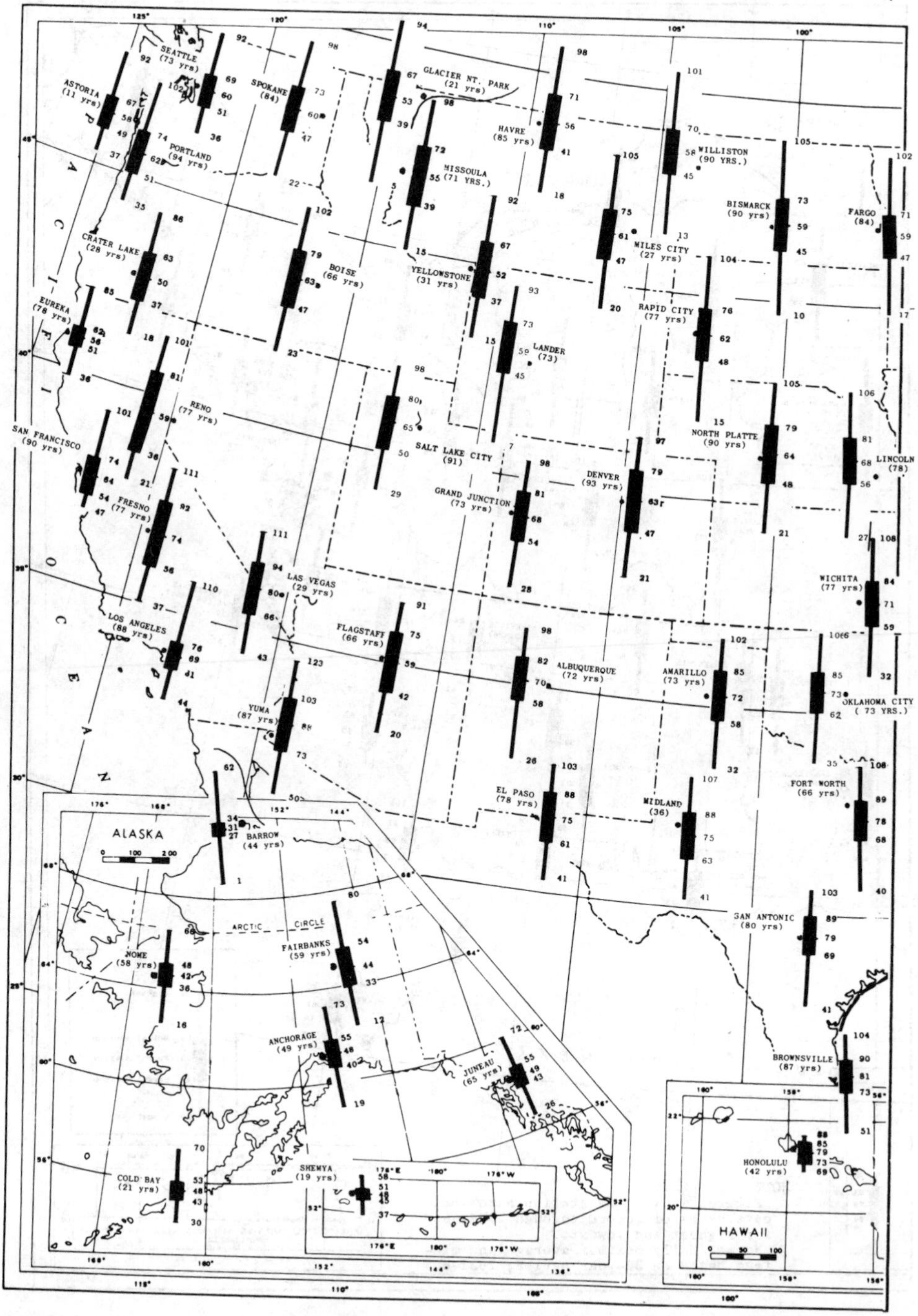

AND EXTREME TEMPERATURES (°F), SEPTEMBER

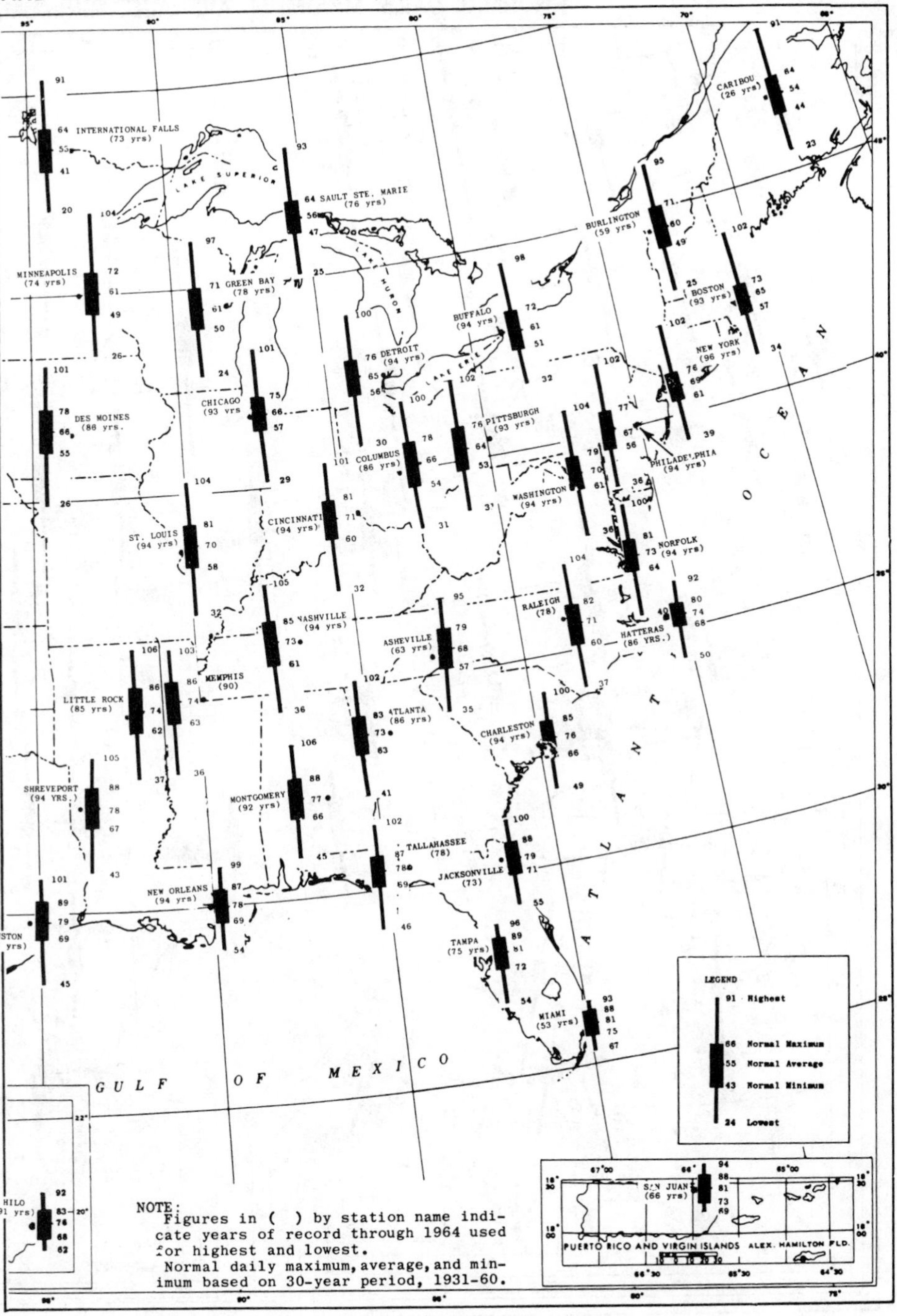

See tables beginning on page 329 for any adjustments indicated by 1941-1970 updates of normals, means, and extremes data.

NORMAL DAILY MAXIMUM, AVERAGE, MINIMUM,

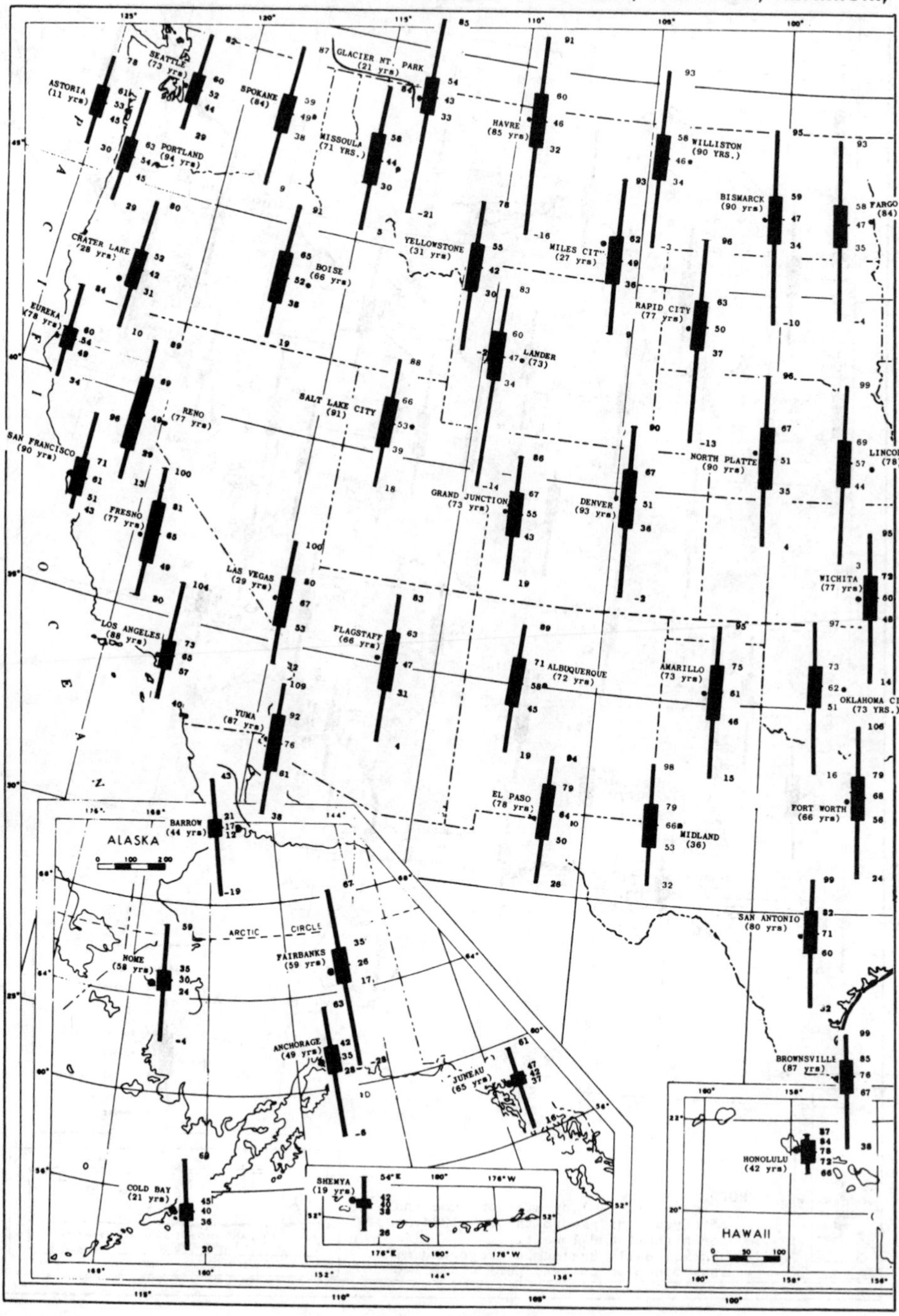

AND EXTREME TEMPERATURES (°F), OCTOBER

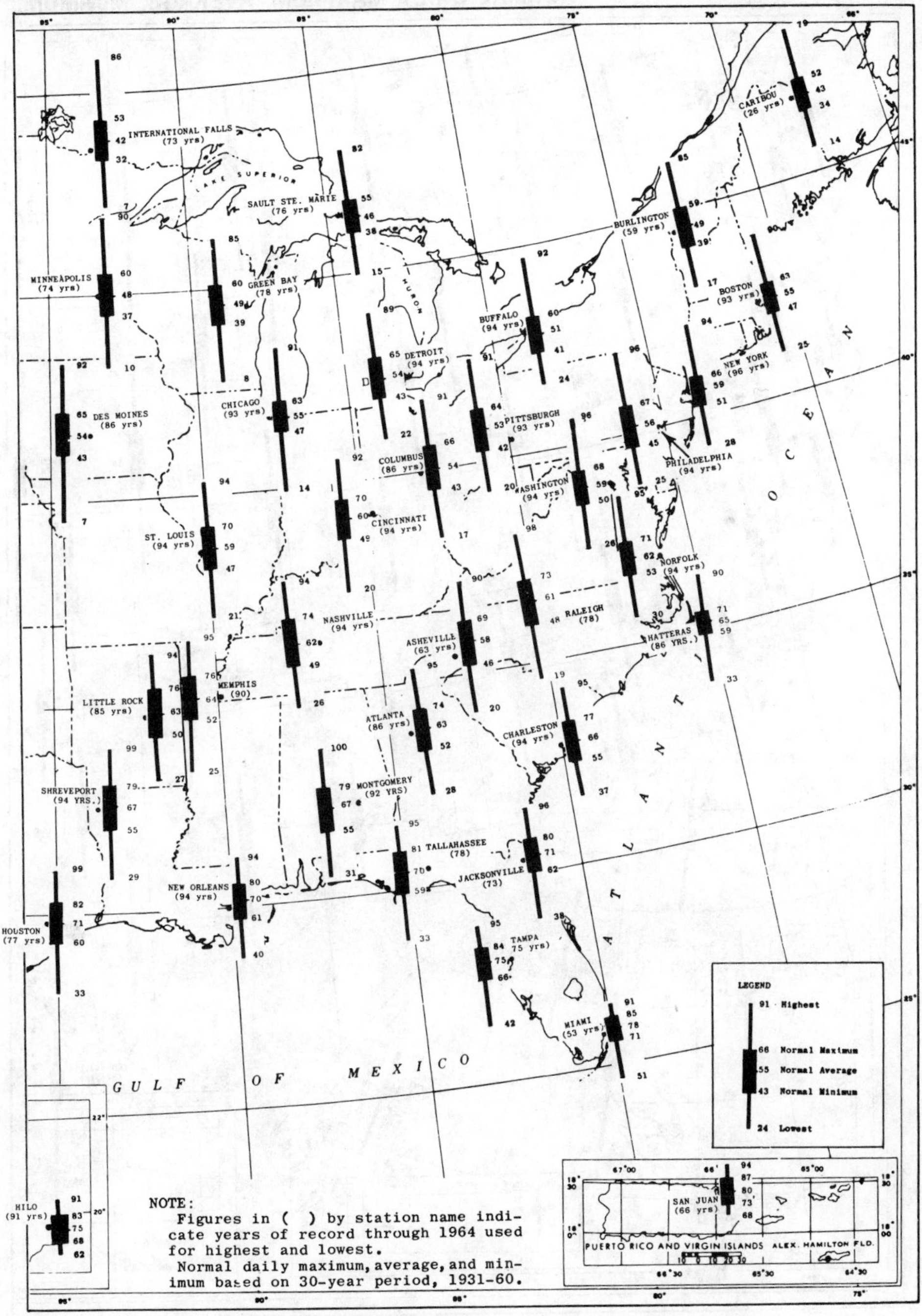

See tables beginning on page 329 for any adjustments indicated by 1941-1970 updates of normals, means, and extremes data.

NORMAL DAILY MAXIMUM, AVERAGE, MINIMUM,

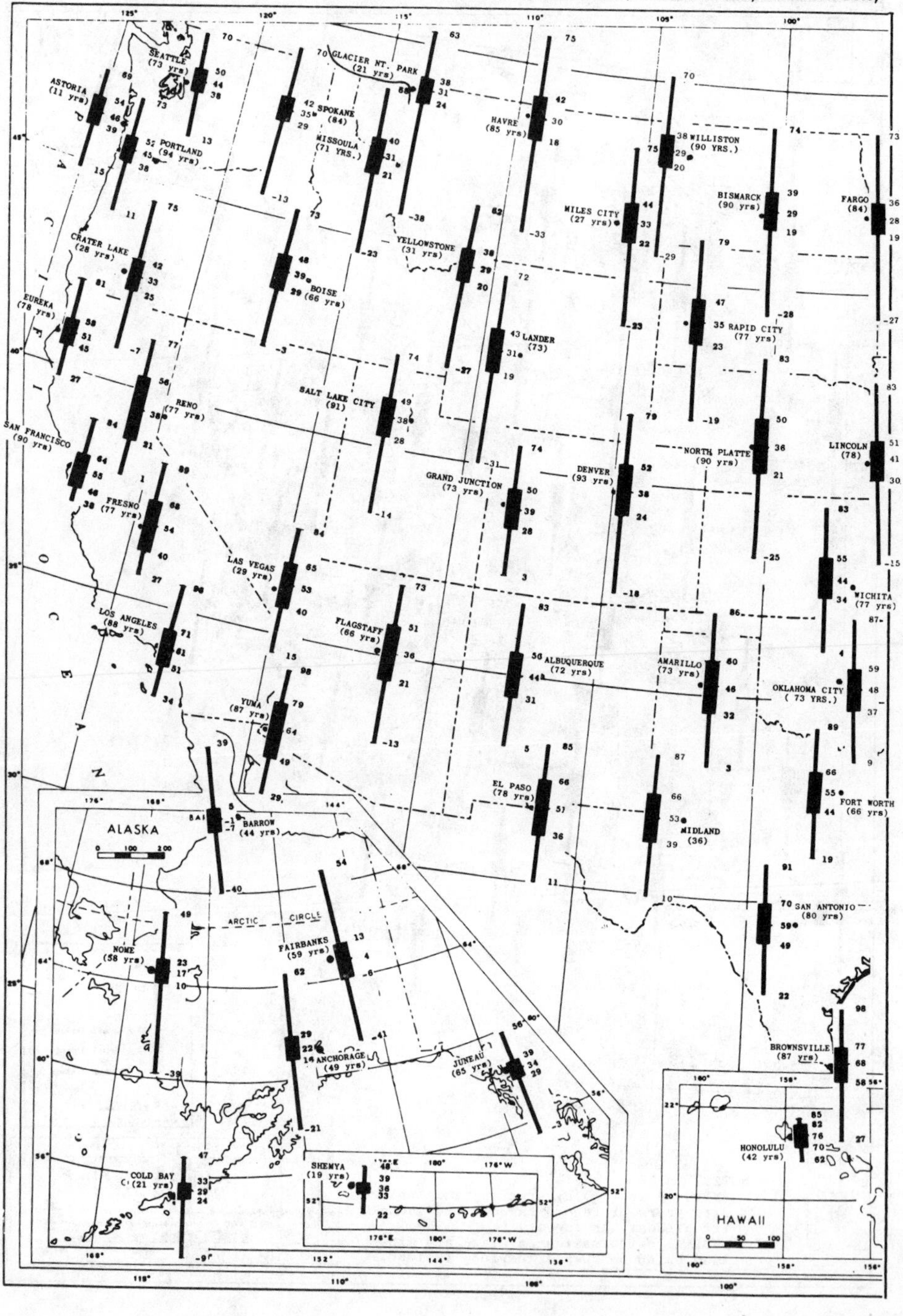

AND EXTREME TEMPERATURES (°F), NOVEMBER

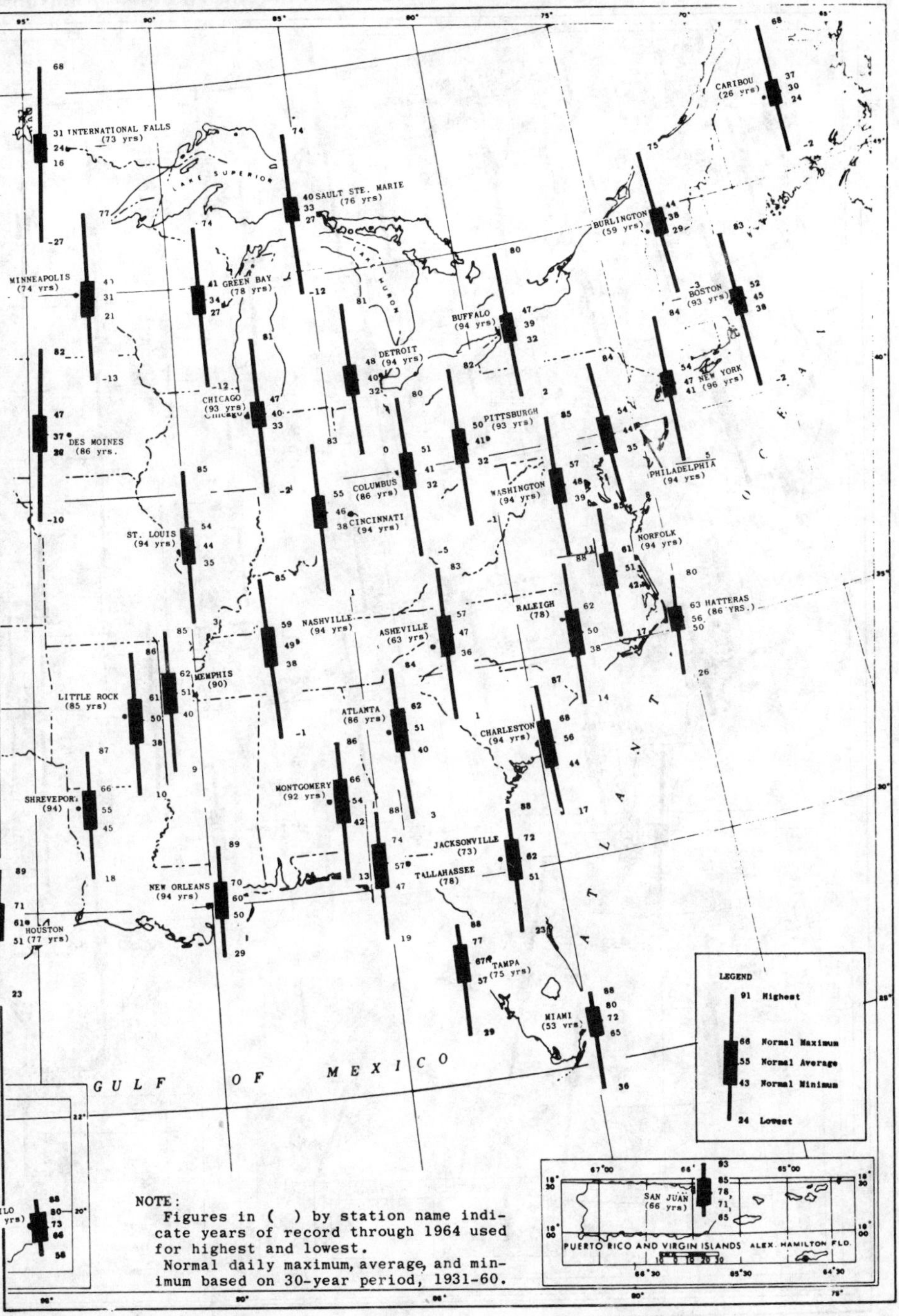

NOTE:
Figures in ( ) by station name indicate years of record through 1964 used for highest and lowest.
Normal daily maximum, average, and minimum based on 30-year period, 1931-60.

See tables beginning on page 329 for any adjustments indicated by 1941-1970 updates of normals, means, and extremes data.

NORMAL DAILY MAXIMUM, AVERAGE, MINIMUM,

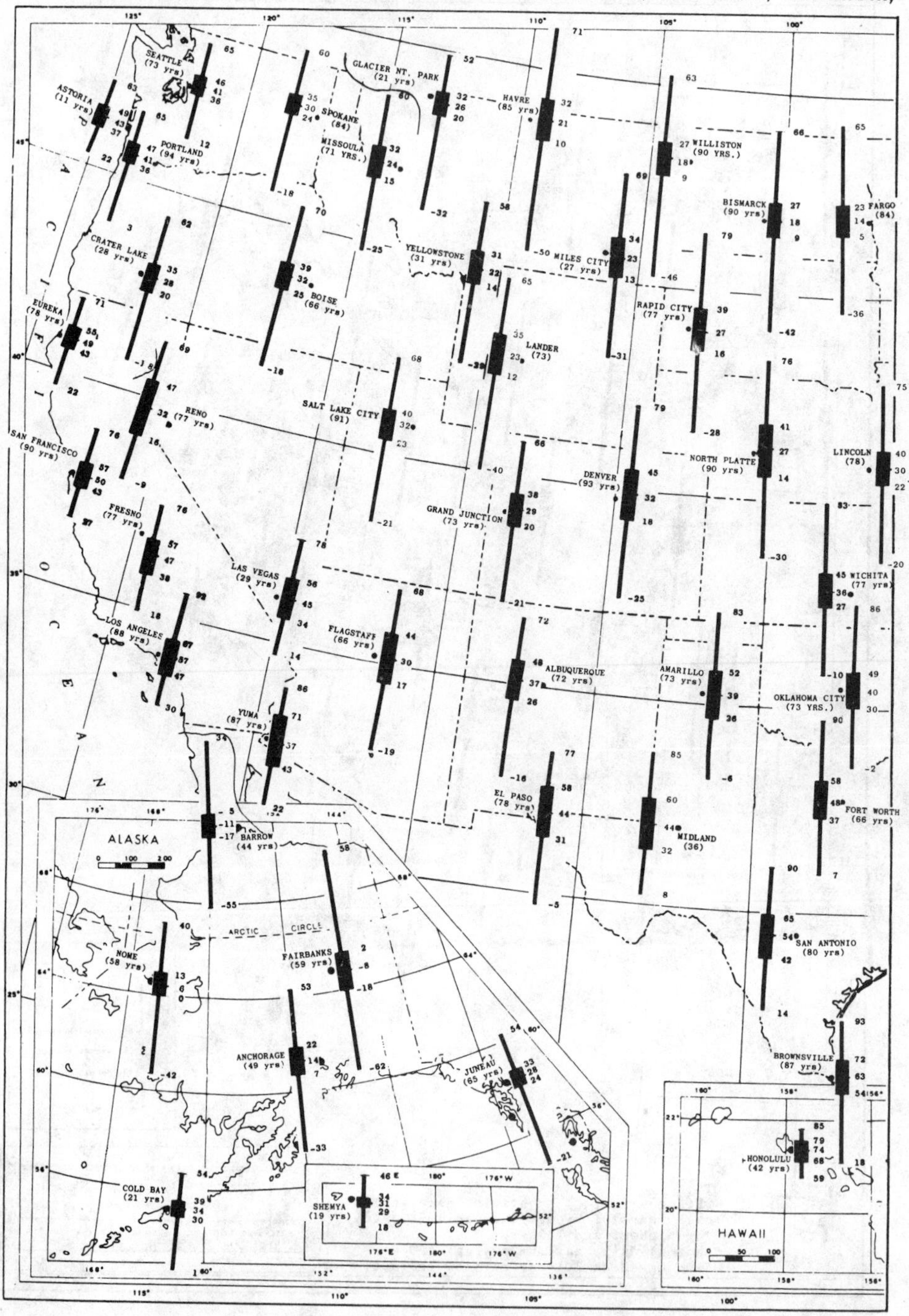

AND EXTREME TEMPERATURES (°F), DECEMBER

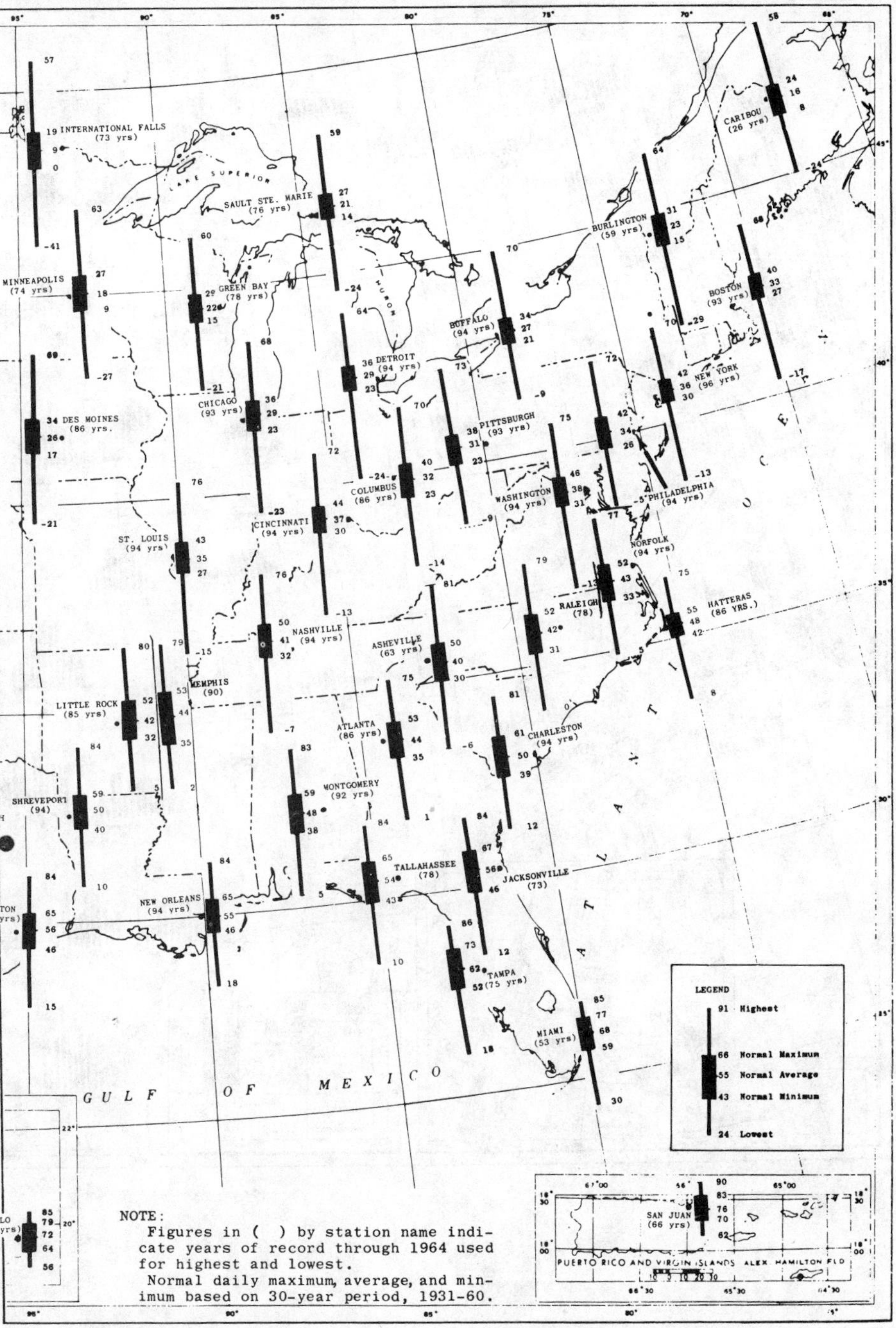

See tables beginning on page 329 for any adjustments indicated by 1941-1970 updates of normals, means, and extremes data.

NORMAL MONTHLY TOTAL PRECIPITATION (Inches)

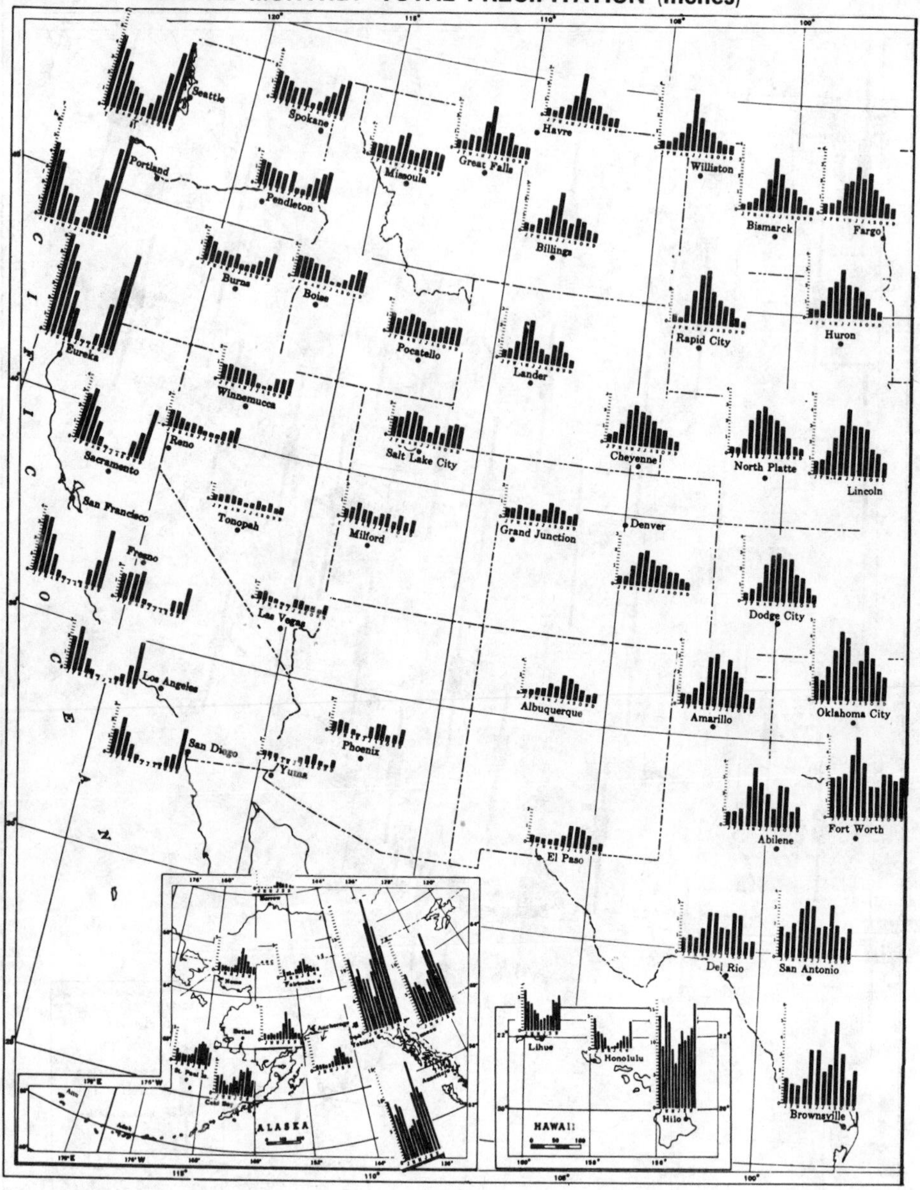

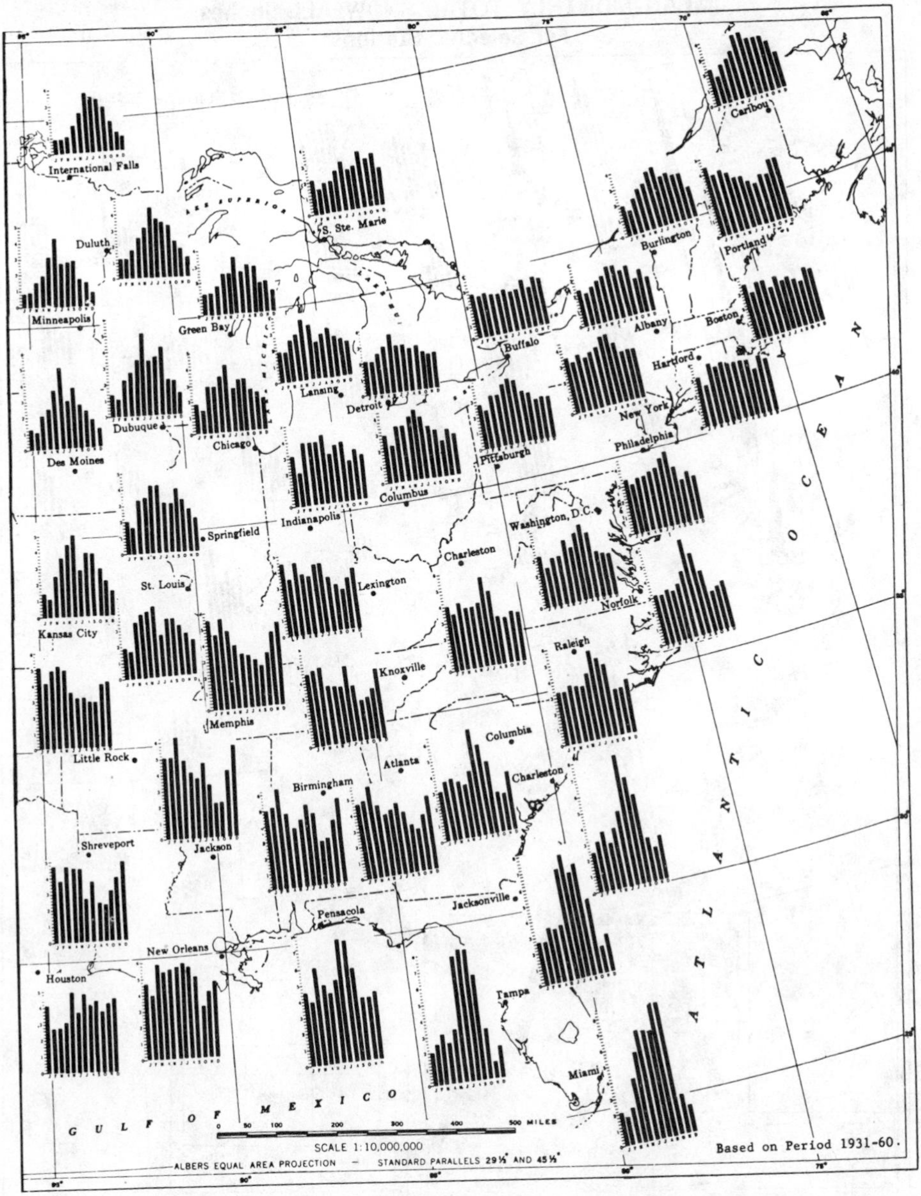

See tables beginning on page 329 for any adjustments indicated by 1941-1970 updates of normals, means, and extremes data.

MEAN MONTHLY TOTAL SNOWFALL (Inches)
For Selected Stations*

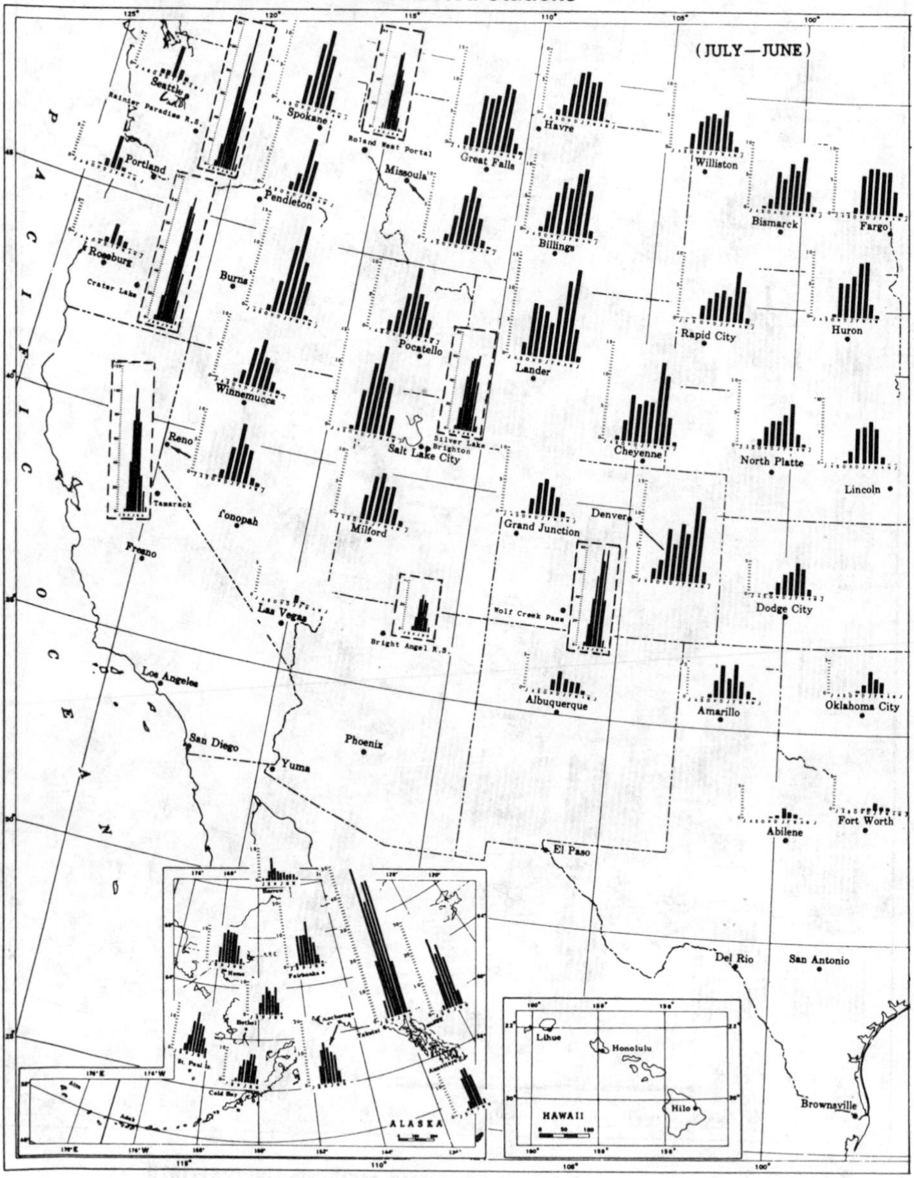

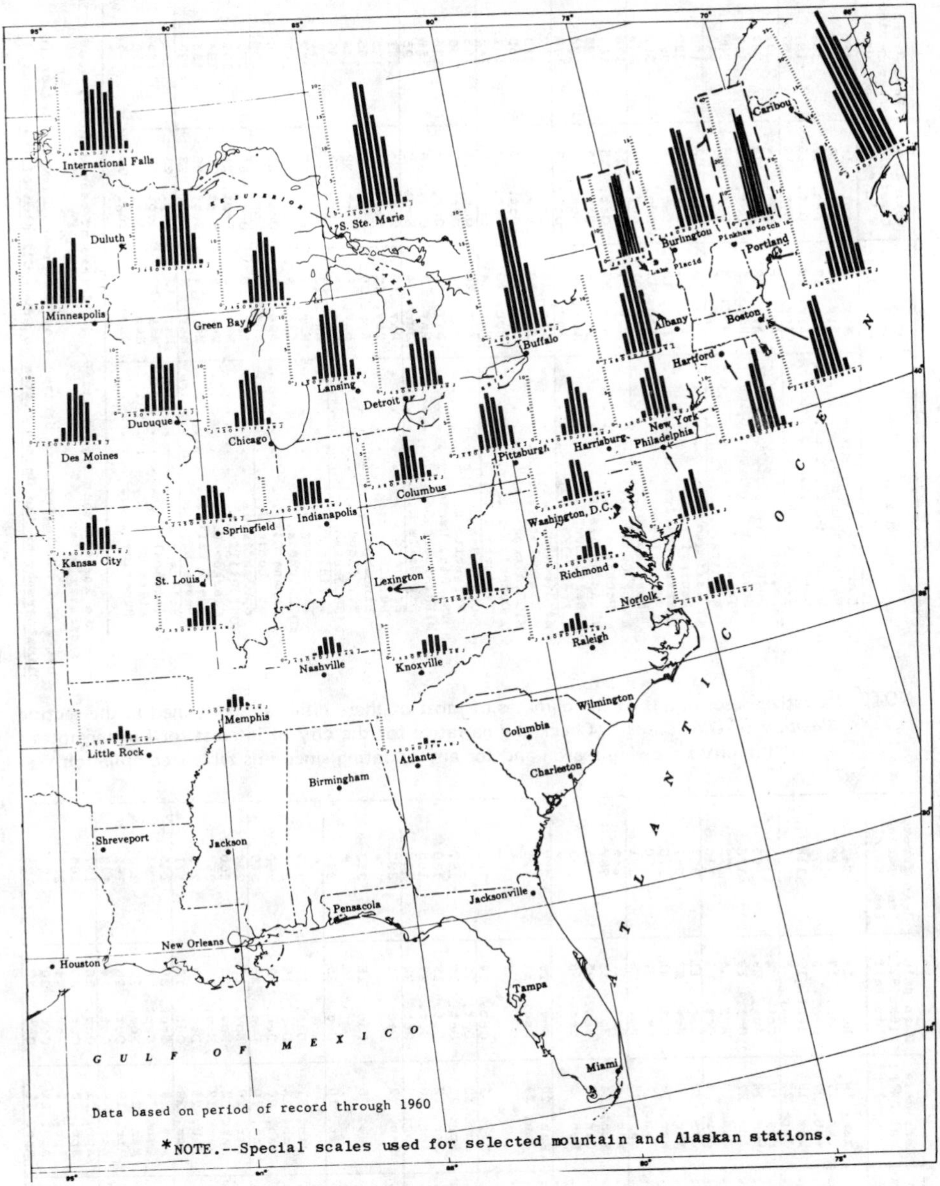

See tables beginning on page 329 for any adjustments indicated by 1941-1970 updates of normals, means, and extremes data.

FREEZE DATA AND GROWING SEASON

MEAN DATE OF LAST 32 F. TEMPERATURE IN SPRING, FIRST 32 F. IN AUTUMN, AND MEAN LENGTH OF FREEZE-FREE PERIOD (DAYS)

State and Station	Mean date last 32°F. in spring	Mean date first 32°F. in fall	Mean freeze-free period (no. days)
ALA.Birmingham	Mar. 19	Nov. 14	241
Mobile U	Feb. 17	Dec. 12	298
Montgomery U	Feb. 27	Dec. 3	279
ALASKA.Anchorage	May 18	Sept. 13	118
Barrow	June 27	July 5	8
Cordova	May 10	Oct. 2	145
Fairbanks	May 24	Aug. 29	97
Juneau	Apr. 27	Oct. 19	176
Nome	June 12	Aug. 24	73
ARIZ.Flagstaff	June 8	Oct. 2	116
Phoenix	Jan. 27	Dec. 11	317
Tucson	Mar. 6	Nov. 23	261
Winslow	Apr. 28	Oct. 21	176
Yuma U	Jan. 11	Dec. 27	350
ARK.Fort Smith	Mar. 23	Nov. 9	231
Little Rock	Mar. 16	Nov. 15	244
CALIF.Bakersfield	Feb. 14	Nov. 28	287
Eureka U	Jan. 24	Dec. 25	335
Fresno	Feb. 3	Dec. 3	303
Los Angeles U	*	*	*
Red Bluff	Feb. 25	Nov. 29	277
Sacramento	Jan. 24	Dec. 11	321
San Diego	*	*	*
San Francisco U	*	*	*
COLO.Denver U	May 2	Oct. 14	165
Palisades	Apr. 22	Oct. 17	178
Pueblo	Apr. 28	Oct. 12	167
CONN.Hartford	Apr. 22	Oct. 19	180
New Haven	Apr. 15	Oct. 27	195
D.C.Washington U	Apr. 10	Oct. 28	200
FLA.Apalachicola U	Feb. 2	Dec. 21	322
Fort Myers	*	*	*
Jacksonville U	Feb. 6	Dec. 16	313
Key West	*	*	*
Lakeland	Jan. 10	Dec. 25	349
Miami	*	*	*
Orlando	Jan. 31	Dec. 17	319
Pensacola U	Feb. 18	Dec. 15	300
Tallahassee	Feb. 26	Dec. 3	280
Tampa	Jan. 10	Dec. 26	349
GA.Atlanta U	Mar. 20	Nov. 19	244
Augusta	Mar. 7	Nov. 22	260
Macon	Mar. 12	Nov. 19	252
Savannah	Feb. 21	Dec. 9	291
IDAHO.Boise	Apr. 29	Oct. 16	171
Pocatello	May 8	Sept. 30	145
Salmon	June 4	Sept. 6	94
ILL.Cairo U	Mar. 23	Nov. 11	233
Chicago U	Apr. 19	Oct. 28	192
Freeport	May 8	Oct. 4	149
Peoria	Apr. 22	Oct. 16	177
Springfield U	Apr. 8	Oct. 30	205
IND.Evansville	Apr. 2	Nov. 4	216
Fort Wayne	Apr. 24	Oct. 20	179
Indianapolis U	Apr. 17	Oct. 27	193
South Bend	May 3	Oct. 16	165
IOWA.Des Moines U	Apr. 20	Oct. 19	183
Dubuque U	Apr. 19	Oct. 19	184
Koekuk	Apr. 12	Oct. 26	197
Sioux City	Apr. 28	Oct. 12	167
KANS.Concordia U	Apr. 16	Oct. 24	191
Dodge City	Apr. 22	Oct. 24	184
Goodland	May 5	Oct. 9	157
Topeka U	Apr. 9	Oct. 26	200
Wichita	Apr. 5	Nov. 1	210
KY.Lexington	Apr. 13	Oct. 28	198
Louisville U	Apr. 1	Nov. 7	220
LA.Lake Charles	Feb. 18	Dec. 6	291
New Orleans	Feb. 13	Dec. 12	302
Shreveport	Mar. 1	Nov. 27	272
MAINE.Greenville	May 27	Sept. 20	116
Portland	Apr. 29	Oct. 15	169
MD.Annapolis	Mar. 4	Nov. 15	225
Baltimore U	Mar. 28	Nov. 17	234
Frederick	Mar. 24	Oct. 17	176
MASS.Boston	Apr. 16	Oct. 25	192
Nantucket	Apr. 12	Nov. 16	219
MICH.Alpena U	May 6	Oct. 9	156
Detroit	Apr. 25	Oct. 23	181
Escanaba U	May 14	Oct. 6	145
Grand Rapids U	Apr. 25	Oct. 27	185
Marquette U	May 14	Oct. 17	156
S. Ste. Marie	May 18	Oct. 3	138
MINN.Albert Lee	May 3	Oct. 6	156
Big Falls R.S.	June 4	Sept. 7	95
Brainerd	May 16	Sept. 24	131
Duluth	May 22	Sept. 24	125
Minneapolis	Apr. 30	Oct. 13	166
St. Cloud	May 9	Sept. 29	144
MISS.Jackson	Mar. 10	Nov. 13	248
Meridian	Mar. 13	Nov. 14	246
Vicksburg U	Mar. 8	Nov. 15	252
MO.Columbia	Apr. 9	Oct. 24	198
Kansas City	Apr. 5	Oct. 31	210
St. Louis U	Apr. 2	Nov. 8	220
Springfield	Apr. 10	Oct. 31	203
MONT.Billings	May 15	Sept. 24	132
Glasgow U	May 19	Sept. 20	124
Great Falls	May 14	Sept. 26	135
Havre U	May 9	Sept. 23	138
Helena	May 12	Sept. 23	134
Kalispell	May 12	Sept. 23	135
Miles City	May 5	Oct. 3	150
Superior	June 5	Aug. 30	85

* Occurs in less than 1 year in 10. No freeze of record in Key West, Fla.
U Indicates urban.

Charts and tabulation were derived from the Freeze Data tabulation in Climatography of the United States No. 60 - Climates of the States.

NOTE: Narrative descriptions of the climates of most of these cities are contained in the section, *"Weather of U.S. Cities"*. Check the narrative for the city of interest for further notes about the city's growing season and for any updating since this table's compilation.

MEAN DATE OF LAST 32 F. TEMPERATURE IN SPRING, FIRST 32 F. IN AUTUMN, AND MEAN LENGTH OF FREEZE-FREE PERIOD (continued)

State and Station	Mean date last 32°F. in spring	Mean date first 32°F. in fall	Mean freeze-free period (no. days)
NEBR.Grand Island	Apr. 29	Oct. 6	160
Lincoln	Apr. 20	Oct. 17	180
Norfolk	May 4	Oct. 3	152
North Platte	Apr. 30	Oct. 7	160
Omaha	Apr. 14	Oct. 20	189
Valentine Lakes	May 7	Sept. 30	146
NEV.Elko	June 6	Sept. 3	89
Las Vegas	Mar. 13	Nov. 13	245
Reno	May 14	Oct. 2	141
Winnemucca	May 18	Sept. 21	125
N.H.Concord	May 11	Sept. 30	142
N.J.Cape May	Apr. 4	Nov. 15	225
Trenton U	Apr. 8	Nov. 5	211
N.MEX.Albuquerque	Apr. 16	Oct. 29	196
Roswell	Apr. 9	Nov. 2	208
N.Y.Albany	Apr. 27	Oct. 13	169
Binghamton U.	May 4	Oct. 6	154
Buffalo	Apr. 30	Oct. 25	179
New York U.	Apr. 7	Nov. 12	219
Rochester	Apr. 28	Oct. 21	176
Syracuse	Apr. 30	Oct. 15	168
N.C.Asheville U	Apr. 12	Oct. 24	195
Charlotte U	Mar. 21	Nov. 15	239
Greenville	Mar. 28	Nov. 5	222
Hatteras	Feb. 25	Dec. 18	296
Raleigh U	Mar. 24	Nov. 16	237
Wilmington U.	Mar. 8	Nov. 24	262
N.DAK.Bismarck	May 11	Sept. 24	136
Devils Lake U	May 18	Sept. 22	127
Fargo	May 13	Sept. 27	137
Williston U	May 14	Sept. 23	132
OHIO.Akron-Canton	Apr. 29	Oct. 20	173
Cincinnati (Abbe)	Apr. 15	Oct. 25	192
Cleveland	Apr. 21	Nov. 2	195
Columbus U.	Apr. 17	Oct. 30	196
Dayton	Apr. 20	Oct. 21	184
Toledo	Apr. 24	Oct. 25	184
OKLA.Okla.City U.	Mar. 28	Nov. 7	223
Tulsa	Mar. 31	Nov. 2	216
OREG.Astoria	Mar. 18	Nov. 24	251
Bend	June 17	Aug. 17	62
Medford	Apr. 25	Oct. 20	178
Pendleton	Apr. 27	Oct. 8	163
Portland U.	Feb. 25	Dec. 1	279
Salem	Apr. 14	Oct. 27	197
PA.Allentown	Apr. 20	Oct. 16	180
Harrisburg	Apr. 10	Oct. 28	201
Philadelphia U.	Mar. 30	Nov. 17	232
Pittsburgh	Apr. 20	Oct. 23	187
Scranton U.	Apr. 24	Oct. 14	174
R.I.Providence U.	Apr. 13	Oct. 27	197
S.C.Charleston U.	Feb. 19	Dec. 10	294
Columbia U.	Mar. 14	Nov. 21	252
Greenville	Mar. 23	Nov. 17	239
S.DAK.Huron U	May 4	Sept. 30	149
Rapid City U.	May 7	Oct. 4	150
Sioux Falls U	May 5	Oct. 3	152
TENN.Chattanooga U.	Mar. 26	Nov. 10	229
Knoxville U	Mar. 31	Nov. 6	220
Memphis U	Mar. 20	Nov. 12	237
Nashville U	Mar. 28	Nov. 7	224
TEX.Albany	Mar. 30	Nov. 9	224
Balmorhea	Apr. 1	Nov. 12	226
Beeville	Feb. 21	Dec. 6	288
College Station	Mar. 1	Dec. 1	275
Corsicana	Mar. 13	Nov. 27	259
Dalhart Exp. Sta.	Apr. 23	Oct. 18	178
Dallas	Mar. 18	Nov. 22	249
Del Rio	Feb. 12	Dec. 9	300
Encinal	Feb. 15	Dec. 12	301
Houston	Feb. 5	Dec. 11	309
Lampasas	Apr. 1	Nov. 10	223
Matagorda	Feb. 12	Dec. 17	308
Midland	Apr. 3	Nov. 6	218
Mission	Jan. 30	Dec. 21	325
Mount Pleasant	Mar. 23	Nov. 12	233
Nacogdoches	Mar. 15	Nov. 13	243
Plainview	Apr. 10	Nov. 6	211
Presidio	Mar. 20	Nov. 13	238
Quanah	Mar. 31	Nov. 7	221
San Angelo	Mar. 25	Nov. 15	235
Ysleta	Apr. 6	Oct. 30	207
UTAH.Blanding	May 18	Oct. 14	148
Salt Lake City	Apr. 12	Nov. 1	202
VT.Burlington	May 8	Oct. 3	148
VA.Lynchburg	Apr. 6	Oct. 27	205
Norfolk U	Mar. 18	Nov. 27	254
Richmond U.	Apr. 2	Nov. 8	220
Roanoke	Apr. 20	Oct. 24	187
WASH.Bumping Lake	June 17	Aug. 16	60
Seattle U	Feb. 23	Dec. 1	281
Spokane	Apr. 20	Oct. 12	175
Tatoosh Island	Jan. 25	Dec. 20	329
Walla Walla U	Mar. 28	Nov. 1	218
Yakima	Apr. 19	Oct. 15	179
W.VA.Charleston	Apr. 18	Oct. 28	193
Parkersburg	Apr. 16	Oct. 21	189
WIS.Green Bay	May 6	Oct. 13	161
La Crosse U	May 1	Oct. 8	161
Madison U	Apr. 26	Oct. 19	177
Milwaukee U	Apr. 20	Oct. 25	188
WYO.Casper	May 18	Sept. 25	130
Cheyenne	May 20	Sept. 27	130
Lander	May 15	Sept. 20	128
Sheridan	May 21	Sept. 21	123

* Occurs in less than 1 year in 10. No freeze of record in Key West, Fla.
U Indicates urban.

Charts and tabulation were derived from the Freeze Data tabulation in Climatography of the United States No. 60 - Climates of the States.

MEAN PERCENTAGE OF POSSIBLE SUNSHINE

STATE AND STATION	YEARS	JAN.	FEB.	MAR.	APR.	MAY	JUNE	JULY	AUG.	SEPT.	OCT.	NOV.	DEC.	ANNUAL
ALA. BIRMINGHAM	56	43	49	56	63	66	67	62	65	66	67	58	44	59
MONTGOMERY	49	51	53	61	69	73	72	66	69	69	71	64	48	64
ALASKA. ANCHORAGE	19	39	46	56	58	50	51	45	39	35	32	33	29	45
FAIRBANKS	20	34	50	61	68	55	53	45	35	31	28	38	29	44
JUNEAU	14	30	32	39	37	34	35	28	30	25	18	21	18	30
NOME	29	44	46	48	53	51	48	32	26	34	35	36	30	41
ARIZ. PHOENIX	64	76	79	83	88	93	94	84	84	89	88	84	77	85
YUMA	52	83	87	91	94	97	98	92	91	93	93	90	83	91
ARK. LITTLE ROCK	66	44	53	57	62	67	72	71	73	71	74	58	47	62
CALIF. EUREKA	49	40	44	50	53	54	56	51	46	52	48	42	39	49
FRESNO	55	46	63	72	83	89	94	97	97	93	87	73	47	78
LOS ANGELES	63	70	69	70	67	68	69	80	81	80	76	79	72	73
RED BLUFF	39	50	60	65	75	79	86	95	94	89	77	64	50	75
SACRAMENTO	48	44	57	67	76	82	90	96	95	92	82	65	44	77
SAN DIEGO	68	68	67	68	66	60	60	67	70	70	70	76	71	68
SAN FRANCISCO	64	53	57	63	69	70	75	68	63	70	70	62	54	66
COLO. DENVER	64	67	67	65	63	61	69	68	68	71	71	67	65	67
GRAND JUNCTION	57	58	62	64	67	71	79	76	72	77	74	67	58	69
CONN. HARTFORD	48	46	55	56	54	57	60	62	60	57	55	46	46	56
D. C. WASHINGTON	66	46	53	56	57	61	64	64	62	62	61	54	47	58
FLA. APALACHICOLA	26	59	62	62	71	77	70	64	63	62	74	66	53	65
JACKSONVILLE	60	58	59	66	71	71	63	62	63	58	58	61	53	62
KEY WEST	45	68	75	78	78	76	70	69	71	65	65	69	66	71
MIAMI BEACH	48	66	72	73	73	68	62	65	67	62	62	65	65	67
TAMPA	63	63	67	71	74	75	66	61	64	64	67	67	61	68
GA. ATLANTA	65	48	53	57	65	68	68	62	63	65	67	60	47	60
HAWAII. HILO	9	48	42	41	34	31	41	44	38	42	41	34	36	39
HONOLULU	53	62	64	60	62	64	66	67	70	70	68	63	60	65
LIHUE	9	48	48	48	46	51	60	58	59	67	58	51	49	54
IDAHO. BOISE	20	40	48	59	67	68	75	89	86	81	66	46	37	66
POCATELLO	21	37	47	58	64	66	72	82	81	78	66	48	36	64
ILL. CAIRO	30	46	53	59	65	71	77	82	79	75	73	56	46	65
CHICAGO	66	44	49	53	56	63	69	73	70	65	61	47	41	59
SPRINGFIELD	59	47	51	54	58	64	69	76	72	73	64	53	45	60
IND. EVANSVILLE	48	42	49	55	61	67	73	78	76	73	67	52	42	64
FT. WAYNE	48	38	44	51	55	62	69	74	69	64	58	41	38	57
INDIANAPOLIS	63	41	47	49	55	62	68	74	70	68	64	48	39	59
IOWA. DES MOINES	66	56	56	56	59	62	66	75	70	64	64	53	48	62
DUBUQUE	54	48	52	52	58	60	63	73	67	61	55	44	40	57
SIOUX CITY	52	55	58	58	59	63	67	75	72	67	65	53	50	63
KANS. CONCORDIA	52	60	60	62	63	65	73	79	76	72	70	64	58	67
DODGE CITY	70	67	66	68	68	68	74	78	78	76	75	70	67	71
WICHITA	46	61	63	64	64	66	73	80	77	73	69	67	59	69
KY. LOUISVILLE	59	41	47	52	57	64	68	72	69	68	64	51	39	59
LA. NEW ORLEANS	69	49	50	57	63	66	64	58	60	64	70	60	46	59
SHREVEPORT	18	48	54	58	60	69	78	79	80	79	77	65	60	69
MAINE. EASTPORT	58	45	51	52	52	51	53	55	57	54	50	37	40	50
MASS. BOSTON	67	47	56	57	56	59	62	64	63	61	58	48	48	57
MICH. ALPENA	45	29	43	52	56	59	64	70	64	52	44	24	22	51
DETROIT	69	34	42	48	52	58	65	69	66	61	54	35	29	53
GRAND RAPIDS	56	26	37	48	54	60	66	72	67	58	50	31	22	49
MARQUETTE	55	31	40	47	52	53	56	63	57	47	38	24	24	47
S. STE. MARIE	60	28	44	50	54	54	59	63	58	45	36	21	22	47
MINN. DULUTH	49	47	55	60	58	58	60	68	63	53	47	36	40	55
MINNEAPOLIS	45	49	54	55	57	60	64	72	69	60	54	40	40	56
MISS. VICKSBURG	66	46	50	57	64	69	73	69	72	74	71	60	45	64
MO. KANSAS CITY	69	55	57	59	60	64	70	76	73	70	67	59	52	65
ST. LOUIS	68	48	49	56	59	64	68	72	68	67	65	54	44	61
SPRINGFIELD	45	48	54	57	60	63	69	77	72	71	65	58	48	63
MONT. HAVRE	55	49	58	61	63	63	65	78	75	64	57	48	46	62
HELENA	65	46	55	58	60	59	63	77	74	63	57	48	43	60
KALISPELL	50	28	40	49	57	58	60	77	73	61	50	28	20	53
NEBR. LINCOLN	55	57	59	60	60	63	69	76	71	67	66	59	55	64
NORTH PLATTE	53	63	63	64	62	64	72	78	74	72	70	62	58	68
NEV. ELY	21	61	64	68	65	67	79	79	81	81	73	67	62	72
LAS VEGAS	19	74	77	78	81	85	91	84	86	92	84	83	75	82
RENO	51	59	64	69	75	77	82	90	89	86	76	68	56	76
WINNEMUCCA	53	52	60	64	70	76	83	90	90	86	75	62	53	74

These charts and tabulation derived from "Normals, Means, and Extremes" table in U. S. Weather Bureau publication Local Climatological Data.

STATE AND STATION	YEARS	JAN.	FEB.	MAR.	APR.	MAY	JUNE	JULY	AUG.	SEPT.	OCT.	NOV.	DEC.	ANNUAL
N. H. CONCORD	44	48	53	55	53	51	56	57	58	55	50	43	43	52
N. J. ATLANTIC CITY	62	51	57	58	59	62	65	67	66	65	54	58	52	60
N. MEX. ALBUQUERQUE	28	70	72	72	76	79	84	76	75	81	80	79	70	76
ROSWELL	47	69	72	75	77	76	80	76	75	74	74	74	69	74
N. Y. ALBANY	63	43	51	53	53	57	62	63	61	58	54	39	38	53
BINGHAMTON	63	31	39	41	44	50	56	54	51	47	43	29	26	44
BUFFALO	49	32	41	49	51	59	67	70	67	60	51	31	28	53
CANTON	43	37	47	50	48	54	61	63	61	54	45	30	31	49
NEW YORK	83	49	56	57	59	62	65	66	64	64	61	53	50	59
SYRACUSE	49	31	38	45	50	58	64	67	63	56	47	29	26	50
N. C. ASHEVILLE	57	48	53	56	61	64	63	59	59	62	64	59	48	58
RALEIGH	61	50	56	59	64	67	65	62	62	63	64	62	52	61
N. DAK. BISMARCK	65	52	58	56	57	58	61	73	69	62	59	49	48	59
DEVILS LAKE	55	53	60	59	60	59	62	71	67	59	56	44	45	58
FARGO	39	47	55	56	58	62	63	73	69	60	57	39	46	59
WILLISTON	43	51	59	60	63	66	66	78	75	65	60	48	48	63
OHIO, CINCINNATI	44	41	46	52	56	62	69	72	68	68	60	46	39	57
CLEVELAND	65	29	36	45	52	61	67	71	68	62	54	32	25	50
COLUMBUS	65	36	44	49	54	63	68	71	68	66	60	44	35	55
OKLA. OKLAHOMA CITY	62	57	60	63	64	65	74	78	78	74	68	64	57	68
OREG. BAKER	46	41	49	56	61	63	67	83	81	74	62	46	37	60
PORTLAND	69	27	34	41	49	52	55	70	65	55	42	28	23	48
ROSEBURG	29	24	32	40	51	57	59	79	77	68	42	28	18	51
PA. HARRISBURG	60	43	52	55	57	61	65	68	63	62	58	47	43	57
PHILADELPHIA	66	45	56	57	58	61	62	64	61	62	61	53	49	57
PITTSBURGH	63	32	39	45	50	57	62	64	61	62	54	39	30	51
R. I. BLOCK ISLAND	48	45	54	47	56	58	60	62	62	60	59	50	44	56
S. C. CHARLESTON	61	58	60	65	72	73	70	66	66	67	68	68	57	66
COLUMBIA	55	53	57	62	68	69	68	63	65	64	68	64	51	63
S. DAK. HURON	62	55	62	60	62	65	68	76	72	66	61	52	49	63
RAPID CITY	53	58	62	63	62	61	66	73	73	69	66	58	54	64
TENN. KNOXVILLE	62	42	49	53	59	64	66	64	59	64	64	53	41	57
MEMPHIS	55	44	51	57	64	68	74	73	74	70	69	58	45	64
NASHVILLE	63	42	47	54	60	65	69	69	68	69	65	55	42	59
TEX. ABILENE	14	64	68	73	66	73	86	83	85	73	71	72	66	73
AMARILLO	54	71	71	75	75	75	82	81	81	79	76	76	70	76
AUSTIN	33	46	50	57	60	62	72	76	79	70	70	57	49	63
BROWNSVILLE	37	44	49	51	57	65	73	78	78	67	70	54	44	61
DEL RIO	36	53	55	61	63	60	66	75	80	69	66	58	52	63
EL PASO	53	74	77	81	85	87	87	78	78	80	82	80	73	80
FT. WORTH	33	56	57	65	66	67	75	78	78	74	70	63	58	68
GALVESTON	66	50	50	55	61	69	76	72	71	70	74	62	49	63
SAN ANTONIO	57	48	51	56	58	60	69	74	75	69	67	55	49	62
UTAH, SALT LAKE CITY	22	48	53	61	68	73	78	82	82	84	73	56	49	69
VT. BURLINGTON	54	34	43	48	47	53	59	62	59	51	43	25	24	46
VA. NORFOLK	60	50	57	60	63	67	66	66	66	63	64	60	51	62
RICHMOND	56	49	55	59	63	67	66	65	62	63	64	58	50	61
WASH. NORTH HEAD	44	28	37	42	48	48	48	50	46	48	41	31	27	41
SEATTLE	26	27	34	42	48	53	48	62	56	53	36	28	24	45
SPOKANE	62	26	41	53	63	64	68	82	79	68	53	28	22	58
TATOOSH ISLAND	49	26	36	39	45	47	46	48	44	47	38	26	23	40
WALLA WALLA	44	24	35	51	63	67	72	86	84	72	59	33	20	60
YAKIMA	18	34	49	62	70	72	74	86	86	74	61	38	29	65
W. VA. ELKINS	55	33	37	42	47	55	55	56	53	55	51	41	33	48
PARKERSBURG	62	30	36	42	49	56	60	63	60	60	53	37	29	48
WIS. GREEN BAY	57	44	51	55	56	58	64	70	65	58	52	40	40	55
MADISON	59	44	49	52	53	58	64	70	66	60	56	41	38	56
MILWAUKEE	59	44	48	53	56	60	65	73	67	62	56	44	39	57
WYO. CHEYENNE	63	65	66	64	61	59	68	70	68	69	69	65	63	66
LANDER	57	66	70	71	66	65	74	76	75	72	67	61	62	69
SHERIDAN	52	56	61	62	61	61	67	76	74	67	60	53	52	64
YELLOWSTONE PARK	35	39	51	55	57	56	63	73	71	65	57	45	38	56
P. R. SAN JUAN	57	64	69	71	66	59	62	65	67	61	63	63	65	65

Based on period of record through December 1959, except in a few instances.

See tables beginning on page 329 for any adjustments indicated by 1941-1970 updates of normals, means, and extremes data.

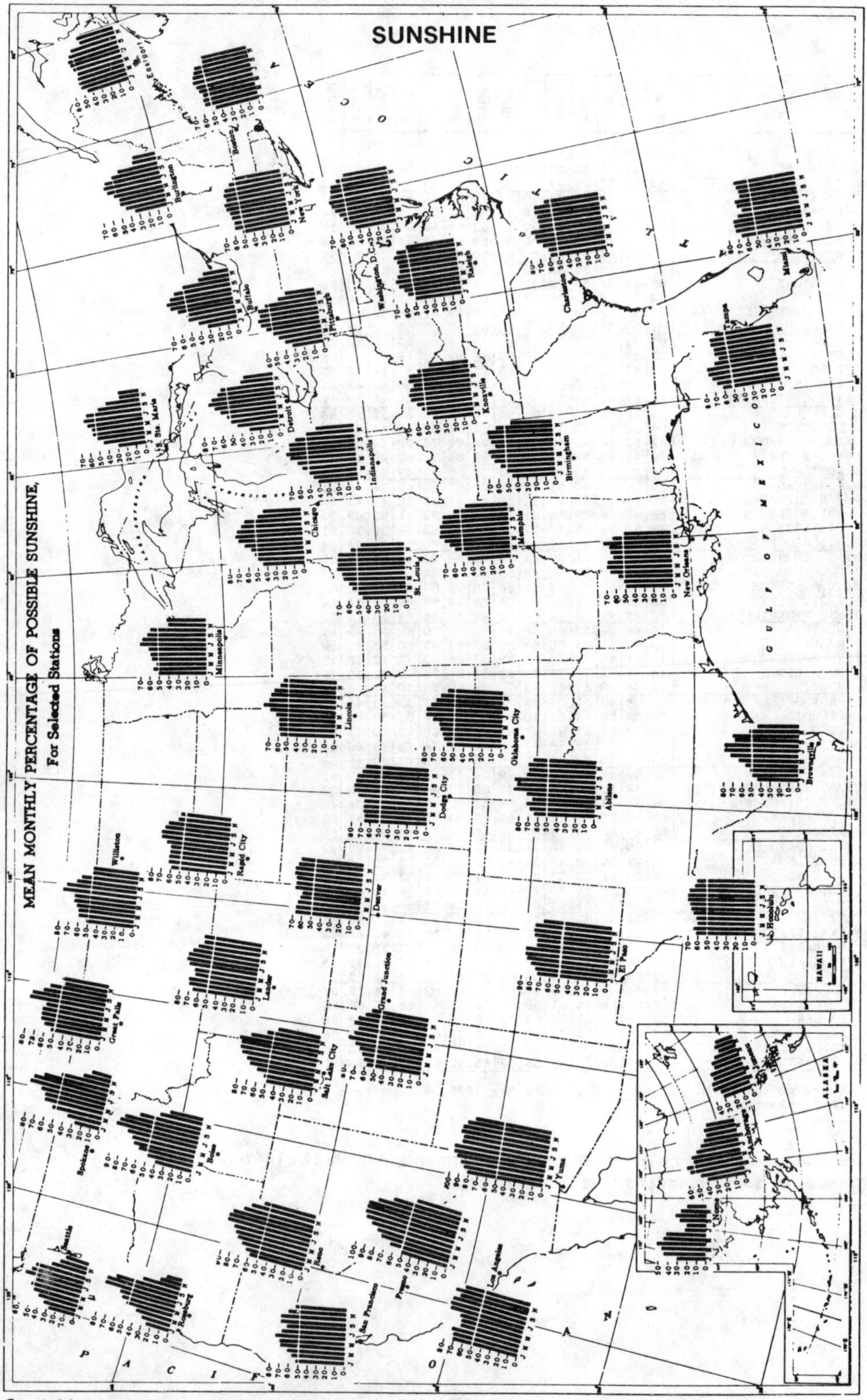

See tables beginning on page 329 for any adjustments indicated by 1941-1970 updates of normals, means, and extremes data.

PREVAILING WIND DIRECTION

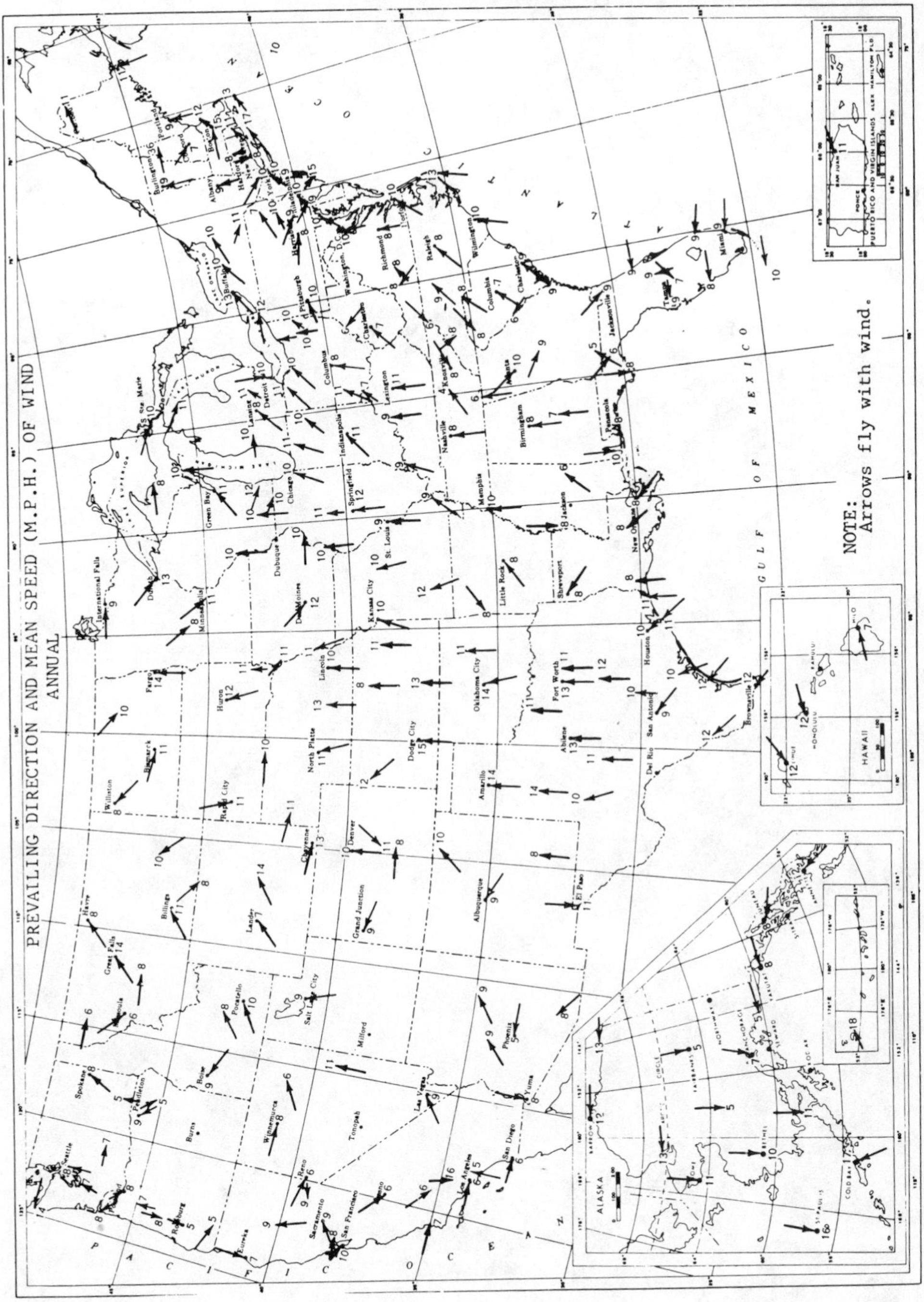

STORMS AND SEVERE WEATHER

HURRICANES

They are tropical children, the offspring of ocean and atmosphere, powered by heat from the sea, driven by the easterly trades and temperate westerlies, the high planetary winds, and their own fierce energy. In their cloudy arms and around their tranquil core, winds blow with lethal velocity, the ocean develops an inundating surge, and, as they move toward land, tornadoes now and then flutter down from the advancing wall of thunderclouds.

Compared to the great cyclonic storm systems of the temperate zone they are of moderate size, and their worst winds do not approach tornado velocities. Still, their broad spiral base may dominate weather over thousands of square miles, and from the earth's surface into the lower stratosphere. Their winds may reach 200 miles per hour, and their lifespan is measured in days or weeks, not minutes or hours. No other atmospheric disturbance combines duration, size, and violence more destructively.

As they occur in different oceans and hemispheres, they bear names given locally; *baguio* in the Philippines, *cyclone* in the Indian Ocean, *typhoon* in the Pacific. In our hemisphere, the name is *Hurricane** – the greatest storm on earth.

When do hurricanes develop?

The direct rays of the sun touch the Equator and strike northward toward the Tropic of Cancer, following the annual track of the sun across the earth's surface. In the Southern Hemisphere winter has begun, and it is summer north of the Equator. Behind the sun's passage the sea and air grow warmer; the polar air of winter begins its gradual retreat.

The northward shift of the sun also brings the season of tropical cyclone to the Northern Hemisphere, a season that is ending for the Pacific and Indian Oceans south of the Equator. Along our coasts and those of Asia, it is time to look seaward, to guard against the season's storms. Over the Pacific, the tropical cyclone season is never quite over; but varies in intensity. Every year, conditions east of the Philippines send a score of violent storms howling toward Asia, but it is worst from June through October. Southwest of Mexico, a few Pacific hurricanes will grow during spring and summer, but most will die at sea or perish over the desert or strike the lower California coast as squalls.

Along our Atlantic and Gulf coasts, the nominal hurricane season is from June through November. Early in the season, the Caribbean and Gulf of Mexico are the principal areas of origin; in July and August, the center shifts eastward and by September spreads from the Bahamas southeastward to the Lesser Antilles, and eastward to the Cape Verde islands off the west coast of Africa. After mid-September, principal areas of origin shift back to the western Caribbean and the Gulf of Mexico. If this is an average year, there will be fewer than 10 tropical cyclones, of which about six will develop into hurricanes. These will kill 50 or 100 persons between Texas and Maine and cause property damage of more than $100 million. If it is a worse-than-average year, we will suffer several hundred deaths, and property damage will run to billions of dollars.

From the National Hurricane Center in Miami, a radar fence reaches westward to Texas, northward to New England, providing NOAA National Weather Service stations along the coast a 200-mile look into offshore disturbances. In Maryland, the giant

---

*From the Spanish *huracan*, probably derived from the Mayan storm god, *Hunraken*; the Quiche god of thunder and lightning, *hurakan*; and numerous other Caribbean Indian terms for evil spirit, big wind, and the like.

computers of the National Meteorological Center digest the myriad bits of data – atmospheric pressure, temperature, surface winds and winds aloft, humidity – received from weather stations and ships monitoring the atmospheric setting hour to hour, day to day. Cloud photographs from NOAA spacecraft orbiting the earth are received at the National Environmental Satellite Service in Maryland, and studied for the telltale spiral on the warming sea. The crews of U.S. Navy, Air Force, and Coast Guard aircraft over the Gulf of Mexico, Caribbean, and Atlantic watch the sky with special emphasis – waiting for the storm that will bear a lady's name.

What causes a hurricane?

Hurricane formation was once believed to result from an intensification of the convective forces which produce the cumulonimbus towers of the doldrums, whose light winds have filled our literature with ships becalmed and thirsty sailors. This view of hurricane generation held that surface heating caused warm moist air to ascend convectively to levels where condensation produced cumulonimbus clouds, which, after an inexplicable drop in atmospheric pressure, coalesced and were spun into a cyclonic motion by coriolis force.

This hypothesis left much to be desired. Although some hurricanes develop from disturbances beginning in the doldrums, very few reach maturity in that region. Also, the high incidence of seemingly ideal convective situations does not match the low incidence of Atlantic hurricanes. Finally, the hypothesis did not explain the drop in atmospheric pressure, so essential to development of hurricane-force winds.

There is still no exact understanding of the triggering mechanism involved in hurricane generation, the balance of conditions needed to generate hurricane circulation, and the relationships between large- and small-scale atmospheric processes. But scientists today, treating the hurricane system as an atmospheric heat engine, present a more comprehensive and convincing view.

They begin with a starter mechanism in which either internal or external forces intensify the initial disturbance – the intruding polar trough, easterly wave, or an eddy from an active ITC* – as when diverging flow at upper levels becomes superimposed above the area of convergence in the low-altitude disturbance, setting up a vertical circulation which may be organized into a hurricane.

The initial disturbance becomes a region into which low-level air from the surrounding area begins to flow, accelerating the convection already occurring inside the disturbance. The vertical circulation becomes increasingly well organized as water vapor in the ascending moist layer is condensed (releasing large amounts of heat energy to drive the wind system) and as the system is swept into a counterclockwise cyclonic spiral. But this incipient hurricane would soon fill up because of inflow at lower levels unless the chimney in which converging air surges upward is provided the exhaust mechanism of high-altitude winds.

These pump ascending air out of the cyclonic system into a high-altitude anticyclone, which transports the air well away from the disturbance before sinking occurs. Thus, a large-scale vertical circulation is set up in which low-level air is spiraled up the cyclonic twisting of the disturbance, and, after a trajectory over the sea, returned to lower altitudes some distance from the storm. This pumping action – and the heat released by the ascending air – may account for the sudden drop of atmospheric pressure at the surface, which produces the steep pressure gradient along which winds reach hurricane proportions.

It is believed that the interaction of low-level and high-altitude wind systems determines the intensity the hurricane will attain. If less air is pumped out than

---

* ITC – intertropical convergence (zone). Also known as "doldrums.'

converges at low levels, the system will fill and die out. If more is pumped out than flows in, the circulation will be sustained and will intensify. It is also believed that planetary wind systems, displaced northward, set up an essential large-scale flow which supports the budding storm.

Research has shown that any process which increases the rate of low-level inflow is favorable for hurricane development, provided the inflowing air carries sufficient heat and moisture to fuel the hurricane's power system. It has also been shown that air above the developing disturbance at altitudes between 20,000 and 40,000 feet increases one to three degrees in temperature about 24 hours before the disturbance develops into a hurricane. But it is not known whether low-level inflow and high-level warming *cause* hurricanes. They could very well be measurable symptoms of another effect which actually triggers the storm's increase to hurricane intensity.

The view of hurricanes as atmospheric engines is necessarily a general one. The exact role of each contributor is not completely understood. The engine seems to be both inefficient and unreliable; a myriad of delicate conditions must be satisfied for the atmosphere to produce a hurricane. Their relative infrequency indicates that many a potentially healthy hurricane ends early as a misfiring dud of a disturbance, somewhere over the sea.

Portrait of a hurricane—

Given the cyclonic circulation, the disturbance is distinguished by its form and intensity as it changes from tropical disturbance, to tropical depression, to tropical storm—to hurricane. The early forms are a kind of adolesence. The hurricane, as a young adult taking strength from the warm ocean, is unique in both structure and ferocity.

It stands upon the sea as a whirlwind of awful violence. On average, its great spiral covers an area some 100 miles in diameter with winds greater than 74 miles per hour, and spreads gale-force winds—winds above 40 miles per hour—over a 400-mile-diameter area. Its cyclonic spiral is marked by heavy cloud bands from which torrential rains fall, separated by areas of light rain or no rain at all; these spiral bands ascend in decks of cumulus and cumulonimbus clouds to the convective limit of cloud formation, where condensing water vapor is swept off as ice-crystal wisps of cirrus clouds. Thunderstorm electrical activity is observed in these bands, both as lightning and as tiny electrostatic discharges.

In the lower few thousand feet, air flows in through the cyclone, and is whipped upward through ascending columns of air near the center. The size and intensity decrease with altitude, the cyclonic circulation being gradually replaced above 40,000 feet by an anticyclonic circulation centered hundreds of miles away—the enormous high-altitude pump which is the exhaust system of the hurricane heat engine.

At lower levels, where the hurricane is most intense, winds on the rim of the storm follow a wide pattern, like the slower currents around the edge of a whirlpool; and, like those currents, these winds accelerate as they approach the center of the vortex. The outer band has light winds at the rim of the storm, perhaps no more than 30 miles per hour; within 30 miles of the center, winds may have velocities exceeding 150 miles per hour. The inner band is the region of maximum wind velocity, where the storm's worst winds are felt, and where ascending air is chimneyed upward, releasing heat to drive the storm. In most hurricanes, these winds reach 100 miles per hour—and more than 200 miles per hour in the most memorable ones.

Hurricane winds are produced, as are all winds, by differences in atmospheric pressure, or density. The pressure gradient—the rate of pressure change with distance—produced in hurricanes is the most severe in the atmosphere, excepting only the pressure change across the narrow funnel of a tornado.

Atmospheric pressure is expressed as the height of a column of mercury that can be supported by the weight of the overlying air at a given time. In North America, barometric measurements at sea level seldom go below 29 inches of mercury, and in the Tropics it is generally close to 30 inches under normal conditions. Around a hurricane, however, pressure drops with increasing sharpness from a few points below 30 inches on the periphery to pressures of the order of 28 inches near the center. The lowest barometric reading of record for the United States is the 26.35 inches obtained during a hurricane at Lower Matecumbe Key in September 1935. Pressure has been observed to drop more than an inch per hour, with a pressure gradient amounting to a change of 0.11 inch per mile.

Weather maps show atmospheric pressure in millibars, units equal to 1/1000 bar. The bar is a unit of pressure equal to 29.53 inches of mercury, in the English system; and to 1 million dynes per square centimeter in the centimeter-gram-second (metric) system. Use of the millibar notation permits worldwide compatibility of meteorological data.

Winds flow inward toward the low pressure of the eye—

In the hurricane, winds flow toward the low pressure in the warm, comparatively calm core. There, converging air is whirled upward by convection, the mechanical thrusting of other converging air, and the pumping action of high-altitude circulations. This spiral is marked by the thick cloud walls curling inward toward the storm center, releasing heavy precipitation and enormous quantities of heat energy. At the center, surrounded by a band in which this strong vertical circulation is greatest, is the core—the eye of the hurricane.

The eye, like spiral rainbands, is unique to the hurricane; no other atmospheric phenomenon has this calm core. On the average, eye diameter is about 14 miles, although diameters of 25 miles are not unusual. From the heated tower of maximum winds and cumulonimbus clouds, winds diminish rapidly to something less than 15 miles per hour in the eye; at the opposite wall, winds increase again, but come from the opposite direction because of the cyclonic circulation of the storm. To primitive man, this transformation of storm into comparative calm, and calm into violence from another quarter must have seemed an excessive whim of arbitrary gods. Still, it is spectacular. The eye's existence in the midst of opaque rainsqualls and hurricane winds, the intermittent bursts of blue sky and sunlight through light clouds in the core of the cyclone, the relatively calm sea beneath, the galleried cumulus and cumulonimbus clouds— these make lyricists of all who see them.

That is how an average hurricane is structured. But every hurricane is individual, and the more or less orderly circulation described here omits the extreme variability and instability within the storm system. Pressure and temperature gradients fluctuate wildly across the storm as the hurricane maintains its erratic life in the face of forces which will ultimately destroy it. If it is an August storm, its average life expectancy is 12 days; if a July or November storm, it lives an average of 8.

While a hurricane lives, the transaction of energy within its circulation is immense. If a hurricane is taken to be a heat engine, the efficiency with which it converts thermal to mechanical energy is quite low, near 3 percent. Nevertheless, the condensation heat energy released by a hurricane in one day often is the equivalent of that released by fusion of 400 20-megaton hydrogen bombs. Put in more comprehensible terms, one day's released energy, converted to electricity, would supply the United States' electrical needs for more than six months. There is no satisfactory way of scaling down a hurricane; it is immense to us, like the ocean and atmosphere themselves.

When a hurricane moves toward land—

Once generated, a hurricane tends to survive while it is over warm water, for it is the temperature difference between air and water that drives and sustains the storm system. But the forces which control its movement are destructive; they drive the storm ashore or over the colder water beyond the tropics where it will fill and die, or be resurrected as a storm of another type. This thrust away from the tropics is the clockwise curve which takes typhoons of the tropical Pacific across the coastlines of Japan and northern Asia, and the hurricanes of the tropical North Atlantic Caribbean, and Gulf of Mexico across the eastern United States.

Even before a hurricane forms, the embryonic storm has forward motion, driven by the easterly flow in which it is embedded. While the easterly drift is small—less than 20 miles per hour—intensification is favored; greater movement generally inhibits intensification during the early stages. When the hurricane matures, greater forward motion is frequently accompanied by intensification. The intensification which often follows acceleration is usually shortlived. At temperate latitudes, a few hurricanes reach forward speeds of 60 miles per hour.

Forecasting the direction this steering current will take the hurricane is complicated by several factors. The hurricane winds mask the basic current over a large area, both horizontally and vertically. Also, the steering mechanism is incompletely understood. It is not known, for example, what fraction of the storm's forward motion comes from its own internal energy and what portion is applied by the basic current, which is ordinarily the dominant force.

The tracks of hurricanes are as individual as the storms themselves. No two tracks are precisely superimposed, and only the most general trends can be established. A hurricane drifting westward past Cuba may seem poised to recurve north and east across Florida, only to dither, then spin off through the Gulf of Mexico—to Yucatan or New Orleans or Brownsville. Or a hurricane may follow a course from birth to death whose only consistency is an erratic, aimless looping across the tropics. Although most hurricanes ultimately recurve, there have been numerous exceptions. Hurricane Inez of September 1966, which doubled back instead of recurving and finally died in central Mexico, is a case in point.

Without heat energy from the sea a hurricane dies—

From generation, a hurricane is acted upon by those forces which finally destroy it. At middle altitudes, air flows through the cyclonic vortex, cooling the warm core and acting as a thermal brake on storm intensity. Friction between the storm and ocean is only slightly inhibiting. It is possible that, without frictional effects, there would not be enough low-level inflow to keep the storm fueled with moist, warm air. Over land, frictional effects are greater and contribute to filling and dissipating the storm—although it is the loss of energy from the sea, not friction, which finally kills a hurricane.

Hurricane intensity is unquestionably linked to the warmth of ocean waters in its path. The storms do not form over water much below 80° Fahrenheit (F.), and decreases in water temperature have a direct influence on the rate at which the hurricane decays. Off California, small hurricanes deteriorate rapidly once they reach the cold eastern Pacific waters; larger hurricanes in the Atlantic may travel for longer periods over cold North Atlantic water, the rate of decay also being a function of storm size and intensity.

Over land, a hurricane decays rapidly. Without its heat source, and with the added effects of frictional drag, the circulation is rapidly destroyed. Hurricane rains, however, may continue even after the winds are much depleted. It has been estimated that hurricane rainfall—with or without destructive winds—accounts for nearly a fourth of the southeastern United States' annual precipitation.

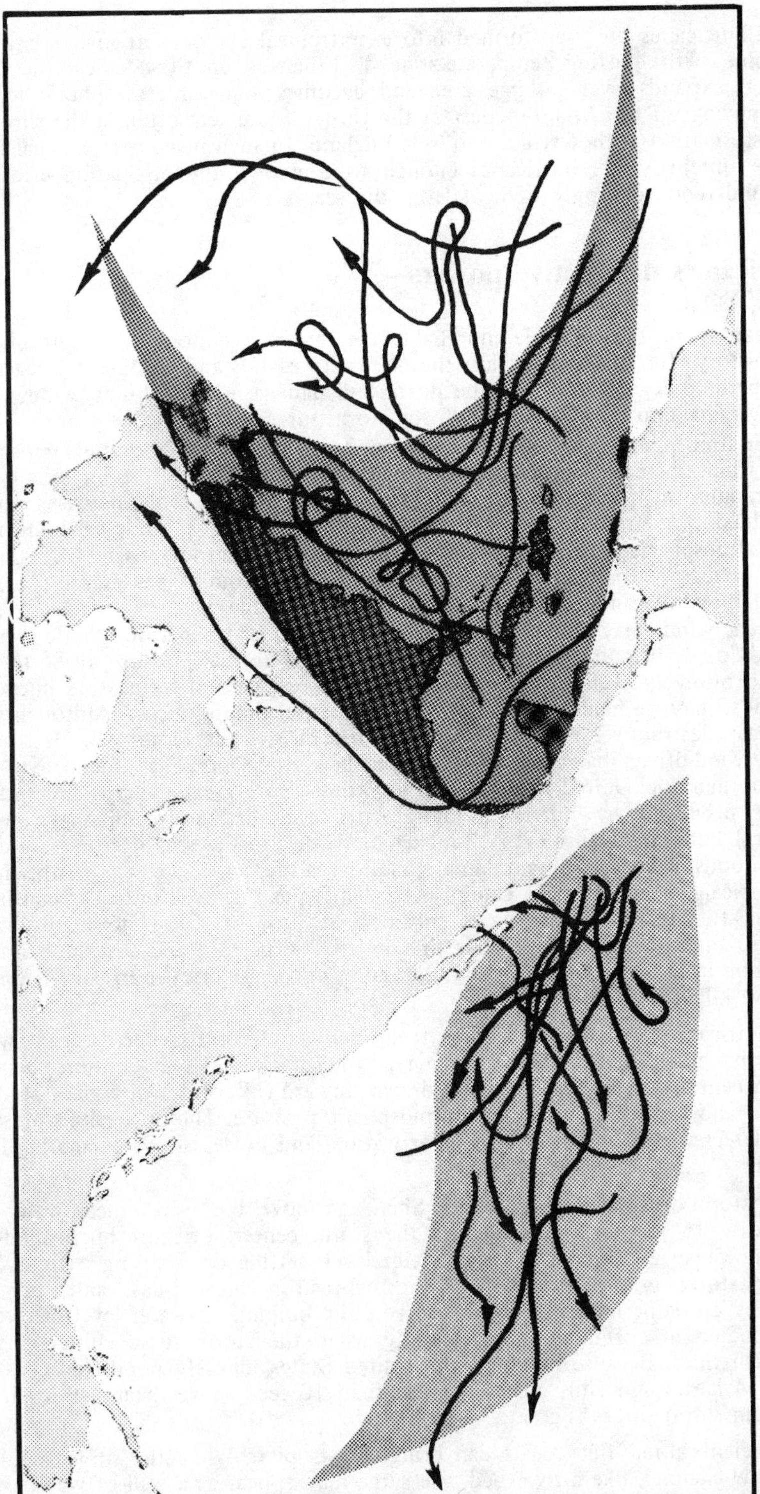

The paths followed by selected, individual hurricanes are shown on the map above as thin black lines. Exactly why the storms change direction as they do—sometimes retracing their previous paths, sometimes looping before continuing—is not completely understood.

Many hurricanes are transformed into extratropical cyclones at higher latitudes, or combine with existing temperate-zone disturbances. In these cases, the storm circulation expands over a large area and becomes a major atmospheric feature. Storms moving up the Atlantic coast of the United States are often in the throes of this transformation as they strike into New England. In such instances, external forces sometimes intensify the hurricanes enough to overcome the dissipating effects of friction and reduced supply of heat from the sea.

A hurricane's destructive powers—

Hurricanes are the unstable, unreliable creatures of a moment in our planet's natural history. But the destruction they bring to islands and continental coastlines in their paths is legend. Most of the death and damage is brought by wind, flood-producing rains, and most lethal of all, the storm surge.

Normal atmospheric pressure at sea level is approximately 2,000 pounds per square foot. As winds increase, pressure against objects is added at a disproportionate rate. Pressure mounts with the square of wind velocity, and over a tenfold increases in wind speed, added pressure increases 100-fold. For example, a 25-mile-per-hour wind increases atmospheric pressure by about 2 pounds per square foot; a wind of 200 miles per hour increases atmospheric pressure by about 220 pounds per square foot. For some structures, the added force is sufficient to cause failure.

Hurricane winds may also produce an inverse effect, as when atmospheric pressure outside a closed structure is reduced enough to cause normal pressure inside to flow outward explosively. Tall structures like radio towers, fretted by gusting hurricane-force winds, may be made to oscillate until structural failure occurs. Although wind is the least destructive and least lethal of the hurricane's battery of destructive elements, wind-driven barrages of debris can be quite dangerous, and in areas less developed than the United States, hurricane winds cause great damage and fatality.

Floods produced by hurricane rainfall are more destructive than the winds. The typical hurricane brings 6 to 12 inches of rainfall to the area it crosses, and the resulting floods have caused great damage and loss of life, particularly in mountainous areas. Hurricane Diane of 1955 caused little damage as it moved onto the continent; but, long after its hurricane winds subsided, it brought floods to Pennsylvania, New York, and New England–floods that killed 200 persons and cost an estimated $700 million in damage. In the West Indies and Central America, hurricane-triggered floods have killed thousands.

The hurricane's worst killer comes from the sea. Over the deep ocean, waves generated by hurricane-force winds may reach heights of 50 feet or more, beneath the storm center, the ocean surface is drawn upward (like water in a giant straw) a foot or so above normal by reduced atmospheric pressure. The hurricane's presence may be detected well in advance of its arrival on land by sea swells emanating from the storm.

As the storm crosses the Continental Shelf and moves coastward, mean water level may increase 15 feet or more. Behind the storm center, offshore hurricane-force winds may cause a decrease in mean water level, setting up a strong current. The advancing storm is superimposed on normal astronomical tides, and, in turn, wind waves are superimposed on the surge; this buildup of water level can cause severe flooding in costal areas, particularly when the storm surge coincides with normal high tides. Because much of the United States' densely populated coastline along the Atlantic and Gulf coasts lies less than 10 feet above mean sea level, the danger from storm surges is great.

Surge heights along flat coasts can bring catastrophe. When the surge is forced up a narrow channel, like a river bed, the surge may appear as a wall of water–what is incorrectly called a "tidal wave."

Wave and current action associated with the surge also causes extensive damage. Water weights some 1,700 pounds per cubic yard; extended pounding by giant waves can demolish any structure not specifically designed to withstand such forces. Currents set up along the coast by the gradient in storm-surge heights and wind combine with the waves to weaken coastal structures. Many buildings withstand hurricane winds until, their foundations undermined by erosion, they are weakened and fail. Waves and currents severely erode beaches and highways, and, in confined harbors, damage to shipping may be extreme. In estuarine and bayou areas, intrusions of salt water endanger the public health–and create bizarre effects like the salt-crazed snakes fleeing Louisiana's flooded bayous.

Hurricane deaths come mostly from flooding

The greatest loss of life associated with hurricanes is caused by flooding due to the storm surge. History is filled with such catastrophes.

In Asia, the price in life has been tragically high. In 1737, storm surges killed 300,000 near Calcutta, and another 50,000 in 1864. In 1876, 100,000 were killed by a storm surge in Backergunge, India. In 1970, a cyclone's storm surge on the coast of East Pakistan killed 200,000 persons according to official figures. Unofficial estimates ran as high as 500,000 dead.

Our hemisphere has had its share of storm-surge deaths. In August 1893, a great storm wave drowned between 1,000 and 2,000 persons in Charleston, S. C.; in October of that same year, a storm surge drowned 1,800 along the Gulf coast. More than 6,000 persons perished in Galveston in 1900, and, in 1928, some 2,000 persons drowned in Florida when a hurricane caused Lake Okeechobee to overflow. A storm surge in November 1932 killed 2,500 in Cuba, and 400 were killed in Florida by the intense hurricane of September 2, 1935. The September 21, 1938, hurricane killed 600 in New England. About 380 persons drowned when Hurricane Audrey struck Louisiana in June 1957.

Over the years, the toll in life has diminished encouragingly. In the United States, reduction in hurricane deaths has been the effect of timely warning for the people along the nation's coasts.

But given the increased population and development of areas affected by hurricanes, damage to fixed property continues to mount. Betsy, in 1965, caused some $1.4 billion in property damage, and the $1.42 billion in damages caused by Camille in 1969 made her the most destructive hurricane ever to strike the U. S. It is expected that this trend will continue until these powerful storms can not only be predicted, but neutralized as well.

Why ladies' names for hurricanes?

The National Hurricane Center flexes the warning service when a tropical disturbance is detected and confirmed by aerial reconnaissance. These initial messages are in the form of bulletins, which alert the system that a suspicious area is under surveillance. Bulletins are also picked up by news media, where the word goes out that NOAA is watching a disturbance for future developments over the Atlantic, Gulf, or Caribbean. If the disturbance intensifies into a tropical cyclone, it is given a lady's name–and gender, for, almost unconsciously, forecasters and news media begin to call the storm "she."

The early Caribbean practice of naming hurricanes for the saint on whose day they occurred was never used in this country, but our substitute was a cumbersome latitude-longtitude identification. The advent of high-speed communications, together with the confusion which arose when more than one tropical cyclone was in progress in the same area, forced a change. For a time, tropical cyclones were designated by

20 JUNE 1972 TIME OF PHOTO 1800 GMT *

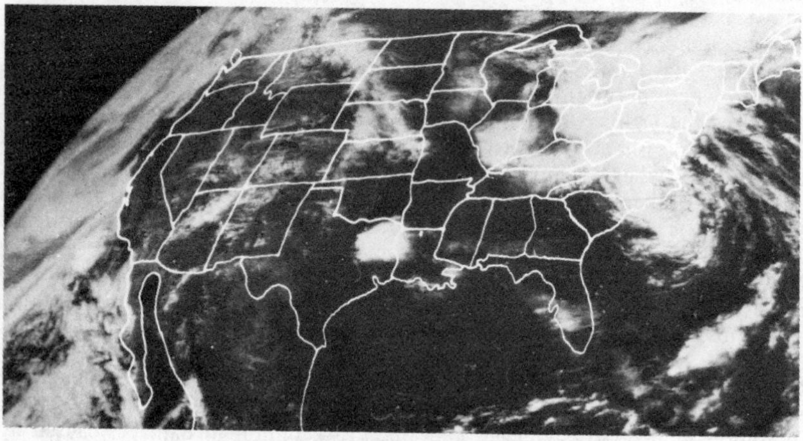

21 JUNE 1972 TIME OF PHOTO 1800 GMT

22 JUNE 1972 TIME OF PHOTO 1800 GMT

*Greenwich Mean Time

23 JUNE 1972

TRACKING A HURRICANE FROM SPACE

Tracking tropical storms by means of special satellites is one of the space age methods of coping with these meteorological monsters. Here, Hurricane Agnes is watched by an orbiting camera over a four day span. Earlier warnings which reduce deaths and destruction have resulted from this TV eye hoisted aloft by NASA's rockets.

letters of the alphabet (e. g., A–1943,) and by the World War II phonetic alphabet, (Able, Baker, Charlie); and it has been suggested that the storms be named from the International Civil Aviation Organization's phonetic system (Apha, Bravo, Cocoa), the letters of the Greek alphabet (Alpha, Beta, Gamma), the names of animals (Antelope, Bear, Coyote), and descriptive adjectives (Annoying, Blustery, Churning). It has also been suggested that the storms carry the names of well-known personalities, places, and things, and the name of mythological figures.

It appears that the feminization of tropical cyclones began during World War II, when weathermen plotting the movement of storms across vast theaters of operations identified them alphabetically, using the names of girls. George R. Stewart's novel, *Storm* (Random House, 1941). may have been the first published account of this practice. Whatever the origin, the use of ladies' names for tropical cyclones has been persistent. Even though some alternative recommendations have had merit, the practice continues, and has been official Weather Service policy since 1953.

HURRICANE NAMES
Atlantic, Caribbean and Gulf of Mexico—

1976—Anna, Belle, Candice, Dottie, Emmy, Frances, Gloria, Holly, Inga, Jill, Kay, Lilias, Maria, Nola, Orpha, Pamela, Ruth, Shirley, Trixie, Vilda, Wynne

1977—Anita, Babe, Clara, Dorothy, Evelyn, Frieda, Grace, Hannah, Ida, Jodie, Kristina, Lois, Mary, Nora, Odel, Penny, Raquel, Sophia, Trudy, Virginia, Willene

1978—Amelia, Bess, Cora, Debra, Ella, Flossie, Greta, Hope, Irma, Juliet, Kendra, Louise, Martha, Noreen, Ora, Paula, Rosalie, Susan, Tanya, Vanessa, Wanda

1979—Angie, Barbara, Cindy, Dot, Eve, Franny, Gwyn, Hedda, Iris, Judy, Karen, Lana, Molly, Nita, Ophelia, Patty, Roberta, Sherry, Tess, Vesta, Wenda

1980—Abby, Bertha, Candy, Dinah, Elsie, Felicia, Georgia, Hedy, Isabel, June, Kim, Lucy, Millie, Nina, Olive, Phyllis, Rosie, Suzy, Theda, Violet, Willette

1981—Arlene, Beth, Chloe, Doria, Edith, Fern, Ginger, Heidi, Irene, Janice, Kristy, Laura, Margo, Nona, Orchid, Portia, Rachel, Sandra, Terese, Verna, Wallis

1982—Agnes, Betty, Carrie, Dawn, Edna, Felice, Gerda, Harriet, Ilene, Jane, Kara, Lucile, Mae, Nadine, Odette, Polly, Rita, Sarah, Tina, Velma, Wendy

1983—Alice, Brenda, Christine, Delia, Ellen, Fran, Gilda, Helen, Imogene, Joy, Kate, Loretta, Madge, Nancy, Ona, Patsy, Rose, Sally, Tam, Vera, Wilda

1984—Alma, Becky, Carmen, Dolly, Elaine, Fifi, Gertrude, Hester, Ivy, Justine, Kathy, Linda, Marsha, Nelly, Olga, Pearl, Roxanne, Sabrina, Thelma, Viola, Wilma

1985—Amy, Blanche, Caroline, Doris, Eloise, Faye, Gladys, Hallie, Ingrid, Julia, Kitty, Lilly, Mabel, Niki, Opal, Peggy, Ruby, Sheila, Tilda, Vicky, Winnie

NOTE: If a storm is large enough to have great historical significance its name may be withdrawn from this "re-cycling" list. (e.g., "Eloise", a major storm in 1975 may be withdrawn and another name beginning with "E" may be placed in the list for 1985.)

In 1960, a semi-permanent list of four sets of names in alphabetical order was introduced. In 1971, the list was expanded to ten sets of names. A separate set of names is used each year, beginning with the first name in each set. The letters Q, U, X, Y, and Z are not included because of the scarcity of names beginning with those letters. After ten years, when the ten sets of names have been used, the sets will be used over again in the same manner.

Typhoons and Pacific hurricanes have also been feminized. In the eastern North Pacific, the alphabetical listing of names is prepared in sets of four, and designations are cycled from year to year. In the central and western North Pacific, the practice differs because of the high incidence of tropical cyclones. The four sets prepared for typhoons originating there are not cycled annually, instead, all names are used consecutively, regardless of the year–for example, if the 1971 typhoon season ended with Virginia, then 1972 would begin with typhoon Wendy, both from the same set of names.

HURRICANE NAMES

Eastern North Pacific

1976 —Annette, Bonny, Celeste, Diana,
1980 Estelle, Fernanda, Gwen, Hyacinth,
1984 Iva, Joanne, Kathleen, Liza, Madeline, Naomi, Orla, Pauline, Rebecca, Simone, Tara, Valerie, Willa

1977 —Ava, Bernice, Claudia, Doreen,
1981 Emily, Florence, Glenda, Heather,
1985 Irah, Jennifer, Katherine, Lillian, Mona, Natalie, Odessa, Prudence, Roslyn, Sylvia, Tillie, Victoria, Wallie

1978 —Aletta, Blanca, Connie, Dolores,
1982 Eileen, Francesca, Gretchen,
1986 Helga, Ione, Joyce, Kirsten, Lorraine, Maggie, Norma, Orlene, Patricia, Rosalie, Selma, Toni, Vivian, Winona

1979 —Agatha, Bridget, Carlotta, Denise,
1983 Eleanor, Francene, Georgette,
1987 Hilary, Ilsa, Jewel, Katrina, Lily, Monica, Nanette, Olivia, Priscilla, Ramona, Sharon, Terry, Veronica, Winifred

Central and Western North Pacific

(List rotates without regard to year)

Alice, Betty, Cora, Doris, Elsie, Flossie, Grace, Helen, Ida, June, Kathy, Lorna, Marie, Nancy, Olga, Pamela, Ruby, Sally, Therese, Violet, Wilda.

Anita, Billie, Clara, Dot, Ellen, Fran, Georgia, Hope, Iris, Joan, Kate, Louise, Marge, Nora, Opal, Patsy, Ruth, Sarah, Thelma, Vera, Wanda.

Amy, Babe, Carla, Dinah, Emma, Freda, Gilda, Harriet, Ivy, Jean, Kim, Lucy, Mary, Nadine, Olive, Polly, Rose, Shirley, Trix, Virginia, Wendy

Agnes, Bess, Carmen, Della, Elaine, Faye, Gloria, Hester, Irma, Judy, Kit, Lola, Mamie, Nina, Ora, Phyllis, Rita, Susan, Tess, Viola, Winnie.

High winds make dramatic and awesome pictures, but it is the flooding from hurricane rains which make the tropical storms such death and destruction dealers.

Tropical Cyclone Classification—

By international agreement, tropical cyclone is the general term for all cyclonic circulations originating over tropical waters, classified by form and intensity as follows:

Tropical disturbance: rotary circulation slight or absent at surface but sometimes better developed aloft, no closed isobars (lines of equal atmospheric pressure) and no strong winds, a common phenomenon in the tropics.

Tropical depression: one or more closed isobars and some rotary circulation at surface, highest wind speed 39 miles per hour (34 knots).

Tropical storm: closed isobars, distinct rotary circulation, highest wind speed 39-73 miles per hour (34-63 knots).

Hurricane: closed isobars, strong and very pronounced rotary circulation, wind speed of 74 miles per hour (64 knots) or more.

Words of Warning—

Small-craft warning: When a hurricane moves within a few hundred miles of the coast, advisories warn small-craft operators to take precautions and not to venture into the open ocean.

Gale warning: When winds of 38-55 miles per hour (33-48 knots) are expected, a gale warning is added to the advisory message.

Storm warning: When winds of 55-74 miles per hour (48-64 knots) are expected, a storm warning is added to the advisory message.

Gale and storm warnings indicate the coastal area to be affected by the warning, the time during which the warning will apply, and the expected intensity of the disturbance. **When gale or storm warnings are part of a tropical cyclone advisory, they may change to a hurricane warning if the storm continues along the coast.**

Hurricane watch: If the hurricane continues its advance and threatens coastal and inland regions, a hurricane watch is added to the advisory, covering a specified area and duration. A hurricane watch means that hurricane conditions are a real possibility; it does not mean they are imminent. When a hurricane watch is issued, everyone in the area covered by the watch should listen for further advisories and be prepared to act quickly if hurricane warnings are issued.

Hurricane warning: When hurricane conditions are expected within 24 hours, a hurricane warning is added to the advisory. Hurricane warnings identify coastal areas where winds of at least 74 miles per hour are expected to occur. A warning may also describe coastal areas where dangerously high water or exceptionally high waves are forecast, even though winds may be less than hurricane force.

When the hurricane warning is issued, all precautions should be taken immediately. Hurricane warnings are seldom issued more than 24 hours in advance. If the hurricane's path is unusual or erratic, the warnings may be issued only a few hours before the beginning of huricane conditions. Precautionary actions should begin as soon as a hurricane warning is announced.

HURRICANE SAFETY RULES

1. ENTER EACH HURRICANE SEASON PREPARED. **Every June through November, recheck your supply of boards, tools, batteries, nonperishable foods, and the other equipment you will need when a hurricane strikes your town.**
2. WHEN YOU HEAR THE FIRST TROPICAL CYCLONE ADVISORY, **listen for future messages; this will prepare you for a hurricane emergency well in advance of the issuance of watches and warnings.**
3. WHEN YOUR AREA IS COVERED BY A HURRICANE WATCH, **continue normal activities, but stay tuned to radio or television for all National Weather Service advisories. Remember, a hurricane watch means possible danger within 24 hours; if the danger materializes, a hurricane warning will be issued. Meanwhile, keep alert. Ignore rumors.**
4. WHEN YOUR AREA RECEIVES A HURRICANE WARNING, PLAN YOUR TIME **before the storm arrives and avoid the last-minute hurry which might leave you marooned, or unprepared.**

   KEEP CALM **until the emergency has ended.**

   LEAVE LOW-LYING AREAS **that may be swept by high tides or storm waves.**

   LEAVE MOBILE HOMES **for more substantial shelter. They are particularly vulnerable to overturning during strong winds. Damage can be minimized by securing mobile homes with heavy cables anchored in concrete footing.**

   MOOR YOUR BOAT SECURELY **before the storm arrives, or evacuate it to a designated safe area. When your boat is moored, leave it, and don't return once the wind and waves are up.**

   BOARD UP WINDOWS **or protect them with storm shutters or tape. Danger to small windows is mainly from wind-driven debris. Larger windows may be broken by wind pressure.**

   SECURE OUTDOOR OBJECTS **that might be blown away or uprooted. Garbage cans, garden tools, toys, signs, porch furniture, and a number of other harmless items become missiles of destruction in hurricane winds. Anchor them or store them inside before the storm strikes.**

   STORE DRINKING WATER **in clean bathtubs, jugs, bottles, and cooking utensils; your town's water supply may be contaminated by flooding or damaged by hurricane floods.**

   CHECK YOUR BATTERY-POWERED EQUIPMENT. **Your radio may be your only link with the world outside the hurricane, and emergency cooking facilities, lights, and flashlights will be essential if utilities are interrupted.**

   KEEP YOUR CAR FUELED. **Service stations may be inoperable for several days after the storm strikes, due to flooding or interrupted electrical power.**

STAY AT HOME, if it is sturdy and on high ground; if it is not, move to a designated shelter, and stay there until the storm is over.

REMAIN INDOORS DURING THE HURRICANE. Travel is extremely dangerous when winds and tides are whipping through your area.

MONITOR THE STORM'S POSITION through National Weather Service advisories.

BEWARE THE EYE OF THE HURRICANE

If the calm storm center passes directly overhead, there will be a lull in the wind lasting from a few minutes to half an hour or more. Stay in a safe place unless emergency repairs are absolutely necessary. But remember, at the other side of the eye, the winds rise very rapidly to hurricane force, and come from the opposite direction.

5. WHEN THE HURRICANE HAS PASSED:

SEEK NECESSARY MEDICAL CARE AT RED CROSS disaster stations or hospitals.

STAY OUT OF DISASTER AREAS. Unless you are qualified to help, your presence might hamper first-aid and rescue work.

DRIVE CAREFULLY along debris-filled streets. Roads may be undermined and may collapse under the weight of a car. Slides along cuts are also a hazard.

AVOID LOOSE OR DANGLING WIRES, and report them immediately to your power company or the nearest law enforcement officer.

REPORT BROKEN SEWER OR WATER MAINS to the water department.

PREVENT FIRES. Lowered water pressure may make fire fighting difficult.

CHECK REFRIGERATED FOOD for spoilage if power has been off during the storm.

REMEMBER THAT HURRICANES MOVING INLAND CAN CAUSE SEVERE FLOODING. STAY AWAY FROM RIVER BANKS AND STREAMS.

Tornadoes spawned by hurricanes are among the storms' worst killers. When a hurricane approaches, listen for tornado watches and warnings. A tornado watch means tornadoes are expected to develop. A tornado warning means a tornado has actually been sighted. When your area receives a tornado warning, seek inside shelter immediately, preferably below ground level. If a tornado catches you outside, move away from its path at a right angle. If there is no time to escape, lie flat in the nearest depression, such as a ditch or ravine.

NORTH ATLANTIC TROPICAL CYCLONES FOR PAST YEARS

TOTAL NUMBER OF TROPICAL CYCLONES, LOSS OF LIFE AND DAMAGE

	Total Number Tropical Cyclones*		Total Number Hurricanes		Loss of Life		Damage by Categories**	
Year	All Areas	Reaching U.S. Coast	All Areas	Reaching U.S. Coast	Total All Areas	United States	Total All Areas	United States
1931	9	2	2	0		0		#
1932	11	5	6	2		0		#
1933	21	7	9	5		63		7
1934	11	5	6	3		17		6
1935	6	2	5	2		414		7
	58	21	28	12				
1936	16	7	7	3		9		6
1937	9	4	3	0		0		4
1938	8	4	3	2		600		8
1939	5	3	3	1		3		3
1940	8	3	4	2		51		6
	46	21	20	8				
1941	6	4	4	2		10		7
1942	10	3	4	2	17	8	7	7
1943	10	4	5	1	19	16	7	7
1944	11	4	7	3	1,076	64	8	8
1945	11	5	5	3	29	7	8	8
	48	20	25	11				
1946	6	4	3	1	5	0	7	7
1947	9	7	5	3	72	53	8	8
1948	9	4	6	3	24	3	7	7
1949	13	3	7	2	4	4	8	8
1950	13	4	11	3	27	19	7	7
	50	22	32	12				
1951	10	1	8	0	244	0	7	6
1952	7	2	6	1	16	3	6	6
1953	14	6	6	2	3	2	7	7
1954	11	4	8	3	720+	193	9	9
1955	12	5	9	3	1,518+	218	9	9
	54	18	37	9				
1956	8	2	4	1	76	21	8	7
1957	8	5	3	1	475	395	8	8
1958	10	1	7	0	49	2	7	7
1959	11	7	7	3	57	24	7	7
1960	7	5	4	2	185	65	8	8
	44	20	25	7				
1961	11	3	8	1	345	46	8	8
1962	5	1	3	0	4	4	6	6
1963	9	1	7	1	7,218+	11	9	7
1964	12	6	6	4	266	49	9	9
1965	6	2	4	1	76	75	9	9
	43	13	28	7				
1966	11	2	7	2	1,040	54	8	7
1967	8	2	6	1	68	18	8	8
1968	7	3	4	1	11	9	7	7
1969	13	3	10	2	364	256	9	9
1970	7	4	3	1	74	11	9	8
	46	14	30	7				
1971	12	5	5	3	44	8	8	8
1972	4	3	3	1	128	121	9	9
1973	7	1	4	0	16	5	7	7
1974	7	1	4	1	3,000+	1	8	8
Total	419	159	241	78				
Mean	9.5	3.6	5.5	1.8				

**The Environmental Data Service has for some time recognized that, without detailed expert appraisal of damage, all figures published are merely approximations. Since errors in dollar estimates vary in proportion of the total damage, storms are placed in categories varying from 1 to 9 as follows:

1 Less than $50
2 $50 to $500
3 $500 to $5,000
4 $5,000 to $50,000
5 $50,000 to $500,000
6 $500,000 to $5,000,000
7 $5,000,000 to $50,000,000
8 $50,000,000 to $500,000,000
9 $500,000,000 to $5,000,000,000

*Including hurricanes
Not reported in literature, believed minor.
+ Additional deaths for which figures are not available.

NORTH ATLANTIC TROPICAL CYCLONES FOR PAST YEARS

Frequency of Tropical Cyclones (Including Hurricanes) by Months and Years

	Feb.	May	June	July	Aug.	Sept.	Oct.	Nov.	Dec.	Total
1931			1	1	2	3	1	1		9
1932		1			3	3	3	1		11
1933		1	1	3	7	5	3	1		21
1934		1	1	1	2	2	3	1		11
1935					3	1	2			6
1936			3	2	6	4	1			16
1937				1	2	6				9
1938					3	1	3	1		8
1939			1		1	1	2			5
1940		1			3	2	2			8
1941						4	2			6
1942					3	3	3	1		10
1943				1	2	4	3			10
1944				3	2	4	2			11
1945			1	1	4	3	2			11
1946			1	1	1	1	2			6
1947				1	2	3	3			9
1948		1		1	2	3	1	1		9
1949					3	7	2	1		13
1950					4	3	6			13
1951		1			3	4	2			10
1952	(Feb.) 1				2	2	2			7
1953		1			3	4	4	1	1	14
1954			1	1	2	4	1	1	1	11
1955				1	4	5	2			12
1956			1	1	1	4	1			8
1957			2		1	4	1			8
1958			1		4	4	1			10
1959		1	2	2	1	3	2			11
1960			1	2	1	3				7
1961				1		6	2	2		11
1962					2	2	1			5
1963				1	1	5	2			9
1964			1	1	4	4	1	1		12
1965			1		2	2	1			6
1966			1	4	1	4		1		11
1967					1	4	3			8
1968			3		1	2	1			7
1969				1	6	2	3	1		13
1970		1		2	1	3				7
1971				1	3	6	1	1		12
1972			1		2	1				4
1973				1	2	2	2			7
1974					3	4				
Totals	1	9	24	35	106	147	79	16	2	419

Frequency of Tropical Cyclones Reaching Hurricane Intensity by Months and Years

	May	June	July	Aug.	Sept.	Oct.	Nov.	Dec.	Total
1931					2				2
1932				3	1	1	1		6
1933		1	1	3	3	1			9
1934		1	1	1	1	1	1		6
1935				2	1	2			5
1936		1	1	3	2				7
1937					3				3
1938				2	1				3
1939				1		2			3
1940				3	1				4
1941					3	1			4
1942				3			1		4
1943			1	1	2	1			5
1944			2	1	3	1			7
1945		1		1	1	2			5
1946			1		1	1			3
1947				2	1	2			5
1948				1	3	1	1		6
1949				2	4	1			7
1950				4	3	4			11
1951	1			2	3	2			8
1952				2	2	2			6
1953				2	3	1			6
1954		1		2	3	1		1	8
1955				3	5	1			9
1956			1	1	1	1			4
1957		1			2				3
1958				3	3	1			7
1959		1	2		3	1			7
1960			1	1	2				4
1961			1		5	1	1		8
1962				1	1	1			3
1963			1	1	4	1			7
1964				2	3	1			6
1965				2	1	1			4
1966		1	3	1	1		1		7
1967				1	3	2			6
1968		2		1		1			4
1969				5	2	2	1		10
1970	1		1		1				3
1971				1	4				5
1972		1		1	1				3
1973			1	1	1	1			4
1974				2	2				
Totals	2	11	18	68	92	42	7	1	241

TORNADOES

A tornado is a local storm of short duration formed of winds rotating at very high speeds, usually in a counter-clockwise direction. This storm is visible as a vortex, a whirlpool structure of winds rotating about a hollow cavity in which centrifugal forces produce a partial vacuum. As condensation occurs around the vortex, a pale cloud appears — the familiar and frightening tornado funnel. Air surrounding the funnel is also part of the tornado vortex; as the storm moves along the ground, this outer ring of rotating winds becomes dark with dust and debris, which may eventually darken the entire funnel.

These small, severe storms form several thousand feet above the earth's surface, usually during warm, humid, unsettled weather, and usually in conjunction with a severe thunderstorm. Sometimes a series of two or more tornadoes is associated with a parent thunderstorm. As the thunderstorm moves, tornadoes may form at intervals along its path, travel for a few miles, and dissipate. The forward speed of tornadoes has been observed to range from almost no motion to 70 miles per hour.

Funnels usually appear as an extension of the dark, heavy cumulonimbus clouds of thunderstorms, and stretch downward toward the ground. Some never reach the surface; others touch and rise again.

Size, speed, and duration–

On the average, tornado paths are only a quarter of a mile wide and seldom more than 16 miles long. But there have been spectacular instances in which tornadoes have caused heavy destruction along paths more than a mile wide and 300 miles long. A tornado traveled 293 miles across Illinois and Indiana on May 26, 1917, and lasted 7 hours and 20 minutes. Its forward speed was 40 miles an hour, an average figure for tornadoes.

Where do tornadoes occur? When?

Tornadoes occur in many parts of the world and in all 50 states. But no area is more favorable to their formation than the continental plains of North America, and no season is free of them. Normally, the number of tornadoes is at its lowest in the United States during December and January, and at its peak in May. The months of greatest total frequency are April, May, and June.

In February, when tornado frequency begins to increase, the center of maximum frequency lies over the central Gulf States. Then, during March, this center moves eastward to the southeast Atlantic states, where tornado frequency reaches a peak in April. During May, the center of maximum frequency moves to the southern plains states, and in June, northward to the northern plains and Great Lakes area as far east as western New York state. The reason for this drift is the increasing penetration of warm, moist air while contrasting cool, dry air still surges in from the north and northwest; tornadoes are generated with greatest frequency where these air masses wage their wars. Thus, when the Gulf states are substantially "occupied" by warm air systems after May, there is no cold air intrusion to speak of, and tornado frequency drops. This is the case across the nation after June. Winter cooling permits fewer and fewer encounters between warm and overriding cold systems, and tornado frequency returns to its lowest level by December.

The mathematical chance that a specific location will be struck by a tornado in any one year is quite small. For example, the probability of a tornado striking a given point in the area most frequently subject to tornadoes is 0.0363, or about once in 250 years. In the far western states, the probability is close to zero.

But tornadoes have provided many unmathematical exceptions. Oklahoma City has been struck by tornadoes 26 times since 1892. Baldwyn, Mississippi, was struck twice by tornadoes during a 25-minute period on March 16, 1942. A third of Irving, Kansas, was left in ruins by two tornadoes which occurred 45 minutes apart on May 30, 1879. Austin, Texas, had two tornadoes in rapid succession on May 4, 1922; and Codell, Kansas, was struck three times in 1916, 1917, and 1918—on May 20.

During the period 1953-1969, an average of 642 tornadoes per year occurred in the United States, about half of them during three months—April, May, and June. For the same period, the annual average number of tornado days—days on which one or more tornadoes were reported—was 159. Average annual frequency by states for this period ranges from 103 tornadoes in Texas to less than three in most of the northeastern and far western states.

Tornadoes may occur at any hour of the day or night, but, because of the meteorological combinations which create them, they form most readily during the warmest hours of the day. The greatest number of tornadoes—82 percent of the total—occurs between noon and midnight, and the greatest single concentration—23 percent of total tornado activity—falls between 4 and 6 p.m.

Major tornadoes

The most death-dealing series of tornadoes on record occurred during the late afternoon on March 18, 1925, in portions of Missouri, Indiana, Illinois, Kentucky, and Tennessee. Eight separate and distinct tornadoes were observed. One of these killed 689 persons, injured 1,890 and caused more than 16 million dollars in property damage. The other seven tornadoes of the series increased the total loss of life to 740 and contributed significantly to the total casualty and property damage.

Another major series of tornadoes killed 268 people and injured 1,874 in Alabama on March 21, 1932. Property damage amounted to approximately 5 million dollars.

Trends

From 1916 through 1952, fewer than 300 tornadoes were reported in any one year. In 1953, when the U.S. Department of Commerce initiated its tornado forecasting effort, more than 437 tornadoes were observed and reported, beginning the first period of reliable statistical history. Since 1953, partly through improved equipment and techniques, partly through increasing public participation, essentially complete tornado records have been available. This publication summarizes tornado incidence for the period 1953-1969. More tornadoes occurred in 1967 than in any prior year of record for the United States. In 44 States, 912 tornadoes killed 116 persons and caused property damage in the millions of dollars. In 1969, 604 tornadoes in 41 States killed 66 persons, 32 of them in Mississippi on January 23.

How a tornado is formed—

Tornado formation requires the presence of layers of air with contrasting characteristics of temperature, moisture, density, and wind flow. Compli-

1

2

A few seconds in the violent, devastating life of a tornado are recorded in this remarkable photo series. Winds surrounding a tornado's vortex, which reach peaks too high to clock, are estimated at up to 300 miles per hour, plus.

3

4

The average tornado's life is measured in minutes, and its path seldom more than 16 miles long. But one moved 293 miles, going on for seven hours and twenty minutes.

cated energy transformations produce the tornado vortex.

Many theories have been advanced as to the type of energy transformation necessary to generate a tornado, and none has won general acceptance. The two most frequently encountered visualize tornado generation as either the effect of thermally induced rotary circulations, or as the effect of converging rotary winds. Currently, scientists seem to agree that neither process generates tornadoes independently. It is more probable that tornadoes are produced by the combined effects of thermal and mechanical forces, with one or the other force being the stronger generating agent.

Numerous observations of lightning strokes and a variety of luminous features in and around tornado funnels have led scientists to speculate about the relationship between tornado formation and thunderstorm electrification. This hypothesis explores the alternative possibilities that atmospheric electricity accelerates rotary winds to tornado velocities, or that those high-speed rotary winds generate large electrical charges. Here, as in most attempts to understand complex atmospheric relationships, the reach of theory exceeds the grasp of proof.

Tornado damage—

If there is some question as to the causes of tornadoes, there is none on the destructive effects of these violent storms. The dark funnel of a tornado can destroy solid buildings, make a deadly missile of a piece of straw, uproot large trees, and hurl people and animals for hundreds of yards. In 1931, a tornado in Minnesota carried an 83-ton railroad coach and its 117 passengers 80 feet through the air, and dropped them in a ditch.

Tornadoes do their destructive work through the combined action of their strong rotary winds and the partial vacuum in the center of the vortex. As a tornado passes over a building, the winds twist and rip at the outside at the same time that the abrupt pressure reduction in the tornado's "eye" causes explosive over-pressures inside the building. Walls collapse or topple outward, windows explode, and the debris of this destruction is driven through the air in a dangerous barrage. Heavy objects like machinery and railroad cars are lifted and carried by the wind for considerable distances.

Where there is such complete destruction there is usually also loss of life. On April 11, 1965, Palm Sunday, 37 tornadoes struck the midwest, killing 271 persons and injuring more than 5,000; property damage was estimated at $300 million. Since the early 1950's, the tornado death toll has averaged about 120 per year.

Tornado warnings—

Although it is not possible to predict exactly where and when severe thunderstorms and tornadoes will occur, it is possible to predict general areas where the probability of severe thunderstorm and tornado development is greatest by detecting the larger-scale events which are usually associated with such storms.

This important function is performed by the National Severe Storms Forecast Center in Kansas City, Missouri. The Kansas City facility is one of several environmental hazards centers of action operated by the National Weather Service (formerly the Weather Bureau), a major element of NOAA, the National Oceanic and Atmospheric Administration of the U.S. Department of Commerce.

Meteorologists at Kansas City monitor conditions in the North American atmosphere, using surface data from hundreds of points and radar summaries, satellite photographs, meteorological upper-air profile (obtained by sounding balloons), and reports from pilots. From these thousands of pieces of information, weathermen determine the area that is most likely to experience severe thunderstorms or tornadoes. Information on this area is then issued to National Weather Service offices and the public in the form of a **watch** bulletin.

A severe thunderstorm watch or tornado watch bulletin issued by the Center usually identifies an area about 140 miles wide by 240 miles long. Although the **watch** bulletin states approximately where and for how long the severe local storm threat will exist, it does not mean that severe local storms will not occur outside the **watch** area or time frame—the **watch** is only an indication of where and when the probabilities are highest.

Watch bulletins are transmitted to all National Weather Service offices. Designated offices prepare and issue a redefining statement which specifies the affected area in terms of counties, towns, and locally well-known geographic landmarks. These messages are disseminated to the public by all possible means, and are used to guide the activities of local government, law enforcement, and emergency agencies in preparing for severe weather.

Watches are not warnings. Until a severe thunderstorm or tornado warning is issued, persons in watch areas should maintain their normal routines, but watch for threatening weather and listen to the radio or television for further severe weather information.

A severe thunderstorm warning or tornado warning bulletin is issued by a local office of the National Weather Service when a severe thunderstorm or tornado has actually been sighted in the area or indicated by radar. **Warnings** describe the location of the severe thunderstorm or tornado at the time of detection, the area (usually the counties) that could be affected, and the time period (usually one hour) covered by the **warning.** The length of this area is equal to the distance the storm is expected to travel in one hour.

When a **warning** is received, persons close to the storm should take cover immediately, especially in the case of a tornado **warning.** Persons farther away from the storm should be prepared to take cover if threatening conditions are sighted.

Severe weather statements are prepared by local offices of the National Weather Service to keep the public fully informed of all current information, particularly when **watch** or **warning** bulletins are in effect. Statements are issued at least once each hour, and more frequently when the severe weather situation is changing rapidly. In this way, a close watch is kept on weather developments, and information is quickly disseminated to the counties for which the National Weather Service office has responsibility.

All-clear bulletins are issued whenever the threat of severe thunderstorms or tornadoes has ended in the area previously warned in a tornado or a severe thunderstorm **warning** bulletin. When a **warning** is cancelled, but a **watch** continues in effect for the same area or a **warning** is in effect for an adjacent area, a "Severe Weather Bulletin" is issued; this qualified message is also issued when a portion, but not all, of a **watch** area is cancelled. This permits a continuous alert in the path of the storm, with the alert being cancelled as the severe weather moves through the **watch** area.

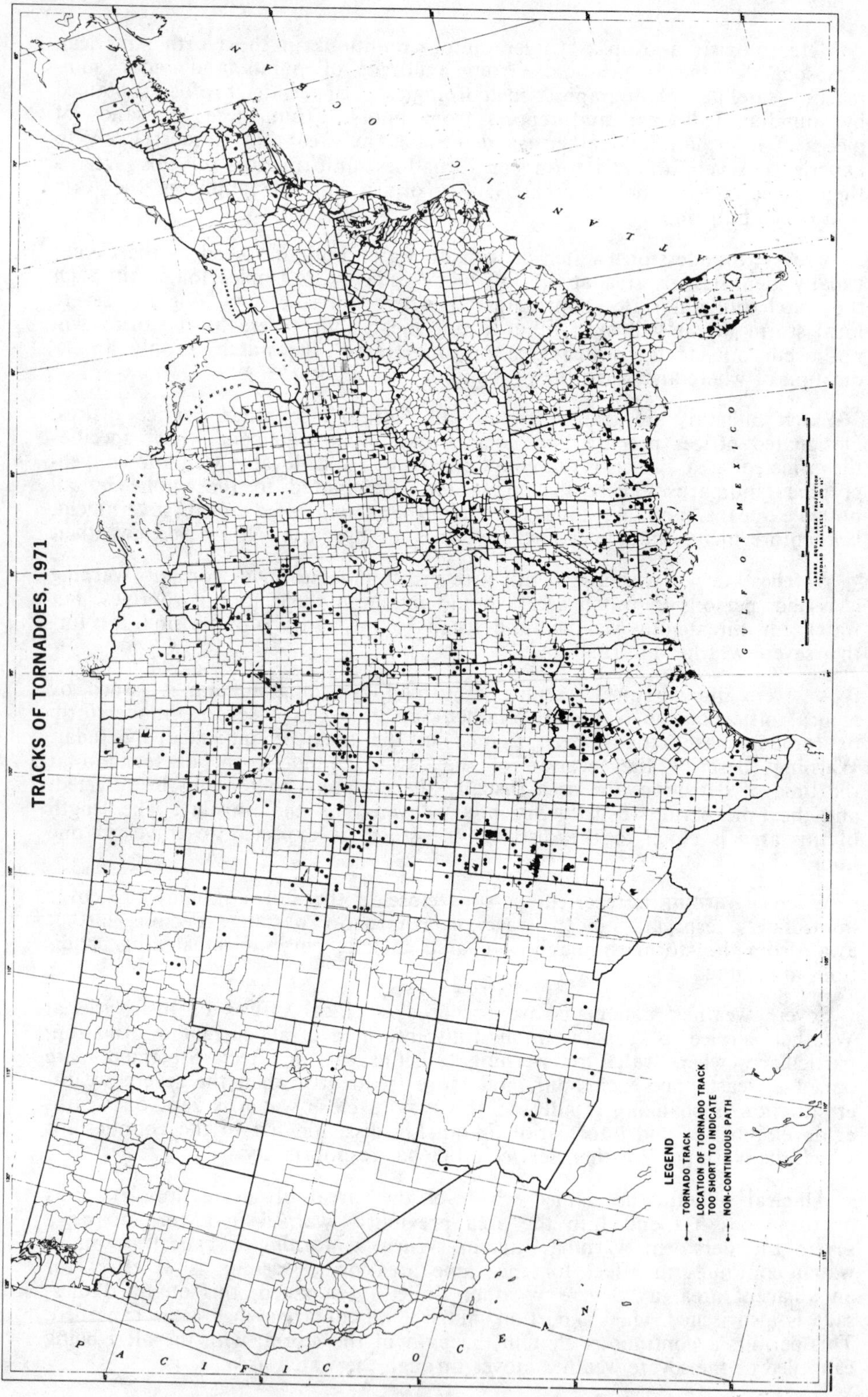
TRACKS OF TORNADOES, 1971
LEGEND
TORNADO TRACK
LOCATION OF TORNADO TRACK TOO SHORT TO INDICATE
NON-CONTINUOUS PATH
A T L A N T I C O C E A N
G U L F O F M E X I C O
P A C I F I C O C E A N

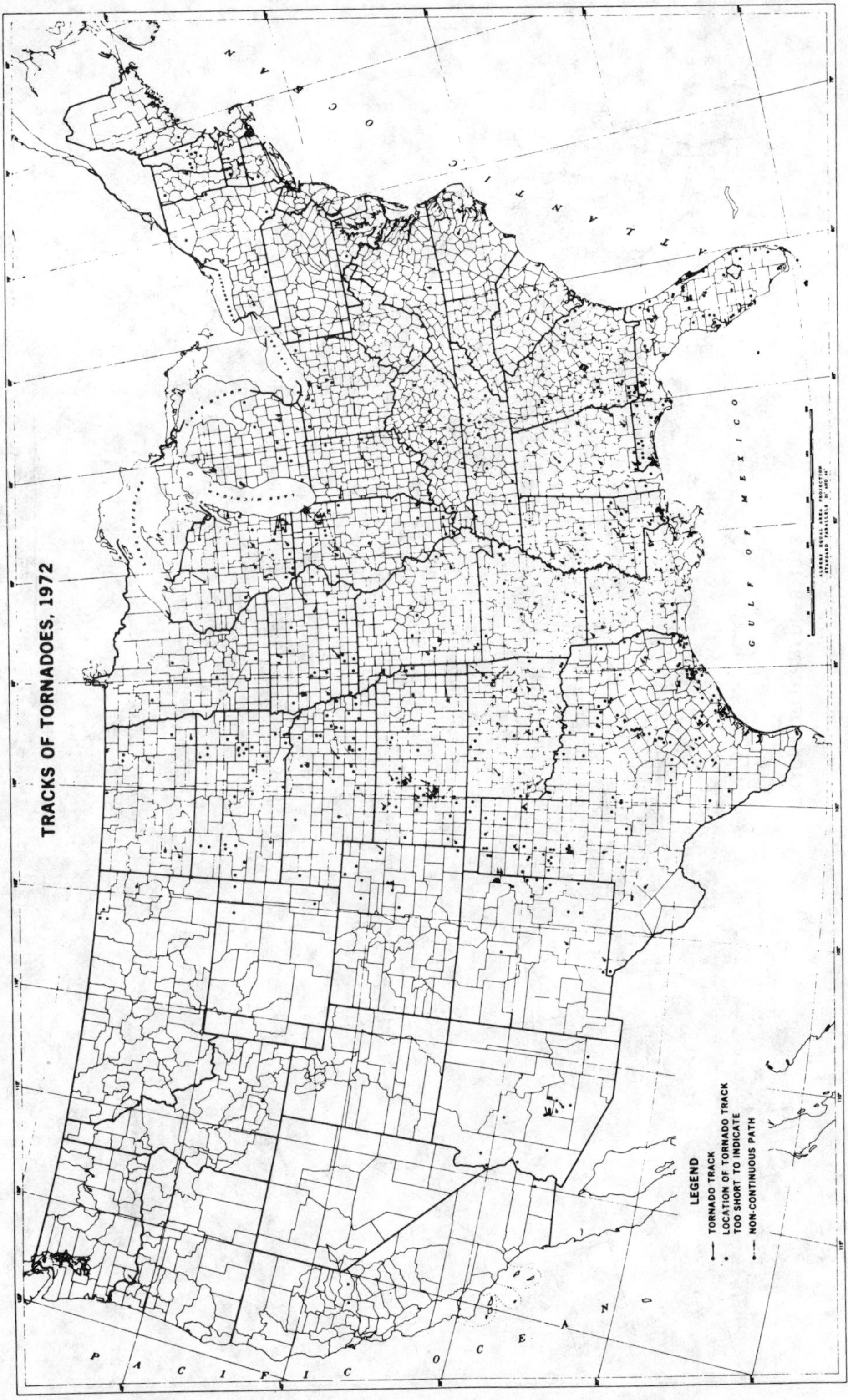
TRACKS OF TORNADOES, 1972
ATLANTIC OCEAN
GULF OF MEXICO
PACIFIC OCEAN
LEGEND
TORNADO TRACK
LOCATION OF TORNADO TRACK TOO SHORT TO INDICATE
NON-CONTINUOUS PATH

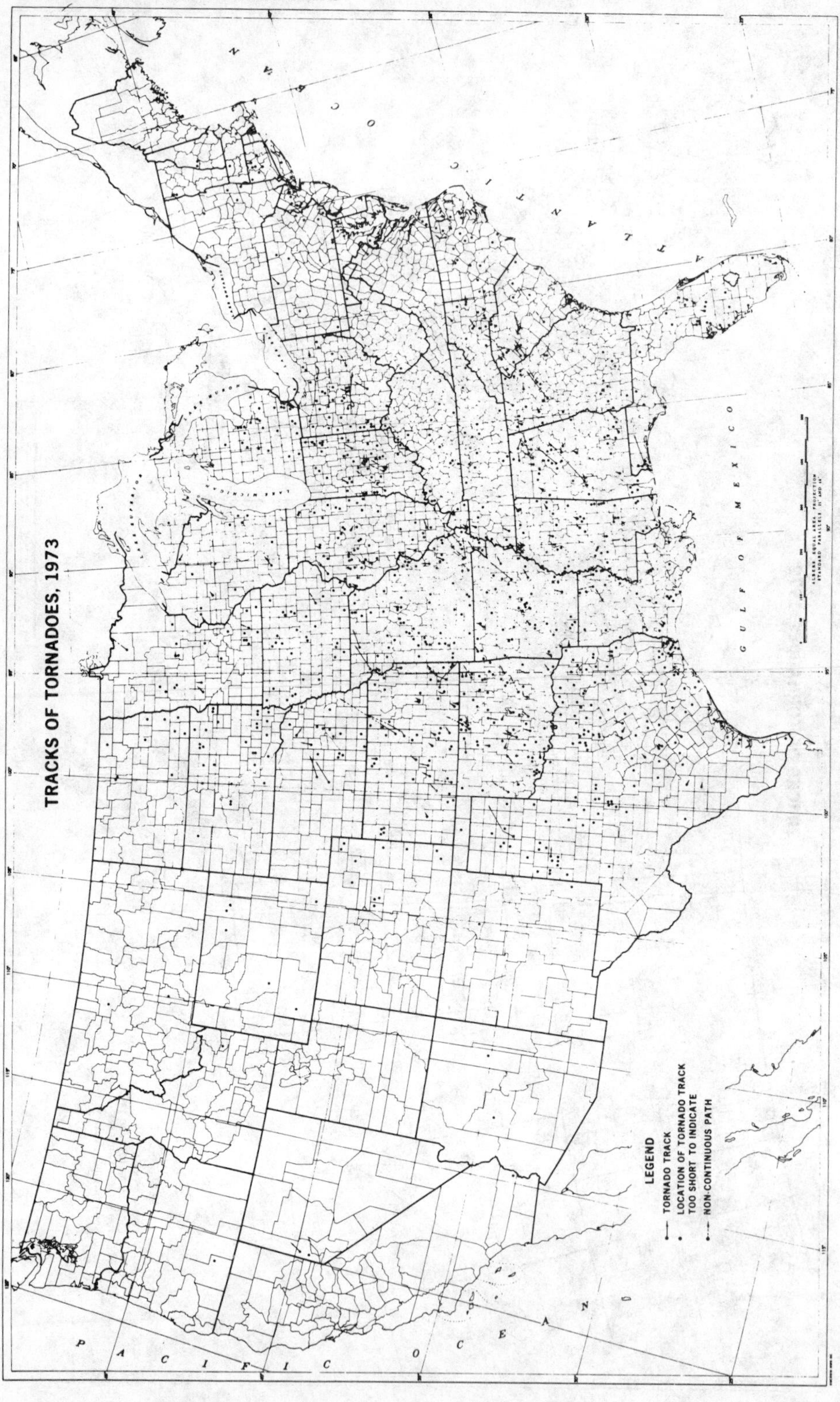
TRACKS OF TORNADOES, 1973
LEGEND
TORNADO TRACK
LOCATION OF TORNADO TRACK TOO SHORT TO INDICATE
NON-CONTINUOUS PATH
ATLANTIC OCEAN
GULF OF MEXICO
PACIFIC OCEAN
LAKE MICHIGAN

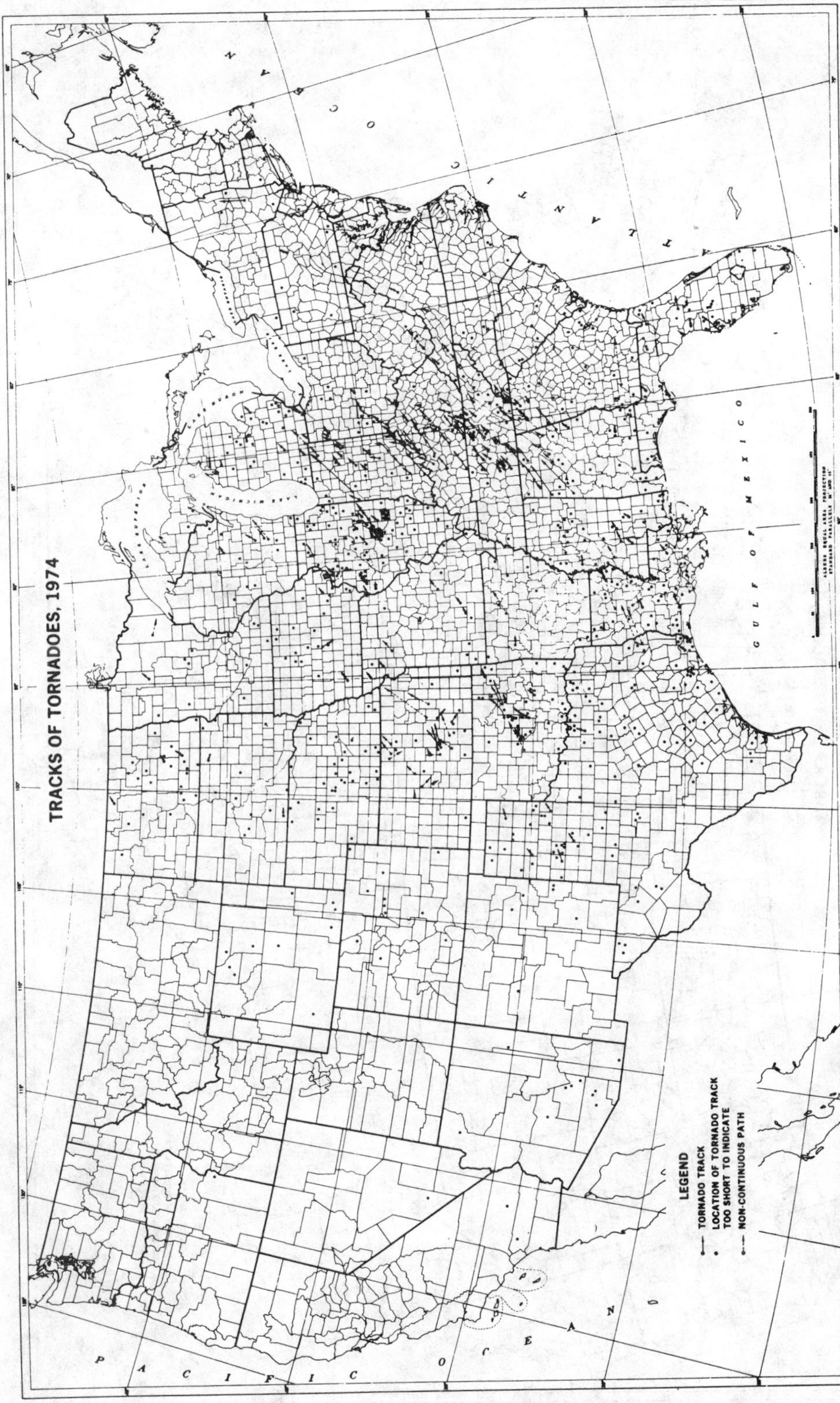
TRACKS OF TORNADOES, 1974
LEGEND
TORNADO TRACK
LOCATION OF TORNADO TRACK TOO SHORT TO INDICATE
NON-CONTINUOUS PATH
GULF OF MEXICO
ATLANTIC OCEAN
PACIFIC OCEAN
LAKE SUPERIOR
LAKE MICHIGAN
LAKE HURON

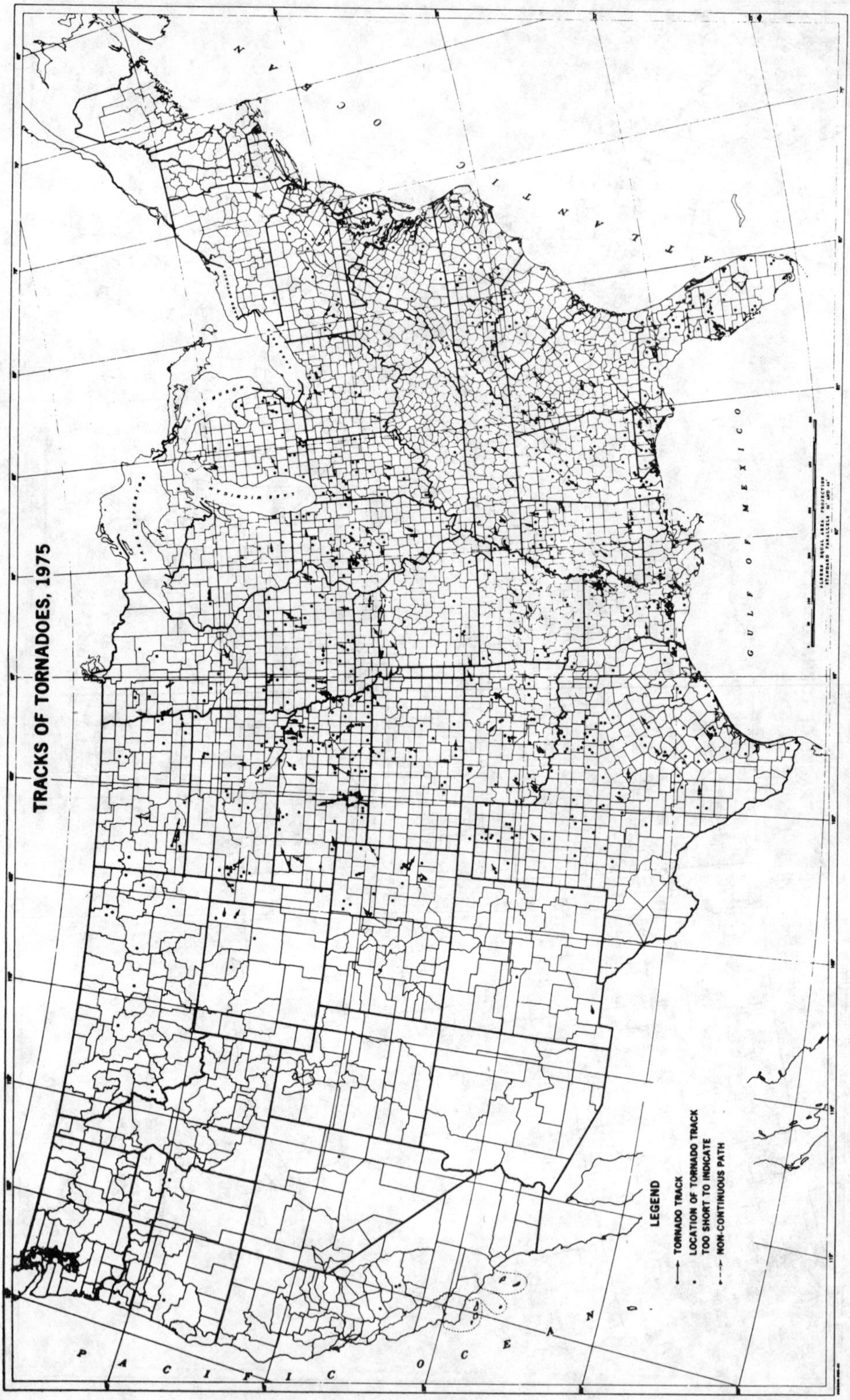
TRACKS OF TORNADOES, 1975
ATLANTIC OCEAN
GULF OF MEXICO
PACIFIC OCEAN
LEGEND
TORNADO TRACK
LOCATION OF TORNADO TRACK TOO SHORT TO INDICATE
NON-CONTINUOUS PATH

Tornado Characteristics—

Time of Day during which tornadoes are most likely to occur is mid-afternoon, generally between 3 and 7 p.m., but they have occurred at all times of day.

Direction of Movement is usually from southwest to northeast. (Note: Tornadoes associated with hurricanes may move from an easterly direction.)

Length of Path averages 4 miles, but may reach 300 miles. A tornado traveled 293 miles across Illinois and Indiana on May 26, 1917, and lasted 7 hours and 20 minutes.

Width of Path averages about 300 to 400 yards but tornadoes have cut swaths a mile and more in width.

Speed of Travel averages from 25 to 40 miles per hour, but speeds ranging from stationary to 68 miles per hour have been reported.

The Cloud directly associated with a tornado is a dark, heavy cumulonimbus (the familiar thunderstorm cloud) from which a whirling funnel-shaped pendant extends to the ground.

Precipitation associated with the tornado usually occurs first as rain just preceding the storm, frequently with hail, and as a heavy downpour immediately to the left of the tornado's path.

Sound occurring during a tornado has been described as a roaring, rushing noise, closely approximating that made by a train speeding through a tunnel or over a trestle, or the roar of many airplanes.

TORNADO SAFETY RULES

A tornado watch means tornadoes are expected to develop. Keep a battery-operated radio or television set nearby, and listen for weather advisories—even if the sky is blue. A tornado warning means a tornado has actually been sighted or indicated by weather radar. Seek inside shelter (in a storm cellar or reinforced building) and stay away from windows. Curl up so that your head and eyes are protected. Keep a battery-operated radio or television nearby, and listen for further advisories.

ON THE STREET OR IN A CAR, **leave your car and take shelter in civil defense or other inside shelter areas with basements or storm cellars. Be sure to stay away from large glassed in areas. If no building is available or if caught out in the open countryside take shelter in a ditch or ravine or lie flat on the ground upwind of your parked car. If an overpass or concrete viaduct is available then take shelter behind the concrete pilings in such a way as to put the concrete between you and approaching tornado.**

IN HIGH-RISE OFFICE BUILDINGS AND LARGE APARTMENT BUILDINGS, **if possible post a trained spotter or lookout on the roof with a two-way radio. Go to the lower floors or the basement. Take shelter in small interior rooms such as rest rooms, closets and utility rooms as well as interior corridors. Be sure to cover and protect the head from flying and falling debris.**

IN HOMES, **take shelter in the basement under sturdy items. Concrete laundry tubs, heavy duty work benches, pool tables and staircases offer the greatest safety. If there is no basement take cover under heavily stuffed furniture in the center of the home or in a bathroom or interior closet. Open some windows on at least two different sides of the home, preferably those on the east and west side, but take shelter away from all windows. Caution: Avoid bathrooms with an out-side wall on the south or west side of the home. Also do not lock yourself in a closet that has no inside latch or door handle.**

(Continued on next page)

TORNADO SAFETY RULES

IN SHOPPING CENTERS OR SHOPPING MALLS, **if possible post a trained security guard or lookout on the west or south side of the complex with a two way radio. Take shelter in the basement or in shops below ground level. If there is no basement take shelter in interior hallways, small interior rooms or shops on the east or north side of the center. If only one large building or room exists then take shelter in the north end of the room. Be sure to protect your head from flying or falling debris. Caution: Avoid large open malls or walkways with glass or plastic skylights as well as large glass signs and display cases.**

IN SCHOOLS, **go to a storm cellar or underground shelter if available. If there is no underground shelter area move the pupils into interior hallways or small interior rooms on the lowest floor and on the east or north side of the building. Caution: Avoid auditoriums, gymnasiums and other large rooms with long freespan roofs as well as southwest to northeast oriented corridors with exposed or unbaffled entrances on the south and west side of the building. Also avoid glass display cases, glassed in stairwells and all door ways.**

IN FACTORIES, **post a trained spotter or lookout on the roof with a two-way radio. Workers should move to sections of the plant that are below ground level. If this is not possible then have the workers take shelter in interior corridors or in small interior rooms such as rest rooms, closets and storage rooms on the east or north side of the building. Caution: Avoid the southwest corner of the plant as well as large rooms or work areas with long freespan roofs. Stay away from all windows.**

IN MOBILE HOMES, **leave your trailer and take shelter in an administration building with a basement or an approved community shelter area. If no shelter is available go to a ditch or ravine on the west or south side of the trailer park and lie down flat against the ground. Make sure you protect your head from flying debris.**

IN A BUS, TRUCK OR LARGE VAN, **try to move away from the storm by driving at right angles to its path. If this is not possible or if you experience strong cross winds then park the vehicle pointing into the wind, pull the hand break and unload your passengers. Open as many windows as time will allow on both sides of the vehicles then leave the vehicle and take shelter in a ditch, ravine or other depression in the ground that is upwind from your truck or bus.**

CONSTRUCTING A SHELTER

IN parts of the country where tornadoes are comparatively frequent, a form of shelter is vital for protection from tornadoes. The shelter may never be needed; but during a tornado emergency, it can be worth many times the effort and cost of preparing it. One of the safest tornado shelters is an underground excavation, known as a storm cellar.

LOCATION — **When possible, the storm cellar should be located outside and near the residence, but not so close that falling walls or debris could block the exit. If there is a rise in the ground, the cellar may be dug into it to make use of the rise for protection. The cellar should not be connected in any way with house drains, cesspools, or sewer and gas pipes.**

SIZE — **The size of the shelter depends on the number of persons to be accommodated and the storage needs. A structure 8 feet long by 6 feet wide and 7 feet high will protect eight people for a short time and provide limited storage space.**

MATERIAL — **Reinforced concrete is the best material for a tornado shelter. Other suitable building materials include split logs, 2-inch planks (treated with creosote and covered with tar paper), cinder block, hollow tile, and brick. The roof should be covered with a 3-foot mound of well-pounded dirt, sloped to divert surface water. The entrance door should be of heavy construction, hinged to open inward.**

DRAINAGE — **The floor should slope to a drainage outlet if the terrain permits. If not, a dry well can be dug. An outside drain is better, because it will aid ventilation.**

VENTILATION — **A vertical ventilating shaft about 1 foot square can extend from near the floor level through the ceiling. This can be converted into an emergency escape hatch if the opening through the ceiling is made 2 feet square and the 1-foot shaft below is made easily removable. Slat gratings of heavy wood on the floor also will improve air circulation.**

EMERGENCY EQUIPMENT — **A lantern and tools—crowbar, pick, shovel, hammer, pliers, screwdriver— should be stored in the cellar to ensure escape if cellar exits are blocked by debris. Stored metal tools should be greased to prevent rusting.**

QUOTES FROM WEATHER FOLKLORE–

A veering wind, fair weather;
A backing wind, foul weather.
If the wind back against the sun,
Trust it not, for back it will run.

Cats have the reputation of being weather wise, an old notion which has given rise to the most extensive folklore.
It is almost universally believed that good weather may be expected when the cat washes herself, but bad when she licks her coat against the grain, or washes her face over her ears, or sits with her tail to the fire.

NUMBER OF TORNADOES, TORNADO DAYS AND RESULTING LOSSES BY YEARS, 1916-75

YEAR	Number Tornadoes	Tornado Days	Total Deaths	Most Deaths in Single Tornado	Total Property Losses †	PROPERTY LOSS FREQUENCY* Category 5	Category 6	Category 7 and Over
1916	90	36	150	30	6	7	1	0
1917	121	38	551	101	7	21	9	0
1918	81	45	136	36	7	20	5	0
1919	64	35	206	59	7	10	2	0
1920	87	50	499	87	7	14	10	0
1921	105	55	202	61	7	22	3	0
1922	108	64	135	16	7	27	5	0
1923	102	59	110	23	6	21	1	0
1924	130	57	376	85	7	26	11	1
1925	119	65	794	689	7	34	2	1
1926	111	57	144	23	6	28	0	0
1927	163	62	540	92	7	42	9	1
1928	203	79	95	14	7	40	7	0
1929	197	74	274	40	7	48	4	0
1930	192	72	179	41	7	38	6	0
1931	94	57	36	6	6	14	1	0
1932	151	67	394	37	7	23	1	1
1933	258	96	362	34	7	46	9	0
1934	147	77	47	6	6	10	3	0
1935	180	77	71	11	6	29	0	0
1936	151	71	552	216	7	17	5	1
1937	147	75	29	5	6	24	0	0
1938	213	76	183	32	7	29	6	0
1939	152	75	91	27	7	21	3	0
1940	124	62	65	18	7	13	2	0
1941	118	57	53	25	6	24	1	0
1942	167	66	384	65	7	42	10	0
1943	152	61	58	5	7	28	8	0
1944	169	68	275	100	7	50	9	0
1945	121	66	210	69	7	21	10	1
1946	106	65	78	15	7	29	7	0
1947	165	78	313	169	7	46	7	1
1948	183	68	139	33	7	62	11	2
1949	249	80	211	58	7	54	13	0
1950	199	88	70	18	7	47	9	0
1951	262	113	34	6	7	35	11	2
1952	240	98	229	57	7	53	19	0
1953	421	136	515	116	8	63	18	7
1954	550	159	36	6	7	63	8	1
1955	593	153	126	80	7	74	13	1
1956	504	155	83	25	7	83	24	1
1957	856	154	192	44	8	129	26	3
1958	564	166	66	19	7	70	8	1
1959	604	156	58	21	7	70	4	1
1960	616	172	46	16	7	65	11	1
1961	697	169	51	16	7	103	21	1
1962	657	152	28	17	7	51	10	0
1963	464	141	31	5	7	77	15	1
1964	704	156	73	22	7	113	17	5
1965	906	181	296	44	8	126	30	11
1966	585	150	98	58	8	79	13	4
1967	926	173	114	33	8	125	33	8
1968	660	171	131	34	8	82	26	6
1969	608	155	66	32	8	98	16	3
1970	653	171	72	26	8	97	24	6
1971	888	192	156	58	8	71	30	5
1972	741	194	27	6	8	100	28	1
1973	1102	206	87	7	9	219	67	9
1974	947	184	361	34	9	166	82	25
1975	918	204	60	9	9	189	31	11
Means: 1956-75	730	170	105	---	---	106	26	5

NOTE: - - The above estimated losses are based on values at time of occurrence.

† Storm damages in categories:

5. $50,000 to $500,000
6. $500,000 to $5 million
7. $5 million to $50 million
8. $50 million to $500 million
9. $500 million and over.

* Number of times property losses reported in Storm Data in Categories 5, 6, 7 and over.

NUMBER OF TORNADOES, TORNADO DAYS, AND DEATHS BY STATES, 1956-75

STATE	TORNADOES							DAYS		DEATHS		
	TOTAL	AVERAGE	GREATEST	YEAR	LEAST	YEAR	Per # 10,000 Sq.Mi.	TOTAL	AVERAGE	TOTAL	AVERAGE	Per @ 10,000 Sq.Mi.
Alabama	403	20	45	1973+	5	1956	3.90	224	11	158	8	31
Alaska	1	0	1	1959	0	1975+	.00	1	0	0	0	0
Arizona	84	4	17	1972	0	1965	.37	69	3	3	0	0
Arkansas	354	18	50	1973	2	1969+	3.33	182	9	105	5	20
California	55	3	10	1958	0	1968+	.17	44	2	0	0	0
Colorado	264	13	32	1965	1	1959	1.27	190	10	2	0	0
Connecticut	35	2	8	1973	0	1969+	3.49	33	2	1	0	2
Delaware	17	1	5	1975	0	1974+	4.13	15	1	0	0	0
District of Columbia	0	0	0	-	0	-	.00	0	0	0	0	0
Florida	767	38	97	1975	12	1965	6.55	450	23	43	2	7
Georgia	438	22	46	1971+	7	1960	3.72	265	13	39	2	7
Hawaii	13	1	4	1971	0	1972+	1.01	11	1	0	0	0
Idaho	29	1	5	1967	0	1975+	.17	20	1	0	0	0
Illinois	615	31	107	1974	7	1964	5.45	281	14	115	6	20
Indiana	463	23	48	1973	6	1972	6.38	212	11	190	10	52
Iowa	549	27	54	1964	7	1956	4.88	258	13	37	2	7
Kansas	913	46	94	1964	17	1975+	5.55	408	20	62	3	8
Kentucky	179	9	34	1974	1	1975+	2.22	97	5	97	5	24
Louisiana	410	21	55	1974	5	1958+	4.22	253	13	65	3	13
Maine	61	3	11	1971	0	1964	.92	51	3	0	0	0
Maryland	48	2	10	1975	0	1970+	2.27	42	2	1	0	1
Massachusetts	93	5	12	1958	0	1959+	5.63	64	3	7	0	8
Michigan	280	14	39	1974	2	1959	2.40	159	8	95	5	16
Minnesota	341	17	34	1968	5	1972	2.03	199	10	57	3	7
Mississippi	455	23	44	1973	5	1964	4.77	239	12	263	13	55
Missouri	633	32	79	1973	11	1972	4.54	301	15	113	6	16
Montana	71	4	10	1975+	0	1974+	.24	54	3	0	0	0
Nebraska	700	35	78	1975	10	1966	4.53	328	16	18	1	2
Nevada	14	1	4	1964	0	1972+	.06	12	1	0	0	0
New Hampshire	50	3	9	1963	0	1975+	2.69	44	2	0	0	0
New Jersey	37	2	8	1973	0	1972+	2.36	29	1	0	0	0
New Mexico	194	10	18	1972	2	1973+	.80	144	7	3	0	0
New York	69	3	7	1969	1	1966+	.70	61	3	2	0	0
North Carolina	219	11	38	1973	2	1970	2.08	132	7	17	1	3
North Dakota	277	14	41	1965	2	1961	1.96	171	9	12	1	2
Ohio	291	15	43	1973	3	1966	3.53	159	8	128	6	31
Oklahoma	1115	56	107	1957	30	1972+	7.97	455	23	133	7	19
Oregon	22	1	3	1975+	0	1964+	.11	18	1	0	0	0
Pacific	1	0	1	1975	0	1974+	.00	1	0	0	0	0
Pennsylvania	106	5	15	1975	0	1959	1.17	85	4	3	0	1
Puerto Rico	7	0	2	1969	0	1975+	1.02	6	0	0	0	0
Rhode Island	1	0	1	1972	0	1975+	.41	1	0	0	0	0
South Carolina	194	10	23	1973	1	1970	3.12	126	6	21	1	7
South Dakota	498	25	64	1965	1	1958	3.23	250	13	7	0	1
Tennessee	227	11	44	1974	1	1962	2.69	117	6	68	3	16
Texas	2384	119	232	1967	56	1956	4.46	975	49	161	8	6
Utah	27	1	5	1970+	0	1975+	.16	21	1	0	0	0
Vermont	21	1	5	1962	0	1975+	1.09	17	1	0	0	0
Virginia	105	5	20	1975	1	1963+	1.29	75	4	14	1	3
Virgin Islands	0	0	0	-	0	-	.00	0	0	0	0	0
Washington	23	1	4	1972	0	1975+	.17	17	1	6	0	1
West Virginia	40	2	6	1974	0	1960+	.83	32	2	1	0	0
Wisconsin	379	19	33	1964	6	1956	3.37	210	11	47	2	8
Wyoming	125	6	17	1962	0	1970	.64	98	5	1	0	0
TOTAL: United States	*14600	730	1102	1973	464	1963	2.02	†3404	170	2095	105	6

+ Also in earlier year(s).
* Corrected for boundary-crossing tornadoes.
† Tornado Days for Country as a whole.

Mean annual tornadoes per 10,000 square miles.
@ Number of deaths per 10,000 square miles -- 1956-75

NUMBER OF TORNADOES, TORNADO DAYS, AND DEATHS BY MONTHS, 1956-75

	JANUARY			FEBRUARY			MARCH			APRIL			MAY			JUNE		
YEAR	NUMBER	DAYS	DEATHS	NUMBER	DAYS	DEATHS	NUMBER	DAYS	DEATHS	NUMBER	DAYS	DEATHS	NUMBER	DAYS	DEATHS	NUMBER	DAYS	DEATHS
1956	2	2	0	47	12	8	31	7	1	85	15	67	79	24	4	65	21	0
1957	17	3	13	5	3	0	38	7	1	216	21	29	227	26	87	147	25	14
1958	12	7	0	20	5	13	15	10	0	76	19	4	68	21	0	127	27	42
1959	16	2	3	20	5	21	43	11	9	30	12	1	226	28	8	73	25	2
1960	9	4	0	28	10	0	28	10	0	70	20	7	201	26	34	124	27	3
1961	1	1	0	31	8	0	124	17	7	74	19	3	137	25	23	107	23	2
1962	12	3	1	25	7	0	37	9	17	41	8	1	200	22	3	171	29	0
1963	15	5	1	6	3	0	50	12	8	82	14	16	71	21	1	91	23	0
1964	14	3	10	2	2	0	36	11	6	157	23	15	135	20	16	136	24	0
1965	21	11	0	32	4	0	34	9	2	129	20	264	275	25	17	147	28	6
1966	1	1	0	28	5	0	12	6	58	80	20	12	98	17	0	126	28	19
1967	39	4	7	8	5	0	42	14	3	149	18	73	116	25	3	210	28	6
1968	5	3	0	7	3	0	28	8	0	102	15	40	145	26	72	136	27	11
1969	3	1	32	5	5	0	8	2	1	68	15	2	145	25	4	137	28	7
1970	9	5	0	16	3	0	25	12	2	117	16	29	88	19	26	134	24	6
1971	18	7	1	83	12	131	40	13	2	75	14	11	166	24	7	199	28	1
1972	33	10	5	7	4	0	69	17	0	96	20	16	140	27	0	114	25	2
1973	33	7	1	10	4	0	80	16	17	150	22	10	250	26	35	224	26	2
1974	24	8	2	23	9	0	36	12	1	269	22	313	144	28	10	194	26	31
1975	53	7	12	45	12	7	84	16	12	108	20	13	188	30	5	196	28	6
1956–75:																		
TOTAL	337	94	88	448	121	180	860	219	147	2174	353	926	3099	485	355	2858	520	160
MEAN	17	5	4	22	6	9	43	11	7	109	18	46	155	24	18	143	26	8

	JULY			AUGUST			SEPTEMBER			OCTOBER			NOVEMBER			DECEMBER			ANNUAL		
YEAR	NUMBER	DAYS	DEATHS	NUMBER	DAYS	DEATHS	NUMBER	DAYS	DEATHS	NUMBER	DAYS	DEATHS	NUMBER	DAYS	DEATHS	NUMBER	DAYS	DEATHS	NUMBER	DAYS	DEATHS
1956	91	26	1	43	20	2	16	10	0	29	8	0	7	6	0	9	4	0	504	155	83
1957	55	19	0	20	14	0	17	10	2	18	11	2	58	11	25	38	4	18	856	154	191
1958	121	30	1	46	20	1	24	14	1	9	6	4	45	6	0	1	1	0	564	166	66
1959	63	24	0	38	18	0	58	15	14	24	10	0	11	4	0	2	2	0	604	156	58
1960	43	22	0	47	23	1	22	13	0	18	10	1	25	6	0	1	1	0	616	172	46
1961	77	27	0	27	16	0	53	16	15	14	5	0	36	7	1	16	5	0	697	169	51
1962	78	26	0	51	21	6	24	11	0	11	10	0	5	4	0	2	2	0	657	152	28
1963	62	26	0	26	13	2	33	13	3	13	5	0	15	6	0	0	0	0	464	141	31
1964	63	23	0	79	23	2	25	10	0	22	4	22	17	8	0	18	5	2	704	156	73
1965	86	26	0	61	23	1	64	21	0	16	4	1	34	6	5	7	4	0	906	181	296
1966	100	27	3	58	21	0	22	13	0	29	6	6	20	3	0	11	3	0	585	150	98
1967	90	25	1	28	16	2	139	16	5	36	7	4	8	5	0	61	10	10	926	173	114
1968	56	22	2	66	23	2	25	14	0	14	9	0	44	12	3	32	9	1	660	171	131
1969	99	27	0	69	21	19	20	11	0	26	10	0	5	3	0	23	7	1	608	155	66
1970	81	26	3	55	21	0	54	20	0	50	13	6	10	4	0	14	8	0	653	171	72
1971	100	30	1	50	21	0	47	15	0	38	12	0	16	7	0	56	9	2	888	192	156
1972	115	29	0	59	23	2	49	19	0	34	10	0	17	4	2	8	6	0	741	194	27
1973	80	26	0	51	23	4	69	22	3	25	11	0	81	11	12	49	12	3	1102	206	87
1974	59	19	0	107	26	0	25	11	0	45	10	4	13	8	0	8	5	0	947	184	361
1975	76	26	2	60	25	2	34	17	0	12	7	0	40	8	0	22	8	1	918	204	60
1956–75:																					
TOTAL	1595	506	14	1041	411	46	820	291	43	483	168	50	507	129	48	378	105	38	14600	3402	2095
MEAN	80	25	1	52	21	2	41	15	2	24	8	3	25	6	2	19	5	2	730	170	105

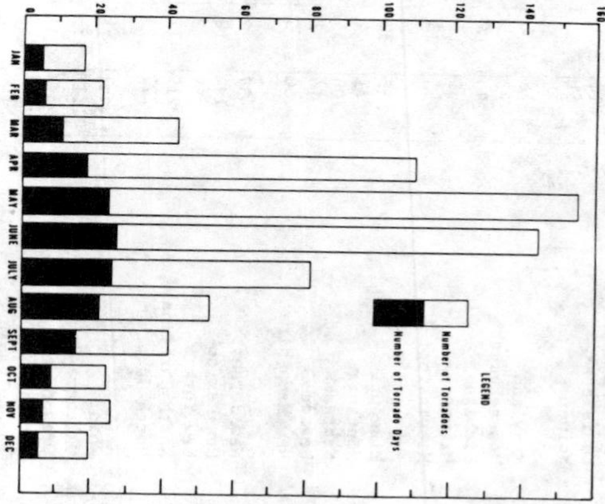

AVERAGE NUMBER OF TORNADOES AND TORNADO DAYS EACH MONTH IN THE UNITED STATES

(Based on 14,600 Tornadoes that Occurred from 1956 - 1975)

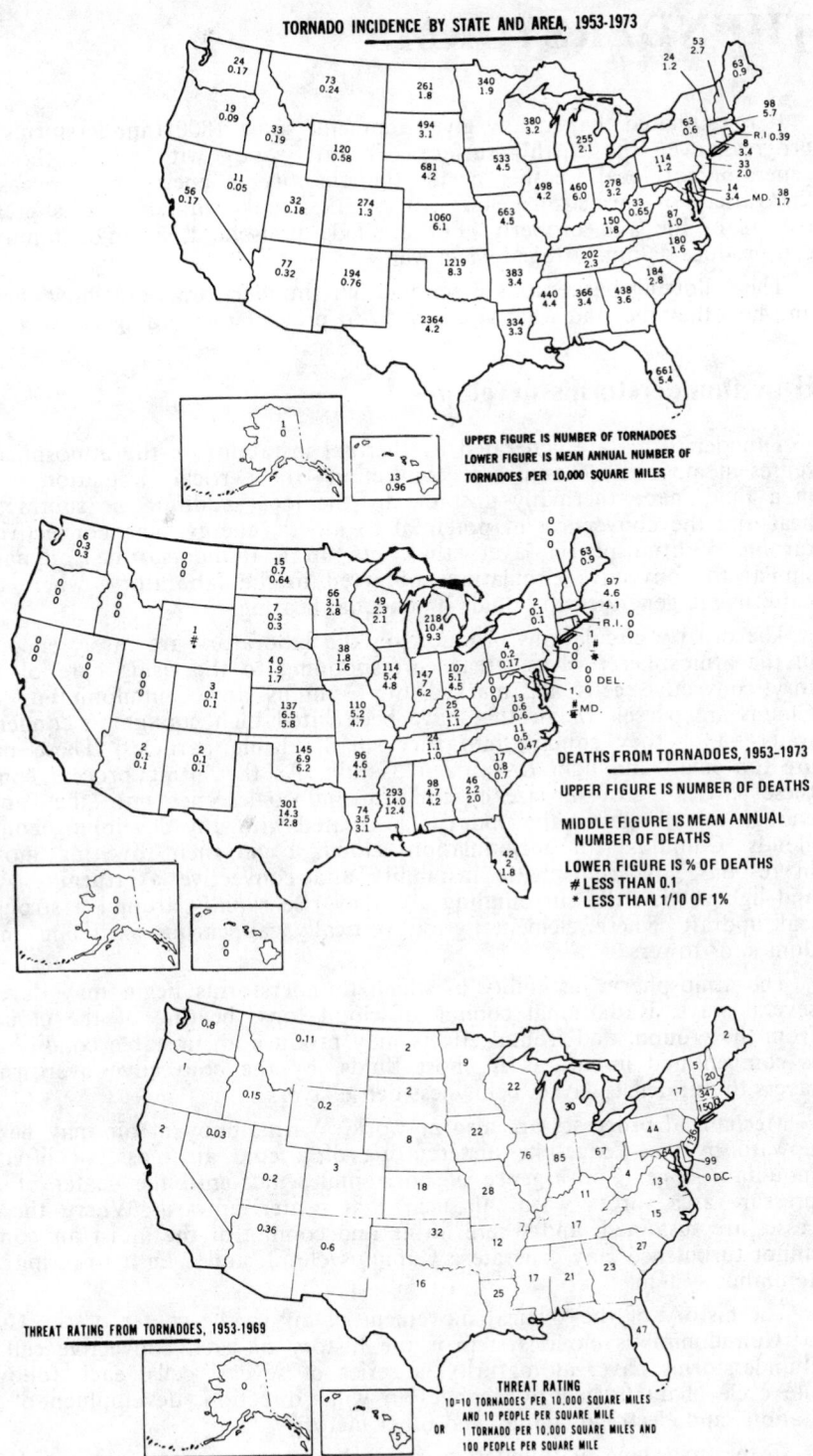

TORNADO INCIDENCE BY STATE AND AREA, 1953-1973

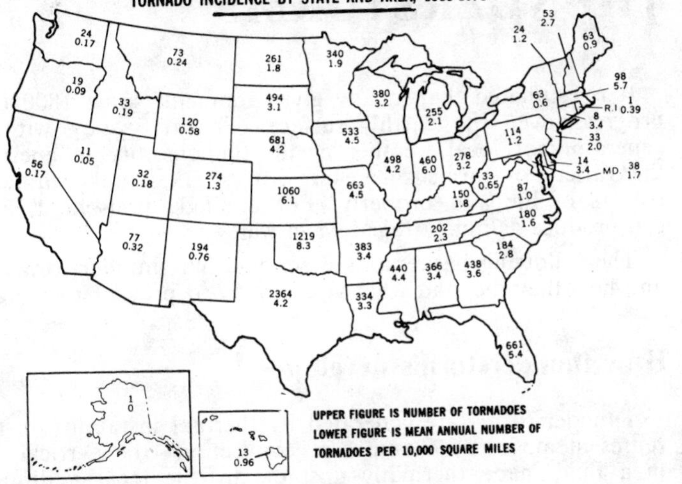

UPPER FIGURE IS NUMBER OF TORNADOES
LOWER FIGURE IS MEAN ANNUAL NUMBER OF TORNADOES PER 10,000 SQUARE MILES

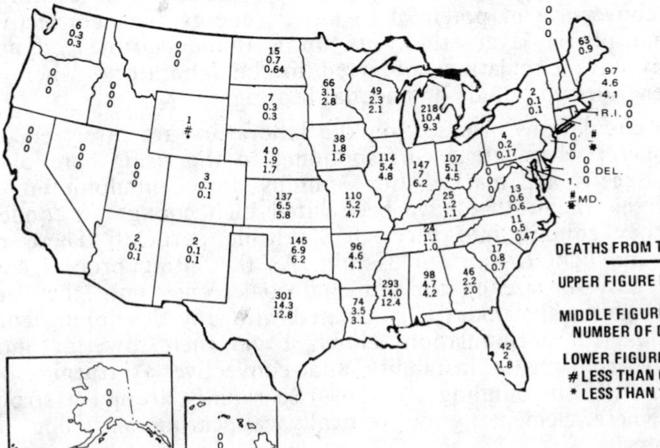

DEATHS FROM TORNADOES, 1953-1973

UPPER FIGURE IS NUMBER OF DEATHS

MIDDLE FIGURE IS MEAN ANNUAL NUMBER OF DEATHS

LOWER FIGURE IS % OF DEATHS
LESS THAN 0.1
* LESS THAN 1/10 OF 1%

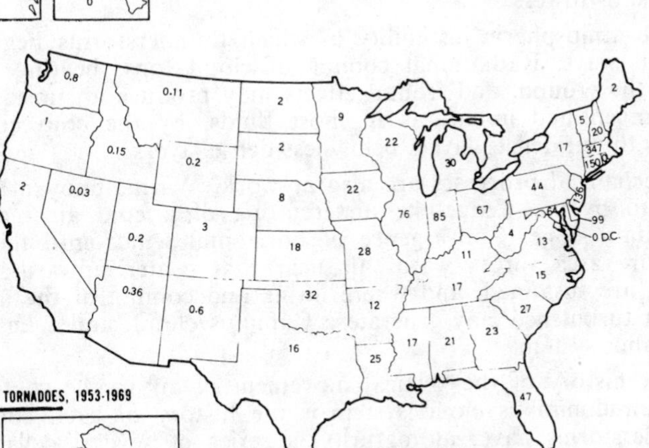

THREAT RATING FROM TORNADOES, 1953-1969

THREAT RATING
10=10 TORNADOES PER 10,000 SQUARE MILES AND 10 PEOPLE PER SQUARE MILE
OR 1 TORNADO PER 10,000 SQUARE MILES AND 100 PEOPLE PER SQUARE MILE

THUNDERSTORMS

It is estimated that at any given moment, some 1800 thunderstorms are in progress over the earth's surface. The frequency with which these giant generators of local weather occur, the quantity of energy they release, and the variety of forms this energy may take, make thunderstorms great destroyers of life and property. For a single household, a single family, they can produce as much tragedy as a war.

The following paragraphs describe what thunderstorms are, how they form and how they die, and what you can do to prevent their doing violence to you.

How thunderstorms develop—

Thunderstorms are generated by thermal instability in the atmosphere, and represent a violent example of convection—the vertical circulation produced in a fluid made thermally unstable by the local addition or subtraction of heat and the conversion of potential to kinetic energy. The convective overturning of atmospheric layers that sets up a thunderstorm is dynamically similar to convective circulations observed in the laboratory, where distinct patterns are generated in liquids by unequal heating.

The orderly circulations produced in the laboratory are rarely encountered in the atmosphere, where areas corresponding to the rising core of laboratory convective cells are marked by Cumulus and Cumulonimbus clouds. Clouds are parcels of air that have been lifted high enough to condense the water vapor they contain into very small, visible particles. These particles are too small and light to fall out as rain. As the lifting process continues, these particles grow in size, by collision and coalescence until they are large enough to fall against the updrafts associated with any developing convective clouds. Cumulus (for accumulation) clouds begin their towering movement in response to atmospheric instability and convective overturning. Warmer and lighter than the surrounding air, they rise rapidly around a strong, central updraft. These elements grow vertically, appearing as rising mounds, domes, or towers.

The atmospheric instability in which thunderstorms begin may develop in several ways. Radiational cooling of cloud tops, heating of the cloud base from the ground, and frontal effects may produce an unstable condition. This is compensated in air, as in most fluids, by the convective overturning of layers to put denser layers below less dense layers.

Mechanical processes are also at work. Warm, buoyant air may be forced upward by the wedge-like undercutting of a cold air mass, or lifted by a mountain slope. Convergence of horizontal winds into the center of a low-pressure area forces warm air near that center upward. Where these processes are sustained, and where lifting and cooling of the moist air continues, minor turbulence may generate a Cumulus cloud, and then a towering cumulonimbus system.

The history of the vertical movement of air in the center of the Cumulus or Cumulonimbus cloud system is the history of each convective cell. Most thunderstorms have, at maturity, a series of several cells, each following a life cycle characterized by changes in wind direction, development of precipitation and electrical charge, and other factors.

In the first stage of thunderstorm development, an updraft drives warm air up beyond condensation levels, where clouds form, and where continued upward movement produces Cumulus formations. The updraft develops in a region of gently converging surface winds in which the atmospheric pressure is slightly lower than in surrounding areas. As the updraft continues, air flows in through the cloud's sides in a process called entrainment, mixing with and feeding the updraft. The updraft may be further augmented by a chimney effect produced by high winds at altitude.

Heat energy from water—

But a developing thunderstorm also feeds on another source of energy. Once the cloud has formed, the phase changes of water result in a release of heat energy, which increases the momentum of the storm's vertical development. The rate at which this energy is released is directly related to the amount of gaseous water vapor converted to liquid water.

As water vapor in the burgeoning cloud is raised to saturation levels, the air is cooled sufficiently to liberate solid and liquid particles of water, and rain and snow begin to fall within the cloud. The cloud tower rises beyond the level (3-5 kilometers) where fibrous streamers of frozen precipitation elements appear; this apparent ice phase is thought to be a condition of thunderstorm precipitation. The formation and precipitation of particles large enough and in sufficient quantity to fall against the updraft marks the beginning of the second, mature state of the thunderstorm cell.

A thunderstorm's mature stage is marked by a transition in wind direction within the storm cells. The prevailing updraft which initiated the cloud's growth is joined by a downdraft generated by precipitation. The downdraft is fed and strengthened, as the updraft was, by the addition of entrained air, and by evaporational cooling caused by interactions of entrained air and falling precipitation. The mature storm dominates the electrical field and atmospheric circulation for several miles around. Lightning—the discharge of electricity between large charges of opposite sign—occurs soon after precipitation begins, a clue to the relationship of thunderstorm electrification and formation of ice crystals and raindrops.

At maturity, the thunderstorm cloud is several miles across its base and may tower to altitudes of 40,000 feet or more. The swift winds of the upper troposphere shred the cloud top into the familiar anvil form, visible in dry regions as lonely giants, or as part of a squall line.

On the ground directly beneath the storm system, the mature stage is initially felt as rain, which is soon joined by the strong downdraft. The downdraft spreads out from the cloud in gusting, divergent winds, and brings a marked drop in temperature. Even where the rain has not reached the ground, the thunderstorm's mature stage can be recognized by this cold air stream flowing over the surface. This is nature's warning that the thunderstorm is in its most violent phase. It is in this phase that the thunderstorm unleashes its lightning, hail, heavy rain, high wind, and—most destructive of all—the tornado. But even as it enters maturity, the storm has begun to die. The violent downdraft initially shares the circulation with the sustaining updraft, then strangles it. As the updraft is cut off from its converging low-level winds, the storm loses its source of moisture and heat energy. Precipitation weakens, stops, and the cold downdraft ceases. And the thunderstorm, violent creature of an instant, spreads and dies.

The thunderstorm cloud at maturity is several miles across its base and may tower to altitudes of 40,000 feet, or more. The swift winds of the upper troposphere shred the cloud top into the familiar anvil form, visible in dry regions as lonely giants, or as part of a squall line.

THUNDERSTORM SAFETY RULES

1. KEEP AN EYE ON THE WEATHER DURING WARM PERIODS AND DURING THE PASSAGE OF COLD FRONTS. **When Cumulus clouds begin building up and darkening, you are probably in for a thunderstorm. Check the latest weather forecast.**

2. KEEP CALM. **Thunderstorms are usually of short duration; even squall lines pass in a matter of a few hours. Be cautious, but don't be afraid. Stay indoors and keep informed.**

3. KNOW WHAT THE STORM IS DOING. **Remember that the mature stage may be marked on the ground by a sudden reversal of wind direction, a noticeable rise in wind speed, and a sharp drop in temperature. Heavy rain, hail, tornadoes, and lightning generally occur only in the mature state of the thunderstorm.**

4. CONDITIONS MAY FAVOR TORNADO FORMATION. **Tune in your radio or television receiver to determine whether there is a tornado watch or tornado warning out for your area. A tornado watch means tornado formation is likely in the area covered by the watch. A tornado warning means one has been sighted or radar-indicated in your area. If you receive a tornado warning, seek inside shelter in a storm cellar, below ground level, or in reinforced concrete structures; stay away from windows.**

5. LIGHTNING IS THE THUNDERSTORM'S WORST KILLER. **Stay indoors and away from electrical appliances while the storm is overhead. If lightning catches you outside, remember that it seeks the easiest—not necessarily the shortest—distance between positive and negative centers. Keep yourself lower than the nearest highly conductive object, and maintain a safe distance from it. If the object is a tree, twice its height is considered a safe distance.**

6. THUNDERSTORM RAIN MAY PRODUCE FLASH FLOODS. **Stay out of dry creek beds during thunderstorms. If you live along a river, listen for flash-flood warnings from the National Weather Service.**

LIGHTNING

It is estimated that lightning strikes the earth 100 times each second. The average annual death toll for lightning is greater than for tornadoes or hurricanes.

According to data assembled by the National Center for Health Statistics, lightning kills about 150 Americans per year and injures about 250. Property loss—fire and other damage to structures, aircraft damage, livestock deaths and injuries, forest fires, disruption of electromagnetic transmissions, and other effects—is estimated at more than $100 million annually.

What causes lightning?

Lightning is a secondary effect of electrification within a thunderstorm cloud system. Updrafts of warm, moist air rising into cold air can cause small cumulus clouds to grow into the large cumulonimbus cloud systems we associate with thunderstorms. These turbulent cloud systems tower about their companions, and dominate the atmospheric circulation and electrical field over a wide area. The transition from a small cloud to a turbulent, electrified giant can occur in as little as 30 minutes.

As a thunderstorm cumulonimbus develops, interactions of charged particles, external and internal electrical fields, and complex energy exchanges produce a large electrical field within the cloud. No completely acceptable theory explaining the complex processes of thunderstorm electrification has yet been advanced. But it is believed that electrical charge is important to formation of raindrops and ice crystals, and that thunderstorm electrification closely follows precipitation.

The distribution of electricity in a thunderstorm cloud is usually a concentration of positive charge in the frozen upper layers, and a large negative charge around a positive area in the lower portions of the cloud.

The earth is normally negatively charged with respect to the atmosphere. As the thunderstorm passes over the ground, the negative charge in the base of the cloud induces a positive charge on the ground below and several miles around the storm. The ground charge follows the storm like an electrical shadow, growing stronger as the negative cloud charge increases. The attraction between positive and negative charges makes the positive ground current flow up buildings, trees, and other elevated objects in an effort to establish a flow of current. But air, which is a poor conductor of electricity, insulates the cloud and ground charges, preventing a flow of current until large electrical charges are built up.

Lightning occurs when the difference between the positive and negative charges—the electrical potential—becomes great enough to overcome the resistance of the insulating air, and to force a conductive path for current to flow between the two charges. Potential in these cases can be as much as 100 million volts. Lightning strokes represent a flow of current from negative to positive (in most cases), and may proceed from cloud to cloud, cloud to ground, or, where high structures are involved, from ground to cloud.

The typical cloud-to-ground stroke we see most frequently begins as a pilot leader, too faint to be visible, advances downward from the cloud, and sets up the initial portion of the stroke path. A surge of current called a step leader follows the pilot, moving 100 feet or more at a time toward the ground, pausing, then repeating the sequence until the conductive path of electrified (ionized) particles is near the ground. There, discharge streamers extending from the ground intercept the leader path and complete the conductive channel between ground and cloud charges. When this path is complete, a return stroke leaps upward at speeds approaching that of light, illuminating the branches of the descending leader track. Because these tracks point downward, the stroke appears to come from the cloud. The bright light of the return stroke is the result of glowing atoms and molecules of air energized by the stroke.

Once the channel has been established and the return stroke has ended, dart leaders from the cloud initiate secondary returns, until the opposing charges are dissipated or the channel is gradually broken up by air movement. Even when luminous lightning is not visible, current may continue to flow along the ionized channel set up by the initial step leader.

Ground-to-cloud discharges are less frequently observed than the familiar cloud-to-ground stroke. In these cases, step leaders generally proceed from a tall conductive or semiconductive structure to the clouds; the initial leader stroke is not followed by a return stroke from the cloud, possibly because charges are less mobile in the cloud than in the highly conducting earth. Once the conductive path is established, however, current flow may set up cloud-to-ground sequences of dart leaders and returns.

Thunder—

Thunder is the crash and rumble associated with lightning, and is caused by explosive expansion of air heated by the stroke. When lightning is close by, the thunder is a sharp explosive sound. More distant strokes produce the familiar growl and rumble of thunder, a result of sound being refracted and modified by the turbulent environment of a thunderstorm. Because the speed of light is about a million times that of sound, the distance (in miles) to a lightning stroke can be estimated by counting the number of seconds between lightning and thunder, and dividing by five.

Lightning comes in many forms. Streak lightning, a single or multiple line from cloud to ground, is the form seen most frequently. Forked lightning shows the conductive channel. Sheet lightning is a shapeless flash covering a broad area, often seen in cloud-to-cloud discharges. Heat lightning is seen along the horizon during hot weather, and is believed to be the reflection of lightning occurring beyond the horizon. Ribbon lightning is streak lightning whose conductive channel is moved by high winds, making successive strokes seem to parallel one another. Beaded lightning appears as an interrupted stroke.

Ball lightning—

Ball lightning is in some ways the most interesting—and most controversial—form. As reported, ball lightning appears as a luminous globe, toroid (doughnut-shape), or ellipsoid which hisses as it hurtles from cloud to earth, maneuvers at high speeds, rolls along structures, or hangs suspended in the air.

The electromagnetic impulses of a lightning stroke produce whistlers—gliding tones which travel along lines of force in the earth's magnetic field from their lightning source in one hemisphere to a similar point in the opposite hemisphere, often echoing back and forth several times. Their sound is something like the whistle of World War II bombs, occasionally modified in a way that produces musical variations.

The dual character of lightning—it is a carrier of high currents and produces destructive thermal effects—makes it doubly dangerous. The current peaks, which may reach magnitudes of 200,000 amperes or more, produce forces which have a crushing effect upon conductors, and which can build to explosive levels in non-conducting or semiconducting materials like wood or brick. The continuous current produces heat, and is responsible for the numerous fires attributed to lightning.

Work on the lightning problem—

At NOAA, the National Oceanic and Atmospheric Administration of the U.S. Department of Commerce, lightning is the subject of considerable scientific interest. The severe storm warnings of NOAA's National Weather Service carry implicit alerts that lightning can be expected—and avoided. Commerce Department scientists at NOAA's Environmental Research Laboratories are experimenting with lightning suppression techniques, measuring atmospheric electricity over the open ocean, and studying the apparent but elusive connections between lightning and other events in the atmosphere, ionosphere, earth, and geomagnetic field.

LIGHTNING SAFETY RULES

THESE SAFETY RULES WILL HELP YOU SAVE YOUR LIFE WHEN LIGHTNING THREATENS.

1. **Stay indoors, and don't venture outside, unless absolutely necessary.**
2. **Stay away from open doors and windows, fireplaces, radiators, stoves, metal pipes, sinks, and plug-in electrical appliances.**
3. **Don't use plug-in electrical equipment like hair dryers, electric tooth brushes, or electric razors during the storm.**
4. **Don't use the telephone during the storm—lightning may strike telephone lines outside.**
5. **Don't take laundry off the clothesline.**
6. **Don't work on fences, telephone or power lines, pipelines, or structural steel fabrication.**
7. **Don't use metal objects like fishing rods and golf clubs. Golfers wearing cleated shoes are particularly good lightning rods.**
8. **Don't handle flammable materials in open containers.**
9. **Stop tractor work, especially when the tractor is pulling metal equipment, and dismount. Tractors and other implements in metalic contact with the ground are often struck by lightning.**
10. **Get out of the water and off small boats.**
11. **Stay in your automobile if you are traveling. Automobiles offer excellent lightning protection.**
12. **Seek shelter in buildings. If no buildings are available, your best protection is a cave, ditch, canyon, or under high-high clumps of trees in open forest glades.**
13. **When there is no shelter, avoid the highest object in the area. If only isolated trees are nearby, your best protection is to crouch in the open, keeping twice as far away from isolated trees as the trees are high.**
14. **Avoid hill tops, open spaces, wire fences, metal clothes lines, exposed sheds, and any electrically conductive elevated objects.**
15. **When you feel the electrical charge—if your hair stands on end or your skin tingles—lightning may be about to strike you. Drop to the ground immediately.**

Persons struck by lightning receive a severe electrical shock and may be burned, but they carry no electrical charge and can be handled safely. A person "killed" by lightning can often be revived by prompt mouth-to-mouth resuscitation, cardiac massage, and prolonged artificial respiration. In a group struck by lightning, the apparently dead should be treated first; those who show vital signs will probably recover spontaneously, although burns and other injuries may require treatment. Recovery from lightning strikes is usually complete except for possible impairment or loss of sight or hearing.*

*See Taussing, H. B. "Death From Lightning and the Possibility of Living Again," Annals of Internal Medicine, Vol. 68, No. 6 June 1968.

FLOODS

Flood danger—

The transformation of a tranquil river into a destructive flood occurs hundreds of times each year, in every part of the United States. Every year, some 75,000 American are driven from their homes by floods; on the average, 80 persons are killed each year. These destructive overflows have caused property damage in some years estimated at more than $1,000,000,000. Floods are also great wasters of water—and water is a priceless national resource.

Why floods?

Floods begin when soil and vegetation cannot absorb falling rain or melting snow, and when water runs off the land in such quantities that it cannot be carried in normal stream channels or retained in natural ponds and manmade reservoirs. River Forecast Centers issue flood forecasts and warnings when the rain that has fallen is enough to cause rivers to overflow their banks, and when melting snow combines with rainfall to produce similar effects.

Flood warnings—

Early flood warnings allow time for residents to leave low-lying areas, and to move personal property, mobile equipment, and livestock to higher ground. Sometimes valuable crops can be harvested in advance of a destructive flood. Emergency and relief organizations can prepare to handle refugees and to combat the inevitable health hazards caused by floods.

Flood warnings can be issued hours to days in advance of the flood peak on major tributaries. Main river flood forecasts can be issued as far as several days or even weeks in advance. In general, the time lapse between rainfall or snowmelt and the rise in river height increases with the size of the river.

Flood warnings are forecasts of impending floods, and are distributed to the public by radio and television, and through local emergency forces. The warning message tells the expected severity of flooding (minor, moderate, or major), the affected river, and when and where flooding will begin. Careful preparation and prompt response will reduce property loss and ensure personal safety.

Community sand bagging efforts tell more dramatically than river pictures of heavy rains and swelling streams. This Jack Shere, American Red Cross photo shows college and high school students preparing Minot, North Dakota to battle April 1969 flood waters.

FLOOD SAFETY RULES

BEFORE THE FLOOD:

1. **Keep on hand materials like sandbags, plywood, plastic sheeting, and lumber.**
2. **Install check valves in building sewer traps, to prevent flood water from backing up in sewer drains.**
3. **Arrange for auxiliary electrical supplies for hospitals and other operations which are critically affected by power failure.**
4. **Keep first aid supplies at hand.**
5. **Keep your automobile fueled; if electric power is cut off, filling stations may not be able to operate pumps for several days.**
6. **Keep a stock of food which requires little cooking and no refrigeration; electric power may be interrupted.**
7. **Keep a portable radio, emergency cooking equipment, lights and flashlights in working order.**

WHEN YOU RECEIVE A FLOOD WARNING:

8. **Store drinking water in clean bathtubs, and in various containers. Water service may be interrupted.**
9. **If forced to leave your home and time permits, move essential items to safe ground; fill tanks to keep them from floating away; grease immovable machinery.**
10. **Move to a safe area before access is cut off by flood water.**

DURING THE FLOOD:

11. **Avoid areas subject to sudden flooding.**
12. **Do not attempt to cross a flowing stream where water is above your knees.**
13. **Do not attempt to drive over a flooded road—you can be stranded, and trapped.**

AFTER THE FLOOD:

14. **Do not use fresh food that has come in contact with flood waters.**
15. **Test drinking water for potability; wells should be pumped out and the water tested before drinking.**
16. **Seek necessary medical care at nearest hospital. Food, clothing, shelter, and first aid are available at Red Cross shelters.**
17. **Do not visit disaster area; your presence might hamper rescue and other emergency operations.**
18. **Do not handle live electrical equipment in wet areas; electrical equipment should be checked and dried before returning to service.**
19. **Use flashlights, not lanterns or torches, to examine buildings; flammables may be inside.**
20. **Report broken utility lines to appropriate authorities. During any flood emergency, stay tuned to your radio or television station. Information from NOAA and civil emergency forces may save your life.**

FLASH FLOODS

Flash flood waves, moving at incredible speeds, can roll boulders, tear out trees, destroy buildings and bridges, and scour out new channels. Killing walls of water can reach 10 to 20 feet. You won't always have a warning that these deadly, sudden floods are coming. But you can save yourself — your family — if you know what to expect and how to react.

On small streams, especially near the headwaters of river basins, water levels may rise quickly in heavy rainstorms, and flash floods can begin before the rain stops falling. There is little time between detection of flood crest. Swift action is essential to the protection of life and property.

NOAA's Weather Service has helped set up flash flood warning systems in about 100 communities. In these, a volunteer network of rainfall and river observing stations is established in the area, and a local flood warning representative is appointed to collect reports from the network. The representative is authorized to issue official flash flood warnings based on a series of graphs prepared by the Weather Service . These graphs show the local flooding that will occur under different conditions of soil moisture and rainfall. On the basis of reported rainfall, the representative can prepare a flood forecast from these graphs, and spread a warning within minutes. Communities within range of a Weather Service radar have the additional protection of advance warning when flood-producing storms approach.

Successful operation of a flash flood warning system requires active community participation and planning, but very little financial outlay. Still, the communities with cooperative flash flood warning systems are only a small fraction of the thousands of communities which need them.

Flash flood warnings are the most urgent type of flood warning issued, and are transmitted to the public over radio, television, and by sirens and other signals.

Learn these flash flood terms used in forecasts and warnings:

FLASH FLOOD means the occurrence of a dangerous rise in water level of a stream or over a land area in a few hours or less caused by heavy rain, ice jam breakup, earthquake, or dam failure.

FLASH FLOOD WATCH means that heavy rains occurring or expected to occur may soon cause flash flooding in certain areas and citizens should be alert to the possibility of a flood emergency which will require immediate action.

FLASH FLOOD WARNING means that flash flooding is occurring or imminent on certain streams or designated areas and immediate precautions should be taken by those threatened.

FLASH FLOOD SAFETY RULES

BEFORE THE FLOOD **know the elevation of your property in relation to nearby streams and other waterways. Investigate the flood history of your area and how man-made changes may affect future flooding. Make advance plans of what you will do and where you will go in a flash flood emergency.**

WHEN A FLASH FLOOD WATCH IS ISSUED **listen to area radio and television stations for possible Flash Flood Warnings and reports of flooding in progress from the National Weather Service and public safety agencies. Be prepared to move out of danger at a moment's notice. If you are on the road, watch for flooding at highway dips, bridges, and low areas due to heavy rain not observable to you, but which may be indicated by thunder and lightning.**

WHEN A FLASH FLOOD WARNING IS ISSUED **for your area act quickly to save yourself. You may have only seconds:**

1. **Get out of areas subject to flooding. Avoid already flooded areas.**

2. **Do not attempt to cross a flowing stream on foot where water is above your knees.**

3. **If driving, know the depth of water in a dip before crossing. The road may not be intact under the water. If the vehicle stalls, abandon it immediately and seek higher ground — rapidly rising water may engulf the vehicle and its occupants and sweep them away.**

4. **Be especially cautious at night when it is harder to recognize flood dangers.**

5. **When you are out of immediate danger, tune in area radio or television stations for additional information as conditions change and new reports are received.**

AFTER THE FLASH FLOOD WATCH OR WARNING IS CANCELLED **stay tuned to radio or television for follow-up information. Flash flooding may have ended, but general flooding may come later in headwater streams and major rivers.**

LOSS OF LIFE AND PROPERTY IN THE UNITED STATES FROM FLOODS

PROPERTY LOSSES IN THOUSANDS OF DOLLARS
By Months and Years, 1925-1973

	January		February		March		April		May		June		July		August		September		October		November		December		Total	
Year	Property	Life	Property	Life	Property	Life	Property	Life	Property	Life	Property	Life	Property	Life	Property	Life	Property	Life	Property	Life	Property	Life	Property	Life	Property	Life
1925	3,614	2	141	0	74	0	-	0	65	6	3,980	14	140	0	275	0	1,171	14	380	0	83	0	-	0	9,923	36
1926	19	0	600	0	77	0	293	0	-	0	-	1	55	0	7	0	7,729	6	12,699	6	135	0	1,854	3	23,468	16
1927	2,626	8	1,867	0	407	0	283,207	232	7,566	95	1,125	0	241	0	3,460	0	-	0	1,627	0	45,093	88	437	0	347,656	423
1928	4	0	9	0	758	0	1,168	0	105	0	12,296	1	13,339	0	9,272	3	4,047	5	-	0	3,567	6	46	0	44,611	15
1929	122	0	2,964	0	21,947	47	1,937	0	15,668	5	10,268	5	4,959	32	130	0	92	0	9,379	0	556	0	76	0	68,098	89
1930	7,110	0	7	0	146	0	-	0	5,021	14	3,042	0	244	0	251	0	-	0	29	0	-	0	-	0	15,850	14
1931	-	0	30	0	572	0	-	0	8	0	13	0	1,215	0	201	0	2	0	1	0	744	0	22	0	2,808	0
1932	1,207	0	-	0	165	0	373	0	1,552	0	1,245	0	1,627	0	763	0	2,666	11	335	0	3	0	359	0	10,295	11
1933	308	0	87	0	2,008	1	2,709	4	10,785	4	2,650	4	1,117	0	6,516	4	489	0	10	0	-	0	10,000	16	36,679	33
1934	5,002	45	9	0	706	0	1,693	34	-	0	899	0	178	0	322	9	84	0	28	0	1,287	0	154	0	10,362	88
1935	297	0	1	0	2,177	4	2,698	5	16,903	40	62,702	122	29,370	52	159	5	7,551	0	2,691	0	61	0	2,517	8	127,127	236
1936	341	0	2,107	6	145,936	24	124,743	82	1,118	6	124	0	2,248	20	205	0	5,046	4	378	0	118	0	5	0	282,549	142
1937	411,481	65	7,691	75	62	0	4,524	0	2,627	0	5,429	0	124	2	760	0	140	0	256	0	97	0	7,546	0	440,738	142
1938	260	0	3,712	2	27,819	86	3,008	0	12,402	0	3,624	58	10,373	9	232	8	39,641	17	3	0	5	0	19	0	101,098	180
1939	3	0	1,657	4	738	0	1,982	0	37	0	4,271	1	1,725	78	3,408	0	13	0	-	0	-	0	-	0	13,834	83
1940	58	0	7,246	0	1,048	2	2,185	0	438	0	2,790	12	5,314	0	18,853	40	2,135	6	88	0	95	0	217	0	40,467	60
1941	3	0	516	0	820	2	1,970	4	3,081	7	12,718	12	314	0	23	0	6,247	15	10,446	7	3,361	0	25	0	39,524	47
1942	131	0	1,901	1	327	0	18,369	2	14,837	31	25,586	1	13,064	17	267	0	3,234	0	5,678	2	-	0	15,113	14	98,507	68
1943	3,579	4	69	5	7,183	8	10,161	5	130,478	57	41,771	0	2,870	3	3,651	25	-	0	-	0	-	0	-	0	199,732	107
1944	3	0	35	1	2,633	3	42,646	13	24,103	0	24,535	16	3,198	0	928	0	1,708	0	108	0	-	0	1,182	0	101,079	33
1945	146	0	5,882	0	33,202	14	54,054	36	23,530	0	28,866	8	8,280	3	2,942	13	1,059	3	1,424	3	-	0	6,413	11	165,798	91
1946	13,385	0	4,015	0	631	0	2	0	12,587	12	20,343	3	1,656	4	1,148	0	7,346	9	1,965	0	1,134	0	6,441	0	70,813	28
1947	486	3	96	0	1,458	0	56,037	2	18,032	1	193,134	48	652	1	1,431	0	455	0	248	0	5	0	304	0	272,328	55
1948	6,479	6	11,429	1	17,896	4	28,667	15	107,244	35	22,160	15	17,550	2	1,144	0	590	0	-	0	3,553	0	13,247	4	229,959	82
1949	9,772	6	5,073	2	11,676	3	9,261	2	18,195	10	32,861	17	3,762	5	568	0	618	0	1,551	2	578	1	16	0	93,931	48
1950	4,619	3	6,925	7	3,451	7	14,668	0	51,126	21	22,340	34	19,224	6	1,687	0	3,718	4	5,562	3	6,638	3	36,092	5	176,050	93
1951	884	0	5,823	2	7,264	1	18,287	2	15,166	6	5,383	8	972,458	25	2,509	7	621	0	-	0	-	0	346	0	1,028,741	51
1952	9,139	14	926	1	1,909	9	199,127	10	6,438	3	22,775	2	3,858	9	296	0	9,376	6	-	0	30	0	190	0	254,064	54
1953	8,575	1	368	0	10,675	2	-	0	41,656	5	53,572	29	3,873	1	1,926	2	887	0	42	0	300	0	330	0	122,204	40
1954	2,554	4	84	0	20	0	557	0	6,213	1	52,076	20	2,215	2	6,606	3	3,170	8	33,341	17	0	0	3	0	106,842	55
1955	-	0	1,620	4	17,372	17	2,653	4	9,231	2	3,825	1	1,071	0	712,085	193	3,471	0	52,442	18	1,168	0	190,553	63	995,491	302
1956	9,455	0	2,731	3	3,403	2	1,202	0	24,799	10	2,300	4	5,849	15	11,671	4	-	0	1,892	0	137	3	1,249	0	64,688	42
1957	61,383	15	29,750	2	-	0	106,130	18	44,182	13	101,696	32	4,669	0	722	2	335	0	2,663	0	8,610	0	163	0	360,303	82
1958	273	0	12,501	11	11,193	0	21,145	3	24,884	2	67,537	0	42,779	29	18,631	1	14,560	0	2,336	1	2,416	0	-	0	218,255	47
1959	95,601	8	2,448	0	2,031	6	427	0	7,181	8	890	0	557	0	5,550	0	1,844	0	19,602	3	4,970	0	154	0	141,255	25
1960	534	1	713	2	29,988	4	28,056	0	2,214	3	9,956	13	9,038	1	677	0	5,266	0	5,818	6	360	0	356	0	92,976	32
1961	32	0	13,870	1	14,242	3	5,053	0	67,785	6	4,324	4	5,825	25	3,974	6	26,041	7	580	0	[illegible]	0	10,666	0	154,033	52
1962	884	0	24,906	9	28,417	4	8,920	0	1,893	0	2,265	2	2,428	1	708	0	3,266	3	-	0	580	0	970	0	75,237	19
1963	2,343	0	16,392	0	99,429	31	2,302	0	1,573	0	14,682	3	4,261	4	36,926	1	38	0	-	0	-	0	-	0	177,946	39
1964	787	0	15	0	97,945	14	16,763	1	1,313	0	71,666	37	29	0	517	0	5,477	3	16,432	1	750	2	439,948	42	651,642	100
1965	11,084	0	2,566	2	4,158	1	180,337	16	36,328	3	495,750	66	24,705	17	193	0	9,652	0	894	0	-	0	22,379	14	788,046	119
1966	13,114	0	12,823	2	2,012	1	40,460	16	1,315	0	4,377	1	840	4	17,773	0	658	0	-	0	528	2	23,104	5	117,004	31
1967	2,213	0	-	0	42,182	4	6,453	0	3,043	1	104,097	5	1,191	4	7,877	0	101,135	11	140	0	-	2	106,887	7	375,218	34
1968	7,436	4	2,971	0	45,925	2	2,053	0	245,670	17	11,216	0	16,350	3	4,009	3	594	0	104	0	-	0	3,071	2	339,399	31
1969	302,378	64	108,781	8	4,065	1	179,999	9	8,798	4	35,403	3	118,455	33	123,524	157	4,557	0	4,931	2	2,000	3	9,763	13	902,654	297
1970	50,941	18	257	1	10,147	3	13,914	8	28,622	6	29,417	3	4,002	4	3,595	10	16,214	25	67,045	53	111	3	1,188	1	225,453	135
1971	8,347	0	12,354	1	3,343	0	2,781	0	[illegible],354	2	6,366	2	6,274	5	157,450	29	50,814	22	2,630	7	1,096	0	28,716	6	287,525	74
1972	16,253	4	14,815	128	9,480	0	19,238	4	29,950	23	4,229,819	350	24,222	2	26,758	1	40,015	9	32,837	24	108	3	21,640	6	4,465,135	554
1973	10,478	1	16,023	3	438,544	14	409,591	38	540,262	21	209,489	30	7,709	11	43,897	8	74,706	4	128,246	10	6,019	2	9,529	6	1,894,493	148
Total	1,085,743	276	346,806	284	1,167,662	324	1,929,493	565	1,633,378	480	6,077,653	987	1,405,661	429	1,246,447	534	468,478	194	426,861	165	98,117	118	973,290	227	16,859,589	4,583
Average	22,158	6	7,078	6	23,830	7	39,377	12	33,334	10	124,034	20	28,687	9	25,438	11	9,561	4	8,711	3	2,002	2	19,863	5	344,073	94

FLOOD DAMAGE ESTIMATES BY STATE

1955-1973
Flooa Losses in Thousands of Dollars

States	1955	1956	1957	1958	1959	1960	1961	1962	1963	1964	1965	1966
Alabama	3,379	720	2,324	872	-	670	12,625	3,529	1,280	5,343	723	2,366
Alaska	-	*	-	-	-	-	**	***	-	-	-	-
Arizona	226	-	-	-	100	-	325	1,000	-	55	11,330	3,050
Arkansas	61	255	27,938	6,202	3,090	580	3,503	91	2,500	598	143	5,055
California	165,767	8,745	13	33,063	4	516	95	2,780	11,834	229,168	11,321	24,347
Colorado	2,567	5,135	2,901	240	-	-	-	80	50	-	452,293	707
Connecticut	379,360	-	-	-	-	750	-	-	-	-	-	-
Delaware	117	-	-	-	-	-	-	-	-	-	-	-
District of Columbia	-	51	-	60	-	-	-	-	-	-	-	-
Florida	105	1,891	-	-	150	12,047	317	1,481	-	426	144	548
Georgia	1	212	1,068	323	-	392	5,236	-	445	3,641	397	1,628
Hawaii	-	-	-	400	-	-	-	-	2,300	-	-	-
Idaho	1,371	6,222	20,896	3	500	-	939	8,112	2,766	11,704	4,184	-
Illinois	102	1,026	1,206	17,970	1,506	7,503	11,553	891	513	3,044	30,564	577
Indiana	1,003	4,021	66,748	52,302	12,958	2,649	13,306	670	8,266	12,327	20	3,098
Iowa	35	51	1,543	7,508	128	7,612	9,389	6,778	70	240	32,462	904
Kansas	474	33	9,164	4,606	4,061	1,947	13,397	1,826	168	370	29,792	97
Kentucky	6,629	568	55,233	3,817	2,480	3	12,969	16,885	36,917	35,476	1,044	1,671
Louisiana	30	-	4,147	2,842	-	112	6,074	1,908	-	30	-	250
Maine	-	-	-	-	61	-	800	-	-	-	-	528
Maryland	5,450	837	-	40	-	-	-	-	-	-	53	-
Massachusetts	155,982	-	-	-	-	6,400	-	-	-	-	-	-
Michigan	-	1,278	-	-	-	1,181	-	-	-	-	-	-
Minnesota	-	11	9,128	17	50	212	552	1,290	26	-	97,603	4,300
Mississippi	3,132	1,270	2,693	13,826	280	744	15,918	1,982	19	3,152	1,931	2,706
Missouri	666	167	9,618	38,718	6,018	13,506	27,375	557	152	6,591	33,976	2,781
Montana	63	317	33	1	82	57	-	147	148	54,389	253	-
Nebraska	1,500	865	5,983	3,064	3,753	8,884	674	2,630	13,394	5,146	1,368	11,628
Nevada	7,398	237	-	-	-	-	891	762	2,858	2,454	4	307
New Hampshire	-	-	-	-	4,500	100	-	-	-	-	-	-
New Jersey	23,102	-	-	3	-	-	-		-	-	-	-
New Mexico	1,066	-	-	-	-	-	-	-	620	1,235	4,833	1,048
New York	30,072	1,089	166	42	5,667	7,229	608	-	33,102	3,275	-	-
North Carolina	625	831	788	3,201	506	100	1,400	-	-	15,816	88	198
North Dakota	2	-	100	-	28	136	-	-	-	-	5,192	9,700
Ohio	753	1,056	7	4,867	54,840	191	1,217	6,512	22,359	28,039	-	1,893
Oklahoma	977	-	35,665	169	8,907	2,638	2,483	792	413	798	2,508	12
Oregon	9,515	6,376	310	363	20	360	757	1,550	299	187,101	5,679	2,283
Pennsylvania	141,381	7,199	1,048	3,582	21,109	3,072	612	15	5,397	16,938	-	705
Rhode Island	28,830	-	-	-	-	-	-	-	-	-	-	-
South Carolina	74	-	60	680	122	72	369	97	89	1,809	268	140
South Dakota	11	10	3,969	-	-	3,417	1	3,030	-	-	740	470
Tennessee	977	279	5,118	128	-	226	2,263	651	6,262	156	2,472	1,608
Texas	5,165	3,715	78,881	18,101	2,886	8,093	2,846	1,948	20	5,435	39,395	28,001
Utah	226	210	169	10	4	-	281	1,272	64	70	1,746	1,577
Vermont	-	-	3	-	-	-	-	-	-	692	-	-
Virginia	10,695	-	139	-	28	211	231	-	5,937	-	2	-
Washington	1,165	6,472	1,664	50	4,914	-	130	-	1,013	11,817	1,012	592
West Virginia	5,187	3,185	11,052	1,170	709	370	3,455	5,914	17,624	4,169	49	1,868
Wisconsin	50	335	-	-	1,791	996	1,442	57	142	-	14,067	361
Wyoming	200	11	526	3	-	-	-	-	899	138	390	-
TOTAL	995,491	64,688	360,303	218,255	141,255	92,976	154,033	75,237	177,946	651,642	788,046	117,004

States	1967	1968	1969	1970	1971	1972	1973
Alabama	1,695	408	88	10,891	2,170	2,278	5,439
Alaska	98,550	-	-	-	8,631	1,090	1,500
Arizona	3,576	188	-	5,000	3,476	20,868	-
Arkansas	1,497	21,099	3,411	639	2,549	1,780	129,579
California	1,370	-	423,296	47,798	3,522	1,132	9,480
Colorado	-	-	66	2,040	-	15	121,383
Connecticut	-	100	528	-	-	15,414	1,950
Delaware	-	-	-	-	50	-	-
District of Columbia	-	-	-	-	-	2,533	-
Florida	95	46	2,858	145	476	41,206	2,282
Georgia	23	133	79	348	243	328	5,143
Hawaii	1,029	2,500	-	-	500	-	-
Idaho	792	-	111	38	1,187	355	-
Illinois	2,629	2,576	9,095	9,124	462	5,927	258,704
Indiana	4,618	22,463	6,672	2,300	1,690	4,700	6,326
Iowa	4,416	1,650	6,233	977	684	13,262	12,724
Kansas	15,093	2,304	10,991	4,138	1,644	1,646	53,772
Kentucky	17,583	6,036	8,075	707	6,099	15,841	10,491
Louisiana	-	2,810	251	1,000	-	100	334,904
Maine	-	-	300	-	-	-	11,200
Maryland	125	-	200	15	8,600	218,206	-
Massachusetts	-	35,000	-	-	-	10	-
Michigan	-	100	13	-	-	10	530
Minnesota	-	1,197	67,168	4,350	15	64,318	242
Mississippi	1,192	6,269	1,900	3,586	12,431	10,248	226,885
Missouri	39,080	890	36,601	14,926	191	5,783	231,438
Montana	2,947	-	388	581	412	595	-
Nebraska	40,644	6,029	1,826	-	5,941	73	10,388
Nevada	45	1	-	138	-	-	-
New Hampshire	-	800	400	-	-	-	19,100
New Jersey	1,438	166,690	580	-	138,700	15,050	50,868
New Mexico	-	-	-	-	-	6,613	251
New York	777	-	3,383	3,953	1,080	747,674	5,000
North Carolina	1,168	-	1,338	2,326	965	10,772	39,004
North Dakota	-	-	37,436	13,832	1,266	537	-
Ohio	6,622	20,074	87,916	2,478	782	12,929	8,317
Oklahoma	3	3,021	762	5,212	23,166	12,006	38,119
Oregon	1,044	538	938	2,518	4,350	12,977	2,699
Pennsylvania	7,251	421	3,310	365	20,899	2,786,294	5,935
Rhode Island	588	9,000	-	-	-	-	-
South Carolina	579	-	625	52	295	69	7,674
South Dakota	1,125	123	31,898	19	-	165,086	-
Tennessee	1,090	648	1,090	13,260	86	6,634	66,273
Texas	98,259	24,267	12,878	3,150	26,538	20,605	136,758
Utah	453	1,260	237	222	1,033	358	2,270
Vermont	-	100	680	-	-	40	66,466
Virginia	581	-	123,552	148	1,158	180,770	1,615
Washington	1,910	611	2,722	380	3,908	21,029	-
West Virginia	14,235	47	5,996	297	1,653	37,974	3,359
Wisconsin	-	-	4,763	-	-	-	6,121
Wyoming	1,096	-	-	500	503	-	304
TOTAL	375,218	339,399	900,654	157,453	287,275	4,465,135	1,894,493

*Major flood in May 1956 **Major flood in June 1961 ***Ice jam flooding May 1962; also serious flooding in June 1962

LOSSES IN INDIVIDUAL SEVERE FLOODS

Property Losses in Thousands of Dollars

Date *	Location	Lives **	Property
May-June 1903	Kansas, Lower Missouri, and Upper Mississippi Rivers	100	$ 40,000
March 1912	Lower Mississippi River	---	70,000
March 1913	Ohio River and tributaries	467	147,000
December 1913	Texas Rivers	177	9,000
June 1921	Arkansas River in State of Colorado	120	25,000
September 1921	Texas Rivers	215	19,000
Spring of 1927	Mississippi Valley	313	284,118
November 1927	New England Rivers	88	45,578
May-June 1935	Republican and Kansas Rivers	110	18,000
July 1935	Upper Susquehanna Tributaries	52	26,000
March-April 1936	Rivers in Eastern United States	107	270,000
Jan.-Feb. 1937	Ohio and Lower Mississippi River Basins	137	417,685
March 1938	Streams in Southern California	79	24,500
September 1938	Rivers in New England	---	37,000
July 1939	Licking and Kentucky Rivers	78	1,715
August 1940	Rivers in Southern Virginia, the Carolinas, and Eastern Tennessee	40	12,000
May 1942	Delaware and Susquehanna River Basins	33	13,000
July 1942	Upper Allegheny River and Sinnamahoning Creek Basins	15	10,000
Nov.-Dec. 1942	Willamette River	10	6,900
April-June 1943	Maumee, Wabash, Upper Mississippi, Missouri, White, and Arkansas River Basins	60	172,500
August 1943	Little Kanawha River	23	1,300
April-June 1944	Upper Mississippi, Missouri, Arkansas, Red, and Lower Mississippi River Basins and East Texas Rivers	17	82,000
Feb.-March 1945	Ohio River	18	30,000
May-July 1947	Lower Missouri and Middle Mississippi River Basins	29	235,000
May-June 1948	[1]Columbia River Basin	35	101,725
May 1949	Trinity River	10	14,000
June 1949	Shenandoah and Potomac Rivers	11	8,850
June 1950	Rivers in Central West Virginia	31	4,020
June-July 1951	[2]Kansas and Missouri	28	923,224
April 1952	[3]Red River of the North, Upper Mississippi, and Missouri River Basins	11	198,000
April-May 1953	Louisiana and Texas	12	38,959
June 1953	Northwestern Iowa	14	32,950
June 1954	Middle Rio Grande and Lower Pecos Rivers	16	19,079
October 1954	Pecos River in New Mexico	13	1,783
March 1955	Ohio River Basin	15	14,396
August 1955	[4]Hurricane "Dianne" Floods in the Northeast	187	714,079
December 1955	[5]West Coast Rivers	61	154,532
Jan.-Feb. 1957	[6]Streams in Southeastern Kentucky, Southwestern West Virginia, and adjacent areas in Tennessee and Virginia	14	58,000
February 1957	Snake River and Tributaries	---	20,500
April-June 1957	Rivers in Texas, Arkansas, Kansas, Louisiana, Missouri and Oklahoma	18	105,000
June-July 1957	Wabash River and Tributaries	---	63,000
June 1958	White and Wabash Rivers	---	57,000
July 1958	Flash Flood on East Nishnabotna River (Iowa)	19	5,850
January 1959	Ohio River Basin	---	81,921
July 1961	Flash Flooding on Small Streams in Charleston, W.Va.	22	3,238

IN THE UNITED STATES SINCE JULY 1902

Property Losses in Thousands of Dollars

Date*	Location	Lives **	Property
March 1963	Ohio River Basin	26	97,600
June 1964	Montana	31	54,279
December 1964	California and Oregon	40	415,832
March 1964	Ohio River Basin	13	81,602
March-May 1965	[7]Upper Mississippi, Missouri, and Red River of the North River Basins	16	181,325
May 1965	Brazos River	---	30,802
June 1965	South Platte River Basin	16	415,076
June 1965	Sanderson, Texas Flash Flood	26	2,715
June 1965	Arkansas River Basin	16	58,340
April-May 1966	Sabine and Trinity Basins, Texas	14	$ 20,100
June 1967	Platte River Basin in Nebraska	---	35,275
September 1967	Hurricane "Beulah" floods in Texas	---	98,239
August 1967	Tanana and Chena Rivers in Alaska	---	98,550
May 1968	Rivers in Northern New Jersey	---	166,690
Jan.-Feb. 1969	Floods in California	60	399,233
March-April 1969	[8]Snowmelt Floods in Upper Midwest	---	151,000
July 1969	Northern Ohio	30	87,915
August 1969	[9]James River Basin in Virginia	153	116,000
January 1970	Sacramento River Basin	18	38,120
September 1970	Arizona	23	5,000
October 1970	Puerto Rico	50	62,000
August 1971	New Jersey ("Doria" rainfall)	---	138,700
September 1971	Southeastern Pennsylvania	13	19,010
February 1972	Buffalo Creek, West Virginia	125	10,000
May 1972	South-central Texas Flash Floods	18	17,500
June 1972	Black Hills of South Dakota	237	164,947
June 1972	Eastern U.S. (Hurricane "Agnes" floods)	105	4,019,721
Spring 1973	Mississippi System	33	1,154,770
May 1973	South Platte Basin in Colorado	---	120,400
May 1973	Flash Flooding in Mountains of North Carolina and Southwest Virginia	12	29,485
June 1973	Connecticut Basin in Vermont, Connecticut and New Hampshire	11	64,000
June 1973	San Jacinto Basin and small adjacent basins in southeast Texas	10	62,500

* The 1966 to 1972 Annual Issues of Climatological Data, National Summary (as well as various earlier issues) contain this table which lists additional significant severe floods during the period of record.

** No entry indicates that fewer than ten lives were lost.

References

1. Monthly Weather Review, January 1949
2. Technical Paper No. 17
3. Technical Paper No. 23
4. Technical Paper No. 26
5. Climatological Data, National Summary, December 1955
6. Climatological Data, National Summary, January 1957
7. Technical Paper No. WB-3
8. NOAA Technical Report No. 13
9. Climatological Data, National Summary, October 1970
10. Climatological Data, National Summary, June 1972; Geological Survey Professional Paper 924

WINTER STORMS

Winter storms can kill without breaking climatological records. Their danger is persistent, year to year. From 1936 through 1969, snowstorms caused more than 3,000 deaths, directly and indirectly. Of those reported deaths, more than a third were attributed to automobile and other accidents; just less than one-third to over-exertion, exhaustion, and consequent fatal heart attack; fewer than 400 to exposure and fatal freezing; and the rest to such causes as home fires, carbon monoxide poisoning in stalled cars, falls on slippery walks, electrocution from downed wires, and building collapse. The greatest number of snow-related deaths—354—in this period occured in 1960; 1958 is second with 345 deaths. About half of those reported occurred in New England, New York, and Pennsylvania.

Winter storm impact—

Nearly everyone east of the Pacific coastal ranges remembers significant winter storms—days of heavy snow, interminable blizzard, inconvenience, economic loss, and, sometimes, personal tragedy. Winter brings them all. For Wyoming or Kansas or Texas the blizzard of 1888 was one of the worst on record. The period January 11-13, in that year brought the most disastrous blizzard ever known in Montana, the Dakotas, and Minnesota, combining gale winds, blowing snow, and extreme cold into a lethal, destructive push from the Rockies eastward. The eastern seaboard got its big storm the same year. March 11-14, 1888, saw the seaboard from Chesapeake Bay to Maine stricken with a blizzard that dumped an average of 40 inches of snow over southeastern New York and southern New England. The storm killed 200 in New York City alone; total deaths were over 400.

But every winter is a bad year for someone. The 1966 season saw the eastern seaboard paralyzed by snow from Virginia to New England, with more than 50 deaths, and thousands marooned. A March storm buried the Dakotas, Minnesota, and Nebraska, with 30-foot drifts pushed up by winds gusting to more than 100 miles per hour. The 1967 winter storm season was not much better, and included a May Day blizzard in the Dakotas and a nor'easter which brought snow and hurricane-force winds to northern New England late in May. Snowfall across middle America was as much as four times normal in early 1968, and 1969 was called "the year of the big snows" in the midwest.

Where and why winter storms occur—

The storms are generated, as are many of the thunderstorms of summer, from disturbances along the boundary between cold polar and warm tropical air masses, the fronts where air masses of different temperatures and densities wage their perpetual war of instability and equilibrium. The disturbances may become intense lowpressure systems, churning over tens of thousands of square miles in a great counter-clockwise sweep.

In the Pacific, these disturbances form along polar fronts off the east coast of Asia and travel northeastward toward Alaska. But some, particularly those forming along the mid-Pacific polar front, take a more southerly track, striking the United States as far south as southern California. Few Pacific disturbances cross the Rockies, but some do, redeveloping to the east. One region of such redevelopment lies east of the Colorado Rockies; the storms which come out of that region are called Colorado Cyclones. Another region of storm redevelopment is east of the Canadian Rockies, from which come the so-called Alberta Cyclones. Both types take an eastward path, their most frequent ones converging over the Great Lakes. The Lakes themselves are generators of severe local winter storms, and forge others from northward-drifting disturbances originating over the Gulf of Mexico and our southern plains.

On our east coast, winter storms often form along the Atlantic polar front near the coast of Virginia and the Carolinas and in the general area east of the southern Appalachians. These are the notorious Cape Hatteras storms —nor'easters—which develop to great intensity as they move up the coast, then drift seaward toward Iceland, where they finally decay.

Because they form over water, these storms are difficult to forecast, and occasionally surprise the Atlantic megalopolis with paralyzing snows. In 1969, the U.S. Departments of Commerce, Transportation, and Defense tightened winter storm surveillance with reconnaissance aircraft, an ocean buoy, and a new weather ship. With better hour-to-hour information on the storms, weathermen ashore have begun to ease the burden of unexpected heavy snows in eastern cities.

For some parts of the United States—the Northern Rockies, for example—storms with snow followed by cold are a threat from mid-September to mid-May; during one of the colder months from November to March, it is not unusual for eight separate storms to affect some area across the continent. Intense winter storms are frequently accompanied by cold waves, ice or glaze, heavy snow, blizzards, or a combination of these; often, in a single winter storm, precipitation type changes several times as the storm passes. Their common feature is the ability to completely immobilize large areas and to isolate and kill persons and livestock in their path. In our northland, the severity of these storms makes their threat a seasonal one. Farther south, the occasional penetration of severe winter storms into more moderate climates causes severe hardship and great loss of warm-weather crops.

Freezing rain (ice storms)—

Freezing rain or freezing drizzle is rain or drizzle occurring when surface temperatures are below freezing (32° Fahrenheit, F). The moisture falls in liquid form but freezes upon impact, resulting in a coating of ice glaze on all exposed objects. The occurrence of freezing rain or drizzle is often called an ice storm when a substantial glaze layer accumulates. Ice forming on exposed objects generally ranges from a thin glaze to coatings about an inch thick; but much thicker deposits have been observed. For example, ice deposits to eight inches in diameter were reported on wires in northern Idaho in January 1961, and loadings of 11 pounds per foot of telephone wire were found in Michigan in February 1922. It has been estimated that an evergreen tree 50 feet high with an average width of 20 feet may be coated with as much as five tons of ice during a severe ice storm. A heavy accumulation of ice, especially when accompanied by high winds, devastates trees and transmission lines. Sidewalks, streets, and highways become extremely hazardous to pedestrians and motorists—over 85 per cent of ice-storm deaths are traffic-related. Freezing rain and drizzle frequently occur for a short time as a transitory condition between the occurrence of rain or drizzle and snow, and therefore usually occur at temperatures slightly below freezing.

Some of the most destructive ice storms have occurred in the southern states, where neither buildings nor crops are designed with severe winter conditions in mind. The most damaging ice storm in the United States was probably that which struck the southland from January 28 to February 4, 1951, causing some $50 million damage in Mississippi, $15 million in Louisiana, and nearly $2 million in Arkansas; this storm also caused 22 deaths. The region of greatest incidence, however, is a broad belt from Nebraska, Kansas, and Oklahoma eastward through the middle Atlantic and New England states.

Ice storms are not sleet storms—

Ice storms are sometimes incorrectly referred to as sleet storms. Sleet can be easily identified as frozen rain drops (ice pellets) which bounce when hitting the ground or other objects. Sleet does not stick to trees and wires; but sleet in sufficient depth does cause hazardous driving conditions.

Winter warnings—

The terms **watch** and **warning** are used for winter storms, as for other natural hazards. The **watch** alerts the public that a storm has formed and is approaching the area. People in the alerted area should keep listening for the latest advisories over radio and television, and begin to take precautionary measures. The warning means that a storm is imminent and immediate action should be taken to protect life and property.

The word **snow** in a forecast, without a qualifying word such as **occasional** or **intermittent,** means that the fall of snow is of a steady nature and will probably continue for several hours without letup.

Heavy snow warnings are issued to the public when a fall of four inches or more is expected in a 12-hour period, or a fall of six inches or more is expected in a 24-hour period. Some variations on these rules may be used in different parts of the country. Where four-inch snowfalls are common, for example, the emphasis on heavy snow is generally associated with six or more inches of snow. In other parts of the country where heavy snow is infrequent or in metropolitan areas with heavy traffic, a snowfall of two or three inches will justify a heavy snow warning.

Snow flurries are defined as snow falling for short durations at intermittant periods; however, snowfall during the flurries may reduce visibilities to an eighth of a mile or less. Accumulations from snow flurries are generally small.

Snow squalls are brief, intense falls of snow and are comparable to summer rain showers. They are accompanied by gusty surface winds.

Blowing and drifting snow generally occur together and result from strong winds and falling snow or loose snow on the ground. **Blowing snow** is defined as snow lifted from the surface by the wind and blown about to a degree that horizontal visibility is greatly restricted.

Drifting snow is used in forecasts to indicate that strong winds will blow falling snow or loose snow on the ground into significant drifts. In the northern plains, the combination of blowing and drifting snow, **after** a substantial snowfall has ended, is often referred to as a ground blizzard.

Blizzards are the most dramatic and perilous of all winter storms, characterized by low temperatures and by strong winds bearing large amounts of snow. Most of the snow accompanying a blizzard is in the form of fine, powdery particles of snow which are whipped in such great quantities that at times visibility is only a few yards.

Blizzard warnings are issued when winds with speeds of at least 35 miles per hour are accompanied by considerable falling or blowing snow and temperatures of 20°F or lower are expected to prevail for an extended period of time.

Severe blizzard warnings are issued when blizzards of extreme proportions are expected and indicate wind with speeds of at least 45 miles per hour plus a great density of falling or blowing snow and a temperature of 10°F or lower.

Hazardous driving (travelers') warnings are issued to indicate that falling, blowing or drifting snow, freezing rain or drizzle, sleet or strong winds will make driving difficult.

Livestock (stockmen's) warnings alert ranchers and farmers that livestock will require protection from a large accumulation of snow or ice, a rapid drop in temperature, or strong wind.

A cold wave warning indicates an expected rapid fall in temperature within a 24-hour period which will require substantially increased protection to agricultural, industrial, commercial, and social activities. The temperature falls and minimum temperatures required to justify cold wave warnings vary with the changing of the season and with geographic location. Regardless of the month or the section of the country, a cold wave warning is a red flag alert to the public that during a forthcoming forecast period **a change to very cold weather will require greater than normal protective measures.**

The terms **ice storm**, **freezing rain,** and **freezing drizzle** warn the public that a coating of ice is expected on the ground and on other exposed surfaces. The qualifying term **heavy** is used to indicate ice coating which, because of the extra weight of the ice, will cause significant damage to trees, overhead wires, and the like. Damage will be greater if the freezing rain or drizzle is accompanied by high winds.

BLIZZARD SAFETY FOR CATTLE

Blizzards take a terrible toll in livestock. For both humane and economic reasons, stockmen should take necessary precautions in advance of severe winter storms.

MOVE LIVESTOCK, ESPECIALLY YOUNG LIVESTOCK, INTO SHELTERED AREAS. **Shelter belts, properly oriented and laid out, provide better protection for range cattle than shed type shelters, which may cause cattle to overcrowd, with consequent overheating and respiratory disorders.**

HAUL EXTRA FEED TO FEEDING AREAS **before the storm arrives. Storm duration is the largest determinant of livestock losses; if the storm last more than 48 hours, emergency feed methods are required. Range cattle are hardy and can survive extreme winter weather providing they have some non-confining type of shelter from the wind and are able to feed at frequent intervals.**

Autopsies of cattle killed by winter storms have shown the cause of death to be dehydration, not cold or suffocation. Because cattle cannot lick enough snow to satisfy their thirst, stockmen are advised to use heaters in water tanks to provide livestock with water and feed after prolonged exposure to winter storm conditions.

WINTER STORM SAFETY RULES

Keep ahead of the winter storm by listening to the latest weather warnings and bulletins on radio and television.

CHECK BATTERY POWERED EQUIPMENT BEFORE THE STORM ARRIVES. **A portable radio or television set may be your only contact with the world outside the winter storm. Also check emergency cooking facilities and flashlights.**

CHECK YOUR SUPPLY OF HEATING FUEL. **Fuel carriers may not be able to move if a winter storm buries your area in snow.**

CHECK YOUR FOOD **and stock an extra supply. Your supplies should include food that requires no cooking or refrigeration in case of power failure.**

PREVENT FIRE HAZARDS **due to overheated coal or oil burning stoves, fireplaces, heaters, or furnaces.**

STAY INDOORS DURING STORMS **and cold snaps unless in peak physical condition. If you must go out, avoid overexertion.**

DON'T KILL YOURSELF SHOVELING SNOW. **It is extremely hard work for anyone in less than prime physical condition, and can bring on a heart attack, a major cause of death during and after winter storms.**

RURAL RESIDENTS: MAKE NECESSARY TRIPS FOR SUPPLIES BEFORE THE STORM DEVELOPS OR NOT AT ALL; **arrange for emergency heat supply in case of power failure; be sure camp stoves and lanterns are filled.**

DRESS TO FIT THE SEASON. **If you spend much time outdoors, wear loose-fitting, lightweight, warm clothing in several layers; layers can be removed to prevent perspiring and subsequent chill. Outer garments should be tightly woven, water repellent, and hooded. The hood should protect much of your face and cover your mouth to ensure warm breathing and protect your lungs from the extremely cold air. Remember that entrapped, insulating air, warmed by body heat, is the best protection against cold. Layers of protective clothing are more effective and efficient than single layers of thick clothing; and mittens, snug at the wrists, are better protection than fingered gloves.**

AUTOMOBILE PREPARATIONS. **Your automobile can be your best friend—or worst enemy—during winter storms, depending on your preparations. Get your car winterized before the storm season begins. Everything on the checklist shown below should be taken care of before winter storms strike your area.**

__ignition system
__battery
__lights
__tire tread
__cooling system
__fuel system
__lubrication
__exhaust system tight
__heater
__brakes perfectly adjusted
__wiper blades
__defroster
__snow tires installed
__chains
__winter-grade oil

Keep water out of your fuel by maintaining a FULL tank of gasoline.

BE EQUIPPED FOR THE WORST. Carry a winter storm car kit, especially if cross country travel is anticipated or if you live in the northern states.

Suggested Winter Storm Car Kit: blankets or sleeping bags, matches and candles, empty 3-pound coffee can with plastic cover, facial tissue, paper towels, extra clothing, high-calorie, nonperishable food, compass and road maps, knife, first aid kit, shovel, sack of sand, sand, flashlight or signal light, windshield scraper, booster cables, two tow chains, fire extinguisher, catalytic heater, axe.

Winter auto travel safety—

Winter travel by automobile is serious business. Take your travel seriously.

If the storm exceeds or even tests your limitations, seek available refuge immediately.

Plan your travel and select primary and alternate routes.

Check latest weather information on your radio.

Try not to travel alone; two or three persons are preferable.

Travel in convoy with another vehicle, if possible.

Always fill gasoline tank before entering open country, even for a short distance.

Drive carefully, defensively.

IF A BLIZZARD CATCHES YOU IN YOUR CAR

AVOID OVEREXERTION AND EXPOSURE. Exertion from attempting to push your car, shovel heavy drifts, and perform other difficult chores during the strong winds, blinding snow, and bitter cold of a blizzard may cause a heart attack—even for persons in apparently good physical condition.

STAY IN YOUR VEHICLE. Do not attempt to walk out of a blizzard. Disorientation comes quickly in blowing and drifting snow. Being lost in open country during a blizzard is almost certain death. You are more likely to be found, and more likely to be sheltered, in your car.

DON'T PANIC.

KEEP FRESH AIR IN YOUR CAR. Freezing wet snow and wind-driven snow can completely seal the passenger compartment.

BEWARE THE GENTLE KILLERS: CARBON MONOXIDE AND OXYGEN STARVATION. Run the motor and heater sparingly, and only with the downwind window open for ventilation.

EXERCISE by clapping hands and moving arms and legs vigorously from time to time, and do not stay in one position for long.

TURN ON DOME LIGHT AT NIGHT, to make the vehicle visible to work crews.

KEEP WATCH. Do not permit all occupants of car to sleep at once.

WIND CHILL (EQUIVALENT TEMPERATURES)

How cold will you feel?

The temperature of the air is not always a reliable indicator of how cold a person will feel outdoors. Other weather elements, such as wind speed, relative humidity and sunshine (solar radiation), also exert an influence. In addition, the type of clothing worn, together with the state of health and the metabolism of an individual also will have an influence upon how cold he will feel. Generally, "coldness" is related to the loss of heat from exposed flesh; it can be assumed to be proportional to the measured rate of heat loss from an object.

Figure 1 (Wind Chill Equivalent Temperature Table) gives equivalent temperatures for various combinations of wind and temperature. In the example shown, a combination of 20° F. and a 10 mph wind has the same cooling power as a temperature of 3° F. and a wind speed of 4 mph.

The next time you want to know how cold it is outdoors, go ahead and check that thermometer! But keep in mind that other things (wind speed, state of nourishment, individual metabolism and protective clothing) all help to determine how "chilly" you feel at a given time and place.

WIND CHILL EQUIVALENT TEMPERATURE TABLE

DRY BULB TEMPERATURE (°F)

WIND VELOCITY (MPH)	45	40	35	30	25	20	15	10	5	0	-5	-10	-15	-20	-25	-30	-35	-40	-45	WIND VELOCITY (MPH)
4	45	40	35	30	25	20	15	10	5	0	-5	-10	-15	-20	-25	-30	-35	-40	-45	4
5	43	37	32	27	22	16	11	6	0	-5	-10	-15	-21	-26	-31	-36	-42	-47	-52	5
10	34	28	22	16	10	3	-3	-9	-15	-22	-27	-34	-40	-46	-52	-58	-64	-71	-77	10
15	29	23	16	9	2	-5	-11	-18	-25	-31	-38	-45	-51	-58	-65	-72	-78	-85	-92	15
20	26	19	12	4	-3	-10	-17	-24	-31	-39	-46	-53	-60	-67	-74	-81	-88	-95	-103	20
25	23	16	8	1	-7	-15	-22	-29	-36	-44	-51	-59	-66	-74	-81	-88	-96	-103	-110	25
30	21	13	6	-2	-10	-18	-25	-33	-41	-49	-56	-64	-71	-79	-86	-93	-101	-109	-116	30
35	20	12	4	-4	-12	-20	-27	-35	-43	-52	-58	-67	-74	-82	-89	-97	-105	-113	-120	35
40	19	11	3	-5	-13	-21	-29	-37	-45	-53	-60	-69	-76	-84	-92	-100	-107	-115	-123	40
45	18	10	2	-6	-14	-22	-30	-38	-46	-54	-62	-70	-78	-85	-93	-102	-109	-117	-125	45

VERY COLD · BITTER COLD · EXTREME COLD

Figure 1

EXAMPLE OF TABLE USE-

Suppose the temperature outside is 25°F, and wind velocity is 10 miles-per-hour. To determine wind-chill equivalent temperature, first scan across the top of the chart until 25°F is reached (5th vertical column of the chart). This is the vertical column to be checked. Now scan down the left side of the chart until 10 is reached. This numeral 10, which designates the 3rd horizontal column, is the wind velocity measured in miles-per-hour. Now follow these two vertical and horizontal columns until they intersect. **THE NUMBER IN THE SQUARE IN WHICH THE TWO COLUMNS INTERSECT IS THE WIND-CHILL EQUIVALENT TEMPERATURE YOU SEEK.**

	45	40	35	30	**25**	20
4	45	40	35	30	25	20
5	43	37	32	27	22	16
10	34	28	22	16	**10**	3
15	29	23	16	9	2	-5

VERY COLD

Development of wind chill index –

A reasonably satisfactory solution to that elusive characteristic of weather known as "coldness" was first proposed by Dr. Paul Siple in 1939. The term "Wind Chill" was used to describe the relative discomfort resulting from combinations of wind and temperature. The method used was not applicable to temperatures above 0° C. and high wind speeds caused exaggerated wind chill values. During the Antarctic winter of 1941, Siple and Passel developed a new formula to determine Wind Chill from experiments made at Little America. Measurements were made of the time required for the freezing of 250 grams of water in a plastic cylinder under a variety of conditions of wind and temperature. They assumed that the rate of heat loss was proportional to the difference in temperature between the cylinder and the temperature of the surrounding air. The results, expressed in kilocalories per square meter per hour per degree Celsius, were plotted against wind speed in meters per second.

Heat loss occurs by means of radiation, conduction and convection. Combining all effects, the general equation for heat loss "H" is:

$$H = (A + B\sqrt{v} + Cv)\,\Delta t$$

where H = Heat loss (wind chill) in kg. cals/m^2/hr

v = Wind speed in meters per second

Δt = Difference in degrees Celsius between neutral skin temperature of 33° and air temperature

Constants

$A = 10.45$
$B = 10.00$
$C = -1.00$

The constant "A" includes the cooling caused by radiation and conduction. The value of the constants "A," "B," and "C" varies widely in formulae presented by different investigators. This is to be expected since "H" also depends on certain properties of the body being cooled. The above formula measures the cooling power of the wind and temperature in complete shade and does not consider the gain of heat from incoming radiation, either direct or diffuse. Under conditions of bright sunshine, the wind chill index should be reduced by about 200 kg/cals/m^2/hr.

The wind chill index, or equivalent temperature, is based upon a neutral skin temperature of 33° C. (91.4° F.). With physical exertion, the body heat production rises, perspiration begins, and heat is removed from the body by vaporization. The body also loses heat through conduction to cold surfaces with which it is in contact, and in breathing cold air which results in the loss of heat from the lungs. The index, therefore, does not take into account all possible losses of the body. It does, however, give a good measure of the convective cooling which is the major source of body heat loss.

Figure 2 (Wind Chill Index Nomogram) illustrates the amount of cooling produced by various combinations of wind and temperature. The line for 4 mph is accented because this is roughly the wind speed generated by someone walking briskly under calm conditions and is the generally accepted standard wind speed for calculating equivalent temperature. To obtain the temperature equivalent of 4 mph from the graph, move horizontally to the left from the intersection of a given wind and temperature until the 4 mph line is reached. The vertical line intersected is the equivalent temperature. In the example shown, a combination of 20° F. temperature and a 10 mph wind has an equivalent temperature of 3° F.

WIND CHILL INDEX NOMOGRAM

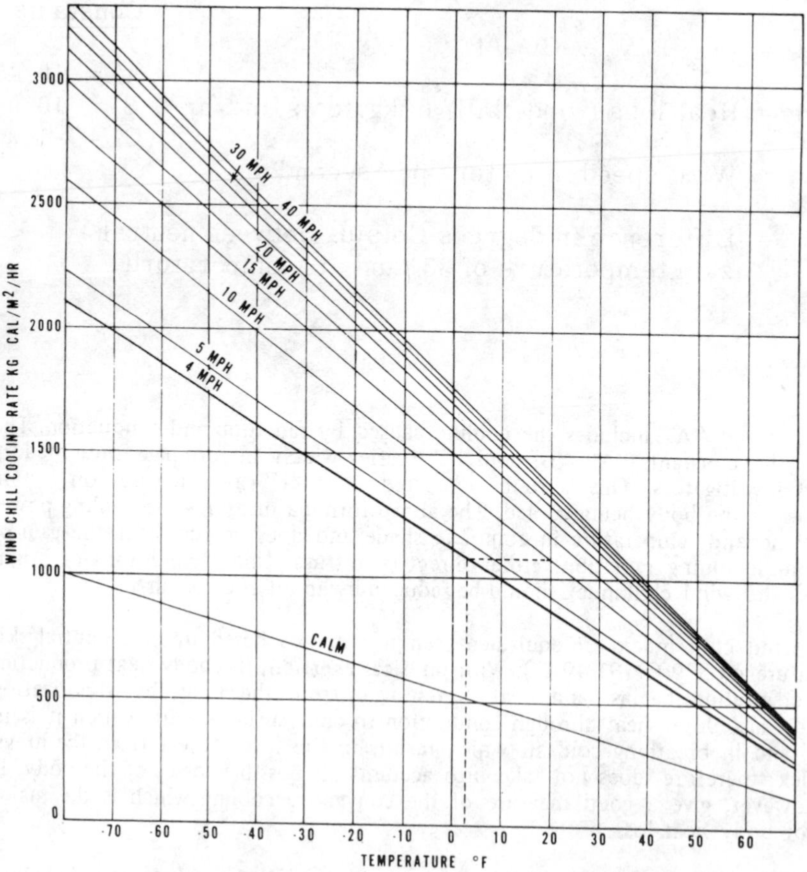

Figure 2

B

HEAT WAVE DANGERS

In a "normal" year, about 175 Americans die from summer heat and too much sun—"excessive heat and insolation" is the vital statistics category. Among our family of natural hazards, only the excessive cold of winter—not lightning, hurricanes, tornadoes, floods, earthquakes, or tsunamis—takes a greater average toll.

Heat waves make a tragic difference—

In the period 1950 through 1967, more than 8,000 persons were killed in the United States by the effects of heat and solar radiation. The 1,401 dead in 1952, the 978 in 1954, and the several years with death tolls closer to 600 push the yearly average for this period to about 452 deaths, a high price to pay for warm weather.

These are direct casualties. It is not known how many deaths are encouraged by excessive heat or solar radiation—for example, how many diseased or aging hearts surrender that would not have under better conditions. Heat waves bring great stresses to the human body; among the aged or infirm are many who cannot run another summer race.

Most summers see heat waves in one section or another of the United States. East of the Rockies, they tend to be periods of high temperatures and humidities—those oppressive, muggy days when human comfort is just an expression—although the worst have been catastrophically dry.

Among the big ones are the hot summer of 1830, which scorched the north central interior, and that of 1860, which dried up the Great Plains. July 1901 may still be talked about by old timers in the middle west, remembering high temperatures, or thinking about someone the heat killed—there were 9,508 heat deaths in that year.

Heat waves of the past—

There is nothing in American climatological annals to touch the heat waves which came with the Dust Bowl droughts of the 1930s. The years 1930, 1934, and 1936 brought progressively more severe summer weather. Record highs of 121 degrees in North Dakota and Kansas, and 120 degrees in South Dakota, Oklahoma, Arkansas, and Texas were observed in the ugly summer of 1936; July and August of that year saw record highs of 109 degrees or better tied or broken in Indiana. Louisiana, Maryland, Michigan, Minnesota, Nebraska, New Jersey, Pennsylvania, West Virginia, and Wisconsin.

These were cruel years in terms of heat deaths. From 1930 through 1936, ranging from a low of 678 deaths in 1932 to 4,768 in 1936, heat killed nearly 15,000 persons. The toll is consistently high, but tends sharply upward with increases in average July temperatures. This relationship between excessive July heat and significant jumps in heat deaths persists to the present day, despite the softening effects of modern consumer technology.

The first half of the 1950's was on the hot side, and its heat death toll is correspondingly high. Many states had their hottest summer of record in 1952; that year's death toll, 1,401, is the highest for the 1950-1967 period. The summer of 1954, a year when heat killed 978, was almost as bad.

The July-August 1955 heat wave brought no record extremes, but the persistent conditions of high temperature and humidity were memorably oppressive, especially in cities. Although average temperatures were not too bad in July, August averages were the highest in the 1950-1967 period—two bad months can make a long, hot summer.

The heat wave of July 1966 covered much of the eastern and middle continent with high temperatures and very high humidity. The portrait of a heat wave illustrated by charts with this text presents some of the meteorological and mortality particulars of the 1966 hot spell.

How ordinary summer heat develops—

Given terrain and geographic situation, North American summers are bound to be hot. As the advancing sun drives back the polar air, the land is opened up to light and solar heat, and occupied by masses of moist warm air spun landward off the tropical ocean. With these rain-filled visitors come the tongues of dry desert air that flick northward out of Mexico, and, occasionally, the hot winds called chinooks which howl down the Rockies' eastern slopes.

Inequalities of atmospheric heating and cooling, of moistness and aridity, are regulated at middle latitudes by horizontal and vertical mixing. The mixing apparatus is the parade of cyclones (low-pressure centers, or Lows) and anticyclones (high-pressure centers, or Highs) which lie at the heart of most weather, good and bad.

The cyclones and anticyclones drift in the midlatitude westerlies, the prevailing eastward-blowing winds which follow a scalloped path around the northern hemisphere. The large-scale undulations of these winds may extend for thousands of miles, and are called planetary waves. Their high-speed core is the jet stream, which snakes across the continent some six to eight miles up, keeping mainly to the cool side of Highs and Lows as they form and spin and die below it.

The kind of weather predominating in an area over a period of time depends largely on the prevailing position and orientation of the jet stream. As the continent warms, the jet stream shifts northward, along with the tracks of surface weather disturbances. Cyclones like the ones which brought April rains to the Gulf states bring June thundershowers to the Plains; the humid spring of Georgia becomes the muggy summer of Illinois.

These semi-regular alternations of instability and equilibrium, hot and cool, moist and dry, combine year-in and year-out to generate the average June-to-September climate for North America.

How heat waves occur—

When these alternating processes are somehow interrupted, the climatic "norm" of summer is marred by a heat wave. The anomaly is usually associated with a change in the planetary waves, so that the prevailing winds from the southwestern deserts sweep farther north than usual and blanket a large region with hot, often humid air at ground level. An upper-level High may settle over the mid-continent, destroying cloud cover with its descending, compression-heated currents, until the blessing of fair weather turns to the curse of drought. In addition, heat from the hot, dry ground feeds back into the atmosphere, tending to perpetuate the heat wave circulation.

Whatever the cause, the effect is uncomfortable and dangerous. Continental heat waves live in human memory the way fierce winters do.

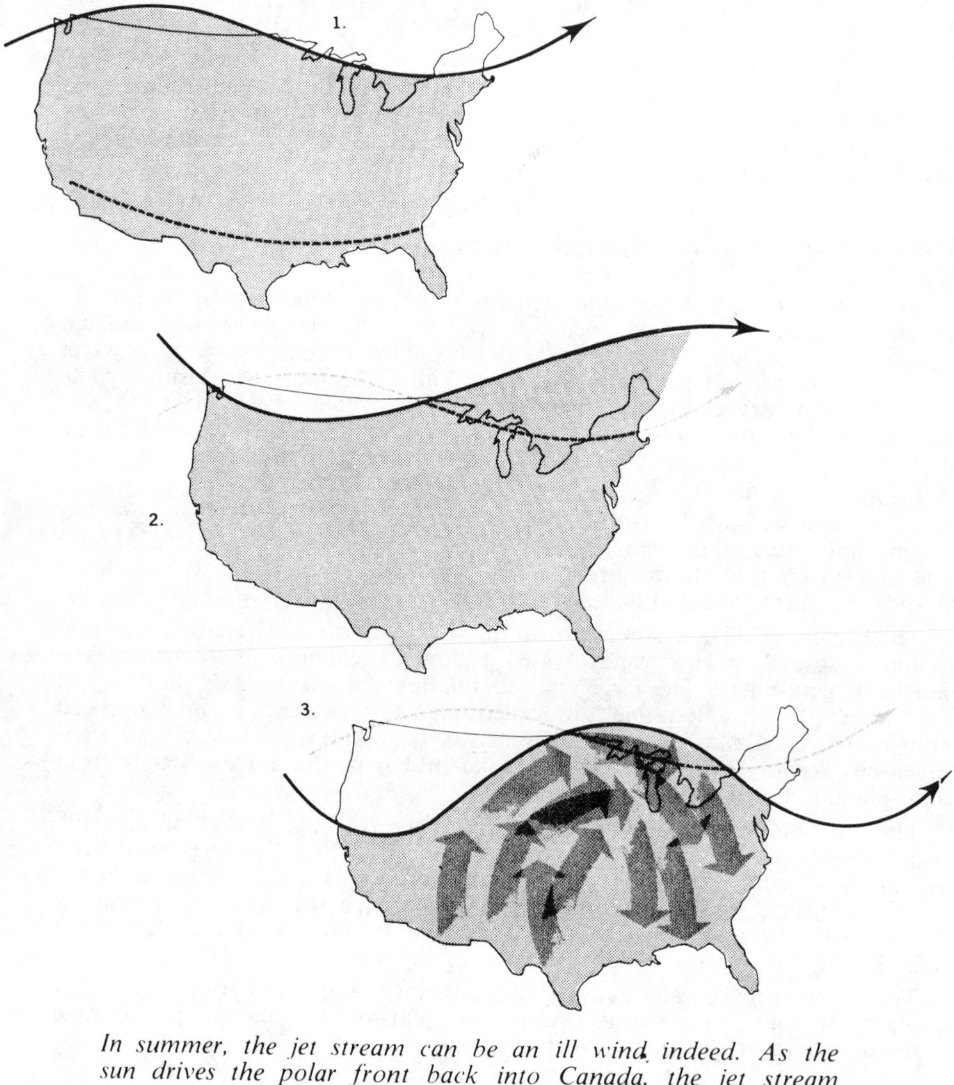

In summer, the jet stream can be an ill wind indeed. As the sun drives the polar front back into Canada, the jet stream keeps to the cool side of the boundary, and shifts northward (1). The summer is a "normal" one—hot but not too hot; humid but not too humid. But the polar front and jet stream may be oriented so that their eastern segment is displaced farther to the north (2), setting the atmospheric stage for a midwestern and eastern heat wave. A persistent High can block the jet stream northward (3), its clockwise, sinking circulation drawing in hot dry air from the southwestern deserts, and dry air from the northwest. This classical Dust Bowl pattern brings hot, dry weather to the mid-continent, but often means cooler-than-normal conditions in New England and the far northwest (Jet stream position at 500 mb level is shown here.)

The human body's reaction to heat—

To keep on the cool side of their upper thermal limits, our bodies dissipate heat by varying the rate and depth of blood circulation, by losing water through the skin and sweat glands, and, as the last extremity is reached, by panting. Under normal conditions, these reflex activities are kept in balance and controlled by the brain's hypothalamus, a comparatively simple sensor of rising and falling environmental temperatures, and a sophisticated manager of temperatures inside.

Like the hot light in a car, the hypothalamus responds to the temperature of coolant, in this case, blood. A surge of blood heated above 98.6 degrees sends the hypothalamus into action. As its orders go out, the heart begins to pump more blood, blood vessels dilate to accommodate the increased flow, and the bundles of tiny capillaries threading through the upper layers of the skin are put into operation. The body's blood is circulated closer to the skin's surface, and excess heat drains off into the cooler atmosphere. At the same time, water diffuses through the skin as insensible perspiration, so-called because it evaporates before it becomes visible, and the skin seems dry to the touch.

Heat loss from increased circulation and insensible perspiration is a comparatively minor correction. If the hypothalamus continues to sense overheating, it calls upon the millions of sweat glands which perforate the outer layer of our skin. These tiny glands can shed great quantities of water (and heat) in what is called sensible perspiration, or sweating. Between sweating and insensible perspiration, the skin handles about 90 percent of the body's heat-dissipating function.

As environmental temperature approaches normal body temperature, physical discomfort is replaced by physical danger. The body loses its ability to get rid of heat through the circulatory system, because there is no heat-drawing drop in temperature between the skin and the surrounding aid. At this point, the skin's elimination of heat by sweating becomes virtually the only means of maintaining constant temperature. Now it is not the heat but the humidity, as they say.

Most water enters the atmosphere via the process of evaporation, the jump from liquid to vapor phase; to do this, a water molecule must absorb enough energy to break the tenacious clutch of its fellow molecules. Evaporation, consequently, has the effect of absorbing large quantities of energy in the form of latent heat, which cools the parent body. This is familiar to anyone who has stepped from a bath into a dry room. The breakdown of the evaporation process when one steps from a bath into a hot, moist room is just as familiar.

Sweating, by itself, does nothing to cool the body, unless the water is removed by evaporation—and high relative humidity retards evaporation. Under conditions of high temperature (above 90 degrees) and high relative humidity (above 75 percent), the body is doing everything it can to maintain 98.6 inside. The heart is pumping a torrent of blood through dilated circulatory vessels; the sweat glands are pouring liquids—and essential dissolved chemicals, like sodium and chloride—onto the surface of the skin. And the body's metabolic heat production goes on, down in the vital organs.

Still, the thermal limits are there. When they are exceeded by very much or for very long, the warm-blooded organism does not doze, reptile fashion. It dies.

Much of the information on the human thermoregulatory system and heat syndrome is from Burch, G., and DePasquale, N., *Hot Climates, Man and His Heart.* Courtesy of Charles C. Thomas, Publisher

A study of three September heat waves in Los Angeles and Orange County, California, shows what excessive temperature alone can do. Without the complicating factors of high humidity or air pollution, the heat waves were accompanied by an increased mortality, especially among the elderly. The California study agreed with other researchers that increased mortality in a heat wave tends to follow maximum temperatures by about one day—the day it takes to overwork a tired circulatory system. The causes of "extra" deaths in September 1963 would seem to bear this out. Most were assigned to coronary and cerebrovascular disease. Heat syndrome was almost absent.

Heat syndrome refers to several clinically recognizable disturbances of the human thermoregulatory system. The disorders generally have to do with a reduction or collapse of the body's ability to shed heat by circulatory changes and sweating, or a chemical (salt) imbalance caused by too much sweating. Ranging in severity from the vague malaise of heat asthenia to the extremely lethal heat stroke, heat syndrome disorders share one common feature: the individual has overexposed or overexercised for his age and physical condition for the thermal environment.

Portrait of a Heat Wave

The summer of 1966 ended the mild period of the 1960s, and the relationship between heat deaths and summer temperatures repeated itself with a vengeance (1). In many States, high heat death tolls came with July temperatures several degrees above the average (2), and the monthly heat-death rate for the United States was dramatically different from that of milder 1965 (3).

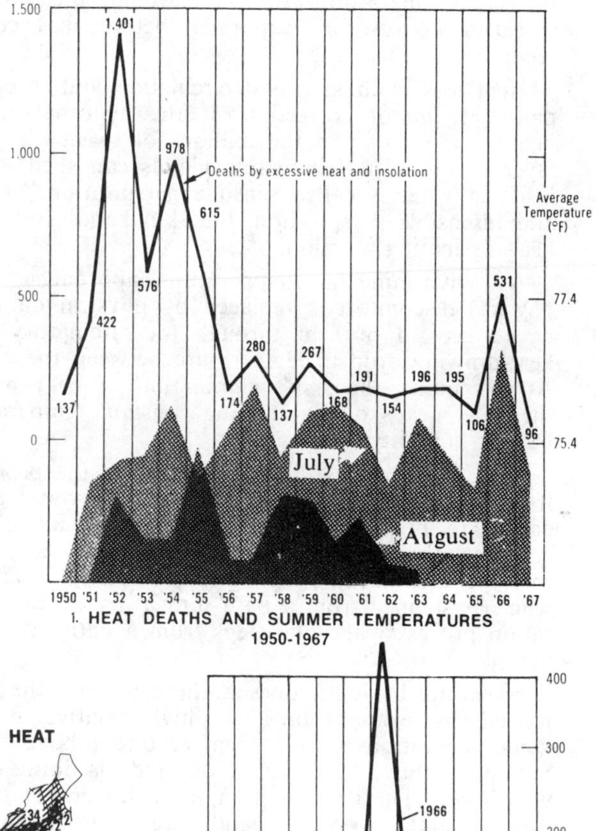

1. HEAT DEATHS AND SUMMER TEMPERATURES 1950-1967

2. HEAT DEATHS AND EXCESSIVE HEAT BY STATE, JULY 1966

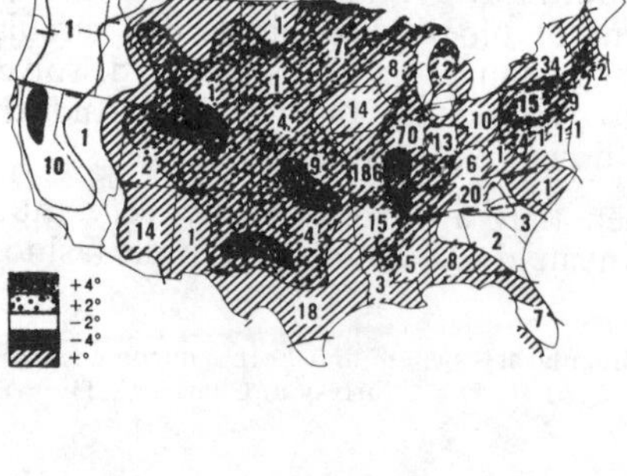

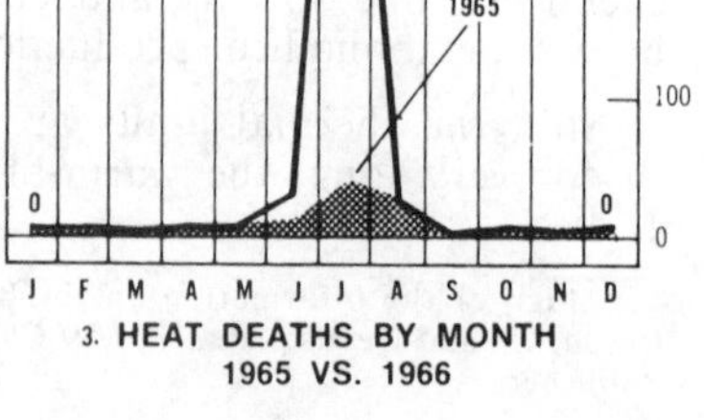

3. HEAT DEATHS BY MONTH 1965 VS. 1966

Sunburn, while not categorized as heat syndrome, is pertinent here, for ultraviolet radiation burns can significantly retard the skin's ability to shed excess heat.

Studies of heat syndrome and its victims indicate that it occurs at all ages of man, but, other things being equal, the severity of the disorder tends to increase with age—heat cramps in a 17-year-old may be heat exhaustion in someone 40, and heat stroke in a person over 60.

There is evidence that heat waves are worse in the airless, brick, and asphalt canyons of the "inner cities" than in the better lawned, more open suburbs. The July 1966 tragedy in St. Louis is a case in point.

Acclimatization has to do with adjusting sweatsalt concentrations, among other things. In winter and summer, this concentration changes, just as it does when one moves from Boston to Panama. The idea is to lose enough water to regulate body temperature, with the least possible chemical disturbance. Because females appear to be better at this than males—females excrete less sweat and so less salt—heat syndrome usually strikes fewer females.

For people with heart disease, climatic stress is worse than for others. In a hot, humid environment, impaired evaporation and water loss hamper thermal regulation, while physical exertion and heart failure increase the body's rate of heat production. The ensuing cycle is vicious in the extreme.

HEAT WAVE SAFETY RULES

1. SLOW DOWN. **Your body can't do its best in high temperatures and humidities, and might do its worst.**
2. HEED YOUR BODY'S EARLY WARNINGS THAT HEAT SYNDROME IS ON THE WAY. **Reduce your level of activities immediately and get to a cooler environment.**
3. DRESS FOR SUMMER. **Lightweight, light-colored clothing reflects heat and sunlight, and helps your thermoregulatory system maintain normal body temperature.**
4. PUT LESS FUEL ON YOUR INNER FIRES. **Foods (like proteins) that increase metabolic heat production also increase water loss.**
5. DON'T DRY OUT. **Heat wave weather can wring you out before you know it. Drink plenty of water while the hot spell lasts.**
6. STAY SALTY. **Unless you're on a salt-restricted diet, take an occasional salt tablet or some salt solution when you've worked up a sweat.**
7. AVOID THERMAL SHOCK. **Acclimatize yourself gradually to warmer weather. Treat yourself extra gently for those first critical two or three hot days.**
8. VARY YOUR THERMAL ENVIRONMENT. **Physical stress increases with exposure time in heat wave weather. Try to get out of the heat for at least a few hours each day. If you can't do this at home, drop in on a cool store, restaurant, or theater—anything to keep your exposure time down.**
9. DON'T GET TOO MUCH SUN. **Sunburn makes the job of heat dissipation that much more difficult.**
10. KNOW THE HEAT SYNDROME SYMPTOMS AND FIRST AID.

HEAT AND SUN FIRST-AID

Heat Syndrome	Caused by	Symptoms	First Aid
HEAT ASTHENIA (OR CALASTHENIA)	Excessively hot, humid environment.	Easy fatigue, headache, mental and physical inefficiency, poor appetite, insomnia, heavy sweating, high pulse rate, shallow breathing, and sometimes circulatory stress in the ill.	**Respite from heat heat and humidity, plenty of fluids, and, if sweating is heavy (and no dietary restrictions prevent it) a salt tablet and rest.**
HEAT CRAMPS	Strenuous activity under conditions of high heat and humidity, when evaporative cooling is impaired, stimulating excessive sweating and loss of salts from blood and tissue, causing cramps.	Painful spasms of voluntary muscles, contraction in flexor muscles in fingers, then larger muscles in legs and abdominal wall. Pupils dilate with each spasm, there may be heavy sweating, skin becomes cold and clammy. Unlike severe abdominal disease symptoms, heat cramps are intermittent.	**Usually respond better to firm pressure on cramping muscles than to vigorous kneading. Application of warm wet towels also gives relief. Three or four doses of salt solution (½ teaspoon dissolved in 4 fl. oz. water) administered at 15-minute intervals. Large quantities of water without salt may precipitate the disease.**
HEAT EXHAUSTION	Prolonged hot spell, excessive exposure, physical exertion cause thermoregulatory breakdown involving loss of vasomotor (blood-vessel diameter) control and circulatory shock.	Profuse sweating, weakness, vertigo, and sometimes heat cramps; symptoms similar to calasthenia may herald by several days. Skin is cold and pale, clammy with sweat; pulse is thready and blood pressure is low. Body temperature is normal or sub-normal. Vomiting may occur. Unconsciousness is rare.	**Move to cooler environment immediately. Provide bed rest, salt solution (see above); victims, sometimes nauseated at first, can usually take fluids after a period of rest. Seek medical help for severe heat exhaustion.**

HEAT STROKE (or sunstroke, heat collapse, thermic fever, heat hyperexia)	Failure of thermoregulatory and cardiovascular systems brought about when intensive sweating under conditions of high heat and humidity restrict heat dissipation by sweating, which finally ceases. Advanced age and hot, humid, windless environment are factors.	Weakness, vertigo, nausea, headache, heat cramps, mild heat exhaustion, excessive sweating. Sweating stops just before heat stroke. Then temperature rises sharply, often to 106° or more, pulse is bounding and full, blood pressure elevated. Delirium or coma is common. Armpit and groin areas are dry (they are wet in heat exhaustion). Skin is flushed and pink at first; however, in later stages, it appears ashen or purplish.	**Heat stroke is a very serious emergency. Medical care is urgently needed. Move the victim into cooler, indoor environment, remove his clothing, put him to bed. Primary objective is to reduce body temperature, preferably by iced bath (or by sponging the body with alcohol or lukewarm water) until a tolerable level (about 103° or a pulse rate below 110 per minute) is reached. Caution is necessary here.**
SUNBURN	Overexposure to ultraviolet radiation.	Redness and pain caused by dilation of small blood vessels in skin. In more severe cases, tissue injury brings swelling of skin, blisters, and often fever and headache. Because it impairs thermoregulatory efficiency, sunburn may be accompanied by other heat syndrome disorders.	**Prevent severe sunburn by limiting the time of initial exposure, depending on comfort and conditions. Treat mild sunburn with cold cream or certain oils or greases (e.g., salad oil, shortening). Wash hands before applying. Do not apply butter or oleomargarine. Dressing should be used if blistering appears, injured area should not be exposed to sunlight until healed. Medical care is needed for extensive or severe cases.**

HEAT STROKE IS A SEVERE MEDICAL EMERGENCY. SUMMON A PHYSICIAN OR GET THE PATIENT TO A HOSPITAL IMMEDIATELY. DELAY CAN BE FATAL.

SOURCE: U.S. Dept. of Commerce
National Oceanic and Atmospheric Administration

TEMPERATURE-HUMIDITY INDEX

A useful guide to summer time comfort is the Temperature-Humidity Index. A single number can be used to approximately express the reaction of most people to the heat-humidity complex, although it is known that individual responses vary considerably from person to person and from time to time. Table 1 relates various degrees of sheltered air temperature and relative humidity to equivalent THI values. The table is read in the manner of some road map mileage tables and provides index values to the nearest whole number. A brief discussion of the index is also provided.

Table 1 The Temperature-Humidity Index

TEMPERATURE	RELATIVE HUMIDITY									
	10%	20%	30%	40%	50%	60%	70%	80%	90%	100%
66°F	62	63	63	63	64	64	65	65	66	66
67°	63	63	64	64	65	65	66	66	67	67
68°	63	64	64	65	65	66	67	67	68	68
69°	64	64	65	65	66	67	67	68	68	69
70°	64	65	65	66	67	67	68	69	69	70
71°	65	65	66	67	67	68	69	70	70	71
72°	65	66	67	67	68	69	70	71	71	72
73°	66	66	67	68	69	70	70	71	72	73
74°	66	67	68	69	70	71	71	72	73	74
75°	67	67	68	69	70	71	72	73	74	75
76°	67	68	69	70	71	72	73	74	75	76
77°	68	69	70	71	72	73	74	75	76	77
78°	68	69	70	71	73	74	75	76	77	78
79°	69	70	71	72	73	74	76	77	78	79
80°	69	70	72	73	74	75	76	78	79	80
81°	70	71	72	73	75	76	77	78	80	81
82°	70	72	73	74	75	77	78	79	81	82
83°	71	72	73	75	76	78	79	80	82	83
84°	71	73	74	75	77	78	79	81	83	84
85°	72	73	75	76	78	79	80	82	84	85
86°	72	74	75	77	78	80	81	83	84	86
87°	73	74	76	77	79	81	82	84	85	87
88°	73	75	76	78	80	81	83	85	86	88
89°	74	75	77	79	81	82	84	86	87	89
90°	74	76	77	79	81	83	85	87	88	90
91°	75	76	78	80	82	84	85	87	89	91
92°	75	77	79	81	83	85	86	88	90	92
93°	76	78	80	81	83	85	87	89	91	93
94°	76	78	80	82	84	86	88	90	92	94
95°	77	79	81	83	85	87	89	91	93	95
96°	77	79	81	84	86	88	90	92	94	96
97°	78	80	82	84	86	88	91	93	95	
98°	78	80	83	85	87	89	91	94	96	
99°	79	81	83	85	88	90	92	95		
100°	79	82	84	86	89	91	93	95		
101°	80	82	84	87	89	91	94	96		
102°	80	83	35	88	90	92	95			
103°	81	83	86	88	91	93	96			
104°	81	84	86	89	91	94	96			
105°	82	84	87	90	92	95				
106°	82	85	87	90	93	96				
107°	83	85	88	91	94	96				
108°	83	86	89	92	95					
109°	84	87	89	92	95					
110°	84	87	90	93	96					

few people feel uncomfortable

about one-half of all people feel uncomfortable

nearly everyone feels uncomfortable

rapidly decreasing work efficiency

extreme danger

The table progresses downward and to the right from a zone of comfort to a zone of dangerous heat stress. The values are for appropriately clothed persons engaged in sedentary activities in nearly calm air.

Why a Temperature-Humidity Index?

"It isn't the heat; it's the humidity." As noted in the chapter entitled, "Heat Waves", the job of keeping the body cool falls increasingly upon the **evaporation of sweat** as the temperature rises. Meanwhile, the other forms of heat dissipation such as radiation and convection, which depend upon temperature differences between the skin and the surroundings, are reduced in effectiveness. In turn, the rate of evaporation of sweat is influenced by the humidity in the surrounding air. (Wind speed and thermal radiation are also factors.) Hence, the common assertion.

Discomfort is usually a complaint as soon as sweating begins, although to be sure the discomfort and heat stress on the body would be much greater if one could not sweat. "Politeness" aside, it is unfortunate that some people do not sweat as soon or as much as others. Clothing reduces the effectiveness of sweating, but it is needed for protection from the sun. In order to reflect heat and enhance circulation of air, hot weather clothing should be light colored, light weight, porous, and loose fitting. **Weather Almanac** believes that cotton or high cotton blends are still the best hot weather fabrics for most people.

A single number can be used to express the combined temperature-humidity effect and thereby provide a fairly good index of equivalent heat stress. In engineering, this combined index is referred to as "effective temperature." Briefly, in the Weather Bureau, it was referred to as the Discomfort Index or DI. Currently, in Weather Bureau practice, it is called simply the Temperature-Humidity Index or THI.

What the Temperature-Humidity Index tells you

The THI represents the heat sensations reported by a panel of sedentary persons experimentally subjected to a series of temperature and humidity values, in comparison with a temperature of the same value in calm indoor air saturated with water vapor (relative humidity 100%). The "votes" of relative comfort or discomfort when tabulated showed considerable variation, as is to be expected. Among the factors in the variation are age, diet, exertion, type and amount of clothing, bodily functioning, state of health, state of mind, and past climatic experience especially within the previous several weeks. The results can be generalized as follows:

Relatively few people in summer will feel discomfort from heat and humidity at THI values of 70 or below.

EXAMPLE OF USE: Assume the outside temperature is 79°F and the relative humidity is 60 percent. Suppose you wish to know what Temperature-Humidity Index number this equals. Use the table like this to find out: 1. Look down the first vertical column of the chart (the column on the far left) until you reach "79°". A row of numbers appears to the right; remember that row for you will use it in the next step. 2. Now return to the top of the chart and move across until the caption "60%" is reached. (It heads the seventh column). Now let your eye travel down this vertical column until the column crosses the horizontal row which you located in step #1. **The number at this intersection is 74. It is the TH Index number for 79°F when the relative humidity stands at 60%.** Other values can be found by using the same method.

Air conditioning may be appropriate for THI values of 73 or higher.

About half of the people will be uncomfortable by the time the THI value reaches 75.

Nearly everyone feels uncomfortable by the time the THI value reaches 79, with some people experiencing acute discomfort. Restraint in exercise and care in the selection of clothing is very important.

With THI values rising into the 80s, discomfort becomes acute for everyone. Work efficiency begins to drop markedly. Mistakes and accidents increase.

THI values near 90 are in the danger zone for almost everyone. The THI values infrequently reach as high as 90 in some parts of the United States. A study several years ago found no THI values higher than 92. Higher values in the nation might be found under special local conditions or in poorly ventilated enclosed places.

Direct sunshine and hot radiating surfaces such as pavements, walls and windows decrease these tolerance limits somewhat. A light wind will increase them. Lacking detailed knowledge of local outdoor climates or special industrial conditions, the Temperature-Humidity Index and the limits given can serve as a rough guide.

Infants and old persons are generally comfortable at higher THI values than young healthy persons, but they probably have a lower tolerance for acute discomfort and dangerous heat stress. Persons of any age with cardiovascular problems also experience discomfort and dangerous heat stress at lower THI values than other people.

Everyone is more easily stressed in the first half of the hot season.

Light but active physical exertion may lower the various limits by about 5 units. Heavy work may reduce them by about 10 units.

Any of the following equations may be used to calculate THI values:

1) $THI = 0.4(td + tw) + 15$

2) $THI = 0.55td + 0.2tdp + 17.5$

3) $THI = td - (0.55 - 0.55RH).(td - 58)$

Where THI is Temperature-Humidity Index; td is dry bulb temperature in °F; tw is wet bulb temperature in °F; tdp is dew point temperature in °F; RH is relative humidity expressed in decimal form, e.g., 60% is written as 0.60.

For convenience, Equation 3 relating temperature and relative humidity has been reduced to Table 1 above. If a wet-bulb temperature is available from a sling psychrometer or a ventilated thermometer whose bulb is kept wet with a saturated muslin sleeve, Equation 1 can be used.

LIVESTOCK WEATHER SAFETY INDEX

Livestock, like human beings, are subject to heat stress that is variable not only with temperature but with different combinations of *temperature* **and** *relative humidity*. This is particularly true for animals that are confined or being loaded or transported. Thus, the Temperature-Humidity Index, as explained in the previous text, is a useful tool in animal care.

The research which established this connection was primarily focused on hogs; but the relationship for cattle and other animals was found to be very similar; so pet owners may also wish to consider adapting the TH Index in caring for their animals.

The same TH calculations shown in the preceeding table can be used when they are given the following meaning for animals:

SAFETY INDEX (THI) READINGS OF 79-THROUGH-83 = LIVESTOCK DANGER!

An index in this category is dangerous for confined livestock, particularly hogs. There is also a need for precautionary measures in anticipation of a higher index. In fact, disaster can strike at the upper level of this range unless proper safety steps are taken by stockmen. An increase of 25% or more can be expected in transit loss.

SAFETY INDEX (THI) READINGS OF 84 OR HIGHER = LIVESTOCK EMERGENCY!

An increase of 45% or more can be expected in transit loss.

Additional hazard: the effect of calm, cloudless days

Lack of cloud cover and little or no movement of air are additional hazards which can increase stress and should be considered. An emergency situation is most likely to develop when the temperature is 90 to 95 degrees early in the day, and higher temperatures are forecast for the period that the livestock will be in the marketing process. Additional stress created by handling livestock *should be kept at an absolute minimum*.

Reduction of hazard: the effect of wind

The cooling effect of wind can lower the THI value a few degrees in open areas. However, when the air temperature approaches the skin temperature of the animal, the cooling effect of wind becomes minimal.

Acclimatization

Hot, humid weather is more detrimental to livestock in the early summer than in mid- or late summer and during any season following an extended cool period. This heat tolerance has not been qualified but should be considered during periods of marginal danger or emergency categories.

National Weather Service Warnings

Many Forecast Offices of the National Weather Service (U. S. Department of Commerce, National Oceanic and Atmospheric Administration) issue Danger and/or Emergency Warnings. If potential users are unaware of this program they should contact their local weather service office or agricultural extension agent for information on service in their region.

What the index means

Most livestock do not adjust readily to high temperatures (heat stress). Hogs are especially vulnerable when *closely confined* in a vehicle, building, or pen. A careful study by Livestock Conservation Inc.* of the relationship of hog deaths during the marketing process shows that high temperatures, especially with high relative humidity, cause abnormally *high losses*.

When the outside temperature is above 80°, the high death loss is quite closely related to the National Weather Service "Temperature Humidity Index." Although this index was originally developed to indicate comfort ranges for humans, research by Livestock Conservation, Inc. points to similar ranges of comfort for animals. High values adversely influence efficiency of production, meat quality, health and survival.

Why hogs are a special problem

Heat build up internally in the hog's body if it cannot be thrown off by the lungs or skin. If the internal temperature reaches 105-106°, heat exhaustion occurs and will be *followed by death* unless the situation is relieved.

Hogs lose about 80% of their body heat through the lungs when the environmental temperature is above 80°; only 20% is lost from the skin by radiation and air movement. Hogs must breathe approximately 20 times as much air at 100° as at 80° to maintain a safe internal body temperature (around 102° when their environmental temperature is 100°).

---

*19 West Chicago Avenue, Hinsdale, Illinois 60521

QUOTES FROM WEATHER FOLKLORE–

If the cock goes crowing to bed,
He'll certainly rise with a watery head.

If on Candlemas day (February 2) it is bright and clear, the ground-hog will stay in his den, thus indicating that more snow and cold are to come; But if it snows or rains he will creep out, as the winter is ended. (German)

If Candlemas Day be fine and clear,
Corn and fruits will then be dear.

If the November goose bone be thick,
So will the winter weather be;
If the November goose bone be thin,
So will the winter weather be.

Human hair (red) curls and kinks at the approach of a storm, and restraightens after the storm.

When the moon lies on her back,
She sucks the wet into her lap.
– Ellesmere.

The shepard would rather see the wolf enter his fold on Candlemas Day than the sun.

March in January, January in March, I fear.

Who doffs his coat on a winter's day
Will gladly put it on in May.

EARTHQUAKES

Most natural hazards can be detected before their threat matures. But seisms (from the Greek seismos, earthquake) have no known precursors, and so they come without warning, like the vengeance of an ancient, lunatic god. For this reason, they continue to kill in some areas at a level usually reserved for wars and epidemics—the 68,000 dead in Peru died on May 31, 1970, not in antiquity. Nor is the horror of a lethal earthquake completed with a heavy death toll. The homeless living are left to cope with fire, looting, pestilence, fear, and the burden of rebuilding what the planet so easily shrugs away.

Earthquakes have not been the killers in the United States they have in Eurasia and Africa. Thus far (through February 1972) this century, fewer than 1,600 deaths have been caused by earthquakes and tsunamis (so-called "tidal waves") in the U.S., and 700 of these came in the 1906 San Francisco earthquake and fire. Of more than 115,000 deaths from major earthquakes worldwide since 1960, fewer than 300 occurred in the United States.

Property damage is a different story. The San Francisco earthquake did an estimated $24 million property damage, and the ensuing fire $500 million more. Since San Francisco, Americans have paid something over $1 billion to the earthquake, about $400 million of it to the Alaskan earthquake of March 1964, and about $600 million of it to the San Fernando, Calif., earthquake of February 1971. The price goes up, year by year. There is every reason to believe our worst seismic disasters are ahead of us.

LISTENING POST. In the global network of standardized seismograph stations, three-component (vertical, north-south, east-west motion) seismometers (1) sense earthquake vibrations, and relay them in the form of electrical signals to galvanometers (2) and recorders (3) installed in dark vaults. The seismogram is written by a light beam from the galvanometer, directed onto photo-sensitive paper on the recorder. As variations in seismometer signals deflect the galvanometer beam, the familiar ups and downs of an earthquake record appear.

Where earthquakes occur—

Our planet's most active earthquake-producing feature is the circum-Pacific seismic belt, which trends along the major geologic faults and the deep oceanic trenches of island arcs decorated here and there with the volcanic "Ring of Fire." The mid-Atlantic Ridge, with its fish-skelton figure of transverse cracks, is also quite active. Other major seismic belts branch from the circum-Pacific system and arc across southeastern and southern Asia into southern Europe, through the Indian Ocean up through the eastern Mediterranean, and up through southern Asia into China.

In an average year, these belts will generate several million tremors, ranging in severity from barely detectable wiggles to great earthquakes of the size which ravaged San Francisco in 1906, and tilted a third of Alaska in 1964. There is always an earthquake in progress somewhere.

Epicenters of damaging earthquakes are superimposed on a seismic risk map included with this article. That map divides the conterminous United States into four zones; zone 0, where there is no reasonable expectance of earthquake damage; zone 1, where minor earthquake damage can be expected; zone 2, where moderate damage can be expected; and zone 3, where major destructive earthquakes may occur. Similar maps for Alaski and Hawaii, and updated versions of this one are under development by the Environmental Research Laboratories. If you live in a high-risk area, check your homes' construction against your city's earthquake construction codes; build on solid ground, not fill; and use earthquake-resistant design.

WHAT IS AN EARTHQUAKE?

Earthquake conditions—

The planet Earth is believed to consist of a thin crust two or three miles thick under the oceans and as much as 25 miles thick beneath the continents that covers the large, solid sphere of the rock mantle, which descends to about 1800 miles. Below the mantle is the fluid outer core, and, at about 3200 miles' depth, the apparently solid inner core. The province of earthquakes recorded thus far is from the crust to a maximum depth of about 450 miles.

Conditions thought to prevail in this hot, dark, high-pressure land cannot be simulated in existing laboratories—at the base of the mantle, pressure is about 11,000 tons per square inch, temperature, 10,000 degrees Fahrenheit. These diamond-mashing pressures produce a rigidity in mantle rock about four times that of ordinary steel, with an average density about that of titanium.

This very solid mantle rock seems to behave, over periods of millions of years, like a very sluggish fluid. Something, perhaps the temperature difference between the white-hot region near the core and the cooler region near the crust, drives slow-moving cycles of rising and descending currents in the mantle rock itself.

Evidently, these currents rise beneath the thin-crusted ocean floor, thrust up the mid-ocean ridges, and generate the stresses which produce their spinelike transverse cracks and shallow earthquakes. This is believed to be the force which causes material to well up through the crust, replacing and spreading the old seafloor, and pushing drifting continents apart.

Where the currents begin their descent at the edges of continents, they produce compressive pressures, and massive folding in the form of trenches and mountain ranges. These regions are the sites of the deeper earthquakes, and of most volcanism.

Earth stresses and strains and then releases—

Stresses generated in the crust and upper mantle by convective currents are stored in the form of strain–physical deformation of the rock structure. Under normal circumstances, the "solid" rocks deform plastically, releasing pent-up energy before it builds to catastrophic levels. But, when stresses accumulate too rapidly to be removed by plastic flow, some structural compensation is necessary. Large blocks of material are slowly forced into highly strained positions along faults, and held in place by a supporting structure of stronger materials. These energy-absorbing zones of weakness continue to shift, like longbows being pulled to the breaking point. Finally, more stress causes the supporting rocks to rupture, triggering the "cocked" fracture back toward equilibrium. The sides of the rebounding fault move horizontally with respect to one another (strike-slip), vertically (dip-slip), or in combinations of such motion, as in the large-scale tilting which accompanied the March 1964 Alaska earthquake.

Foreshocks and aftershocks—

Sometimes all the energy to be released goes out in one large wrench, followed by trains of smaller tremors, or aftershocks, produced by continuing collapse and slippage along the fracture. Sometimes the fault shift is preceded by the small structural failures we detect as foreshocks. The magnitude 5.9 earthquake which shook Fairbanks, Alaska, on June 21, 1967, was preceded by a magnitude 5.6 foreshock, followed by a magnitude 5.5 aftershock, and then, over the next 24 hours, by more than 2,000 smaller aftershocks. Small tremors were detected for days after the initial event. But all small tremors or earthquake "swarms" do not necessarily indicate that a big one is on the way. The Matsushiro, Japan, swarm maintained an intermittent tremble for more than a year, probably doing more psychic than physical damage. Of more than 600,000 tremors recorded between August 3, 1965, and the end of 1966, 60,000 were strong enough to be felt, and 400 were damaging. During the most active period, in April and May 1966, Matsushiro felt hundreds of tremors daily, all under magnitude 5.

Whatever the time period involved, the energy of strain flows out through the shifted fault in the form of heat, sound, and earthquake waves. These last are the shakers and wreckers, the global messages sent out by earthquakes.

They are also man's only window to his planet's deep interior.

How earthquake waves travel—

There are four basic seismic waves: two preliminary "body" waves which travel through the earth, and two which travel only at the surface. Combinations, reflections, and diffractions produce a virtual infinity of other types. The behavior of these is well enough understood that wave speed and amplitude have been the major means of describing the earth's interior. In addition, a large earthquake generates elastic waves which echo through the planet like vibrations in a ringing bell, and which actually cause the planet to expand and contract infinitesimally.

The primary (P) wave is longitudinal, like a sound wave, propagates through both liquids and solids, and is usually the first signal that an earthquake has occurred. Where the disturbance is near enough or large enough to be felt, the P wave arrives at the surface like a hammerblow from the inside. This is the swiftest seismic wave, its speed varying with the material through which it passes. In the heterogeneous crustal structure, P-wave velocity is usually less than 4 miles per second—nearly 15,000 miles per hour. Just below the crust, at a layer called the Mohorovicic discontinuity (popularly, the Moho), these speeds jump to 5 miles per second and subsequently increase to about 8½ miles per second (more than 30,000 miles per hour) through the core.

As the compressional phase of the P wave passes through the earth, particles are pushed together and displaced away from the disturbance. The rarefactional phase dilates the particles and displaces them toward the earthquake source. For an object imbedded in the ground, the result is a series of sharp pushes and pulls parallel to the wave path—motions similar to those which the passengers feel when a long train gets under way.

The secondary (S) wave is transverse, like a light or radio wave, and travels barely more than half as fast as the primary wave. Because S waves require a rigid medium to travel in coherent rays, their apparent absence below the mantle gives credence to the theory of a fluid core. About twice the period and amplitude of the associated P waves, these shear waves displace particles at right angles to the direction of wave travel. The vertical component of this movement is somewhat dampened by the opposing force of gravity; but side-to-side shaking in the horizontal can be quite destructive. Where the motion is perceptible, the arrival of the S waves marks the beginning of a new series of shocks, often worse than the P-wave tremor.

Surface waves, named for their discoverers, Love and Rayleigh, are of much greater length and period—e.g., 30 seconds or more, vs. less than one second for P waves. Love waves are shear in the horizontal dimension, and the Rayleigh wave induces a retrograde, elliptical motion, something like that in wind-driven ocean waves. The speed of the Love wave is about 2½ miles per second; the Rayleigh wave is about 10 percent slower. Despite the large proportion of earthquake energy represented by these waves, their long period smooths out the motion they impart, reducing their destructiveness.

Wave motion is not considered in describing the travel of seismic waves through the earth. Instead, the P and S body waves, and their large family of reflected, combined, or resonated offspring, are treated as rays. If the planet were homogeneous, like a ball of wax, these rays would be straight lines. But in the heterogeneous earth the rays describe concavely spherical paths away from the earthquake source, and from points of reflection at the surface.

Because they travel at different speeds, seismic waves arrive at a given point on the earth's surface at different times. Near the source, the ground will shake over a slightly longer interval of time than it took the fault to slip. At great distances, the same energy released by a single event may be detected instrumentally for days.

Measuring an earthquake—

Intensity is an indication of an earthquake's apparent severity at a specified location, as determined by experienced observers. Through interviews with persons in the stricken area, damage surveys, and studies of earth movement, an earthquake's regional effects can be systematically described. For seismologists and emergency workers, intensity becomes an efficient shorthand for describing what an earthquake has done to a given area.

The Modified Mercalli Intensity Scale generally used in the United States grades observed effects into twelve classes ranging from I, felt only under especially favorable circumstances, to XII, damage total. The older Rossi-Forel Intensity scale, or R.F., has ten categories of observed effects, and is still used in Europe. Still other intensity scales are in use in Japan and the the U.S.S.R.

Rating earthquakes by intensity has the disadvantage of being always relative. In recent years, intensity ratings have been supplemented by an "objective" scale of earthquake magnitude.

Magnitude expresses the amount of energy released by an earthquake as determined by measuring the amplitudes produced on standardized recording instruments. The persistent misconception that the "Richter Scale" rates the size of earthquakes on a "scale of ten" is extremely misleading, and has tended to mask the clear distinction between magnitude and intensity.

Earthquake magnitudes are similar to stellar magnitudes in that they describe the subject in absolute, not relative, terms, and that they refer to a logarithmic, not an arithmetic, scale. An earthquake of magnitude 8, for example, represents seismograph amplitudes ten times larger than those of a magnitude 7 earthquake, 100 times larger than those of a magnitude 6 earthquake, and so on. There is no highest or lowest value, and it is possible here, as with temperature, to record negative values. The largest earthquakes of record were rated at magnitude 8.9; the smallest, about minus 3. Preliminary magnitude determinations may vary with the observatory, equipment, and methods of estimating—the Alaska earthquake of March 1964, for example, was described variously as magnitude 8.4, 8.5, 8.6 by different stations.

Magnitude also provides an indication of earthquake energy release, which intensity does not. In terms of ergs,* a magnitude 1 earthquake releases about one billionth the energy of a magnitude 7 earthquake; a magnitude 5, about one thousandth that of a magnitude 7.

* In the centimeter-gram-second system, an erg is the unit of work equal to a force of 1 dyne acting through a distance of 1 centimeter; a dyne is the force required to accelerate a freestanding gram mass 1 centimeter per second.

EARTHQUAKE SAFETY RULES

An earthquake strikes your area and for a minute or two the "solid" earth moves like the deck of a ship. What you do during and immediately after the tremor may make life-and-death differences for you, your family, and your neighbors. These rules will help you survive.

DURING THE SHAKING:

1. Don't panic. The motion is frightening but, unless it shakes something down on top of you, it is harmless. The earth does not yawn open, gulp down a neighborhood, and slam shut. Keep calm and ride it out.
2. If it catches you indoors, stay indoors. Take cover under a desk, table, bench, or in doorways, halls, and against inside walls. Stay away from glass.
3. Don't use candles, matches, or other open flames, either during or after the tremor. Douse all fires.
4. If the earthquake catches you outside, move away from buildings and utility wires. Once in the open, stay there until the shaking stops.
5. Don't run through or near buildings. The greatest danger from falling debris is just outside doorways and close to outer walls.
6. If you are in a moving car, stop as quickly as safety permits, but stay in the vehicle. A car is an excellent seismometer, and will jiggle fearsomely on its springs during the earthquake; but it is a good place to stay until the shaking stops.

AFTER THE SHAKING:

1. Check your utilities, but do not turn them on. Earth movement may have cracked water, gas, and electrical conduits.
2. If you smell gas, open windows and shut off the main valve. Then leave the building and report gas leakage to authorities. Don't re-enter the house until a utility official says it is safe.
3. If water mains are damaged, shut off the supply at the main valve.
4. If electrical wiring is shorting out, close the switch at the main meter box.
5. Turn on your radio or television (if conditions permit) to get the latest emergency bulletins.
6. Stay off the telephone except to report an emergency.
7. Don't go sight-seeing.
8. Stay out of severly damaged buildings; aftershocks can shake them down.

See next page for earthquake risk map

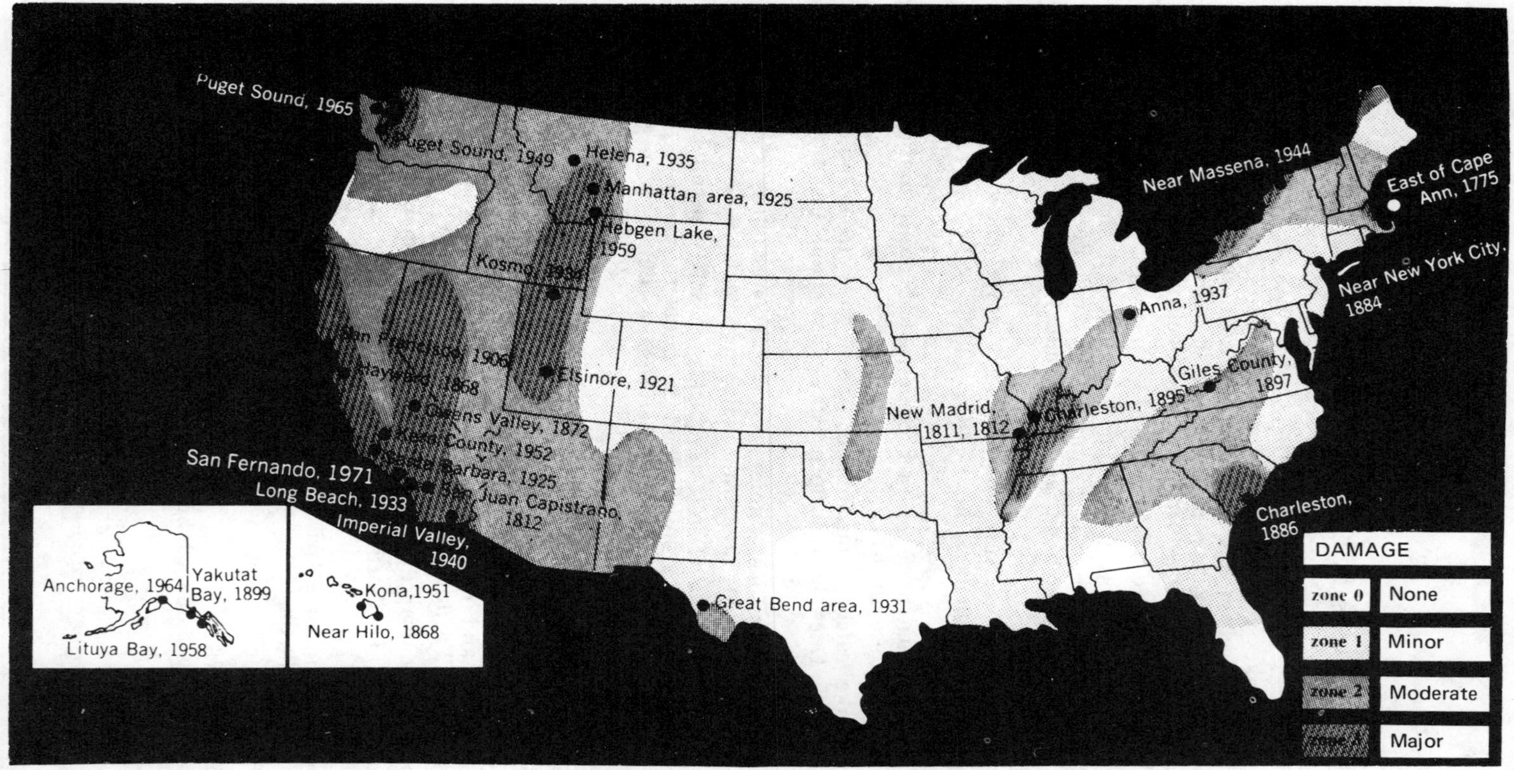

The four zones indicated by shadings on this map suggest the relative probability that earthquake damage may sometime occur in given areas. The epicenters of major earthquakes which have occured in the U.S. and the years of occurrence are also noted. Estimates of earthquake risk are based on the history of seismic disturbances, evidences of strain release and consideration of major geologic structures.

Earthquakes (intensity V and above) in the United States through 1970

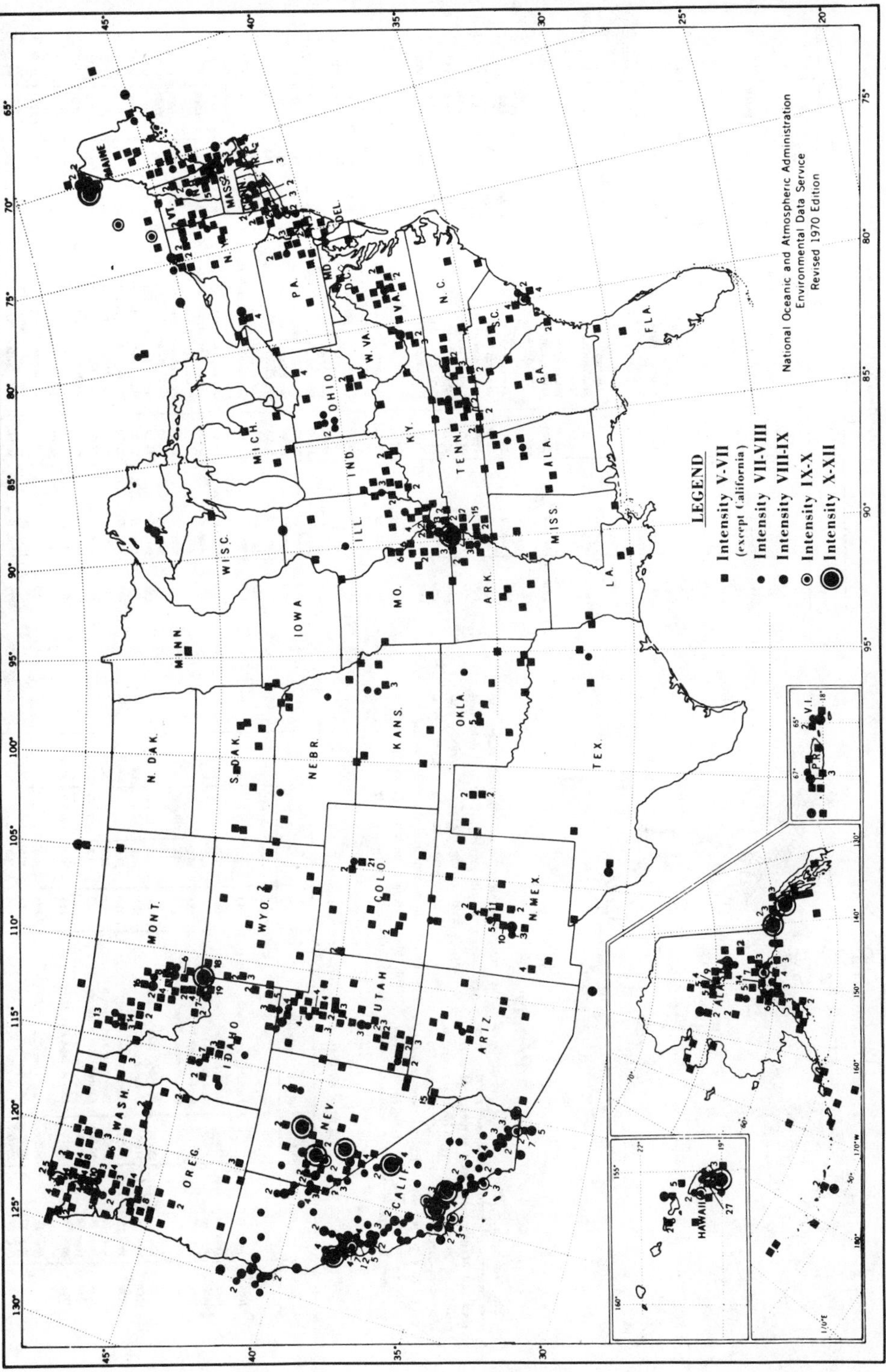

Northeastern Region

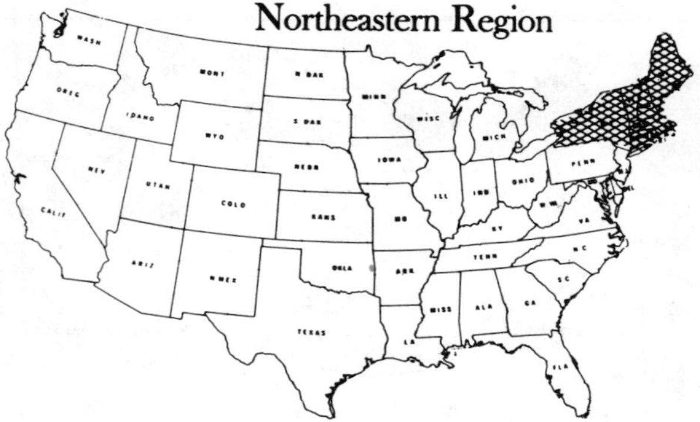

Résumé

The Northeastern Region of the country contains zones of relatively high seismic activity. New York and Massachusetts have experienced numerous shocks, several quite severe. This region also is affected by large earthquakes originating in adjacent Canada, principally in the St. Lawrence Valley and the Laurentian Trough. Earthquakes in this region may be explained by the readjustment of the crust, subsequent to the relatively recent Ice Age. Some geologists suggest the ice load deformed the earth's crust during the glacial periods, and now it is gradually coming back to its normal position. As the adjustments may occur deep within the earth, major surface faulting (a rarity in this region) need not be present.

List of Earthquakes in Northeastern Region

Year	Date	Time (EST)	Locality	N. lat.	W. long.	Area	Intensity
				degrees	degrees	sq. mi.	
1638	June 11	14:00 / 16:00	Probably St. Lawrence Valley	46.5	72.5	....	IX
1643	June 11	13:00	Newbury, Mass	42.8	70.8	....	....
1658	Apr. 14	......	New England	......	......	....	VII
1661	Feb. 10	......	St. Lawrence Valley	45.5	73.0	....	(*)
1663	Feb. 5	17:30	St. Lawrence River region	47.6	70.1	750,000	X
1727	Nov. 9	22:40	Newbury, Mass	42.8	70.8	75,000	VIII
1732	Sept. 16	11:00	St. Lawrence Valley	45.5	73.6	....	IX
1737	Feb. 17	16:30	Boston, Mass	42.4	71.0	....	....
	Dec. 18	23:00	Near New York City, N.Y	40.8	74.0	....	VII
1741	June 24	10:35	Eastern Massachusetts	42.2	71.2	1,000	....
1744	June 14	10:15	do	......	......	....	....
1755	Nov. 18	04:11	East of Cape Ann, Mass	42.5	70.0	300,000	VIII
	Nov. 18	05:29	do	42.5	70.0	....	....
	Nov. 22	20:27	do	42.5	70.0	....	V
	Dec. 19	22:00	do	42.5	70.0	....	....

See footnotes at end of table.

List of Earthquakes in Northeastern Region—Continued

Year	Date	Time (EST)	Locality	N. lat.	W. long.	Area	Intensity
				degrees	degrees	sq. mi.	
1783	Nov. 29	21:00 / 23:00	New Hampshire to Pennsylvania	......	......	....	....
1791	May 18	22:00	East Haddam, Conn	41.5	72.5	35,000	VIII
1792	Aug. 28	22:00	do	41.5	72.5	....	....
1793	Jan. 11	08:00	do	41.5	72.5	....	....
1794	Mar. 6	14:00 / 23:00	do	41.5	72.5	....	....
1805	Aug. 11	19:00	do	41.5	72.5	....	....
1810	Nov. 9	21:15	Exeter, N.H	43.0	70.9	....	VI
1817	May 22	15:00	Central Maine	46.0	69.0	....	VI
	Oct. 5	11:45	Woburn, Mass	42.5	71.2	....	VII–VIII
1827	Aug. 23	......	New London, Conn	41.4	72.7	....	IV–V
1837	Apr. 12	......	Hartford, Conn	41.7	72.7	....	V
1840	Aug. 9	15:30	Southern Connecticut	41.5	72.9	7,500	V
1841	Jan. 25	a.m.	New York	......	......	....	....
1847	Aug. 8	10:00	Southeastern Massachusetts	42	71	....	....
1848	Sept. 9	22:00	Connecticut, New Jersey, Pennsylvania, and Rhode Island.	......	......	....	....
1852	Nov. 27	23:45	Northeastern Massachusetts	42.8	71.0	2,000	V
1853	Mar. 12	02:03	Northern New York	43.7	75.5	....	VI
1854	Dec. 10	12:30	Newburyport, Mass	42.8	70.8	600	V
1855	Feb. 8	06:30	Canada, felt to south	46.0	64.5	85,000	VI*
1857	Oct. 23	15:15	Western New York	43.2	78.6	18,000	VI
1858	June 30	22:45	New Haven, Conn	41.8	73.0	1,000	V
1860	Oct. 17	06:00	Canada, felt to south	47.5	70.0	700,000	VIII–IX
1861	July 12	21:00	do	45.4	75.4	100,000	VII
1867	Dec. 18	03:00	Vermont	44	73	....	V
1869	Oct. 22	06:00	Bay of Fundy	45.0	66.2	250,000	VIII
1870	Oct. 20	11:25	Canada, felt to south	47.4	70.5	1,000,000	IX
1872	Jan. 9	19:54	do	47.5	70.5	100,000	VII
	July 11	05:25	Westchester County, N.Y	40.9	73.8	100	V
	Nov. 18	14:00	Concord, N.H	43.2	71.6	1,000	IV–V
1873	July 6	09:30	Ontario, Canada	43.0	79.5	30,000	V
1874	Feb. 27	22:40	Southeastern Maine	44.8	68.7	6,000	V
	Dec. 10	22:25	Westchester, N.Y	40.9	73.8	5,000	VI
1875	July 28	04:10	Connecticut	41.8	73.2	2,000	V
1876	Sept. 21	23:30	Southeastern Massachusetts	42.8	70.9	500	IV–V
1877	Nov. 4	01:56	Northern New York	44.5	74.0	90,000	VII
1878	Oct. 4	02:30	Hudson River, N.Y	41.5	74.0	600	V
1879	Aug. 21	03:00	Canada, northwest of Buffalo, N.Y.	43.2	79.2	1,300	V
1880	May 12	07:45	Northeastern Massachusetts	42.8	70.9	500	IV–V
1881	Jan. 20	21:40	Bath, Maine	44	70	2,000	IV–V
1882	Dec. 19	17:20	New Hampshire	43.2	71.4	1,000	V
	Dec. 31	22:00	Maine and New Brunswick	45	67	80,000	V
1883	Feb. 27	22:30	Rhode Island	41.5	71.5	....	V
1884	Jan. 18	02:00	Contoocook, N.H	43.2	71.7	(*)	....
	Aug. 10	14:07	Near New York City, N.Y	40.6	74.0	70,000	VII
	Nov. 23	00:30	Southern New Hampshire	43.2	71.7	8,000	V–VI
1891	May 1	19:10	do	43.2	71.6	3,000	V
1893	Mar. 9	00:30	New York City, N.Y	40.6	74.0	(*)	V
1896	Mar. 22	19:56	Maine and New Brunswick	45.2	67.2	8,000	IV–V
1897	May 27	22:16	Northeastern New York	44.5	74.5	150,000	VI
1898	Sept. 17	10:54	Near Belfast, Maine	44.3	69.1	(*)	IV–V

See footnotes at end of table.

List of Earthquakes in Northeastern Region—Continued

Year	Date	Time (EST)	Locality	N. lat.	W. long.	Area	Intensity
				degrees	*degrees*	*sq. mi.*	
1903	Jan. 21	a.m.	Eastern Massachusetts	42.1	70.9	500	V
	Apr. 24	07:30	Northeastern Massachusetts	42.7	71.0	350	V
	Dec. 25	07:30	Near Madrid, N.Y	44.7	75.5	1,500	V
1904	Mar. 21	01:04	Southeastern Maine	45.0	67.2	150,000	VII
1905	July 15	05:10	Maine and New Hampshire	44.3	69.8	20,000	V
	Aug. 30	05:42	Rockingham County, N.H	43	71	400	IV–V
	Oct. 22	a.m.	Northern Vermont	44.9	72.2	([4])	IV–V
1907	Jan. 24	06:30	Schenectady, N.Y	42.8	74.0	([4])	IV–V
	Oct. 15	19:10	Northeastern Massachusetts and southeastern New Hampshire.	42.8	71.0	1,200	V
1908	Feb. 5	03:20	Housatonic Valley, Conn	......	......	......	......
1910	Jan. 22	20:15	Cumberland County, Maine	43.8	70.4	150	V
1912	Dec. 11	05:15	Near Calais, Maine	45.0	68.0	20,000	V–VI
1913	Apr. 28	19:30	Near Potsdam, N.Y	44.8	75.3	3,000	VI
	Aug. 10	00:15	Lake Placid, N.Y	44	74	2,500	V
1914	Jan. 13	03:00	Maine and New Brunswick	45.1	67.2	([4])	V
	Feb. 10	13:31	Canada, felt to south	45.0	76.9	200,000	VII [3]
	Feb. 21	19:15	Western Maine	45.0	70.5	8,000	V
1916	Jan. 5	08:56	Near Lake George, N.Y	43.7	73.7	300	V
	Feb. 2	23:26	Mohawk Valley, N.Y	43	74	8,000	V
	June 8	16:15	Near New York City, N.Y	41.0	73.8	([4])	IV–V
	Nov. 1	21:32	Glens Falls, N.Y	43.3	73.7	300	V
1917	May 22	04:00	St. Lawrence Valley	45	75	15,000	IV–V
1918	Aug. 20	23:12	Southern Maine	44.2	70.6	15,000	VII
1924	Sept. 30	03:52	Probably St. Lawrence Valley	47.6	69.7	30,000	V [3]
1925	Jan. 7	08:07	Eastern Massachusetts	42.6	70.6	20,000	V
	Feb. 28	21:19[1]	St. Lawrence River region	47.7	70.5	2,000,000	VIII
	Apr. 24	02:56	Southeastern Massachusetts	41.8	70.8	1,600	V
	Oct. 9	08:56	Southeastern New Hampshire and Maine.	43.7	70.7	15,000	VI
	Nov. 14	08:04	Near Hartford, Conn	41.5	72.5	850	VI
1926	Mar. 18	16:11	Near Manchester, N.H	42.9	71.4	800	VI
	May 11	22:30	New Rochelle, N.Y	40.9	73.9	150	V
	Aug. 28	16:00	Western Maine	44.7	70.0	3,000	V
1927	Mar. 8	23:08	Concord, N.H	43.3	71.4	600	V
1928	Feb. 8	....	Milo, Maine	45.5	69.0	([4])	VI
	Mar. 18	10:20	Saranac Lake, N.Y	44.5	74.3	12,000	V–VI
	Apr. 25	18:38	Berlin, N.H	44.5	71.2	3,000	V
1929	Aug. 12	06:25[1]	Attica, N.Y	42.9	78.3	100,000	VIII
	Nov. 18	15:32[1]	Grand Banks of Newfoundland	44	56	[5] 80,000	X
	Dec. 2	17:14[1]	Attica, N.Y	42.8	78.3	([4])	V
1931	Jan. 7	19:14	Canada, felt to south	47.4	70.5	......	IV [3]
	Apr. 20	14:56[1]	Lake George, N.Y	43.4	73.7	60,000	VII
1933	Oct. 29	p.m.	St. Johnsville, N.Y	43.0	74.7	......	IV
1934	Apr. 14	21:58[1]	Adirondack Mountains, N.Y	44.5	73.9	8,000	V–VI
1935	Apr. 23	20:24[1]	Near Cape Cod, Mass	42.2	70.2	......	IV
	Nov. 1	01:04[1]	Timiskaming, Canada	46.8	79.1	1,000,000	VI [3]
1938	Aug. 22	07:48	Vicinity of Bangor, Maine	44.7	68.8	3,500	V
1939	Oct. 19	06:54[1]	Canada, at confluence of Saguenay and St. Lawrence Rivers.	47.8	70.0	[5] 90,000	V [3]
1940	Jan. 28	18:12[1]	Buzzards Bay, Mass	41.6	70.8	2,000	V
	Dec. 20	02:27[1]	Lake Ossipee, N.H	43.8	71.3	150,000	VII
	Dec. 24	08:44[1]	do	43.8	71.3	......	VII
1943	Jan. 14	16:33[1]	Dover-Foxcroft area, Maine	45.3	69.6	50,000	V

See footnotes at end of table.

List of Earthquakes in Northeastern Region—Continued

Year	Date	Time (EST)	Locality	N. lat.	W. long.	Area	Intensity
				degrees	*degrees*	*sq. mi.*	
1944	Sept. 4	23:39[1]	Massena, N.Y., and Cornwall, Ontario, Canada.	44.9	74.8	[5] 175,000	VIII
1947	Dec. 28	14:58[1]	Dover-Foxcroft, Maine	45.2	69.2	6,000	V
1949	Oct. 4	21:34[1]	Southwestern Maine	44.8	70.5	16,000	V
1951	Sept. 3	20:26	Rockland County, N.Y	41.2	74.1	5,500	V
1952	Jan. 29	23:00	Burlington, Vt	44.5	73.2	([4])	VI
	Aug. 24	19:07	Mohawk Valley, N.Y	43.0	74.5	400	V
	Oct. 8	16:40	Poughkeepsie, N.Y	41.7	74.0	......	V
	Oct. 14	17:04[1]	South-central Quebec, Canada	48.0	69.8	......	V [3]
1953	Mar. 27	03:50	Stamford, Conn	41.1	73.5	......	V
	Mar. 31	07:59	West-central Vermont	43.7	73.0	......	V
1954	July 29	15:57	Maine-Massachusetts-New Hampshire coastal areas.	......	......	......	V
1955	Feb. 2	p.m.	Burlington, Vt	44.5	73.2	([4])	V
	Aug. 16	02:35	Attica, N.Y	42.9	78.3	......	V
1957	Apr. 23	19:42	St. Johnsbury, Vt	44.4	72.0	([4])	V
	Apr. 26	06:40[1]	Near coast of Maine	43.6	69.8	31,500	VI
1958	Sept. 19	About 12:45	Cape Elizabeth, Maine	43.5	70.2	([4])	V
1961	Apr. 20	08:15	Massena, N.Y	44.9	74.9	......	V
1962	Mar. 27	01:37	Niagara Falls, N.Y	43.1	79.1	......	V
	Apr. 10	09:31[1]	Vermont	44.1	73.4	20,000	V
	June 20	21:07[1]	Southern Quebec, Canada	45.4	72.7	......	V [3]
	Dec. 29	01:19	Milford, N.H	42.8	71.6	......	V
1963	Oct. 16	10:31[1]	Near coast of Massachusetts	42.5	70.8	6,800	VI
	Oct. 30	17:37[1]	Northeast of Peabody, Mass	42.7	70.8	......	VI
	Dec. 4	16:33[1]	Tilton-Laconia, N.H	43.6	71.6	......	V
1964	Mar. 29	About 04:16	Massena, N.Y	44.9	74.9	([4])	V
1964	June 26	07:05[1]	Near Warner, N.H	43.3	71.9	3,000	VI
	Nov. 17	12:08	Westchester County, N.Y	41.2	73.7	......	V
1965	Oct. 24	About 12:45	Nantucket, Mass	41.3	70.1	([4])	V
	Dec. 7	22:03[1]	Narragansett Bay, R.I	41.7	71.4	375	V
1966	Jan. 1	08:24[1]	Attica-Varysburg, N.Y	42.8	78.2	3,500	VI
	July 23	21:00[1]	Jonesport, Maine	44.5	67.6	([4])	V
	Oct. 23	18:06[1]	Manchester, N.H	43.0	71.8	......	V
1967	Feb. 2	08:40[1]	Narragansett Bay, R.I	41.4	71.4	350	V
	June 13	14:09[1]	Attica-Alabama, N.Y	42.9	78.2	3,000	VI
	July 1	{09:09[1] 11:06[1]}	Kennebec County, Maine	44.4	69.9	2,000	V
	Nov. 22	17:10	Westchester County, N.Y	41.0	73.7	400	V
1968	Oct. 19	05:37[1]	Southern Ontario, Canada	45.4	74.0	......	V [3]
	Nov. 3	03:34	Southern Connecticut	......	......	......	V
1969	Aug. 6	11:03	Moultonboro, N.H	43.8	71.4	([4])	V

[1] Instrumental origin time and epicenter.

[2] Violent.
[3] Intensity in the United States.
[4] Local.
[5] United States area affected.

Eastern Region

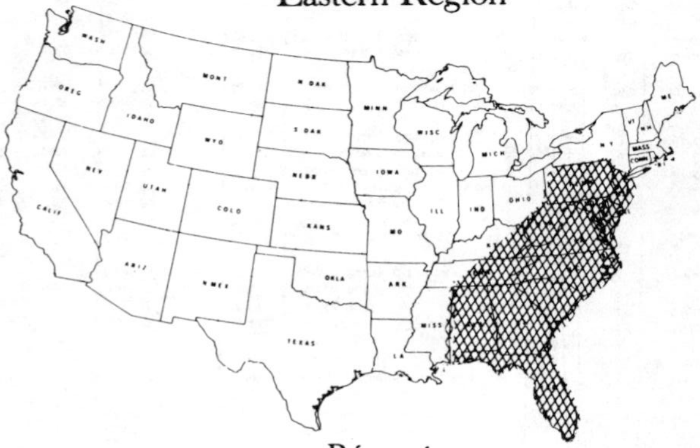

Résumé

This region, with the exception of the Charleston, S.C., earthquake, has a moderate amount of low-level earthquake activity. It is possible that the processes that have resulted in the present condition of the Appalachian Mountains system have reached a state of relative inactivity. Earthquakes occur throughout the region and the axis of principal activity roughly parallels the coast.

The earthquakes in the mountain regions are not surprising, as there seems to be a process of adjustment generally continuing in such regions, but the occurrence of the Charleston shock in a sandy plain is more difficult to explain.

List of Earthquakes in Eastern Region

Year	Date	Time (EST)	Locality	N. lat.	W. long.	Area	Intensity
				degrees	*degrees*	*sq. mi.*	
1758	Apr. 24	21:30	Annapolis, Md	38.9	76.5	....	....
1774	Feb. 21	14:00	Eastern Virginia	....	....	58,000	....
1800	Mar. 17	....	Philadelphia, Pa	39.8	75.2	....	....
	Nov. 29	....	do	39.8	75.2	....	....
1807	Apr. 30 or May 1.	04:00	Lynchburg-Richmond, Va., area	....	....	....	V
1828	Mar. 9	22:00 to 23:00	Probably Virginia	....	....	218,000	V
1833	Aug. 27	06:00	Central Virginia	....	....	52,000	V
1840	Nov. 11 and 14	....	Philadelphia, Pa	39.8	75.2	....	....
1843	Feb. 8	10:40	West Indies, felt in U.S	16	62	....	....
1852	Apr. 29	13:00	Probably Virginia	....	....	162,000	VI
1853	May 2	09:20	Virginia-West Virginia region	....	....	72,000	V
1855	Feb. 2	03:00	Charlotte Court House, Va	37.0	78.6	9,000	V
1857	Dec. 19	09:04	Charleston, S.C	32.9	80.0	....	....

See footnotes at end of table.

List of Earthquakes in Eastern Region—Continued

Year	Date	Time (EST)	Locality	N. lat.	W. long.	Area	Intensity
				degrees	*degrees*	*sq. mi.*	
1861	Aug. 31	05:22	Probably Virginia	....	....	300,000	VI
1871	Oct. 9	09:40	Wilmington, Del	39.7	75.5	....	VII
1872	June 17	15:00	Milledgeville, Ga	33.1	83.3	....	V
1874	Feb. 10 to Apr. 17.	....	McDowell County, N.C	35.7	82.1	(*)	V
1875	Nov. 1	21:55	Northern Georgia	33.8	82.5	25,000	VI
	Dec. 22	23:45	Arvonia, Va., area	37.6	78.5	50,000	VII
1877	Sept. 10	09:59	Delaware Valley	40.3	74.9	300	IV–V
	Nov. 16	02:38	North Carolina-Tennessee region	35.5	84.0	5,000	V
1879	Jan. 12	23:45 / 23:55	Near St. Augustine, Fla	29.5	82.0	25,000	VI
	Mar. 25	19:30	Delaware River	39.2	75.5	600	IV–V
	Dec. 13	02:00	Charlotte, N.C	35.2	80.8	....	V
1880	Jan. 22	22:23	Cuba, felt in Florida	22.8	80.8	65,000	VIII*
	Jan. 23	04:00	do	22.8	80.8	....	....
1883	Mar. 11	18:57	Harford County, Md	39.5	76.4	(*)	IV–V
	Mar. 12	00:00 / 01:00	do	39.5	76.4	(*)	IV–V
1884	Jan. 18	08:00	Wilmington, N.C	34.3	78.0	(*)	V
	May 31	....	Allentown, Pa	40.6	75.5	(*)	V
1885	Jan. 2	21:16	Maryland-Virginia region	39.2	77.5	3,500	V
	Aug. 6	08:00	Watauga County, N.C	36.2	81.6	(*)	IV–V
	Oct. 9	23:35	Virginia	37.7	78.8	20,000	VI
1886	Feb. 4	20:00	Alabama	32.8	88.0	1,600	V
	Feb. 13	....	do	32.8	88.0	....	....
	Aug. 31	21:51 / 21:59	Charleston, S.C	32.9	80.0	2,000,000	IX–X
	Oct. 22	05:20	do	32.9	80.0	30,000	VI
	Oct. 22	14:45	do	32.9	80.0	30,000	VII
	Nov. 5	12:20	do	32.9	80.0	30,000	VI
1889	Mar. 8	18:40	Pennsylvania	40	76	4,000	V
1895	Sept. 1	06:09	West of Newark, N.J	40.7	74.8	35,000	VI
1897	May 3	12:18	Pulaski, Va	37.1	80.7	29,000	VI
	May 31	13:58	Giles County, Va	37.3	80.7	280,000	VII
	Oct. 21	22:20	Southwestern Virginia	37	81	20,000	V
	Dec. 18	18:45	Ashland, Va	37.7	77.5	7,500	V
1898	Feb. 5	15:00	Pulaski, Va	37.0	80.7	34,000	VI
	Nov. 25	15:00	Southwestern Virginia	....	....	65,000	V
1899	Feb. 13	04:30	do	37	81	30,000	V
1900	Oct. 31	11:15	Jacksonville, Fla	30.4	81.7	(*)	V
1902	May 29	02:30	Chattanooga, Tenn	35.1	85.3	(*)	V
	Oct. 18	17:00	Tennessee-Georgia region	35.0	85.3	1,500	V
1903	Jan. 23	20:15	Georgia-South Carolina region	32.1	81.1	10,000	VI
1904	Mar. 4	19:30	Eastern Tennessee	35.7	83.5	5,000	V
1905	Jan. 27 and 28	....	Gadsden, Ala	34	86	250,000	VII
1906	May 8	12:41	Near Seaford, Del	38.7	75.7	400	V
1907	Feb. 11	08:22	Arvonia, Va	37.7	78.4	5,600	VI
	Apr. 19	03:30	Charleston, S.C	32.9	80.0	10,000	V

See footnotes at end of table.

List of Earthquakes in Eastern Region—Continued

Year	Date	Time (EST)	Locality	N. lat.	W. long.	Area	Intensity
				degrees	*degrees*	*sq. mi.*	
1908	May 31	12:42	Allentown, Pa	40.6	75.5	(1)	VI
	Aug. 23	04:30	Powhatan, Va	37.5	77.9	1,500	V
1909	Apr. 2	02:25	Charles Town-Martinsburg, W. Va.	39.4	78.0	2,500	V–VI
1910	May 8	16:10	Arvonia, Va	37.7	78.4	4,000	V
1911	Apr. 20	....	North Carolina-South Carolina area.	35.2	82.7	600	V
1912	June 12	05:30	Summerville, S.C	33.0	80.2	35,000	VII
	June 20	....	Savannah, Ga	32	81	....	V
1913	Jan. 1	13:28	Union County, S.C	34.7	81.7	43,000	VI–VII
	Mar. 28	16:50	Near Knoxville, Tenn	36.2	83.7	2,700	VII
	Apr. 17	11:30	Southeastern Tennessee	35.3	84.2	3,500	V
1914	Jan. 23	22:24	do	35.6	84.5	(1)	V
	Mar. 5	15:05	Near Atlanta, Ga	33.5	83.5	50,000	VI
	Sept. 22	02:04	Summerville, S.C	33.0	80.2	30,000	V
1915	Oct. 29	About 01:00	Near Marshall, N.C	35.8	82.7	1,200	V
1916	Feb. 21	17:39	Near Asheville, N.C	35.5	82.5	200,000	VI
	Aug. 26	14:36	Western North Carolina	36	81	3,800	V
	Oct. 18	16:04	Northeastern Alabama	33.5	86.2	100,000	VII
1917	June 29	20:23	Western Alabama	32.7	87.5	(1)	V
1918	Apr. 9	21:09	Luray, Va	38.7	78.4	60,000	VI
	June 21	20:00	Lenoir City, Tenn	36.1	84.1	3,000	V
1919	Sept. 5	21:46	Near Front Royal, Va	38.8	78.2	....	VI
1920	Dec. 24	02:30	Rockwood, Tenn., area	36	85	(1)	V
1921	Jan. 26	18:40	New Jersey	40	75	150	V
	July 15	....	Near Mendota, Va	36.6	82.3	(1)	VI
	Aug. 7	01:30	New Canton, Va., area	37.8	78.4	2,800	V
1924	Oct. 20	03:30	Pickens County, S.C	35.0	82.6	56,000	V
	Dec. 25	23:30	Roanoke, Va	37.3	79.9	(1)	V
1926	July 8	04:50	Southern Mitchell County, N.C	35.9	82.1	(1)	VI
1927	June 1	07:20	Asbury Park, N.J., area	40.3	74.0	3,000	VII
	June 10	02:16	Near Charlottesville, Va	38	79	2,500	V
	June 16	07:00	Northeastern Alabama	34.7	86.0	2,500	V
1928	Nov. 2	23:03	Western North Carolina	36.0	82.6	40,000	VI
1929	Dec. 26	21:56	Central Virginia	38.1	78.5	....	VI
1931	May 5	07:18	Northern Alabama	33.7	86.6	6,500	V–VI
1933	Jan. 24	21:00	Near Trenton, N.J	40.2	74.7	600	V
	Dec. 19	09:12	Summerville, S.C	33.0	80.2	(1)	IV–V
1934	Oct. 29	15:07	Erie, Pa	42.0	80.2	(1)	V
1935	Jan. 1	03:15*	North Carolina-Georgia border	35.1	83.6	7,000	V
1938	July 15	17:45*	Southern Blair County, Pa	40.4	78.2	100	VI
	Aug. 22	22:36*	Central New Jersey	40.1	74.5	5,000	V
1939	May 4	21:45	Anniston, Ala	33.7	85.8	....	V
	Nov. 14	21:54*	Salem County, N.J	39.6	75.2	6,000	V
1945	June 13	21:25	Cleveland, Tenn	35	84½	....	V
	July 26	05:32*	Murray Lake, S.C	34.3	81.4	25,000	IV–V
1952	Nov. 19	....	Charleston, S.C	32.9	80.0	....	V

List of Earthquakes in Eastern Region—Continued

Year	Date	Time (EST)	Locality	N. lat.	W. long.	Area	Intensity
				degrees	*degrees*	*sq. mi.*	
1954	Jan. 7	02:25	Sinking Spring, Pa	40.3	76.0	....	VI
	Feb. 21	15:00	Wilkes-Barre, Pa	41.2	75.9	(1)	VII
	Feb. 23	22:55	do	41.2	75.9	(1)	VI
1955	Sept. 28	02:02	Virginia-North Carolina border	....	....	1,700	V
1956	Sept. 7	08:36* 08:49*	Knoxville, Tenn., area	35.5	84.0	8,300	VI
1957	Mar. 23	14:03	West-central New Jersey	40¾	74¾	....	VI
	Apr. 23	04:24*	Birmingham, Ala., area	34½	86¾	11,500	VI
	May 13	09:25	Western North Carolina	35¾	82	8,100	VI
	June 23	01:34*	East-central Tennessee	36½	84½	....	V
	July 2	04:33	Western North Carolina	35½	82½	....	VI
	Nov. 24	15:06*	Hartford, Tenn., area	35	83½	4,100	VI
1958	Mar. 5	06:54	Wilmington, N.C., and vicinity	34¼	77¾	....	V
	Oct. 20	01:16	Anderson, S.C	34½	82¾	(1)	V
1959	Apr. 23	15:59*	Virginia-West Virginia border	37½	80½	3,000	VI
	Aug. 3	01:08*	Near Charleston, S.C	33	79½	25,000	VI
	Aug. 12	13:06*	Alabama-Tennessee border	35	87	2,800	VI
	Oct. 26	21:07	Northeastern South Carolina	34½	80¼	4,800	VI
1960	Mar. 12	07:48*	Off coast of South Carolina	33	79	3,500	V
	Apr. 15	05:10	Eastern Tennessee	35¾	84	1,300	V
1960	July 23	22:37	Near Charleston, S.C	33	80	(1)	V
1961	Sept. 14	21:17	Lehigh Valley, Pa	40¾	75½	(1)	V
	Dec. 27	12:06	Pennsylvania-New Jersey border	40½	74¾	....	V
1963	Oct. 28	17:39*	Near Galax, Va	36.7	81.0	1,300	V
1964	Feb. 18	04:31*	Alabama-Georgia border	34.8	85.5	....	V
	Mar. 12	20:20*	Central Georgia	33.2	83.4	400	V
	Apr. 20	14:05*	Columbia, S.C., area	34	81	....	V
	May 12	04:45*	Cornwall, Pa	40.2	76.5	(1)	VI
1966	May 31	01:19*	West of Richmond, Va	37.6	78.0	28,000	V
1967	Apr. 8	00:41*	Columbus, Ohio	39.6	82.5	4,000	V
	Oct. 23	04:04*	Near Summerville, S.C	33.4	80.7	....	V
1968	Dec. 10	04:13*	Southern New Jersey	39.7	74.6	....	V
	Dec. 11	10:00	Louisville, Ky	38.3	85.7	....	V
1969	July 13	16:51*	Eastern Tennessee	36.1	74.3	20,000	V
	Nov. 19	20:00*	Southern West Virginia	37.4	81.0	100,000	VI
	Dec. 11	18:45*	Richmond, Va	37.8	77.4	6,500	V
	Dec. 13	05:20*	Western North Carolina	35.1	83.0	3,500	V
1970	Sept. 9	20:41*	Northwestern North Carolina	36.1	81.4	2,000	V

*Instrumental origin time and epicenter.

[1] Local.

[2] Intensity at epicenter.

Central Region

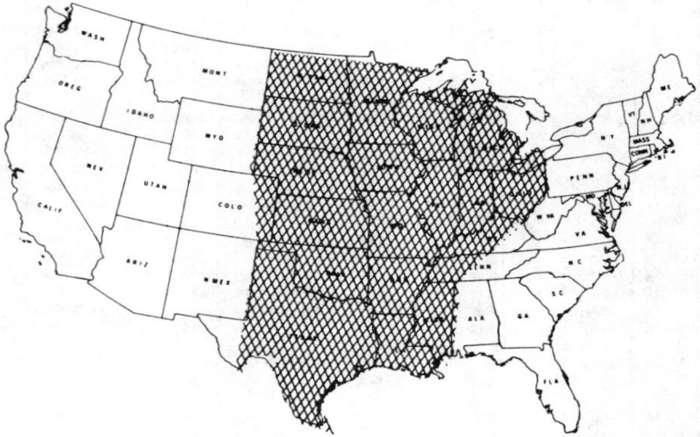

Résumé

Except for the flat beds of some oceans, the non-mountainous interior portions of continents usually are considered less earthquake prone than any part of the earth. However, this does not hold true for the Central United States. The Upper Mississippi and Ohio Valleys are regions of relatively frequent earthquakes. Three of the great earthquakes of known history occurred in the Upper Mississippi region in 1811–12. Only the sparse settlement of the area prevented grave damage. The extent, and severity, of topographic effects from these shocks has not been equaled by any other earthquake in the contiguous United States. The reason for most of the earthquakes in the Central Region is not fully understood. The Rough Creek Fault is believed responsible for the 1811–12 shocks. But most of the slips have occurred in formations deep in alluvial material and geologists have been able to study only the incidental effects on the alluvial soil. It is important that more studies be conducted in this seismic region.

List of Earthquakes in Central Region

Year	Date	Time (CST)	Locality	N. lat.	W. long.	Area	Intensity
				degrees	*degrees*	*sq. mi.*	
1776	Summer	08:00	Muskingum River, Ohio	......	......	......	......
1779	Unknown	......	Northern Kentucky	......	......	......	......
1791 or 1792	April or May	07:00	Northern and eastern Kentucky	......	......	......	......

See footnotes at end of table.

List of Earthquakes in Central Region—Continued

Year	Date	Time (CST)	Locality	N. lat.	W. long.	Area	Intensity
				degrees	*degrees*	*sq. mi.*	
1795	Jan. 8	03:00	Kaskaskia, Ill	......	......	......	......
1804	Aug. 24	14:10	Fort Dearborn (Chicago), Ill	42.0	87.8	30,000	......
1811	Dec. 16	02:00	New Madrid, Mo	36.6	89.6	2,000,000	XII
1812	Jan. 23	......	do	36.6	89.6	......	XII
	Feb. 7	......	do	36.6	89.6	......	XII
1820	Nov. 9	16:00	Cape Girardeau, Mo	37.3	89.5	......	IV–V
1827	Aug. 6	22:30	New Albany, Ind	38.3	85.8	......	VI
	Aug. 7	01:00	do	38.3	85.8	......	VI
1834	Nov. 20	13:40	Northern Kentucky	......	......	......	V
1838	June 9	08:45	St. Louis, Mo	38.5	90.3	......	VI
1841	Dec. 27	23:50	Near Hickman, Ky	......	......	......	V
1843	Jan. 4	20:45	Western Tennessee	35.2	90.0	400,000	VIII
	Feb. 16	23:00	St. Louis, Mo	......	......	(*)	III–IV
1844	Nov. 28	07:00	Knoxville, Tenn	36.0	84.0	......	VI
1857	Oct. 8	04:00 } 04:07 }	St. Louis, Mo	38.5	90.3	7,500	VI
1860	Unknown	......	Central Minnesota	......	......	......	......
1865	Aug. 17	09:00	Southeastern Missouri	36.5	89.5	24,000	VII
1867	Apr. 24	14:22	Lawrence, Kans	39.5	96.7	300,000	VII
1872	Feb. 6	08:00	Wenona, Mich	43.5	83.8	(*)	V
	Oct. 9	10:00	Sioux City, Iowa	42.7	97.0	3,000	V
1875	June 18	07:43	Western Ohio	40.2	84.0	40,000	VII
	Nov. 8	04:40	Kansas	39.3	95.5	8,000	V
1876	Sept. 25	00:15	Near Evansville, Ind	38.5	87.7	60,000	VI
1877	Aug. 17	10:50	Southeastern Michigan	42.3	83.3	200	IV–V
	Nov. 15	11:45 } 12:30 }	Eastern Nebraska	41	97	140,000	VII
1878	Mar. 12	04:00	Columbus, Ky	36.8	89.2	(*)	V
	Nov. 18	23:52	Southeastern Missouri	36.7	90.4	150,000	VI
1879	Dec. 29	00:30	South Dakota	42.9	97.3	(*)	V
1882	Feb. 9	14:00	Ohio	......	......	......	V
	July 20	04:00	Southern Illinois	38	90	3,000	V
	Sept. 27	04:20	do	39	90	40,000	VI
	Oct. 15	00:00 } 05:00 }	do	39	90	40,000	V
	Oct. 22	16:15	Arkansas	35	94	135,000	VI–VII
1883	Jan. 11	01:12	Cairo, Ill	37.0	89.2	80,000	VI

See footnotes at end of table.

List of Earthquakes in Central Region—Continued

Year	Date	Time (CST)	Locality	N. lat.	W. long.	Area	Intensity
				degrees	*degrees*	*sq. mi.*	
1883	Feb. 4	05:00	Kalamazoo, Mich	42.3	85.6	8,000	VI
	Apr. 12	02:30	Cairo, Ill	37.0	89.2	([1])	VI–VII
	Dec. 5	09:20	Izard County, Ark	36.3	91.8	([1])	V
1884	Sept. 19	14:14	Near Columbus, Ohio	40.7	84.1	125,000	VI
1887	Feb. 6	16:15	Vincennes, Ind	38.7	87.5	75,000	VI
	Aug. 2	12:36	Cairo, Ill	37.0	89.2	([1])	V
1889	July 19	19:32	Memphis, Tenn	35.2	90.0	([1])	VI
1891	Jan. 8	00:00	Rusk, Tex	31.7	95.2	....	VII
	July 26	20:28	Evansville, Ind	37.9	87.5	....	VI
	Sept. 26	22:55	Near Cairo, Ill	......	......	....	....
1895	Oct. 11	17:55 / 19:25	Black Hills, S. Dak	43.9	103.3	....	IV–V
	Oct. 31	05:08	Charleston, Mo	37.0	89.4	1,000,000	VIII
1897	Apr. 30	22:00	Tennessee, Illinois, Indiana, and Kentucky.	......	......	....	IV–V
1899	Apr. 29	20:05	Southwestern Indiana and southeastern Illinois.	38.5	87.0	40,000	VI–VII
1901	May 17	01:00	Ohio	39.3	82.5	7,000	V
1902	Jan. 24	04:48	Missouri	38.6	90.3	40,000	VI
	July 28	12:00	Eastern Nebraska	42.5	97.5	35,000	V
1903	Feb. 8	13:21	St. Louis, Mo	38.5	90.3	70,000	VI
	Nov. 4	12:18 / 13:14	.... do	38.5	90.3	70,000	VI–VII
	Nov. 27	03:20	New Madrid, Mo	36.5	89.5	70,000	V
1904	Oct. 27	p.m.	Kansas	37.7	100.0	2,700	V
1905	Mar. 13	10:30	Menominee, Mich	45.0	87.7	([1])	V
	Apr. 13	10:30	Keokuk, Iowa	40.4	91.4	5,000	V
	July 26	18:20	Calumet, Mich	47.3	88.4	16,000	VII
	Aug. 21	23:08	Mississippi Valley	......	......	40,000	VI
1906	Jan. 7	18:15	Manhattan, Kans	39.3	96.6	10,000	VII
	May 9	18:27	South Dakota-Nebraska border	43.0	101.3	8,000	VI
	May 11	00:15	Southwestern Indiana	38.5	87.2	800	V
	May 21	13:00	Flora, Ill	38.8	88.5	....	V
	May 26	About 09:00	Keweenaw Peninsula, Mich	47.3	88.4	1,000	VIII
	June 27	16:10	Fairport, Ohio	41.4	81.6	400	V
1907	July 4	03:00	Farmington, Mo	37.7	90.4	400	IV–V
1908	Sept. 28	13:34	New Madrid, Mo	36.5	89.5	5,000	IV–V
	Oct. 27	18:27	Cairo, Ill	37.0	89.2	5,000	V
1909	Jan. 22	21:15	Houghton, Mich	47.2	88.6	([1])	V
	May 15	a.m.	Canada, felt to south	50	105	500,000	VI–VII
	May 26	08:42	Illinois	42.5	89.0	500,000	VII

See footnotes at end of table.

List of Earthquakes in Central Region—Continued

Year	Date	Time (CST)	Locality	N. lat.	W. long.	Area	Intensity
				degrees	*degrees*	*sq. mi.*	
1909	July 18	22:34	Illinois	40.2	90.0	40,000	VII
	Aug. 16	16:45	Southwestern Illinois	38.3	90.2	....	....
	Sept. 22	....	Ohio Valley	38.7	86.5	4,000	V
	Sept. 27	03:45 / 03:50	Indiana	39.0	87.6	30,000	VII
	Oct. 23	01:10	Southeastern Missouri	37.0	89.5	40,000	V
	Oct. 23	03:47	Near Robinson, Ill	39.0	87.7	8,000	V
1910	Feb. 26	02:00	Columbus, Nebr	41.4	97.3	([1])	IV–V
1911	Mar. 31	10:57 / 12:10	Rison, Ark	33.8	92.2	18,000	V
	June 2	16:34	South Dakota	44.2	98.2	40,000	V
1912	Jan. 2	10:21	Illinois	41.5	88.5	40,000	VI
1915	Apr. 28	17:40	New Madrid-Tiptonville, Mo	36.4	89.5	200	IV–V
	Oct. 23	00:05	Kadoka, S. Dak	43.8	101.5	([1])	V
	Oct. 26	01:40	Mayfield, Ky	36.7	88.6	([1])	V
	Dec. 7	12:40	Near mouth of Ohio River	36.7	89.1	60,000	V–VI
1916	Dec. 18	23:42	Hickman, Ky	36.6	89.3	([1])	VI–VII
1917	Mar. 27	13:56	Panhandle, Tex	35.3	101.2	([1])	VI
	Apr. 9	14:52	Eastern Missouri	38.1	90.6	200,000	VI
	Sept. 3	15:30	Staples, Minn	46.3	94.5	10,000	VI
1918	Sept. 10	10:30	El Reno, Okla	35.5	98.0	([1])	V
	Oct. 4	03:21	Arkansas	34.7	92.3	30,000	V
	Oct. 13	03:30	Black Rock, Ark	36.1	91.1	([1])	V
	Oct. 15	21:30	Western Tennessee	35.2	89.2	20,000	V
1919	May 25	03:45	Southern Indiana	38.5	87.5	18,000	V
	Nov. 3	14:40	Vicinity of Pocahontas, Ark	36.2	90.9	([1])	IV–V
1920	May 1	09:15	Missouri	38.5	90.5	10,000	V
1922	Mar. 22	16:30 / 20:20	Southern Illinois	37.3	88.6	25,000	V
	Mar. 23	15:45	Western Kentucky	......	......	....	V
1923	Oct. 28	11:10	Marked Tree, Ark	35.5	90.3	40,000	VII
	Nov. 9	22:00	Tallula, Ill	......	......	....	V
	Dec. 31	21:05	Arkansas	35.4	90.3	30,000	V
1924	Mar. 2	05:18	Kentucky	36.9	89.1	15,000	V
1925	Mar. 26	22:06	Southwestern Ohio	......	......	....	V
	Apr. 26	22:05	Indiana	38.0	87.5	100,000	V
	May 13	06:00	Kentucky	36.7	88.6	3,000	V
	July 30	06:17	Panhandle region, Tex	35.4	101.3	200,000	V
	Sept. 2	05:55	Kentucky	37.8	87.6	75,000	V–VI

See footnotes at end of table.

List of Earthquakes in Central Region—Continued

Year	Date	Time (CST)	Locality	N. lat.	W. long.	Area	Intensity
				degrees	*degrees*	*sq. mi.*	
1926	Nov. 5	09:53	Southeastern Ohio	39.1	82.1	350	VI–VII
1927	Mar. 18	11:25	White Cloud, Kans	40.0	95.3	300	V
	May 7	02:28	Mississippi Valley	36.5	89.0	130,000	VII
1928	Sept. 9	15:00	Lorain and Cleveland, Ohio	41.5	82.0	1,500	V
	Nov. 16	07:45	Black Hills, S. Dak	44.0	103.7	2,000	V
1929	Mar. 8	04:06*	Bellefontaine, Ohio	40.4	84.2	5,000	V
	Sept. 23	04:00 } 05:00 }	Northeastern Kansas	39.0	96.6	15,000	V
	Oct. 21	15:30	do	39.2	96.5	8,000	V
	Dec. 7	02:02	do	39.2	96.5	1,000	V
	Dec. 27	18:30	El Reno, Okla	35.5	98.0	8,000	VI
1930	Sept. 30	14:40*	Ohio	40.3	84.3	....	VII
	Oct. 19	06:17	Louisiana	30.0	91.0	15,000	VI
1931	Jan. 5	20:51	Elliston, Ind	39.0	87.0	500	V
	Sept. 20	17:05*	Anna, Ohio	40.4	84.2	40,000	VII
	Dec. 16	21:40*	Northern Mississippi	34.1	89.8	65,000	VI–VII
1932	Apr. 9	04:15	Mexia-Wortham, Tex	31.7	96.4	1,000	V–VI
1933	Feb. 20	11:00	Norton, Kans	39.8	99.8	6,000	V
	May 28	10:10	Maysville, Ky	38.7	83.7	600	V
	Aug. 19	13:30	El Reno, Okla	35.5	98.0	200	VI
	Dec. 9	02:40	Manila, Ark	35.8	90.2	100	VI
1934	Apr. 11	11:40	Texas-Oklahoma border	33.9	95.5	3,000	V
	July 30	01:20	Chadron, Nebr	42.7	103.0	23,000	VI
	Aug. 19	18:47*	Rodney, Mo	37.0	89.2	28,000	VII
	Nov. 12	08:45	Rock Island, Ill	41.5	90.5	....	VI
1935	Mar. 1	05:00*	Nebraska	40.3	96.2	50,000	VI
1936	Mar. 14	11:20	Southeastern Oklahoma	34.0	95.2	900	V
	June 19	21:24	Texas Panhandle	35.8	101.3	40,000	V
1937	Mar. 2	08:48*	Western Ohio	40.4	84.2	70,000	VII
	Mar. 3	03:50	Ohio	......	......	......	V
	Mar. 8	23:45*	Western Ohio	40.4	84.2	150,000	VII–VIII
	May 16	18:50*	Northeastern Arkansas	36.1	90.6	25,000	IV–V
	Nov. 17	11:05*	Centralia, Ill	38.6	89.1	8,000	V
1938	Sept. 16	21:34*	Northeastern Arkansas	35.5	90.3	90,000	IV–V
	Oct. 11	03:37	Sioux Falls, S.Dak	43.3	96.4	3,000	V
1939	June 19	15:43	Arkadelphia, Ark	34.1	93.1	....	V
	Nov. 23	09:15*	Near Griggs, Ill	38.2	90.1	150,000	V
1941	Nov. 16	21:09*	Covington, Tenn	35.5	89.7	(*)	V–VI
1943	Mar. 8	21:26*	Lake Erie area	41.6	81.3	40,000	IV–V
1946	July 23	00:45	Wessington, S.Dak	44.3	98.4	....	VI
1947	June 29	22:24*	Near St. Louis, Mo	38.4	90.2	15,000	VI
	Aug. 9	20:47*	South-central Michigan	42.0	85.0	50,000	VI
1950	Feb. 8	04:37	Near Lebanon, Mo	37.4	92.4	....	V
1952	Feb. 20	16:35*	Tennessee-Missouri border	36.4	89.5	....	V
	Apr. 9	10:29*	El Reno, Okla	35.4	97.8	140,000	VII
	Apr. 16	00:05	do	35.4	97.8	....	V
	June 20	03:38*	Southeastern Ohio	39.7	82.2	10,000	VI
	July 16	17:48*	Dyersburg, Tenn	36.2	89.6	....	VI
1953	Mar. 17	07:12 } 08:25 }	Concho, Okla	35.6	97.8	....	VI

See footnotes at end of table.

List of Earthquakes in Central Region—Continued

Year	Date	Time (CST)	Locality	N. lat.	W. long.	Area	Intensity
				degrees	*degrees*	*sq. mi.*	
1953	Sept. 11	12:26*	Southwestern Illinois	38.6	90.1	....	VI
1954	Jan. 1	21:25	Middlesboro, Ky	36.6	83.7	....	VI
	Jan. 22	p.m.	Athens and Etowah, Tenn	35.3	84.4	....	V
	Feb. 2	10:53	Missouri-Arkansas border	36.7	90.3	....	VI
	Apr. 26	20:09	Memphis, Tenn	35.2	90.0	....	V
1955	Jan. 25	01:24*	Tennessee-Arkansas-Missouri border.	35.6	90.3	30,000	VI
	Feb. 1	08:45	Gulfport, Miss	30.4	89.1	....	V
	Mar. 29	03:03	Finley, Tenn	36.0	89.5	....	VI
	Apr. 9	07:01*	West of Sparta, Ill	38.1	89.8	20,000	VI
	May 26	12:09	Cleveland, Ohio	41.5	81.7	(*)	V
	June 28	19:16	do	41.5	81.7	(*)	V
	Sept. 5	19:45	Finley, Tenn	36.0	89.5	....	V
	Dec. 13	01:43	Dyer County, Tenn	36.0	89.5	....	V
1956	Jan. 6	05:58*	Southern Kansas	37.3	98.5	16,000	VI
	Jan. 27	06:03	West-central Ohio	......	......	....	V
	Jan. 28	22:14*	Tennessee-Arkansas border	35.6	89.6	....	VI
	Feb. 16	17:30	Edmond, Okla	35.4	97.3	....	VI
	Apr. 2	10:03	Southeastern Oklahoma	34.2	95.4	....	V
	Oct. 29	03:24	Caruthersville, Mo	36.1	89.4	....	V
	Oct. 30	04:36	Northeastern Oklahoma	36.2	95.9	3,700	VII
	Nov. 25	22:13*	Wayne County, Mo	37.1	90.6	21,500	VI
1957	Mar. 19	10:38	Northeastern Texas	32	95	10,000	V
	Mar. 26	02:27	Paducah, Ky	37.0	88.4	(*)	V
1958	Jan. 26	10:56	Memphis, Tenn	35.2	90.0	(*)	V
	Jan. 27	23:57	Illinois-Kentucky-Missouri border	37	89	300	V
	Apr. 8	16:26	Obion County, Tenn	36.2	89.1	400	V
	Apr. 26	01:30	Lake County, Tenn	36.3	89.5	....	V
	May 1	16:47	Cleveland, Ohio	41.5	81.7	(*)	V
	Nov. 7	20:42*	Illinois-Indiana border	38.4	87.9	33,000	VI
	Nov. 19	12:15	Baton Rouge, La	30.3	91.1	(*)	V
1959	Feb. 13	02:37	Bogota, Tenn	36.2	89.5	170	V
	June 15	06:45	Seminole, Pontotoc, and Johnston Counties, Okla.	......	......	....	V
	June 17	04:27*	Southwestern Oklahoma	34.5	98.5	12,000	VI
	Dec. 21	10:25	Finley, Tenn	36.0	89.5	400	V
1960	Jan. 28	15:38	Dyer County, Tenn	36.0	89.5	(*)	V
	Apr. 21	04:45	Lake County, Tenn	36.3	89.5	(*)	V
1961	Jan. 10	19:40	Southeastern Oklahoma	......	......	....	V
	Feb. 22	03:45	Northwestern Ohio	41.2	83.4	....	V
	Apr. 13	15:15*	Kansas-Nebraska border	39.9	100.0	....	V
	Apr. 27	About 01:30	Southeastern Oklahoma	35	95	....	V
	Dec. 25	06:20 } 06:58 }	Kansas-Missouri border	39.1	94.6	11,000	V
	Dec. 31	10:36*	Central South Dakota	44.4	100.5	....	VI
1962	Feb. 2	00:44*	New Madrid, Mo	36.5	89.6	35,000	VI
	June 26	19:29*	Southern Illinois	37.7	88.5	....	V
	July 23	00:05*	Southern Missouri	36.1	89.8	....	VI
1963	Mar. 3	11:30*	Southeastern Missouri	36.7	90.1	100,000	VI
	Aug. 2	18:38*	Illinois-Kentucky border	37.0	88.8	....	V

See footnotes at end of table.

List of Earthquakes in Central Region—Continued

Year	Date	Time (CST)	Locality	N. lat.	W. long.	Area	Intensity
				degrees	*degrees*	*sq. mi.*	
1964	Mar. 24	00:12	Hot Springs, S.Dak	43.5	103.5	(2)	V
	Mar. 27	About 21:00	Near Van Tassell, Wyo	42.7	104.1	....	V
	Mar. 28	04:09*	Nebraska	42.9	101.6	90,000	VII
	Apr. 28	15:19*	Texas-Louisiana border	31.7	93.6	....	V
	Aug. 16	05:36	Hemphill, Tex., area	31.4	93.8	....	V
1965	Aug. 14	07:14*	Southwestern Illinois	37.1	89.2	....	VII
	Aug. 15	00:07* 22:19*	do	37.4	89.5	....	V
	Oct. 20	20:05*	Eastern Missouri	37.8	91.1	160,000	VI
1966	June 26	06:00*	South Dakota	44.3	103.4	....	VI
	July 20	03:05*	Texas Panhandle region	35.7	101.2	....	V
	Aug. 14	09:26*	Western Texas	32.0	102.6	....	VI
1967	Apr. 7	23:41*	Ohio	39.6	82.5	4,000	V
	June 4	10:14*	Near Greenville, Miss	33.6	90.9	25,000	VI
	June 29	07:57*	do	33.6	90.9	....	V
	July 21	03:15*	Missouri	37.5	90.4	....	VI
	Nov. 23	00:24*	South Dakota	43.7	99.4	....	V
1968	Oct. 14	08:43*	Durant, Okla	34.0	96.8	(3)	VI
	Nov. 9	11:02*	South-central Illinois	38.0	88.5	580,000	VII
1969	Jan. 1	17:36*	Central Arkansas	34.8	92.6	23,000	VI
	May 2	05:33*	Eastern Oklahoma	35.2	96.3	13,000	V
1970	Nov. 16	20:14*	Northeastern Arkansas	35.9	89.9	30,000	VI

*Instrumental origin time and epicenter.

[2] Widespread.
[3] Local.
[4] Intensity at epicenter.

Western Mountain Region

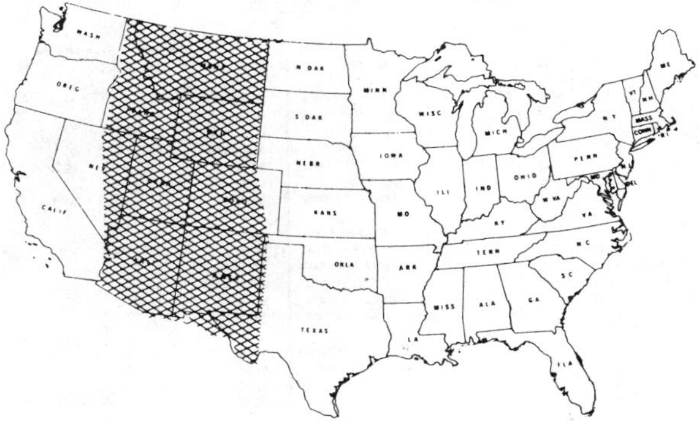

Résumé

Less is known about the earthquake history of this part of the United States than of any other section. The list begins with 1852, a very recent date compared to other regions, and for some time even after that date accounts are very inadequate. There has been much activity in this region, but many of the earthquakes have occurred in sparsely populated regions. Montana, Utah, and Nevada have been subject to earthquakes of considerable severity, and there is a region in Mexico, just south of the border, which has had one major earthquake and many minor ones. Less damage in loss of lives and property is likely in much of this region because of the wide separation of towns. However, a danger of considerable importance was shown in the Montana earthquake of 1959, when a great avalanche claimed 28 lives, formed a barrier which blocked the Madison River, and created a lake.

List of Earthquakes in Western Mountain Region

Year	Date	Time (MST)	Locality	N. lat.	W. long.	Area	Intensity
				degrees	*degrees*	*sq. mi.*	
1852	Nov. 9	....	Near Fort Yuma, Ariz	33	114½	....	VIII–IX
1853	December	....	Fort Yuma, Ariz	....	....	....	....

See footnotes at end of table.

List of Earthquakes in Western Mountain Region—Continued

Year	Date	Time (MST)	Locality	N. lat.	W. long.	Area	Intensity
				degrees	*degrees*	*sq. mi.*	
1853	Dec. 1	11:15	Nephi, Utah	39.7	111.8	...	V
1868	Apr. 28	...	Socorro, N. Mex	34.0	107.0	...	V
1869	Unknown	...	do	34.0	107.0	...	VII
	May 22	a.m.	Helena, Mont	46.6	112.0	...	VI
1872	Dec. 10	16:30	Western Montana	46.4	112.5	...	VI
	Dec. 11	06:55	do	46.4	112.5	...	...
1873	July 30	20:15	Beaver, Utah	38.3	112.7	1,000	VI
1879	Unknown	...	Socorro, N. Mex	34.0	107.0	...	V
1880	July 11	22:00	Portage, Utah	42.0	112.3	(a)	VI
	Sept. 16	22:27	Salt Lake City, Utah	40.8	112.0	3,000	V
1881	Mar. 25	19:15	Hebron, Utah	...	...	2,000	V
1882	Nov. 7	18:30	Colorado	40	105	11,000	V
1884	Nov. 9	02:00	Utah	41.5	111.2	6,000	VI
1886	July 6	...	Socorro, N. Mex	34.0	107.0	...	V
1887	May 3	14:13	Sonora, Mexico	31	109	...	VIII–IX
	Dec. 5	08:30	Kanab, Utah	37.1	112.5	(a)	VI
1891	Apr. 20	06:55	Washington County, Utah	...	...	1,000	VI
	Sept. 12	20:48	Cedar City, Utah	37.7	113.0	...	...
1893	July 12	06:00–07:00	Albuquerque, N. Mex	35.0	106.4	...	V
	Sept. 7	...	New Mexico	34.7	106.6	...	VII
1894	June 8	11:00	Fish Springs, Utah	...	...	(a)	V
	June 25	...	Casper, Wyo	42.9	106.3	...	V
	July 18	15:50	Ogden, Utah	41.2	112.0	(a)	VI–VII
1895	Mar. 22	...	Colorado	...	...	1,500	V
	Oct. 7	...	New Mexico	34.5	106.7	...	V
	Oct. 31	05:00	Socorro, N.Mex	34.0	107.0	...	VI
1897	Nov. 4	02:29	Montana	45	113	...	VI
	Unknown	...	Socorro, N.Mex	34.0	107.0	...	VI
	Nov. 14	...	Casper, Wyo	42.9	106.3	...	VI–VII
1899	Dec. 13	06:50	Utah	41	112	5,000	V
1900	Aug. 1	12:45	do	39.8	112.2	600	VI–VII
1901	July 26	14:40	Nevada	40.8	115.7	3,500	VII
	Nov. 13	21:30	Southern Utah	38.7	112.1	50,000	VIII
	Nov. 15	a.m.	Colorado	38.8	106.2	(a)	VI–VII
1902	Nov. 17	12:53	Pine Valley, Utah	37.4	113.5	10,000	VII
	Dec. 5	...	Southeastern Utah	...	...	...	...
1904	Jan. 19 to Sept. 10.	...	Socorro, N.Mex	34.0	107.0	...	V–VI
	Aug. 3	20:00	Montana	45.5	111.8	(a)	V
1905	Nov. 11	14:26	Shoshone, Idaho	42.9	114.5	...	VII
1906	Jan. 25	13:33	Flagstaff, Ariz	35.2	111.7	15,000	VII
	May 24	14:10	West Weber, Utah	41.2	112.0	(a)	V
	July 12	05:15	Socorro, N.Mex	34.0	107.0	40,000	VII–VIII
	July 16	12:00	do	34.0	107.0	100,000	VIII
	Oct. 18	19:06	Idaho	42.5	111.4	3,000	V
1906	Nov. 15	05:15	Socorro, N.Mex	34.0	107.0	100,000	VII–VIII
1908	Dec. 20 to 29	16:30	Virginia City, Mont	45.3	111.9	(a)	VI
1909	Oct. 5 to Dec.	...	Utah	42	113	(a)	VII
1910	Jan. 10 to 12	...	Richfield, Utah	38.7	112.1	(a)	VI
	May 22	07:28	Salt Lake City, Utah	40.8	111.9	3,500	VII
	July 25	18:30	Rock Springs, Wyo	41.5	109.3	(a)	V
	Sept. 23	21:05	Northeastern Arizona	36.0	111.1	45,000	VI
1912	Aug. 18	14:12	Northeast of Williams, Ariz	36.5	111.5	55,000	VI–VII
1913	Apr. 12	01:25	Southeastern Idaho	42	112	8,000	V
	July 18	...	Socorro, N.Mex	34.0	107.0	...	...
	Nov. 11	14:55 } 15:18 } 16:45 }	Southwestern Colorado	38.2	107.7	7,500	V
	Dec. 5	17:15	Arizona and New Mexico	34.1	106.8	(a)	...
1914	Apr. 8	09:06	Utah	...	...	1,000	V
	May 13	10:15	do	42	112	8,000	VII
	Dec. 20	22:25	Enterprise, Utah, and vicinity	37.6	113.8	...	V
1915	May 8	09:10	Wyoming	44.9	110.7	10,000	V
	July 15	15:00	Utah	40.3	111.7	5,000	VI
	July 30	11:50	Northern Utah	41.8	112.2	(a)	V
	Aug. 11	03:20	do	40.5	112.7	(a)	V
	Oct. 5	01:00	Near Utah-Nevada border	40.1	114.0	...	V
	Nov. 17	15:35	Elko, Nev	40.9	115.8	...	V
1916	Feb. 4	23:25	Utah	40.0	111.7	(a)	V
	May 12	19:30	Boise, Idaho	43.7	116.2	50,000	VII
	May 25	23:36	Idaho City, Idaho	43.8	116.0	10,000	V
	Aug. 3	06:21	Nevada	41.0	117.5	(a)	IV–V
	Sept. 9	19:57	Hailey Center, Idaho	43.5	114.3	(a)	V
	Dec. 12	04:45	Eastern Arizona	34	110	70,000	V
1917	Apr. 19	21:30	Pierson, Idaho	44.0	114.8	(a)	V
	Dec. 12	05:00	Southern Idaho	43.0	111.3	8,000	V
1918	Mar. 11	20:26	Near Rathdrum, Idaho	47.6	117.0	6,000	V
	May 28	04:30	Santa Fe County, N.Mex	35.5	106.6	7,500	VII–VIII
1919	Jan. 31	21:30	Socorro, N.Mex	34.0	107.0	(a)	IV–V
	Feb. 1	13:30	do	34.0	107.0	(a)	V
1920	Sept. 18	14:05	Northern Utah	41.5	112.0	2,000	V–VI
	Sept. 19	06:50	do	41.5	112.0	(a)	...
	Nov. 19	22:40	do	41.5	112.0	(a)	...
	Nov. 25	17:00	St. George, Utah	37.1	113.5	(a)	V
1921	Sept. 29	07:12	Elsinore, Utah	38.8	112.2	(a)	VIII
	Sept. 29	19:30	do	38.8	112.2	...	VII

See footnotes at end of table.

List of Earthquakes in Western Mountain Region—Continued

Year	Date	Time (MST)	Locality	N. lat.	W. long.	Area	Intensity
				degrees	*degrees*	*sq. mi.*	
1921	Oct. 1	08:32	Elsinore, Utah	38.8	112.2	....	VIII
	Oct. 27	07:15	do	38.8	112.2	....	....
	Nov. 1	08:35	do	38.8	112.2	....	....
1923	Mar. 23 to Apr. 12.	21:00	Kelly, Wyo	43.6	110.6	1,500	V
1924	Aug. 12	21:23	New Mexico	36.0	104.5	....	V
	Nov. 25	07:10	Southeastern Idaho	42.5	111.5	20,000	V
1925	June 27	18:21*	East of Helena, Mont	46.0	111.2	310,000	VIII
	July 10	07:45	do	46.0	111.2	....	VI
	Aug. 10	09:30	Sweet Grass, Mont	49.3	112.5	25,000	V
	Nov. 17	18:50	Wyoming	44.6	107.0	3,000	V
1926	May 31	05:25	Three Forks, Mont	46.0	111.4	1,000	V
	Nov. 27	18:25	Idaho	47.5	116.0	2,000	V
	Dec. 12	17:44	South-central Montana	46.1	111.2	30,000	V
1928	Feb. 13	07:00	Central Wyoming	43.5	108.2	3,000	V
	Apr. 20 to May 10.	Various	Creede, Colo	37.8	107.0	(*)	IV–V
	Oct. 31	21:16	Mexico, felt in Texas	26	106	....	V*
1929	Feb. 15	20:00	Montana	46.1	111.3	40,000	V
1930	Mar. 16	06:00?	Helena, Mont	46.6	112.0	(*)	VI
	June 12	02:15	Grover, Wyo	42.6	111.0	(*)	VI
	July 9	18:00	Western Montana	47	115	*large	V
	Aug. 24 to Dec. 22.	Various	Yellowstone National Park, Wyo	44	111	....	IV–V
	Dec. 3	14:36	Albuquerque, N.Mex	35.0	106.4	(*)	V–VI
1931	Feb. 4	21:48	do	35.0	106.4	(*)	VI
	Apr. 17	05:38	Eastern Arizona	34.0	110.5	3,500	V
	July 28	01:40*	Cottonwood, Ariz	35.0	112.0	1,500	V
	Aug. 16	05:40*	Western Texas	30.9	104.2	450,000	VIII
	Aug. 18	13:36	do	30.6	104.1	(*)	V
1932	Jan. 26	03:13	Western Wyoming	43.6	110.8	1,000	V–VI
1933	Jan. 20	06:05	Parowan, Utah	38	113	1,000	VI
	June 10	22:59	Helena, Mont	46.6	112.0	(*)	V
	Aug. 19	03:13	Logan, Mont	45.8	111.3	(*)	V
	Nov. 2	09:26	Gray, Idaho	43.0	111.3	(*)	V
	Nov. 29	10:00	Virginia City, Mont	45.3	111.9	200	IV–V
1934	Jan. 7	18:32	Socorro, N.Mex	34.0	107.0	(*)	V
	Mar. 12	08:06* / 11:20*	Kosmo, Utah	41.7	112.8	170,000	VIII
	May 6	01:10*	Northern Utah	42	113	17,500	VI
	May 6	22:22	Silver City, N.Mex	32.7	108.2	200	V
	Nov. 23	16:40	Lander, Wyo	43	109	8,000	V
1935	Jan. 2	00:30?	Wellton, Ariz	32.8	114.2	(*)	VI
	Jan. 10	01:10	Grand Canyon, Ariz	36.1	112.2	(*)	VI
	Feb. 20	18:25	Bernardo, N.Mex	34.5	106.8	(*)	VI
	Mar. 29	00:39	Rollins, Mont	47.8	114.2	(*)	V
	Oct. 3	19:47	Helena, Mont	46.6	112.0	(*)	V
	Oct. 7	12:30	Craig, Mont	47.0	111.9	(a)	VI

See footnotes at end of table.

List of Earthquakes in Western Mountain Region—Continued

Year	Date	Time (MST)	Locality	N. lat.	W. long.	Area	Intensity
				degrees	*degrees*	*sq. mi.*	
1935	Oct. 12	00:51*	Helena, Mont	46.6	112.0	70,000	VII
	Oct. 18	21:48*	do	46.6	112.0	230,000	VIII
	Oct. 27	12:00	do	46.6	112.0	(*)	VI
	Oct. 31	11:38*	do	46.6	112.0	140,000	VIII
	Nov. 21	20:58	do	46.6	112.0	13,000	VI
	Nov. 28	07:42	do	46.6	112.0	90,000	VI
	Dec. 17 to 30	22:33*	Belen, N.Mex	34.7	106.8	2,000	V–VI
1936	Jan. 11	11:02	Great Falls, Mont	47.0	111.3	750	V
	Jan. 14	21:40	Yellowstone National Park, Wyo	44	111	1,200	VI
	Feb. 13	16:55 / 17:30	Helena, Mont	46.6	112.0	....	VI
	Mar.	Various	Marysville, Mont	46.8	112.3	....	V
	May 9	03:25	Zion National Park, Utah	37.5	113.0	1,500	V–VI
	June 11	16:13	Helena, Mont	46.6	112.0	(*)	V–VI
	June 22	20:30	Marysville, Mont	46.8	112.3	(*)	V
	Sept. 19	21:13	Hoover Dam, Nev	36	115	(*)	V
1937	Feb. 17	21:15	Southern Utah	38.0	112.5	2,000	V
	Apr. 24	20:28*	West-central Nevada	39	117	20,000	V
	Apr. 27	21:15	Hoover Dam, Nev	36	115	(*)	V
	June 18	10:18	do	36	115	(*)	V
	Nov. 11	17:39	do	36	115	(*)	V–VI
	Dec. 18	04:00	Cascade, Idaho	44.5	116.0	1,200	V
1938	Sept. 17	10:20	Arizona-New Mexico border	33.2	108.6	8,000	VI
	Sept. 19	22:40	do	....	....	(*)	V–VI
	Sept. 29	16:34	do	....	....	(*)	V–VI
	Nov. 1	01:26*	do	33.0	108.7	(*)	V–VI
1939	May 4	13:44*	Near Las Vegas, Nev	36.0	114.8	7,000	VI
	May 11	16:40	Trident, Mont	....	....	(*)	V–VI
1940	Dec. 23	14:50*	Helena, Mont	46.5	112.5	7,000	VI
1942	June 4	08:26	Boulder City, Nev	36.0	114.9	(*)	V
	June 4	16:04	Northern Sanpete County, Utah	....	....	(*)	V
	Aug. 5	14:34	Yellowstone National Park, Wyo	44	111	(*)	V
	Aug. 30	16:08	Cedar City, Utah	37.7	113.0	(*)	VI
	Sept. 8	22:15	Boulder City, Nev	36.0	114.9	(*)	V
	Nov. 1	11:50*	Sandpoint, Idaho	48.0	116.7	25,000	VI
1943	Feb. 22	07:20*	Near Salt Lake City, Utah	41.0	111.5	(*)	VI
	June 24	21:25*	Southern Sheridan County, Mont	48.5	105.0	(*)	VI
1944	July 12	12:30*	Seafoam, Idaho	44.7	115.2	70,000	VII
	Sept. 8	21:12*	Western Colorado	39.0	107.5	3,000	VI
1945	Feb. 13	20:01*	Near Clayton, Idaho	44.7	115.4	60,000	VI
	June 1	09:55*	Helena, Mont	46.6	112.0	6,000	V
	Sept. 23	02:59*	Western Montana	48.0	114.2	36,000	VI
1946	May 5	21:30	Northern Utah	41.8	112.0	....	V
	Dec. 11	08:09	Northwestern Montana	48.4	114.4	3,000	VI
1947	Mar. 14	11:00	Seeley Lake, Mont	47.2	113.5	....	VI
	Nov. 6	09:50	San Antonito, N.Mex	35.0	106.4	....	VI
	Nov. 23	02:46*	Southwestern Montana	44.8	112.0	150,000	VIII
	Dec. 17	05:38*	Western Montana	46.5	112.0	....	V
1948	Feb. 23	19:39*	Northwestern Wyoming	43.5	111.0	1,500	VI
	Mar. 11	21:29*	Northwestern Texas	36	102½	50,000	VI

See footnotes at end of table.

List of Earthquakes in Western Mountain Region—Continued

Year	Date	Time (MST)	Locality	N. lat.	W. long.	Area	Intensity
				degrees	*degrees*	*sq. mi.*	
1948	May 15	23:45	Western Montana	46.0	111.5	....	V
	Nov. 2	09:48*	Hoover Dam area, Nev	35.9	114.8	....	VI
1949	Mar. 6	23:50	Salt Lake City, Utah	40.8	111.9	....	V–VI
	Mar. 7	00:09	do	40.8	111.9	....	V–VI
	May 23	00:22	East Vaughn, N.Mex	34.6	105.2	....	VI
	Nov. 1	19:30	Southwestern Utah	37.2	113.3	700	VI
1950	Jan. 16	17:53	Apache County, Ariz	35.5	109.5	....	VI
	Jan. 17	18:56*	Near Soldier Summit, Utah	40½	110½	....	V
	May 8	15:35	Payson, Utah	40.0	111.4	(*)	V
	June 27	21:31*	West Yellowstone, Mont	44¾	110½	....	VI
	Aug. 19	18:45*	Western Montana	47¼	113½	4,000	VI
	Oct. 18	02:30 07:00 10:30 15:30	Cascade, Idaho	44.5	116.0	(*)	V
1951	June 20	12:37*	Northern Texas	35½	103	....	VI
	Aug. 5	17:37	Butte, Mont	46.0	112.5	(*)	V
	Dec. 9	00:08	Helena, Mont	46.6	112.0	....	V
1952	Feb. 8	01:59	Boulder City, Nev., area	36.0	114.9	....	V
	Feb. 20	06:41	do	36.0	114.9	....	VI
	Mar. 31	17:38*	Northwestern Montana	48.0	113.8	35,000	VII
	Apr. 14	13:37	Moiese and St. Ignatius, Mont	47.2	114.1	....	V
	Apr. 22	09:55*	Western Montana	46.2	111.4	1,500	VI
	May 23	21:15*	Arizona-Nevada border	36.1	114.7	1,000	V
	May 29	20:15	Western Montana	46.2	111.4	....	V
	Aug. 3	20:42*	Cimarron, N.Mex	36.5	105.0	....	V
	Aug. 17	03:45	Los Alamos, N.Mex	35.5	106.2	....	V
	Sept. 28	13:00 13:30	Lehi, Utah	40.2	111.5	....	V
	Oct. 7	02:20	Colorado-New Mexico border region.	37.0	106.0	....	V
1953	May 23	19:54*	North-central Utah	40½	111½	....	VI
	Aug. 8	09:50	Flathead Lake, Mont	48	114	....	VI
	Oct. 21	20:00	Panguitch, Utah	37.5	112.3	....	V
	Nov. 23	06:30	Helmville, Mont	46.5	112.6	(*)	V
1954	Jan. 20	13:50*	Southeastern Wyoming	41½	105½	2,000	V
	June 7	17:16*	Northern Idaho	47.5	116.0	....	V
	July 4	09:33*	Yellowstone National Park, Wyo	44.9	110.8	....	V
	Nov. 3	13:39	Albuquerque, N.Mex	35.1	106.7	....	V
1955	Jan. 10	03:07*	Southeastern Nevada	37.0	114½	....	V
	Feb. 2	12:23	Salt Lake City, Utah	40.8	111.9	....	V
	Feb. 10	10:30*	Northwestern Colorado	40.5	107.0	....	V
	May 12	15:57	Davis and Salt Lake Counties, Utah	41	112	....	V
	May 31	21:56	Southwestern Montana	45.8	111.5	....	V
	Aug. 2	23:40	Southwestern Colorado	38	107	2,000	VI
	Aug. 12	09:20	Santa Fe, N.Mex	35.7	106.1	....	V
1956	Aug. 6	21:06*	Western Idaho	44.5	115.0	1,200	V
	Dec. 25	06:58	Helena, Mont	46.6	112.0	....	V
1957	May 17	10:41	Southwestern Montana	....	....	....	V
	Dec. 18	23:25	Wallace, Idaho	47.5	116.0	....	VI
1958	Feb. 13	15:52*	North-central Utah	40½	111½	1,200	VI

See footnotes at end of table.

List of Earthquakes in Western Mountain Region—Continued

Year	Date	Time (MST)	Locality	N. lat.	W. long.	Area	Intensity
				degrees	*degrees*	*sq. mi.*	
1958	Apr. 19	02:01	Boulder City, Nev	36.0	114.9	(*)	VI
	Apr. 28	13:59	Yellowstone National Park, Wyo	44	111	(2)	V
	May 28	09:46*	Georgetown Lake area and Philipsburg, Mont.	46½	113	4,500	VI
	Nov. 28	06:31	Nephi, Utah	39.7	111.8	(2)	V
	Dec. 1	13:51*	Northern Utah	40½	112½	200	V
	Dec. 1	20:23*	do	40½	112½	(2)	V
1959	Jan. 4	00:23	Southeastern Idaho	....	....	500	V
	Feb. 11	07:01	Flagstaff, Ariz	35.2	111.7	(2)	V
	Feb. 27	15:20*	Southwestern Utah	38	112½	1,500	VI
	May 17	03:57*	Northwestern Montana	47½	113	3,000	V
	July 21	10:39*	Arizona-Utah border	37	112½	8,000	VI
	Aug. 17	23:37*	Hebgen Lake, Mont	44.8	111.1	600,000	X
	Aug. 18	01:42*	Yellowstone National Park, Wyo	44.8	110.7	....	VI
	Aug. 18	21:04*	Southwestern Montana	44.9	111.6	....	V
	Aug. 20	12:11*	Hebgen Lake, Mont., area	45	111	....	V
	Aug. 23	01:40	do	45	111	....	VI
	Aug. 30	00:50	West Yellowstone, Mont	44.7	111.1	....	V
	Sept. 4	12:18	Whitehall, Mont	45.9	112.1	....	V
	Sept. 5	05:10	Yellowstone National Park, Wyo	44¾	111	(2)	VI
	Sept. 25	05:40	do	44¾	111	(2)	V
	Sept. 26	02:04	do	44¾	111	(2)	V
	Sept. 28	01:06*	Gallatin Gateway, Mont	45	111	(2)	V
	Sept. 29	18:36*	Yellowstone National Park, Wyo	45	111	(2)	VI
	Oct. 13	01:15*	Flagstaff, Ariz	35½	111½	(2)	V
	Oct. 18	05:09	West Yellowstone, Mont	44.7	111.1	....	V
	Oct. 19	02:00 06:50	do	44.7	111.1	(2)	V
	Nov. 1	16:03*	Yellowstone National Park, Wyo	45	111	(2)	V
	Nov. 3	10:03	Duck Creek, Mont	....	....	....	VI
	Nov. 4	21:42	Yellowstone National Park, Wyo	44¾	111	(2)	V
	Dec. 8	00:14	Ennis, Mont	45.4	111.7	....	V
	Dec. 11	23:23	West Yellowstone, Mont	44.7	111.1	....	V
	Dec. 12	10:47	do	44.7	111.1	....	V
	Dec. 13	00:50*	do	45	110½	....	V
	Dec. 13	00:57	Yellowstone National Park, Wyo	44¾	111	(2)	V
	Dec. 25	09:50	Foxpark, Wyo	41.1	106.2	(2)	V
1960	Jan. 4	21:04*	Hebgen Lake, Mont	44½	111½	(2)	V
	Feb. 3	11:30	Ennis, Mont	45.4	111.7	(2)	V
	Mar. 22	20:15*	Hebgen Lake, Mont	44½	111	....	V
	Apr. 21	10:49*	do	45	111	....	V
	Apr. 26	21:32*	do	44½	111	....	V
	July 22	08:49*	Lajoya, N.Mex	34	106½	....	V
	July 23	07:15*	do	34	106½	3,000	VI
	July 24	03:37	Near Bernardo, N.Mex	34.5	106.8	(2)	V
	Aug. 7	09:27*	Southeastern Idaho	42.4	111.5	900	VI
	Aug. 10	00:42*	do	42.5	111.5	....	V
	Aug. 20	01:02*	do	42.3	111.3	....	V
	Oct. 11	01:06*	Southwestern Colorado	38.3	107.6	10,000	VI
	Oct. 17	09:00	Aspen, Colo	39.2	106.9	(2)	V

See footnotes at end of table.

List of Earthquakes in Western Mountain Region—Continued

Year	Date	Time (MST)	Locality	N. lat.	W. long.	Area	Intensity
				degrees	*degrees*	*sq. mi.*	
1961	Mar. 13	12:28	Hebgen Dam, Mont	44.9	111.4	(a)	V
	Apr. 6	22:51*	Southern Madison County, Mont	44.8	112.0	2,500	V
	Apr. 15	22:03*	Central Utah	39.3	111.5	2,000	VI
	May 6	09:12*	East-central Utah	39.6	110.2	....	V
	June 26	06:05	Papoose Creek at Madison River, Mont.	......	......	(a)	V
	June 29	04:45	Yellowstone National Park, Wyo	44¾	111	(a)	V
	July 3	00:06*	Central New Mexico	33.6	106.9	(a)	VI
	Dec. 3	18:41 20:25	Virginia City, Mont	45.3	111.9	(a)	V
1962	Feb. 5	07:46*	Southwestern Colorado	38.2	107.6	....	V
	Feb. 15	00:13*	Arizona-Utah border	36.9	112.4	....	V
	Feb. 25	10:18*	Western Montana	45.2	111.2	....	V
	June 18	21:55	Dupont, Colo	......	......	(a)	V
	Aug. 6	About 17:50	Dupont, Colo., area	......	......	....	V
	Aug. 26	05:15 06:22	Yellowstone National Park, Wyo	......	......	(a)	V
	Aug. 30	06:35*	Northern Utah	41.8	111.8	65,000	VII
	Sept. 4	About 20:00	Logan, Utah	41.7	111.8	(a)	V
	Sept. 5	09:04*	Near Salt Lake City, Utah	40.7	112.0	9,000	VI
	Sept. 7	a.m.	Lewiston, Utah	42	111.8	(a)	V
	Dec. 4	10:50*	Northeast of Denver, Colo	39.8	104.7	....	VI
	Dec. 5	06:48*	North-central Colorado	39.9	104.6	6,000	VI
	Dec. 18	06:49 06:50 06:52	Northwestern Montana	......	......	....	V
	Dec. 28	03:01*	do	48.4	113.9	....	V
1963	Jan. 27	08:25*	Central Idaho	44.4	114.6	6,000	VI
	Jan. 29	22:51*	Yellowstone National Park, Wyo	45.0	110.8	(a)	V
	Feb. 1	09:39*	Central Idaho	44.3	114.5	....	V
	Feb. 15	20:02*	Southwestern Montana	46.1	111.0	6,000	V
	Feb. 25	11:45*	Western Wyoming	42.6	109.2	....	V
	Mar. 8	01:36*	Yellowstone National Park, Wyo	44.8	110.2	(a)	VI
	Mar. 21	21:35*	do	44.8	110.5	(a)	V
	Mar. 25	02:29*	Near Boulder City, Nev	36.0	114.9	9,000	VI
	Apr. 18	03:43*	Yellowstone National Park, Wyo	44.8	110.3	(a)	V
	Apr. 23	01:13	Hoover Dam, Nev	36	115	(a)	V
	May 11	16:07	Papoose Creek at Madison River, Mont.	......	......	(a)	V
	May 25	03:45*	Northeastern Colorado	39.8	104.7	900	V
	June 6	12:48	Gibbon Meadow area, Wyo	......	......	(a)	V
	July 2	01:03*	Northern Colorado	39.8	104.6	3,000	V
	July 7	12:21*	Central Utah	39.6	111.9	1,600	VI
	Sept. 9	03:45*	Central Idaho	44.4	114.7	....	V
	Sept. 10	19:09*	do	44.4	114.7	3,500	VI
	Sept. 11	05:00*	Southeastern Arizona	33.2	110.7	2,500	V
	Sept. 14	08:58*	Central Idaho	44.3	114.8	....	V
	Sept. 16	05:06*	do	44.3	114.7	....	V

See footnotes at end of table.

List of Earthquakes in Western Mountain Region—Continued

Year	Date	Time (MST)	Locality	N. lat.	W. long.	Area	Intensity
				degrees	*degrees*	*sq. mi.*	
1963	Sept. 23	23:36*	Yellowstone National Park, Wyo	44.9	111.0	(a)	V
	Dec. 17	02:30*	do	44.9	111.0	(a)	V
	Dec. 20	06:01*	Hebgen Lake, Mont., area	44.9	111.7	3,000	V
1964	Feb. 20	13:20*	Eastern Nevada	39.4	114.2	....	V
	Mar. 20	05:20	Polson, Mont., area	47.7	114.2	(a)	V
	Mar. 27	19:36	Near Ennis, Mont	45.4	111.7	(a)	V
	Mar. 28	03:10	Swan Lake, Mont	47.9	113.8	(a)	VI
	Aug. 21	20:28*	Eastern Wyoming	42.9	104.7	1,500	V
	Sept. 23	10:10*	Near Boulder City, Nev	35.9	114.8	3,000	V
	Oct. 8	19:26*	Flathead Lake, Mont	47.8	114.2	....	V
	Oct. 21	00:39*	Hebgen Lake, Mont	44.8	111.6	25,000	V
1965	Jan. 5	19:01*	Southwestern Montana	44.9	112.7	12,000	VI
	Jan. 6	03:26	Polson, Mont	47.7	114.2	650	V
	Jan. 12	20:44*	Eastern Idaho	44.9	112.7	(a)	V
	Feb. 16	15:22*	Denver, Colo., area	39.9	105.0	300	VI
	Apr. 6	07:46*	Virginia City, Mont	45.6	111.9	(a)	V
	Apr. 27	06:50	Northwestern Montana	......	......	450	V
	Apr. 28	19:00	Nordman, Idaho	48.6	116.9	(a)	V
	July 18	14:41*	Denver, Colo., area	39.8	104.8	....	V
	July 31	06:42*	do	39.7	104.9	....	V
	Sept. 13	02:58*	do	39.8	104.8	....	V
	Sept. 14	15:46*	do	39.9	104.6	....	VI
	Sept. 29	12:00*	do	39.8	105.1	....	VI
	Oct. 8	12:35*	Hebgen Lake, Mont	44.8	111.1	....	V
	Oct. 26	04:28*	Western Montana	47.4	113.2	....	V
	Nov. 20	21:02*	Denver, Colo., area	39.8	104.8	3,000	VI
1966	Jan. 4	17:37*	do	39.8	104.7	....	V
	Jan. 22	18:57*	New Mexico-Colorado border region.	37.0	107.0	15,000	VII
	Jan. 23	16:48*	Lumberton, N.Mex., area	36.9	107.0	....	V
	Mar. 7	11:10*	West-central Montana	46.3	111.5	12,500	V
	Mar. 17	04:48*	Northeastern Utah	41.7	111.5	6,000	V
	Apr. 29	23:28*	Flathead Lake, Mont	48.0	113.8	500	V
	Aug. 16	11:03*	Southern Nevada	37.4	114.2	20,000	VI
	Sept. 19	03:07*	Southwestern Montana	45.9	111.2	....	V
	Sept. 22	11:58*	Southern Nevada	37.4	114.2	....	V
	Oct. 2	19:26*	Southeastern Colorado	37.4	104.1	15,000	VI
	Oct. 11	00:30*	Hebgen Lake, Mont	44.9	111.1	....	V
	Oct. 11	04:48	West Yellowstone, Mont	44.7	111.1	(a)	V
	Oct. 11	10:53*	Hebgen Lake, Mont	44.8	111.2	(a)	V
	Nov. 14	13:03*	Denver, Colo., area	39.9	104.7	....	VI
1967	Jan. 10	04:53*	Hebgen Lake, Mont	45.0	111.5	(a)	V
	Feb. 2	22:28*	Commerce City, Colo., area	39.7	104.8	....	V
	Feb. 14	20:28*	Rangely, Colo	40.1	109.0	(a)	V
	Apr. 10	12:00*	Commerce City-Denver, Colo., area	39.9	104.8	6,500	VI
	Apr. 27	10:25*	Denver, Colo., area	39.9	104.7	....	VI
	Aug. 9	06:25*	Denver, Colo., region	39.9	104.7	15,000	VII
	Sept. 23	21:47*	Salt Lake City, Utah, area	40.7	112.1	....	V
	Oct. 4	03:20*	Marysvale, Utah, area	38.5	112.1	15,000	VII
	Nov. 15	00:10*	Denver, Colo., area	39.9	104.6	....	V
	Nov. 26	22:09*	do	40.0	104.7	17,000	VI

See footnotes at end of table.

List of Earthquakes in Western Mountain Region—Continued

Year	Date	Time (MST)	Locality	N. lat.	W. long.	Area	Intensity
				degrees	*degrees*	*sq. mi.*	
1968	Jan. 16	02:42*	Central Utah	39.3	112.1	....	V
	Jan. 30	08:20*	North-central Nevada	41.0	117.4	3,500	V
	Feb. 21	01:16*	Central Nevada	38.6	116.3	....	V
	Mar. 26	11:22*	Northwestern Montana	47.7	114.4	....	V
	July 6	07:03*	North-central Nevada	41.0	117.4	9,500	V
	July 15	11:33*	North-central Colorado	39.9	104.8	....	V
1969	Jan. 29	22:18*	New Mexico	34.3	106.9	....	V
	Apr. 1	09:45*	Northwestern Montana	47.9	114.3	10,000	VII
	Apr. 26	03:42*	Western Idaho	44.2	114.5	9,000	VI
	Apr. 30	20:10*	Northwestern Montana	46.7	112.8	3,000	V
	May 5	00:09*	Western Idaho	44.1	114.5	....	V
	May 6	06:40	Proctor, Mont	47.9	114.5	(2)	V
	May 12	02:26* / 02:49*	Texas-Mexico border region	31.8	106.4	....	VI
	May 23	02:01	Commerce City, Colo	39.9	105.1	....	V
	June 9	01:54*	Northwestern Montana	47.9	114.3	3,500	V
	June 21	04:07*	Proctor, Mont	47.9	114.5	(2)	V
	Sept. 14	17:03*	Northwestern Montana	47.9	114.2	2,000	VI
	Oct. 7	08:11	Proctor, Mont	47.9	114.5	(2)	V
	Oct. 13	22:16*	Flathead Lake, Mont., area	47.8	114.2	(2)	V
	Nov. 6	17:11*	do	47.9	114.2	....	VI
1970	Jan. 12	04:21*	Amistad, N.Mex	36.1	103.2	3,700	VI
	Feb. 4	16:40*	Proctor, Mont	47.9	114.2	....	V
	Mar. 29	05:41*	Grouse Creek, Utah	41.6	113.7	....	V
	Apr. 21	01:54*	Rangely, Colo	40.1	108.9	....	V
	May 23	01:55*	Commerce City, Colo	39.9	105.1	....	V
	May 23	08:08*	Proctor, Mont	47.8	114.2	(3)	V
	June 25	18:27*	Southwestern Montana	45.6	111.8	....	V
	Sept. 1	05:34*	Proctor, Mont	47.9	114.4	....	V
	Oct. 18	13:07*	Western Montana	46.2	111.5	3,500	V
	Nov. 28	00:40*	Albuquerque, N.Mex	35.0	106.7	1,200	VI

*Instrumental origin time and epicenter.

[2] Local earthquake.
[3] Uncertain.
[4] Intensity in the United States.

Washington and Oregon

Résumé

From 1841 to 1970, many earthquakes of intensity V or greater centered in Washington and Oregon. Others were felt, but centered either offshore in the Pacific, in British Columbia to the north, or in neighboring states. Most of the activity occurred in the western part of the region, while the stronger shocks were in the neighborhood of Puget Sound. Indications are that the heaviest activity occurred in 1946 a few miles west of Tacoma, in 1949 near Olympia, and in 1965 near Seattle. A few of the earlier shocks may have equaled or possibly exceeded the 1946 shocks in intensity, but lack of detailed information prevents satisfactory comparison.

List of Earthquakes in Washington and Oregon

Year	Date	Time (PST)	Locality	N. lat.	W. long.	Area	Intensity
				degrees	*degrees*	*sq. mi.*	
1841	Dec. 2	16:00	Vancouver, Wash	45.6	122.7	(1)	V
1856	Dec. 26	....	Port Townsend, Wash	48	123		....
1859	Apr. 2	02:30	Olympia, Wash	47	123	(1)	V
1860	May 7	....	Port Townsend, Wash	48	123		....
1864	Oct. 29	18:10	Victoria, B.C	48.5	123.5	....	VI [4]
1865	Aug. 25	21:00	Vancouver Island, B.C	48.5	123.5	....	VI [4]

See footnotes at end of table

List of Earthquakes in Washington and Oregon—Continued

Year	Date	Time (PST)	Locality	N. lat.	W. long.	Area	Intensity
				degrees	*degrees*	*sq. mi.*	
1868	May 30	....	Mukilteo, Wash	48	122	....	....
1871	May 19	....	Mt. Rainier, Wash	....	....	....	....
1872	Dec. 14 to 16	Various	Puget Sound, Wash	....	....	150,000	VI
	Dec. 16 to Jan. 4, 1873.	....	Walla Walla, Wash	46.0	118.3	....	....
1877	Oct. 12	13:53	Cascade Mountains, Oreg	....	....	....	VII
1880	Aug. 22	13:25	Northwestern Washington	....	....	....	....
	Dec. 12	20:40	Puget Sound, Wash	....	....	....	VI
1883	Sept. 28	00:00	Portland, Oreg	45.5	122.6	(3)	....
1885	Oct. 9	08:00	Olympia, Wash	47	123	....	V
	Dec. 8	22:40	Puget Sound, Wash	47.5	122.5	(3)	V
1891	Sept. 22	03:40	Port Angeles, Wash	48.0	123.5	(3)	V
	Nov. 29	15:21	Puget Sound region, Wash	....	....	4,000	V–VI
1892	Feb. 3	20:30	Portland, Oreg	45.5	122.8	10,000	VI
	Apr. 17	14:50	Near Olympia, Wash	47	123	....	VI
1893	Mar. 6	17:03	Umatilla, Oreg	46	119	(3)	VI–VII
1895	Feb. 25	04:47	Green River, Wash	46.5	122.4	....	V
	Apr. 16	00:02	Port Townsend, Wash	48	123	(3)	V–VI
1896	Jan. 3	22:15	Victoria, B.C	....	....	....	VI [4]
	Feb. 6	21:55	East Clallam, Wash	48.3	124.3	(3)	VI
	Apr. 2	03:17	McMinnville, Oreg	45.3	123.3	1,000	VI
1897	Dec. 15	....	Lakeside, Wash	47.8	120.0	....	....
1903	Mar. 13	18:15	Sand Point, Wash	47.7	122.2	10,000	V
1904	Mar. 16	20:20	Victoria, B.C	48.5	122.8	20,000	V [4]
1906	Jan. 2	05:45	Northeastern Washington	....	....	7,000	VI
	Apr. 19	01:30	Paisley, Oreg	42.7	120.6	....	V
	Nov. 1	17:49	Colville, Wash	48.5	117.9	....	V
1909	Jan. 11	15:49	Northwestern Washington	49.0	122.7	25,000	VII
	May 24	09:20	Waterville, Wash	47.6	120.0	(3)	....
1911	Sept. 28	18:39	Northwestern Washington	48.8	122.7	....	VI
1913	July 29	08:15	Mt. Rainier, Wash	47	122	1,500	V
	Oct. 14	15:00	Seven Devils District, Oreg	45.7	117.1	....	V
	Dec. 25	06:40	Puget Sound, Wash	47.7	122.5	8,000	V
1914	Sept. 5	01:35	Olympia, Wash	47	123	1,000	V
1915	May 18	19:00	Portland, Oreg	45.5	122.7	(3)	V
	Aug. 18	10:00	Northwestern Washington	48.5	121.4	30,000	V
1916	Jan. 1	16:52	Puget Sound, Wash	47.3	122.3	12,000	V
	Feb. 22	03:45	Marietta, Wash	48.8	122.6	....	V
1917	Nov. 12	02:47	Mt. Rainier, Wash	46.8	121.8	1,000	VI
1918	Feb. 28	15:45	Yakima, Wash	46.5	120.5	(3)	V
	Nov. 1	09:20	Corfu, Wash	46.7	119.5	(3)	V–VI
	Dec. 6	00:41•	Vancouver, B.C	49.7	126.5	....	V [4]
1920	Jan. 23	23:09	Northwestern Washington	49.0	122.7	....	VII
	Apr. 14	15:45	Crater Lake, Oreg	42.9	122.1	....	V
	Nov. 28	03:30	Spokane, Wash., region	....	....	....	....
1921	Feb. 25	12:00	Cascadia, Oreg	44.4	122.4	....	V
1923	Jan. 10	20:30	Oregon	42.0	120.5	....	V
	Feb. 12	10:30	Bellingham, Wash	49.0	122.7	(3)	V

See footnotes at end of table

List of Earthquakes in Washington and Oregon—Continued

Year	Date	Time (PST)	Locality	N. lat.	W. long.	Area	Intensity
				degrees	*degrees*	*sq. mi.*	
1923	Sept. (?)	....	Sultan, Wash	47.8	121.8	(1)	....
1926	Dec. 4	05:55	Victoria, B.C	48.5	123.5	4,000	V [4]
	Dec. 30	09:57	East-central Washington	....	....	15,000	V
1927	Apr. 8	21:00	Eastern Oregon	44.8	117.2	400	V
1928	Feb. 2	04:52	Startup, Wash	47.8	121.7	(3)	VI
	Feb. 9	03:05	Vancouver Island, B.C	48.5	125.0	10,000	V [4]
1930	July 18	18:38	Near Perrydale, Oreg	45.0	123.2	....	V–VI
1931	Apr. 17	20:00	Bellingham, Wash	48.7	122.2	5,000	VI
	Aug. 16	19:20	Talent, Oreg	42.3	122.8	(3)	V
	Dec. 31	07:25	Puget Sound, Wash	47.5	123.0	10,000	VI
1932	Jan. 5	15:13	Near Sultan, Wash	48.0	121.8	1,500	V
	July 17	22:03	do	48.0	121.8	14,000	V
	Aug. 6	14:16	Seattle, Wash	47.7	122.3	500	VI
1934	May 4	20:06	Puget Sound, Wash., region	48	123	10,000	V
	Sept. 18	00:00	Ellensburg, Wash	47	121	(3)	V
	Sept. 26	16:15	do	47	121	(3)	V
	Oct. 19	23:31	do	47	121	(3)	V
	Nov. 1	07:28	do	47	121	(3)	V
	Nov. 2	15:17	do	47	121	(3)	V
	Nov. 3	06:50	Cascade Mountains, Wash	48	121	10,000	IV–V
1935	July 9	14:45	Chelan Falls, Wash	47.7	120.0	(3)	V
1936	July 15	23:08•	Northern Oregon	46.0	118.3	105,000	VII
	July 18	08:30	do	46.0	118.3	(3)	V
	Aug. 4	01:19	do	45.8	118.6	(3)	V
	Aug. 27	20:39	Milton-Freewater, Oreg	....	....	....	V
1938	Jan. 6	05:11	Puget Sound, Wash	47.8	122.4	....	V
1939	Nov. 12	23:46•	Olympia, Wash	47.4	122.6	60,000	VII
1940	Oct. 27	14:30	Puget Sound, Wash	47.2	123.4	12,000	V
1941	Apr. 7	01:25	Mazama, Wash	48.3	119.6	5,500	VI
	Dec. 29	10:37	Portland, Oreg	45.5	122.7	5,000	VI
1942	May 12	16:52	Corvallis, Oreg	44.6	123.4	(1)	V
	June 12	01:30	Halfway, Oreg	44.9	117.1	(1)	V
	Oct. 14	03:30	Stehekin, Wash	48.3	120.6	(1)	V
	Nov. 1	09:00	Portland, Oreg	45.5	122.6	(1)	V
1943	Apr. 23	15:11	Entiat, Wash	47.8	120.6	10,000	V
	Nov. 28	16:43	Puget Sound, Wash	48.4	122.9	9,000	VI
1944	Mar. 31	13:15	Olympia, Wash	47	123	2,500	V
	Oct. 31	03:34	Entiat, Wash	47.8	120.6		V
1945	Apr. 29	12:16•	Southeast of North Bend, Wash	47.4	121.7	50,000	VI–VII
	Apr. 29	23:46	do	47.4	121.7	....	VI
	May 1	11:46	do	47.4	121.7	....	V
1946	Feb. 14	19:18•	Puget Sound, Wash	47.3	122.9	70,000	VII
	June 23	09:13•	Georgia Strait, B.C	49.9	125.3	100,000	VIII [4]
1948	Sept. 24	14:35	Port Gamble, Wash	47.8	122.6	....	V
1949	Apr. 13	11:56•	Olympia, Wash	47.1	122.7	150,000	VIII
	Aug. 21	20:01•	Queen Charlotte Islands region	54	133	2,220,000	....
1950	Apr. 14	03:04•	Near Langley, Wash	48	122½	7,000	VI
	Dec. 2	17:57	Mukilteo, Wash	48.0	122.3		V
1952	Aug. 6	09:31	Seattle, Wash	47.4	122.2	....	V
1953	Dec. 15	20:32	Northwestern Oregon	45.5	122.7	3,000	VI

See footnotes at end of table

List of Earthquakes in Washington and Oregon—Continued

Year	Date	Time (PST)	Locality	N. lat.	W. long.	Area	Intensity
				degrees	*degrees*	*sq. mi.*	
1954	Mar. 16	07:56*	Western Washington	47.1	121.8	3,000	V
	May 4	17:42*	Northwestern Washington	47.3	122.4	1,500	V
	May 15	05:02*	Puget Sound, Wash	47.4	122.3	17,000	VI
	May 23	05:42	Methow Valley, Wash	....	....	....	V
1955	Jan. 11	02:20*	Western Olympic Mountains, Wash	47.8	124.0	....	V
	Mar. 25	22:56*	Near Hartford, Wash	48.0	122.0	8,500	VI
	Sept. 10	08:53*	Neah Bay, Wash	48.4	124.6	....	V
	Nov. 2	17:40*	Near Robe, Wash	48.1	121.7	....	V
1956	Jan. 6	20:30*	Puget Sound, Wash	47.3	122.4	2,500	V
	Feb. 8	16:57*	Northwestern Washington	48.3	122.6	4,000	V
1957	Jan. 25	17:16*	do	48.3	122.4	15,000	VI
	Feb. 11	09:05*	do	47.5	121.1	4,000	VI
	May 4	13:09*	Puget Sound, Wash	47.3	122.4	2,000	V
	Nov. 1	02:12*	Near Mount Rainier, Wash	47	121	1,500	V
	Nov. 16	22:00*	Northwest of Salem, Oreg	45.3	123.8	4,500	VI
1958	Apr. 12	14:37*	North-central Washington	48	120	8,000	VI
	Aug. 22	21:00	Eastsound, Wash	48.7	122.9	....	V
	Oct. 6	21:08*	Willapa Bay, Wash	46.7	124.0	1,800	VI
1959	Jan. 20	About 23:15	Milton-Freewater, Oreg	....	....	....	V
	Aug. 4	15:53*	Southwestern Washington	45.7	122.3	600	V
	Aug. 5	19:45* 20:36*	Near Chelan, Wash	47.8	120.0	25,000	VI
	Oct. 14	13:36*	Near Monroe, Wash	47.8	122.0	2,800	V
	Nov. 23	10:15*	Near Longmire, Wash	46.7	121.7	1,000	V
	Dec. 11	22:24*	Northwestern Washington	48.7	123.3	8,000	V
1960	Jan. 7	01:16*	Southwestern Washington	46.7	122.7	3,500	V
	Apr. 10	22:48*	Western Washington	47.6	122.3	600	VI
	Sept. 10	07:07*	Northwestern Washington	47.7	123.1	14,000	VI
1961	Jan. 3	23:26*	Southwestern Washington	46.0	122.1	2,000	V
	Feb. 1	21:50	Mt. Rainier National Park, Wash	46.7	121.9	....	V
	Aug. 18	20:56*	Northwestern Oregon	44.7	122.5	7,000	VI
	Sept. 15	19:25*	Southwestern Washington	46.0	122.2	7,000	VI
	Sept. 16	03:45	Amboy, Wash	46.0	122.2	([2])	V
	Sept. 17	07:56*	Southwestern Washington	46.0	122.2	9,000	VI
	Oct. 30	19:35*	Okanogan County, Wash	48.4	120.0	1,200	V
	Nov. 6	17:29*	Northwest of Portland, Oreg	45.7	122.9	9,000	VI
	Nov. 7	13:30	Portland, Oreg	45.5	122.6	....	V
1962	Jan. 14	21:29*	North-central Washington	47.8	120.2	3,000	V
	Nov. 5	19:37*	Near Vancouver, Wash	45.6	122.7	20,000	VII
	Dec. 31	12:50*	West-central Washington	47.0	122.0	13,000	VI
1963	Jan 24	13:43*	Western Washington	47.4	122.1	5,500	VI
	Mar. 7	15:53*	Northwestern Oregon	44.9	123.5	....	V
	Dec. 21	18:54*	Okanogan County, Wash	48.3	119.3	3,000	V
	Dec. 26	18:36*	Northwestern Oregon	45.7	123.4	4,000	VI
1964	Jan. 26	13:41*	Merrill Lake, Wash	46.1	122.4	2,000	V
	July 14	07:50*	Near Bellingham, Wash	48.9	122.5	8,000	VI
	July 30	04:45*	British Columbia-Washington border region.	49.2	122.3	3,000	V
	July 30	07:33*	Near Seattle, Wash	47.7	122.1	1,500	V

See footnotes at end of table

List of Earthquakes in Washington and Oregon—Continued

Year	Date	Time (PST)	Locality	N. lat.	W. long.	Area	Intensity
				degrees	*degrees*	*sq. mi.*	
1964	Oct. 1	04:31*	Washington-Oregon border region	45.7	122.8	....	V
	Oct. 15	06:33*	Near Seattle, Wash	47.7	122.1	900	V
1965	Apr. 29	07:29*	do	47.4	122.3	130,000	VII–VIII
1967	Mar. 6	19:51*	Puget Sound, Wash., area	47.8	122.7	7,500	V
1968	May 29	About 21:00	Adel, Oreg	42.2	119.9	([1])	V
	June 3	05:28*	California-Oregon border	42.2	119.8	....	V
	June 3	18:34*	do	42.3	119.9	7,000	VI
	June 3	18:38*	Southern Oregon	42.3	119.8	([1])	V
	Sept. 6	04:17*	Northwestern Washington	47.8	122.8	4,000	V
	Nov. 30	06:40*	Southwestern Washington	46.5	122.4	1,000	V
1969	Feb. 14	00:34*	Vancouver Island region, B.C	48.7	123.0	5,000	V [4]
	Oct. 9	09:08*	Near Elbe, Wash	46.8	121.7	2,000	V
	Nov. 1	07:44*	Northwestern Washington	47.9	121.9	7,000	V
	Nov. 9	23:39*	do	48.5	121.4	7,000	V
1970	Feb. 10	12:21*	do	47.7	122.3	1,500	V
	Oct. 24	14:32*	do	47.3	122.4	2,300	V

*Instrumental origin time and epicenter.
[1] Uncertain.
[2] Local earthquake.

[4] Intensity in United States.

Alaska

Résumé

Alaska and the Aleutian Islands are part of the great seismic belt that circumscribes the Pacific. Although earthquake activity here is greater than in any other state, few of the shocks have caused severe damage because of the absence of large population centers. The activity is separated into two zones. One zone, approximately 200 miles wide, extends from Fairbanks through the Kenai Peninsula to the Near Islands. The second zone begins north of Yakutat Bay and extends southeastward to the west coast of Vancouver Island.

In 1899, the Yakutat Bay area experienced one of the notable earthquakes of the last century. The shore was raised over a considerable length, and at one point, there was a vertical fault slip of 47½ feet—one of the greatest fault movements known. On July 9, 1958, a major shock near Lituya Bay was felt as far south as Seattle, Wash., and eastward to Whitehorse, Yukon Territory. On March 27, 1964, one of the greatest geotectonic events of our time occurred in southern Alaska. In minutes, thousands of people were made homeless, 131 lives were lost, and the economy of the entire State was disrupted. Tsunamis swept the Pacific Ocean from the Gulf of Alaska to Antarctica, causing extensive damage along coastal Alaska, British Columbia, and California.

Time of occurrence for this region has been standardized to 150° meridian time.

List of Earthquakes in Alaska

Year	Date	Time (AST)	Locality	N. lat.	W. long.	Area	Intensity
				degrees	*degrees*	*sq. mi.*	
1786	Unknown	....	Alaska Peninsula	59	154	....	....
1788	July 27	....	Sanak Island, Shumagin Islands, and Alaska Peninsula.	55	161	....	....
1796	May	....	Unalaska Island	54	167	....	....
1802	Unknown	....	.... do	54	167	....	....
1812	Unknown	....	Atka Island	52	174½	....	....
1817	April	....	Umnak Island	53	168	....	....
1818	Unknown	....	Vicinity of Makushin, Unalaska Island.	54	167	....	....
1826	June	....	Unalaska Island	54	167	....	....
1835	Apr. 14	....	Pribilof Islands	57	170	....	....
1836	Apr. 2 and August.	....	St. Paul and St. George Islands, Pribilof Islands.	57	170	....	....
1843	Dec. 15	01:20	Sitka	57	136	....	....
	Dec. 16	{13:30 16:00}	.... do	57	136	....	....

See footnotes at end of table

List of Earthquakes in Alaska—Continued

Year	Date	Time (AST)	Locality	N. lat.	W. long.	Area	Intensity
				degrees	*degrees*	*sq. mi.*	
1847	Unknown	....	Sitka	57	136	....	....
1857	Sept. 8	11:–	Kodiak Island	58	152	....	....
1861	May 3	....	St. George Island, Pribilof Islands	59½	170	....	....
1866	Sept. 5	....	Kodiak Island	58	152	....	....
1867	July 19	23:00	Ikogmut, Lower Yukon River	62	161	....	....
1868	Unknown	....	Unga, Shumagin Islands	55	161	....	....
1878	Aug. 29	....	Makushin, Unalaska Island	54	167	....	....
1879	June 3	09:32	Atka Island	52	174½	....	....
1880	Sept. 28	18:–	Ukamok or Chirikof Island	56	156	....	....
	Oct. 26	20:45	Sitka and Hoonah Village	58	136	....	....
1883	Oct. 6	08:–	Alaska Peninsula	59	154	....	....
1896	Late May	....	Mount St. Elias and Prince William Sound region.	61	146	....	....
1897	Jan. 11	....	Yakutat Bay	60	140	....	....
	May 6	....	Southeastern Alaska	....	....	....	....
1898	August	....	Susitna Station	61	150	....	....
	Aug. 24	22:–	Valdez	61	146	....	....
1899	Apr. 1	16:45	Shumagin Islands	55½	161	....	....
	July 11	....	Tyonek	61	151	....	....
	Sept. 3	14:22•	Near Cape Yakataga	60	142	....	XI
	Sept. 10	11:40•	Yakutat Bay	60	140	....	XI
	Sept. 22	21:30	Unga, Shumagin Islands	55	161	....	....
1900	Aug. 10	....	Skagway and Dawson	....	....	....	....
	Oct. 7	....	Tyonek	61	151	....	....
	Oct. 9	02:28•	Chugach Mountains area	60	142	120,000	VII–VIII
1901	March	....	Fort Gibbon	65	152	....	....
	Dec. 30 to 31	....	Kenai, on Cook Inlet	60½	151	....	....
1902	Aug. 17	....	Between Muir and Yakutat	....	....	....	....
1903	March	....	Valdez	61	146	....	....
	June 2	15:45	.... do	61	146	....	....
	July 26	....	Dry Bay	59	138	....	....
1904	Aug. 27	11:56•	Rampart	64.0	151.0	....	VI
1905	Dec. 8	....	Kuskokwim River	61	162	....	....
1907	Sept. 24	03:58	Skagway	59½	135¼	....	V–VI
	Dec. 29	....	Northwest of Nome	66	168	....	....
1908	Feb. 14	01:25	Prince William Sound	61	146¼	....	....
	May 14	22:32•	Southeastern Alaska	59	141	....	VI
	Oct. 29 and Nov. 2.	....	Northeast of Katalla	60½	144	....	V–VI
1909	Feb. 16	....	Near Yakutat	....	....	....	....
	May 6	....	Yakutat	59½	139½	....	....
	Sept. 8	06:50•	Aleutian Islands	52½	169	....	....
	Sept. 19	10:00	Seward and Kenai Peninsulas	....	....	....	....
1910	Mar. 14	05:09	Skagway	59½	135¼	....	V
	Aug. 5	....	Yakutat Bay	60	140	....	....
	Sept. 1	....	Dutch Harbor	54	166	....	....
	Nov. 20	23:32	Nome	64	165	....	V
1911	Jan. 7	04:43	Near Fairbanks	65	148	....	V
	Early September	....	Yakutat	59½	139½	....	....

See footnotes at end of table

List of Earthquakes in Alaska—Continued

Year	Date	Time (AST)	Locality	N. lat.	W. long.	Area	Intensity
				degrees	*degrees*	*sq. mi.*	
1911	Sept. 21	19:01*	Prince William Sound and Kenai Peninsula.	60.5	149.0	120,000	VII–VIII
	Oct. 17		Southwestern Alaska				
1912	Early January		Aleutian Islands				
	Jan. 31	10:12*	Prince William Sound area	61.0	147.5	150,000	
	June 4 to 5		Kanatak, Nushagak, and Uyak				
	June 6	23:56*	Cook Inlet	59	153		
	June 6		Kodiak	58	152½		
	June 7	About 22:00	Kanatak	57½	156		
	July 6	21:58*	Central Alaska	64.0	147.0	200,000	
	Aug. 17		Naknek	58½	157		
	Nov. 6	21:40*	Kodiak Island region	57.5	155.0		
	Nov. 21	15:56	British Columbia, Canada	50	124		
1914	May 29	06:03	Near Fairbanks	65	148		
1915	Oct. 15	19:10	Kenai Peninsula	62	146		V–VI
1917	May 30	22:47	Unga, Shumagin Islands	55	161		
	Dec. 14	16:10	Sitka	57	136		
1920	June 25	16:41	Fairbanks	65	148		
1922	Sept. 21	Early a.m.	Anchorage	61	150		
1925	Feb. 23	13:55	Kenai Peninsula	62	146		VII
	Feb. 24	03:00	Latouche	60	148		VI
	Feb. 24	03:45	Matanuska	61½	149		V
1926	Nov. 14	18:23	Prince William Sound region				V
1927	Oct. 24	06:00*	Southeastern Alaska	57.5	137.0		VI
	Nov. 12	12:56*	do	57.5	137.0		VI
	Nov. 21	06:14	Sitka	57	136		V
	Dec. 31	10:07	Southeastern Alaska				V
1928	Jan. 24	16:35	Seward	60	150		VI
	Feb. 6	20:03	Prince William Sound	61	149		
	Feb. 19	11:08	Prince William Sound and Kenai Peninsula.	61	147		
	June 8	00:30	Cordova	60	146		V
	June 21	06:27*	South-central Alaska	60.0	146.5		VI
	Oct. 29	21:13	Prince William Sound	61	149		
1929	Jan. 21	00:31* / 04:20*	South of Fairbanks	64.0	148.0	200,000	
	Mar. 6	15:35*	Dutch Harbor	51	170		
	Apr. 6	00:33*	Matanuska	61½	149		V
	May 26	12:40*	Near Queen Charlotte Islands, B.C.	51	131		VI–VII
	Aug. 19	07:40	Kodiak Island	58	152		
	Nov. 11	19:45	Southeastern Alaska				
1931	May 28	19:16*	Girdwood	63	149		
	May 30	00:00	Attu Island	53	173 E		VI
	June 11	12:40	Chitina and Valdez				V
	July 6	12:04	Kanatak	57½	156		V
	July 13	02:30*	Girdwood	60½	149		V
	Oct. 17	02:30*	Girdwood and Wasilla	61	149		V

See footnotes at end of table

List of Earthquakes in Alaska—Continued

Year	Date	Time (AST)	Locality	N. lat.	W. long.	Area	Intensity
				degrees	*degrees*	*sq. mi.*	
1931	Nov. 20	00:30	Girdwood and Valdez				V
	Nov. 21	04:28*	Girdwood	60½	149		V
	Dec. 23	17:41*	Near Kodiak Island	60.0	152.0		
1932	Mar. 3	02:31	Girdwood	60½	149		V
	Mar. 25	13:59*	South-central Alaska	62.5	152.5		VII
	Sept. 13	22:43*	Prince William Sound and Kenai Peninsula.	61	148		V
	Oct. 6	07:05	Homer	59½	151½		V
1933	Jan. 3	17:59*	Near Seward	61.0	148.0		VI
	Apr. 26	16:36*	Northwest of Anchorage	61.2	150.7		VII
	Apr. 26	17:03	Homer	59½	151½		V
	Apr. 26	18:50	Anchorage	61	150		V
	June 13	12:20*	Old Tyonek	61	151		
	June 28	13:35*	Fox Islands	53.5	165.0		
	July 28	01:49	Dutch Harbor, Unalaska Island	54	166		
	Aug. 30	16:52*	Southeastern Alaska	59.2	137.5		V
	Sept. 19	13:40*	Yukon Territory	60	138		V
1934	Feb. 11	21:50	Juneau	58	134½		V
	Apr. 19	08:52	Anchorage	61	150		V
	May 3	18:36*	South-central Alaska	61.2	147.5		VI
	May 14	12:13*	Kodiak Island	57.7	152.2		VI
	May 15	12:–	Kodiak and Seward				V
	June 17	23:14*	South-central Alaska	60.5	151.0		V
	Aug. 1	21:13*	do	61.5	147.5		V
	Nov. 28	19:13	Gustavus	58	136		V
1935	Aug. 23	12:09	Anchorage	61	150		V
1936	Oct. 22	20:24*	South-central Alaska	61.1	149.2		VI
1937	July 22	07:09*	Central Alaska	64.7	146.7		VIII
	Oct. 24	01:36*	South-central Alaska	62	150		V
1938	Nov. 10	10:18*	East of Shumagin Islands	55.5	158.0		
1939	Feb. 13	21:52	Fairbanks	65	148		V
	Feb. 24	04:16*	Fox Islands	53.0	164.5		V
	Mar. 31	05:30	Ellamar	61	147		V
	Aug. 19	21:17*	Fox Islands	54.0	164.0		V
	Oct. 16	11:47	Southeast of Fairbanks				
1940	Jan. 6		Big Delta and Fairbanks				V
	Feb. 11	23:18*	False Pass and Port Moller	55	161½		V
	Mar. 5	12:37 / 13:01 / 13:55	McKinley Park and Healy				
	July 19	04:47	Near Anchorage	61	150		VI
	Aug. 29	21:32*	Fairbanks	65	148		V
1941	July 29	15:51*	Kenai Peninsula area	61.0	151.0		VI
1943	Nov. 3	04:32*	South-central Alaska	61.7	151.0		V
1946	Apr. 1	02:29*	South of Unimak Island	52.8	162.5		VI
1947	Oct. 15	16:10*	Fairbanks area	64.5	148.8		VIII
1949	Sept. 27	05:31*	South-central Alaska	59.8	149.0		V
1950	Aug. 25	18:39*	Seward Peninsula	64.3	161.8		V
1951	June 25	06:13*	Near Anchorage	61	150		V

See footnotes at end of table

List of Earthquakes in Alaska—Continued

Year	Date	Time (AST)	Locality	N. lat.	W. long.	Area	Intensity
				degrees	*degrees*	*sq. mi.*	
1952	Mar. 9	10:00*	Alaska-Canada border	59½	136		V
	Nov. 21	07:27	Lost River area	66	166		V
	Dec. 6	14:58	Shemya Air Force Base, Shemya Island.	53	174 E		VI
1954	Mar. 3	10:46*	Valdez	61½	146½		V
	May 16	03:00	St. George Island, Pribilof Islands	56½	170		V
	Aug. 23	04:58*	Kenai Peninsula	61	148½		V
	Oct. 3	01:19*	do	60½	151		VIII
1956	Mar. 31	01:54	McGrath	63	155½		V
	May 17	18:19	Fairbanks	65	148		V
	June 8	16:27*	Hot Springs	64	148		V
1957	Mar. 9	04:07*	Fairbanks area	65	149		V
	Mar. 9	04:22*	Andreanof Islands	51.3	175.8		VIII
1958	Jan. 13	00:29	College	65	148		V
	Feb. 16	12:20	McGrath	63	155½		V
	Mar. 31	05:50	Huslia	65½	156		V
	Apr. 7	05:31*	Central Alaska	66.1	156.8	150,000	VIII
	Apr. 8	20:15*	Gulf of Alaska	56½	139		V
	Apr. 11	02:18	Kotzebue	66	162½		V
	Apr. 12	23:07*	Central Alaska	66	156		V
	May 5	13:53*	Near coast of southeastern Alaska	57½	136½		V
	May 10	12:55*	Central Alaska	65	152½		V
	May 10	13:13*	do	64½	152½		V
	May 10	19:24*	do	65	152½		V
	July 9	20:16*	Southeastern Alaska	58.6	137.1	400,000	XI
	Aug. 31	13:00*	Central Alaska	63	144½		V
	Aug. 31	16:30	Tanacross	63	144		V
	Nov. 19	05:02*	Kenai Peninsula	60½	150½		V
	Nov. 25	20:15	Yakutat	59½	139½		V
1960	Jan. 3	01:38*	South-central Alaska	61	152		V
	Feb. 18	19:09*	Kenai Peninsula	60½	151		VI
	Mar. 2	18:59*	Central Alaska	64½	150	8,000	V
	Mar. 9	14:24*	do	64	149		V
	July 16	11:20* } 12:03* }	Seward Peninsula	65½	167½		V
	Oct. 14	03:12*	Southeastern Alaska	60.0	136.4		V
1961	Jan. 30	02:13*	Central Alaska	65.3	149.9		V
	Sept. 5	01:35*	Kenai Peninsula	60.0	150.6		VI
1962	May 9	14:04*	Southern Alaska	62.0	150.1		V
	July 16	02:55*	do	62.3	153.1		V
	Aug. 18	06:44* } 07:46* }	South-central Alaska	62.3	152.5		V
	Oct. 20	16:05*	Vicinity of Anchorage	61.1	149.7		VI
	Dec. 13	04:57*	Kenai Peninsula	61.4	147.2		V
1963	June 23	18:27*	Cook Inlet	59.5	151.7		VII
	Dec. 7	18:18	Fairbanks-College area	65	148		V
1964	Jan. 6	08:31	Homer	59½	151½		V
	Feb. 6	03:07*	South of Alaska	55.7	155.8		V
	Mar. 27	17:36*	Southern Alaska	61.0	147.8	700,000	IX–X
	Apr. 3	12:00* } 12:34* }	do	61.6	147.6		V

See footnotes at end of table

List of Earthquakes in Alaska—Continued

Year	Date	Time (AST)	Locality	N. lat.	W. long.	Area	Intensity
				degrees	*degrees*	*sq. mi.*	
1964	Apr. 14	12:56*	Kodiak Island region	58.0	152.6		VI
	Dec. 12	14:33*	Nome	64.9	156.7		VI
1965	Feb. 3	19:01*	Rat Islands	51.3	178.6 E		VI
	Apr. 16	13:22*	Central Alaska	64.7	160.1		VI
	Apr. 26	10:29*	Alaska Peninsula	54.5	162.6		V
	July 2	10:59*	Fox Islands	53.1	167.6		VI
	Dec. 22	09:41*	Kodiak Island region	58.4	153.1		V
1966	Aug. 26	00:20*	Kotzebue	67.1	161.5		V
	Aug. 30	10:21* } 10:23* }	South-central Alaska	61.3	147.5	30,000	V
1967	Feb. 6	04:49*	Central Alaska	64.8	147.4	20,000	V
	June 20	15:00	Dot Lake	64	144		VI
	June 21	08:13*	Central Alaska	64.8	147.4	90,000	VII
	June 23	01:55*	do	64.8	147.4		VI
1968	Oct. 29	12:16*	East-central Alaska	65.4	150.1	250,000	VII–VIII
	Nov. 10	22:54*	Alaska Peninsula	57.3	155.3		V
	Dec. 17	02:02*	Southern Alaska	60.2	152.8	100,000	VI
1969	Feb. 5	23:34*	Andreanof Islands	51.6	176.2		V
	May 14	09:33*	do	51.3	179.9		V
	May 17	22:44*	Southern Alaska	60.3	146.0		V
	Nov. 23	23:42	Near Cold Bay	55.2	162.5		V
	Dec. 25	16:30	King Cove	55.0	162.3		V
1970	Jan. 15	22:06*	Southern Alaska	60.3	152.7		V
	Mar. 11	12:39*	Kodiak Island region	57.5	153.9		V
	Apr. 17	22:51*	Southern Alaska	59.9	152.8		V
	Aug. 13	17:40*	Central Alaska	64.9	147.8		V
	Nov. 2	16:30*	do	62.0	151.2		V

*Instrumental origin time and epicenter.

Hawaii

Résumé

Seismic activity in the islands centers on the Island of Hawaii. Much of this activity is associated directly with volcanic processes because this is an active volcanic region. However, the stronger shocks that are sometimes felt throughout the islands are of tectonic origin. The greatest known earthquake, in 1868, was extremely violent and destructive, considering the sparsely settled nature of the island. Shocks north of Hawaii are often felt strongly on Maui, Lanai, and Molokai.

List of Earthquakes in Hawaii

Year	Date	Time (HST)	Locality	N. lat.	W. long.	Area	Intensity
				degrees	*degrees*	*sq. mi.*	
1834	Feb. 19		Island of Hawaii				
1838	Dec. 12		do				
1868	Apr. 2	About 16:00	Near south coast of Hawaii	19	155½		X
1871	Mar. 19		Oahu				
1878	Jan. 20		Maui				
1881	Sept. 30		Oahu and Maui				
1909	Mar. 13		Island of Hawaii				
1912	Oct. 13		Hawaii				
1913	Sept. 8	12:08	Kilauea, Hawaii, area				V
	Oct. 25	01:28	do				V
1918	Nov. 2	00:03	Mauna Loa, Hawaii				VII
1919	Jan. 28	17:53	Hawaii				V
	Aug. 26	02:34	Island of Hawaii				V
	Sept. 14	17:50	Kilauea, Hawaii				VII
1923	Jan. 14	02:58	Island of Hawaii				
	Feb. 9	21:11	do				
	Dec. 14	06:04	do				
	Dec. 25	19:16	Hawaii				
1924	Aug. 20	06:50	Island of Hawaii				
1925	July 8	06:15	do				
1926	Feb. 7		Oahu and Maui				
	Feb. 28	07:11	Island of Hawaii				
	Mar. 19	23:03	do				
	Apr. 22	05:02	Mauna Loa, Hawaii				
	June 9	10:05	Island of Hawaii				
1927	Mar. 20	05:22	do				
	Aug. 3	10:12	do				

See footnote at end of table

List of Earthquakes in Hawaii—Continued

Year	Date	Time (HST)	Locality	N. lat.	W. long.	Area	Intensity
				degrees	*degrees*	*sq. mi.*	
1929	Sept. 25	18:51*	Kona, Hawaii	19¾	156		VII
	Sept. 28	07:40	Hilo, Hawaii				VII
	Oct. 5	21:52*	Holualoa, Hawaii	19¾	156		VII
1930	May 20	19:22	Hualalai region, Hawaii				V
	May 25	20:47	Kilauea, Hawaii				V
1931	Jan. 30	00:08	Waiohinu, Hawaii				V
1933	Dec. 2	06:30	Hilo, Hawaii				VI
1934	May 10	10:39*	Near Hakalau, Hawaii	19.6	155.4		V
1935	Jan. 2	07:17*	Kilauea, Hawaii	19.4	155.3		V
	June 28	09:30*	Mauna Loa, Hawaii	19.6	155.2		V
	Sept. 30	23:06*	do	19.4	155.7		V
	Oct. 1	00:28*	do	19.6	155.4		V
	Nov. 21	01:41*	do	19.5	155.5		V
1936	Apr. 15	08:57*	Kilauea, Hawaii	19.4	155.2		V
1938	Jan. 22	22:33*	North of Maui	21.2	156.1		VIII
	Feb. 17	02:48*	Mauna Loa, Hawaii	19.6	155.4		V
1939	May 15	10:58*	Kilauea, Hawaii	19.4	155.1		V
	May 23	14:44*	do	19.5	155.4		V
	May 24	13:29*	do	19.4	155.2		V
	May 29	19:45*	South of Maui	19.5	156.8		V
	May 31	21:21*	Kilauea, Hawaii	19.6	155.2		V
	June 12	01:41*	Kau Desert, Hawaii				V
	July 14	04:21*	Kilauea, Hawaii	19.3	155.1		V
1940	June 17	00:27*	North of Island of Hawaii	20.5	155.3		VI
	July 15	17:18*	do	20.9	155.1		
	Sept. 1	22:45*	do	21.0	155.3		V
1941	Sept. 25	07:48*	Mauna Loa, Hawaii	19.2	155.5		VII
	Nov. 16	10:11	Near Waimea, Hawaii				V
	Nov. 18	03:26	do				V
	Nov. 22	21:53	do				V
1943	Nov. 10	16:52	Southern Hawaii				VI
1944	Nov. 12	05:26	Southwest of Halemaumau, Hawaii				V
	Dec. 27	04:12*	Mokuaweoweo, Hawaii	19½	155½		VI
1945	Mar. 4	00:00	Mauna Loa, Hawaii				V
	May 19	01:48	do				V
	Sept. 19	05:33	Saddle area, Hawaii				V
1947	Mar. 19	23:06	Island of Hawaii				V
	Sept. 30	04:04	do				V
1948	June 28	01:38	Oahu				V
1949	Feb. 26	13:54	Mauna Loa, Hawaii				V
	May 2	05:02	do				V
1950	Mar. 25	05:43	do				V
	May 29	15:16*	do	19½	156		VI
1951	Apr. 22	14:52*	Kilauea, Hawaii	19	155½		VII
	Aug. 21	00:57*	Kona, Hawaii	19¾	156		IX
	Sept. 16	01:43*	Kaoiki Fault, Hawaii	19.2	155.5		V
	Nov. 8	09:34	Mauna Loa, Hawaii	19.2	155.5		VI
1952	Feb. 2	01:16	Near Kaumana, Hawaii				V
	Mar. 17	17:58*	Off coast of Hawaii	19.1	155.0		V
	Apr. 6	21:10*	South of Molokai	21	157		V

See footnotes at end of table.

List of Earthquakes in Hawaii—Continued

Year	Date	Time (HST)	Locality	N. lat.	W. long.	Area	Intensity
				degrees	*degrees*	*sq. mi.*	
1952	May 23	12:12*	Kona, Hawaii	19.5	155.5	...	VI
	July 12	13:53	do	...	...	...	V
1953	Jan. 9	21:10*	Mauna Loa, Hawaii	19.4	155.5	...	V
	Jan. 15	02:05*	do	19.3	155.4	...	V
	Aug. 21	19:47	Hawaii	...	...	...	V
1954	Mar. 30	08:42*	Near Kalapana, Hawaii	20	155	...	VII
	July 3	11:53*	Kilauea, Hawaii	20½	155½	...	VI
1955	Mar. 27	16:02	do	...	...	...	VII
	Apr. 1	04:24*	do	19½	155	...	V
	Aug. 7	07:18*	Off north coast of Hawaii	20½	155½	...	V
	Aug. 14	02:28*	Kilauea, Hawaii	19½	155½	...	...
	Oct. 26	16:56*	Near Mokuaweoweo, Hawaii	19½	155½	...	V
1956	May 13	21:54*	Off north coast of Hawaii	20.3	155.3	...	V
	Oct. 16	00:45*	West of Hawaii	20	157	...	V
1957	Aug. 18	00:42*	Near Hana, Maui	21	156	...	V
1958	Feb. 23	04:01	Near Ulupau Head, Oahu	...	...	...	V
1961	July 23	05:24	Off coast of Island of Hawaii	...	...	...	V
	Sept. 22	17:02*	Kilauea, Hawaii	19.4	155.1	...	V
	Sept. 24	19:29*	do	19.4	155.1	...	V
1962	June 27	18:27*	Kaoiki Fault, Hawaii	19.4	155.4	...	VI
1963	Oct. 23	10:24*	do	19.4	155.4	...	V
1966	Nov. 5	09:43*	Southeast of Kealakekua, Hawaii	19.5	155.9	...	V
1970	Oct. 25	09:55*	South of Molokai	21.0	156.8	...	...

*Instrumental origin time and epicenter.

Puerto Rico Region

Résumé

Many earthquakes have been felt on Puerto Rico since the settlement of the Island by Europeans, and several of the shocks have resulted in severe property damage. There is much geologic and topographic evidence that earthquakes have been of relatively frequent occurrence in this region for thousands of years.

There has not been a destructive earthquake near Puerto Rico since the October 11, 1918, shock that centered in northwestern Mona Passage. The Island sustained much damage in its western portions and 116 lives were lost.

List of Earthquakes in Puerto Rico Region

Year	Date	Time (Local)	Locality	N. lat.	W. long.	Intensity
				degrees	*degrees*	
1785	July 11	...	Probably Anegada Passage	18½	64	...
1824	Apr. 20	...	St. Thomas, V.I.	18.4	64.9	VII
1843	Feb. 8	...	Guadeloupe and Antigua, Leeward Islands.	...	...	...
1844	Apr. 16	...	Probably north of Puerto Rico	...	...	VII
1846	Nov. 28	...	Probably Mona Passage	...	...	VI
1851	Feb. 22	...	Puerto Rico	...	...	V
1855	Dec. 14	...	Salinas, P.R.	18.0	60.3	V
1860	Oct. 23	...	Mayagüez, P.R.	...	...	VI
1865	May 12	...	St. Thomas, V.I.	18.4	64.9	V–VI
	Aug. 30	...	Puerto Rico region	...	...	V–VI
1867	Nov. 18	14:45	Virgin Islands	18.2	65	VIII
1868	Mar. 17	...	Puerto Rico and Virgin Islands	...	...	VII
1875	Dec. 8	...	Arecibo, P.R.	18.5	66.7	VII
1900	Oct. 2	...	Cidra, P.R.	18.2	66.2	...
1901	Oct. 22	...	do	18.2	66.2	V
1906	Sept. 27	...	Puerto Rico region	19	66½	VI–VII
1908	Aug. 13	...	Ponce, P.R.	18.0	66.6	...
	Sept. 5	...	Puerto Rico region	...	...	V
1909	Feb. 17	...	do	...	...	V
1910	Sept. 9	...	do	...	...	V
1913	July 24	...	Probably Anegada Passage	18½	64	...
1916	Apr. 24	00:27*	Santo Domingo, Dominican Republic	18½	68	VIII[a]
1917	July 26	21:01*	Northwest of Puerto Rico	19	67½	V

See footnotes at end of table.

List of Earthquakes in Puerto Rico Region—Continued

Year	Date	Time (Local)	Locality	N. lat.	W. long.	Intensity
				degrees	*degrees*	
1917	Aug. 7	....	Punta Higüero, P.R	18.4	67.3	V
	October or November.	....	Mayagüez, P.R	18.2	67.2	V–VI
1918	Oct. 11	10:15*	Northwestern Mona Passage	18.5	67.5	VIII–IX
	Oct. 24	....	do	......	......	VI
	Nov. 12	....	do	......	......	V–VI
1928	Nov. 18	22:35	Puerto Rico region	......	......	V
1929	Oct. 16	05:25	do	......	......	V
	Oct. 16	06:20	do	......	......	V
1934	Aug. 2	03:41	do	......	......	V
1943	July 28	23:02*	Northwest of Puerto Rico	19¼	67½	V
	July 29	21:02*	do	19¼	67¾	V
1946	Aug. 4	13:51*	Dominican Republic	19¼	69	VI
1951	Sept. 15	04:11	Puerto Rico region	......	......	VI
1956	Feb. 13	11:33*	North of Puerto Rico	19	66½	V
1959	Jan. 26	20:20*	Eastern Dominican Republic	18	68½	V
	Mar. 29	01:40*	Virgin Islands region	19	64½	V
1961	Aug. 2	23:08*	Puerto Rico region	18.4	66.3	V
1962	Apr. 20	01:48*	Near north coast of Haiti	20.6	72.2	V
	July 23	18:12*	Virgin Islands region	19.0	65.1	....
1966	Nov. 3	12:25*	Mona Passage	19.2	68.0	V
1967	Feb. 1	19:23	Guayanilla, P.R	18.0	66.8	V
	Feb. 3	01:20	do	18.0	66.8	V
	Feb. 13	19:56	do	18.0	66.8	V
1970	July 8	00:49*	Virgin Islands	18.0	64.6	V

*Instrumental origin time and epicenter.

[1] Intensity at epicenter or at location named.

California and Western Nevada

Résumé

It has been estimated that earthquakes in California and western Nevada represent approximately 90 percent of the seismic activity of the contiguous United States. The majority of these shocks occur at relatively shallow focal depths of 10 to 15 miles and along known rupture zones or faults. The shallow focal depths partly account for the greater violence of earthquakes in this region, compared with those occurring in the Central or Eastern United States. The principal fault in this area—the San Andreas—extends over 600 miles through California, from near the Salton Sea in southern California northwest to Point Arena. Movement along this fault was responsible for the great earthquakes in 1857 (near Fort Tejon) and 1906 (San Francisco), and many of lesser magnitudes.

List of Earthquakes in California and Western Nevada

Year	Date	Time (PST)	Locality	N. lat.	W. long.	Area	Intensity
				degrees	*degrees*	*sq. mi.*	
1769	July 28	13:00	Los Angeles region	34	118	....	....
1775	Dec. 26	17:00	Southeast of Hemet	......	......	....	....
1790 (?)	....	....	Owens Valley region	......	......	....	....
1800	Oct. 11(?)	....	San Juan Bautista	37	121½	....	....
	Nov. 22	13:30	San Diego area	......	......	....	VII
	....	....	Santa Barbara	34½	119½	....	....

See footnotes at end of table

List of Earthquakes in California and Western Nevada—Continued

Year	Date	Time (PST)	Locality	N. lat.	W. long.	Area	Intensity
				degrees	*degrees*	*sq. mi.*	
1803	May 25		San Diego	32½	117		
1806	Mar. 24		Santa Barbara	34½	119½		
1808	June 21 (?)		Presidio of San Francisco	38	122½		
1812	Dec. 8	About 07:00	Southern California				VIII–IX
	Dec. 21	About 11:00	Off coast of southern California	34	120		X
1822			San Jose and Santa Clara	37½	122		
1827	Sept. 23 (?)		Los Angeles	34	118		
1830			San Luis Obispo	35	121		
1836	June 10	07:30	San Francisco Bay	38	122		IX–X
1838	June	p.m.	San Francisco region	37½	122½		X
1841	July 3	14:07	Monterey	36½	122		
1843	June 23	15:30	California-Mexico border region				
1851	May 15	08:10	San Francisco	37½	122½		VI
1851 (?)	Nov. 26		Coast of northern California				
1852	Oct. 26		Southern California				
	Nov. 22 to 24		San Francisco Peninsula	37½	122½		
	Nov. 27 to 30		Southern California	34½	119		
	Dec. 17		San Luis Obispo	35	121		VII–VIII
1853	Feb. 1	13:00	San Simeon	35½	121		
	Oct. 23		Humboldt Bay	41	124		
1855	Jan. 24	22:00	Downieville	39½	121		
	July 10 or 11	20:15	Los Angeles County	34	118½		VIII
1856	Feb. 15	05:25	San Francisco	37½	122½		
	Sept. 20	23:30	San Diego County	33	116½		VII
1857	Jan. 9	About 08:00	Near Fort Tejon	35	119		X–XI
	Feb. 5	19:00	San Francisco	38	122		
1858	Nov. 26	00:35	San Jose	37½	122		VIII
1860	Mar. 15	11:00	Western Nevada				
	Nov. 12		Humboldt Bay	41	124		VIII
1861	July 3	16:11	Contra Costa and Alameda Counties.	37½	122		VIII
1862	May 27		San Diego County	33	117½		
			Goleta	34½	120		
1864	Mar. 5	08:49	San Francisco	37½	122½		VI
1865	Mar. 8	06:00	Sonoma County	38½	122½		VII
	May 24	03:21	Central and Southern California				
	Oct. 1	09:15	Fort Humboldt and Eureka	41	124½		VIII–IX
	Oct. 8	12:46	Santa Cruz Mountains	37	122		VIII–IX
1866	Mar. 26	12:12	San Francisco region				
1867	Dec. 1	23:12	Nevada City	39½	121		
1868	May		Dos Palmas	33½	115½		
	May 24 (?)	21:00	Nevada				
	May 29	21:00	California-Nevada				
	Sept. 4	08:00	Inyo County	37	118		
	Sept. 26	00:40	Ukiah	39	123		
	Oct. 21	07:53	Hayward	37½	122		IX–X
1869	Dec. 20	20:00	Downieville	39½	121		

See footnotes at end of table

List of Earthquakes in California and Western Nevada—Continued

Year	Date	Time (PST)	Locality	N. lat.	W. long.	Area	Intensity
				degrees	*degrees*	*sq. mi.*	
1869	Dec. 26	17:30	California-Nevada	39½	120		
	Dec. 27	02:00	do	39½	120		VI–VII
1871	Mar. 2	13:05	Humboldt and Mendocino Counties.	40½	124		VII
	July 5		Inyo County	37	118		VI
	July 9		Kern County				
	July 11	19:30	Swansea, Inyo County	37	118		
			Imperial Valley				
1872	Mar. 17		Lone Pine	36½	118		
	Mar. 23	13:41	Northeast of Austin, Nev	40	117½	12,000	VI
	Mar. 26	02:30	Owens Valley	36½	118	125,000	X–XI
	Apr. 18		Cerro Gordo, Inyo County				
	May 17	13:00	Lone Pine	36½	118		
1873	Nov. 22	21:00	Del Norte County	42	124	70,000	VII
1876	Jan. 3	10:55	Sonoma County	38½	123		VI–VII
1877	June 11		Imperial County	33	115½		
1878	Late summer		Inglewood	34	118½		
1881	Apr. 10	02:00	Modesto region	38	121	50,000	VII
1882	Mar. 6	14:00	Hollister	37	121½		
1883	Mar. 30	07:45	do	37	121½		VI
	Sept. 5	04:30	Ventura	34	119		
1884	Mar. 25	16:40	San Francisco	37½	122½		
1885	Jan. 30	10:45	Lassen County	40½	120½		VII
	Mar. 30	23:56	Southeast of Hollister	36½	121		VII
	Apr. 11	20:05	Monterey County	36	121	125,000	VII–VIII
	July 31	16:10	Sonoma County	39	123		
1887	June 3	02:48	Carson City, Nev	39	120		VII
1888	Feb. 18	02:50	Point Arena Lighthouse	39	124		
	Feb. 29	14:50	Petaluma	38	122½		VII
	Apr. 28	20:48	Nevada City	39½	121		VII
	Nov. 18	14:28	Oakland	37½	122½		VII
1889	May 19	03:10	Collinsville and Antioch	38	122		VII
	June 19	22:00	Lassen County	40½	120½		VII
	July 31	04:47	San Francisco Bay	37½	122		VII
	Aug. 27	18:15	Pomona area	34	118		VI
	Sept. 29	20:10	Near Bishop				
1890	Feb. 9	04:06	Southern California	34	117½		VI
	Apr. 24	03:36	Monterey Bay region	37	121½		VII
	July 26	01:40	Petrolia	40½	124½		VII
	Aug. 10 (?)		Mono Lake				
1891	Jan. 2	12:00	Mount Hamilton	37½	121½		VI
	Oct. 11	22:28	Napa and Sonoma Counties	38½	122½		VII–VIII
1892	Feb. 23	23:20	Northern Baja California	31½	116½		VIII–IX[a]
	Apr. 19	02:50	Vacaville	38½	122½		IX
	Apr. 21	09:43	Winters	38½	122		IX
	Nov. 13	04:45	Monterey	36½	122		VI
1893	Apr. 4	11:40	Northwest of Los Angeles	34½	118½		VIII–IX
	May 18	16:35	Southeast of Ventura	34	119		
	Aug. 9	01:15	Santa Rosa	38½	122½		VII
1894	July 13	20:50	Northeast of Fresno	37	120		

See footnotes at end of table

List of Earthquakes in California and Western Nevada—Continued

Year	Date	Time (PST)	Locality	N. lat.	W. long.	Area	Intensity
				degrees	*degrees*	*sq. mi.*	
1894	July 29	21:12	Mojave area	35	118		
	Sept. 30	09:36	Humboldt County				
	Oct. 23	15:03	San Diego	33	117		VII
	Nov. 18	02:40	Virginia City, Nev.	39½	119½		
1895	Mar. 1	01:00	Off Cape Mendocino				
1896	Jan. 27	13:00	Carson City, Nev.	39	120		VI
1897	June 20	12:14	Near Hollister	37	121½	50,000	VIII
1898	Mar. 30	23:43	Mare Island	38	122		VII
	Apr. 14	23:07	Mendocino County	39	124		VIII–IX
1899	Apr. 16	02:41	Eureka	41	124		
	Apr. 30	14:41	Watsonville	37	121½	20,000	VII
	June 1	23:19	San Francisco	37½	122½		VI
	July 6	12:10	Watsonville	37	121½	40,000	
	July 22	12:32	San Bernardino County	34½	117½		VIII
	Oct. 12	21:00	Santa Rosa	38½	122½		VII
	Dec. 25	04:25	San Jacinto and Hemet	33½	116½	100,000	IX
1901	Mar. 2	23:45	Monterey County	36	120½	40,000	VII–VIII
1902	May 19	10:31	Elmira	38½	122	20,000	VII–VIII
	July 27	22:57	Santa Barbara County	34½	120½		VIII
	July 31	01:20 / 19:30	do	34½	120½		
	Dec. 12		Los Alamos	34½	120½		VII
1903	Jan. 23	21:30	Baja California	31½	115½		
	June 11	05:12	Near San Jose	37½	122	40,000 to 100,000	VII
	July 24	12:26	Willows	39½	122		VII
	Aug. 2	22:49	Santa Clara County	37½	122	50,000	VII
	Dec. 25	09:45	Los Angeles area	34	118		VI
1905	Dec. 23	14:23	Bakersfield	35½	119		
1906	Mar. 3	12:25	Southern California				
	Apr. 18	05:12	Northwest of San Francisco	38	123	375,000	XI
	Apr. 18	16:30	Brawley, Imperial Valley	33	115		VIII
	Apr. 23	01:10	Ferndale	41	124		VII
	May 1	21:30	Guerneville, Sonoma County	38½	123		VI
	Dec. 6	22:40	San Luis Obispo County	35½	121		
1907	Aug. 11	04:19	Humboldt County	40½	124		
	Sept. 19	17:54	Near San Bernardino	34	117	50,000	VII
1908	Jan. 26	About 18:00	Honey Lake region				VII
	Aug. 18	02:59	Eureka	41	124	6,000	VII
	Nov. 4	00:37	Death Valley District	36	117	50,000 to 75,000	
1909	May 17	17:19	Upper Mattole	41	124		VII–VIII
	June 22	23:34	Sierra County	39½	121	50,000	VII
	Oct. 28	22:45	Humboldt County	40½	124	100,000	VIII
1910	Mar. 10	22:52	Monterey Bay			60,000	VI
	Mar. 18	16:11	Humboldt County	40	125		
	May 6	08:40	Near Bishop	37½	119	50,000	

See footnotes at end of table

List of Earthquakes in California and Western Nevada—Continued

Year	Date	Time (PST)	Locality	N. lat.	W. long.	Area	Intensity
				degrees	*degrees*	*sq. mi.*	
1910	May 15	07:47	Lake Elsinore region	33½	117½		VII
	Nov. 21	15:23	Tonopah Junction, Nev.	38	117		
	Dec. 31	04:11	San Benito and Monterey Counties	36½	121½		
1911	Mar. 11	13:30	Hollister	37	121		VI
	July 1	14:00*	South of San Jose	37	122	60,000	VII–VIII
1912	Jan. 4	19:53	Bishop, Inyo County	37½	118½	50,000	
	Dec. 14		Near Oxnard, Ventura County	34	119		VI–VII
1914	Feb. 18	10:15	Near Reno, Nev.	39½	120		VI
	Apr. 24	00:35	do	39½	120	100,000	VII
	Nov. 8	18:31	Santa Cruz Mountains	37	122	30,000	VII
1915	Jan. 11	20:31	Los Alamos	34½	120½	50,000	VIII
	Feb. 21	p.m.	Near Lassen Peak	40½	121		
	Apr. 5	15:11	Coleville region	38½	119½	25,000	
	June 22	19:59 / 20:56	El Centro, Calexico, and Mexicali	32.8	115.5	50,000 to 100,000	VIII
	Oct. 2	22:53*	Pleasant Valley, Nev.	40½	117½	500,000	X
	Oct. 7	21:26	Piedmont	37½	122		VI
	Nov. 20	16:14*	Baja California	32	115	120,000	VII*
	Dec. 31	04:20*	Off Humboldt County coast	41	126		
1916	Feb. 2	21:02	Western Nevada	40½	119½	100,000	VI
	July 4	20:40	Humboldt County	40½	124½		VI
	Aug. 6	11:38	Paicines, San Benito County	36½	121	30,000	VII
	Oct. 22	18:44*	Tejon Pass	34.9	118.9	25,000 to 50,000	VII
	Nov. 10	01:11	Near Death Valley				
	Dec. 1	14:53	Avila	35	121		VII
1917	May 27	22:06	Imperial Valley	33	115½	40,000	
	July 6	03:01	Owens Valley				VI–VII
	July 9	14:22	Lopez Canyon				VI
1918	Mar. 12	02:30	Sierra County	39½	121		VII
	Apr. 21	14:32*	Riverside County	33¾	117	150,000	IX
	Apr. 22	13:15	Corona	34	117½		VI
	Apr. 30	20:32	Calexico	32½	115½	31,000	VI*
	June 6	14:32	Riverside County	33½	117		
	July 14	16:23*	Off coast of Humboldt County	41	125		VI
	Nov. 19	12:18	Santa Monica Bay	34	118½		VI
1919	Jan. 4	15:00	Shasta County	40½	122		
	Feb. 16	07:57	South of Maricopa	35	119	30,000	VII
	Sept. 15	06:07	Eureka	41	124		VII
	Sept. 29	23:37	Baja California	32½	115		
	Oct. 1	05:07	do	32½	115		
	Dec. 31	18:35	Mesa Grande and Warner Springs	33	117		VI
1920	June 21	18:48	Inglewood	34	118½	11,000	VIII
	July 16	10:08	Los Angeles	34	118½		VI
	July 22	19:55	Hot Springs	40½	121½		VII
1921	July 21	12:17	Eagle Lake	40½	120½		VI
	Sept. 8	11:24	South of Imperial Valley	32½	115½		
1922	Jan. 31	05:17*	Northwest of Cape Mendocino	41	125½	400,000	VI

See footnotes at end of table

List of Earthquakes in California and Western Nevada—Continued

Year	Date	Time (PST)	Locality	N. lat.	W. long.	Area	Intensity
				degrees	*degrees*	*sq. mi.*	
1922	Mar. 10	03:21*	Cholame Valley	35¾	120¼	100,000	IX
	Aug. 17	21:12	Cholame region	35½	120½	25,000	....
1923	Jan. 22	01:04*	Off Cape Mendocino	40½	124½	....	VII–VIII
	July 22	23:30*	San Bernardino Valley	34	117¼	70,000	VII
	Nov. 5	14:07	Calexico	32½	115½	....	VII[3]
	Nov. 7	15:57	Baja California	32½	115½	....	VII[3]
1924	Dec. 27	20:18	Near Salinas	36.7	121.6	....	VI
1925	Apr. 15	....	Calexico	32½	115½	....	VI[3]
	June 29	06:42*	Santa Barbara and vicinity	34.3	119.8	....	VIII–IX
1926	Feb. 18	10:18	Southwest of Ventura	34	119½	....	VI
	Apr. 3	12:08	Northeast of Banning	34	116	60,000	....
	Apr. 19	07:17	Baja California	32½	115	....	....
	June 29	15:21	Santa Barbara	34½	119½	30,000	VII
	June 30	05:31	Kern River Canyon	....	....	30,000	....
	July 25	09:58	Near Idria	36½	120½	30,000	VI
	Oct. 22	04:35*, 05:35*	Monterey Bay	36¾	122	100,000	VIII
1927	Jan. 1	00:17*, 01:13*	Imperial Valley, near Mexican border.	32½	115½	50,000	VIII[3]
	Feb. 15	15:54	Near Santa Cruz	37	122	30,000	VI
	May 28	09:38	Near San Jose	37.3	121.8	3,000	VI
	Aug. 4	04:24	Santa Monica Bay	34	118½	8,000	VI
	Aug. 20	12:05	Humboldt Bay	41	124	....	VIII
	Sept. 17	18:07*	Near Bishop	37½	118¾	75,000	VII
	Nov. 4	05:51*	West of Point Arguello	34½	121½	....	IX–X
	Nov. 18	19:32	Santa Maria	35	120½	....	VI
1928	June 3	p.m.	Weaverville	41	123	....	VII
	Sept. 5	06:42	Colorado Desert region, near Twentynine Palms.	34	116	....	V
1929	July 8	08:46*	Whittier	34	118	....	VII
	Nov. 28	11:49	Northwest of Bishop	36.9	118.2	35,000	VII
1930	Jan. 15	16:25*, 16:34	Fawnskin and Summit	34.2	116.9	50,000	VII
	Feb. 25	18:30	Imperial Valley	33	115½	20,000	VIII
	Mar. 1	15:44	do	33	115½	11,000	VIII
	Apr. 9	14:00	Lake Tahoe	39	120	19,000	VI
	Apr. 12	04:57	Fernley, Nev	39½	119	15,000	VI
	Aug. 5	03:25	Santa Barbara	34½	119½	....	VII
	Aug. 30	16:41*	Santa Monica Bay	33.9	118.6	12,000	VII
	Sept. 22	18:58	Humboldt Bay	41	124	10,000	VII
	Dec. 11	01:00	Southwest of Cape Mendocino	40½	124½	25,000	VI
1931	Aug. 23	10:02*	West of Cape Mendocino	40.2	125.6	4,500	VI
	Sept. 9	05:41*	Northwest of Cape Mendocino	40.8	125.0	15,000	VI
1932	June 6	00:44*	Humboldt County	40.8	124.3	50,000	VIII
	July 25	22:52	Upper Kern River	35.8	118.5	....	VI
	Dec. 20	22:10*	Western Nevada	38.7	117.8	500,000	X
1933	Mar. 10	17:54*	Long Beach	33.6	118.0	100,000	IX
	May 16	03:47	Niles Canyon	38	122	8,000	VII
	June 25	12:45*	Wabuska, Nev	39.1	119.3	70,000	VII
	Oct. 2	01:10*	Signal Hill	33.8	118.1	6,000	VI

See footnotes at end of table

List of Earthquakes in California and Western Nevada—Continued

Year	Date	Time (PST)	Locality	N. lat.	W. long.	Area	Intensity
				degrees	*degrees*	*sq. mi.*	
1934	Jan. 30	11:24, 12:17*	Southeast of Hawthorne, Nev	38.3	118.4	110,000	VIII–IX
	June 7	20:30, 20:48*	Parkfield	36	120½	34,000	VIII
	Dec. 30	05:52*	South of Calexico	32¼	115½	60,000	VI[3]
	Dec. 31	10:46*	do	32	114¾	80,000	VII[3]
1935	Oct. 24	06:48*	Southern California	34.1	116.9	29,000	V
1936	May 10	09:40	North of Bishop	37.5	118.5	6,000	VI
1937	Feb. 6	20:42*	Northwest of Ferndale	40½	125¼	10,000	V
	Mar. 8	02:31	Near Berkeley	37.8	122.2	5,000	VI–VII
	Mar. 25	08:49*	Terwilliger Valley	33.5	116.6	30,000	VII
1938	May 31	00:34*	Santa Ana Mountains	33.7	117.5	30,000	VI
	Aug. 30	19:18*	Near Long Beach	33.8	118.2	1,200	VI
	Sept. 11	22:11*	West of Cape Mendocino	40.3	124.8	20,000	VI
	Dec. 3	09:42*	West of Bishop	37.5	118.8	24,000	VI–VII
1939	Jan. 11	14:00	Southeast of Minden, Nev	38.8	119.6	8,000	VI
	May 11	10:05*	Northeast of Mina, Nev	38.6	117.8	38,000	VI
	June 24	05:02	Near Hollister	36.8	121.4	10,000	VII
	Dec. 27	11:29*	Long Beach	33.8	118.1	2,500	VI
1940	Feb. 8	00:06*	Chico area	39¾	121¼	30,000	VI–VII
	May 18	20:37*	Southeast of El Centro	32.7	115.5	[1] 60,000	X
	Oct. 10	21:57*	Off Redondo Beach	33.8	118.4	10,000	VI
	Nov. 19	10:34	Off Cape Mendocino	....	....	8,000	VI
1941	Feb. 9	01:44*	do	40.9	125.4	17,000	VI
	May 13	08:02*	do	40.3	125.0	....	V
	June 30	23:51*	Santa Barbara and Carpinteria	34.4	119.6	20,000	VIII
	Sept. 14	08:44*, 10:39*	Owens Valley	37.6	118.7	30,000	VI–VII
	Sept. 21	11:53*	Near Cuddy Valley	34.9	118.9	26,000	VI
	Oct. 3	08:13*	Off Cape Mendocino	40.6	124.6	12,000	VI–VII
	Oct. 21	22:57*	Gardena area	33.8	118.2	2,000	VII
	Nov. 14	00:42*	Torrance-Gardena area	33.8	118.2	3,600	VII–VIII
	Dec. 30	22:49*	Owens Valley	37.6	118.7	28,000	VI
1942	Oct. 21	08:22*	Near Borrego Valley	33.0	116.0	35,000	VII
	Dec. 3	01:45*	West of Wadsworth, Nev	39.9	119.0	24,000	VI
	Dec. 17	07:08*	Central California-Nevada border	38.9	119.5	....	V
1943	Aug. 8	21:30*	Excelsior Mountains, Nev	38.2	118.2	34,000	VI
	Aug. 28	19:45*	San Bernardino Mountains	34.3	117.0	16,000	VI
	Oct. 25	20:51*	Northwest of Mount Hamilton	37.4	121.7	20,000	VI
1944	June 12	02:46*, 03:17*	North of Cabazon	34.0	116.8	16,000	VI
	June 18	16:04*, 19:06*	Near Dominguez Junction	33.9	118.2	12,000	VI
1945	Jan. 7	14:26*	San Benito County	36.7	121.2	13,000	VI
	Apr. 1	15:44*	Santa Rosa Island	34.0	120.0	1,000	IV
	May 17	07:07*	Near Hollister	36.8	121.4	6,000	VI
	May 19	07:07*	Off Cape Mendocino	40.6	126.4	1,500	V
	Aug. 15	09:56*	Borrego Valley	33.2	116.1	15,000	VI
	Aug. 27	01:13*	San Jose	37.3	121.8	13,000	VI
1946	Jan. 8	10:54*	Southeast of Borrego Valley	33.0	115.8	12,000	V

See footnotes at end of table

List of Earthquakes in California and Western Nevada—Continued

Year	Date	Time (PST)	Locality	N. lat.	W. long.	Area	Intensity
				degrees	*degrees*	*sq. mi.*	
1946	Mar. 15	05:50*	North of Walker Pass	35.7	118.1	65,000	VIII
	July 18	06:28*	San Bernardino County	34.5	116.0	27,000	VI
	Sept. 27	23:19*	North of Beaumont	34.0	116.9	9,000	VI
1947	Apr. 10	07:58*	East of Barstow	35.0	116.6	75,000	VII
	June 22	15:30*	Gilroy	37.0	121.8	7,000	VI
	July 24	14:11*	Morongo Valley	34.0	116.5	35,000	V
	Aug. 10	13:58*	Near Hollister	36.9	121.4	3,500	VI
	Sept. 23	05:53*	Humboldt County	40.4	125.2	4,000	VI
1948	Feb. 10	19:29*	Tulare County	36.1	118.8	18,000	VI
	Dec. 4	15:43*	Desert Hot Springs	33.9	116.4	65,000	VII
	Dec. 29	04:53*	Near Verdi, Nev	39.5	120.1	40,000	VII
	Dec. 31	17:18*	Near Hollister	36.9	121.6	3,500	VII
1949	Feb. 11	13:05*	Northern Inyo County	37.1	117.8	18,000	VI
	Mar. 9	04:29*	Hollister	37.0	121.5	20,000	VII
	May 2	03:26*	Riverside County	34.0	115.7	16,000	VI
	June 9	19:07*	East of San Jose	37.4	121.6	8,000	VI
	Aug. 27	06:52*	Near Point Conception	34.5	120.5	350	VI
	Nov. 4	12:43*	Baja California	32.2	116.5	[1] 9,000	VI [*]
	Nov. 17	17:20*	Terminal Island, San Pedro Bay	33.8	118.3	....	V
1950	Feb. 25	16:06*	Sespe Hot Springs	34.6	119.1	2,500	VI
	Mar. 20	07:22*	Lassen Peak	40.5	121.5	4,000	V
	July 29	06:37*	Imperial Valley	33.1	115.6	[1] 18,500	VIII
	Aug. 1	00:37*	do	33.1	115.6	....	VI
	Sept. 5	11:20*	Northwest of Anza	33.7	116.8	10,000	VI
	Dec. 14	05:24*	Near Herlong	40.1	120.1	20,000	VII
1951	Jan. 23	23:17*	Near Calipatria	33.1	115.6	14,000	VII
	Jan. 25	13:00*	San Francisco Bay	37.8	122.2	....	VI
	Feb. 15	02:48* / 02:50*	Near Santa Rosa Mountains	33.5	116.5	7,000	V
	July 23	18:25* / 19:04*	Berkeley Hills	37.9	122.3	....	VI
	July 29	02:54*	Southeast of Mulberry	36.6	121.2	10,000	VI
	Aug. 6	01:05*	do	36.6	121.2	2,500	VI
	Aug. 14	23:23*	Terminal Island	33.5	118.2	....	V
	Oct. 7	20:11*	Off Cape Mendocino	40.3	124.8	9,000	VII
	Oct. 31	12:58*	Near Hollister	36.9	121.4	2,500	VI
	Nov. 14	00:40*	Near Scotia	40.4	124.0	3,000	VI
	Dec. 5	07:53*	Imperial Valley	33.1	115.4	3,000	VII
	Dec. 25	16:47*	San Clemente Island	32.8	118.4	18,000	VI
	Dec. 27	18:49*	Near Owens River Gorge	37.6	118.6	10,000	VI
1952	Feb. 9	00:43*	Northeast of Lone Pine	36.7	117.9	....	VI
	May 9	08:32*	North of Carson City, Nev	39.4	119.7	3,000	VI
	July 21	03:52*	Kern County	35.0	119.0	160,000	XI
	July 21	04:06*	do	35.0	118.8	....	V
	July 21	11:41*	do	35.1	119.0	....	V
	July 22	16:39*	do	35.4	118.6	....	V
	July 22	23:53*	do	35.0	118.8	....	VII
	July 23	05:17*	do	35.2	118.8	....	VII
	July 23	10:14*	do	35.0	118.8	....	VI
	July 25	11:10* / 11:43*	do	35.3	118.5	....	VII

See footnotes at end of table

List of Earthquakes in California and Western Nevada—Continued

Year	Date	Time (PST)	Locality	N. lat.	W. long.	Area	Intensity
				degrees	*degrees*	*sq. mi.*	
1952	July 28	23:04*	Kern County	35.4	118.9	....	VII
	July 31	04:09*	do	35.3	118.6	....	VI
	Aug. 13	09:39*	do	35.2	118.7	....	VI
	Aug. 22	14:41*	Bakersfield	35.3	118.9	40,000	VIII
	Aug. 23	02:09*	Near Acton	34.5	118.2	35,000	VI
	Aug. 29	20:56*	Kern County	35.3	118.5	....	VI
	Sept. 2	04:42*	do	35.1	118.7	....	VI
	Sept. 2	08:38*	do	35.3	118.5	....	VI
	Sept. 22	03:41*	Petrolia	40.2	124.4	4,000	VII
	Oct. 12	16:34*	Oakland, Near Dimond District	37.8	122.2	3,500	V
	Oct. 21	16:46*	San Francisco Bay	37.9	122.4	2,500	V
	Nov. 21	23:47*	Near Bryson	35.8	121.2	20,000	VII
1953	May 24	19:24*	Wheeler Ridge	35.0	119.0	....	VI
	May 24	20:08*	Calpella	39.4	123.3	....	VI
	June 13	20:17*	Imperial Valley	32.8	115.7	4,800	VII
	Sept. 25	19:34*	Near Reno, Nev	39.6	119.8	12,000	VI
	Dec. 16	21:13*	Watsonville	36.9	121.7	3,500	VI
1954	Jan. 12	15:34*	West of Wheeler Ridge	35.0	119.0	35,000	VII–VIII
	Jan. 27	06:20*	West of Tehachapi	35.2	118.6	12,000	VI
	Mar. 19	01:54*	Santa Rosa Mountains	33.3	116.2	40,000	VI
	Mar. 22	20:15*	do	33.3	116.2	....	VI
	Apr. 22	10:50*	East of Watsonville	36.9	121.7	2,500	VI
	Apr. 25	12:33*	do	36.9	121.7	12,000	VIII
	July 6	03:13*	East of Fallon, Nev	39.4	118.5	130,000	IX
	July 6	14:08*	Southeast of Fallon, Nev	39.3	118.5	....	VIII
	Aug. 12	04:50*	East of Watsonville	36.9	121.7	....	VI
	Aug. 23	21:52*	East of Fallon, Nev	39.6	118.5	150,000	IX
	Aug. 26	05:48*	Near Anacapa Island	33.9	119.5	....	VI
	Aug. 31	14:21*	Dixie Valley, Nev	39.6	118.2	....	VII
	Sept. 15	20:51*	East of Merced	37.3	120.0	....	VI
	Nov. 10	10:07*	Lake and Mendocino Counties	39.1	123.0	2,500	VI
	Nov. 12	04:27*	Baja California	31½	116	....	V [*]
	Nov. 25	03:17*	Off Cape Mendocino	40.3	125.6	9,000	V
	Dec. 16	03:07* / 03:11*	Dixie Valley, Nev	39.3	118.2	200,000	X
	Dec. 16	23:09*	East of San Leandro	37.7	122.1	4,500	VI
	Dec. 21	11:56*	Eureka-Arcata areas	40.8	124.1	50,000	VII
	Dec. 30	01:16*	do	40.8	124.1	....	VI
1955	Jan. 10	05:16*	Southeast of Lovelock, Nev	39.9	118.4	....	VI
	Jan. 25	04:23	Terminal Island area	33.8	118.2	....	IV
	Mar. 2	07:59*	Near San Ardo	36.0	120.9	7,000	VI
	Apr. 29	07:15*	Near Kelseyville	39.0	122.8	900	VI
	May 7	03:51*	do	38.9	122.9	2,000	VI
	Aug. 7	19:22*	North of Caliente	35.4	118.6	6,000	V
	Aug. 8	02:36*	Near Hawthorne, Nev	38.5	118.8	9,000	V
	Sept. 4	18:01*	East of San Jose	37.4	121.8	12,000	VII
	Oct. 23	20:11*	Near Concord	38.0	122.1	12,000	VII
	Nov. 2	11:40*	Near San Ardo	36.0	120.9	7,000	VI
	Nov. 21	12:55*	North of Bena	35.4	118.7	4,000	V
	Dec. 16	22:07*	Near Brawley	33.0	115.5	9,000	VII

See footnotes at end of table

List of Earthquakes in California and Western Nevada—Continued

Year	Date	Time (PST)	Locality	N. lat.	W. long.	Area	Intensity
				degrees	*degrees*	*sq. mi.*	
1956	Jan. 2	16:26*	Near Glen Ivy, Temescal Canyon	33.8	117.5	9,000	VI
	Jan. 3	06:24*	Baja California	32.4	116.0	[1] 3,500	V [2]
	Feb. 6	18:18* 19:17*	North of Castaic	34.6	118.6	3,000	VI
	Feb. 9	06:33*	Baja California	31.8	115.9	[1] 30,000	VI [2]
	Feb. 14	10:34* 17:21*	do	31.5	115.5	Large area	V [2]
	Mar. 9	21:56*	Near Petrolia	40.3	124.2	2,500	V
	Mar. 16	12:30*	Near Baldwin Lake	34.3	116.8	8,000	VI
	Mar. 18	02:18* 02:22*	Near Manzanita Lake	40.0	121.6	....	VI
	Apr. 4	20:29* 20:30*	Near Saint Helena	38.5	122.5	4,500	VI
	May 11	08:31*	Near Baldwin Lake	34.3	116.8	9,000	V
	July 23	00:04*	Northwest of King City	36.3	121.3	4,000	V
	Sept. 23	03:25*	Riverside County	33.5	116.6	1,500	VI
	Oct. 11	08:49*	West of Ferndale	40.7	125.8	3,500	V
	Nov. 15	19:23*	Northwest of Parkfield	36.0	120.5	8,000	VI
	Dec. 1	06:11*	West of Hollister	36.9	121.6	3,200	V
	Dec. 31	09:39*	Near Hawthorne, Nev	38.3	119.0	6,000	VI
1957	Jan. 24	12:55*	Southeast of Palomar	33.1	116.4	6,000	V
	Jan. 29	13:20*	Off coast, southwest of Big Sur	35.9	122.1	5,000	V
	Jan. 31	23:52*	Little San Bernardino Mountains	34.0	116.3	3,000	V
	Mar. 18	10:56*	South of Oxnard	34.1	119.2	3,000	VI
	Mar. 22	11:44*	West of Daly City	37.7	122.5	12,000	VII
	Mar. 23	00:14*	do	37.7	122.5	3,500	VI
	Apr. 25	13:58*	Southwest end of the Salton Sea	33.2	115.9	12,000	VII
	May 26	08:00*	Southwest of the Salton Sea	33.2	116.0	7,000	V
	Oct. 30	18:48*	Near Comptche	39.2	123.7	4,000	VI
1958	May 24	15:05*	Near Petrolia	40.3	124.2	3,500	VI
	July 8	21:24*	Near Morgan Hill	37.3	121.7	3,000	V
	July 13	21:26*	Off Carpinteria	34.4	119.5	5,000	VI
	Sept. 30	23:25*	Southeast of Soledad	36.4	121.1	....	VI
	Oct. 1	13:42*	Southeast of Sierraville	39.6	120.3	5,000	VI
	Oct. 10	05:05*	Northwest of Parkfield	35.9	120.5	3,500	V
	Oct. 30	16:26*	Northeast of San Jose	37.5	121.8	1,500	VI
	Nov. 30	19:21*	Baja California	32.3	115.8	[1] 15,000	VI [2]
	Dec. 11	01:52*	Southwest of San Francisco	37.7	122.5	6,500	VI
1959	Mar. 2	15:27*	Near Gilroy	37.0	121.6	8,000	VI
	Mar. 22	23:10*	Dixie Valley, Nev	39.6	118.0	50,000	VI
	Apr. 1	10:19*	Northeast of Loyalton	39.7	120.2	25,000	VII
	Apr. 5	22:08*	North of Ukiah	39.3	123.2	1,200	VI
	May 26	07:58*	Near Salinas	36.7	121.6	4,500	VI
	June 13	17:27*	Near the Sierra Buttes	39.7	120.6	4,500	V
	June 17	16:30*	Northwest of Bishop	37.6	118.6	3,000	VI
	June 23	06:35*	North of Schurz, Nev	39.1	118.8	35,000	VI
	July 1	15:49*	South of Bannister	35.2	119.1	6,000	V
	Aug. 3	23:37*	West of Bishop	37.4	118.6	12,000	VI
	Aug. 25	21:33*	Morongo Valley	34.1	116.6	10,000	V
	Sept. 24	09:02*	Northeast of Ukiah	39.4	123.0	....	VI
	Sept. 30	20:36*	Off coast of southern California	34.4	120.6	4,500	VI

See footnotes at end of table

List of Earthquakes in California and Western Nevada—Continued

Year	Date	Time (PST)	Locality	N. lat.	W. long.	Area	Intensity
				degrees	*degrees*	*sq. mi.*	
1959	Oct. 24	07:35*	Near Owens Park	35.7	118.0	....	VI
	Dec. 21	18:39*	Off Punta Gorda	40.3	124.5	3,000	V
	Dec. 28	18:33*	Northwest of Hollister	36.9	121.5	5,000	VI
1960	Jan. 19	19:26*	South of Hollister	36.8	121.4	7,500	VI
	June 4	23:47*	Northwest of Bishop	37.5	118.6	4,800	V–VI
	June 5	17:18*	West of Arcata	40.8	124.9	8,000	VI
	Aug. 8	23:39*	Off coast of northern California	40.3	126.1	6,500	V
1961	Jan. 28	00:13*	Near Walker Pass	35.8	118.0	13,000	VI
	Apr. 4	13:32	Terminal Island, Long Beach Harbor.	......	......	....	IV
	Apr. 5	20:05*	Off coast of northern California	40.1	124.8	3,500	VI
	Apr. 8	23:23* 23:26*	About 13 miles south of Hollister	36.7	121.3	13,500	VII
	May 28	05:00*	Northeast of Indio	33.8	116.1	5,000	VI
	July 3	20:56*	West of Winnemucca, Nev	40.9	118.4	10,000	V
	July 30	16:07*	Near Shandon	35.8	120.3	5,000	V
	Oct. 18	21:10*	East of Brown	35.8	117.8	12,000	VII
	Oct. 20	11:50*	Near Huntington Beach	33.6	118.0	1,200	VI
	Nov. 14	21:39*	Near Wheeler Ridge	34.9	119.0	10,000	VI
1962	Apr. 27	01:13*	Near Perris	33.7	117.2	4,500	VI
	June 6	09:50*	Near Lakeport	39.1	123.1	6,500	VII
	July 20	01:02*	Near Dixie Valley, Nev	39.8	118.1	13,500	V
	Aug. 23	11:29*	Off coast of Del Norte County	41.8	124.3	15,000	VI
	Sept. 4	09:17* 09:33*	Northwest of Arcata	41.0	124.2	7,000	VI
	Sept. 15	21:36*	Near Walker Pass	35.7	118.0	16,000	VI
	Oct. 28	18:43*	Near Big Bear	34.3	116.9	9,500	VI
1963	Feb. 28	16:26*	Near Fort Tejon	34.9	119.0	8,000	VI
	May 22	14:41*	Sunnyvale	37.3	122.2	1,500	VI
	May 22	22:44*	Imperial Valley	33.0	115.7	4,000	VI
	June 7	04:05*	Near Antioch	38.0	121.8	1,500	VI
	June 11	07:24*	Baja California	31.8	116.2	[1] 5,500	V [2]
	Sept. 14	11:46* 12:28*	Vicinity of Chittenden and Soda Lake.	36.8	121.6	5,000	VII
	Sept. 23	06:42*	Near San Jacinto	33.8	117.0	10,000	VI
	Dec. 6	00:34*	Bishop-Paradise area	37.5	118.7	10,000	VI
1964	Jan. 6	15:47*	San Bernardino County	34.3	116.5	4,500	V
	Mar. 22	08:31*	North of Hawthorne, Nev	38.8	118.7	7,500	V
	May 13	04:19*	San Benito	36.5	121.1	3,000	V
	June 21	07:33*	San Diego	32.7	117.1	[1] 2,000	VI
	June 22	20:55*	do	32.7	117.1	....	VI
	Oct. 30	11:03*	Dyer, Nev	37.7	118.0	....	VI
	Nov. 15	18:47*	North of Watsonville	37.0	121.7	12,000	VII
	Dec. 22	12:55*	Off coast, northwest of Ensenada, Mexico.	31.9	117.1	[1] 9,000	VI [2]
1965	Jan. 1	00:04*	Southwest of Fontana	34.0	117.6	4,000	VI
	Apr. 15	12:09*	San Bernardino Valley	34.1	117.5	4,000	VI
	June 3	08:26*	Bridgeport	38.3	119.2	4,000	V
	June 15	18:42*	Imperial Valley	33.0	115.5	1,000	VI
	July 15	23:46*	West of Saugus	34.4	118.6	3,000	VI

See footnotes at end of table

List of Earthquakes in California and Western Nevada—Continued

Year	Date	Time (PST)	Locality	N. lat.	W. long.	Area	Intensity
				degrees	*degrees*	*sq. mi.*	
1965	Sept. 10	13:29*	Pittsburg	38.0	121.9	3,000	VI
	Sept. 19	07:42*	Kings County	35.9	120.1	3,500	V
	Sept. 25	09:44*	Southeast of Newberry Springs	34.7	116.5	25,000	VII
	Oct. 17	01:45*	Near Palm Springs	33.9	116.8	6,000	VI
	Oct. 21	00:43*	East of Yucaipa	34.0	116.7	....	VI
	Nov. 12	15:55*	South of Glendale	34.0	118.2	800	VI
1966	Mar. 4	04:40*	Near Imperial	32.8	115.5	....	VI
	Apr. 2	04:49*	South of Luning, Nev	38.4	118.1	....	VI
	May 23	19:50*	Near Chico	39.7	121.8	12,000	VI
	June 27	20:26*	Parkfield	35.9	120.9	20,000	VII
	Aug. 7	09:36*	Gulf of California	31.8	114.5	....	VI[2]
	Sept. 12	08:41*	Near Boca	39.4	120.1	45,000	VII
	Oct. 1	21:13*	Palos Verdes Peninsula	33.9	118.3	....	VI
	Oct. 14	12:34*	Watsonville area	37.0	121.8	....	VI
1967	May 21	06:43*	Near Anza	33.5	116.6	9,000	VI
	June 14	20:58*	Near Whittier	34.0	118.0	....	VI
	June 26	07:16*	Near Ukiah	39.3	123.3	1,500	VI
	July 22	01:23*	Southeast of Paicines	36.5	121.1	....	VI
	Sept. 7	04:39*	Corralitos	37.0	121.8	6,500	VI
	Sept. 28	07:39*	Morgan Hill area	37.2	121.6	7,500	VI
	Dec. 10	04:07*	Ferndale area	40.5	124.6	6,000	VI
	Dec. 18	09:25*	Corralitos	37.0	121.8	9,000	VI
1968	Feb. 5	16:42*	Mount Montgomery, Nev., area	38.0	118.4	8,000	VI
	Mar. 21	13:55*	Corralitos area	37.0	121.7	3,500	V
	Mar. 28	13:22*	East of White Water	34.0	116.1	4,000	V
	Apr. 8	18:29*	South of Ocotillo Wells	33.2	116.1	60,000	VII
	Apr. 8	19:48*	Calexico area	33.1	116.0	....	VI
	Apr. 18	09:42*	South of Big Bear Lake	34.3	116.9	3,600	V
	Apr. 25	11:50*	Santa Rosa	38.5	122.7	5,000	VII
	Apr. 28	16:22*	South of Willows	39.5	122.0	10,500	VI
	May 22	05:27*	Salton City area	33.3	116.2	3,500	V
	June 25	17:42*	Petrolia-Honeydew area	40.1	124.4	5,000	VII
	June 29	11:14*	Goleta	34.3	119.6	....	VI
	July 4	16:45*	do	34.1	119.7	8,000	VI
1969	Jan. 23	15:01*	East of Palm Springs	33.9	116.0	5,000	V
	Feb. 7	13:26*	Ferndale area	40.4	124.5	4,000	VI
	Feb. 27	20:56*	Palmdale area	34.6	118.1	4,800	VI
	Apr. 28	15:21*	Borrego Springs area	33.4	116.4	30,000	VII
	May 19	06:41*	do	33.4	116.2	6,500	V
	June 7	03:27*	Capetown region	40.8	125.8	....	VI
	Oct. 1	20:57* 22:20*	Santa Rosa	38.5	122.7	10,500	VII–VIII
	Oct. 27	03:00	Hollister region	36.8	121.4	4,000	VI
	Oct. 27	05:16*	Near Laguna Beach	33.5	117.8	4,500	V
	Nov. 17	12:49*	Pine Canyon area	36.4	121.0	4,000	V
	Nov. 18	22:29*	do	36.4	121.6	3,500	V
1970	Jan. 2	18:52*	Cupertino area	37.3	122.1	1,200	VI
	Mar. 30	23:02*	Gilroy-Hollister	36.9	121.4	4,800	V
	May 18	07:08*	Fort Jones area	41.4	122.8	4,500	V
	June 11	19:30*	Danville	37.8	121.9	1,300	VI
	June 12	08:04*	do	37.8	121.9	....	VI

See footnotes at end of table

List of Earthquakes in California and Western Nevada—Continued

Year	Date	Time (PST)	Locality	N. lat.	W. long.	Area	Intensity
				degrees	*degrees*	*sq. mi.*	
1970	Aug. 3	20:14*	Carmel Valley region	36.6	122.2	5,500	VI
	Sept. 12	06:31*	Lytle Creek area	34.3	117.5	25,000	VII

*Instrumental origin time and epicenter.
[1] United States area affected.
[2] Intensity in United States.

TSUNAMI (TIDAL WAVE)

What is a tsunami?

The phenomenon we call "tsunami" is a series of traveling ocean waves of great length and long period, generated by disturbances associated with earthquakes in oceanic and coastal regions. As the tsunami crosses the deep ocean, its length from crest to crest may be a hundred miles or more, its height from trough to crest only a few feet. It **cannot** be felt aboard ships in deep water, and **cannot** be seen from the air. But in deep water, tsunami waves may reach forward speeds exceeding 600 miles per hour.

As the tsunami enters the shoaling water of coastlines in its path, the velocity of its waves diminishes and wave height **increases. It is in these shallow waters that tsunamis become a threat to life and property,** for they can crest to heights of more than 100 feet, and strike with devastating force.

The warning system—

Development of the NOAA Coast and Geodetic Survey's Pacific Tsunami Warning System was impelled by the disastrous waves of April 1946, which surprised Hawaii and took a heavy toll in life and property. The locally disastrous tsunami caused by the March 1964 Alaska earthquake impelled the development of another type of warning apparatus—the Regional Tsunami Warning System in Alaska.

The Regional Tsunami Warning System is headquartered at the Coast and Geodetic Survey's Seismological Observatory at Palmer, Alaska. This is the nerve center for an elaborate telemetry network linking Palmer with remote seismic and tidal stations along the Alaska coast and in the Aleutian Islands. Seismograph stations in the network are at Palmer Observatory and its two remote stations 25 miles south and west, and at Biorka, Sitka, Gilmore Creek, Kodiak, and Adak. Tide stations are at Seward, Sitka, Kodiak, Cold Bay, Unalaska, Adak, Yakutat, and Shemya. Data from these stations are recorded continuously at Palmer, where a 24-hour watch is kept.

When an earthquake occurs in the Alaska-Aleutian area, seismologists at Palmer Observatory rapidly determine its epicenter (the point on the earth's surface above the underground source of the earthquake) and magnitude. If the epicenter falls in the Aleutian Island arc or near Alaskan coastal area, and if the earthquake magnitude is great enough to generate a tsunami, Palmer Observatory issues a TSUNAMI WARNING through the Alaska Disaster Office, Alaska Command, and Federal Aviation Administration (FAA) covering the area near the epicenter. A TSUNAMI WATCH is issued for the rest of the Alaskan coastline, alerting the public to the possibility of a tsunami threat. If a tsunami is detected by tide stations, Palmer Observatory extends the TSUNAMI WARNING to cover the entire coastline of Alaska. If no tsunami is observed, both the WATCH and WARNING bulletins are cancelled.

Subsidiary warning centers have been established at Sitka and Adak Ob-

The tsunami churned up by Alaska's 1964 earthquake left this scene of destruction behind when the wall of water ebbed.

servatories. These facilities operate small seismic arrays and have a limited warning responsibility for local areas.

The Pacific Tsunami Warning System has its headquarters at the Coast and Geodetic Survey's Honolulu Observatory. There, seismologists monitor data received from seismic and tidal instruments in Hawaii and around the Pacific Ocean, and provide ocean-wide tsunami watches and warnings. The Pacific system works very closely with its regional counterpart in Alaska. Potentially tsunami-generating earthquakes in the Alaska-Aleutian area are detected and evaluated at Palmer Observatory, and the data relayed directly to Honolulu Observatory. Where there is tidal evidence of a tsunami, the warning is extended by Honolulu to cover the Pacific Ocean basin. For tsunamis generated elsewhere in the Pacific area, tsunami watch and warning bulletins are prepared at Honolulu Observatory and disseminated in Alaska by the Alaska Disaster Office, the military, and FAA.

TSUNAMI (TIDAL WAVE) SAFETY RULES –

Tsunamis are the so-called "tidal waves" generated by some earthquakes. When you hear a tsunami warning, you must assume a dangerour wave is on its way. History shows that when the great waves finally strike, they claim those who have ignored the warning.

REMEMBER:

1. **All earthquakes do not cause tsunamis, but many do. When you hear that an earthquake has occurred, stand by for a tsunami emergency.**
2. **A strong earthquake felt in a low-lying coastal area is a natural warning of possible, immediate danger. Keep calm and move to higher ground, away from the coast.**
3. **A tsunami is not a single wave, but a series of waves. Stay out of danger areas until an "all-clear" is issued by competent authority.**
4. **Approaching tsunamis are sometimes heralded by a noticeable rise or fall of coastal water. This is nature's tsunami warning and should be heeded.**
5. **A small tsunami at one beach can be a giant a few miles away. Don't let the modest size of one make you lose respect for all.**
6. **All tsunamis—like hurricanes—are potentially dangerous, even though they may not damage every coastline they strike.**
7. **Never go down to the beach to watch for a tsunami. When you can see the wave you are too close to escape it.**
8. **During a tsunami emergency, your local Civil Defense, police, and other emergency organizations will try to save your life. Give them your fullest cooperation.**

Stay tuned to your radio or television stations during a tsunami emergency—bulletins issued through Civil Defense and NOAA offices can help you save your life!

RETIREMENT AND HEALTH WEATHER

A REVIEW OF SOME ATMOSPHERIC FACTORS IN HEALTH AND DISEASE

The illusion that perfect health and happiness are within man's possibilities has flourished in many different forms throughout history.

Rene Dubos in Mirage of Health

Physicians since before the time of Hippocrates, the "father of medicine," have recognized the inexorable bond between the human organism and its physical environment. Hippocrates'[1] work *On Airs, Waters, and Places,* justly regarded as a medical classic and a source of philosophical inspiration in medical analysis, opens with this advice:

> *Whoever wishes to investigate medicine properly, should proceed thus: in the first place to consider the seasons of the year, and what effects each of them produce (for they are not at all alike, but differ much in themselves and in their changes). Then the winds, the hot and the cold, especially such as are common to all countries, and then such as are peculiar to each locality. We must also consider the qualities of the waters, for as they differ from one another in taste and weight, so also do they differ much in their qualities. In the same manner, when one comes into a city to which he is a stranger, he ought to consider its situation, how it lies as to the winds and the rising of the sun; for its influence is not the same whether it lies to the north or the south, to the rising sun [east] or to the setting sun [west].*

Claude Bernard, the great pioneer of scientific medicine in the mid-nineteenth century, recognised that the conditions necessary to life are found neither in the organism nor in the outer environment, but in both at once. The germ theory of disease which is almost exactly one hundred years old did much however to focus medical research on micro-organisms and away from the weaker but more pervasive influences of diet and the physical environment. Nevertheless, a hardy and, indeed, at times even foolhardy band of scientists and physicians have continued to probe for an understanding of the vexing relationships between nature and nurture in health and disease.

Scientific disciplines such as Biometeorology and Medical Geography which cut across many research specialties have been developed with increasing success in recent years. The information retrieval problem in cross-disciplinary subjects such as these is difficult because relevant findings may be scattered widely among 50,000 or more scientific and medical publications. Yet, the greatest problems arise because of inherent difficulties in the subject matters of investigation.

The weather is noted for its restless variability. As Frederick Sargent II[2] points out the atmospheric ingredients of weather "are rarely present in exactly the same proportion, and, as a consequence, it has been exceedingly difficult to conceive exact models of the physical environment." Yet, he continues, "the variability of the organism is no less simple. The individual organism, be it plant or animal, has biochemical and physiological individuality. Biochemical, physiological, and behavioral events in plants and animals vary in time [and] are regulated by biological clocks." These clocks have multiple rhythms. Approximate periods vary from one day, to a week, a month, a season, a year, and longer. Given such multiple controls, the variation in factors such as the chemical properties of the blood, functions of important organs or body systems, and overt behavior may be greater in a single individual over a long period of time than between different individuals at the same time.

The theme of the biological and behavioral uniqueness of individuals is an important one. Nothing can be done with it in this review except to note the extraordinary difficulty in making sense of fluctuating series of unique environmental and organismic events. The resulting literature can be exceedingly confusing and contradictory. It is founded too often upon statistical correlations of doubtful significance with the physiological linkages poorly established, for as Nelson Dingle[3] indicates, "in the search for cause and effect relationship in bioclimatological work, one needs to give careful attention to the question whether the data actually contain the required information." As R.E. Munn[4] concludes, "there is a vast literature on medical climatology. In many cases the evidence is inductive and not very convincing." The task of the reviewer is to try to sort the wheat from the chaff.*

Meteorotropisms

The Greek term "meteor" refers to atmospheric disturbances and "tropic" to turnings or changes. Hence, a scientific term has been coined to refer to a turn of events related to atmospheric disturbances: meteorotropism. The identification and analysis of such biological events is at the heart of the science of biometeorology. Having stated his ideas on the variability of living individuals, Sargent proceeds as follows:

> *The main inquiry of biometeorology is to find out how much of this organismic variability is due to the changing atmospheric environment within which the organisms exist . . . When biological events are ordered in time, deviations from the expected aggregate about certain hours, days, months, etc. When sizable human populations are investigated, it has been found that sudden death, attacks of angina, joint pain, insomnia, and traffic accidents occur with unusual frequency on certain days, or in certain seasons. In some cases, it has been possible to demonstrate by appropriate statistical procedures that characteristic changes in the atmospheric environment are correlated with the biological aggregations. The biological event is then identified as a meteorotropism.*

The convincing isolation of a weather related biological change from those related to some other form of environmental or internally induced stress is not an easy one, as Sargent is the first to acknowledge. Something of the problem can be seen by considering cases of aggravated duodenal ulcers.

Duodenal ulcer aggravation

The monthly summary of the number of patients admitted to the Philadelphia General Hospital with hemorrhaging duodenal ulcers over the period 1949-1953 records cases in every month but shows a tendency to peak in March-April and October-November of any given year. The peak in the fall is somewhat greater than the spring peak. Francis K. Davis, Jr.[5] notes that "since hemorrhage from ulcers is intimately connected with the circulatory system and since this system definitely reacts to temperature changes, an attempt was made to find some relationship between temperature changes and ulcer hemorrhages." The greatest decrease in average temperature from one month to the next during the period under study did in fact occur from October to November, and the greatest increase occurred between March and April. One particular January-February period had a higher incidence of admission than the other comparable periods. This January was characterized by an unusually high monthly average temperature and was followed by an unusually cold February. Moreover, this particular January experienced 16 day to day changes of more than 10 F° in maximum temperature, nine of which were from warm to cold. Thus, the plausible suggestion that "the period of negative temperature change contributes more strongly to circulatory stresses than the period of positive temperature change" receives some support, but "more detailed data than are presently

* A discussion of the effects of thermal stress on the body is found in the sections of this book dealing with "heat wave dangers" and "winter storms and wind chill."

available would be necessary to decide this point.'' Nevertheless, Davis concludes:

So, there is strong evidence that hemorrhage from duodenal ulcers may be brought on by marked variations in temperatures and the stress that such variations put on the body as it is forced to adjust. This fact, together with the observation that the number of cases is least in midsummer, would suggest that a warm climate with relatively little daily and seasonal variation in temperature would afford the most suitable residence for those prone to suffer from duodenal ulcers. Meanwhile, those northerners who are afflicted with duodenal ulcers might well be on the lookout for cold wave warnings in the fall. Such warnings cause construction workers to stop pouring concrete, prod farmers into taking special precautions to save crops, and serve to make fuel oil companies prepare for extra deliveries. They might be used to equal advantage by ulcer patients.

Or, can they?

Another study in southern Australia found an increase of reported ulcer cases during May-June, the equivalent of Philadelphia's November-December, thereby seeming to confirm the latter study. Yet, as Munn[4] points out, still another study in Hawaii, where there is a climate like that described by Davis as most suitable for ulcer patients, revealed a variation in frequency of ulcer aggravation through the months similar to that found in Philadelphia. Does this latter finding indicate that the hemorrhages have nothing to do with the weather? Does it indicate that they are related to some weather or environmental circumstance common to both types of settings but as yet not detected? Or does it indicate that the body is somewhat sterotyped in its response to stress and that very different factors can help to bring about the same variation in clinical condition? The prudent person with ulcers may want to follow Davis's advice, at least in so far as it implies elimination of outside activities during periods when the temperature is forecast to change sharply. More properly, that person would also want to consult with a well-read specialist in internal medicine.

Asthma and "Hay Fever"

The atmosphere is a carrier of countless gases and particles or droplets from natural and man-made sources. Some perons are extremely sensitive by way of allergic reactions to many substances that are quite common in the air. Different types of pollen and fungi spores are found in enormous numbers in various seasons. Asthma symptoms ranging from wheezes to near suffocation result from exposure to many of these substances. Various man-made air pollutants also seem to be implicated.

Fairly good correlations can be found between reported asthma attack rate and levels of air pollution measured variously by indices of sulfur dioxide, nitrates, suspended particulate, and total oxidant — the terms are treated further in the air pollution section of the book. Arlan A. Cohen, M.D. and co-workers[6] conducted an intensive study in New Cumberland, West Virginia where "significant correlations were found between . . . attack rate and pollution levels after the effects of temperature had been removed from the analysis. These temperature independent air pollution effects occurred at levels of pollution commonly found in large cities, and appeared greater at moderate than at low temperatures." The weather related effects, in themselves, are very interesting and fairly well established by independent investigators.

Sudden changes in the weather can be a very important trigger for the beginning of all types of asthma attacks whether characterized by an allergic reaction to air borne particles or by bronchial infections. Solco Tromp[7] of the Netherlands has concluded that the frequency of asthma increases rapidly after a sudden increase in the general turbulence of the air combined with rapidly falling temperature. In other words, the increase occurs during the advance and passage of an active fast-moving cold front. The increase is most striking after a long quiet period with moderate temperatures.

On a seasonal basis, the average asthma frequency is low during the winter and spring with significant increases, at least in the Netherlands, at the end of June. The maximum frequency generally occurs sometime between September and November. Studies in the United States seem to indicate that the effects are most pronounced in the early fall during the first or second invasion of cold air when indoor heating has to be reinitiated. Cold frontal passages later in the winter produce less spectacular increases in both the frequency and severity of asthma attacks. These meteorotropisms have been attributed variously to the stirring of allergenic substances in the house with the renewed heating and to the difficulty the body has in adjusting to cold stress after lengthy adaption to warm conditions. Either condition may be expected to decline over the winter months.

A sharp decrease in asthma frequency is observed during the influx of warm tropical air associated with an active warm front and during periods of mild but calm and settled weather. A rapid succession of cold and warm fronts can set up waves of increasing and decreasing asthma frequency. On the other hand, in warm climates, great heat stress is associated with an increase of asthma complaints. To further complicate the picture, Tromp notes that, contrary to patients suffering from non-infectious asthma, the bronchitic patients have the highest degree of complaints in winter, particularly in January and February, and a minimum in the summer.

''Hay fever'' (seasonal vasomotor rhinitis) is neither caused by hay nor very often associated with fever. It is caused by seasonal allergens produced by plants that often flower around the hay season. The characteristic symptoms such as excessive sneezing, stuffiness, profuse nasal discharge, fatigue, itching eyes, nose, mouth and so forth may also occur on a non-seasonal basis as the result of allergies to substances such as house-dust, animal products, or foods. The weather factors associated with the production, release, and transport of various ragweed pollens of the ''late season'' from August until first frost have been studied in greater depth than those associated with the aeroallergens of other seasons.

The highest ragweed pollen indices are found in a triangular portion of the United States bounded by the eastern Great Plains, the Gulf of Mexico and the Appalachian Mountains, and the middle Great Lakes. In the southern part of Michigan, a particularly bad area for hay fever, it has been found that high May rainfall and low July rainfall promote the maximum annual yield of pollen. Dingle[3] reports that ''on an average midsummer day, with dew at sunrise and sunny weather, the mature flowers begin to swell outward before the dew disappears . . . . As the relative humidity drops with solar warming, the anthers open in quick succession throughout the local ragweed population.'' He also notes that the openings take place quickly when the humidity is low, much more slowly when it is high, and perhaps not at all under steady rain.

The vast majority of ragweed pollen falls out within a few hundred feet of the source. Local up-drafts that produce fair weather or ''bubble'' clouds or the turbulence associated with thunderstorms or approaching cold fronts may, if timed properly with the release of pollen, carry large amounts of pollen to considerable heights. The grains may be swept along for hundreds of miles before falling out or being washed-out by precipitation. Dingle believes that the likelihood of the reflotation of pollen which has fallen out is small in comparison with the amount of fresh daily emissions.

Heart diseases

According to the Department of Health, Education, and Welfare about 1,250,000 heart attacks (acute myocardial infarction) occur annually in the United States of which about 400,000 are deadly. Some 25,000,000 persons suffer from various forms of heart and vascular disease such as stroke and high blood pressure leading to more than 1,000,000 deaths each year. Many studies in Western Europe and various parts of the United States have shown significant correlations between these diseases and some form of temperature stress. It is said that persons with coronary artery disease cannot tolerate exposure to cold wind combined with high humidity without experiencing severe chest pain. Such sensitivity of course cannot explain the rather frequent occurrence of heart attacks during rest in a comfortable room or during sleep in a warm bed. Still, certain patterns emerge from the study of weather stresses that help to explain some of the seasonal variations, where they occur. An early study in Los Angeles before World War II could establish no significant seasonal variation in that mild climate. What the situation might be like today with many more social and environmental stresses added to the life of Angelenos would make the basis for an interesting study.

Solco Tromp,[7] who is perhaps the leading European biometeorologist, summarizes the major observed cardiovascular meteorotropic correlations as follows:

(1) In the Northern countries the mortality rate of coronary heart diseases, being considerably higher in males than in females, is almost every year highest in January-February and lowest around July-August.

(2) The mortality rate for stroke, being higher in females than in males, shows each year the same seasonal pattern as the coronary heart diseases.

(3) In very warm countries, such as the southern part of the United States, highest mortality incidence is observed in summer, lowest in winter.

Tromp notes further that winters with abnormally low temperatures are characterized by very high mortality and that during relatively warm winters mortality is relatively low. Similarly, during the summer, even in regions that have relatively low mortality rates in that season, the higher the temperature the more people seem to die from stroke and coronary heart disease. Studies in Philadelphia and Kentucky, where the seasonal extremes are fairly great, reveal a double peak in winter and in summer, at least in males.

One of the most suggestive studies was made in Dallas, Texas. The highest number of heart attacks occurred in the summer and the lowest during the winter season. But a more careful analysis conducted with an eye to strong frontal passages and sudden air mass changes rather than simply to average monthly temperatures revealed an increased frequency of heart attacks in any season during periods of sudden inflow of polar or tropical air masses. The winter cold waves may not last very long, but they can be quite severe, as can the summer heat waves. Thus, while the weather patterns in Dallas and Philadelphia are quite different, as are the patterns of heart disease, the correlations in both places with rapid changes toward hot or cold air masses show considerably unity of result.

Although the basic correlations between heart attacks and weather factors are not clearly established, the findings and opinions of different investigators do not have to be regarded as so widely divergent as they sometimes seem to be. Tromp notes that the findings of significant correlations between meteorological stress (particularly heat and cold) and increased incidence of diseases such as myocardial infarction, angina pectoris, and stroke have been confirmed in artifical climate chambers.

Arthritis

Some persons have an almost legendary sensitivity to weather changes. They have been called variously, "cyclonopaths,' 'weather birds,' 'human barometers," and other terms suggesting sensitivity to changing conditions of the atmosphere. Twinges of gout and sciatica are popularly supposed to forecast rain. Most familiar is the conviction expressed in folklore that pains from scars and from arthritis sharpen during weather in the vicinity of a front separating one air mass from another type. For few indeed are those persons who doubt that

A coming storm our shooting corns presage
Our aches will throb, our hollow tooth will rage.

Such folk wisdom has received a great deal of medical support. Indeed, Hippocrates, or one of his followers, tried to relate atmospheric conditions and the personality of individuals in a treatise *On Temperaments and Humors*. The ideas survived in one form or another well past the time of Shakespeare. In the present day, some of the relations between mood or pain and the weather are being put on a fairly sound basis. Some of the more interesting results have been obtained in the Climatron or controlled climate chamber at the Hospital of the University of Pennsylvania.[8]

It should be clear by now that studies of human populations in their usual habitats are frustratingly difficult. Thus, many investigators have taken recourse to artificial chambers where experimental subjects can live for several weeks. Five or more factors can be varied singly or in various combinations. Some of the meteorotropic relations may be clarified in such chambers, although considerable difficulties remain in the attempt to generalize to the "real" world.

The Pennsylvania Climatron can control temperature, humidity, pressure, air flow, and ionization. Experiments with arthritic patients in which the environmental factors were varied one at a time in random order with a return to "standard" conditions in between resulted in no significant effect on the clinical index of well being and joint condition. Large effects however were produced in a group of eight patients with rheumatoid arthritis when they were subjected to simultaneous variations of pressure and humidity. Seven patients were afflicted with greatly increased arthritis in 57% to 100% of their trial exposures. One patient was insensitive to the same changes through six cycles. Typically, the effects occurred in a cycle when relative humidity was increased from 30% to 80% while the atmospheric pressure was simulataneously decreased by 10% over a six hour period. It should be noted that these rates of change are considerably higher than those that occur naturally in the atmosphere, except perhaps in rapidly moving hurricanes. The details of the clinical indices varied considerably from patient to patient and for different features of the programmed environmental changes, but the general effects were clear enough to justify the conclusion that

From these results, it would appear that at least one condition of changing weather factors – rising humidity with falling barometric pressure – fairly consistently exerts a detrimental effect on arthritic symptoms and signs. It would also appear that the changing conditions, rather than the high humidity or low barometric pressure, are responsible. It now seems reasonable to conclude that weather effect on arthritis is a definite phenomena, and not just another old wives' tale. It is not implied that climatic changes have any direct bearing on the cause of arthritis, nor is it believed that a constant climate would have any fundamentally curative effect.

On changing climate

The effects of many drugs change with changes in the weather. Digitalis, a drug widely used in heart disease, in experimental doses in animals is more toxic during storms than in stable atmospheric conditions. Its toxicity also rises with increased body temperature and increased elevations. It may be the case that these variations in toxicity as well as the variations in the effects of other drugs are related to the permeability of various membranes in the body and thereby to the ease with which the drugs can enter the blood stream. Weather may trigger the body responses that result in these changes, but little is known about the relevant biological mechanisms. At any rate, Helmut Landsberg[9] notes that some sleep inducing drugs have reduced effects at high temperatures, the response to insulin is apparently slowed by exposure to cold, atropine taken internally to relieve spasms also inhibits sweating and can thereby be dangerous in a hot environment, and some diuretics can cause excess loss of sodium leading to circulatory complications in persons not acclimated to a hot environment. Thus, in this era of high speed business and recreational travel from one climate zone to another, the traveler is well advised to check with a physician about possible changes in medication or dosage.

Jet-lag, or rapid time zone travel fatigue, has made people aware of the difficulties that even healthy individuals may experience in forcing their organism to adapt quickly to a new environment. Some persons can adapt fairly quickly with few ill effedts, but many individuals adjust only slowly and with considerable strain.

Many older persons as well as a few younger ones, who are otherwise healthy, may have organic responses to day to day weather changes that are slow enough so that their bodies are never quite "in balance" with the environment. Even though no particular disease may be present, feelings of dis-ease may result. On the other hand, there are schools of medical thought stemming from Hippocrates' time which do not draw sharp distinction between conditions of disease and feelings of dis-ease.

In trying to find an "ideal" climate, people frequently ask whether a move to a different area would be beneficial to their health. Vacations have traditionally been an attempt for many people to find a more ideal environment, at least for a short period of time. Yet, contemporary folk wisdom tells of the need to take a rest on returning from an otherwise delightful vacation. This bit of folk wisdom has some bearing on the question of moving to a different area. There are many reasons for this advice. One reason is the slowness with which human organisms adapt to major climatic changes. Acclimatization to a new area may take ten years or longer in the opinion of some investigators. It is certainly a process that can take weeks to occur. Clothing habits change quickly enough, and thirst brings about rapid changes in the amount of fluid intake — although to be sure the nature of the fluid imbibed in recreational settings is often inappropriate for a well functioning organism. The quantity and quality of food intake and physical exertion is even more frequently inappropriate to the new setting, and the process of acclimatization can be a long drawn out affair indeed. Motivation plays an important role in speeding the process.

An important consideration for the person thinking of making a "permanent" move to a new location is a possibility of a return to the original environment. Acclimatization is a two way process. After an experience of several years in a new environment, adaptation may be more or less complete. The process of readaptation to the original setting, however, may be even more difficult than the former process. The body is older and, for lack of a better term, may have less "elasticity" in the various vital systems. Also, there may have been adaptive changes that are in principle difficult to reverse. This latter point is highly speculative.

The search for an "ideal" climate may be a never ending one. Each person is affected in an individual way by his environment and no group could agree on the ideal. The process of acclimation is a complicated interplay of physiological, behavioral, and physhological responses. A person has to feel "at home and wanted." The health and well-being of many persons may be served best by staying in the "native" setting even though it may be regarded as far from ideal. "Air conditioning" in both summer and winter can be a big help in making the old environment do. Of course, in the face of continued ecological decay and energy supplies that will be critical for some time to come and increasingly expensive, people need to consider the possibility of reducing their less essential demands in exchange for the goods and services that make for a healthier way of life.

"Inadvertant" changes in climate

A major maladaption of modern societies concerns the disposition of industrial, commercial, transportation, and household wastes. Man has long disposed of these wastes into the air, water, and soil on the assumption that the vastness of these resources could cope adequately with the necessary dispersal, dilution, and assimulation of the waste products. Even before Hippocrates wrote *On Airs, Waters, and Places,* air, water, and soil have been known to be vital resources for all living things. It is now clear that these resources cannot continue to be polluted at the accelerating pace of modern society. The possible would wide effects on climate and environmental quality will not be discussed in this review, but the local and regional health effects of air pollutants will be treated briefly.

The large number of deaths in excess of seasonal normals associated with air pollution episodes in places such as Donora, Pennsylvania and London, England until as recently as ten or twenty years ago are hopefully things of the past. These earlier episodes involved changes in the expected death rates of 50% or more! They probably were triggered by extraordinarily high levels of pollutants such as sulfur dioxide and particulates: — the pollutants produced by uncontrolled heavy industrial processes and the burning of any but the highest grades of coal and fuel oil. In these earlier episodes, the pollutants accumulated to intolerably high levels when the weather pattern over the particular region stagnated for three or more days. Technological remedies of long standing (dating back 40 to 100 years or more!) and newer control techniques coupled with shifts from coal to gas and high grade fuel oil as energy sources finally have been instituted in most highly populated regions of the developed world. Some of the control techniques have not been adequately developed yet and the existing ones have not been universally adopted. With regard to the "old fashioned pollutants, most cities are in far better shape today than they were a decade ago. But the difficult improvements lie ahead.

The problem of urban air pollution by the old standby sulfer dioxide and respirable particles has by no means been solved. Out-patient and emergency ward counts in large cities continue to show low correlations with existing air pollution levels of these substances. The effects are truly marginal, and require very nice analytical techniques. Using the best studies available, the correlations involving the various measures of sulfur dioxide, suspended particulate, and total oxidant can be translated even today into thousands of excess hospital and doctor visits for respiratory ailments and associated cardiovascular problems. The dramatic death dealing episodes may be over, at least for a while, but air pollution related deaths continue to occur at lower levels where they tend to be hidden in the "noise of normal day-to-day and season-to-season variations in death rates.

Lester Lave and Eugene Seskin[10] believe they have developed techniques of analysis sensitive enough to isolate the proportion of deaths associated with air pollution described by indices of particulates and sulfates. The statistical significance of their findings remains even when climate, home heating, and various social or economic variables are added. They have available only crude measures of the various factors believed to be responsible for most of the observed variation, and one can question whether their air quality and other social and environmental data really contain the necessary information. Still, based on the best available measurements, they conclude that a 50% reduction in the urban levels of particulates and sulfates could cut the urban death rates by 4% and add one full year to life expectancy at birth. According to Lave and Seskin, the social and economic benefits of such a reduction in pollution, which is technologically feasible, would be comparable to the complete eradication of cancer, which is not medically possible at present. The economic cost of such reduction are varied according to different strategies economic management. With no offsetting governmental intervention, for example, the prices of manufactured goods — exclusive of automobiles — might be expected to rise between 0% and 5% for an average rise of about 2% and net unemployment might be expected to rise by about 0.2% during the first few years of such a phased abatement program.

The sickness and mortality effects of the types of air pollutants associated with automobile exhausts such as hydorcarbons, carbon monoxide, nitrogen oxides, and the oxides of heavy metal additives are more subtle and hence more difficult to isolate than similar effects in the case of heavy industrial effluents and the combustion products of raw coal and low grade oil. Even so, statistical analysis and prudent concern establishes well enough the need for new combustion technology and alternative forms of transportation. The goals set by the Clean Air Act of 1970 for the automobile industry to meet for the 1975 and 1976 model years are very stringent. The economic costs of meeting those standards are roughly twice those mentioned above and they include a significant penalty in consumption of limited fuel resources. Some people argue that the goals for the automobile industry are excessive. More realistically, it might be argued that those goals go somewhat beyond the level required for balanced progress in environmental management. The issue is not one of need, but one of priorities and strategy in achieving responsible environmental stewardship.

The truth is that only a brief respite will have been achieved from Man's habit of fouling his nest — someone's waste spaces are someone else's living spaces — unless the search for better technological palliatives is coupled with a less demanding way of life. The sad part of the picture is that the areas with the highest potential for air pollution episodes are precisely the areas with the most stable weather patterns and hence the areas most desirable for many health, recreational, and retirement living purposes. As the pressure mounts to continue the rapid subdivision and economic development of the desirable southeastern, southwestern and west coast areas of the United States, the high potential that they have for weather stagnation and serious air pollution episodes will be fullfilled with increasing frequency. The same conclusion applies to comparable areas in Europe. Existing social and technological mechanisms will have to be maintained even when the economic shoe begins to pinch a little, and new ones developed to make further significant cuts in the witches brew of chemicals that continue to degrade the quality of the air and other life resources. As an aid to the general public in thinking about these issues more deeply, this book draws together for the first time in a single convenient source the best judgments from members of the Environmental Protection Agency about the existing air quality in the various analysis regions of the nation.

Spirit willing and pocketbook able

Americans have always been a mobile people. Freedom of movement for business, recreational, and retirement purposes is a valued privilege of the American way of life. It should not be treated lightly or abused. Knowledge of all the effects of any given movement is, of course, impossible to obtain. Nevertheless, considerable insight about the atmospheric conditions to be found in or near the major urban settings of the nation can be derived from this book. One of its purposes is to provide the basis for that insight in one convenient source. It is like an almanac, the more it is used, the more connections can be seen, and the more valuable the book becomes. On the basis of experience, conversation, and intuition, everyone has some idea of desirable, if not quite ideal, weather patterns. Everyone can extrapolate from known situations to plan for the visit or move that has to be made.

The various tables in this book summarize as far as possible in popular or semi-popular terms the recent weather and air quality history of more than 100 locations in the United States and many additional cities abroad. Each of the standard elements of the observed weather is presented in a way that indicates a great deal about the averages and the amount of deviation that may be expected to occur in any given month. The reader will want to pay attention especially to the information on temperature means and extremes,

the persistence of extreme conditions in any month, humidity, sky cover and sunshine. A complete guide to the information in the climatic summaries is found in the section, "How to get answers to your weather questions." Information is also presented to facilitate easy comparisons of the average air quality that may be expected.

It is impossible to make forecasts from this book. Not even the Farmer's Almanac (!) can do that in any meaningful way. The judicious examination of the various tables of the book, in comparison with the tables for an area known well from first hand experience, can be an aid in planning for both short term and longer term "changes of climate."

J.A.R.

Suggestions for Further Reading

The subject of biometeorology is treated simply and succinctly in

Landsberg, Helmut E., *Weather and Health*, Doubleday Anchor Science Studies Series S 59 ($1.45), 1969

A very readable introduction to the philosophy of medicine and biological change is

Dubos, Rene, *Mirage of Health*, Doubleday Anchor A258 ($1.25), 1959

The best elementary introduction to air pollution meteorology is

Battan, Louis J., *The Unclean Sky*, Doubleday Anchor Science Studies Series S 46 ($1.25), 1966

A simple but more general approach to air pollution is

[Corman, Rena], *Air Pollution Primer*, published in 1969 by the National Tuberculosis and Respiratory Disease Association (now, the American Lung Association) A copy can be obtained from the offices of your local chapter.

Somewhat more advanced treatments of these subjects can be found in the following books:
Dubos, Rene, *Man Adapting,* Yale University Press, 1965
Licht, Sidney-M.D. (Ed.), *Medical Climatology,* Elizabeth Licht, Publisher, 1964

Reference Notes

1. Hippocrates. A useful collection that includes *On Airs, Waters, and Places* along with other treatises or extracts is *The Theory and Practice of Medicine,* Citadel Press, 1964

2. Sargent, Frederick, II, "The Nature and Nurture of Biometeorology," *Bulletin of the American Meteorological Society,* Vol. 44, No. 8 (August 1963), pp. 483-448.

3. Dingle, A.N., comment, p. 148 in Tromp, S.W. (ed.), *Biometeorology,* Pergamon Press, 1962. Dingle's ideas on pollution by ragweed pollen are found in Licht, Sidney (ed.), *Medical Meteorology,* Licht, 1964, pp. 96-130.

4. Munn, R.E., *Biometeorological Methods,* Academic Press, 1970, p. 255.

5. Davis, Francis K., Jr., "Ulcers and Temperature Changes," *Bulletin of American Meteorological Society,* Vol. 39, No. 12 (December 1958), pp. 652-654

6. Cohen, Arlan A., M.D., *et. al.,*"Asthma and Air Pollution from a Coal-Fueled Power Plant", *American Journal of Public Health,* Vol. 62, No. 9 (September 1972), pp. 1181-1188.

7. Tromp, Solco W., "Biometeorological Aspects of Architectural and Urban Planning and Their Significance for the Thermoregulatory Efficiency, and Physico-Chemical State of the Blood of Human Subjects," Conference on Urban Environment and Second Conference on Biometeorology, 1972. *Preprint Volume* of papers available from the American Meteorological Society, 45 Beacon Street, Boston, Mass., 02108. Tromp's work is also reported extensively in two volumes he edited, *Biometeorology,* Pergamon Press, 1962 and *Medical Meteorology,* Elsevier, 1962. All three of these volumes are first rate.

8. Hollander, Joseph L. and S.J. Yeostros, "The Effect of Simultaneous Variations of Humidity and Barometric Pressure on Arthritis," *Bulletin of the American Meteorological Society,* Vol. 44, No. 8 (August 1963), pp. 489-494.

9. Landsberg, Helmut E., *Weather and Health,* Doubleday Anchor, 1969, pp. 126-128. Essential; the next book to be read.

10. Lave, Lester B. and Eugene P. Seskin, "Air Pollution, Climate, and Home Heating: Their Effects on U.S. Mortality Rates," *American Journal of Public Health,* Vol. 62, No. 7 (July 1972), pp. 909-916.

JET-LAG OR TIME-ZONE FATIGUE

The modern jet airplane makes it possible for a person to travel great distances in a few hours under conditions of great comfort and safety. An exception is the physiological and mental stress that most persons encounter if four or more time zones are crossed creating the effects of what is commonly called "jet-lag" or "time-zone fatigue."

More than 100 biological functions and human activities are geared to fluctuate between maximum and minimum values in about 24 hours, the so-called "circadian rhythms" (from the Latin words "circa" and "dies" for approximately one day) or "body clocks." After a jet flight of several hours across a continent or an ocean, a traveler's "body clocks" will be badly out of phase or "desynchronized" with respect to local time. The body rhythms will tend to be in phase with the time of the place of departure rather than the local time of the place of arrival.

The travel induced phase shift between "body time" and "local time" will cause some discomfort and, more dangerously, lapses in alertness, immediate memory, and impairment of normal judgments. Hunger, sleep, elimination patterns, and mental functioning may take several days to return to normal. Deep body temperatures, which are commonly highest around 5 PM and lowest around 4 or 5 AM, and the associated biochemical processes, may take a little longer to become resynchronized.

One easy to remember rule of thumb is that most travelers readjust to the new time zone at the rate of about one hour per day, although each function has its own rate of return and there is marked individual variability in the severity of desynchronization and the rate of recovery.

North-south flights produce few of these effects, although, for reasons to be made clear, such travel within a time zone can cause a high degree of subjective fatigue as well as certain physiological effects keyed to drugs, alcohol, and smoking that need attention by the wise traveler.

In nearly all cases, the effects increase with the age of the traveler.

Social factors

Some studies of adaption to time zone shifts seem to show the importance of social and psychological factors in the readjustment process. Less deterioration seems to take place when persons travel in groups. Related observations reveal that fatigue seems to be less and resynchronization may occur more rapidly in relation to familiar surroundings. The problems may be reduced when the person experiences a high degree of motivation and generally feels "at home."

Anything that interferes with the oxygen up-take of body and brain cells produces an anemia, fatigue, and an impairment of mental functioning. Alcohol from drinking and carbon monoxide from smoking are two common sources of such deterioration. The reduced oxygen pressure at altitudes above 10,000 feet produces physiological effects similar to those of moderate drinking and smoking in persons acclimatized to near sea level pressures. Fatigue occurs rapidly in such persons at pressure altitudes above about 12,000 feet. With modern airplanes pressurized to between 6,000 and 8,000 feet, even though flying at altitudes well above 30,000 feet, fatigue and mental impairment are minimized. The various effects are additive, however. A person who drinks or smokes during, or for several hours prior, to a flight can experience a physiological altitude of 10,000 to 12,000 feet or more, with the alcohol and smoke having twice the effect of similar amounts at sea level. Thus, for example, two drinks immediately before and during flight might suddenly induce the effects of four drinks undeı normal circumstances. The effects of these habits on the cardio-vascular system and mental functioning are bad enough for north-sourth flights within a time zone. They aggravate considerably the jet-lag effects of easterly or westerly flights.

Time-zone travel tips

Various common sense rules can be developed from these generalizations. Persons with chronic or acute respiratory and circulatory disorders should abstain from smoking and drinking during and for several hours before any air flight, even if they have not managed to change their behavior for the better in normal circumstances. Consultation with a physician is prudent. All persons should at least moderate their drinking and smoking habits, if not abstain altogether, in order to minimize fatigue and the other effects of long distance high speed travel.

A person should try to adjust sleeping and eating patterns over several days before departure. Eating smaller amounts, more frequently than usual, and, in any case, avoiding a heavy meal just before or just after the flight can be helpful. If possible, sleeping and awakening should be adjusted about an hour a day in each of several days before departure. Thus, before flying toward the east, bedtime and wakeup time can be set one hour earlier in each of several days, or set one hour later in preparation for a westbound flight. Flights of more than 10,000 miles should include a 24 hour stopover.

A flight can be selected profitably to arrive in the afternoon or evening rather than in the morning in order to move more quickly into the crucial sleep patterns of the new time zone. Evening entertainment or business activities should be avoided on the day of arrival. If adaption is to take place after arrival, important decisions or strenuous sight-seeing should be postponed for a day or two. Avoid sleep inducing medications, which reduce the most refreshing REM or rapid eye movement phase of sleep. Light meals, mild exercise such as walking, and warm baths should help to speed adaption to the new sleep cycle.

As a final suggestion, since the effects of many medications can change considerably with pressure altitude, it would be wise to check with your physician before departure about changes in schedule or dosage that might prove to be beneficial.

Recommended further reading on body clocks and jet lag:

Aschoff, J., "Circadian rhythms in man," *Science*, V. 148 (June 11, 1965), 1427-32.

Brown, F. A. Jr., "The 'clocks' timing biological rhythms," *American Scientist*, V. 60 (December 1972), 756-66.

McFarland, R. A., "Air travel across time zones," *American Scientist*, V. 63 (January-February 1975), 23-30.

Siegel, P. V., *et. al.*, "Time zone effects," *Science*, V. 164 (June 13, 1969), 1249-55.

Strughold, Hubertus, M.D., *Your Body Clock, its significance for the jet traveler*, Charles Scribner's Sons, New York, 1971.

QUOTES FROM WEATHER FOLKLORE–

If three days old her face be bright and clear,
No rain or stormy gale the sailors fear;
But if she rise with bright and blushing cheek,
The blustering winds the bending mast will
shake,
If dull her face and blunt her horns appear,
On the fourth day a breeze or rain is near.
If on the third she moves with horns direct,
Not pointing downward or to heaven erect,
The western wind expect; and drenching rain,
If on the fourth her horns direct remain.
If to the earth her upper horn she bend,
Cold Boreas from the north his blast will send;
If upward she extend it to the sky,
Loud Notus with his blustering gale is nigh.
When the fourth day around her orb is spread
A circling ring of deep and murky red,
Soon from his cave the God of Storms will rise,
Dashing with foamy waves the lowering skies.
And when fair Cynthia her full orb displays,
Or when unveiled to sight are half her rays,
Then mark the various hues that paint her face,
And thus the fickle weather's changes trace.
If smile her pearly face benign and fair,
Calm and serene will breathe the balmy air;
If with deep blush her maiden cheek be red,
Then boisterous wind the caution sailors dread;
If sullen blackness hang upon her brow,
From clouds as black will rainy torrents flow.
Not through the month their power these
signs extend,
But all their influence with the quarter end.
– J. Lamb's "Aratus."

AIR POLLUTION

AIR POLLUTION

We all are responsible for air pollution to some degree depending upon our economic demands and manner of living. We all are victims to some extent of its harmful consequences depending upon our physical state and where we live and work. Precise determination of these consequences, which vary considerably with time, place, and person, is not easy to make. It is certain, however, that no one completely escapes the ill effects of polluted air. The booklet, *A Citizen's Guide to Clean Air*, prepared by the Conservation Foundation under contract with the Environmental Protection Agency interpreted the seriousness of air pollution as follows:

> *Air pollution can kill. In London, New York, and Donora, Pennsylvania, polluted air–sustained and heavy for several days–has caused serious illness and death, especially among infants, the elderly, and people with weakened hearts or lungs.**

The examples are overworked and badly dated, but they remind us that one of the prices of clean air is continuing hard work. While the "death harvests" of the killer episodes have been greatly reduced since the 1950s and 60s, it is likely that thousands of preventable (pollution related) deaths per year remain in the national totals.

Other serious consequences of dirty air described in the *Citizen's Guide* can stand without comment:

> *Air pollution can impair health. Dirty air makes eyes water and smart; it stings the throat and upsets breathing. People with chronic lung or heart disease are particularly vulnerable to air pollution. We are just beginning to measure the adverse health effects that can result from continuous exposure to relatively low concentrations of pollutants. Epidemiological studies indicate that direct relationships exist between prolonged exposure to polluted air and the incidence of emphysema, bronchitis, asthma, and lung cancer.*
>
> *More obviously, of course, air pollution reduces visibility. It can spoil scenic vistas. It can ground planes and making driving hazardous. Its corrosive qualities cause vast economic losses and contribute to the deterioration of cities. It rots and soils clothes, discolors house paints, and rusts metals. By eating away stone and metal, it mars monuments and public buildings and increases housekeeping chores and costs for cities, families, and businesses. The Library of Congress says its books and manuscripts deteriorate more rapidly because of air pollution. The National Gallery of Art suspects that air pollution is damaging masterpieces.*
>
> *Damage from air pollution is not just an urban phenomenon. It affects rural areas, too, by injuring vegetation, stunting the growth of shrubs and flowers, severely damaging crops and trees, and causing illness among livestock. To many farmers, these costs are apparent and direct. But to most*

*See pages 160–170

of us, they come indirectly – in the form of higher food bills and, from time to time, contaminated foods . . . . And there is growing evidence that air pollution may be having adverse effects on the growth and reproduction of some of our forests.

A commonly cited estimate of the dollar costs of air pollution — in terms of damage to health, materials, property, and vegetation — is $16 billion per year, with the economic costs of human illness and excess mortality set at about $6 billion. The base year was 1968. More recent studies, using somewhat different procedures, place the cost of damage and avoidance action at $25 billion or more per year in 1976 dollars. All such estimates of the "social costs" of air pollution, or what economists call "externalities," have serious flaws in them wholly separate from the absence of equations for suffering, anxiety, or grief. Perhaps, they provide a ball-park figure. Recent estimates indicate that control costs can be expected to increase over the next decade from about $10 billion a year to at least $25 billion annually in constant 1976 dollars. How much the social costs will be reduced by such expenditures is not clear. The reduction in cost should be substantial but they will not go to zero. The clamour for cost-benefit determination of policy will continue to rise.

Concern about air pollution in U.S. cities is at least a century old. Comprehensive control action is less than a decade old. The pioneer activities before World War II scored a few modest victories and probably can be credited with keeping many locally bad situations from getting worse. The early post war efforts, aided greatly by the rapid displacement of coal by oil and natural gas in small furnaces and boilers, showed that real, if limited, improvement was possible where local laws were enforced vigorously. The problem was one of using local "police" powers to force the widespread adoption and maintenance of known control remedies, many of which were of long standing development. These local approaches were directed mainly against dense smoke. They were fragmented, uneven in quality, and of limited effectiveness. The changing character of urban complexes, population distribution and mobility patterns, and the emergence of new emission problems or the more complete appraisal of old emission problems led to the development of increasingly comprehensive state and ultimately federal programs. Many forcing actions were required, as in the case of the automobile, to develop new or improved control techniques. Over the years, progress has been made, but many knotty technological, economic, and regulatory problems remain in the effort to clean up our air.

The first major attack on air pollution was mounted by the cities in the, so called, Progressive Era before World War I. One by one, cities enacted or upgraded laws governing their jurisdictions. The efforts at city and state levels were revitalized in the 1940s and 50s. Finally, in the years since 1955, the Congress has enacted a series of laws intended to encourage training, research, and development and to provide a framework for effective action coordinated by federal authorities, but implemented by state authorities. The two most important of these federal laws were the Clean Air Act of 1967 and the Clean Air Act Amendments of 1970. In particular, the 1970 amendments mandated the development and enforcement of ambient air quality standards for various pollutants. As noted below, these standards are of two types. The amendments specifically require that primary air quality standards be set to fully protect public health and that the standards contain an adequate margin of safety. Moreover, the amendments required that the primary or health related standards be achieved throughout the nation by mid 1975 with allowances for a two year extension to 1977 in certain cases. The various standards for the five major classes of pollutants established so far are given in Table 5.1.

Table 5.1

National Ambient Air Quality Standards

Pollutant	*Primary*	*Secondary*
Particulate Matter		
Annual geometric mean	75	60
Maximum 24-hour concentration*	260	150
Sulfur Oxides		
Annual arithmetic mean	80 (.03 ppm)	60 (.02 ppm)
Maximum 24-hour concentration*	365 (.14 ppm)	260 (.1 ppm)
Maximum 3-hour concentration*		1,300 (.5 ppm)
Carbon Monoxide		
Maximum 8-hour concentration*	10 (9 ppm)	
Maximum 1-hour concentration*	40 (35 ppm)	same as primary
Photochemical Oxidants		
Maximum 1-hour concentration*	160 (.08 ppm)	same as primary
Nitrogen Oxides		
Annual arithmetic mean	100 (.05 ppm)	same as primary

(All measurements are expressed in micrograms per cubic meter ($\mu g/m^3$) except for those for carbon monoxide, which are expressed in milligrams per cubic meter (mg/m^3). Equivalent measurements in parts per million (ppm) are given for the gaseous pollutants.)

* Not to be exceeded more than once a year.

A national ambient **air quality standard** is the maximum level which will be permitted for a given pollutant. But there are two kinds of such standards: primary and secondary. **Primary standards** are to be sufficiently stringent to protect the public health; **secondary standards** must protect the public welfare including property and aesthetics.

EPA sets these standards after it issues a criteria document and a control-technology document on the pollutant in question.

Both the primary and secondary standards apply to all control regions.

A recent review by EPA research personnel of a variety of health effects studies has led to a general reaffirmation of the original primary standards. All of the studies have shortcomings, but best judgment estimates of the short and long term ambient air quality levels indicate that the primary standards generally are on target with some margin of safety as required by law.

The review does point up however the need for continuing concern about the amount of sulfur dioxide gas in the air, for which standards with little or no margin of safety exist, and an increased concern about particulate sulfate salts and sulfuric acid aerosols, for which standards have not yet been established. The sulfate problem is treated more fully below. With more and more sulfur bearing coal being programmed to be burned as fuel in the generation of electricity as a contribution to energy independence, the issues of sulfur standards and appropriate control technologies will become even more heated than they have been in recent years. Table 5.2 summarizes the results of the review of health effects.

Table 5.2
Safety Factors Contained in Primary Ambient Air Quality Standards

Pollutant	Lowest Best Judgment Estimates for an Effects Threshold	Adverse Effect	Standard	Safety Margin for Lowest Best Judgment Estimate, %*
Sulfur Dioxide	300 to 400 μg/m³ (Short-Term)	Mortality Harvest	365 μg/m³ (24 hour)	None
	91 μg/m³ (Long-Term)	Increased Frequency of Acute Respiratory Disease	80 ug/m³ (yearly)	14
Acid Aerosols	8 μg/m³ (Short-Term)	Increased Asthmatic Attack	None	None
	15 μg/m³ (Long-Term)	Increased Infections in Children	None	None
Total Suspended Particulates	70 to 250 μg/m³ (Short-Term)	Aggravation of Respiratory Diseases	260 μg/m³ (24 hour)	None
	100 μg/m³ (Long-Term)	Increased Prevalence in Chronic Bronchitis	75 μg/m³ (yearly)	33
Nitrogen Dioxide	141 μg/m³ (Long-Term)	Increased Severity of Acute Respiratory illness	100 μg/m³ (8 hour) (yearly)	41
Carbon Monoxide	23 (8 Hr.) mg/m³ 73 (1 Hr.) mg/m³	Diminished Exercise Tolerance in Heart Patients	10 mg/m³ 40 mg/m³ (1 Hour)	130 82
Photochemical Oxidants	200 (Short-Term)	Increased Susceptibility to Infection	160 (1 Hour)	25

* Safety margin=Effects Threshold Minus Standard, Divided by Standard Multiplied by 100.

SOURCE: J. F. Finklea, et. al., "The Role of Environmental Health Assessment in the Control of Air Pollution," draft (Environmental Protection Agency, August, 1974.)

Air quality (pollution) to be controlled region-by-region—

EPA, assisted by the states, designated air quality control regions. These are the basic geographic units in which the control process takes place. Regional boundaries are based on considerations of climate, meteorology, topography, urbanization, and other factors affecting air quality conditions in each area. A region can cover only part of one state or it can include portions of several states which share a common air pollution problem. The country has been divided into about 250 regions. As pollution patterns change or as more information about problems is gathered, the boundaries of some of the regions may change.

Federal Air Quality Control Regions

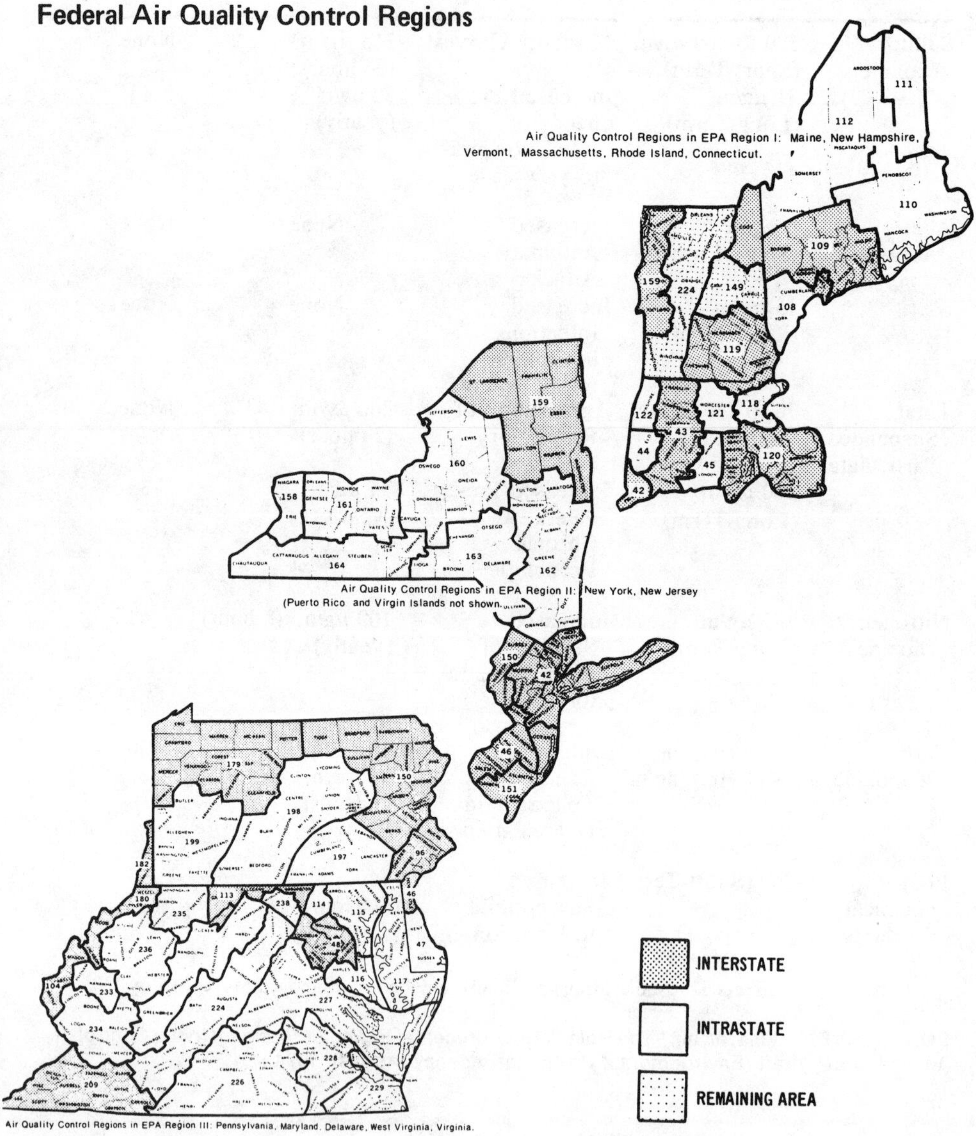

Air Quality Control Regions in EPA Region I: Maine, New Hampshire, Vermont, Massachusetts, Rhode Island, Connecticut.

Air Quality Control Regions in EPA Region II: New York, New Jersey (Puerto Rico and Virgin Islands not shown.)

Air Quality Control Regions in EPA Region III: Pennsylvania, Maryland, Delaware, West Virginia, Virginia.

Air Quality Control Regions in EPA Region V: Minnesota, Wisconsin, Michigan, Ohio, Illinois, Indiana.

Federal Air Quality Control Regions

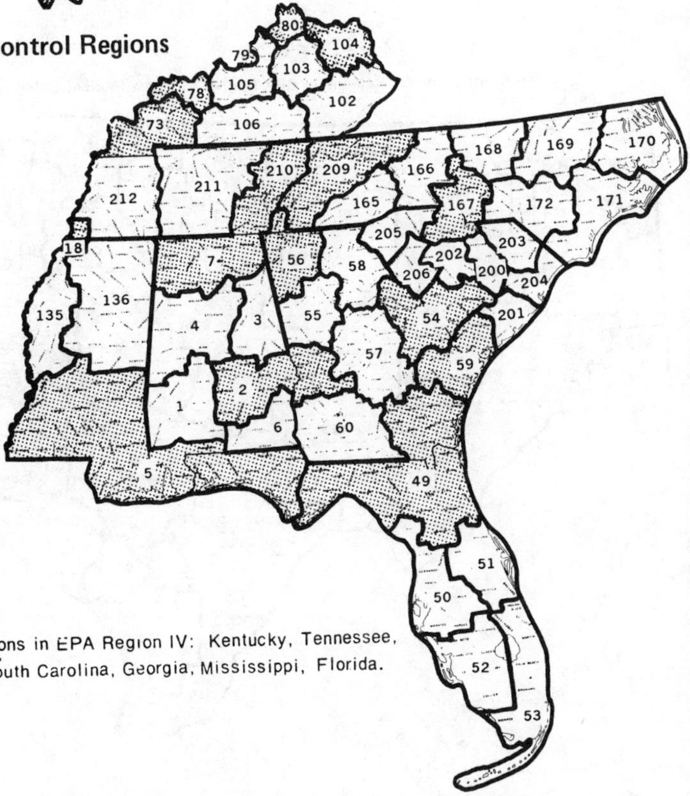

Air Quality Control Regions in EPA Region IV: Kentucky, Tennessee, North Carolina, Alabama, South Carolina, Georgia, Mississippi, Florida.

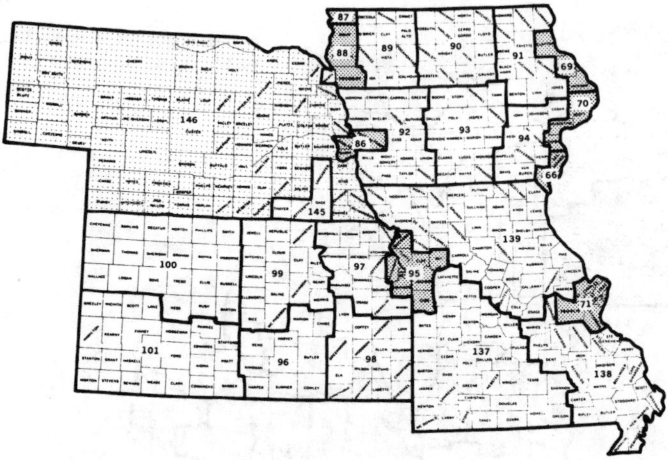

Air Quality Control Regions in EPA Region VII: Nebraska, Iowa; Kansas, Missouri.

Federal Air Quality Control Regions

Air Quality Control Regions in EPA Region VI: New Mexico, Oklahoma, Arkansas, Texas, Louisiana.

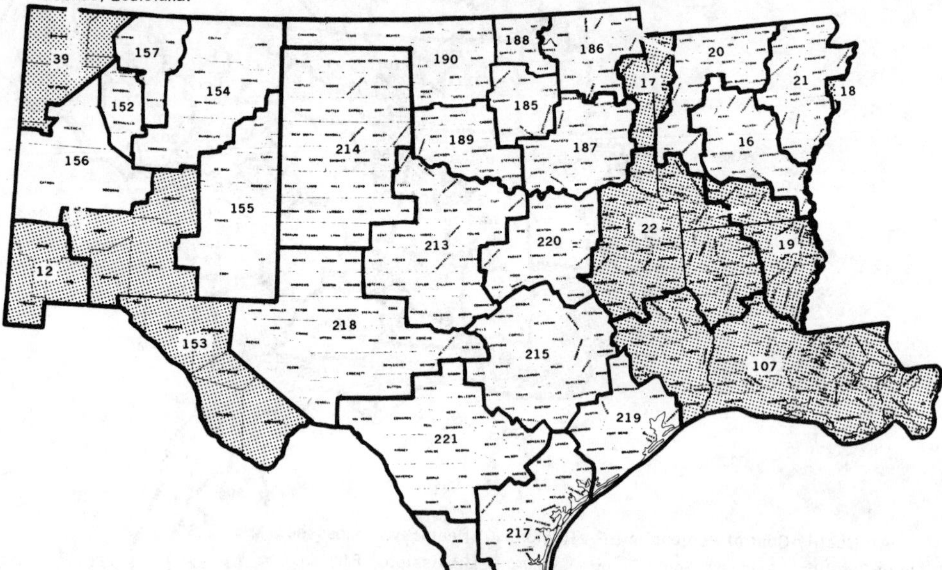

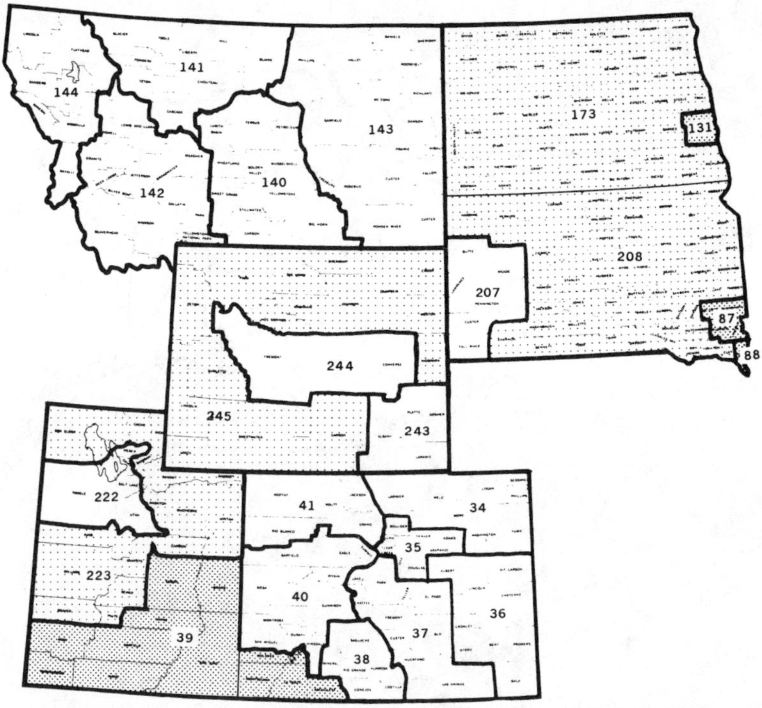

Air Quality Control Regions in EPA Region VIII: Montana, Utah, North Dakota, South Dakota, Wyoming, Colorado.

Federal Air Quality Control Regions

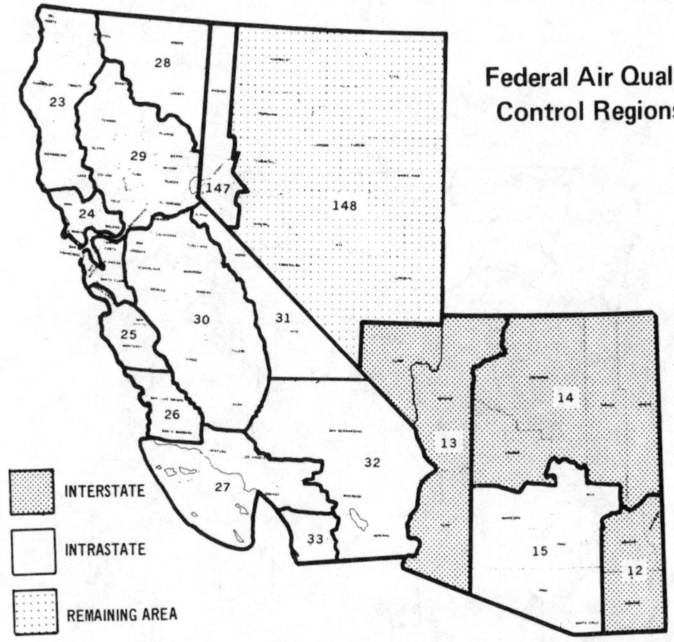

Air Quality Control Regions in EPA Region IX: California, Nevada, Arizona. (Hawaii, American Samoa, and Guam not shown. See Figures 23, 64, and 65.)

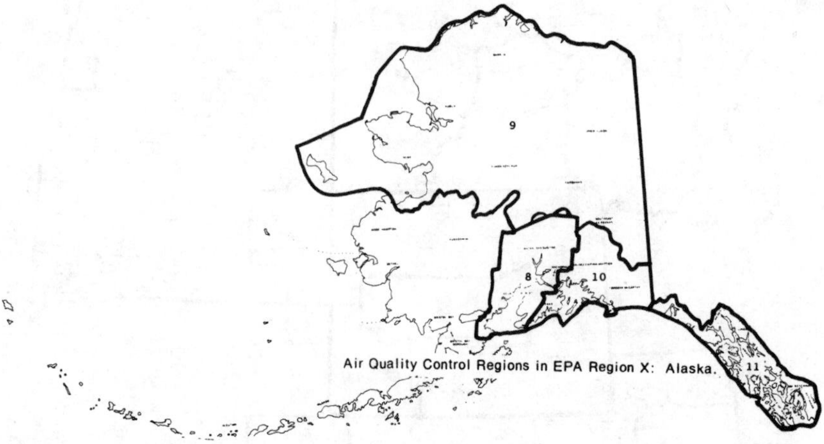

Air Quality Control Regions in EPA Region X: Alaska.

Federal Air Quality Control Regions

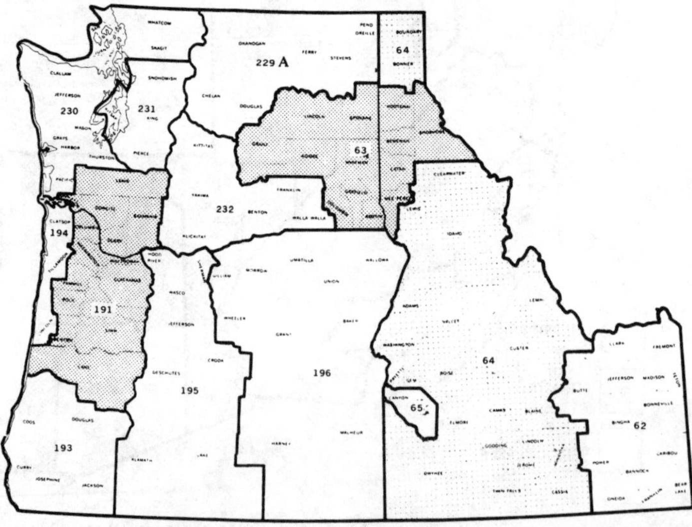

Air Quality Control Regions in EPA Region X: Washington, Oregon, Idaho.

Federal Air Quality Control Regions

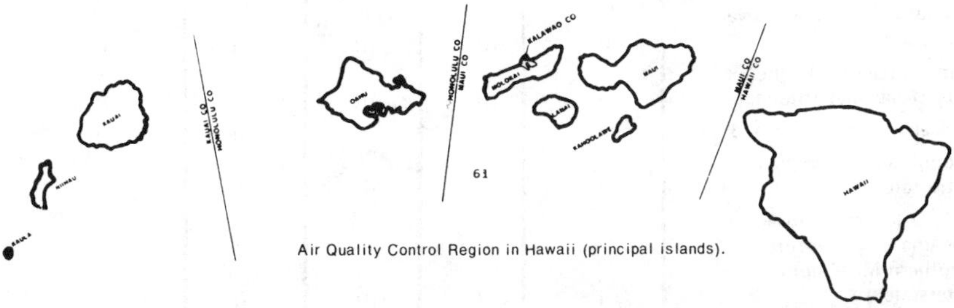

Air Quality Control Region in Hawaii (principal islands).

Large states often contain several regions, among which are widely varying pollution levels and problems. One state (Hawaii) itself comprises a single control region. And the boundaries of some control regions encompass parts of two or more states. Obviously, different control measures will be needed from region to region, depending on their location, the nature of the pollution, and the degree of urbanization.

To accommodate these differences in the implementation process, EPA has devised a classification system. Its purpose is, in EPA's words, to ensure that "the time and resources to be expended in developing the plan for that region, as well as the substantive content of the plan, will be commensurate with the complexity of the air pollution problem."

The ratings in Table 5.3 represent EPA's best regional estimates of air quality as of the end of 1971. The law required attainment of priority III status or better by mid 1975 with allowance for a two year extension on a case by case basis. Tables 5.4 to 5.9 give the regions judged to be in violation of the standards in mid 1975 according to the best information then available (see below).

System for rating the regions for clean air—

The classification system works like this. Each control region is graded by EPA as Priority I, Priority II, or Priority III, on the basis of the known or estimated levels of the six pollutants presently covered by national standards. Hence, the most heavily polluted regions are PRIORITY I; regions with less pollution are PRIORITY II; and those with pollution levels below or just above standard levels are PRIORITY III.

Moreover, a given control region may have different classifications for different pollutants. It could be classified as Priority I for sulfur oxides and Priority III for carbon monoxide. And some regions, where precise air quality data are lacking, may be classified according to population — for example, any region with an urban concentration exceeding 200,000 people will generally be classified as Priority I. If several regions within one state share the same classification for a given pollutant, the state may develop one plan for that pollutant with provisions applicable to all of those control regions.

(Continued on page 200)

Table 5.3

Air quality control region (See maps)*	POLLUTANT: Particulate matter	Sulphur oxides	Nitrogen dioxide	Carbon monoxide	Photochemical oxidants (hydrocarbons)
ALABAMA					
Alabama & Tombigbee Rivers Intrastate –1*	II	III	III	III	III
Columbus (Georgia)- Phenix City (Alabama) Interstate – 2	I	III	III	III	III
East Alabama Intrastate – 3	I	III	III	III	III
Metropolitan Birmingham Intrastate – 4	I	II	III	I	I
Mobile (Alabama)-Pensacola-Panama City (Florida)-Southern Mississippi Interstate – 5	I	I	III	III	I
Southeast Alabama Intrastate – 6	II	III	III	III	III
Tennessee River Valley (Alabama)-Cumberland Mountains (Tennessee) –7 Interstate	I	I	III	III	III
ALASKA					
Cook Inlet Intrastate – 8	I	III	III	III	III
Northern Alaska Intrastate – 9	I	III	III	I	III
South Central Alaska Intrastate – 10	III	III	III	III	III
Southeastern Alaska Intrastate – 11	III	IA	III	III	III
ARIZONA					
Arizona-New Mexico Southern Border Interstate –12	I-A	I-A	III	III	III
Clark-Mohave Interstate – 13	I	I-A	I	I	I
Four Corners Interstate – 14	I-A	I-A	I-A	III	III
Phoenix-Tucson Intrastate – 15	I	I	I	I	I
ARKANSAS					
Central Arkansas Intrastate – 16	II	III	III	III	III
Metropolitan Fort Smith Interstate –17	II	III	III	III	III
Metropolitan Memphis Interstate – 18	I	III	I	III	I
Monroe (Louisiana)-El Dorado (Arkansas) Interstate – 19	II	III	III	III	III
Northeast Arkansas Intrastate –20	III	III	III	III	III
Northwest Arkansas Intrastate–21	III	III	III	III	III
Shreveport-Texarkana-Tyler Interstate –22	II	III	III	III	III
CALIFORNIA					
North Coast Intrastate – 23	II	III	III	III	III
San Francisco Bay Area Intrastate – 24	II	II	I	I	I
North Central Coast Intrastate –25	II	II	III	III	I
South Central Coast Intrastate-26	III	III	III	III	III
Metropolitan Los Angeles Intrastate – 27	I	II	I	I	I

Source: Federal Register, Wed., May 31, 1972

Table 5.3 (continued)

Air quality control region (See maps)*	POLLUTANT Particulate matter	Sulphur oxides	Nitrogen dioxide	Carbon monoxide	Photochemical oxidants (hydrocarbons)
Northeast Plateau Intrastate – 28	III	III	III	III	III
Sacramento Valley Intrastate – 29	II	III	III	I	I
San Joaquin Valley Intrastate – 30	I	III	III	I	I
Great Basin Valley Intrastate – 31	III	III	III	III	III
Southeast Desert Intrastate – 32	I	III	III	III	I
San Diego Intrastate – 33	II	III	I	I	I
COLORADO					
Pawnee Intrastate – 34	I	III	III	III	III
Metropolitan Denver Intrastate – 35	I	III	III	I	I
Comanche Intrastate – 36	III	III	III	III	III
San Isabel Intrastate – 37	I	III	III	III	III
San Luis Intrastate – 38	III	III	III	III	III
Four Corners Interstate – 39	IA	IA	IA	III	III
Grand Mesa Intrastate – 40	III	III	III	III	III
Yampa Intrastate – 41	III	III	III	III	III
CONNECTICUT					
New Jersey-New York-Connecticut Interstate – 42	I	I	I	I	I
Hartford-New Haven-Springfield Interstate – 43	I	I	I	I	I
Northwestern Intrastate – 44	III	III	III	III	III
Eastern Intrastate – 45	II	III	III	III	III
DELAWARE					
Metropolitan Philadelphia Interstate – 46	I	I	I	I	I
Southern Delaware Intrastate – 47	III	III	III	III	III
DISTRICT OF COLUMBIA					
National Capital Interstate – 48	I	I	I	I	I
FLORIDA					
Mobile (Alabama)-Pensacola-Panama City (Florida) Southern Mississippi Interstate – 5	I	I	III	III	I
Jacksonville (Florida)-Brunswick (Georgia) Interstate – 49	I	II	III	III	I
West Central Florida Intrastate – 50	I	I	I	III	III
Central Florida Intrastate – 51	II	III	III	III	III
Southwest Florida Intrastate – 52	III	III	III	III	III
Southeast Florida Intrastate – 53	II	III	I	III	III
GEORGIA					
Augusta (Georgia)-Aiken (South Carolina) Interstate – 54	I	II	III	III	III
Metropolitan Atlanta Intrastate – 55	I	I	I	III	III
Chattanooga Interstate – 56	I	II	I	III	III

Table 5.3 (continued)

Air quality control region (See maps)*	POLLUTANT Particulate matter	Sulphur oxides	Nitrogen dioxide	Carbon monoxide	Photochemical oxidants (hydrocarbons)
Columbus (Georgia)-Phenix City (Alabama) Interstate – 2	I	III	III	III	III
Central Georgia Intrastate – 57	I	II	III	III	III
Jacksonville (Florida)-Brunswick (Georgia) – 49 Interstate	I	II	III	III	I
Northeast Georgia Intrastate – 58	II	III	III	III	III
Savannah (Georgia)-Beaufort (South Carolina) Interstate – 59	I	I	III	III	III
Southwest Georgia Intrastate – 60	II	II	III	III	III
HAWAII – 61	II	III	III	III	III
IDAHO					
Eastern Idaho Intrastate – 62	I	IA	III	III	III
Eastern Washington-Northern Idaho Interstate – 63	I	IA	III	I	III
Idaho Intrastate – 64	I	III	III	III	III
Metropolitan Boise Intrastate – 65	II	III	III	III	III
ILLINOIS					
Burlington-Keokuk Interstate – 66	I	I	III	III	III
East Central Illinois Intrastate – 67	III	II	III	III	III
Metropolitan Chicago Interstate (Indiana-Illinois) – 68	I	I	I	I	I
Metropolitan Dubuque Interstate – 69	I	III	IA	III	III
Metropolitan Quad Cities Interstate – 70	I	III	III	III	III
Metropolitan St. Louis Interstate (Missouri-Illinois) – 71	I	I	I	I	I
North Central Illinois Intrastate – 72	II	IA	III	III	III
Paducah (Kentucky)-Cairo (Illinois) Interstate – 73	I	II	III	III	III
Rockford (Illinois)-Janesville-Beloit (Wisconsin) Interstate – 74	II	III	III	III	III
Southeast Illinois Intrastate – 75	III	II	III	III	III
West Central Illinois Intrastate – 76	I	IA	III	III	III
INDIANA					
East Central Indiana Intrastate – 77	II	II	III	III	III
Evansville (Indiana)-Owensboro-Henderson (Kentucky) Interstate – 78	I	II	III	III	III
Louisville Interstate – 79	I	I	I	III	I
Metropolitan Chicago Interstate (Indiana-Illinois) – 68	I	I	I	I	I
Metropolitan Cincinnati Interstate – 80	I	I	III	I	I
Metropolitan Indianapolis Intrastate – 81	I	I	I	I	I
Northeast Indiana Intrastate – 82	II	III	III	III	III

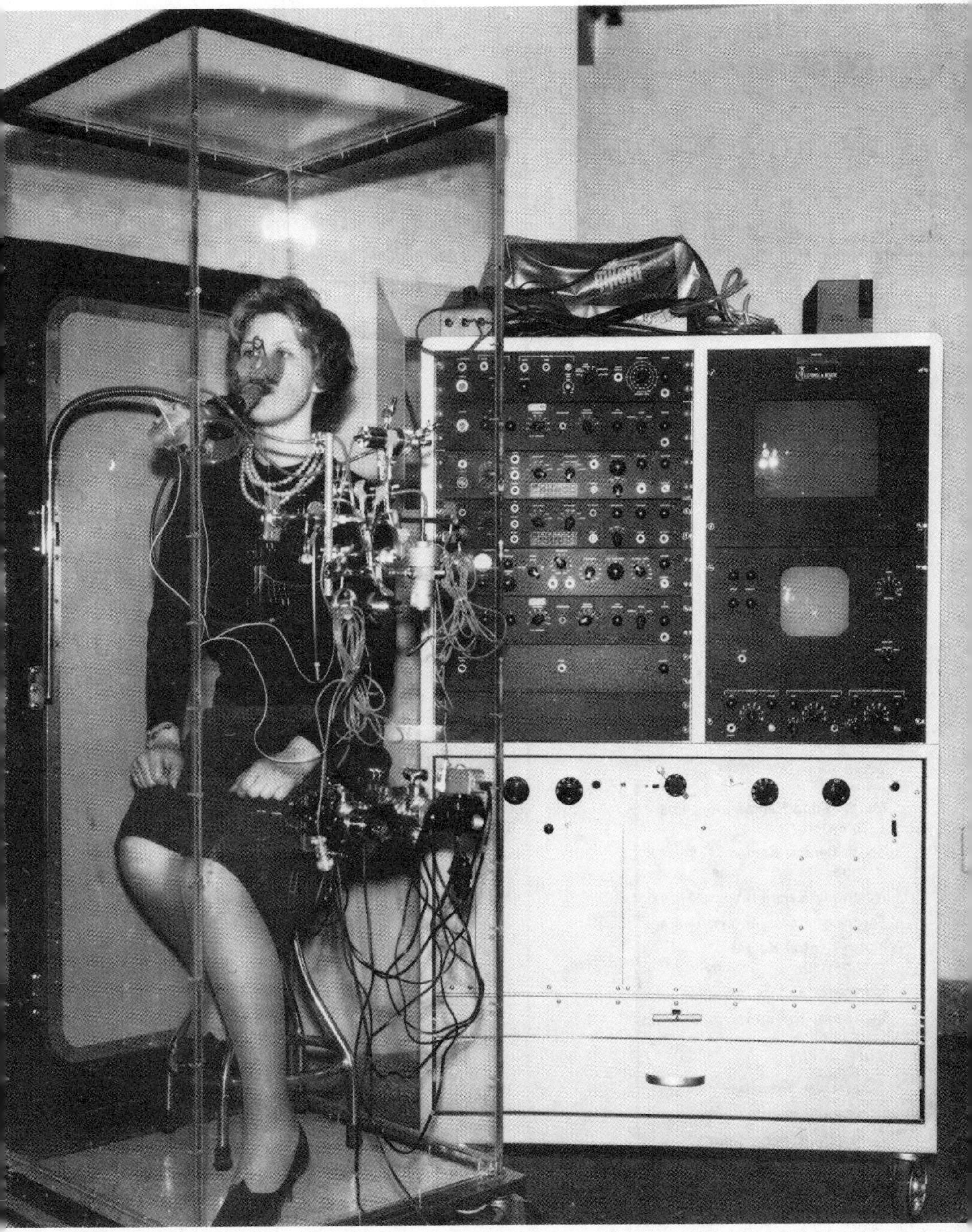

In this special facility for testing human reactions to "smog" at St. Vincent's Hospital in New York City, the physician can completely control the air. He can vary the atmosphere inside from the worst smog to 100 per cent oxygen, making continuous measurements of patient lung function as he changes the mix.

Table 5.3 (continued)

Air quality control region (See maps)*	Particulate matter	Sulphur oxides	Nitrogen dioxide	Carbon monoxide	Photochemical oxidants (hydrocarbons)
South Bend-Elkhart (Indiana)-Benton Harbor(Michigan) Interstate – 83*	I	IA	III	III	III
Southern Indiana Intrastate – 84	IA	IA	III	III	III
Wabash Valley Intrastate – 85	I	I	III	III	III
IOWA					
Metropolitan Omaha-Council Council Bluffs Interstate – 86	I	II	II	III	III
Metropolitan Sioux Falls Interstate – 87	II	III	III	III	III
Metropolitan Sioux City Interstate – 88	III	III	III	III	III
Metropolitan Dubuque Interstate – 69	I	III	IA	III	III
Metropolitan Quad Cities Interstate – 70	I	III	III	III	III
Burlington-Keokuk Interstate – 66	I	I	III	III	III
Northwest Iowa Intrastate – 89	III	III	III	III	III
North Central Iowa Intrastate – 90	IA	III	III	III	III
Northeast Iowa Intrastate – 91	I	III	III	III	III
Southwest Iowa Intrastate – 92	III	III	III	III	III
South Central Iowa Intrastate – 93	I	III	III	III	I
Southeast Iowa Intrastate – 94	III	III	III	III	III
KANSAS					
Metropolitan Kansas City – 95 Interstate	I	III	III	I	I
South Central Kansas Intrastate – 96	I	III	III	III	I
Northwèst Kansas Intrastate – 97	I	III	III	III	III
Southeast Kansas Intrastate – 98	III	III	III	III	III
North Central Kansas Intrastate – 99	I	III	III	III	III
Northwest Kansas Intrastate – 100	I	III	III	III	III
Southwest Kansas Intrastate – 101	I	III	III	III	III
KENTUCKY					
Appalachian Intrastate – 102	II	III	III	III	III
Bluegrass Intrastate – 103	II	III	III	III	III
Evansville (Indiana)-Owensboro-Henderson (Kentucky) Interstate – 78	I	II	III	III	III
Huntington (West Virginia)-Ashland (Kentucky)-Portsmouth-Ironton (Ohio) Interstate – 104	I	III	III	III	III
Louisville Interstate – 79	I	I	I	III	I
Metropolitan Cincinnati Interstate – 80	I	II	I	III	I
North Central Kentucky Intrastate – 105	II	III	III	III	III

Source: Federal Register, Wed., May 31, 1972

Table 5.3 (continued)

Air quality control region (See maps)*	POLLUTANT				
	Particulate matter	Sulphur oxides	Nitrogen dioxide	Carbon monoxide	Photochemical oxidants (hydrocarbons)
Paducah (Kentucky)-Cairo (Illinois) Interstate – 73*	I	II	III	III	III
South Central Kentucky Intrastate – 106	III	III	III	III	III
LOUISIANA					
Southern Louisiana-Southeast Texas Interstate – 107	II	I	III	III	I
Shreveport-Texarkana-Tyler Interstate – 108	II	III	III	III	III
Monroe-El Dorado Interstate – 19	II	III	III	III	III
MAINE					
Metropolitan Portland Intrastate – 108	I	II	III	III	III
Androscoggin Valley Interstate – 109	IA	IA	III	III	III
Down East Intrastate – 110	IA	IA	III	III	III
Aroostook Intrastate – 111	III	III	III	III	III
Northwest Maine Intrastate – 112	III	III	III	III	III
MARYLAND					
Cumberland-Keyser Interstate – 113	I	I	III	III	III
Central Maryland Intrastate – 114	II	II	III	III	III
Metropolitan Baltimore Intrastate – 115	I	I	I	I	I
National Capital Interstate – 48	I	I	I	I	I
Southern Maryland Intrastate – 116	III	III	III	III	III
Eastern Shore Intrastate – 117	II	III	III	III	III
MASSACHUSETTS					
Metropolitan Boston Intrastate – 118	I	I	I	I	I
Merrimack Valley-Southern New Hampshire Interstate – 119	I	I	III	III	III
Metropolitan Providence Interstate – 120	I	I	I	III	III
Central Massachusetts Intrastate – 121	I	II	I	III	III
	I	II	I	III	III
Hartford-New Haven-Springfield Interstate – 43	I	I	I	I	I
Berkshire Intrastate – 122	II	III	III	III	III
MICHIGAN					
Metropolitan Detroit-Port Huron Intrastate – 123	I	I	I	III	III
Metropolitan Toledo Interstate – 124	I	I	I	III	I
South Central Michigan Intrastate – 125	II	II	III	III	III
South Bend-Elkhart (Indiana)-Benton Harbor (Michigan) Interstate – 83	I	IA	III	III	III
Central Michigan Intrastate – 126	II	III	I	III	III
Upper Michigan Intrastate – 127	III	III	III	III	III

Table 5.3 (continued)

Air quality control region (See maps)*	POLLUTANT Particulate matter	Sulphur oxides	Nitrogen dioxide	Carbon monoxide	Photochemical oxidants (hydrocarbons)
MINNESOTA					
Central Minnesota Intrastate – 128*	II	III	III	III	III
Southeast Minnesota-La Crosse (Wisconsin) Interstate – 129	II	IA	III	III	III
Duluth (Minnesota)-Superior (Wisconsin) Interstate – 130	I	II	III	III	III
Metropolitan Fargo-Moorhead Interstate – 131	II	III	III	III	III
Minneapolis-St. Paul Intrastate -132	I	I	I	I	III
Northwest Minnesota Intrastate -133	II	III	III	III	III
Southwest Minnesota Intrastate – 134	III	III	III	III	III
MISSISSIPPI					
Mobile (Alabama)-Pensacola-Panama City (Florida-Gulfport (Mississippi) – 5	I	I	III	III	I
Metropolitan Memphis Interstate – 18	I	III	I	III	I
Mississippi Delta Intrastate – 135	III	III	III	III	III
Northeast Mississippi Intrastate – 136	II	III	III	III	III
MISSOURI					
Metropolitan Kansas City Interstate – 95	I	III	III	I	I
Southwest Missouri Intrastate –137	I	III	III	III	III
Southeast Missouri Intrastate – 138	III	III	III	III	III
Northern Missouri Intrastate – 139	II	III	III	III	III
Metropolitan St. Louis Interstate – 71	I	I	I	I	I
MONTANA					
Billings Intrastate – 140	II	II	III	III	III
Great Falls Intrastate – 141	III	IA	III	III	III
Helena Intrastate – 142	IA	IA	III	III	III
Miles City Intrastate – 143	III	III	III	III	III
Missoula Intrastate – 144	I	III	III	III	III
NEBRASKA					
Metropolitan Omaha-Council Bluffs Interstate – 86	I	II	I	III	III
Lincoln-Beatrice-Fairbury Intrastate – 145	II	III	III	III	III
Metropolitan Sioux City Interstate – 88	III	III	III	III	III
Nebraska Intrastate– 146	III	III	III	III	III
NEVADA					
Clark-Mohave Interstate – 13	I	IA	I	I	I
Northwest Nevada Intrastate -147	I	III	III	III	III
Nevada Intrastate – 148	IA	IA	III	III	III

Source: Federal Register, Wed., May 31, 1972

Table 5.3 (continued)

Air quality control region (See maps)*	POLLUTANT				
	Particulate matter	Sulphur oxides	Nitrogen dioxide	Carbon monoxide	Photochemical oxidants (hydrocarbons)
NEW HAMPSHIRE					
Androscoggin Valley Interstate – 109*	IA	IA	III	III	III
Central New Hampshire Intrastate – 149	III	III	III	III	III
Merrimack Valley-Southern New Hampshire Interstate – 119	I	I	III	III	III
NEW JERSEY					
New Jersey-New York-Connecticut Interstate – 42	I	I	I	I	I
Metropolitan Philadelphia Interstate – 46	I	I	I	I	I
Northeast Pennsylvania-Upper Delaware Valley Interstate – 150	I	II	I	III	III
New Jersey Intrastate – 151	III	IA	III	I	III
NEW MEXICO					
Albuquerque-Mid Rio Grande Intrastate – 152	I	III	III	III	I
Arizona-New Mexico Southern Border Interstate – 12	IA	IA	III	III	III
El Paso-Las Cruces-Alamogordo Interstate – 153	I	I	III	I	I
Four Corners Interstate – 39	IA	IA	IA	III	III
Northeastern Plains Intrastate – 154	III	III	III	III	III
Pecos-Permian Basin Intrastate – 155	III	III	III	III	III
Southwestern Mountains-Augustine Plains Intrastate – 156	III	III	III	III	III
Upper Rio Grande Valley Intrastate – 157	III	III	III	III	III
NEW YORK					
Niagara Frontier Intrastate – 158	I	I	I	III	I
Champlain Valley Interstate – 159	II	II	III	III	III
Central New York Intrastate – 160	I	II	III	I	I
Genesee-Finger Lakes Intrastate – 161	II	II	I	III	I
Hudson Valley Intrastate – 162	I	II	III	III	III
Southern Tier East Intrastate – 163	II	II	III	III	III
Southern Tier West Intrastate – 164	II	II	III	III	III
New Jersey-New York-Connecticut Interstate – 42	I	I	I	I	I
NORTH CAROLINA					
Western Mountain Intrastate – 165	I	III	III	III	III
Eastern Mountain Intrastate – 166	I	III	III	III	III
Metropolitan Charlotte Interstate – 167	I	II	III	III	I
Northern Piedmont Intrastate – 168	I	III	III	III	III
Eastern Piedmont Intrastate – 169	I	III	III	III	III
Northern Coastal Intrastate – 170	I	III	III	III	III
Southern Coastal Intrastate – 171	II	III	III	III	III
Sandhills Intrastate – 172	II	III	III	III	III

On Saturday afternoon, November 26, 1966, the newcomer to New York City might not have suspected from just looking around that people there must contend with air pollution. But if the visitor had arrived a day before John Pedin of the N.Y. Daily News took this picture his impression might have been a little different, as the photo on the opposite page illustrates.

This "smog" scene was shot by Fred Morgan on Friday, November 25, 1966 at 10:30 AM, just hours before favorable air currents and changing meteorological conditions rescued Manhattan as the photo on the opposite page indicates. New York City is by no means alone in its fight with air pollution, since almost every major American city has been given a "must clean up" mark on its air-quality report card.

Table 5.3 (continued)

Air quality control region (See maps)*	POLLUTANT Particulate matter	Sulphur oxides	Nitrogen dioxide	Carbon monoxide	Photochemical oxidants (hydrocarbons)
NORTH DAKOTA					
Metropolitan Fargo-Moorhead Interstate – 131 *	II	III	III	III	III
North Dakota Intrastate – 173	II	III	III	III	III
OHIO					
Greater Metropolitan Cleveland Intrastate – 174	I	I	I	III	I
Huntington (West Virginia)-Ashland (Kentucky)-Portsmouth-Ironton (Ohio) Interstate – 104	I	III	III	III	III
Mansfield-Marion Intrastate – 175	II	II	III	III	III
Metropolitan Cincinnati Interstate – 80	I	II	I	III	I
Metropolitan Columbus Intrastate – 176	I	III	I	III	I
Metropolitan Dayton Intrastate 177	I	II	I	III	I
Metropolitan Toledo Interstate 124	I	I	I	III	I
Northwest Ohio Intrastate – 178	II	I	III	III	III
Northwest Pennsylvania-Youngstown Interstate – 179	I	II	III	III	III
Parkersburg (West Virginia)-Marietta (Ohio) Interstate – 180	I	II	III	III	III
Sandusky Intrastate – 181	III	III	III	III	III
Steubenville-Weirton-Wheeling Interstate – 182	I	I	III	III	III
Wilmington-Chillicothe-Logan Intrastate – 183	III	III	III	III	III
Zanesville-Cambridge Intrastate – 184	II	IA	III	III	III
OKLAHOMA					
Central Oklahoma Intrastate – 185	I	III	III	III	I
Northeastern Oklahoma Intrastate – 186	I	III	III	III	I
Southeastern Oklahoma Intrastate – 187	III	III	III	III	III
North Central Oklahoma Intrastate – 188	III	III	III	III	III
Southwestern Oklahoma Intrastate – 189	III	III	III	III	III
Northwestern Oklahoma Intrastate – 190	III	III	III	III	III
Metropolitan Fort Smith Interstate – 17	II	III	III	III	III
Shreveport-Texarkana-Tyler Interstate – 22	II	III	III	III	III
OREGON					
Portland Interstate – 191	I	IA	III	I	I
Southwest Oregon Intrastate 193	II	III	III	III	III
Northwest Oregon Intrastate 194	III	III	III	III	III
Central Oregon Intrastate – 195	II	III	III	III	III
Eastern Oregon Intrastate – 196	II	III	III	III	III

Source: Federal Register, Wed., May 31, 1972

Table 5.3 (continued)

Air quality control region (See maps)*	Particulate matter	Sulphur oxides	Nitrogen dioxide	Carbon monoxide	Photochemical oxidants (hydrocarbons)
PENNSYLVANIA					
Metropolitan Philadelphia Interstate – 96*	I	I	I	I	I
Northeast Pennsylvania-Upper Delaware Valley Interstate - 150	I	II	I	III	III
South Central Pennsylvania Intrastate – 197	I	II	I	III	III
Central Pennsylvania Intrastate – 198	I	III	I	III	III
Southwest Pennsylvania Intrastate – 199	I	I	I	I	I
Northwest Pennsylvania-Youngstown Interstate – 179	I	II	III	III	III
RHODE ISLAND					
Metropolitan Providence Interstate – 120	I	I	I	III	III
SOUTH CAROLINA					
Augusta (Georgia)-Aiken – 59 (South Carolina) Interstate	I	II	III	III	III
Metropolitan Charlotte Interstate – 167	I	II	III	III	I
Camden-Sumter Intrastate – 200	II	III	III	III	III
Charleston Intrastate – 201	I	I	III	III	III
Columbia Intrastate – 202	II	III	III	III	III
Florence Intrastate – 203	III	III	III	III	III
Georgetown Intrastate – 204	II	III	III	III	III
Greenville-Spartanburg Intrastate – 205	I	III	III	III	III
Greenwood Intrastate – 206	III	III	III	III	I
Savannah (Georgia)-Beaufort (South Carolina) Interstate – 59	I	I	III	III	III
					III
SOUTH DAKOTA					I
Metropolitan Sioux City Interstate – 88	III	III	III	III	III
Metropolitan Sioux Falls Interstate – 87	II	III	III	III	III
Black Hills - Rapid City Intrastate – 207	III	III	III	III	
South Dakota Intrastate – 208	III	III	III	III	
					III
TENNESSEE					III
Eastern Tennessee-South- – 20 western Virginia Interstate	I	I	III	III	III
					III
Tennessee River Valley-Cumberland Mountains Intrastate – 210	I	I	III	III	
Middle Tennessee Intrastate – 211	I	II	III	III	
Western Tennessee Intrastate – 212	I	III	III	III	
Chattanooga Interstate – 56	I	II	I	III	III
Metropolitan Memphis Interstate – 18	I	III	I	III	III

Table 5.3 (continued)

Air quality control region (See maps)*	Particulate matter	Sulphur oxides	Nitrogen dioxide	Carbon monoxide	Photochemical oxidants (hydrocarbons)
TEXAS					
Abilene-Wichita Falls Intrastate – 213*	II	II	III	III	III
Amarillo-Lubbock Intrastate – 214	II	I	III	III	III
Austin-Waco Intrastate –215	II	III	III	III	I
Brownsville-Laredo Intrastate 216	I	III	III	III	III
Corpus Christi-Victoria Intrastate – 217	I	I	I	III	I
Midland-Odessa-San Angelo Intrastate – 218	II	II	III	III	III
Metropolitan Houston-Galveston Intrastate – 219	I	I	I	III	I
Metropolitan Dallas-Fort Worth Intrastate – 220	II	III	I	III	I
Metropolitan San Antonio Intrastate – 221	II	III	III	III	I
Southern Louisiana-Southeast Texas Interstate – 107	II	I	III	III	I
El Paso-Las Cruces Alamogordo Interstate – 153	I	I	III	I	I
Shreveport-Texarkana-Tyler Interstate – 22	II	III	III	III	III
UTAH					
Wasatch Front Intrastate – 222	I	I	I	I	I
Four Corners Interstate – 39	IA	IA	IA	III	III
Utah Intrastate – 223	III	III	III	III	III
VERMONT					
Champlain Valley Interstate – 159	II	II	III	III	III
Vermont Intrastate – 224	II	II	III	III	III
VIRGINIA					
Eastern Tennessee-South- – 209 western Virginia Interstate	I	I	III	III	III
Valley of Virginia Intrastate – 224	II	III	III	III	III
Central Virginia Intrastate – 226	I	III	III	III	III
Northeastern Virginia Intrastate – 227	IA	III	III	III	III
State Capital Intrastate – 228	I	III	I	III	I
Hampton Roads Intrastate – 229	I	II	I	III	I
National Capital Interstate – 48	I	I	I	I	I
WASHINGTON					
Eastern Washington-Northern Idaho Interstate – 63	I	IA	III	I	III
Olympic-Northwest Washington Intrastate – 230	II	II	III	III	III
Portland Interstate – 191	I	IA	III	I	I
Puget Sound Intrastate – 231	I	IA	I	I	I
South Central Washington Intrastate – 232	I	III	III	III	III

Source: Federal Register, Wed., May 31, 1972

Table 5.3 (continued)

Air quality control region (See maps)*	POLLUTANT				
	Particulate matter	Sulphur oxides	Nitrogen dioxide	Carbon monoxide	Photochemical oxidants (hydrocarbons)
WEST VIRGINIA					
Steubenville-Weirton-Wheeling Interstate – 182*	I	I	III	III	III
Parkersburg-Marietta Interstate – 180	I	II	III	III	III
Huntington-Ashland-Portsmouth Ironton Interstate – 104	I	III	III	III	III
Kanawha Valley Intrastate – 233	I	III	III	III	III
Southern West Virginia Intrastate – 234	III	III	III	III	III
North Central West Virginia Intrastate – 235	I	III	III	III	III
Cumberland-Keyser Interstate – 113	I	I	III	III	III
Central West Virginia Intrastate – 236	III	III	III	III	III
Allegheny Intrastate – 237	III	III	III	III	III
Easten Panhandle Intrastate – 238	III	III	III	III	III
WISCONSIN					
Duluth (Minnesota)-Superior (Wisconsin) Interstate – 130	I	II	III	III	III
North Central Wisconsin Intrastate – 239	II	III	III	III	III
Lake Michigan Intrastate – 240	II	III	III	III	III
Southeast Minnesota-La Crosse (Wisconson) Interstate – 129	II	IA	III	III	III
Southern Wisconsin Intrastate – 241	II	III	III	III	III
Southeastern Wisconsin Intrastate – 242	I	II	I	III	I
Rockford (Illinois)-Jamesville – 74 Beloit (Wisconsin) Interstate	II	III	III	III	III
Metropolitan Dubuque Interstate – 69	I	III	IA	III	III
WYOMING					
Cheyenne Intrastate – 243	II	III	III	III	III
Casper Intrastate – 244	II	III	III	III	III
Wyoming Intrastate – 245	III	III	III	III	III
GUAM					
Guam – 246	III	II	III	III	III
PUERTO RICO					
Puerto Rico – 247	IA	IA	III	III	III
VIRGIN ISLANDS					
U. S. Virgin Islands – 248	IA	IA	III	III	III
AMERICAN SAMOA					
American Samoa – 249	III	III	III	III	III

Source: Federal Register, Wed., May 31, 1972

(Continued from page 185)

The goals were to be achieved under federally approved state implementation plans. The 1970 amendments permitted various administrative extensions in certain circumstances. As it became clear that energy supply problems for specific clean fuels would impede the meeting of some of the goals, the Energy Supply and Environmental Coordination Act of 1974 authorized more extended delays under certain explicit conditions. The basic standards remain intact, however, and the original goals are being approached. Actual measured values of the various standard pollutants in 1975 will not be available in final form until late 1976. EPA pressure on the states to meet their legal responsibilities in a more timely fashion is being increased. According to unpublished estimates cited in *Environmental Quality*, EPA officials expected that the primary standard levels would be fully achieved by the original 1975 target date in only 91 of the nation's 247 Air Quality Control Regions:

> *At monitoring sites in nearly two-thirds of the regions, the pollution levels designated by the standards were still being exceeded (violated) for one or more pollutants. The standards are exceeded for suspended particulates in 118 of the 247 regions, for sulfur dioxide in 34 regions, carbon monoxide in 69 regions, oxidants in 79 regions, and nitrogen dioxide in 16 regions.*
>
> *The highest levels of particulates and sulfur oxides, the major pollutants from stationary sources (smokestacks), occur mainly in the Northeastern and North Central states. California continues to have the most severe automotive pollution problems. Occurrences of poor air quality are by no means restricted to any region or state, however. In such widely separated large cities as Los Angeles, Chicago, and Philadelphia, primary standards for all the criteria pollutants are still exceeded at times. There are also problems in many small cities and in rural areas.*
>
> *Of the nation's 20,000 largest stationary sources which collectively account for about 85 percent of all stationary source pollution, 15,600 were in compliance with emission regulations or were meeting compliance schedules by mid-1975.*
>
> *Efforts to reduce air pollution have encountered a number of obstacles. Scientific knowledge and available technological and legal tools are sometimes insufficient. Moreover, the nation's economic and energy difficulties are not always compatible with environmental goals. Some facilities have been granted extensions or variances which permit the burning of coal or oil with a high sulfur content. The full effects of such variances on ambient air quality are still uncertain.*
>
> *Yet it is evident that the nation's efforts to improve air quality have accomplished a great deal in the relatively short period of 5 years.*

Tables 5.4 to 5.9 list the various Air Quality Control Regions that probably had not reached the national primary standards for the given pollutant according to the best estimates or measurements available in mid 1975. Listed in Table 5.4 are the 33 regions for which non-attainment appears to be caused by "uncontrollable" sources of particulates, such as fugitive dust, which includes desert dust storms and blown dust from farms, unpaved roads, and construction areas. Note that the listings are in numerical order by Air Quality Control Region as indicated on the maps above. The order of listing is not given according to severity of pollution. The principal city is given to identify the region and not to pinpoint the location of violations which may be in another part of the region.

Actual air-quality data for 1975 will not be available until late 1976. Definite identification of which AQCR have not met the National Ambient Air Quality Standard until that data is ready.

Table 5.4

Air Quality Control Regions Expected To Exceed the National Standards for Total Suspended Particulates by the Statutory Deadline Because of Fugitive Dust

Air quality control region	Principal city [1]	Air quality control region	Principal city [1]
12	Silver City, New Mexico	89	Mason City, Iowa
13	Kingman, Arizona	92	Des Moines, Iowa
14	Flagstaff, Arizona	95	Topeka, Kansas
15	Phoenix, Arizona	96	Salina, Kansas
18	Marion, Arkansas	99	Wichita, Kansas
20	Newport, Arkansas	146	Grand Island, Nebraska
23	Death Valley, California	147	Ely, Nevada
26	Eureka, California	148	Reno, Nevada
28	Sacramento, California	152	Albuquerque, New Mexico
31	Fresno, California	153	El Paso, Texas
33	Lancaster, California	187	Woodward, Oklahoma
36	Denver, Colorado	205	Rapid City, South Dakota
37	Fort Collins, Colorado	207	Knoxville, Tennessee
38	Pueblo, Colorado	213	Brownsville, Texas
40	Craig, Colorado	222	Danville, Virginia
85	Omaha, Nebraska	226	Roanoke, Virginia
88	Cedar Rapids, Iowa		

[1] The term "principal city" refers to the principal population center in the particular AQCR and has no relation to the actual locations of air quality measurements which violate NAAQS. For interstate AQCR's, "principal city" is the principal city in that state portion which is not considered likely to attain NAAQS by the statutory attainment date. In cases where more than one state portion of an interstate AQCR is considered unlikely to attain NAAQS by the statutory attainment date, the principal city in the AQCR as a whole is indicated.

Source: Environmental Protection Agency.

Table 5.5

Air Quality Control Regions Expected To Exceed the National Standards for Total Suspended Particulates by the Statutory Deadline [1]

Air quality control region	Principal city [2]	Air quality control region	Principal city [2]
05	Pensacola, Florida	124	Toledo, Ohio
07	Huntsville, Alabama	126	Traverse City, Michigan
16	Little Rock, Arkansas	128	Rochester, Minnesota
17	Fort Smith, Arkansas	129	Duluth, Minnesota
22	Shreveport, Louisiana	131	Minneapolis, Minnesota
24	Los Angeles, California	132	Fergus Falls, Minnesota
29	San Diego, California	133	Wilmar, Minnesota
42	Hartford, Connecticut	137	Jefferson City, Missouri
45	Philadelphia, Pennsylvania	142	Helena, Montana
47	Washington, D.C.	143	Miles City, Montana
49	Jacksonville, Florida	144	Missoula, Montana
50	Miami, Florida	145	Lincoln, Nebraska
52	Tampa, Florida	151	Scranton, Pennsylvania
55	Chattanooga, Tennessee	159	Burlington, Vermont
65	Burlington, Illinois	173	Dayton, Ohio
67	Chicago, Illinois	174	Cleveland, Ohio
68	Dubuque, Iowa	175	Mansfield-Marion, Ohio
69	Davenport, Iowa	176	Columbus, Ohio
70	St. Louis, Missouri	178	Youngstown, Ohio
73	Beloit, Wisconsin	179	Marietta, Ohio
75	Springfield, Illinois	180	Sandusky, Ohio
77	Henderson, Kentucky	181	Steubenville, Ohio
78	Louisville, Kentucky	184	Oklahoma City, Oklahoma
79	Cincinnati, Ohio	186	Tulsa, Oklahoma
80	Indianapolis, Indiana	195	Altoona, Pennsylvania
84	Terre Haute, Indiana	196	Harrisburg, Pennsylvania
86	Sioux City, Iowa	197	Pittsburgh, Pennsylvania
87	Sioux Falls, South Dakota	199	Charleston, South Carolina
90	Spencer, Iowa	208	Nashville, Tennessee
91	Iowa City, Iowa	211	Amarillo, Texas
94	Kansas City, Missouri	214	Corpus Christi, Texas
97	Great Bend, Kansas	215	Dallas, Texas
98	Coffeyville, Kansas	216	Houston, Texas
100	Dodge City, Kansas	217	San Antonio, Texas
101	Hazard, Kentucky	220	Salt Lake City, Utah
103	Ashland, Kentucky	223	Norfolk, Virginia
115	Baltimore, Maryland	225	Richmond, Virginia
118	Worchester, Massachusetts	234	Charleston, West Virginia
119	Boston, Massachusetts	238	Wausau, Wisconsin
120	Providence, Rhode Island	239	Milwaukee, Wisconsin
121	Great Falls, Montana	243	Sheridan, Wyoming
122	Flint, Michigan	246	Guam
123	Detroit, Michigan		

[1] Excludes AQCR's that will exceed standards because of fugitive dust.

[2] "Principal city" refers to the principal population center in the particular AQCR and has no relation to the actual locatians of air quality measurements that violate NAAQS. For interstate AQCR's, "principal city" is the principal city in that state portion which is not considered likely to attain NAAQS by the statutory attainment date. In cases where more than one state portion of an interstate AQCR is considered unlikely to attain NAAQS by the statutory attainment date, the principal city in the AQCR as a whole is indicated.

Source: Environmental Protection Agency.

Table 5.6

Air Quality Control Regions Expected To Exceed National Standards for Sulfur Dioxide by the Statutory Deadline

Air quality control region	Principal city [1]	Air quality control region	Principal city [1]
007	Huntsville, Alabama	079	Cincinnati, Ohio
012	Hurley, New Mexico	080	Indianapolis, Indiana
024	Los Angeles, California	082	South Bend, Indiana
042	Hartford, Connecticut	083	Bloomington, Indiana
045	Philadelphia, Pennsylvania	084	Terre Haute, Indiana
047	Washington, D.C.	103	Huntington, West Virginia
052	Tampa, Florida	120	Providence, Rhode Island
062	Kellogg, Idaho [2]	122	Flint, Michigan
065	Burlington, Illinois	123	Detroit, Michigan
067	Chicago, Illinois	125	Lansing, Michigan
070	St. Louis, Missouri	131	Minneapolis, Minnesota
071	Dixon, Illinois	142	Helena, Montana
072	Paducah-Cairo, Illinois	209	Memphis, Tennessee
074	Carbondale, Illinois	216	Galveston, Texas
075	Springfield, Illinois	235	Clarksburg, West Virginia
077	Evansville, Indiana	239	Milwaukee, Wisconsin
078	Louisville, Kentucky [2]	246	Guam

[1] The term "principal city" refers to the principal population center in the particular AQCR and has no relation to the actual locations of air quality measurements which violate NAAQS. For interstate AQCR's, "principal city" is the principal city in that state portion which is not considered likely to attain NAAQS by the statutory attainment date. In cases where more than one state portion of an interstate AQCR is considered unlikely to attain NAAQS by the statutory attainment date, the principal city in the AQCR as a whole is indicated.

[2] Has 2-year extension from the statutory date.

Source: Environmental Protection Agency.

Table 5.7

Air Quality Control Regions with Ambient Nitrogen Dioxide Concentrations at or above National Standards

Air quality control region	Principal urban area reporting violations	Air quality control region	Principal urban area reporting violations
015	Phoenix, Arizona	056	Atlanta, Georgia
024	Los Angeles, California	067	Chicago, Illinois
029	San Diego, California	115	Baltimore, Maryland
030	San Francisco, California	119	Boston, Massachusetts
036	Denver, Colorado	123	Detroit, Michigan
042	Springfield, Massachusetts	174	Canton, Ohio
043	New York, New York	220	Salt Lake City, Utah
045	Philadelphia, Pennsylvania	225	Richmond, Virginia

Source: Environmental Protection Agency.

Table 5.8

Air Quality Control Regions Exceeding National Standards for Oxidants/Ozone in 1973 and/or 1974

Air quality control region	Principal urban area reporting violations
004	Birmingham, Alabama
005	Mobile, Alabama
013	Las Vegas, Nevada
015	Phoenix, Arizona (TCP) [1]
018	Memphis, Tennessee
024	Los Angeles, California (TCP) [2]
025	Salinas, California
028	Sacramento, California (TCP) [2]
029	San Diego, California (TCP) [2]
030	San Francisco, California (TCP) [2]
031	Fresno, California (TCP) [2]
032	San Luis Obispo, California
033	Lancaster, California
036	Denver, Colorado (TCP) [2]
043	New York City, New York (TCP) [2]
045	Philadelphia, Pennsylvania (TCP) [2]
047	Washington, D.C. (TCP) [2]
050	Miami, Florida
051	Naples, Florida
056	Atlanta, Georgia
060	Honolulu, Hawaii
067	Chicago Illinois (TCP) [1]
070	St. Louis, Missouri
072	Paducah, Kentucky
075	Springfield, Illinois
077	Owensboro, Kentucky
078	Louisville, Kentucky
079	Newport, Kentucky
080	Indianapolis, Indiana (TCP) [3]
085	Omaha, Nebraska
092	Des Moines, Iowa
095	Topeka, Kansas
099	Wichita, Kansas
103	Ashland, Kentucky
106	New Orleans, Louisiana
107	Berlin, New Hampshire
115	Baltimore, Maryland (TCP) [2]
117	Pittsfield, Maine
118	Worchester, Massachusetts
119	Boston, Massachusetts (TCP) [2]
120	Providence, Rhode Island (TCP) [1]
121	Nashua, New Hampshire
123	Detroit, Michigan
124	Toledo, Ohio
131	Minneapolis, Minnesota (TCP) [1]
151	Scranton, Pennsylvania
152	Albuquerque, New Mexico
153	Dona Ana County, New Mexico
158	Utica, New York
159	Glen Falls, New York
160	Rochester, New York (TCP) [3]
161	Schenectady, New York
162	Buffalo, New York
167	Charlotte, North Carolina
171	Asheville, North Carolina
173	Dayton, Ohio
174	Akron, Ohio
176	Columbus, Ohio
178	Youngstown, Ohio
184	Oklahoma City, Oklahoma
186	Tulsa, Oklahoma
193	Vancouver, Washington (TCP) [2]
195	Johnstown, Pennsylvania
196	Harrisburg, Pennsylvania
197	Baden, Pennsylvania (TCP) [2]
200	Richland County, South Carolina
207	Kingsport, Tennessee
208	Nashville, Tennessee
212	Austin, Texas (TCP) [3]
214	Corpus Christi, Texas (TCP) [3]
215	Dallas, Texas (TCP) [3]
216	Houston, Texas (TCP) [3]
217	San Antonio, Texas (TCP) [3]
220	Salt Lake City, Utah (TCP) [1]
223	Norfolk, Virginia
225	Richmond, Virginia
229	Seattle, Washington (TCP) [1]
239	Milwaukee, Wisconsin
240	Columbia County, Wisconsin

[1] Transportation Control Plan designed for carbon monoxide only.

[2] Transportation Control Plan designed for both carbon monoxiae and photochemical oxidants.

[3] Transportation Control Plan designed for photochemical oxidants only.

Source: Environmental Protection Agency.

Table 5.9

Air Quality Control Regions Exceeding National Standards for Carbon Monoxide in 1973 and/or 1974

Air quality control region	Principal urban area reporting violations	Air quality control region	Principal urban area reporting violations
004	Birmingham, Alabama	113	Cumberland, Maryland
008	Anchorage, Alaska [1]	115	Baltimore, Maryland (TCP) [3]
009	Fairbanks, Alaska (TCP) [2]	118	Worcester, Massachusetts
013	Las Vegas, Nevada	119	Boston, Massachusetts (TCP) [3]
015	Phoenix, Arizona [2]	120	Providence, Rhode Island (TCP) [2]
018	Memphis, Tennessee	121	Nashua, New Hampshire
024	Los Angeles, California (TCP) [3]	124	Toledo, Ohio
028	Sacramento, California (TCP) [3]	131	Minneapolis, Minnesota (TCP) [2]
029	San Diego, California (TCP) [3]	145	Lincoln, Nebraska
030	San Francisco, California (TCP) [3]	148	Reno, Nevada
031	Fresno, California (TCP) [3]	150	Atlantic City, New Jersey
032	San Luis Obispo, California	151	Phillipsburg, New Jersey [1]
033	Lancaster, California [1]	152	Albuquerque, New Mexico
036	Denver, Colorado (TCP) [3]	153	Las Cruces, New Mexico
042	Springfield, Massachusetts	157	Santa Fe, New Mexico
043	New York City, New York (TCP) [3]	158	Syracuse, New York
045	Philadelphia, Pennsylvania (TCP) [3]	159	Burlington, Vermont [1]
047	Washington, D.C. (TCP) [3]	160	Rochester, New York (TCP) [4]
056	Atlanta, Georgia	161	Schenectady, New York
060	Honolulu, Hawaii	162	Buffalo, New York [1]
062	Spokane, Washington (TCP) [2]	167	Charlotte, North Carolina
067	Chicago (Illinois (TCP) [2]	173	Dayton, Ohio
070	St. Louis, Missouri	174	Cleveland, Ohio
072	Paducah, Kentucky	176	Columbus, Ohio [1]
077	Owensboro, Kentucky	184	Oklahoma City, Oklahoma
078	Louisville, Kentucky	186	Tulsa, Oklahoma [1]
085	Omaha, Nebraska [1]	193	Portland, Oregon (TCP) [3]
092	Des Moines, Iowa	197	Pittsburgh, Pennsylvania (TCP) [3]
094	Kansas City, Kansas	208	Nashville, Tennessee
095	Topeka, Kansas [1]	216	Houston, Texas (TCP) [4]
099	Wichita, Kansas	220	Salt Lake City, Utah (TCP) [2]
102	Lexington, Kentucky [1]	223	Hampton, Virginia
103	Ashland, Kentucky	225	Richmond, Virginia
106	New Orleans, Louisiana	229	Seattle, Washington (TCP) [2]
		239	Milwaukee, Wisconsin

[1] Less than 20 percent above primary standards and thus probably not a problem at this time. (Additional CO reductions will occur as a result of the Federal Motor Vehicle Control Program.)

[2] Transportation Control Plan designed for carbon monoxide only.

[3] Transportation Control Plan designated for both carbon monoxide and photochemical oxidants.

[4] Transportation Control Plan designed for photochemical oxidants only.

Source: Environmental Protection Agency.

Unregulated Pollutants

It is becoming increasingly evident that the air pollutants upon which our standards and monitoring have been focusing do not represent all the important parameters of air quality. In some cases, they may not even represent the most important or informative ones.

Present ambient air quality standards and most monitoring of suspended particulates, for example, are concerned only with the total weight of airborne particulate matter, as measured by high-volume samplers. But total weight is at best only a crude indicator of trends in the kinds of particulates that are most important to human health. By itself such a measurement is inadequate for many scientific purposes and therefore may be inadequate as a regulatory guide.

There are two major reasons for this inadequacy. First, the total weight of airborne particulates does not distinguish between tiny particles, which can penetrate the human respiratory system efficiently and thus pose considerable hazard to health, and the larger particles which generally do not. The proportion of respirable (small) particles — less than 3 microns in diameter — varies roughly from less than one-third to more than two-thirds of the total suspended particulates.

The second important reason is that most of the public health effects of particles in the air depend upon their chemical composition, which can also vary greatly. Toxic substances like acid sulfates, nitrates, trace metals, and organic compounds are important and potentially harmful constituents of airborne particulate matter, but there are no ambient standards and their is very little monitoring for these constituents now.

Table 5.10

Estimates of Adverse Health Effects of Aerosol Acid Sulfates

Effect	Threshold concentration (micrograms per cubic meter)	Duration of exposure
Increased daily mortality (four studies)	25	24 hours or longer
Aggravation of heart and lung disease in elderly (two studies)	25	24 hours or longer
Aggravation of asthma (four studies)	6–10	24 hours or longer
Increased acute respiratory diseases in children (four studies)	13	Several years
Increased risk of chronic bronchitis		
Cigarette smokers	15	Up to 10 years
Nonsmokers	10	Up to 10 years

Source: J. F. Finklea, et al., "Health Effects of Increasing Sulfur Oxides Emissions," Environmental Protection Agency (draft, 1975).

Particulate Sulfates

Suspended sulfate aerosols are believed among the air pollutants most damaging to human health; some of their estimated effects are listed in Table 5.10. A relatively small proportion of the sulfates in air was directly emitted as particulates, however. Most sulfates are formed through secondary chemical reactions in the atmosphere from other kinds of sulfur compounds which originate from both natural and manmade sources.

Continuous air monitoring network station in Philadelphia at 20th and Franklin Parkway houses instruments to keep tabs on air quality.

On a worldwide scale, most of the airborne sulfur compounds are believed to originate from natural sources such as volcanic activity, ocean salts, and decomposition of dead plants and animals. In an industrialized nation like the United States, however, manmade sulfur emissions — mostly in gaseous form — are believed to outweigh emissions from natural sources.

At least 95 percent of all manmade sulfur emissions is in the form of sulfur dioxide. The remainder is emitted as hydrogen sulfide or sulfur trioxide and a small amount of particulate sulfates. Once in the air, these sulfur compounds can be converted to sulfates by a variety of chemical reactions.

The best available data on ambient levels of sulfates and other noncriteria air pollutants are those of EPA's National Air Surveillance Network. This federal network consists of about 250 monitoring sites generally located in urban areas. As shown in Figure 5.11, as of 1970, the particulate sulfate levels observed at 164 urban NASN sites were highest in the Northeast. Findings were similar at 25 non-urban sites, but urban sulfate concentrations were substantially higher than nonurban. Only in rural areas of the Western states were sulfate levels near the average global background range of 1-2 micrograms per cubic meter.

Figure 5.11

Urban Sulfate Concentrations, 1970

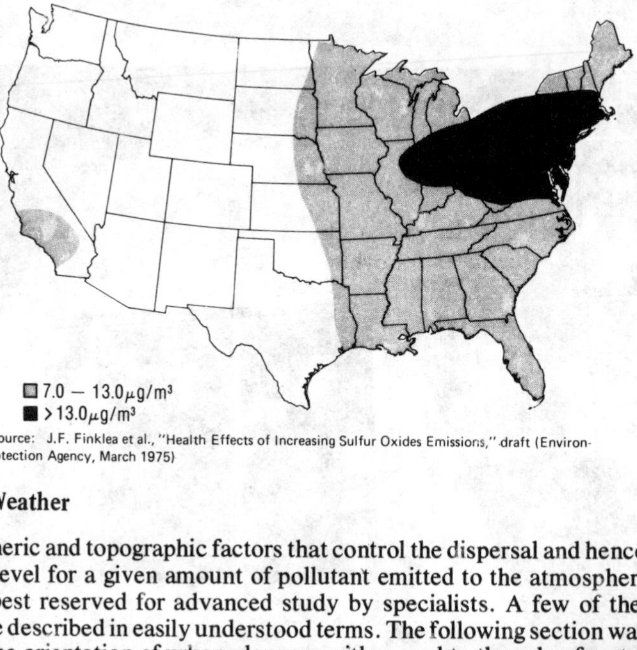

Source: J.F. Finklea et al., "Health Effects of Increasing Sulfur Oxides Emissions," draft (Environmental Protection Agency, March 1975)

Air Pollution Weather

The atmospheric and topographic factors that control the dispersal and hence affect the local ambient level for a given amount of pollutant emitted to the atmosphere are very complex and best reserved for advanced study by specialists. A few of these factors however can be described in easily understood terms. The following section was prepared originally for the orientation of urban planners with regard to the role of meteorology in the planning and air pollution control process. The section from *A Guide For Considering Air Quality in Urban Planning*, EPA, March 1974, provides a good general introduction to a complex subject. Information is provided also on the High Air Pollution Potential Advisory forecasts prepared by National Weather Service forecasters. Figure 5.18 illustrates the likely susceptibility of various large regions of the nation in any five year period to conditions favorable for the accumulation of air pollutants. The expected averages are derived from about ten years of forecast experience.

Natural Phenomena Affecting Air Quality

The concentration of atmospheric pollutants observed at different locations depends on more than just the quantity of pollutants emitted at the various sources. The atmosphere is the agent that transports and disperses pollutants between sources and receptors. Consequently, the state of the atmosphere helps to determine the concentrations of pollutants observed at receptors. Unlike emissions sources, which can be controlled, the state of the atmosphere is not at present susceptible to man's control.

Some skill has been attained, however, in predicting the future state of the atmosphere. Since the meteorological conditions that favor high concentrations of pollutants are known, severe air pollution episodes can therefore be forecast.

In general, three parameters are used to describe atmospheric transport and dispersion processes. These are wind speed, wind direction, and atmospheric stability. For emissions at a given source, a higher wind speed provides the pollutants with a greater air volume within which to disperse. This causes ground level pollutant concentrations, other things being equal, to be inversely proportional to wind speed.

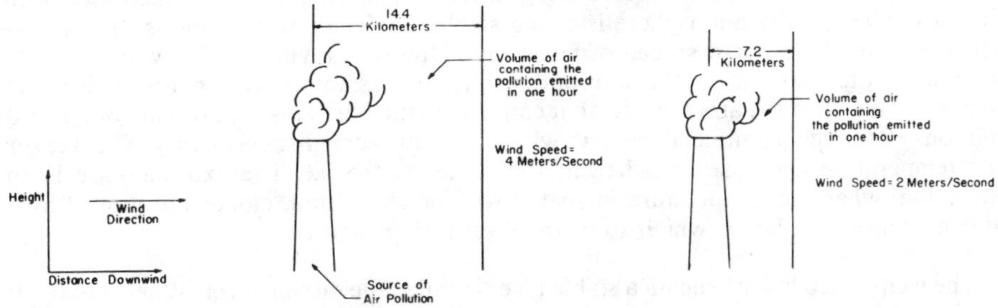

Figure 5.12 The influence of wind speed on ground level pollutant concentrations

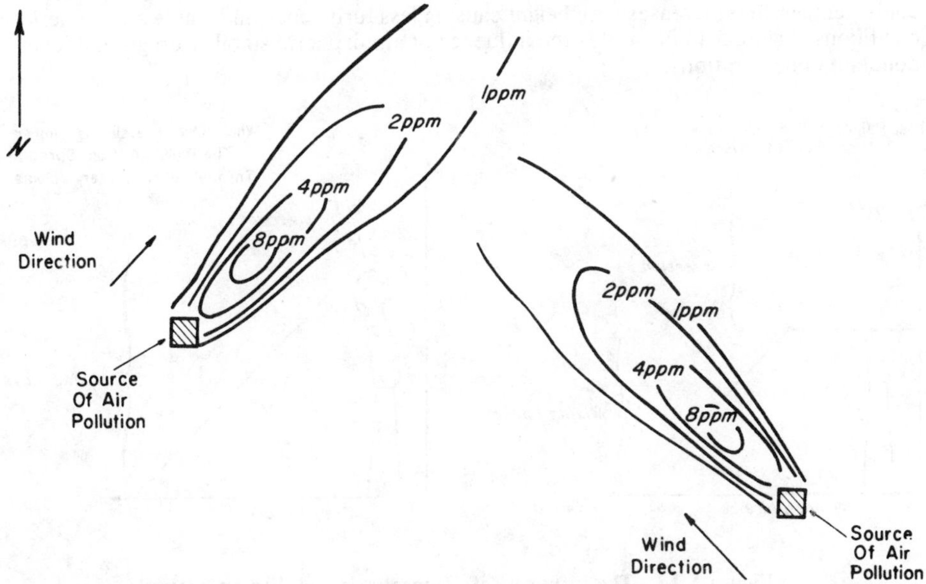

Figure 5.13 The influence of wind direction on ground level pollutant concentrations

Horizontally, the wind direction is the strongest factor affecting pollutant concentrations. For a given wind direction, nearly all the pollutant transport and dispersion will be downwind. Wind direction determines which sector of the area surrounding a source will receive pollutants from that source. The influences of wind speed and direction on pollution dispersion volumes and hence, on ground level concentrations are illustrated in Figures 5.12 and 5.13.

Atmospheric stability directly affects the vertical dispersion of atmospheric pollutants. Unlike wind direction and wind speed, atmospheric stability cannot be measured directly. Atmospheric stability is a measure of air turbulence and may be defined in terms of the vertical atmospheric temperature profile. When the temperature decreases rapidly with height, vertical motions in the atmosphere are enhanced, and the atmosphere is called unstable. An unstable atmosphere, with its enhanced vertical motions, is more effective for dispersing pollutants, and because of the large volume of air available for the spread of pollutants, ground-level concentrations can be relatively low. When the temperature does not decrease rapidly with height, vertical motions are neither enhanced nor repressed and the stability is described as neutral. Under these conditions, pollutants are also allowed to disperse vertically in the atmosphere, although not as rapidly as for the unstable case.

When the temperature decreases very little, remains the same, or increases with increasing height, the atmosphere is called stable. Under these conditions, the atmosphere inhibits the upward spread of pollutants. Upward-moving smoke, which rapidly assumes the temperature of the surrounding air, reaches a point where it is colder, and hence denser, than the air above it, so it can rise no further. This suppression of upward motions effectively forms a lid beneath which pollutants can disperse freely. The weaker the temperature decrease with height, the higher is the lid. The extreme case is an inversion, when the temperature increases with height. Often, clouds are topped by a stable or inversion layer, which stops their vertical growth.

The well-mixed layer beneath a stable layer is called the mixing layer. When it extends to the ground its vertical extent is known as the mixing height or the mixing depth. Generally, turbulence is enhanced in the early morning hours as the sun heats the ground and temperature decreases with height causing unstable conditions. At night, as the earth cools, temperature increases with height causing less turbulence and stable atmospheric conditions. Figure 5.14 illustrates the influence of atmospheric stability on ground level pollutant concentrations.

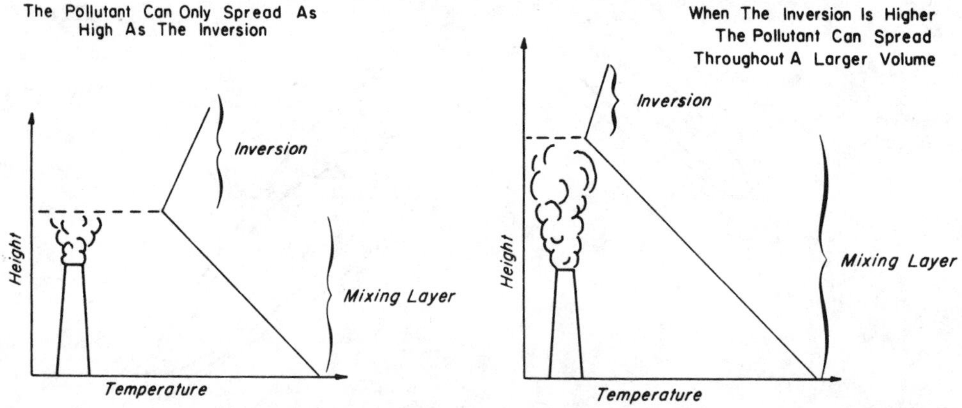

Figure 5.14 The influence of atmospheric stability on ground level pollutant concentrations

Wind speed, wind direction, and atmospheric stability will vary greatly with time. For a certain location, some combinations occur more frequently than others.

Where detailed meteorological records have been kept for a year or more, a stability wind rose can be calculated. This wind rose is a set of tables, one for each stability class (ranging from very stable to very unstable), listing the frequency of occurence of all possible combinations of wind speed and wind direction. Such wind roses are available for many locations in the United States from the National Climatic Center in Asheville, North Carolina. It should be noted that topographical features such as mountains, hills, valleys, bodies of water, buildings, and other terrain features can change airflow patterns resulting in unexpected pollution effects.

Near a large body of water, local sea breezes influence the spread of pollutants. Early in the morning, when the air is still or the wind is off the land, pollutants can accumulate over their sources or downwind of them. Later in the day, when a local sea breeze develops, a fresh breeze blows in the direction from the water toward land. This breeze brings with it not only the pollutants emitted from the sources at this time of day, but also those accumulated earlier in the day, because they are carried back from water to land. Unexpectedly high pollutant concentrations can occur near the shore when the high pollutant loading blows past. In addition to this effect, which generally occurs close to land, the seabreeze itself can penetrate as far inland as 40 miles or more.

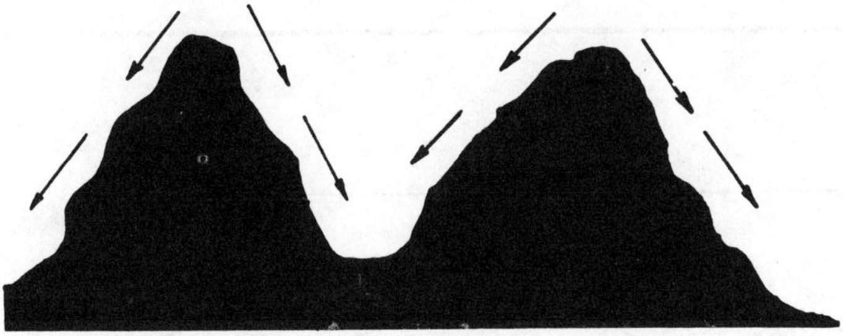

Figure 5.15 Nighttime airflow into valleys

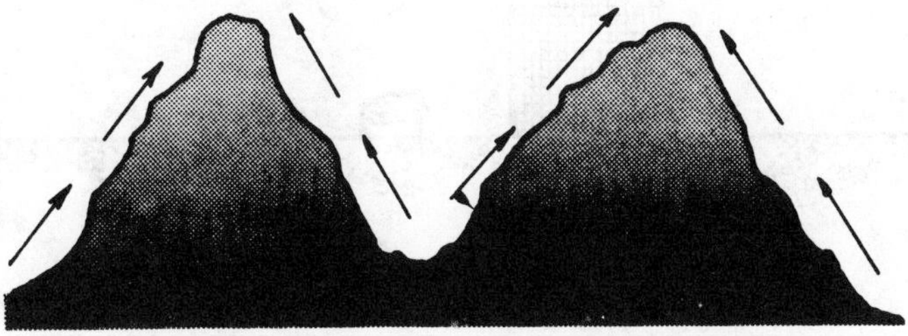

Figure 5.16 Daytime airflow out of valleys

Mountains and valleys have characteristic airflow patterns, too. In the evening, as the earth and the air close to the earth cools, the coldest air will sink into the lowest part of the valley, as illustrated in Figure 5.15. This creates a stable inversion layer because lighter, warmer air stays above the valley. In this way, pollutants are trapped in the valleys all night. During the daytime when heating occurs, the air in the valley is warmed and rises, permitting the pollutants to escape (Figure 5.16). Unfortunately, this heating and upward motion does not always occur. During periods when high pressure settles over a region and the air is stagnant, the atmosphere is stable all day long, and pollutants continue to accumulate in the valley. Some of the worst episodes of air pollution have occurred in mountain chains like the Appalacians, where industries are located in the valleys between adjacent hills.

In cities, buildings form the topography. Where rows of tall buildings front on narrow streets the air flows through the streets as though they were canyons. Since ventilation is determined by building configuration, many distortions in wind, and hence pollution flows, take place in a city. Figure 5.17 shows an example. Air flows over a building and into a street downwind of it. The lines show the direction of airflow. The building, because the air cannot flow through it, creates an obstruction in the pattern of the smooth airflow. Downwind of the building, an eddy, or circular movement of air at variance with the main airflow, is formed in its wake, such as the one shown in the figure. The eddy can trap pollutants emitted by cars in the street, and can cause concentrations of pollutants, for example, carbon monoxide, to be as much as three times higher on the side of the street further downwind than at the site of pollutant origin.

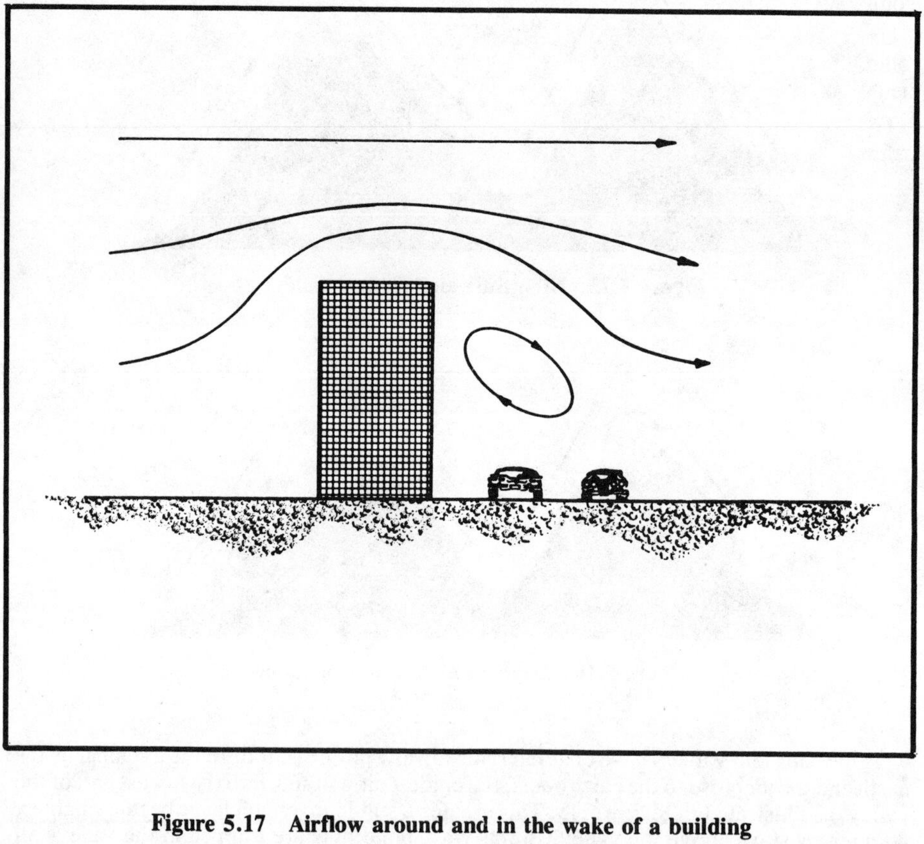

Figure 5.17 Airflow around and in the wake of a building

High Air Pollution Potential Advisories

High Air Pollution Potential Advisories (HAPPA) are prepared at the National Meteorological Center (NMC) in Suitland, Maryland, by meteorologists of the National Oceanographic and Atmospheric Administration (NOAA), Department of Commerce.

Advisories are based both on reports received hourly via teletype from Weather Service stations in the United States and on numerous analyses and forecasts prepared by the NMC. With its electronic computer facilities, the NMC prepares mixing-depth and wind-speed data from all upper-air-observing stations in the contiguous United States (about 70 stations). These data are analyzed, interpreted, and integrated with other meteorological information.

National air pollution potential advisories based on these data are transmitted daily at 12:20 p.m., E.S.T., to Weather Service stations. When meteorological conditions do not warrant issuance of a HAPPA, the teletype message is "none today." When the forecast indicates that an advisory of high air pollution potential should be issued, the message designates the affected areas. The daily message indicates significant changes in the boundaries of advisory areas, including termination of an episode.

Because conditions of atmospheric transport and dispersion typically vary with location and time, the forecasting staff cannot prepare advisories for each city in the United States. For this reason, the NOAA meteorologists limit their forecasts to areas at least as large as 75,000 square miles (roughly the size of Oklahoma), in which stagnation conditions are expected to persist for at least 36 hours. Individual Weather Service stations may modify these generalized forecasts on the basis of local meteorological conditions.

Users of the service should realize that boundaries of the forecast areas of high air pollution potential cannot be delineated exactly. For practical purposes, the lines defining the advisory areas should be interpreted as bands roughly 100 miles wide.

To be notified of these advisories, air pollution control or research officials must initiate arrangements with the nearest Weather Service station.

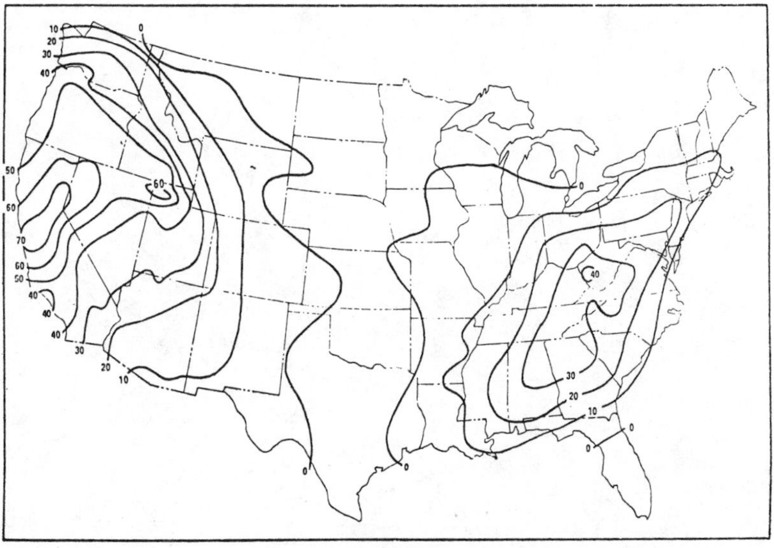

Figure 5.18 Isopleths of total number of forecast-days of high meteorological potential for air pollution expected in a 5-year period. Data are based on forecasts issued since the program began, 1 August 1960 and 1 October 1963 for eastern and western parts of the United States, respectively, through 3 April 1970.

Source: G.C. Holzworth, "MIXING HEIGHTS, WIND SPEEDS, AND URBAN AIR POLLUTION POTENTIAL". EPA 1972.

WEATHER FUNDAMENTALS (INCLUDING FAHRENHEIT/CELSIUS CONVERSION)

WEATHER FUNDAMENTALS

The following is intended to serve as a sort of "weather primer". It attempts to analyze in everyday language the fundamental factors and processes which are the components of weather.

THE EARTH'S ATMOSPHERE

Composition of our atmosphere

Air is a mixture of several gases. When completely dry, it is about 78% nitrogen and 21% oxygen. The remaining 1% is other gases such as Argon, Carbon Dioxide, Neon, Helium, and others. However, in nature, air is never completely dry. It always contains some water vapor in amounts varying from *almost* zero to about 5% by volume. As water vapor content increases, the other gases decrease proportionately.

Vertical structure

We classify the atmosphere into layers, or spheres, by characteristics exhibited in these layers.

The TROPOSPHERE is the layer from the surface to an average altitude of about 7 miles. It is characterized by an overall decrease of temperature with increasing altitude. The height of the troposphere varies with latitude and seasons. It slopes from about 20,000 feet over the poles to about 65,000 feet over the Equator; and it is higher in summer than in winter.

At the top of the troposphere is the TROPOPAUSE, a very thin layer marking the boundary between the troposphere and the layer above. The height of the tropopause and certain weather phenomena are related, as will be explained later.

Above the tropopause is the STRATOSPHERE. This layer is typified by relatively small changes in temperature with height except for a warming trend near the top.

Density

Air is matter and has weight. Since it is gaseous, it is compressible. Pressure the atmosphere exerts on the surface is the result of the weight of the air above. Thus, air near the surface is much more dense than air at high altitudes.

TEMPERATURE

Temperature scales

Two commonly used temperature scales are Celsius (Centigrade) and Fahrenheit. The Celsius scale is used exclusively for upper air temperatures and is rapidly becoming the world standard for surface temperatures also.

Traditionally, two common temperature references are the melting point of pure ice and the boiling point of pure water at sea level. The melting point of ice is 0° C or 32° F; the boiling point of water is 100° C or 212° F. Thus, the difference between melting and boiling is 100 degrees Celsius or 180 degrees Fahrenheit; the ratio between degrees Celsius and Fahrenheit is 100/180 or 5/9. Since 0° F is 32 Fahrenheit degrees colder than 0° C, you must apply this difference when comparing temperatures on the two scales. You can convert from one scale to the other using one of the following formulae:

$$C = \frac{5}{9}(F - 32) \qquad F = \frac{9}{5}C + 32$$

where C is degrees Celsius and F is degrees Fahrenheit. (See conversion chart, page 255)

Temperature is measured with a thermometer. But what makes a thermometer work? Simply the addition or removal of heat. Heat and temperature are not the same; how are they related?

Heat and temperature

Heat is a form of energy. When a substance contains heat, it exhibits the property we measure as temperature—the degree of "hotness" or "coldness." A specific amount of heat absorbed by or removed from a substance raises or lowers its temperature a definite amount. However, the amount of temperature change depends on characteristics of the substance. Each substance has its unique temperature change for the specific change in heat. For example, if a land surface and a water surface have the same temperature and an equal amount of heat is added, the land surface becomes hotter than the water surface. Conversely, with equal heat loss, the land becomes colder than the water.

The Earth receives energy from the sun in the form of solar radiation. The Earth and its atmosphere reflect about 55 percent of the radiation and absorb the remaining 45 percent converting it to heat. The Earth, in turn, radiates energy, and this outgoing radiation is "terrestrial radiation." It is evident that the average heat gained from incoming solar radiation must equal heat lost through terrestrial radiation in order to keep the earth from getting progressively hotter or colder. However, this balance is world-wide; we must consider regional and local imbalances which create temperature variations.

Temperature variations

The amount of solar energy received by any region varies with time of day, with seasons, and with latitude. These differences in solar energy create temperature variations. Temperatures also vary with differences in topographical surface and with altitude. These temperature variations create forces that drive the atmosphere in its endless motions.

Day-to-night (diurnal) variation of temperature

Diurnal variation is the change in temperature from day to night brought about by the daily rotation of the Earth. The Earth receives heat during the day by solar radiation but continually loses heat by terrestrial radiation. Warming and cooling depend on an imbalance of solar and terrestrial radiation. During the day, solar radiation exceeds terrestrial radiation and the surface becomes warmer. At night, solar radiation ceases, but terrestrial radiation continues and cools the surface. Cooling continues after sunrise until solar radiation again exceeds terrestrial radiation. Minimum temperature usually occurs after sunrise, sometimes as much as one hour after. The continued cooling after sunrise is one reason that fog sometimes forms shortly after the sun is above the horizon.

Seasonal variation of temperature

In addition to its daily rotation, the Earth revolves in a complete orbit around the sun once each year. Since the axis of the Earth tilts to the plane of orbit, the angle of incident solar radiation varies seasonally between hemispheres. The Northern Hemisphere is warmer in June, July, and August because it receives more solar energy than does the Southern Hemisphere. During December, January, and February, the opposite is true; the Southern Hemisphere receives more solar energy and is warmer.

Temperature variation with latitude

The shape of the Earth causes a geographical variation in the angle of incident solar radiation. Since the Earth is essentially spherical, the sun is more nearly overhead in equatorial regions than at higher latitudes. Equatorial regions, therefore, receive the most radiant energy and are warmest.Slanting rays of the sun at higher latitudes deliver less energy over a given area with the least being received at the poles. Thus, temperature varies with latitude from the warm Equator to the cold poles.

Temperature variations with topography

Not related to movement or shape of the earth are temperature variations induced by water and terrain. As stated earlier, water absorbs and radiates energy with less temperature change than does land. Large, deep water bodies tend to minimize temperature changes, while continents favor large changes. Wet soil such as in swamps and marshes is almost as effective as water in suppressing temperature changes. Thick vegetation tends to control temperature changes since it contains some water and also insulates against heat transfer between the ground and the atmosphere. Arid, barren surfaces permit the greatest temperature changes.

These topographical influences are both diurnal and seasonal. For example, the difference between a daily maximum and minimum may be 10° or less over water, near a shore line, or over a swamp or marsh, while a difference of 50° or more is common over rocky or sandy deserts. In the Northern Hemisphere in July, temperatures are warmer over continents than over oceans; in January they are colder over continents than over oceans. The opposite is true in the Southern Hemisphere, but not as pronounced because of more water surface in the Southern Hemisphere.

To compare land and water effect on seasonal temperature variation, consider northern Asia and southern California near San Diego. In the deep continental interior of northern Asia, July average temperature is about 50° F; and January average, about —30° F. Seasonal range is about 80° F. Near San Diego, due to the proximity of the Pacific Ocean, July average is about 70° F and January average, 50° F. Seasonal variation is only about 20° F.

Abrupt temperature differences develop along lake and ocean shores. These variations generate pressure differences and local winds which will be studied further on in this text.

Prevailing wind is also a factor in temperature controls. In an area where prevailing winds are from large water bodies, temperature changes are rather small. Most islands enjoy fairly constant temperatures. On the other hand, temperature changes are more pronounced where prevailing wind is from dry, barren regions.

Air transfers heat slowly from the surface upward. Thus, temperature changes aloft are more gradual than at the surface. The following looks at particulars of temperature changes with altitude.

Temperature variation with altitude

Temperature normally decreases with increasing altitude throughout the troposphere. This *decrease of temperature with altitude* is defined as *lapse rate*. The average decrease of temperature—average lapse rate—in the troposphere is 2° C per 1,000 feet. But since this is an average, the exact value seldom exists. In fact, temperature sometimes increases with height through a layer. *An increase in temperature with altitude is* defined as *an inversion,* i.e., lapse rate is inverted.

An inversion often develops near the ground on clear, cool nights when wind is light. The ground radiates and cools much faster than the overlying air. Air in contact with the

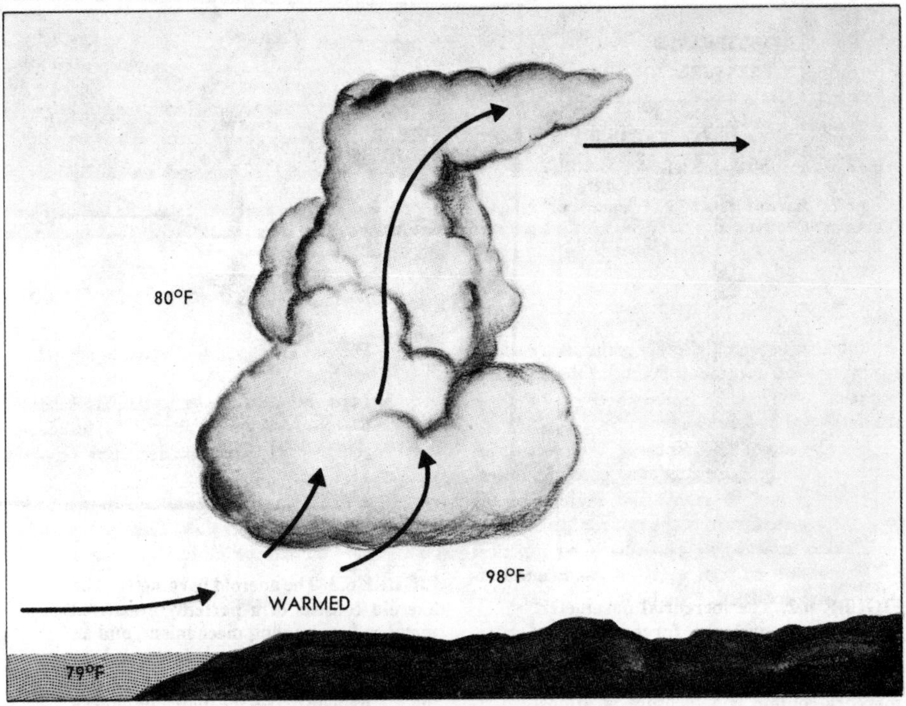

FIGURE 6.1. Temperature differences create air movement and, at times, cloudiness.

ground becomes cold while the temperature a few hundred feet above changes very little. Thus, temperature increases with height. Inversions may also occur at any altitude when conditions are favorable. For example, a current of warm air aloft overrunning cold air near the surface produces an inversion aloft. Inversions are common in the stratosphere.

ATMOSPHERIC PRESSURE AND THE BAROMETER

Atmospheric pressure

Atmospheric pressure is the force per unit area exerted by the weight of the atmosphere. Since air is not solid, we cannot weigh it with conventional scales. Yet, Toricelli proved three centuries ago that he could weigh the atmosphere by balancing it against a column of mercury. He actually measured pressure converting it directly to weight.

Measuring pressure

The instrument Toricelli designed for measuring pressure is the barometer. Weather services and the aviation community use two types of barometers in measuring pressure—the mercurial and aneroid.

The Mercurial Barometer—The mercurial barometer, consists of an open dish of mercury into which we place the open end of an evacuated glass tube. Atmospheric pressure forces mercury to rise in the tube. At stations near sea level, the column of mercury rises on the average to a height of 29.92 inches or 760 millimeters. In other words,

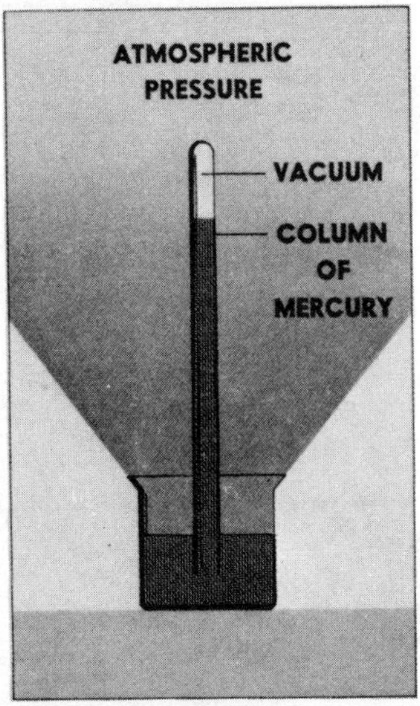

FIGURE 6.2. The mercurial barometer. Atmospheric pressure forces mercury from the open dish upward into the evacuated glass tube. The height of the mercury column is a measure of atmospheric pressure.

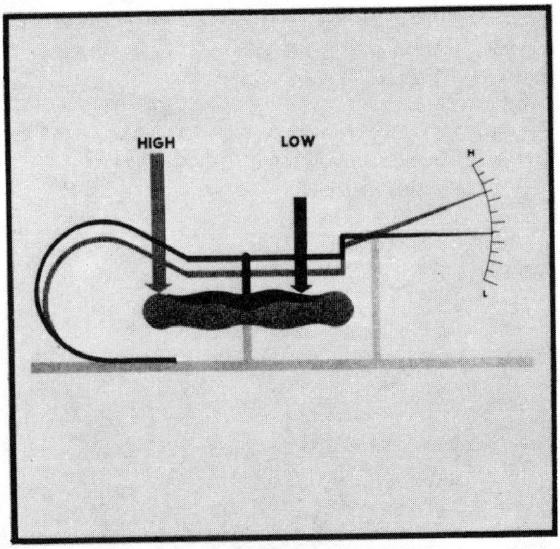

FIGURE 6.3. The aneroid barometer. The aneroid consists of a partially evacuated metal cell, a coupling mechanism, and an indicator scale. The cell contracts and expands with changing pressure. The coupling mechanism drives the indicator along a scale graduated in pressure units.

a column of mercury of that height weighs the same as a column of air having the same cross section as the column of mercury and extending from sea level to the top of the atmosphere.

Why is mercury used in the barometer? Mercury is the heaviest substance available which remains liquid at ordinary temperatures. It permits the instrument to be of manageable size. Water could be used but at sea level the water column would be about 34 feet high.

The aneroid barometer

Essential features of an aneroid barometer are a flexible metal cell and the registering mechanism. The cell is partially evacuated and contracts or expands as pressure changes. One end of the cell is fixed, while the other end moves the registering mechanism. The coupling mechanism magnifies movement of the cell driving an indicator hand along a scale graduated in pressure units.

Pressure units

Pressure is expressed in many ways throughout the world. The term used depends somewhat on its application and the system of measurement. Two popular units are "inches of mercury" or "millimeters of mercury." Since pressure is force per unit area, a more explicit expression of pressure is "pounds per square inch" or "grams per square centimeter." The term "millibar" precisely expresses pressure as a force per unit area, one millibar being a force of 1,000 dynes per square centimeter. The millibar is rapidly becoming a universal pressure unit.

Station pressure

Obviously, pressure can be measured only at the point of measurement. The pressure measured at a station or airport is "station pressure" or the actual pressure at field elevation. For instance, station pressure at Denver is less than at New Orleans. Now look more closely at some factors influencing pressure.

Pressure variation

Pressure varies with altitude and temperature of the air as well as with other minor influences.

Altitude—Moving upward through the atmosphere, weight of the air above becomes less and less. Within the lower few thousand feet of the troposphere, pressure decreases roughly one inch for each 1,000 feet increase in altitude.

Sea Level Pressure—Since pressure varies with altitude, it is not easy to compare station pressures between stations at different altitudes. To make them comparable, pressure readings must be adjusted to some common level. Mean sea level seems the most feasible common reference. Pressure measured at a 5,000-foot station is 25 inches; pressure increases about 1 inch for each 1,000 feet or a total of 5 inches. Sea level pressure is approximately 25 + 5 or 30 inches. The weather observer takes temperature and other effects into account, but this simplified example explains the basic principle of sea level pressure reduction.

Sea level pressure is usually expressed in millibars. Standard sea level pressure is 1013.2 millibars, 29.92 inches of mercury, 760 millimeters of mercury, or about 14.7 pounds per square inch.

Pressure Analyses (Using Isobars)—Sea level pressure are commonly plotted on a map and lines are drawn connecting points of equal pressure. These lines of equal pressure are *isobars*. Hence, the surface map is an *isobaric analysis* showing identifiable, organized pressure patterns. Five pressure systems are defined as follow:

1. LOW—a center of pressure surrounded on all sides by higher pressure; also called a cyclone. Cyclonic curvature is the curvature of isobars to the left when you stand with lower pressure to your left.
2. HIGH—a center of pressure surrounded on all sides by lower pressure, also called an anticyclone. Anticyclonic curvature is the curvature of isobars to the right when you stand with lower pressure to your left.
3. TROUGH—an elongated area of low pressure with the lowest pressure along a line marking maximum cyclonic curvature.
4. RIDGE—an elongated area of high pressure with the highest pressure along a line marking maximum anticyclonic curvature.
5. COL—the neutral area between two highs and two lows. It also is the intersection of a trough and a ridge. The col on a pressure surface is analogous to a mountain pass on a topographic surface. We simply contour the heights of the pressure surface. For example, a 700-millibar constant pressure analysis is a contour map of the heights of the 700-millibar pressure surface. While the contour map is based on variations in height, these variations are small when compared to flight levels, and for all practical purposes, you may regard the 700-millibar chart as a weather map at approximately 10,000 feet or 3,048 meters.

WIND

What causes wind?

Differences in temperature create differences in pressure. These pressure differences drive a complex system of winds in a never ending attempt to reach equilibrium. Wind also transports water vapor and spreads fog, clouds, and precipitation. To help the reader relate wind to pressure patterns and the movement of weather systems, this text explains *convection* and the *pressure gradient force*, describes the effects of the *Coriolis* and frictional forces, relates convection and these forces to the general circulation, discusses local and small-scale wind systems, introduces the concept of wind shear, and associates wind with weather.

Convection currents cause wind

When two surfaces are heated unequally, they heat the overlying air unevenly. The warmer air expands and becomes lighter or less dense than the cool air. The more

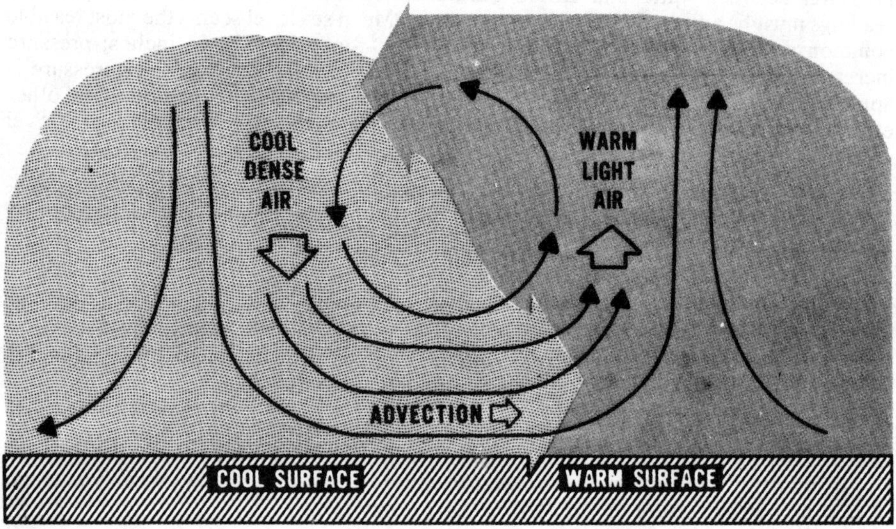

FIGURE 6.4. Convective current resulting from uneven heating of air by contrasting surface temperatures. The cool, heavier air forces the warmer air aloft establishing a convective cell. Convection continues as long as the uneven heating persists.

dense, cool air is drawn to the ground by its greater gravitational force lifting or forcing the warm air upward much as oil is forced to the top of water when the two are mixed. Figure 6.4 shows the convective process. The rising air spreads and cools, eventually descending to complete the convective circulation. As long as the uneven heating persists, convection maintains a continuous "convective current."

The horizontal air flow in a convective current is "wind." Convection of both large and small scales accounts for systems ranging from hemispheric circulations down to local eddies. This horizontal flow, wind, is sometimes called "advection." However, the term "advection" more commonly applies to the transport of atmospheric properties by the wind, i.e., warm advection; cold advection; advection of water vapor, etc.

Pressure gradient force of wind

Pressure differences must create a force in order to drive the wind. This force is the *pressure gradient force*. The force is from higher pressure to lower pressure and is perpendicular to isobars or contours. Whenever a pressure difference develops over an area, the pressure gradient force begins moving the air directly across the isobars. The closer the spacing of isobars, the stronger is the pressure gradient force. The stronger the pressure gradient force, the stronger is the wind. Thus, closely spaced isobars mean strong winds; widely spaced isobars mean lighter wind. From a pressure analysis, the reader can get a general idea of wind speed from contour or isobar spacing.

Because of uneven heating of the Earth, surface pressure is low in warm equatorial regions and high in cold polar regions. A pressure gradient develops from the poles to the Equator. If the Earth did not rotate, this pressure gradient force would be the only force acting on the wind. Circulation would be two giant hemispheric convective currents. Cold air would sink at the poles; wind would blow straight from the poles to the Equator; warm air at the Equator would be forced upward; and high level winds would blow directly toward the poles. However, the Earth does rotate; and because of its rotation. this simple circulation is greatly distorted.

Coriolis force: it modifies wind direction

A moving mass travels in a straight line until acted on by some outside force. However, if one views the moving mass from a rotating platform, the path of the moving mass relative to his platform appears to be deflected or curved. To illustrate, start rotating the turntable of a record player. Then using a piece of chalk and a ruler, draw a "straight" line from the center to the outer edge of the turntable. To you, the chalk traveled in a straight line. Now stop the turntable; on it, the line spirals outward from the center. To a viewer on the turntable, some "apparent" force deflected the chalk to the right.

A similar apparent force deflects moving particles on the earth. Because the Earth is spherical, the deflective force is much more complex than the simple turntable example. Although the force is termed "apparent," to us on Earth, it is very real. The principle was

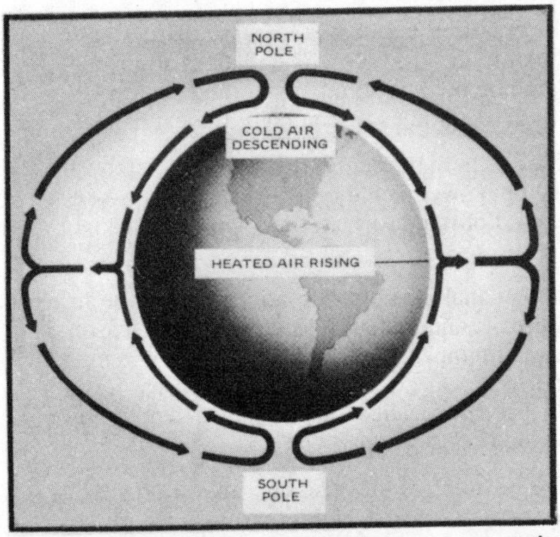

FIGURE 6.5 Circulation as it would be on a nonrotating globe. Intense heating at the Equator lowers the density. More dense air flows from the poles toward the Equator forcing the less dense air aloft where it flows toward the poles. The circulation would be two giant hemispherical convective currents.

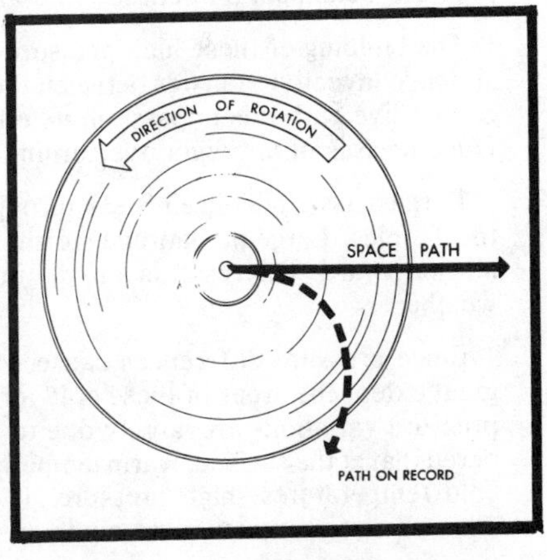

FIGURE 6.6. Apparent deflective force due to rotation of a horizontal platform. The "space path" is the path taken by a piece of chalk. The "path of record" is the line traced on the rotating record. Relative to the record, the chalk appeared to curve; in space, it traveled in a straight line.

first explained by a Frenchman, Coriolis, and carries his name—the Coriolis force.

The Coriolis force affects the paths of aircraft; missiles; flying birds; ocean currents; and, most important to the study of weather, air currents. The force deflects air to the right in the Northern Hemisphere and to the left in the Southern Hemisphere. This text concentrates mostly on deflection to the right in the Northern Hemisphere.

Coriolis force is at a right angle to wind direction and directly proportional to wind speed. That is, as wind speed increases, Coriolis force increases. At a given latitude, double the wind speed and you double the Coriolis force. Why at a given latitude?

Coriolis force varies with latitude from zero at the Equator to a maximum at the poles. It influences wind direction everywhere except immediately at the Equator; but the effects are more pronounced in middle and high latitudes.

Remember that the pressure gradient force drives the wind and is perpendicular to isobars. When a pressure gradient force is first established, wind begins to blow from higher to lower pressure directly across the isobars. However, the instant air begins moving, Coriolis force deflects it to the right. Soon the wind is deflected a full 90° and is parallel to the isobars or contours. At this time, Coriolis force exactly balances pressure gradient force. With the forces in balance, wind will remain parallel to isobars or contours. Surface friction disrupts this balance as we discuss later; but first let's see how Coriolis force distorts the fictitious global circulation.

The general circulation of earth's air

As air is forced aloft at the Equator and begins its high-level trek northward, the Coriolis force turns it to the right or to the east. Wind becomes westerly at about 30° latitude temporarily blocking further northward movement. Similarly, as air over the poles begins its low-level journey southward toward the Equator, it likewise is deflected to the right and becomes an east wind, halting for a while its southerly progress. As a result, air literally "piles up" at about 30° and 60° latitude in both hemispheres. The added weight of the air increases the pressure into semipermanent high pressure belts. Maps of mean surface pressure for the months of July and January show clearly the subtropical high pressure belts near 30° latitude in both the Northern and Southern Hemispheres.

The building of these high pressure belts creates a temporary impasse disrupting the simple convective transfer between the Equator and the poles. The restless atmosphere cannot live with this impasse in its effort to reach equilibrium. Something has to give. Huge masses of air begin overturning in middle latitudes to complete the exchange.

Large masses of cold air break through the northern barrier plunging southward toward the Tropics. Large midlatitude storms develop between cold outbreaks and carry warm air northward. The result is a midlatitude band of migratory storms with ever changing weather.

Since pressure differences cause wind, seasonal pressure variations determine to a great extent the areas of these cold air outbreaks and midlatitude storms. But, seasonal pressure variations are largely due to seasonal temperature changes. It will be remembered that at the surface, warm temperatures to a great extent determine low pressure and cold temperatures, high pressure. It will also be recalled that seasonal temperature changes over continents are much greater than over oceans.

During summer, warm continents tend to be areas of low pressure and the relatively cool oceans, high pressure. In winter, the reverse is true—high pressure over the cold continents and low pressure over the relatively warm oceans. The same pressure variations occur in the warm and cold seasons of the Southern Hemisphere, although the effect is not as pronounced because of the much larger water areas of the Southern Hemisphere.

Cold outbreaks are strongest in the cold season and are predominantly from cold continental areas. Summer outbreaks are weaker and more likely to originate from cool water surfaces. Since these outbreaks are masses of cool, dense air, they characteristically are high pressure areas.

As the air tries to blow outward from the high pressure, it is deflected to the right by the Coriolis force. Thus, the wind around a high blows clockwise. The high pressure with its associated wind system is an *anticyclone*.

The storms that develop between high pressure systems are characterized by low pressure. As winds try to blow inward toward the center of low pressure, they also are deflected to the right. Thus, the wind around a low is counterclockwise. The low pressure and its wind system is a *cyclone*.

The high pressure belt at about 30° north latitude forces air outward at the surface to the north and to the south. The northbound air becomes entrained into the midlatitude storms. The southward moving air is again deflected by the Coriolis force becoming the well-known subtropical northeast trade winds. In midlatitudes, high level winds are predominantly from the west and are known as the prevailing westerlies. Polar easterlies dominate low-level circulation north of about 60° latitude.

There are three major wind belts. *Northeasterly trade* winds carry tropical storms from east to west. The *prevailing westerlies* drive midlatitude storms generally from west to east. Few major storm systems develop in the comparatively small Arctic region; the chief influence of the *polar easterlies* is their contribution to the development of midlatitude storms.

Friction effect on wind

This discussion so far has said nothing about friction. Wind flow patterns aloft follow isobars or contours where friction has little effect. However, friction is a significant factor near the surface.

Friction between the wind and the terrain surface slows the wind. The rougher the terrain, the greater is the frictional effect. Also, the stronger the wind speed, the greater is the friction. One may not think of friction as a force, but it is a very real and effective force always acting opposite to wind direction.

As frictional force slows the windspeed, Coriolis force decreases. However, friction does not affect pressure gradient force. Pressure gradient and Coriolis forces are no longer in balance. The stronger pressure gradient force turns the wind at an angle across the isobars toward lower pressure until the three forces balance. Frictional and Coriolis forces combine to just balance pressure gradient force. Surface wind spirals outward from high pressure into low pressure crossing isobars at an angle.

The angle of surface wind to isobars is about 10° over water increasing with roughness of terrain. In mountainous regions, one often has difficulty relating surface wind to pressure gradient because of immense friction and also because of local terrain effects on pressure.

The jet stream

A discussion of the general circulation is incomplete when it does not mention the "jet stream." Winds on the average increase with height throughout the troposphere culminating in a maximum near the level of the tropopause. These maximum winds tend to be further concentrated in narrow bands. A jet stream, then, is a narrow band of strong winds meandering through the atmosphere at a level near the tropopause. Further discussion of the jet stream is taken up later in this text.

Local and small scale winds

Until now, this text has dealt only with the general circulation and major wind systems. Local terrain features such as mountains and shore lines influence local winds and weather.

Mountain and valley winds

In the daytime, air next to a mountain slope is heated by contact with the ground as it receives radiation from the sun. This air usually becomes warmer than air at the same altitude but farther from the slope.

Colder, denser air in the surroundings settles downward and forces the warmer air near the ground up the mountain slope. This wind is a "valley wind" so called because the air is flowing up out of the valley.

At night, the air in contact with the mountain slope is cooled by terrestrial radiation and becomes heavier than the surrounding air. It sinks along the slope, producing the "mountain wind" which flows like water down the mountain slope. Mountain winds are usually stronger than valley winds, especially in winter. The mountain wind often continues down the more gentle slopes of canyons and valleys, and in such cases takes the name "drainage wind." It can become quite strong over some terrain conditions and in extreme cases can become hazardous when flowing through canyon restrictions.

Katabatic wind

A katabatic wind is any wind blowing down an incline when the incline is influential in causing the wind. Thus, the mountain wind is a katabatic wind. Any katabatic wind originates because cold, heavy air spills down sloping terrain displacing warmer, less dense air ahead of it. Air is heated and dried as it flows down slope. Sometimes the descending air becomes warmer than the air it replaces.

Many katabatic winds recurring in local areas have been given colorful names to highlight their dramatic, local effect. Some of these are the Bora, a cold northerly wind blowing from the Alps to the Mediterranean coast; the Chinook, a warm wind down the east slope of the Rocky Mountains often reaching hundreds of miles into the high plains; the Taku, a cold wind in Alaska blowing off the Taku glacier; and the Santa Ana, a warm wind descending from the Sierras into the Santa Ana Valley of California.

Land and sea breezes

As frequently stated earlier, land surfaces warm and cool more rapidly than do water surfaces; therefore, land is warmer than the sea during the day; wind blows from the cool water to warm land—the "sea breeze" so called because it blows from the sea. At night, the wind reverses, blows from cool land to warmer water, and creates a "land breeze."

Land and sea breezes develop only when the overall pressure gradient is weak. Wind with a stronger pressure gradient mixes the air so rapidly that local temperature and pressure gradients do not develop along the shore line.

Wind shear

Rubbing two objects against each other creates friction. If the objects are solid, no exchange of mass occurs between the two. However, if the objects are fluid currents, friction creates eddies along a common shallow mixing zone, and a mass transfer takes place in the shallow mixing layer. This zone of induced eddies and mixing is a shear zone.

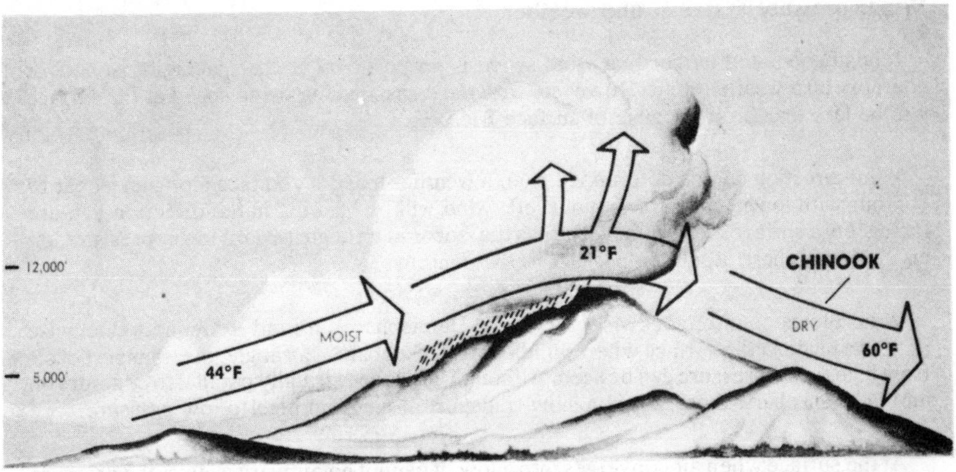

FIGURE 6.7. The "Chinook" is a katabatic (downslope) wind. Air cools as it moves upslope and warms as it blows downslope. The Chinook occasionally produces dramatic warming over the plains just east of the Rocky Mountains.

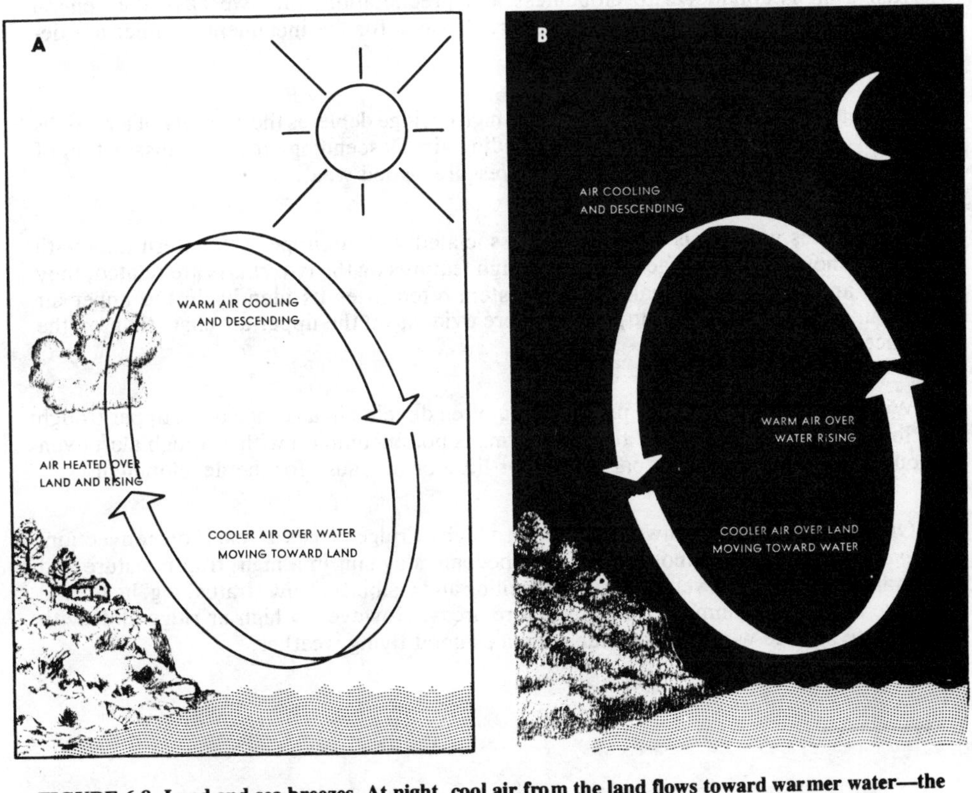

FIGURE 6.8. Land and sea breezes. At night, cool air from the land flows toward warmer water—the land breeze. During the day, wind blows from the water to the warmer land—the sea breeze.

Wind, pressure systems, and weather

It has been noted earlier that wind speed is proportional to the spacing of isobars or contours on a weather map. However, with the same spacing, wind speed at the surface will be less than aloft because of surface friction.

Wind direction can be determined from a weather map. If you face along an isobar or contour with lower pressure on your left, wind will be blowing in the direction you are facing. On a surface map, wind will cross the isobar at an angle toward lower pressure; on an upper air chart, it will be parallel to the contour.

Wind blows counterclockwise (Northern Hemisphere) around a low and clockwise around a high. At the surface where winds cross the isobars at an angle, the transport of air from high to low pressure can be seen. Although winds are virtually parallel to contours on an upper air chart, there still is a slow transport of air from high to low pressure.

At the surface when air converges into a low, it cannot go outward against the pressure gradient, nor can it go downward into the ground; it must go upward.* Therefore, a low or trough is an area of rising air.

Rising air is conducive to cloudiness and precipitation; thus we have the general association of low pressure—bad weather. Reasons for the inclement weather are developed further on in this text.

By similar reasoning, air moving out of a high or ridge depletes the quantity of air. Highs and ridges, therefore, are areas of descending air. Descending air favors dissipation of cloudiness; hence the association, high pressure—good weather.

Many times weather is more closely associated with an upper air pattern than with features shown by the surface map. Although features on the two charts are related, they seldom are identical. A weak surface system often loses its identity in the upper air pattern, while another system may be more evident on the upper air chart than on the surface map.

Widespread cloudiness and precipitation often develop in advance of an upper trough or low. A line of showers and thunderstorms is not uncommon with a trough aloft even though the surface pressure pattern shows little or no cause for the development.

On the other hand, downward motion in a high or ridge places a "cap" on convection, preventing any upward motion. Air may become stagnant in a high, trap moisture and contamination in low levels, and restrict ceiling and visibility. Low stratus, fog, haze, and smoke are not uncommon in high pressure areas. However, a high or ridge aloft with moderate surface winds most often produces good flying weather.

---

* Earlier it was stated that air "piles up" in the vicinity of 30° latitude increasing pressure and forming the subtropical high pressure belt. Why, then, does not air flowing into a low or trough increase pressure and fill the system? Dynamic forces maintain the low or trough; and these forces differ from the forces that maintain the subtropical high.

MOISTURE, CLOUD FORMATION, AND PRECIPITATION

Water vapor

Water evaporates into the air and becomes an ever-present but variable constituent of the atmosphere. Water vapor is invisible just as oxygen and other gases are invisible. However, water vapor can be readily measured and expressed in different ways. Two commonly used terms are (1) relative humidity, and (2) dew point.

Relative humidity

Relative humidity routinely is expressed in percent. As the term suggests, *relative humidity* is "relative." It relates *the actual water vapor present to that which could be present*.

Temperature largely determines the maximum amount of water vapor air can hold. Warm air can hold more water vapor than cool air. Actually, relative humidity expresses the degree of saturation. Air with 100% relative humidity is saturated; less than 100% is unsaturated.

If a given volume of air is cooled to some specific temperature, it can hold no more water vapor than is actually present, relative humidity becomes 100%, and saturation occurs. What is that temperature?

Dew point

Dew point is the temperature to which air must be cooled to become saturated by the water vapor already present in the air. Aviation weather reports normally include the air temperature and dew point temperature. Dew point when related to air temperature reveals qualitatively how close the air is to saturation.

Temperature—dew point spread

The difference between air temperature and dew point temperature is popularly called the "spread." As spread becomes less, relative humidity increases, and it is 100% when temperature and dew point are the same. Surface temperature—dew point spread is important in anticipating fog but has little bearing on precipitation. To support precipitation, air must be saturated through thick layers aloft.

Sometimes the spread at ground level may be quite large, yet at higher altitudes the air is saturated and clouds form. Some rain may reach the ground or it may evaporate as it falls into the drier air. Our never ending weather cycle involves a continual reversible change of water from one state to another. A closer look at change of state follows in this text.

Change of state

Evaporation, condensation, sublimation, freezing, and melting are changes of state. Evaporation is the changing of liquid water to invisible water vapor. Condensation is the reverse process. Sublimation is the changing of ice directly to water vapor, or water vapor to ice, bypassing the liquid state in each process. Snow or ice crystals result from the sublimation of water vapor directly to the solid state. The freezing and melting processes need no explanation.

Latent heat

Any change of state involves a heat transaction with no change in temperature. Evaporation requires heat energy that comes from the nearest available heat source. This heat energy is known as the "latent heat of vaporization," and its removal cools the source it comes from. An example is the cooling of your body by evaporation of perspiration.

What becomes of this heat energy used by evaporation? Energy cannot be created or destroyed, so it is hidden or stored in the invisible water vapor. When the water vapor condenses to liquid water or sublimates directly to ice, energy originally used in the evaporation reappears as heat and is released to the atmosphere. This energy is "latent heat" and is quite significant as will be shown later. Melting and freezing involve the exchange of "latent heat of fusion" in a similar manner. The latent heat of fusion is much less than that of condensation and evaporation; however, each in its own way plays an important role in weather.

As air becomes saturated, water vapor begins to condense on the nearest available surface. What surfaces are in the atmosphere on which water vapor may condense?

Condensation nuclei

The atmosphere is never completely clean; an abundance of microscopic solid particles suspended in the air are condensation surfaces. These particles, such as salt, dust, and combustion byproducts are "condensation nuclei." Some condensation nuclei have an affinity for water and can induce condensation or sublimation even when air is almost but not completely saturated.

As water vapor condenses or sublimates on condensation nuclei, liquid or ice particles begin to grow. Whether the particles are liquid or ice does not depend entirely on temperature. Liquid water may be present at temperatures well below freezing.

Supercooled water

Freezing is complex and liquid water droplets often condense or persist at temperatures colder than 0° C. Water droplets colder than 0° C are supercooled. When they strike an exposed object, the impact induces freezing. For example, impact freezing of supercooled water can result in aircraft icing.

Supercooled water drops very often are in abundance in clouds at temperatures between 0° C and –15° C, with decreasing amounts at colder temperatures. Usually, at temperatures colder than –15° C, sublimation is prevalent; and clouds and fog may be mostly ice crystals with a lesser amount of supercooled water. However, strong vertical currents may carry supercooled water to great heights where temperatures are much colder than –15° C. Supercooled water has been observed at temperatures colder than –40° C.

Dew and frost

During clear nights with little or no wind, vegetation often cools by radiation to a temperature at or below the dew point of the adjacent air. Moisture than collects on the leaves just as it does on a pitcher of ice water in a warm room. Heavy dew often collects on grass and plants when none collects on pavements or large solid objects. These more massive objects absorb abundant heat during the day, lose it slowly during the night, and cool below the dew point only in rather extreme cases.

Frost forms in much the same way as dew. The difference is that the dew point of surrounding air must be colder than freezing. Water vapor then sublimates directly as ice crystals or frost rather than condensing as dew. Sometimes dew forms and later freezes; however, frozen dew is easily distinguished from frost. Frozen dew is hard and transparent while frost is white and opaque.

To now, little has been said here about clouds. What brings about the condensation or sublimation that results in cloud formation?

Cloud formation

Normally, air must become saturated for condensation or sublimation to occur. Saturation may result from cooling temperature, increasing dew point, or both. Cooling is far more predominant.

Cooling processes

Three basic processes may cool air to saturation. They are (1) air moving over a colder surface, (2) stagnant air overlying a cooling surface, and (3) expansional cooling in upward moving air. Expansional cooling is the major cause of cloud formation.

Clouds and fog

A cloud is a visible aggregate of minute water or ice particles suspended in air. If the cloud is on the ground, it is fog. When entire layers of air cool to saturation, fog or sheet-like clouds result. Saturation of a localized updraft produces a towering cloud. A cloud may be composed entirely of liquid water, of ice crystals, or a mixture of the two.

Precipitation

Precipitation is an all inclusive term denoting drizzle, rain, snow, ice pellets, hail, and ice crystals. Precipitation occurs when these particles grow in size and weight until the atmosphere no longer can suspend them and they fall. These particles grow primarily in two ways.

Particle growth

Once a water droplet or ice crystal forms, it continues to grow by added condensation or sublimation directly onto the particle. This is the slower of the two methods and usually results in drizzle or very light rain or snow.

Cloud particles collide and merge into a larger drop in the more rapid growth process. This process produces larger precipitation particles and does so more rapidly than the simple condensation growth process. Upward currents enhance the growth rate and also support larger drops. Precipitation formed by merging drops with mild upward currents can produce light to moderate rain and snow. Strong upward currents support the largest drops and build clouds to great heights. They can produce heavy rain, heavy snow, and hail.

Liquid, freezing, and frozen

Precipitation forming and remaining liquid falls as rain or drizzle. Sublimation forms snowflakes, and they reach the ground as snow if temperatures remain below freezing.

Precipitation can change its state as the temperature of its environment changes. Falling snow may melt in warmer layers of air at lower altitudes to form rain. Rain falling through colder air may become supercooled, freezing on impact as freezing rain; or it may freeze during its descent, falling as ice pellets. Ice pellets always indicate freezing rain at higher altitude.

Sometimes strong upward currents sustain large supercooled water drops until some freeze; subsequently, other drops freeze to them forming hailstones.

Precipitation versus cloud thickness

To produce significant precipitation, clouds usually are 4,000 feet thick or more. The heavier the precipitation, the thicker the clouds are likely to be.

Land and water effects on clouds

Land and water surfaces underlying the atmosphere greatly affect cloud and precipitation development. Large bodies of water such as oceans and large lakes add water vapor to the air.

The greatest frequency of low ceilings, fog, and precipitation can be expected in areas where prevailing winds have an over-water trajectory. The aviator should be especially alert for these hazards when moist winds are blowing upslope.

In winter, cold air frequently moves over relatively warm lakes. The warm water adds heat and water vapor to the air causing showers to the lee of the lakes. In other seasons, the air may be warmer than the lakes. When this occurs, the air may become saturated by evaporation from the water while also becoming cooler in the low levels by contact with the cool water. Fog often becomes extensive and dense to the lee of a lake. Strong cold winds across the Great Lakes often carry precipitation to the Appalachians.

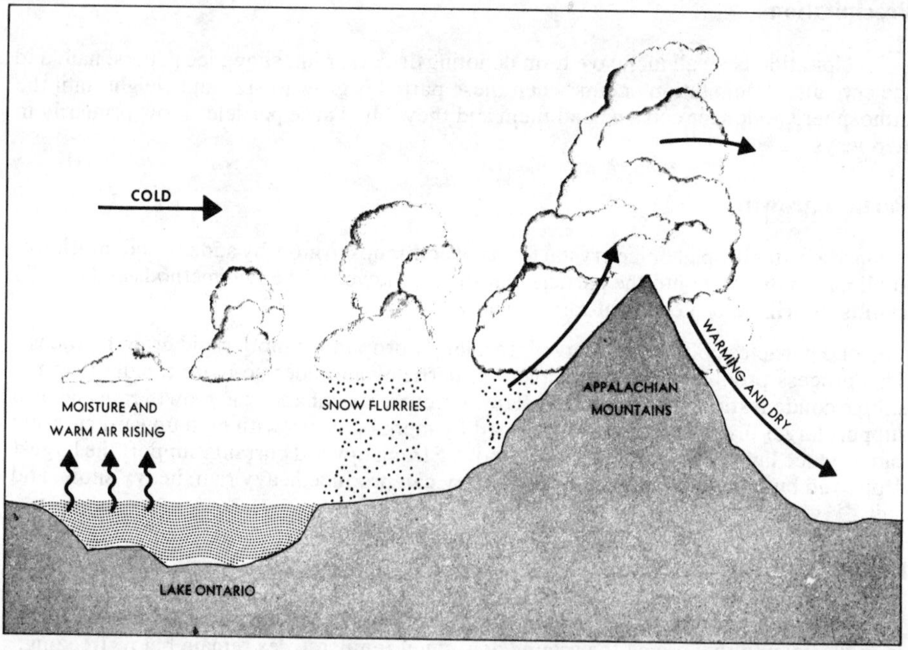

FIGURE 6.9. Strong cold winds across the Great Lakes absorb water vapor and may carry showers as far eastward as the Appalachians.

A lake only a few miles across can influence convection and cause a diurnal fluctuation in cloudiness. During the day, cool air over the lake blows toward the land, and convective clouds form over the land. At night, the pattern reverses; clouds tend to form over the lake as cool air from the land flows over the lake creating convective clouds over the water.

Water exists in three states—solid, liquid, and gaseous. Water vapor is an invisible gas. Condensation or sublimation of water vapor creates many common weather extremes. These things may be anticipated:

1. Fog when temperature-dew point spread is 5° F or less and decreasing.

2. Lifting or clearing of low clouds and fog when temperature-dew point spread is increasing.

3. Frost on a clear night when temperature-dew point spread is 5° F or less, is decreasing, and dew point is colder than 32° F.

4. More cloudiness, fog, and precipitation when wind blows from water than when it blows from land.

5. Cloudiness, fog, and precipitation over higher terrain when moist winds are blowing uphill.

6. Showers to the lee of a lake when air is cold and the lake is warm. Expect fog to the lee of the lake when the air is warm and the lake is cold.

7. Clouds to be at least 4,000 feet thick when significant precipitation is reported. The heavier the precipitation, the thicker the clouds are likely to be.

STABLE AND UNSTABLE AIR

Changes within upward and downward moving air

Anytime air moves upward, it expands because of decreasing atmospheric pressure. Conversely, downward moving air is compressed by increasing pressure. But as pressure and volume change, temperature also changes.

When air expands, it cools; and when compressed, it warms. These changes are *adiabatic*, meaning that no heat is removed from or added to the air. We frequently use the terms *expansional* or *adiabatic cooling* and *compressional* or *adiabatic heating*. The adiabatic rate of change of temperature is virtually fixed in unsaturated air but varies in saturated air.

Unsaturated air

Unsaturated air moving upward and downward cools and warms at about 3.0° C (5.4° F) per 1,000 feet. This rate is *the "dry adiabatic rate of temperature change"* and *is independent of the temperature of the mass of air through which the vertical movements occur*. Figure 6.10 illustrates a "Chinook Wind"—an excellent example of dry adiabatic warming.

Saturated air

Condensation occurs when *saturated* air moves upward. Latent heat released through

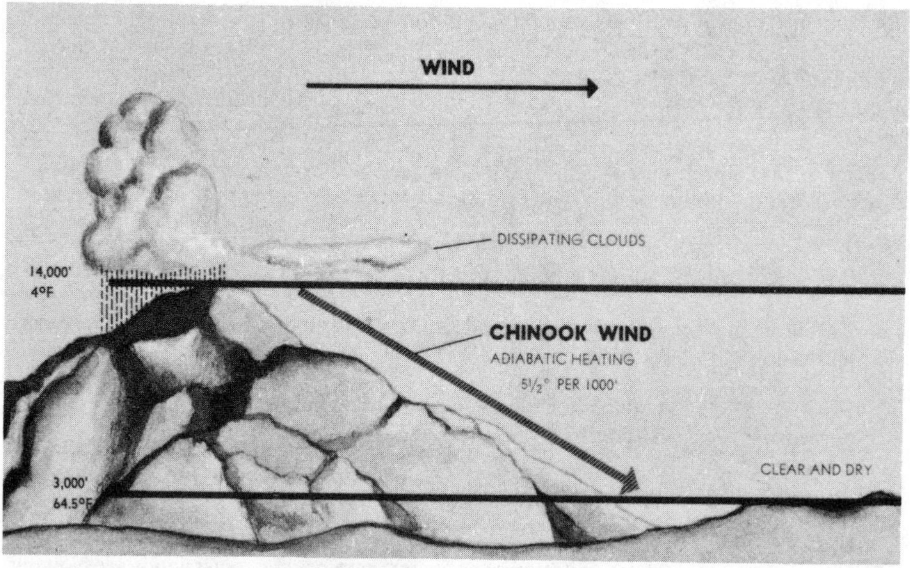

FIGURE 6.10. Adiabatic warming of downward moving air produces the warm Chinook wind.

condensation partially offsets the expansional cooling. Therefore, *the saturated adiabatic rate of cooling is slower than the dry adiabatic rate*. The saturated rate depends on saturation temperature or dew point of the air. Condensation of copious moisture in saturated warm air releases more latent heat to offset expansional cooling than does the scant moisture in saturated cold air. Therefore, *the saturated adiabatic rate of cooling is less in warm air than in cold air*.

When saturated air moves downward, it heats at the same rate as it cools on ascent *provided* liquid water evaporates rapidly enough to maintain saturation. Minute water droplets evaporate at virtually this rate. Larger drops evaporate more slowly and complicate the moist adiabatic process in downward moving air.

Adiabatic cooling and vertical air movement

If a sample of air is forced upward into the atmosphere, two possibilities must be considered:

(1) The air may become colder than the surrounding air, or

(2) Even though it cools, the air may remain warmer than the surrounding air.

If the upward moving air becomes colder than surrounding air, it sinks; but if it remains warmer, it is accelerated upward as a convective current. Whether it sinks or rises depends on the ambient or existing temperature lapse rate.

Do not confuse existing lapse rate with adiabatic rates of cooling in vertically moving air.* The difference between the existing lapse rate of a given mass of air and the adiabatic rates of cooling in upward moving air determines if the air is stable or unstable.

* Sometimes the dry and moist adiabatic rates of cooling will be called the dry adiabatic lapse rate and the moist adiabatic lapse rate. In this text, *lapse rate* refers exclusively to the existing, or actual, decrease of temperature with height in a real atmosphere. The dry or moist adiabatic lapse rate signifies a prescribed rate of expansional cooling or compressional heating. An adiabatic lapse rate becomes real *only* when it becomes a condition brought about by vertically moving air.

CLOUDS

Clouds—stable or unstable?

Earlier it was stated that when air is cooling and first becomes saturated, condensation or sublimation begins to form clouds. Further on in this text cloud types are explained along with their significance as "signposts in the sky." Whether the air is stable or unstable within a layer largely determines cloud structure.

Stratiform Clouds—Since stable air resists convection, clouds in stable air form in horizontal, sheet-like layers or "strata." Thus, within a *stable* layer, clouds are *stratiform*. Adiabatic cooling may be by upslope flow; by lifting over cold, more dense air; or by converging winds. Cooling by an underlying cold surface is a stabilizing process and may produce fog. If clouds are to remain stratiform, the layer must remain stable after condensation occurs.

Cumuliform Clouds—Unstable air favors convection. A "cumulus" cloud, meaning "heap," forms in a convective updraft and builds upward. Thus, within an *unstable* layer, clouds are *cumuliform*; and the vertical extent of the cloud depends on the depth of the unstable layer.

Initial lifting to trigger a cumuliform cloud may be the same as that for lifting stable air. In addition, convection may be set off by surface heating. Air may be unstable or slightly stable before condensation occurs; but for convective cumuliform clouds to develop, it must be unstable after saturation. Cooling in the updraft is now at the slower moist adiabatic rate because of the release of latent heat of condensation. Temperature in the saturated updraft is warmer than ambient temperature, and convection is spontaneous. Updrafts accelerate until temperature within the cloud cools below the ambient temperature. This condition occurs where the unstable layer is capped by a stable layer often marked by a temperature inversion. Vertical heights range from the shallow fair weather cumulus to the giant thunderstorm cumulonimbus—the ultimate in atmospheric instability capped by the tropopause.

When unstable air lies above stable air, convective currents aloft sometimes form middle and high level cumuliform clouds. In relatively shallow layers they occur as altocumulus and ice crystal cirrocumulus clouds. Altocumulus castellanus clouds develop in deeper midlevel unstable layers.

Identification

For identification purposes, one needs to be concerned only with the more basic cloud types, which are divided into four "families." The families are: high clouds, middle clouds, low clouds, and clouds with extensive vertical development. The first three families are further classified according to the way they are formed. Clouds formed by vertical currents in unstable air are *cumulus* meaning *accumulation* or *heap*; they are characterized by their lumpy, billowy appearance. Clouds formed by the cooling of a stable layer are *stratus* meaning *stratified* or *layered*; they are characterized by their uniform, sheet-like appearance.

In addition to the above, the prefix *nimbo* or the suffix *nimbus* means raincloud. Thus, stratified clouds from which rain is falling are *nimbostratus*. A heavy, swelling cumulus type cloud which produces precipitation is a *cumulonimbus*. Clouds broken into fragments are often identified by adding the suffix *fractus*; for example, fragmentary cumulus is *cumulus fractus*.

High clouds

The high cloud family is cirriform and includes cirrus, cirrocumulus, and cirrostratus.

They are composed almost entirely of ice crystals. The height of the bases of these clouds ranges from about 16,500 to 45,000 feet in middle latitudes.

Middle clouds

In the middle cloud family are the altostratus, altocumulus, and nimbostratus clouds. These clouds are primarily water, much of which may be supercooled. The height of the bases of these clouds ranges from about 6,500 to 23,000 feet in middle latitudes.

Low clouds

In the low cloud family are the stratus, stratocumulus, and fair weather cumulus clouds. Low clouds are almost entirely water, but at times the water may be supercooled. Low clouds at sub-freezing temperatures can also contain snow and ice particles. The bases of these clouds range from near the surface to about 6,500 feet in middle latitudes.

Clouds with extensive vertical development

The vertically developed family of clouds includes towering cumulus and cumulonimbus. These clouds usually contain supercooled water above the freezing level. But when a cumulus grows to great heights, water in the upper part of the cloud freezes into ice crystals forming a cumulonimbus. The heights of cumuliform cloud bases range from 1,000 feet or less to above 10,000 feet.

CLOUD RECOGNITION

LOW-BASE CLOUDS
(Continued next page)

FIGURE 6.11. CUMULUS. Fair weather cumulus clouds form in convective currents and are characterized by relatively flat bases and dome-shaped tops. Fair weather cumulus do not show extensive vertical development and do not produce precipitation.

LOW-BASE CLOUDS (Continued)

FIGURE 6.12. CUMULONIMBUS. Cumulonimbus are the ultimate manifestation of instability. They are vertically developed clouds of large dimensions with dense *boiling* tops when crowned with thick veils of dense cirrus (the anvil).

FIGURE 6.13. STRATUS. Stratus is a gray, uniform, sheet-like cloud with relatively low bases. When associated with fog or precipitation, the combination can become troublesome for visual flying.

LOW-BASE CLOUDS (Continued)

FIGURE 6.14. NIMBOSTRATUS. Nimbostratus is a gray or dark massive cloud layer, diffused by more or less continuous rain, snow, or ice pellets.

FIGURE 6.15. STRATOCUMULUS. Stratocumulus bases are globular masses or rolls unlike the flat, sometimes indefinite, bases of stratus. They usually form at the top of a layer mixed by moderate surface winds. Sometimes, they form from the breaking up of stratus or the spreading out of cumulus.

MIDDLE-BASE CLOUDS

FIGURE 6.16. ALTOSTRATUS. Altostratus is a bluish veil or layer of clouds. It is often associated with altocumulus and sometimes gradually merges into cirrostratus. The sun may be dimly visible through it.

FIGURE 6.17. ALTOCUMULUS. Altocumulus are composed of white or gray colored layers or patches of solid cloud. The cloud elements may have a waved or roll-like appearance.

HIGH-BASE CLOUDS

FIGURE 6.18. CIRRUS. Cirrus are thin, feather-like crystal clouds in patches or narrow bands. Larger ice crystals often trail downward in well-defined wisps called "mares' tails."

FIGURE 6.19. CIRROSTRATUS. Cirrostratus is a thin whitish cloud layer appearing like a sheet or veil. Cloud elements are diffuse, sometimes partially striated or fibrous. Due to their ice crystal makeup, these clouds are associated with halos—large luminous circles surrounding the sun or moon.

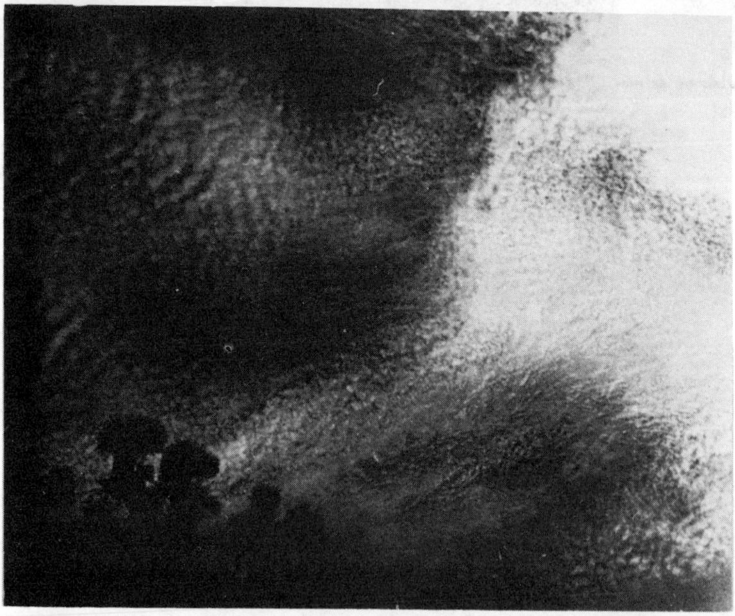

FIGURE 6.20. CIRROCUMULUS. Cirrocumulus are thin clouds, the individual elements appearing as small white flakes or patches of cotton. May contain highly supercooled water droplets.

FOG

Fog

Fog is a surface based cloud composed of either water droplets or ice crystals.

Small temperature-dew point spread is essential for fog to form. Therefore, fog is prevalent in coastal areas where moisture is abundant. However, fog can occur anywhere. Abundant condensation nuclei enhances the formation of fog. Thus, fog is prevalent in industrial areas where by-products of combustion provide a high concentration of these nuclei. Fog occurs most frequently in the colder months, but the season and frequency of occurrence vary from one area to another.

Fog may form (1) by cooling air to its dew point, or (2) by adding moisture to air near the ground. Fog is classified by the way it forms. Formation may involve more than one process.

Radiation fog

Radiation fog is relatively shallow fog. It may be dense enough to hide the entire sky or may conceal only part of the sky. "Ground fog" is a form of radiation fog.

Conditions favorable for radiation fog are clear sky, little or no wind, and small temperature-dew point spread (high relative humidity). The fog forms almost exclusively at night or near daybreak. Terrestrial radiation cools the ground; in turn, the cool ground cools the air in contact with it. When the air is cooled to its dew point, fog forms. When rain soaks the ground, followed by clearing skies, radiation fog is not uncommon the following morning.

Radiation fog is restricted to land because water surfaces cool little from nighttime radiation. It is shallow when wind is calm. Winds up to about 5 knots mix the air slightly and tend to deepen the fog by spreading the cooling through a deeper layer. Stronger winds disperse the fog or mix the air through a still deeper layer with stratus clouds forming at the top of the mixing layer.

Ground fog usually "burns off" rather rapidly after sunrise. Other radiation fog generally clears before noon unless clouds move in over the fog.

Advection fog

Advection fog forms when moist air moves over colder ground or water. It is most common along coastal areas but often develops deep in continental areas. At sea it is called "sea fog." Advection fog deepens as wind speed increases up to about 15 knots. Wind much stronger than 15 knots lifts the fog into a layer of low stratus or stratocumulus.

The west coast of the United States is quite vulnerable to advection fog. This fog frequently forms offshore as a result of cold water and then is carried inland by the wind. During the winter, advection fog over the central and eastern United States results when moist air from the Gulf of Mexico spreads northward over cold ground. The fog may extend as far north as the Great Lakes. Water areas in northern latitudes have frequent dense sea fog in summer as a result of warm, moist, tropical air flowing northward over colder Arctic waters.

Advection fog is usually more extensive and much more persistent than radiation fog. Advection fog can move in rapidly regardless of the time of day or night.

Upslope fog

Upslope fog forms as a result of moist, stable air being cooled adiabatically as it moves up sloping terrain. Once the upslope wind ceases, the fog dissipates. Unlike radiation fog, it can form under cloudy skies. Upslope fog is common along the eastern slopes of the Rockies and somewhat less frequent east of the Appalachians. Upslope fog often is quite dense and extends to high altitudes.

Precipitation-induced fog

When relatively warm rain or drizzle falls through cool air, evaporation from the precipitation saturates the cool air and forms fog. Precipitation-induced fog can become quite dense and continue for an extended period of time. This fog may extend over large areas, completely suspending air operations. It is most commonly associated with warm fronts, but can occur with slow moving cold fronts and with stationary fronts.

Ice fog

Ice fog occurs in cold weather when the temperature is much below freezing and water vapor sublimates directly as ice crystals. Conditions favorable for its formation are the same as for radiation fog except for cold temperature, usually –25° F or colder. It occurs mostly in the Arctic regions, but is not unknown in middle latitudes during the cold season.

Low stratus clouds

Stratus clouds, like fog, are composed of extremely small water droplets or ice crystals suspended in air. An observer on a mountain in a stratus layer would call it fog. Stratus and fog frequently exist together. In many cases there is no real line of distinction between the fog and stratus; rather, one gradually merges into the other. Stratus tends to be lowest during night and early morning, lifting or dissipating due to solar heating during the late morning or afternoon. Low stratus clouds often occur when moist air mixes with a colder air mass or in any situation where temperature-dew point spread is small.

Haze and smoke

Haze is a concentration of salt particles or other dry particles not readily classified as dust or other phenomenon. It occurs in stable air, is usually only a few thousand feet thick, but sometimes may extend as high as 15,000 feet. Haze layers often have definite tops above which horizontal visibility is good. However, downward visibility from above a haze layer is poor, especially on a slant. Visibility in haze varies greatly depending upon whether the observer is facing the sun.

Smoke concentrations form primarily in industrial areas when air is stable. It is most prevalent at night or early morning under a temperature inversion but it can persist throughout the day.

AIR MASSES AND FRONTS

Air masses

When a body of air comes to rest or moves slowly over an extensive area having fairly uniform properties of temperature and moisture, the air takes on those properties. Thus, the air over the area becomes somewhat of an entity and has fairly uniform horizontal distribution of its properties. The area over which the air mass acquires its identifying distribution of moisture and temperature is its "source region."

Source regions are many and varied, but the best source regions for air masses are large snow or ice covered polar regions, cold northern oceans, tropical oceans, and large desert areas. Midlatitudes are poor source regions because transitional disturbances dominate these latitudes giving little opportunity for air masses to stagnate and take on the properties of the underlying region.

Air mass modification

Just as an air mass took on the properties of its source region, it tends to take on properties of the underlying surface when it moves away from its source region, thus becoming modified.

The degree of modification depends on the speed with which the air mass moves, the nature of the region over which it moves, and the temperature difference between the new surface and the air mass. Some ways air masses are modified are: (1) warming from below, (2) cooling from below, (3) addition of water vapor, and (4) subtraction of water vapor:

1. Cool air moving over a warm surface is heated from below, generating instability and increasing the possibility of showers.

2. Warm air moving over a cool surface is cooled from below, increasing stability. If air is cooled to its dew point, stratus and/or fog forms.

3. Evaporation from water surfaces and falling precipitation adds water vapor to the air. When the water is warmer than the air, evaporation can raise the dew point sufficiently to saturate the air and form stratus or fog.

4. Water vapor is removed by condensation and precipitation.

Stability

Stability of an air mass determines its typical weather characteristics. When one type of air mass overlies another, conditions change with height. Characteristics typical of an unstable and a stable air mass are as follows:

Unstable Air	*Stable Air*
Cumuliform clouds	Stratiform clouds and fog
Showery precipitation	Continuous precipitation
Rough air (turbulence)	Smooth air
Good visibility, except in blowing obstructions	Fair to poor visibility in haze and smoke

Fronts

As air masses move out of their source regions, they come in contact with other air masses of different properties. The zone between two different air masses is a frontal zone or front. Across this zone, temperature, humidity and wind often change rapidly over short distances.

Discontinuities

When you pass through a front, the change from the properties of one air mass to those of the other is sometimes quite abrupt. Abrupt changes indicate a narrow frontal zone. At other times, the change of properties is very gradual indicating a broad and diffuse frontal zone.

Temperature—Temperature is one of the most easily recognized discontinuities across a front. At the surface, the passage of a front usually causes noticeable temperature change.

Dew Point—Dew point temperature is a measure of the amount of water vapor in the air. Temperature—dew point spread is a measure of the degree of saturation. Dew point and temperature—dew point spread usually differ across a front. The difference helps identify the front and may give a clue to differences of cloudiness and/or fog.

Wind—Wind always changes across a front. Wind discontinuity may be in direction, in speed, or in both.

Pressure—A front lies in a pressure trough, and pressure generally is higher in the cold air. Thus, when a front is crossed directly into colder air, pressure usually rises abruptly. When a front is approached toward warm air, pressure generally falls until the front is crossed, and then remains steady or falls slightly in the warm air. However, pressure patterns vary widely across fronts.

Types of fronts

The three principal types of fronts are the cold front, the warm front, and the stationary front.

Cold Front—The leading edge of an advancing cold air mass is a cold front. At the surface, cold air is overtaking and replacing warmer air. Cold fronts move at about the speed of the wind component perpendicular to the front just above the frictional layer. A shallow cold air mass or a slow moving cold front may have a frontal slope more like a warm front.

Warm Front—The edge of an advancing warm air mass is a warm front—warmer air is overtaking and replacing colder air. Since the cold air is denser than the warm air, the cold air hugs the ground. The warm air slides up and over the cold air and lacks direct push on the cold air. Thus, the cold air is slow to retreat in advance of the warm air. This slowness of the cold air to retreat produces a frontal slope that is more gradual than the cold frontal slope. Consequently, warm fronts on the surface are seldom as well marked as cold fronts, and they usually move about half as fast when the general wind flows is the same in each case.

Stationary Fronts—When neither air mass is replacing the other, the front is stationary. The opposing forces exerted by adjacent air masses of different densities are such that the frontal surface between them shows little or no movement. In such cases, the surface winds tend to blow parallel to the frontal zone. Slope of a stationary front is normally shallow, although it may be steep depending on wind distribution and density difference.

Frontal waves and occlusion

Frontal waves and cyclones (areas of low pressure) usually form on slow-moving cold fronts or on stationary fronts. The life cycle and movement of a cyclone is dictated to a great extent by the upper wind flow.

In the initial condition of frontal wave development in figure 6.21, the winds on both sides of the front are blowing parallel to the front (A). Small disturbances then may start a wavelike bend in the front (B).

If this tendency persists and the wave increases in size, a cyclonic (counterclockwise) circulation develops. One section of the front begins to move as a warm front, while the section next to it begins to move as a cold front (C). This deformation is a frontal wave.

The pressure at the peak of the frontal wave falls, and a low-pressure center forms. The cyclonic circulation becomes stronger, and the surface winds are now strong enough to move the fronts; the cold front moves faster than the warm front (D). When the cold front catches up with the warm front, the two of them *occlude* (close together). The result is an *occluded front* or, for brevity, an *occlusion* (E). This is the time of maximum intensity for the wave cyclone. Note that the symbol depicting the occlusion is a combination of the symbols for the warm and cold fronts.

As the occlusion continues to grow in length, the cyclonic circulation diminishes in intensity and the frontal movement slows down (F). Sometimes a new frontal wave begins to form on the long westward-trailing portion of the cold front (F,G), or a secondary low pressure system forms at the apex where the cold front and warm front come together to form the occlusion. In the final stage, the two fronts may have become a single stationary front again. The low center with its remnant of the occlusion is disappearing (G).

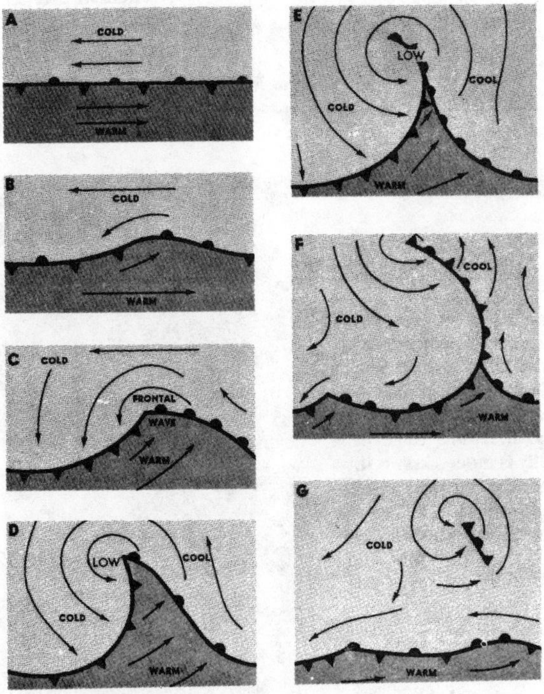

FIGURE 6.21. The life cycle of a frontal wave.

Figure 6.25 indicates a warm-front occlusion in vertical cross section. This type of occlusion occurs when the air is colder in advance of the warm front than behind the cold front, lifting the cold front aloft.

Non-frontal lows

Since fronts are boundaries between air masses of different properties, fronts are not associated with lows lying solely in a homogeneous air mass. Nonfrontal lows are infrequent east of the Rocky Mountains in midlatitudes but do occur occasionally during the warmer months. Small nonfrontal lows over the western mountains are common as is

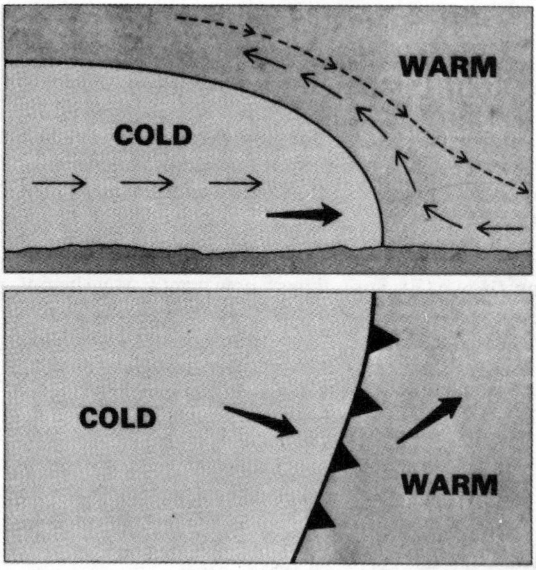

FIGURE 6.22. Cross section of a cold front (above) with the weather map symbol (below). The symbol is a line with pointed barbs pointing in the direction of movement. If a map is in color, a blue lines represents the cold front. The vertical scale is expanded in the top illustration to show the frontal slope. The frontal slope is steep near the leading edge as cold air replaces warm air. The solid heavy arrow shows movement of the front. Warm air may descend over the front as indicated by the dashed arrows; but more commonly, the cold air forces warm air upward over the frontal surface as shown by the solid arrows.

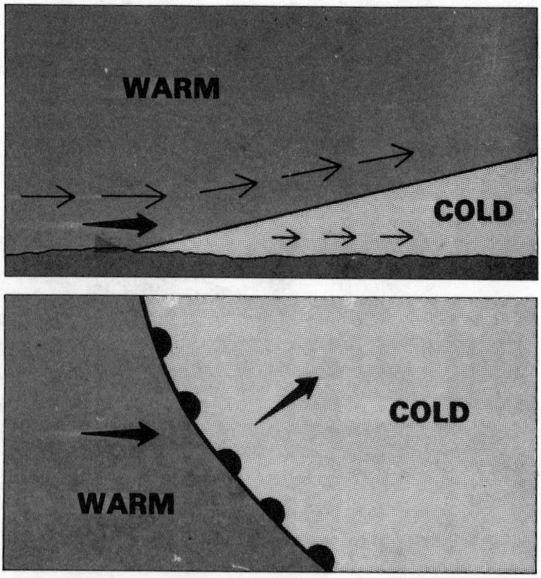

FIGURE 6.23. Cross section of a warm front (top) with the weather map symbol (bottom). The symbol is a line with rounded barbs pointing in the direction of movement. If a map is in color, a red line represents the warm front. Slope of a warm front generally is more shallow than slope of a cold front. Movement of a warm front shown by the heavy black arrow is slower than the wind in the warm air represented by the light solid arrows. The warm air gradually erodes the cold air.

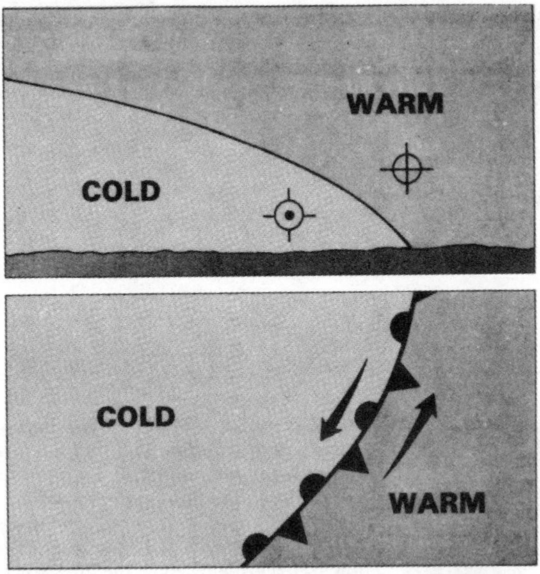

FIGURE 6.24. Cross section of a stationary front (top) and its weather map symbol (bottom). The symbol is a line with alternating pointed and rounded barbs on opposite sides of the line, the pointed barbs pointing away from the cold air and the rounded barbs away from the warm air. If a map is in color, the symbol is a line of alternating red and blue segments. The front has little or no movement and winds are nearly parallel to the front. The symbol in the warm air is the tail of a wind arrow into the page. The symbol in the cold air is the point of a wind arrow out of the page. Slope of the front may vary considerably depending on wind and density differences across the front.

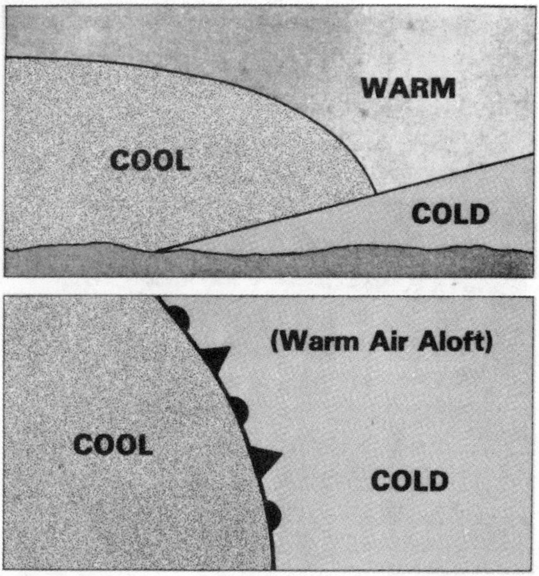

FIGURE 6.25. Cross section of a warm-front occlusion (top) and its weather map symbol (bottom). The symbol is a line with alternating pointed and rounded barbs on the same side of the line pointing in the direction of movement. Shown in color on a weather map, the line is purple. In the warm front occlusion, air under the cold front is not as cold as air ahead of the warm front; and when the cold front overtakes the warm front, the less cold air rides over the colder air. In a warm front occlusion, cool air replaces cold air at the surface.

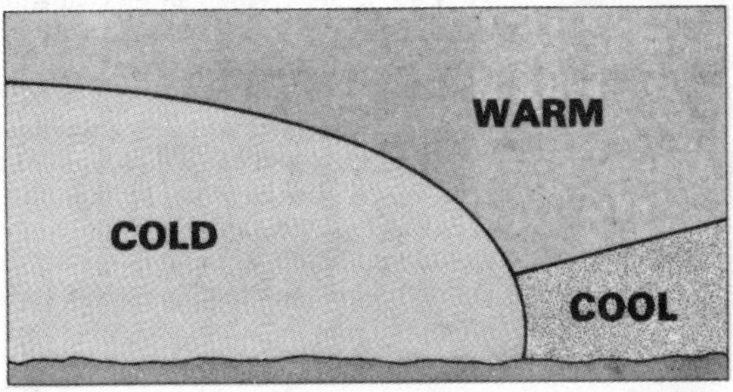

FIGURE 6.26. Cross section of a cold-front occlusion. Its weather map symbol is the same as for a warm-front occlusion shown in Figure 6.25. In the cold-front occlusion, the coldest air is under the cold front. When it overtakes the warm front, it lifts the warm front aloft; and cold air replaces cool air at the surface.

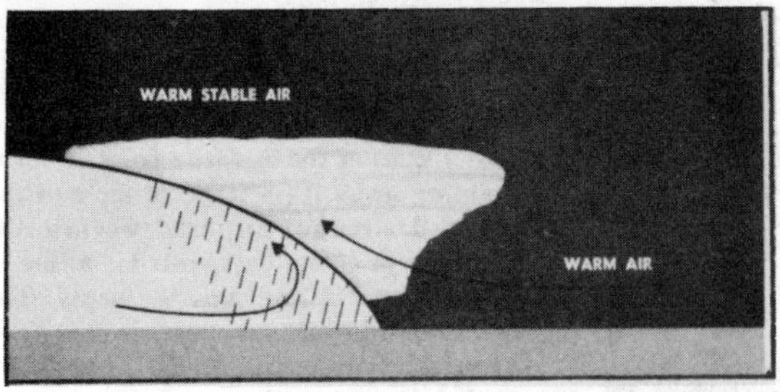

FIGURE 6.27. A cold front underrunning warm, moist, stable air. Clouds are stratified and precipitation continuous. Precipitation induces stratus in the cold air.

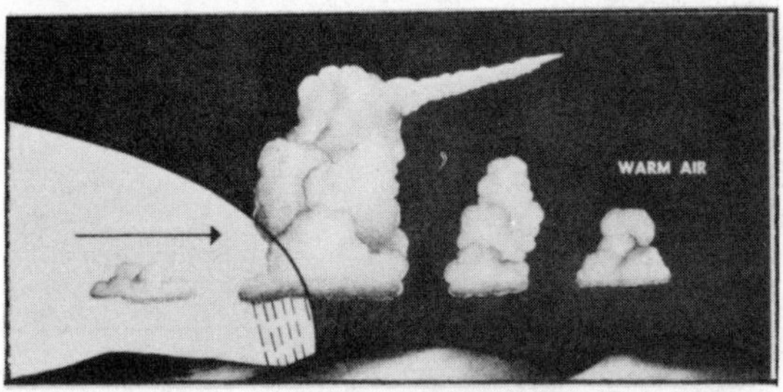

FIGURE 6.28. A cold front underrunning warm, moist, unstable air. Clouds are cumuliform with possible showers or thunderstorms near the surface position of the front. Convective clouds often develop in the warm air ahead of the front. The warm, wet ground behind the front generates low-level convection and fair weather cumulus in the cold air.

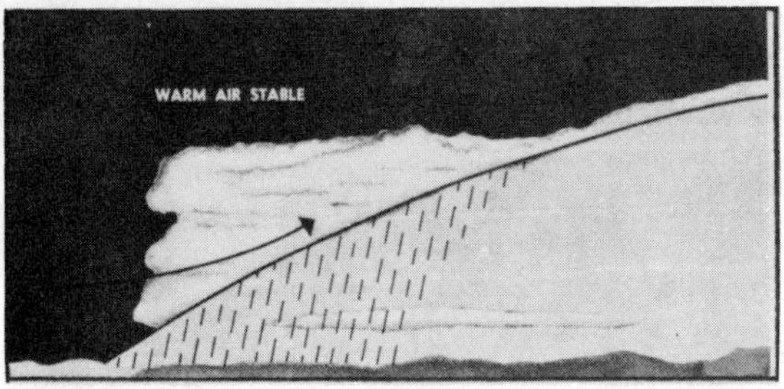

FIGURE 6.29. A warm front with overrunning moist, stable air. Clouds are stratiform and widespread over the shallow front. Precipitation is continuous and induces widespread stratus in the cold air.

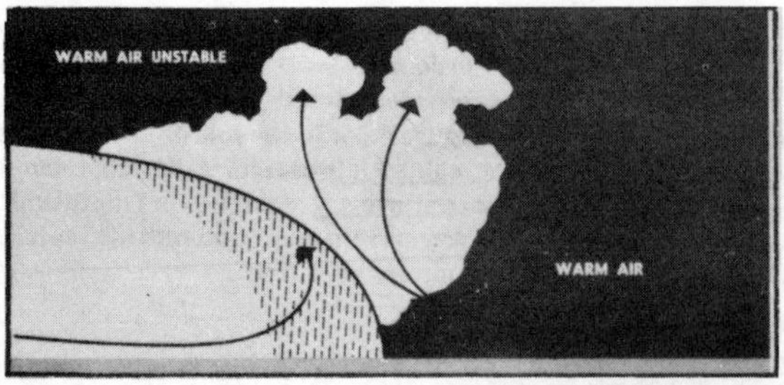

FIGURE 6.30. A slow-moving cold front underrunning warm, moist, unstable air. Note that the front is more shallow than the fast-moving front shown in figure 6.28. Clouds are stratified with embedded cumulonimbus and thunderstorms. This type of frontal weather is especially hazardous since the individual thunderstorms are hidden and cannot be avoided unless the aircraft is equipped with airborne radar.

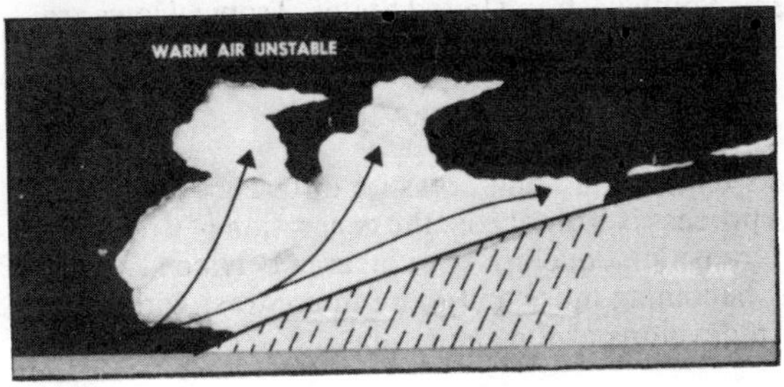

FIGURE 6.31. A warm front with over-running warm, moist, unstable air. Weather, clouds, and hazards are similar to those described in figure 6.30 except that they generally are more widespread.

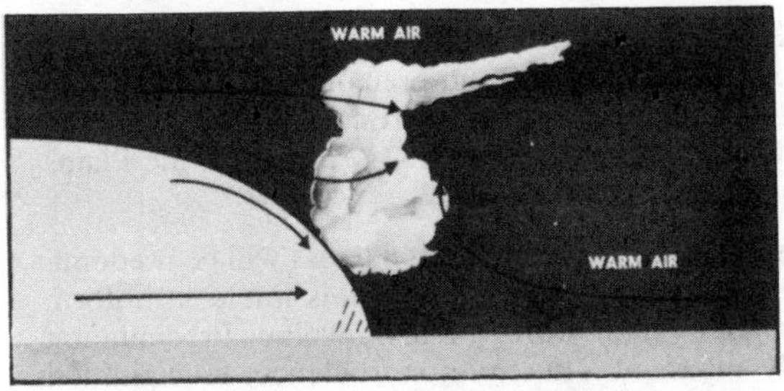

FIGURE 6.32. A fast moving cold front underrunning warm, moist, unstable air. Showers and thunderstorms develop along the surface position of the front.

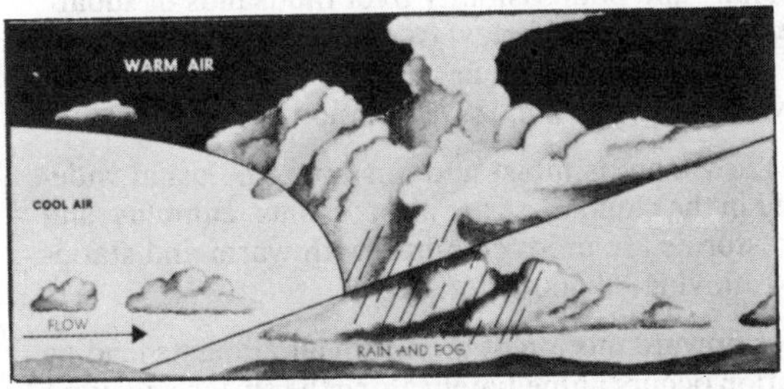

FIGURE 6.33. A warm front occlusion lifting warm, moist, unstable air. Note that the associated weather is complex and encompasses all types of weather associated with both the warm and cold fronts when air is moist and unstable.

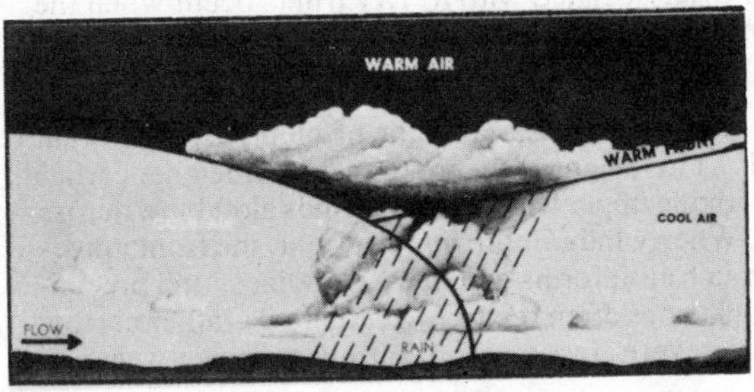

FIGURE 6.34. A cold front occlusion lifting warm, moist, stable air. Associated weather encompasses types of weather associated with both warm and cold fronts when air is moist and stable.

the semistationary thermal low in extreme Southwestern United States. Tropical lows are also nonfrontal.

Frontolysis and frontogenesis

As adjacent air masses modify and as temperature and pressure differences equalize across a front, the front dissipates. This process is frontolysis, the generation of a front. It occurs when a relatively sharp zone of transition develops over an area between two air masses which have densities gradually becoming more and more in contrast with each other. The necessary wind flow pattern develops at the same time.

Frontal weather

Weather occuring with a front depends on (1) the amount of moisture available, (2) the degree of stability of the air that is forced upward, (3) the slope of the front, (4) the speed of frontal movement, and (5) the upper wind flow.

Sufficient moisture must be available for clouds to form, or there will be no clouds. As an inactive front comes into an area of moisture, clouds and precipitation may develop rapidly. A good example of this is a cold front moving eastward from the dry slopes of the Rocky Mountains into a tongue of moist air from the Gulf of Mexico over the Plains States. Thunderstorms may build rapidly.

The degree of stability of the lifted air determines whether cloudiness will be predominately stratiform or cumuliform. If the warm air overriding the front is stable, stratiform clouds develop. If the warm air is unstable, cumuliform clouds develop. Precipitation from stratiform clouds is usually steady and there is little or no turbulence. Precipitation from cumuliform clouds is of a shower type and the clouds are turbulent.

Shallow frontal surfaces tend to give extensive cloudiness with large precipitation areas. Widespread precipitation associated with a gradual sloping front often causes low stratus and fog. In this case, the rain raises the humidty of the cold air to saturation. This and related effects may produce low ceiling and poor visibility over thousands of square miles. If temperature of the cold air near the surface is below freezing but the warmer air aloft is above freezing, precipitation falls as freezing rain or ice pellets; however, if temperature of the warmer air aloft is well below freezing, precipitation forms as snow.

When the warm air overriding a shallow front is moist and unstable, the usual widespread cloud mass forms; but embedded in the cloud mass are altocumulus, cumulus, and even thunderstorms. These embedded storms are more common with warm and stationary fronts but may occur with a slow moving, shallow cold front.

A fast moving, steep cold front forces upward motion of the warm air along its leading edge. If the warm air is moist, precipitation occurs immediately along the surface position of the front.

Since an occluded front develops when a cold front overtakes a warm front, weather with an occluded front is a combination of both warm and cold frontal weather.

A front may have little or no cloudiness associated with it. Dry fronts occur when the warm air aloft is flowing down the frontal slope or the air is so dry that any cloudiness that occurs is at high levels.

The upper wind flow dictates to a great extent the amount of cloudiness and rain accompanying a frontal system as well as movement of the front itself. Remember earlier it was said that systems tend to move with the upper winds. When winds aloft blow across a front, it tends to move with the wind. When winds aloft parallel a front, the front moves slowly if at all. A deep, slow moving trough aloft forms extensive cloudiness and precipitation, while a rapid moving minor trough more often restricts weather to a rather narrow band. However, the latter often breeds severe, fast moving, turbulent spring weather.

Instability line

An instability line is a narrow, nonfrontal line or band of convective activity. If the activity is fully developed thunderstorms, the line is a *squall line*. Instability lines form in moist unstable air. An instability line may develop far from any front. More often, it develops ahead of a cold front, and sometimes a series of these lines move out ahead of the front. A favored location for instability lines which frequently erupt into severe thunderstorms is a dew point front or dry line.

Dew point front or dry line

During a considerable part of the year, dew point fronts are common in Western Texas and New Mexico northward over the Plains States. Moist air flowing north from the Gulf of Mexico abuts the dryer and therefore slightly denser air flowing from the southwest. Except for moisture differences, there is seldom any significant air mass contrast across this "Front"; and therefore, it is commonly called a "dry line." Nighttime and early morning fog and low-level clouds often prevail on the moist side of the line while generally clear skies mark the dry side. In spring and early summer over Texas, Oklahoma, and Kansas, and for some distance eastward, the dry line is a favored spawning area for squall lines and tornadoes.

TURBULENCE

Convective currents

Convective currents are localized vertical air movements, both *ascending* and *descending*. For every rising current, there is a compensating downward current. The downward currents frequently occur over broader areas than do the upward currents, and therefore, they have a slower vertical speed than do the rising currents.

Convective currents are most active on warm summer afternoons when winds are light. Heated air at the surface creates a shallow, unstable layer, and the warm air is forced upward. Convection increases in strength and to greater heights as surface heating increases. Barren surfaces such as sandy or rocky wastelands and plowed fields become hotter than open water or ground covered by vegetation. Thus, air at and near the surface heats unevenly. Because of uneven heating, the strength of convective currents can vary considerably within short distances.

When cold air moves over a warm surface, it becomes unstable in lower levels. Convective currents extend several thousand feet above the surface resulting in rough, choppy turbulence. This condition often occurs in any season after the passage of a cold front.

THUNDERSTORMS
(See special text, page 80)

TORNADOES
(See special text, page 60)

HIGH ALTITUDE WEATHER

The tropopause

Earlier it was noted that the tropopause is a thin layer forming the boundary between the troposphere and stratosphere. Height of the tropopause varies from about 65,000 feet over the Equator to 20,000 feet or lower over the poles. The tropopause is not continuous but generally descends step-wise from the Equator to the poles. These steps occur as "breaks."

An abrupt change in temperature lapse rate characterizes the tropopause.

Maximum winds generally occur at levels near the tropopause. These strong winds create narrow zones of wind shear which often generate hazardous turbulence for aircraft.

The jet stream

The jet stream is a narrow, shallow, meandering river of maximum winds extending around the globe in a wavelike pattern. A second jet stream is not uncommon, and three at one time are not unknown. A jet may be as far south as the northern Tropics. A jet in midlatitudes generally is stronger than one in or near the Tropics. The jet stream typically occurs in a break in the tropopause. Therefore, a jet stream occurs in an area of intensified temperature gradients characteristic of the break.

The concentrated winds, by arbitrary definition, must be 50 knots or greater to classify as a jet stream. The jet maximum is not constant; rather, it is broken into segments, shaped something like a boomerang.

Jet stream segments move with pressure ridges and troughs in the upper atmosphere. In general they travel faster than pressure systems, and maximum wind speed varies as the segments progress through the systems. In midlatitude, wind speed in the jet stream averages considerably stronger in winter than in summer. Also the jet shifts farther south in winter than in summer.

Condensation trails

A condensation trail, popularly contracted to "contrail," is generally defined as a cloud-like streamer which frequently is generated in the wake of aircraft flying in clear, cold, humid air. Two distinct types are observed—exhaust trails and aerodynamic trails.

Exhaust contrails

The exhuast contrail is formed by the addition to the atmosphere of sufficient water vapor from aircraft exhaust gases to cause saturation or super-saturation of the air. Since heat is also added to the atmosphere in the wake of an aircraft, the addition of water vapor must be of such magnitude that it saturates or supersaturates the atmosphere in spite of the added heat. There is evidence to support the idea that the nuclei which are necessary for condensation or sublimation may also be donated to the atmosphere in the exhaust gases of aircraft engines, further aiding contrail formation. These nuclei are relatively large. Recent experiments, however, have revealed that visible exhaust contrails may be prevented by adding very minute nuclei material (dust, for example) to the exhaust. Condensation and sublimation on these smaller nuclei result in contrail particles too small to be visible.

Aerodynamic contrails

In air that is almost saturated, aerodynamic pressure reduction around airfoils, engine nacelles, and propellers cools the air to saturation leaving condensation trails from these

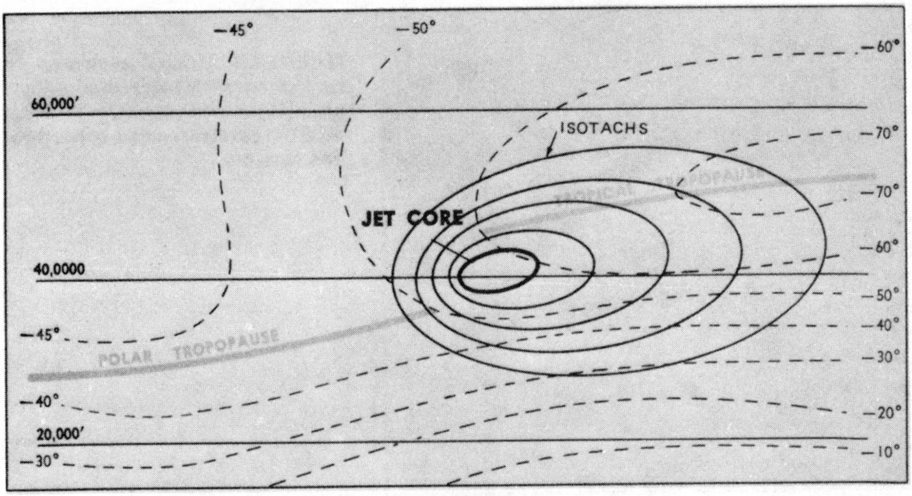

FIGURE 6.35. A cross section of the upper troposphere and lower stratosphere showing the tropopause and associated features. Note the "break" between the high tropical and the lower polar tropopause. Maximum winds occur in the vicinity of this break.

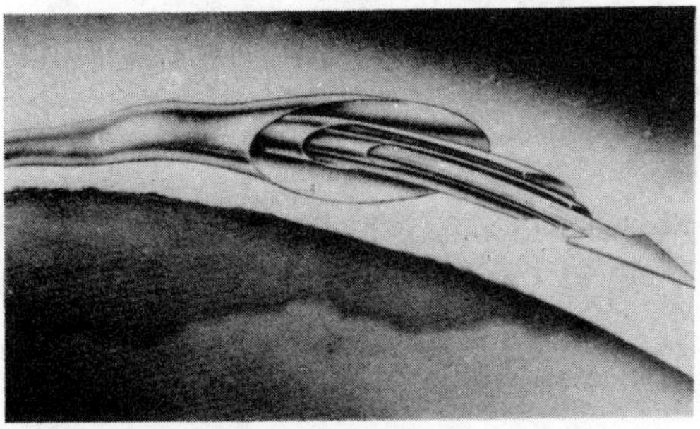

FIGURE 6.36. Artist's concept of the jet stream. Broad arrow shows direction of wind.

FIGURE 6.37. A jet stream segment.

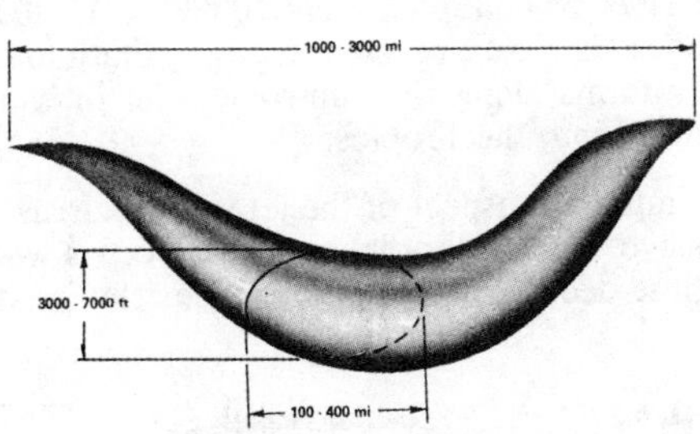

components. This type of trail usually is neither as dense nor as persistent as exhaust trails. However, under critical atmospheric conditions, an aerodynamic contrail may trigger the formation and spreading of a deck of cirrus clouds.

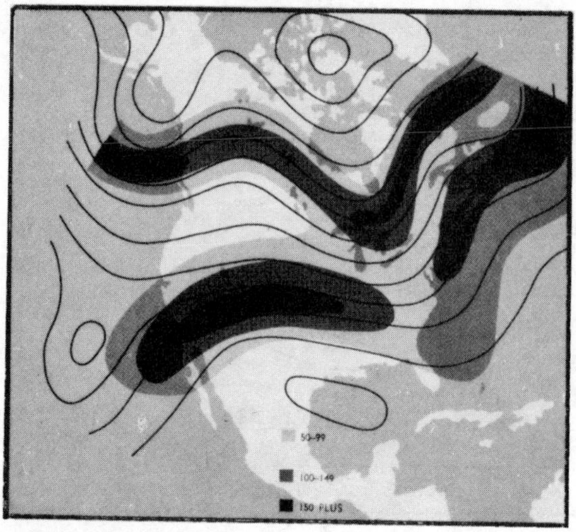

FIGURE 6.38. Multiple jet streams. Note the "segments" of maximum winds embedded in the general pattern. Turbulence usually is greatest on the polar sides of these maxima.

Cirrus Clouds

Air travels in a "corkscrew" path around the jet core with upward motion on the equatorial side. Therefore, when high level moisture is available, cirriform clouds form on the equatorial side of the jet. Jet stream cloudiness can form independently of well-defined pressure systems. Such cloudiness ranges primarily from scattered to broken coverage in shallow layers or streaks. Their sometimes fish hook and streamlined, wind-swept appearance always indicates very strong upper wind usually quite far from developing or intense weather systems.

The most dense cirriform clouds occur with well-defined systems. They appear in broad bands. Cloudiness is rather dense in an upper trough, thickens downstream, and becomes most dense at the crest of the downwind ridge. The clouds taper off after passing the ridge crest into the area of descending air. The poleward boundary of the cirrus band often is quite abrupt and frequently casts a shadow on lower clouds, especially in an occluded frontal system.

The upper limit of dense, banded cirrus is near the tropopause; a band may be either a single layer of multiple layers 10,000 to 12,000 feet thick. Dense, jet stream cirriform cloudiness is most prevalent along midlatitude and polar jets. However, a cirrus band usually forms along the subtropical jet in winter when a deep upper trough plunges southward into the Tropics.

An important aspect of the jet stream cirrus shield is its association with turbulence. Extensive cirrus cloudiness often occurs with deepening surface and upper lows and these deepening systems produce the greatest turbulence.

FIGURE 6.39. Mean jet positions relative to surface systems. Cyclogenesis (development) of a surface low usually is south of the jet as shown on the left. The deepening low moves nearer the jet, center. As it occludes, the low moves north of the jet, right; the jet crosses the frontal system near the point of occlusion.

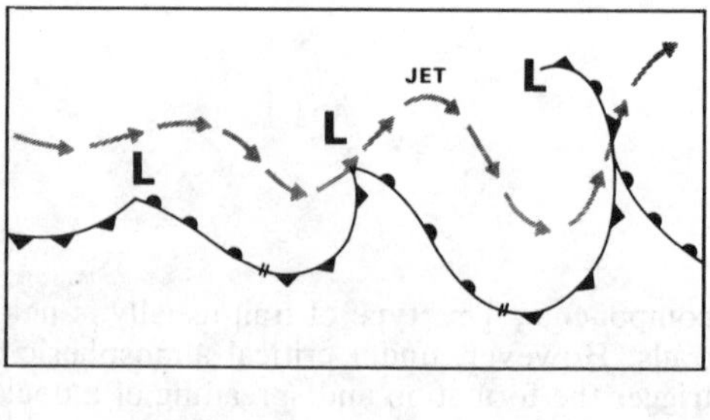

Temperature Conversion

Fahrenheit to Celsius

°F	°C	°F	°C	°F	°C
120	48.9	**63**	17.2	**6**	−14.4
119	48.3	**62**	16.7	**5**	−15.0
118	47.8	**61**	16.1	**4**	−15.6
117	47.2	**60**	15.6	**3**	−16.1
116	46.7	**59**	15.0	**2**	−16.7
115	46.1	**58**	14.4	**+1**	−17.2
114	45.6	**57**	13.9	**0**	−17.8
113	45.0	**56**	13.3	**−1**	−18.3
112	44.4	**55**	12.8	**−2**	−18.9
111	43.9	**54**	12.2	**−3**	−19.4
110	43.3	**53**	11.7	**−4**	−20.0
109	42.8	**52**	11.1	**−5**	−20.6
108	42.2	**51**	10.6	**−6**	−21.1
107	41.7	**50**	10.0	**−7**	−21.7
106	41.1	**49**	9.4	**−8**	−22.2
105	40.6	**48**	8.9	**−9**	−22.8
104	40.0	**47**	8.3	**−10**	−23.3
103	39.4	**46**	7.8	**−11**	−23.9
102	38.9	**45**	7.2	**−12**	−24.4
101	38.3	**44**	6.7	**−13**	−25.0
100	37.8	**43**	6.1	**−14**	−25.6
99	37.2	**42**	5.6	**−15**	−26.1
98	36.7	**41**	5.0	**−16**	−26.7
97	36.1	**40**	4.4	**−17**	−27.2
96	35.6	**39**	3.9	**−18**	−27.8
95	35.0	**38**	3.3	**−19**	−28.3
94	34.4	**37**	2.8	**−20**	−28.9
93	33.9	**36**	2.2	**−21**	−29.4
92	33.3	**35**	1.7	**−22**	−30.0
91	32.8	**34**	1.1	**−23**	−30.6
90	32.2	**33**	+0.6	**−24**	−31.1
89	31.7	**32**	0.0	**−25**	−31.7
88	31.1	**31**	−0.6	**−26**	−32.2
87	30.6	**30**	−1.1	**−27**	−32.8
86	30.0	**29**	−1.7	**−28**	−33.3
85	29.4	**28**	−2.2	**−29**	−33.9
84	28.9	**27**	−2.8	**−30**	−34.4
83	28.3	**26**	−3.3	**−31**	−35.0
82	27.8	**25**	−3.9	**−32**	−35.6
81	27.2	**24**	−4.4	**−33**	−36.1
80	26.7	**23**	−5.0	**−34**	−36.7
79	26.1	**22**	−5.6	**−35**	−37.2
78	25.6	**21**	−6.1	**−36**	−37.8
77	25.0	**20**	−6.7	**−37**	−38.3
76	24.4	**19**	−7.2	**−38**	−38.9
75	23.9	**18**	−7.8	**−39**	−39.4
74	23.3	**17**	−8.3	**−40**	−40.0
73	22.8	**16**	−8.9	**−41**	−40.6
72	22.2	**15**	−9.4	**−42**	−41.1
71	21.7	**14**	−10.0	**−43**	−41.7
70	21.1	**13**	−10.6	**−44**	−42.2
69	20.6	**12**	−11.1	**−45**	−42.8
68	20.0	**11**	−11.7	**−46**	−43.3
67	19.4	**10**	−12.2	**−47**	−43.9
66	18.9	**9**	−12.8	**−48**	−44.4
65	18.3	**8**	−13.3	**−49**	−45.0
64	17.8	**7**	−13.9	**−50**	−45.6

Celsius to Fahrenheit

°C	°F	°C	°F
50	122.0	**−7**	19.4
49	120.2	**−8**	17.6
48	118.4	**−9**	15.8
47	116.6	**−10**	14.0
46	114.8	**−11**	12.2
45	113.0	**−12**	10.4
44	111.2	**−13**	8.6
43	109.4	**−14**	6.8
42	107.6	**−15**	5.0
41	105.8	**−16**	3.2
40	104.0	**−17**	+1.4
39	102.2	**−18**	−0.4
38	100.4	**−19**	−2.2
37	98.6	**−20**	−4.0
36	96.8	**−21**	−5.8
35	95.0	**−22**	−7.6
34	93.2	**−23**	−9.4
33	91.4	**−24**	-11.2
32	89.6	**−25**	-13.0
31	87.8	**−26**	-14.8
30	86.0	**−27**	-16.6
29	84.2	**−28**	-18.4
28	82.4	**−29**	-20.2
27	80.6	**−30**	-22.0
26	78.8	**−31**	-23.8
25	77.0	**−32**	-25.6
24	75.2	**−33**	-27.4
23	73.4	**−34**	-29.2
22	71.6	**−35**	-31.0
21	69.8	**−36**	-32.8
20	68.0	**−37**	-34.6
19	66.2	**−38**	-36.4
18	64.4	**−39**	-38.2
17	62.6	**−40**	-40.0
16	60.8	**−41**	-41.8
15	59.0	**−42**	-43.6
14	57.2	**−43**	-45.4
13	55.4	**−44**	-47.2
12	53.6	**−45**	-49.0
11	51.8	**−46**	−50.8
10	50.0		
9	48.2		
8	46.4		
7	44.6		
6	42.8		
5	41.0		
4	39.2		
3	37.4		
2	35.6		
1	33.8		
0	+32.0		
−1	30.2		
−2	28.4		
−3	26.6		
−4	24.8		
−5	23.0		
−6	21.2		

MARINE WEATHER

and

BE YOUR OWN FORECASTER

NOAA VHF-FM Radio Weather

Alabama	
Huntsville	162.40 MHz
Mobile	162.55 MHZ
Alaska	
Anchorage	162.55 MHz
Seward	162.55 MHz
Arizona	
Phoenix	162.55 MHz
California	
Coachella	162.40 MHz
Crescent City	162.55 MHz
Brookings, Ore.	
Eureka	162.40 MHz
Los Angeles	162.55 MHz
Monterey	162.40 MHz
Point Arena	162.40 MHz
Sacramento	162.40 MHz
San Diego	162.40 MHz
San Francisco	162.55 MHz
San Luis Obispo	162.55 MHz
Santa Barbara	162.40 MHz
Colorado	
Denver	162.55 MHz
Connecticut	
New London	162.40 MHz
Florida	
Daytona Beach	162.40 MHz
Jacksonville	162.55 MHz
Key West	162.40 MHz
Miami	162.55 MHz
Panama City	162.55 MHz
Pensacola	162.40 MHz
Tallahassee	162.40 MHz
Tampa	162.55 MHz
West Palm Beach	162.40 MHz
Georgia	
Atlanta	162.55 MHz
Savannah	162.40 MHz
Hawaii	
Hilo	162.55 MHz
Honolulu	162.55 MHz
Kokee	162.40 MHz
Mt. Haleakala	162.40 MHz
Illinois	
Chicago	162. 5 MHz
Indiana	
Evansville	162.55 MHz
Indianapolis	162.55 MHz
Iowa	
Des Moines	162.55 MHz
Kansas	
Wichita	162.55 MHz
Kentucky	
Ashland	162.55 MHz
Bowling Green	162.40 MHz
Covington	162.55 MHz
Hazard	162.475 MHz
Lexington	162.40 MHz
Louisville	162.475 MHz
Mayfield	162.475 MHz
Somerset	162.55 MHz
Louisiana	
Baton Rouge	162.40 MHz
Lake Charles	162.55 MHz
Morgan City	162.475 MHz
New Orleans	162.55 MHz
Maine	
Ellsworth	162.40 MHz
Portland	162.55 MHz
Maryland	
Baltimore	162.40 MHz
Salisbury	162.40 MHz
Massachusetts	
Boston	162.40 MHz
Hyannis	162.55 MHz
Michigan	
Alpena	162.55 MHz
Clio	162.40 MHz
Detroit	162.55 MHz
Grand Rapids	162.55 MHz
Marquette	162.55 MHz
Sault Sainte Marie	162.55 MHz
Traverse City	162.55 MHz
Minnesota	
Duluth	162.55 MHz
Minneapolis	162.55 MHz
Mississippi	
Gulfport	162.40 MHz
Jackson	162.40 MHz
Missouri	
Kansas City	162.55 MHz
St. Joseph	162.40 MHz
St. Louis	162.55 MHz
New Jersey	
Atlantic City	162.40 MHz
New Mexico	
Albuquerque	162.40 MHz
New York	
Buffalo	162.55 MHz
New York City	162.55 MHz
New York (cont.)	
Rochester	162.40 MHz
North Carolina	
Cape Hatteras	162.55 MHz
New Bern	162.40 MHz
Wilmington	162.55 MHz
Ohio	
Akron	162.40 MHz
Cleveland	162.55 MHz
Columbus	162.55 MHz
Sandusky	162.40 MHz
Oklahoma	
Tulsa	162.55 MHz
Oregon	
Astoria	162.40 MHz
Coos Bay	162.40 MHz
Eugene	162.40 MHz
Newport	162.55 MHz
Portland	162.55 MHz
Pennsylvania	
Erie	162.40 MHz
Philadelphia	162.475 MHz
Pittsburgh	162.55 MHz
South Carolina	
Charleston	162.55 MHz
Myrtle Beach	162.40 MHz
Tennessee	
Nashville	162.55 MHz
Texas	
Brownsville	162.55 MHz
Corpus Christi	162.55 MHz
Dallas	162.40 MHz
Fort Worth	162.55 MHz
Galveston	162.55 MHz
Houston	162.40 MHz
Pharr	162.40 MHz
Utah	
Salt Lake City	162.55 MHz
Vermont	
Burlington	162.40 MHz
Virginia	
Manassas	162.55 MHz
Norfolk	162.55 MHz
Washington	
Neah Bay	162.55 MHz
Seattle	162.55 MHz
Yakima	162.55 MHz
Wisconsin	
Green Bay	162.55 MHz
Milwaukee	162.40 MHz

NOAA Weather Radio is a service of NOAA, the National Oceanic and Atmospheric Administration of the U.S. Department of Commerce, designed to speed warnings of natural disasters and national emergencies to the general public and emergency action units. NOAA Weather Radio broadcasts (on frequencies of 162.400 MHz and 162.550 MHz*) are made from National Weather Service Offices 24-hours a day. Taped weather forecast messages are repeated every 4 to 6 minutes and are routinely revised every 2 to 3 hours or more frequently if needed.

The routine broadcasts are tailored to the weather information needs of the people within the receiving area. Stations located along the coast and Great Lakes provide specialized weather information for boaters, fishermen, and others engaged in coastal activities.

During emergency situations, National Weather Service forecasters can interrupt the routine weather broadcast and substitute special warning messages. The forecasters can also activate specially designed warning receivers. These receivers will either sound an alarm (siren), indicating that an emergency exists and the listener should tune-in the appropriate frequency; or, when operated in a muted mode, will be automatically turned on so that the warning message will be heard.

Several radio manufacturers offer weather radios with and without the emergency warning alarm. In either case, the National Weather Service recommends receivers having a sensitivity of one microvolt or less and a quieting factor of 20 db. Messages can usually be received 40 to 60 miles from the antenna site, but the effective range depends on terrain and the type of receiver used. Where transmitting antennas are on high ground, the range is somewhat greater.

* MHz = Megahertz. One million cycles per second.

Warning display signals –

SMALL CRAFT

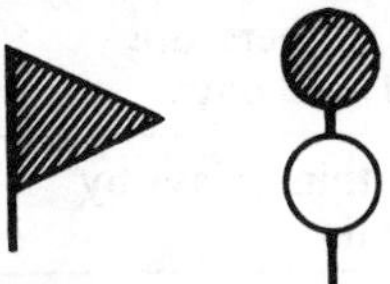

DAYTIME: Red Pennant.

NIGHTTIME: Red Light Over White Light.

Indicates: Forecast winds as high as 33 knots and sea conditions considered dangerous to small-craft operations.

GALE

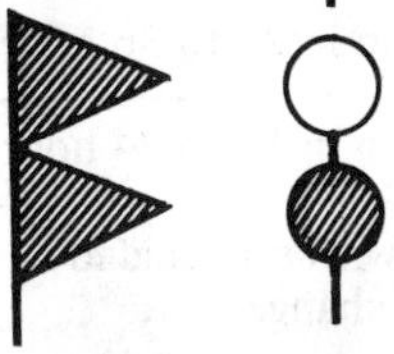

DAYTIME: Two Red Pennants.

NIGHTTIME: White Light over Red Light.

Indicates: Forecast winds in the range 34-47 knots.

STORM

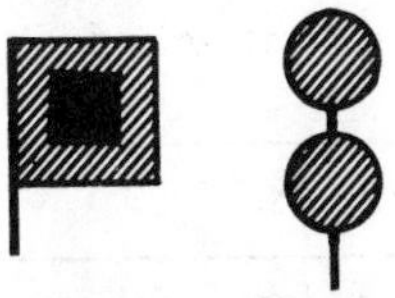

DAYTIME: Square Red Flag With Black Square Centered.

NIGHTTIME: Two Red Lights.

Indicates: Forecast winds 48 knots and above no matter how high the wind speed. If the winds are associated with a tropical cyclone (hurricane), storm warnings indicate forecast winds of 48-63 knots.

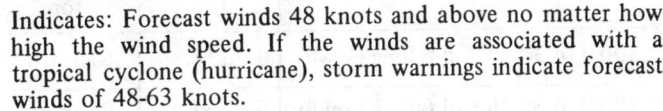

HURRICANE

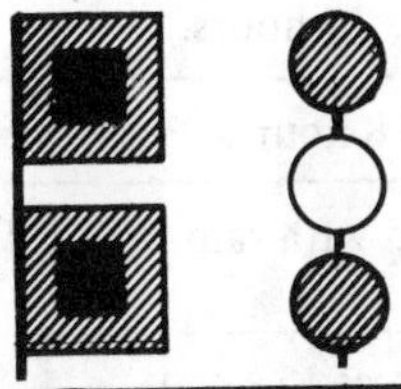

DAYTIME: Two Square Red Flags With Black Square Centered.

NIGHTTIME: White Light Between Two Red Lights.

Indicates: Forecast winds of 64 knots and above, displayed only in connection with a hurricane.

SAFE BOATING WEATHER RULES

BEFORE SETTING OUT

1. **Check local weather and sea conditions.**
2. **Obtain the latest weather forecast for your area from radio broadcasts**

When warnings are in effect, don't go out unless you are confident your boat can be navigated safely under forecast conditions of wind and sea. Be cautious when you see warning displays at U. S. Coast Guard stations, yacht clubs, marinas, and at other coastal points.

WHILE AFLOAT:

1. **Keep a weather eye out for the approach of dark, threatening clouds, which may foretell a squall or thunderstorm; any steady increase in wind or sea; any increase in wind velocity opposite in direction to a strong tidal current. A dangerous rip tide condition may form steep waves capable of broaching a boat.**
2. **Heavy static on your AM radio may be an indication of nearby thunderstorm activity.**
3. **Check radio weather broadcasts for latest forecasts and warnings.**
4. **If a thunderstorm catches you afloat: –stay below deck if possible. –keep away from metal objects that are not grounded to the boat's protection system. –don't touch more than one grounded object at the same time (or you may become a shortcut for electrical surges through the protection system).**

What about navigation? Do you have the NOAA National Ocean Survey charts and other publications covering your part of coastal or Great Lakes waters? Check your local office of the National Weather Service or National Ocean Survey and other essential aids to navigation.

Barometer reduced to sea level.	Wind direction.	Character of weather indicated
30.10 to 30.20 and steady	SW. to NW.	Fair with slight temperature changes for 1 to 2 days.
30.10 to 30.20 and rising rapidly	SW. to NW.	Fair followed within 2 days by warmer and rain.
30.10 to 30.20 and falling slowly	SW. to NW.	Warmer with rain in 24 to 36 hours.
30.10 to 30.20 and falling rapidly	SW. to NW.	Warmer with rain in 18 to 24 hours.
30.20 and above and stationary	SW. to NW.	Continued fair with no decided temperature change.
30.20 and above and falling slowly	SW. to NW.	Slowly rising temperature and fair for 2 days.
30.10 to 30.20 and falling slowly	S. to SE.	Rain within 24 hours.
30.10 to 30.20 and falling rapidly	S. to SE.	Wind increasing in force with rain within 12 to 24 hours.
30.10 to 30.20 and falling slowly	SE. to NE.	Rain in 12 to 18 hours.
30.10 to 30.20 and falling rapidly	SE. to. NE.	Increasing wind with rain within 12 hours.
30.10 and above and falling slowly	E. to NE.	In summer with light winds, rain may not fall for several days. In winter rain within 24 hours.
30.10 and above and falling rapidly	E. to NE.	In summer rain probable within 12 to 24 hours. In winter rain or snow, with increasing winds, will often set in, when the barometer begins to fall and the wind sets in from the NE.
30 or below and falling slowly	SE. to NE.	Rain will continue 1 to 2 days.
30 or below and falling rapidly	SE. to NE.	Rain with high wind, followed within 24 hours by clearing and cooler.
30 or below and rising slowly	S. to SW.	Clearing within a few hours, and continued fair for several days.
29.80 or below and falling rapidly	S. to E.	Severe storm of wind and rain or snow imminent, followed within 24 hours by clearing and colder.
29.80 or below and falling rapidly	E. to N.	Severe northeast gales and heavy rain or snow, followed in winter by a cold wave.
29.80 or below and rising rapidly	Going to W.	Clearing and colder.

BEAUFORT SCALE OF WIND EFFECTS

Wind speed (miles per hour)	Beaufort Number	Wind Effects on Land	Official Description
Less than 1	0	Calm; smoke rises vertically.	LIGHT
1 – 3	1	Wind direction is seen in direction of smoke; but is not revealed by weather vane.	
4 – 7	2	Wind can be felt on face; leaves rustle; wind vane moves.	
8 – 12	3	Leaves and small twigs in motion; wind extends light flag.	GENTLE
13 – 18	4	Wind raises dust and loose papers. Small branches move.	MODERATE
19 – 24	5	Small trees with leaves begin to sway; crested wavelets appear on inland waters.	FRESH
25 – 31	6	Large branches move; telegraph wires whistle; Umbrellas become difficult to control.	STRONG
32 – 38	7	Whole trees sway and walking into the wind becomes difficult.	
39 – 46	8	Twigs break off trees; cars veer on roads.	GALE
47 – 54	9	Slight structural damage occurs (roof slates may blow away, etc.)	
55 – 63	10	Trees are uprooted; considerable structural damage is caused.	WHOLE GALE
64 – 72	11	Widespread damage is caused.	
73 or more	12	Widespread damage is caused.	HURRICANE

FOR THE ARMCHAIR FORECASTER

Above is the Beaufort Scale which permits the estimating of wind speeds from observations. It also gives the basis for converting wind descriptions used in weather reports to wind speed equivalents, and vice-versa.

Use your barometer and wind indicator to do your own forecasting. It's one of the most popular hobbies in the world. The opposite page gives you a chart combining the weather observations of both professionals and amateurs dating back to such observers as Ben Franklin.

RECORD-SETTING WEATHER

HIGHS

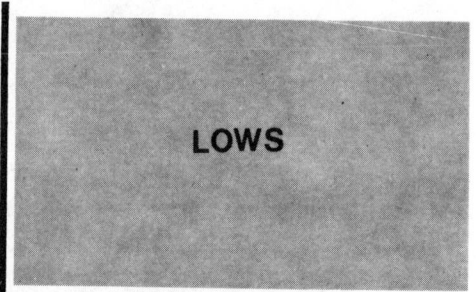

RECORD HIGHEST TEMPERATURES BY STATION

State	Temp. °F.	Date	Station	Elevation Feet
Ala.	112	Sept. 5, 1925	Centerville	345
Alaska	100	June 27, 1915	Fort Yukon	---
Ariz.	127	July 7, 1905*	Parker	345
Ark.	120	Aug. 10, 1936	Ozark	396
Calif.	134	July 10, 1913	Greenland Ranch	-178
Colo.	118	July 11, 1888	Bennett	---
Conn.	105	July 22, 1926	Waterbury	400
Del.	110	July 21, 1930	Millsboro	20
D. C.	106	July 20, 1930*	Washington	112
Fla.	109	June 29, 1931	Monticello	207
Ga.	112	July 24, 1952	Louisville	337
Hawaii	100	Apr. 27, 1931	Pahala	850
Idaho	118	July 28, 1934	Orofino	1,027
Ill.	117	July 14, 1954	E. St. Louis	410
Ind.	116	July 14, 1936	Collegeville	672
Iowa	118	July 20, 1934	Keokuk	614
Kans.	121	July 24, 1936*	Alton (near)	1,651
Ky.	114	July 28, 1930	Greensburg	581
La.	114	Aug. 10, 1936	Plain Dealing	268
Maine	105	July 10, 1911*	North Bridgton	450
Md.	109	July 10, 1936*	Cumberland & Frederick	623 - 325
Mass.	106	July 4, 1911*	Lawrence	51
Mich.	112	July 13, 1936	Mio	963
Minn.	114	July 6, 1936*	Moorhead	904
Miss.	115	July 29, 1930	Holly Springs	600
Mo.	118	July 14, 1954*	Warsaw & Union	687 - 560
Mont.	117	July 5, 1937	Medicine Lake	1,950
Nebr.	118	July 24, 1936*	Minden	2,169
Nev.	122	June 23, 1954*	Overton	1,240
N. H.	106	July 4, 1911	Nashua	125
N. J.	110	July 10, 1936	Runyon	18
N. Mex.	116	July 14, 1934*	Orogrande	4,171
N. Y.	108	July 22, 1926	Troy	35
N. C.	109	Sept. 7, 1954*	Weldon	81
N. Dak.	121	July 6, 1936	Steele	1,857
Ohio	113	July 21, 1934*	Gallipolis (near)	673
Okla.	120	July 26, 1943*	Tishomingo	670
Oreg.	119	Aug. 10, 1898*	Pendleton	1,074
Pa.	111	July 10, 1936*	Phoenixville	100
R. I.	102	July 30, 1949	Greenville	420
S. C.	111	June 28, 1954*	Camden	170
S. Dak.	120	July 5, 1936	Gannvalley	1,750
Tenn.	113	Aug. 9, 1930*	Perryville	377
Tex.	120	Aug. 12, 1936	Seymour	1,291
Utah	116	June 28, 1892	Saint George	2,880
Vt.	105	July 4, 1911	Vernon	310
Va.	110	July 15, 1954	Balcony Falls	725
Wash.	118	Aug. 5, 1961*	Ice Harbor Dam	475
W. Va.	112	July 10, 1936*	Martinsburg	435
Wis.	114	July 13, 1936	Wisconsin Dells	900
Wyo.	114	July 12, 1900	Basin	3,500

* Also on earlier dates at the same or other places.

HIGHEST TEMPERATURES IN CONTERMINOUS UNITED STATES BY MONTHS

Month	Temp. °F.	Year	Day	State	Place	Elevation Feet
Jan.	98	1936	17	Tex.	Laredo	421
Feb.*	105	1963	3	Ariz.	Montezuma	735
Mar.*	108	1954	31	Tex.	Rio Grande City	168
Apr.	118	1898	25	Calif.	Volcano Springs	-220
May*	124	1896	27	Calif.	Salton	-263
June*†	127	1896	15	Ariz.	Ft. Mohave	555
July	134	1913	10	Calif.	Greenland Ranch	-178
Aug. †	127	1933	12	Calif.	Greenland Ranch	-178
Sept.	126	1950	2	Calif.	Mecca	-175
Oct. *	116	1917	5	Ariz.	Sentinel	685
Nov. *	105	1906	12	Calif.	Craftonville	1.759
Dec.	100	1938	8	Calif.	La Mesa	539

* Two or more occurrences, most recent given.

† Slightly higher temperatures in old records are not used owing to lack of information on exposure of instruments.

LOWS

RECORD LOWEST TEMPERATURES BY STATES

State	Temp. °F.	Date	Station	Elevation Feet
Ala.	-24	Jan. 31, 1966	Russellville	880
Alaska	-80	Jan. 23, 1971	Prospect Creek	1,100
Ariz.	-40	Jan. 7, 1971	Hawley Lake	8,180
Ark.	-29	Feb. 13, 1905	Pond	1,250
Calif.	-45	Jan. 20, 1937	Boca	5,532
Colo.	-60	Feb. 1, 1951	Taylor Park	9,206
Conn.	-32	Feb. 16, 1943	Falls Village	585
Del.	-17	Jan. 17, 1893	Millsboro	20
D. C.	-15	Feb. 11, 1899	Washington	112
Fla.	- 2	Feb. 13, 1899	Tallahassee	193
Ga.	-17	Jan. 27, 1940	CCC Camp F-16	---
Hawaii	14	Jan. 2, 1961	Haleakala, Maui Island	9,750
Idaho	-60	Jan. 18, 1943	Island Park Dam	6,285
Ill.	-35	Jan. 22, 1930	Mount Carroll	817
Ind.	-35	Feb. 2, 1951	Greensburg	954
Iowa	-47	Jan. 12, 1912	Washta	1,157
Kans.	-40	Feb. 13, 1905	Lebanon	1,812
Ky.	-34	Jan. 28, 1963	Cynthiana	684
La.	-16	Feb. 13, 1899	Minden	194
Maine	-48	Jan. 19, 1925	Van Buren	510
Md.	-40	Jan. 13, 1912	Oakland	2,461
Mass.	-34	Jan. 18, 1957	Birch Hill Dam	840
Mich.	-51	Feb. 9, 1934	Vanderbilt	785
Minn.	-59	Feb. 16, 1903*	Pokegama Dam	1,280
Miss.	-19	Jan. 30, 1966	Corinth	420
Mo.	-40	Feb. 13, 1905	Warsaw	700
Mont.	-70	Jan. 20, 1954	Rogers Pass	5,470
Nebr.	-47	Feb. 12, 1899	Camp Clarke	3,700
Nev.	-50	Jan. 8, 1937	San Jacinto	5,200
N. H.	-46	Jan. 28, 1925	Pittsburg	1,575
N. J.	-34	Jan. 5, 1904	River Vale	70
N. Mex.	-50	Feb. 1, 1951	Gavilan	7,350
N. Y.	-52	Feb. 9, 1934	Stillwater Reservoir	1,670
N. C.	-29	Jan. 30, 1966	Mt. Mitchell	6,525
N. Dak.	-60	Feb. 15, 1936	Parshall	1,929
Ohio	-39	Feb. 10, 1899	Milligan	800
Okla.	-27	Jan. 18, 1930*	Watts	958
Oreg.	-54	Feb. 10, 1933*	Seneca	4,700
Pa.	-42	Jan. 5, 1904	Smethport	---
R. I.	-23	Jan. 11, 1942	Kingston	100
S. C.	-13	Jan. 26, 1940	Longcreek (near)	1,631
S. Dak.	-58	Feb. 17, 1936	McIntosh	2,277
Tenn.	-32	Dec. 30, 1917	Mountain City	2,471
Tex.	-23	Feb. 8, 1933*	Seminole	3,275
Utah	-50	Jan. 5, 1913*	Strawberry Tunnel	7,650
Vt.	-50	Dec. 30, 1933	Bloomfield	915
Va.	-29	Feb. 10, 1899	Monterey	---
Wash.	-48	Dec. 30, 1965	Mazama & Winthrop	2,120 - 1,765
W. Va.	-37	Dec. 30, 1917	Lewisburg	2,200
Wis.	-54	Jan. 24, 1922	Danbury	908
Wyo.	-63	Feb. 9, 1933	Moran	6,770

* Also on earlier dates at the same or other places.

LOWEST TEMPERATURES IN CONTERMINOUS UNITED STATES BY MONTHS

Month	Temp. °F.	Year	Day	State	Place	Elevation Feet
Jan.	-70	1954	20	Mont.	Rogers Pass	5,470
Feb.	-66	1933	9	Mont.	Riverside R. S.	6,700
Mar.	-50	1906	17	Wyo.	Snake River	6,862
Apr.	-36	1945	5	N. Mex.	Eagle Nest	8,250
May	-15	1964	7	Calif.	White Mountain 2	12,470
June	2	1907	13	Calif.	Tamarack	8,000
July*	10	1911	21	Wyo.	Painter	6,800
Aug. *	5	1910	25	Mont.	Bowen	6,080
Sept. *	- 9	1926	24	Mont.	Riverside R. S.	6,700
Oct.	-33	1917	29	Wyo.	Soda Butte	6,600
Nov.	-53	1959	16	Mont.	Lincoln 14 NE	5,130
Dec. *	-59	1924	19	Mont.	Riverside R. S.	6,700

* Two or more occurrences, most recent given.

TEMPERATURE EXTREMES, HIGHEST

Temperature extremes depend upon a number of factors, important among which are altitude, latitude, surface conditions, and the density and length of record of observing stations.

The World's highest temperatures as well as the greatest range of extremes and the greatest and most rapid temperature fluctuations occur over continental areas in the Temperate Zones.

A reading of 136° F., observed at Azizia (elevation about 380 feet), Tripolitania, Libya, North Africa, on Sept. 13, 1922, is generally accepted as the World's highest temperature recorded under standard conditions.

The highest temperature ever observed in Canada was 115° at Gleichen, Alberta on July 28, 1903. A high of 120° or higher has been recorded on all the Continents except Antarctica where the high is only 58.3°.

Greenland Ranch, Calif., with 134° on July 10, 1913, holds the record for the highest temperature ever officially recorded in the United States. This station is located in barren Death Valley which is about 140 miles long and 4 to 16 miles wide and runs north and south in southeastern California and southwestern Nevada. The valley is below sea level and is flanked by towering mountain ranges with Mt. Whitney, the highest landmark in the 48 States, rising to 14,495 feet, less than 100 miles to the west. Death Valley has the hottest summers in the Western Hemisphere, and is the only known place in the United States where nighttime temperatures sometime remain above 100°.

The highest average annual temperature in the World is probably the 88° at Lugh, Somalia, East Africa. In the United States the station normally having the highest annual average is Key West, Fla., 77.7°; the highest summer average, Death Valley, Calif., 98.2° and the highest winter average, Key West, Fla., 70.2°.

Amazing temperature rises of 40° to 50° in a few minutes occasionally may be brought about by chinook winds. Some outstanding extreme temperature rises in short periods are:

12 hours:	83°, Granville, N. Dak., Feb. 21, 1918, from –33° to 50° from early morning to late afternoon.
15 minutes:	42°, Fort Assiniboine, Mont., Jan. 19, 1892, from –5° to 37°.
7 minutes:	34°, Kipp, Mont., Dec. 1, 1896; observer also reported that a total rise of 80° occurred in a few hours and that 30 inches of snow disappeared in one-half day.
2 minutes:	49°, Spearfish, S. Dak., Jan. 22, 1943, from –4° at 7:30 a. m., to 45° at 7:32 a. m.

The range of temperature extremes over large bodies of water is much less than over land. The absolute extremes over the sea, as far as can be ascertained, range from 100° recorded by the SS TITAN on Aug. 8, 1920, in the Red Sea to –40° observed by the SS BAYCHINO, Jan. 27, 1932, when beset by ice at latitude 70° 50' N., longtitude 159° 11' W. In the Persian Gulf sea-surface temperatures average as high as 88° for July and August, and a high of 96° measured by the SS FRANKENFELS on Aug. 5, 1924, is at least among the highest if not the highest sea-surface temperatures ever observed.

TEMPERATURE EXTREMES, LOWEST

Antarctica, a vast elevated, snow-covered continent at the South Pole is one of the most favorable regions in the World for extremely low temperatures. Several stations there now have records dating back through 1957. During the early part of this period, a new World record low temperature was observed on several occasions. The latest, −126.9° F (−88.3° C), was recorded at Vostok (Russian station) on August 24, 1960. At the Amundsen-Scott station (elevation 9,186 ft.) located on a snow plain within a few hundred yards of the geographical South Pole, the average annual temperature for the period 1957 - 1964 was −59°. For July the average maximum temperature was −69°, the minimum −80° and for January these values were −17° and −22°, respectively. The average temperature at Vostok for the 2-year period 1958 - 59 was −67°. Even colder locations may exist on the continent.

Other regions favorable for unusually low winter extremes include Greenland, a high snow-covered area located mostly in the north polar regions, and north-central Siberia, part of a great land mass at high latitudes. Minima of −90° (Verhoyansk −89.7° F, Feb. 5 & 7, 1892 and Oimekon −89.9° F, Feb. 6, 1933) in the latter region stood as the World's lowest temperatures prior to observations in Antarctica. The lowest temperature on the Greenland Icecap, −86.8° F (−66.0° C) was observed at Northice January 9, 1954. Canada's lowest temperature, −81° F, was observed at Snag, Yukon territory, near the border of Alaska at an altitude of 2,120 feet on February 3, 1947.

In the United States, the lowest temperature on record, −79.8°, was recorded at Prospect Creek Camp which is located in the Endicott Mountains of Northern Alaska at Latitude 66° 48' N. Longtitude 150° 40' W. The lowest temperature in the 48 States, −69.7°, occurred at Rogers Pass, in Lewis and Clark County, Montana. This location is in mountainous and heavily forested terrain, about 1/2 mile east of and 140 feet below the summit of the Continental Divide.

The lowest average annual temperature recorded in the United States is 9.6° at Barrow, Alaska, which lies on the Arctic coast. Barrow also has the coolest summers (June, July, August) with an average of 36.7°. The lowest average winter (December, January, February) temperature is −15.6° at Barter Island on the Arctic coast of northeast Alaska. In Hawaii, average annual temperatures range from 44.0° at Mauna Loa Slope Oberservatory (elevation 11,146 feet) on the island of Hawaii to 75.9° at Honolulu on the island of Oahu.

In the 48 States, Mt. Washington, N. H. (elevation 6,262 feet) has the lowest mean annual temperature, 27.0° F, and the lowest mean summer (June, July, August) temperature, 47.2°. A few stations in the North-east and upper Rockies have mean annuals in the high 30's, and at the same stations in the latter area summers may average in the high 40's. Winter (December, January, February) mean temperature are lowest in northeastern North Dakota where the average is 5.9° at the Langdon Experiment Farm and northwestern Minnesota where the average is 6.1° at Hallock.

In continental areas of the Temperate Zone, 40° to 50° temperature falls in a few hours caused by advection of cold air masses are not uncommon. Sometimes, following these large drops due to advection, radiation may cause a further temperature fall resulting in remarkable changes. Some outstanding extreme temperature falls are:

24 hours:	100°, Browning, Mont., Jan. 23 - 24, 1916, from 44° to −56°.
12 hours:	84°, Fairfield, Mont., Dec. 24, 1924, from 63° at noon to −21° at midnight.
2 hours:	62°, Rapid City, S. Dak., Jan. 12, 1911, from 49° at 6 a. m ., to −13° at 8 a. m.
27 minutes:	58°, Spearfish, S. Dak., Jan. 22, 1943, from 54° at 9. a. m., to −4° at 9:27 a. m.
15 minutes	47°, Rapid City, S. Dak., Jan. 10, 1911, from 55° at 7 a. m., to 8° at 7:15 a. m.

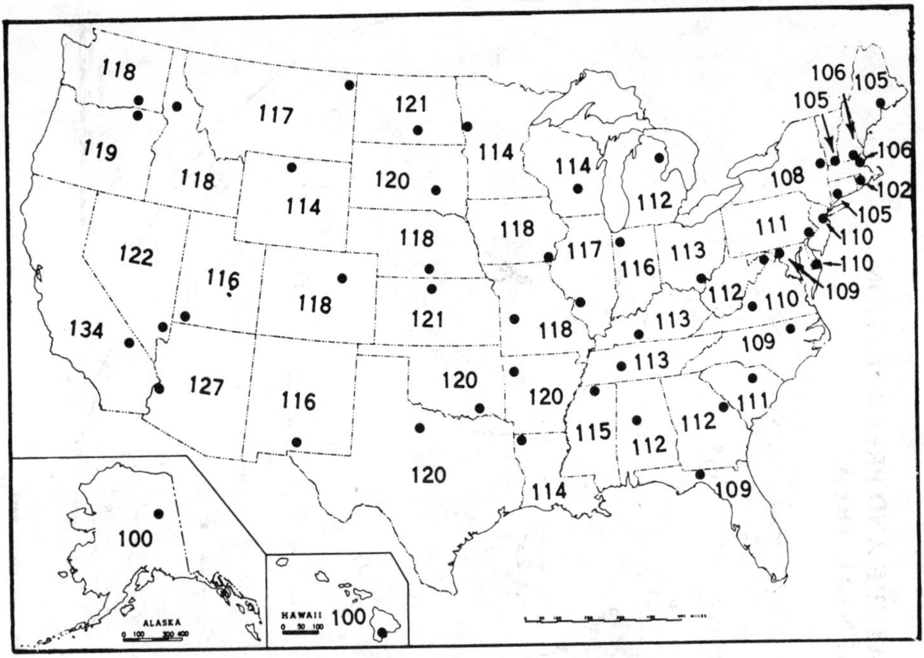

HIGHEST TEMPERATURES OF RECORD
AND LOCATIONS, BY STATES

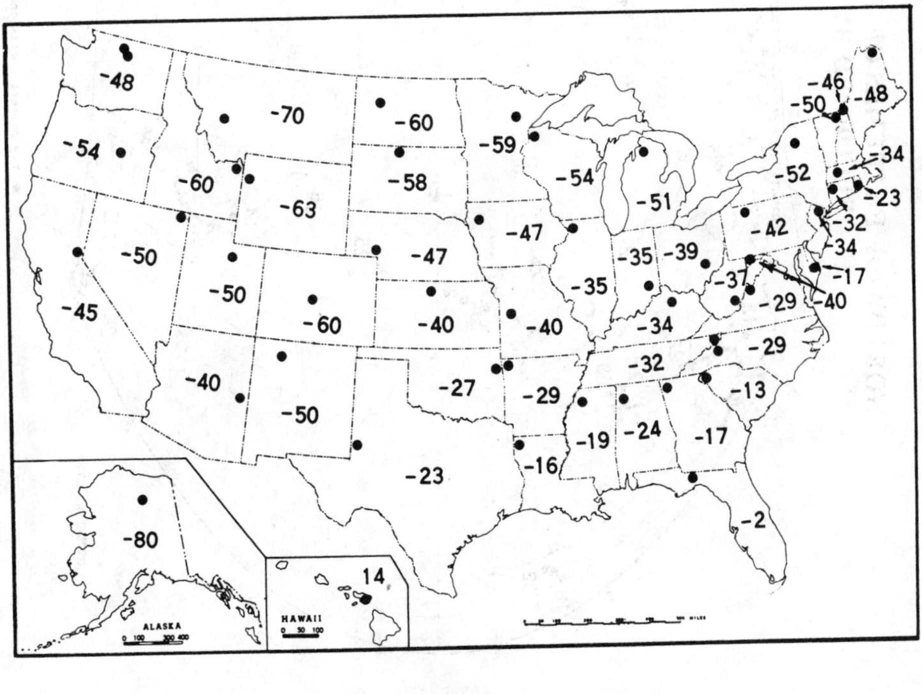

LOWEST TEMPERATURES OF RECORD
AND LOCATIONS, BY STATES

WORLDWIDE EXTREMES OF TEMPERATURE AND PRECIPITATION RECORDED BY CONTINENTAL AREA

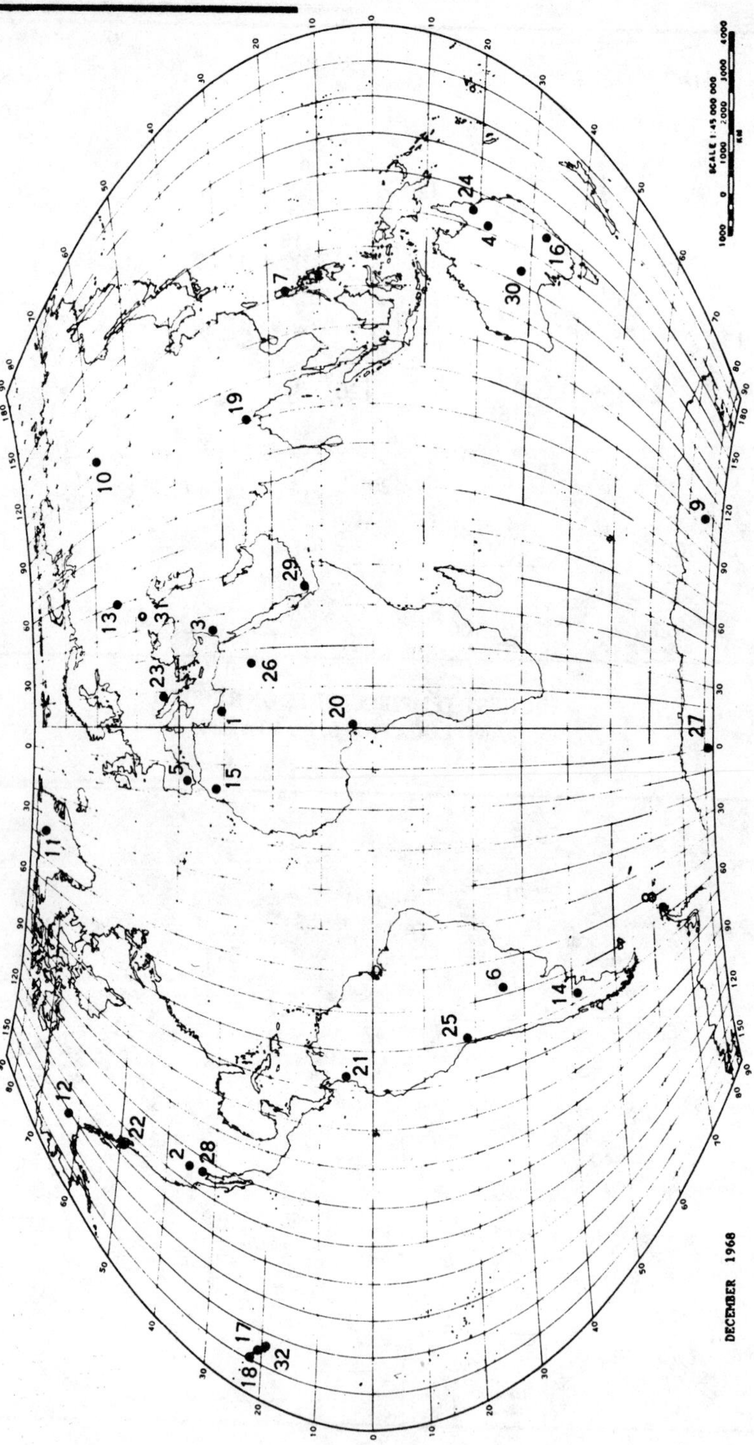

● Key numbers correspond to data entries on following page.

TEMPERATURE EXTREMES

Key No.	Area	Highest °F	Place	Elevation Feet	Date
1	Africa	136	Azizia, Libya	380	Sep. 13, 1922
2	North America	134	Death Valley, Calif.	-178	July 10, 1913
3	Asia	129	Tirat Tsvi, Israel	-722	June 21, 1942
4	Australia	128	Cloncurry, Queensland	622	Jan. 16, 1889
5	Europe	122	Seville, Spain	26	Aug. 4, 1881
6	South America	120	Rivadavia, Argentina	676	Dec. 11, 1905
7	Oceania	108	Tuguegarao, Philippines	72	Apr. 29, 1912
8	Antarctica	58	Esperanza, Palmer Pen.	26	Oct. 20, 1956

Key No.	Area	Lowest °F	Place	Elevation Feet	Date
9	Antarctica	-127	Vostok	11,220	Aug. 24, 1960
10	Asia	- 90	Oymykon, U.S.S.R.	2,625	Feb. 6, 1933
11	Greenland	- 87	Northice	7,690	Jan. 9, 1954
12	North America	- 81	Snag, Yukon, Canada	1,925	Feb. 3, 1947
13	Europe	- 67	Ust'Shchugor, USSR	279	January +
14	South America	- 27	Sarmiento, Argentina	879	June 1, 1907
15	Africa	- 11	Ifrane, Morocco	5,364	Feb. 11, 1935
16	Australia	- 8	Charlotte Pass, N.S.W.	---	July 22, 1947*
17	Oceania	14	Haleakala Summit, Maui	9,750	Jan. 2, 1961

\+ exact date unknown; lowest in 15-year period
* and earlier date
--- elevation unknown

EXTREMES OF AVERAGE ANNUAL PRECIPITATION

Key No.	Area	Greatest Amount Inches	Place	Elevation Feet	Years of Record
18	Oceania	460.0	Mt. Waialeale, Kauai, Hawaii	5,075	32
19	Asia	450.0	Cherrapunji, India	4,309	74
20	Africa	404.6	Debundscha, Cameroon	30	32
21	South America	353.9	Quibdo, Colombia	240	10-16
22	North America	262.1	Henderson Lake, B. C., Canada	12	14
23	Europe	182.8	Crkvica, Yugoslavia	3,337	22
24	Australia	179.3	Tully, Queensland	---	31

Key No.	Area	Least Amount Inches	Place	Elevation Feet	Years of Record
25	South America	0.03	Arica, Chile	95	59
26	Africa	<0.1	Wadi Halfa, Sudan	410	39
27	Antarctica	* 0.8	South Pole Station	9,186	10
28	North America	1.2	Batagues, Mexico	16	14
29	Asia	1.8	Aden, Arabia	22	50
30	Australia	4.05	Mulka, South Australia	---	34
31	Europe	6.4	Astrakhan, USSR	45	25
32	Oceania	8.93	Puako, Hawaii	5	13

* The value given is the average amount of solid snow accumulating in one year as indicated by snow markers. The liquid content of the snow is undetermined.

ROUND-THE-WORLD WEATHER

Look closely. It's our planet, Earth. This is the way NASA's cameras see it from 22,300 miles in space. Such satellite photos have opened a new doorway to meteorology by allowing the global movement of weather to be tracked with precise accuracy.

CLIMATES OF THE WORLD

Temperature Distribution

The distribution of temperature over the world and its variations through the year depend primarily on the amount of distribution of the radiant energy received from the sun in different regions. This in turn depends mainly on latitude but is greatly modified by the distribution of continents and oceans, prevailing winds, oceanic circulation, topography, and other factors.

Maps showing average temperatures over the surface of the earth for January and for July are given in figures 1 and 2.

In the winter of the Northern Hemisphere, it will be noted, the poleward temperature gradient (that is, the rate of fall in temperature) north of latitude 15° is very steep over the interior of North America. This is shown by the fact that the lines indicating changes in temperature come very close together. The temperature gradient is also steep toward the cold pole over Asia –the area marked –50°. In western Europe, to the east of the Atlantic Ocean and the North Atlantic Drift, and in the region of prevailing westerly winds, the temperature gradient is much more gradual, as indicated by the fact that the isotherms, or lines of equal temperature, are far apart. In the winter of the Southern Hemisphere, as shown on the map for July (a winter month south of the Equator), the temperature gradient toward the South Pole is very gradual, and the isothermal deflections from the east-west direction (that is, the dipping of the isothermal lines) are of minor importance because continental effects are largely absent.

In the summers of the two hemispheres–July in the north and January in the south– the temperature gradients poleward are very much diminished as compared with those during the winter. This is especially marked over the middle and higher northern latitudes because of the greater warming of the extensive interiors of North America and Eurasia than of the smaller land areas in middle and higher southern latitudes.

Distribution of Precipitation

Whether precipitation (see the map, fig. 3) occurs as rain or snow or in the rarer forms of hail or sleet depends largely on the temperature climate, which may be influenced more by elevation than by latitude, as in the case of the perpetually snowcapped mountain peaks and glaciers on the Equator in both South America and Africa.

The quantity of precipitation is governed by the amount of water vapor in the air and the nature of the process that leads to its condensation into liquid or solid form through cooling. Air may ascend to great elevations through local convection, as in thunderstorms and in tropical regions generally; it may be forced up over topographical elevations across the prevailing wind direction, as on the southern or windward slopes of the Himalayas in the path of the southwest monsoon in India; or it may ascend more or less gradually in migratory low-pressure formations such as those that govern the main features of weather in the United States.

The areas of heaviest precipitation on the map (fig. 3) are generally located, as would be expected, in tropical regions, where because of high temperature the greatest amount of water vapor may be present in the atmosphere and the greatest evaporation takes place–although only where conditions favor condensation can rainfall occur. Outstanding exceptions are certain regions in high latitudes, such as southern Alaska, western Norway, and southern Chile, where relatively warm, moist winds from the sea undergo forced ascent over considerable elevations.

In marked contrast to the rainy regions just named are the dry polar regions, where the water-vapor content of the air is always very low because of the low

AVERAGE JANUARY TEMPERATURE (F°)

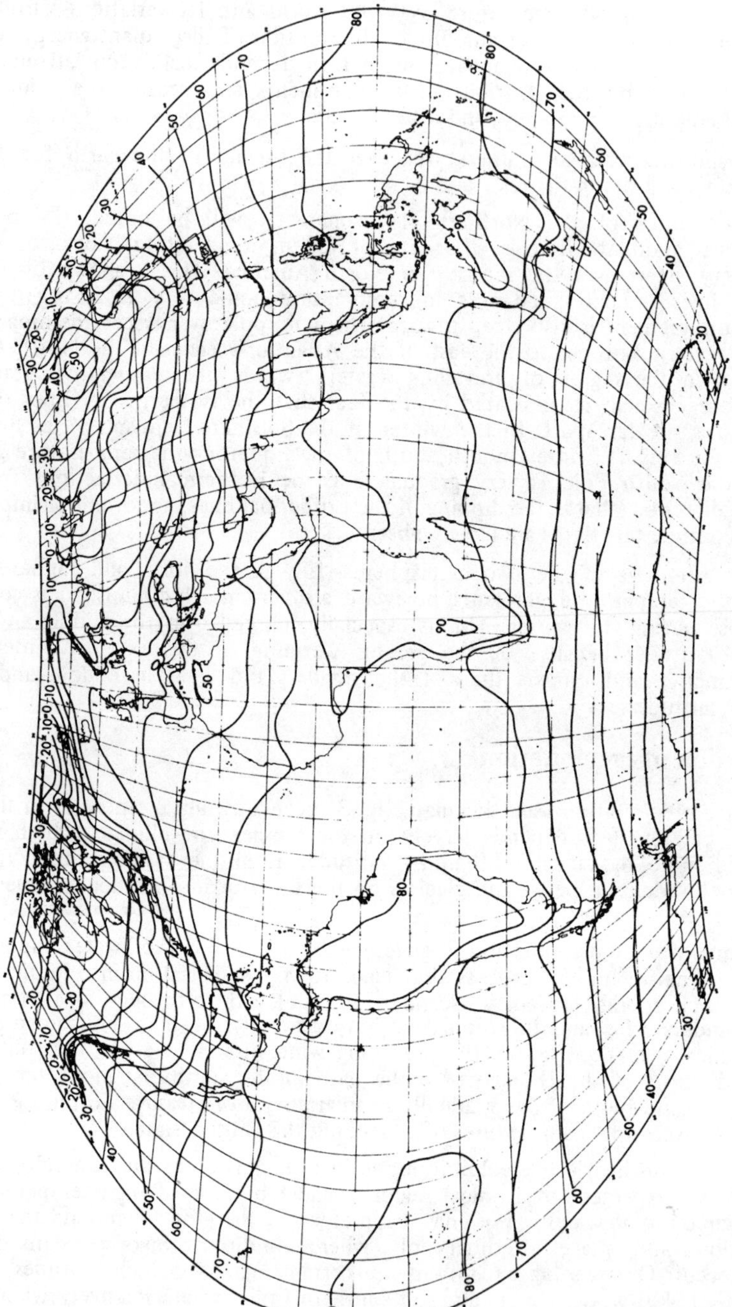

Figure 1.

AVERAGE JULY TEMPERATURE (F°)

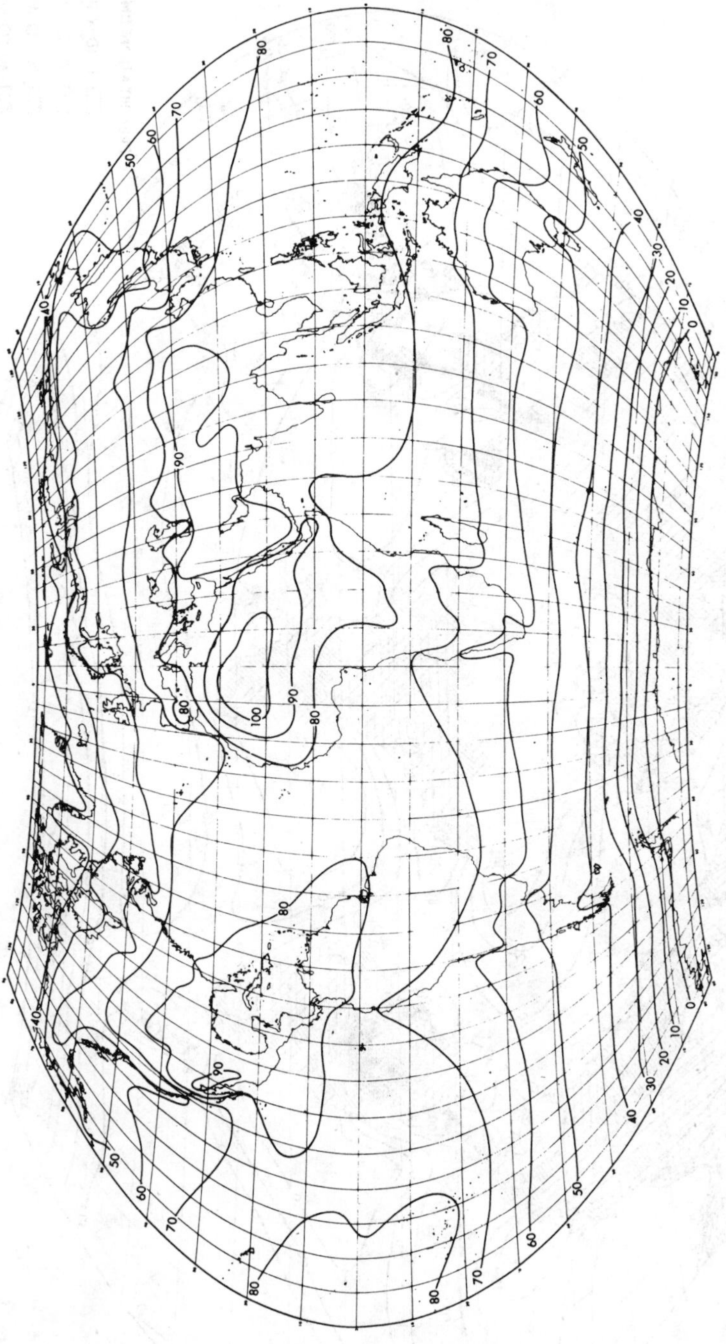

Figure 2.

GENERAL PATTERN OF ANNUAL WORLD PRECIPITATION (INCHES)

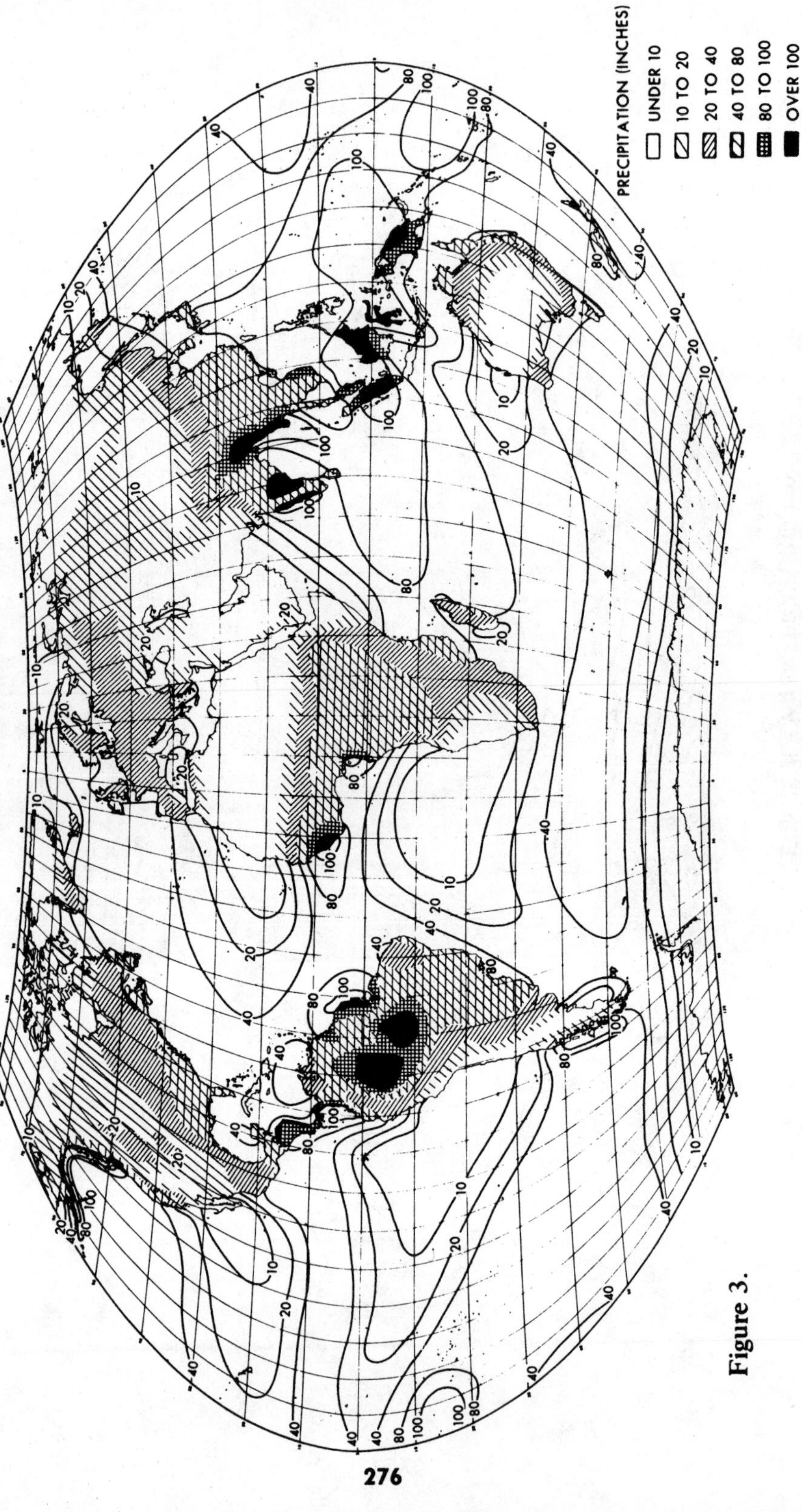

Figure 3.

temperature and very limited evaporation. The dry areas in the subtropical belts of high atmospheric pressure (in the vicinity of latitude 30° on all continents, and especially from the extreme western Sahara over a broad, somewhat broken belt to the Desert of Gobi) and the arid strips on the lee sides of mountains on whose windward slopes precipitation is heavy to excessive, are caused by conditions which, even though the temperature may be high, are unfavorable to the condensation of whatever water vapor may be present in the atmosphere.

In the tables following are data on mean maximum and minimum temperatures for January, April, July, and October, with extremes recorded in the period of record, and monthly and annual precipitation for about 800 selected stations well distributed over the earth.

North America

North America is nearly all within middle and northern latitudes. Consequently it has a large central area in which the continental type of climate with marked seasonal temperature is to be found.

Along the coasts of northern Alaska, western Canada, and the northwestern part of the United States, moderate midsummer temperatures are in marked contrast to those prevailing in the interior east of the mountains. (Note, for example, the great southward dip of the 60° isotherm along the west coast in fig. 2.) Again, the mild midwinter temperatures in the coastal areas stand out against the severe conditions to be found from the Great Lakes region northward and northwestward (fig. 1).

In the West Indian region, temperature conditions are subtropical; and in Mexico and Central America, climatic zones depend on elevation, ranging from subtropical to temperate in the higher levels.

The prevailing westerly wind movement carries the continental type of climate eastward over the United States, so that the region of maritime climate along the Atlantic Ocean is very narrow.

From the Aleutian Peninsula to northern California west of the crests of the mountains, there is a narrow strip where annual precipitation is over 40 inches; it exceeds 100 inches locally on the coast of British Columbia (see fig.3). East of this belt there is an abrupt fall-off in precipitation to less than 20 inches annually over the western half of the continent from Lower California northward, and to even less than 5 inches in parts of what used to be called the "Great American Desert." in the southwestern part of the United States.

In the eastern part of the continent–that is, from the southeastern part of the United States northeastward to Newfoundland–the average annual precipitation is more than 40 inches. Rainfall in the West Indies, southern Mexico, and Central America is generally abundant. It is very spotty, however, varying widely even within short distances, especially from the windward to the leeward sides of the mountains.

The northern areas are, of course, very cold; but the midwinter low temperatures fall far short of the records set in the cold-pole area of northeastern Siberia, where the vast extent of land becomes much colder than the partly ice-covered area of northern Canada .

South America

A large part of South America lies within the Tropics and has a characteristically tropical climate. The remaining rather narrow southern portion is not subject to the extremes of heat and cold that are found where wide land areas give full sway to the continental type of climate with its hot summers and cold winters, as in North America and Asia. Temperature anomalies unusual for a given latitude are to be found mainly at the elevated levels of the Andean region stretching from the Isthmus of Panama to Cape Horn.

The Antarctic Current and its cool Humboldt branch skirting the western shores northward to the Equator, together with the prevailing on-shore winds, exert a strong cooling influence over the coastal regions of all the western countries of South America except Colombia. On the east the southerly moving Brazilian current from tropical waters has the opposite, or warming, effect except along southern Argentina.

In the northern countries of South America the sharply contrasted dry and wet seasons are related to the regime of the trade winds. In the dry season (corresponding to winter in the Northern Hemisphere) these winds sweep the entire region, while the wet season (corresponding to summer in the Northern Hemisphere) calms and variable winds prevail. In the basin of the Amazon River the rainfall is related to the equatorial belt of low pressure and to the trade winds, which give the maximum amounts of rainfall in the extreme west, where they ascend the Andean slopes.

The desert areas on the west coast of South America, extending from the Equator to the latitude of Santiago, are due primarily to the cold Humboldt or Peruvian Current and upwelling coastal water. The moist, cool ocean air is warmed in passing over the land, with a consequent decrease in relative humidity, so that the dew point is not reached and condensation of vapor does not occur until the incoming air has reached high elevations in the Andes, where temperatures are very much lower than along the coast.

In southern Chile the summer has moderate rainfall, and winters are excessively wet. The conditions that prevail farther north are not present here, and condensation of moisture from the ocean progresses from the shores up to the crests of the Andes. By the time the air passes these elevations, however, the moisture has been so depleted that the winds in the leeward slopes are dry, becoming more and more so as they are warmed on reaching lower levels. The mountains can be looked upon as casting a great "rain shadow"–an area of little rain–over southern Argentina.

Europe

In Europe there is no extensive north-south mountain system such as is found in both the Americas, and the general east-west direction of the ranges in the south allows the conditions in the maritime west to change rather gradually toward Asia. Generally rainfall is heaviest on the western coast, where locally it exceeds 60 inches annually, and diminishes toward the east–except in the elevated Alpine and Caucasus regions–to less than 20 inches in eastern Russia. There is a well-defined rain shadow in Scandinavia, with over 60 inches of rain in western Norway and less than 20 inches in eastern Sweden.

Over much of Europe rainfall is both abundant and rather evenly distributed throughout the year. The chief feature of seasonal distribution of precipitation is the marked winter maximum and the extremely dry, even droughty, summers in most of the Mediterranean lands.

Isothermal lines have the general direction of the parallels of latitude except in winter, when the waters of the western ocean, warmed by the Gulf Stream, give them a north-south trend. Generally there are no marked dips in isotherms due to elevation and continental type of climate such as are found in North America. In Scandinavia, however, the winter map shows an abrupt fall in temperature from the western coast of Norway to the eastern coast of Sweden and thence a continued fall eastward, under a type of exposure more and more continental in contrast to the oceanic exposure on the west.

Asia

The vast extent of Asia gives full opportunity for continental conditions to develop a cold area of high barometric pressure in winter and a low-pressure, hot area in summer, the former northeast of the Himalayas and the latter stretching widely from west to east in the latitude of northern India. (See the area marked 90° on the map, fig. 2.) These distributions of pressure give to India the well-known monsoon seasons, during which the wind comes from one direction for several months, and also affect the yearly distribution of rainfall over eastern Asia.

In winter, the air circulation is outward over the land from the cold pole, and precipitation is very light over the entire continent. In summer, on the contrary, there is an inflow of air from the oceans; even the southeast trade winds flow across the Equator and merge into the southwest monsoon which crosses India. This usually produces abundant rain over most of that country, with excessively heavy amounts when the air is forced to rise, even to moderate elevations, in its passage the land. At Cherrapunji (4,455 feet), on the southern side of the Khasi Hills in Assam, the average rainfall in a winter month is about 1 inch, while in both June and July it is approximately 100 inches. However, this heavy summer rainfall meets an impassable barrier in the Himalaya Mountains, while the much lighter summer monsoon rainfall over Japan and eastern Asia does not extend far into China because of lesser elevations. Consequently, while the southeast quadrant of Asia, including the East Indies, also with monsoon winds, has heavy to excessive annual rainfall, the remainder of the continent is dry, with vast areas receiving less than 10 inches annually.

North of the Himalayas the low plains are excessively cold in winter and temperatures rise rather high in summer. At Verkhoyansk in the cold-pole area, and north of the Arctic Circle, the mean temperature in January is about -59° F, and in July approximately 64°; the extreme records are a maximum of 98°, from readings at 1 p.m., and a minimum of -90°.

In southwestern Asia the winter temperature control is still the interior high-pressure area, and temperatures are generally low, especially at high elevations; in summer at low elevations excessively high maxima are recorded, as, for example, in the Tigris-Euphrates Valley

Africa

Africa, like South America, lies very largely within the Tropics. There too, temperature distribution is determined mainly by altitude. Moreover, along the southern portion of the western coast the cool Benguela Current moves northward, and on the eastern coast are the warm tropical currents of the Indian Ocean, which create conditions closely paralleling those found around the South American Continent. In the strictly tropical areas of Africa conditions are characterized by prevailing low barometric pressure, with conventional rainfall and alternate northward and southward movement of the heat equator, while in both the north and the south the ruling influences are the belts of high barometric pressure.

Except in the Atlas Mountains in the northwest where the considerable elevations set up a barrier in the path of trade winds and produce moderate rainfall, the desert conditions typified by the Sahara extend from the Atlantic to the Red Sea and from the Mediterranean southward well beyond the northern Tropic to about the latitudes of southern Arabia.

South of the Sahara, rainfall increases rapidly, becoming abundant to heavy from the west coast to the central lakes, with annual maxima of over 80 inches in the regions bordering the eastern and western extremes of the Guinea coast. This marked increase in precipitation does not extend to the eastern portion of the middle region of the continent, where the annual amounts received are below 40 inches and decrease to less than 10 inches on the coasts of Somalia. Also to the south of the central rainy area there is a rapid fall in precipitation toward the arid regions of Southwest Africa, where conditions are similar to those in Somalia.

The heavy rainfall over sections of Ethiopia from June to October, when more than 40 inches fall and bring the overflowing of the otherwise arid Nile Valley, is one of the earth's outstanding features of seasonal distribution of rainfall.

Moist equatorial climate is typified by conditions in the Democratic Republic of the Congo; arid torrid climate by those of the United Arab Republic and the Sahara; and moderate plateau climate by those found in parts of Ethiopia, Kenya and Tanzania.

Australia

In the southern winter the high-pressure belt crosses the interior of Australia, and all except the southernmost parts of the continent are dry. In summer, on the other hand, this pressure belt has moved south of the continent, still giving dry conditions over the southern and western areas. Thus the total annual precipitation is less than 20 inches except in the extreme southwest and in a strip circling from southeast to northwest. The average annual precipitation is even less than 10 inches in a large south-central area.

In the south the winter precipitation is the cyclonic type; the heavy summer rains of the north are of monsoon origin; and those of the eastern borders are in large part orographic, owing to the presence of the highlands in the immediate vicinity of the coasts. In the outer border of the rainfall strip along the coastal region, the mean annual rainfall is over 40 inches and in many localities over 60 inches. This is true for the monsoon rains in the north.

Because of the location of Australia, on both sides of the southern Tropic, temperatures far below freezing are to be found only in a small part of the continent, in the south at high elevations. In the arid interior extreme maximum temperatures are very high, ranking with those of the hottest regions on the earth

ROUND-THE-WORLD WEATHER →

Travel plans demand some research about climate and what weather to expect and prepare for along your route. The following pages let you check on weather expectations for all four seasons for more than 550 key cities of the world. Of course, one season's weather, or even one year's weather may, and often does deviate considerably from averages. That is true in Greece or Spain the same as in New York or Denver, meaning that averages can never serve as a guarantee that this year or this season mightn't be the exception. A traveler should assess that for himself, after determining what is "normal" for the area, and what he might ordinarily expect the weather there to be.

U.S. cities appear in these tables, but far more detailed studies of the weather and climate of more than 100 U.S. cities await the reader in a special section of this book.

COUNTRY AND STATION	LATITUDE (° ′)	LONGITUDE (° ′)	ELEVATION (FEET)	TEMPERATURE: LENGTH OF RECORD (YEAR)	AVERAGE DAILY: JANUARY MAXIMUM (°F)	JANUARY MINIMUM (°F)	APRIL MAXIMUM (°F)	APRIL MINIMUM (°F)	JULY MAXIMUM (°F)	JULY MINIMUM (°F)	OCTOBER MAXIMUM (°F)	OCTOBER MINIMUM (°F)	EXTREME MAXIMUM (°F)	EXTREME MINIMUM (°F)
NORTH AMERICA														
United States (Conterminous):														
Albuquerque, N. Mex.	35 03N	106 37W	5,311	30	46	24	69	42	91	66	71	45	104	-16
Asheville, N.C.	35 26N	82 32W	2,140	30	48	28	67	42	84	61	68	45	99	- 7
Atlanta, Ga.	33 39N	84 26W	1,010	30	52	37	70	50	87	71	72	52	103	- 9
Austin, Tex.	30 18N	97 42W	597	30	60	41	78	57	95	74	82	60	109	- 2
Birmingham, Ala.	33 34N	86 45W	620	30	57	36	76	50	93	71	79	52	107	-10
Bismark, N. Dak.	46 46N	100 45W	1,647	30	20	0	55	32	86	58	59	34	114	-45
Boise, Idaho	43 34N	116 13W	2,838	30	36	22	63	37	91	59	65	38	112	-28
Brownsville, Tex.	25 54N	97 26W	16	30	71	52	82	66	93	76	85	67	104	12
Buffalo, N.Y.	42 56N	78 44W	705	30	31	18	53	34	80	59	60	41	99	-21
Cheyenne, Wyo.	41 09N	104 49W	6,126	30	37	14	56	30	85	55	63	32	100	-38
Chicago, Ill.	41 47N	87 45W	607	30	33	19	57	41	84	67	63	47	105	-23
Des Moines, Iowa	41 32N	93 39W	938	30	29	11	59	38	87	65	66	43	110	-30
Dodge City, Kans.	37 46N	99 58W	2,582	30	42	20	66	41	93	68	71	46	109	-26
El Paso, Tex.	31 48N	106 24W	3,918	30	56	30	78	49	95	69	79	50	109	- 8
Indianapolis, Ind.	39 44N	86 17W	792	30	37	21	61	40	86	64	67	44	107	-25
Jacksonville, Fla.	30 25N	81 39W	20	30	67	45	80	58	92	73	80	62	105	10
Kansas City, Mo.	39 07N	94 36W	742	30	40	23	66	46	92	71	72	49	113	-22
Las Vegas, Nev.	36 05N	115 10W	2,162	30	54	32	78	51	104	76	80	53	117	8
Los Angeles, Calif.	33 56N	118 23W	97	30	64	45	67	52	76	62	73	57	110	23
Louisville, Ky.	38 11N	85 44W	477	30	44	27	66	43	89	67	70	46	107	-20
Miami, Fla.	25 48N	80 16W	7	30	76	58	83	66	89	75	85	71	100	28
Minneapolis, Minn.	44 53N	93 13W	834	30	22	2	56	33	84	61	61	37	108	-34
Missoula, Mont.	46 55N	114 05W	3,190	30	28	10	57	31	85	49	58	30	105	-33
Nasheville, Tenn.	36 07N	86 41W	590	30	49	31	71	48	91	70	74	49	107	-15
New Orleans, La.	29 59N	90 15W	3	30	64	45	78	58	91	73	80	61	102	7
New York, N.Y.	40 47N	73 58W	132	30	40	27	60	43	85	68	66	50	106	-15
Oklahoma City, Okla.	35 24N	97 36W	1,285	30	46	28	71	49	93	72	74	52	113	-17
Phoenix, Ariz.	33 26N	112 01W	1,117	30	64	35	84	50	105	75	87	55	118	16
Pittsburgh, Pa.	40 27N	80 00W	747	30	40	25	63	42	85	65	65	45	103	-20
Portland, Maine	43 39N	70 19W	47	30	32	12	53	32	80	57	60	37	103	-39
Portland, Oreg.	45 36N	122 36W	21	30	44	33	62	42	79	56	63	45	107	- 3
Reno, Nev.	39 30N	119 47W	4,404	30	45	16	65	31	89	46	69	29	106	-19
Salt Lake City, Utah	40 46N	111 58W	4,220	30	37	18	63	36	94	60	65	38	107	-30
San Francisco, Calif.	37 37N	122 23W	8	30	55	42	64	47	72	54	71	51	106	20
Sault Ste. Marie, Mich.	46 28N	84 22W	721	30	23	8	46	30	76	54	55	38	98	-37
Seattle, Wash.	47 27N	122 18W	400	30	44	33	58	40	76	54	60	44	100	0
Sheridan, Wyo.	44 46N	106 58W	3,964	30	34	9	56	31	87	56	62	33	106	-41
Spokane, Wash.	47 38N	117 32W	2,356	30	31	19	59	36	86	55	60	38	108	-30
Washington, D.C.	38 51N	77 03W	14	30	44	30	66	46	87	69	68	50	106	-15
Wilmington, N.C.	34 16N	77 55W	28	30	58	37	74	51	89	71	76	55	104	5

COUNTRY AND STATION	AVERAGE PRECIPITATION: LENGTH OF RECORD (YEAR)	JANUARY (IN.)	FEBRUARY (IN.)	MARCH (IN.)	APRIL (IN.)	MAY (IN.)	JUNE (IN.)
Albuquerque, N. Mex.	30	0.4	0.4	0.5	0.5	0.8	0.6
Asheville, N.C.	30	4.2	4.0	4.8	4.0	3.7	3.5
Atlanta, Ga.	30	4.4	4.5	5.4	4.5	3.2	3.8
Austin, Tex.	30	2.4	2.6	2.1	3.6	3.7	3.2
Birmingham, Ala.	30	5.0	5.3	6.0	4.5	3.4	4.0
Bismark, N. Dak.	30	0.4	0.4	0.8	1.2	2.0	3.4
Boise, Idaho	30	1.3	1.3	1.3	1.2	1.3	0.9
Brownsville, Tex.	30	1.4	1.5	1.0	1.6	2.4	3.0
Buffalo, N.Y.	30	2.8	2.7	3.2	3.0	3.0	2.5
Cheyenne, Wyo.	30	0.5	0.6	1.2	1.9	2.5	2.1
Chicago, Ill.	30	1.9	1.6	2.7	3.0	3.7	4.1
Des Moines, Iowa	30	1.3	1.1	2.1	2.5	4.1	4.7
Dodge City, Kans.	30	0.6	0.7	1.2	1.8	3.2	3.0
El Paso, Tex.	30	0.5	0.4	0.4	0.3	0.4	0.7
Indianapolis, Ind.	30	3.1	2.3	3.4	3.7	4.0	4.6
Jacksonville, Fla.	30	2.5	2.9	3.5	3.6	3.5	6.3
Kansas City, Mo.	30	1.4	1.2	2.5	3.6	4.4	4.6
Las Vegas, Nev.	30	0.5	0.4	0.4	0.2	0.1	*
Los Angeles, Calif.	30	2.7	2.9	1.8	1.1	0.1	0.1
Louisville, Ky.	30	4.1	3.3	4.6	3.8	3.9	4.0
Miami, Fla.	30	2.0	1.9	2.3	3.9	6.4	7.4
Minneapolis, Minn.	30	0.7	0.8	1.5	1.9	3.2	4.0
Missoula, Mont.	30	0.9	0.9	0.7	1.0	1.9	1.9
Nasheville, Tenn.	30	5.5	4.5	5.2	3.7	3.7	3.3
New Orleans, La.	30	3.8	4.0	5.3	4.6	4.4	4.4
New York, N.Y.	30	3.3	2.8	4.0	3.4	3.7	3.3
Oklahoma City, Okla.	30	1.3	1.4	2.0	3.1	5.2	4.5
Phoenix, Ariz.	30	0.7	0.9	0.7	0.3	0.1	0.1
Pittsburgh, Pa.	30	2.8	2.3	3.5	3.4	3.8	4.0
Portland, Maine	30	4.4	3.8	4.3	3.7	3.4	3.2
Portland, Oreg.	30	5.4	4.2	3.8	2.1	2.0	1.7
Reno, Nev.	30	1.2	1.0	0.7	0.5	0.5	0.4
Salt Lake City, Utah	30	1.4	1.2	1.6	1.8	1.4	1.0
San Francisco, Calif.	30	4.0	3.5	2.7	1.3	0.5	0.1
Sault Ste. Marie, Mich.	30	2.1	1.5	1.8	2.2	2.8	3.3
Seattle, Wash.	30	5.7	4.2	3.8	2.4	1.7	1.6
Sheridan, Wyo.	30	0.6	0.7	1.4	2.2	2.6	2.6
Spokane, Wash.	30	2.4	1.9	1.5	0.9	1.2	1.5
Washington, D.C.	30	3.0	2.5	3.2	3.2	4.1	3.2
Wilmington, N.C.	30	2.9	3.4	4.0	2.9	3.5	4.3

COUNTRY AND STATION	JULY (IN.)	AUGUST (IN.)	SEPTEMBER (IN.)	OCTOBER (IN.)	NOVEMBER (IN.)	DECEMBER (IN.)	YEAR (IN.)
Albuquerque, N. Mex.	1.2	1.3	1.0	0.8	0.4	0.5	8.4
Asheville, N.C.	5.9	4.9	3.6	3.1	2.8	3.6	48.1
Atlanta, Ga.	4.7	3.6	3.3	2.4	3.0	4.4	47.2
Austin, Tex.	2.2	1.9	3.4	2.8	2.1	2.5	32.5
Birmingham, Ala.	5.2	4.9	3.3	3.0	3.5	5.0	53.1
Bismark, N. Dak.	2.2	1.7	1.2	0.9	0.6	0.4	15.2
Boise, Idaho	0.2	0.2	0.4	0.8	1.2	1.3	11.4
Brownsville, Tex.	1.7	2.8	5.0	3.5	1.3	1.7	26.9
Buffalo, N.Y.	2.6	3.1	3.1	3.0	3.6	3.0	35.6
Cheyenne, Wyo.	1.8	1.4	1.1	0.8	0.6	0.5	15.0
Chicago, Ill.	3.4	3.2	2.7	2.8	2.2	1.9	33.2
Des Moines, Iowa	3.1	3.7	2.9	2.1	1.8	1.1	30.5
Dodge City, Kans.	2.3	2.4	1.5	1.4	0.6	0.5	19.2
El Paso, Tex.	1.3	1.2	1.1	0.9	0.3	0.5	8.0
Indianapolis, Ind.	3.5	3.0	3.2	2.6	3.1	2.7	39.2
Jacksonville, Fla.	7.7	6.9	7.6	5.2	1.7	2.2	53.6
Kansas City, Mo.	3.2	3.8	3.3	2.9	1.8	1.5	34.2
Las Vegas, Nev.	0.5	0.5	0.3	0.2	0.3	0.4	3.8
Los Angeles, Calif.	*	*	0.2	0.4	1.1	2.4	12.8
Louisville, Ky.	3.4	3 0	2.6	2.3	3.2	3.2	41.4
Miami, Fla.	6.8	7.0	9.5	8.2	2.8	1.7	59.9
Minneapolis, Minn.	3.3	3.2	2.4	1.6	1.4	0.9	24.9
Missoula, Mont.	0.9	0.7	1.0	1.0	0.9	1.1	12.9
Nasheville, Tenn.	3.7	2.9	2.9	2.3	3.3	4.2	45.2
New Orleans, La.	6.7	5.3	5.0	2.8	3.3	4.1	53.7
New York, N.Y.	3.7	4.4	3.9	3.1	3.4	3.3	42.3
Oklahoma City, Okla.	2.4	2.5	3.0	2.5	1.6	1.4	30.9
Phoenix, Ariz.	0.8	1.1	0.7	0.5	0.5	0.9	7.3
Pittsburgh, Pa.	3.6	3.5	2.7	2.5	2.3	2.5	36.9
Portland, Maine	2.9	2.4	3.5	3.2	4.2	3.9	42.9
Portland, Oreg.	0.4	0.7	1.6	3.6	5.3	6.4	37.2
Reno, Nev.	0.3	0.2	0.2	0.5	0.6	1.1	7.2
Salt Lake City, Utah	0.6	0.9	0.5	1.2	1.3	1.2	14.1
San Francisco, Calif.	*	*	0.2	0.7	1.6	4.1	18.7
Sault Ste. Marie, Mich.	2.5	2.9	3.8	2.8	3.3	2.3	31.3
Seattle, Wash.	0.8	1.0	2.1	4.0	5.4	6.3	39.0
Sheridan, Wyo.	1.2	0.9	1.2	1.1	0.8	0.6	15.9
Spokane, Wash.	0.4	0.4	0.8	1.6	2.2	2.4	17.2
Washington, D.C.	4.2	4.9	3.8	3.1	2.8	2.8	40.8
Wilmington, N.C.	7.7	6.9	6.3	3.0	3.1	3.4	51.4

(See footnotes at end of tables)

COUNTRY AND STATION	LATITUDE	LONGITUDE	ELE-VATION	TEMPERATURE: LENGTH OF RECORD	AVERAGE DAILY: JANUARY MAXIMUM	JANUARY MINIMUM	APRIL MAXIMUM	APRIL MINIMUM	JULY MAXIMUM	JULY MINIMUM	OCTOBER MAXIMUM	OCTOBER MINIMUM	EXTREME: MAXIMUM	EXTREME: MINIMUM	AVERAGE PRECIPITATION: LENGTH OF RECORD	JANUARY	FEBRUARY	MARCH	APRIL	MAY	JUNE	JULY	AUGUST	SEPTEMBER	OCTOBER	NOVEMBER	DECEMBER	YEAR
	° ′	° ′	FEET	YEAR	°F	°F	°F	°F	°F	°F	°F	°F	°F	°F	YEAR	IN.	IN.	IN.	IN.	IN.	IN.	IN.	IN.	IN.	IN.	IN.	IN.	IN.
United States, Alaska:																												
Anchorage	61 13N	149 52W	85	30	21	4	44	28	65	50	42	28	86	-38	30	0.8	0.7	0.5	0.4	0.5	1.0	1.9	2.6	2.5	1.9	1.0	0.9	14.7
Annette	55 02N	131 34W	110	30	38	30	50	37	63	51	51	42	90	-4	30	11.4	8.5	9.6	9.1	7.1	5.7	6.0	7.5	9.9	16.9	14.7	12.1	118.5
Barrow	71 18N	156 47W	31	30	-9	-23	7	-7	45	33	21	12	78	-56	30	0.2	0.2	0.1	0.1	0.1	0.4	0.8	0.9	0.6	0.5	0.2	0.2	4.3
Bethel	60 47N	161 48W	125	30	11	-4	34	18	62	48	38	25	90	-52	30	1.1	1.1	1.0	0.6	1.0	1.2	2.0	4.2	2.6	1.5	1.1	1.0	18.4
Cold Bay	55 12N	162 43W	96	30	33	23	38	28	54	45	45	36	78	-9	30	2.3	3.2	1.8	1.5	2.3	2.0	1.8	4.3	4.3	4.6	3.8	2.6	34.5
Fairbanks	64 49N	147 52W	436	30	-1	-21	42	17	72	48	35	17	99	-66	30	0.9	0.5	0.4	0.3	0.7	1.4	1.8	2.2	1.1	0.9	0.6	0.5	11.3
Juneau	58 22N	134 35W	12	30	30	20	45	31	63	48	47	37	89	-21	30	4.0	3.1	3.3	2.9	3.2	3.4	4.5	5.0	6.7	8.3	6.1	4.2	54.7
King Salmon	58 41N	156 39W	49	30	21	6	41	25	63	47	43	29	88	-40	30	1.1	1.0	1.0	0.6	1.0	1.4	2.1	3.4	3.1	2.2	1.5	1.0	19.4
Nome	64 30N	165 26W	13	30	12	-3	28	14	55	44	35	24	84	-47	30	1.0	0.9	0.9	0.8	0.7	0.9	2.3	3.8	2.7	1.7	1.2	1.0	17.9
St. Paul Island	57 09N	170 13W	22	30	30	21	33	24	49	42	41	33	64	-26	30	1.8	1.2	1.1	1.0	1.3	1.2	2.3	3.3	3.1	3.2	2.5	1.8	23.8
Shemya	52 43N	174 06E	122	30	34	29	38	33	49	44	42	38	63	16	30	2.5	2.3	2.6	2.1	2.4	1.3	2.2	2.1	2.3	2.8	2.7	2.1	27.4
Yakutat	59 31N	139 40W	28	30	34	20	45	29	61	48	49	35	86	-24	30	10.9	8.2	8.7	7.2	8.0	5.1	8.4	10.9	16.6	19.6	16.1	12.3	132.0
Canada:																												
Aklavik, N.W.T.	68 14N	135 00W	30	22	-10	-26	19	-2	66	47	25	15	93	-62	22	0.5	0.5	0.4	0.5	0.5	0.8	1.4	1.4	0.9	0.9	0.8	0.4	9.0
Alert, N.W.T.	82 31N	62 20W	95	9	-19	-29	-8	-18	44	36	2	-7	67	-53	10	0.2	0.3	0.3	0.3	0.5	0.6	0.5	1.1	1.0	0.9	0.2	0.4	6.3
Calgary, Alta.	51 06N	114 01W	3,540	55	24	2	53	27	76	47	54	29	97	-49	55	0.5	0.5	0.8	1.0	2.3	3.1	2.5	2.3	1.5	0.7	0.7	0.6	16.7
Charlottetown, P.E.I.	46 17N	63 08W	181	65	26	10	43	30	73	58	54	41	98	-27	65	3.8	3.0	3.2	2.8	2.7	2.6	3.0	3.4	3.4	4.1	3.8	4.0	39.8
Chatham, N.B.	47 00N	65 27W	109	50	23	2	47	28	77	56	55	37	102	-43	50	3.4	2.7	3.3	3.0	3.2	3.6	3.9	4.0	3.1	4.0	3.4	3.2	40.8
Churchhill, Man.	58 45N	94 04W	94	30	-11	-27	24	4	64	43	34	20	96	-57	30	0.5	0.6	0.9	0.9	0.9	1.9	2.2	2.7	2.3	1.4	1.0	0.7	16.0
Edmonton, Alta.	53 34N	113 31W	2,219	71	16	-3	52	28	74	50	51	30	99	-57	71	0.9	0.7	0.7	1.0	1.9	3.2	3.3	2.4	1.3	0.8	0.9	0.9	18.0
Fort Nelson, B.C.	58 50N	122 35W	1,253	12	1	-15	47	25	74	51	43	25	98	-61	13	0.9	1.2	0.7	0.8	1.4	2.5	2.4	1.5	1.3	1.0	1.4	1.2	16.3
Fort Simpson, N.W.T.	61 45N	121 14W	554	42	-10	-27	38	14	74	50	36	21	97	-70	42	0.7	0.7	0.5	0.7	1.4	1.5	2.0	1.5	1.3	1.1	0.9	0.8	13.1
Frobisher Bay, N.W.T.	63 45N	68 33W	110	18	-9	-23	16	-1	53	39	29	18	76	-49	10	0.7	0.9	0.8	0.8	0.7	0.9	1.5	2.0	1.8	1.1	1.1	1.0	13.3
Gander, Nfld.	48 57N	54 34W	496	14	27	13	40	27	71	52	51	37	96	-17	14	2.6	3.3	2.8	2.6	2.6	2.8	3.6	3.6	3.7	4.1	4.2	3.7	39.6
Halifax, N.S.	44 39N	63 34W	83	75	32	15	47	31	74	55	57	41	99	-21	71	5.4	4.4	4.9	4.5	4.1	4.0	3.8	4.4	4.1	5.4	5.3	5.4	55.7
Kapuskasing, Ont.	49 25N	82 28W	743	19	10	-14	43	19	75	50	47	31	101	-53	19	2.0	1.1	1.6	1.8	2.1	2.3	3.4	2.9	3.5	2.5	2.4	1.9	27.5
Knob Lake, Que.	54 48N	66 49W	1,712	30	-3	-21	30	12	64	46	37	25	88	-59	10	1.9	1.9	1.4	1.6	1.7	3.3	3.3	4.4	3.4	2.9	2.4	1.5	29.7
Montreal, Que.	45 30N	73 34W	187	67	21	6	50	33	78	61	54	40	97	-35	77	3.8	3.0	3.5	2.6	3.1	3.4	3.7	3.5	3.7	3.4	3.5	3.6	40.8
North Bay, Ont.	46 21N	79 25W	1,216	17	22	2	48	28	78	56	49	36	99	-46	23	2.0	1.5	1.8	2.2	2.5	3.2	3.2	2.7	3.7	3.2	2.7	2.1	30.8
Ottowa, Ont.	45 19N	75 40W	374	65	21	3	51	31	81	58	54	37	102	-38	65	2.9	2.2	2.8	2.7	2.5	3.5	3.4	2.6	3.2	2.9	3.0	2.6	34.3
Penticton, B.C.	49 28N	119 36W	1,129	32	32	21	61	35	84	53	59	38	105	-16	32	1.0	0.7	0.7	0.7	1.1	1.2	0.8	0.8	1.0	0.8	0.9	1.1	10.8
Port Arthur, Ont.	48 22N	89 19W	644	62	17	-4	44	26	74	52	50	34	104	-42	59	0.9	0.8	1.0	1.5	2.1	2.8	3.6	2.8	3.4	2.5	1.5	0.9	23.8
Prince George, B.C.	53 53N	122 41W	2,218	27	23	3	54	27	75	44	52	30	102	-58	27	1.8	1.2	1.4	0.8	1.3	2.1	1.6	1.9	2.0	2.0	1.9	1.9	19.9
Prince Rupert, B.C.	54 17N	130 23W	170	26	39	30	50	37	62	49	53	42	90	-3	26	9.8	7.6	8.4	6.7	5.3	4.1	4.8	5.1	7.7	12.2	12.3	11.3	95.3
Quebec, Que.	46 48N	71 23W	239	72	18	2	44	29	76	57	51	37	97	-34	72	3.5	2.7	3.0	2.4	3.1	3.7	4.0	4.0	3.6	3.4	3.2	3.2	39.8
Regina, Sask.	50 26N	104 40W	1,884	55	10	-11	50	26	79	51	52	27	110	-56	49	0.5	0.3	0.7	0.7	1.8	3.3	2.4	1.8	1.3	0.9	0.6	0.4	14.7
Resolute, N.W.T.	74 43N	94 59W	220	13	-20	-33	-1	-16	45	35	11	0	61	-61	7	0.1	0.1	0.2	0.2	0.5	0.8	0.9	1.1	0.8	0.5	0.2	0.1	5.5
St. John, N.B.	45 17N	66 04W	119	61	28	11	43	32	69	54	54	41	93	-24	61	4.1	3.1	3.7	3.2	3.1	3.2	3.1	3.6	3.7	4.1	3.9	3.8	42.6
St. Johns, Nfld.	47 32N	52 44W	211	68	30	18	41	29	69	51	53	40	93	-21	58	5.3	5.1	4.6	3.8	3.9	3.1	3.1	4.0	3.7	4.8	5.7	6.0	53.1
Saskatoon, Sask.	52 08N	106 38W	1,690	38	9	-11	49	26	77	52	51	27	104	-55	38	0.9	0.5	0.7	0.7	1.4	2.6	2.4	1.9	1.5	0.9	0.5	0.6	14.6

COUNTRY AND STATION	LATITUDE	LONGITUDE	ELEVATION	TEMPERATURE: LENGTH OF RECORD	AVERAGE DAILY: JANUARY MAXIMUM	JANUARY MINIMUM	APRIL MAXIMUM	APRIL MINIMUM	JULY MAXIMUM	JULY MINIMUM	OCTOBER MAXIMUM	OCTOBER MINIMUM	EXTREME: MAXIMUM	EXTREME: MINIMUM	AVERAGE PRECIPITATION: LENGTH OF RECORD	JANUARY	FEBRUARY	MARCH	APRIL	MAY	JUNE	JULY	AUGUST	SEPTEMBER	OCTOBER	NOVEMBER	DECEMBER	YEAR
	° ′	° ′	FEET	YEAR	°F	°F	°F	°F	°F	°F	°F	°F	°F	°F	YEAR	IN.	IN.	IN.	IN.	IN.	IN.	IN.	IN.	IN.	IN.	IN.	IN.	IN.
The Pas, Man.	53 49N	101 15W	890	27	1	-18	45	21	75	54	45	26	100	-54	27	0.6	0.5	0.7	0.8	1.4	2.2	2.2	2.1	2.0	1.2	1.0	0.8	15.5
Toronto, Ont.	43 40N	79 24W	379	105	30	16	50	34	79	59	56	40	105	-26	105	2.7	2.4	2.6	2.5	2.9	2.7	3.0	2.7	2.9	2.4	2.8	2.6	32.2
Vancouver, B.C.	49 17N	123 05W	127	43	41	32	58	40	74	54	57	44	92	2	41	8.6	5.8	5.0	3.3	2.8	2.5	1.2	1.7	3.6	5.8	8.3	8 8	57.4
Whitehorse, Y.T.	60 43N	135 04W	2,303	10	13	- 3	41	22	67	45	41	28	91	-62	10	0.6	0.5	0.6	0.4	0.6	1.0	1.6	1.5	1.3	0.7	1.0	0.8	10.6
Winnipeg, Man.	49 54N	97 14W	783	66	7	-13	48	27	79	55	51	31	108	-54	66	0.9	0.9	1.2	1.4	2.3	3.1	3.1	2.5	2.3	1.5	1.1	0.9	21.2
Yellow Knife, N.W.T.	62 28N	114 27W	674	13	- 8	-23	29	9	69	52	36	26	90	-60	13	0.8	0.6	0.7	0.4	0.7	0.6	1.5	1.4	1.0	1.3	1.0	0.8	10.8
Greenland:																												
Angmagssalik	65 36N	37 33W	95	30	23	10	35	16	54	37	35	25	77	-26	38	2.9	2.4	2.6	2.1	2.0	1.8	1.5	2.1	3.3	4.7	3.0	2.7	31.1
Danmarkshaven	76 46N	19 00W	7	2	- 1	-15	6	-13	47	34	13	2	63	-42	2	1.2	0.7	0.7	0.1	0.2	0.2	0.5	0.6	0.3	0.3	1.0	0.7	6.0
Eismitte	70 53N	40 42W	9,843	1	-33	-53	-14	-37	19	1	-23	-42	27	-85	1	0.6	0.2	0.3	0.2	0.1	0.1	0.1	0.4	0.3	0.5	0.5	1.0	4.3
Godthaab	64 10N	51 43W	66	40	19	10	31	20	52	38	35	26	76	-20	45	1.4	1.7	1.6	1.2	1.7	1.4	2.2	3.1	3.3	2.5	1.9	1.5	23.5
Ivigtut	61 12N	48 10W	98	48	24	12	38	24	57	42	40	29	86	-20	50	3.3	2.6	3.4	2.5	3.5	3.2	3.1	3.7	5.9	5.7	4.6	3.1	44.6
Jacobshavn	69 13N	51 02W	104	32	8	- 7	24	6	51	40	31	20	71	-46	52	0.4	0.4	0.5	0.5	0.6	0.8	1.2	1.4	1.3	0.9	0.7	0.5	9.2
Nord	81 36N	16 40W	118	8	-15	-28	- 5	-18	44	35	3	- 6	61	-60	8	0.8	0.8	0.5	0.3	0.1	0.3	1.0	1.4	1.2	0.6	1.4	0.5	8.9
Scoresbysund	70 29N	21 58W	56	12	12	- 3	22	6	49	36	25	15	63	-42	12	1.8	1.4	0.9	1.4	0.4	0.8	1.5	0.7	1.7	1.4	1.1	1.9	15.0
Thule	76 31N	68 44W	251	12	- 4	-17	10	- 7	46	38	19	8	63	-44	12	0.4	0.3	0.2	0.2	0.3	0.2	0.7	0.6	0.6	0.7	0.5	0.2	4.9
Upernivik	72 47N	56 07W	59	40	- 1	-13	15	- 1	48	35	29	21	69	-44	50	0.4	0.5	0.7	0.6	0.6	0.5	0.9	1.1	1.1	1.1	1.1	0.6	9.2
Mexico:																												
Acapulco	16 50N	99 56W	10	8	85	70	87	71	89	75	88	74	97	60	40	0.3	*	0.0	*	1.4	12.8	9.1	9.3	13.9	6.7	1.2	0.4	55.1
Chihuahua	28 42N	105 57W	4,429	9	65	36	81	51	89	66	79	51	102	12	22	0.2	0.4	0.3	0.2	0.2	1.7	3.6	3.7	3.3	0.9	0.5	0.4	15.4
Guadalajara	20 41N	103 20W	5,194	26	73	45	85	53	79	60	78	56	101	26	33	0.4	0.2	0.2	0.2	1.1	8.8	9.4	8.5	7.2	2.2	0.8	0.7	39.7
Guaymas	27 57N	110 55W	58	9	74	57	84	65	96	82	91	75	117	41	41	0.5	0.2	0.2	0.1	*	0.1	1.7	2.7	2.1	0.7	0.3	0.8	9.4
La Paz	24 07N	110 17W	85	9	74	54	86	58	96	73	90	68	108	31	12	0.2	0.1	0.0	0.0	0.0	0.2	0.4	1.2	1.4	0.6	0.5	1.1	5.7
Lerdo	25 30N	103 32W	3,740	10	72	45	86	57	90	68	82	58	105	23	14	0.4	0.1	0.2	0.3	0.8	1.5	1.5	1.3	2.0	0.8	0.8	0.5	10.2
Manzanillo	19 04N	104 20W	26	17	86	68	87	67	93	76	91	76	103	54	17	0.1	0.2	*	0.0	0.1	4.7	5.7	6.4	14.5	5.1	0.9	1.8	39.5
Mazatlan	23 11N	106 25W	256	10	71	61	76	65	86	77	85	76	93	52	46	0.8	0.5	0.2	0.1	0.1	1.5	5.9	8.3	8.0	2.6	0.9	1.3	30.2
Merida	20 58N	89 38W	72	22	83	62	92	69	92	73	87	71	106	51	40	1.2	0.9	0.7	0.8	3.2	5.6	5.2	5.6	6.8	3.8	1.3	1.3	36.5
Mexico City	19 26N	99 04W	7,340	42	66	42	78	52	74	54	70	50	92	24	48	0.2	0.3	0.5	0.7	1.9	4.1	4.5	4.3	4.1	1.6	0.5	0.3	23.0
Monterrey	25 40N	100 18W	1,732	11	68	48	84	62	90	71	80	64	107	25	33	0.6	0.7	0.8	1.3	1.3	3.0	2.3	2.4	5.2	3.0	1.5	0.8	22.9
Salina Cruz	16 12N	95 12W	184	10	85	72	88	76	89	76	87	75	98	62	22	*	0.4	0.6	0.5	3.3	11.6	4.5	5.5	7.1	4.0	0.9	0.1	38.5
Tampico	22 16N	97 51W	78	12	75	59	83	69	89	75	85	71	104	34	12	1.5	1.2	1.0	1.5	1.9	8.7	4.9	4.8	10.8	5.0	2.0	1.6	44.9
Vera Cruz	19 12N	96 08W	52	10	77	66	83	72	87	74	85	73	98	53	40	0.9	0.6	0.6	0.8	2.6	10.4	4.1	11.1	13.9	6.9	3.0	1.0	65.7
CENTRAL AMERICA																												
British Honduras:																												
Belize	17 31N	88 11W	17	27	81	67	86	74	87	75	86	72	97	49	33	5.4	2.4	1.5	2.2	4.3	7.7	6.4	6.7	9.6	12.0	8.9	7.3	74.4
Canal Zone:																												
Balboa Heights	08 57N	79 33W	118	34	88	71	90	74	87	74	85	73	97	63	46	1.0	0.4	0.7	2.9	8.0	8.4	7.1	7.9	8.2	10.1	10.2	4.8	69.7
Cristobal	09 21N	79 54W	35	36	84	76	86	77	85	76	86	75	97	66	73	3.4	1.5	1.5	4.1	12.5	13.9	15.6	15.3	12.7	15.8	22.3	11.7	130.3
Costa Rica:																												
San Jose	09 56N	84 08W	3,760	8	75	58	79	62	77	62	77	60	92	49	34	0.6	0.2	0.8	1.8	9.0	9.5	8.3	9.5	12.0	11.8	5.7	1.6	70.8

(See footnotes at end of tables)

COUNTRY AND STATION	LATITUDE	LONGITUDE	ELEVATION	TEMPERATURE: LENGTH OF RECORD	AVERAGE DAILY: JANUARY MAXIMUM	JANUARY MINIMUM	APRIL MAXIMUM	APRIL MINIMUM	JULY MAXIMUM	JULY MINIMUM	OCTOBER MAXIMUM	OCTOBER MINIMUM	EXTREME: MAXIMUM	EXTREME: MINIMUM	AVERAGE PRECIPITATION: LENGTH OF RECORD	JANUARY	FEBRUARY	MARCH	APRIL	MAY	JUNE	JULY	AUGUST	SEPTEMBER	OCTOBER	NOVEMBER	DECEMBER	YEAR
	° ′	° ′	FEET	YEAR	°F	°F	°F	°F	°F	°F	°F	°F	°F	°F	YEAR	IN.	IN.	IN.	IN.	IN.	IN.	IN.	IN.	IN.	IN.	IN.	IN.	IN.
El Salvador:																												
San Salvador	13 42N	89 13W	2,238	39	90	60	93	65	89	65	87	65	105	45	39	0.3	0.2	0.4	1.7	7.7	12.9	11.5	11.7	12.1	9.5	1.6	0.4	70.0
Guatemala:																												
Guatemala City	14 37N	90 31W	4,855	6	73	53	82	58	78	60	76	60	90	41	29	0.3	0.1	0.5	1.2	6.0	10.8	8.0	7.8	9.1	6.8	0.9	0.3	51.8
Honduras:																												
Tela	15 46N	87 27W	41	4	82	67	87	72	88	73	86	71	96	58	20	8.9	5.1	2.6	3.3	4.3	5.0	6.4	9.4	7.7	13.5	15.9	14.0	96.1
WEST INDIES																												
Bridgetown, Barbados	13 08N	59 36W	181	35	83	70	86	72	86	74	86	73	95	61	22	2.6	1.1	1.3	1.4	2.3	4.4	5.8	5.8	6.7	7.0	8.1	3.8	50.3
Camp Jacob, Guadaloupe	16 01N	61 42W	1,750	19	77	64	79	65	81	68	81	68	92	54	21	9.2	6.1	8.1	7.3	11.5	14.1	17.6	15.3	16.4	12.4	12.3	10.1	140.4
Ciudad Trujillo, Dominican Rep.	18 29N	69 54W	57	26	84	66	85	69	88	72	87	72	98	59	25	2.4	1.4	1.9	3.9	6.8	6.2	6.4	6.3	7.3	6.0	4.8	2.4	55.8
Fort-de-France, Martinique	14 37N	61 05W	13	22	83	69	86	71	86	74	87	73	96	56	31	4.7	4.3	2.9	3.9	4.7	7.4	9.4	10.3	9.3	9.7	7.9	5.9	80.4
Hamilton, Bermuda	32 17N	64 46W	151	59	68	58	71	59	85	73	79	69	99	40	62	4.4	4.7	4.8	4.1	4.6	4.4	4.5	5.4	5.2	5.8	5.0	4.7	57.6
Havana, Cuba	23 08N	82 21W	80	25	79	65	84	69	89	75	85	73	104	43	72	2.8	1.8	1.8	2.3	4.7	6.5	4.9	5.3	5.9	6.8	3.1	2.3	48.2
Kingston, Jamaica	17 58N	76 48W	110	33	86	67	87	70	90	73	88	73	97	56	59	0.9	0.6	0.9	1.2	4.0	3.5	1.5	3.6	3.9	7.1	2.9	1.4	31.5
La Guerite, St. Christopher (St. Kitts)	17 20N	62 45W	157	19	80	71	83	73	86	76	85	75	91	61	21	4.1	2.0	2.3	2.3	3.8	3.6	4.4	5.2	6.0	5.4	7.3	4.5	50.9
Nassau, Bahamas	25 05N	77 21W	12	35	77	65	81	69	88	75	85	73	94	41	57	1.4	1.5	1.4	2.5	4.6	6.4	5.8	5.3	6.9	6.5	2.8	1.3	46.4
Port-au-Prince, Haiti	18 33N	72 20W	121	42	87	68	89	71	94	74	90	72	101	58	70	1.3	2.3	3.4	6.3	9.1	4.0	2.9	5.7	6.9	6.7	3.4	1.3	53.3
Saint Clair, Trinidad	10 40N	61 31W	67	49	87	69	90	69	88	71	89	71	101	52	97	2.7	1.6	1.8	2.1	3.7	7.6	8.6	9.7	7.6	6.7	7.2	4.9	64.2
Saint Thomas, Virgin Is.	18 20N	64 58W	11	9	82	71	85	74	88	77	87	76	92	63	9	2.5	1.9	1.7	2.2	4.6	3.2	3.2	4.1	6.9	5.6	3.9	3.9	43.7
San Juan, Puerto Rico	18 26N	66 00W	13	30	81	67	84	69	87	74	87	73	94	60	30	4.7	2.9	2.2	3.7	7.1	5.7	6.3	7.1	6.8	5.8	6.5	5.4	64.2
SOUTH AMERICA																												
Argentina:																												
Bahia Blanca	38 43S	62 16W	95	33	88	62	71	51	57	39	71	48	109	18	46	1.7	2.2	2.5	2.3	1.2	0.9	1.0	1.0	1.6	2.2	2.1	1.9	20.6
Buenos Aires	34 35S	58 29W	89	23	85	63	72	53	57	42	69	50	104	22	70	3.1	2.8	4.3	3.5	3.0	2.4	2.2	2.4	3.1	3.4	3.3	3.9	37.4
Cipolletti	38 57S	67 59W	889	9	89	56	72	40	55	29	72	43	107	9	24	0.4	0.4	0.7	0.4	0.6	0.6	0.5	0.3	0.6	0.9	0.5	0.5	6.4
Corrientes	27 28S	58 50W	177	39	93	71	81	63	71	53	82	60	112	30	40	4.7	4.5	5.3	5.6	3.3	1.9	1.7	1.5	2.8	4.7	5.2	5.2	46.4
La Quiaca	22 06S	65 36W	11,345	23	70	41	69	32	60	16	71	32	95	0	25	3.5	2.6	1.8	0.3	*	0.0	*	*	0.1	0.3	1.0	2.7	12.3
Mendoza	32 53S	68 49W	2,625	23	90	60	73	47	59	35	76	50	109	15	46	0.9	1.2	1.1	0.5	0.4	0.3	0.2	0.3	0.5	0.7	0.7	0.7	7.5
Parana	31 44S	60 31W	210	12	91	67	77	58	62	45	75	54	113	21	23	3.1	3.1	3.9	4.9	2.6	1.2	1.2	1.6	2.4	2.8	3.7	4.5	35.0
Puerto Madryn	42 47S	65 01W	26	50	81	57	70	46	55	36	68	45	104	10	50	0.4	0.6	0.7	0.5	0.9	0.6	0.6	0.4	0.6	0.7	0.4	0.6	7.0
Santa Cruz	50 01S	68 32W	39	12	70	48	57	39	41	28	58	39	94	1	20	0.6	0.3	0.3	0.6	0.4	0.5	0.4	0.5	0.3	0.3	0.4	0.7	5.3
Santiago del Estero	27 46S	64 18W	653	28	97	69	82	59	70	44	87	59	116	19	20	3.4	3.0	3.0	1.3	0.6	0.3	0.2	0.2	0.5	1.4	2.5	4.1	20.4
Ushuaia	54 50S	68 20W	26	16	57	41	48	33	39	25	52	35	85	- 6	21	2.0	2.6	1.9	2.1	1.5	1.2	1.2	1.1	1.3	1.6	1.5	1.9	19.9
Bolivia:																												
Concepcion	16 15S	62 03W	1,607	5	85	66	86	62	81	54	88	62	101	32	16	7.2	4.7	4.4	1.8	2.0	1.5	1.1	0.9	1.2	2.9	5.0	5.9	38.6
La Paz	16 30S	68 08W	12,001	31	63	43	65	40	62	33	66	40	80	26	50	4.5	4.2	2.6	1.3	0.5	0.3	0.4	0.5	1.1	1.6	1.9	3.7	22.6
Sucre	19 03S	65 17W	9,344	5	63	48	63	45	61	37	65	46	88	25	52	7.3	4.9	3.7	1.6	0.2	0.1	0.2	0.3	1.0	1.6	2.6	4.3	27.8
Brazil:																												
Barra do Corda	05 35S	45 28W	266	9	89	71	89	71	92	64	94	72	103	45	9	6.7	8.7	8.0	6.1	2.3	1.0	0.7	0.7	1.0	2.5	3.9	5.7	47.2

COUNTRY AND STATION	LATITUDE	LONGITUDE	ELEVATION	TEMPERATURE: LENGTH OF RECORD	AVERAGE DAILY JANUARY MAXIMUM	JANUARY MINIMUM	APRIL MAXIMUM	APRIL MINIMUM	JULY MAXIMUM	JULY MINIMUM	OCTOBER MAXIMUM	OCTOBER MINIMUM	EXTREME MAXIMUM	EXTREME MINIMUM	AVERAGE PRECIPITATION: LENGTH OF RECORD	JANUARY	FEBRUARY	MARCH	APRIL	MAY	JUNE	JULY	AUGUST	SEPTEMBER	OCTOBER	NOVEMBER	DECEMBER	YEAR
	° ′	° ′	FEET	YEAR	°F	°F	°F	°F	°F	°F	°F	°F	°F	°F	YEAR	IN.	IN.	IN.	IN.	IN.	IN.	IN.	IN.	IN.	IN.	IN.	IN.	IN.
Bela Vista	22 06S	56 22W	525	13	91	67	85	61	77	49	87	61	108	20	20	6.6	4.9	4.4	4.3	5.0	2.8	1.3	1.8	2.9	5.4	5.8	7.0	52.2
Belem	01 27S	48 29W	42	16	87	72	87	73	88	71	89	71	98	61	20	12.5	14.1	14.1	12.6	10.2	6.7	5.9	4.4	3.5	3.3	2.6	6.1	96.0
Brasilia	15 51S	47 56W	3,481	3	80	65	82	62	78	51	82	64	93	46	3	9.0	7.8	4.8	3.4	1.4	*	0.0	*	1.3	4.9	9.7	11.7	54.0
Conceicao do Araguaia	08 15S	49 12W	53	5	88	70	91	68	95	63	93	68	102	55	5	14.9	12.1	10.8	4.1	1.9	0.4	*	0.5	1.5	6.6	4.9	8.6	66.2
Corumba	19 00S	57 39W	381	8	94	73	92	73	84	64	93	70	106	33	11	7.3	5.9	5.1	4.6	2.9	1.9	0.3	1.2	2.6	4.0	5.6	7.1	48.5
Florianopolis	27 35S	48 33W	96	17	83	72	74	64	68	57	73	63	102	32	25	7.6	5.6	6.3	4.1	3.6	3.5	2.2	3.7	4.3	5.1	3.5	4.3	53.1
Goias	15 58S	50 04W	1,706	11	86	63	91	63	89	56	94	63	104	41	11	12.5	9.9	10.2	4.6	0.4	0.3	0.0	0.3	2.3	5.3	9.4	9.5	64.8
Guarapuava	25 16S	51 30W	3,592	10	79	61	73	55	66	47	74	53	94	23	5	8.7	5.8	5.4	4.5	4.6	6.5	2.7	3.6	4.6	6.9	6.6	6.1	65.8
Manaus	03 08S	60 01W	144	11	88	75	87	75	89	75	92	76	101	63	25	9.8	9.1	10.3	8.7	6.7	3.3	2.3	1.5	1.8	4.2	5.6	8.0	71.3
Natal	05 46S	35 12W	52	18	87	76	86	73	82	69	85	75	100	61	18	1.9	4.8	7.0	9.2	7.1	8.7	7.7	3.8	1.4	0.8	0.7	1.1	54.2
Parana	12 26S	48 06W	853	19	90	58	90	58	91	48	94	58	105	37	19	11.3	9.3	9.4	4.0	0.5	*	0.1	0.2	1.1	5.0	9.1	12.2	62.3
Porto Alegre	30 02S	51 13W	33	22	87	67	78	60	66	49	74	57	105	25	22	3.5	3.2	3.9	4.1	4.5	5.1	4.5	5.0	5.2	3.4	3.1	3.5	49.1
Quixeramobim	05 12S	39 18W	653	9	92	79	86	76	88	74	93	77	100	63	13	0.7	5.0	6.6	5.0	7.0	1.7	0.7	0.6	0.4	0.6	0.7	0.6	29.6
Recife	08 04S	34 53W	97	27	86	77	85	75	80	71	84	75	94	50	56	2.1	3.3	6.3	8.7	10.5	10.9	10.0	6.0	2.5	1.0	1.0	1.1	63.4
Rio de Janeiro	22 55S	43 12W	201	38	84	73	80	69	75	63	77	66	102	46	84	4.9	4.8	5.1	4.2	3.1	2.1	1.6	1.7	2.6	3.1	4.1	5.4	42.6
Salvador (Bahia)	13 00S	38 30W	154	25	86	74	84	74	79	69	83	71	100	50	20	2.6	5.3	6.1	11.2	10.8	9.4	7.2	4.8	3.3	4.0	4.5	5.6	74.8
Santarem	02 30S	54 42W	66	22	86	73	85	73	87	71	91	73	99	65	22	6.8	10.9	13.2	12.9	11.3	6.9	4.1	1.7	1.5	1.9	2.3	4.1	77.9
Sao Paulo	23 37S	46 39W	2,628	44	77	63	73	59	66	53	68	57	100	32	24	8.8	7.8	6.0	2.2	3.0	2.4	1.5	2.1	3.5	4.6	6.0	9.4	57.3
Sena Madureira	09 04S	68 39W	443	12	92	69	91	68	91	63	93	69	100	41	17	11.2	11.3	10.2	9.4	4.1	2.2	1.1	1.5	4.0	7.0	7.5	11.7	81.2
Uaupes	00 08S	67 05W	272	15	88	72	88	72	85	70	89	71	100	52	10	10.3	7.7	10.0	10.6	12.0	9.2	8.8	7.2	5.1	6.9	7.2	10.4	105.4
Uruguaiana	29 46S	57 07W	246	15	91	69	78	59	66	48	77	55	108	27	12	3.6	3.6	5.6	5.1	3.7	4.2	3.2	2.8	3.6	4.1	2.9	4.1	46.6
Chile:																												
Ancud	41 47S	73 52W	184	30	62	51	57	47	50	42	55	45	82	30	46	3.1	3.7	5.3	7.4	9.9	11.0	10.3	9.4	6.5	4.2	4.7	4.6	80.1
Antofagasta	23 42S	70 24W	308	22	76	63	70	58	63	51	66	55	86	37	32	0.0	0.0	0.0	*	*	0.1	0.2	0.1	*	0.1	*	0.0	0.5
Arica	18 28S	70 20W	95	15	78	64	74	60	66	54	69	58	93	39	25	*	0.0	0.0	0.0	0.0	0.0	0.0	*	0.0	0.0	0.0	*	*
Cabo Raper	46 50S	75 38W	131	8	58	46	54	44	47	38	51	40	72	28	10	7.8	5.8	7.1	7.7	7.5	7.9	9.5	7.5	5.6	7.0	6.7	7.0	87.1
Los Evangelistas	52 23S	75 07W	190	16	50	44	48	41	43	36	45	39	66	19	27	11.7	10.0	11.3	11.4	9.6	9.4	9.4	8.6	9.2	8.8	9.9	10.1	119.4
Potrerillos	26 30S	69 27W	9,350	7	65	49	63	47	57	40	61	44	75	20	7	*	*	0.3	*	0.7	*	0.5	0.3	0.2	0.2	0.0	*	2.2
Puerto Aisen	42 24S	72 42W	33	8	63	50	55	43	45	37	55	42	93	18	11	7.8	7.8	8.3	7.5	14.7	10.4	11.1	11.1	6.5	7.8	7.0	7.9	107.9
Punta Arenas	53 10S	70 54W	26	15	58	45	50	39	40	31	51	38	86	11	15	1.5	0.9	1.3	1.4	1.3	1.6	1.1	1.2	0.9	1.1	0.7	1.4	14.4
Santiago	33 27S	70 42W	1,706	14	85	53	74	45	59	37	72	45	99	24	58	0.1	0.1	0.2	0.5	2.5	3.3	3.0	2.2	1.2	0.6	0.3	0.2	14.2
Valdivia	39 48S	73 14W	16	29	73	52	62	46	52	41	63	44	97	19	60	2.6	2.9	5.2	9.2	14.2	17.7	15.5	12.9	8.2	5.0	4.9	4.1	102.4
Valparaiso	33 01S	71 38W	135	30	72	56	67	52	60	47	65	50	94	32	41	0.1	*	0.3	0.6	4.1	5.9	3.9	2.9	1.3	0.4	0.2	0.2	19.9
Colombia:																												
Andagoya	05 06N	76 40W	197	8	90	75	90	75	89	74	90	74	97	62	15	25.0	21.4	19.5	26.1	25.5	25.8	23.3	25.3	24.6	22.7	22.4	19.5	281.1
Bogota	04 42N	74 08W	8,355	10	67	48	67	51	64	50	66	50	75	30	49	2.3	2.6	4.0	5.8	4.5	2.4	2.0	2.2	2.4	6.3	4.7	2.6	41.8
Cartagena	10 28N	75 30W	39	6	84	73	87	76	88	78	87	77	98	61	10	0.4	0.0	0.4	0.9	3.4	3.4	3.0	0.6	0.5	10.8	8.9	4.5	36.8
Ipiales	00 50N	77 42W	9,680	9	61	50	60	49	57	42	62	49	77	32	13	3.1	2.3	3.5	3.5	2.8	1.9	1.3	1.1	1.4	3.1	3.3	2.6	29.9
Tumaco	01 49N	78 45W	7	10	82	75	84	76	82	75	82	75	90	64	10	16.9	11.7	9.6	14.6	17.4	12.0	7.7	7.3	7.3	5.9	4.9	7.0	122.3
Ecuador:																												
Cuenca	02 53S	78 39W	8,301	7	69	50	69	50	65	47	70	49	81	29	10	2.0	1.8	3.2	4.3	4.3	1.7	0.9	1.1	1.6	3.1	1.8	2.5	28.3

(See footnotes at end of tables)

COUNTRY AND STATION	LATITUDE	LONGITUDE	ELEVATION	TEMPERATURE: LENGTH OF RECORD	AVERAGE DAILY: JANUARY MAXIMUM	JANUARY MINIMUM	APRIL MAXIMUM	APRIL MINIMUM	JULY MAXIMUM	JULY MINIMUM	OCTOBER MAXIMUM	OCTOBER MINIMUM	EXTREME: MAXIMUM	EXTREME: MINIMUM	AVERAGE PRECIPITATION: LENGTH OF RECORD	JANUARY	FEBRUARY	MARCH	APRIL	MAY	JUNE	JULY	AUGUST	SEPTEMBER	OCTOBER	NOVEMBER	DECEMBER	YEAR
	° ′	° ′	FEET	YEAR	°F	°F	°F	°F	°F	°F	°F	°F	°F	°F	YEAR	IN.	IN.	IN.	IN.	IN.	IN.	IN.	IN.	IN.	IN.	IN.	IN.	IN.
Guayaquil	02 10S	79 53W	20	5	87	72	88	72	84	67	86	68	98	52	10	8.3	11.4	11.5	8.1	2.1	0.4	0.2	*	*	*	0.1	1.1	43.2
Quito	00 08S	78 29W	9,222	54	67	46	69	47	71	44	71	46	86	25	33	3.9	4.4	5.6	6.9	5.4	1.7	0.8	1.2	2.7	4.4	3.8	3.1	43.9
French Guiana:																												
Cayenne	04 56N	52 27W	20	38	84	74	86	75	88	73	91	74	97	65	51	14.4	12.3	15.8	18.9	21.7	15.5	6.9	2.8	1.2	1.3	4.6	10.7	126.1
Guyana:																												
Georgetown	06 50N	58 12W	6	54	84	74	85	76	85	75	87	76	93	68	35	8.0	4.5	6.9	5.5	11.4	11.9	10.0	6.9	3.2	3.0	6.1	11.3	88.7
Lethem	03 24N	59 38W	270	3	91	73	91	74	87	73	92	76	97	63	9	1.2	1.4	1.3	5.7	11.5	11.9	14.8	9.4	3.4	2.3	4.3	1.3	68.5
Paraguay:																												
Asuncion	25 17S	57 30W	456	15	95	71	84	65	74	53	86	62	110	29	30	5.5	5.1	4.3	5.2	4.6	2.7	2.2	1.5	3.1	5.5	5.9	6.2	51.8
Bahia Negra	20 14S	58 10W	318	20	92	74	87	68	79	61	90	69	106	35	20	5.4	5.3	4.9	2.9	2.3	1.6	1.5	0.6	2.3	4.2	5.3	4.3	40.6
Peru:																												
Arequipa	16 21S	71 34W	8,460	13	67	49	67	48	67	47	68	47	82	25	37	1.3	1.8	0.7	0.2	*	*	*	*	0.0	*	*	0.4	4.4
Cajamarca	07 09S	78 30W	8,662	9	71	48	70	47	70	41	71	47	79	25	9	3.6	4.2	4.6	3.4	1.7	9.5	9.2	9.3	2.3	2.3	1.9	3.2	28.2
Cusco	13 33S	71 59W	10,866	13	68	45	71	40	70	31	72	43	86	16	12	6.4	5.9	4.3	2.0	0.6	0.2	0.2	0.4	1.0	2.6	3.0	5.4	32.0
Iquitos	03 45S	73 13W	384	5	90	71	87	71	88	68	90	70	100	54	5	9.1	10.4	9.4	13.6	10.7	5.7	6.4	5.2	10.5	7.3	9.1	10.3	107.7
Lima	12 05S	77 03W	394	15	82	66	80	63	67	57	71	58	93	49	15	0.1	*	*	*	0.2	0.2	0.3	0.3	0.3	0.1	0.1	*	1.6
Mollendo	17 00S	72 07W	80	10	79	66	76	63	67	57	70	59	90	50	10	*	0.1	*	*	0.1	0.1	*	0.2	0.2	0.1	0.1	*	0.9
Surinam:																												
Paramaribo	05 49N	55 09W	12	35	85	72	86	73	87	73	91	73	99	62	75	8.4	6.5	7.9	9.0	12.2	11.9	9.1	6.2	3.1	3.0	4.9	8.8	91.0
Uruguay:																												
Artigas	30 24S	56 23W	384	13	91	65	77	55	65	45	75	54	107	24	50	4.3	3.9	4.7	5.1	4.1	4.1	2.8	3.0	4.0	4.7	3.8	4.1	48.6
Montevideo	34 52S	56 12W	72	56	83	62	71	53	58	43	68	49	109	25	56	2.9	2.6	3.9	3.9	3.3	3.2	2.9	3.1	3.0	2.6	2.9	3.1	37.4
Venezuela:																												
Caracas	10 30N	66 56W	3,418	30	75	56	81	60	78	61	79	61	91	45	46	0.9	0.4	0.6	1.3	3.1	4.0	4.3	4.3	4.2	4.3	3.7	1.8	32.9
Ciudad Bolivar	08 07N	63 32W	197	10	90	72	93	75	90	75	93	75	100	64	10	1.4	0.8	0.7	1.0	3.8	5.5	6.3	7.1	3.6	4.0	2.8	1.3	38.3
Maracaibo	10 39N	71 36W	20	12	90	73	92	76	94	76	92	76	102	66	36	0.1	*	0.3	0.8	2.7	2.2	1.8	2.2	2.8	5.9	3.3	0.6	22.7
Merida	08 36N	71 10W	5,293	14	73	56	75	60	76	59	75	60	90	48	14	2.5	1.5	3.6	6.7	9.8	7.3	4.7	5.7	6.7	9.5	8.2	3.4	69.7
Santa Elena	04 36N	61 07W	2,976	10	82	61	82	63	81	61	84	61	95	48	10	3.2	3.2	3.2	5.7	9.6	9.5	9.1	7.6	5.3	4.9	4.9	4.5	70.7
PACIFIC ISLANDS																												
Easter Is. (Isla de Pascua)	27 10S	109 26W	98	4	77	64	78	63	70	58	73	58	88	46	10	4.8	3.7	4.6	4.2	4.6	4.3	3.5	3.0	2.7	3.7	4.6	4.9	48.6
Mas a Tierra (Juan Fernandez)	33 37S	78 52W	20	25	72	60	68	57	60	50	61	51	86	39	29	0.8	1.2	1.6	3.4	5.9	6.4	5.8	4.4	2.9	1.9	1.6	1.0	36.9
Seymour Is. (Galapagos Is.)	00 28S	90 18W	36	3	86	72	87	75	81	69	81	67	93	58	3	0.8	1.4	1.1	0.7	*	*	*	*	*	*	*	*	4.0
ATLANTIC ISLANDS																												
Fernando de Noronha	03 50S	32 25W	148	32	84	75	82	75	81	73	82	75	93	63	32	1.7	4.7	7.4	10.5	10.5	7.3	5.4	1.9	0.7	0.3	0.4	0.5	51.3
Cumberland Bay, South Georgia	54 16S	36 30W	8	23	48	35	42	29	34	23	41	28	84	-3	24	3.3	4.3	5.3	5.4	5.2	4.9	5.5	5.3	3.5	2.6	3.4	3.0	51.7
Laurie Is., South Orkneys	60 44S	44 44W	13	48	35	29	31	21	20	4	30	19	54	-40	46	1.4	1.5	1.9	1.6	1.2	1.0	1.3	1.3	1.1	1.1	1.3	1.0	15.7
Stanley, Falkland Isles	51 42S	57 51W	6	25	56	42	49	37	40	31	48	35	76	12	41	2.8	2.3	2.5	2.6	2.6	2.1	2.0	2.0	1.5	1.6	2.0	2.8	26.8

See footnotes at end of table.

COUNTRY AND STATION	LATITUDE	LONGITUDE	ELEVATION	TEMPERATURE: LENGTH OF RECORD	AVERAGE DAILY: JANUARY MAXIMUM	JANUARY MINIMUM	APRIL MAXIMUM	APRIL MINIMUM	JULY MAXIMUM	JULY MINIMUM	OCTOBER MAXIMUM	OCTOBER MINIMUM	EXTREME: MAXIMUM	EXTREME: MINIMUM	AVERAGE PRECIPITATION: LENGTH OF RECORD	JANUARY	FEBRUARY	MARCH	APRIL	MAY	JUNE	JULY	AUGUST	SEPTEMBER	OCTOBER	NOVEMBER	DECEMBER	YEAR
			FEET	YEAR	°F	°F	°F	°F	°F	°F	°F	°F	°F	°F	YEAR	IN.	IN.	IN.	IN.	IN.	IN.	IN.	IN.	IN.	IN.	IN.	IN.	IN.
EUROPE																												
Albania:																												
Durres	41 19N	19 28E	23	10	51	42	63	55	83	74	68	58	95	21	10	3.0	3.3	3.9	2.2	1.6	1.9	0.5	1.9	1.7	7.1	8.5	7.3	42.9
Andorra:																												
Les Escaldes	42 30N	01 31E	3,543	5	43	29	59	39	78	55	61	42	91	0	9	1.5	1.7	2.9	2.4	4.7	3.1	2.2	3.4	3.1	3.5	3.3	2.5	34.3
Austria:																												
Innsbruck	47 16N	11 24E	1,909	34	34	20	60	39	78	55	58	40	97	-16	35	2.1	1.8	1.5	2.2	2.9	4.1	5.1	4.5	3.1	2.4	2.2	1.9	33.8
Vienna (Wien)	48 15N	16 22E	664	50	34	26	57	41	75	59	55	44	98	-14	100	1.5	1.4	1.8	2.0	2.8	2.7	3.0	2.7	2.0	2.0	1.9	1.8	25.6
Bulgaria:																												
Sofiya (Sofia)	42 42N	23 20E	1,805	30	34	22	62	41	82	57	63	42	99	-17	27	1.3	1.1	1.7	2.3	3.3	3.2	2.4	2.0	2.3	2.1	1.9	1.4	25.0
Varna	43 12N	27 55E	115	30	40	30	59	43	84	63	67	50	107	-12	20	1.5	0.9	1.2	1.2	1.8	2.6	1.9	1.2	1.5	1.9	1.9	2.0	19.6
Cyprus:																												
Nicosia	35 09N	33 17E	716	40	58	42	74	50	97	69	81	58	116	23	64	2.9	2.0	1.3	0.8	1.1	0.4	*	*	0.2	0.9	1.7	3.0	14.6
Czechoslovakia:																												
Praha (Prague)	50 05N	14 25E	662	40	34	25	55	40	74	58	54	44	98	-16	70	0.9	0.8	1.1	1.5	2.4	2.8	2.6	2.2	1.7	1.2	1.2	0.9	19.3
Prerov	49 27N	17 27E	702	20	34	25	57	38	77	55	56	40	100	-23	21	1.3	1.1	1.1	2.0	2.4	2.9	3.5	3.2	2.0	2.4	1.5	1.4	24.8
Denmark:																												
Copenhagen (Kobenhavn)	55 41N	12 33E	43	30	36	29	50	37	72	55	53	42	91	- 3	30	1.6	1.3	1.2	1.7	1.7	2.1	2.2	3.2	1.9	2.1	2.2	2.1	23.3
Aarhus	56 08N	10 12E	161	21	35	27	51	37	70	54	53	42	87	-12	21	2.3	1.5	1.4	1.8	1.2	2.2	2.5	3.3	3.2	2.6	2.5	2.1	26.6
Finland:																												
Helsinki	60 10N	24 57E	30	20	27	17	43	31	71	57	45	37	89	-23	50	2.2	1.7	1.7	1.7	1.9	2.0	2.3	3.3	2.8	2.9	2.7	2.4	27.6
Kuusamo	65 57N	29 12E	843	20	17	2	35	18	68	50	36	27	90	-40	20	1.1	1.1	1.1	1.1	1.4	2.3	2.8	3.0	2.1	2.1	1.6	1.1	20.8
Vaasa	63 05N	21 36E	13	18	26	16	41	28	69	55	44	36	89	-29	19	1.1	0.8	0.8	1.0	1.4	1.8	2.4	2.5	2.7	2.3	1.7	1.1	19.6
France:																												
Ajaccio (Corsica)	41 52N	08 35E	243	46	56	40	66	48	85	64	72	55	103	23	86	3.0	2.3	2.6	2.2	1.6	0.9	2.8	0.7	1.7	3.8	4.4	3.1	29.1
Bordeaux	44 50N	00 43W	157	51	48	35	63	44	80	58	66	47	102	9	47	2.7	2.8	2.9	2.6	2.5	2.3	2.0	1.9	2.2	3.0	3.9	3.9	32.7
Brest	48 19N	04 47W	56	56	49	40	57	44	70	56	61	49	95	7	56	3.5	3.0	2.5	2.5	1.9	2.0	2.0	2.2	2.3	3.6	4.2	4.4	34.1
Cherbourg	49 39N	01 38W	30	47	47	40	54	43	67	57	59	50	91	14	47	3.3	2.9	2.7	2.0	1.9	1.8	1.9	3.0	2.9	4.6	5.1	5.2	37.3
Lille	50 35N	03 05W	141	40	42	33	58	40	75	55	59	45	96	0	40	2.5	1.9	2.5	2.0	2.4	2.2	2.8	2.3	2.6	3.0	3.0	3.2	30.3
Lyon	45 42N	04 47E	938	70	41	30	61	42	80	58	61	45	105	-13	70	1.4	1.4	1.8	2.1	2.8	2.9	2.8	2.9	3.1	3.1	2.6	1.9	28.8
Marseille	43 18N	05 23E	246	72	53	38	59	41	78	58	76	57	101	9	102	1.9	1.5	1.8	2.0	1.9	1.0	0.6	0.9	2.6	3.7	3.1	2.2	23.2
Paris	48 49N	02 29E	164	66	42	32	60	41	76	55	59	44	105	1	118	1.5	1.3	1.5	1.7	2.0	2.1	2.1	2.0	2.0	2.2	2.0	1.9	22.3
Strasbourg	48 35N	07 46E	465	20	40	31	59	41	78	57	58	43	101	- 8	20	1.6	1.4	1.7	2.6	2.6	3.1	3.4	3.4	3.1	2.7	2.0	1.9	29.5
Toulouse	43 33N	01 23E	538	47	47	35	62	43	82	59	66	48	111	1	47	1.9	1.7	2.3	2.7	2.9	2.4	1.5	2.1	2.3	2.2	2.4	2.3	26.7
Germany:																												
Berlin	52 27N	13 18E	187	50	35	26	55	38	74	55	55	41	96	-15	40	1.9	1.3	1.5	1.7	1.9	2.3	3.1	2.2	1.9	1.7	1.7	1.9	23.1
Bremen	53 05N	08 47E	52	50	37	30	53	38	71	55	54	43	94	- 7	80	1.9	1.6	1.8	1.5	2.1	2.6	3.2	2.8	2.1	2.2	2.0	2.2	26.0
Frankfurt A/M	50 07N	08 40E	338	50	37	29	58	41	75	56	56	43	100	- 7	80	1.7	1.3	1.6	1.5	2.0	2.5	2.8	2.6	1.9	2.2	2.0	2.0	24.1
Hamburg	53 33N	09 58E	66	50	35	28	51	39	69	56	53	44	92	- 4	80	2.1	1.9	2.0	1.8	2.1	2.7	3.4	3.2	2.5	2.6	2.1	2.5	28.9
Munchen (Munich)	48 09N	11 34E	1,739	50	33	23	54	37	72	54	53	40	92	-14	80	1.7	1.4	1.9	2.7	3.7	4.6	4.7	4.2	3.2	2.2	1.9	1.9	34.1
Munster	51 58N	07 38E	207	50	39	29	56	38	73	54	56	42	96	-17	40	2.6	1.9	2.2	2.0	2.2	2.7	3.3	3.1	2.5	2.7	2.4	2.9	30.5
Nurnberg	49 27N	11 03E	1,050	50	35	26	56	38	74	55	55	41	99	-18	80	1.5	1.2	1.3	1.7	2.2	2.5	3.1	3.1	2.1	2.1	1.9	1.7	24.4

(See footnotes at end of tables)

COUNTRY AND STATION	LATITUDE	LONGITUDE	ELEVATION	TEMPERATURE: LENGTH OF RECORD	AVERAGE DAILY JANUARY MAXIMUM	JANUARY MINIMUM	APRIL MAXIMUM	APRIL MINIMUM	JULY MAXIMUM	JULY MINIMUM	OCTOBER MAXIMUM	OCTOBER MINIMUM	EXTREME MAXIMUM	EXTREME MINIMUM	AVERAGE PRECIPITATION: LENGTH OF RECORD	JANUARY	FEBRUARY	MARCH	APRIL	MAY	JUNE	JULY	AUGUST	SEPTEMBER	OCTOBER	NOVEMBER	DECEMBER	YEAR
	° ′	° ′	FEET	YEAR	°F	°F	°F	°F	°F	°F	°F	°F	°F	°F	YEAR	IN.	IN.	IN.	IN.	IN.	IN.	IN.	IN.	IN.	IN.	IN.	IN.	IN.
Gibraltar:																												
Windmill Hill	36 06N	05 21W	400	12	58	50	64	55	77	66	70	61	97	35	12	4.6	3.4	3.7	2.5	1.4	0.2	*	0.1	0.8	3.5	4.1	5.4	29.7
Greece:																												
Athinai (Athens)	37 58N	23 43E	351	72	54	42	67	52	90	72	74	60	109	20	80	2.2	1.6	1.4	0.8	0.8	0.6	0.2	0.4	0.6	1.7	2.8	2.8	15.8
Iraklion (Crete)	35 20N	25 08E	98	21	60	48	70	54	85	72	77	62	114	32	22	3.7	3.0	1.6	0.9	0.7	0.1	*	0.1	0.7	1.7	2.7	4.0	19.2
Rodhos (Rhodes)	36 26N	28 15E	289	10	59	51	67	59	83	74	76	68	104	30	6	5.7	3.9	2.6	1.7	0.5	0.3	0.0	*	0.4	1.7	5.2	6.7	28.5
Thessaloniki (Salonika)	40 37N	22 57E	78	9	49	37	66	49	90	70	73	56	107	15	26	1.5	1.5	1.6	1.9	2.0	1.2	1.0	0.7	1.2	2.4	2.1	1.9	19.0
Hungary:																												
Budapest	47 31N	19 02E	394	50	35	26	62	44	82	61	61	45	103	-10	50	1.5	1.5	1.7	2.0	2.7	2.6	2.0	1.9	1.8	2.1	2.4	2.0	24.2
Debrecen	47 36N	21 39E	430	50	33	21	61	39	81	57	60	41	102	-22	80	1.2	1.1	1.4	1.8	2.4	2.8	2.5	2.3	1.8	2.2	2.0	1.6	23.1
Iceland:																												
Akureyri	65 41N	18 05W	16	23	34	26	40	30	57	47	43	34	83	- 8	26	1.7	1.5	1.7	1.3	0.6	0.9	1.3	1.6	1.9	2.3	1.9	1.9	18.6
Reykjavik	64 09N	21 56W	92	25	36	28	43	33	58	48	44	36	74	4	30	4.0	3.1	3.0	2.1	1.6	1.7	2.0	2.6	3.1	3.4	3.6	3.7	33.9
Ireland:																												
Cork	51 54N	08 29W	56	27	48	38	55	41	68	53	58	44	85	15	35	4.9	3.6	3.3	2.6	2.9	2.0	2.9	3.1	2.9	3.9	4.5	4.7	41.3
Dublin	53 22N	06 21W	155	30	47	35	54	38	67	51	57	43	86	8	35	2.7	2.2	2.0	1.9	2.3	2.0	2.8	3.0	2.8	2.7	2.7	2.6	29.7
Shannon Airport	52 41N	08 55W	8	9	46	36	55	41	66	53	58	45	87	12	12	3.8	3.0	2.0	2.2	2.4	2.1	3.1	3.0	3.0	3.4	4.2	4.3	36.5
Italy:																												
Ancona	43 37N	13 32E	52	30	46	36	62	50	83	68	67	55	102	18	30	2.6	1.7	1.6	2.3	2.1	1.9	1.5	1.5	3.5	3.7	2.5	3.0	28.0
Cagliari (Sardinia)	39 15N	09 03E	3	30	56	43	66	50	86	67	72	58	102	25	25	2.2	1.5	1.5	1.2	1.5	0.5	0.1	0.4	1.0	3.0	1.8	2.3	17.0
Genova (Genoa)	44 24N	08 55E	318	10	50	41	65	53	82	70	73	58	100	18	10	3.9	4.0	3.3	3.4	4.6	1.4	1.6	2.3	4.7	6.1	7.2	4.1	46.6
Napoli (Naples)	40 51N	14 15E	82	30	54	40	65	52	84	70	71	60	101	24	30	3.7	3.2	3.0	2.6	1.8	1.8	0.6	0.7	2.8	5.1	4.5	5.4	35.2
Palermo (Sicily)	38 07N	13 19E	354	10	58	47	67	53	86	71	75	62	113	31	30	3.8	3.4	2.4	1.9	1.1	0.6	0.2	0.6	2.0	3.7	4.1	4.5	28.3
Rome	41 48N	12 36E	377	10	54	39	68	46	88	64	73	53	104	20	30	3.3	2.9	2.0	2.0	1.9	0.7	0.4	0.7	2.8	4.3	4.4	4.1	29.5
Taranto	40 28N	17 17E	56	10	55	43	59	50	89	70	73	58	108	26	10	1.6	0.9	1.3	0.8	1.0	0.6	0.4	0.7	1.0	2.2	1.8	1.9	14.2
Venezia (Venice)	45 26N	12 23E	82	10	43	33	63	49	82	67	65	52	97	14	30	2.0	2.1	2.4	2.8	3.2	3.3	2.6	2.6	2.6	3.7	3.5	2.6	33.4
Luxembourg:																												
Luxembourg	49 37N	06 03E	1,096	7	36	29	58	40	74	55	56	43	99	-10	100	2.3	2.0	1.9	2.1	2.4	2.5	2.8	2.6	2.4	2.7	2.7	2.8	29.2
Malta:																												
Valletta	35 54N	14 31E	233	90	59	51	66	56	84	72	76	66	105	34	90	3.3	2.3	1.5	0.8	0.4	0.1	*	0.2	1.3	2.7	3.6	3.9	20.3
Monaco:																												
Monaco	43 44N	07 25E	180	60	54	46	61	53	77	70	67	60	93	27	60	2.4	2.3	3.1	2.2	2.1	1.4	0.7	1.1	2.3	4.7	4.3	3.5	30.1
Netherlands:																												
Amsterdam	52 23N	04 55E	5	29	40	34	52	43	69	59	56	48	95	3	29	2.0	1.4	1.3	1.6	1.8	1.8	2.6	2.7	2.8	2.8	2.6	2.2	25.6
Norway:																												
Bergen	60 24N	05 19E	141	49	43	27	55	34	72	51	57	38	89	3	75	7.9	6.0	5.4	4.4	3.9	4.2	5.2	7.3	9.2	9.2	8.0	8.1	78.8
Kristiansand	58 10N	07 59E	175	11	32	25	50	35	71	53	53	39	90	-14	56	5.0	3.6	3.6	2.7	2.5	2.8	3.5	5.3	4.7	6.2	5.7	6.4	52.0
Oslo	59 56N	10 44E	308	44	30	20	50	34	73	56	49	37	93	-21	56	1.7	1.3	1.4	1.6	1.8	2.4	2.9	3.8	2.5	2.9	2.3	2.3	26.9
Tromso	69 39N	18 57E	335	47	30	22	37	27	59	48	40	33	83	- 1	75	4.1	3.8	3.3	2.4	2.1	2.1	2.3	2.9	4.7	4.5	4.0	3.9	40.1
Trondheim	63 25N	10 27E	417	44	31	22	45	32	66	51	46	36	95	-22	65	3.1	2.7	2.6	2.0	1.7	1.9	2.4	3.0	3.4	3.7	2.8	2.8	32.1
Vardo	70 22N	31 06E	43	40	27	19	34	26	53	44	38	32	80	-11	56	2.5	2.5	2.3	1.5	1.3	1.3	1.5	1.7	1.9	2.5	2.1	2.4	23.5

COUNTRY AND STATION	LATITUDE	LONGITUDE	ELEVATION	TEMPERATURE: LENGTH OF RECORD	AVERAGE DAILY: JANUARY MAXIMUM	JANUARY MINIMUM	APRIL MAXIMUM	APRIL MINIMUM	JULY MAXIMUM	JULY MINIMUM	OCTOBER MAXIMUM	OCTOBER MINIMUM	EXTREME: MAXIMUM	EXTREME: MINIMUM	AVERAGE PRECIPITATION: LENGTH OF RECORD	JANUARY	FEBRUARY	MARCH	APRIL	MAY	JUNE	JULY	AUGUST	SEPTEMBER	OCTOBER	NOVEMBER	DECEMBER	YEAR
	° ′	° ′	FEET	YEAR	°F	°F	°F	°F	°F	°F	°F	°F	°F	°F	YEAR	IN.	IN.	IN.	IN.	IN.	IN.	IN.	IN.	IN.	IN.	IN.	IN.	IN.
Poland:																												
Gdansk (Danzig)	54 24N	18 40E	36	36	33	25	49	37	70	56	53	42	94	-16	35	1.2	1.0	1.3	1.5	1.8	2.3	2.8	2.6	2.1	1.8	1.8	1.5	21.7
Krakow	50 04N	19 57E	723	35	32	22	55	38	76	57	56	41	97	-28	35	1.1	1.3	1.4	1.8	2.8	4.0	4.5	3.8	2.7	2.2	1.7	1.3	28.6
Warsaw	52 13N	21 02E	294	25	30	21	54	38	75	56	54	41	98	-22	113	1.2	1.1	1.3	1.5	1.9	2.6	3.0	3.0	1.9	1.7	1.4	1.4	22.0
Wroclaw (Breslau)	51 07N	17 05E	482	50	35	25	55	39	74	57	55	42	98	-26	40	1.5	1.1	1.5	1.7	2.4	2.4	3.4	2.7	1.8	1.7	1.5	1.5	23.2
Portugal:																												
Braganca	41 49N	06 47W	2,395	11	46	31	59	39	80	54	62	42	103	10	11	11.9	6.9	7.7	3.7	3.0	1.6	0.5	0.6	1.5	3.0	6.3	7.1	53.8
Lagos	37 06N	08 38W	46	21	61	47	67	52	83	64	73	58	107	28	17	3.2	2.6	2.8	1.4	0.8	0.2	*	*	0.4	1.5	2.6	2.8	18.3
Lisbon	38 43N	09 08W	313	75	56	46	64	52	79	63	69	57	103	29	75	3.3	3.2	3.1	2.4	1.7	0.7	0.2	0.2	1.4	3.1	4.2	3.6	27.0
Romania:																												
Bucuresti (Bucharest)	44 25N	26 06E	269	41	33	20	63	41	86	61	65	44	105	-18	41	1.5	1.1	1.7	1.6	2.5	3.8	2.3	1.8	1.5	1.6	1.9	1.5	22.8
Cluj	46 47N	23 40E	1,286	15	31	18	58	38	79	56	60	41	100	-26	16	1.3	1.2	1.0	2.1	3.3	3.3	2.6	3.3	2.0	1.7	1.0	1.2	24.0
Constanta	44 11N	28 39E	13	20	37	25	55	42	79	63	62	49	101	-13	39	1.2	1.2	1.1	1.1	1.3	1.7	1.3	1.1	1.1	1.4	1.2	1.4	15.1
Spain:																												
Almeria	36 51N	02 28W	213	20	61	47	69	54	85	69	76	62	108	34	20	0.9	1.0	0.7	0.9	0.7	0.2	*	0.1	0.6	0.9	1.5	1.1	8.6
Barcelona	41 24N	02 09E	312	20	56	42	64	51	81	69	71	58	98	24	30	1.2	2.1	1.9	1.8	1.8	1.3	1.2	1.7	2.6	3.4	2.7	1.8	23.5
Burgos	42 20N	03 42W	2,825	29	42	30	57	38	77	53	61	43	99	0	29	1.5	1.5	2.1	1.9	2.4	1.7	0.8	0.7	1.4	2.0	2.2	2.0	20.2
Madrid	40 25N	03 41W	2,188	30	47	33	64	44	87	62	66	48	102	14	30	1.1	1.7	1.7	1.7	1.5	1.2	0.4	0.3	1.2	1.9	2.2	1.6	16.5
Sevilla	37 29N	05 59W	98	26	59	41	73	51	96	67	78	57	117	27	26	2.2	2.9	3.3	2.3	1.3	0.9	0.1	0.1	1.1	2.6	3.7	2.8	23.3
Valencia	39 28N	00 23W	79	26	58	41	67	51	83	68	73	57	107	20	29	0.9	1.5	0.9	1.2	1.1	1.3	0.4	0.5	2.2	1.6	2.5	1.3	15.4
Sweden:																												
Abisko	68 21N	18 49E	1,273	11	20	6	33	19	61	45	35	24	82	-30	11	0.7	0.6	0.5	0.5	0.7	1.8	1.6	1.8	1.2	1.0	0.6	0.6	11.7
Goteberg	57 42N	11 58E	55	39	35	27	48	36	69	56	51	42	88	-13	61	2.5	2.0	2.0	1.7	1.9	2.2	2.8	3.7	3.1	3.1	2.7	2.8	30.5
Haparanda	65 50N	24 09E	30	20	22	10	38	23	71	53	39	30	89	-34	20	2.2	1.6	1.2	1.5	1.4	1.7	2.1	2.8	2.6	2.8	2.5	2.0	24.4
Karlstad	59 23N	13 30E	164	30	30	20	49	32	73	56	49	38	93	-21	30	1.9	1.2	1.2	1.4	1.9	1.9	2.6	3.1	2.9	2.4	2.4	1.9	24.8
Sarna	61 41N	13 07E	1,504	20	19	4	42	23	69	46	42	28	91	-51	20	1.6	0.8	0.9	1.2	1.6	2.8	3.6	3.3	2.6	2.3	1.8	1.8	24.3
Stockholm	59 21N	18 04E	146	30	31	23	45	32	70	55	48	39	97	-26	30	1.5	1.1	1.1	1.5	1.6	1.9	2.8	3.1	2.1	2.1	1.9	1.9	22.4
Visby (Gotland)	57 39N	18 18E	36	30	35	28	44	33	67	55	50	41	88	1	30	1.7	1.1	1.2	1.4	1.1	1.4	2.0	2.7	1.7	1.9	2.1	2.0	20.3
Switzerland:																												
Berne	46 57N	07 26E	1,877	30	35	26	56	39	74	56	55	42	96	- 9	77	1.9	2.0	2.6	3.0	3.7	4.4	4.4	4.3	3.5	3.5	2.7	2.5	38.5
Geneve (Geneva)	46 12N	06 09E	1,329	30	39	29	58	41	77	58	58	44	101	- 1	125	1.9	1.8	2.2	2.5	3.0	3.1	2.9	3.6	3.6	3.8	3.1	2.4	33.9
Zurich	47 23N	08 33E	1,617	23	38	28	57	39	76	55	57	42	98	-12	23	2.3	1.9	2.9	3.4	4.0	4.9	5.0	4.6	3.3	3.2	2.5	2.9	40.9
Turkey:																												
Edirne (Adrianople)	41 39N	26 34E	154	18	41	28	66	44	88	63	70	49	107	- 8	18	2.2	1.9	1.7	1.9	1.7	2.1	1.5	1.1	1.1	2.1	2.9	3.0	23.2
Istanbul (Constantinople)	40 58N	28 50E	59	18	45	36	61	45	81	65	67	54	100	17	18	3.7	2.3	2.6	1.9	1.4	1.3	1.7	1.5	2.3	3.8	4.1	4.9	31.5
United Kingdom:																												
Belfast	54 35N	05 56W	57	7	42	34	53	38	65	52	55	44	82	14	30	4.2	2.8	2.3	2.4	2.3	2.5	3.5	3.5	3.4	3.8	3.6	3.9	38.2
Birmingham	52 29N	01 56W	535	30	42	35	53	40	69	54	55	45	92	11	30	2.9	2.1	1.7	2.2	2.5	1.8	2.8	2.7	2.3	2.9	3.2	2.6	29.7
Cardiff	51 28N	03 10W	203	30	45	36	55	41	69	54	57	45	91	2	30	4.6	3.0	2.3	2.5	3.0	2.2	3.4	3.9	3.6	4.5	4.6	4.3	41.9
Dublin	53 22N	06 21W	155	30	47	35	54	38	67	51	57	43	86	8	35	2.7	2.2	2.0	1.9	2.3	2.0	2.8	3.0	2.8	2.7	2.7	2.6	29.7
Edinburgh	55 55N	03 11W	441	30	43	35	50	39	65	52	53	44	83	15	30	2.5	1.6	1.6	1.6	2.2	1.9	3.1	3.1	2.6	2.9	2.4	2.1	27.6
London	51 29N	00 00	149	30	44	35	56	40	73	55	58	44	99	9	30	2.0	1.5	1.4	1.8	1.8	1.6	2.0	2.2	1.8	2.3	2.5	2.0	22.9

(See footnotes at end of tables)

ROUND–THE–WORLD WEATHER

COUNTRY AND STATION	LATITUDE ° ′	LONGITUDE ° ′	ELEVATION FEET	TEMPERATURE: LENGTH OF RECORD YEAR	AVERAGE DAILY: JANUARY MAXIMUM °F	JANUARY MINIMUM °F	APRIL MAXIMUM °F	APRIL MINIMUM °F	JULY MAXIMUM °F	JULY MINIMUM °F	OCTOBER MAXIMUM °F	OCTOBER MINIMUM °F	EXTREME: MAXIMUM °F	EXTREME: MINIMUM °F	AVERAGE PRECIPITATION: LENGTH OF RECORD YEAR	JANUARY IN.	FEBRUARY IN.	MARCH IN.	APRIL IN.	MAY IN.	JUNE IN.	JULY IN.	AUGUST IN.	SEPTEMBER IN.	OCTOBER IN.	NOVEMBER IN.	DECEMBER IN.	YEAR IN.
Liverpool	53 24N	03 04W	198	30	44	36	52	41	66	55	55	46	87	15	30	2.7	1.9	1.5	1.6	2.2	2.0	2.8	3.1	2.6	3.0	3.0	2.5	28.9
Perth	56 24N	03 27W	77	30	43	32	53	38	68	51	55	41	89	0	30	3.1	2.2	1.9	1.7	2.3	2.0	3.1	2.9	2.8	3.3	2.7	2.7	30.7
Plymouth	50 21N	04 07W	87	30	47	40	54	43	66	55	58	49	88	16	30	4.3	3.0	2.6	2.3	2.5	2.0	2.6	2.9	2.8	3.8	4.6	4.4	37.8
Wick	58 26N	03 05W	119	30	42	35	48	38	59	50	52	43	80	8	30	2.9	2.1	1.8	2.1	1.8	2.0	2.6	2.6	2.9	3.2	3.1	2.9	30.0
U.S.S.R.:																												
Arkhangelsk	64 33N	40 32E	22	23	9	2	36	23	64	51	36	30	91	-49	25	1.2	1.1	1.1	0.7	1.3	1.9	2.6	2.7	2.2	1.9	1.6	1.3	19.8
Astrakhan	46 21N	48 02E	45	10	23	14	57	40	85	69	56	40	99	-22	25	0.5	0.5	0.4	0.6	0.6	0.7	0.5	0.4	0.6	0.4	0.6	0.6	6.4
Dnepropetrovsk	48 27N	35 04E	259	18	25	16	53	39	80	62	56	40	101	-25	17	1.4	1.1	1.2	1.4	1.8	3.0	1.9	1.6	1.0	1.8	1.6	1.6	19.4
Kaunas	54 54N	23 53E	118	19	26	18	49	34	72	53	50	38	96	-23	19	1.6	1.3	1.3	1.8	2.0	3.2	3.3	3.5	1.9	1.9	1.6	1.6	25.0
Kirov	58 36N	49 41E	594	20	6	- 2	41	27	72	55	37	29	92	-43	29	1.2	1.0	0.9	0.9	1.9	2.5	2.1	2.9	2.3	2.0	1.6	1.3	20.6
Kursk	51 45N	36 12E	773	15	19	11	47	35	74	58	48	36	91	-23	20	1.5	1.3	1.2	1.5	2.2	2.5	3.2	2.3	1.6	1.8	1.5	1.7	22.3
Leningrad	59 56N	30 16E	16	26	23	12	45	31	71	57	45	37	91	-36	95	1.0	0.9	0.9	1.0	1.6	2.0	2.5	2.8	2.1	1.8	1.4	1.2	19.2
Lvov	49 50N	24 01E	978	9	31	22	53	38	77	59	55	43	97	-29	35	1.3	1.5	1.8	2.0	2.8	3.7	4.1	3.1	2.4	2.1	0.8	1.6	28.2
Minsk	53 54N	27 33E	738	12	22	13	47	33	70	54	47	36	92	-27	20	1.4	1.5	1.3	1.5	2.0	2.8	3.0	3.1	1.6	1.5	1.5	1.7	22.9
Moskva (Moscow)	55 46N	37 40E	505	15	21	9	47	31	76	55	46	34	96	-27	11	1.5	1.4	1.1	1.9	2.2	2.9	3.0	2.9	1.9	2.7	1.7	1.6	24.8
Odessa	46 29N	30 44E	214	20	28	22	52	41	79	65	57	47	99	-13	15	1.0	0.7	0.7	1.1	1.1	1.9	1.6	1.4	1.1	1.4	1.1	1.1	14.3
Riga	56 57N	24 06E	67	30	29	20	48	35	72	56	49	39	93	-20	57	1.3	1.0	1.1	1.2	1.7	2.4	3.0	3.0	2.1	2.0	1.9	1.5	22.2
Saratov	51 32N	46 03E	197	14	15	7	50	35	82	64	48	36	102	-27	15	1.0	1.0	0.8	1.0	1.3	1.8	1.2	1.3	1.1	1.4	1.4	1.2	14.5
Sevastopol	44 37N	33 31E	75	20	39	30	55	42	79	65	63	50	97	- 4	30	1.1	1.1	1.1	0.9	0.6	1.1	0.8	0.6	1.1	1.5	1.2	1.1	12.2
Stalingrad	48 42N	44 31E	136	8	15	4	52	36	84	65	53	37	106	-30	12	0.9	1.0	0.6	0.6	1.0	1.9	0.9	0.8	0.7	1.0	1.5	1.3	12.2
Stavropol	45 02N	41 58E	1,886	18	26	17	50	37	76	60	55	42	95	-22	41	1.4	1.1	1.5	2.4	3.0	4.1	3.0	2.0	2.5	2.3	1.8	1.8	26.9
Tallin	59 26N	24 48E	146	15	27	18	42	31	70	55	47	38	89	-19	63	1.1	1.0	0.9	1.1	1.7	1.9	2.1	2.7	2.3	2.1	1.9	1.5	20.2
Tbilisi	41 43N	44 48E	1,325	10	39	26	61	44	83	65	64	48	95	6	10	0.7	0.8	1.3	1.6	3.6	3.1	2.2	1.7	1.9	1.3	2.0	1.2	21.4
Ust'Shchugor	64 16N	57 34E	279	15	4	-14	35	17	65	49	33	23	90	-67	15	1.1	0.8	0.8	0.7	1.4	2.2	3.0	3.2	2.4	2.2	1.5	1.3	20.6
Ufy	54 43N	55 56E	571	20	6	- 3	44	30	75	58	41	31	99	-42	23	1.6	1.3	1.2	0.9	1.6	2.4	2.6	2.2	1.8	2.3	2.2	2.3	22.5
Yugoslavia:																												
Beograd (Belgrade)	44 48N	20 28E	453	16	37	27	64	45	84	61	65	47	107	-14	16	1.6	1.3	1.6	2.2	2.6	2.8	1.9	2.5	1.7	2.7	1.8	1.9	24.6
Skopje	41 59N	21 28E	787	10	40	26	67	42	88	60	65	43	105	-11	10	1.5	1.2	1.3	1.5	1.9	1.9	1.3	1.1	1.1	2.6	2.3	1.8	19.5
Split	43 31N	16 26E	420	14	51	29	65	50	87	68	69	55	100	17	51	3.1	2.5	3.2	3.0	2.5	2.1	1.2	1.6	2.9	4.4	4.2	4.4	35.1
OCEAN ISLANDS																												
Bjornoya, Bear Island	74 31N	19 01E	49	10	26	17	27	16	44	36	36	29	71	-25	25	1.6	1.3	1.3	0.9	0.8	0.7	0.8	1.2	1.8	1.7	1.4	1.6	15.1
Gronfjorden, Spitzbergen	78 02N	14 15E	23	19	10	- 4	15	- 3	46	38	25	17	60	-57	15	1.4	1.3	1.1	0.9	0.5	0.4	0.6	0.9	1.0	1.2	0.9	1.5	11.7
Horta, Azores	38 32N	28 38W	200	30	62	54	64	55	76	65	71	62	88	38	30	4.5	4.1	4.2	3.0	2.9	2.0	1.5	1.9	3.2	4.4	4.1	4.5	40.3
Jan Mayen	71 01N	08 28W	131	5	31	21	31	22	46	38	39	29	60	-18	29	2.1	1.7	1.6	1.4	0.9	0.9	1.4	1.8	2.5	2.5	2.2	2.2	21.2
Lerwick, Shetland Island	60 08N	01 11W	269	30	42	35	46	37	58	49	50	42	71	17	30	4.5	3.4	2.9	2.7	2.2	2.2	2.7	2.9	3.7	4.3	4.5	4.5	40.5
Matochkin Shar, Novaya Zemlya	73 16N	56 24E	61	9	8	- 6	13	- 1	47	36	30	21	68	-41	9	0.6	0.6	0.6	0.4	0.3	0.4	1.4	1.5	1.5	0.6	0.6	0.4	8.9
Ponta Delgada, Azores	37 45N	25 40W	118	30	62	54	64	55	76	64	71	61	85	37	30	4.0	3.5	3.5	2.5	2.3	1.4	1.0	1.2	2.9	3.6	3.7	3.0	32.6
Stornoway, Hebrides	58 11N	06 21W	34	30	44	37	49	39	61	51	53	44	78	11	15	6.4	3.2	3.2	3.1	2.5	2.4	3.0	4.3	4.7	6.2	4.6	5.5	49.1
Thorshavn, Faeroes	62 02N	06 45W	82	50	42	33	45	36	56	47	58	40	70	8	50	6.6	5.2	4.8	3.6	3.4	2.5	3.1	3.5	4.7	5.9	6.3	6.6	56.2

COUNTRY AND STATION	LATITUDE ° ′	LONGITUDE ° ′	ELEVATION FEET	TEMPERATURE LENGTH OF RECORD YEAR	AVERAGE DAILY JANUARY MAXIMUM °F	JANUARY MINIMUM °F	APRIL MAXIMUM °F	APRIL MINIMUM °F	JULY MAXIMUM °F	JULY MINIMUM °F	OCTOBER MAXIMUM °F	OCTOBER MINIMUM °F	EXTREME MAXIMUM °F	EXTREME MINIMUM °F	AVERAGE PRECIPITATION LENGTH OF RECORD YEAR	JANUARY IN.	FEBRUARY IN.	MARCH IN.	APRIL IN.	MAY IN.	JUNE IN.	JULY IN.	AUGUST IN.	SEPTEMBER IN.	OCTOBER IN.	NOVEMBER IN.	DECEMBER IN.	YEAR IN.
AFRICA																												
Algeria:																												
Adrar	27 52N	00 17W	938	15	69	39	92	60	115	82	92	63	124	25	15	*	*	0.1	*	*	*	*	*	*	0.2	0.2	*	0.6
Alger (Algiers)	36 46N	03 03E	194	25	59	49	68	55	83	70	74	63	107	32	25	4.4	3.3	2.9	1.6	1.8	0.6	*	0.2	1.6	3.1	5.1	5.4	30.0
Bone	36 54N	07 46E	66	26	59	46	67	52	85	69	75	61	115	32	26	5.6	4.1	2.9	2.2	1.5	0.6	0.1	0.3	1.2	3.0	4.3	5.2	31.0
El Golea	30 35N	02 53E	1,247	15	63	37	84	56	107	79	87	60	120	23	15	0.1	0.3	0.5	*	*	*	*	*	*	0.3	0.4	0.3	1.9
Fort Flatters	28 06N	06 42E	1,224	15	67	38	90	59	110	78	92	63	124	19	15	0.3	0.1	0.1	0.2	*	*	0.0	*	*	*	0.2	0.2	1.1
Tamanrasset	22 42N	05 31E	4,593	15	67	39	86	56	95	71	85	59	102	20	15	0.2	*	*	0.2	0.4	0.1	0.1	0.4	0.1	*	*	*	1.5
Touggourt	33 07N	06 04E	226	26	62	38	83	55	107	77	84	59	122	26	26	0.2	0.4	0.5	0.2	0.2	0.2	*	*	0.1	0.3	0.5	0.3	2.9
Angola:																												
Cangamba	13 41S	19 52E	4,331	6	84	62	89	58	82	46	87	59	109	20	7	8.9	7.4	6.8	1.8	0.1	0.0	0.0	0.2	0.2	1.6	5.1	8.5	40.6
Luanda	08 49S	13 13E	194	27	83	74	85	75	74	65	79	71	98	58	59	1.0	1.4	3.0	4.6	0.5	*	*	*	0.1	0.2	1.1	0.8	12.7
Mocamedes	15 12S	12 09E	10	15	79	65	82	66	68	56	74	61	102	44	21	0.3	0.4	0.7	0.5	*	*	*	*	*	*	0.1	0.1	2.1
Nova Lisboa	12 48S	15 45E	5,577	14	78	58	78	57	77	47	81	58	90	36	14	8.7	7.8	9.8	5.7	0.4	0.0	*	*	0.6	5.5	9.6	8.9	57.0
Botswana:																												
Francistown	21 13S	27 30E	3,294	20	88	65	83	56	75	41	90	61	107	24	28	4.2	3.1	2.8	0.7	0.2	0.1	*	*	*	0.9	2.3	3.4	17.7
Maun	19 59S	23 25E	3,091	20	90	66	87	58	77	42	95	64	110	24	20	4.3	3.8	3.5	1.1	0.2	*	0.0	0.0	*	0.5	1.9	2.8	18.2
Tsabong	26 03S	22 27E	3,156	10	94	65	83	51	71	34	88	54	107	15	14	2.0	1.9	1.9	1.3	0.4	0.4	0.1	*	0.2	0.7	1.1	1.5	11.5
Cameroon:																												
Ngaoundere	07 17N	13 19E	3,601	9	87	55	87	64	82	63	82	61	102	46	10	*	*	1.1	5.5	7.0	8.4	10.6	9.6	9.2	5.3	0.5	*	57.2
Yaounde	03 53N	11 32E	2,526	11	85	67	85	66	80	66	81	65	96	57	11	0.9	2.6	5.8	6.7	7.7	6.0	2.9	3.1	8.4	11.6	4.6	0.9	61.2
Central African Republic:																												
Bangui	04 22N	18 34E	1,270	5	90	68	91	71	85	69	87	69	101	57	5	1.0	1.7	5.0	5.3	7.4	4.5	8.9	8.1	5.9	7.9	4.9	0.2	60.8
Ndele	08 24N	20 39E	1,939	3	99	67	98	73	86	69	90	68	109	58	3	0.2	1.3	0.6	1.7	8.4	6.1	8.3	10.1	10.7	7.8	0.6	0.0	55.8
Chad:																												
Am Timan	11 02N	20 17E	1,430	3	98	56	105	68	89	70	96	67	113	43	3	0.0	0.0	0.1	1.2	4.3	5.0	7.3	12.3	5.8	1.2	0.0	0.0	37.2
Fort Lamy	12 07N	15 02E	968	5	93	57	107	74	92	72	97	70	114	47	5	0.0	0.0	0.0	0.1	1.2	2.6	6.7	12.6	4.7	1.4	0.0	0.0	29.3
Largeau (Faya)	18 00N	19 10E	837	5	84	54	104	69	109	76	103	72	121	37	5	0.0	0.0	0.0	0.0	*	0.0	*	0.7	*	0.0	0.0	0.0	0.7
Congo, Democratic Republic of the:																												
Albertville	05 54S	29 12E	2,493	5	85	66	83	67	82	58	87	67	92	50	20	4.2	4.7	6.3	8.4	3.3	0.3	0.1	0.3	0.8	2.8	7.9	6.3	45.4
Kinspasa (Leopoldville)	04 20S	15 18E	1,066	8	87	70	89	71	81	64	88	70	97	58	12	5.3	5.7	7.7	7.7	6.2	0.3	0.1	0.1	1.2	4.7	8.7	5.6	53.3
Luluabourg	05 54S	22 25E	2,198	3	85	68	86	68	85	63	85	68	94	57	14	5.4	5.6	7.7	7.6	3.3	0.8	0.5	2.3	4.6	6.5	9.1	8.9	62.3
Stanleyville	00 26N	25 14E	1,370	8	88	69	88	70	84	67	86	68	97	61	14	2.1	3.3	7.0	6.2	5.4	4.5	5.2	6.5	7.2	8.6	7.8	3.3	67.1
Congo, Republic of:																												
Brazzaville	04 15S	15 15E	1,043	15	88	69	91	71	82	63	89	70	98	54	18	6.3	4.9	7.4	7.0	4.3	0.6	*	*	2.2	5.4	11.5	8.4	58.0
Ouesso	01 37N	16 04E	1,132	4	88	69	91	71	85	69	87	69	106	60	4	2.4	3.6	6.4	3.2	5.8	4.6	2.9	3.7	7.9	10.0	5.7	2.4	58.6
Pointe Noire (Loango)	04 39S	11 48E	164	7	85	73	87	74	78	66	83	72	93	59	7	5.4	6.7	6.4	8.0	3.9	0.0	0.0	0.0	0.4	4.1	6.6	6.6	48.1
Dahomey:																												
Cotonou	06 21N	02 26E	23	5	80	74	83	78	78	74	80	75	95	65	10	1.3	1.3	4.6	4.9	10.0	14.4	3.5	1.5	2.6	5.3	2.3	0.5	52.4

(See footnotes at end of tables)

ROUND–THE–WORLD WEATHER

COUNTRY AND STATION	LATITUDE	LONGITUDE	ELEVATION	TEMPERATURE: LENGTH OF RECORD	AVERAGE DAILY: JANUARY MAXIMUM	JANUARY MINIMUM	APRIL MAXIMUM	APRIL MINIMUM	JULY MAXIMUM	JULY MINIMUM	OCTOBER MAXIMUM	OCTOBER MINIMUM	EXTREME: MAXIMUM	EXTREME: MINIMUM	AVERAGE PRECIPITATION: LENGTH OF RECORD	JANUARY	FEBRUARY	MARCH	APRIL	MAY	JUNE	JULY	AUGUST	SEPTEMBER	OCTOBER	NOVEMBER	DECEMBER	YEAR
	° '	° '	FEET	YEAR	°F	°F	°F	°F	°F	°F	°F	°F	°F	°F	YEAR	IN.	IN.	IN.	IN.	IN.	IN.	IN.	IN.	IN.	IN.	IN.	IN.	IN.
Ethiopia:																												
Addis Ababa	09 20N	38 45E	8,038	15	75	43	77	50	69	50	75	45	94	32	37	0.5	1.5	2.6	3.4	3.4	5.4	11.0	11.8	7.5	0.8	0.6	0.2	48.7
Asmara	15 17N	38 55E	7,628	9	74	44	78	51	71	53	72	53	88	31	17	*	*	0.4	1.5	1.5	1.3	6.7	5.0	1.3	0.3	0.4	*	18.4
Diredawa	09 02N	41 45E	3,937	8	81	58	91	69	90	68	89	67	100	49	8	0.8	0.8	3.3	3.0	2.8	1.5	4.3	3.8	2.2	0.5	0.3	0.8	24.1
Gambela	08 15N	34 35E	1,345	26	98	64	98	71	87	69	92	67	111	48	30	0.2	0.4	1.4	3.2	5.9	6.7	8.5	9.5	7.3	3.5	1.8	0.4	48.8
French Territory of Afars and Issas (F.T.A.I.):																												
Djibouti	11 36N	43 09E	23	16	84	73	90	79	106	87	92	80	117	63	46	0.4	0.5	1.0	0.5	0.2	*	0.1	0.3	0.3	0.4	0.9	0.5	46.0
Gabon:																												
Libreville	00 23N	09 26E	115	11	87	73	89	73	83	68	86	71	99	62	21	9.8	9.3	13.2	13.4	9.6	0.5	0.1	0.7	4.1	13.6	14.7	9.8	98.8
Mayoumba	03 25S	10 38E	200	8	84	73	86	73	78	68	82	72	91	60	8	6.5	9.3	6.2	10.2	2.3	0.1	0.0	0.2	2.6	9.3	10.7	4.6	62.0
Gambia:																												
Bathurst	13 21N	16 40W	90	9	88	59	91	65	86	74	89	72	106	45	9	0.1	0.1	*	*	0.4	2.3	11.1	19.7	12.2	4.3	0.7	0.1	51.0
Ghana:																												
Accra	05 33N	00 12W	88	17	87	73	88	76	81	73	85	74	100	59	65	0.6	1.3	2.2	3.2	5.6	7.0	1.8	0.6	1.4	2.5	1.4	0.9	28.5
Kumasi	06 40N	01 37W	942	10	88	66	89	71	82	70	86	70	100	51	10	0.8	2.3	5.7	5.1	7.5	7.9	4.3	3.1	6.8	7.1	3.7	0.8	55.2
Guinea:																												
Conakry	09 31N	13 43W	23	7	88	72	90	73	83	72	87	73	96	63	10	0.1	0.1	0.4	0.9	6.2	22.0	51.1	41.5	26.9	14.6	4.8	0.4	169.0
Kouroussa	10 39N	09 53W	1,217	9	93	60	99	73	87	69	90	69	109	39	10	0.4	0.3	0.9	2.8	5.3	9.7	11.7	13.6	13.4	6.6	1.3	0.4	66.4
Ifni (now in Morocco):																												
Sidi Ifni	29 27N	10 11W	148	14	66	52	71	59	75	64	75	62	124	40	14	1.0	0.6	0.5	0.6	0.1	0.1	*	*	0.4	0.1	0.9	1.8	6.1
Ivory Coast:																												
Abidjan	05 19N	04 01W	65	13	88	73	90	75	83	73	85	74	96	59	10	1.6	2.1	3.9	4.9	14.2	19.5	8.4	2.1	2.8	6.6	7.9	3.1	77.1
Bouake	07 42N	05 00W	1,194	12	91	68	92	70	85	68	89	68	104	57	10	0.4	1.5	4.1	5.8	5.3	6.0	3.1	4.6	8.2	5.2	1.5	1.0	46.7
Kenya:																												
Mombasa	04 03S	39 39E	52	45	87	75	86	76	81	71	84	74	96	61	54	1.0	0.7	2.5	7.7	12.6	4.7	3.5	2.5	2.5	3.4	3.8	2.4	47.3
Nairobi	01 16S	36 48E	5,971	15	77	54	75	58	69	51	76	55	87	41	17	1.5	2.5	4.9	8.3	6.2	1.8	0.6	0.9	1.2	2.1	4.3	3.4	37.7
Liberia:																												
Monrovia	06 18N	10 48W	75	6	89	71	90	72	80	72	86	72	97	62	4	0.2	0.1	4.4	11.7	13.4	36.1	24.2	18.6	29.9	25.2	8.2	2.9	174.9
Libya:																												
Banghazi (Benghazi)	32 06N	20 04E	82	46	63	50	74	58	84	71	80	66	109	37	46	2.6	1.6	0.8	0.2	0.1	*	*	*	0.1	0.7	1.8	2.6	10.5
Cufra	24 12N	23 21E	1,276	7	69	43	90	62	101	75	90	64	122	26	7	*	0.0	0.0	0.0	*	0.0	0.0	0.0	0.0	0.0	0.0	*	*
Sabhah	27 01N	14 26E	1,457	3	64	41	89	60	102	74	91	64	120	24	10	*	*	*	*	0.1	0.1	0.0	0.0	0.0	*	*	*	0.3
Tarabulus (Triopoli)	32 54N	13 11E	72	47	61	47	72	57	85	71	80	65	114	33	56	3.2	1.8	1.1	0.4	0.2	0.1	*	*	0.4	1.6	2.6	3.7	15.1
Malagasy Republic:																												
Diego Suarez	12 17S	49 17E	100	11	88	75	88	75	84	69	86	72	98	63	31	10.6	9.5	7.6	2.2	0.3	0.2	0.2	0.3	0.3	0.7	1.1	5.8	38.7
Tananarive	18 55S	47 33E	4,500	44	79	61	76	58	68	48	80	54	95	34	62	11.8	11.0	7.0	2.1	0.7	0.3	0.3	0.4	0.7	2.4	5.3	11.3	53.4
Tulear	23 20S	43 41E	20	27	92	72	89	64	81	58	86	65	108	43	15	3.1	3.2	1.4	0.3	0.7	0.4	0.1	0.2	0.3	0.7	1.4	1.7	13.5
Malawi:																												
Karonga	09 57S	33 56E	1,596	8	86	71	85	70	81	59	91	66	99	51	8	7.1	7.0	10.8	6.2	1.7	0.1	*	*	0.0	0.3	0.3	4.7	38.3
Zomba	15 23S	35 19E	3,141	27	80	65	78	62	72	53	85	64	95	41	29	12.1	9.9	10.1	2.7	0.7	0.4	0.3	0.3	0.2	1.0	4.3	10.9	52.9

COUNTRY AND STATION	LATITUDE	LONGITUDE	ELEVATION	TEMPERATURE: LENGTH OF RECORD	AVERAGE DAILY: JANUARY MAXIMUM	JANUARY MINIMUM	APRIL MAXIMUM	APRIL MINIMUM	JULY MAXIMUM	JULY MINIMUM	OCTOBER MAXIMUM	OCTOBER MINIMUM	EXTREME: MAXIMUM	EXTREME: MINIMUM	AVERAGE PRECIPITATION: LENGTH OF RECORD	JANUARY	FEBRUARY	MARCH	APRIL	MAY	JUNE	JULY	AUGUST	SEPTEMBER	OCTOBER	NOVEMBER	DECEMBER	YEAR
	° '	° '	FEET	YEAR	°F	°F	°F	°F	°F	°F	°F	°F	°F	°F	YEAR	IN.	IN.	IN.	IN.	IN.	IN.	IN.	IN.	IN.	IN.	IN.	IN.	IN.
Mali:																												
Araouane	18 54N	03 33W	935	8	81	48	110	67	111	79	103	70	130	37	10	*	*	0.0	0.0	0.0	0.2	0.2	0.5	0.6	0.1	0.1	*	1.7
Bamako	12 39N	07 58W	1,116	11	91	61	103	76	89	71	93	71	117	47	10	*	*	0.1	0.6	2.9	5.4	11.0	13.7	8.1	1.7	0.6	*	44.1
Gao	16 16N	00 03W	902	15	83	58	105	77	97	80	100	78	116	44	19	*	0.0	*	0.1	0.4	1.0	2.9	5.4	1.5	0.2	*	0.0	11.5
Mauritania:																												
Atar	20 31N	13 04W	761	7	84	54	97	67	106	81	98	72	117	39	10	*	0.0	*	*	*	0.1	0.3	1.2	1.1	0.1	*	*	2.8
Nema	16 36N	07 16W	883	9	86	62	105	79	99	78	101	79	120	47	10	0.1	*	*	*	0.7	1.1	2.3	4.7	2.1	0.7	*	0.1	11.6
Nouakchott	18 07N	15 36W	69	5	85	57	90	64	89	74	91	71	115	44	10	*	0.1	*	*	*	0.1	0.5	4.1	0.9	0.4	0.1	*	6.2
Morocco:																												
Casablanca	33 35N	07 39W	164	48	63	45	69	52	79	65	76	58	110	31	40	2.1	1.9	2.2	1.4	0.9	0.2	0.0	*	0.3	1.5	2.6	2.8	15.9
Marrakech	31 36N	08 01W	1,509	35	65	40	79	52	101	67	83	57	120	27	31	1.0	1.1	1.3	1.2	0.6	0.3	0.1	0.1	0.4	0.9	1.2	1.2	9.4
Rabat	34 00N	06 50W	213	35	63	46	71	52	82	63	77	58	118	32	29	2.6	2.5	2.6	1.7	1.1	0.3	*	*	0.4	1.9	3.3	3.4	19.8
Tangier	35 48N	05 49W	239	35	60	47	65	51	80	64	72	59	106	28	35	4.5	4.2	4.8	3.5	1.7	0.6	*	*	0.9	3.9	5.8	5.4	35.3
Mozambique:																												
Beira	19 50S	34 51E	28	37	89	75	86	71	77	61	87	71	109	48	39	10.9	8.4	10.1	4.2	2.2	1.3	1.2	1.1	0.8	5.2	5.3	9.2	59.9
Chicoa	15 36S	32 21E	899	8	96	65	93	63	86	55	101	68	117	32	8	7.8	5.7	4.4	0.6	*	*	*	*	*	1.1	2.6	5.2	27.4
Lourenco Marques	25 58S	32 36E	194	42	86	71	83	66	76	55	82	64	114	45	42	5.1	4.9	4.9	2.1	1.1	0.8	0.5	0.5	1.1	1.9	3.2	3.8	29.9
Niger:																												
Agades	16 59N	07 59E	1,706	8	86	50	105	70	104	75	101	68	115	40	10	0.0	0.0	*	*	0.2	0.3	1.9	3.7	0.7	0.0	0.0	0.0	6.8
Bilma	18 41N	12 55E	1,171	9	81	45	101	63	108	75	101	62	116	29	10	0.0	0.0	0.0	*	*	0.0	0.1	0.5	0.3	0.0	0.0	0.0	0.9
Niamey	13 31N	02 06E	709	10	93	58	108	77	94	74	101	74	114	47	10	*	*	0.2	0.3	1.3	3.2	5.2	7.4	3.7	0.5	*	0.0	21.6
Nigeria:																												
Enugu	06 27N	07 29E	763	11	90	72	91	74	83	71	87	71	99	55	33	0.7	1.1	2.6	5.9	10.4	11.4	7.6	6.7	12.8	9.8	2.1	0.5	71.5
Kaduna	10 35N	06 26E	2,113	18	89	59	95	72	83	68	89	66	105	46	34	*	0.1	0.5	2.5	5.9	7.1	8.5	11.9	10.6	2.9	0.1	*	50.1
Lagos	06 27N	03 24E	10	32	88	74	89	77	83	74	85	74	104	60	47	1.1	1.8	4.0	5.9	10.6	18.1	11.0	2.5	5.5	8.1	2.7	1.0	72.3
Maiduguri	11 51N	13 05E	1,162	15	90	54	104	72	90	73	96	68	112	43	40	*	*	*	0.3	1.6	2.7	7.1	8.7	4.2	0.7	*	0.0	25.3
Portuguese Guinea:																												
Bolama	11 34N	15 26W	62	31	88	67	91	73	84	74	87	74	106	59	37	*	*	*	*	0.8	7.8	23.1	27.6	16.9	8.0	1.6	0.1	85.9
Rhodesia:																												
Bulawayo	20 09S	28 37E	4,405	15	81	61	79	56	70	45	85	59	99	28	50	5.6	4.3	3.3	0.7	0.4	0.1	*	*	0.2	0.8	3.2	4.8	23.4
Salisbury	17 50S	31 08E	4,831	15	78	60	78	55	70	44	83	58	95	32	50	7.7	7.0	4.6	1.1	0.5	0.1	*	0.1	0.2	1.1	3.8	6.4	32.6
Senegal:																												
Dakar	14 42N	17 29W	131	25	79	64	81	65	88	76	89	76	109	53	26	*	*	*	*	*	0.7	3.5	10.0	5.2	1.5	0.1	0.3	21.3
Kaolack	14 08N	16 04W	20	9	93	60	103	68	91	75	93	74	114	48	10	*	0.0	*	*	0.3	2.6	6.9	10.7	7.0	2.7	0.1	*	30.3
Sierra Leone:																												
Freetown/Lungi	08 37N	13 12W	92	8	87	73	88	76	82	73	85	72	98	62	8	0.4	0.2	1.2	3.1	9.5	14.3	29.2	36.5	22.3	14.2	5.5	1.2	137.6
Somalia:																												
Berbera	10 26N	45 02E	45	30	84	68	89	77	107	88	92	76	117	58	30	0.3	0.1	0.2	0.5	0.3	*	*	0.1	*	0.1	0.2	0.2	2.0
Mogadishu (Mogadiscio)	02 02N	45 21E	39	13	86	73	90	78	83	73	86	76	97	59	21	*	*	*	2.3	2.3	3.8	2.5	1.9	1.0	0.9	1.6	0.5	16.9

(See footnotes at end of tables)

ROUND–THE–WORLD WEATHER

COUNTRY AND STATION	LATITUDE	LONGITUDE	ELEVATION	TEMPERATURE: LENGTH OF RECORD	AVERAGE DAILY: JANUARY MAXIMUM	JANUARY MINIMUM	APRIL MAXIMUM	APRIL MINIMUM	JULY MAXIMUM	JULY MINIMUM	OCTOBER MAXIMUM	OCTOBER MINIMUM	EXTREME MAXIMUM	EXTREME MINIMUM	AVERAGE PRECIPITATION: LENGTH OF RECORD	JANUARY	FEBRUARY	MARCH	APRIL	MAY	JUNE	JULY	AUGUST	SEPTEMBER	OCTOBER	NOVEMBER	DECEMBER	YEAR
	° ′	° ′	FEET	YEAR	°F	°F	°F	°F	°F	°F	°F	°F	°F	°F	YEAR	IN.	IN.	IN.	IN.	IN.	IN.	IN.	IN.	IN.	IN.	IN.	IN.	IN.
South Africa, Republic of:																												
Capetown	33 54S	18 32E	56	19	78	60	72	53	63	45	70	52	103	28	18	0.6	0.3	0.7	1.9	3.1	3.3	3.5	2.6	1.7	1.2	0.7	0.4	20.0
Durban	29 50S	31 02E	16	15	81	69	78	64	72	52	75	62	107	39	78	4.3	4.8	5.1	3.0	2.0	1.3	1.1	1.5	2.8	4.3	4.8	4.7	39.7
Kimberley	28 48S	24 46E	3,927	19	91	64	77	52	65	36	83	54	103	20	57	2.4	2.5	3.1	1.5	0.7	0.2	0.2	0.3	0.6	1.0	1.6	2.0	16.1
Port Elizabeth	33 59S	25 36E	190	14	78	61	73	55	67	45	70	54	104	31	84	1.2	1.3	1.9	1.8	2.4	1.8	1.9	2.0	2.3	2.2	2.2	1.7	22.7
Port Nolloth	29 14S	16 52E	23	20	67	53	66	50	62	45	64	49	107	31	64	0.1	0.1	0.2	0.2	0.3	0.3	0.3	0.3	0.2	0.1	0.1	0.1	2.3
Pretoria	25 45S	28 14E	4,491	13	81	60	75	50	66	37	80	55	96	24	12	5.0	4.3	4.5	1.7	0.9	0.6	0.3	0.2	0.8	2.2	5.2	5.2	30.9
Walvis Bay	22 56S	14 30E	24	20	73	59	75	55	70	47	67	51	104	25	20	*	0.2	0.3	0.1	0.1	*	*	0.1	*	*	*	*	0.9
Southwest Africa:																												
Keetmanshoop	26 35S	18 08E	3,295	17	95	65	85	57	70	42	87	55	108	26	45	0.8	1.1	1.4	0.6	0.2	*	*	*	0.1	0.2	0.3	0.4	5.2
Windhoek	22 34S	17 06E	5,669	30	85	63	77	55	68	43	84	59	97	25	60	3.0	2.9	3.1	1.6	0.3	*	*	*	0.1	0.4	0.9	1.9	14.3
Spanish Sahara:																												
Semara	26 46N	11 31W	1,509	6	73	47	88	58	99	66	88	61	121	37	6	0.1	*	0.0	*	*	0.0	0.0	*	1.0	*	0.4	0.0	1.5
Villa Cisneros	23 42N	15 52W	35	12	71	56	74	60	78	65	80	65	107	48	14	*	*	*	*	0.1	0.0	*	0.2	1.4	0.1	0.2	1.0	3.0
Sudan:																												
El Fasher	13 38N	25 21E	2,395	17	88	50	102	64	96	70	99	64	113	33	17	*	0.0	*	*	0.3	0.7	4.5	5.3	1.2	0.2	0.0	0.0	12.2
Khartoum	15 37N	32 33E	1,279	46	90	59	105	72	101	77	104	75	118	41	46	*	*	*	*	0.1	0.3	2.1	2.8	0.7	0.2	*	0.0	6.2
Port Sudan	19 37N	37 13E	18	30	81	68	89	71	106	83	93	76	117.	50	40	0.2	0.1	*	*	*	*	0.3	0.1	*	0.4	1.7	0.9	3.7
Wadi Halfa	21 55N	31 20E	410	39	75	46	98	62	106	74	98	67	127	28	39	*	*	*	*	*	0.0	*	*	*	*	*	0.0	*
Wau	07 42N	28 03E	1,443	38	96	64	99	72	89	69	93	69	115	50	38	*	0.2	0.9	2.6	5.3	6.5	7.5	8.2	6.6	4.9	0.6	*	43.3
Tanzania:																												
Dares Salaam	06 50S	39 18E	47	44	83	77	86	73	83	66	85	69	96	59	49	2.6	2.6	5.1	11.4	7.4	1.3	1.2	1.0	1.2	1.6	2.9	3.6	41.9
Iringa	07 47S	35 42E	5,330	14	76	59	75	59	72	52	80	57	90	42	24	6.8	5.1	7.1	3.5	0.5	*	*	*	0.1	0.2	1.5	4.5	29.3
Kigoma	04 53S	29 38E	2,903	26	80	67	81	67	83	63	84	69	100	53	18	4.8	5.0	5.9	5.1	1.7	0.2	0.1	0.2	0.7	1.9	5.6	5.3	36.5
Togo:																												
Lome	06 10N	01 15E	72	5	85	72	86	74	80	71	83	72	94	58	15	0.6	0.9	1.9	4.6	5.7	8.8	2.8	0.4	1.4	2.4	1.1	0.4	31.0
Tunisia:																												
Gabes	33 53N	10 07E	7	50	61	43	74	54	89	71	81	62	122	27	50	0.9	0.7	0.8	0.4	0.3	*	*	0.1	0.5	1.2	1.2	0.6	6.7
Tunis	36 47N	10 12E	217	50	58	43	70	51	90	68	77	59	118	30	50	2.5	2.0	1.6	1.4	0.7	0.3	0.1	0.3	1.3	2.0	1.9	2.4	16.5
Uganda:																												
Kampala	00 20N	32 36E	4,304	15	83	65	79	64	77	62	81	63	97	53	15	1.8	2.4	5.1	6.9	5.8	2.9	1.8	3.4	3.6	3.8	4.8	3.9	46.2
Lira	02 15N	32 54E	3,560	14	91	61	86	64	81	61	86	61	100	50	14	0.7	1.0	3.5	6.9	7.9	4.9	6.4	10.0	8.3	6.1	3.2	1.8	60.7
United Arab Republic:																												
Alexandria	31 12N	29 53E	105	45	65	51	74	59	85	73	83	68	111	37	61	1.9	0.9	0.4	0.1	*	*	*	*	*	0.2	1.3	2.2	7.0
Aswan	24 02N	32 53E	366	46	74	50	96	66	106	79	98	71	124	35	11	*	*	*	*	*	*	0.0	0.0	0.0	*	*	*	*
Cairo	29 52N	31 20E	381	42	65	47	83	57	96	70	86	65	117	34	42	0.2	0.2	0.2	0.1	0.1	*	0.0	0.0	*	*	0.1	0.2	1.1
Upper Volta:																												
Bobo Dioulasso	11 10N	04 15W	1,411	11	92	58	99	71	87	69	90	70	115	46	10	0.1	0.2	1.1	2.1	4.6	4.8	9.8	12.0	8.5	2.5	0.7	0.0	46.4
Ouagadougou	12 22N	01 31W	991	10	92	60	103	79	91	74	95	74	118	48	15	*	0.1	0.5	0.6	3.3	4.8	8.0	10.9	5.7	1.3	*	0.0	35.2
Zambia:																												
Balovale	13 34S	23 06E	3,577	8	82	65	84	61	81	47	91	64	108	38	9	8.5	6.9	5.8	1.2	*	0.0	0.0	*	0.3	2.3	4.4	8.9	38.3

COUNTRY AND STATION	LATITUDE	LONGITUDE	ELE-VATION	TEMPERATURE: LENGTH OF RECORD	AVERAGE DAILY: JANUARY MAXIMUM	JANUARY MINIMUM	APRIL MAXIMUM	APRIL MINIMUM	JULY MAXIMUM	JULY MINIMUM	OCTOBER MAXIMUM	OCTOBER MINIMUM	EXTREME: MAXIMUM	EXTREME: MINIMUM	AVERAGE PRECIPITATION: LENGTH OF RECORD	JANUARY	FEBRUARY	MARCH	APRIL	MAY	JUNE	JULY	AUGUST	SEPTEMBER	OCTOBER	NOVEMBER	DECEMBER	YEAR
	° ′	° ′	FEET	YEAR	°F	°F	°F	°F	°F	°F	°F	°F	°F	°F	YEAR	IN.	IN.	IN.	IN.	IN.	IN.	IN.	IN.	IN.	IN.	IN.	IN.	IN.
Kasama	10 12S	31 11E	4,544	10	79	61	79	60	76	50	87	62	95	39	10	10.7	9.9	10.9	2.8	0.5	*	*	*	*	0.8	6.4	9.5	51.5
Lusaka	15 25S	28 19E	4,191	10	78	63	79	59	73	49	88	64	100	39	10	9.1	7.5	5.6	0.7	0.1	*	*	0.0	*	0.4	3.6	5.9	32.9
ATLANTIC ISLANDS:																												
Funchal, Madeira Island	32 38N	16 55W	82	30	66	56	67	58	75	66	74	65	103	40	30	2.5	2.9	3.1	1.3	0.7	0.2	*	*	1.0	3.0	3.5	3.3	21.5
Georgetown, Ascension Island	07 56S	14 25W	55	29	85	73	88	75	84	72	83	71	95	65	45	0.2	0.4	0.7	1.1	0.5	0.5	0.5	0.4	0.3	0.3	0.2	0.1	5.2
Hutts Gate, St. Helena	15 57S	05 40W	2,062	30	68	60	69	61	62	55	61	54	82	50	30	2.1	3.1	4.2	3.1	2.8	3.2	4.3	2.6	2.2	1.7	1.2	1.6	32.1
Las Palmas, Canary Islands	28 11N	15 28W	20	45	70	58	71	61	77	67	79	67	99	46	48	1.4	0.9	0.9	0.5	0.2	*	*	*	0.2	1.1	2.1	1.6	8.6
Porto da Praia, Cape Verde Is.	14 54N	23 31W	112	25	77	68	79	69	83	75	85	76	94	56	25	0.1	*	*	*	0.0	*	0.2	3.8	4.5	1.2	0.3	0.1	10.2
Santa Isabel, Fernando Po	03 46N	08 46E	-----	2	87	67	89	70	84	69	86	70	102	61	16	1.3	2.5	4.2	7.2	9.4	11.1	7.4	6.6	9.6	10.4	3.5	1.7	74.9
Sao Tome, Sao Tome	00 20N	06 43E	16	10	86	73	86	73	82	69	84	71	91	56	10	3.2	4.2	5.9	5.0	5.3	1.1	*	*	0.9	4.3	4.6	3.5	38.0
Tristan da Cunha	37 03S	12 19W	75	5	66	59	64	57	57	50	59	51	75	38	5	3.5	3.5	6.4	4.7	7.1	5.9	6.1	6.9	7.9	5.8	4.3	4.0	66.1
INDIAN OCEAN ISLANDS:																												
Agalega Island	10 26S	56 40E	10	3	86	77	87	77	83	75	84	75	91	69	2	5.9	10.1	4.9	6.9	13.2	8.9	8.7	3.2	1.8	4.2	7.0	10.0	84.7
Cocos (Keeling) Island	12 05S	96 53E	15	36	86	77	85	78	82	76	84	76	94	68	38	5.4	7.7	8.5	10.4	7.9	9.0	8.7	4.8	3.7	3.3	4.2	4.6	78.2
Heard Island	53 01S	73 23E	16	5	41	35	39	33	34	27	35	28	58	13	5	5.8	5.8	5.7	6.1	5.8	3.9	3.6	2.2	2.5	3.7	4.0	5.1	54.3
Hellburg, Reunion Island	21 04S	55 22E	3,070	5	74	59	73	56	65	48	69	51	84	40	11	22.4	8.0	16.4	7.2	5.3	4.4	3.1	3.0	2.0	2.3	3.5	12.9	90.5
Port Victoria, Seychelles	04 37S	55 27E	15	60	83	76	86	77	81	75	83	75	92	67	64	15.2	10.5	9.2	7.2	6.7	4.0	3.3	2.7	5.1	6.1	9.1	13.4	92.5
Royal Alfred Observatory, Mauritius	20 06S	57 32E	181	40	86	73	82	70	75	62	80	64	95	50	43	8.5	7.8	8.7	5.0	3.8	2.6	2.3	2.5	1.4	1.6	1.8	4.6	50.6
ASIA – FAR EAST																												
China																												
Canton	23 10N	113 20E	59	26	65	49	77	65	91	77	85	67	101	31	36	0.9	1.9	4.2	6.8	10.6	10.6	8.1	8.5	6.5	3.4	1.2	0.9	63.6
Chanasha	28 15	112 58E	161	14	45	35	70	56	94	78	75	59	109	16	26	1.9	3.7	5.3	5.7	8.2	8.7	4.4	4.3	2.7	3.0	2.7	1.5	52.1
Chungking	29 30N	106 33E	855	27	51	42	73	59	93	76	71	61	111	28	60	0.7	0.8	1.5	3.8	5.7	7.1	5.6	4.7	5.8	4.3	1.9	0.8	42.9
Hankow	30 35N	114 17E	75	29	46	34	69	55	93	78	74	60	108	9	55	1.8	1.9	3.6	5.8	7.0	9.0	7.0	4.1	3.0	3.1	1.9	1.2	49.4
Harbin (Ha-erh-pin)	45 45N	126 38E	476	35	7	-14	54	31	84	65	54	31	102	-43	38	0.2	0.2	0.4	0.9	1.7	3.7	6.6	4.7	2.3	1.2	0.5	0.2	22.6
Kashgar	39 24N	76 07E	4,296	27	33	12	71	48	92	68	71	43	106	-15	18	0.6	0.1	0.5	0.2	0.3	0.2	0.4	0.3	0.1	0.1	0.2	0.3	3.2
Kunming	25 02N	102 43E	6,211	32	61	37	76	51	77	62	70	53	91	22	31	0.4	0.5	0.7	0.8	4.3	6.3	8.8	8.6	5.0	3.0	1.7	0.4	40.5
Lanchow	36 06N	103 55E	5,105	8	33	7	65	40	84	61	62	39	100	- 3	4	0.2	0.2	0.2	0.5	0.8	0.7	3.3	5.1	2.2	0.6	0.0	0.3	14.1
Mukden (Shen-yang)	41 47N	123 24E	138	40	20	- 2	60	36	87	69	62	39	103	-28	42	0.2	0.2	0.7	1.2	2.6	3.8	7.0	6.3	2.9	1.7	0.9	0.4	28.2
Shanghai	31 12N	121 26E	16	56	47	32	67	49	91	75	75	56	104	10	81	1.9	2.4	3.3	3.6	3.8	7.0	5.8	5.5	5.2	2.9	2.1	1.5	45.0
Tientsin	39 10N	117 10E	13	24	33	16	68	45	90	73	68	48	109	- 3	25	0.2	0.1	0.4	0.5	1.1	2.4	7.6	6.0	1.7	0.6	0.4	0.2	21.0
Urumchi	43 45N	87 40E	2,972	6	13	-7	60	36	82	58	50	31	112	-30	6	0.6	0.3	0.5	1.5	1.1	1.5	0.7	1.0	0.6	1.7	1.6	0.4	11.5
Hong Kong:	22 18N	114 10E	109	50	64	56	75	67	87	78	81	73	97	32	50	1.3	1.8	2.9	5.4	11.5	15.5	15.0	14.2	10.1	4.5	1.7	1.2	85.1
Japan:																												
Kushiro	43 02N	144 12E	315	41	30	8	44	31	66	55	58	40	87	-19	41	1.8	1.4	2.8	3.6	3.8	4.1	4.4	4.9	6.6	4.0	3.1	2.0	42.9

(See footnotes at end of tables)

COUNTRY AND STATION	LATITUDE	LONGITUDE	ELEVATION	TEMPERATURE: LENGTH OF RECORD	AVERAGE DAILY JANUARY MAXIMUM	JANUARY MINIMUM	APRIL MAXIMUM	APRIL MINIMUM	JULY MAXIMUM	JULY MINIMUM	OCTOBER MAXIMUM	OCTOBER MINIMUM	EXTREME MAXIMUM	EXTREME MINIMUM	AVERAGE PRECIPITATION: LENGTH OF RECORD	JANUARY	FEBRUARY	MARCH	APRIL	MAY	JUNE	JULY	AUGUST	SEPTEMBER	OCTOBER	NOVEMBER	DECEMBER	YEAR
	° ′	° ′	FEET	YEAR	°F	°F	°F	°F	°F	°F	°F	°F	°F	°F	YEAR	IN.	IN.	IN.	IN.	IN.	IN.	IN.	IN.	IN.	IN.	IN.	IN.	IN.
India:																												
Ahmadabad	23 03N	72 37E	180	45	85	58	104	75	93	79	97	73	118	36	45	*	0.1	0.1	*	0.4	3.7	12.2	8.1	4.2	0.4	0.1	*	29.3
Bangalore	12 57N	77 40E	2,937	60	80	57	93	69	81	66	82	65	102	46	60	0.2	0.3	0.4	1.6	4.2	2.9	3.9	5.0	6.7	5.9	2.7	0.4	34.2
Bombay	19 06N	72 51E	27	60	88	62	93	74	88	75	93	73	110	46	60	0.1	0.1	0.1	*	0.7	19.1	24.3	13.4	10.4	2.5	0.5	0.1	71.2
Calcutta	22 32N	88 20E	21	60	80	55	97	76	90	79	89	74	111	44	60	0.4	1.2	1.4	1.7	5.5	11.7	12.8	12.9	9.9	4.5	0.8	0.2	63.0
Cherrapunji	25 15N	91 44E	4,309	35	60	46	71	59	72	65	72	61	87	33	35	0.7	2.1	7.3	26.2	50.4	106.1	96.3	70.1	43.3	19.4	2.7	0.5	425.1
Hyderabad	17 27N	78 28E	1,741	50	85	59	101	75	87	73	88	68	112	43	45	0.3	0.4	0.5	1.2	1.1	4.4	6.0	5.3	6.5	2.5	1.1	0.3	29.6
Jalpaiguri	26 32N	88 43E	272	50	74	50	90	68	89	77	87	70	104	36	55	0.3	0.7	1.3	3.7	11.8	25.9	32.2	25.3	21.2	5.6	0.5	0.2	128.7
Lucknow	26 45N	80 52E	400	60	74	47	101	71	92	80	91	67	119	34	60	0.8	0.7	0.3	0.3	0.8	4.5	12.0	11.5	7.4	1.3	0.2	0.3	40.1
Madras	13 04N	80 15E	51	60	85	67	95	78	96	79	90	75	113	57	60	1.4	0.4	0.3	0.6	1.0	1.9	3.6	4.6	4.7	12.0	14.0	5.5	50.0
Mormugao	15 22N	73 49E	157	10	86	70	88	79	83	75	86	75	98	59	30	*	*	*	0.7	2.6	29.6	31.2	15.9	9.5	3.8	1.3	0.2	94.8
New Delhi	28 35N	77 12E	695	10	71	43	97	68	95	80	93	64	115	31	75	0.9	0.7	0.5	0.3	0.5	2.9	7.1	6.8	4.6	0.4	0.1	0.4	25.2
Silchar	24 49N	92 48E	95	60	78	52	88	69	90	77	88	72	103	41	53	0.8	2.1	7.9	14.3	15.6	21.7	19.7	19.7	14.4	6.5	1.4	0.4	124.5
Indian Ocean Islands:																												
Port Blair, Andaman Is.	11 40N	92 43E	261	60	84	72	89	75	84	75	84	74	97	62	60	1.8	1.1	1.1	2.4	15.1	21.7	15.4	16.3	17.4	12.5	10.5	7.9	123.2
Amini Divi, Laccadive Is.	11 07N	72 44E	13	29	86	74	92	80	86	77	86	77	99	65	30	0.7	*	*	1.5	3.7	14.3	12.0	7.7	6.3	5.8	2.6	1.3	56.0
Minicoy, Maldive Is.	08 18N	73 00E	9	20	85	73	87	80	85	76	85	76	98	63	50	1.8	0.7	0.9	2.3	7.0	11.6	8.9	7.8	6.3	7.3	5.5	3.4	63.5
Car Nicobar, Nicobar Is.	09 09N	92 49E	47	13	86	77	90	77	86	77	85	75	95	66	30	3.9	1.2	2.1	3.5	12.5	12.4	9.3	10.2	12.9	11.6	11.4	7.8	98.8
Iran:																												
Abadan	30 21N	48 13E	10	12	64	44	90	62	112	81	98	63	127	24	10	1.5	1.7	0.6	0.8	0.1	0.0	0.0	0.0	0.0	0.1	1.0	1.8	7.6
Esfahan (Isfahan)	32 37N	51 41E	5,238	45	47	25	72	46	98	67	78	47	108	- 4	45	0.7	0.6	0.8	0.6	0.3	*	0.1	*	*	0.1	0.4	0.7	4.4
Kermanshah	34 19N	47 07E	4,331	15	45	23	68	38	99	56	79	38	108	-13	15	2.6	2.3	2.8	2.2	1.6	*	*	*	*	0.4	2.0	2.4	16.4
Rezaiyeh	37 32N	45 05E	4,364	3	32	17	67	45	91	64	67	47	99	-11	3	1.9	2.3	2.0	1.7	1.2	0.5	*	0.1	0.2	1.5	0.8	1.6	13.8
Tehran	35 41N	51 19E	3,937	24	45	27	71	49	99	72	76	53	109	- 5	33	1.8	1.5	1.8	1.4	0.5	0.1	0.1	0.1	0.1	0.3	0.8	1.2	9.7
Iraq:																												
Baghdad	33 20N	44 24E	111	15	60	39	85	57	110	76	92	61	121	18	15	0.9	1.0	1.1	0.5	0.1	*	*	*	*	0.1	0.8	1.0	5.5
Basra	30 34N	47 47E	8	10	64	45	85	63	104	81	94	64	123	24	10	1.4	1.1	1.2	1.2	0.2	0.0	*	*	*	*	1.4	0.8	7.3
Mosul	36 19N	43 09E	730	26	54	35	77	49	109	72	88	51	124	12	29	2.8	3.1	2.1	1.9	0.7	*	*	*	*	0.2	1.9	2.4	15.2
Israel:																												
Haifa	32 48N	35 02E	23	16	65	49	77	58	88	75	85	68	112	27	30	6.9	4.3	1.6	1.0	0.2	*	*	*	0.1	1.0	3.7	7.3	26.2
Jerusalem	31 47N	35 13E	2,654	19	55	41	73	50	87	63	81	59	107	26	50	5.1	4.7	2.9	0.9	0.1	*	0.0	0.0	*	0.3	2.2	3.5	19.7
Tel Aviv	32 06N	34 46E	33	10	64	50	70	57	82	72	79	65	102	34	10	4.9	2.7	2.0	0.7	0.1	0.0	0.0	0.0	0.1	0.4	4.1	6.1	21.1
Jammu/Kashmir:																												
Srinagar	33 58N	74 46E	5,458	50	41	24	67	45	88	64	74	41	106	- 4	50	2.9	2.8	3.6	3.7	2.4	1.4	2.3	2.4	1.5	1.2	0.4	1.3	25.9
Jordan:																												
Amman	31 58N	35 59E	2,547	25	54	39	73	49	89	65	81	57	109	21	25	2.7	2.9	1.2	0.6	0.2	0.0	0.0	0.0	*	0.2	1.3	1.8	10.9
Kuwait:																												
Kuwait	29 21N	48 00E	16	14	61	49	83	68	103	86	91	73	119	33	10	0.9	0.9	1.1	0.2	*	0.0	0.0	0.0	0.0	0.1	0.6	1.1	5.1
Lebanon:																												
Beirut	33 54N	35 28E	111	62	62	51	72	58	87	73	81	69	107	30	71	7.5	6.2	3.7	2.2	0.7	0.1	*	*	0.2	2.0	5.2	7.3	35.1

COUNTRY AND STATION	LATITUDE	LONGITUDE	ELEVATION	TEMPERATURE: LENGTH OF RECORD	AVERAGE DAILY: JANUARY MAXIMUM	JANUARY MINIMUM	APRIL MAXIMUM	APRIL MINIMUM	JULY MAXIMUM	JULY MINIMUM	OCTOBER MAXIMUM	OCTOBER MINIMUM	EXTREME: MAXIMUM	EXTREME: MINIMUM	AVERAGE PRECIPITATION: LENGTH OF RECORD	JANUARY	FEBRUARY	MARCH	APRIL	MAY	JUNE	JULY	AUGUST	SEPTEMBER	OCTOBER	NOVEMBER	DECEMBER	YEAR
	° ′	° ′	FEET	YEAR	°F	°F	°F	°F	°F	°F	°F	°F	°F	°F	YEAR	IN.	IN.	IN.	IN.	IN.	IN.	IN.	IN.	IN.	IN.	IN.	IN.	IN.
Nepal:																												
Katmandu	27 42N	85 22E	4,423	27	65	36	84	53	84	69	80	56	99	27	9	0.6	1.6	0.9	2.3	4.8	9.7	14.7	13.6	6.1	1.5	0.3	0.1	56.2
Oman and Muscat:																												
Muscat	23 37N	58 35E	15	23	77	66	90	78	97	87	93	80	116	51	38	1.1	0.7	0.4	0.4	*	0.1	*	*	0.0	0.1	0.4	0.7	3.9
Pakistan (West):																												
Karachi	24 48N	66 59E	13	43	77	55	90	73	91	81	91	72	118	39	59	0.5	0.4	0.3	0.1	0.1	0.7	3.2	1.6	0.5	0.1	0.1	0.2	7.8
Multan	30 11N	71 25E	400	60	68	42	95	68	102	86	94	64	122	29	60	0.4	0.4	0.4	0.3	0.3	0.6	2.0	1.8	0.5	0.1	0.1	0.2	7.1
Rawalpindi	33 35N	73 03E	1,676	60	62	38	86	59	98	77	89	57	118	25	60	2.5	2.5	2.7	1.9	1.3	2.3	8.1	9.2	3.9	0.6	0.3	1.2	36.5
Saudi Arabia:																												
Dhahran	26 16N	50 10E	78	10	69	54	90	69	107	86	95	73	120	40	10	1.1	0.6	0.4	0.2	0.1	0.0	0.0	0.0	0.0	0.0	0.2	0.9	3.5
Jidda	21 28N	39 10E	20	5	84	66	91	70	99	79	95	73	117	49	5	0.2	*	*	*	*	0.0	*	*	*	*	1.0	1.2	2.5
Riyadh	24 39N	46 42E	1,938	3	70	46	89	64	107	78	94	61	113	19	3	0.1	0.8	0.9	1.0	0.4	*	0.0	*	0.0	0.0	*	*	3.2
Syria:																												
Deir Ez Zor	35 21N	40 09E	699	5	53	35	80	52	105	78	86	56	114	16	8	1.6	0.8	0.3	0.8	0.1	*	0.0	0.0	0.0	0.2	1.5	0.9	6.2
Dimashq (Damascus)	33 30N	36 20E	2,362	13	53	36	75	49	96	64	81	54	113	21	7	1.7	1.7	0.3	0.5	0.1	*	*	0.0	0.7	0.4	1.6	1.6	8.6
Halab (Aleppo)	36 14N	37 08E	1,280	8	50	34	75	48	97	69	81	54	117	9	10	3.5	2.5	1.5	1.1	0.3	0.1	0.0	*	*	1.0	2.2	3.3	15.5
Trucial Kingdoms:																												
Sharjah	25 20N	55 24E	18	11	74	54	86	65	100	82	92	71	118	37	12	0.9	0.9	0.4	0.2	0.0	0.0	0.0	0.0	0.0	0.0	0.4	1.4	4.2
Turkey:																												
Adana	36 59N	35 18E	82	21	57	39	74	51	93	71	84	58	109	19	31	4.3	4.0	2.5	1.6	2.0	0.7	0.2	0.2	0.7	1.9	2.4	3.8	24.3
Ankara	39 57N	32 53E	2,825	26	39	24	63	40	86	59	69	44	104	-13	24	1.3	1.2	1.3	1.3	1.9	1.0	0.5	0.4	0.7	0.9	1.2	1.9	13.6
Erzurum	39 54N	41 16E	6,402	16	24	8	50	32	78	53	59	37	93	-22	16	1.4	1.6	2.0	2.5	3.1	2.1	1.3	0.9	1.1	2.3	1.8	1.1	21.2
Izmir (Smyrna)	38 27N	27 15E	92	39	55	39	70	49	92	69	76	55	108	12	58	4.4	3.3	3.0	1.7	1.3	0.6	0.2	0.2	0.8	2.1	3.3	4.8	25.5
Samsun	41 17N	36 19E	131	24	50	38	59	45	79	65	69	56	103	20	27	2.9	2.6	2.7	2.3	1.8	1.5	1.5	1.3	2.4	3.2	3.5	2.4	29.1
Yemen:																												
Kamaran I.	15 20N	42 37E	20	26	82	74	89	79	98	85	93	82	105	66	21	0.2	0.2	0.1	0.1	0.1	*	0.5	0.7	0.1	0.1	0.4	0.9	3.4
AUSTRALIA & PACIFIC ISLANDS																												
Australia:																												
Adelaide	34 57S	138 32E	20	86	86	61	73	55	59	45	73	51	118	32	104	0.8	0.7	1.0	1.8	2.7	3.0	2.6	2.6	2.1	1.7	1.1	1.0	21.1
Alice Springs	23 48S	133 53E	1,791	62	97	70	81	54	67	39	88	58	111	19	30	1.7	1.3	1.1	0.4	0.6	0.5	0.3	0.3	0.3	0.7	1.2	1.5	9.9
Bourke	30 05S	145 58E	361	63	99	70	82	55	65	40	85	56	125	25	72	1.4	1.5	1.1	1.1	1.0	1.1	0.9	0.8	0.8	0.9	1.2	1.4	13.2
Brisbane	27 25S	153 05E	17	53	85	69	79	61	68	49	80	60	110	35	91	6.4	6.3	5.7	3.7	2.8	2.6	2.2	1.9	1.9	2.5	3.7	5.0	44.7
Broome	17 57S	122 13E	56	41	92	79	93	72	82	58	91	72	113	40	50	6.3	5.8	3.9	1.2	0.6	0.9	0.2	0.1	*	*	0.6	3.3	22.9
Burketown	17 45S	139 33E	30	31	93	77	91	69	82	55	93	70	110	40	53	8.2	6.3	5.2	1.0	0.2	0.3	*	*	*	0.4	1.5	4.4	27.5
Canberra	35 18S	149 11E	1,886	23	82	55	67	44	52	33	68	43	109	14	25	1.9	1.7	2.2	1.6	1.8	2.1	1.8	2.2	1.6	2.2	1.9	2.0	23.0
Carnarvon	24 53S	113 40E	13	43	88	72	84	66	71	51	78	61	118	37	57	0.4	0.7	0.7	0.6	1.5	2.4	1.6	0.7	0.2	0.1	*	0.2	9.1
Cloncurry	20 40S	140 30E	622	32	99	77	90	67	77	51	95	68	127	35	59	4.4	4.2	2.4	0.7	0.5	0.6	0.3	0.1	0.3	0.5	1.3	2.7	18.0
Esperance	33 50S	121 55E	14	44	77	60	72	54	62	45	68	50	117	31	60	0.7	0.7	1.2	1.8	3.3	4.1	4.0	3.8	2.7	2.2	1.0	0.9	26.4
Laverton	28 40S	122 23E	1,510	30	96	69	81	57	64	41	82	55	115	25	30	0.8	0.8	1.6	0.8	0.9	0.7	0.6	0.5	0.2	0.3	0.8	0.8	8.8
Melbourne	37 49S	144 58E	115	88	78	57	68	51	56	42	67	48	114	27	88	1.9	1.8	2.2	2.3	2.1	2.1	1.9	1.9	2.3	2.6	2.3	2.3	25.7
Mundiwindi	23 52S	120 10E	1,840	15	101	64	87	61	70	41	89	58	112	22	15	1.0	1.9	2.0	0.8	0.6	0.9	0.1	0.3	0.3	0.5	0.5	1.2	10.1

(See footnotes at end of tables)

COUNTRY AND STATION	LATITUDE	LONGITUDE	ELEVATION	TEMPERATURE: LENGTH OF RECORD	AVERAGE DAILY: JANUARY MAXIMUM	JANUARY MINIMUM	APRIL MAXIMUM	APRIL MINIMUM	JULY MAXIMUM	JULY MINIMUM	OCTOBER MAXIMUM	OCTOBER MINIMUM	EXTREME: MAXIMUM	EXTREME: MINIMUM	AVERAGE PRECIPITATION: LENGTH OF RECORD	JANUARY	FEBRUARY	MARCH	APRIL	MAY	JUNE	JULY	AUGUST	SEPTEMBER	OCTOBER	NOVEMBER	DECEMBER	YEAR
	° ′	° ′	FEET	YEAR	°F	°F	°F	°F	°F	°F	°F	°F	°F	°F	YEAR	IN.	IN.	IN.	IN.	IN.	IN.	IN.	IN.	IN.	IN.	IN.	IN.	IN.
Miyako	39 38N	141 59E	98	30	43	23	58	37	77	62	66	46	99	1	30	2.9	3.0	3.2	3.5	4.5	5.0	5.0	7.2	9.5	6.8	3.0	2.6	56.2
Nagasaki	32 44N	129 53E	436	59	49	36	66	50	85	73	72	58	98	22	59	2.8	3.3	4.9	7.3	6.7	12.3	10.1	6.9	9.8	4.5	3.7	3.2	75.5
Osaka	34 47N	135 26E	49	60	47	32	65	47	87	73	72	55	102	19	60	1.7	2.3	3.8	5.2	4.9	7.4	5.9	4.4	7.0	5.1	3.0	1.9	52.6
Tokyo	35 41N	139 46E	19	60	47	29	63	46	83	70	69	55	101	17	60	1.9	2.9	4.2	5.3	5.8	6.5	5.6	6.0	9.2	8.2	3.8	2.2	61.6
Korea:																												
Pusan	35 10N	129 07E	6	36	43	29	62	47	81	71	70	54	97	7	36	1.7	1.4	2.7	5.5	5.2	7.9	11.6	5.1	6.8	2.9	1.6	1.2	53.6
P'yongyang	39 01N	125 49E	94	43	27	8	61	38	84	69	65	43	100	-19	43	0.6	0.4	1.0	1.8	2.6	3.0	9.3	9.0	4.4	1.8	1.6	0.8	36.4
Seoul	37 31N	126 55E	34	22	32	15	62	41	84	70	67	45	99	-12	22	1.2	0.8	1.5	3.0	3.2	5.1	14.8	10.5	4.7	1.6	1.8	1.0	49.2
Mongolia:																												
Ulan Bator	47 54N	106 56E	4,287	13	- 2	-27	45	18	71	50	44	17	97	-48	15	*	*	0.1	0.2	0.3	1.0	2.9	1.9	0.8	0.2	0.2	0.1	7.7
Taiwan:																												
Tainan	22 57N	120 12E	53	13	72	55	82	67	89	77	86	70	95	39	13	0.7	0.7	1.1	3.2	6.3	15.6	16.0	15.8	8.4	1.2	0.9	0.6	70.5
Taipei	25 04N	121 32E	21	12	66	53	77	64	92	76	80	68	101	32	12	3.8	5.3	4.3	5.3	6.9	8.8	8.8	8.7	8.2	5.5	4.2	2.9	72.7
Union of Soviet Socialist Republics:																												
Alma-Ata	43 16N	76 53E	2,543	19	23	7	56	38	81	60	55	35	100	-30	27	1.3	0.9	2.2	4.0	3.7	2.6	1.4	1.2	1.0	2.0	1.9	1.3	23.5
Chita (Tchita)	52 02N	113 30E	2,218	10	-10	-27	42	19	75	51	38	18	99	-52	24	0.1	0.1	0.1	0.4	1.1	1.8	3.3	3.3	1.2	0.5	0.2	0.2	12.3
Dubinka	69 07N	87 00E	141	5	-23	-31	6	-10	59	47	19	11	84	-62	5	0.3	0.4	0.2	0.3	0.6	1.9	1.5	2.1	1.8	0.9	0.4	0.3	10.7
Irkutsk	52 16N	104 19E	1,532	10	3	-15	42	20	70	50	41	21	98	-58	38	0.5	0.4	0.3	0.6	1.3	2.2	3.1	2.8	1.7	0.7	0.6	0.6	14.9
Kazalinsk	45 46N	62 06E	207	10	16	5	58	27	90	65	57	35	108	-27	19	0.4	0.4	0.5	0.5	0.6	0.2	0.2	0.3	0.3	0.4	0.5	0.6	4.9
Khabarovsk	48 28N	135 03E	165	7	- 2	-13	41	28	75	63	48	34	91	-46	8	0.3	0.2	0.3	0.7	2.0	3.5	4.1	3.3	3.0	0.7	0.6	0.5	19.2
Kirensk	57 47N	108 07E	938	18	-14	-28	38	15	74	51	10	- 4	95	-71	19	0.8	0.5	0.5	0.5	1.0	1.8	2.1	2.1	1.7	1.0	1.0	1.0	14.0
Krasnoyarsk	56 01N	92 52E	498	10	3	-10	34	23	67	55	34	26	103	-47	8	0.1	0.2	0.1	0.2	1.0	1.4	1.2	2.1	1.7	0.9	0.5	0.4	9.8
Markovo	64 45N	170 50E	85	15	-19	-29	5	- 8	59	47	16	9	84	-72	16	0.2	0.2	0.3	0.1	0.3	0.8	1.0	1.9	1.1	0.4	0.4	0.3	7.0
Narym	58 50N	81 39E	197	13	- 7	-18	35	19	71	56	35	25	94	-61	14	0.8	0.5	0.8	0.5	1.3	2.6	2.4	2.7	1.7	1.4	1.1	0.9	16.8
Okhotsk	59 21N	143 17E	18	19	- 6	-17	29	10	57	48	33	21	78	-50	25	0.1	0.1	0.2	0.4	0.9	1.6	2.2	2.6	2.4	1.0	0.2	0.1	11.8
Omsk	54 58N	73 20E	279	19	- 1	-14	39	21	74	56	40	27	102	-56	22	0.6	0.3	0.3	0.5	1.2	2.0	2.0	2.0	1.1	1.0	0.7	0.8	12.5
Petropavlovsk	52 53N	158 42E	286	7	23	11	35	25	56	47	46	34	84	-29	35	3.0	2.2	3.4	2.5	2.2	2.0	3.1	3.2	3.8	3.9	3.6	3.0	35.9
Salehkard	66 31N	66 35E	60	18	-13	-21	18	4	61	49	26	20	85	-65	27	0.3	0.3	0.3	0.3	0.7	1.3	1.9	2.0	1.5	0.7	0.5	0.4	10.2
Semipalatinsk	50 24N	80 13E	709	10	8	- 7	45	26	81	57	46	30	101	-47	10	0.9	0.5	0.5	0.6	1.2	1.5	1.1	1.3	0.7	1.2	1.1	1.0	11.6
Sverdlovsk	56 49N	60 38E	894	21	6	- 5	42	26	70	54	37	28	94	-45	29	0.5	0.4	0.5	0.7	1.9	2.7	2.6	2.7	1.6	1.2	1.1	0.8	16.7
Tashkent	41 20N	69 18E	1,569	19	37	21	65	47	92	64	65	41	106	-19	19	2.1	1.1	2.6	2.3	1.4	0.5	0.2	0.1	0.1	1.2	1.5	1.6	14.7
Verkhoyansk	67 34N	133 51E	328	24	-54	-63	19	-10	66	47	12	- 3	98	-90	44	0.2	0.2	0.1	0.2	0.3	0.9	1.1	1.0	0.5	0.3	0.3	0.2	5.3
Vladivostok	43 07N	131 55E	94	14	13	0	46	34	71	60	55	41	92	-22	53	0.3	0.4	0.7	1.2	2.1	2.9	3.3	4.7	4.3	1.9	1.2	0.6	23.6
Yakutsk	62 01N	129 43E	535	19	-45	-53	27	6	73	54	23	11	97	-84	22	0.3	0.2	0.1	0.3	0.4	1.1	1.6	1.3	1.1	0.5	0.4	0.3	7.4
ASIA – SOUTHEAST																												
Brunei:																												
Brunei	04 55N	114 55E	10	5	85	76	87	77	87	76	86	77	99	70	12	14.6	7.6	7.8	9.8	10.9	9.5	9.0	7.3	11.8	14.5	15.2	13.0	131.0

COUNTRY AND STATION	LATITUDE	LONGITUDE	ELEVATION	TEMPERATURE: LENGTH OF RECORD	AVERAGE DAILY: JANUARY MAXIMUM	JANUARY MINIMUM	APRIL MAXIMUM	APRIL MINIMUM	JULY MAXIMUM	JULY MINIMUM	OCTOBER MAXIMUM	OCTOBER MINIMUM	EXTREME MAXIMUM	EXTREME MINIMUM	AVERAGE PRECIPITATION: LENGTH OF RECORD	JANUARY	FEBRUARY	MARCH	APRIL	MAY	JUNE	JULY	AUGUST	SEPTEMBER	OCTOBER	NOVEMBER	DECEMBER	YEAR
	° ′	° ′	FEET	YEAR	°F	°F	°F	°F	°F	°F	°F	°F	°F	°F	YEAR	IN.	IN.	IN.	IN.	IN.	IN.	IN.	IN.	IN.	IN.	IN.	IN.	IN.
Burma:																												
Mandalay	21 59N	96 06E	252	20	82	55	101	77	93	78	89	73	111	44	20	0.1	0.1	0.2	1.2	5.8	6.3	2.7	4.1	5.4	4.3	2.0	0.4	32.6
Moulmein	16 26N	97 39E	150	43	89	65	95	77	83	74	88	75	103	52	60	0.2	0.2	0.5	3.0	19.9	37.1	47.5	44.2	27.1	8.5	1.7	0.3	190.2
Cambodia:																												
Phnom Penh	11 33N	104 51E	39	37	88	71	95	76	90	76	87	76	105	55	49	0.3	0.4	1.4	3.1	5.7	5.8	6.0	6.1	8.9	9.9	5.5	1.7	54.8
Indonesia:																												
Batavia (Jakarta)	06 11S	106 50E	26	80	84	74	87	75	87	73	87	74	98	66	78	11.8	11.8	8.3	5.8	4.5	3.8	2.5	1.7	2.6	4.4	5.6	8.0	70.8
Manokwari	00 53S	134 03E	10	5	86	73	86	74	86	74	87	74	93	68	40	12.0	9.4	13.2	11.1	7.8	7.2	5.4	5.6	4.9	4.7	6.5	10.3	98.1
Mapanget	01 32N	124 55E	264	21	85	73	86	73	87	73	89	72	97	65	63	18.6	13.8	12.2	8.0	6.4	6.5	4.8	4.0	3.3	4.9	8.9	14.7	106.1
Penfui	10 10S	123 39E	335	21	87	75	89	72	88	70	92	72	101	58	63	15.2	13.7	9.2	2.6	1.2	0.4	0.2	0.0	0.0	0.7	3.3	9.1	55.7
Pontianak	00 00N	109 20E	13	20	87	74	89	75	89	74	89	75	96	68	63	10.8	8.2	9.5	10.9	11.1	8.7	6.5	8.0	9.0	14.4	15.3	12.7	125.1
Tabing	00 52S	100 21E	19	21	87	74	87	75	87	74	86	74	94	68	63	13.9	10.1	12.2	14.5	12.8	11.7	10.5	13.7	16.2	20.1	20.5	19.2	175.4
Tarakan	03 19N	117 33E	20	19	85	73	86	75	87	74	87	74	94	67	31	10.9	10.2	14.0	13.9	13.5	12.6	10.3	12.4	11.6	14.3	15.2	13.4	152.3
Laos:																												
Vientiane	17 58N	102 34E	559	13	83	58	95	73	89	75	88	71	108	32	27	0.2	0.6	1.5	3.9	10.5	11.9	10.5	11.5	11.9	4.3	0.6	0.1	67.5
Malaya, Fed.:																												
Kuala Lumpur	03 06N	101 42E	111	19	90	72	91	74	90	72	89	73	99	64	19	6.2	7.9	10.2	11.5	8.8	5.1	3.9	6.4	8.6	9.8	10.2	7.5	96.1
Singapore	01 18N	103 50E	33	39	86	73	88	75	88	75	87	74	97	66	64	9.9	6.8	7.6	7.4	6.8	6.8	6.7	7.7	7.0	8.2	10.0	10.1	95.0
North Borneo:																												
Sanda Kan	05 54N	118 03E	38	45	85	74	89	76	89	75	88	75	99	70	46	19.0	10.9	8.6	4.5	6.2	7.4	6.7	7.9	9.3	10.2	14.5	18.5	123.7
Philippine Islands:																												
Davao	07 07N	125 38E	88	15	87	72	91	73	88	73	89	73	97	65	34	4.8	4.5	5.2	5.8	9.2	9.1	6.5	6.5	6.7	7.9	5.3	6.1	77.6
Manila	14 31N	121 00E	49	61	86	69	93	73	88	75	88	74	101	58	75	0.9	0.5	0.7	1.3	5.1	10.0	17.0	16.6	14.0	7.6	5.7	2.6	82.0
Sarawak:																												
Kuching	01 29N	110 20E	85	5	85	72	90	73	90	72	89	73	98	64	19	24.0	20.1	12.9	11.0	10.3	7.1	7.7	9.2	8.6	10.5	14.1	18.2	153.7
Thailand:																												
Bangkok	13 44N	100 30E	53	10	89	67	95	78	90	76	88	76	104	50	10	0.2	1.1	1.1	2.3	5.2	6.0	6.9	9.2	14.0	9.9	1.8	0.1	57.8
Viet Nam																												
Hanoi	21 03N	105 52E	20	12	68	58	80	70	92	79	84	72	108	41	12	0.8	1.2	2.5	3.6	4.1	11.2	11.9	15.2	10.0	3.5	2.6	2.8	69.4
Saigon	10 49N	106 39E	33	31	89	70	95	76	88	75	88	74	104	57	33	0.6	0.1	0.5	1.7	8.7	13.0	12.4	10.6	13.2	10.6	4.5	2.2	78.1
ASIA – MIDDLE EAST																												
Aden:																												
Riyan	14 39N	49 19E	83	13	82	67	88	74	92	77	88	72	111	57	13	0.3	0.1	0.6	0.2	*	0.1	0.1	0.1	*	*	0.7	0.3	2.5
Afghanistan:																												
Kabul	34 30N	69 13E	5,955	9	36	18	66	43	92	61	73	42	104	- 6	45	1.3	1.5	3.6	3.3	0.9	0.2	0.1	0.1	*	0.4	0.6	0.6	12.6
Kandhar	31 36N	65 40E	3,462	7	56	31	83	50	102	66	85	44	111	14	7	3.1	1.7	0.8	0.3	0.2	*	0.1	*	0.0	*	*	0.8	7.0
Ceylon:																												
Colombo	06 54N	79 52E	22	25	86	72	88	76	85	77	85	75	99	59	40	3.5	2.7	5.8	9.1	14.6	8.8	5.3	4.3	6.3	13.7	12.4	5.8	92.3
East Pakistan:																												
Dacca	23 46N	90 23E	24	60	77	56	92	74	88	79	88	75	108	43	61	0.3	1.2	2.4	5.4	9.6	12.4	13.0	13.3	9.8	5.3	1.0	0.2	73.9

(See footnotes at end of tables)

COUNTRY AND STATION	LATITUDE	LONGITUDE	ELEVATION	TEMPERATURE: LENGTH OF RECORD	AVERAGE DAILY: JANUARY MAXIMUM	JANUARY MINIMUM	APRIL MAXIMUM	APRIL MINIMUM	JULY MAXIMUM	JULY MINIMUM	OCTOBER MAXIMUM	OCTOBER MINIMUM	EXTREME: MAXIMUM	EXTREME: MINIMUM	AVERAGE PRECIPITATION: LENGTH OF RECORD	JANUARY	FEBRUARY	MARCH	APRIL	MAY	JUNE	JULY	AUGUST	SEPTEMBER	OCTOBER	NOVEMBER	DECEMBER	YEAR
	° ′	° ′	FEET	YEAR	°F	°F	°F	°F	°F	°F	°F	°F	°F	°F	YEAR	IN.	IN.	IN.	IN.	IN.	IN.	IN.	IN.	IN.	IN.	IN.	IN.	IN
Perth	31 56S	115 58E	64	44	85	63	76	57	63	48	70	53	112	31	63	0.3	0.4	0.8	1.7	5.1	7.1	6.7	5.7	3.4	2.2	0.8	0.5	34.7
Port Darwin	12 25S	130 52E	104	58	90	77	92	76	87	67	93	77	105	55	70	15.2	12.3	10.0	3.8	0.6	0.1	*	0.1	0.5	2.0	4.7	9.4	58.7
Sydney	33 52S	151 02E	62	87	78	65	71	58	60	46	71	56	114	35	87	3.5	4.0	5.0	5.3	5.0	4.6	4.6	3.0	2.9	2.8	2.9	2.9	46.5
Thursday Island	10 35S	142 13E	200	31	87	77	86	77	82	73	86	76	98	64	49	18.2	15.8	13.9	8.0	1.6	0.5	0.4	0.2	0.1	0.3	1.5	7.0	67.5
Townsville	19 15S	146 46E	18	31	87	76	84	70	75	59	83	71	110	39	67	10.9	11.2	7.2	3.3	1.3	1.4	0.6	0.5	0.7	1.3	1.9	5.4	45.7
William Creek	28 55S	136 21E	247	39	96	69	80	55	65	41	84	56	119	25	30	0.5	0.6	0.3	0.3	0.3	0.5	0.2	0.3	0.3	0.5	0.5	0.7	5.0
Windorah	25 26S	142 36E	390	29	101	74	86	59	70	43	91	61	116	26	50	1.4	1.6	1.6	0.9	0.8	0.8	0.5	0.4	0.5	0.6	0.9	1.4	11.4
Tasmania:																												
Hobart	42 53S	147 20E	177	70	71	53	63	48	52	40	63	46	105	28	100	1.9	1.5	1.8	1.9	1.8	2.2	2.1	1.9	2.1	2.3	2.4	2.1	24.0
New Zealand:																												
Auckland	37 00S	174 47E	23	36	73	60	67	56	56	46	63	52	90	33	92	3.1	3.7	3.2	3.8	5.0	5.4	5.7	4.6	4.0	4.0	3.5	3.1	49.1
Christchurch	43 29S	172 32E	118	52	70	53	62	45	50	35	62	44	96	21	64	2.2	1.7	1.9	1.9	2.6	2.6	2.7	1.9	1.8	1.7	1.9	2.2	25.1
Dunedin	45 55S	170 12E	4	77	66	50	59	45	48	37	59	42	94	23	77	3.4	2.8	3.0	2.8	3.2	3.2	3.1	3.0	2.7	3.0	3.2	3.5	36.9
Wellington	41 17S	174 46E	415	66	69	56	63	51	53	42	60	48	88	29	79	3.2	3.2	3.2	3.8	4.6	4.6	5.4	4.6	3.8	4.0	3.5	3.5	47.4
PACIFIC ISLANDS:																												
Canton, Phoenix Is.	02 46S	171 43W	9	12	88	78	89	78	89	78	90	78	98	70	30	2.6	2.2	2.5	3.6	4.3	2.6	2.6	2.5	1.2	1.1	1.6	2.6	29.4
Guam, Marianas Is.	13 33N	144 50E	361	30	84	72	86	73	87	72	86	73	95	54	30	4.6	3.5	2.6	3.0	4.2	5.9	9.0	12.8	13.4	13.1	10.3	6.1	88.5
Honolulu, Hawaii	21 20N	157 55W	7	30	79	66	80	68	85	73	84	72	93	56	30	3.8	3.3	2.9	1.3	1.0	0.3	0.4	0.9	1.0	1.8	2.2	3.0	21.9
Iwo Jima, Bonin Is.	24 47N	141 19E	353	15	71	64	77	69	86	78	84	76	95	46	17	3.2	2.5	2.1	3.7	4.9	4.0	6.4	6.5	4.6	5.9	4.8	4.3	52.8
Madang, New Guinea	05 12S	145 47E	19	12	87	75	88	74	88	74	88	75	98	62	20	12.1	11.9	14.9	16.9	15.1	10.8	7.6	4.8	5.3	10.0	13.3	14.5	137.2
Midway Is.	28 13N	177 23W	29	21	69	62	71	64	81	74	79	72	92	46	20	4.6	3.7	3.1	2.5	1.9	1.3	2.9	3.9	3.7	3.7	3.6	4.2	40.7
Naha, Okinawa	26 12N	127 39E	96	30	67	56	76	64	89	77	81	69	96	41	30	5.3	5.4	6.1	6.1	8.9	10.0	7.1	10.0	7.1	6.6	5.9	4.3	82.8
Noumea, New Caledonia	22 16S	166 27E	246	24	86	72	83	70	76	62	80	65	99	52	52	3.7	5.1	5.7	5.2	4.4	3.7	3.6	2.6	2.5	2.0	2.4	2.6	43.5
Pago Pago, Samoa	14 19S	170 43W	29	2	87	75	87	76	83	74	85	75	98	67	41	24.5	20.5	19.2	16.5	15.4	12.3	10.0	8.2	13.1	14.9	19.2	19.8	193.6
Ponape, Caroline Is.	06 58N	158 13E	123	30	86	75	86	75	87	73	87	72	96	67	30	11.1	9.7	14.6	20.0	20.3	16.7	16.2	16.3	15.8	16.0	16.9	18.3	191.9
Port Moresby, New Guinea	09 29S	147 09E	126	20	89	76	87	75	83	73	86	75	98	64	38	7.0	7.6	6.7	4.2	2.5	1.3	1.1	0.7	1.0	1.4	1.9	4.4	39.8
Rabaul, New Guinea	04 13S	152 11E	28	19	90	73	90	73	89	73	92	73	100	65	24	14.8	10.4	10.2	10.0	5.2	3.3	5.4	3.7	3.5	5.1	7.1	10.1	88.8
Suva, Fiji Is.	18 08S	178 26E	20	43	86	74	84	73	79	68	81	70	98	55	43	11.4	10.7	14.5	12.2	10.1	6.7	4.9	8.3	7.7	8.3	9.8	12.5	117.1
Tahiti, Society Is.	17 33S	149 36W	7	23	89	72	89	72	86	68	87	70	93	61	27	13.2	11.5	6.5	6.8	4.9	3.2	2.6	1.9	2.3	3.4	6.5	11.9	74.7
Tulagi, Solomon Is.	09 05S	160 10E	8	20	88	76	88	76	86	76	87	76	96	68	37	14.3	15.8	15.0	10.0	8.1	6.8	7.6	8.7	8.0	8.7	10.0	10.4	123.4
Wake Is.	19 17N	166 39E	11	30	82	73	83	74	87	77	86	77	92	64	30	1.1	1.4	1.5	1.9	2.0	1.9	4.6	7.1	5.2	5.3	3.1	1.8	36.9
Yap, Caroline Is.	9 31N	138 08E	62	30	85	76	87	77	88	75	88	75	97	69	30	7.9	4.6	5.4	6.4	9.5	10.7	13.8	14.7	14.0	13.2	11.2	10.2	121.6

COUNTRY AND STATION	LATITUDE (° ′)	LONGITUDE (° ′)	ELEVATION (FEET)	TEMPERATURE: LENGTH OF RECORD (YEAR)	AVERAGE DAILY JANUARY MAXIMUM (°F)	AVERAGE DAILY JANUARY MINIMUM (°F)	AVERAGE DAILY APRIL MAXIMUM (°F)	AVERAGE DAILY APRIL MINIMUM (°F)	AVERAGE DAILY JULY MAXIMUM (°F)	AVERAGE DAILY JULY MINIMUM (°F)	AVERAGE DAILY OCTOBER MAXIMUM (°F)	AVERAGE DAILY OCTOBER MINIMUM (°F)	EXTREME MAXIMUM (°F)	EXTREME MINIMUM (°F)
ANTARCTICA														
Byrd Station	80 01S	119 32W	5,095	6	10	- 2	-11	-30	-25	-45	-15	-33	31	-82
Ellsworth	77 44S	41 07W	139	6	22	12	-10	-25	-21	-35	- 2	-15	36	-70
McMurdo Station	77 53S	166 48W	8	10	30	21	- 1	-13	- 9	-24	2	-12	42	-59
South Pole Station	89 59S	000 00W	9,186	5	-16	-23	-66	-79	-67	-81	-55	-64	6	-107
Wilkes	66 16S	110 31E	31	7	34	28	17	9	8	- 3	16	6	46	-35

COUNTRY AND STATION	AVERAGE PRECIPITATION: LENGTH OF RECORD (YEAR)	JANUARY (IN.)	FEBRUARY (IN.)	MARCH (IN.)	APRIL (IN.)	MAY (IN.)	JUNE (IN.)	JULY (IN.)	AUGUST (IN.)	SEPTEMBER (IN.)	OCTOBER (IN.)	NOVEMBER (IN.)	DECEMBER (IN.)	YEAR (IN.)
ANTARCTICA														
Byrd Station	6	0.4	0.4	0.2	0.3	0.4	0.5	0.7	0.7	0.3	0.7	0.0	0.3	4.9
Ellsworth	6	0.3	0.2	0.3	0.6	0.2	0.2	0.2	0.2	0.3	0.4	0.5	0.2	3.6
McMurdo Station	10	0.5	0.7	0.4	0.4	0.4	0.3	0.2	0.3	0.4	0.2	0.2	0.3	4.3
South Pole Station	5	*	0.1	0.0	0.0	0.0	0.0	0.0	0.0	0.0	*	0.0	*	0.1
Wilkes	7	0.5	0.4	1.7	1.1	1.4	1.2	1.3	0.8	1.5	1.2	0.8	0.3	12.2

NOTES

1. "Length of Record" refers to average daily maximum and minimum temperatures and precipitation. A standard period of the 30 years from 1931-1960 had been used for locations in the United States and some other countries. The length of record of extreme maximum and minimum temperatures includes all available years of data for a given location and is usually for a longer period.

2. * - Less than 0.05"

3. Except for Antarctica, amounts of solid precipitation such as snow or hail have been converted to their water equivalent. Because of the frequent occurrence of blowing snow, it has not been possible to determine the precise amount of precipitation actually falling in Antarctica. The values shown are the average amounts of solid snow accumulating in a given period as determined by snow markers. The liquid content of the accumulation is undetermined.

ENERGY/WEATHER

HEATING AND COOLING DEGREE DAY DATA

Heating Degree Days

Early this century heating engineers developed the concept of heating degree days as a useful index of heating fuel requirements. They found that when the daily mean temperature is lower than 65 degrees, most buildings require heat to maintain an inside temperature of 70 degrees.* The daily mean temperature is obtained by adding together the maximum and minimum temperatures reported for the day and dividing the total by two. Each degree of mean temperature below 65 is counted as one heating degree day. Thus, if the maximum temperature is 70 degrees and the minimum 52 degrees, four heating degree days would be produced. (70 + 52 = 122; 122 divided by 2 = 61; 65 - 61 = 4). If the daily mean temperature is 65 degrees or higher, the heating degree day total is zero.

For every additional heating degree day, more fuel is needed to maintain a comfortable 70 degrees indoors. A day with a mean temperature of 35 degrees — 30 heating degree days — would require twice as much fuel as a day with a mean temperature of 50 — 15 heating degree days, assuming, of course, similar meteorological conditions such as wind speed and cloudiness.

So valuable has the heating degree concept become that daily, monthly and seasonal totals are routinely computed for all temperature observing stations in the National Weather Service's network. Daily figures are used by fuel companies for evaluation of fuel use rates and for efficient scheduling of deliveries. For example, if a heating system is known to use one gallon of fuel for every 5 heating degree days, oil deliveries will be scheduled to meet this burning rate. Gas and Electric Company dispatchers use the data to anticipate demand and to implement priority procedures when demand exceeds capacity.

The amount of heat required to maintain a certain temperature level is proportional to the heating degree days. A fuel bill usually will be twice as high for a month with 1,000 heating degree days as for a month with 500. For example, it can be estimated that about four times as much fuel will be required to heat a building in Chicago, where the annual average is 6,100 heating degree days, as it would to heat a building in New Orleans, where the average is about 1,500. All this is true only if building construction and living habits in these areas are similar. Since such factors are not constant, these ratios must be modified by actual experience. The use of heating degree days has the advantage that consumption rates are fairly constant, i.e., fuel consumed for 100 degree days is about the same whether the 100 heating degree days were accumulated on only three or four days or were spread over seven or eight days.

Accumulation of temperature data for a particular location has resulted in the establishment of "normal" values based on thirty years of record. Maps and tables of heating degree day normals, are published by the National Oceanic and Atmospheric Administration's Environmental Data Service (EDS). The maps are useful only for broad general comparisons, because temperatures, even in a small area, vary considerably depending on differences in altitude, exposure, wind, and other circumstances. FIG. 11.1, NORMAL SEASONAL HEATING DEGREE DAYS, 1941-1970, illustrates the national distribution. Tables of normal monthly and annual heating degree days for U.S. cities provide a more accurate basis for comparison. The tables show, for instance, that Washington, D.C. (National Airport) has a normal annual total of 4,211 heating degree days, while the normal for Boston, Massachusetts (Logan International Airport) is 5,621.

Heating degree day comparisons within a single area are the most accurate. For example, March heating degree day totals in the Midwest average about 70 percent of those for January. In Chicago, the coldest six months in order of decreasing coldness are January, December, February, March, November, and April. Annual heating degree day data are published by heating season which runs from July of one year through June of the next year. This enables direct comparison of seasonal heating degree day data and seasonal heating fuel requirements.

Cooling Degree Days

The cooling degree day statistic — summer sister of the familiar heating degree day — serves as an index of air-conditioning requirements during the year's warmest months.

According to experts, the need for air-conditioning begins to be felt when the daily maximum temperature climbs to 80 degrees and higher. The cooling degree day is therefore a kind of mirror image of the heating degree day. After obtaining the daily mean temperature, by adding together the day's high and low temperatures and dividing the total by two, the base 65 is substracted from the resulting figure to determine the cooling degree day total. For example, a day with a maximum temperature of 82 degrees and a minimum of 60 would produce six cooling degree days. (82 + 60 = 142; 142 divided by 2 = 71; 71 - 65 = 6). If the daily mean temperature is 65 degrees or lower, the cooling degree day total is zero.

The greater the number of cooling degree days, the more energy is required to maintain indoor temperatures at a comfortable level. However, the relationship between cooling degree days and energy use is less precise than that between heating degree days and fuel consumption. There is considerable controversy among meteorologists, as well as air-conditioning engineers, as to what meteorological variables are most closely related to energy consumption by air-conditiong systems. Many experts argue that because high humidity levels make people feel more uncomfortable as temperatures rise, some measure of moisture should be included in calculating energy needs for air-conditioning. The Temperature-Humidity Index has been suggested as an alternative basis for calculating cooling degree days. In addition to humidity some experts feel there are other factors, such as cloudiness and wind speed, that should be included in computation of energy needs for air-conditioning. All agree, however, that there is a need for a more effective measure of the influence of weather on air-conditioning loads.

Until a definitive study of the problem is conducted, NOAA's EDS is continuing to use and publish statistics based on simple cooling degree day calculations, employing air temperatures measured at National Weather Service Offices and cooperating stations throughout the country. As with heating degree days, normals of cooling degree days have been established, based on thirty years of record. FIGURE 11.2, NORMAL SEASONAL COOLING DEGREE DAYS, 1941-1970, illustrates the national distribution.

PLEASE NOTE THAT HEATING AND COOLING DEGREE DAYS DO NOT CANCEL EACH OTHER OUT. TOTALS FOR EACH ARE ACCUMULATED INDEPENDENTLY.

---

* All temperatures are in degrees Fahrenheit unless otherwise specified.

NORMAL SEASONAL HEATING DEGREE DAYS (BASE 65 F) 1941-1970

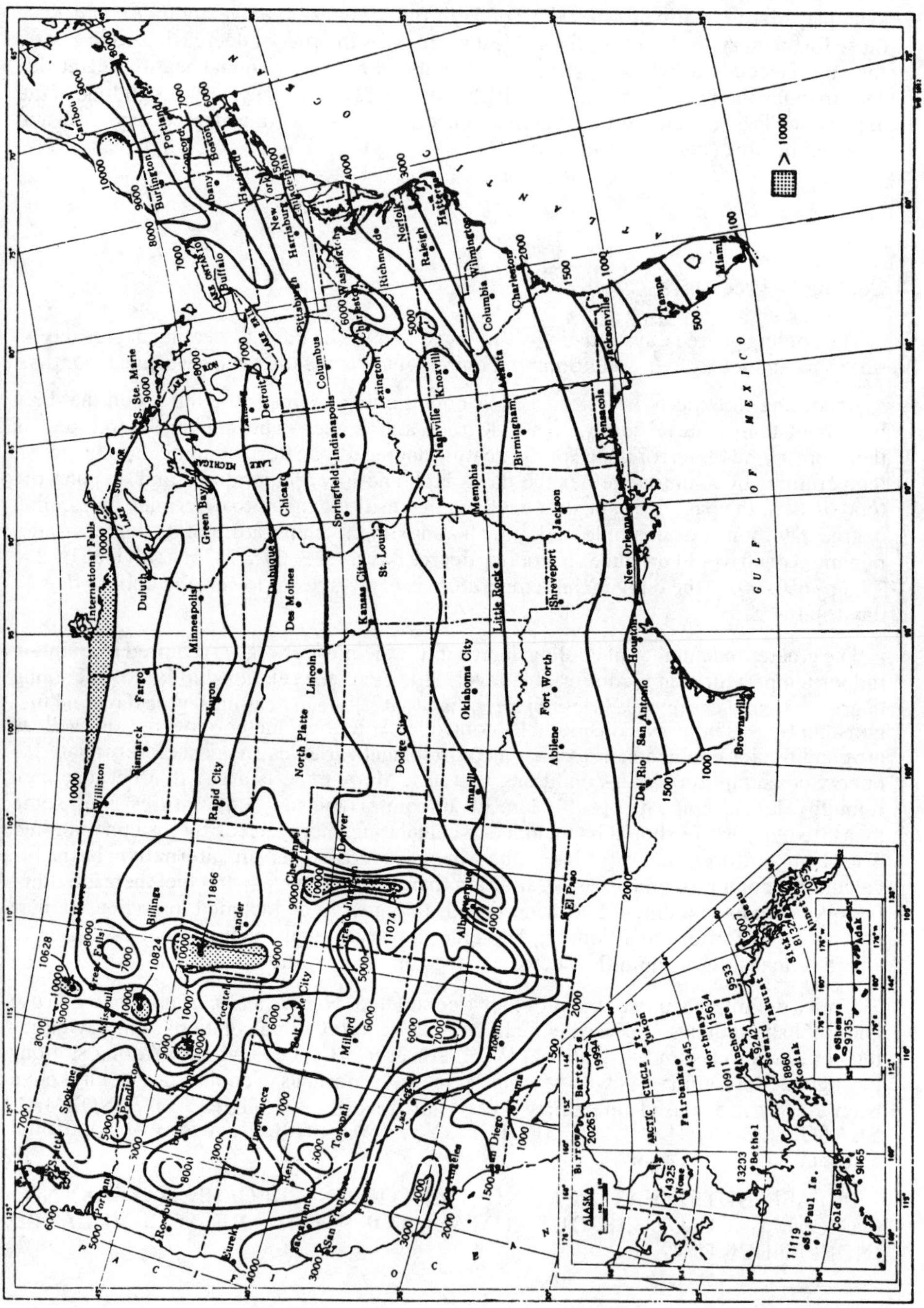

FIG. 11.1

NORMAL SEASONAL COOLING DEGREE DAYS (BASE 65 F) 1941-1970

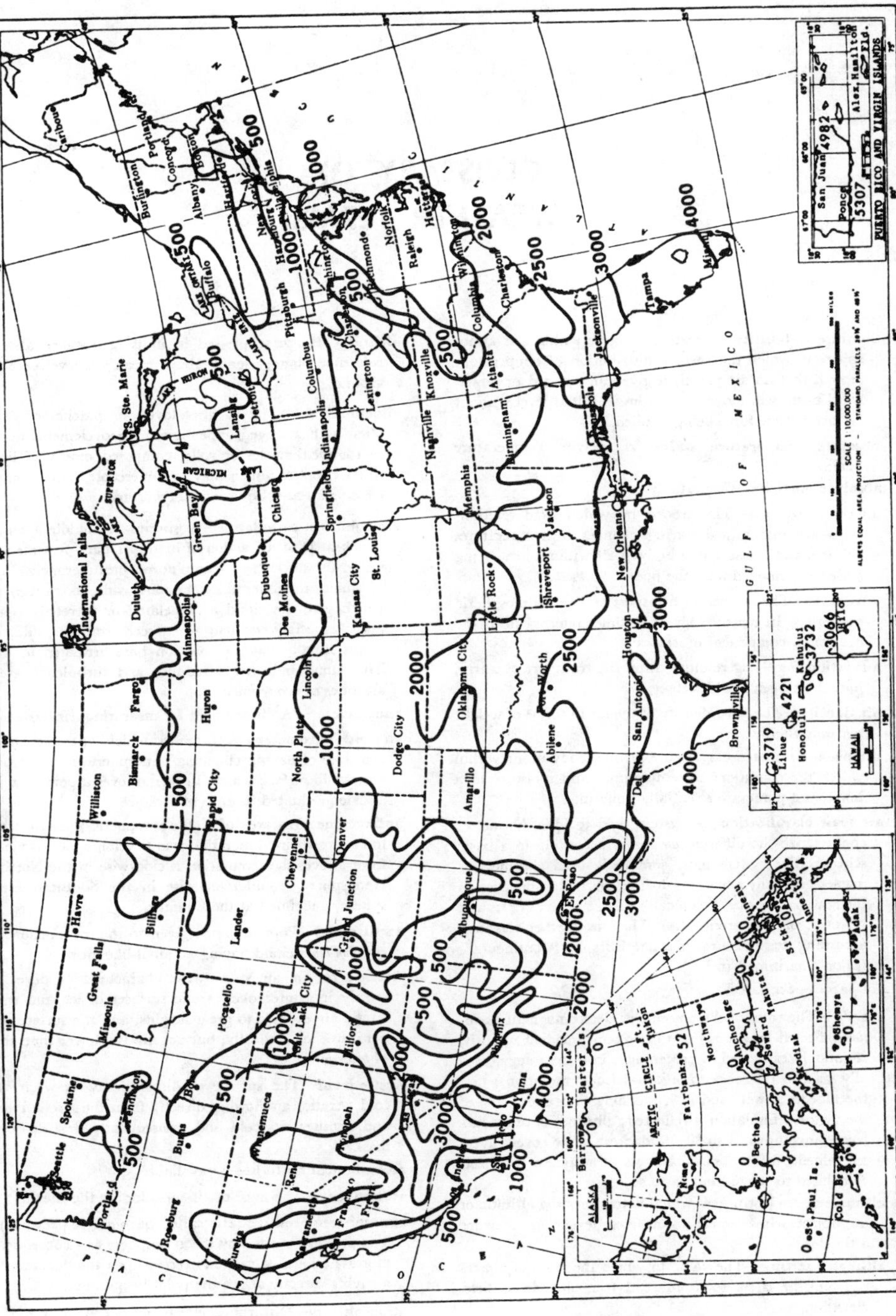

FIG. 11.2

GLOSSARY OF WEATHER TERMS

A

absolute instability—A state of a layer within the atmosphere in which the vertical distribution of temperature is such that an air parcel, if given an upward or downward push, will move away from its initial level without further outside force being applied.

absolute temperature scale—*See* Kelvin Temperature Scale.

absolute vorticity—*See* vorticity.

adiabatic process—The process by which fixed relationships are maintained during changes in temperature, volume, and pressure in a body of air without heat being added or removed from the body.

advection—The horizontal transport of air or atmospheric properties. In meteorology, sometimes referred to as the horizontal component of *convection.*

advection fog—Fog resulting from the transport of warm, humid air over a cold surface.

air density—The mass density of the air in terms of weight per unit volume.

air mass—In meteorology, an extensive body of air within which the conditions of temperature and moisture in a horizontal plane are essentially uniform.

air mass classification—A system used to identify and to characterize the different *air masses* according to a basic scheme. The system most commonly used classifies air masses primarily according to the thermal properties of their *source regions:* "tropical" (T); "polar" (P); and "Arctic" or "Antarctic" (A). They are further classified according to moisture characteristics as "continental" (c) or "maritime" (m).

air parcel—*See* parcel.

albedo—The ratio of the amount of electromagnetic *radiation* reflected by a body to the amount incident upon it, commonly expressed in percentage; in meteorology, usually used in reference to *insolation* (solar radiation); i.e., the albedo of wet sand is 9, meaning that about 9% of the incident insolation is reflected; albedoes of other surfaces range upward to 80–85 for fresh snow cover; average albedo for the earth and its atmosphere has been calculated to range from 35 to 43.

altimeter—An instrument which determines the altitude or an object with respect to a fixed level. *See* pressure altimeter.

altimeter setting—The value to which the scale of a *pressure altimeter* is set so as to read true altitude at field elevation.

altimeter setting indicator—A precision *aneroid barometer* calibrated to indicate directly the altimeter setting.

altitude—Height expressed in units of distance above a reference plane, usually above mean sea level or above ground.

altocumulus—White or gray layers or patches of cloud, often with a waved appearance; cloud elements appear as rounded masses or rolls; composed mostly of liquid water droplets which may be supercooled; may contain ice crystals at subfreezing temperatures.

altocumulus castellanus—A species of middle cloud of which at least a fraction of its upper part presents some vertically developed, cumuliform protuberances (some of which are taller than they are wide, as castles) and which give the cloud a crenelated or turreted appearance; especially evident when seen from the side; elements usually have a common base arranged in lines. This cloud indicates instability and turbulence at the altitudes of occurrence.

anemometer—An instrument for measuring *wind speed.*

aneroid barometer—A *barometer* which operates on the principle of having changing atmospheric pressure bend a metallic surface which, in turn, moves a pointer across a scale graduated in units of pressure.

anticyclone—An area of high atmospheric pressure which has a closed circulation that is anticyclonic, i.e., as viewed from above, the circulation is clockwise in the Northern Hemisphere, counterclockwise in the Southern Hemisphere, undefined at the Equator.

anvil cloud—Popular name given to the top portion of a *cumulonimbus* cloud having an anvil-like form.

Arctic air—An air mass with characteristics developed mostly in winter over Arctic surfaces of ice and snow. Arctic air extends to great heights, and the surface temperatures are basically, but not always, lower than those of *polar air.*

Arctic front—The surface of discontinuity between very cold (Arctic) air flowing directly from the Arctic region and another less cold and, consequently, less dense air mass.

astronomical twilight—*See* twilight.

atmosphere—The mass of air surrounding the Earth.

atmospheric pressure (also called barometric pressure)—The pressure exerted by the atmosphere as a consequence of gravitational attraction exerted upon the "column" of air lying directly above the point in question.

atmospherics—Disturbing effects produced in radio receiving apparatus by atmospheric electrical phenomena such as an electrical storm. Static.

aurora—A luminous, radiant emission over middle and high latitudes confined to the thin air of high altitudes and centered over the earth's magnetic poles. Called "aurora borealis" (northern lights) or "aurora australis" according to its occurrence in the Northern or Southern Hemisphere, respectively.

B

backing—Shifting of the wind in a counterclockwise direction with respect to either space or time; opposite of *veering*. Commonly used by meteorologists to refer to a cyclonic shift (counterclockwise in the Northern Hemisphere and clockwise in the Southern Hemisphere).

backscatter—Pertaining to radar, the energy reflected or scattered by a *target;* an *echo.*

banner cloud (also called cloud banner)—A banner-like cloud streaming off from a mountain peak.

barograph—A continuous-recording *barometer.*

barometer—An instrument for measuring the pressure of the atmosphere; the two principle types are *mercurial* and *aneroid.*

barometric altimeter—*See* pressure altimeter.

barometric pressure—Same as *atmospheric pressure.*

barometric tendency—The change of barometric pressure within a specified period of time. In aviation weather observations, routinely determined periodically, usually for a 3-hour period.

Beaufort scale—A scale of wind speeds.

black blizzard—Same as *duststorm.*

blizzard—A severe weather condition characterized by low temperatures and strong winds bearing a great amount of snow, either falling or picked up from the ground.

blowing dust—A type of *lithometeor* composed of dust particles picked up locally from the surface and blown about in clouds or sheets.

blowing sand—A type of *lithometeor* composed of sand picked up locally from the surface and blown about in clouds or sheets.

blowing snow—A type of *hydrometeor* composed of snow picked up from the surface by the wind and carried to a height of 6 feet or more.

blowing spray—A type of *hydrometeor* composed of water particles picked up by the wind from the surface of a large body of water.

Buys Ballot's law—If an observer in the Northern Hemisphere stands with his back to the wind, lower pressure is to his left.

C

calm—The absence of wind or of apparent motion of the air.

cap cloud (also called cloud cap)—A standing or stationary cap-like cloud crowning a mountain summit.

ceiling—In meteorology in the U.S., (1) the height above the surface of the base of the lowest layer of clouds or *obscuring phenomena* aloft that hides more than half of the sky, or (2) the *vertical visibility* into an *obscuration. See* summation principle.

Celsius temperature scale (abbreviated C)—A temperature scale with zero degrees as the melting point of pure ice and 100 degrees as the boiling point of pure water at standard sea level atmospheric pressure.

Centigrade temperature scale—Same as *Celsius temperature scale.*

change of state—In meteorology, the transformation of water from one form, i.e., solid (ice), liquid, or gaseous (water vapor), to any other form. There are six possible transformations designated by the five terms following:

(1) **condensation**—The change of water vapor to liquid water.

(2) **evaporation**—The change of liquid water to water vapor.

(3) **freezing**—The change of liquid water to ice.

(4) **melting**—The change of ice to liquid water.

(5) **sublimation**—The change of (a) ice to water vapor or (b) water vapor to ice. *See* latent heat.

Chinook—A warm, dry *foehn* wind blowing down the eastern slopes of the Rocky Mountains over the adjacent plains in the U.S. and Canada.

cirriform—All species and varieties of *cirrus, cirrocumulus,* and *cirrostratus* clouds; descriptive of clouds composed mostly or entirely of small ice crystals, usually transparent and white; often producing *halo* phenomena not observed with other cloud forms. Average height ranges upward from 20,000 feet in middle latitudes.

cirrocumulus—A *cirriform* cloud appearing as a thin sheet of small white puffs resembling flakes or patches of cotton without shadows; sometimes confused with *altocumulus.*

cirrostratus—A *cirriform* cloud appearing as a whitish veil, usually fibrous, sometimes smooth; often produces *halo* phenomena; may totally cover the sky.

cirrus—A *cirriform* cloud in the form of thin, white featherlike clouds in patches or narrow bands; have a fibrous and/or silky sheen; large ice crystals often trail downward a considerable vertical distance in fibrous, slanted, or irregularly curved wisps called mares' tails.

civil twilight—*See* twilight.

climate—The statistical collective of the weather conditions of a point or area during a specified interval of time (usually several decades); may be expressed in a variety of ways.

climatology—The study of *climate.*

clinometer—An instrument used in weather observing for measuring angles of inclination; it is used in conjunction with a *ceiling light* to determine cloud height at night.

cloudburst—In popular teminology, any sudden and heavy fall of *rain,* almost always of the *shower* type.

cloud cap—*See* cap cloud.

cold front—Any non-occluded *front* which moves in such a way that colder air replaces warmer air.

condensation—*See* change of state.

condensation level—The height at which a rising *parcel* or layer of air would become saturated if lifted adiabatically.

condensation nuclei—Small particles in the air on which water vapor condenses or sublimates.

condensation trail (or contrail) (also called vapor trail)—A cloud-like streamer frequently observed to form behind aircraft flying in clear, cold, humid air.

conditionally unstable air—Unsaturated air that will become unstable on the condition it becomes saturated. *See* instability.

conduction—The transfer of heat by molecular action through a substance or from one substance in contact with another; transfer is always from warmer to colder temperature.

constant pressure chart—A chart of a constant pressure surface; may contain analyses of height, wind, temperature, humidity, and/or other elements.

continental polar air—*See* polar air.

continental tropical air—*See* tropical air.

contour—In meteorology, (1) a line of equal height on a constant pressure chart; analogous to contours on a relief map; (2) in radar meteorology, a line on a radar scope of equal *echo* intensity.

contouring circuit—On weather radar, a circuit which displays multiple contours of *echo* intensity simultaneously on the *plan position indicator* or *range-height indicator* scope. *See* contour (2).

contrail—Contraction for *condensation trail.*

convection—(1) In general, mass motions within a fluid resulting in transport and mixing of the properties of that fluid. (2) In meteorology, atmospheric motions that are predominantly vertical, resulting in vertical transport and mixing of atmospheric properties; distinguished from *advection.*

convective cloud—*See* cumuliform.

convective condensation level (abbreviated CCL)—The lowest level at which condensation will occur as a result of *convection* due to surface heating. When condensation occurs at this level, the layer between the surface and the CCL will be thoroughly mixed, temperature *lapse rate* will be dry adiabatic, and *mixing ratio* will be constant.

convective instability—The state of an unsaturated layer of air whose *lapse rates* of temperature and moisture are such that when lifted adiabatically until the layer becomes saturated, convection is spontaneous.

convergence—The condition that exists when the distribution of winds within a given area is such that there is a net horizontal inflow of air into the area. In convergence at lower levels, the removal of the resulting excess is accomplished by an upward movement of air; consequently, areas of low-level convergent winds are regions favorable to the occurrence of clouds and precipitation. Compare with *divergence.*

Coriolis force—A deflective force resulting from earth's rotation; it acts to the right of wind direction in the Northern Hemisphere and to the left in the Southern Hemisphere.

corona—A prismatically colored circle or arcs of a circle with the sun or moon at its center; coloration is from blue inside to red outside (opposite that of a *halo*); varies in size (much smaller) as opposed to the fixed diameter of the halo; characteristic of clouds composed of water droplets and valuable in differentiating between middle and cirriform clouds.

corposant—*See* St. Elmo's Fire.

corrected altitude (approximation of true altitude)—*See* altitude.

cumuliform—A term descriptive of all convective clouds exhibiting vertical development in contrast to the horizontally extended *stratiform* types.

cumulonimbus—A cumuliform cloud type; it is heavy and dense, with considerable vertical extent in the form of massive towers; often with tops in the shape of an *anvil* or massive plume; under the base of cumulonimbus, which often is very dark, there frequently exists *virga*, precipitation and low ragged clouds (*scud*), either merged with it or not; frequently accompanied by lightning, thunder, and sometimes hail; occasionally produces a tornado or a waterspout; the ultimate manifestation of the growth of a cumulus cloud, occasionally extending well into the stratosphere.

cumulonimbus mamma—A *cumulonimbus* cloud having hanging protuberances, like pouches, festoons, or udders, on the under side of the cloud; usually indicative of severe turbulence.

cumulus—A cloud in the form of individual detached domes or towers which are usually dense and well defined; develops vertically in the form of rising mounds of which the bulging upper part often resembles a cauliflower; the sunlit parts of these clouds are mostly brilliant white; their bases are relatively dark and nearly horizontal.

cumulus fractus—*See* fractus.

cyclogenesis—Any development or strengthening of cyclonic circulation in the atmosphere.

cyclone—(1) An area of low atmospheric pressure which has a closed circulation that is cyclonic, i.e., as viewed from above, the circulation is counterclockwise in the Northern Hemisphere, clockwise in the Southern Hemisphere, undefined at the Equator. Because cyclonic circulation and relatively low atmospheric pressure usually coexist, in common practice the terms cyclone and low are used interchangeably. Also, because cyclones often are accompanied by inclement (sometimes destructive) weather, they are frequently referred to simply as storms. (2) Frequently misused to denote a *tornado.* (3) In the Indian Ocean, a *tropical cyclone* of hurricane or typhoon force.

D

deepening—A decrease in the central pressure of a pressure system; usually applied to a *low* rather than to a *high*, although technically, it is acceptable in either sense.

density—(1) The ratio of the mass of any substance to the volume it occupies—weight per unit volume. (2) The ratio of any quantity to the volume or area it occupies, i.e., population per unit area, *power density.*

density altitude—*See* altitude.

depression—In meteorology, an area of low pressure; a *low* or *trough.* This is usually applied to a certain stage in the development of a *tropical cyclone*, to migratory lows and troughs, and to upper-level lows and troughs that are only weakly developed.

dew—Water condensed onto grass and other objects near the ground, the temperatures of which have fallen below the initial dew point temperature of the surface air, but is still above freezing. Compare with *frost.*

dew point (or dew-point temperature)—The temperature to which a sample of air must be cooled, while the *mixing ratio* and barometric pressure remain constant, in order to attain saturation with respect to water.

discontinuity—A zone with comparatively rapid transition of one or more meteorological elements.

disturbance—In meteorology, applied rather loosely: (1) any low pressure or cyclone, but usually one that is relatively small in size; (2) an area where weather, wind, pressure, etc., show signs of cyclonic development; (3) any deviation in flow or pressure that is associated with a disturbed state of the weather, i.e., cloudiness and precipitation; and (4) any individual circulatory system within the primary circulation of the atmosphere.

diurnal—Daily, especially pertaining to a cycle completed within a 24-hour period, and which recurs every 24 hours.

divergence—The condition that exists when the distribution of winds within a given area is such that there is a net horizontal flow of air outward from the region. In divergence at lower levels, the resulting deficit is compensated for by subsidence of air from aloft; consequently the air is heated and the relative humidity lowered making divergence a warming and drying process. Low-level divergent regions are areas unfavorable to the occurrence of clouds and precipitation. The opposite of *convergence.*

doldrums—The equatorial belt of calm or light and variable winds between the two tradewind belts. Compare *intertropical convergence zone.*

downdraft—A relative small scale downward current of air; often observed on the lee side of large objects restricting the smooth flow of the air or in precipitation areas in or near *cumuliform* clouds.

drifting snow—A type of *hydrometeor* composed of snow particles picked up from the surface, but carried to a height of less than 6 feet.

drizzle—A form of *precipitation.* Very small water drops that appear to float with the air currents while falling in an irregular path (unlike *rain,* which falls in a comparatively straight path, and unlike *fog* droplets which remain suspended in the air).

dropsonde—A *radiosonde* dropped by parachute from an aircraft to obtain *soundings* (measurements) of the atmosphere below.

dry adiabatic lapse rate—The rate of decrease of temperature with height when unsaturated air is lifted adiabatically (due to expansion as it is lifted to lower pressure). *See* adiabatic process.

dry bulb—A name given to an ordinary thermometer used to determine temperature of the air; also used as a contraction for *dry-bulb temperature.* Compare *wet bulb.*

dry-bulb temperature—The temperature of the air.

dust—A type of *lithometeor* composed of small earthen particles suspended in the atmosphere.

dust devil—A small, vigorous *whirlwind,* usually of short duration, rendered visible by dust, sand, and debris picked up from the ground.

duster—Same as *duststorm.*

duststorm (also called duster, black blizzard)—An unusual, frequently severe weather condition characterized by strong winds and dust-filled air over an extensive area.

D-value—Departure of true altitude from pressure altitude (*see* altitude); obtained by algebraically subtracting true altitude from pressure altitude; thus it may be plus or minus. On a constant pressure chart, the difference between actual height and *standard atmospheric* height of a constant pressure surface.

E

eddy—A local irregularity of wind in a larger scale wind flow. Small scale eddies produce turbulent conditions.

estimated ceiling—A ceiling classification applied when the ceiling height has been estimated by the observer or has been determined by some other method; but, because of the specified limits of time, distance, or precipitation conditions, a more descriptive classification cannot be applied.

evaporation—*See* change of state.

extratropical low (sometimes called extratropical cyclone, extratropical storm)—Any *cyclone* that is not a *tropical cyclone,* usually referring to the migratory frontal cyclones of middle and high latitudes.

eye—The roughly circular area of calm or relatively light winds and comparatively fair weather at the center of a well-developed *tropical cyclone.* A *wall cloud* marks the outer boundary of the eye.

F

Fahrenheit temperature scale (abbreviated F)—A temperature scale with 32 degrees as the melting point of pure ice and 212 degrees as the boiling point of pure water at standard sea level atmospheric pressure (29.92 inches or 1013.2 millibars).

Fall wind—A cold wind blowing downslope. Fall wind differs from *foehn* in that the air is initially cold enough to remain relatively cold despite compressional heating during descent.

filling—An increase in the central pressure of a pressure system; opposite of *deepening;* more commonly applied to a low rather than a high.

first gust—The leading edge of the spreading downdraft, *plow wind,* from an approaching thunderstorm.

flow line—A *streamline.*

foehn—A warm, dry downslope wind; the warmness and dryness being due to adiabatic compression upon descent; characteristic of mountainous regions. *See* adiabatic process, Chinook, Santa Ana.

fog—A *hydrometeor* consisting of numerous minute water droplets and based at the surface; droplets are small enough to be suspended in the earth's atmosphere indefinitely. (Unlike *drizzle,* it does not fall to the surface; differs from cloud only in that a cloud is not based at the surface; distinguished from haze by its wetness and gray color.)

fractus—Clouds in the form of irregular shreds, appearing as if torn; have a clearly ragged appearance; applies only to stratus and cumulus, i.e., *cumulus* fractus and *stratus* fractus.

freezing—*See* change of state.

freezing level—A level in the atmosphere at which the temperature is 0° C (32° F).

front—A surface, interface, or transition zone of discontinuity between two adjacent *air masses* of different densities; more simply the boundary between two different air masses. *See* frontal zone.

frontal zone—A *front* or zone with a marked increase of density gradient; used to denote that fronts are not truly a "surface" of discontinuity but rather a "zone" of rapid transition of meteorological elements.

frontogenesis—The initial formation of a *front* or *frontal zone.*

frontolysis—The dissipation of a *front.*

frost (also hoarfrost)—Ice crystal deposits formed by sublimation when temperature and dew point are below freezing.

funnel cloud—A *tornado* cloud or *vortex* cloud extending downward from the parent cloud but not reaching the ground.

G

glaze—A coating of ice, generally clear and smooth, formed by freezing of supercooled water on a surface.

gradient—In meteorology, a horizontal decrease in value per unit distance of a parameter in the direction of maximum decrease; most commonly used with pressure, temperature, and moisture.

ground fog—In the United States, a *fog* that conceals less than 0.6 of the sky and is not contiguous with the base of clouds.

gust—A sudden brief increase in wind; according to U.S. weather observing practice, gusts are reported when the variation in wind speed between peaks and lulls is at least 10 knots.

H

hail—A form of *precipitation* composed of balls or irregular lumps of ice, always produced by convective clouds which are nearly always *cumulonimbus.*

halo—A prismatically colored or whitish circle or arcs of a circle with the sun or moon at its center; coloration, if not white, is from red inside to blue outside (opposite that of a *corona*); fixed in size with an angular diameter of 22° (common) or 46° (rare); characteristic of clouds composed of ice crystals; valuable in differentiating between *cirriform* and forms of lower clouds.

haze—A type of *lithometeor* composed of fine dust or salt particles dispersed through a portion of the atmosphere; particles are so small they cannot be felt or individually seen with the naked eye (as compared with the larger particles of *dust*), but diminish the visibility; distinguished from *fog* by its bluish or yellowish tinge.

high—An area of high barometric pressure, with its attendant system of winds; an *anticyclone.* Also high pressure system.

hoar frost—*See* frost.

humidity—Water vapor content of the air; may be expressed as *specific humidity, relative humidity,* or *mixing ratio.*

hurricane—A *tropical cyclone* in the Western Hemisphere with winds in excess of 65 knots or 120 km/h.

hydrometeor—A general term for particles of liquid water or ice such as rain, fog, frost, etc., formed by modification of water vapor in the atmosphere; also water or ice particles lifted from the earth by the wind such as sea spray or blowing snow.

hygrograph—The record produced by a continuous-recording *hygrometer.*

hygrometer—An instrument for measuring the water vapor content of the air.

I

ice crystals—A type of *precipitation* composed of unbranched crystals in the form of needles, columns, or plates; usually having a very slight downward motion, may fall from a cloudless sky.

ice fog—A type of fog composed of minute suspended particles of ice; occurs at very low temperatures and may cause *halo* phenomena.

ice needles—A form of *ice crystals.*

ice pellets—Small, transparent or translucent, round or irregularly shaped pellets of ice. They may be (1) hard grains that rebound on striking a hard surface or (2) pellets of snow encased in ice.

indefinite ceiling—A ceiling classification denoting *vertical visibility* into a surface based obscuration.

indicated altitude—*See* altitude.

insolation—Incoming solar *radiation* falling upon the earth and its atmosphere.

instability—A general term to indicate various states of the atmosphere in which spontaneous *convection* will occur when prescribed criteria are met; indicative of turbulence. *See* absolute instability, conditionally unstable air, convective instability.

intertropical convergence zone—The boundary zone between the trade wind system of the Northern and Southern Hemispheres; it is characterized in maritime climates by showery precipitation with cumulonimbus clouds sometimes extending to great heights.

inversion—An increase in temperature with height—a reversal of the normal decrease with height in the *troposphere;* may also be applied to other meteorological properties.

isobar—A line of equal or constant barometric pressure.

isoheight—On a weather chart, a line of equal height; same as *contour* (1).

isoline—A line of equal value of a variable quantity, i.e., an isoline of temperature is an *isotherm,* etc. *See* isobar, isotach, etc.

isoshear—A line of equal *wind shear.*

isotach—A line of equal or constant wind speed.

isotherm—A line of equal or constant temperature.

isothermal—Of equal or constant temperature, with respect to either space or time; more commonly, temperature with height; a zero *lapse rate.*

J

jet stream—A quasi-horizontal stream of winds 50 knots or more concentrated within a narrow band embedded in the westerlies in the high *troposphere.*

K

katabatic wind—Any wind blowing downslope. *See* fall wind, foehn.

Kelvin temperature scale (abbreviated K)—A temperature scale with zero degrees equal to the temperature at which all molecular motion ceases, i.e., absolute zero (0° K = −273° C); the Kelvin degree is identical to the Celsius degree; hence at standard sea level pressure, the melting point is 273° K and the boiling point 373° K.

knot—A unit of speed equal to one nautical mile per hour.

L

land breeze—A coastal breeze blowing from land to sea, caused by temperature difference when the sea surface is warmer than the adjacent land. Therefore, it usually blows at night and alternates with a *sea breeze,* which blows in the opposite direction by day.

lapse rate—The rate of decrease of an atmospheric variable with height; commonly refers to decrease of temperature with height.

latent heat—The amount of heat absorbed (converted to kinetic energy) during the processes of change of liquid water to water vapor, ice to water vapor, or ice to liquid water; or the amount released during the reverse processes. Four basic classifications are:

(1) **latent heat of condensation**—Heat released during change of water vapor to water.

(2) **latent heat of fusion**—Heat released during change of water to ice or the amount absorbed in change of ice to water.

(3) **latent heat of sublimation**—Heat released during change of water vapor to ice or the amount absorbed in the change of ice to water vapor.

(4) **latent heat of vaporization**—Heat absorbed in the change of water to water vapor; the negative of latent heat of condensation.

layer—In reference to sky cover, clouds or other obscuring phenomena whose bases are approximately at the same level. The layer may be continuous or composed of detached elements. The term "layer" does not imply that a clear space exists between the layers or that the clouds or *obscuring phenomena* composing them are of the same type.

lee wave—Any stationary wave disturbance caused by a barrier in a fluid flow. In the atmosphere when sufficient moisture is present, this wave will be evidenced by *lenticular clouds* to the lee of mountain barriers; also called *mountain wave* or *standing wave.*

lenticular cloud (or lenticularis)—A species of cloud whose elements have the form of more or less isolated, generally smooth lenses or almonds. These clouds appear most often in formations of orographic origin, the result of *lee waves*, in which case they remain nearly stationary with respect to the terrain (standing cloud), but they also occur in regions without marked orography.

level of free convection (abbreviated LFC)—The level at which a *parcel* of air lifted dry-adiabatically until saturated and moist-adiabatically thereafter would become warmer than its surroundings in a conditionally unstable atmosphere. *See* conditional instability and adiabatic process.

lifting condensation level (abbreviated LCL)—The level at which a *parcel* of unsaturated air lifted dry-adiabatically would become saturated. Compare *level of free convection* and *convective condensation level.*

lightning—Generally, any and all forms of visible electrical discharge produced by a *thunderstorm.*

lithometeor—The general term for dry particles suspended in the atmosphere such as dust, haze, smoke, and sand.

low—An area of low barometric pressure, with its attendant system of winds. Also called a barometric depression or *cyclone.*

M

mammato cumulus—Obsolete. *See* cumulonimbus mamma.

mare's tail—*See* cirrus.

maritime polar air (abbreviated mP)—*See* polar air.

maritime tropical air (abbreviated mT)—*See* tropical air.

maximum wind axis—On a constant pressure chart, a line denoting the axis of maximum wind speeds at that constant pressure surface.

mean sea level—The average height of the surface of the sea for all stages of tide; used as reference for elevations throughout the U.S.

melting—*See* change of state.

mercurial barometer—A *barometer* in which pressure is determined by balancing air pressure against the weight of a column of mercury in an evacuated glass tube.

meteorology—The science of the *atmosphere.*

microbarograph—An aneroid *barograph* designed to record atmospheric pressure changes of very small magnitudes.

millibar (abbreviated mb.)—An internationally used unit of pressure equal to 1,000 dynes per square centimeter. It is convenient for reporting *atmospheric pressure.*

mist—A popular expression for drizzle or heavy fog.

mixing ratio—The ratio by weight of the amount of water vapor in a volume of air to the amount of dry air; usually expressed as grams per kilogram (g/kg).

moist-adiabatic lapse rate—*See* saturated-adiabatic lapse rate.

moisture—An all-inclusive term denoting water in any or all of its three states.

monsoon—A wind that in summer blows from sea to a continental interior, bringing copious rain, and in winter blows from the interior to the sea, resulting in sustained dry weather.

mountain wave—A *standing wave* or *lee wave* to the lee of a mountain barrier.

N

nautical twilight—*See* twilight.

negative vorticity—*See* vorticity.

nimbostratus—A principal cloud type, gray colored, often dark, the appearance of which is rendered diffuse by more or less continuously falling rain or snow, which in most cases reaches the ground. It is thick enough throughout to blot out the sun.

noctilucent clouds—Clouds of unknown composition which occur at great heights, probably around 75 to 90 kilometers. They resemble thin *cirrus*, but usually with a bluish or silverish color, although sometimes orange to red, standing out against a dark night sky. Rarely observed.

normal—In meteorology, the value of an element averaged for a given location over a period of years and recognized as a standard.

numerical forecasting—*See* numerical weather prediction.

numerical weather prediction—Forecasting by digital computers solving mathematical equations; used extensively in weather services throughout the world.

O

obscuration—Denotes sky hidden by surface-based *obscuring phenomena* and *vertical visibility* restricted overhead.

obscuring phenomena—Any *hydrometeor* or *lithometeor* other than clouds; may be surface based or aloft.

occlusion—Same as *occluded front.*

occluded front (commonly called occlusion, also called frontal occlusion)—A composite of two fronts as a *cold front* overtakes a *warm front* or *quasi-stationary front.*

orographic—Of, pertaining to, or caused by mountains as in orographic clouds, orographic lift, or orographic precipitation.

ozone—An unstable form of oxygen; heaviest concentrations are in the stratosphere; corrosive to some metals; absorbs most ultraviolet solar radiation.

P

parcel—A small volume of air, small enough to contain uniform distribution of its meteorological properties, and large enough to remain relatively self-contained and respond to all meteorological processes. No specific dimensions have been defined, however, the order of magnitude of 1 cubic foot has been suggested.

partial obscuration—A designation of sky cover when part of the sky is hidden by surface based *obscuring phenomena.*

pilot balloon—A small free-lift balloon used to determine the speed and direction of winds in the upper air.

pilot balloon observation (commonly called PIBAL)—A method of winds-aloft observation by visually tracking a *pilot balloon.*

plan position indicator (PPI) scope—A radar indicator scope displaying range and azimuth of *targets* in polar coordinates.

plow wind—The spreading downdraft of a *thunderstorm;* a strong, straight-line wind in advance of the storm. *See* first gust.

polar air—An air mass with characteristics developed over high latitudes, especially within the subpolar highs. Continental polar air (cP) has cold surface temperatures, low moisture content, and, especially in its source regions, has great stability in the lower layers. It is shallow in comparison with *Arctic air.* Maritime polar (mP) initially possesses similar properties to those of continental polar air, but in passing over warmer water it becomes unstable with a higher moisture content. Compare *tropical air.*

polar front—The semipermanent, semicontinuous *front* separating air masses of tropical and polar origins.

positive vorticity—*See* vorticity.

precipitation—Any or all forms of water particles, whether liquid or solid, that fall from the atmosphere and reach the surface. It is a major class of *hydrometeor,* distinguished from cloud and *virga* in that it must reach the surface.

precipitation attenuation—*See* attenuation.

pressure—*See* atmospheric pressure.

pressure altimeter—An *aneroid barometer* with a scale graduated in altitude instead of pressure using *standard atmospheric* pressure-height relationships; shows indicated altitude (not necessarily true altitude); may be set to measure altitude (indicated) from any arbitrarily chosen level.

pressure gradient—The rate of decrease of pressure per unit distance at a fixed time.

pressure jump—A sudden, significant increase in *station pressure.*

pressure tendency—*See* barometric tendency.

prevailing easterlies—The broad current or pattern of persistent easterly winds in the Tropics and in polar regions.

prevailing visibility—In the U.S., the greatest horizontal visibility which is equaled or exceeded throughout half of the horizon circle; it need not be a continuous half.

prevailing westerlies—The dominant west-to-east motion of the atmosphere, centered over middle latitudes of both hemispheres.

prevailing wind—Direction from which the wind blows most frequently.

prognostic chart (contracted PROG)—A chart of expected or forecast conditions.

pseudo-adiabatic lapse rate—*See* saturated-adiabatic lapse rate.

psychrometer—An instrument consisting of a *wet-bulb* and a *dry-bulb* thermometer for measuring wet-bulb and dry-bulb temperature; used to determine water vapor content of the air.

pulse—Pertaining to radar, a brief burst of electromagnetic radiation emitted by the radar; of very short time duration. *See* pulse length.

pulse length—Pertaining to radar, the dimension of a radar pulse; may be expressed as the time duration or the length in linear units. Linear dimension is equal to time duration multiplied by the speed of propagation (approximately the speed of light).

Q

quasi-stationary front (commonly called stationary front)—A *front* which is stationary or nearly so; conventionally, a front which is moving at a speed of less than 5 knots is generally considered to be quasi-stationary.

R

RADAR (contraction for radio detection and ranging)—An electronic instrument used for the detection and ranging of distant objects of such composition that they scatter or reflect radio energy. Since *hydrometeors* can scatter radio energy, *weather radars,* operating on certain frequency bands, can detect the presence of precipitation, clouds, or both.

radarsonde observation—A *rawinsonde observation* in which winds are determined by radar tracking a balloon-borne target.

radiation—The emission of energy by a medium and transferred, either through free space or another medium, in the form of electromagnetic waves.

radiation fog—*Fog* characteristically resulting when radiational cooling of the earth's surface lowers the air temperature near the ground to or below its initial dew point on calm, clear nights.

radiosonde—A balloon-borne instrument for measuring pressure, temperature, and humidity aloft. Radiosonde observation—a *sounding* made by the instrument.

rain—A form of *precipitation;* drops are larger than *drizzle* and fall in relatively straight, although not necessarily vertical, paths as compared to drizzle which falls in irregular paths.

rain shower—*See* shower.

range attenuation—*See* attenuation.

RAOB—A *radiosonde* observation.

rawin—A *rawinsonde* observation.

rawinsonde observation—A combined winds aloft and radiosonde observation. Winds are determined by tracking the *radiosonde* by radio direction finder or radar.

relative humidity—The ratio of the existing amount of water vapor in the air at a given temperature to the maximum amount that could exist at that temperature; usually expressed in percent.

relative vorticity—*See* vorticity.

ridge (also called ridge line)—In meteorology, an elongated area of relatively high atmospheric pressure; usually associated with and most clearly identified as an area of maximum anticyclonic curvature of the wind flow (*isobars, contours,* or *streamlines*).

rocketsonde—A type of *radiosonde* launched by a rocket and making its measurements during a parachute descent; capable of obtaining *soundings* to a much greater height than possible by balloon or aircraft.

roll cloud (sometimes improperly called rotor cloud)—A dense and horizontal roll-shaped accessory cloud located on the lower leading edge of a *cumulonimbus* or less often, a rapidly developing *cumulus;* indicative of turbulence.

rotor cloud (sometimes improperly called *roll cloud*)—A turbulent cloud formation found in the lee of some large mountain barriers, the air in the cloud rotates around an axis parallel to the range; indicative of possible violent turbulence.

S

St. Elmo's Fire (also called corposant)—A luminous brush discharge of electricity from protruding objects, such as masts and yardarms of ships, aircraft, lightning rods, steeples, etc., occurring in stormy weather.

Santa Ana—A hot, dry, *foehn* wind, generally from the northeast or east, occurring west of the Sierra Nevada Mountains especially in the pass and river valley near Santa Ana, California.

saturated adiabatic lapse rate—The rate of decrease of temperature with height as saturated air is lifted with no gain or loss of heat from outside sources; varies with temperature, being greatest at low temperatures. *See* adiabatic process and dry-adiabatic lapse rate.

saturation—The condition of the atmosphere when actual *water vapor* present is the maximum possible at existing temperature.

scud—Small detached masses of stratus *fractus* clouds below a layer of higher clouds, usually *nimbostratus.*

sea breeze—A coastal breeze blowing from sea to land, caused by the temperature difference when the land surface is warmer than the sea surface. Compare *land breeze.*

sea fog—A type of *advection fog* formed when air that has been lying over a warm surface is transported over a colder water surface.

sea level pressure—The *atmospheric pressure* at *mean sea level,* either directly measured by stations at sea level or empirically determined from the *station pressure* and temperature by stations not at sea level; used as a common reference for analyses of surface pressure patterns.

sea smoke—Same as *steam fog.*

sector visibility—*Meteorological visibility* within a specified sector of the horizon circle.

shear—*See* wind shear.

shower—*Precipitation* from a *cumuliform* cloud; characterized by the suddenness of beginning and ending, by the rapid change of intensity, and usually by rapid change in the appearance of the sky; showery precipitation may be in the form of rain, ice pellets, or snow.

slant visibility—For an airborne observer, the distance at which he can see and distinguish objects on the ground.

sleet—*See* ice pellets.

smog—A mixture of *smoke* and *fog.*

smoke—A restriction to visibility resulting from combustion.

snow—Precipitation composed of white or translucent ice crystals, chiefly in complex branched hexagonal form.

snow flurry—Popular term for snow *shower,* particularly of a very light and brief nature.

snow grains—*Precipitation* of very small, white opaque grains of ice, similar in structure to *snow* crystals. The grains are fairly flat or elongated, with diameters generally less than 0.04 inch (1 mm.).

snow pellets—*Precipitation* consisting of white, opaque approximately round (sometimes conical) ice particles having a snow-like structure, and about 0.08 to 0.2 inch in diameter; crisp and easily crushed, differing in this respect from *snow grains;* rebound from a hard surface and often break up.

snow shower—*See* shower.

solar radiation—The total electromagnetic *radiation* emitted by the sun. *See* insolation.

sounding—In meteorology, an upper-air observation; a *radiosonde* observation.

source region—An extensive area of the earth's surface characterized by relatively uniform surface conditions where large masses of air remain long enough to take on characteristic temperature and moisture properties imparted by that surface.

specific humidity—The ratio by weight of *water vapor* in a sample of air to the combined weight of water vapor and dry air. Compare *mixing ratio.*

squall—A sudden increase in wind speed by at least 15 knots to a peak of 20 knots or more and lasting for at least one minute. Essential difference between a *gust* and a squall is the duration of the peak speed.

squall line—Any nonfrontal line or narrow band of active *thunderstorms* (with or without *squalls*).

stability—A state of the atmosphere in which the vertical distribution of temperature is such that a *parcel* will resist displacement from its initial level. (*See also* instability.)

standard atmosphere—A hypothetical atmosphere based on climatological averages comprised of numerous physical constants of which the most important are:

(1) A surface *temperature* of 59° F (15° C) and a surface pressure of 29.92 inches of mercury (1013.2 millibars) at sea level;

(2) A *lapse rate* in the troposphere of 6.5° C per kilometer (approximately 2° C per 1,000 feet);

(3) A *tropopause* of 11 kilometers (approximately 36,000 feet) with a temperature of −56.5° C; and

(4) An *isothermal* lapse rate in the stratosphere to an altitude of 24 kilometers (approximately 80,000 feet).

standing cloud (standing lenticular altocumulus)—*See* lenticular cloud.

standing wave—A wave that remains stationary in a moving fluid. In aviation operations it is used most commonly to refer to a *lee wave* or *mountain wave.*

stationary front—Same as *quasi-stationary front.*

station pressure—The actual *atmospheric pressure* at the observing station.

steam fog—Fog formed when cold air moves over relatively warm water or wet ground.

storm detection radar—A weather radar designed to detect *hydrometeors* of precipitation size; used primarily to detect storms with large drops or hailstones as opposed to clouds and light precipitation of small drop size.

stratiform—Descriptive of clouds of extensive horizontal development, as contrasted to vertically developed *cumuliform* clouds; characteristic of stable air and, therefore, composed of small water droplets.

stratocumulus—A low cloud, predominantly *stratiform* in gray and/or whitish patches or layers, may or may not merge; elements are tessellated, rounded, or roll-shaped with relatively flat tops.

stratosphere—The atmospheric layer above the tropopause, average altitude of base and top, 7 and 22 miles respectively; characterized by a slight average increase of temperature from base to top and is very stable; also characterized by low moisture content and absence of clouds.

stratus—A low, gray cloud layer or sheet with a fairly uniform base; sometimes appears in ragged patches; seldom produces precipitation but may produce *drizzle* or *snow grains*. A *stratiform* cloud.

stratus fractus—*See* fractus.

streamline—In meteorology, a line whose tangent is the wind direction at any point along the line. A flowline.

sublimation—*See* change of state.

subsidence—A descending motion of air in the atmosphere over a rather broad area; usually associated with *divergence*.

summation principle—The principle states that the cover assigned to a layer is equal to the summation of the sky cover of the lowest layer plus the additional coverage at all successively higher layers up to and including the layer in question. Thus, no layer can be assigned a sky cover less than a lower layer, and no sky cover can be greater than 1.0 (10/10).

superadiabatic lapse rate—A *lapse rate* greater than the *dry-adiabatic lapse rate*. *See* absolute instability.

supercooled water—Liquid water at temperatures colder than freezing.

surface inversion—An *inversion* with its base at the surface, often caused by cooling of the air near the surface as a result of *terrestrial radiation*, especially at night.

surface visibility—Visibility observed from eye-level above the ground.

synoptic chart—A chart, such as the familiar weather map, which depicts the distribution of meteorological conditions over an area at a given time.

T

target—In radar, any of the many types of objects detected by radar.

temperature—In general, the degree of hotness or coldness as measured on some definite temperature scale by means of any of various types of thermometers.

temperature inversion—*See* inversion.

terrestrial radiation—The total infrared *radiation* emitted by the Earth and its atmosphere.

thermograph—A continuous-recording *thermometer*.

thermometer—An instrument for measuring *temperature*.

thunderstorm—In general, a local storm invariably produced by a *cumulonimbus* cloud, and always accompanied by lightning and thunder.

tornado (sometimes called cyclone, twister)—A violently rotating column of air, pendant from a cumulonimbus cloud, and nearly always observable as "funnel-shaped." It is the most destructive of all small-scale atmospheric phenomena.

towering cumulus—A rapidly growing *cumulus* in which height exceeds width.

tower visibility—*Prevailing visibility* determined from the control tower.

trade winds—Prevailing, almost continuous winds blowing with an easterly component from the subtropical high pressure belts toward the *intertropical convergence zone;* northeast in the Northern Hemisphere, southeast in the Southern Hemisphere.

tropical air—An air mass with characteristics developed over low latitudes. Maritime tropical air (mT), the principal type, is produced over the tropical and subtropical seas; very warm and humid. Continental tropical (cT) is produced over subtropical arid regions and is hot and very dry. Compare *polar air*.

tropical cyclone—A general term for a *cyclone* that originates over tropical oceans. By international agreement, tropical cyclones have been classified according to their intensity, as follows:

(1) **tropical depression**—winds up to 34 knots (64 km/h);

(2) **tropical storm**—winds of 35 to 64 knots (65 to 119 km/h);

(3) **hurricane or typhoon**—winds of 65 knots or higher (120 km/h).

tropical depression—*See* tropical cyclone.

tropical storm—*See* tropical cyclone.

tropopause—The transition zone between the *troposphere* and *stratosphere*, usually characterized by an abrupt change of *lapse rate*.

troposphere—That portion of the *atmosphere* from the earth's surface to the *tropopause;* that is, the lowest 10 to 20 kilometers of the atmosphere. The troposphere is characterized by decreasing temperature with height, and by appreciable water vapor.

trough (also called trough line)—In meteorology, an elongated area of relatively low atmospheric pressure; usually associated with and most clearly identified as an area of maximum cyclonic curvature of the wind flow (*isobars*, *contours*, or *streamlines*); compare with *ridge*.

true altitude—*See* altitude.

true wind direction—The direction, with respect to true north, from which the wind is blowing.

turbulence—In meteorology, any irregular or disturbed flow in the atmosphere.

twilight—The intervals of incomplete darkness following sunset and preceding sunrise. The time at which evening twilight ends or morning twilight begins is determined by arbitrary convention, and several kinds of twilight have been defined and used; most commonly civil, nautical, and astronomical twilight.

(1) **Civil Twilight**—The period of time before sunrise and after sunset when the sun is not more than 6° below the horizon.

(2) **Nautical Twilight**—The period of time before sunrise and after sunset when the sun is not more than 12° below the horizon.

(3) **Astronomical Twilight**—The period of time before sunrise and after sunset when the sun is not more than 18° below the horizon.

twister—In the United States, a colloquial term for *tornado.*

typhoon—A *tropical cyclone* in the Eastern Hemisphere with winds in excess of 65 knots (120 km/h).

U

undercast—A cloud *layer* of ten-tenths (1.0) coverage (to the nearest tenth) as viewed from an observation point above the layer.

unlimited ceiling—A clear sky or a sky cover that does not meet the criteria for a *ceiling.*

unstable—*See* instability.

updraft—A localized upward current of air.

upper front—A *front* aloft not extending to the earth's surface.

upslope fog—Fog formed when air flows upward over rising terrain and is, consequently, adiabatically cooled to or below its initial *dew point.*

V

vapor pressure—In meteorology, the pressure of water vapor in the atmosphere. Vapor pressure is that part of the total atmospheric pressure due to water vapor and is independent of the other atmospheric gases or vapors.

vapor trail—Same as *condensation trail.*

veering—Shifting of the wind in a clockwise direction with respect to either space or time; opposite of backing. Commonly used by meteorologists to refer to an anticyclonic shift (clockwise in the Northern Hemisphere and counterclockwise in the Southern Hemisphere).

vertical visibility—The distance one can see upward into a surface based *obscuration;* or the maximum height from which a pilot in flight can recognize the ground through a surface based obscuration.

virga—Water or ice particles falling from a cloud, usually in wisps or streaks, and evaporating before reaching the ground.

visibility—The greatest distance one can see and identify prominent objects.

visual range—*See* runway visual range.

vortex—In meteorology, any rotary flow in the atmosphere.

vorticity—Turning of the atmosphere. Vorticity may be imbedded in the total flow and not readily identified by a flow pattern.

(a) **absolute vorticity**—the rotation of the Earth imparts vorticity to the atmosphere; absolute vorticity is the combined vorticity due to this rotation and vorticity due to circulation relative to the Earth (relative vorticity).

(b) **negative vorticity**—vorticity caused by anticyclonic turning; it is associated with downward motion of the air.

(c) **positive vorticity**—vorticity caused by cyclonic turning; it is associated with upward motion of the air.

(d) **relative vorticity**—vorticity of the air relative to the Earth, disregarding the component of vorticity resulting from Earth's rotation.

W

wake turbulence—*Turbulence* found to the rear of a solid body in motion relative to a fluid. In aviation terminology, the turbulence caused by a moving aircraft.

wall cloud—The well-defined bank of vertically developed clouds having a wall-like appearance which form the outer boundary of the *eye* of a well-developed *tropical cyclone.*

warm front—Any non-occluded *front* which moves in such a way that warmer air replaces colder air.

warm sector—The area covered by warm air at the surface and bounded by the *warm front* and *cold front* of a *wave cyclone.*

water equivalent—The depth of water that would result from the melting of snow or ice.

waterspout—*See* tornado.

water vapor—Water in the invisible gaseous form.

wave cyclone—A *cyclone* which forms and moves along a front. The circulation about the cyclone center tends to produce a wavelike deformation of the front.

weather—The state of the *atmosphere,* mainly with respect to its effects on life and human activities; refers to instantaneous conditions or short term changes as opposed to *climate.*

weather radar—Radar specifically designed for observing weather. *See* cloud detection radar and storm detection radar.

weather vane—A *wind vane.*

wedge—Same as *ridge.*

wet bulb—Contraction of either *wet-bulb temperature* or *wet-bulb thermometer.*

wet-bulb temperature—The lowest *temperature* that can be obtained on a *wet-bulb thermometer* in any given sample of air, by evaporation of water (or ice) from the muslin wick; used in computing *dew point* and *relative humidity.*

wet-bulb thermometer—A thermometer with a muslin-covered bulb used to measure wet-bulb temperature.

whirlwind—A small, rotating column of air; may be visible as a dust devil.

willy-willy—A *tropical cyclone* of hurricane strength near Australia.

wind—Air in motion relative to the surface of the earth; generally used to denote horizontal movement.

wind direction—The direction **from** which wind is blowing.

wind speed—Rate of wind movement in distance per unit time.

wind vane—An instrument to indicate wind direction.

wind velocity—A vector term to include both *wind direction* and *wind speed.*

wind shear—The rate of change of *wind velocity* (direction and/or speed) per unit distance; conventionally expressed as vertical or horizontal wind shear.

X—Y—Z

zonal wind—A west wind; the westerly component of a wind. Conventionally used to describe large-scale flow that is neither cyclonic nor anticyclonic.

WEATHER OF SELECTED U.S. CITIES

HOW TO GET ANSWERS TO YOUR WEATHER QUESTIONS

Reading the reports of weather in various cities—

All of the information you want about the weather history of key cities should be easy for you to find. Pages telling about the cities appearing further along in this book were planned so as to be informative, yet simple to read. But packing in so much information means using special forms, so a word about how to get at certain information most quickly is in order.

The climate of each city is first presented as a narrative description, prepared by a local climatologist, whose job puts him in an unequalled position to know the weather of the particular area as no one else would. This narrative may answer all of your questions without requiring you to study the tables of statistics.

The narrative report—

Typically, the report begins with a description of the local area in terms of terrain features, water bodies, and other topographical features, because these features exercise key influences on the local weather. They usually account for it if an area's weather differs sharply from weather in areas only a few miles away. For example, if a lake is near a city it will always influence the city's weather, and in fact, may even create climatic differences from one part of the city to another. Mountains, swamps, even plowed fields each exercise their influences on air masses as they move toward a city, making it worthwhile for you to check this first. The city's report then proceeds to discuss temperature ranges, rainfall patterns, snowfall occurences, and scores of other points before closing ... typically with points about the agricultural adaptability of the climate there. Growing season is usually noted, and first and last frost dates are usually given, along with suggestions about the types of crops for which the area is climatologically suited.

Beyond this narrative is the comprehensive statistical picture of the area's weather.

Statistics—

The statistics are of two different kinds. The first type distills many years of history to give you a sort of profile of the city's weather (NORMALS, MEANS AND EXTREMES). The second group offers data for individual years, going back twenty years, to let you see what variances have tended to occur, and to what extent weather conditions tend to repeat themselves.

Because many readers need to go no farther than the temperature portion of the NORMALS, MEANS, AND EXTREMES, it is broken off and moved forward to the first of the city's pages. The remaining part of this table appears on the city's second page. The year-by-year historical data are on the page that closes the presentation for the city.

Information to help you to quickly understand the individual entries in these tables follows:

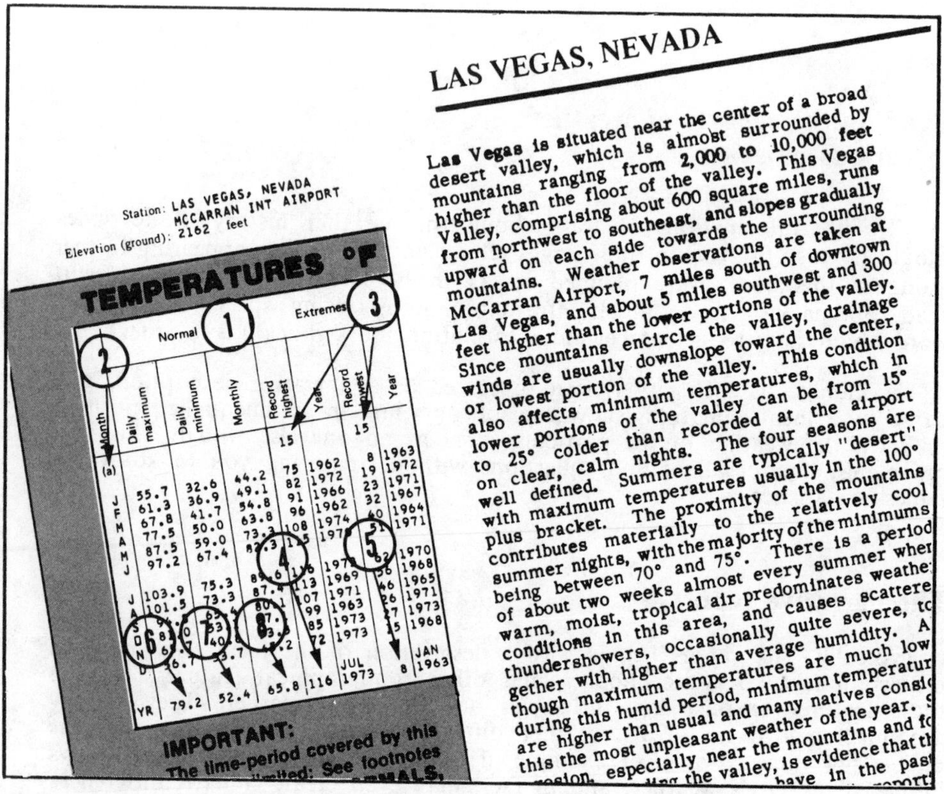

1. **NORMAL** as applied to temperature, degree days, and precipitation refers to the value of that particular element averaged over the period 1941-1970. When the station does not have continuous records from an instrument site with the same "exposure", a "difference factor" between the old site and the new site is used to adjust the observed values to a common series. The difference factor is determined from a period of simultaneous measurements. The base period is revised every ten years by adding the averages for the most recent decade and dropping them for the first decade of the former normal period. Thus, in 1973, the current normals for 1941-1970 replaced the former normals for 1931-1960. In the early 1980s, new normals for the period 1951-1980 will be calculated. *Normal* does not refer to "normalcy" or "expectation," but only to the actual average for a particular thirty year period.

2. **(Note a) MEANS and EXTREMES** are based on the period of years in which observations have been made under comparable conditions of instrument exposure. Data are included for dates through 1975 unless otherwise noted. The DATE OF AN EXTREME is the *most recent* one in cases of repeated occurrences.

3. **LENGTH OF OBSERVATIONAL RECORD** for *Means* and *Extremes* is based on the length of January data for the present instrument site exposure (15 equals 15 years). The Table *does not* give the all time high or low value if it was recorded at a *different*

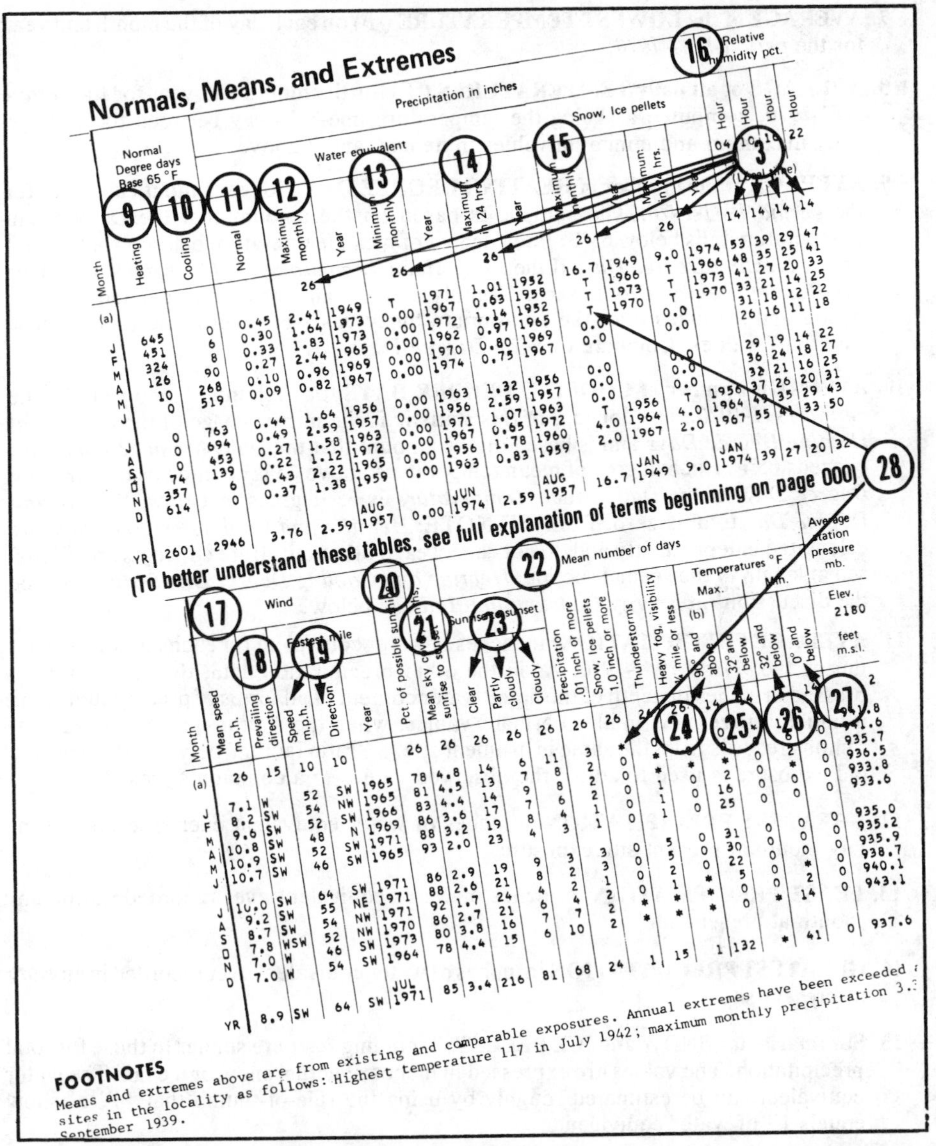

site within the area. The Mean or average values for *Relative Humidity, Wind, Sunshine, Sky Condition,* and the *Mean Number Of Days* with the various other weather conditions listed are also based on the length of record noted in each instance down through 1975.

4. **HIGHEST TEMPERATURE** (in degrees Fahrenheit) ever recorded during any month at present site exposure.

5. **LOWEST TEMPERATURE** (°F) ever recorded during any month (present site).

6. **AVERAGE of the HIGHEST TEMPERATURE** (°F) on each day of the month and year for the *period 1941-1970*. This value is obtained by taking the sum of the highest temperature for each day of the period (adjusted for site exposure if necessary) and dividing by the number of days included.

7. **AVERAGE of the LOWEST TEMPERATURE** (°F) on each day of the month and year for the *period 1941-1970.*

8. **AVERAGE of all daily TEMPERATURES** (°F) for the month and year for the *period 1941-1970*; computed as being the temperature one-half way between the average daily maximum and minimum values in items 6 and 7 above.

9. **AVERAGE of the number of HEATING DEGREE DAYS** for each month and year for the *period 1941-1970.* The statistic is based on the amount that the Daily Mean Temperature falls below 65°F. Each degree of mean temperature below 65 is counted as one *Heating Degree Day.* If the *Daily Mean Temperature* is 65 degrees or higher, the *Heating Degree Day* is zero. Monthly and annual sums are calculated for each period and averaged over the appropriate thirty years of record to establish these "normal" values. Compare *Cooling Degree Days.*

10. **AVERAGE number of COOLING DEGREE DAYS** for each month and year for the *period 1941-1970.* The concept of this statistic is the mirror image of the concept of *Heating Degree Days* and is based on the amount that the *Daily Mean Temperature* exceeds 65°F. Each degree of mean temperature above 65 is counted as one *Cooling Degree Day.* If the *Daily Mean Temperature* is 65 degrees or below, the *Cooling Degree Day* total is zero. PLEASE NOTE: *Heating and Cooling Degree Days* are calculated independently and do not cancel each other out. Both concepts are discussed at length in the special section, *Heating and Cooling Degree Day Data.* Also see the discussion on *Energy Consumption Indices* below.

11. **AVERAGE PRECIPITATION*** in inches of water equivalent for each month and year during the *period 1941-1970.* As in the other precipitation data, the values are expressed in inches of depth of the liquid water content of all forms of precipitation even if initially frozen. As in all "normal" values, when the station does not have continuous records from the same instrument site, a "ratio factor" between the new and old exposure is used to adjust the observed values to a common series.

12. **GREATEST PRECIPITATION** in inches of water equivalent ever recorded during any month at present site exposure.

13. **LEAST PRECIPITATION** in inches of water equivalent ever recorded during any month at present site.

14. **GREATEST PRECIPITATION** in inches of water equivalent ever recorded in any *day* at present site.

15. **Summaries for SNOW and ICE PELLETS** including *sleet* are similar to those for total precipitation. The values are expressed in inches of actual snow or ice fall. The water equivalent can be estimated roughly by using the rule-of-thumb that 10" of snow equals 1" of water equivalent.

16. **AVERAGE RELATIVE HUMIDITY** at various hours of the day. The time is expressed in terms of the 24 hour clock (00 is midnight, 06 is 6 am, 12 is noon, and 18 is 6 pm). Values are for present site only. See the section on *Temperature Humidity Index* for a discussion of warm weather comfort related to humidity.

17. **WINDINESS** — average speed of wind is expressed in miles-per-hour without regard for direction.

---

*See also precipitation information in the next segment of the chart labeled *Mean number of days.*

18. **PREVAILING WIND DIRECTION** — the most common single wind direction without regard for wind speed or any minimum amount of persistence. The aggregate total of wind from the other directions may be very much greater than that from the "prevailing" direction. Direction is coded in two different ways, some reports use letters, some use numbers. When letters are used, they have the usual meaning, such as WSW indicating west-south-west. When numbers are used, they are given in tens of degrees clockwise from true north, so that 09 is 90° clockwise from north (*east*), 18 is 180° (*south*), 27 is 270° (*west*), and 36 is 360° (*north*). The statistic is based on *data through 1963 only*.

19. **HIGH WIND** — the greatest speed in miles per hour of any "mile" of wind passing the station. The accompanying direction and year of occurrence are also given. A mile of wind passing the station in 1 minute has an average speed of 60 mph, 2 minutes—30 mph, 5 minutes—12 mph, etc. The wind cups of the particular instrument involved operate much like the wheel of a car in actuating the car's odometer. The instrument does not record the strength of individual wind gusts which usually last less than 20 seconds and which may be very much greater than the value given here. The fastest mile however does give some idea of the *extremes* of wind that can be encountered.

20. **SUNSHINE** — average percent of daytime hours subject to direct radiation from the sun at the present site. The percentage is given without regard for the intensity of sunshine. That is, thin clouds, light haze, or other minor obstructions to direct solar rays may be present but would not mitigate the full counting of an hour.

21. **VERTICAL OBSERVATION** — Average amount of daytime sky obscured by any type of cover expressed in tenths (e.g., 4.8 equals 4.8/10, or 48%).

22. **ACTIVITY LIMITING WEATHER** — average number of days in month with specified weather conditions based on present exposure. An (*) indicates less than ½ day.

23. **CLOUDINESS** — average number of days in month at the present site with various amounts of cloud cover. *Clear* indicates average daytime cloudiness of 0.3 or less; *partly cloudy* indicates average daytime cloudiness between 0.4 and 0.7; *cloudy* indicates average daytime cloudiness of 0.8 or more.

24. **VERY HOT DAYS** — average number of days in month and year when the temperature at the present site has reached 90° or above. (70°F or above at Alaskan stations).

25. **COLD DAYS** — average number of days at the present site when the temperatures remained below 32°F at all times.

26. **FREEZING DAYS** — average number of days at the present site when the temperature dropped to a minimum of 32°F or below.

27. **VERY COLD DAYS** — average number of days at the present site when the minimum temperature was 0°F or below.

28. **SPECIAL SYMBOLS** that appear on many of the individual summaries:

*	**Less than one-half.**
+	**Also on earlier dates, months, or years.**
T	**Trace, an amount too small to measure.**
–	**Below zero temperatures are preceded by a minus sign.**

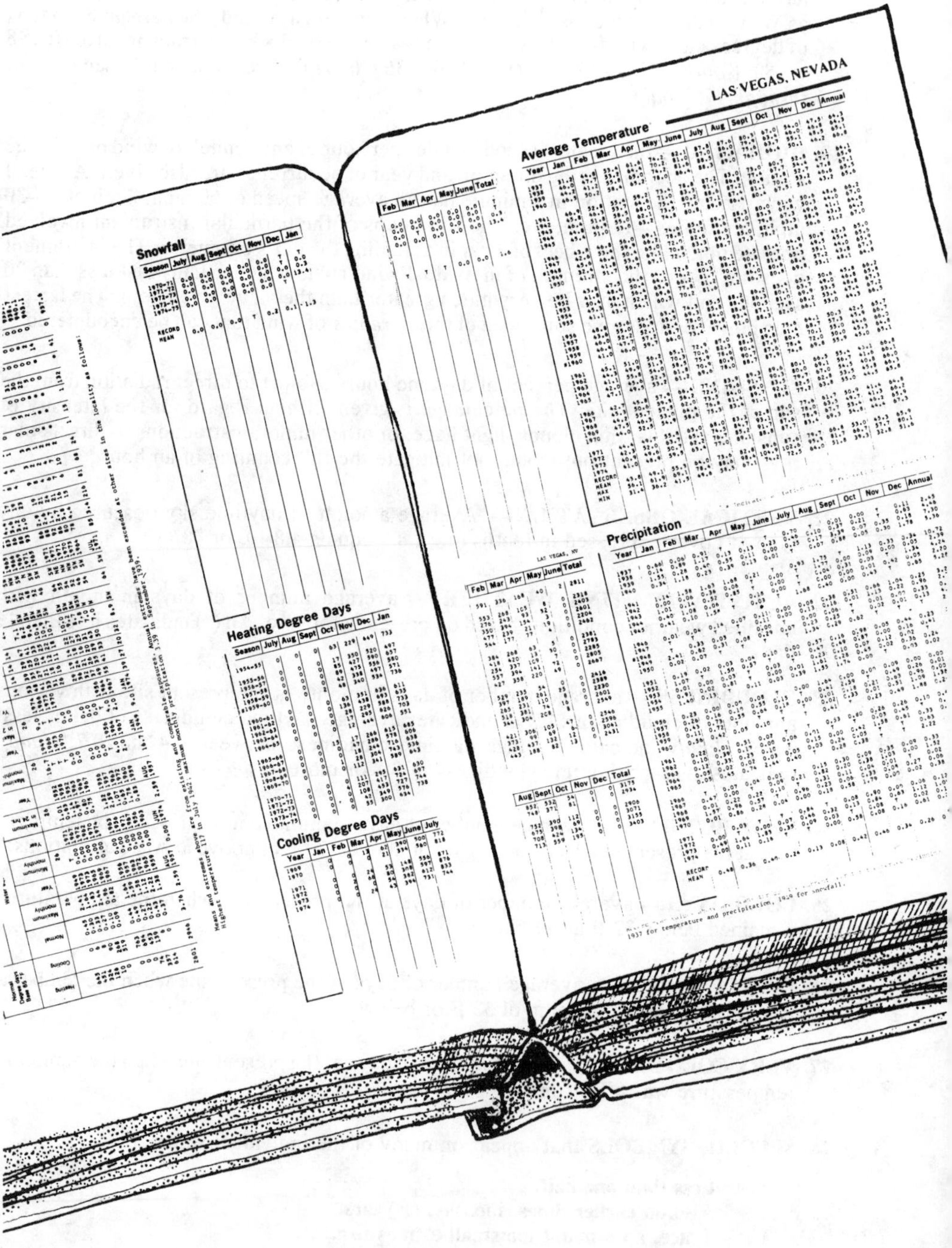
LAS VEGAS, NEVADA
Average Temperature
Snowfall
Heating Degree Days
Cooling Degree Days
Precipitation

Weather Averages Year by Year

AVERAGE TEMPERATURE equals the *average* of the *maximum* and *minimum temperatures* for each day of the month for the given year; afternoon temperatures were typically *higher* than these values and late night/early morning temperatures were typically *below* them.

PRECIPITATION refers to the inches of water equivalent in the total of all forms of liquid or frozen precipitation that fell during each month. *Snowfall* refers to the actual amount of snow in inches that fell during the month. T (trace) is a precipitation amount of less than 0.005 inches. (Note: in estimating the water equivalent of snow a ratio of 10'' of snow equals 1'' of water is customarily employed.)

ENERGY CONSUMPTION INDICES. See the special section, *Heating and Cooling Degree Data,* and items 9 and 10 above. *Heating Degree Days* provide a well established index of relative fuel consumption for space heating in a given place—a month of 2000 *HDD* requires about twice the amount of space heating energy as one of 1000 *HDD,* while 100 *HDD* will require about the same fuel whether accumulated in 2 or 4 days. Regional differences in the *Heating Degree Day Index* are only partially useful in estimating comparative fuel requirements because the building construction and cultural expectations tend to be different in different parts of the country (e.g., subjective ideas of comfort in relation to temperature will vary). For example, the average standards of efficiency in heating equipment and insulation are generally lower in warmer climates so that fuel requirements tend not to decrease as rapidly as the heating degree days decrease.*

The complementary index of *Cooling Degree Days* provides only a rough guide to relative energy consumption in air conditioning. *Cooling Degree Days* are best noted for ease of calculation from standard climatological statistical sources and a very broad data base. A proper air conditioning index will almost certainly require a factor for humidity variation and possibly factors for cloudiness or other weather variables. See section on *Temperature Humidity Index.* Nevertheless, regions with low relative humidity tend to have lower nighttime temperatures than humid regions with comparable maximum daytime temperatures with correspondingly lower cooling degree day departures. Thus, the *Cooling Degree Day Index* will have some usefulness in indicating relative outdoor comfort and relative indoor air conditioning requirements from time-to-time and from place-to-place.

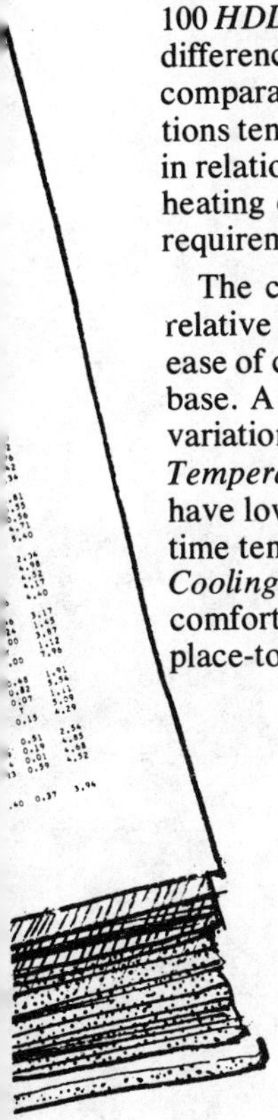

* A useful study of actual differences in regional fuel consumption related to *Heating Degree Days* can be found in the book *Energy Prices, 1960-1973* prepared by Foster Associates for the Ford Foundation Energy Policy Project Study and published by Ballinger, 1974, pages 62-64.

Weather observations taken at sea are important to hurricane forecasting. Balloons, such as this one, lift instruments which radio back wind speeds at various altitudes.

Station: BIRMINGHAM, ALABAMA
MUNICIPAL AIRPORT
Elevation (ground): 620 feet

TEMPERATURES °F

	Normal			Extremes			
Month	Daily maximum	Daily minimum	Monthly	Record highest	Year	Record lowest	Year
(a)				12		12	
J	54.3	34.1	44.2	77	1975	-4	1966
F	57.7	36.1	46.9	79	1972	10	1971
M	64.8	41.8	53.3	87	1967	19	1968
A	75.3	51.0	63.2	89	1970	26	1973
M	82.5	58.4	70.5	95	1970	36	1971
J	88.4	66.4	77.4	99	1964	42	1966
J	90.3	69.5	79.9	102	1966	51	1967
A	89.7	68.7	79.2	98	1968	55	1968
S	84.7	63.0	73.9	96	1975	37	1967
O	75.8	50.8	63.3	91	1963	28	1965
N	64.0	40.1	52.1	83	1974	13	1970
D	55.5	34.9	45.2	78	1971	11	1963
YR	73.6	51.2	62.4	102	JUL 1966	-4	JAN 1966

IMPORTANT:
The time-period covered by this record is limited: See footnotes on next page for explanation and for additional history of EXTREME HIGHS AND LOWS recorded in the general area.

For the period of record, Birmingham's monthly temperatures show a range from a January mean of 44 degrees to a July mean of 80 degrees. This 36 degree annual range reflects the effect of the station's location (2) with respect to the warm body of water to the south and (b) the invasions of relatively cold air from the continental north and west. The occurrence of very low temperatures, although quite rare, effectively prevents the growth of vegetation normally indigenous to sub-tropical climates.

Precipitation, with a minimum occurring during October, has two maxima each year, one during the winter months, and another, slightly lower, in July. Summer precipitation is chiefly in the form of thunderstorms. Snowfall is seldom heavy enough to be important. heavy falls occur occasionally, however, and when in excess of about 2 inches, they produce a real traffic problem. Very low temperatures in this area almost invariably occur under radiation conditions involving a particularly persistent snow cover.

Droughts are infrequent. One of the worst on record occurred in 1924 when no rain fell between September 29 and December 4 with the exception of 0.01 inch on November 21.

Located nearly 300 miles from the Gulf of Mexico, Birmingham's position keeps it safe from the destructive winds of hurricanes passing inland from the Gulf of Mexico. Some very heavy rains have occurred in connection with these storms, however — for example, the three-day fall of 9.71 inches on July 6-8, 1916.

The length of the growing season, averaging 239 days, has been as short as 192 days (in 1953), and as long as 297 (in 1938). The average date of last minimum temperature of 32 degrees in spring is March 17, but it has occurred as late as April 21 and as early as February 1; and the first in autumn, averaging November 10, has occurred as early as October 17 and as late as December 5.

The topography of Birmingham is hilly. The City proper is located in a valley between a ridge of hills, extending from the northeast to the west, and the Red Mountain Range, which extends from the east ot the southwest. This valley is approximately 8 miles long and 2 to 4 miles wide. The Red Mountain Range approaches a height of 600 feet above the valley level. Another ridge, The Shades Mountain Ridge, parallels the Red Mountain Range several miles to the southeast. Rolling terrain extends to the southwest and the west. The hills in the Birmingham area, which extend to the northeast and the north, are the foothills of the Appalachian Mountains and the Cumberland Plateau. The main climatic effect of the topography of Birmingham is that during the winter months, ideal radiation and pronounced cold air drainage produce extreme temperature inversions and rather low minimum temperatures.

Normals, Means, and Extremes

(To better understand these tables, see full explanation of terms beginning on page 322)

Month	Normal Degree days Base 65 °F: Heating	Normal Degree days: Cooling	Precipitation, Water equivalent: Normal	Maximum monthly	Year	Minimum monthly	Year	Maximum in 24 hrs.	Year	Snow, Ice pellets: Maximum monthly	Year	Maximum in 24 hrs.	Year
(a)				32		32		32		32		32	
J	654	9	4.84	11.00	1949	1.49	1961	5.81	1949	5.5	1948	4.5	1948
F	517	10	5.28	17.67	1961	1.20	1968	6.57	1961	2.3	1960	2.3	1960
M	389	26	6.17	11.42	1951	1.79	1967	7.05	1970	0.7	1957	0.7	1957
A	116	62	4.62	9.90	1964	1.35	1967	5.08	1966	T	1971	T	1971
M	20	190	3.62	11.10	1969	1.15	1951	4.63	1969	0.0		0.0	
J	0	372	4.00	8.44	1963	0.67	1968	3.85	1957	0.0		0.0	
J	0	462	5.22	13.70	1950	1.11	1952	4.39	1968	0.0		0.0	
A	0	440	4.31	10.85	1967	0.82	1955	5.13	1952	0.0		0.0	
S	6	273	3.64	9.74	1951	T	1955	3.92	1957	0.0		0.0	
O	137	84	2.58	7.04	1970	0.11	1963	3.26	1959	T	1955	T	1955
N	391	0	3.72	15.25	1948	0.42	1949	4.87	1948	1.4	1950	1.4	1950
D	614	0	5.23	13.98	1961	1.29	1958	5.29	1961	8.0	1963	8.4	1963
YR	2844	1928	53.23	17.67	FEB 1961	T	SEP 1955	7.05	MAR 1970	8.0	DEC 1963	8.4	DEC 1963

Month	Relative humidity pct. Hour 00 (Local time)	Hour 06	Hour 12	Hour 18	Wind: Mean speed m.p.h.	Prevailing direction	Fastest mile: Speed m.p.h.	Direction	Year	Pct. of possible sunshine	Mean sky cover, tenths, sunrise to sunset
(a)	12	12	12	12	32	15	32	32		32	32
J	77	81	63	67	8.5	S	49	W	1975	41	7.0
F	72	78	56	58	9.2	N	59	SE	1960	49	6.6
M	73	79	54	53	9.6	S	65	SW	1955	55	6.4
A	76	83	53	53	8.7	S	56	SW	1956	63	5.8
M	83	86	55	58	6.9	S	65	NW	1951	66	5.9
J	84	86	57	61	6.2	SSW	56	SW	1957	65	5.9
J	87	89	63	67	5.7	SSW	57	SW	1960	60	6.3
A	88	90	63	69	5.5	NE	50	NW	1956	63	5.8
S	86	89	61	71	6.6	ENE	50	SE	1951	62	5.5
O	85	88	56	73	6.2	ENE	43	W	1955	67	4.6
N	81	84	58	69	7.6	N	52	N	1944	56	5.7
D	79	82	63	70	8.1	NNW	41	SE	1954	45	6.5
YR	81	85	58	64	7.4	S	65	SW	MAR 1955	58	6.0

Month	Mean number of days: Sunrise to sunset: Clear	Partly cloudy	Cloudy	Precipitation .01 inch or more	Snow, Ice pellets 1.0 inch or more	Thunderstorms	Heavy fog, visibility ¼ mile or less	Temperatures °F Max. (b) 90° and above	Max. 32° and below	Min. 32° and below	Min. 0° and below	Average station pressure mb. Elev. 630 feet m.s.l.
(a)	32	32	32	32	32	32	32	12	12	12	12	3
J	7	6	18	12	*	2	1	0	1	16	*	998.0
F	7	6	15	11	*	3	1	0	*	15	0	996.3
M	7	9	15	11	*	5	1	0	0	7	0	993.3
A	9	8	13	9	0	5	*	0	0	1	0	995.1
M	8	11	12	9	0	7	*	2	0	0	0	992.2
J	7	13	10	10	0	9	1	9	0	0	0	994.0
J	5	14	12	13	0	11	*	13	0	0	0	994.5
A	7	14	10	10	0	9	*	11	0	0	0	995.9
S	10	9	11	8	0	4	1	5	0	0	0	995.2
O	14	8	9	6	0	1	1	0	0	1	0	998.2
N	10	7	13	9	*	2	1	0	0	8	0	998.2
D	8	7	16	11	*	1	1	0	*	13	0	997.4
YR	99	112	154	118	*	58	9	40	2	60	*	995.7

FOOTNOTES Means and extremes above are from existing and comparable exposures. Annual extremes have been exceeded at other sites in the locality as follows: Highest temperature 107 in July 1930; lowest temperature -10 in February 1899; maximum monthly precipitation 20.12 in July 1916; minimum monthly precipitation 0.00 in October 1924; maximum precipitation in 24 hours 8.84 in July 1916; maximum monthly snowfall 11.8 in January 1936; maximum snowfall in 24 hours 11.0 in January 1936.

Snowfall

Season	July	Aug	Sept	Oct	Nov	Dec	Jan
1936-37	0.0	0.0	0.0	0.0	0.0	0.0	0.0
1937-38	0.0	0.0	0.0	0.0	T	1.5	T
1938-39	0.0	0.0	0.0	0.0	0.5	0.0	0.0
1939-40	0.0	0.0	0.0	0.0	0.0	T	10.0
1940-41	0.0	0.0	0.0	0.0	0.0	0.0	T
1941-42	0.0	0.0	0.0	0.0	T	T	T
#1942-43	0.0	0.0	0.0	0.0	0.0	0.0	0.0
1943-44	0.0	0.0	0.0	0.0	0.0	T	0.3
1944-45	0.0	0.0	0.0	0.0	T	1.5	T
1945-46	0.0	0.0	0.0	0.0	0.0	2.5	T
1946-47	0.0	0.0	0.0	0.0	0.0	0.0	0.0
1947-48	0.0	0.0	0.0	0.0	0.0	0.0	5.5
1948-49	0.0	0.0	0.0	0.0	0.0	T	1.0
1949-50	0.0	0.0	0.0	0.0	0.0	0.0	0.0
1950-51	0.0	0.0	0.0	0.0	1.4	T	T
1951-52	0.0	0.0	0.0	0.0	T	T	0.0
1952-53	0.0	0.0	0.0	0.0	0.0	0.0	T
1953-54	0.0	0.0	0.0	0.0	0.0	T	T
1954-55	0.0	0.0	0.0	0.0	0.0	T	T
1955-56	0.0	0.0	0.0	T	0.0	T	T
1956-57	0.0	0.0	0.0	0.0	T	T	0.0
1957-58	0.0	0.0	0.0	0.0	0.0	T	T
1958-59	0.0	0.0	0.0	0.0	0.0	3.3	T
1959-60	0.0	0.0	0.0	0.0	0.0	T	T
1960-61	0.0	0.0	0.0	0.0	0.0	T	T
1961-62	0.0	0.0	0.0	0.0	0.0	T	3.8
1962-63	0.0	0.0	0.0	0.0	0.0	T	T
1963-64	0.0	0.0	0.0	0.0	0.0	8.0	0.4
1964-65	0.0	0.0	0.0	0.0	0.0	T	T
1965-66	0.0	0.0	0.0	0.0	0.0	0.0	1.2
1966-67	0.0	0.0	0.0	0.0	T	T	T
1967-68	0.0	0.0	0.0	0.0	T	T	1.0
1968-69	0.0	0.0	0.0	0.0	T	T	T
1969-70	0.0	0.0	0.0	0.0	T	T	1.7
1970-71	0.0	0.0	0.0	0.0	T	0.0	T
1971-72	0.0	0.0	0.0	0.0	T	0.0	T
1972-73	0.0	0.0	0.0	0.0	0.0	0.0	T
1973-74	0.0	0.0	0.0	0.0	0.0	T	0.C
1974-75	0.0	0.0	0.0	0.0	T	0.4	T
1975-76	0.0	0.0	0.0	0.0	T	T	
RECORD MEAN	0.0	0.0	0.0	T	T	0.5	0.5

Heating Degree Days

Season	July	Aug	Sept	Oct	Nov	Dec	Jan
1955-56	0	0	0	185	450	607	719
1956-57	0	0	2	62	436	322	530
1957-58	0	0	24	217	344	519	788
1958-59	0	0	0	107	319	711	696
1959-60	0	0	1	99	427	525	622
#1960-61	0	0	0	99	346	723	798
1961-62	0	0	3	93	301	556	718
#1962-63	0	0	9	100	382	686	822
1963-64	0	0	4	35	350	869	680
1964-65	0	0	0	196	305	520	591
1965-66	0	0	13	171	305	583	840
1966-67	0	0	3	203	331	635	643
1967-68	0	0	41	162	492	510	690
1968-69	0	0	1	148	434	723	687
1969-70	0	0	4	110	443	663	830
1970-71	0	0	10	104	493	523	657
1971-72	0	0	0	28	437	320	548
1972-73	0	0	9	135	486	534	749
1973-74	0	0	3	73	285	615	374
1974-75	0	0	19	159	378	542	493
1975-76	0	0	49	105	349	626	

Cooling Degree Days

Year	Jan	Feb	Mar	Apr	May	June	July
1969	0	0	0	33	156	346	523
1970	0	0	2	115	227	330	492
1971	1	0	0	35	90	394	393
1972	4	6	7	88	93	291	379
1973	0	0	24	28	132	333	452
1974	4	3	52	48	204	238	450
1975	8	0	26	61	241	351	416

Feb	Mar	Apr	May	June	Total
0.0	0.0	0.0	0.0	0.0	0.0
0.0	0.0	0.0	0.0	0.0	1.5
0.0	0.0	0.0	0.0	0.0	0.5
T	T	0.0	0.0	0.0	10.0
3.5	0.0	0.0	0.0	0.0	3.5
T	2.5	0.0	0.0	0.0	2.5
T	T	0.0	0.0	0.0	T
0.0	0.0	0.0	0.0	0.0	0.3
0.0	0.0	0.0	0.0	0.0	1.5
0.0	0.0	0.0	0.0	0.0	2.5
T	T	0.0	0.0	0.0	T
0.0	0.0	0.0	0.0	0.0	5.5
T	0.0	0.0	0.0	0.0	1.0
0.0	0.0	0.0	0.0	0.0	0.0
0.2	T	0.0	0.0	0.0	1.6
T	T	0.0	0.0	0.0	T
T	T	0.0	0.0	0.0	T
T	T	0.0	0.0	0.0	T
T	T	0.0	0.0	0.0	T
0.0	T	0.0	0.0	0.0	T
0.0	0.7	0.0	0.0	0.0	0.7
2.2	0.0	0.0	0.0	0.0	2.2
0.0	T	0.0	0.0	0.0	3.3
2.3	T	0.0	0.0	0.0	2.3
T	0.0	0.0	0.0	0.0	T
0.0	T	0.0	0.0	0.0	3.8
0.5	0.0	0.0	0.0	0.0	0.5
T	0.0	0.0	0.0	0.0	8.4
T	T	0.0	0.0	0.0	T
T	T	0.0	0.0	0.0	1.2
0.8	T	0.0	0.0	0.0	0.8
0.7	T	0.0	0.0	0.0	1.7
T	T	0.0	0.0	0.0	T
0.1	T	0.0	0.0	0.0	1.8
0.8	T	T	0.0	0.0	0.8
T	T	0.0	0.0	0.0	T
0.0	0.0	0.0	0.0	0.0	T
T	0.0	0.0	0.0	0.0	T
T	T	0.0	0.0	0.0	0.4
0.2	T	T	0.0	0.0	1.2

Average Temperature

Year	Jan	Feb	Mar	Apr	May	June	July	Aug	Sept	Oct	Nov	Dec	Annual
1936	41.6	43.7	59.4	60.9	74.2	81.8	80.7	80.4	78.4	66.2	51.4	49.0	64.0
1937	56.4	46.4	52.0	62.6	72.5	80.4	79.7	81.0	73.3	61.4	50.2	45.6	63.5
1938	46.0	54.6	61.7	62.9	72.4	77.0	80.2	81.8	75.1	68.0	55.4	46.0	65.1
1939	49.4	51.9	58.2	61.0	69.9	78.6	80.7	78.4	77.0	66.6	52.2	48.8	64.4
1940	30.6	44.0	53.7	61.3	68.0	76.4	77.9	80.6	74.2	67.1	53.4	50.6	61.5
1941	46.7	42.3	48.6	65.9	73.6	78.7	80.4	79.2	78.8	72.0	53.6	49.8	64.1
1942	42.8	43.2	54.8	65.4	70.7	78.4	81.0	78.8	72.8	65.1	56.8	46.8	63.0
#1943	47.7	49.0	51.8	63.4	73.2	82.6	81.0	81.4	70.8	60.4	48.8	43.2	62.8
1944	44.5	51.6	55.0	60.6	72.0	79.6	78.8	78.4	74.8	61.4	52.2	43.1	62.7
1945	43.1	49.5	61.8	63.5	66.8	77.8	79.7	79.4	76.4	61.4	54.5	39.2	62.8
1946	45.0	48.4	59.8	65.0	68.6	74.9	78.4	76.2	71.8	63.5	58.6	48.9	63.3
1947	48.2	38.8	46.7	63.8	67.9	75.6	76.2	81.0	76.3	69.1	50.2	46.0	61.6
1948	36.8	49.3	57.2	66.0	69.8	78.8	81.0	78.0	72.5	60.5	54.4	48.8	62.8
1949	52.5	51.6	53.8	60.5	71.5	77.2	81.0	78.6	71.5	68.8	50.8	47.4	63.8
1950	58.9	52.4	51.9	59.1	73.6	76.8	77.6	76.7	71.8	65.8	47.2	39.9	62.6
1951	46.8	49.0	54.7	60.4	68.9	78.1	81.0	82.3	75.4	65.0	47.8	49.8	63.2
1952	51.4	50.2	52.5	60.3	70.8	82.6	82.9	79.5	71.7	56.8	51.7	45.0	63.0
1953	49.3	49.0	57.8	60.6	73.5	81.4	79.7	79.5	74.1	65.2	51.6	43.4	63.8
1954	46.2	51.2	53.4	67.2	65.1	79.2	83.7	83.6	78.4	64.5	50.7	43.8	63.9
1955	43.5	48.6	57.6	66.3	72.9	72.4	79.9	81.1	77.6	61.4	50.7	45.3	63.1
1956	41.6	52.3	53.8	60.8	73.4	76.5	80.2	80.5	72.4	64.5	50.3	54.5	63.4
1957	47.8	55.2	51.8	64.9	71.3	79.2	79.9	80.3	73.5	58.5	53.8	48.1	63.7
1958	39.3	37.6	49.9	63.0	71.2	78.6	80.0	79.7	75.2	62.3	54.9	41.9	61.1
1959	42.3	48.1	51.9	62.5	72.9	77.2	81.1	81.3	74.8	65.8	50.6	47.8	63.0
1960	44.7	43.6	44.2	64.3	68.2	78.3	82.3	80.1	74.4	64.4	53.2	41.5	61.6
#1961	39.0	52.1	57.3	59.2	67.3	75.0	78.4	78.7	76.4	64.2	55.9	46.9	62.6
1962	41.7	55.2	52.1	62.2	78.6	79.0	82.6	82.1	74.8	66.4	52.0	42.6	64.1
#1963	38.2	40.8	58.4	65.2	70.5	77.3	78.7	80.0	73.5	67.5	53.5	36.8	61.7
1964	42.8	42.7	53.9	65.3	71.7	78.2	77.7	78.1	76.0	59.6	55.3	48.0	62.5
1965	45.8	44.6	49.8	64.8	71.8	75.0	77.7	78.0	73.7	60.0	54.8	46.0	61.9
1966	37.7	46.2	52.3	62.2	66.9	73.6	81.3	77.0	71.8	58.8	54.1	44.3	60.5
1967	44.0	41.8	58.3	67.2	67.7	76.2	75.7	74.2	68.4	60.7	48.4	48.5	60.9
1968	42.5	38.7	52.8	62.9	68.3	77.9	78.8	79.4	72.1	63.2	50.3	41.5	60.7
1969	42.6	44.5	46.6	62.7	69.0	76.2	81.7	77.8	70.9	63.9	50.1	43.3	60.8
1970	37.9	44.5	52.6	65.6	71.3	75.7	80.6	78.7	77.0	63.3	48.4	47.9	62.0
1971	43.6	44.2	48.5	60.2	65.3	77.9	77.5	77.8	75.0	67.2	50.7	54.8	61.9
1972	47.2	46.9	53.7	63.1	67.2	74.2	76.9	78.8	75.1	61.7	48.9	47.7	61.8
1973	40.7	42.3	58.6	58.1	67.5	75.9	79.4	77.2	77.2	66.6	56.2	45.0	62.1
1974	52.8	47.3	61.2	61.5	71.0	72.7	79.2	78.4	70.1	60.6	52.7	47.3	62.9
1975	49.1	50.1	53.9	60.5	72.4	76.4	78.1	79.1	70.2	63.5	54.1	44.6	62.7
RECORD MEAN	45.6	47.1	55.0	62.9	70.7	77.8	79.9	79.6	75.2	64.6	53.4	46.3	63.2
MAX	54.7	56.7	65.6	74.0	81.6	88.2	89.8	89.6	85.5	75.9	64.0	55.5	73.4
MIN	36.5	37.4	44.3	51.8	59.8	67.3	70.0	69.6	64.8	53.2	42.7	37.1	52.9

\# Indicates a station move or relocation of instruments.

BIRMINGHAM, AL

Feb	Mar	Apr	May	June	Total
366	354	173	5	7	2866
281	402	120	31	0	2186
762	462	116	25	0	3257
466	400	124	12	0	2835
613	637	97	72	0	3093
356	252	199	48	4	2825
285	398	154	1	0	2509
672	225	84	25	0	3005
639	348	71	5	0	3001
571	478	85	2	0	2748
520	393	149	34	9	3017
645	248	51	65	2	2826
755	387	108	30	0	3175
566	563	95	26	4	3247
568	377	91	23	0	3109
578	500	171	74	0	3110
526	348	138	21	7	2373
629	217	228	48	0	3035
491	161	147	9	0	2158
412	361	190	2	0	2556

Aug	Sept	Oct	Nov	Dec	Total
402	188	84	2	0	1734
432	377	58	0	0	2033
403	309	105	10	13	1753
434	318	40	8	2	1670
385	376	129	28	0	1887
418	180	28	15	0	1640
447	211	66	29	2	1858

Precipitation

Year	Jan	Feb	Mar	Apr	May	June	July	Aug	Sept	Oct	Nov	Dec	Annual
1936	10.07	7.34	2.87	5.20	0.65	1.81	8.52	4.00	2.70	1.64	1.62	7.78	54.20
1937	13.37	4.03	3.70	6.01	5.27	1.77	4.11	5.27	2.81	6.60	1.71	2.04	56.69
1938	3.69	1.65	9.05	11.58	2.34	3.35	8.39	2.61	1.59	0.05	4.01	2.09	50.40
1939	4.57	8.24	4.35	4.47	5.88	4.97	3.39	8.50	7.69	0.17	0.75	2.82	55.80
1940	5.39	8.27	6.46	3.14	3.02	4.27	8.27	2.14	1.39	2.57	3.81	4.32	53.05
1941	2.48	2.91	5.44	3.02	1.05	2.62	10.33	9.93	1.77	3.43	1.67	5.40	50.05
1942	1.89	3.62	5.85	1.03	3.95	4.68	2.15	2.08	4.84	1.40	1.57	11.03	44.09
#1943	1.16	2.03	9.35	4.49	2.04	1.31	4.99	2.23	2.31	1.26	2.43	3.26	36.86
1944	2.59	6.55	7.17	7.82	3.58	3.76	3.76	3.48	2.22	0.46	2.49	4.46	48.34
1945	2.64	7.76	5.86	6.20	3.24	1.06	3.34	3.45	3.79	6.54	3.85	5.54	53.27
1946	8.68	9.10	5.34	1.54	6.32	7.06	6.61	5.33	6.29	3.10	4.17	3.67	67.21
1947	9.04	1.86	5.67	7.28	3.83	4.54	1.41	5.52	0.36	1.20	5.83	4.94	51.48
1948	3.73	7.90	6.73	3.55	2.43	3.78	6.55	4.10	3.63	0.70	15.25	4.28	62.63
1949	11.00	8.29	7.98	4.90	3.37	2.84	2.98	5.22	4.31	3.00	0.42	3.44	57.75
1950	4.51	4.28	5.47	1.97	4.55	4.97	13.70	5.49	2.50	2.41	1.69	3.92	55.46
1951	3.68	4.36	11.42	6.19	1.15	7.31	4.10	2.98	9.74	2.78	1.98	8.71	64.40
1952	4.35	3.05	5.44	1.38	3.31	4.15	1.11	8.18	2.69	2.03	2.50	4.96	43.15
1953	7.82	6.01	4.31	4.97	4.27	1.22	4.71	2.80	2.98	0.21	1.62	9.04	49.96
1954	6.35	3.37	3.51	3.20	3.23	1.93	3.58	2.74	1.24	1.77	3.96	5.78	40.66
1955	4.70	6.47	4.16	6.42	4.81	2.06	6.85	0.82	T	3.73	4.69	1.64	46.35
1956	1.85	8.98	6.09	5.47	2.38	1.69	7.97	7.12	2.26	3.49	2.18	4.16	53.64
1957	6.00	3.73	6.08	5.41	2.96	7.70	2.62	4.19	9.59	1.81	5.67	4.01	59.77
1958	3.42	5.14	3.03	3.51	2.33	3.10	6.79	1.98	5.74	2.31	3.38	1.29	42.02
1959	4.16	3.52	5.13	2.81	8.27	2.09	3.61	3.64	5.95	6.21	3.84	2.46	51.69
1960	5.05	3.36	6.31	2.24	2.28	2.74	2.06	4.09	2.73	3.45	3.24	3.21	40.76
1961	1.49	17.67	9.22	4.33	2.45	4.85	10.17	3.56	2.42	2.05	4.29	13.98	76.48
1962	8.64	4.39	5.21	2.99	1.26	3.59	3.89	3.49	3.69	2.03	6.41	2.55	48.14
1963	7.32	3.25	6.31	6.70	3.72	8.44	6.54	1.53	1.21	0.11	4.00	5.94	55.07
1964	5.37	4.11	9.44	9.90	3.20	4.08	4.34	2.78	3.26	2.95	3.24	5.09	57.76
1965	3.21	6.22	6.10	2.54	1.37	8.17	4.87	3.55	2.60	0.67	2.80	2.06	44.16
1966	4.74	8.67	3.77	8.37	3.30	2.87	4.99	6.48	5.12	3.13	2.28	2.34	56.06
1967	2.84	4.74	1.79	1.35	9.32	4.37	6.60	10.85	2.84	4.23	6.42	11.49	66.84
1968	5.56	1.20	6.17	6.23	3.51	0.67	9.39	1.81	3.42	1.20	4.66	7.38	51.20
1969	7.78	3.17	5.19	5.32	11.10	3.75	2.91	1.76	6.85	2.51	2.66	6.07	59.07
1970	2.47	2.35	11.36	5.56	2.27	3.55	3.37	7.01	1.05	7.04	2.31	3.32	51.66
1971	3.58	9.28	6.65	4.25	2.64	6.57	8.90	3.68	3.35	1.21	1.76	5.92	57.79
1972	9.30	2.15	4.79	2.56	3.82	[illegible]	3.55	2.01	8.09	3.35	4.47	5.76	52.55
1973	6.85	2.33	9.71	5.33	8.29	3.74	8.36	5.41	2.64	0.96	4.91	7.58	66.11
1974	6.85	4.94	2.43	5.43	5.43	1.42	4.69	8.28	4.94	1.49	4.13	5.97	56.00
1975	7.23	4.96	7.57	3.19	4.15	2.44	7.33	3.33	3.69	3.74	4.15	3.49	55.27
RECORD MEAN	5.02	4.99	6.02	4.70	4.03	4.03	5.46	4.40	3.38	2.69	3.57	5.17	53.46

Record mean values above are means through the current year for the period beginning in 1896, 1944 for snowfall. Data are from City Office locations through June 1943 and from Airport locations thereafter.

Station: MOBILE, ALABAMA
BATES FIELD
Elevation (ground): 211 feet

TEMPERATURES °F

Month	Normal: Daily maximum	Normal: Daily minimum	Normal: Monthly	Extremes: Record highest	Extremes: Year	Extremes: Record lowest	Extremes: Year
(a)				14		14	
J	61.1	41.3	51.2	79	1975	8	1963
F	64.1	43.9	54.0	81	1975	11	1962
M	69.5	49.2	59.4	89	1967	11	1962
A	78.0	57.7	67.9	91	1971	36	1973
M	85.0	64.5	74.8	99	1962	46	1971
J	89.8	70.7	80.3	101	1969	56	1966
J	90.5	72.6	81.6	100	1968	62	1967
A	90.6	72.3	81.5	102	1968	60	1967
S	86.5	68.4	77.5	98	1964	42	1967
O	79.7	58.0	68.9	93	1963	38	1968
N	69.5	47.5	58.5	87	1971	24	1970
D	63.0	42.8	52.9	81	1974	10	1962
YR	77.3	57.4	67.4	102	AUG 1968	8	JAN 1963

IMPORTANT:
The time-period covered by this record is limited: See footnotes following table of **NORMALS, MEANS AND EXTREMES** for explanation and for additional history of **EXTREME HIGHS AND LOWS** recorded in the general area.

Mobile is located at the head of Mobile Bay and approximately 30 miles from the Gulf of Mexico. Its weather is influenced to a considerable extent by the Gulf.

The summers are consistently warm, but maximum temperatures are seldom as high as they are at inland stations. Normally, in summer, the day begins with a minimum in the low seventies and the temperature rises rapidly before noon to the high eighties or low nineties where it is checked by onset of the sea breeze. On the rare occasions when northerly winds prevail throughout the day, the maxima may reach the high nineties or go slightly above 100°.

Winter weather is usually mild except for occasional invasions of cold air that last about three days. January is the coldest month in the year. An average winter will have less than 20 days with below freezing minima and the lowest reading will be about 23°. However, unusual winters may produce much lower readings that require extensive protective measures as some citrus fruit is grown in the area and outdoor nurseries are numerous. The growing season will average about 274 days.

The normal annual rainfall is among the highest in the United States. It is fairly evenly distributed throughout the year with a slight maximum at the height of the summer thunderstorm season and a slight minimum during the late fall. Rainfall is usually of the shower type and long periods of continuous rain are rare. (Continued page 334)

Snowfall

Season	July	Aug	Sept	Oct	Nov	Dec	Jan
1970-71	0.0	0.0	0.0	0.0	0.0	0.0	0.0
1971-72	0.0	0.0	0.0	0.0	0.0	0.0	0.0
1972-73	0.0	0.0	0.0	0.0	0.0	0.0	T
1973-74	0.0	0.0	0.0	0.0	0.0	T	0.0
1974-75	0.0	0.0	0.0	0.0	0.0	0.0	0.0
1975-76	0.0	0.0	0.0	0.0	0.0	0.0	
RECORD MEAN	0.0	0.0	0.0	0.0	T	0.1	0.1

Heating Degree Days

Season	July	Aug	Sept	Oct	Nov	Dec	Jan
1955-56	0	0	0	74	278	370	489
1956-57	0	0	0	1	292	200	302
1957-58	0	0	7	108	179	389	608
1958-59	0	0	0	37	170	466	525
1959-60	0	0	0	27	299	396	482
#1960-61	0	0	0	36	170	482	604
#1961-62	0	0	0	42	193	339	511
1962-63	0	0	0	41	242	441	575
1963-64	0	0	0	17	186	616	486
1964-65	0	0	0	78	167	347	387
1965-66	0	0	0	43	100	345	554
1966-67	0	0	0	32	173	374	370
1967-68	0	0	23	46	202	273	448
1968-69	0	0	0	50	284	474	420.
1969-70	0	0	0	20	220	345	618
1970-71	0	0	0	7	273	265	361
1971-72	0	0	0	8	204	136	244
1972-73	0	0	0	33	284	308	442
1973-74	0	0	0	18	91	377	108
1974-75	0	0	0	58	215	336	276
1975-76	0	0	9	11	211	402	

Cooling Degree Days

Year	Jan	Feb	Mar	Apr	May	June	July
1969	5	10	4	134	303	527	582
1970	6	2	16	229	335	467	564
1971	18	13	37	151	260	531	541
1972	47	15	40	173	309	478	513
1973	0	1	80	98	303	508	598
1974	85	19	91	88	332	392	539
1975	21	44	57	115	363	475	529

Feb	Mar	Apr	May	June	Total
0.0	T	0.0	0.0	0.0	T
0.0	0.0	0.0	0.0	0.0	0.0
3.6	0.0	0.0	0.0	0.0	3.6
0.0	0.0	0.0	0.0	0.0	T
0.0	0.0	0.0	0.0	0.0	0.0
0.2	T	0.0	0.0	0.0	0.4

MOBILE, AL

Feb	Mar	Apr	May	June	Total
191	183	63	0	0	1648
155	209	64	7	0	1230
569	256	51	7	0	2174
293	254	71	0	0	1816
450	357	44	32	0	2087
214	123	131	7	0	1767
141	270	83	0	0	1579
473	108	6	3	0	1889
484	187	25	0	0	2001
342	240	4	0	0	1565
333	208	27	1	0	1611
363	100	0	3	0	1415
525	251	12	0	0	1780
320	342	8	0	0	1898
375	190	14	10	0	1792
308	190	57	6	0	1467
295	131	35	0	0	1053
368	86	75	0	0	1596
288	106	49	0	0	1037
185	183	70	0	0	1323

Aug	Sept	Oct	Nov	Dec	Total
490	380	220	17	4	2676
567	505	184	6	36	2917
534	441	261	37	94	2918
575	505	224	46	20	2945
518	462	293	110	10	2981
517	323	81	45	36	2548
524	325	183	85	11	2732

Average Temperature

Year	Jan	Feb	Mar	Apr	May	June	July	Aug	Sept	Oct	Nov	Dec	Annual
#1936	51.4	51.2	63.0	65.6	74.7	82.6	82.3	82.2	81.2	70.9	57.6	54.2	68.1
1937	63.0	53.0	56.5	67.0	76.2	80.6	81.9	82.0	76.7	66.8	55.2	51.8	67.6
1938	51.8	58.6	67.2	66.4	74.9	80.2	81.5	83.4	77.5	69.4	58.8	51.2	68.4
1939	55.8	56.7	62.3	66.2	73.8	80.6	82.0	80.8	79.4	70.1	57.0	54.8	68.3
1940	39.6	50.1	59.4	65.2	72.2	79.0	80.7	81.6	75.9	69.1	58.8	57.0	65.7
#1941	52.8	50.0	55.2	68.6	75.0	80.4	81.9	83.8	80.7	75.6	58.0	55.6	68.1
1942	47.8	48.6	56.9	65.7	72.6	79.3	81.0	80.0	74.7	69.3	60.3	53.5	65.8
1943	52.5	54.3	57.4	67.5	76.5	81.4	82.7	82.6	74.7	65.0	56.1	52.1	66.9
1944	50.7	60.6	60.9	65.0	74.2	84.1	80.7	80.6	78.5	69.1	59.5	51.2	67.9
1945	50.3	57.5	67.3	68.4	71.8	80.9	79.6	81.3	79.4	66.8	60.7	46.9	67.6
1946	51.6	54.9	63.2	69.3	73.6	77.8	80.2	80.3	75.9	69.3	63.8	56.2	68.0
1947	55.5	47.8	54.5	68.8	73.4	79.8	79.8	81.3	78.0	72.7	57.6	53.3	66.9
1948	44.8	55.6	63.2	70.3	75.2	80.5	82.0	80.5	74.6	66.7	60.5	57.7	67.6
1949	58.6	60.3	59.5	65.9	75.1	79.7	80.4	81.1	76.1	72.7	57.2	56.0	68.6
#1950	64.6	59.0	56.1	62.5	76.1	81.7	79.0	80.7	76.8	75.6	54.1	48.9	67.9
1951	53.2	54.7	60.6	64.8	74.4	80.0	82.0	84.6	78.4	71.0	54.0	56.7	67.9
1952	58.9	56.7	58.4	65.0	75.4	82.8	82.9	82.3	75.8	63.0	56.8	52.0	67.5
1953	54.5	54.0	64.5	65.5	77.7	83.2	81.2	80.9	77.1	69.9	58.1	50.5	68.1
1954	53.5	57.7	58.3	71.4	70.5	81.3	83.1	84.6	81.2	68.8	56.4	51.1	68.2
1955	50.6	55.8	63.7	69.7	77.0	77.6	80.5	81.8	79.8	66.8	56.9	53.4	67.8
1956	49.0	59.5	59.5	66.1	76.5	78.4	80.3	80.7	75.0	69.3	56.3	59.4	67.5
1957	56.7	61.2	58.5	67.3	74.5	80.0	82.6	80.5	75.5	63.8	59.4	52.2	67.7
1958	45.1	44.5	56.6	67.0	73.6	79.1	80.2	80.2	78.2	67.2	61.0	49.8	65.2
1959	47.9	54.8	56.8	65.1	75.3	78.9	80.3	81.1	77.9	70.5	55.7	52.0	66.4
1960	49.4	49.3	53.8	67.2	70.7	80.5	82.4	79.8	77.1	69.9	59.7	49.2	65.8
1961	45.4	57.9	62.2	62.5	72.3	77.0	80.6	80.2	78.1	67.5	60.5	54.9	66.6
#1962	48.9	61.7	57.0	65.6	80.1	80.6	83.4	82.1	78.0	71.0	56.9	50.6	68.0
1963	46.2	47.8	63.9	71.2	76.1	80.4	82.7	83.5	77.3	71.7	59.2	44.9	67.1
1964	49.2	48.1	59.4	69.6	74.9	80.4	80.5	81.5	78.2	64.3	61.1	54.2	66.8
1965	52.5	53.4	58.2	71.4	75.7	79.4	82.4	81.2	79.1	68.7	63.9	53.7	68.3
1966	47.2	52.8	58.8	68.4	75.1	79.1	83.8	81.2	77.9	68.0	60.7	53.2	67.2
1967	53.0	52.2	64.5	74.6	74.6	82.5	81.5	79.8	74.2	66.7	59.5	57.9	68.4
1968	50.3	46.7	58.1	70.3	76.0	83.2	82.7	83.1	78.1	70.1	56.3	49.5	67.0
1969	51.5	53.7	53.8	68.9	74.5	82.4	83.5	80.6	77.5	71.2	58.0	53.7	67.4
1970	45.0	51.4	59.2	71.9	75.3	80.2	83.0	83.0	81.7	70.5	55.9	57.4	67.9
1971	53.7	54.3	59.9	67.9	73.0	82.4	82.3	82.1	79.5	72.9	59.2	63.5	69.2
1972	58.4	55.0	61.8	69.4	74.7	80.7	81.4	83.4	81.6	71.0	56.8	55.5	69.2
1973	50.5	51.7	64.6	65.6	74.6	81.6	84.1	81.4	80.2	73.6	65.3	52.9	68.9
1974	64.0	55.2	64.3	66.1	75.5	77.8	82.2	81.4	75.5	65.5	59.2	55.1	68.5
1975	56.6	59.8	60.7	66.2	76.5	80.7	81.8	81.7	75.3	70.3	60.5	52.1	68.5
RECORD MEAN	51.9	54.4	60.1	67.1	74.3	80.3	81.8	81.5	78.1	68.9	58.9	53.1	67.6
MAX	60.6	63.3	68.9	75.9	83.1	88.8	89.9	89.7	86.4	78.4	68.5	61.8	76.3
MIN	43.2	45.5	51.3	58.3	65.4	71.7	73.6	73.3	69.7	59.4	49.3	44.3	58.8

\# Indicates a station move or relocation of instruments.

Precipitation

Year	Jan	Feb	Mar	Apr	May	June	July	Aug	Sept	Oct	Nov	Dec	Annual
#1936	14.59	4.03	1.52	5.94	3.77	1.75	6.13	6.29	2.18	0.42	2.86	4.03	53.51
1937	4.03	3.29	6.96	7.49	4.62	7.21	7.27	4.45	3.16	11.43	2.23	3.28	65.42
1938	2.87	1.88	2.15	2.37	2.02	4.62	12.83	2.04	0.97	0.48	1.72	3.20	37.15
1939	2.64	7.44	2.11	2.58	8.52	9.12	7.02	8.81	4.81	0.13	0.69	2.55	56.42
1940	2.65	5.56	4.19	4.78	4.37	12.49	9.82	2.24	4.86	0.57	3.00	7.74	62.27
#1941	3.53	4.21	5.49	2.34	1.42	10.11	13.60	3.71	5.21	3.91	3.72	7.34	64.59
1942	3.36	7.73	7.18	1.98	4.00	12.70	10.86	6.38	7.27	4.06	0.90	5.62	72.04
1943	6.01	2.82	8.35	3.18	3.62	4.35	6.00	2.78	8.76	0.76	5.00	4.74	56.37
1944	4.46	2.05	12.32	15.59	2.25	4.18	9.21	11.46	12.72	0.81	7.51	2.92	85.48
1945	5.60	5.33	4.22	8.90	2.52	6.12	14.11	7.54	3.64	3.71	1.92	9.07	72.68
1946	5.52	4.81	15.58	0.86	11.17	5.10	9.19	4.91	6.60	0.05	3.03	2.25	69.07
1947	8.52	2.26	14.53	10.45	6.71	6.60	2.83	8.78	9.00	3.65	10.28	6.92	90.53
1948	6.48	1.31	11.95	5.79	3.72	5.24	6.03	11.09	7.56	1.45	13.65	5.85	80.12
1949	3.13	7.33	7.76	10.69	3.10	6.08	19.29	4.23	8.35	4.03	0.44	6.02	80.45
#1950	2.22	1.92	9.43	6.07	4.71	7.78	14.16	8.61	7.05	2.42	0.68	7.49	72.54
1951	2.58	2.38	11.83	6.64	1.39	10.09	11.65	4.04	7.44	1.19	3.99	3.96	67.18
1952	3.94	8.12	5.57	3.56	7.07	5.28	4.76	7.56	12.13	0.06	1.89	9.35	69.29
1953	3.30	6.29	4.42	8.12	1.85	6.11	8.42	10.61	1.73	0.18	4.54	11.38	66.95
1954	1.18	1.54	4.18	0.48	2.93	1.94	7.66	3.92	4.29	3.21	4.77	6.25	42.35
1955	3.35	6.52	1.47	17.69	3.88	2.22	11.38	10.88	2.93	3.71	1.47	8.24	73.74
1956	5.16	4.30	9.74	2.15	4.23	11.92	10.13	4.96	11.58	4.19	1.09	4.32	73.77
1957	1.45	5.41	8.69	7.33	7.99	3.61	4.32	8.53	13.61	1.26	7.38	3.10	72.68
1958	5.86	4.80	9.26	4.52	4.98	10.06	9.54	6.77	8.19	0.90	3.56	1.45	69.89
1959	4.38	7.19	5.08	8.17	7.40	9.47	8.46	4.51	8.47	6.56	0.67	2.97	73.33
1960	7.92	4.88	5.27	5.57	5.24	1.68	9.21	6.67	3.87	3.81	0.25	4.16	58.53
1961	6.14	6.61	10.35	6.86	4.62	13.07	4.80	5.69	6.63	1.47	5.57	10.92	82.73
1962	4.75	6.57	6.97	1.89	0.45	7.15	5.44	3.01	4.87	2.41	2.75	4.54	50.80
1963	7.14	4.11	1.48	1.83	2.02	7.16	8.25	9.26	0.58	0.06	4.48	6.46	52.83
1964	7.36	2.73	4.23	13.45	4.32	4.27	8.83	6.20	2.19	2.42	3.73	4.12	63.85
1965	9.35	4.94	4.97	0.60	4.33	3.70	8.13	4.72	10.45	1.59	0.73	3.97	57.48
1966	5.52	9.01	3.21	2.37	4.66	1.19	5.20	6.48	4.32	4.44	1.35	4.60	52.35
1967	5.46	6.13	0.59	2.26	5.05	2.88	7.80	8.86	7.76	6.69	0.36	7.50	61.34
1968	0.98	2.88	1.30	2.24	3.17	3.71	3.08	4.59	6.13	1.13	4.05	10.70	43.96
1969	2.79	3.40	8.15	4.53	7.95	1.33	14.14	12.05	1.95	0.67	0.44	5.58	62.98
1970	3.85	5.32	8.60	1.67	8.84	7.68	9.19	9.20	2.56	5.71	1.54	5.77	69.93
1971	2.15	7.15	6.49	0.99	3.16	2.88	7.75	10.46	7.30	0.03	1.23	5.58	55.17
1972	5.94	4.46	5.87	1.81	7.72	3.65	2.16	2.35	3.28	1.26	5.67	5.59	49.76
1973	1.96	3.40	11.63	9.91	2.97	5.33	6.24	5.46	12.68	2.15	4.52	4.57	70.82
1974	3.89	6.47	6.16	5.91	2.31	3.48	6.60	7.03	10.60	0.88	3.91	4.31	61.55
1975	3.43	3.75	7.45	9.05	7.12	3.76	11.82	8.50	7.37	6.72	12.63	4.98	86.58
RECORD MEAN	4.69	5.04	6.55	5.08	4.47	5.58	7.57	6.65	5.57	3.20	3.64	5.22	63.26

Record mean values above are means through the current year for the period beginning in 1871 for temperature and precipitation, 1942 for snowfall. Data are from City Office locations through November 1941 and from Airport locations thereafter.

MOBILE, ALABAMA

(Continued)

Frontal thunderstorms may occur in any month of the year and airmass storms are frequent in summer. July and August will average a thunderstorm every other day. The summer storms are usually not too violent and seldom produce hail.

While the Mobile area has not had a destructive hurricane since 1926, this seems to be due more to chance than to location. Past records show that this area is subject to hurricanes from the West Indies, as well as to those from the western Caribbean and the southwestern Gulf of Mexico.

Normals, Means, and Extremes

Month	Normal Degree days Base 65 °F: Heating	Cooling	Precipitation in inches — Water equivalent: Normal	Maximum monthly	Year	Minimum monthly	Year	Maximum in 24 hrs.	Year	Snow, Ice pellets: Maximum monthly	Year	Maximum in 24 hrs.	Year	Relative humidity pct. Hour 00 (Local time)	Hour 06	Hour 12	Hour 18
(a)				34		34		34		34		34		13	13	13	13
J	451	23	4.71	9.35	1965	0.98	1968	8.34	1965	3.5	1955	3.5	1955	80	82	64	72
F	337	30	4.76	9.01	1966	1.31	1948	5.00	1952	3.6	1973	3.6	1973	76	81	56	62
M	221	46	7.07	15.58	1946	0.59	1967	6.52	1951	1.6	1954	1.6	1954	80	84	56	64
A	40	127	5.59	17.69	1955	0.48	1954	13.36	1955	0.0		0.0		84	87	55	65
M	0	304	4.52	11.17	1946	0.45	1962	4.47	1972	0.0		0.0		83	86	53	62
J	0	459	6.09	13.07	1961	1.19	1966	7.38	1961	0.0		0.0		84	86	54	65
J	0	515	8.86	19.29	1949	2.16	1972	5.34	1975	0.0		0.0		87	89	61	72
A	0	512	6.93	12.05	1969	2.35	1972	6.62	1969	0.0		0.0		87	90	62	74
S	0	375	6.59	13.61	1957	0.58	1963	6.82	1974	0.0		0.0		86	88	60	72
O	39	160	2.55	6.72	1975	0.03	1971	4.30	1967	0.0		0.0		82	85	52	67
N	211	16	3.39	13.65	1948	0.25	1960	7.02	1975	T	1966	T	1966	83	85	56	70
D	385	10	5.92	11.38	1953	1.45	1958	5.50	1968	3.0	1963	3.0	1963	81	84	63	73
YR	1684	2577	66.98	19.29	JUL 1949	0.03	OCT 1971	13.36	APR 1955	3.6	FEB 1973	3.6	FEB 1973	83	86	58	68

(To better understand these tables, see full explanation of terms beginning on page 322)

Month	Wind: Mean speed m.p.h.	Prevailing direction	Fastest mile: Speed m.p.h.	Direction	Year	Pct. of possible sunshine	Mean sky cover, tenths, sunrise to sunset	Mean number of days — Sunrise to sunset: Clear	Partly cloudy	Cloudy	Precipitation .01 inch or more	Snow, Ice pellets 1.0 inch or more	Thunderstorms	Heavy fog, visibility ¼ mile or less	Temperatures °F Max.: (b) 90° and above	32° and below	Min.: 32° and below	0° and below	Average station pressure mb. Elev. 221 feet m.s.l.
(a)	27	14	17	17			27	27	27	27	34	34	34	34	13	13	13	13	3
J	10.8	N	44	18	1959		6.7	7	7	17	11	*	2	6	0	*	7	0	1012.2
F	11.0	N	46	23	1960		6.2	8	6	14	10	*	2	4	0	0	5	0	1011.0
M	11.3	N	40	27	1962		6.1	9	8	14	11	*	5	5	0	0	1	0	1008.0
A	10.7	S	44	01	1964		5.9	8	10	12	8	0	5	5	*	0	0	0	1009.6
M	9.1	S	51	32	1963		5.7	9	11	11	8	0	7	2	6	0	0	0	1006.3
J	7.9	S	44	05	1959		5.8	7	14	9	12	0	12	1	19	0	0	0	1007.7
J	7.1	S	46	18	1960		6.7	3	15	13	17	0	18	1	23	0	0	0	1008.3
A	6.9	NE	63	14	1969		6.1	6	15	10	14	0	14	1	20	0	0	0	1009.6
S	8.2	NE	36	11	1960		5.9	8	11	11	10	0	7	2	11	0	0	0	1007.8
O	8.4	N	46	36	1964		4.3	15	8	8	6	0	2	2	2	0	0	0	1011.4
N	9.6	N	37	36	1959		5.2	11	8	11	8	0	2	4	0	0	1	0	1012.3
D	10.3	N	38	32	1959		6.2	9	6	16	11	*	2	5	0	0	5	0	1012.2
YR	9.3	N	63	14	AUG 1969		5.9	100	119	146	124	*	80	39	81	*	19	0	1009.7

FOOTNOTE

Means and extremes above are from existing and comparable exposures. Annual extremes have been exceeded at other sites in the locality as follows: Highest temperature 104 in July 1952; lowest temperature -1 in February 1899; maximum monthly snowfall 6.0 in February 1895; highest wind 87 from East in October 1916.

Station: ANCHORAGE, ALASKA
INTERNATIONAL AIRPORT
Elevation (ground): 114 feet

TEMPERATURES °F

Month	Normal			Extremes			
	Daily maximum	Daily minimum	Monthly	Record highest	Year	Record lowest	Year
(a)				22		22	
J	20.0	3.5	11.8	50	1961	-34	1975
F	26.6	8.9	17.8	48	1968	-26	1956
M	32.8	14.6	23.7	49	1974	-24	1971
A	43.8	26.8	35.3	62	1965	3	1972
M	55.2	37.2	46.2	77	1969	17	1964
J	62.9	46.2	54.6	85	1969	33	1961
J	65.6	50.1	57.9	81	1955	38	1964
A	63.8	48.0	55.9	82	1968	33	1969
S	55.7	40.4	48.1	73	1957	20	1956
O	41.8	27.8	34.8	61	1969	-5	1956
N	28.3	13.9	21.1	53	1967	-21	1956
D	20.6	5.3	13.0	47	1969	-30	1964
YR	43.1	26.9	35.0	85	JUN 1969	-34	JAN 1975

IMPORTANT:
The time-period covered by this record is limited: See footnotes on next page for explanation and for additional history of EXTREME HIGHS AND LOWS recorded in the general area.

Anchorage is in a broad valley with adjacent narrow bodies of water. Cook Inlet, including Knik Arm and Turnagain Arm, lies approximately 2 miles to the west, north, and south. The terrain rises gradually to the east for about 10 miles, with marshes interspersed with glacial moraines, shallow depressions, small streams, and knolls. Beyond this area, the Chugach Mountains rise abruptly into a range oriented north-northeast to south-southwest, with average elevation 4,000 to 5,000 feet and some peaks to 8,000 or 10,000 feet. The Chugach Range acts as a barrier to the influx of warm, moist air from the Gulf of Alaska, so the average annual precipitation is only 10 to 15 percent of that at stations located on the Gulf of Alaska side of the Chugach Range.

The Alaska Mountain Range lies in a long arc from southwest, through northwest, to northeast, approximately 100 miles distant from Anchorage. During the winter, this Range is an effective barrier to the influx of very cold air from the north side of the Range. Extreme cold winter weather, associated with a high pressure system over interior Alaska, may lead to a succession of clear days in Anchorage, with temperatures dropping to -15° to -30°, as contrasted to the -50° and even -60° readings in the interior. There are some factors, however, which tend to offset the sheltering effect of this mountain barrier. Chief among these is cold air entrapment in various suburban areas during periods of light winds. This results occasionally in temperatures on the outskirts of Anchorage as much as 15° to 20° colder than observed at the official observation sites.

The four seasons are well marked in the Anchorage area, but in length, and in some major characteristics, they differ considerably from the usually accepted standards in middle latitudes.

Winter is considered to be the period during which the ponds, streams, and lakes are frozen; this normally extends from mid-October to mid-April. The shortest day of the year has 5 hours and 28 minutes of possible sunshine. Periods of clear, cold weather normally alternate with cloudy, mild weather during the Anchorage winter. The clear, cold weather is frequently accompanied by significant fog because of the important low-level moisture source provided by the arms of Cook Inlet which surround the area on three sides; while considerable floating ice is prevalent, the high tides maintain some open water throughout the winter. Visibilities of 1/2 mile, or less, occur about 5 percent of the time during December and January, and most of these low visibilities are associated with fog. Snow visibilities generally range from 1 to 3 miles though heavier snowfalls will, of course, restrict visibilities to less than a mile on a few occasions. The first measurable snow occurs, on the average, on October 15, but has been as early as September 20; latest measurable snow in the spring averages April 14, but has been as late as May 6. Snow occurs on 20 to 25 percent of the midwinter days, and most of the snow falls in relatively small daily amounts, with only 2 percent of the midwinter days having more than 4 inches. The heavier snows occur in conjunction with vigorous storm centers moving northward across south-central Alaska. Normally, the depth of snowfall on the ground does not exceed 15 inches. Strong, gusty, north winds which occur, on the average, once or twice during the winter will, under favorable snow conditions, cause drifting and packing of snow cover. Although normally an area of light winds, strong "Northers" at Anchorage occasionally result from the rapid deepening of storms in the nearby Gulf of Alaska at a time when the interior is covered by an extensive mass of quite cold air.

(Continued page 338)

ANCHORAGE, ALASKA

Normals, Means, and Extremes

(To better understand these tables, see full explanation of terms beginning on page 322)

Month	Normal Degree days Base 65 °F: Heating	Normal Degree days Base 65 °F: Cooling	Precipitation in inches, Water equivalent: Normal	Maximum monthly	Year	Minimum monthly	Year	Maximum in 24 hrs.	Year	Snow, Ice pellets: Maximum monthly	Year	Maximum in 24 hrs.	Year
(a)				22		22		22		22		22	
J	1649	0	0.84	2.09	1963	0.02	1974	1.19	1961	21.1	1955	10.5	1955
F	1322	0	0.84	3.07	1955	0.07	1958	1.16	1956	48.5	1955	12.4	1956
M	1280	0	0.56	1.48	1963	0.10	1969	0.53	1963	26.1	1959	14.5	1959
A	891	0	0.56	1.78	1963	T	1969	0.69	1975	27.6	1963	9.1	1955
M	583	0	0.59	1.60	1968	0.02	1957	0.83	1968	3.9	1963	3.9	1963
J	312	0	1.07	3.40	1962	0.18	1969	1.84	1962	0.0		0.0	
J	220	0	2.07	4.44	1958	0.42	1972	2.06	1956	0.0		0.0	
A	282	0	2.32	3.40	1973	0.33	1969	1.68	1955	0.0		0.0	
S	507	0	2.37	5.43	1961	0.76	1973	1.92	1961	4.6	1965	3.5	1965
O	936	0	1.43	2.89	1972	0.35	1960	1.03	1972	21.3	1955	9.6	1955
N	1317	0	1.02	2.71	1964	0.10	1975	1.66	1964	32.4	1956	16.4	1964
D	1612	0	1.07	2.67	1955	0.19	1956	1.62	1955	41.6	1955	17.7	1955
YR	10911	0	14.74	5.43	SEP 1961	T	APR 1969	2.06	JUL 1956	48.5	FEB 1955	17.7	DEC 1955

Month	Relative humidity pct. Hour 02	Hour 08	Hour 14	Hour 20 (Local time)	Wind: Mean speed m.p.h.	Prevailing direction	Fastest mile: Speed m.p.h.	Direction	Year	Pct. of possible sunshine	Mean sky cover, tenths, sunrise to sunset	Mean number of days, Sunrise to sunset: Clear	Partly cloudy	Cloudy	Precipitation .01 inch or more	Snow, Ice pellets 1.0 inch or more	Thunderstorms	Heavy fog, visibility ¼ mile or less	Temperatures °F Max. (b) 90° and above	32° and below	Min. 32° and below	0° and below	Average station pressure mb. Elev. 132 feet m.s.l.
(a)	14	14	14	14	22	10	22	22		22	22	22	22	22	11	11	22	22	11	11	11	11	3
J	70	71	70	70	5.8	NNE	61	03	1971	44	6.3	10	4	17	5	3	0	7	0	29	31	16	1004.7
F	74	75	69	71	6.4	N	44	36	1963	44	7.2	6	4	18	10	4	0	4	0	21	27	8	1000.7
M	71	70	58	68	6.7	N	35	34	1963	55	6.5	8	6	17	8	3	0	1	0	14	27	4	1001.5
A	72	67	55	64	7.0	N	35	15	1964	54	7.1	5	7	18	7	2	0	1	0	3	21	0	1005.1
M	73	64	50	58	8.2	S	33	35	1964	53	7.5	4	7	20	7	0	*	*	*	0	4	0	1005.0
J	76	69	57	63	8.1	S	30	17	1971	47	8.0	3	6	21	8	0	*	*	2	0	0	0	1006.8
J	81	74	62	69	7.0	S	29	16	1957	44	7.8	4	6	21	11	0	*	*	7	0	0	0	1009.8
A	82	78	64	75	6.5	S	30	23	1955	41	8.0	3	6	22	13	0	*	1	2	0	0	0	1010.1
S	84	83	65	78	5.9	NNE	33	18	1956	41	7.8	4	5	21	13	*	*	2	*	0	3	0	1006.0
O	77	78	65	75	6.3	N	40	03	1966	40	7.4	6	5	20	11	2	0	2	0	5	21	*	996.8
N	78	77	73	76	5.9	NNE	37	34	1970	38	7.2	6	5	19	9	3	0	4	0	22	28	4	1000.7
D	75	75	75	76	5.8	NNE	41	05	1964	34	7.1	7	4	20	11	5	0	5	0	26	30	9	994.9
YR	76	73	64	70	6.6	N	61	03	JAN 1971	46	7.3	66	65	234	113	21	1	27	11	120	192	43	1003.5

FOOTNOTES

Means and extremes above are from existing and comparable exposures. Annual extremes have been exceeded at other sites in the locality as follows: Highest temperature 86 in June 1953; lowest temperature -38 in February 1947; maximum monthly precipitation 5.91 in August 1934; minimum monthly precipitation 0.00 in December 1933.

Snowfall

Season	July	Aug	Sept	Oct	Nov	Dec	Jan
1942-43							
1943-44	0.0	0.0	0.0	T	6.8	14.4	24.4
1944-45	0.0	0.0	T	T	5.4	16.2	2.7
1945-46	0.0	0.0	0.0	10.6	9.5	2.1	9.4
1946-47	0.0	0.0	0.0	0.4	17.9	16.7	11.1
1947-48	0.0	0.0	0.4	3.7	11.5	14.9	14.9
1948-49	0.0	0.0	0.0	7.8	10.4	11.1	36.1
1949-50	0.0	0.0	0.0	7.3	8.2	25.9	13.6
1950-51	0.0	0.0	0.0	T	1.9	27.9	12.2
1951-52	0.0	0.0	0.0	3.6	3.3	19.7	20.1
1952-53	0.0	0.0	0.0	12.6	8.4	13.3	4.0
#1953-54	0.0	0.0	0.0	0.9	2.0	20.0	8.1
1954-55	0.0	0.0	0.0	8.7	8.0	19.0	21.1
1955-56	0.0	0.0	0.0	21.3	11.8	41.6	5.9
1956-57	0.0	0.0	T	13.4	32.4	2.7	3.9
1957-58	0.0	0.0	T	T	5.7	4.3	16.3
1958-59	0.0	0.0	T	4.4	24.3	10.8	6.5
1959-60	0.0	0.0	0.0	7.1	11.7	31.2	14.2
1960-61	0.0	0.0	T	0.5	9.6	4.9	1.7
1961-62	0.0	0.0	0.0	18.5	13.9	11.0	12.1
1962-63	0.0	0.0	0.0	3.0	3.0	4.9	15.5
1963-64	0.0	0.0	0.0	4.0	2.6	9.8	7.6
1964-65	0.0	0.0	0.0	10.6	25.8	16.2	8.5
1965-66	0.0	0.0	4.6	16.7	17.9	23.9	9.7
1966-67	0.0	0.0	0.0	1.9	13.5	13.4	16.7
1967-68	0.0	0.0	0.0	4.8	2.5	26.5	7.3
1968-69	0.0	0.0	1.3	15.1	14.7	7.9	6.5
1969-70	0.0	0.0	0.0	0.2	2.6	8.7	16.1
1970-71	0.0	0.0	T	4.2	4.2	11.2	1.2
1971-72	0.0	0.0	0.0	11.9	8.2	11.4	9.6
1972-73	0.0	0.0	1.5	3.3	10.7	6.5	8.1
1973-74	0.0	0.0	0.0	6.6	10.6	6.7	0.5
1974-75	0.0	0.0	0.0	4.4	8.4	29.2	5.7
1975-76	0.0	0.0	0.0	T	2.0	11.5	
RECORD MEAN	0.0	0.0	0.2	6.3	10.0	15.0	11.0

Heating Degree Days

Season	July	Aug	Sept	Oct	Nov	Dec	Jan
1955-56	226	323	554	1029	1664	1758	1654
1956-57	265	271	563	1128	1448	1881	1545
1957-58	206	191	445	823	955	1722	1433
1958-59	260	290	552	1094	1357	1531	1700
#1959-60	284	278	514	998	1241	1450	1482
1960-61	227	295	530	860	1267	1226	1359
#1961-62	221	318	489	1112	1450	1884	1593
1962-63	197	249	578	836	1274	1499	1415
#1963-64	192	242	383	866	1583	1237	1573
1964-65	240	315	485	922	1303	1980	1701
1965-66	178	261	333	1055	1328	1603	1713
1966-67	214	324	553	1008	1419	1674	1791
1967-68	172	200	501	901	1042	1513	1625
1968-69	153	208	530	982	1280	1816	1869
1969-70	168	330	478	732	1235	1128	1722
1970-71	239	312	552	1003	1201	1550	1934
1971-72	291	302	561	1008	1396	1508	1814
1972-73	185	252	608	1025	1308	1627	1925
1973-74	216	342	573	1012	1532	1440	1797
1974-75	235	263	452	937	1263	1425	1643
1975-76	192	252	463	937	1517	1654	

Cooling Degree Days

Year	Jan	Feb	Mar	Apr	May	June	July
1969	0	0	0	0	0	5	1
1970	0	0	0	0	0	0	0
1971	0	0	0	0	0	0	1
1972	0	0	0	0	0	0	5
1973	0	0	0	0	0	0	0
1974	0	0	0	0	0	0	1
1975	0	0	0	0	0	0	2

Feb	Mar	Apr	May	June	Total
3.3	2.4	3.1	T	0.0	
7.4	15.2	1.4	0.0	0.0	69.6
14.7	9.0	1.1	8.8	0.0	57.9
19.0	5.8	1.9	0.0	0.0	58.3
1.3	7.1	T	1.7	0.0	56.2
8.1	14.0	T	0.0	0.0	67.5
12.4	12.9	16.4	3.9	0.0	111.0
T	4.9	T	0.0	0.0	59.9
14.3	7.7	T	0.0	0.0	64.0
5.9	13.1	3.2	0.4	0.0	69.3
6.6	4.6	1.5	T	0.0	51.0
2.5	14.9	0.7	0.0	0.0	49.1
48.5	8.6	18.7	0.0	0.0	132.6
33.1	4.6	10.5	0.0	0.0	128.8
11.8	3.2	T	0.0	0.0	67.4
0.6	2.5	1.0	0.0	0.0	30.4
13.7	26.1	8.7	0.0	0.0	94.5
8.5	5.1	3.5	0.0	0.0	81.3
9.6	5.8	6.4	0.0	0.0	38.5
1.4	14.2	3.0	0.0	0.0	74.1
19.8	11.4	27.6	3.9	0.0	89.1
17.9	15.1	6.8	0.4	0.0	64.2
11.5	3.0	2.8	0.2	0.0	78.6
10.7	5.2	6.1	T	0.0	94.8
16.3	8.8	4.0	0.0	0.0	74.6
26.1	3.2	7.8	T	0.0	78.2
10.6	1.1	T	0.0	0.0	57.2
8.7	1.4	4.1	0.0	0.0	41.8
18.5	11.1	8.3	T	0.0	58.7
8.9	12.0	12.6	T	0.0	74.6
1.0	16.1	1.3	0.0	0.0	48.5
23.3	8.2	1.9	0.0	0.0	57.8
15.4	8.3	16.1	0.4	0.0	87.9
12.5	8.7	5.5	0.6	0.0	69.8

Average Temperature

Year	Jan	Feb	Mar	Apr	May	June	July	Aug	Sept	Oct	Nov	Dec	Annual
1943		22.0	23.6	34.8	46.2	54.6	55.9	53.6	46.0	36.4	28.1	22.4	36.1
1944	14.6	25.8	20.6	31.9	45.0	54.4	56.2	55.4	47.0	36.8	22.5	17.3	35.6
1945	22.6	21.5	23.6	31.8	42.4	52.4	57.3	54.2	46.6	34.8	12.4	13.0	34.4
1946	15.8	17.8	15.9	32.8	44.8	53.7	58.4	53.2	47.4	39.4	17.2	5.0	33.4
1947	-1.0	18.1	30.3	36.1	46.6	53.4	59.6	55.2	47.2	36.0	27.8	22.7	36.0
1948	18.0	12.2	19.8	31.4	46.2	53.9	56.2	53.2	45.6	35.8	14.2	5.8	32.7
1949	12.6	6.0	29.4	31.4	44.8	50.6	56.0	54.8	49.8	35.2	26.0	6.8	33.6
1950	5.1	7.5	27.5	35.2	45.1	53.1	56.7	58.0	48.8	33.2	12.0	12.1	32.9
1951	5.1	13.2	12.5	37.3	46.9	52.9	59.4	55.9	47.3	31.6	22.7	10.8	33.0
1952	3.8	18.6	22.6	33.0	42.0	51.9	57.2	55.1	46.2	38.0	31.3	17.7	34.8
#1953	6.9	20.4	21.8	38.0	47.3	59.1	60.5	56.6	47.1	34.4	20.6	17.9	35.9
1954	9.8	6.7	22.4	33.3	48.4	54.7	57.9	56.1	48.5	39.8	27.6	6.0	34.3
1955	18.2	15.4	23.1	31.1	43.9	51.2	57.5	54.4	46.3	31.6	9.4	8.1	32.5
1956	5.1	10.3	19.6	34.7	44.0	52.4	56.3	56.0	46.1	28.4	16.5	4.3	31.1
1957	15.0	13.5	28.7	37.1	48.6	58.0	58.1	58.5	49.9	38.1	33.0	9.4	37.3
1958	18.6	19.1	28.9	38.8	47.5	55.1	56.4	55.5	46.4	29.5	19.5	15.4	35.9
1959	10.1	20.8	14.0	33.7	47.6	56.6	55.7	55.8	47.7	32.5	23.4	18.0	34.7
#1960	17.0	22.7	21.0	34.1	49.1	55.1	57.6	55.3	47.1	37.0	22.5	25.2	37.0
#1961	20.9	17.9	16.3	36.0	47.8	54.9	57.7	54.5	48.5	29.0	16.5	4.2	33.7
1962	13.5	19.5	19.9	36.9	44.7	53.5	58.4	56.8	45.6	37.8	22.3	16.6	35.4
1963	19.2	23.5	24.0	31.9	46.9	51.6	58.6	57.0	52.0	36.8	12.1	24.8	36.5
#1964	14.1	20.1	17.3	33.7	41.2	55.9	57.1	54.6	48.7	35.0	21.3	1.0	33.3
1965	10.0	10.3	36.5	39.7	45.4	52.9	59.0	56.3	53.7	30.7	20.5	13.1	35.7
1966	9.7	14.7	16.7	35.3	44.2	55.4	57.9	54.4	46.3	32.3	17.5	10.8	32.9
1967	7.1	14.4	23.2	35.1	47.1	56.1	59.3	58.3	48.1	35.7	30.0	16.0	35.9
1968	12.5	23.1	28.4	35.0	48.2	54.8	59.9	58.2	47.1	33.1	22.1	6.3	35.7
1969	4.6	17.9	28.6	39.4	47.7	57.7	59.3	54.2	48.9	41.2	23.7	28.4	37.7
1970	9.2	29.6	35.4	36.4	48.1	54.8	57.1	54.6	46.4	32.5	24.9	14.9	37.0
1971	2.7	20.6	14.2	33.4	41.6	51.2	55.4	55.0	46.1	32.3	18.3	16.2	32.3
1972	6.4	13.5	15.7	26.8	43.3	51.9	59.0	56.6	44.5	31.7	21.3	12.4	31.9
1973	2.9	13.1	24.2	35.8	43.6	51.4	57.8	53.8	45.7	32.2	13.6	18.3	32.7
1974	6.8	14.1	23.3	37.9	47.9	55.5	57.3	56.3	49.8	34.5	22.6	18.8	35.4
1975	11.9	12.9	22.5	32.9	46.3	53.0	58.6	56.6	49.3	34.6	14.2	11.6	33.7
RECORD MEAN	10.9	16.9	22.8	34.6	45.8	54.0	57.7	55.5	47.6	34.5	20.8	13.7	34.6
MAX	18.6	25.1	31.7	42.6	54.3	62.0	65.3	63.0	55.0	41.0	27.4	20.5	42.2
MIN	3.2	8.6	13.8	26.6	37.2	46.0	50.0	48.0	40.2	27.9	14.2	6.9	26.9

ANCHORAGE, AK

Feb	Mar	Apr	May	June	Total
1584	1403	904	644	369	12312
1437	1119	830	500	201	11188
1279	1115	776	533	291	9769
1229	1575	931	530	245	11294
1223	1357	923	483	289	10522
1312	1500	865	526	294	10261
1267	1394	837	621	338	11524
1156	1266	986	557	393	10406
1297	1476	936	733	263	10781
1530	879	754	598	357	11064
1402	1493	882	641	285	11174
1411	1292	890	547	261	11384
1209	1129	894	510	301	9997
1312	1124	761	527	217	10779
983	910	852	515	298	9351
1238	1574	940	717	410	11670
1488	1521	1138	666	384	12077
1448	1258	866	654	399	11555
1416	1265	805	526	279	11223
1454	1313	954	575	354	10868

Aug	Sept	Oct	Nov	Dec	Total
2	0	0	0	0	8
0	0	0	0	0	0
0	0	0	0	0	1
0	0	0	0	0	5
0	0	0	0	0	0
0	0	0	0	0	1
0	0	0	0	0	2

Precipitation

# Indicates a station move or relocation of instruments.

Year	Jan	Feb	Mar	Apr	May	June	July	Aug	Sept	Oct	Nov	Dec	Annual
1943		0.28	0.39	0.17	0.64	1.20	2.54	3.27	3.97	0.47	1.27	1.39	
1944	1.29	0.47	0.44	0.23	0.51	0.86	2.53	4.01	2.50	1.20	0.33	1.08	15.45
1945	0.36	1.13	1.23	0.34	1.27	1.62	1.49	3.88	2.70	2.32	0.59	0.13	17.06
1946	0.51	1.22	0.32	0.18	1.23	0.74	0.97	1.69	1.24	0.80	1.39	0.97	11.26
1947	0.96	0.12	0.47	0.33	0.57	0.30	1.27	2.59	4.28	0.89	1.23	0.68	13.69
1948	1.04	0.43	0.67	0.08	0.03	0.42	3.28	1.86	2.34	1.75	1.36	0.50	13.76
1949	2.13	0.69	1.05	0.82	0.41	2.94	1.26	1.80	2.45	1.25	0.62	1.45	16.87
1950	0.83	T	0.29	0.04	0.10	1.90	0.97	0.92	1.07	0.52	0.26	1.71	8.61
1951	0.71	0.84	0.42	0.53	0.05	2.51	1.83	2.41	5.16	0.88	0.27	1.02	16.63
1952	1.47	0.50	0.65	0.32	0.32	0.44	2.47	2.95	2.32	3.80	0.96	0.79	16.99
#1953	0.20	0.48	0.21	0.15	0.76	0.57	1.14	5.06	1.85	0.81	0.11	1.11	12.45
1954	0.56	0.18	0.97	0.03	0.15	0.91	2.08	2.13	1.66	2.02	0.93	1.00	12.62
1955	1.12	3.07	0.51	1.32	0.02	1.18	1.72	3.26	1.27	1.82	0.59	2.67	18.55
1956	0.52	2.49	0.28	0.50	0.44	0.52	3.07	1.60	2.00	2.19	2.33	0.19	16.13
1957	1.36	0.67	0.20	0.01	0.02	0.56	1.64	2.02	3.21	0.93	1.51	0.36	12.49
1958	1.05	0.07	0.19	0.25	1.05	2.19	4.44	1.67	1.31	1.93	1.41	0.54	16.10
1959	0.27	0.95	0.85	1.32	0.49	0.26	4.43	3.11	1.42	1.12	0.67	1.34	16.23
1960	0.72	0.45	0.22	0.27	0.44	0.26	2.71	2.70	4.79	0.35	0.56	1.04	14.51
1961	1.51	0.46	0.34	1.38	0.47	1.12	2.22	1.94	5.43	2.81	0.64	0.95	19.27
1962	0.88	0.74	0.58	0.25	1.52	3.40	0.72	1.92	1.45	1.56	0.49	1.06	14.57
1963	2.09	1.35	1.48	1.78	0.44	1.82	2.75	2.80	0.98	1.01	0.12	1.49	18.11
1964	0.35	1.15	1.07	0.89	0.97	1.73	1.08	2.16	0.83	2.31	2.71	0.64	15.89
1965	0.57	0.67	0.83	0.30	0.51	0.96	1.74	1.58	4.60	1.44	1.86	1.44	16.50
1966	0.63	0.80	0.44	0.70	0.75	0.27	0.71	2.47	2.45	0.86	1.11	1.06	12.25
1967	1.25	1.01	0.98	0.49	1.07	1.44	2.47	2.96	2.86	0.51	1.72	2.40	19.16
1968	0.83	1.67	0.29	0.85	1.60	0.62	1.34	0.69	1.05	1.61	1.08	0.45	12.08
1969	0.28	0.73	0.10	T	0.86	0.18	2.14	0.33	0.78	0.90	0.84	0.94	8.08
1970	0.86	0.57	0.29	0.27	0.43	0.85	2.03	2.23	1.11	1.62	1.21	1.62	13.09
1971	0.24	1.49	0.70	0.63	0.52	0.37	2.86	2.58	1.79	2.16	0.67	0.87	14.88
1972	0.56	0.63	0.68	0.73	0.81	0.61	0.42	1.40	4.42	2.89	0.76	0.72	14.63
1973	0.72	0.11	0.65	0.33	0.14	1.07	0.60	3.40	0.76	1.74	0.78	0.38	10.68
1974	0.02	1.15	0.60	0.61	0.34	0.69	1.22	1.62	1.53	2.63	1.01	2.00	13.42
1975	0.43	0.77	0.54	1.71	0.40	0.47	1.33	1.19	4.52	0.69	0.10	0.89	13.04
RECORD MEAN	0.82	0.83	0.57	0.54	0.59	1.06	1.92	2.31	2.43	1.51	0.95	1.06	14.59

Record mean values above are means through the current year for the period beginning in 1943 for temperature and precipitation.

ANCHORAGE, ALASKA

(Continued)

Spring is the period immediately following the famed Alaska "Break-up". This season is characterized by warm, pleasant days and chilly nights; the mean temperature rises rapidly; precipitation amounts are exceedingly small.

Summer comprises the period from June through early September, and is, in reality, two seasons of about equal length, the first of which is dry, the second wet. At the time of the summer solstice, possible sunshine in Anchorage amounts to almost 19-1/2 hours, and the sound of singing birds and pounding hammers is nearly as common at midnight as at noon. About the middle of July average cloudiness increases markedly, and the remainder of the summer usually accounts for about 40 percent of the annual precipitation.

Autumn is brief in Anchorage, beginning shortly before mid-September and lasting until mid-October. The frequency of cloudy days and precipitation drops sharply in early October. Measurable amounts of snow are rare in September, but substantial snowfalls sometimes reaching 10 to 12 inches occasionally occur in mid-October. Some of the stronger southerly winds, a few with damaging effects, occur in the late summer or fall; these are post-frontal winds following the movement of a storm from the southern Bering Sea or Bristol Bay, northeastward across the Alaskan interior. Somewhat less frequent, but more damaging, are the southeasterly "Chugach" winds which are funneled down the creek canyons on the northwestern slopes of the Chugach mountains east of the city; gusts estimated at 80 to 100 mph have caused considerable damage to roofs, power lines and trailers on a few occasions.

The growing season in Anchorage averages 124 days, with the mean daily temperature above freezing from April 8 to October 23. May 15 is the average date for the occurrence of a temperature as low as 32°, while September 16 is the average first date with 32° in the fall. The latest date with 32° in spring has been June 6, and the earliest with 32° in the fall August 14.

Note: A special report, detailing climate along the route of the Alaska pipeline, begins on page 702 .

Station: FAIRBANKS, ALASKA INTERNATIONAL AIRPORT
Elevation (ground): 436 feet

TEMPERATURES °F

Month	Normal			Extremes			
	Daily maximum	Daily minimum	Monthly	Record highest	Year	Record lowest	Year
(a)				12		12	
J	-2.2	-21.6	-11.9	38	1965	-61	1969
F	9.3	-14.3	-2.5	43	1970	-56	1968
M	23.3	-4.3	9.5	51	1970	-46	1964
A	40.4	17.3	28.9	65	1973	-21	1964
M	58.8	35.7	47.3	81	1964	-1	1964
J	70.7	47.2	59.0	96	1969	37	1970
J	71.8	49.6	60.7	94	1975	37	1964
A	65.8	44.9	55.4	85	1966	30	1965
S	54.4	34.4	44.4	80	1963	11	1972
O	33.5	16.9	25.2	65	1969	-27	1975
N	11.7	-6.2	2.8	46	1970	-43	1964
D	-1.5	-19.3	-10.4	42	1969	-56	1964
YR	36.3	15.0	25.7	96	JUN 1969	-61	JAN 1969

IMPORTANT:
The time-period covered by this record is limited: See footnotes on next page for explanation and for additional history of EXTREME HIGHS AND LOWS recorded in the general area.

Fairbanks is located in the Tanana Valley of interior Alaska, and is well sheltered from maritime influences by mountain ranges on practically all sides. The area, consequently, has a definite continental climate, conditioned in large measure by the ready response of the land mass to variations in solar heat received by the area throughout the year. The sun is above the horizon from 18 to 21 hours each day during the months of June and July; and during this period daily average maximum temperatures reach the lower seventies, and extreme highs of 90° or more have occurred in May, June, and July. Conversely, during the period from November to March, when the sunshine period ranges from 10 to less than 4 hours per day, the lowest temperature readings normally fall below zero quite regularly and extremes of near or below -60° have occurred in three midwinter months. The surrounding upland areas tend to aid the drainage or settling of cold air into the Tanana Valley lowlands.

The persistent snow cover during the winter months is a major contributing factor to the development of extreme cold, since the white surface prevents the absorption of heat from the rather limited amount of sunshine realized during the winter season. During December and January maximum temperatures are usually below zero.

Ice fog and smoke conditions frequently occur with the extremely low temperatures during anticyclonic conditions and these tend to persist for periods of a few days to one or two weeks. During such periods most, if not all, aircraft operations are suspended. Amounts of cloudiness are low, on the average, the year around, and are particularly low during the period February through April. Wind speeds are particularly light during the winter months. These facts, together with the relative scarcity of heavy fog during March and April, indicate that flying conditions are quite favorable during the early spring months when the daylight hours are rapidly increasing.

Precipitation normally follows a fairly regular pattern. By stateside standards the total annual precipitation of about 12 inches is relatively light, being a little less than is received at Denver and a little more than is received at San Diego. Growing season precipitation, which begins with the occurrence of light rain showers in May, builds up through the summer months to a maximum in August. There is a noticeable decline in precipitation from September on through December. April, which averages the lightest monthly precipitation during the year, realizes the greatest percentage of possible sunshine.

(Continued page 342)

FAIRBANKS, ALASKA

Normals, Means, and Extremes

(To better understand these tables, see full explanation of terms beginning on page 322)

Month	Normal Degree days Base 65 °F: Heating	Normal Degree days Base 65 °F: Cooling	Precipitation in inches, Water equivalent: Normal	Maximum monthly	Year	Minimum monthly	Year	Maximum in 24 hrs.	Year	Snow, Ice pellets: Maximum monthly	Year	Maximum in 24 hrs.	Year	Relative humidity pct. Hour 02 (Local time)	Hour 08	Hour 14	Hour 20	Wind: Mean speed m.p.h.	Prevailing direction	Fastest mile: Speed m.p.h.	Direction	Year	Pct. of possible sunshine	Mean sky cover, tenths, sunrise to sunset	Mean number of days, Sunrise to sunset: Clear	Partly cloudy	Cloudy	Precipitation .01 inch or more	Snow, Ice pellets 1.0 inch or more	Thunderstorms	Heavy fog, visibility ¼ mile or less	Temperatures °F Max. 90° and above (b)	Max. 32° and below	Min. 32° and below	Min. 0° and below	Average station pressure mb. Elev. 454 feet m.s.l.
(a)				24		24		24		24		24		12	12	12	12	24	12	24	24			24	24	24	24	24	24	24	24	12	12	12	12	3
J	2384	0	0.60	1.92	1957	0.01	1966	0.58	1968	26.3	1957	9.4	1968	67	67	68	67	2.8	N	29	27	1954		6.0	10	6	15	7	3	0	6	0	31	31	28	999.6
F	1890	0	0.53	1.75	1966	0.04	1975	0.97	1966	43.1	1966	20.1	1966	63	63	61	63	3.9	N	33	27	1955		6.5	7	6	15	7	3	0	2	0	26	28	24	995.8
M	1720	0	0.48	2.10	1963	T	1968	0.92	1963	29.6	1963	12.6	1963	63	62	52	60	5.0	N	40	22	1970		6.0	9	7	15	6	3	0	1	0	22	31	19	993.0
A	1083	0	0.33	0.84	1967	T	1969	0.31	1965	11.1	1967	4.9	1962	64	59	46	54	6.5	N	31	23	1965		6.8	6	7	17	5	1	0	*	0	6	28	2	994.3
M	549	0	0.65	1.67	1955	0.07	1957	0.88	1955	4.7	1964	4.5	1964	64	51	36	43	7.6	N	31	29	1955		7.0	5	10	16	6	*	*	*	3	*	8	*	991.9
J	211	31	1.42	3.52	1955	0.19	1966	1.52	1955	T	1974	T	1974	69	58	40	46	6.9	SW	40	25	1974		7.3	3	10	17	10	0	2	*	18	0	0	0	992.1
J	148	15	1.90	4.35	1962	0.40	1957	1.63	1962	0.0		0.0		78	68	50	56	6.4	SW	29	09	1957		7.6	3	8	20	12	0	2	1	21	0	0	0	994.8
A	304	6	2.19	6.20	1967	0.40	1957	3.42	1967	T	1969	T	1969	82	77	54	67	6.1	N	34	27	1954		7.9	2	7	22	13	0	1	2	9	0	1	0	996.9
S	618	0	1.08	3.05	1960	0.15	1968	1.21	1954	7.8	1972	7.0	1972	76	74	50	65	6.0	N	30	22	1975		7.4	5	6	19	9	*	*	2	2	*	9	0	994.3
O	1234	0	0.73	1.84	1970	0.08	1954	0.68	1970	24.4	1974	10.4	1974	76	76	66	74	5.4	N	40	25	1958		7.9	4	5	22	10	4	0	2	0	18	29	4	989.0
N	1866	0	0.66	3.32	1970	T	1953	0.84	1970	54.0	1970	14.6	1970	72	72	70	71	3.9	N	35	25	1970		6.8	7	5	18	10	4	0	1	0	28	30	19	994.2
D	2337	0	0.65	2.29	1970	T	1969	1.25	1968	33.5	1965	14.7	1968	67	67	67	67	3.1	N	37	24	1970		6.9	7	6	18	8	4	0	4	0	30	31	26	988.9
YR	14344	52	11.22	6.20	AUG 1967	T	DEC 1969	3.42	AUG 1967	54.0	NOV 1970	20.1	FEB 1966	70	66	55	61	5.3	N	40	25	JUN 1974		7.0	68	83	214	102	22	5	21	53	162	224	123	993.7

FOOTNOTES

Means and extremes above are from existing and comparable exposures. Annual extremes have been exceeded at other sites in the locality as follows: Highest temperature 99 in July 1919; lowest temperature -66 in January 1934; maximum monthly precipitation 6.88 in August 1930; minimum monthly precipitation 0.00 in February 1919; maximum monthly snowfall 65.6 in January 1937.

Snowfall

Season	July	Aug	Sept	Oct	Nov	Dec	Jan
1936-37	0.0	0.0	T	12.3	19.9	18.2	65.6
1937-38	0.0	0.0	0.0	4.3	9.1	10.4	15.4
1938-39	0.0	0.0	0.7	1.2	7.9	9.7	13.1
1939-40	0.0	0.0	T	12.8	11.7	1.5	27.1
1940-41	0.0	0.0	T	6.1	6.7	5.7	1.5
#1941-42	0.0	0.0	T	8.3	8.3	2.7	5.3
#1942-43	0.0	0.0	T	9.1	11.5	1.7	8.1
1943-44	0.0	0.0	T	5.0	1.3	13.0	3.0
1944-45	0.0	0.0	T	6.2	4.1	7.3	2.1
1945-46	0.0	0.0	0.0	17.3	9.8	3.0	8.0
1946-47	0.0	0.0	T	17.5	3.1	9.2	17.8
1947-48	0.0	0.0	2.8	11.2	10.6	3.3	8.6
1948-49	0.0	T	2.1	5.9	5.9	21.1	17.9
1949-50	0.0	0.0	0.0	5.7	5.8	11.5	30.9
1950-51	T	0.0	T	14.0	17.6	7.7	8.7
#1951-52	T	T	T	6.4	14.7	13.5	9.3
1952-53	0.0	0.0	2.6	8.3	2.4	0.4	1.7
1953-54	0.0	0.0	T	1.2	0.2	5.5	18.6
1954-55	0.0	0.0	T	2.8	7.5	9.8	10.3
1955-56	0.0	T	T	14.4	6.1	27.5	9.5
1956-57	0.0	0.0	T	13.8	14.1	7.5	26.3
1957-58	0.0	0.0	4.9	8.5	8.0	4.5	6.2
1958-59	0.0	0.0	0.1	11.9	11.4	8.1	5.6
1959-60	0.0	0.0	T	4.2	12.1	12.1	23.6
1960-61	0.0	0.0	T	3.9	10.1	3.8	7.4
1961-62	0.0	0.0	T	24.2	9.4	6.3	8.9
1962-63	0.0	0.0	0.5	2.8	3.1	6.0	17.5
1963-64	0.0	0.0	0.0	11.6	4.6	8.8	4.8
1964-65	0.0	0.0	0.0	4.7	18.1	14.0	3.0
1965-66	0.0	0.0	T	15.7	18.8	33.5	0.7
1966-67	0.0	0.0	0.0	5.5	36.6	2.9	13.0
1967-68	0.0	0.0	T	5.8	14.4	16.8	22.6
1968-69	0.0	0.0	0.9	6.7	8.0	20.2	10.8
1969-70	0.0	T	0.0	3.7	11.4	T	3.6
1970-71	0.0	0.0	4.1	21.9	54.0	32.5	8.5
1971-72	0.0	0.0	3.5	20.4	9.8	29.6	12.6
1972-73	0.0	0.0	7.8	6.9	12.2	26.9	14.2
1973-74	0.0	0.0	1.2	8.2	17.5	2.5	3.0
1974-75	0.0	0.0	0.3	24.4	22.5	17.9	14.1
1975-76	0.0	0.0	T	14.4	11.4	6.7	
RECORD MEAN	0.0	T	1.1	10.2	13.5	12.7	10.7

Heating Degree Days

Season	July	Aug	Sept	Oct	Nov	Dec	Jan
1955-56	144	362	634	1268	2247	2300	2651
1956-57	135	278	685	1481	2097	2895	1969
1957-58	150	178	634	1102	1496	2499	2102
1958-59	102	257	660	1555	1910	2238	2643
1959-60	285	320	637	1262	1746	2315	2134
1960-61	124	299	701	1190	1978	1846	2078
1961-62	179	294	622	1353	2078	2759	2258
1962-63	86	223	696	1055	1816	2218	1959
#1963-64	169	312	505	1189	2267	1890	2509
1964-65	165	256	595	1133	1876	2841	2574
1965-66	152	374	496	1580	1833	2455	2872
1966-67	92	247	441	1255	1929	2643	2496
1967-68	178	213	545	1239	1661	2064	2358
1968-69	50	208	657	1320	1881	2567	2849
1969-70	170	467	472	955	1914	1892	2524
1970-71	96	244	722	1425	1630	2318	3002
1971-72	134	271	600	1143	1932	2195	2524
1972-73	63	184	738	1177	1739	2091	2582
1973-74	111	302	523	1231	1968	2124	2535
1974-75	85	195	402	1342	1935	2370	2497
1975-76	33	270	570	1270	2195	2513	

Cooling Degree Days

Year	Jan	Feb	Mar	Apr	May	June	July
1969	0	0	0	0	0	83	2
1970	0	0	0	0	0	0	22
1971	0	0	0	0	0	73	16
1972	0	0	0	0	0	40	55
1973	0	0	0	0	0	13	24
1974	0	0	0	0	1	9	44
1975	0	0	0	0	0	28	146

Feb	Mar	Apr	May	June	Total
9.6	T	7.9	1.0	0.0	134.5
13.3	3.0	1.8	T	0.0	57.3
4.9	6.8	T	0.4	0.0	44.7
2.0	1.3	T	0.0	0.0	56.4
0.3	5.6	8.4	T	0.0	34.3
3.8	4.2	0.5	T	0.0	33.1
2.5	18.4	0.2	1.3	0.0	52.8
21.4	14.1	0.2	T	0.0	58.0
4.0	8.9	1.7	1.9	0.0	36.2
8.8	4.4	3.5	T	0.0	54.8
0.5	1.7	4.6	0.1	0.0	54.5
6.8	9.2	25.1	1.0	0.0	78.6
16.9	5.4	5.3	1.0	T	81.5
3.5	6.7	0.8	T	0.0	64.9
9.8	5.3	0.3	T	T	63.4
1.8	3.5	2.1	3.1	T	54.4
4.4	3.1	T	T	T	22.9
4.5	8.6	0.1	0.0	0.0	38.7
16.4	12.4	2.3	0.0	0.0	61.5
21.0	3.1	2.4	0.0	0.0	84.0
9.3	2.2	0.9	0.3	0.0	74.4
1.6	4.0	0.6	0.6	0.0	38.9
19.7	3.2	1.0	0.0	0.0	61.0
6.5	4.4	6.9	T	0.0	69.8
7.1	1.7	7.0	0.0	0.0	41.0
26.4	12.6	7.6	2.4	0.0	97.8
5.0	29.6	5.8	T	0.0	70.3
9.9	3.5	8.8	4.7	0.0	56.7
7.6	1.4	5.8	0.7	0.0	55.3
43.1	8.9	1.5	1.7	0.0	123.9
5.2	28.4	11.1	T	0.0	102.7
4.8	0.1	5.0	2.7	0.0	72.2
1.4	11.3	0.4	T	0.0	59.7
6.4	4.2	7.1	T	0.0	36.4
16.3	6.4	0.9	1.1	0.0	145.7
4.5	5.7	4.3	0.0	0.0	90.4
1.8	8.7	1.0	T	0.0	79.5
8.7	7.0	1.3	0.0	T	49.4
1.6	5.0	4.4	T	0.0	90.2
9.8	7.5	3.7	0.7	T	69.9

Average Temperature

Year	Jan	Feb	Mar	Apr	May	June	July	Aug	Sept	Oct	Nov	Dec	Annual
1936	-8.2	-14.4	4.6	27.6	48.6	62.6	60.5	57.7	42.5	30.2	10.8	-12.7	25.8
1937	11.4	-10.7	5.9	23.8	43.6	61.8	60.3	52.0	47.8	30.7	10.4	-7.2	27.5
1938	-18.1	-11.4	10.0	34.2	47.7	57.2	59.2	54.6	49.3	37.8	9.5	-3.1	27.2
1939	-10.6	-2.9	4.5	32.0	47.1	59.2	60.4	53.6	42.0	20.6	-5.2	0.0	25.1
1940	-1.6	-0.1	12.6	43.6	49.2	60.1	62.0	57.6	45.7	29.4	6.4	-4.0	30.1
1941	-13.8	10.0	15.0	37.5	47.8	61.6	58.6	58.3	44.0	23.2	-1.6	-8.6	27.7
#1942	0.9	11.5	8.1	34.9	51.9	61.4	60.8	56.9	48.8	28.0	-6.4	-24.6	27.7
#1943	-22.2	4.8	10.0	30.6	47.2	59.4	59.4	52.6	43.6	29.5	12.0	-1.2	27.1
1944	-5.6	9.4	6.8	25.0	48.6	58.6	61.0	52.6	42.1	29.0	4.4	-2.2	27.5
1945	0.0	5.6	10.4	24.5	42.2	53.8	59.1	53.6	43.2	26.2	-7.6	-5.8	25.4
1946	-4.6	0.8	1.4	27.0	48.4	61.4	61.7	52.3	42.6	31.0	-6.6	-22.6	24.4
1947	-22.2	0.4	14.6	30.6	48.8	55.8	62.0	50.9	41.2	24.2	12.4	-0.4	26.5
1948	-4.4	-6.6	5.4	23.2	45.8	58.8	58.0	50.2	40.5	25.2	-2.0	-15.6	23.2
1949	-8.8	-9.1	20.0	23.8	44.0	51.6	59.8	55.6	48.2	28.0	11.4	-10.4	26.2
1950	-1.0	-22.5	17.5	28.9	47.4	58.8	62.0	57.7	46.8	26.0	-6.1	-5.4	25.8
#1951	-23.2	-7.6	-0.6	34.4	49.3	57.0	60.3	57.8	46.9	22.3	11.6	-7.5	25.1
1952	-19.4	-2.5	9.0	27.9	41.6	58.4	60.0	53.9	42.6	30.5	15.4	-3.3	26.2
#1953	-22.5	2.6	7.6	37.2	51.5	61.8	62.0	56.0	45.2	24.0	2.2	-4.1	27.0
1954	-14.6	-16.9	11.7	26.4	50.5	58.6	58.2	56.5	42.7	31.2	12.6	-21.5	24.7
1955	-3.2	-12.3	10.1	21.6	46.0	55.6	61.3	53.1	43.6	23.8	-9.8	-9.0	23.4
1956	-20.2	-10.6	5.9	31.2	48.5	57.7	61.0	55.8	41.9	17.1	-4.8	-28.2	21.3
1957	1.5	-2.6	18.1	32.5	48.4	64.1	60.7	59.1	43.6	29.2	14.9	-15.6	29.5
1958	-2.7	1.4	16.0	34.5	48.3	62.6	62.5	56.4	42.8	14.7	1.4	-7.2	27.6
1959	-20.0	5.9	-6.7	26.0	47.2	61.5	55.5	54.5	43.6	24.0	6.7	-9.4	24.1
1960	-3.8	3.0	4.7	26.7	53.1	56.0	62.1	55.1	41.4	26.4	-1.0	5.4	27.4
1961	-2.0	-4.4	0.7	25.1	49.3	58.8	59.2	55.3	44.1	21.2	-4.2	-23.9	23.3
1962	-7.8	7.1	8.0	30.1	44.9	58.6	63.5	58.0	41.5	30.8	4.4	-6.5	27.7
#1963	1.7	-0.3	7.7	24.5	49.4	53.4	60.0	54.7	47.9	26.4	-10.5	4.0	26.6
1964	-15.7	0.7	-2.2	25.8	38.6	60.1	59.7	56.5	44.9	28.4	2.4	-26.5	22.8
1965	-18.0	-18.1	24.5	30.9	42.9	55.2	60.2	52.7	48.2	13.9	3.9	-14.1	23.5
1966	-27.4	-7.6	-2.5	27.1	45.4	63.3	62.5	57.1	50.1	24.3	0.6	-20.1	22.7
1967	-15.3	-6.9	9.8	31.7	45.7	61.8	59.8	58.3	46.6	24.8	9.5	-1.6	27.1
1968	-11.0	-5.0	12.8	29.2	47.6	59.5	65.8	58.5	42.8	22.1	2.3	-17.7	25.6
1969	-26.7	-7.3	10.1	36.3	49.4	64.9	59.4	49.8	49.1	34.0	1.2	4.0	27.0
1970	-16.2	-8.0	20.9	32.0	51.8	58.0	62.4	56.9	40.8	18.9	10.7	-9.8	27.9
1971	-31.7	-4.6	-0.4	26.7	47.3	63.4	61.0	56.1	44.7	27.9	0.5	-5.8	23.8
1972	-16.3	-10.1	-2.8	20.8	47.4	59.4	64.5	58.9	40.1	26.8	7.0	-2.5	24.5
1973	-18.2	-1.5	11.9	35.3	50.6	60.3	62.0	55.0	47.3	25.1	-0.7	-3.4	27.0
1974	-16.7	-17.8	7.6	34.9	51.4	58.7	63.5	59.1	51.4	21.4	0.6	-11.3	25.2
1975	-15.5	-3.4	12.6	30.5	53.5	63.4	68.4	56.1	45.8	23.9	-8.0	-16.1	25.9
RECORD MEAN	-12.4	-3.8	8.5	29.7	47.4	58.9	60.7	55.1	44.5	25.8	2.6	-9.5	25.7
MAX	-3.3	7.5	22.3	40.9	58.6	70.4	71.5	65.3	54.1	33.4	10.9	-1.2	35.9
MIN	-21.5	-15.1	-5.3	18.4	36.1	47.4	49.9	44.9	34.8	18.1	-5.7	-17.8	15.4

# Indicates a station move or relocation of instruments.

FAIRBANKS, AK

Feb	Mar	Apr	May	June	Total
2193	1830	1009	505	215	15358
1891	1446	968	506	75	14426
1780	1514	909	515	101	12960
1650	2225	1166	544	135	15085
1798	1885	1143	378	260	14163
1948	1995	1189	481	180	14009
1620	1765	1040	617	201	14786
1830	1777	1208	482	342	13692
1862	2085	1166	810	148	14912
2334	1249	1019	680	287	15009
2039	2092	1132	600	63	15688
2014	1704	991	594	138	14544
2029	1613	1069	533	169	13671
2024	1698	855	475	80	14664
1595	1365	981	401	203	12939
1948	2030	1141	542	117	15215
2178	2102	1318	539	205	15141
1864	1637	883	439	150	13547
2322	1778	895	414	188	14391
1918	1620	1028	347	69	13808

Aug	Sept	Oct	Nov	Dec	Total
0	0	0	0	0	85
0	0	0	0	0	22
0	0	0	0	0	89
0	0	0	0	0	95
2	0	0	0	0	39
20	0	0	0	0	74
1	0	0	0	0	175

Precipitation

Year	Jan	Feb	Mar	Apr	May	June	July	Aug	Sept	Oct	Nov	Dec	Annual
1936	0.09	0.15	0.49	T	1.03	0.67	0.81	2.12	0.76	2.02	1.88	1.12	11.14
1937	6.71	0.54	T	0.42	0.38	0.74	1.32	3.83	0.34	1.39	0.53	0.28	16.48
1938	0.54	0.40	0.23	0.10	0.13	0.40	2.72	2.69	0.58	0.10	0.42	0.52	8.83
1939	0.68	0.27	0.48	T	0.89	2.16	2.18	1.44	1.16	0.79	0.63	0.05	10.75
1940	1.34	0.08	0.03	0.27	1.39	2.16	0.94	2.13	0.75	0.53	0.54	0.29	10.45
1941	0.13	0.04	0.38	0.87	1.39	1.20	1.78	0.97	0.62	0.88	0.54	0.18	8.98
#1942	0.26	0.26	0.29	0.07	0.48	2.75	1.65	3.49	2.85	0.91	1.14	0.07	14.22
#1943	0.45	0.35	1.21	0.05	0.43	0.26	0.68	3.11	1.12	0.87	0.11	0.87	9.51
1944	0.19	2.10	0.88	0.01	1.75	1.03	0.90	2.81	1.09	0.69	0.21	0.45	12.11
1945	0.07	0.27	0.53	0.09	0.72	2.31	2.04	4.39	1.48	1.40	0.83	0.25	14.38
1946	0.70	0.73	0.29	0.24	1.30	1.49	1.32	1.80	0.81	1.88	0.24	0.53	11.33
1947	1.23	0.03	0.16	0.39	0.36	0.56	1.06	1.58	1.73	0.61	0.66	0.15	8.52
1948	0.47	0.50	0.55	2.30	1.39	1.80	4.24	3.51	0.57	0.42	0.54	1.09	17.38
1949	0.93	1.12	0.38	0.23	0.52	3.52	3.47	1.19	0.12	0.43	0.36	0.77	13.04
1950	2.00	0.25	0.52	0.03	0.52	0.86	2.50	1.17	0.31	0.51	0.99	0.39	10.05
#1951	0.57	0.91	0.22	0.04	0.44	1.24	1.77	1.94	0.72	0.46	0.68	1.28	10.27
1952	0.84	0.14	0.35	0.18	0.33	1.21	1.79	1.14	1.73	0.47	0.15	0.04	8.37
1953	0.12	0.27	0.20	0.01	0.64	1.85	1.37	2.97	1.32	0.11	T	0.13	8.99
1954	0.55	0.21	0.60	T	0.17	1.78	3.22	0.84	1.82	0.08	0.42	0.48	10.17
1955	0.49	0.60	0.52	0.19	1.67	3.52	2.51	1.93	1.45	0.94	0.21	1.83	15.86
1956	0.43	0.99	0.15	0.12	0.61	1.02	1.41	2.22	1.94	0.91	0.98	0.59	11.37
1957	1.92	0.56	0.15	0.08	0.07	0.21	0.40	0.40	0.47	0.74	0.30	0.25	5.55
1958	0.31	0.07	0.24	0.09	0.57	1.01	1.42	0.61	0.46	0.84	0.40	0.41	6.43
1959	0.09	0.93	0.15	0.12	1.02	1.19	2.80	1.81	0.92	0.68	0.55	0.56	10.82
1960	0.97	0.38	0.20	0.40	0.26	0.73	1.38	1.71	3.05	0.92	0.41	0.23	10.64
1961	0.25	0.17	0.11	0.37	0.24	0.66	2.61	2.85	1.91	1.17	0.47	0.59	11.40
1962	0.69	1.26	0.66	0.38	0.62	2.22	4.35	4.03	1.40	0.28	0.17	0.56	16.62
1963	1.78	0.27	2.10	0.49	0.11	2.00	1.36	3.60	0.19	1.51	0.18	0.38	13.97
1964	0.21	0.46	0.18	0.68	0.97	1.33	1.28	2.37	0.85	0.53	0.86	0.34	10.06
1965	0.07	0.32	0.27	0.47	0.14	1.16	1.39	1.48	2.11	0.74	1.21	1.92	11.28
1966	0.01	1.75	0.34	0.32	0.38	0.19	0.83	0.59	0.15	0.29	2.06	0.16	7.07
1967	0.40	0.25	1.90	0.84	0.43	1.13	3.34	6.20	0.25	0.32	0.93	1.34	17.33
1968	1.19	0.15	T	0.29	0.67	1.52	0.84	0.96	0.15	0.31	0.27	1.38	7.73
1969	0.55	0.10	0.60	T	0.95	0.39	1.33	2.04	0.28	0.10	0.54	T	6.88
1970	0.10	0.32	0.25	0.45	0.42	2.57	1.81	1.98	0.65	1.84	3.32	2.29	16.00
1971	0.33	0.63	0.20	0.11	0.16	0.31	2.08	2.32	2.45	1.35	0.54	1.83	12.31
1972	0.73	0.16	0.27	0.20	0.35	0.55	0.63	1.09	2.08	0.86	0.46	1.13	8.51
1973	0.44	0.11	0.40	0.05	0.99	0.97	1.92	2.19	0.19	0.91	0.80	0.15	9.12
1974	0.14	0.33	0.27	0.21	0.11	1.22	1.17	1.14	0.47	1.08	1.03	0.55	7.72
1975	0.60	0.04	0.22	0.47	0.49	0.99	1.81	2.10	0.20	0.79	0.44	0.31	8.46
RECORD MEAN	0.75	0.48	0.44	0.28	0.63	1.33	1.84	2.34	1.03	0.84	0.70	0.64	11.30

Record mean values above are means through the current year for the period beginning in 1930 for temperature and precipitation, 1952 for snowfall. Data are from Cooperative records through June 1929 and from locations listed in the table thereafter.

(Continued)

The average last date of freezing temperatures in the spring is May 21; and the average first occurrence of freezing temperatures in the fall is August 30, resulting in a growing season averaging around 100 days. The dairy industry and potato and vegetable farming represent the primary agricultural pursuits in the area, potatoes being the chief money crop. Summers are not sufficiently warm to mature corn, peppers, and tomatoes. However, cabbage, turnips, and the leafy vegetables grow luxuriantly, and there is a better chance of maturing grain crops in the Tanana Valley than in other agricultural areas of Alaska.

Ice begins running in the Chena Slough at Fairbanks during October, varying in time from the freeze-up, which averages about the first week in the month, to the date when ice will support a man's weight, averaging October 27. The Chena remains frozen and safe for man until the middle of April. Break-up usually occurs about the first week in May.

Note: A special report, detailing climate along the route of the Alaska pipeline, begins on page 702.

QUOTES FROM WEATHER FOLKLORE–

The moon and the weather
May change together;
But change of the moon
Does not change the weather.
If we'd no moon at all,
And that may seem strange,
We still should have weather
That's subject to change.

"Notes and Queries"

Station: JUNEAU, ALASKA MUNICIPAL AIRPORT
Elevation (ground): 12 feet

TEMPERATURES °F

Month	Normal			Extremes			
	Daily maximum	Daily minimum	Monthly	Record highest	Year	Record lowest	Year
(a)				32		32	
J	29.1	17.8	23.5	57	1958	-22	1972
F	33.9	22.1	28.0	50	1968	-22	1968
M	38.2	25.6	31.9	55	1965	-15	1972
A	46.5	31.3	38.9	71	1958	6	1963
M	55.4	38.2	46.8	82	1947	25	1972
J	62.0	44.4	53.2	86	1969	31	1971
J	63.6	47.7	55.7	90	1975	36	1950
A	62.3	46.2	54.3	83	1957	27	1948
S	56.1	42.3	49.2	72	1949	23	1972
O	47.2	36.4	41.8	61	1954	12	1971
N	37.3	27.6	32.5	56	1949	-5	1966
D	32.0	22.5	27.3	54	1944	-21	1949
YR	47.0	33.5	40.3	90	JUL 1975	-22	JAN 1972

IMPORTANT:
The time-period covered by this record is limited: See footnotes on next page for explanation and for additional history of EXTREME HIGHS AND LOWS recorded in the general area.

Juneau lies well within the area of maritime influences which prevail over the coastal areas of southeastern Alaska, and is in the path of most storms that cross the Gulf of Alaska. Consequently, the area has little sunshine, generally moderate temperatures, and abundant precipitation. In contrast with the characteristic lack of sunshine there are greatly appreciated intervals, sometimes lasting for several days at a stretch, during which clear skies prevail. The rugged terrain exerts a fundamental influence upon local temperatures and the distribution of precipitation, creating considerable variations in both weather elements within relatively short distances.

Temperature variations, both daily and seasonal, are usually confined to relatively narrow limits by the dominant maritime influences. Although variations between maximum and minimum temperatures may vary as much as 40° during clear periods, the differences between normal daily maximum and normal daily mimimum temperatures range from as little as 7° in December to around 18° in June. Variations on a seasonal basis range from a monthly normal temperature of near 25° in January to 55° in July. Extremes of record cover a range of 111°, from the maximum of 89° in July to the minimum of - 22° in February. Extreme maximum readings above 80° have occurred in May through August. Low temperature extremes of around - 20° have occurred in December, January, and February. Periods of comparatively severe cold, which usually start with strong northerly winds, are most often caused by the flow of cold air from northwestern Canada through nearby mountain passes and over the Juneau ice field, and are generally of brief duration. During such periods gusty winds, known locally as " Taku Winds, " often occur in the city of Juneau and other local areas but generally do not occur at the Airport or in the Mendenhall Valley. At these times gusty winds extend through channels to the northwest and southeast, and are sometimes strong enough to cause considerable damage. During periods of calm or light winds, temperature differences within short distances are frequently very pronounced. Variations in local radiation and drainage produce wide differences in temperatures particularly between upland or sloping areas and the low, flat terrain which is greatly affected by drainage from higher elevations. The Airport Station, located on relatively low, flat terrain, and in the path of drainage air from the Mendenhall Glacier, averages about 10 days a year with minimum readings below zero. The city of Juneau, located on a noticeable slope portion of a rugged mountain area, experiences on the average only about one day each year with minimum readings below zero. At the airport the growing season averages 146 days, from May 4 to September 28; while in the city of Juneau the average is 181 days, from April 22 to October 21.

The months February to June mark the period of lightest precipitation, with monthly averages of about 3 inches. After June the monthly amounts increase gradually, reaching a maximum during October when the monthly fall averages over 7 inches. Monthly averages of precipitation then tend to decline from November until February. Due to the rugged topography, precipitation throughout the year tends to vary greatly in different localities, even in adjacent areas. Juneau Airport has about 65 percent of the total precipitation realized in the City though the rain gages are only 8 miles apart. The maximum yearly amount received in the City is almost double the maximum received at the Juneau Airport.

Although a trace of snow has fallen as early as September 9, first falls usually occur in the latter part of October, and sometimes not until the first part of December. On the average there is very little accumulation on the ground

(Continued page 346)

JUNEAU, ALASKA

Normals, Means, and Extremes

(To better understand these tables, see full explanation of terms beginning on page 322)

Month	Normal Degree days Base 65 °F: Heating	Cooling	Precipitation in inches — Water equivalent: Normal	Maximum monthly	Year	Minimum monthly	Year	Maximum in 24 hrs.	Year	Snow, Ice pellets: Maximum monthly	Year	Maximum in 24 hrs.	Year
(a)				32		32		32		32		32	
J	1287	0	3.94	7.75	1965	0.94	1969	2.74	1948	63.8	1973	20.1	1975
F	1036	0	3.44	8.48	1964	0.68	1969	2.37	1949	86.3	1965	23.7	1949
M	1026	0	3.57	6.36	1966	1.15	1974	1.81	1948	52.6	1948	31.0	1948
A	783	0	2.99	4.33	1947	0.27	1948	1.57	1952	46.3	1963	24.2	1963
M	564	0	3.31	6.33	1966	1.25	1946	1.39	1948	1.2	1964	0.7	1945
J	354	0	2.93	5.34	1949	1.08	1950	1.92	1953	T	1970	T	1970
J	288	0	4.69	7.88	1969	1.15	1972	1.88	1968	0.0		0.0	
A	332	0	5.00	12.31	1961	1.11	1954	2.62	1974	0.0		0.0	
S	474	0	6.90	11.51	1948	2.34	1965	3.17	1952	T	1974	T	1974
O	719	0	7.85	15.25	1974	2.71	1950	4.66	1946	15.6	1956	8.8	1956
N	975	0	5.53	11.22	1956	1.46	1965	3.34	1949	32.5	1975	16.5	1963
D	1169	0	4.57	9.89	1956	1.90	1968	3.56	1956	54.7	1964	25.6	1962
YR	9007	0	54.67	15.25	OCT 1974	0.27	APR 1948	4.66	OCT 1946	86.3	FEB 1965	31.0	MAR 1948

Month	Relative humidity pct. Hour 04 (Local time)	Hour 10	Hour 16	Hour 22	Wind: Mean speed m.p.h.	Prevailing direction	Fastest mile: Speed m.p.h.	Direction	Year	Pct. of possible sunshine	Mean sky cover, tenths, sunrise to sunset	Mean number of days — Sunrise to sunset: Clear	Partly cloudy	Cloudy	Precipitation .01 inch or more	Snow, Ice pellets 1.0 inch or more	Thunderstorms	Heavy fog, visibility ¼ mile or less	Temperatures °F Max. (b) 90° and above	Max. 32° and below	Min. 32° and below	Min. 0° and below	Average station pressure mb. Elev. 24 feet m.s.l.
(a)	32	32	32	32	32	20	16	16		30	32	32	32	32	32	32	32	32	32	32	32	32	3
J	79	79	76	79	8.5	ESE	38	12	1968	33	7.6	6	3	22	18	7	*	2	0	18	27	5	1009.3
F	82	81	75	82	8.8	ESE	44	13	1970	32	8.1	4	3	21	17	6	0	2	0	10	23	2	1009.5
M	84	79	69	81	8.8	ESE	40	11	1963	37	8.1	4	3	24	17	5	0	2	0	5	25	1	1008.7
A	87	75	64	81	8.9	ESE	40	11	1962	38	8.2	3	4	23	17	1	0	1	*	*	17	0	1014.2
M	89	74	63	79	8.4	ESE	40	12	1965	38	7.9	4	4	23	17	0	0	1	1	0	5	0	1013.0
J	89	75	64	78	7.9	N	32	13	1965	34	8.1	3	5	22	15	0	*	*	5	0	*	0	1013.4
J	90	81	70	81	7.6	N	32	12	1970	30	8.2	3	5	23	17	0	*	*	7	0	0	0	1016.0
A	91	84	74	85	7.6	N	35	12	1969	30	8.1	4	4	23	18	0	*	1	5	0	*	0	1015.7
S	92	87	77	90	8.0	N	48	12	1967	25	8.5	3	3	24	20	0	*	3	*	0	2	0	1015.3
O	90	87	80	88	9.7	ESE	49	12	1965	19	8.8	2	2	27	23	*	0	3	0	*	9	0	1005.9
N	86	85	82	86	8.7	ESE	58	11	1968	23	8.4	4	2	24	19	4	*	3	0	7	20	*	1007.0
D	83	82	81	83	9.4	ESE	55	11	1963	20	8.5	4	1	26	21	6	0	2	0	13	24	3	1004.2
YR	87	81	73	83	8.5	ESE	58	11	NOV 1968	31	8.2	44	39	282	220	30	*	22	19	53	152	11	1011.0

FOOTNOTES

Means and extremes are from existing and comparable exposures. Annual extremes have been exceeded at other sites in the locality as follows: Maximum monthly precipitation 25.87 in November 1936; minimum monthly precipitation 0.25 in July 1915; maximum precipitation in 24 hours 5.54 in September 1918.

Snowfall

Season	July	Aug	Sept	Oct	Nov	Dec	Jan
1943-44	0.0	0.0	0.0	T	0.0	13.4	14.0
1944-45	0.0	0.0	0.0	0.0	16.7	5.6	9.8
1945-46	0.0	0.0	0.0	0.2	10.5	22.3	35.4
1946-47	0.0	0.0	T	0.3	9.6	21.9	20.7
1947-48	0.0	0.0	0.0	T	6.7	6.6	9.0
1948-49	0.0	0.0	0.0	0.0	27.5	35.9	25.0
1949-50	0.0	0.0	0.0	2.1	1.0	19.8	13.4
1950-51	0.0	0.0	0.0	T	16.7	28.5	9.5
1951-52	0.0	0.0	0.0	T	17.5	20.7	28.2
1952-53	0.0	0.0	0.0	0.0	0.1	9.3	12.3
1953-54	0.0	0.0	0.0	T	9.2	4.8	10.4
1954-55	0.0	0.0	0.0	0.0	2.0	23.5	20.2
1955-56	0.0	0.0	0.0	0.3	7.7	39.2	33.6
1956-57	0.0	0.0	T	15.6	5.2	44.8	3.4
1957-58	0.0	0.0	0.0	0.0	4.6	39.0	19.5
1958-59	0.0	0.0	0.0	3.4	28.1	28.3	13.6
1959-60	0.0	0.0	0.0	T	8.8	12.0	26.6
1960-61	0.0	0.0	0.0	0.0	7.0	13.1	18.9
1961-62	0.0	0.0	0.0	0.6	6.0	26.4	31.5
1962-63	0.0	0.0	0.0	0.0	6.5	41.3	12.2
1963-64	0.0	0.0	0.0	T	20.1	7.2	13.4
1964-65	0.0	0.0	0.0	T	3.1	54.7	45.2
1965-66	0.0	0.0	0.0	0.3	9.6	16.9	54.8
1966-67	0.0	0.0	0.0	4.3	20.0	19.6	38.2
1967-68	0.0	0.0	0.0	0.0	9.5	21.1	31.1
1968-69	0.0	0.0	0.0	T	8.7	35.6	28.2
1969-70	0.0	0.0	0.0	0.0	18.2	0.7	15.8
1970-71	0.0	0.0	T	0.4	24.3	26.2	51.0
1971-72	0.0	0.0	0.0	6.9	20.5	37.1	45.1
1972-73	0.0	0.0	0.0	2.2	2.8	31.6	63.8
1973-74	0.0	0.0	0.0	T	18.6	15.7	36.0
1974-75	0.0	0.0	T	0.9	3.5	17.3	41.5
1975-76	0.0	0.0	0.0	5.3	32.5	51.0	
RECORD MEAN	0.0	0.0	T	1.3	12.0	24.3	26.0

Heating Degree Days

Season	July	Aug	Sept	Oct	Nov	Dec	Jan
1955-56	247	396	534	809	1289	1447	1396
1956-57	263	337	500	843	793	1279	1369
1957-58	288	225	371	709	808	1097	995
1958-59	230	316	521	736	928	1076	1449
1959-60	328	378	498	757	911	926	1146
1960-61	321	355	466	660	915	956	1062
1961-62	262	339	511	760	1027	1246	1182
1962-63	250	305	486	645	810	1132	1147
1963-64	288	244	375	625	1093	993	1098
1964-65	324	347	453	614	980	1496	1291
1965-66	292	297	435	654	1045	1182	1746
1966-67	265	382	466	812	1191	1188	1291
1967-68	340	303	444	671	973	1162	1432
1968-69	248	281	516	802	920	1405	1801
1969-70	343	448	521	724	975	921	1329
1970-71	387	405	553	783	1110	1343	1607
1971-72	227	290	504	811	1001	1360	1519
1972-73	207	293	535	810	907	1275	1423
1973-74	343	404	505	732	1253	1143	1550
1974-75	349	315	437	690	851	957	1296
1975-76	281	337	402	712	1088	1244	

Cooling Degree Days

Year	Jan	Feb	Mar	Apr	May	June	July
1969	0	0	0	0	0	7	0
1970	0	0	0	0	0	0	0
1971	0	0	0	0	0	0	0
1972	0	0	0	0	0	0	0
1973	0	0	0	0	0	0	0
1974	0	0	0	0	0	0	0
1975	0	0	0	0	0	0	7

Feb	Mar	Apr	May	June	Total
7.1	4.1	15.1	0.0	0.0	53.7
6.7	9.3	5.9	0.7	0.0	54.7
13.4	18.6	2.4	0.0	0.0	102.8
19.7	0.7	4.0	0.0	0.0	76.9
10.6	52.6	4.7	0.0	0.0	90.2
39.6	1.7	1.6	T	0.0	131.3
27.8	4.1	1.5	0.0	0.0	69.7
17.4	23.1	T	0.0	0.0	95.2
12.6	18.2	4.7	T	0.0	101.9
6.5	14.4	T	0.0	0.0	42.6
13.8	14.3	9.5	0.0	0.0	62.0
23.6	19.4	4.1	0.0	0.0	92.8
33.8	33.9	6.6	0.0	0.0	155.1
54.3	5.2	1.0	0.0	0.0	129.5
13.4	1.6	T	0.0	0.0	78.1
19.2	28.3	6.9	0.0	0.0	127.8
2.3	17.9	1.3	0.0	0.0	68.9
25.9	16.3	6.3	0.0	0.0	87.5
7.7	37.4	1.8	T	0.0	111.4
15.7	28.9	46.3	0.0	0.0	150.9
19.4	38.9	4.4	1.2	0.0	104.6
86.3	4.0	0.8	0.2	0.0	194.3
17.6	49.0	1.5	T	0.0	149.7
32.0	6.6	3.0	0.0	0.0	123.7
17.0	8.2	6.1	T	0.0	93.0
17.1	27.9	T	0.0	0.0	117.5
2.0	1.1	3.5	0.0	T	41.3
21.5	50.6	1.1	T	0.0	175.1
31.1	27.1	10.3	0.0	0.0	178.1
20.9	9.6	0.5	0.0	0.0	131.4
32.8	15.3	0.5	0.0	0.0	118.9
16.5	18.9	4.5	0.0	0.0	103.1
21.4	19.0	5.0	0.1	T	109.1

Average Temperature

Year	Jan	Feb	Mar	Apr	May	June	July	Aug	Sept	Oct	Nov	Dec	Annual
1943							53.4	53.4	49.6	42.3	39.6	37.0	
1944	34.8	31.2	33.0	39.6	46.2	54.4	55.6	53.8	50.2	44.8	34.1	31.2	42.4
1945	32.0	31.5	35.4	37.0	49.2	51.4	52.7	53.6	48.4	42.4	24.1	28.2	40.5
1946	30.4	31.6	34.0	39.2	49.3	56.8	54.3	52.4	49.4	40.8	29.4	21.7	40.8
1947	21.0	25.0	35.8	39.2	47.7	52.7	56.2	54.0	49.5	43.1	37.4	35.2	41.4
1948	32.6	21.7	27.8	34.5	48.0	55.4	56.9	53.4	48.2	42.0	31.8	19.1	39.3
1949	25.6	16.2	35.2	39.6	45.8	49.3	53.4	53.2	50.8	41.6	39.3	21.0	39.3
1950	7.9	23.4	32.7	37.4	44.8	56.2	54.4	55.9	49.6	38.9	22.3	29.3	37.7
1951	18.5	21.6	26.0	39.0	46.8	52.2	60.3	55.5	50.6	38.0	31.1	22.4	38.5
1952	14.4	30.6	31.5	37.5	44.7	52.2	55.5	54.1	48.7	44.9	38.4	33.3	40.5
1953	18.7	34.3	31.4	41.0	49.2	56.3	57.3	54.9	49.1	43.2	33.1	32.3	41.7
1954	20.7	23.6	30.8	33.1	46.3	53.8	54.3	56.1	49.2	42.8	38.4	28.1	39.8
1955	32.1	29.3	27.8	38.0	42.9	50.5	56.8	52.0	47.0	38.7	21.8	18.1	37.9
1956	19.8	21.8	28.0	38.7	45.2	50.0	56.3	54.0	48.2	37.5	38.4	23.5	38.4
1957	20.6	25.3	32.8	38.6	47.9	54.9	55.5	57.6	52.4	41.9	37.9	29.4	41.2
1958	32.8	27.1	32.9	42.5	48.1	56.5	57.4	54.5	47.4	41.1	33.9	30.0	42.0
1959	18.0	28.2	33.8	38.8	46.0	55.2	54.1	52.6	48.2	40.3	34.4	34.9	40.4
1960	27.8	33.4	31.9	40.9	49.5	51.1	54.4	53.3	49.2	43.5	34.3	33.9	41.9
1961	30.5	31.5	34.5	39.9	47.4	52.4	56.3	53.9	47.7	40.3	30.6	24.6	40.8
1962	26.7	25.7	29.4	39.6	44.5	49.9	56.7	54.8	48.5	43.9	37.8	28.3	40.5
1963	27.7	33.1	31.9	36.6	48.7	50.4	55.4	56.9	52.2	44.6	28.3	32.7	41.5
1964	29.3	35.9	28.8	38.6	45.1	53.6	54.3	53.6	49.7	45.0	32.1	16.6	40.2
1965	23.1	23.6	35.0	37.7	42.4	48.5	55.4	55.1	50.3	43.7	29.9	26.6	39.3
1966	8.6	25.9	30.2	38.1	43.3	52.9	56.2	52.4	49.2	38.6	25.1	26.5	37.2
1967	23.1	30.4	24.1	37.3	45.6	54.8	53.8	55.1	50.0	43.1	32.3	27.3	39.7
1968	18.7	28.8	33.1	37.9	48.4	52.2	56.8	55.7	47.6	39.0	34.1	19.4	39.3
1969	6.8	21.2	30.7	40.6	49.9	57.8	53.7	50.3	47.4	41.4	32.3	35.1	38.9
1970	22.0	35.1	36.5	39.1	45.3	50.7	52.3	51.7	46.3	39.6	27.8	21.6	39.0
1971	13.0	28.1	28.9	38.6	43.5	53.2	57.5	55.4	48.1	38.5	31.4	20.9	38.1
1972	15.8	19.5	26.5	34.6	44.8	50.4	58.0	55.4	47.0	38.7	34.5	23.6	37.4
1973	18.9	24.6	32.9	39.6	45.9	51.3	53.7	51.8	48.0	41.2	23.0	28.0	38.2
1974	14.8	28.8	24.7	39.3	46.8	50.2	53.5	54.7	50.1	42.5	36.4	33.8	39.6
1975	23.1	24.5	30.6	38.3	47.4	51.4	55.9	53.9	51.4	41.8	28.5	24.7	39.3
RECORD MEAN	22.2	27.3	31.2	38.4	46.4	52.8	55.5	54.1	49.0	41.5	32.0	26.9	39.8
MAX	27.8	33.1	37.5	45.8	54.9	61.5	63.7	62.0	55.8	46.8	36.9	31.6	46.5
MIN	16.5	21.4	24.9	31.0	37.9	44.0	47.2	46.2	42.2	36.2	27.1	22.1	33.1

JUNEAU, AK

Feb	Mar	Apr	May	June	Total
1247	1144	780	605	441	10335
1105	992	785	521	296	9083
1057	988	668	518	250	7974
1022	959	781	582	285	8885
911	1019	713	470	409	8466
932	938	746	538	371	8260
1097	1095	756	627	447	9349
885	1023	846	500	431	8460
835	1118	785	610	336	8400
1154	923	813	693	487	9575
1090	1071	805	667	355	9639
963	1261	824	592	300	9535
1043	984	808	508	374	9042
1219	1054	727	464	218	9655
830	876	770	601	422	8760
1029	1112	784	658	346	10117
1315	1186	906	618	432	10169
1126	986	752	584	404	9302
1006	1242	765	556	437	9936
1129	1063	791	541	402	8821

Aug	Sept	Oct	Nov	Dec	Total
0	0	0	0	0	7
0	0	0	0	0	0
0	0	0	0	0	0
0	0	0	0	0	0
0	0	0	0	0	0
0	0	0	0	0	0
0	0	0	0	0	7

# Indicates a station move or relocation of instruments.

Precipitation

Year	Jan	Feb	Mar	Apr	May	June	July	Aug	Sept	Oct	Nov	Dec	Annual
1943							6.65	5.66	11.24	9.26	6.50	9.86	
1944	4.55	1.76	5.75	3.65	4.27	3.04	3.72	4.71	3.69	12.39	7.52	4.43	59.48
1945	3.49	3.17	4.54	2.82	1.33	4.66	7.76	4.17	7.31	11.05	2.43	2.57	55.30
1946	4.24	2.03	3.50	3.11	1.25	1.08	6.61	5.52	4.90	10.52	7.31	2.47	52.54
1947	4.76	2.18	5.80	4.33	3.25	4.77	2.01	8.47	11.09	4.89	4.89	4.36	60.80
1948	6.77	1.14	4.16	0.27	4.39	2.52	5.54	3.39	11.51	11.04	10.38	2.95	64.06
1949	7.33	4.03	2.09	4.32	3.38	5.34	3.97	3.52	7.80	8.50	9.22	2.35	61.85
1950	0.94	2.22	1.29	2.09	3.38	1.08	7.07	4.95	7.32	2.71	2.13	3.43	38.61
1951	2.09	2.31	3.75	3.54	2.12	4.06	2.67	2.76	3.85	3.65	4.70	2.30	37.80
1952	3.50	2.85	3.32	3.72	6.19	2.44	3.71	5.90	10.84	13.29	7.11	2.86	65.73
1953	1.46	6.28	3.65	2.95	2.51	2.98	2.95	5.45	6.17	12.33	2.72	5.02	54.47
1954	2.01	4.22	1.49	1.95	2.98	1.48	3.50	1.11	5.03	6.32	5.67	5.42	41.18
1955	4.03	3.30	4.72	2.46	4.89	2.22	2.37	6.53	5.39	7.47	2.65	2.86	48.89
1956	2.83	4.05	4.69	3.00	4.83	3.42	2.96	9.99	4.59	6.50	11.22	9.89	67.97
1957	1.05	3.99	1.35	3.65	2.44	1.44	2.83	1.50	5.61	3.94	8.55	3.76	40.11
1958	4.90	2.00	1.20	1.96	4.13	2.65	4.31	4.20	5.06	9.39	4.31	7.45	51.56
1959	1.39	4.15	4.56	3.42	3.79	1.36	7.39	5.39	5.51	6.04	6.82	5.88	55.70
1960	3.86	2.05	4.84	3.13	1.52	3.51	4.31	4.77	8.47	8.95	4.97	7.39	57.77
1961	3.76	4.07	2.67	3.92	4.75	3.22	6.04	12.31	7.01	10.20	6.12	4.04	68.11
1962	6.99	0.96	5.00	1.99	2.85	4.75	4.75	5.21	9.75	7.39	4.03	8.16	61.83
1963	6.55	6.03	3.69	3.85	2.02	4.53	5.22	1.20	8.05	7.78	3.91	4.56	57.39
1964	3.19	8.48	4.38	4.04	4.35	3.37	6.94	3.48	2.59	7.35	4.89	5.22	58.28
1965	7.75	5.10	1.66	3.33	4.45	3.11	2.26	4.17	2.34	7.99	1.46	4.26	47.88
1966	4.34	3.13	6.36	2.08	6.33	1.74	3.91	6.37	8.20	6.97	4.39	4.48	58.30
1967	4.04	4.74	1.34	1.12	2.94	2.87	4.26	5.46	8.53	5.71	5.81	3.25	50.07
1968	3.25	5.30	3.85	3.25	1.45	1.95	4.60	2.39	10.14	4.60	5.34	1.90	48.02
1969	0.94	0.68	4.17	1.74	3.38	2.41	7.88	7.54	5.44	3.77	8.69	4.36	51.00
1970	2.37	3.35	4.08	3.69	3.92	2.97	5.01	7.47	9.86	5.87	2.01	2.58	53.18
1971	5.56	3.93	3.33	2.44	4.30	1.74	1.67	6.89	5.36	5.80	4.38	3.23	48.63
1972	3.73	2.71	4.19	3.62	4.03	3.98	1.15	8.62	6.24	8.49	3.35	3.56	53.67
1973	4.37	3.94	3.01	2.41	4.09	2.80	3.65	6.64	4.95	6.07	1.63	2.30	45.86
1974	2.37	6.23	1.15	2.59	1.66	4.92	3.12	5.78	5.96	15.25	7.79	7.03	63.85
1975	4.10	3.76	2.17	3.04	3.59	2.48	4.96	2.78	7.25	3.55	2.83	5.81	46.32
RECORD MEAN	3.83	3.57	3.49	2.92	3.46	2.97	4.35	5.27	6.74	7.68	5.29	4.38	53.95

Record mean values above are means through the current year for the period beginning in 1944. Data are from airport locations.

(Continued)

at low levels until the last of November, although at higher elevations, and particularly on mountain tops, a cover is usually established in early October. Snow accumulation usually reaches its greatest depth during the middle of February when it averages around 10 inches at the airport. December, January, February, and March have the largest amounts of snowfall, averaging from 18 to around 23 inches per month. Individual storms may produce heavy falls as late as the first part of April and light falls as late as the first half of May. However, snow cover is usually gone before the middle of April. During some winters, when temperatures are above normal, there is a great deal of thawing which causes slush that later freezes; and there are occasional intervals of rain which freezes into glaze ice on contact with the ground.

Note: A special report, detailing climate along the route of the Alaska pipeline, begins on page 702.

QUOTES FROM WEATHER FOLKLORE–

Observe which way the hedgehog builds her nest,
To front the north or south, or east or west;
For if 'tis true what common peole say,
The wind will blow the quite contrary way.
If by some secret art the hedgehog knows,
So long before, the way in which the winds will blow,
She has an art which many a person lacks
That thinks himself fit to make our almanacks.
– Poor Robin's Almanack, 1733.

Station: FLAGSTAFF, ARIZONA
PULLIAM AIRPORT
Elevation (ground): 7006 feet

TEMPERATURES °F

Month	Normal			Extremes			
	Daily maximum	Daily minimum	Monthly	Record highest	Year	Record lowest	Year
(a)				26		26	
J	41.4	14.4	27.9	66	1971	-22	1971
F	44.0	17.0	30.5	67	1963	-16	1965
M	47.9	20.4	34.2	73	1966	-16	1966
A	56.9	27.3	42.1	78	1962	-2	1975
M	66.6	33.5	50.1	87	1974	14	1975
J	76.0	40.4	58.2	96	1970	22	1955
J	80.8	50.4	65.6	97	1973	32	1955
A	77.9	49.3	63.6	90	1975	24	1968
S	73.7	41.2	57.5	90	1950	23	1971
O	62.9	31.1	47.0	83	1950	-2	1971
N	50.9	21.8	36.4	74	1973	-13	1958
D	43.2	16.3	29.8	68	1950	-18	1971
YR	60.2	30.3	45.3	97	JUL 1973	-22	JAN 1971

IMPORTANT:
The time-period covered by this record is limited: See footnotes on next page for explanation and for additional history of EXTREME HIGHS AND LOWS recorded in the general area.

Flagstaff, elevation 7,000 feet, is situated on a volcanic plateau at the base of the highest mountains in Arizona. The climate may be classified as vigorous: cold winters, mild, pleasantly cool summers, moderate humidity, and considerable diurnal temperature change. Only limited farming exists due to the short growing season that averages 120 days, with the longest and shortest on record being 164 and 73 (based on a temperature threshold of 32°). The normal annual rainfall is a little over 19 inches and the average annual snowfall is over 80 inches. The stormy months are January, February, March, July, and August. Snow conditions provide excellent winter sports.

Temperatures in Flagstaff are characteristic of high altitude climates. The average daily range of temperature is relatively high, especially in the winter months (October to March) as a result of extensive snow cover and clear skies causing maximum radiation.

FLAGSTAFF, ARIZONA

Normals, Means, and Extremes

(To better understand these tables, see full explanation of terms beginning on page 322)

Month	Normal Degree days Base 65 °F: Heating	Normal Degree days Base 65 °F: Cooling	Precipitation in inches, Water equivalent: Normal	Maximum monthly	Year	Minimum monthly	Year	Maximum in 24 hrs.	Year	Snow, Ice pellets: Maximum monthly	Year	Maximum in 24 hrs.	Year
(a)				26		26		26		26		26	
J	1150	0	1.89	6.46	1957	0.00	1972	1.78	1952	44.3	1955	16.6	1962
F	966	0	1.47	4.15	1962	T	1967	1.72	1965	42.1	1969	17.6	1959
M	955	0	1.83	6.75	1970	T	1972	2.96	1970	77.4	1973	26.3	1970
A	687	0	1.33	5.62	1965	0.09	1962	1.47	1965	58.3	1965	15.9	1967
M	462	0	0.56	2.02	1957	T	1974	1.11	1965	8.2	1975	6.6	1965
J	219	15	0.57	2.92	1955	0.00	1971	2.79	1956	T	1955	T	1955
J	52	70	2.48	5.23	1964	0.32	1963	2.55	1964	0.0		0.0	
A	93	49	2.65	5.50	1951	0.26	1962	2.65	1951	0.0		0.0	
S	231	6	1.68	6.60	1958	T	1973	3.43	1965	2.0	1965	2.0	1965
O	558	0	1.37	9.86	1972	T	1952	2.73	1972	24.7	1971	13.5	1974
N	858	0	1.33	4.97	1965	0.05	1956	2.30	1957	25.2	1975	18.1	1975
D	1091	0	2.15	7.30	1967	T	1958	3.11	1951	86.0	1967	27.3	1967
YR	7322	140	19.31	9.86	OCT 1972	0.00	JAN 1972	3.43	SEP 1965	86.0	DEC 1967	27.3	DFC 1967

Month	Relative humidity pct. Hour 05 (Local time)	Hour 11	Hour 17	Hour 23	Wind: Mean speed m.p.h.	Prevailing direction	Fastest mile $: Speed m.p.h.	Direction	Year	Pct. of possible sunshine #	Mean sky cover, tenths, sunrise to sunset	Mean number of days, Sunrise to sunset: Clear	Partly cloudy	Cloudy	Precipitation .01 inch or more	Snow, Ice pellets 1.0 inch or more	Thunderstorms	Heavy fog, visibility ¼ mile or less	Temperatures °F Max. (b) 90° and above	Max. 32° and below	Min. 32° and below	Min. 0° and below	Average station pressure mb. Elev. 7018 feet m.s.l.
(a)	21	21	14	14	14	2	10	10		3	26	26	26	26	26	26	26	26	26	26	26	26	3
J	73	52	49	69	7.9	NE	37	02	1962	70	5.3	12	6	13	7	4	*	2	0	5	30	4	786.0
F	73	49	43	64	7.5	S	30	02	1963	74	5.0	12	6	10	6	3	*	1	0	3	28	2	786.3
M	71	43	39	62	8.2	SSW	31	23	1966	66	5.1	12	7	12	7	5	1	1	0	2	30	1	782.9
A	65	35	31	54	8.9	SSW	35	20	1969	84	4.5	13	8	9	6	3	1	1	0	*	26	*	784.3
M	63	27	24	47	8.2	SSW	29	01	1967	91	3.8	16	9	6	3	1	3	*	0	0	15	0	786.8
J	56	24	21	41	8.0	SSW	31	16	1962	89	2.9	19	7	4	3	0	4	*	1	0	3	0	789.2
J	70	34	40	62	6.2	SSW	23	21	1971	76	5.4	9	13	9	11	0	16	*	1	0	*	0	791.7
A	77	40	46	70	5.6	S	35	30	1970	80	5.2	10	13	8	11	0	16	*	*	0	*	0	791.7
S	75	37	38	66	6.5	S	40	01	1965	84	3.4	17	9	4	6	*	7	*	*	0	3	0	790.8
O	72	38	35	62	6.6	N	28	05	1967	77	3.4	18	6	7	5	1	2	1	0	*	19	*	789.7
N	71	43	43	65	7.7	NNE	32	02	1964	75	4.1	16	6	8	5	2	1	1	0	1	28	1	787.9
D	73	50	55	75	7.8	NE	29	23	1966	77	4.6	14	7	10	6	3	*	2	0	5	30	3	787.6
YR	70	39	38	61	7.4	SSW	40	01	SEP 1965	80	4.4	168	97	100	75	21	51	10	3	17	214	10	787.9

FOOTNOTES Means and extremes above are from existing and comparable exposures. Annual extremes have been exceeded at other sites in the locality as follows: Lowest temperature -30 in January 1937; maximum precipitation in 24 hours 3.59 in November 1919; maximum monthly snowfall 104.8 inches in January 1949.

Snowfall

Season	July	Aug	Sept	Oct	Nov	Dec	Jan
1936-37	0.0	0.0	0.0	0.0	T	30.0	42.8
1937-38	0.0	0.0	0.0	0.0	0.0	2.0	5.5
1938-39	0.0	0.0	0.0	T	1.2	17.0	16.0
1939-40	0.0	0.0	0.0	1.0	1.5	T	15.6
1940-41	0.0	0.0	0.0	1.5	6.5	13.5	14.0
1941-42	0.0	0.0	0.0	0.8	0.8	19.9	8.0
#1942-43	0.0	0.0	0.0	T	1.0	8.0	31.0
1943-44	0.0	0.0	0.0	T	0.1	20.9	20.0
1944-45	0.0	0.0	0.0	T	9.7	13.5	18.2
1945-46	0.0	0.0	0.0	0.0	0.7	9.8	9.9
1946-47	0.0	0.0	0.0	T	13.4	6.3	10.5
1947-48	0.0	0.0	0.0	0.2	12.0	20.6	15.1
1948-49	0.0	0.0	0.0	T	T	22.2	104.8
#1949-50	0.0	0.0	T	6.9	3.0	15.0	17.7
1950-51	0.0	0.0	0.0	0.0	T	4.0	17.9
1951-52	0.0	0.0	0.0	0.0	11.9	16.4	23.7
1952-53	0.0	0.0	0.0	0.0	25.0	14.2	4.0
1953-54	0.0	0.0	0.0	0.0	4.8	5.4	28.3
1954-55	0.0	0.0	0.0	0.0	1.2	4.5	44.3
1955-56	0.0	0.0	0.0	0.0	7.7	4.2	12.5
1956-57	0.0	0.0	0.0	2.9	1.0	5.0	32.8
1957-58	0.0	0.0	0.0	0.6	8.2	1.6	2.2
1958-59	0.0	0.0	0.0	0.3	13.0	T	6.0
1959-60	0.0	0.0	0.0	3.9	2.0	17.4	14.4
1960-61	0.0	0.0	0.0	0.2	0.8	5.3	11.2
1961-62	0.0	0.0	0.0	8.2	11.7	29.6	30.8
1962-63	0.0	0.0	0.0	0.0	2.9	3.8	9.9
1963-64	0.0	0.0	0.0	0.0	10.9	4.6	10.3
1964-65	0.0	0.0	0.0	0.0	14.3	13.7	15.1
1965-66	0.0	0.0	2.0	2.2	2.9	38.5	14.5
1966-67	0.0	0.0	0.0	T	11.3	13.4	9.8
1967-68	0.0	0.0	0.0	0.0	5.1	86.0	15.2
1968-69	0.0	0.0	0.0	T	4.3	27.5	12.0
1969-70	0.0	0.0	0.0	1.5	3.0	4.6	5.2
1970-71	0.0	0.0	0.0	0.0	2.0	24.5	0.8
1971-72	0.0	0.0	T	24.7	4.9	18.8	0.0
1972-73	0.0	0.0	0.0	11.8	23.2	28.9	21.0
1973-74	0.0	0.0	0.0	T	20.7	1.2	35.3
1974-75	0.0	0.0	0.0	16.6	8.2	15.6	20.1
1975-76	0.0	0.0	0.0	T	25.2	18.9	
RECORD MEAN	0.0	0.0	0.1	2.8	8.7	15.7	16.0

Heating Degree Days

Season	July	Aug	Sept	Oct	Nov	Dec	Jan
1955-56	105	22	219	480	857	958	979
1956-57	51	134	103	594	928	1071	1091
1957-58	47	73	225	603	961	919	1062
1958-59	27	11	235	508	894	879	1034
1959-60	6	66	254	528	819	1034	1303
1960-61	7	55	156	613	839	1116	1072
1961-62	21	50	330	628	919	1203	1168
1962-63	32	38	184	536	747	1026	1218
1963-64	0	49	168	467	804	1071	1225
1964-65	9	72	245	417	1001	1070	1034
1965-66	22	69	326	467	753	1071	1281
1966-67	14	32	185	556	757	1089	1111
1967-68	11	33	207	461	733	1292	1218
1968-69	38	164	267	554	872	1234	1021
1969-70	21	37	200	753	926	978	1051
1970-71	6	16	310	643	758	1125	1098
1971-72	24	40	352	809	938	1310	1126
1972-73	22	78	241	584	1055	1330	1297
1973-74	39	45	212	458	829	987	1147
1974-75	19	34	195	522	841	1178	1150
1975-76	23	66	207	566	821	1101	

Cooling Degree Days

Year	Jan	Feb	Mar	Apr	May	June	July
1969	0	0	0	0	0	1	64
1970	0	0	0	0	0	44	99
1971	0	0	0	0	0	28	108
1972	0	0	0	0	0	4	76
1973	0	0	0	0	0	34	69
1974	0	0	0	0	0	120	66
1975	0	0	0	0	0	0	60

Feb	Mar	Apr	May	June	Total
8.0	11.0	T	0.0	0.0	91.8
21.5	9.0	4.0	T	0.0	42.0
30.5	4.5	1.0	0.0	0.0	70.2
15.0	2.0	13.3	0.0	0.0	48.4
4.0	7.5	14.5	T	0.0	61.5
22.5	6.5	6.5	0.0	0.0	65.0
11.5	2.7	10.2	0.0	0.0	64.4
28.5	15.7	11.2	3.3	0.0	99.7
2.7	35.2	4.7	T	0.0	84.0
9.1	14.6	7.4	T	0.0	51.5
T	1.6	0.6	T	T	32.4
28.5	29.7	0.9	0.0	0.0	107.0
26.9	6.9	0.4	5.8	T	167.0
6.7	10.4	0.5	3.1	0.0	63.3
19.0	12.9	12.5	7.1	0.0	73.4
8.1	44.4	1.4	T	0.0	105.9
6.0	7.3	2.5	1.0	0.0	60.0
16.0	26.0	5.0	3.5	0.0	89.0
15.6	1.0	0.5	0.7	T	67.8
9.8	3.4	5.1	0.0	0.0	42.7
T	3.0	7.4	0.9	0.0	53.0
15.5	28.6	14.8	0.0	0.0	71.5
33.5	1.0	T	T	0.0	53.8
24.7	4.5	7.1	3.6	0.0	77.6
3.2	29.3	0.8	3.1	0.0	53.9
32.4	13.0	0.0	3.2	0.0	128.9
10.9	8.0	11.8	0.0	0.0	47.3
1.4	38.5	19.9	3.8	0.0	89.4
23.9	34.4	58.3	7.0	0.0	166.7
10.8	7.4	5.1	0.0	0.0	83.4
T	10.9	17.7	0.0	0.0	63.1
9.3	10.1	22.7	2.0	0.0	150.4
42.1	43.6	0.6	4.6	0.0	134.7
2.8	67.3	11.3	0.0	0.0	95.7
15.1	3.1	5.0	6.1	0.0	56.6
0.4	T	1.5	0.0	0.0	50.3
33.8	77.4	10.9	3.0	0.0	210.0
2.4	8.8	1.6	0.0	0.0	70.0
18.2	29.1	25.1	8.2	0.0	141.1
13.9	20.1	9.6	2.3	T	89.2

FLAGSTAFF, AZ

Feb	Mar	Apr	May	June	Total
1114	864	723	406	121	6848
771	845	735	583	156	7062
858	1054	718	338	136	6994
1054	850	572	466	98	6628
1130	786	635	440	87	7088
868	925	619	495	116	6881
965	1135	517	518	213	7667
788	940	757	372	255	6893
1105	1061	752	477	224	7403
983	985	768	560	353	7497
1109	854	603	343	171	7069
824	799	816	498	265	6946
839	861	733	453	172	7013
1105	1164	693	383	207	7702
775	962	821	378	174	7076
943	862	683	557	210	7211
956	768	749	573	220	7865
1006	1176	801	370	164	8124
960	754	650	310	67	6458
1041	978	856	536	231	7581

Aug	Sept	Oct	Nov	Dec	Total
48	0	0	0	0	113
64	1	0	0	0	208
17	0	0	0	0	153
20	0	0	0	0	100
40	0	0	0	0	143
33	13	0	0	0	232
28	0	0	0	0	88

Average Temperature

Year	Jan	Feb	Mar	Apr	May	June	July	Aug	Sept	Oct	Nov	Dec	Annual
1936	30.4	31.2	37.1	46.6	53.2	63.2	66.9	65.2	55.8	47.5	37.8	31.5	47.2
1937	12.6	27.6	34.2	43.2	52.5	58.7	66.4	66.4	60.5	49.9	40.3	34.7	45.6
1938	34.2	30.4	35.4	43.8	50.8	59.6	65.0	64.4	59.8	47.0	33.5	32.1	46.3
1939	27.6	19.5	37.4	46.2	52.5	60.0	67.6	66.6	58.2	46.4	40.0	37.0	46.6
1940	31.8	22.7	39.8	44.6	54.3	63.8	67.4	66.0	57.6	48.5	36.3	33.6	47.2
1941	29.4	36.4	37.6	38.4	51.3	56.6	64.2	63.0	54.6	43.5	39.2	30.4	45.4
1942	29.8	26.5	34.6	43.1	49.8	59.2	68.4	65.1	58.8	48.6	41.8	36.0	46.8
#1943	31.4	34.0	40.4	47.2	53.3	58.7	67.6	66.2	60.5	49.4	36.6	29.1	47.9
1944	29.2	30.2	33.8	40.5	50.9	56.8	65.6	67.5	60.4	50.6	35.0	32.8	46.1
1945	29.3	35.0	33.3	42.0	51.9	58.2	68.0	67.2	60.7	50.7	39.0	28.2	47.0
1946	28.9	32.6	38.8	48.4	51.2	63.1	67.4	65.4	60.4	45.4	35.9	36.0	47.8
1947	28.0	38.2	40.8	44.7	55.4	59.4	68.0	63.9	62.1	49.8	32.8	28.1	47.6
1948	33.2	29.2	29.9	46.0	53.0	59.4	66.7	65.5	60.3	48.6	35.3	30.7	46.5
#1949	19.6	24.0	35.4	48.0	50.8	59.5	67.2	64.6	60.8	45.2	44.8	27.1	45.6
1950	26.7	34.8	37.7	46.2	48.6	58.0	64.2	62.2	54.8	52.1	40.9	35.8	46.8
1951	28.7	31.0	34.6	42.2	50.7	56.7	67.8	62.6	57.9	46.6	34.1	26.7	45.0
1952	25.8	28.0	28.6	43.1	52.3	57.8	63.7	64.4	58.3	51.1	30.7	26.3	44.2
1953	35.1	30.6	36.1	41.9	45.0	59.0	66.4	62.6	57.7	44.9	38.0	28.3	45.4
1954	28.5	34.6	32.3	46.3	53.0	58.4	66.5	61.6	57.8	48.5	39.6	29.5	46.4
1955	22.2	22.5	34.9	40.0	48.1	55.9	61.7	64.4	57.6	49.3	36.3	33.8	42.9
1956	33.2	26.3	36.9	40.6	51.7	61.0	64.3	60.8	61.5	45.6	33.9	30.3	45.5
1957	29.6	37.2	37.6	40.2	45.9	60.0	64.8	63.4	57.4	45.3	37.7	35.1	45.8
1958	30.5	34.1	30.7	40.8	53.9	61.1	65.8	66.4	57.0	48.4	35.0	36.5	46.7
1959	31.4	27.2	37.3	45.7	49.8	61.8	67.5	62.9	56.4	47.7	37.4	31.4	46.4
1960	22.7	25.8	39.4	43.7	50.5	62.3	67.4	65.3	59.7	45.0	36.8	28.7	45.6
1961	30.2	33.8	34.9	44.1	48.8	63.1	66.7	64.1	53.8	44.5	34.2	26.0	45.3
1962	27.1	30.3	28.1	47.6	48.0	58.2	64.6	64.9	58.7	47.5	39.8	31.6	45.5
1963	25.4	36.7	34.5	39.6	52.7	56.3	68.0	63.8	59.2	49.8	37.9	30.3	46.2
1964	25.3	26.6	30.5	39.7	49.4	57.4	66.9	63.3	56.7	51.3	31.3	30.3	44.1
1965	31.4	29.7	33.0	39.2	46.7	53.0	65.0	63.7	53.8	49.7	39.7	30.2	44.6
1966	23.5	25.1	37.2	44.7	53.7	59.1	66.4	65.2	58.6	46.9	39.5	29.7	45.8
1967	29.1	35.3	39.0	37.6	48.7	56.2	66.6	64.4	57.9	50.0	40.4	23.1	45.7
1968	25.5	35.8	37.0	40.3	50.2	59.9	64.9	59.5	55.9	46.9	35.7	25.0	44.7
1969	31.8	25.4	27.3	41.7	52.4	57.9	66.2	65.1	58.2	40.5	33.9	33.3	44.5
1970	30.9	37.1	33.7	37.5	52.6	60.4	67.7	66.3	54.4	43.9	39.5	28.5	46.1
1971	29.3	31.1	37.0	41.9	46.8	58.7	67.5	64.0	53.0	38.6	33.5	22.5	43.6
1972	28.4	31.8	40.0	39.8	46.4	57.6	66.5	62.9	56.7	45.9	29.6	21.9	43.9
1973	22.9	28.7	26.8	38.0	52.8	60.5	65.7	64.6	57.7	50.0	37.1	33.0	44.8
1974	27.8	30.5	40.4	43.2	54.8	66.5	66.3	64.7	58.7	47.9	36.8	26.8	47.0
1975	27.7	27.6	33.2	36.2	47.5	57.1	65.9	63.5	57.9	46.5	37.3	29.2	44.2
RECORD MEAN	27.8	30.7	35.7	42.6	50.2	59.1	65.7	63.8	57.3	46.9	36.7	29.5	45.5
MAX	41.2	43.8	49.2	57.4	66.6	77.0	80.9	78.3	73.1	62.8	51.5	42.9	60.4
MIN	14.3	17.6	22.1	27.7	33.8	41.2	50.5	49.3	41.5	31.0	21.9	16.0	30.6

# Indicates a station move or relocation of instruments.

Precipitation

Year	Jan	Feb	Mar	Apr	May	June	July	Aug	Sept	Oct	Nov	Dec	Annual
1936	0.22	2.73	1.63	0.10	0.09	0.26	4.36	2.70	1.41	2.37	0.43	3.00	19.30
1937	3.19	2.79	2.87	0.16	0.31	1.07	2.69	2.51	1.83	T	0.08	1.91	19.41
1938	1.39	3.72	4.39	0.40	0.13	0.87	2.11	2.87	1.07	0.51	0.28	2.84	20.58
1939	1.26	1.52	0.84	0.57	0.08	T	0.90	2.45	3.47	0.34	1.45	0.03	12.91
1940	1.56	2.43	0.27	1.71	0.15	1.18	0.52	2.26	3.63	3.45	0.92	3.14	21.22
1941	1.19	1.77	2.31	3.12	0.70	0.55	1.71	1.31	4.54	4.90	0.81	2.11	25.02
1942	0.54	1.40	0.58	0.96	T	0.00	1.07	2.08	0.65	1.00	0.24	1.38	9.90
#1943	3.26	1.24	1.66	1.18	0.18	0.15	1.72	2.45	1.67	1.57	0.19	2.51	17.78
1944	1.72	2.98	2.00	1.84	0.99	0.10	1.74	0.67	1.33	0.35	1.96	1.82	17.50
1945	1.94	0.51	4.21	0.55	T	0.06	4.14	2.91	0.18	0.76	0.08	2.27	17.61
1946	0.98	0.77	1.46	3.45	0.46	T	4.78	3.46	1.53	2.10	1.60	1.15	21.74
1947	0.85	0.18	0.59	0.14	0.98	T	1.21	4.25	0.64	1.39	0.88	2.02	13.13
1948	0.82	2.33	2.10	0.38	0.13	0.46	0.73	2.10	1.05	1.87	T	3.38	15.35
#1949	6.91	1.64	0.75	0.31	1.03	2.19	2.74	1.26	3.47	3.84	0.86	1.49	26.49
1950	1.07	1.29	1.01	0.28	0.35	0.37	3.42	1.47	0.89	T	0.45	0.16	10.76
1951	1.61	0.99	0.91	1.74	1.00	T	4.47	5.50	0.60	2.26	1.26	5.45	25.79
1952	3.48	0.82	3.03	1.63	T	0.09	2.10	2.92	2.09	T	2.84	1.06	20.06
1953	0.45	0.38	0.87	1.16	0.27	T	2.50	4.21	0.12	0.49	1.83	0.53	12.81
1954	1.97	1.27	3.90	0.80	0.44	1.17	3.51	1.53	3.14	0.89	0.32	0.61	19.55
1955	2.67	1.56	0.17	0.51	0.21	2.92	3.49	3.73	T	0.05	1.78	0.88	17.97
1956	1.62	1.06	0.12	0.86	0.17	2.79	1.19	1.42	0.02	0.68	0.05	0.39	10.37
1957	6.46	0.85	0.92	1.04	2.02	1.59	1.57	1.65	T	3.66	4.24	0.59	24.59
1958	0.22	3.04	2.98	1.23	0.45	0.70	0.75	3.02	6.60	0.86	1.39	T	21.24
1959	0.34	3.63	0.08	1.49	0.64	0.77	2.93	4.96	0.28	2.35	0.31	3.68	21.46
1960	1.03	1.82	0.66	1.34	0.71	0.39	0.96	3.28	1.18	3.57	1.27	0.39	16.60
1961	1.15	0.12	2.89	0.35	0.28	0.37	2.03	3.37	1.92	1.89	1.43	3.15	18.95
1962	2.65	4.15	1.30	0.09	0.99	0.52	2.36	0.26	2.48	1.23	1.23	0.85	18.11
1963	0.96	1.28	1.03	2.13	0.05	T	0.32	4.96	0.79	1.25	1.39	0.36	14.52
1964	1.07	0.14	3.08	2.17	0.84	0.17	5.23	1.32	0.99	0.02	1.27	2.74	19.04
1965	3.05	2.34	3.33	5.62	1.88	0.30	2.34	1.01	4.85	0.27	4.97	6.63	36.59
1966	1.10	1.06	0.95	0.27	T	0.21	1.62	3.55	2.03	0.99	2.33	6.17	20.28
1967	0.93	T	1.11	1.90	0.41	1.05	3.80	2.68	2.25	0.30	0.54	7.30	22.27
1968	1.55	1.29	1.15	2.09	0.55	0.16	3.61	1.13	0.04	1.38	0.87	2.71	16.53
1969	4.63	3.91	3.00	0.11	1.06	0.01	3.81	1.90	1.34	1.14	2.04	0.46	23.41
1970	0.51	0.41	6.75	1.16	T	0.07	2.58	5.15	3.79	0.11	1.37	2.12	24.02
1971	0.08	1.48	0.25	0.55	1.23	0.00	1.97	4.48	2.02	4.37	0.40	4.18	21.01
1972	0.00	0.02	T	0.72	0.14	1.93	1.90	2.82	0.81	9.86	2.34	4.13	24.67
1973	1.89	3.69	6.18	1.21	1.17	0.40	1.87	1.25	T	0.03	1.90	0.12	19.71
1974	3.63	0.26	1.01	0.57	T	T	3.00	2.16	0.93	3.64	1.03	1.18	17.41
1975	1.76	1.90	2.92	2.20	1.16	0.05	2.24	0.74	1.89	0.33	2.96	1.95	20.10
RECORD MEAN	1.89	1.81	1.91	1.30	0.66	0.53	2.74	2.82	1.72	1.54	1.36	1.91	20.19

Record mean values above are means through the current year for the period beginning in 1900 for temperature and precipitation, 1950 for snowfall.

QUOTES FROM WEATHER FOLKLORE –

A red morn, that ever yet betokened
Wreck to the seamen, tempest to the field,
Sorrow to shepherds, woe unto the birds,
Gust and foul flaws the herdmen and herds.
– Shakespeare.

Cranes soaring aloft and quietly in the air
foreshows fair weather,
but if they make much noise,
as if consulting which way to go,
it foreshadows a storm that's near at hand.
– Thomas Willsford.

Station: PHOENIX, ARIZONA
SKY HARBOR AIRPORT
Elevation (ground): 1112 feet

TEMPERATURES °F

Month	Normal: Daily maximum	Normal: Daily minimum	Normal: Monthly	Extremes: Record highest	Extremes: Year	Extremes: Record lowest	Extremes: Year
(a)				15		15	
J	64.8	37.6	51.2	88	1971	19	1971
F	69.3	40.8	55.1	89	1963	26	1964
M	74.5	44.8	59.7	95	1972	25	1966
A	83.6	51.8	67.7	101	1962	37	1968
M	92.9	59.6	76.3	110	1974	40	1967
J	101.5	67.7	84.6	116	1974	51	1965
J	104.8	77.5	91.2	115	1973	67	1968
A	102.2	76.0	89.1	116	1975	61	1968
S	98.4	69.1	83.8	110	1974	47	1965
O	87.6	56.8	72.2	103	1974	34	1971
N	74.7	44.8	59.8	93	1975	31	1966
D	66.4	38.5	52.5	82	1965	24	1968
YR	85.1	55.4	70.3	116	AUG 1975	19	JAN 1971

IMPORTANT:
The time-period covered by this record is limited: See footnotes on next page for explanation and for additional history of EXTREME HIGHS AND LOWS recorded in the general area.

Phoenix is located in about the center of the Salt River Valley, a broad, oval-shaped, nearly flat plain. The Salt River runs from east to west through the valley but, owing to impounding dams upstream, it is usually dry. The climate is of a desert type with low annual rainfall and low relative humidity. Daytime temperatures are high throughout the summer months. The winters are mild. Nighttime temperatures frequently drop below freezing during the three coldest months, but afternoons are usually sunny and warm.

At an elevation of about 1100 feet, the station is in a level or gently sloping valley running east and west. The Salt River Mountains are located about 6 miles to the south and rise to 2600 feet m.s.l. The Phoenix Mountains lie 8 miles to the north-northwest and have a maximum elevation of 2300 feet m.s.l. Eighteen miles to the southwest lies the 3300-foot Estrella Mountain, and 25 miles to the west are found the White Tank Mountains with an elevation of 4000 feet m.s.l. The Superstition Mountains are approximately 40 miles to the east and rise to 4600 feet m.s.l.

The central floor of the Salt River Valley is irrigated by water from dams built on the Salt River system. To the north and west of the gravity flow irrigated district there is considerable agricultural land irrigated by pump water. There is no evidence that the irrigation has in any way affected the relative humidity in the valley. The average daytime relative humidity is about 30 percent based on observations at 11:00 a.m. and 5:00 p.m.

There are two separate rainfall seasons. The first occurs during the winter months from November to March when the area is subjected to occasional storms from the Pacific Ocean. While this is classed as a rainfall season, there can be periods of a month or more in this or any other season when practically no precipitation occurs. Snowfall occurs very rarely in the Salt River Valley, while light snows occasionally fall in the higher mountains surrounding the valley. The second rainfall period occurs during July and August when Arizona is subjected to widespread thunderstorm activity whose moisture supply originates in the Gulf of Mexico and along Mexico's west coast. These thunderstorms are extremely variable in intensity and location.

The spring and fall months are generally dry, although precipitation in substantial amounts has fallen on occasion during every month of the year.

Since the Phoenix area is primarily agricultural, minimum temperatures and their variation over the valley have been studied closely. During the winter months the temperature is marginal for some types of crops, such as citrus. Areas with milder temperatures around the edges of the valley are utilized by these crops. However, the valley is subject to occasional killing and hard freezes in which no area escapes damage.

The valley floor, in general, is rather free of wind. During the spring months southwest and west winds predominate and are associated with the passage of low pressure throughs. During the thunderstorm season there are often local gusty winds, usually flowing from an easterly direction. Throughout the year there are periods, often several days in length, in which winds remain under 10 miles an hour.

Sunshine in the Phoenix area averages 86 percent of the possible amount, ranging from a minimum monthly average

(Continued page 354)

PHOENIX, ARIZONA

Normals, Means, and Extremes

(To better understand these tables, see full explanation of terms beginning on page 322)

Month	Normal Degree days Base 65 °F		Precipitation in inches											Relative humidity pct.				Wind					Pct. of possible sunshine †	Mean sky cover, tenths, sunrise to sunset $	Mean number of days											Average station pressure mb.
			Water equivalent							Snow, Ice pellets				Hour 05	Hour 11	Hour 17	Hour 23			Peak gust Ø					Sunrise to sunset							Temperatures °F				
														(Local time)																		Max.		Min.		Elev. 1107
Month	Heating	Cooling	Normal	Maximum monthly	Year	Minimum monthly	Year	Maximum in 24 hrs.	Year	Maximum monthly	Year	Maximum in 24 hrs.	Year	05	11	17	23	Mean speed m.p.h.	Prevailing direction	Speed m.p.h.	Direction	Year			Clear	Partly cloudy	Cloudy	Precipitation .01 inch or more	Snow, Ice pellets 1.0 inch or more	Thunderstorms	Heavy fog, visibility ¼ mile or less	(b) 90° and above	32° and below	32° and below	0° and below	feet m.s.l.
(a)				38		38		38		38		38		15	15	15	15	30	18	38	38		80	30	38	38	38	36	38	36	38	15	15	15	15	3
J	428	0	0.71	2.41	1955	0.00	1972	1.31	1951	T	1962	T	1962	66	44	30	55	5.1	E	51	SW	1974	78	4.7	14	7	10	4	0	*	1	0	0	6	0	978.1
F	292	14	0.60	2.23	1944	0.00	1967	1.07	1944	0.6	1939	0.6	1939	59	37	25	47	5.7	E	49	SSE	1959	80	4.4	13	6	9	4	0	1	*	0	0	2	0	977.9
M	185	21	0.76	4.16	1941	0.00	1959	1.32	1941	0.0		0.0		58	33	23	44	6.4	E	50	WNW	1956	83	4.3	15	7	9	3	0	1	*	2	0	1	0	973.9
A	60	141	0.32	2.10	1941	0.00	1962	1.38	1941	T	1949	T	1949	44	23	15	29	6.8	E	45	NW	1957	89	3.3	17	7	6	2	0	1	0	7	0	0	0	973.0
M	0	355	0.14	0.94	1944	0.00	1974	0.94	1944	0.0		0.0		36	17	12	22	6.8	E	59	SSE	1954	93	2.6	21	6	4	1	0	1	0	23	0	0	0	970.8
J	0	588	0.12	1.70	1972	0.00	1974	1.64	1972	0.0		0.0		35	18	12	22	6.8	E	59	S	1972	94	1.8	23	5	2	1	0	1	0	29	0	0	0	969.4
J	0	812	0.75	4.19	1955	T	1947	1.97	1955	0.0		0.0		46	28	20	33	7.1	W	71	N	1959	85	3.7	17	10	4	4	0	6	0	31	0	0	0	971.2
A	0	747	1.22	5.56	1951	T	1975	3.07	1943	0.0		0.0		53	34	24	39	6.5	E	60	SSW	1953	85	3.3	17	10	4	5	0	7	0	31	0	0	0	971.3
S	0	564	0.69	4.23	1939	0.00	1973	2.43	1970	0.0		0.0		53	31	23	40	6.2	E	75	SW	1950	89	2.0	22	5	3	3	0	3	0	27	0	0	0	971.8
O	17	240	0.46	4.40	1972	0.00	1973	2.27	1972	0.0		0.0		53	30	22	42	5.7	E	48	SSW	1956	88	2.6	21	6	4	3	0	1	*	14	0	0	0	974.3
N	182	26	0.46	3.04	1952	0.00	1956	1.07	1952	0.0		0.0		61	38	28	52	5.2	E	55	S	1975	83	3.5	18	6	6	2	0	1	*	*	0	*	0	976.7
D	388	0	0.82	3.98	1967	0.00	1973	1.89	1967	T	1974	T	1974	69	48	35	60	5.0	E	68	W	1953	77	4.0	15	7	9	4	0	1	1	0	0	3	0	978.9
YR	1552	3508	7.05	5.56	AUG 1951	0.00	JUN 1974	3.07	AUG 1943	0.6	FEB 1939	0.6	FEB 1939	53	32	22	41	6.1	E	75	SW	SEP 1950	86	3.4	213	82	70	34	0	23	2	165	0	13	0	973.9

FOOTNOTES

Ø Peak Gust observed during Airway observational program from January 1938 through October 1953; from recorder charts thereafter.
† Combined record from Post Office, August 1895 through October 1953, and from Sky Harbor Airport, November 1953 to date.
$ Broken record: 1940, 1941, and 1948 to date.
Means and extremes above are from existing and comparable exposures. Annual extremes have been exceeded at other sites in the locality as follows: Highest temperature 118 in July 1958+; lowest temperature 16 in January 1913; maximum monthly precipitation 6.47 in July 1911; maximum precipitation in 24 hours 4.98 in July 1911; maximum monthly snowfall 1.0 in January 1937 and earlier; maximum snowfall in 24 hours 1.0 in January 1937 and earlier.

Snowfall

Season	July	Aug	Sept	Oct	Nov	Dec	Jan
#1936-37	0.0	0.0	0.0	0.0	0.0	0.0	1.0
#1937-38	0.0	0.0	0.0	0.0	0.0	0.0	0.0
1938-39	0.0	0.0	0.0	0.0	0.0	0.0	0.0
1939-40	0.0	0.0	0.0	0.0	0.0	0.0	0.0
1940-41	0.0	0.0	0.0	0.0	0.0	0.0	0.0
1941-42	0.0	0.0	0.0	0.0	0.0	0.0	0.0
1942-43	0.0	0.0	0.0	0.0	0.0	0.0	0.0
1943-44	0.0	0.0	0.0	0.0	0.0	0.0	0.0
1944-45	0.0	0.0	0.0	0.0	0.0	0.0	0.0
1945-46	0.0	0.0	0.0	0.0	0.0	0.0	0.0
1946-47	0.0	0.0	0.0	0.0	0.0	0.0	0.0
1947-48	0.0	0.0	0.0	0.0	0.0	0.0	0.0
1948-49	0.0	0.0	0.0	0.0	0.0	0.0	0.0
1949-50	0.0	0.0	0.0	0.0	0.0	0.0	0.0
1950-51	0.0	0.0	0.0	0.0	0.0	0.0	T
1951-52	0.0	0.0	0.0	0.0	0.0	0.0	0.0
#1952-53	0.0	0.0	0.0	0.0	0.0	0.0	0.0
1953-54	0.0	0.0	0.0	0.0	0.0	0.0	0.0
1954-55	0.0	0.0	0.0	0.0	0.0	0.0	0.0
1955-56	0.0	0.0	0.0	0.0	0.0	0.0	0.0
1956-57	0.0	0.0	0.0	0.0	0.0	0.0	0.0
#1957-58	0.0	0.0	0.0	0.0	0.0	0.0	0.0
1958-59	0.0	0.0	0.0	0.0	0.0	0.0	0.0
1959-60	0.0	0.0	0.0	0.0	0.0	0.0	0.0
1960-61	0.0	0.0	0.0	0.0	0.0	0.0	0.0
1961-62	0.0	0.0	0.0	0.0	0.0	0.0	T
1962-63	0.0	0.0	0.0	0.0	0.0	0.0	0.0
1963-64	0.0	0.0	0.0	0.0	0.0	0.0	0.0
1964-65	0.0	0.0	0.0	0.0	0.0	0.0	0.0
1965-66	0.0	0.0	0.0	0.0	0.0	0.0	0.0
1966-67	0.0	0.0	0.0	0.0	0.0	0.0	0.0
1967-68	0.0	0.0	0.0	0.0	0.0	T	0.0
1968-69	0.0	0.0	0.0	0.0	0.0	T	0.0
1969-70	0.0	0.0	0.0	0.0	0.0	0.0	0.0
1970-71	0.0	0.0	0.0	0.0	0.0	0.0	0.0
1971-72	0.0	0.0	0.0	0.0	0.0	0.0	0.0
1972-73	0.0	0.0	0.0	0.0	0.0	0.0	0.0
1973-74	0.0	0.0	0.0	0.0	0.0	0.0	0.0
1974-75	0.0	0.0	0.0	0.0	0.0	T	0.0
1975-76	0.0	0.0	0.0	0.0	0.0	0.0	
RECORD MEAN	0.0	0.0	0.0	0.0	0.0	T	T

Heating Degree Days

Season	July	Aug	Sept	Oct	Nov	Dec	Jan
1955-56	0	0	0	1	181	278	271
1956-57	0	0	0	47	214	356	334
#1957-58	0	0	0	12	253	303	365
1958-59	0	0	0	4	124	271	341
1959-60	0	0	0	26	119	342	506
#1960-61	0	0	0	16	153	445	326
1961-62	0	0	0	51	233	388	414
1962-63	0	0	0	1	115	301	507
1963-64	0	0	0	0	133	403	558
1964-65	0	0	0	0	281	396	375
1965-66	0	0	4	7	116	370	516
1966-67	0	0	0	8	139	397	437
1967-68	0	0	0	6	72	512	384
1968-69	0	0	0	0	173	473	306
1969-70	0	0	0	12	95	307	393
1970-71	0	0	0	19	119	376	396
1971-72	0	0	0	79	185	455	414
1972-73	0	0	0	38	205	395	422
1973-74	0	0	0	2	156	291	333
1974-75	0	0	0	21	112	439	388
1975-76	0	0	0	15	159	310	

Cooling Degree Days

Year	Jan	Feb	Mar	Apr	May	June	July
1969	0	0	22	123	433	582	878
1970	0	4	4	58	459	700	938
1971	7	2	76	107	265	614	934
1972	0	11	200	212	419	691	919
1973	0	0	0	109	499	701	894
1974	0	2	69	182	477	825	858
1975	0	0	12	42	374	654	913

Feb	Mar	Apr	May	June	Total
0.0	0.0	0.0	0.0	0.0	1.0
0.0	0.0	0.0	0.0	0.0	0.0
0.6	0.0	0.0	0.0	0.0	0.6
0.0	0.0	0.0	0.0	0.0	0.0
0.0	0.0	0.0	0.0	0.0	0.0
0.0	0.0	0.0	0.0	0.0	0.0
0.0	0.0	0.0	0.0	0.0	0.0
0.0	0.0	0.0	0.0	0.0	0.0
0.0	0.0	0.0	0.0	0.0	0.0
0.0	0.0	0.0	0.0	0.0	0.0
0.0	0.0	0.0	0.0	0.0	0.0
0.0	0.0	0.0	0.0	0.0	0.0
0.0	0.0	T	0.0	0.0	T
0.0	0.0	0.0	0.0	0.0	0.0
0.0	0.0	0.0	0.0	0.0	T
0.0	0.0	0.0	0.0	0.0	0.0
0.0	0.0	0.0	0.0	0.0	0.0
0.0	0.0	0.0	0.0	0.0	0.0
0.0	0.0	0.0	0.0	0.0	0.0
0.0	0.0	0.0	0.0	0.0	0.0
0.0	0.0	0.0	0.0	0.0	0.0
0.0	0.0	0.0	0.0	0.0	0.0
0.0	0.0	0.0	0.0	0.0	0.0
0.0	0.0	0.0	0.0	0.0	0.0
0.0	0.0	0.0	0.0	0.0	T
0.0	0.0	0.0	0.0	0.0	0.0
0.0	0.0	0.0	0.0	0.0	0.0
0.0	0.0	0.0	0.0	0.0	0.0
0.0	0.0	0.0	0.0	0.0	0.0
0.0	0.0	0.0	0.0	0.0	0.0
0.0	0.0	0.0	0.0	0.0	T
0.0	0.0	0.0	0.0	0.0	0.0
0.0	0.0	0.0	0.0	0.0	0.0
0.0	0.0	0.0	0.0	0.0	0.0
0.0	0.0	0.0	0.0	0.0	0.0
0.0	0.0	0.0	0.0	0.0	0.0
0.0	0.0	0.0	0.0	0.0	T
0.0	0.0	0.0	0.0	0.0	T
0.0	0.0	0.0	0.0	0.0	0.0
0.0	0.0	0.0	0.0	0.0	0.0
0.0	0.0	0.0	0.0	0.0	0.0
0.0	0.0	0.0	0.0	0.0	0.0
0.0	0.0	0.0	0.0	0.0	0.0
0.0	0.0	0.0	0.0	0.0	T
T	0.0	T	0.0	0.0	T

PHOENIX, AZ

Feb	Mar	Apr	May	June	Total
402	131	55	0	0	1319
117	107	48	7	0	1230
191	245	68	0	0	1437
306	66	0	3	0	1115
388	56	14	0	0	1451
259	166	6	0	0	1371
255	277	2	0	0	1620
148	151	50	0	0	1273
450	277	69	23	0	1913
346	269	133	14	0	1814
423	145	12	0	0	1593
256	102	93	10	0	1442
151	167	39	0	0	1331
327	265	12	13	0	1569
134	166	60	0	0	1167
241	123	53	0	0	1327
174	22	12	0	0	1341
200	254	39	0	0	1553
229	77	5	0	0	1093
301	191	107	4	0	1563

Aug	Sept	Oct	Nov	Dec	Total
918	638	158	16	0	3768
862	527	151	18	0	3721
773	623	220	30	0	3651
780	599	259	4	0	4094
885	598	302	36	0	4024
821	673	365	13	0	4285
839	640	265	45	1	3785

Average Temperature

Year	Jan	Feb	Mar	Apr	May	June	July	Aug	Sept	Oct	Nov	Dec	Annual
#1936	52.8	56.4	64.6	73.1	81.7	90.3	93.2	91.1	83.6	73.2	61.8	53.2	72.9
#1937	43.2	54.7	59.9	67.6	78.6	85.3	91.8	92.2	86.9	74.8	62.3	56.9	71.2
1938	52.6	54.4	57.8	66.6	78.7	83.4	88.8	88.2	84.4	69.2	53.2	53.6	69.2
1939	50.7	47.0	61.0	70.2	77.5	84.6	92.0	90.3	82.0	69.4	62.5	55.5	70.2
1940	54.6	55.2	63.6	69.5	80.8	89.1	92.0	91.3	85.0	72.7	57.7	55.6	72.3
1941	53.3	57.3	58.4	61.6	74.5	80.6	88.6	86.2	79.2	66.4	60.0	52.3	68.2
1942	52.4	51.0	57.0	64.8	73.4	83.2	91.8	87.6	83.3	70.6	61.9	54.5	69.3
1943	51.7	57.6	63.2	70.7	77.5	83.6	91.0	87.4	84.0	71.1	59.4	52.4	70.8
1944	49.9	51.6	56.0	64.0	74.0	79.6	88.6	90.3	83.0	73.2	56.6	52.0	68.2
1945	50.4	54.6	55.8	65.4	75.1	81.2	91.1	89.6	83.8	73.8	57.6	49.3	69.0
1946	49.6	52.0	60.8	72.4	75.8	86.2	90.1	88.8	83.8	66.4	54.3	53.6	69.5
1947	48.5	58.1	62.7	68.2	78.8	83.7	92.9	88.8	86.2	72.7	55.0	49.2	70.4
1948	51.6	52.6	56.3	69.2	76.4	84.2	91.2	91.4	85.6	73.6	54.8	50.1	69.8
1949	43.7	51.8	59.1	70.6	76.0	85.3	90.4	87.6	86.1	68.5	64.4	51.3	69.6
1950	49.7	58.9	62.6	72.5	76.0	84.9	90.5	90.3	82.2	78.3	64.2	57.5	72.3
1951	51.9	56.1	60.7	67.8	76.7	83.0	92.5	87.2	83.2	71.9	58.6	52.1	70.1
#1952	51.4	54.2	55.6	67.5	79.6	84.5	89.9	90.9	85.8	76.8	57.1	51.0	70.4
1953	54.5	53.3	61.5	66.6	70.9	85.0	90.8	89.3	84.1	71.6	61.5	49.3	69.9
1954	52.3	61.1	58.3	71.6	78.2	84.7	91.3	88.4	86.2	74.9	64.6	54.0	72.1
1955	48.7	50.9	61.6	66.7	75.6	83.7	86.7	86.6	82.9	75.7	59.1	55.8	69.5
1956	56.0	50.9	61.6	66.1	76.9	86.9	87.9	85.8	84.6	69.7	57.8	53.3	69.8
1957	54.0	61.4	61.8	66.5	72.9	87.1	91.4	88.0	83.2	70.6	56.4	55.0	70.7
#1958	53.0	58.0	57.0	66.7	81.3	89.1	93.6	92.7	86.6	76.6	61.4	56.0	72.7
1959	53.8	53.9	63.6	73.5	76.3	90.3	94.0	88.1	83.3	72.7	60.9	53.6	72.0
#1960	48.5	51.5	65.1	70.4	77.8	90.0	92.4	89.7	85.9	70.6	60.5	50.5	71.1
1961	54.2	55.6	59.6	69.2	75.6	88.6	91.7	88.6	80.6	69.6	57.1	52.3	70.2
1962	51.5	55.7	56.0	72.3	73.5	83.1	90.2	91.7	84.3	71.6	61.9	55.0	70.6
1963	48.4	60.2	61.0	65.8	80.0	81.7	92.0	87.1	85.1	76.2	61.9	51.8	71.0
1964	46.7	49.3	56.5	65.2	73.7	82.6	90.6	86.2	80.9	74.9	55.5	52.0	67.8
1965	52.7	52.4	56.1	63.4	71.8	79.0	91.0	89.0	79.2	73.8	62.1	52.9	68.6
1966	48.2	49.7	61.2	69.8	80.1	86.8	93.0	90.9	82.9	70.9	60.5	52.0	70.5
1967	50.7	55.7	62.8	62.4	75.1	81.1	91.6	91.0	84.8	73.5	63.9	48.2	70.1
1968	52.4	59.7	59.9	66.7	76.6	86.2	90.2	86.5	83.6	72.7	59.2	49.5	70.3
1969	54.9	53.0	56.9	68.5	78.3	84.2	93.1	94.4	86.0	69.5	62.1	54.8	71.3
1970	52.1	60.2	59.5	64.7	79.6	88.1	95.0	92.5	82.2	69.1	61.4	52.6	71.4
1971	52.2	56.3	63.3	66.5	73.3	85.3	94.9	89.6	85.6	69.3	59.7	50.2	70.5
1972	51.4	59.1	70.6	71.4	78.3	87.8	94.4	89.9	84.8	71.9	58.1	52.1	72.5
1973	51.2	57.5	56.6	67.2	80.9	88.1	93.5	93.4	84.7	74.4	60.8	55.4	72.0
1974	54.0	56.7	64.5	70.6	80.2	92.2	92.4	91.2	87.2	75.9	61.5	50.6	73.1
1975	52.3	54.0	59.0	62.6	76.7	86.6	94.3	91.9	86.2	72.9	60.9	54.8	71.0
RECORD MEAN	51.6	55.4	60.5	67.7	76.0	85.2	90.8	89.0	83.6	71.7	59.8	52.4	70.3
MAX	65.0	69.1	74.7	82.9	91.9	101.5	104.1	101.9	97.8	86.8	74.6	65.8	84.7
MIN	38.1	41.7	46.2	52.4	60.0	68.8	77.5	76.1	69.3	56.5	45.0	38.9	55.9

# Indicates a station move or relocation of instruments.

Precipitation

Year	Jan	Feb	Mar	Apr	May	June	July	Aug	Sept	Oct	Nov	Dec	Annual
#1936	0.80	1.01	0.50	0.14	T	T	2.49	0.32	0.43	0.13	0.35	2.12	8.29
#1937	0.83	0.76	1.58	T	0.08	T	0.49	0.05	1.17	T	0.00	0.41	5.37
1938	0.51	0.68	0.77	0.02	T	0.36	0.08	0.97	T	0.00	0.00	1.62	5.01
1939	0.27	0.59	0.11	0.11	0.00	0.00	0.77	1.18	4.23	0.10	0.47	T	7.83
1940	0.01	0.51	T	0.04	T	T	0.33	0.54	1.47	1.05	0.29	3.94	8.18
1941	0.97	2.02	4.16	2.10	0.81	T	0.79	0.85	1.82	0.52	1.16	1.06	16.26
1942	0.36	0.21	0.22	0.69	0.00	0.00	1.14	1.29	0.07	0.60	T	0.29	4.87
1943	0.66	0.06	0.55	0.05	0.01	0.02	0.38	4.91	0.78	0.19	0.00	1.42	9.03
1944	0.37	2.23	0.99	0.49	0.94	0.00	0.65	0.07	0.23	0.33	1.12	1.28	8.70
1945	1.01	0.10	0.79	T	0.00	0.00	1.31	0.58	T	0.53	0.00	0.44	4.76
1946	1.16	0.15	0.02	0.02	0.00	0.00	1.50	2.41	2.42	0.05	0.82	0.83	9.38
1947	0.03	0.13	T	T	0.32	T	T	1.10	0.34	0.04	0.59	0.45	3.00
1948	0.00	1.31	0.16	T	T	0.08	0.91	0.41	T	0.60	0.00	0.68	4.15
1949	1.71	0.12	0.35	0.18	0.09	0.33	0.44	0.48	0.99	0.82	0.31	0.92	6.74
1950	0.41	1.15	0.26	T	T	0.11	0.76	0.37	0.49	0.00	0.04	0.03	3.62
1951	1.58	0.29	0.44	1.02	0.20	T	1.06	5.56	0.33	0.52	0.73	0.64	12.37
#1952	0.56	0.29	2.20	1.94	0.00	0.06	0.54	1.11	0.23	0.00	3.04	0.68	10.65
1953	0.23	0.53	0.74	0.02	0.71	T	0.88	0.31	0.00	T	0.07	0.07	3.56
1954	0.88	0.58	1.22	0.02	0.11	0.02	0.36	0.55	0.44	0.12	T	0.01	4.31
1955	2.41	0.09	T	T	0.02	0.95	4.19	1.80	T	0.13	0.05	0.18	9.82
1956	0.67	0.64	0.00	0.03	T	0.01	0.92	0.46	0.02	0.06	0.00	0.01	2.82
1957	1.57	0.21	0.53	0.12	0.43	0.26	0.72	0.85	0.00	2.66	0.02	0.23	7.60
#1958	0.07	1.15	1.94	0.89	0.08	0.05	0.31	0.72	2.25	0.50	0.16	0.00	8.12
1959	0.23	0.63	0.00	0.05	T	T	0.45	1.36	0.04	1.75	0.43	3.46	8.40
1960	0.85	0.04	0.57	0.00	T	T	0.25	0.82	0.12	0.67	T	0.07	3.39
1961	0.23	0.01	0.41	T	T	T	0.40	2.11	0.22	0.08	0.12	0.85	4.43
1962	1.20	0.83	0.50	0.00	T	0.12	0.10	0.25	0.39	T	0.03	0.48	3.90
1963	0.55	1.16	0.30	0.33	T	0.00	0.03	2.68	T	1.46	0.73	T	7.24
1964	0.22	0.01	0.37	0.10	T	0.00	0.60	1.29	1.80	0.17	0.35	1.09	6.00
1965	1.22	0.91	1.39	1.35	0.16	0.91	0.16	0.18	0.60	0.20	0.92	3.19	11.19
1966	0.35	0.95	0.34	T	T	0.22	0.09	2.17	2.00	0.25	0.38	0.52	7.27
1967	0.25	0.00	0.43	0.08	0.05	0.47	0.99	0.02	0.13	0.67	1.27	3.98	8.34
1968	0.19	1.20	1.04	T	T	0.00	1.70	0.59	0.00	0.35	0.91	0.69	6.67
1969	1.37	0.78	0.56	0.03	0.26	0.00	0.28	0.14	2.11	0.08	0.65	0.68	6.94
1970	T	0.30	2.26	T	T	0.00	0.48	1.02	2.85	0.44	0.02	0.26	7.63
1971	0.22	0.35	T	0.13	T	0.00	0.24	0.99	0.92	0.27	T	0.47	3.59
1972	0.00	T	T	T	T	1.70	0.72	1.20	0.28	4.40	1.01	1.56	10.87
1973	0.13	1.36	1.69	0.07	0.10	T	1.30	T	0.00	0.00	1.36	0.00	6.01
1974	0.57	0.02	1.37	0.01	0.00	0.00	0.84	1.15	1.07	2.12	0.44	0.59	8.18
1975	0.02	0.33	0.63	0.43	T	T	0.38	T	0.82	0.23	0.55	1.12	4.51
RECORD MEAN	0.74	0.72	0.68	0.35	0.11	0.11	0.90	1.03	0.78	0.51	0.60	0.88	7.41

Record mean values above are means through the current year for the period beginning in 1896 for temperature and precipitation, 1938 for snowfall. Temperature, precipitation, and snowfall are from City Office locations through 1937. Heating degree days are from City Office locations through June 1938. All data for later periods are from Airport locations.

(Continued)

of 77 percent in January and December to a maximum of 94 percent in June. During the winter, skies are sometimes cloudy, but clear skies predominate and temperatures are mild. During the spring, skies are also predominately clear with warm temperatures during the day and mild pleasant evenings. Beginning with June, daytime weather is hot. During July and August, there is often considerable afternoon cloudiness associated with cumulus clouds building up over the nearby mountains. Summer thundershowers seldom occur in the valley before evening.

The autumn season, beginning during the latter part of September, is characterized by sudden changes in temperature. The change from the heat of summer to mild winter temperatures usually occurs during October. The normal temperature change from the beginning to the end of this month is the greatest of any of the twelve months in central Arizona. By November, the mild winter season is definitely established in the Salt River Valley region.

QUOTES FROM WEATHER FOLKLORE–

Mackerel scales and mare's tails
Make lofty ships carry low sails.

Station: TUCSON, ARIZONA INTERNATIONAL AIRPORT
Elevation (ground): 2584 feet

TEMPERATURES °F

Month	Normal			Extremes			
	Daily maximum	Daily minimum	Monthly	Record highest	Year	Record lowest	Year
(a)				35		35	
J	63.5	38.2	50.9	87	1953	16	1949
F	67.0	39.9	53.5	92	1957	20	1955
M	71.5	43.6	57.6	92	1950	20	1965
A	80.7	50.3	65.5	102	1943	27	1945
M	89.6	57.5	73.6	107	1958	38	1950
J	97.9	66.2	82.1	111	1970	47	1955
J	98.3	74.2	86.3	111	1958	63	1973
A	95.3	72.3	83.8	109	1944	61	1956
S	93.1	67.1	80.1	107	1950	44	1965
O	83.8	56.4	70.1	101	1955	26	1971
N	72.2	44.8	58.5	90	1947	24	1958
D	64.8	39.1	52.0	84	1954	16	1974
YR	81.5	54.1	67.8	111	JUN 1970	16	DEC 1974

IMPORTANT:
The time-period covered by this record is limited: See footnotes on next page for explanation and for additional history of EXTREME HIGHS AND LOWS recorded in the general area.

Within 10 to 15 miles of the station the terrain is flat or gently rolling, with many dry washes. There is a general increase in elevation from north and northwest to south and southeast. Rugged mountain ranges and jutting hills encircle the valley floor. The higher mountains to the north, east, and south reach up to over 5,000 feet above the airport, and are at distances of 25 to 40 miles. To the west, the hills and smaller mountains range from 500 to 4,000 feet above the airport; all are more than 5 miles distant.

The soil cover is rather sandy, and native vegetation is mostly brush, cacti, and small trees, typical of the low latitude desert climate. The metropolitan area of Tucson lies at the foot of the Catalina Mountains, to the north of the airport. As a result of the lower elevation and more protected location of the City, recorded maximum temperatures are usually higher there than at the airport and minimum temperatures are correspondingly lower than at the airport.

As might be expected from its geographical situation, the climate of Tucson is prominently characterized by a long, hot season, beginning in April and ending in October. From May through September, maximum temperatures above 90° are the rule, with the mean maximum occasionally exceeding 100° in July. Under usual conditions, the diurnal temperature range is large, averaging almost 30°, although it may exceed 40°. Clear skies or very thin high clouds permit intense surface heating during the day and active radiational cooling at night, a process enhanced by the characteristic atmospheric dryness. The average growing season in the Tucson area approximates 250 days.

The distribution of precipitation through the year is such that more than 50 percent of the annual amount usually falls between July 1 and September 15 and a secondary maximum from December through March provides over 20 percent of the yearly precipitation. During the July-September period scattered convective or orographic showers and thunderstorms occur that often fill dry washes to overflowing. On occasion, brief, torrential downpours cause spectacular and destructive flash floods in sections of the metropolitan area, sometimes from short-period falls of over 1.50 inches. Hail rarely falls in thunderstorms, and sleet is an almost unknown form of precipitation. The December through March precipitation is more general and occurs as prolonged rainstorms that provide much needed replenishment of ground water. During these storms, snow often falls on the higher mountains, but snow in Tucson itself is infrequent, particularly in accumulations exceeding an inch in depth.

Relative humidity shows a pronounced daily oscillation in line with the usual large daily range in temperature. From near the first of the year, the average relative humidity decreases steadily until July and the beginning of the thunderstorm season, when it shows a marked increase. By the middle of September, and end of the thunderstorm season, it decreases again, resuming the upward climb in late November. Only occasionally during the summer is relative humidity high enough to produce appreciable physical discomfort, and then only for short periods. During the hot season, relative humidity values may fall below 10 percent during afternoons, and sometimes below 5 percent. The low average wet bulb temperature during

(Continued page 358)

TUCSON, ARIZONA

Normals, Means, and Extremes

(To better understand these tables, see full explanation of terms beginning on page 322)

Month	Normal Degree days Base 65 °F: Heating	Normal Degree days Base 65 °F: Cooling	Precipitation in inches, Water equivalent: Normal	Maximum monthly	Year	Minimum monthly	Year	Maximum in 24 hrs.	Year	Snow, Ice pellets: Maximum monthly	Year	Maximum in 24 hrs.	Year	Relative humidity pct. Hour 05 (Local time)	Hour 11	Hour 17	Hour 23
(a)				35		35		35		35		34		35	35	35	35
J	442	0	0.77	2.37	1957	T	1970	1.40	1946	4.7	1949	3.5	1949	62	39	32	56
F	333	11	0.70	2.27	1941	0.00	1972	1.49	1942	3.9	1965	3.9	1965	58	34	26	49
M	243	13	0.64	2.26	1952	0.00	1956	1.19	1952	5.7	1964	5.7	1964	52	28	23	42
A	81	96	0.35	1.66	1951	0.00	1972	0.75	1952	1.0	1956	1.0	1956	42	21	16	31
M	0	272	0.14	0.89	1943	0.00	1974	0.89	1943	0.0		0.0		33	16	12	23
J	0	513	0.20	1.46	1954	0.00	1975	1.27	1954	0.0		0.0		33	17	13	24
J	0	660	2.38	5.20	1958	0.27	1947	3.93	1958	0.0		0.0		58	33	28	47
A	0	583	2.34	7.93	1955	0.32	1975	2.48	1961	0.0		0.0		66	39	33	54
S	0	453	1.37	5.11	1964	0.00	1953	3.05	1964	0.0		0.0		55	32	27	44
O	29	187	0.66	4.51	1972	0.00	1973	1.86	1972	T	1959	T	1959	52	30	25	43
N	221	26	0.56	1.90	1952	0.00	1970	1.86	1968	6.4	1958	6.4	1958	54	32	28	48
D	403	0	0.94	5.02	1965	0.00	1973	1.54	1967	6.8	1971	6.8	1971	62	39	35	56
YR	1752	2814	11.05	7.93	AUG 1955	0.00	JUN 1975	3.93	JUL 1958	6.8	DEC 1971	6.8	DEC 1971	52	30	25	43

Month	Wind: Mean speed m.p.h.	Prevailing direction	Fastest mile: Speed m.p.h.	Direction	Year	Pct. of possible sunshine	Mean sky cover, tenths, sunrise to sunset	Mean number of days, Sunrise to sunset: Clear	Partly cloudy	Cloudy	Precipitation .01 inch or more	Snow, Ice pellets 1.0 inch or more	Thunderstorms	Heavy fog, visibility ¼ mile or less	Temperatures °F Max. (b) 90° and above	Max. 32° and below	Min. 32° and below	Min. 0° and below	Average station pressure mb. Elev. 2555 feet m.s.l.
(a)	30	15	28	28		28	34	35	35	35	35	35	35	35	35	35	35	35	3
J	7.8	SE	40	E	1962	81	4.6	14	7	10	4	*	*	*	0	0	7	0	927.3
F	8.1	SE	59	E	1952	83	4.4	13	7	8	3	*	*	*	*	0	5	0	927.2
M	8.5	SE	41	SE	1955	86	4.5	15	6	10	4	*	*	*	*	0	1	0	924.2
A	8.8	SE	46	SE	1952	91	3.3	17	8	5	2	*	1	0	4	0	*	0	923.8
M	8.6	SE	42	NE	1965	94	2.7	21	6	4	1	0	1	0	17	0	0	0	922.7
J	8.5	SSE	50	SE	1961	93	2.1	22	6	2	1	0	2	0	28	0	0	0	922.3
J	8.2	SE	71	SE	1971	78	5.3	10	12	9	10	0	14	0	29	0	0	0	924.3
A	7.6	SE	54	NE	1969	81	4.5	13	12	6	9	0	13	0	28	0	0	0	924.5
S	8.1	SE	54	SE	1960	87	2.8	20	6	4	4	0	5	0	23	0	0	0	924.2
O	8.2	SE	47	SE	1948	89	2.8	20	7	4	3	0	2	0	9	0	*	0	925.7
N	8.0	SE	55	E	1951	85	3.4	18	6	6	3	*	*	*	*	0	1	0	927.1
D	7.8	SE	44	W	1949	80	4.4	15	6	10	4	*	*	*	0	0	6	0	928.1
YR	8.2	SE	71	SE	JUL 1971	86	3.7	198	89	78	50	1	40	1	139	0	21	0	925.1

FOOTNOTES

Means and extremes above are from existing and comparable exposures. Annual extremes have been exceeded at other sites in the locality as follows: Highest temperature 112 in June 1902; lowest temperature 6 in January 1913.

Snowfall

Season	July	Aug	Sept	Oct	Nov	Dec	Jan
1936-37	0.0	0.0	0.0	0.0	0.0	0.0	5.8
1937-38	0.0	0.0	0.0	0.0	0.0	0.0	0.0
1938-39	0.0	0.0	0.0	0.0	0.0	0.0	0.0
# 1939-40	0.0	0.0	0.0	0.0	0.0	0.0	0.0
1940-41	0.0	0.0	0.0	0.0	0.0	0.0	0.0
1941-42	0.0	0.0	0.0	0.0	0.0	1.2	0.0
1942-43	0.0	0.0	0.0	0.0	0.0	0.0	0.0
1943-44	0.0	0.0	0.0	0.0	0.0	0.0	0.0
1944-45	0.0	0.0	0.0	0.0	0.0	0.0	0.0
1945-46	0.0	0.0	0.0	0.0	0.0	0.0	T
1946-47	0.0	0.0	0.0	0.0	0.0	0.0	0.0
1947-48	0.0	0.0	0.0	0.0	0.0	T	0.0
# 1948-49	0.0	0.0	0.0	0.0	0.0	0.0	4.7
1949-50	0.0	0.0	0.0	0.0	0.0	1.4	0.0
1950-51	0.0	0.0	0.0	0.0	0.0	T	2.8
1951-52	0.0	0.0	0.0	0.0	0.0	0.0	0.0
1952-53	0.0	0.0	0.0	0.0	0.0	0.0	0.0
1953-54	0.0	0.0	0.0	0.0	0.0	0.0	0.0
1954-55	0.0	0.0	0.0	0.0	0.0	0.0	0.0
1955-56	0.0	0.0	0.0	0.0	0.0	0.0	0.0
1956-57	0.0	0.0	0.0	0.0	0.0	0.0	0.0
1957-58	0.0	0.0	0.0	0.0	0.0	0.0	0.0
1958-59	0.0	0.0	0.0	0.0	6.4	0.0	0.0
1959-60	0.0	0.0	0.0	T	0.0	T	1.3
1960-61	0.0	0.0	0.0	0.0	0.0	0.0	0.0
1961-62	0.0	0.0	0.0	0.0	0.0	0.0	0.0
1962-63	0.0	0.0	0.0	0.0	0.0	0.0	0.0
1963-64	0.0	0.0	0.0	0.0	0.0	0.0	0.0
1964-65	0.0	0.0	0.0	0.0	0.1	0.0	0.0
1965-66	0.0	0.0	0.0	0.0	0.0	0.3	T
1966-67	0.0	0.0	0.0	0.0	0.0	T	0.0
1967-68	0.0	0.0	0.0	0.0	0.0	1.6	0.0
1968-69	0.0	0.0	0.0	0.0	0.0	0.4	0.0
1969-70	0.0	0.0	0.0	0.0	0.0	T	0.0
1970-71	0.0	0.0	0.0	0.0	0.0	0.0	T
1971-72	0.0	0.0	0.0	0.0	0.0	6.8	0.0
1972-73	0.0	0.0	0.0	0.0	0.0	0.0	T
1973-74	0.0	0.0	0.0	0.0	0.0	0.0	0.4
1974-75	0.0	0.0	0.0	0.0	0.0	T	0.0
1975-76	0.0	0.0	0.0	0.0	T	T	
RECORD MEAN	0.0	0.0	0.0	T	0.2	0.3	0.3

Heating Degree Days

Season	July	Aug	Sept	Oct	Nov	Dec	Jan
1955-56	0	0	0	0	198	288	268
1956-57	0	0	0	47	223	378	340
1957-58	0	0	0	41	314	306	416
#1958-59	0	0	0	27	215	284	340
1959-60	0	0	0	45	189	416	556
1960-61	0	0	0	37	183	486	381
1961-62	0	0	0	61	312	444	491
1962-63	0	0	0	13	137	336	515
1963-64	0	0	0	2	186	372	533
1964-65	0	0	0	5	293	383	348
1965-66	0	0	8	33	110	396	532
1966-67	0	0	0	20	126	386	416
1967-68	0	0	0	14	89	502	384
1968-69	0	0	0	4	204	440	288
1969-70	0	0	0	55	188	384	455
1970-71	0	0	0	58	143	403	445
1971-72	0	0	0	120	249	548	444
1972-73	0	0	0	96	358	489	533
1973-74	0	0	0	23	216	390	451
1974-75	0	0	0	53	218	552	465
1975-76	0	0	0	38	191	365	

Cooling Degree Days

Year	Jan	Feb	Mar	Apr	May	June	July
1969	0	0	15	87	348	477	658
1970	0	5	0	25	333	561	693
1971	6	0	45	51	152	493	706
1972	0	1	82	82	236	506	678
1973	0	0	0	21	272	495	603
1974	0	0	18	87	301	664	581
1975	0	0	4	11	184	471	604

Feb	Mar	Apr	May	June	Total
0.0	0.0	0.0	0.0	0.0	5.8
0.0	0.0	0.0	0.0	0.0	0.0
T	0.0	0.0	0.0	0.0	T
0.0	0.0	0.0	0.0	0.0	0.0
0.0	0.0	0.0	0.0	0.0	0.0
0.0	0.0	0.0	0.0	0.0	1.2
0.0	0.0	0.0	0.0	0.0	0.0
0.0	0.0	0.0	0.0	0.0	0.0
T	0.0	0.0	0.0	0.0	T
1.1	T	0.0	0.0	0.0	1.1
0.0	0.0	0.0	0.0	0.0	0.0
0.0	0.0	0.0	0.0	0.0	T
T	0.1	0.0	0.0	0.0	4.8
0.0	0.0	0.0	0.0	0.0	1.4
0.0	0.0	0.0	0.0	0.0	2.8
0.0	3.4	0.0	0.0	0.0	3.4
0.5	0.0	0.0	0.0	0.0	0.5
0.0	0.0	0.0	0.0	0.0	0.0
T	0.0	0.0	0.0	0.0	T
1.0	0.0	1.0	0.0	0.0	2.0
0.0	0.0	0.0	0.0	0.0	0.0
0.0	T	0.0	0.0	0.0	T
0.0	0.0	0.0	0.0	0.0	6.4
T	0.0	0.0	0.0	0.0	1.3
0.0	0.0	0.0	0.0	0.0	0.0
T	0.0	0.0	0.0	0.0	T
0.0	0.0	0.0	0.0	0.0	0.0
0.0	5.7	0.0	0.0	0.0	5.7
3.9	0.0	0.0	0.0	0.0	4.0
1.2	0.0	0.0	0.0	0.0	1.5
0.0	0.0	T	0.0	0.0	T
0.0	0.0	0.0	0.0	0.0	1.6
0.0	T	0.0	0.0	0.0	0.4
0.0	T	T	0.0	0.0	T
T	0.0	0.0	0.0	0.0	T
0.0	0.0	0.0	0.0	0.0	6.8
0.0	0.0	0.0	0.0	0.0	T
0.0	T	0.0	0.0	0.0	0.4
T	0.5	0.0	0.0	0.0	0.5
0.2	0.3	T	0.0	0.0	1.3

TUCSON, AZ

Feb	Mar	Apr	May	June	Total
468	167	84	0	0	1473
128	167	50	18	0	1351
252	329	100	0	0	1758
370	205	8	10	0	1459
493	136	68	5	0	1908
331	206	41	9	0	1674
285	357	5	7	0	1962
215	234	79	0	0	1529
497	321	107	27	0	2045
383	305	114	21	0	1852
473	166	26	0	0	1744
256	115	113	20	0	1452
170	200	91	0	0	1450
328	339	34	35	0	1672
224	274	132	8	0	1720
350	200	111	12	0	1722
259	73	50	0	0	1743
320	410	174	19	0	2399
362	161	49	5	0	1657
393	299	217	29	0	2226

Aug	Sept	Oct	Nov	Dec	Total
669	493	118	1	0	2866
620	347	68	4	0	2656
514	430	101	12	0	2510
563	414	150	1	0	2713
615	445	206	26	2	2685
564	387	185	1	0	2788
651	458	182	27	0	2592

Average Temperature

Year	Jan	Feb	Mar	Apr	May	June	July	Aug	Sept	Oct	Nov	Dec	Annual
1936	48.8	53.2	59.0	66.9	75.3	83.8	86.8	83.8	77.6	68.6	59.9	50.8	67.9
1937	41.2	52.8	56.0	62.8	73.8	81.2	86.3	86.0	81.8	71.0	59.4	54.3	67.2
1938	52.4	54.2	57.6	65.5	71.3	81.8	84.4	83.3	81.2	70.0	54.8	53.0	67.5
1939	50.4	45.5	59.2	67.2	74.0	82.6	87.2	84.6	79.4	67.5	62.2	56.2	68.0
#1940	52.6	52.8	59.6	65.4	76.0	83.4	87.2	84.4	80.8	70.7	56.8	56.5	68.9
1941	52.6	56.5	56.9	59.8	72.9	80.2	86.4	83.2	79.4	67.2	60.6	52.0	67.3
1942	53.0	50.8	55.8	63.6	73.1	82.9	89.8	85.2	81.6	69.4	63.2	54.2	68.5
1943	52.8	58.7	61.8	70.4	76.3	83.2	88.0	83.9	82.0	70.8	61.6	52.5	70.2
1944	50.4	50.7	56.4	63.0	73.4	80.6	87.4	86.4	79.6	72.8	55.9	52.3	67.4
1945	50.7	53.6	54.6	63.4	73.6	78.9	86.5	84.2	80.9	71.6	58.5	50.4	67.2
1946	48.0	52.0	59.4	70.6	73.0	85.4	86.0	84.0	80.9	65.9	54.8	55.6	68.0
1947	48.4	57.8	59.6	64.8	76.8	82.1	88.2	83.7	83.0	70.4	54.2	48.2	68.1
#1948	51.5	50.8	54.0	68.0	75.1	83.4	86.8	85.2	82.6	71.1	53.6	51.2	67.8
1949	43.0	50.2	57.6	67.4	73.4	83.0	85.0	84.2	82.2	66.4	64.3	50.8	67.3
1950	50.4	57.2	60.7	69.2	71.6	81.6	82.8	84.7	78.3	76.8	63.0	56.9	69.4
1951	50.3	53.7	57.4	64.4	74.0	80.5	88.8	84.9	83.2	72.5	58.5	51.5	68.3
1952	51.7	51.6	52.7	65.1	76.8	83.4	86.0	85.3	83.3	76.4	56.4	50.1	68.2
1953	53.9	52.2	60.6	65.2	68.9	84.1	86.8	86.4	82.9	71.0	61.6	48.6	68.5
1954	53.5	60.3	59.3	71.5	75.9	83.1	86.8	83.4	82.9	74.2	62.7	53.3	70.6
1955	46.7	48.8	59.6	64.4	71.8	82.3	84.6	81.8	81.2	74.3	58.5	55.5	67.4
1956	56.1	48.7	60.2	64.2	75.8	86.2	85.4	84.0	84.3	70.2	57.8	52.5	68.8
1957	53.8	61.1	59.6	66.2	71.2	85.3	88.1	84.2	81.3	67.9	54.3	54.9	69.0
#1958	51.4	55.8	54.2	64.5	79.1	84.9	86.9	84.5	80.5	71.9	57.8	55.6	68.9
1959	53.8	51.5	58.2	69.2	72.5	85.4	86.6	81.8	80.2	69.7	58.5	51.4	68.2
1960	46.8	47.8	61.0	65.7	71.9	83.5	86.0	84.2	81.2	67.3	59.2	49.1	67.0
1961	52.5	53.0	58.2	66.2	72.9	84.7	86.1	81.8	77.1	68.5	54.4	50.5	67.1
1962	49.0	54.7	53.3	70.1	71.7	80.3	84.9	87.0	81.3	70.6	61.5	54.0	68.2
1963	48.3	57.5	57.7	64.0	77.3	80.5	87.6	82.3	82.4	73.2	59.3	52.7	68.6
1964	47.5	47.7	54.8	63.2	73.2	82.0	86.2	81.6	76.3	72.1	55.2	52.4	66.0
1965	53.6	51.1	55.1	64.5	70.1	77.6	85.0	84.0	76.8	71.9	62.6	52.1	67.1
1966	47.7	47.8	60.1	66.8	76.1	82.8	85.3	82.9	78.3	68.1	61.1	52.4	67.4
1967	51.4	55.6	62.1	62.1	71.9	80.7	85.4	84.6	80.7	71.6	62.9	48.6	68.1
1968	52.4	59.1	58.7	63.2	73.3	83.5	84.9	81.3	80.7	71.7	58.3	50.6	68.1
1969	55.5	53.1	54.3	66.6	74.9	80.7	86.1	86.3	81.2	66.8	58.6	52.4	68.0
1970	50.0	57.0	55.9	61.1	75.2	83.4	87.2	84.8	76.4	65.1	60.1	51.8	67.3
1971	50.5	52.3	59.8	62.8	69.3	81.2	87.5	81.3	79.1	64.2	56.8	47.1	66.0
1972	50.4	55.8	65.0	65.8	72.3	81.6	86.6	82.9	78.6	66.5	53.0	49.0	67.3
1973	47.6	53.4	51.6	59.7	73.0	81.4	84.3	84.7	79.6	70.7	58.4	52.3	66.4
1974	50.2	51.9	60.1	66.1	74.3	86.9	83.5	83.0	77.8	69.1	57.5	47.0	67.3
1975	49.8	50.7	55.3	57.9	69.8	80.5	84.2	85.8	80.0	69.5	59.3	53.0	66.3
RECORD MEAN	50.2	53.0	57.7	64.4	72.6	81.9	86.0	83.9	79.9	69.4	58.1	51.2	67.4
MAX	64.4	67.5	73.0	80.7	89.5	98.7	99.1	96.6	94.0	84.9	73.2	65.2	82.2
MIN	36.0	38.5	42.4	48.1	55.6	65.1	72.8	71.2	65.8	53.8	43.0	37.1	52.5

Precipitation

\# Indicates a station move or relocation of instruments.

Year	Jan	Feb	Mar	Apr	May	June	July	Aug	Sept	Oct	Nov	Dec	Annual
1936	0.96	0.92	0.55	0.07	T	0.06	2.82	3.03	1.51	0.34	1.13	0.85	12.24
1937	1.62	0.23	0.63	0.01	0.25	T	2.06	1.29	1.43	0.05	0.19	0.67	8.43
1938	0.65	0.88	0.43	0.08	0.11	2.07	0.78	2.37	0.50	0.00	0.09	0.93	8.89
1939	0.35	1.60	0.69	0.04	0.00	T	0.61	1.24	1.53	0.18	0.54	0.27	7.05
#1940	0.45	1.42	0.04	0.21	0.52	1.19	0.68	3.51	1.89	0.17	1.75	3.07	14.90
1941	1.43	2.27	1.46	1.06	0.74	T	2.51	1.99	1.20	0.53	0.65	2.01	15.85
1942	0.50	1.92	0.23	0.79	0.00	0.00	0.68	0.90	1.78	0.60	T	0.47	7.87
1943	0.44	0.39	1.27	0.03	0.89	0.13	1.09	3.04	3.59	0.25	0.00	0.79	11.91
1944	0.36	1.10	1.01	0.56	0.37	0.04	1.77	1.78	2.08	1.13	1.78	1.55	13.53
1945	0.58	0.47	0.53	0.11	0.00	0.00	2.84	4.31	0.14	1.13	0.00	0.47	10.58
1946	2.22	0.22	0.50	0.14	0.00	0.04	2.44	3.61	2.26	0.82	1.10	0.46	13.81
1947	0.14	0.02	0.39	T	0.04	0.05	0.27	2.24	0.47	0.80	0.70	0.41	5.53
#1948	T	2.00	0.29	T	0.00	0.06	3.02	1.08	1.11	0.56	0.06	0.93	9.11
1949	1.19	0.20	0.19	0.38	0.00	0.02	1.42	1.92	0.81	0.52	0.17	0.84	7.66
1950	0.30	1.48	0.26	T	0.01	1.24	3.72	0.86	1.15	T	T	0.27	9.29
1951	1.12	0.13	0.12	1.66	0.01	T	1.49	2.66	0.34	1.91	1.27	0.99	11.70
1952	0.24	0.08	2.26	1.51	0.02	0.30	3.25	1.56	0.80	0.00	1.90	0.73	12.65
1953	0.06	0.96	0.60	0.06	T	0.03	2.87	0.46	0.00	T	0.18	0.12	5.34
1954	0.78	0.75	1.01	0.00	0.47	1.46	2.03	2.00	3.05	0.02	0.00	0.06	11.63
1955	1.89	0.19	0.03	T	0.03	0.03	5.10	7.93	0.05	0.32	T	0.33	15.90
1956	1.08	0.54	0.00	0.31	T	0.36	2.77	1.12	0.37	0.27	T	0.22	7.04
1957	2.37	0.36	0.93	0.16	0.33	0.17	1.25	3.92	T	2.62	0.56	0.89	13.56
1958	T	1.15	1.82	0.48	0.02	0.51	5.20	0.91	0.21	1.21	1.09	0.00	12.60
1959	0.03	0.28	T	0.01	0.00	T	3.92	2.79	T	0.70	0.29	1.97	9.99
1960	2.01	0.42	0.25	0.00	0.08	0.25	0.73	2.09	1.20	0.71	0.07	0.93	8.74
1961	0.95	0.01	0.41	T	0.00	0.26	1.81	4.28	0.51	0.65	0.44	1.57	10.89
1962	1.39	0.33	0.25	T	0.00	0.25	1.38	0.48	2.86	0.22	0.49	0.93	8.58
1963	0.59	0.81	0.34	0.32	T	T	1.66	2.86	1.45	0.60	1.26	0.08	9.97
1964	0.14	0.13	0.81	0.67	0.00	0.01	4.82	3.90	5.11	0.91	0.68	0.81	17.99
1965	0.45	0.64	0.27	0.23	T	0.01	2.13	1.12	0.82	0.07	0.77	5.02	11.53
1966	1.74	2.25	0.19	0.12	0.11	0.02	2.57	3.31	3.53	0.32	0.06	0.19	14.41
1967	0.04	0.13	0.41	0.29	0.62	0.42	2.72	2.00	1.35	1.03	0.48	3.44	12.93
1968	0.18	0.99	1.79	0.62	T	0.00	1.97	1.12	T	0.09	1.86	0.32	8.94
1969	0.74	0.50	0.34	0.60	0.46	0.00	1.51	2.57	1.31	0.03	1.06	0.82	9.94
1970	T	0.34	1.13	0.45	0.03	0.33	2.53	1.43	3.58	1.73	0.00	0.43	11.98
1971	0.04	0.50	T	0.56	0.01	T	2.18	3.29	1.75	1.18	0.69	1.97	12.17
1972	0.00	0.00	0.01	0.00	0.24	0.68	3.49	2.93	1.09	4.51	1.30	0.61	14.86
1973	0.06	1.60	2.20	0.02	0.09	0.50	1.74	0.54	T	0.00	0.47	0.00	7.22
1974	0.93	T	0.55	T	0.00	0.01	4.44	1.04	1.69	2.12	0.81	0.33	11.92
1975	0.36	0.13	0.95	0.27	0.11	0.00	2.38	0.32	1.26	T	0.34	0.52	6.64
RECORD MEAN	0.77	0.80	0.71	0.36	0.18	0.26	2.26	2.14	1.27	0.62	0.77	1.01	11.15

Record mean values above are means through the current year for the period beginning in 1900 for temperature and precipitation, 1941 for snowfall. Temperature and precipitation are from the University of Arizona location through May 1940 and from Airport locations thereafter. Heating degree days from Airport locations for the entire period of the table.

(Continued)

hot weather makes evaporative air coolers effective most of the time.

Tucson lies in the zone receiving more sunshine than any other section of the United States; the persistence of the bright sunshine is one of the most noteworthy features of this desert climate. Cloudless days are commonplace, and average cloudiness, much of it being very thin cirriform clouds, is low.

Surface winds are generally light, with no important seasonal changes in either velocities or prevailing direction. Occasional windstorms cause localized duststorms, particularly in the outlying sections of Tucson where the ground has been disturbed in numerous development areas. During the spring months, winds may briefly be strong enough to cause some damage to trees and buildings. Wind velocities and directions are influenced to an important extent by the surrounding mountains, as well as by the general slope of the terrain. With weak pressure gradients, local winds tend to be in the SE quadrant during the night and early morning hours, veering to NW during the day. Highest velocities usually occur with winds from the SW and E to S.

While dust and haze of local origin are frequently visible, their effect on the general clarity of the atmosphere is not great. Visibility values are normally high; and fog is extremely rare.

QUOTES FROM WEATHER FOLKLORE —

A severe autumn denotes a windy summer,
a windy winter a rainy spring,
A rainy spring a severe summer,
A severe summer a windy autumn;
So that the air in balance is
Seldom debtor unto itself. — *Bacon.*

Station: LITTLE ROCK, ARKANSAS
ADAMS FIELD

Elevation (ground): 257 feet

TEMPERATURES °F

Month	Normal Daily maximum	Normal Daily minimum	Normal Monthly	Extremes Record highest	Year	Record lowest	Year
(a)				16		16	
J	50.1	28.9	39.5	81	1969	-4	1962
F	53.8	31.9	42.9	83	1962	10	1963
M	61.8	38.7	50.3	91	1974	17	1965
A	73.5	49.9	61.7	90	1965	28	1971
M	81.4	58.1	69.8	98	1964	40	1971
J	89.3	66.8	78.1	102	1963	46	1969
J	92.6	70.1	81.4	105	1974	54	1972
A	92.6	68.6	80.6	108	1964	52	1967
S	85.8	60.8	73.3	102	1963	38	1967
O	76.0	48.7	62.4	97	1963	31	1965
N	62.4	38.1	50.3	85	1964	17	1975
D	52.1	31.1	41.6	79	1970	-1	1963
YR	72.6	49.3	61.0	108	AUG 1964	-4	JAN 1962

IMPORTANT:
The time-period covered by this record is limited: See footnotes on next page for explanation and for additional history of EXTREME HIGHS AND LOWS recorded in the general area.

Little Rock is located on the Arkansas River near the geographical center of the State. It is situated on the dividing line between the Ouachita Mountains to the west and the flat lowlands comprising the Mississippi River Valley to the east. Elevations range from 222 feet at the river level to 257 feet over much of the flat land, including the airport in the southeast, to near 600 feet in the hilly residential area of the western portions of the City. Two minor temperature variations are observed due to the terrain: (1) somewhat lower minimum temperatures are observed in the airport vicinity; and, (2) a slight downslope adiabatic heating effect accompanies airflow from the ridges and hills in the west and northwest.

The modified continental climate of Little Rock includes exposure to all of the North American airmass types. However, with its proximity to the Gulf of Mexico the summer season is marked by prolonged periods of warm and humid weather. The growing season averages 233 days in which 62 percent of the normal precipitation occurs. Winters are mild, but polar and arctic outbreaks are not uncommon.

Precipitation is fairly well distributed throughout the year. Summer rainfall is almost completely of the convective and airmass variety with the driest period occurring in the late summer and early fall. The combination of active fronts, plus ample moisture during the winter and early spring months results in abundant rain amounts. Snow is almost a negligible form of precipitation. On an average of one out of every four or five winters, seasonal snowfall accumulates to less than 1 inch on the ground. Glaze and ice storms, although infrequent, are at times severe. Warm front weather characterized by shallow surface cold air flow from the north under warm moist Gulf air results in excellent conditions for the production of freezing precipitation.

LITTLE ROCK, ARKANSAS

Normals, Means, and Extremes

(To better understand these tables, see full explanation of terms beginning on page 322)

Month	Normal Degree days Base 65 °F: Heating	Cooling	Precipitation in inches, Water equivalent: Normal	Maximum monthly	Year	Minimum monthly	Year	Maximum in 24 hrs.	Year	Snow, Ice pellets: Maximum monthly	Year	Maximum in 24 hrs.	Year	Relative humidity pct. Hour 00 (Local time)	Hour 06	Hour 12	Hour 18
(a)				34		34		34		34		34		15	15	15	15
J	791	0	4.24	12.53	1950	0.75	1961	5.18	1969	12.0	1966	11.3	1960	77	82	62	65
F	619	0	4.42	11.02	1956	0.51	1947	5.15	1950	9.6	1966	9.6	1966	74	79	57	58
M	470	14	4.93	9.49	1953	0.73	1966	3.40	1944	7.0	1971	6.7	1971	71	78	56	55
A	139	40	5.25	14.20	1973	1.05	1960	7.96	1974	T	1973	T	1973	74	82	56	56
M	21	169	5.30	12.74	1968	0.69	1970	7.71	1955	0.0		0.0		82	87	57	58
J	0	393	3.50	7.82	1974	T	1952	4.61	1960	0.0		0.0		82	86	54	57
J	0	508	3.38	7.60	1951	0.86	1942	3.41	1959	0.0		0.0		84	88	58	61
A	0	484	3.01	14.46	1966	0.26	1968	7.32	1966	0.0		0.0		84	88	57	61
S	5	254	3.55	9.09	1973	0.28	1956	4.05	1967	0.0		0.0		86	90	60	66
O	143	63	2.99	9.68	1949	0.01	1944	4.07	1949	0.0		0.0		82	86	52	63
N	441	0	3.86	9.54	1957	0.28	1949	5.07	1957	4.8	1971	4.8	1971	78	83	58	64
D	725	0	4.09	8.33	1944	1.26	1958	3.63	1971	9.8	1963	9.8	1963	78	82	63	67
YR	3354	1925	48.52	14.46	AUG 1966	T	JUN 1952	7.96	APR 1974	12.0	JAN 1966	11.3	JAN 1960	79	84	57	61

Month	Wind: Mean speed m.p.h.	Prevailing direction	Fastest mile: Speed m.p.h.	Direction	Year	Pct. of possible sunshine	Mean sky cover, tenths, sunrise to sunset	Mean number of days, Sunrise to sunset: Clear	Partly cloudy	Cloudy	Precipitation .01 inch or more	Snow, Ice pellets 1.0 inch or more	Thunderstorms	Heavy fog, visibility ¼ mile or less	Temperatures °F Max.: 90° and above (b)	32° and below	Min.: 32° and below	0° and below	Average station pressure mb. Elev. 265 feet m.s.l.
(a)	33	15	34	34		32	33	33	33	33	33	33	33	33	15	15	15	15	3
J	8.9	S	44	S	1950	46	6.6	8	6	17	10	1	2	3	0	4	20	*	1010.5
F	9.4	SW	57	SW	1971	54	6.0	9	5	14	9	*	2	2	0	*	15	0	1009.3
M	10.1	WNW	56	SE	1959	57	6.2	9	7	15	11	*	5	1	*	*	5	0	1004.6
A	9.6	S	65	NW	1961	61	6.1	9	7	14	10	0	7	1	*	0	1	0	1006.2
M	8.1	S	61	NW	1952	68	6.0	8	11	12	10	0	7	1	4	0	0	0	1003.5
J	7.6	SSW	60	NE	1953	73	5.3	10	11	9	8	0	8	*	17	0	0	0	1005.2
J	7.0	SW	56	NW	1960	71	5.6	9	13	9	8	0	9	1	22	0	0	0	1006.2
A	6.6	SW	54	NW	1956	73	5.0	12	10	9	7	0	6	1	19	0	0	0	1007.5
S	7.0	NE	50	NW	1952	68	5.1	12	8	10	7	0	4	1	8	0	0	0	1008.0
O	7.0	SW	58	SSW	1956	69	4.4	15	7	9	6	0	2	2	2	0	*	0	1010.6
N	8.2	SW	49	SW	1952	56	5.5	11	6	13	8	*	3	2	0	0	6	0	1009.8
D	8.5	SW	48	SW	1971	48	6.3	9	6	16	9	*	2	2	0	1	16	*	1009.7
YR	8.2	SW	65	NW	APR 1961	63	5.7	121	97	147	104	2	58	16	71	5	63	*	1007.6

FOOTNOTES

Means and extremes above are from existing and comparable exposures. Annual extremes have been exceeded at other sites in the locality as follows: Highest temperature 110 in August 1936; lowest temperature -13 in February 1899; maximum monthly precipitation 18.04 in January 1937; maximum precipitation in 24 hours 9.58 in April 1913; maximum monthly snowfall 19.4 in January 1918; maximum snowfall in 24 hours 13.0 in January 1893.

Note: Precipitation and Sunshine data are from North Little Rock Airport beginning December 15, 1975.

Snowfall

Season	July	Aug	Sept	Oct	Nov	Dec	Jan
1936-37	0.0	0.0	0.0	0.0	T	T	T
1937-38	0.0	0.0	0.0	0.0	T	0.1	T
1938-39	0.0	0.0	0.0	0.0	T	T	0.0
1939-40	0.0	0.0	0.0	0.0	0.0	0.1	5.8
1940-41	0.0	0.0	0.0	0.0	0.0	0.0	0.4
#1941-42	0.0	0.0	0.0	0.0	0.0	T	2.7
1942-43	0.0	0.0	0.0	0.0	0.0	T	2.2
1943-44	0.0	0.0	0.0	0.0	0.0	T	5.5
1944-45	0.0	0.0	0.0	0.0	0.0	T	T
1945-46	0.0	0.0	0.0	0.0	0.0	2.0	2.9
1946-47	0.0	0.0	0.0	0.0	0.0	2.5	T
1947-48	0.0	0.0	0.0	0.0	0.0	0.5	4.8
1948-49	0.0	0.0	0.0	0.0	T	T	3.0
1949-50	0.0	0.0	0.0	0.0	0.0	T	2.3
1950-51	0.0	0.0	0.0	0.0	T	1.3	3.2
1951-52	0.0	0.0	0.0	0.0	0.4	T	0.0
1952-53	0.0	0.0	0.0	0.0	1.0	T	T
1953-54	0.0	0.0	0.0	0.0	0.0	T	4.0
1954-55	0.0	0.0	0.0	0.0	0.0	T	0.5
1955-56	0.0	0.0	0.0	0.0	0.0	T	2.8
1956-57	0.0	0.0	0.0	0.0	0.0	0.0	T
1957-58	0.0	0.0	0.0	0.0	0.8	T	T
1958-59	0.0	0.0	0.0	0.0	0.2	5.0	0.2
1959-60	0.0	0.0	0.0	0.0	0.0	T	11.6
1960-61	0.0	0.0	0.0	0.0	0.0	6.0	T
1961-62	0.0	0.0	0.0	0.0	T	T	6.0
1962-63	0.0	0.0	0.0	0.0	0.0	1.5	0.7
1963-64	0.0	0.0	0.0	0.0	0.0	9.8	T
1964-65	0.0	0.0	0.0	0.0	0.0	0.2	T
1965-66	0.0	0.0	0.0	0.0	0.0	0.0	12.0
1966-67	0.0	0.0	0.0	0.0	T	0.2	1.6
1967-68	0.0	0.0	0.0	0.0	T	1.1	1.0
1968-69	0.0	0.0	0.0	0.0	0.0	0.0	T
1969-70	0.0	0.0	0.0	0.0	T	T	4.0
1970-71	0.0	0.0	0.0	0.0	0.0	T	T
1971-72	0.0	0.0	0.0	0.0	4.8	0.6	0.1
1972-73	0.0	0.0	0.0	0.0	T	0.7	2.6
1973-74	0.0	0.0	0.0	0.0	0.0	T	0.3
1974-75	0.0	0.0	0.0	0.0	T	T	1.4
1975-76	0.0	0.0	0.0	0.0	0.2	1.0	
RECORD MEAN	0.0	0.0	0.0	0.0	0.2	1.0	2.2

Heating Degree Days

Season	July	Aug	Sept	Oct	Nov	Dec	Jan
1955-56	0	0	0	124	459	693	769
1956-57	0	0	0	32	433	492	773
1957-58	0	0	0	164	378	487	753
1958-59	0	0	10	115	314	755	776
#1959-60	0	0	0	106	543	562	733
1960-61	0	0	0	103	431	841	894
1961-62	0	0	10	120	425	719	857
1962-63	0	0	17	78	421	714	954
1963-64	0	0	4	26	350	973	742
1964-65	0	0	14	175	336	646	639
1965-66	0	0	19	137	257	561	916
1966-67	0	0	3	198	309	679	717
1967-68	0	0	39	162	472	685	840
1968-69	0	0	3	124	412	700	665
1969-70	0	0	0	175	458	745	905
1970-71	0	0	4	153	442	554	737
1971-72	0	0	9	6	437	466	659
1972-73	0	0	8	142	530	736	777
1973-74	0	0	2	61	261	680	690
1974-75	0	0	23	111	401	634	630
1975-76	0	0	48	130	414	681	

Cooling Degree Days

Year	Jan	Feb	Mar	Apr	May	June	July
1969	4	0	0	21	176	386	622
1970	3	0	0	77	243	416	471
1971	0	0	11	19	79	435	470
1972	2	0	3	81	174	440	484
1973	0	0	14	41	135	415	506
1974	0	0	45	37	206	288	572
1975	6	0	4	73	245	416	475

Feb	Mar	Apr	May	June	Total
T	1.2	0.0	0.0	0.0	1.2
T	0.0	0.0	0.0	0.0	0.1
1.0	0.0	0.0	0.0	0.0	1.0
3.0	0.0	0.0	0.0	0.0	8.9
3.3	T	0.0	0.0	0.0	3.7
0.5	6.2	0.0	0.0	0.0	9.4
0.7	T	0.0	0.0	0.0	2.9
T	0.0	0.0	0.0	0.0	5.5
0.3	0.0	0.0	0.0	0.0	0.3
3.4	0.0	0.0	0.0	0.0	8.3
1.3	0.7	0.0	0.0	0.0	4.5
T	T	0.0	0.0	0.0	5.3
0.0	T	0.0	0.0	0.0	3.0
T	T	0.0	0.0	0.0	2.3
0.1	0.1	0.0	0.0	0.0	4.7
0.6	0.0	0.0	0.0	0.0	1.0
0.0	0.0	0.0	0.0	0.0	1.0
0.0	0.0	0.0	0.0	0.0	4.0
0.8	T	0.0	0.0	0.0	1.3
T	T	0.0	0.0	0.0	2.8
0.0	T	T	0.0	0.0	T
4.2	T	0.0	0.0	0.0	5.0
T	T	0.0	0.0	0.0	5.4
9.6	5.4	0.0	0.0	0.0	26.6
T	0.0	0.0	0.0	0.0	6.0
T	T	0.0	0.0	0.0	6.0
0.4	T	0.0	0.0	0.0	2.6
0.0	T	0.0	0.0	0.0	9.8
2.9	4.3	0.0	0.0	0.0	7.4
9.6	0.0	0.0	0.0	0.0	21.6
T	T	0.0	0.0	0.0	1.8
4.3	T	0.0	0.0	0.0	6.4
2.3	T	0.0	0.0	0.0	2.3
T	T	0.0	0.0	0.0	4.0
0.7	7.0	T	0.0	0.0	7.7
0.3	0.0	0.0	0.0	0.0	5.8
T	0.0	T	0.0	0.0	3.3
T	0.0	0.0	0.0	0.0	0.3
0.4	2.4	0.0	0.0	0.0	4.2
1.3	0.6	T	0.0	0.0	5.3

Average Temperature

Year	Jan	Feb	Mar	Apr	May	June	July	Aug	Sept	Oct	Nov	Dec	Annual
1936	38.2	36.8	58.0	59.8	72.2	80.6	82.6	84.9	79.4	62.2	49.6	46.1	62.5
1937	41.8	44.2	48.8	62.0	71.9	79.7	80.6	83.0	73.5	61.0	48.7	43.0	61.5
1938	43.0	51.0	60.6	62.8	71.0	76.6	82.8	84.0	76.6	68.0	51.4	44.6	64.4
1939	46.2	44.0	56.6	59.6	69.8	78.8	82.4	80.8	80.8	66.0	50.0	47.0	63.5
1940	29.0	42.5	52.4	60.4	67.5	76.0	78.8	78.6	72.6	66.6	51.0	48.2	60.3
1941	44.3	41.0	47.8	64.7	72.5	77.0	81.4	81.4	76.1	68.7	51.2	45.8	62.7
#1942	39.8	42.0	54.1	63.2	68.8	78.2	82.6	79.4	72.4	63.8	54.3	43.1	61.8
1943	42.0	48.6	47.3	63.2	72.6	81.6	84.4	85.4	72.2	62.1	49.8	40.5	62.5
1944	42.6	48.9	51.6	61.0	71.4	81.0	82.7	81.0	75.7	65.4	52.9	38.0	62.7
1945	40.8	43.5	59.6	63.9	67.1	76.7	79.3	80.0	74.4	61.4	53.8	38.0	61.5
1946	41.7	48.5	59.4	65.6	67.4	76.8	81.5	79.8	72.5	64.1	54.2	49.2	63.4
1947	43.9	38.1	45.7	62.4	68.6	77.8	79.3	85.0	75.8	69.7	48.2	45.4	61.7
1948	34.9	42.2	51.8	67.5	69.9	79.6	82.0	79.2	73.8	61.2	52.5	45.8	61.7
1949	43.6	47.6	52.0	62.0	73.0	79.5	82.2	79.0	70.1	64.4	54.1	45.9	62.8
1950	49.7	47.7	49.9	60.6	71.2	77.8	78.8	77.0	71.2	67.1	48.4	38.8	61.5
1951	43.2	45.9	52.5	59.2	71.0	77.6	81.9	82.8	72.6	63.7	46.0	45.0	61.8
1952	47.9	49.9	51.1	59.3	70.5	84.2	83.6	82.0	73.2	57.0	50.2	44.0	62.7
1953	46.9	46.6	57.1	59.0	71.8	85.0	81.9	81.5	77.1	66.3	51.0	42.2	63.9
1954	41.8	51.7	52.8	67.8	66.6	82.3	86.7	87.2	78.7	65.0	52.7	44.2	64.8
1955	42.5	44.6	54.1	67.0	73.2	74.7	83.4	81.4	77.5	63.6	50.9	42.5	62.9
1956	40.0	47.5	53.0	60.9	74.0	78.2	82.7	83.5	74.1	67.4	50.6	49.4	63.4
1957	39.8	50.4	51.1	62.9	72.4	78.8	82.7	80.2	72.6	60.9	52.2	49.1	62.7
1958	40.5	38.9	46.6	61.6	71.5	77.5	81.9	81.2	74.8	63.2	54.7	40.4	61.0
1959	39.7	45.1	53.1	62.2	74.8	77.4	79.6	81.9	75.2	64.1	47.0	46.6	62.2
#1960	41.1	39.9	41.3	64.9	68.4	78.4	80.7	81.4	76.3	63.5	50.7	37.6	60.4
1961	35.9	47.7	55.9	60.4	67.9	75.8	80.7	78.8	74.3	63.4	51.1	41.7	61.1
1962	37.2	49.2	49.5	59.5	75.3	77.7	81.9	82.8	73.2	66.3	50.7	41.8	62.1
1963	34.0	39.4	57.7	64.3	71.4	80.4	81.5	81.1	74.7	70.1	53.3	33.4	61.8
1964	40.8	41.6	52.7	64.7	72.3	80.6	83.2	79.3	73.7	60.1	54.0	43.9	62.3
1965	44.2	43.2	44.5	65.8	72.7	78.2	82.9	81.7	74.3	61.6	56.5	46.7	62.7
1966	35.4	42.9	54.6	62.4	68.4	78.0	84.2	77.9	72.0	59.2	54.8	43.2	61.1
1967	41.7	40.4	58.9	66.7	68.6	79.5	77.9	75.5	69.0	60.9	49.1	42.7	60.9
1968	37.7	38.0	50.8	60.9	67.6	77.8	77.8	81.4	70.7	62.9	51.2	42.2	59.9
1969	43.5	43.0	45.5	61.8	69.9	77.6	84.8	79.0	72.9	62.4	49.4	40.7	60.9
1970	35.7	42.1	48.2	63.1	71.9	78.7	79.9	81.2	78.1	61.5	50.3	47.2	61.5
1971	41.0	44.4	50.0	59.4	65.6	79.3	80.0	78.0	76.4	69.3	50.5	49.9	62.0
1972	43.6	46.7	53.3	62.5	69.8	79.4	80.4	81.1	75.8	62.6	47.3	41.0	62.0
1973	39.7	42.1	58.2	59.9	68.2	78.6	81.1	80.4	75.7	67.6	56.6	42.8	62.6
1974	42.4	45.7	58.1	60.7	71.3	74.3	83.2	79.0	69.0	62.3	51.9	44.4	61.9
1975	44.6	44.6	48.7	60.7	72.5	78.6	80.2	79.5	69.2	63.0	51.4	42.9	61.3
RECORD MEAN	41.7	44.8	52.9	62.5	70.1	78.2	81.3	80.5	74.1	63.8	51.9	43.8	62.1
MAX	50.3	53.9	62.6	72.4	79.8	87.8	90.8	90.2	84.3	74.5	61.5	52.3	71.7
MIN	33.1	35.6	43.2	52.5	60.4	68.5	71.8	70.8	63.9	53.1	42.2	35.3	52.5

# Indicates a station move or relocation of instruments.

LITTLE ROCK, AR

Feb	Mar	Apr	May	June	Total
506	386	167	12	0	3116
409	427	140	22	0	2728
725	562	132	26	0	3227
550	364	146	4	0	3034
723	729	83	64	0	3543
480	295	200	44	0	3288
445	471	198	5	0	3250
709	258	97	35	0	3283
673	376	71	9	0	3224
604	629	70	0	0	3113
611	327	115	42	0	2985
682	240	52	33	0	2913
778	440	147	30	0	3593
611	595	108	16	1	3235
636	516	124	23	0	3582
571	470	182	55	0	3168
525	360	149	20	0	2631
637	216	186	28	0	3260
533	255	163	4	0	2649
566	499	196	5	0	3065

Aug	Sept	Oct	Nov	Dec	Total
439	243	100	0	0	1991
511	404	51	9	9	2194
411	355	146	10	3	1939
507	341	76	3	0	2111
485	330	147	17	0	2090
441	148	36	14	0	1787
455	178	73	14	2	1941

Precipitation

Year	Jan	Feb	Mar	Apr	May	June	July	Aug	Sept	Oct	Nov	Dec	Annual
1936	0.93	1.30	2.35	3.10	1.24	3.27	7.51	0.27	1.92	4.42	3.67	4.90	34.88
1937	18.04	2.00	2.22	1.90	2.78	1.66	1.62	4.68	5.75	5.00	3.74	3.57	52.96
1938	9.80	4.87	7.18	4.04	3.42	2.92	2.50	3.46	0.99	1.37	6.07	3.34	49.96
1939	7.86	8.59	2.47	7.97	6.95	3.14	2.11	2.92	2.36	0.66	3.93	1.41	50.37
1940	1.40	3.21	1.31	5.58	3.10	2.26	1.60	3.55	2.17	1.91	5.55	3.02	34.66
1941	2.15	2.65	1.58	4.97	4.10	5.99	5.97	3.15	2.40	6.10	1.29	4.94	45.29
#1942	2.72	3.52	4.14	10.76	3.76	3.94	0.86	4.95	1.07	3.34	2.76	4.71	46.53
1943	1.20	0.96	7.61	4.57	4.41	2.81	1.85	0.40	2.19	4.40	0.81	3.34	34.55
1944	2.06	5.98	7.86	4.71	5.02	1.54	3.35	2.82	1.07	0.01	6.08	8.33	48.83
1945	2.26	7.41	6.99	6.61	6.99	7.79	4.57	2.99	9.01	2.20	4.53	1.91	63.26
1946	8.22	3.09	8.22	4.81	9.67	3.39	2.56	0.69	0.83	2.56	7.88	3.23	55.15
1947	2.14	0.51	1.53	6.10	6.87	4.95	1.03	1.09	2.96	5.57	6.27	4.34	43.36
1948	1.56	7.14	6.43	4.54	4.56	2.25	3.41	3.31	1.20	3.11	8.00	2.70	48.21
1949	11.91	4.04	7.33	2.07	2.37	5.71	3.55	6.01	2.75	9.68	0.28	4.78	60.48
1950	12.53	9.27	4.90	2.75	8.37	2.07	1.87	7.59	6.77	1.29	3.90	1.55	62.86
1951	4.32	4.06	1.98	3.81	1.60	4.89	7.60	0.80	4.00	3.73	4.35	5.29	46.43
1952	3.49	5.02	5.61	4.06	4.69	T	2.85	2.50	2.55	0.58	6.84	5.39	43.58
1953	6.11	3.29	9.49	7.28	6.19	0.12	1.19	2.67	1.14	1.02	1.72	2.95	43.17
1954	7.76	3.80	2.14	4.13	6.74	0.63	1.27	0.33	1.78	3.64	1.45	4.15	37.82
1955	1.49	4.24	4.75	3.70	11.55	3.84	2.17	1.22	4.75	1.17	1.80	1.93	42.61
1956	5.77	11.02	3.81	4.64	3.21	5.08	5.47	2.25	0.28	3.04	5.12	2.65	52.34
1957	5.95	5.32	5.12	11.34	11.58	3.39	2.80	4.31	1.96	5.42	9.54	3.88	70.61
1958	4.41	1.93	4.20	8.21	7.84	7.20	3.58	3.80	7.18	0.31	5.35	1.26	55.27
1959	3.58	7.10	3.33	2.57	1.66	6.16	6.36	3.29	7.02	2.07	2.34	8.12	53.60
1960	4.21	4.37	3.67	1.05	5.29	7.25	2.38	2.17	6.23	2.96	1.77	4.09	45.44
1961	0.75	3.65	8.07	3.38	5.68	1.48	2.64	3.14	1.60	0.85	6.11	7.15	44.50
1962	6.84	7.19	5.17	2.90	2.31	6.26	3.10	2.40	3.83	3.54	1.69	1.65	46.88
1963	0.87	2.70	3.81	3.29	1.29	1.25	5.54	0.62	1.81	0.10	4.50	2.48	28.26
1964	0.98	2.87	8.22	11.06	1.40	0.31	3.79	3.71	5.46	0.37	3.70	4.37	46.24
1965	4.45	5.73	3.63	1.19	5.42	2.49	2.51	2.03	7.67	0.21	1.54	2.05	38.92
1966	3.03	5.02	0.73	7.29	2.23	0.69	3.54	14.46	1.42	1.95	3.08	4.21	47.65
1967	2.13	2.31	3.11	7.58	8.69	3.02	4.29	1.73	6.25	4.96	1.73	4.95	50.75
1968	4.76	1.08	5.55	4.85	12.74	6.77	5.98	0.26	5.99	2.81	5.30	4.56	60.65
1969	8.06	2.41	3.65	4.30	3.60	2.98	3.40	2.73	2.33	3.60	3.94	8.10	49.10
1970	1.05	4.57	4.87	7.99	0.69	2.30	3.02	2.15	2.82	7.68	2.09	3.85	43.08
1971	2.07	2.21	3.24	1.70	5.37	7.66	4.01	8.62	0.78	2.55	3.38	6.97	48.56
1972	1.71	1.55	3.32	1.81	2.07	2.62	1.77	3.58	6.43	7.63	7.38	5.14	45.01
1973	5.64	2.95	7.89	14.20	3.96	2.66	6.59	1.26	9.09	5.93	9.03	5.19	74.39
1974	5.77	2.60	2.07	9.76	6.26	7.82	4.09	3.20	4.31	3.36	5.73	2.99	57.96
1975	4.64	4.38	7.67	4.14	5.87	1.56	3.98	2.73	1.86	1.62	3.68	2.95	45.08
RECORD MEAN	4.69	3.93	4.65	5.12	4.92	3.64	3.43	3.34	3.31	2.88	4.10	4.16	48.17

Record mean values above are means through the current year for the period beginning in 1880 for temperature and precipitation, 1943 for snowfall. Data are from City Office locations through March 1942.

EUREKA, CALIFORNIA

Station: EUREKA, CALIFORNIA
POST OFFICE BLDG.
Elevation (ground) 43 feet

TEMPERATURES °F

Month	Normal			Extremes			
	Daily maximum	Daily minimum	Monthly	Record highest	Year	Record lowest	Year
(a)				65		65	
J	53.5	41.1	47.3	75	1943	25	1937
F	54.4	42.3	48.4	85	1930	27	1962
M	54.1	42.5	48.3	78	1914	29	1917
A	54.9	44.4	49.7	79	1918	32	1929
M	57.2	47.8	52.5	84	1939	36	1954
J	59.6	50.7	55.2	85	1945	41	1966
J	60.4	52.1	56.3	76	1931	45	1924
A	61.2	52.7	57.0	82	1968	44	1935
S	61.9	51.2	56.6	85	1958	41	1946
O	60.4	48.4	54.4	82	1917	32	1971
N	57.9	45.5	51.7	77	1950	29	1935
D	54.6	42.6	48.6	77	1963	21	1972
YR	57.5	46.8	52.2	85	SEP 1958	21	DEC 1972

IMPORTANT:
The time-period covered by this record is limited: See footnotes following table of NORMALS, MEANS AND EXTREMES for explanation and for additional history of EXTREME HIGHS AND LOWS recorded in the general area.

Humboldt Bay is 1/4 mile north and 1 mile west of the station. There are no hills in Eureka of any consequence. The land slopes upward gently from the Bay towards the Coast Range, which begins about 3 miles east of the station and reaches the top of its first ridge approximately 10 miles to the east. The average elevation of the ridge is about 2,000 feet. This ridge extends in a semi-circle from a point 20 miles north of Eureka to a point 25 miles south.

The climate of Eureka being completely maritime, high humidity prevails the entire year, which is divided into the "rainy" season and the "dry" season. The rainy season begins in October and continues through April. About 90 percent of the year's precipitation falls during this period. The dry season extends from May through September and is marked by considerable fog or low cloudiness. Usually, however, the fog clears in the late forenoon with the early afternoons generally sunny.

Temperatures are moderate the entire year. Although the highest ever recorded was 85°, and the lowest 20°, the usual range is from a low of about 35° to a high of about 75°. The daily range of temperature averages from about 9° in the summer months to 13° in the winter months, and is occasionally not over 2° to 3°.

(Continued page 364)

Snowfall

Season	July	Aug	Sept	Oct	Nov	Dec	Jan
1970-71	0.0	0.0	0.0	0.0	0.0	0.0	T
1971-72	0.0	0.0	0.0	0.0	0.0	0.0	1.6
1972-73	0.0	0.0	0.0	0.0	0.0	1.9	0.0
1973-74	0.0	0.0	0.0	0.0	0.0	0.0	T
1974-75	0.0	0.0	0.0	0.0	0.0	T	0.0
1975-76	0.0	0.0	0.0	0.0	0.0	0.0	
RECORD MEAN	0.0	0.0	0.0	0.0	0.0	T	0.2

Heating Degree Days

Season	July	Aug	Sept	Oct	Nov	Dec	Jan
1955-56	291	352	298	386	451	451	487
1956-57	279	246	254	353	489	577	665
1957-58	254	200	167	267	397	465	420
1958-59	227	220	176	317	373	385	458
1959-60	276	267	209	283	431	535	505
1960-61	325	293	336	318	408	496	441
1961-62	250	234	281	377	459	567	607
1962-63	339	219	229	312	375	469	579
1963-64	234	239	163	241	366	456	564
1964-65	256	243	288	306	444	505	544
1965-66	309	183	324	285	305	551	531
1966-67	254	275	209	358	368	472	541
1967-68	257	249	170	243	345	611	565
1968-69	260	179	220	354	388	566	644
1969-70	284	282	247	295	404	419	392
1970-71	308	292	274	379	338	539	590
1971-72	299	154	242	440	463	612	624
1972-73	217	204	269	328	389	590	542
1973-74	287	308	230	393	399	419	559
1974-75	222	220	274	360	407	501	587
1975-76	244	290	286	328	486	542	

Cooling Degree Days

Year	Jan	Feb	Mar	Apr	May	June	July
1969	0	0	0	0	0	0	0
1970	0	0	0	0	1	0	0
1971	0	0	0	0	0	0	0
1972	0	0	0	0	0	0	0
1973	0	0	0	0	0	1	0
1974	0	0	0	0	0	0	0
1975	0	0	0	0	0	0	0

Feb	Mar	Apr	May	June	Total
T	0.0	0.0	0.0	0.0	T
0.0	0.0	0.0	0.0	0.0	1.6
0.0	T	0.0	0.0	0.0	1.[illegible]
0.0	0.0	0.0	0.0	0.0	T
0.0	0.0	T	0.0	0.0	T
T	T	T	0.0	0.0	0.2

EUREKA, CA

Feb	Mar	Apr	May	June	Total
573	540	458	356	293	4936
440	459	426	309	228	4725
307	528	404	295	165	3869
487	478	428	386	262	4197
476	443	417	356	310	4508
409	464	467	379	253	4589
478	517	431	388	347	4936
266	484	440	336	312	4360
515	591	529	446	299	4643
533	505	441	459	385	4909
510	519	433	443	280	4673
482	561	560	399	307	4786
337	441	498	384	279	4379
519	508	449	352	246	4685
374	462	521	385	313	4378
518	548	502	438	318	5044
456	422	472	423	306	4913
395	537	439	393	293	4596
523	455	454	423	321	4771
469	532	547	417	347	4883

Aug	Sept	Oct	Nov	Dec	Total
0	0	0	0	0	0
0	1	0	0	0	2
2	0	0	0	0	2
1	0	0	0	0	1
0	0	0	0	0	1
0	0	0	0	0	0
0	0	0	0	0	0

Average Temperature

Year	Jan	Feb	Mar	Apr	May	June	July	Aug	Sept	Oct	Nov	Dec	Annual
1936	49.6	49.6	47.8	51.0	55.6	59.8	58.0	56.5	56.0	54.0	48.6	47.4	52.8
1937	40.4	45.8	50.1	49.5	52.2	58.0	55.8	56.4	56.4	56.8	54.1	51.7	52.3
1938	49.9	48.5	48.2	52.0	51.6	53.2	55.3	55.9	57.0	55.6	48.8	48.7	52.1
1939	46.5	44.4	48.0	51.2	54.0	54.0	56.6	56.8	57.6	54.8	50.4	52.6	52.2
1940	51.8	51.7	51.4	52.7	55.2	54.4	58.0	58.0	59.8	56.7	51.2	50.6	54.3
1941	51.6	52.6	52.8	51.8	55.8	58.4	57.8	59.3	57.6	54.2	54.6	49.4	54.7
1942	50.3	47.3	48.4	51.6	53.1	56.2	59.8	57.4	55.5	53.9	52.0	49.8	52.9
1943	47.0	51.2	50.9	52.0	51.7	54.5	56.8	57.2	57.6	55.0	53.2	49.4	53.0
1944	49.8	46.5	47.7	49.9	51.8	54.6	55.2	56.8	54.6	55.4	52.0	50.6	52.1
1945	48.8	48.6	47.2	48.0	53.3	55.3	56.2	55.6	55.0	53.4	51.0	50.2	51.9
1946	46.4	46.6	47.2	50.0	52.4	56.8	58.2	55.8	56.5	52.0	49.6	48.7	51.7
1947	44.6	50.4	50.8	52.4	53.9	56.6	60.2	58.2	57.6	57.2	49.0	48.2	53.3
1948	47.4	45.4	46.8	48.6	52.0	56.0	56.4	58.0	55.2	53.6	47.7	44.0	50.9
1949	40.3	45.6	49.8	50.6	53.6	54.0	54.8	58.7	56.6	50.7	54.4	45.6	51.2
1950	43.3	47.8	48.0	49.2	49.7	54.3	55.4	57.3	55.5	57.1	54.6	53.7	52.2
1951	46.9	48.5	45.7	49.0	52.9	53.1	55.8	55.4	55.1	55.0	52.0	46.5	51.3
1952	45.0	47.1	45.2	49.6	52.6	53.7	55.3	55.9	55.6	54.3	49.5	48.2	51.0
1953	51.0	47.2	47.2	48.8	52.1	54.1	55.1	58.8	58.2	54.5	53.6	48.2	52.4
1954	47.0	48.3	47.2	50.3	51.5	54.5	55.6	56.7	57.5	54.0	53.4	48.2	52.0
1955	44.2	44.6	45.8	46.9	50.2	52.9	55.5	53.4	54.8	52.3	49.7	50.1	50.1
1956	49.1	45.0	47.4	49.5	53.2	55.0	55.7	56.8	56.4	53.5	48.5	46.2	51.4
1957	43.3	49.0	49.9	50.6	54.8	57.2	56.7	58.3	59.3	56.2	51.5	49.8	53.0
1958	51.2	53.9	47.7	51.3	55.2	59.3	57.5	57.6	59.1	54.5	52.4	52.4	54.3
1959	50.1	47.4	49.3	50.6	52.3	56.0	55.9	56.1	57.8	55.6	50.5	47.5	52.5
1960	48.5	48.4	50.5	50.9	53.3	54.5	54.3	55.4	53.6	54.6	51.1	48.8	52.0
1961	50.5	50.2	49.7	49.2	52.5	56.4	56.7	57.2	55.3	52.6	49.5	46.4	52.2
1962	45.2	47.7	48.1	50.4	52.3	53.2	53.8	57.7	57.1	54.6	52.3	49.7	51.8
1963	46.0	55.3	49.2	50.1	53.9	54.4	57.2	57.1	59.4	57.0	52.5	50.1	53.5
1964	46.6	47.0	45.7	47.1	50.4	54.8	56.6	57.0	55.2	54.9	50.0	48.5	51.1
1965	47.3	45.7	48.5	50.1	49.9	51.9	54.8	58.9	53.9	55.7	54.6	47.0	51.6
1966	47.7	46.5	48.0	50.4	50.4	55.5	56.6	55.9	58.0	53.2	52.6	49.5	52.0
1967	47.4	47.6	46.7	46.2	51.9	54.6	56.5	56.8	59.1	56.9	53.3	45.1	51.8
1968	46.6	53.2	50.6	48.1	52.4	55.5	56.3	59.3	57.5	53.3	51.8	46.5	52.6
1969	44.0	46.2	48.3	49.8	53.4	56.6	55.6	55.8	56.5	55.2	51.3	51.3	52.0
1970	52.1	51.4	49.9	47.4	52.3	54.3	54.8	55.3	55.7	52.6	53.5	47.4	52.2
1971	45.7	46.3	47.1	48.1	50.6	54.3	55.2	60.0	56.7	50.6	49.4	45.0	50.8
1972	44.6	49.0	51.2	49.1	51.2	54.6	57.8	58.2	55.8	54.2	51.8	45.7	52.0
1973	47.3	50.7	47.4	50.1	52.0	55.1	55.6	54.8	57.1	52.1	51.4	51.2	52.1
1974	46.7	46.1	50.1	49.7	51.1	54.1	57.7	57.7	55.6	53.2	51.2	48.7	51.8
1975	45.8	48.0	47.6	46.5	51.4	53.2	56.9	55.3	55.2	54.2	48.5	47.4	50.8
RECORD MEAN	47.2	47.9	48.5	49.9	52.4	54.9	56.0	56.6	56.1	53.9	51.3	48.2	51.9
MAX	53.2	53.9	54.3	55.3	57.1	59.4	60.1	60.8	61.3	59.8	57.5	54.4	57.3
MIN	41.1	41.9	42.7	44.5	47.6	50.3	51.8	52.3	50.8	48.0	45.0	42.0	46.5

\# Indicates a station move or relocation of instruments.

Precipitation

Year	Jan	Feb	Mar	Apr	May	June	July	Aug	Sept	Oct	Nov	Dec	Annual
1936	8.84	5.89	1.77	2.13	2.23	1.34	0.09	T	0.04	0.49	0.01	3.97	26.80
1937	4.27	5.41	7.19	6.55	0.88	1.35	0.03	0.05	0.19	4.33	10.96	4.26	45.47
1938	6.28	13.94	13.97	2.23	0.31	0.01	T	T	1.74	3.34	3.12	5.97	50.91
1939	4.49	4.41	5.03	0.37	1.85	0.56	0.23	0.06	0.05	1.82	0.91	12.13	31.91
1940	4.37	9.62	7.70	0.81	2.54	0.32	0.00	0.00	0.91	4.03	2.29	8.87	41.46
1941	11.37	6.68	4.31	4.49	3.61	1.52	0.06	0.18	0.48	2.64	3.91	12.87	52.12
1942	4.08	6.22	1.77	4.05	5.43	0.57	0.07	0.06	0.06	1.21	8.60	8.52	40.64
1943	5.23	3.51	5.83	3.23	4.25	0.47	0.04	0.21	0.01	4.61	3.59	1.67	32.65
1944	2.92	3.62	2.25	4.25	3.49	1.19	0.10	0.19	0.19	2.79	9.11	5.92	36.02
1945	3.64	9.55	6.03	2.27	3.43	T	T	0.10	1.09	3.38	9.47	9.93	48.89
1946	4.32	5.09	4.68	0.42	1.26	0.30	0.12	0.01	0.32	2.26	4.36	1.56	24.70
1947	3.93	1.33	3.91	1.84	0.17	1.58	1.20	0.10	0.59	6.50	1.72	3.09	25.96
1948	8.23	5.20	6.16	6.53	2.16	0.77	0.25	0.13	1.71	3.33	3.19	7.35	45.01
1949	1.63	6.09	6.94	0.41	2.56	0.06	0.16	0.02	0.50	2.03	3.23	4.49	28.12
1950	13.79	4.61	7.71	1.93	1.30	1.03	0.05	0.07	0.35	13.04	3.43	5.99	53.30
1951	8.47	7.56	3.94	2.05	1.38	T	0.05	0.02	0.79	3.88	7.80	9.10	45.04
1952	10.67	6.22	3.78	1.34	1.77	1.98	T	0.01	0.73	0.62	2.13	11.87	41.12
1953	12.63	3.44	5.95	3.18	5.83	1.24	T	0.41	0.61	3.84	9.57	3.62	50.32
1954	11.78	3.29	3.76	2.78	0.16	2.57	0.04	1.24	0.87	1.47	5.09	9.65	42.70
1955	5.73	1.83	1.82	5.56	0.03	0.11	0.21	T	1.18	2.64	5.77	11.63	36.51
1956	11.51	7.47	2.36	0.31	1.58	1.71	0.06	T	0.33	5.47	0.49	7.18	38.47
1957	4.22	4.36	8.77	1.96	3.42	0.30	0.34	0.02	1.37	6.00	4.44	5.69	40.89
1958	8.57	10.80	6.09	3.67	1.26	0.71	0.05	T	0.78	1.17	3.71	4.06	40.87
1959	7.23	10.65	3.37	0.52	0.91	0.25	T	0.01	1.54	0.74	0.28	3.64	29.14
1960	3.87	7.48	8.13	2.92	6.05	T	0.02	0.04	0.01	1.31	9.87	5.08	44.78
1961	4.54	7.53	7.90	3.49	3.97	0.50	0.03	0.30	0.53	2.28	5.65	3.44	40.16
1962	3.26	6.08	4.04	2.62	0.60	0.11	T	1.92	0.71	6.49	6.77	2.58	35.18
1963	1.70	4.74	6.28	10.68	1.74	0.33	0.11	0.07	0.68	5.41	6.91	3.20	41.85
1964	11.13	1.20	5.91	0.67	1.59	0.72	0.83	0.03	0.07	1.82	12.11	10.96	47.04
1965	5.82	1.36	1.23	5.60	0.44	0.35	T	0.36	T	0.70	5.20	5.22	26.28
1966	9.44	3.12	6.57	1.34	0.06	0.30	0.25	0.50	1.33	1.02	9.86	6.52	40.31
1967	8.87	1.47	7.44	5.29	1.52	0.32	0.00	T	1.32	2.15	4.40	4.34	37.12
1968	7.59	2.93	3.85	0.40	1.04	0.20	0.04	1.98	0.60	2.81	5.88	8.32	35.64
1969	13.92	7.82	1.56	3.22	1.01	0.34	0.05	T	0.36	3.20	3.49	9.60	44.57
1970	12.46	3.15	2.70	1.54	1.38	0.29	T	T	0.32	2.11	13.20	10.24	47.39
1971	5.41	3.28	7.91	2.92	1.28	1.51	0.16	0.55	2.08	0.92	6.36	6.36	38.76
1972	7.96	5.93	5.08	2.27	1.11	0.88	0.01	0.07	1.06	1.97	5.41	7.42	39.17
1973	6.47	3.85	7.10	0.35	0.85	0.23	T	0.08	2.35	4.14	16.58	7.02	49.02
1974	6.02	5.98	6.98	3.15	0.42	0.33	0.11	0.32	T	1.76	2.75	6.40	34.22
1975	5.20	7.68	10.73	3.29	1.05	0.58	0.10	0.58	0.01	6.77	4.72	5.38	46.09
RECORD MEAN	6.99	5.84	5.35	3.06	1.87	0.74	0.12	0.21	0.86	2.71	5.44	6.40	39.59

Record mean values above are means through the current year for the period beginning in 1887 for temperature and precipitation, 1911 for snowfall.

EUREKA, CALIFORNIA

(Continued)

The principal industries are lumbering, fishing, and dairy farming. Owing to the low temperatures and lack of sunshine, there is very little truck farming, but the climate is nearly ideal for berries and flowers.

Normals, Means, and Extremes

Month	Normal Degree days Base 65 °F: Heating	Cooling	Precipitation in inches — Water equivalent: Normal	Maximum monthly	Year	Minimum monthly	Year	Maximum in 24 hrs.	Year	Snow, Ice pellets: Maximum monthly	Year	Maximum in 24 hrs.	Year	Relative humidity pct.: Hour (Local time)	Hour	Hour	Hour
(a				65		65		65		65		65					
J	549	0	7.42	13.92	1969	1.63	1949	4.42	1912	3.0	1935	3.0	1935				
F	465	0	5.15	13.94	1938	0.50	1923	4.88	1959	0.8	1955	0.8	1955				
M	518	0	4.83	13.97	1938	0.07	1926	4.02	1975	1.0	1966	1.0	1966				
A	459	0	2.95	10.68	1963	0.31	1956	2.56	1963	T	1975	T	1975				
M	388	0	2.11	6.05	1960	0.03	1955	2.23	1943	0.0		0.0					
J	294	0	0.66	2.57	1954	0.00	1917	1.73	1943	0.0		0.0					
J	270	0	0.14	1.34	1916	0.00	1967	1.18	1916	0.0		0.0					
A	248	0	0.27	1.98	1968	0.00	1940	0.93	1965	0.0		0.0					
S	252	0	0.65	3.56	1925	0.00	1929	1.32	1966	0.0		0.0					
O	329	0	3.23	13.04	1950	0.00	1917	5.83	1950	0.0		0.0					
N	399	0	5.77	16.58	1973	T	1929	4.55	1926	0.0		0.0					
D	508	0	6.58	12.87	1941	1.17	1917	4.17	1939	1.9	1972	1.9	1972				
YR	4679	0	39.76	16.58	NOV 1973	0.00	JUL 1967	5.83	OCT 1950	3.0	JAN 1935	3.0	JAN 1935				

(To better understand these tables, see full explanation of terms beginning on page 322)

Month	Wind: Mean speed m.p.h.	Prevailing direction	Fastest mile: Speed m.p.h.	Direction	Year	Pct. of possible sunshine	Mean sky cover, tenths, sunrise to sunset	Mean number of days — Sunrise to sunset: Clear	Partly cloudy	Cloudy	Precipitation .01 inch or more	Snow, Ice pellets 1.0 inch or more	Thunderstorms	Heavy fog, visibility ¼ mile or less	Temperatures °F Max. (b): 90° and above	32° and below	Min.: 32° and below	0° and below	Average station pressure mb. Elev. 60 feet m.s.l.
(a)	54	54	65	65		65	33	65	65	65	65	65	54	54	65	65	65	65	
J	6.9	SE	54	S	1955	42	7.3	6	6	19	17	*	1	4	0	0	2	0	
F	7.2	SE	48	SW	1960	46	7.4	6	5	17	14	0	1	3	0	0	1	0	
M	7.6	N	48	SW	1953	50	7.4	6	7	18	15	0	*	2	0	0	*	0	
A	8.0	N	49	N	1915	55	7.0	6	9	15	12	0	*	2	0	0	*	0	
M	7.9	N	40	NW	1955	55	6.9	6	10	15	8	0	*	1	0	0	0	0	
J	7.4	N	39	NW	1949	57	6.5	7	10	13	5	0	*	2	0	0	0	0	
J	6.8	N	35	N	1921	52	6.6	6	11	14	2	0	*	3	0	0	0	0	
A	5.8	NW	34	N	1920	47	6.8	6	11	14	2	0	*	5	0	0	0	0	
S	5.5	N	44	N	1941	53	6.0	9	8	13	4	0	*	7	0	0	0	0	
O	5.6	N	56	SW	1962	49	6.5	8	9	14	9	0	*	9	0	0	0	0	
N	6.0	SE	43	S	1946	42	7.3	6	7	17	13	0	1	7	0	0	*	0	
D	6.4	SE	56	S	1931	40	7.5	6	6	19	16	*	1	4	0	0	1	0	
YR	6.8	N	56	SW	OCT 1962	50	6.9	78	99	188	118	*	5	49	0	0	5	0	

FOOTNOTES

Means and extremes above are from existing and comparable exposures. Annual extremes have been exceeded at other sites in the locality as follows: Lowest temperature 20 in January 1888; maximum monthly precipitation 19.49 in February 1902; maximum monthly snowfall 6.9 in January 1907; maximum snowfall in 24 hours 3.4 in January 1907.

Station: FRESNO, CALIFORNIA
FRESNO AIR TERMINAL
Elevation (ground): 328 feet

TEMPERATURES °F

Month	Normal			Extremes			
	Daily maximum	Daily minimum	Monthly	Record highest	Year	Record lowest	Year
(a)				12		12	
J	54.8	35.8	45.3	75	1974	22	1971
F	60.8	39.0	49.9	76	1967	25	1971
M	66.6	41.2	53.9	90	1972	26	1966
A	74.3	46.2	60.3	95	1965	32	1975
M	82.9	51.9	67.4	104	1974	36	1975
J	90.3	57.5	73.9	110	1964	45	1971
J	98.2	62.9	80.6	111	1972	52	1974
A	96.0	60.6	78.3	108	1971	49	1966
S	91.0	56.5	73.8	105	1971	41	1968
O	79.8	48.6	64.2	96	1971	27	1972
N	66.1	40.8	53.5	88	1966	26	1975
D	54.6	36.9	45.8	71	1969	21	1967
YR	76.3	48.2	62.3	111	JUL 1972	21	DEC 1967

IMPORTANT:
The time-period covered by this record is limited: See footnotes on next page for explanation and for additional history of EXTREME HIGHS AND LOWS recorded in the general area.

Fresno is located about midway and toward the eastern edge of the San Joaquin Valley, which is oriented northwest to southeast and has a length of about 225 miles and an average width of about 50 miles. The terrain around Fresno itself is generally level with an abrupt upward slope about 15 miles eastward to the foothills of the Sierra Nevadas. The main Sierra Nevada Range is located about 50 miles to the east and extends from 12,000 to more than 14,000 feet in elevation. About 45 miles west of Fresno lie the foothills of the Coastal Range.

The climate of Fresno is dry - mild in winter and hot in summer, and nearly nine-tenths of the year's precipitation falls in the six months from November to April.

Thanks to clear skies during the summer and the comparative isolation of the San Joaquin Valley from marine effects, the normal daily maximum temperature advances to a high of 101° during the latter part of July. The daily maximum temperature during this warmest month has ranged from 76° to 115°. Low relative humidities and some wind movement substantially lower the sensible temperature during periods of high readings. Even on the warmest days, the high rate of evaporation of perspiration from the body and the constant movement of air combine to keep the skin temperature much below the air temperature. Sunstroke is practically unknown. Humidity readings of 15 percent are common on summer afternoons, and readings as low as 8 percent have been recorded. In contrast to this, humidity readings average 90 percent during the morning hours of December and January.

Winds flow with the major axis of the San Joaquin Valley; as the Valley is oriented from the northwest to southeast, the winds are generally from one of these directions with northwest prevailing most of the time. This feature is especially beneficial since, during the warmest months, the northwest winds increase during the evenings as a result of heating or thermal effects that have occurred during the day. These refreshing breezes and the normally large temperature variation of about 35° between the highest and lowest readings of the day result in comfortable evening and night temperatures generally.

Winter temperatures are usually mild but during infrequent cold spells minimum readings occasionally drop below freezing. Heavy frost occurs almost every year, and the first heavy frost in the autumn usually occurs during the last week of November. The last frost in the spring is early in March; however, one year in five will have the last heavy frost after the first of April. The average growing season in this area is 291 days.

The mean annual precipitation is less than 11 inches, with 67 percent falling from December through March, and 95 percent falling from October through April. Although the heaviest rain recorded at Fresno for short periods occurred in June, usually any rainfall during the summer is very light. On an average, over 40 rainy days are experienced each year. Although light amounts have fallen. snow is a rare occurrence in Fresno.

Fresno enjoys a very high percentage of sunshine, receiving more than 70 percent of the possible amount during all but the four months of November December, January, and February. Reduction of sunshine during these months is caused by fog and short periods of stormy weather. During foggy periods, sometimes of nearly two weeks duration, winter fog reduces sunshine to a minimum. This fog frequently lifts to a few hundred feet above the surface of the Valley and presents the appearance of a heavy, solid cloud layer.

Spring and autumn are very enjoyable seasons in Fresno, with clear skies, light rainfall and winds, and mild temperatures.

FRESNO, CALIFORNIA

Normals, Means, and Extremes

(To better understand these tables, see full explanation of terms beginning on page 322)

Month	Normal Degree days Base 65 °F: Heating	Normal Degree days Base 65 °F: Cooling	Precipitation in inches, Water equivalent: Normal	Maximum monthly	Year	Minimum monthly	Year	Maximum in 24 hrs.	Year	Snow, Ice pellets: Maximum monthly	Year	Maximum in 24 hrs.	Year	Relative humidity pct. Hour 04 (Local time)	Hour 10	Hour 16	Hour 22
(a)				26		26		26		26		26		12	12	12	12
J	611	0	1.84	8.56	1969	0.37	1972	2.59	1969	2.2	1962	1.5	1962	92	85	68	89
F	423	0	1.72	5.97	1962	T	1964	1.99	1969	0.0		0.0		91	77	56	84
M	344	0	1.62	5.79	1958	0.00	1972	1.63	1958	T	1973	T	1973	87	64	46	76
A	182	41	1.24	4.41	1967	0.02	1962	1.23	1969	0.0		0.0		83	52	35	64
M	51	125	0.32	1.56	1957	T	1975	0.96	1957	0.0		0.0		74	43	25	50
J	9	276	0.06	0.60	1972	0.00	1975	0.60	1972	0.0		0.0		68	40	24	46
J	0	484	0.00	0.04	1969	0.00	1973	0.04	1969	0.0		0.0		64	39	23	42
A	0	412	0.02	0.25	1964	0.00	1972	0.25	1964	0.0		0.0		69	42	25	47
S	0	267	0.07	0.92	1959	0.00	1974	0.91	1959	0.0		0.0		75	45	28	54
O	90	66	0.42	1.54	1968	0.00	1966	1.13	1964	T	1974	T	1974	79	52	35	67
N	345	0	1.22	3.50	1972	0.00	1959	1.35	1953	0.0		0.0		88	74	57	84
D	595	0	1.71	6.73	1955	0.07	1960	1.76	1955	1.2	1968	1.2	1968	94	87	73	91
YR	2650	1671	10.24	8.56	JAN 1969	0.00	JUN 1975	2.59	JAN 1969	2.2	JAN 1962	1.5	JAN 1962	80	58	41	66

Month	Wind: Mean speed m.p.h.	Prevailing direction	Fastest mile: Speed m.p.h.	Direction	Year	Pct. of possible sunshine	Mean sky cover, tenths, sunrise to sunset	Mean number of days, Sunrise to sunset: Clear	Partly cloudy	Cloudy	Precipitation .01 inch or more	Snow, Ice pellets 1.0 inch or more	Thunderstorms	Heavy fog, visibility ¼ mile or less	Temperatures °F Max.: (b) 90° and above	Max.: 32° and below	Min.: 32° and below	Min.: 0° and below	Average station pressure mb. Elev. 327 feet m.s.l.
(a)	26	14	26	26		26	26	26	26	26	26	26	26	26	12	12	12	12	3
J	5.4	SE	32	SE	1952	50	7.2	6	7	18	8	*	*	12	0	0	9	0	1008.8
F	5.7	NW	38	W	1951	66	6.0	8	8	12	7	0	*	7	0	0	5	0	1007.9
M	6.7	NW	41	NW	1964	79	5.1	12	8	11	6	0	1	2	*	0	1	0	1004.2
A	7.2	NW	36	NW	1973	85	4.2	15	8	7	5	0	1	1	2	0	*	0	1004.8
M	7.9	NW	38	N	1952	89	3.1	19	7	5	2	0	1	*	11	0	0	0	1001.1
J	8.0	NW	34	W	1950	94	1.8	24	4	2	1	0	1	0	19	0	0	0	999.7
J	7.1	NW	25	NE	1958	96	1.1	27	3	1	*	0	*	0	29	0	0	0	1000.1
A	6.5	NW	31	S	1961	96	1.2	27	3	1	*	0	*	0	28	0	0	0	1000.4
S	5.9	NW	29	SW	1958	95	1.4	25	3	2	1	0	1	*	18	0	0	0	1000.7
O	5.3	NW	40	NE	1959	88	2.7	20	6	5	2	0	1	1	4	0	*	0	1004.3
N	4.8	NW	29	NW	1974	67	5.1	12	7	11	5	0	*	6	0	0	3	0	1007.6
D	5.0	SE	43	NW	1949	46	6.9	7	6	18	7	*	*	12	0	*	10	0	1010.5
YR	6.3	NW	43	NW	DEC 1949	82	3.8	202	70	93	44	*	6	41	110	*	28	0	1004.2

FOOTNOTES Means and extremes above are from existing and comparable exposures. Annual extremes have been exceeded at other sites in the locality as follows: Highest temperature 115 in July 1905; lowest temperature 17 in January 1913; maximum precipitation in 24 hours 2.86 in November 1900; maximum monthly snowfall 2.5 in January 1930; maximum snowfall in 24 hours 2.5 in January 1930; fastest mile of wind 54 from Northwest in March 1916.

Snowfall

Season	July	Aug	Sept	Oct	Nov	Dec	Jan
1970-71	0.0	0.0	0.0	0.0	0.0	0.0	T
1971-72	0.0	0.0	0.0	0.0	0.0	0.0	T
1972-73	0.0	0.0	0.0	0.0	0.0	T	0.0
1973-74	0.0	0.0	0.0	0.0	0.0	0.0	0.0
1974-75	0.0	0.0	0.0	T	0.0	0.0	0.0
1975-76	0.0	0.0	0.0	0.0	0.0	0.0	
RECORD MEAN	0.0	0.0	0.0	T	0.0	T	0.1

Heating Degree Days

Season	July	Aug	Sept	Oct	Nov	Dec	Jan
1955-56	0	0	1	53	426	455	517
1956-57	0	0	0	135	347	627	692
1957-58	0	0	0	79	386	604	568
1958-59	0	0	2	21	313	470	486
1959-60	0	0	6	54	292	571	556
1960-61	0	0	0	96	394	656	694
#1961-62	0	0	0	126	382	654	724
1962-63	0	0	0	69	291	538	698
#1963-64	0	0	2	56	382	767	651
1964-65	0	3	3	41	410	492	572
1965-66	0	0	12	41	302	707	664
1966-67	0	0	1	65	238	606	579
1967-68	0	0	0	29	239	686	619
1968-69	0	0	12	73	387	665	619
1969-70	0	0	0	166	349	574	485
1970-71	0	0	0	108	282	573	593
1971-72	0	0	20	209	423	678	750
1972-73	0	0	2	108	437	740	610
1973-74	0	0	0	94	360	544	522
1974-75	0	0	0	59	350	628	661
1975-76	0	0	0	154	455	648	

Cooling Degree Days

Year	Jan	Feb	Mar	Apr	May	June	July
1969	0	0	4	15	206	241	500
1970	0	0	0	0	212	353	573
1971	0	0	0	8	64	296	529
1972	0	0	17	18	195	383	518
1973	0	0	0	32	264	419	484
1974	0	0	0	20	179	384	512
1975	0	0	0	0	164	303	413

FRESNO, CALIFORNIA

Average Temperature

Year	Jan	Feb	Mar	Apr	May	June	July	Aug	Sept	Oct	Nov	Dec	Annual
1936	50.5	51.6	58.1	63.6	70.7	76.5	84.8	83.1	76.4	67.6	56.4	45.8	65.4
1937	40.7	51.0	56.3	60.2	70.6	75.6	83.4	82.3	75.2	67.9	57.0	50.8	64.2
1938	46.6	52.4	52.4	60.8	69.4	77.6	82.4	80.0	76.8	64.6	53.6	49.4	63.8
#1939	47.0	47.7	56.2	66.4	69.4	76.5	81.8	81.0	75.9	63.3	55.7	49.9	64.2
1940	48.8	52.8	57.6	63.1	72.2	80.4	80.4	80.2	71.3	65.1	51.8	51.0	64.6
1941	49.8	53.6	57.2	58.8	69.8	73.8	82.4	76.8	70.5	61.0	55.0	49.0	63.1
1942	47.3	49.0	54.4	59.8	65.4	75.8	83.4	80.4	72.4	65.4	52.6	45.9	62.6
1943	45.6	51.6	56.4	62.1	70.4	71.6	81.0	77.2	75.8	64.4	54.0	47.8	63.2
1944	46.8	48.6	54.8	58.2	69.6	72.0	80.0	78.8	75.2	66.4	51.4	47.4	62.4
1945	43.6	50.8	50.5	61.0	66.8	76.0	84.2	79.4	75.5	66.7	53.4	47.6	63.0
1946	44.4	49.3	54.8	64.4	68.5	74.6	82.0	81.1	74.7	61.6	50.6	45.6	62.6
1947	41.0	52.4	59.0	64.7	73.0	76.4	79.0	77.6	77.0	65.2	50.6	45.2	63.4
1948	51.2	49.0	53.2	59.8	65.2	75.8	80.2	78.8	73.8	65.0	52.9	44.4	62.4
#1949	39.6	47.2	54.4	65.6	68.6	78.5	81.2	76.8	75.2	62.6	57.4	44.1	62.6
1950	42.7	51.5	53.4	62.9	68.4	72.8	82.4	79.3	72.2	65.9	58.2	51.0	63.4
1951	45.6	49.9	53.6	61.0	68.3	74.2	79.2	77.9	75.0	63.1	55.5	44.8	62.4
1952	45.2	49.9	50.1	60.9	69.6	69.1	81.7	79.1	75.5	68.2	52.6	46.9	62.4
1953	50.5	48.4	53.3	59.4	61.7	69.3	82.5	75.5	75.5	63.3	54.3	45.7	61.7
1954	46.7	49.6	51.8	63.9	69.7	71.7	81.4	74.5	71.2	63.7	52.4	43.8	61.7
1955	41.6	47.1	53.9	54.8	65.6	72.3	76.2	80.2	74.6	65.0	50.6	50.1	61.0
1956	48.2	45.5	53.8	59.6	66.9	74.3	79.7	76.0	74.4	61.5	53.2	44.5	61.4
1957	42.5	53.3	54.9	60.5	65.1	77.1	80.2	76.4	74.2	62.5	51.9	45.3	62.0
1958	46.4	53.8	51.8	59.1	69.9	72.7	79.5	83.3	75.0	69.2	54.4	49.6	63.7
1959	49.0	49.7	57.7	65.6	64.9	76.4	83.2	77.8	71.9	66.5	55.0	46.4	63.7
1960	46.9	49.5	56.8	60.1	66.1	80.0	82.9	78.5	75.2	63.1	51.6	43.7	62.9
#1961	42.4	51.5	53.4	61.4	63.9	78.8	82.5	81.1	72.4	64.3	51.9	43.8	62.3
1962	41.4	48.3	52.1	64.8	65.0	75.9	80.9	78.8	74.7	64.0	55.2	47.4	62.4
#1963	42.2	56.4	53.3	55.9	67.6	73.2	78.5	78.2	76.6	65.4	52.1	40.0	61.6
1964	43.8	47.4	51.3	58.8	64.9	73.3	81.0	78.9	71.0	68.3	51.2	49.0	61.6
1965	46.3	49.6	55.5	60.8	67.5	71.4	78.9	78.8	68.6	65.8	54.7	42.0	61.6
1966	43.4	47.2	56.3	65.5	70.9	76.3	78.2	81.0	72.8	64.8	56.9	45.2	63.2
1967	46.1	48.9	54.4	52.6	68.8	74.3	83.8	83.6	77.4	66.0	56.8	42.6	62.9
1968	44.8	55.8	55.8	61.5	68.1	78.0	82.4	77.2	73.7	63.3	51.9	43.3	63.0
1969	44.8	47.5	53.1	59.7	70.4	72.9	80.9	79.7	75.7	59.7	53.1	46.2	62.0
1970	49.1	52.7	55.3	57.0	70.8	76.5	83.3	79.9	73.0	63.4	55.4	46.3	63.5
1971	45.7	47.6	54.4	59.1	64.2	74.4	81.9	81.1	73.4	60.9	50.7	42.9	61.4
1972	40.6	52.5	60.7	61.1	69.9	77.5	81.5	79.7	71.8	62.6	50.2	40.9	62.4
1973	45.1	51.9	50.4	61.2	72.9	78.6	80.4	78.5	72.0	63.3	52.9	47.2	62.9
1974	47.9	49.1	56.3	60.0	69.5	77.7	81.3	79.3	77.5	66.0	53.1	44.5	63.5
1975	43.4	49.9	51.5	53.9	68.4	74.7	78.1	75.9	75.8	61.4	49.5	43.9	60.6
RECORD MEAN	45.8	51.0	55.1	60.8	67.7	75.2	81.7	79.9	73.9	64.6	54.2	46.3	63.0
MAX	54.3	61.2	66.5	74.1	82.3	91.1	98.7	96.8	89.8	78.8	66.1	54.7	76.2
MIN	37.3	40.8	43.6	47.5	53.0	59.3	64.6	62.9	57.9	50.4	42.3	37.8	49.8

# Indicates a station move or relocation of instruments.

Precipitation

Year	Jan	Feb	Mar	Apr	May	June	July	Aug	Sept	Oct	Nov	Dec	Annual
1936	0.68	4.70	1.36	0.54	0.04	0.01	T	T	0.00	2.55	T	3.11	12.99
1937	1.97	2.46	2.32	0.33	0.00	T	T	0.00	T	0.11	0.05	3.00	10.24
1938	2.14	3.98	5.19	1.32	0.01	0.05	T	0.00	0.13	0.69	0.10	1.47	15.08
#1939	1.99	0.77	1.88	0.37	0.02	1.66	0.00	T	0.17	0.99	0.04	0.11	8.00
1940	5.89	3.22	0.92	0.16	T	T	0.00	0.00	0.00	0.55	0.05	5.24	16.03
1941	1.56	5.04	1.86	2.61	T	0.12	0.00	0.07	0.00	0.76	0.56	4.16	16.74
1942	1.34	0.67	1.09	1.32	0.27	0.00	T	T	0.00	T	0.84	1.44	6.97
1943	1.48	0.85	3.21	0.90	0.00	T	0.00	0.00	0.00	0.06	0.23	1.48	8.21
1944	0.95	2.60	0.17	1.13	0.29	0.02	0.00	0.00	0.01	0.89	1.37	1.45	8.88
1945	0.92	2.31	2.25	0.12	0.04	0.24	T	T	T	1.04	1.45	1.11	9.48
1946	0.28	1.40	2.01	0.03	1.02	0.00	0.02	0.00	0.14	0.73	1.94	1.95	9.52
1947	0.20	0.60	0.46	0.41	0.20	0.02	T	T	T	0.81	0.43	0.42	3.55
1948	T	0.77	2.28	2.28	0.96	0.01	0.00	0.00	0.00	0.08	0.02	1.23	7.63
#1949	0.60	0.73	3.60	0.01	0.39	T	T	T	0.00	T	0.46	0.78	6.57
1950	3.01	1.84	1.84	0.82	0.05	0.00	0.02	T	0.13	1.19	1.85	1.60	12.35
1951	1.94	1.60	0.31	1.58	0.02	0.06	0.00	0.00	0.00	0.33	1.03	2.82	9.69
1952	3.59	0.53	3.57	2.07	T	0.01	T	0.00	0.09	0.02	1.61	4.05	15.54
1953	1.49	0.09	0.59	0.96	0.48	0.32	T	T	0.00	0.18	1.51	0.51	6.13
1954	1.80	1.13	2.90	0.48	0.09	0.29	T	0.00	0.00	0.00	1.32	1.82	9.83
1955	3.51	1.46	0.07	1.47	0.63	0.00	T-	T	0.00	T	1.34	6.73	15.21
1956	2.41	0.65	0.08	1.38	0.81	0.00	T	0.00	T	1.00	0.00	0.31	6.64
1957	1.75	1.51	0.53	1.38	1.56	0.16	T	0.00	0.19	0.43	1.02	1.90	10.43
1958	2.03	4.11	5.79	2.71	0.79	0.02	0.02	0.01	0.46	T	0.21	0.32	16.47
1959	1.47	3.66	0.09	0.54	0.09	0.00	0.00	0.01	0.92	0.00	0.00	0.43	7.21
1960	2.08	2.37	0.67	1.50	0.02	0.00	T	0.00	0.02	0.09	2.75	0.07	9.57
#1961	1.52	0.40	1.04	0.57	0.40	0.01	T	0.10	T	T	1.60	1.32	6.96
1962	1.12	5.97	1.04	0.02	0.20	T	T	0.00	T	0.73	0.03	0.48	9.59
1963	2.16	2.01	2.10	3.66	0.39	0.03	0.00	0.01	0.15	0.95	2.54	0.27	14.27
1964	0.66	T	1.27	0.50	0.35	0.06	T	0.25	0.00	1.23	1.49	2.63	8.44
1965	1.05	0.43	2.38	1.74	T	T	T	0.02	0.00	0.30	2.69	1.73	10.34
1966	0.53	0.54	0.01	0.15	0.10	0.07	0.03	0.00	0.03	0.00	1.57	3.04	6.07
1967	2.21	0.22	3.15	4.41	0.19	0.14	T	T	T	0.07	1.55	1.04	12.98
1968	1.05	1.10	1.49	0.70	0.24	0.00	T	T	0.00	1.54	1.94	2.44	10.50
1969	8.56	5.60	1.16	1.64	0.06	0.04	0.04	0.00	0.04	0.06	0.80	1.14	19.14
1970	3.83	1.27	1.65	0.21	0.00	0.08	T	0.00	0.00	0.01	2.30	2.51	11.86
1971	0.40	0.29	0.58	1.04	1.40	0.00	T	T	0.04	0.03	0.65	2.56	6.99
1972	0.37	0.67	0.00	0.27	0.15	0.60	T	0.00	0.29	0.22	3.50	1.40	7.47
1973	1.91	3.69	2.84	0.09	T	T	0.00	T	0.00	1.02	1.39	1.74	12.68
1974	2.82	0.25	2.56	0.64	0.00	0.00	T	T	0.00	1.44	0.34	1.26	9.31
1975	0.69	0.97	2.44	0.55	T	0.00	T	0.05	0.22	1.07	0.20	0.14	6.33
RECORD MEAN	1.78	1.57	[illegible]	0.98	0.36	0.10	0.01	0.01	0.14	0.54	0.99	1.58	9.66

Record mean values above are means through the current year for the period beginning in 1888 for temperature, 1878 for precipitation and 1950 for snowfall. Data are from City Office locations through June 1939.

Feb	Mar	Apr	May	June	Total
0.0	0.0	0.0	0.0	0.0	T
0.0	0.0	0.0	0.0	0.0	T
0.0	T	0.0	0.0	0.0	T
0.0	0.0	0.0	0.0	0.0	0.0
0.0	0.0	0.0	0.0	0.0	T
0.0	T	0.0	0.0	0.0	0.1

FRESNO, CA

Feb	Mar	Apr	May	June	Total
558	340	183	49	4	2586
321	308	156	64	0	2650
309	402	183	18	1	2550
422	218	38	59	0	2031
443	255	161	54	0	2392
369	352	138	57	1	2757
461	392	66	65	6	2876
234	356	266	30	0	2482
502	417	201	92	12	3082
423	287	191	58	8	2488
492	271	60	7	1	2557
444	322	366	59	11	2691
258	278	139	37	2	2287
480	366	168	30	0	2800
340	291	232	25	0	2462
480	322	181	81	8	2628
357	142	128	37	0	2744
358	444	140	12	2	2853
438	260	160	33	0	2411
419	409	325	53	3	2907

Aug	Sept	Oct	Nov	Dec	Total
462	331	10	0	0	1769
466	245	67	3	0	1919
505	279	89	0	0	1770
464	213	42	0	0	1850
423	218	47	4	0	1891
448	381	96	0	0	2020
344	329	49	0	0	1602

LOS ANGELES, CALIFORNIA

The climate of Los Angeles is normally pleasant and mild through the year. The Pacific Ocean is the primary moderating influence, but coastal mountain ranges lying along the north and east sides of the Los Angeles coastal basin act as a buffer against extremes of summer heat and winter cold occurring in desert and plateau regions in the interior. A variable balance between mild sea breezes, and either hot or cold winds from the interior, results in some variety in weather conditions, but temperature and humidity are usually well within the limits of human comfort. An important, and somewhat unusual aspect of the climate of the Los Angeles metropolitan area, is the pronounced difference in temperature, humidity, cloudiness, fog, rain, and sunshine over fairly short distances.

These differences are closely related to the distance from, and elevation above, the Pacific Ocean. Both high and low temperatures become more extreme and the average relative humidity becomes lower as one goes inland and up foothill slopes. On the coast and in the lower coastal plain, average daily temperature ranges are about 15° in summer and 20° in winter, but in foothill and inland valley communities these ranges increase to about 30° in summer and 25° in winter. Relative humidity is frequently high near the coast, but may be quite low along the foothills. During periods of high temperatures, the relative humidity is usually below normal so that discomfort is rare, except for infrequent periods when high temperatures and high humidities occur together.

Like other Pacific Coast areas, most rainfall comes during the winter with nearly 85 percent of the annual total occurring from November through March, while summers are practically rainless. As in many semiarid regions, there is a marked variability in monthly and seasonal totals. Annual precipitation may range from less than a third of the normal value to nearly three times normal, while some customarily rainy months may be either completely rainless, or receive from three to four times the average for the month. Precipitation generally increases with distance from the ocean from a yearly total of around 12 inches in coastal sections to the south of the City up to over 20 inches in foothill areas. Destructive flash floods occasionally develop in and below some mountain canyons. Snow is often visible on nearby mountains in the winter, but is extremely rare in the coastal basin. Thunderstorms are infrequent.

Prevailing winds are from the west during the spring, summer, and early autumn, with northeasterly wind predominating the remainder of the year. Average wind speeds are rather low. At times, the lack of air movement, combined with a frequent and persistent temperature inversion, is associated with concentrations of air pollution in the Los Angeles coastal basin and some adjacent areas. In fall, winter, and early spring months, occasional foehn-like descending (Santa Ana) winds come from the northeast over ridges and through passes in the coastal mountains. These Santa Ana winds may pick up considerable amounts of dust and reach speeds of 35 to 50 m.p.h. in north and east sections of the City, with higher speeds in outlying areas to the north and east, but rarely reach coastal portions of the City.

Sunshine, fog, and clouds depend a great deal on topography and distance from the ocean. Low clouds are common at

Station: LOS ANGELES, CALIFORNIA CIVIC CENTER
Elevation (ground): 270 feet

TEMPERATURES °F

Month	Normal			Extremes			
	Daily maximum	Daily minimum	Monthly	Record highest	Year	Record lowest	Year
(a)				35		35	
J	66.5	46.8	56.7	95	1971	28	1949
F	67.6	48.5	58.1	91	1971	34	1949
M	68.6	49.8	59.2	94	1972	38	1971
A	70.5	52.9	61.7	99	1966	39	1975
M	73.2	56.1	64.7	102	1967	46	1964
J	76.5	59.5	68.0	106	1973	50	1953
J	82.9	63.5	73.2	103	1959	54	1952
A	83.7	64.4	74.1	103	1967	53	1943
S	82.5	62.8	72.7	110	1955	51	1948
O	78.0	58.7	68.4	104	1958	41	1971
N	73.2	52.1	62.7	100	1966	39	1964
D	68.0	48.1	58.1	89	1958	32	1951
YR	74.3	55.3	64.8	110	SEP 1955	28	JAN 1949

IMPORTANT:
The time-period covered by this record is limited: See footnotes following table of **NORMALS, MEANS AND EXTREMES** for explanation and for additional history of **EXTREME HIGHS AND LOWS** recorded in the general area.

(Continued)

night and in the morning along the coast during spring and summer, but form later and clear earlier near the foothills so that average annual cloudiness and fog frequencies are greatest near the ocean, and sunshine totals are highest on the inland side of the City. The sun shines about 75 percent of daytime hours at the Civic Center. Light fog may accompany the usual night and morning low clouds, but dense fog is more likely to occur during the night and early morning hours of the winter months.

QUOTES FROM WEATHER FOLKLORE–

Hogs crying and running unquietly up and down with hay or litter in their mouths foreshadow a storm to be near at hand.

– Thomas Willsford.

LOS ANGELES, CALIFORNIA

Normals, Means, and Extremes

(To better understand these tables, see full explanation of terms beginning on page 322)

Month	Normal Degree days Base 65 °F: Heating	Normal Degree days Base 65 °F: Cooling	Precipitation in inches, Water equivalent: Normal	Maximum monthly	Year	Minimum monthly	Year	Maximum in 24 hrs.	Year	Snow, Ice pellets: Maximum monthly	Year	Maximum in 24 hrs.	Year	Relative humidity pct. $ Hour 04 (Local time)	Hour 10	Hour 16	Hour 22	Wind: Mean speed m.p.h.	Prevailing direction	Fastest mile: Speed m.p.h.	Direction	Year	Pct. of possible sunshine	Mean sky cover, tenths, sunrise to sunset	Mean number of days, Sunrise to sunset: Clear	Partly cloudy	Cloudy	Precipitation .01 inch or more	Snow, Ice pellets 1.0 inch or more	Thunderstorms %	Heavy fog, visibility ¼ mile or less %	Temperatures °F Max. (b) 90° and above	Max. 32° and below	Min. 32° and below	Min. 0° and below	Average station pressure mb. Elev. feet m.s.l.
(a)				35		35		35		35		35		17	10	23	11	24	23	35	35		32	33	33	33	33	35	35	23	23	35	35	35	35	
J	268	10	3.00	14.94	1969	0.00	1972	6.11	1956	0.3	1949	0.3	1949	63	51	50	67	6.8	NE	49	N	1946	69	4.5	14	8	9	6	0	1	2	*	0	*	0	
F	207	14	2.77	12.42	1941	T	1964	4.02	1944	T	1951	T	1951	71	54	52	70	6.9	W	40	NW	1961	72	4.7	12	7	9	5	0	1	2	*	0	0	0	
M	190	10	2.19	8.14	1941	0.00	1959	3.41	1943	0.0		0.0		74	52	52	72	7.0	W	47	NW	1964	73	4.7	13	9	9	6	0	1	1	*	0	0	0	
A	124	25	1.27	6.02	1965	0.00	1973	2.05	1956	0.0		0.0		78	53	54	74	6.6	W	40	NW	1955	70	4.7	12	10	8	4	0	1	1	1	0	0	0	
M	60	51	0.13	1.43	1955	0.00	1970	1.07	1955	0.0		0.0		81	56	55	75	6.3	W	39	NW	1945	66	4.8	12	11	8	1	0	*	1	1	0	0	0	
J	25	115	0.03	0.32	1964	0.00	1975	0.32	1964	0.0		0.0		85	59	56	78	5.7	W	32	N	1949	65	4.3	13	11	6	1	0	*	1	1	0	0	0	
J	0	258	0.00	0.03	1969	0.00	1975	0.03	1969	0.0		0.0		84	54	53	79	5.4	W	21	W	1947	82	2.7	21	9	1	*	0	*	1	4	0	0	0	
A	0	282	0.04	0.39	1958	0.00	1975	0.38	1958	0.0		0.0		84	56	55	79	5.3	W	24	E	1945	83	2.6	22	8	1	1	0	*	1	4	0	0	0	
S	5	236	0.17	1.80	1965	0.00	1975	1.45	1965	0.0		0.0		78	52	54	76	5.3	W	27	NW	1941	79	2.9	19	8	3	1	0	*	1	6	0	0	0	
O	35	140	0.27	1.53	1941	0.00	1970	0.62	1941	0.0		0.0		76	55	56	74	5.7	W	48	N	1959	73	3.8	16	9	6	2	0	*	3	3	0	0	0	
N	113	44	2.02	9.68	1965	0.00	1975	4.07	1970	0.0		0.0		61	45	49	62	6.4	W	42	N	1946	74	3.7	16	8	6	3	0	1	2	1	0	0	0	
D	218	0	2.16	6.57	1971	T	1963	3.92	1965	T	1947	T	1947	62	45	50	62	6.6	NE	44	SE	1943	71	4.3	15	8	8	5	0	1	2	0	0	*	0	
YR	1245	1185	14.05	14.94	JAN 1969	0.00	NOV 1975	6.11	JAN 1956	0.3	JAN 1949	0.3	JAN 1949	75	53	53	72	6.2	W	49	N	JAN 1946	73	4.0	185	106	74	34	0	6	17	20	0	*	0	

FOOTNOTES

Means and extremes above are from existing and comparable exposures. Annual extremes have been exceeded at other sites in the locality as follows: Maximum monthly precipitation 15.80 in December 1889; maximum precipitation in 24 hours 7.36 in December 1933; maximum monthly snowfall 2.0 in January 1932; maximum snowfall in 24 hours 2.0 in January 1932.

% Through 1964. The station did not operate 24 hours daily. Fog and thunderstorm data may be incomplete

$ Through 1963.

Snowfall

Season	July	Aug	Sept	Oct	Nov	Dec	Jan
1970-71	0.0	0.0	0.0	0.0	0.0	0.0	0.0
1971-72	0.0	0.0	0.0	0.0	0.0	0.0	0.0
1972-73	0.0	0.0	0.0	0.0	0.0	0.0	0.0
1973-74	0.0	0.0	0.0	0.0	0.0	0.0	0.0
1974-75	0.0	0.0	0.0	0.0	0.0	0.0	0.0
1975-76	0.0	0.0	0.0	0.0	0.0	0.0	
RECORD MEAN	0.0	0.0	0.0	0.0	0.0	T	T

Heating Degree Days

Season	July	Aug	Sept	Oct	Nov	Dec	Jan
1955-56	0	0	6	59	144	279	271
1956-57	0	0	0	34	42	136	328
1957-58	0	0	0	16	131	112	164
1958-59	0	0	0	2	80	132	155
1959-60	0	0	0	2	23	145	319
1960-61	0	0	0	22	135	194	116
1961-62	0	0	2	32	161	243	240
1962-63	0	0	0	33	138	228	286
1963-64	0	0	0	1	103	145	250
1964-65	0	0	0	5	186	256	224
1965-66	0	0	0	1	98	264	281
1966-67	0	0	0	0	88	145	179
1967-68	0	0	0	0	32	287	207
1968-69	0	0	0	4	76	267	219
1969-70	0	0	0	22	52	182	222
1970-71	0	0	0	9	72	243	255
1971-72	0	0	0	94	153	369	288
1972-73	0	0	0	14	97	230	266
1973-74	0	0	1	8	156	174	300
1974-75	0	0	0	25	73	268	243
1975-76	0	0	0	31	132	247	

Cooling Degree Days

Year	Jan	Feb	Mar	Apr	May	June	July
1969	19	0	30	39	81	73	276
1970	0	11	17	17	106	155	326
1971	71	28	16	46	50	131	291
1972	0	4	27	34	122	223	409
1973	9	2	0	25	64	220	236
1974	3	5	8	51	58	223	288
1975	21	0	0	0	11	48	241

Feb	Mar	Apr	May	June	Total
0.0	0.0	0.0	0.0	0.0	0.0
0.0	0.0	0.0	0.0	0.0	0.0
0.0	0.0	0.0	0.0	0.0	0.0
0.0	0.0	0.0	0.0	0.0	0.0
0.0	0.0	0.0	0.0	0.0	0.0
T	0.0	0.0	0.0	0.0	T

Average Temperature

Year	Jan	Feb	Mar	Apr	May	June	July	Aug	Sept	Oct	Nov	Dec	Annual
1936	59.4	56.5	59.0	60.6	65.6	69.0	74.1	73.4	70.5	67.4	67.8	58.6	65.2
1937	47.8	55.3	58.5	62.3	64.0	67.8	71.4	71.6	72.4	67.6	61.7	61.9	63.5
1938	61.2	56.8	57.8	61.6	63.3	65.4	69.6	73.9	74.0	66.7	62.7	62.3	64.6
1939	57.0	54.0	56.8	63.0	63.6	66.9	70.6	73.0	76.6	71.6	67.1	64.2	65.4
#1940	59.8	59.4	61.2	62.8	66.0	66.0	70.6	70.6	69.6	68.3	63.4	61.2	64.9
1941	57.6	58.8	60.6	59.1	67.9	66.0	70.7	71.2	68.0	66.0	65.4	57.0	64.0
1942	58.6	55.7	58.8	59.4	62.8	65.9	71.8	71.0	67.8	67.6	63.5	58.8	63.5
1943	57.6	60.1	58.8	61.4	65.5	66.4	70.7	71.3	70.6	66.6	65.0	56.8	64.2
1944	57.2	53.7	59.6	58.8	62.4	63.4	66.6	71.3	69.2	64.8	59.0	60.0	62.2
1945	56.6	56.6	54.6	59.4	61.9	64.6	71.0	73.3	73.2	67.2	61.6	57.2	63.1
1946	58.0	54.8	57.4	62.0	61.1	68.7	71.8	72.3	73.0	64.5	58.8	56.4	63.2
1947	55.9	59.8	60.4	62.6	64.0	66.9	73.0	71.4	72.2	66.3	59.0	57.2	64.0
#1948	58.6	54.6	55.2	60.4	63.9	67.0	71.0	71.2	71.6	66.3	62.1	53.4	63.0
1949	46.8	52.6	56.0	63.3	64.3	69.7	71.8	73.7	72.9	66.2	67.2	55.6	63.3
1950	50.4	56.7	58.8	62.7	62.2	66.6	73.3	70.9	68.9	69.5	63.7	62.1	63.8
1951	55.7	56.4	60.2	60.4	63.1	66.7	72.8	71.3	71.0	68.8	61.9	54.3	63.6
1952	52.8	58.8	55.3	61.1	66.7	65.7	72.3	74.1	74.3	67.0	59.1	56.1	63.6
1953	60.6	58.9	58.9	58.7	63.9	66.8	74.9	70.7	70.2	69.1	63.6	59.1	64.6
1954	55.6	64.1	57.0	60.9	63.8	67.6	76.7	73.1	72.5	65.7	64.3	58.1	64.9
1955	53.7	57.0	61.3	61.3	63.0	66.7	70.5	75.2	74.5	64.2	61.1	55.9	63.7
1956	56.0	53.1	60.5	58.7	64.4	69.8	71.8	71.9	76.5	66.5	67.2	60.5	64.8
1957	54.2	60.7	61.6	61.7	64.2	72.5	76.0	76.2	72.2	67.1	60.7	61.7	65.7
1958	59.6	60.3	56.9	65.4	68.0	71.0	72.8	75.2	75.9	74.0	63.3	62.0	67.1
1959	60.1	56.3	64.7	66.2	65.0	71.5	77.8	75.5	73.5	70.2	66.6	60.7	67.3
1960	54.6	57.0	62.0	65.3	67.7	70.1	75.5	73.2	75.6	68.0	60.3	58.7	65.7
1961	62.0	61.0	60.1	64.0	63.4	68.8	74.2	74.3	71.0	67.9	60.2	56.9	65.3
1962	57.5	53.8	55.2	64.3	62.9	66.3	70.1	74.1	70.9	65.7	60.6	57.4	63.2
1963	55.6	62.7	58.3	59.6	64.1	66.4	72.1	73.7	77.3	69.1	62.3	60.6	65.1
1964	56.7	59.0	58.6	60.5	61.7	64.8	71.8	73.4	70.2	70.5	59.8	56.5	63.6
1965	58.3	58.0	59.0	61.7	63.4	64.1	70.1	75.6	69.6	73.1	62.0	56.9	64.3
1966	55.7	56.2	61.3	64.4	64.5	70.2	74.4	76.6	73.4	71.2	63.6	60.7	66.0
1967	59.2	62.9	61.0	56.1	67.3	66.3	75.7	79.2	75.2	72.5	66.6	55.6	66.5
1968	58.5	63.8	62.9	64.0	65.5	69.2	74.7	74.1	73.4	69.2	63.3	56.2	66.2
1969	58.3	54.9	59.7	63.8	66.6	67.2	73.8	77.0	71.7	67.3	65.2	59.2	65.4
1970	57.6	61.4	61.2	60.9	67.4	70.0	75.3	76.2	74.4	68.3	63.3	57.2	66.1
1971	58.8	59.2	60.3	62.0	64.0	68.8	74.2	78.9	74.6	67.4	60.2	52.8	65.1
1972	55.5	60.3	63.7	63.9	67.6	72.2	78.0	77.4	72.3	67.2	62.2	58.1	66.5
1973	56.4	60.0	57.9	63.1	65.8	72.0	72.4	73.6	70.0	68.8	60.0	59.9	65.0
1974	55.2	59.2	59.6	64.7	65.7	72.2	74.1	72.3	73.2	67.6	64.0	56.2	65.3
1975	57.6	55.8	55.7	56.0	62.7	65.7	72.5	71.9	74.0	66.4	61.2	57.0	63.0
RECORD MEAN	55.9	56.9	58.5	60.8	63.3	67.0	71.5	72.3	70.7	66.5	62.1	57.6	63.6
MAX	65.1	66.1	67.6	70.0	72.2	76.4	81.9	82.6	81.2	76.7	72.5	67.0	73.3
MIN	46.6	47.7	49.3	51.5	54.4	57.6	61.0	61.9	60.2	56.3	51.7	48.1	53.9

LOS ANGELES, CA
CIVIC CENTER

Feb	Mar	Apr	May	June	Total
338	150	191	74	0	1511
146	123	111	44	0	964
130	246	82	13	0	894
237	49	29	24	0	708
224	111	65	24	0	913
111	146	74	61	11	870
309	298	66	97	38	1486
101	202	161	37	24	1210
169	211	169	113	36	1197
196	183	168	70	38	1326
244	126	58	34	0	1106
81	133	260	43	25	954
70	99	70	50	7	822
277	186	68	25	1	1123
106	128	134	27	1	874
184	154	127	77	11	1131
132	61	61	35	0	1193
136	214	77	32	2	1068
160	171	54	32	1	1057
254	283	262	75	21	1504

Aug	Sept	Oct	Nov	Dec	Total
377	209	100	65	10	1279
352	287	118	28	10	1427
435	296	176	17	0	1557
391	225	89	21	25	1570
272	157	133	9	21	1148
235	254	115	53	2	1295
221	277	82	26	4	931

# Indicates a station move or relocation of instruments.

Precipitation

Year	Jan	Feb	Mar	Apr	May	June	July	Aug	Sept	Oct	Nov	Dec	Annual
1936	0.51	7.25	1.34	0.95	0.00	0.20	0.01	0.02	0.03	1.25	0.05	6.63	18.24
1937	1.99	7.87	4.04	0.24	0.28	0.00	0.00	0.00	0.00	0.01	0.00	3.54	17.97
1938	1.63	9.81	7.94	0.48	0.02	T	0.00	T	0.01	0.01	T	7.26	27.16
1939	2.96	1.13	1.44	0.24	0.02	T	T	0.01	5.67	0.13	0.08	0.38	12.06
#1940	4.33	5.43	1.55	1.61	0.02	T	T	0.00	0.01	1.47	0.34	5.50	20.26
1941	2.21	12.42	8.14	2.67	T	T	T	0.04	0.00	1.53	0.05	4.22	31.28
1942	0.59	1.05	1.26	2.44	T	T	0.00	0.23	T	0.58	0.24	1.01	7.40
1943	7.98	3.07	4.55	0.50	T	0.01	T	0.00	T	0.18	0.05	6.23	22.57
1944	0.97	8.65	2.47	0.60	0.02	0.05	T	T	0.01	0.06	3.72	0.90	17.45
1945	0.04	3.34	3.43	0.08	T	0.01	T	0.04	T	0.56	0.23	5.05	12.78
1946	0.11	1.52	3.66	0.44	0.04	T	T	0.00	0.02	0.92	6.04	3.47	16.22
1947	0.38	0.86	0.79	0.04	0.12	0.02	0.00	0.01	0.09	0.14	0.06	1.62	4.13
1948	T	1.29	3.07	0.78	T	0.16	T	T	T	0.09	T	2.20	7.59
1949	2.43	1.41	1.40	T	0.46	T	T	0.01	0.01	0.01	2.18	2.72	10.63
1950	2.57	1.67	0.87	0.56	T	T	0.01	0.00	0.38	0.24	1.05	0.03	7.38
1951	2.80	1.48	0.44	1.54	0.24	T	T	0.15	0.00	0.59	1.29	5.80	14.33
1952	10.03	0.63	6.14	1.58	T	T	T	T	0.13	0.00	3.13	3.31	24.95
1953	1.08	0.33	0.48	0.91	0.03	0.06	0.00	0.00	T	T	1.11	0.08	4.08
1954	4.60	2.98	2.99	0.13	0.02	0.08	T	T	T	T	2.03	0.86	13.69
1955	4.30	0.68	0.56	2.07	1.43	0.01	T	0.05	T	T	1.68	1.11	11.89
1956	8.39	0.59	T	3.72	0.46	T	0.00	T	0.00	0.12	0.00	0.34	13.62
1957	4.41	1.47	1.02	1.47	0.63	0.08	T	T	0.00	1.51	0.51	2.14	13.24
1958	2.08	6.46	5.30	3.09	0.04	0.00	T	0.39	0.07	0.06	T	T	17.49
1959	1.24	3.32	0.00	0.50	T	T	T	T	0.01	T	0.07	1.09	6.23
1960	2.94	2.26	0.31	1.45	0.05	T	0.00	0.00	T	0.01	2.40	0.15	9.57
1961	1.28	0.15	0.57	0.29	T	T	T	0.03	0.05	T	2.02	1.44	5.83
1962	2.56	11.57	1.10	T	0.02	T	0.00	0.00	0.00	0.12	T	T	15.37
1963	0.52	2.88	2.78	1.94	T	0.14	0.00	0.02	1.31	0.57	2.15	T	12.31
1964	1.43	T	1.79	0.33	0.01	0.32	T	0.00	0.00	0.33	1.72	2.05	7.98
1965	0.84	0.23	2.49	6.02	0.00	0.01	T	0.01	1.80	0.00	9.68	5.73	26.81
1966	0.96	1.51	0.53	0.00	0.22	0.00	T	T	0.30	0.06	4.07	5.26	12.91
1967	5.93	0.11	2.50	3.76	0.01	0.00	0.00	T	1.02	0.00	8.67	1.66	23.66
1968	0.90	0.49	3.34	0.49	0.00	0.01	0.01	0.11	0.03	0.55	0.37	1.28	7.58
1969	14.94	8.03	1.49	0.63	0.03	T	0.03	0.00	T	0.00	1.11	0.06	26.32
1970	1.59	2.58	2.36	0.00	0.00	0.04	0.00	0.00	0.00	0.00	5.05	4.92	16.54
1971	0.43	0.67	0.53	0.50	0.22	0.00	T	0.00	T	0.04	0.30	6.57	9.26
1972	0.00	0.13	T	0.03	0.03	0.07	0.00	0.35	0.02	0.29	3.26	2.36	6.54
1973	4.39	7.89	2.70	0.00	T	0.00	0.00	0.00	0.00	0.12	1.68	0.67	17.45
1974	8.35	0.14	3.78	0.10	0.08	0.00	0.00	0.00	0.00	0.58	0.07	3.59	16.69
1975	0.12	3.54	4.83	1.53	0.09	0.00	0.00	0.00	0.00	0.27	0.00	0.32	10.70
RECORD MEAN	3.04	3.03	2.51	1.08	0.30	0.06	0.01	0.03	0.20	0.51	1.38	2.63	14.78

Record mean values above are means through the current year for the period beginning in 1878 for temperature and precipitation, 1941 for snowfall.

Station: SACRAMENTO, CALIFORNIA
EXECUTIVE AIRPORT

Elevation (ground): 17 feet

TEMPERATURES °F

Month	Normal Daily maximum	Normal Daily minimum	Normal Monthly	Extremes Record highest	Year	Record lowest	Year
(a)				25		25	
J	53.0	37.1	45.1	69	1953	23	1963
F	59.1	40.4	49.8	76	1964	26	1972
M	64.1	41.9	53.0	86	1966	26	1971
A	71.3	45.3	58.3	92	1951	32	1953
M	78.8	49.8	64.3	102	1973	36	1974
J	86.4	54.6	70.5	115	1961	41	1952
J	92.9	57.5	75.2	114	1972	49	1955
A	91.3	56.9	74.1	108	1971	49	1966
S	87.7	55.3	71.5	108	1955	43	1971
O	77.1	49.5	63.3	101	1970	36	1971
N	63.6	42.4	53.0	87	1960	26	1961
D	53.3	38.3	45.8	72	1967	20	1972
YR	73.2	47.4	60.3	115	JUN 1961	20	DEC 1972

IMPORTANT:
The time-period covered by this record is limited: See footnotes following table of NORMALS, MEANS AND EXTREMES for explanation and for additional history of EXTREME HIGHS AND LOWS recorded in the general area.

The lower Sacramento Valley, where Sacramento is located, enjoys a mild climate and abundance of sunshine the year round. Cloudless skies prevail during the summer and largely in the spring and autumn. The summers are remarkably dry, with warm days and pleasant nights. In the winter "rainy season" (December, January, and February) over one-half of the total annual precipitation falls, yet rain in measurable amounts occurs only on about 10 days monthly during winter. Mountains surround the valley to the west, north, and east. The Sierra Nevada snow fields are only 70 miles east of Sacramento and usually provide a plentiful supply of water in the valley streams during the dry season. Because of the shielding influence of the high mountains around the valley, winter storms reach valley districts in modified form. However, torrential rain and heavy snow frequently fall on the western Sierra slopes, the southern Cascades, and to a lesser extent the Coastal Range. As a result, flood conditions occasionally occur along the Sacramento River and its tributaries. Excessive rainfall and damaging windstorms are rare in the valley.

Prevailing winds at Sacramento are southerly every month except November, when they are northerly. This is due to the north-south direction of the valley and the deflecting effect of the towering Sierra Ranges on the prevailing oceanic winds which move through the Carquinez Straits at the junction fo the Sacramento and San Joaquin Rivers. No other tidewater gap exists in the coastal mountains to admit marine air into the Sacramento or the San Joaquin Valley. Occasionally a steep northerly barometric pressure gradient develops and air is forced over the Siskiyou Mountains to the north, warmed dynamically with descent, and reaches the valley floor as a warm, dry, north wind. These

(Continued page 374)

Snowfall

Season	July	Aug	Sept	Oct	Nov	Dec	Jan
1970-71	0.0	0.0	0.0	0.0	0.0	0.0	0.0
1971-72	0.0	0.0	0.0	0.0	0.0	0.0	0.0
1972-73	0.0	0.0	0.0	0.0	0.0	T	0.0
1973-74	0.0	0.0	0.0	0.0	0.0	0.0	T
1974-75	0.0	0.0	0.0	0.0	0.0	0.0	0.0
1975-76	0.0	0.0	0.0	0.0	0.0	0.0	
RECORD MEAN	0.0	0.0	0.0	0.0	0.0	T	T

Heating Degree Days

Season	July	Aug	Sept	Oct	Nov	Dec	Jan
1960-61	0	0	0	27	357	591	695
1961-62	0	0	6	122	378	640	709
#1962-63	0	0	0	97	303	581	736
1963-64	0	0	0	65	398	734	612
1964-65	0	4	10	49	436	469	602
1965-66	0	0	19	32	303	738	591
1966-67	1	0	4	60	303	580	584
1967-68	0	0	0	33	259	643	663
1968-69	0	3	2	97	374	662	644
1969-70	0	0	1	129	323	519	478
1970-71	0	0	4	129	286	578	603
1971-72	0	0	33	191	363	673	731
1972-73	0	0	6	115	451	749	636
1973-74	0	0	0	77	384	553	571
1974-75	7	0	0	44	347	569	661
1975-76	0	0	0	72	306	539	

Cooling Degree Days

Year	Jan	Feb	Mar	Apr	May	June	July
1969	0	0	0	1	108	136	361
1970	0	0	0	0	143	208	374
1971	0	0	0	0	22	186	355
1972	0	0	6	5	129	245	351
1973	0	0	0	19	156	295	373
1974	0	0	0	5	61	180	296
1975	0	0	0	0	177	258	388

SACRAMENTO, CALIFORNIA

Feb	Mar	Apr	May	June	Total
0.0	0.0	0.0	0.0	0.0	0.0
0.0	0.0	0.0	0.0	0.0	0.0
0.0	0.0	0.0	0.0	0.0	T
0.0	0.0	0.0	0.0	0.0	T
0.0	0.0	0.0	0.0	0.0	0.0
T	0.0	0.0	0.0	0.0	T

Average Temperature

Year	Jan	Feb	Mar	Apr	May	June	July	Aug	Sept	Oct	Nov	Dec	Annual
1941	49.7	52.9	56.7	57.2	64.5	69.3	75.9	72.2	69.1	61.4	54.6	40.9	61.0
1942	45.8	49.3	52.6	56.8	60.8	70.5	75.8	73.5	69.4	64.2	52.6	45.7	59.8
1943	46.0	51.0	54.6	58.1	65.9	66.3	74.4	72.0	71.7	61.9	53.7	47.6	60.3
1944	46.6	49.0	54.4	54.6	64.1	67.2	72.2	73.9	73.4	64.4	50.7	46.9	59.8
1945	43.9	51.1	49.8	59.4	61.1	71.9	76.6	72.9	71.8	64.8	51.7	46.5	60.1
1946	44.6	45.6	52.1	58.1	63.1	68.5	74.6	73.3	70.8	60.3	50.2	45.3	58.9
1947	41.5	49.7	55.0	61.3	68.1	71.3	72.6	72.0	72.9	61.7	49.5	44.8	60.0
1948	48.2	47.2	49.6	53.4	59.9	69.1	73.0	72.0	70.0	62.6	51.9	42.0	58.2
1949	38.4	45.4	52.8	61.4	64.2	72.4	73.8	71.5	71.3	61.3	55.1	43.1	59.2
1950	42.0	50.0	51.8	60.5	64.5	68.6	75.6	75.4	71.0	63.4	57.1	50.1	60.8
1951	45.3	49.7	53.3	58.1	64.9	69.2	72.9	72.6	71.2	62.2	53.7	44.8	59.8
1952	44.0	48.7	50.4	59.1	65.7	65.3	74.7	73.9	73.1	65.6	50.4	46.9	59.8
1953	50.9	50.5	52.6	57.4	59.8	67.3	76.5	71.1	72.8	62.2	53.7	47.3	60.2
1954	46.4	48.8	50.8	61.6	65.7	69.4	75.7	70.2	68.7	61.9	51.1	43.5	59.5
1955	42.0	47.6	53.9	53.6	65.2	69.2	72.5	74.9	71.5	63.5	51.5	49.5	59.6
1956	47.5	47.1	54.0	58.6	64.7	72.1	74.3	72.1	71.0	60.9	53.1	44.2	60.0
1957	43.4	52.2	54.4	60.5	64.1	74.9	75.7	72.7	71.4	61.0	51.6	45.3	60.6
1958	45.8	54.0	50.8	59.7	66.9	70.8	74.5	78.5	73.8	67.3	54.4	50.3	62.2
1959	49.1	49.4	57.2	63.8	64.6	74.2	77.7	73.9	69.7	66.3	54.5	46.7	62.3
#1960	46.4	50.8	56.3	59.9	64.9	77.1	78.9	75.5	72.4	65.7	53.1	45.8	62.2
1961	42.4	51.8	53.0	59.6	62.4	76.4	79.2	77.2	70.4	64.0	52.1	44.1	61.1
1962	41.8	47.6	51.1	61.4	63.5	71.6	75.1	74.9	70.9	62.3	54.6	46.0	60.1
1963	41.1	55.9	51.0	53.6	62.1	70.1	73.9	75.1	73.9	64.2	51.6	41.1	59.5
1964	45.1	49.4	52.3	58.9	63.0	70.0	75.9	75.8	70.3	66.7	50.3	49.7	60.6
1965	45.4	49.2	53.0	57.3	64.4	67.0	74.4	75.7	67.6	65.9	54.7	41.0	59.6
1966	45.7	47.5	54.3	62.9	66.4	72.6	72.9	76.9	72.0	64.1	54.7	46.1	61.4
1967	45.9	48.4	50.8	49.6	65.2	69.4	78.0	79.0	74.9	65.5	56.2	44.0	60.6
1968	43.4	54.5	55.1	59.8	64.7	73.9	76.2	73.0	72.2	62.0	52.3	43.5	60.9
1969	44.0	47.4	52.4	57.1	66.9	69.0	76.3	77.9	74.0	61.0	53.9	48.0	60.7
1970	49.3	51.9	54.9	56.1	67.6	71.5	76.8	74.7	72.8	62.1	55.3	46.1	61.6
1971	45.3	48.2	52.6	56.4	61.8	70.5	76.2	76.8	72.2	61.2	52.7	43.0	59.8
1972	41.0	51.4	58.6	58.6	66.9	72.5	76.0	75.9	69.5	62.0	49.7	40.6	60.2
1973	44.3	53.1	51.1	60.8	69.4	74.6	76.8	74.2	70.8	63.4	51.9	46.9	61.5
1974	46.3	48.4	54.1	56.6	63.8	70.5	74.1	74.0	72.2	66.3	53.2	46.4	60.5
1975	43.4	49.2	50.3	51.8	68.2	73.2	77.3	76.9	77.4	65.1	54.6	47.4	61.2
RECORD													
MEAN	44.9	49.8	53.1	58.1	64.5	70.8	75.4	74.3	71.6	63.4	52.9	45.7	60.4
MAX	52.7	59.1	64.0	71.1	79.1	86.8	93.0	91.5	87.8	77.1	63.3	53.1	73.2
MIN	37.0	40.5	42.1	45.1	49.9	54.7	57.7	57.1	55.4	49.7	42.5	38.2	47.5

# Indicates a station move or relocation of instruments.

SACRAMENTO, CA

Feb	Mar	Apr	May	June	Total
363	364	172	84	0	2653
482	425	121	82	4	2969
249	428	333	115	2	2844
448	389	194	99	22	2961
434	363	246	86	21	2720
485	326	96	36	14	2640
461	435	456	98	34	3016
296	299	171	80	2	2446
486	384	230	41	6	2929
359	304	258	56	9	2436
466	379	249	114	14	2822
390	197	190	63	11	2842
325	424	141	15	1	2863
456	332	251	93	9	2726
435	449	389	69	1	2971

Aug	Sept	Oct	Nov	Dec	Total
409	278	13	0	0	1306
305	245	46	0	0	1321
375	254	82	0	0	1274
349	147	30	0	0	1262
293	181	34	0	0	1351
285	222	89	0	0	1138
375	375	81	0	0	1654

Precipitation

Year	Jan	Feb	Mar	Apr	May	June	July	Aug	Sept	Oct	Nov	Dec	Annual
1940	6.67	7.16	3.44	0.83	0.78	T	0.00	0.00	0.01	0.97	1.28	7.33	28.47
1941	4.78	3.98	2.86	4.76	1.35	0.02	0.00	T	T	0.85	0.99	5.02	24.61
1942	4.34	2.55	2.68	4.70	0.85	0.00	T	0.00	0.02	0.17	1.45	2.70	19.46
1943	5.90	1.19	3.94	1.60	0.18	0.04	T	0.00	0.00	0.20	0.62	1.82	15.49
1944	2.50	6.41	1.36	1.79	0.91	0.10	0.00	0.00	T	1.40	3.12	2.05	19.64
1945	1.44	3.88	2.33	0.10	0.40	0.04	T	T	0.00	2.63	1.45	4.84	17.11
1946	0.56	0.73	1.81	0.10	0.54	0.00	T	0.00	0.01	0.58	2.42	1.24	7.99
1947	0.47	2.06	2.32	0.16	0.15	0.25	0.00	0.00	0.01	2.51	1.01	0.53	9.47
1948	0.38	0.80	3.26	2.63	3.13	T	0.00	0.00	0.01	1.39	0.45	4.84	16.89
1949	1.47	1.76	3.73	0.00	0.21	0.00	0.02	0.03	0.01	0.13	1.12	1.93	10.41
1950	3.96	2.88	1.78	0.62	0.40	0.02	0.01	0.00	0.35	2.44	4.80	4.55	21.81
1951	1.97	1.62	0.66	0.69	0.47	T	0.00	0.00	0.14	1.33	2.85	4.71	14.44
1952	7.96	1.13	4.13	1.32	0.03	0.25	0.01	0.00	T	T	2.00	7.10	23.93
1953	2.56	0.20	1.22	2.13	0.41	0.63	0.00	0.07	0.00	0.32	1.48	0.55	9.57
1954	2.67	3.58	3.02	1.62	0.20	T	0.00	0.34	0.00	0.01	3.01	4.41	18.86
1955	2.87	1.02	0.44	2.31	0.57	T	0.00	T	0.67	0.47	1.27	12.64	22.26
1956	6.10	1.91	0.17	1.44	0.86	T	0.00	0.00	0.84	1.23	0.06	0.17	12.78
1957	2.11	4.19	2.07	1.50	1.61	T	T	0.00	1.08	0.92	0.51	2.99	16.98
1958	4.87	7.72	5.62	4.00	0.76	0.23	0.00	0.01	0.08	0.24	0.09	0.76	24.38
1959	4.93	4.11	0.53	0.21	T	0.00	T	T	1.61	0.00	0.02	1.36	12.77
1960	3.43	3.34	1.43	1.32	0.55	0.00	0.01	0.00	T	T	4.25	0.87	15.20
1961	3.47	1.25	2.02	0.46	0.18	0.01	T	0.03	0.17	0.03	3.13	2.47	13.22
1962	1.00	8.77	1.69	0.15	0.03	0.01	0.00	0.13	0.06	7.51	0.39	1.84	21.58
1963	4.71	2.09	4.25	3.54	0.69	T	0.00	T	0.47	1.09	4.35	0.45	21.64
1964	3.83	0.15	1.36	0.17	0.23	0.39	0.01	0.11	0.00	1.72	2.70	6.03	16.70
1965	3.01	0.41	1.47	2.70	0.09	T	T	0.65	T	0.11	2.93	2.44	13.81
1966	1.91	1.56	0.14	0.47	0.25	0.02	0.10	T	0.07	0.00	5.73	3.53	13.78
1967	8.42	0.41	3.91	3.40	0.13	0.60	T	0.00	0.04	0.24	1.18	1.29	19.62
1968	3.77	2.13	2.39	0.42	0.16	0.15	T	0.02	0.00	0.60	2.49	2.77	14.90
1969	8.50	6.98	0.94	1.63	0.04	0.08	T	0.00	0.02	0.72	0.60	4.41	23.92
1970	7.88	1.58	1.62	0.18	T	0.16	0.00	0.00	0.00	0.84	7.41	3.40	23.07
1971	0.90	0.56	2.05	0.44	0.77	0.01	0.00	0.00	T	0.13	0.87	4.05	9.78
1972	0.81	1.28	0.29	1.39	0.28	0.19	0.00	0.00	0.90	1.75	5.14	1.88	13.91
1973	6.87	5.64	2.76	0.05	0.13	0.00	0.00	0.00	0.33	1.64	6.27	2.79	26.48
1974	3.58	1.37	3.27	0.96	0.01	0.50	0.79	T	0.00	1.16	0.66	2.86	15.16
1975	0.73	4.59	4.28	0.81	T	T	0.04	0.23	T	2.03	0.29	0.18	13.18
RECORD													
MEAN	3.65	2.81	2.26	1.41	0.48	0.10	0.03	0.05	0.19	1.04	2.18	3.13	17.33

Record mean values above are means through the current year for the period beginning in 1941 for temperature, 1940 for precipitation, and 1949 for snowfall. Data are from Airport locations.

SACRAMENTO, CALIFORNIA

(Continued)

occasionally disagreeable winds, known as "northers" in the valley, are the counterpart of the well-known "chinook" winds of the Rocky Mountains, and they, or modifications of them, produce the pronounced heat waves in summer. Fortunately, they are of infrequent occurrence and produce an unstable atmospheric condition that is usually followed within two or three days by the normally cool southerly breezes, especially at night. Summer nights in the lower Sacramento Valley are, with few exceptions, cool and invigorating, the result of a prevailing oceanic influence. While it is true that "northers" cause dry, hot weather for brief periods during the summer, it is equally true they are the modifications of cold waves in the winter. Winter northers, with only a few exceptions, are comparatively warm, drying winds.

As is well know, relative humidity has a marked influence on the reactions of plants and animals to temperature. The extremely low relative humidity that accompanies high temperatures in this valley should be considered when comparing temperatures here with those of cities in more humid regions.

Thunderstorms are few in number and usually mild in character. Snow falls so rarely, and in such small amounts, that its ocurrence may be disregarded as a climatic feature. Heavy fog occurs mostly in midwinter, never in summer, and seldom in spring or autumn. Light and moderate fog are more frequent, and may come anytime during the wet, cold season. An occasional winter fog, under stagnant atmospheric conditions, may continue for several days.

Sacramento is the geographical center of the great interior valleys of California. This region produces a wide and abundant variety of fruits, cereals, and vegetables ranging from the semi-tropical to hardier varieties.

Normals, Means, and Extremes

Month	Normal Degree days Base 65 °F		Precipitation in inches												Relative humidity pct.			
			Water equivalent							Snow, Ice pellets							
	Heating	Cooling	Normal	Maximum monthly	Year	Minimum monthly	Year	Maximum in 24 hrs.	Year	Maximum monthly	Year	Maximum in 24 hrs.	Year	Hour 04 (Local time)	Hour 10	Hour 16	Hour 22
(a)				36		36		27		27		27		15	15	15	15
J	617	0	3.73	8.50	1969	0.38	1948	3.41	1967	T	1974	T	1974	90	86	71	86
F	426	0	2.68	8.77	1962	0.15	1964	2.51	1958	T	1949	T	1949	87	79	61	81
M	372	0	2.17	5.62	1958	0.14	1966	2.07	1963	0.0		0.0		83	68	52	76
A	227	26	1.54	4.76	1941	0.00	1949	2.22	1958	0.0		0.0		80	58	43	72
M	120	98	0.51	3.13	1948	T	1975	0.78	1957	0.0		0.0		81	52	37	71
J	20	185	0.10	0.63	1953	0.00	1973	0.63	1953	0.0		0.0		79	48	32	65
J	0	316	0.01	0.79	1974	0.00	1973	0.78	1974	0.0		0.0		76	48	28	61
A	0	286	0.05	0.65	1965	0.00	1973	0.65	1965	0.0		0.0		76	49	28	62
S	5	200	0.19	1.61	1959	0.00	1974	1.56	1959	0.0		0.0		76	50	31	64
O	101	48	0.99	7.51	1962	0.00	1966	5.59	1962	0.0		0.0		79	58	40	69
N	360	0	2.13	7.41	1970	0.02	1959	2.95	1970	0.0		0.0		86	77	61	81
D	595	0	3.12	12.64	1955	0.17	1956	3.64	1955	T	1972	T	1972	90	86	73	87
YR	2843	1159	17.22	12.64	DEC 1955	0.00	SEP 1974	5.59	OCT 1962	T	JAN 1974	T	JAN 1974	82	63	46	73

(To better understand these tables, see full explanation of terms beginning on page 322)

Month	Wind					Pct. of possible sunshine	Mean sky cover, tenths, sunrise to sunset	Mean number of days											Average station pressure mb.
			Fastest mile					Sunrise to sunset							Temperatures °F				
															Max.		Min.		
	Mean speed m.p.h.	Prevailing direction	Speed m.p.h.	Direction	Year			Clear	Partly cloudy	Cloudy	Precipitation .01 inch or more	Snow, Ice pellets 1.0 inch or more	Thunderstorms	Heavy fog, visibility ¼ mile or less	(b) 90° and above	32° and below	32° and below	0° and below	Elev. 25 feet m.s.l.
(a)	27	14	27	27		27	27	27	27	27	36	27	27	27	25	25	25	25	3
J	8.0	SE	60	SE	1954	45	7.1	6	6	19	10	0	*	10	0	*	8	0	1019.4
F	8.0	SSE	51	SE	1959	61	6.2	8	6	14	9	0	*	6	0	0	1	0	1018.5
M	9.0	SW	66	S	1952	70	5.5	11	8	12	8	0	1	2	0	0	1	0	1014.9
A	9.1	SW	45	SW	1955	80	4.6	13	9	8	6	0	1	*	*	0	*	0	1015.9
M	9.4	SW	35	S	1957	86	3.6	17	9	5	3	0	*	*	5	0	0	0	1012.5
J	10.0	SW	47	SW	1950	92	2.2	22	5	3	1	0	*	0	12	0	0	0	1010.9
J	9.2	SSW	36	SW	1956	97	1.0	27	3	1	*	0	*	0	23	0	0	0	1011.3
A	8.7	SW	38	SW	1954	96	1.4	26	4	1	*	0	*	*	21	0	0	0	1011.4
S	7.9	SW	42	NW	1965	94	1.6	24	4	2	1	0	*	*	13	0	0	0	1011.6
O	6.9	SW	68	SE	1950	84	3.3	19	6	6	3	0	*	2	2	0	0	0	1015.0
N	6.5	NNW	70	SE	1953	64	5.7	10	7	13	7	0	*	6	0	0	1	0	1018.3
D	7.2	SSE	70	SE	1952	46	6.9	7	6	18	10	0	*	9	0	*	6	0	1021.6
YR	8.3	SW	70	SE	NOV 1953	79	4.1	190	73	102	58	0	5	35	77	*	17	0	1015.1

FOOTNOTES

Means and extremes above are from existing and comparable exposures. Annual extremes have been exceeded at other sites in the locality as follows: Lowest temperature 17 in December 1932; maximum monthly precipitation 15.04 in January 1862; maximum precipitation in 24 hours 7.24 in April 1880.

Station: SAN DIEGO, CALIFORNIA
LINDBERGH FIELD
Elevation (ground): 13 feet

TEMPERATURES °F

Month	Normal			Extremes			
	Daily maximum	Daily minimum	Monthly	Record highest	Year	Record lowest	Year
(a)				15		15	
J	64.6	45.8	55.2	86	1969	31	1963
F	65.6	47.8	56.7	85	1963	38	1965
M	66.0	50.1	58.1	85	1964	39	1971
A	67.6	53.8	60.7	91	1971	44	1965
M	69.4	57.2	63.3	91	1967	48	1967
J	71.1	59.9	65.5	90	1973	51	1967
J	75.3	63.9	69.6	92	1972	57	1964
A	77.3	65.4	71.4	90	1972	58	1975
S	76.5	63.2	69.9	111	1963	56	1966
O	73.8	58.4	66.1	107	1961	43	1971
N	70.1	51.5	60.8	97	1966	38	1964
D	66.1	47.2	56.7	88	1963	36	1974
YR	70.3	55.4	62.9	111	SEP 1963	31	JAN 1963

IMPORTANT:
The time-period covered by this record is limited: See footnotes on next page for explanation and for additional history of EXTREME HIGHS AND LOWS recorded in the general area.

The city of San Diego is located on San Diego Bay in the southwest corner of southern California. The prevailing winds and weather are tempered by the Pacific Ocean, with the result that summers are cool and winters warm in comparison with other places along the same general latitude. Temperatures freezing or below have occurred only 11 times at the station since the record began in 1871, but hot weather (90° F. or above) is more frequent.

Dry easterly winds sometimes blow in the vicinity for several days at a time, bringing temperatures in the nineties, and at times even in the hundreds, in the eastern sections of the City and outlying suburbs. At the Weather Bureau station itself, however, there have been only 14 days on which 100° or higher was reached.

As these hot winds are predominant in the fall, highest temperatures occur in the months of September and October. Records show that 62 percent of the days with 90° or higher have occurred in these two months. High temperatures are almost invariably accompanied by very low relative humidities, which often drop below 20 percent and occasionally below 10 percent.

A marked feature of the climate is the wide variation in temperature within short distances. In nearby valleys daytimes are much warmer in summer and nights noticeably cooler in winter, and freezing occurs much more frequently than in the City. Although records show unusually small daily temperature ranges, averaging only about 15° between the highest and lowest readings, a few miles inland these ranges increase to 30° or more.

Strong winds and gales are infrequent in the region, and in San Diego harbor (which is landlocked) velocities over 30 m.p.h. occur only about once each year on the average.

The seasonal rainfall is near 10 inches in the City, but increases with elevation and distance from the coast, and in the mountains to the north and east the average is between 20 and 40 inches, depending on slope and elevation. Most of the precipitation falls in winter, except in the mountains where there is an occasional thundershower. Seventy-five percent of the rainfall occurs from November through March, but wide variations take place in monthly and seasonal totals. Irrigation is extensively practiced, not only during the long dry summers and autumns, but also in years with deficient rainfall. Infrequent measurable amounts of sleet and hail occur in San Diego, but only twice has snow been observed at the Weather Bureau Office location. The first occurrence was on January 10, 1949. Light snow, mixed with rain, melted as it fell. On December 13, 1967, snow pellets (or graupel) fell between 7:30 and 8:50 a.m. A trace was recorded, and remained on the ground for about 5 minutes before melting. Some nearby areas within 5 miles of the station, received larger amounts of snow, both in pellet and flake form. In some locations amounts up to or slightly exceeding a half-inch fell, and remained on the ground for an hour or more.

As on the rest of the Pacific Coast, a dominant characteristic of spring and summer is the nighttime and early morning cloudiness. Low clouds form regularly, and frequently extend inland over the coastal valleys and foothills, but they usually dissipate during the morning and the afternoons are generally clear.

Considerable fog occurs along the coast, but the amount decreases with distance inland. The fall and winter months are usually the foggiest. Thunderstorms are rare, averaging about three a year in the City. Visibilities are good as a rule. The sunshine is plentiful for a marine location, with a marked increase towards the interior.

SAN DIEGO, CALIFORNIA

Normals, Means, and Extremes

(To better understand these tables, see full explanation of terms beginning on page 322)

Month	Normal Degree days Base 65 °F: Heating	Cooling	Precipitation in inches – Water equivalent: Normal	Maximum monthly	Year	Minimum monthly	Year	Maximum in 24 hrs.	Year	Snow, Ice pellets: Maximum monthly	Year	Maximum in 24 hrs.	Year
(a)				35		35		35		35		35	
J	314	10	1.88	6.26	1943	T	1948	2.65	1943	T	1949	T	1949
F	237	0	1.48	5.31	1941	0.00	1967	1.71	1941	0.0		0.0	
M	219	0	1.55	5.89	1941	T	1972	2.40	1952	0.0		0.0	
A	144	15	0.81	3.58	1965	T	1966	1.40	1965	0.0		0.0	
M	79	26	0.15	0.95	1971	0.00	1952	0.42	1957	0.0		0.0	
J	52	67	0.05	0.38	1972	0.00	1946	0.28	1972	0.0		0.0	
J	6	149	0.01	0.13	1968	0.00	1964	0.10	1968	0.0		0.0	
A	0	201	0.07	0.87	1945	0.00	1970	0.83	1951	0.0		0.0	
S	16	163	0.13	1.90	1963	0.00	1964	0.90	1963	0.0		0.0	
O	43	77	0.34	2.90	1941	0.00	1967	1.20	1941	0.0		0.0	
N	140	14	1.25	5.82	1965	0.00	1956	2.44	1944	0.0		0.0	
D	257	0	1.73	7.60	1943	0.03	1953	3.07	1945	T	1967	T	1967
YR	1507	722	9.45	7.60	DEC 1943	0.00	AUG 1970	3.07	DEC 1945	T	DEC 1967	T	DEC 1967

Month	Relative humidity pct. (Local time): Hour 04	Hour 10	Hour 16	Hour 22	Wind: Mean speed m.p.h.	Prevailing direction	Fastest mile: Speed m.p.h.	Direction	Year	Pct. of possible sunshine	Mean sky cover, tenths, sunrise to sunset
(a)	15	15	15	15	35	15	32	32		35	35
J	68	54	55	68	5.6	NE	39	SW	1955	71	4.9
F	72	56	57	71	6.3	WNW	35	S	1969	72	5.0
M	74	59	59	72	7.2	WNW	46	SW	1945	70	5.2
A	74	58	58	71	7.6	WNW	37	S	1958	65	5.2
M	76	64	63	74	7.6	WNW	27	SW	1947	58	5.7
J	80	69	67	78	7.5	SSW	26	S	1948	56	5.6
J	81	69	66	79	7.1	WNW	23	NW	1968	68	4.5
A	80	67	66	78	7.0	WNW	23	SW	1945	69	4.1
S	78	65	64	77	6.7	NW	25	W	1955	68	4.0
O	74	58	61	73	6.3	WNW	31	N	1961	67	4.3
N	73	57	63	73	5.7	NE	51	SE	1944	73	4.1
D	70	55	57	70	5.5	NE	34	S	1951	71	4.7
YR	75	61	61	74	6.7	WNW	51	SE	NOV 1944	67	4.8

Month	Mean number of days – Sunrise to sunset: Clear	Partly cloudy	Cloudy	Precipitation .01 inch or more	Snow, Ice pellets 1.0 inch or more	Thunderstorms	Heavy fog, visibility ¼ mile or less	Temperatures °F Max.: (b) 90° and above	32° and below	Min.: 32° and below	0° and below	Average station pressure mb. Elev. 28 feet m.s.l.
(a)	35	35	35	35	35	35	35	15	15	15	15	3
J	13	7	11	6	0	*	4	0	0	*	0	1017.6
F	11	7	10	6	0	*	3	0	0	0	0	1017.8
M	11	10	10	7	0	*	2	0	0	0	0	1015.4
A	10	10	10	5	0	*	1	*	0	0	0	1015.4
M	9	11	11	2	0	*	1	*	0	0	0	1013.7
J	9	12	9	1	0	*	1	*	0	0	0	1012.2
J	13	13	5	*	0	*	1	*	0	0	0	1012.6
A	15	12	4	*	0	*	1	*	0	0	0	1012.5
S	16	9	5	1	0	*	3	1	0	0	0	1012.0
O	15	9	7	2	0	*	4	1	0	0	0	1014.4
N	15	8	7	5	0	*	4	*	0	0	0	1016.2
D	14	8	9	6	0	*	4	0	0	0	0	1018.2
YR	151	116	98	41	0	3	28	3	0	*	0	1014.8

FOOTNOTES

Means and extremes above are from existing and comparable exposures. Annual extremes have been exceeded at other sites in the locality as follows: Lowest temperature 25 in January 1913; maximum monthly precipitation 9.26 in December 1921; maximum precipitation in 24 hours 3.62 in December 1940; fastest mile of wind 53 from Southeast in February 1938.

Snowfall

Season	July	Aug	Sept	Oct	Nov	Dec	Jan
1970-71	0.0	0.0	0.0	0.0	0.0	0.0	0.0
1971-72	0.0	0.0	0.0	0.0	0.0	0.0	0.0
1972-73	0.0	0.0	0.0	0.0	0.0	0.0	0.0
1973-74	0.0	0.0	0.0	0.0	0.0	0.0	0.0
1974-75	0.0	0.0	0.0	0.0	0.0	0.0	0.0
1975-76	0.0	0.0	0.0	0.0	0.0	0.0	
RECORD MEAN	0.0	0.0	0.0	0.0	0.0	T	T

Heating Degree Days

Season	July	Aug	Sept	Oct	Nov	Dec	Jan
1955-56	0	0	1	54	154	236	290
1956-57	0	0	0	35	75	156	259
1957-58	0	0	0	8	126	117	170
1958-59	0	0	0	1	93	108	156
1959-60	0	0	0	11	23	150	309
#1960-61	0	0	0	25	129	261	136
1961-62	0	0	0	33	152	269	257
1962-63	0	0	1	25	154	258	299
1963-64	0	0	0	6	115	202	296
1964-65	0	0	0	8	187	280	277
1965-66	3	0	0	9	118	303	335
1966-67	0	0	0	4	113	236	302
1967-68	0	0	0	3	42	288	239
1968-69	0	0	0	9	104	306	214
1969-70	0	0	0	14	44	178	240
1970-71	0	0	0	12	107	290	331
1971-72	0	0	0	78	160	326	310
1972-73	0	0	0	29	149	224	286
1973-74	0	0	0	6	132	205	243
1974-75	0	0	0	14	97	265	273
1975-76	0	0	0	19	141	246	

Cooling Degree Days

Year	Jan	Feb	Mar	Apr	May	June	July
1969	5	0	1	9	3	31	144
1970	0	1	1	1	21	40	172
1971	5	3	0	19	7	31	142
1972	0	0	0	4	33	68	247
1973	0	0	0	10	17	97	133
1974	0	0	0	2	9	69	204
1975	0	0	0	0	1	18	142

Feb	Mar	Apr	May	June	Total
0.0	0.0	0.0	0.0	0.0	0.0
0.0	0.0	0.0	0.0	0.0	0.0
0.0	0.0	0.0	0.0	0.0	0.0
0.0	0.0	0.0	0.0	0.0	0.0
0.0	0.0	0.0	0.0	0.0	0.0
0.0	0.0	0.0	0.0	0.0	T

SAN DIEGO, CA

Feb	Mar	Apr	May	June	Total
327	208	182	57	8	1517
146	161	122	53	4	1011
122	221	79	11	0	854
216	73	29	25	0	701
228	151	89	45	4	1010
160	182	100	103	43	1139
231	280	103	77	33	1435
114	227	180	43	21	1322
234	222	154	125	40	1394
249	195	138	73	35	1442
284	209	107	40	4	1412
197	183	245	72	48	1400
119	135	85	47	8	966
274	248	101	63	9	1328
142	133	143	58	12	964
266	215	143	109	29	1502
203	139	78	34	0	1328
131	208	107	61	1	1196
184	176	85	55	4	1090
237	225	182	83	10	1386

Aug	Sept	Oct	Nov	Dec	Total
247	154	53	26	5	678
247	145	58	7	0	693
327	224	107	1	0	866
230	117	53	0	1	753
176	121	70	8	1	633
169	164	75	19	0	711
124	201	54	8	0	548

Average Temperature

Year	Jan	Feb	Mar	Apr	May	June	July	Aug	Sept	Oct	Nov	Dec	Annual
1936	56.6	56.3	57.4	58.2	63.2	65.3	70.6	71.4	68.0	65.0	63.7	58.1	62.8
1937	49.2	54.4	56.6	59.7	62.1	64.9	68.4	68.8	69.4	64.6	60.0	60.2	61.5
1938	58.4	57.2	57.2	60.0	61.6	63.2	66.8	69.5	70.4	63.6	59.2	59.6	62.2
1939	55.6	52.4	55.2	61.0	62.2	64.8	68.1	70.1	72.8	67.8	63.8	61.0	62.9
#1940	58.6	57.9	60.3	62.6	64.8	65.2	68.4	69.0	68.7	66.4	61.1	60.8	63.6
1941	57.6	59.9	62.0	60.9	67.2	66.4	69.4	70.8	68.0	65.6	63.4	57.6	64.1
1942	57.7	55.6	57.9	60.2	63.3	64.9	69.6	70.0	67.8	66.0	61.0	57.5	62.6
1943	57.0	59.7	60.0	61.0	65.0	65.2	69.0	71.2	68.7	65.8	61.7	57.8	63.5
1944	56.4	54.6	58.7	59.5	62.8	64.2	66.8	69.4	66.9	64.6	59.8	58.2	61.8
1945	55.2	56.8	55.8	58.4	62.6	65.0	69.0	71.8	71.4	67.4	60.0	57.3	62.6
1946	56.1	54.4	57.1	62.4	63.7	68.0	70.8	72.4	71.0	64.2	58.2	57.1	63.0
1947	53.5	58.5	60.8	62.7	63.9	66.7	69.4	71.0	71.1	66.6	58.4	55.8	63.2
1948	55.7	54.2	55.9	61.2	62.4	64.6	67.0	68.2	68.3	64.1	60.0	53.6	61.3
1949	47.8	52.7	56.2	61.3	63.0	67.2	69.4	70.2	70.0	64.3	64.6	54.8	61.8
1950	52.1	55.6	58.3	60.7	61.2	64.1	69.7	68.2	67.5	66.8	62.5	59.8	62.2
1951	55.7	55.6	58.7	60.7	62.2	65.7	69.3	69.0	67.8	66.8	61.6	55.5	62.4
1952	54.4	57.8	55.9	59.7	64.1	63.9	68.3	70.2	70.5	65.2	59.6	56.4	62.2
1953	60.0	57.0	57.7	58.9	62.9	64.8	70.8	69.9	68.1	67.4	63.1	57.7	63.2
1954	55.0	61.2	57.2	61.0	62.9	65.0	71.9	71.0	69.3	64.2	63.7	58.2	63.4
1955	53.9	55.5	59.7	59.6	61.7	64.7	68.3	72.4	71.5	63.3	60.0	57.1	62.3
1956	55.4	53.5	58.1	58.8	64.5	66.3	69.4	69.7	72.1	65.7	64.2	59.9	63.1
1957	56.5	60.1	59.7	60.7	63.2	68.2	71.3	73.3	70.1	65.6	60.7	61.4	64.2
1958	59.5	60.5	57.6	63.8	65.9	68.0	70.1	73.0	72.7	70.9	61.9	61.9	65.5
1959	59.7	57.1	63.3	64.7	64.3	68.2	73.7	73.6	71.6	67.2	65.3	60.2	65.7
1960	54.9	56.9	60.0	62.9	64.8	66.4	71.2	71.2	72.3	66.0	60.5	56.3	63.6
#1961	60.7	59.0	58.9	61.9	61.5	64.7	70.1	72.6	69.6	66.7	60.3	56.1	63.5
1962	56.7	56.5	55.7	61.8	62.6	63.9	68.3	70.5	68.4	64.6	59.8	56.4	62.1
1963	55.1	61.2	57.5	58.7	63.6	64.7	68.2	72.1	74.3	68.2	61.2	58.5	63.6
1964	55.3	56.7	57.8	60.2	60.9	64.0	69.2	70.7	67.7	68.6	59.1	55.6	62.1
1965	56.0	55.9	58.6	60.7	62.5	63.7	67.7	72.0	68.5	69.4	60.9	55.1	62.6
1966	53.9	54.6	58.1	61.3	63.5	66.5	69.2	72.6	69.9	67.6	61.9	57.2	63.0
1967	55.0	57.8	59.0	56.5	63.5	63.6	70.4	73.1	72.0	68.1	64.1	55.5	63.2
1968	57.2	60.7	60.7	62.4	63.9	65.8	71.7	72.2	71.3	66.6	61.7	54.9	64.1
1969	58.1	54.9	56.8	61.7	62.9	65.5	69.4	72.8	69.9	66.0	64.1	59.1	63.4
1970	57.0	59.7	60.5	60.1	63.6	65.6	70.4	72.8	69.7	66.3	61.4	55.4	63.5
1971	54.3	55.4	57.8	60.7	61.5	64.9	69.4	75.4	72.2	65.7	59.5	54.2	62.6
1972	54.9	57.8	60.2	62.3	64.7	67.0	72.7	72.2	68.7	65.6	59.8	57.5	63.6
1973	55.6	59.9	58.1	61.5	63.4	68.0	69.1	70.5	68.8	66.8	60.6	58.2	63.4
1974	56.9	58.2	59.1	62.0	63.3	66.9	71.4	70.2	70.3	66.8	62.2	56.3	63.6
1975	56.1	56.4	57.5	58.7	62.2	65.0	69.4	68.9	71.5	65.9	60.4	56.9	62.4
RECORD MEAN	55.1	56.1	57.6	59.7	61.9	64.7	68.4	69.8	68.3	64.7	60.6	56.8	62.0
MAX	63.4	63.9	64.8	66.3	67.4	69.9	73.7	75.2	74.4	71.8	69.1	65.2	68.8
MIN	46.7	48.2	50.3	53.1	56.4	59.4	63.0	64.3	62.2	57.5	52.0	48.3	55.1

# Indicates a station move or relocation of instruments.

Precipitation

Year	Jan	Feb	Mar	Apr	May	June	July	Aug	Sept	Oct	Nov	Dec	Annual
1936	0.75	5.18	0.92	0.48	T	0.01	0.01	0.28	0.04	1.86	0.44	4.45	14.42
1937	1.52	4.22	2.65	0.13	0.32	0.01	0.16	0.00	T	T	0.02	1.06	10.09
1938	0.89	3.26	3.73	0.44	0.15	0.01	T	0.03	0.00	0.23	0.02	4.25	13.01
1939	2.38	1.23	1.17	0.47	0.01	0.00	T	T	2.58	0.61	1.04	0.48	9.97
#1940	1.75	3.56	0.82	0.46	T	T	T	T	0.08	1.50	0.49	6.09	14.75
1941	2.03	5.31	5.89	3.35	T	T	0.06	0.03	0.28	2.90	2.23	2.85	24.93
1942	0.21	1.06	1.91	1.40	0.11	0.01	0.00	T	0.00	0.27	0.27	0.69	5.93
1943	6.26	1.40	1.66	0.52	0.02	0.01	0.00	T	0.04	0.20	0.03	7.60	17.74
1944	1.22	3.65	0.80	0.61	0.22	0.10	T	T	T	T	4.93	1.53	13.06
1945	0.42	1.91	2.03	0.03	0.04	0.15	T	0.87	0.03	T	0.13	3.62	9.23
1946	0.89	0.60	2.67	0.52	0.01	0.00	0.00	T	T	0.34	2.53	1.18	8.74
1947	0.35	0.43	0.97	0.36	0.17	T	0.00	0.00	0.18	0.08	0.72	3.02	6.28
1948	T	1.07	1.60	0.13	0.01	0.02	T	0.00	T	1.32	0.10	2.38	6.63
1949	3.56	1.81	0.75	0.09	0.41	T	T	T	T	0.23	1.16	0.86	8.87
1950	3.31	1.62	1.00	0.28	0.09	T	0.08	0.00	T	0.01	1.23	0.05	7.67
1951	1.60	0.50	0.50	1.95	0.00	T	0.00	0.85	0.04	0.68	1.23	3.87	11.22
1952	4.24	0.60	4.97	1.54	0.00	0.14	T	T	T	T	1.83	2.20	15.52
1953	0.58	0.58	0.79	0.33	0.09	0.14	T	T	T	0.07	0.80	0.03	3.41
1954	2.76	1.03	4.31	0.09	0.01	0.03	T	T	0.00	0.00	0.74	0.55	9.52
1955	3.59	0.56	0.38	0.90	0.49	T	T	0.11	T	T	0.55	0.33	6.91
1956	1.65	0.22	T	1.56	0.10	T	T	T	T	0.68	0.00	0.18	4.39
1957	4.80	0.50	0.75	0.84	0.88	0.26	T	T	0.37	1.76	0.59	1.38	12.13
1958	0.62	3.15	3.98	1.65	0.40	T	T	T	0.62	0.01	0.44	0.06	10.93
1959	0.08	3.76	T	0.31	T	T	T	T	0.04	0.23	0.02	1.44	5.88
1960	2.99	1.45	0.55	0.56	0.17	T	T	0.00	0.06	0.04	1.01	C.22	7.05
1961	1.21	0.06	0.85	T	0.01	T	T	0.04	T	0.20	0.79	1.45	4.61
1962	2.71	3.08	0.64	0.01	0.62	0.09	T	T	0.00	0.01	0.01	0.22	7.39
1963	0.11	1.22	1.33	0.71	0.09	0.28	0.00	T	1.90	0.13	1.85	0.10	7.72
1964	1.30	0.37	0.97	0.20	0.15	0.08	0.00	T	0.00	0.02	1.01	1.17	5.27
1965	0.40	0.52	1.79	3.58	T	0.01	0.02	T	0.29	T	5.82	6.60	19.03
1966	1.29	0.86	0.17	T	0.02	T	T	0.00	T	0.80	0.82	3.22	7.18
1967	2.20	0.00	1.14	2.24	0.05	0.16	0.01	0.14	0.08	0.00	3.53	1.66	11.21
1968	0.35	0.22	1.55	0.34	0.08	T	0.13	T	T	0.04	0.36	0.61	3.68
1969	4.78	4.34	0.94	0.21	0.17	0.02	T	0.01	T	0.04	0.79	0.46	11.76
1970	0.86	2.58	1.50	0.09	0.01	T	T	0.00	T	0.07	2.05	2.22	9.38
1971	0.30	1.27	0.20	0.93	0.95	0.01	T	0.03	T	1.66	0.06	3.27	8.68
1972	0.07	0.10	T	0.02	0.10	0.38	T	0.02	0.44	0.58	3.16	1.61	6.48
1973	1.68	1.63	2.26	0.05	T	T	T	T	0.02	0.01	1.63	0.19	7.47
1974	2.96	0.04	1.70	0.02	0.01	0.02	0.01	T	T	1.03	0.14	2.20	8.13
1975	0.49	0.96	3.79	2.00	0.01	0.02	T	T	T	0.09	0.64	0.37	8.37
RECORD MEAN	1.83	1.87	1.49	0.70	0.27	0.06	0.04	0.C8	0.12	0.42	0.96	1.87	9.71

Record mean values above are means through the current year for the period beginning in 1875 for temperature, 1850 for precipitation and 1941 for snowfall. Data are from City Office locations through January 1940 and from Airport locations thereafter.

San Francisco's unique location at the northern end of a narrow peninsula which separates San Francisco Bay from the Pacific Ocean and forms the southern shore of the Golden Gate -- the only sea level entrance through the Coastal Mountains into the Great Valley -- causes San Francisco to be known as the air conditioned City with cool pleasant summers and mild winters. Flowers bloom throughout the year, and warm clothing is needed in every month.

Sea fogs, and the low stratus cloudiness associated with them, constitute another striking characteristic of San Francisco's climate. In the summertime, the temperature of the Pacific Ocean is unusually low near the coast and atmospheric pressure relatively high, while the interior of California is characterized by the opposite in both elements. This tends strongly to intensify the landward movement of air and to make the prevailing westerly winds brisk and persistent, especially during the period from May to August. The fog or low-lying stratus cloudiness off the coast is carried inland by strong westerly winds during the afternoon or night and evaporated during the subsequent forenoon. Notwithstanding the occurrence of these stratus clouds, the sun shines on an average of 66 percent of the daylight hours in downtown San Francisco.

As a result of the steady sweep of air from the Pacific, there are few extremes of heat or cold. During the entire 88 years of temperature records in San Francisco, temperatures have risen to 90° or higher on an average of but once a year and dropped below freezing less than once a year. As a rule, abnormally warm or cool periods last but a few days.

The diurnal land- and sea-breeze characteristic of many coastal regions does not prevail here. Winds from the land are extremely rare, and it is during these infrequent and brief interludes in the normal west wind of the warm months that the occasional hot days occur.

Pronounced wet and dry seasons are another characteristic of this climate. On the average, 84 percent of the total annual precipitation falls during the five-month period, November to March, leaving but 16 percent for the remaining seven months of the year. Measurable amounts of precipitation fall on less than 70 days a year.

There are wide contrasts in climate within short distances in the San Francisco Bay area, some of which are described briefly for the Peninsula in the Local Climatological Data for San Francisco Airport, and for the East Bay area in the Oakland Airport Local Climatological Data. Moreover, even within the city of San Francisco there are differences in climate, the most obvious being the greater frequency and duration of fogs or low cloudiness along the western or Pacific coastal side of the City.

The nearby communities in Marin County, lying just to the north across the Golden Gate and sheltered from the prevailing ocean winds by the fairly high peaks and ridges of the Coast Range, enjoy generally warmer and sunnier weather than San Francisco. Their climate is further modified by proximity to San Francisco and San Pablo Bays to the eastward. In general, temperatures increase from south to north, with correspondingly greater daily ranges, and also increase slightly with distance from the bays. Daily maximum temperatures for July average 16° warmer at San Rafael and 18° warmer at Kentfield than at San Francisco.

Station: SAN FRANCISCO, CAL
FEDERAL OFFICE BLDG.

Elevation (ground): 52 feet

TEMPERATURES °F

Month	Normal			Extremes			
	Daily maximum	Daily minimum	Monthly	Record highest	Year	Record lowest	Year
(a)				39		39	
J	56.0	45.7	50.9	79	1962	30	1937
F	58.9	47.9	53.4	75	1964	36	1951
M	60.1	48.5	54.3	83	1952	38	1942
A	61.2	49.3	55.3	86	1947	40	1967
M	62.5	50.9	56.7	93	1975	44	1964
J	64.5	52.8	58.7	101	1961	47	1955
J	63.8	53.2	58.5	92	1972	47	1953
A	64.8	54.0	59.4	96	1968	48	1969
S	68.8	55.5	62.2	101	1971	48	1955
O	68.2	54.6	61.4	94	1961	45	1949
N	63.2	51.5	57.4	86	1966	41	1961
D	56.8	47.2	52.0	76	1958	30	1972
YR	62.4	50.9	56.7	101	SEP 1971	30	DEC 1972

IMPORTANT:

The time-period covered by this record is limited: See footnotes following table of **NORMALS, MEANS AND EXTREMES** for explanation and for additional history of **EXTREME HIGHS AND LOWS** recorded in the general area.

(Continued)

As in San Francisco, there are well defined wet and dry seasons, but rainfall amounts are strongly influenced by the topography of the Coast Range. Annual average rainfall varies from 26 inches at Hamilton Field to about 40 inches at San Rafael and 49 inches at Kentfield. During the summer stratus season, low overcast frequently covers the entire area during the early morning hours, but clearing begins early in the forenoon, especially in the more northern portions of the County. Wind direction is a critical factor in the occurrence of late afternoon and evening fogs or clouds in the Sausalito and Belvedere areas on the north side of the Golden Gate. Fog with winds from a direction slightly north of west seldom affects these areas, but ocean fog usually reaches them when the wind is a few points south of west. This fog extends less frequently to more northern communities of the County.

The climate of the coastal strip from Half Moon Bay to the south, to Bolinas Bay to the north is characterized by cool, foggy summers and mild winters. July and August are the foggiest months, but even then there is often some midday clearing. Rainfall along the coastal strip averages slightly more than at San Francisco.

Normals, Means, and Extremes

(To better understand these tables, see full explanation of terms beginning on page 322)

Month	Normal Degree days Base 65 °F: Heating	Normal Degree days Base 65 °F: Cooling	Precipitation in inches, Water equivalent: Normal	Water equivalent: Maximum monthly	Year	Water equivalent: Minimum monthly	Year	Water equivalent: Maximum in 24 hrs.	Year	Snow, Ice pellets $: Maximum monthly	Year	Snow, Ice pellets $: Maximum in 24 hrs.	Year
(a)				39		39		39		36		36	
J	437	0	4.51	10.69	1952	1.00	1948	3.49	1956	T	1962	T	1962
F	325	0	2.97	8.49	1938	0.04	1953	2.34	1940	T	1951	T	1951
M	332	0	2.77	8.22	1958	0.12	1956	3.65	1940	T	1951	T	1951
A	291	0	1.63	5.47	1958	T	1949	2.36	1953	0.0		0.0	
M	257	0	0.54	3.19	1957	T	1972	1.28	1957	0.0		0.0	
J	194	5	0.17	1.42	1967	0.00	1973	1.36	1967	0.0		0.0	
J	202	0	0.01	0.62	1974	0.00	1973	0.61	1974	0.0		0.0	
A	177	0	0.05	0.49	1965	0.00	1974	0.49	1965	0.0		0.0	
S	102	18	0.17	2.06	1959	0.00	1975	2.06	1959	0.0		0.0	
O	127	16	1.06	5.51	1962	T	1959	3.11	1962	0.0		0.0	
N	233	0	2.60	7.80	1973	T	1959	2.72	1973	0.0		0.0	
D	403	0	4.18	11.47	1955	0.18	1975	3.14	1945	T	1972	T	1941
YR	3080	39	20.66	11.47	DEC 1955	0.00	SEP 1975	3.65	MAR 1940	T	DEC 1972	T	JAN 1962

Month	Relative humidity pct. $: Hour 04 (Local time)	Hour 10	Hour 16	Hour 22	Wind: Mean speed m.p.h. ¢	Wind: Prevailing direction	Fastest mile $: Speed m.p.h.	Fastest mile $: Direction	Fastest mile $: Year	Pct. of possible sunshine @	Mean sky cover, tenths, sunrise to sunset	Mean number of days, Sunrise to sunset: Clear	Partly cloudy	Cloudy	Precipitation .01 inch or more	Snow, Ice pellets $ 1.0 inch or more	Thunderstorms %	Heavy fog, visibility ¼ mile or less	Temperatures °F Max. (b) 90° and above	Max. 32° and below	Min. 32° and below	Min. 0° and below	Average station pressure mb. Elev. 155 feet m.s.l.
(a)	7	7	7	7	28	28	36	36		38					39	36	28		39	39	39	39	
J	81	72	63	76	6.7	N	47	SE	1965	56					11	0	*		0	0	*	0	
F	83	70	63	78	7.5	W	47	SW	1938	62					10	0	*		0	0	0	0	
M	81	61	61	76	8.5	W	44	S	1948	69					10	0	*		0	0	0	0	
A	82	59	61	80	9.5	W	38	W	1965	73					6	0	*		0	0	0	0	
M	89	65	68	86	10.4	W	38	W	1965	72					3	0	*		*	0	0	0	
J	89	70	72	88	10.9	W	40	W	1965	73					1	0	*		*	0	0	0	
J	92	73	74	90	11.2	W	38	W	1939	66					1	0	*		*	0	0	0	
A	93	73	73	90	10.5	W	34	W	1966	65					1	0	*		*	0	0	0	
S	87	64	66	82	9.1	W	32	W	1956	72					1	0	*		1	0	0	0	
O	81	62	60	74	7.6	W	43	SE	1950	70					5	0	*		*	0	0	0	
N	82	69	63	76	6.3	W	41	S	1953	62					8	0	*		0	0	0	0	
D	80	71	63	74	6.5	N	45	SE	1965	53					11	0	*		0	0	*	0	
YR	85	67	66	81	8.7		47	SE	JAN 1965	67					68	0	2		1	0	*	0	

FOOTNOTES

Means and extremes above a.e from existing and comparable exposures. Annual extremes have been exceeded at other sites in the locality as follows: Lowest temperature 27 in December 1932; maximum monthly precipitation 24.36 in January 1862; maximum precipitation in 24 hours 4.67 in January 1881; maximum monthly snowfall 3.7 in February 1887; maximum snowfall in 24 hours 3.7 in February 1887; fastest mile of wind 51 from Northeast in December 1923 and earlier.

% Through 1964. The station did not operate 24 hours daily. Thunderstorm data therefore may be incomplete.

¢ Through 1964.

$ Through 1972.

@ Through 1973.

Snowfall

Season	July	Aug	Sept	Oct	Nov	Dec	Jan
1936-37	0.0	0.0	0.0	0.0	0.0	0.0	0.0
1937-38	0.0	0.0	0.0	0.0	0.0	0.0	0.0
1938-39	0.0	0.0	0.0	0.0	0.0	0.0	0.0
1939-40	0.0	0.0	0.0	0.0	0.0	0.0	0.0
1940-41	0.0	0.0	0.0	0.0	0.0	0.0	0.0
1941-42	0.0	0.0	0.0	0.0	0.0	T	0.0
1942-43	0.0	0.0	0.0	0.0	0.0	0.0	0.0
1943-44	0.0	0.0	0.0	0.0	0.0	0.0	0.0
1944-45	0.0	0.0	0.0	0.0	0.0	0.0	0.0
1945-46	0.0	0.0	0.0	0.0	0.0	0.0	0.0
1946-47	0.0	0.0	0.0	0.0	0.0	0.0	0.0
1947-48	0.0	0.0	0.0	0.0	0.0	0.0	0.0
1948-49	0.0	0.0	0.0	0.0	0.0	0.0	0.0
1949-50	0.0	0.0	0.0	0.0	0.0	0.0	0.0
1950-51	0.0	0.0	0.0	0.0	0.0	0.0	0.0
1951-52	0.0	0.0	0.0	0.0	0.0	0.0	0.0
1952-53	0.0	0.0	0.0	0.0	0.0	0.0	0.0
1953-54	0.0	0.0	0.0	0.0	0.0	0.0	0.0
1954-55	0.0	0.0	0.0	0.0	0.0	0.0	0.0
1955-56	0.0	0.0	0.0	0.0	0.0	0.0	0.0
1956-57	0.0	0.0	0.0	0.0	0.0	0.0	T
1957-58	0.0	0.0	0.0	0.0	0.0	0.0	0.0
1958-59	0.0	0.0	0.0	0.0	0.0	0.0	0.0
1959-60	0.0	0.0	0.0	0.0	0.0	0.0	0.0
1960-61	0.0	0.0	0.0	0.0	0.0	0.0	0.0
1961-62	0.0	0.0	0.0	0.0	0.0	0.0	T
1962-63	0.0	0.0	0.0	0.0	0.0	0.0	0.0
1963-64	0.0	0.0	0.0	0.0	0.0	0.0	0.0
1964-65	0.0	0.0	0.0	0.0	0.0	0.0	0.0
1965-66	0.0	0.0	0.0	0.0	0.0	0.0	0.0
1966-67	0.0	0.0	0.0	0.0	0.0	0.0	0.0
1967-68	0.0	0.0	0.0	0.0	0.0	0.0	0.0
1968-69	0.0	0.0	0.0	0.0	0.0	0.0	0.0
1969-70	0.0	0.0	0.0	0.0	0.0	0.0	0.0
1970-71	0.0	0.0	0.0	0.0	0.0	0.0	0.0
1971-72	0.0	0.0	0.0	0.0	0.0	0.0	0.0
1972-73	0.0	0.0	0.0	0.0	0.0	T	0.0
1972-73	0.0	0.0	0.0	0.0	0.0	T	0.0
RECORD MEAN	0.0	0.0	0.0	0.0	0.0	T	T

Heating Degree Days

Season	July	Aug	Sept	Oct	Nov	Dec	Jan
1955-56	246	256	181	176	273	362	405
1956-57	238	182	91	169	172	372	494
1957-58	162	165	56	81	239	413	373
1958-59	178	121	39	112	205	224	333
1959-60	165	119	72	73	146	307	425
1960-61	206	219	170	141	276	415	486
1961-62	167	127	91	156	246	456	398
1962-63	270	157	196	130	182	369	445
1963-64	166	160	39	67	244	514	427
1964-65	186	152	139	100	284	343	414
1965-66	230	123	120	73	199	509	393
1966-67	205	188	78	102	241	417	375
1967-68	184	173	67	47	158	398	465
1968-69	213	98	92	148	258	462	505
1969-70	221	171	132	107	166	277	334
1970-71	231	246	95	201	208	439	433
1971-72	225	120	85	229	275	490	506
1972-73	144	139	110	115	298	546	455
1973-74	199	239	137	134	285	396	423
1974-75	167	153	153	119	243	422	428
1975-76	185	170	177	164	276	352	

Cooling Degree Days

Year	Jan	Feb	Mar	Apr	May	June	July
1969	0	0	5	0	1	1	0
1970	0	0	5	0	19	1	17
1971	0	0	0	0	0	7	0
1972	0	0	3	0	1	4	22
1973	0	0	0	2	5	43	8
1974	0	0	0	3	4	3	4
1975	0	0	0	0	23	0	4

Feb	Mar	Apr	May	June	Total
0.0	0.0	0.0	0.0	0.0	0.0
0.0	0.0	0.0	0.0	0.0	0.0
0.0	0.0	0.0	0.0	0.0	0.0
0.0	0.0	0.0	0.0	0.0	0.0
0.0	0.0	0.0	0.0	0.0	0.0
0.0	0.0	0.0	0.0	0.0	T
0.0	0.0	0.0	0.0	0.0	0.0
0.0	0.0	0.0	0.0	0.0	0.0
0.0	0.0	0.0	0.0	0.0	0.0
0.0	0.0	0.0	0.0	0.0	0.0
0.0	0.0	0.0	0.0	0.0	0.0
0.0	0.0	0.0	0.0	0.0	0.0
0.0	0.0	0.0	0.0	0.0	0.0
0.0	0.0	0.0	0.0	0.0	0.0
T	T	0.0	0.0	0.0	T
0.0	0.0	0.0	0.0	0.0	0.0
0.0	0.0	0.0	0.0	0.0	0.0
0.0	0.0	0.0	0.0	0.0	0.0
0.0	0.0	0.0	0.0	0.0	0.0
0.0	0.0	0.0	0.0	0.0	0.0
0.0	0.0	0.0	0.0	0.0	T
0.0	0.0	0.0	0.0	0.0	0.0
0.0	0.0	0.0	0.0	0.0	0.0
0.0	0.0	0.0	0.0	0.0	0.0
0.0	0.0	0.0	0.0	0.0	0.0
0.0	0.0	0.0	0.0	0.0	T
0.0	0.0	0.0	0.0	0.0	0.0
0.0	0.0	0.0	0.0	0.0	0.0
0.0	0.0	0.0	0.0	0.0	0.0
0.0	0.0	0.0	0.0	0.0	0.0
0.0	0.0	0.0	0.0	0.0	0.0
0.0	0.0	0.0	0.0	0.0	0.0
0.0	0.0	0.0	0.0	0.0	0.0
0.0	0.0	0.0	0.0	0.0	0.0
0.0	0.0	0.0	0.0	0.0	0.0
0.0	0.0	0.0	0.0	0.0	0.0
0.0	0.0	0.0			
0.0	0.0	0.0			
T	T	0.0	0.0	0.0	T

Average Temperature

Year	Jan	Feb	Mar	Apr	May	June	July	Aug	Sept	Oct	Nov	Dec	Annual
#1936	53.8	53.4	57.4	58.9	61.5	61.7	59.4	59.3	63.0	62.2	58.0	51.6	58.4
1937	43.6	49.9	54.8	54.5	57.2	61.4	59.3	58.9	61.4	63.4	58.2	54.8	56.4
1938	51.4	53.0	52.8	54.9	56.6	57.5	58.8	60.1	61.2	61.6	56.8	53.6	56.5
1939	52.0	51.2	52.8	55.8	57.0	57.8	59.0	60.6	66.2	63.0	59.2	55.3	57.5
1940	52.6	55.4	57.4	57.8	58.0	59.0	60.2	60.0	65.0	62.3	57.0	55.4	58.3
1941	54.0	55.4	58.4	55.8	61.2	60.0	60.2	61.2	63.5	60.8	58.4	53.4	58.5
1942	51.2	53.4	55.2	55.6	56.8	58.6	59.7	58.5	60.2	60.9	56.0	52.1	56.5
1943	51.9	54.8	55.6	55.6	58.6	57.4	59.0	59.8	63.4	61.2	59.0	53.6	57.5
1944	51.8	51.6	55.8	53.2	56.8	57.8	57.3	58.9	60.6	61.4	55.7	54.2	56.3
1945	50.2	54.4	51.8	55.9	55.4	61.3	59.6	58.6	62.6	61.6	56.4	52.8	56.7
1946	51.4	50.6	53.2	55.2	55.6	58.8	60.4	58.1	62.8	60.4	54.6	51.4	56.0
1947	47.2	53.6	56.0	58.4	57.8	61.8	60.2	61.8	61.4	62.0	55.3	51.0	57.2
1948	54.7	50.8	51.7	53.6	55.6	59.4	59.3	59.6	60.0	60.4	56.6	47.8	55.8
1949	44.7	48.3	53.2	55.6	56.7	58.8	57.6	59.4	62.4	58.5	59.8	50.6	55.4
1950	46.9	51.9	53.2	56.1	54.7	56.8	57.8	59.6	61.9	61.7	61.0	53.7	56.3
1951	50.3	52.2	54.1	52.4	57.3	56.3	56.3	57.3	59.8	61.5	56.3	50.0	55.3
1952	48.1	52.2	51.7	55.4	57.4	56.6	58.7	57.9	61.5	58.8	55.9	51.6	55.5
1953	54.4	54.0	53.2	52.7	56.6	57.8	57.3	59.5	62.5	61.6	56.7	55.0	56.8
1954	51.5	54.0	52.1	57.0	56.2	58.5	59.1	57.9	61.8	61.5	56.6	49.9	56.3
1955	48.1	52.2	54.8	52.3	56.6	57.0	56.9	56.4	59.1	59.7	56.3	53.1	55.2
1956	51.7	51.4	53.7	54.4	57.6	58.9	57.1	58.9	62.6	59.5	59.4	52.7	56.5
1957	48.8	54.0	54.2	57.7	57.9	61.4	59.6	59.5	63.6	62.3	56.8	51.5	57.3
1958	52.8	56.2	53.1	57.1	59.5	62.5	58.9	61.0	66.8	61.8	58.1	57.5	58.8
1959	54.0	53.5	58.2	57.9	56.8	59.4	60.0	61.9	62.9	65.2	60.2	54.9	58.7
1960	51.0	54.3	55.8	56.0	56.9	59.6	58.1	57.7	59.8	60.9	55.5	51.4	56.4
1961	49.1	55.4	54.3	56.9	55.7	60.2	60.0	61.0	63.4	61.2	56.5	50.0	57.0
1962	51.9	51.8	52.7	57.0	55.2	57.5	56.0	60.0	58.3	60.8	58.8	52.9	56.1
1963	50.4	58.4	54.1	54.4	57.2	58.1	59.7	59.8	64.7	62.9	56.7	48.3	57.1
1964	51.0	55.0	53.2	53.8	53.4	57.8	58.9	60.0	62.4	63.1	55.3	53.7	56.5
1965	51.4	54.0	54.4	55.7	54.9	56.2	57.4	61.2	61.2	65.0	58.1	48.3	56.5
1966	52.1	51.8	53.8	57.9	55.1	59.4	58.2	58.8	63.6	62.6	57.2	51.3	56.8
1967	52.6	53.2	52.7	50.8	57.9	57.1	58.9	59.2	63.5	65.5	60.0	51.9	57.0
1968	49.8	56.7	56.7	56.2	55.7	59.0	58.0	62.3	63.1	60.5	56.2	49.8	57.0
1969	48.6	50.1	54.3	54.2	57.0	58.7	57.6	59.4	60.9	61.9	59.3	55.8	56.5
1970	54.0	57.4	57.8	53.3	57.7	56.8	57.8	57.2	64.4	58.6	57.9	50.6	57.0
1971	50.8	51.9	53.3	53.1	54.6	57.3	57.5	61.1	64.7	57.8	55.6	49.0	55.6
1972	48.5	54.0	55.8	55.5	55.5	57.5	60.9	60.2	61.5	61.7	54.9	47.2	56.1
1973	50.1	54.9	52.5	57.2	56.3	60.7	58.6	57.1	61.3	61.0	55.3	52.0	56.4
1974	51.1	52.2	53.3	55.4	54.9	58.2	59.6	59.9	60.3	62.2	56.6	51.1	56.3
1975	51.0	53.3	53.1	51.9	57.2	56.9	58.9	59.5	59.5	59.7	55.6	53.4	55.8
RECORD MEAN	50.2	53.0	54.4	55.6	56.9	58.8	58.9	59.4	61.8	61.0	56.9	51.6	56.5
MAX	55.3	58.6	60.4	61.9	63.0	65.2	64.7	65.1	68.5	67.9	62.9	56.4	62.5
MIN	45.1	47.3	48.3	49.2	50.7	52.4	53.0	53.6	55.0	54.0	50.9	46.7	50.5

# Indicates a station move or relocation of instruments.

SAN FRANCISCO-FEDERAL, CA

Feb	Mar	Apr	May	June	Total
390	346	310	235	187	3367
302	330	222	215	128	2915
242	359	235	171	73	2569
315	209	213	247	165	2361
305	282	268	243	176	2581
262	327	241	277	167	3187
364	376	242	297	231	3151
179	332	313	234	201	3008
284	360	338	356	219	3174
302	319	280	306	259	3084
362	336	217	300	182	3044
325	372	420	230	229	3182
235	254	263	280	174	2698
412	333	315	242	185	3263
210	222	341	237	242	2660
359	354	351	317	230	3464
312	279	278	287	226	3312
277	380	225	267	167	3123
353	354	284	309	202	3315
320	360	386	257	238	3246

Aug	Sept	Oct	Nov	Dec	Total
0	14	20	3	0	44
8	82	10	0	0	142
6	83	12	0	0	108
0	13	20	0	0	63
0	34	15	0	0	107
3	19	41	0	0	77
8	15	5	0	0	55

Precipitation

Year	Jan	Feb	Mar	Apr	May	June	July	Aug	Sept	Oct	Nov	Dec	Annual
#1936	5.77	10.06	1.01	1.09	0.49	0.28	0.03	0.02	T	0.69	0.01	2.94	22.39
1937	5.26	4.88	7.05	0.86	0.06	0.59	T	T	T	0.90	2.46	3.73	25.79
1938	2.65	8.49	5.73	1.52	T	0.00	0.01	0.00	0.15	1.33	0.88	1.48	22.24
1939	3.07	1.94	2.62	0.42	0.63	T	T	T	1.06	0.17	0.20	1.05	11.16
1940	9.98	7.81	5.32	0.94	0.63	0.01	T	T	0.59	1.05	2.22	6.25	34.80
1941	8.24	6.71	4.75	4.05	1.18	0.01	0.01	0.03	T	0.93	1.99	7.29	35.19
1942	4.76	4.27	2.62	3.65	1.11	T	0.01	T	0.18	0.95	4.45	2.87	24.87
1943	6.15	1.95	3.18	1.88	0.13	0.13	T	0.00	0.02	0.74	0.80	2.69	17.67
1944	4.31	5.34	0.83	2.07	0.94	0.12	0.01	0.02	0.00	1.70	6.24	3.97	25.55
1945	1.33	3.43	4.15	0.32	0.64	0.01	T	T	0.04	1.95	3.24	9.84	24.95
1946	1.76	2.03	2.34	0.05	0.37	0.02	0.06	T	0.06	0.15	2.73	2.77	12.34
1947	1.35	2.65	3.64	0.17	0.67	0.64	T	T	T	2.09	1.39	1.84	14.44
1948	1.00	2.32	3.36	3.04	0.54	0.01	0.02	0.02	0.09	0.20	1.18	4.75	16.53
1949	2.20	3.04	5.85	T	0.93	T	0.06	0.04	T	0.08	1.18	2.77	16.15
1950	7.40	2.33	1.65	0.87	0.37	0.03	T	T	T	2.72	4.96	6.01	26.34
1951	4.41	3.00	1.32	0.89	0.65	0.04	0.01	0.43	0.08	0.81	3.33	7.92	22.89
1952	10.69	2.62	4.90	1.08	0.30	0.39	T	0.01	T	0.07	2.42	9.06	31.54
1953	3.26	0.04	1.83	3.42	0.38	0.61	T	0.07	T	0.34	1.88	0.82	12.65
1954	3.11	2.42	4.56	0.82	0.11	0.14	0.03	0.20	T	0.24	2.55	5.67	19.85
1955	4.05	1.18	0.29	1.49	0.04	T	0.02	T	0.02	0.03	2.38	11.47	20.97
1956	8.72	2.03	0.12	1.68	0.68	0.02	T	0.01	0.33	1.14	0.04	0.37	15.14
1957	2.84	3.58	2.39	1.09	3.19	0.06	0.01	T	1.46	3.46	1.13	3.60	22.81
1958	4.38	7.78	8.22	5.47	0.88	0.09	0.05	T	0.04	0.12	0.09	1.48	28.60
1959	3.96	4.04	0.30	0.36	0.02	T	T	0.02	2.06	T	T	1.71	12.47
1960	4.04	3.57	2.06	1.16	0.85	T	T	T	T	0.48	3.35	2.31	17.82
1961	2.79	0.96	2.27	0.79	0.88	0.04	T	0.02	0.22	0.09	4.44	2.13	14.63
1962	1.08	6.58	2.76	0.36	T	T	T	0.07	0.22	5.51	0.60	2.81	19.99
1963	3.35	1.92	3.87	3.35	0.45	T	T	T	0.06	1.39	3.52	0.87	18.78
1964	3.37	0.19	2.12	0.01	0.22	0.57	T	0.01	T	1.90	3.99	5.35	17.73
1965	3.97	0.94	2.92	3.21	T	T	0.02	0.49	T	0.01	4.79	3.51	19.86
1966	3.27	2.72	0.80	0.36	0.19	0.17	0.06	0.10	0.10	0.01	4.80	3.87	16.45
1967	9.49	0.22	4.35	4.90	0.09	1.42	0.00	T	0.04	0.53	1.10	2.12	24.26
1968	4.54	2.28	3.15	0.48	0.22	T	T	0.03	0.06	0.62	2.67	3.91	17.96
1969	7.74	7.26	1.01	1.74	T	0.05	T	T	0.01	2.61	0.45	6.15	27.02
1970	7.81	1.56	1.55	0.06	0.03	0.57	T	T	0.00	0.84	6.44	5.39	24.25
1971	2.04	0.26	2.91	0.72	0.19	T	0.01	0.01	0.22	0.11	1.92	3.93	12.32
1972	1.32	2.13	0.23	1.07	T	0.11	0.01	0.04	0.54	5.41	6.40	3.53	20.79
1973	9.38	6.32	2.63	0.02	0.08	0.00	0.00	0.00	0.30	1.62	7.80	3.65	31.80
1974	3.40	1.53	4.49	2.34	0.00	0.10	0.62	0.00	0.00	0.85	0.40	1.53	15.26
1975	2.57	3.72	5.15	1.25	0.02	0.04	0.20	0.02	0.00	2.44	0.43	0.18	16.02
RECORD MEAN	4.65	3.54	3.01	1.52	0.62	0.15	0.02	0.03	0.27	1.01	2.44	4.24	21.50

Record mean values above are means through the current year for the period beginning in 1875 for temperature, 1850 for precipitation, and 1938 for snowfall.

COLORADO SPRINGS, COLORADO

Station: COLORADO SPRINGS, COLORADO
PETERSON FIELD

Elevation (ground): 6145 feet

TEMPERATURES °F

Month	Normal: Daily maximum	Normal: Daily minimum	Normal: Monthly	Extremes: Record highest	Extremes: Year	Extremes: Record lowest	Extremes: Year
(a)				15		15	
J	41.0	16.1	28.6	72	1974	-21	1963
F	43.6	18.9	31.3	76	1963	-16	1962
M	47.7	22.8	35.3	81	1971	-8	1960
A	59.2	33.1	46.2	81	1960	4	1975
M	68.4	42.6	55.5	92	1964	23	1962
J	78.1	51.1	64.6	98	1963	33	1975
J	84.4	57.0	70.7	99	1964	44	1961
A	82.4	55.8	69.1	96	1969	43	1972
S	74.9	46.9	60.9	94	1960	25	1971
O	64.2	36.8	50.5	86	1964	5	1969
N	49.8	25.1	37.5	74	1973	-1	1972
D	43.1	18.9	31.0	71	1973	-16	1972
YR	61.4	35.4	48.4	99	JUL 1964	-21	JAN 1963

IMPORTANT:
The time-period covered by this record is limited: See footnotes following table of **NORMALS, MEANS AND EXTREMES** for explanation and for additional history of **EXTREME HIGHS AND LOWS** recorded in the general area.

At an elevation near 6,200 feet m.s.l., Colorado Springs is located in relatively flat semi-arid country on the eastern slope of the Rocky Mountains. Immediately to the west the mountains rise abruptly to heights ranging from 10,000 to 14,000 feet but generally averaging near 11,000 feet. To the east lie gently undulating prairie lands. The land slopes upward to the north, reaching an average height of about 8,000 feet in 20 miles at the top of Palmer Lake Divide.

Colorado Springs is in the Arkansas River drainage basin. The principal tributary feeding the Arkansas from this area is Fountain Creek, which rises in the high mountains west of the City and is fed by Monument Creek originating to the north in the Palmer Lake Divide area.

Other topographical features of the average area, and particularly its wide range of elevations, help to give Colorado Springs the various and altogether delightful plains-and-mountain mixture of climate that has established the locality as a highly desirable and healthful place to live. The contents of the "Means and Extremes" record table, pinpointing records for the City itself, necessarily omits interesting essentials about the general locality of which the City is the center. For example: The temperature difference between the City and the summit of Pikes Peak, 12 airline miles away is about the same as the difference between Colorado Springs and Iceland; precipitation amounts at higher elevations in the Colorado Springs neighborhood are approximately twice those at nearby lower elevations and the number of rainy days almost triple.

In Colorado Springs itself, precipitation is relatively light and over 80 percent of it falls between April 1 and September 30 - much of it as heavy downpours accompanying summer thunderstorms. Temperatures in view of the station's latitude and elevation are mild. Uncomfortable

(Continued page 384)

Snowfall

Season	July	Aug	Sept	Oct	Nov	Dec	Jan
1948-49	0.0	0.0	0.0	T	0.4	3.5	7.0
1949-50	0.0	0.0	0.0	6.5	T	0.9	5.1
1950-51	0.0	0.0	T	0.0	2.1	0.8	7.7
1951-52	0.0	0.0	0.8	3.3	5.9	1.3	0.2
1952-53	0.0	0.0	0.0	T	3.5	1.8	T
1953-54	0.0	0.0	0.0	1.9	5.9	3.8	2.6
1954-55	0.0	0.0	0.0	0.1	2.2	2.7	3.2
1955-56	0.0	0.0	0.0	T	3.7	1.2	12.7
1956-57	0.0	0.0	0.0	0.4	9.0	3.9	8.7
1957-58	0.0	0.0	0.8	1.0	18.3	0.2	1.8
1958-59	0.0	0.0	T	2.8	2.9	1.4	5.2
1959-60	0.0	0.0	27.9	9.0	0.8	0.4	1.5
1960-61	0.0	0.0	0.0	1.9	2.0	7.4	3.0
1961-62	0.0	0.0	4.2	5.1	5.0	7.1	6.4
1962-63	0.0	0.0	T	0.0	8.3	0.5	5.8
1963-64	0.0	0.0	0.0	3.0	4.2	9.2	T
1964-65	0.0	0.0	0.0	0.0	4.9	4.9	3.2
1965-66	0.0	0.0	0.1	T	T	6.1	6.0
1966-67	0.0	0.0	0.0	3.4	1.7	2.9	4.1
1967-68	0.0	0.0	0.0	T	3.1	11.7	3.0
1968-69	0.0	0.0	0.0	0.2	12.3	4.9	5.7
1969-70	0.0	0.0	0.0	21.7	5.6	7.3	0.8
1970-71	0.0	0.0	0.8	4.6	1.5	T	8.7
1971-72	0.0	0.0	9.7	2.9	0.3	3.8	5.2
1972-73	0.0	0.0	0.0	14.4	16.4	11.4	3.9
1973-74	0.0	0.0	0.0	3.9	1.8	9.1	2.4
1974-75	0.0	0.0	T	T	1.5	6.3	2.8
1975-76	0.0	0.0	0.0	4.3	9.8	0.9	
RECORD MEAN	0.0	0.0	1.6	3.3	4.9	4.1	4.3

Heating Degree Days

Season	July	Aug	Sept	Oct	Nov	Dec	Jan
1955-56	0	1	134	369	886	920	1036
1956-57	2	33	74	372	898	971	1204
1957-58	1	3	173	423	950	839	995
1958-59	16	7	123	399	740	919	1099
#1959-60	2	8	224	597	851	938	1141
1960-61	24	23	116	440	780	1095	1075
1961-62	29	5	321	503	898	1246	1324
1962-63	6	11	124	335	728	910	1331
1963-64	0	4	34	211	680	1165	1068
1964-65	0	22	151	385	790	992	910
1965-66	10	31	304	366	632	931	1232
1966-67	0	33	111	489	728	1099	981
1967-68	6	52	138	397	758	1223	1057
1968-69	22	52	149	409	906	1096	969
1969-70	1	8	104	720	833	1053	1135
1970-71	2	3	235	637	797	987	1086
1971-72	33	5	285	481	806	1067	1080
1972-73	41	34	136	476	1049	1261	1221
1973-74	32	1	194	378	754	1041	1172
1974-75	1	17	229	376	789	1143	1102
1975-76	0	10	200	391	852	916	

Cooling Degree Days

Year	Jan	Feb	Mar	Apr	May	June	July
1969	0	0	0	0	11	27	216
1970	0	0	0	0	15	89	200
1971	0	0	0	0	1	126	158
1972	0	0	0	2	0	96	168
1973	0	0	0	0	0	104	145
1974	0	0	0	0	18	130	241
1975	0	0	0	0	0	59	195

Feb	Mar	Apr	May	June	Total
3.3	6.8	5.1	0.2	0.0	26.3
0.2	4.3	1.6	1.1	T	19.7
2.5	3.5	1.3	T	0.1	18.0
1.1	15.1	1.2	0.3	0.0	29.2
1.9	2.7	11.5	3.2	0.0	24.6
0.8	4.7	3.3	2.4	0.0	25.4
9.0	4.2	3.4	T	0.0	24.8
2.1	10.4	4.7	T	0.0	34.8
4.3	5.5	42.7	14.9	T	89.4
3.8	16.1	9.1	0.0	0.0	51.1
7.8	10.3	25.5	0.0	0.0	55.9
9.5	8.6	2.4	2.8	0.0	62.9
8.8	9.5	5.8	0.9	0.0	39.3
3.7	8.8	2.0	0.0	0.0	42.3
2.1	8.1	T	0.0	0.0	24.8
2.7	20.5	0.1	0.0	0.0	39.7
9.0	14.4	2.2	0.0	0.0	38.6
9.7	0.1	4.1	4.2	0.0	30.3
3.6	2.1	13.9	T	0.0	31.7
4.8	5.7	2.8	0.2	0.0	31.3
2.0	11.3	6.6	0.0	T	43.0
2.4	19.9	7.0	T	T	64.7
11.5	3.0	2.8	T	0.0	32.9
3.6	7.0	3.3	T	0.0	35.8
2.3	15.6	11.2	0.8	0.0	76.0
2.4	6.8	10.0	0.0	T	36.4
4.8	3.5	6.9	0.2	1.1	27.1
4.4	8.5	7.1	1.2	T	39.4

Average Temp.

Year	Jan	Feb	Mar	Apr	May	June	July	Aug	Sept	Oct	Nov	Dec	Annual
1936	34.1	28.3	40.8	47.7	57.4	67.4	71.4	69.4	61.6	48.5	40.3	34.0	50.1
1937	21.6	33.0	35.6	46.3	56.2	63.2	71.2	72.0	62.2	51.5	39.2	32.8	48.7
1938	31.2	35.4	41.8	47.0	53.6	63.3	68.8	70.4	62.0	52.9	36.0	35.8	49.8
1939	33.2	25.1	40.5	47.4	57.2	64.6	71.3	68.1	64.0	51.9	41.2	37.2	50.1
1940	22.3	32.1	41.6	46.2	56.2	66.0	70.4	67.6	61.4	53.2	36.2	33.6	48.9
1941	31.6	35.6	35.3	44.5	57.0	61.6	68.8	67.0	59.0	49.3	41.4	34.0	48.8
1942	29.0	25.5	36.4	49.2	55.6	62.6	68.0	66.7	59.0	49.8	43.0	34.8	48.3
1943	32.4	39.0	35.7	52.4	51.6	64.8	71.4	69.5	59.9	50.6	39.8	31.4	49.9
1944	30.8	32.6	35.4	41.2	55.7	63.8	67.9	68.0	60.0	52.2	38.8	31.4	48.2
1945	31.8	31.4	41.4	41.4	54.9	59.9	67.4	67.0	58.6	53.0	39.0		
#1946		31.4	42.6	52.6	49.8	63.0			61.5	47.3	36.4	36.8	
1947													
#1948				48.0	55.8	64.0	70.0	68.9	64.4	50.0	34.0	29.6	
1949	19.7	29.2	37.6	46.4	55.4	63.2	70.5	68.8	61.8	47.6	47.4	31.0	48.2
1950	31.3	36.9	36.3	45.5	52.4	64.9	66.0	66.1	58.8	57.5	38.3	34.6	49.1
1951	25.7	33.3	33.2	41.7	55.8	59.0	71.3	67.9	59.1	47.7	36.1	29.8	46.7
1952	34.0	32.4	32.1	45.3	54.6	70.5	70.1	70.1	62.4	51.4	31.5	30.8	48.8
1953	37.6	30.4	40.8	41.9	51.3	67.5	71.8	67.8	63.9	51.7	41.2	30.1	49.7
1954	35.4	41.1	34.1	52.0	54.2	67.9	74.0	70.3	64.8	50.7	42.3	33.9	51.7
1955	27.2	26.4	35.6	47.4	56.4	62.3	72.8	70.3	62.2	52.9	35.3	35.2	48.7
1956	31.4	26.7	37.8	44.1	58.7	70.3	70.0	67.6	64.3	52.7	34.8	33.4	49.3
1957	25.9	38.9	37.2	39.3	51.9	63.5	71.5	69.8	59.6	51.1	33.2	37.7	48.3
1958	32.7	36.6	31.3	43.2	60.2	66.2	68.8	70.7	62.6	52.0	40.2	35.0	50.0
1959	29.3	31.3	36.3	43.9	56.5	68.1	69.9	70.6	59.0	45.5	36.4	34.5	48.4
#1960	28.0	21.7	35.6	48.5	54.7	65.6	69.0	70.0	63.4	50.5	38.7	29.4	48.0
1961	30.1	32.9	36.2	43.6	54.7	63.4	68.2	68.4	54.3	48.6	34.9	24.7	46.6
1962	22.1	31.8	33.6	46.1	58.6	62.9	68.9	70.6	62.1	53.9	40.5	35.4	49.1
1963	21.9	38.7	38.4	51.0	60.2	69.0	75.5	69.8	65.4	58.2	42.1	27.2	51.5
1964	30.3	26.1	30.9	46.2	57.6	65.0	75.3	69.3	61.9	52.3	38.4	32.8	48.8
1965	35.4	27.8	25.6	48.3	54.9	62.1	69.4	65.8	55.0	52.9	43.8	34.7	48.0
1966	25.1	26.8	40.8	44.4	57.1	65.7	73.9	66.8	62.1	48.9	40.6	29.4	48.5
1967	33.1	33.0	42.9	48.2	52.4	62.0	69.3	66.1	60.6	52.3	39.6	25.3	48.8
1968	30.7	32.6	38.6	42.5	51.5	66.9	68.4	65.8	60.3	51.5	34.5	29.4	47.7
1969	33.4	33.8	29.6	48.9	56.8	59.7	71.7	70.2	61.9	41.5	37.0	30.8	48.0
1970	28.2	37.2	32.6	42.6	58.2	64.6	71.2	71.4	57.7	44.2	38.2	32.9	48.3
1971	29.8	29.8	37.7	45.3	53.3	67.8	68.8	69.1	56.7	49.3	37.9	30.4	48.0
1972	30.0	36.1	43.3	49.1	55.9	67.8	68.9	67.7	60.8	49.4	29.8	23.5	48.5
1973	25.4	32.3	36.5	40.9	53.3	65.6	68.4	70.6	58.8	52.6	39.6	31.2	48.0
1974	27.0	33.9	42.1	46.0	59.7	66.2	72.6	67.9	58.0	52.6	38.5	28.0	49.4
1975	29.1	29.8	35.6	44.4	53.4	63.8	71.0	70.2	59.4	52.3	36.4	35.3	48.4
RECORD MEAN	29.2	32.1	36.0	45.5	55.5	65.3	70.6	68.9	60.6	50.8	38.1	31.4	48.7
MAX	42.6	45.3	49.0	58.9	68.9	79.4	84.4	82.6	74.4	64.6	51.3	44.5	62.2
MIN	15.8	18.9	23.0	32.0	42.1	51.1	56.8	55.2	46.8	36.9	24.8	18.2	35.1

# Indicates a station move or relocation of instruments.

COLORADO SPRINGS, CO

Feb	Mar	Apr	May	June	Total
1107	838	622	203	1	6117
724	856	766	400	97	6397
791	1037	647	166	50	6075
937	881	628	258	30	6037
1247	904	489	310	69	6780
892	885	634	324	94	6382
924	967	503	202	96	7018
730	817	415	167	30	5604
1119	1051	555	253	73	6213
1034	1214	497	306	107	6408
1061	744	613	249	63	6236
889	679	496	401	95	6001
932	812	669	411	49	6504
868	1090	477	260	180	6478
772	998	664	218	95	6601
980	837	584	357	32	6537
832	665	469	273	6	6002
912	877	715	359	76	7177
866	700	566	176	88	5968
980	904	608	350	88	6587

Precipitation

Year	Jan	Feb	Mar	Apr	May	June	July	Aug	Sept	Oct	Nov	Dec	Annual
1936	0.13	0.20	0.73	0.62	2.23	1.43	2.30	2.68	1.35	0.50	0.22	0.06	12.45
1937	0.08	0.37	0.70	0.45	1.11	2.32	1.41	1.55	1.44	0.19	0.24	0.24	10.10
1938	0.21	0.29	1.12	1.28	3.13	1.27	1.57	1.92	3.98	0.11	0.18	0.19	15.25
1939	0.15	0.49	0.98	0.68	0.37	0.98	0.55	0.94	0.33	0.01	0.50	0.09	6.07
1940	0.47	0.83	0.33	1.11	3.80	0.76	2.25	0.19	2.67	0.01	0.39	0.23	13.04
1941	0.05	0.07	2.59	4.68	1.52	2.91	1.89	4.06	1.60	2.61	0.20	0.26	22.44
1942	0.20	0.47	0.42	5.06	0.37	5.02	1.49	2.99	0.88	0.88	T	0.17	17.95
1943	0.32	0.31	0.83	1.37	3.21	2.40	2.02	2.64	0.08	0.13	0.35	0.12	13.78
1944	0.12	0.13	0.97	3.55	1.59	0.63	3.73	3.73	0.12	0.38	0.20	0.15	15.30
1945	0.39	0.88	0.38	1.99	1.74	1.52	5.85	4.07	0.02	1.88	0.03	0.43	19.18
#1946	0.17	0.02	T	1.29	2.69	0.35	2.35	3.66	0.36	1.25	1.60	1.10	14.84
1947													
#1948				1.07	1.90	4.01	1.44	4.62	0.40	0.12	0.02	0.29	
1949	0.32	0.13	0.67	0.68	1.14	4.22	3.59	0.54	0.26	0.98	T	0.08	12.61
1950	0.32	0.03	0.33	0.42	1.00	1.59	4.50	0.84	2.82	0.12	0.14	0.06	12.17
1951	0.59	0.22	0.36	0.31	1.54	1.38	4.42	4.31	0.85	1.52	0.53	0.11	16.14
1952	0.04	0.10	1.13	1.36	2.21	0.37	1.19	3.79	0.37	0.04	0.23	0.13	10.96
1953	T	0.13	0.21	1.58	1.33	1.30	2.19	1.88	T	0.74	0.57	0.23	10.16
1954	0.22	0.06	0.59	0.62	2.57	3.69	3.13	1.98	1.91	0.22	0.23	0.21	15.43
1955	0.29	0.57	0.32	0.33	4.88	0.43	2.34	2.46	1.35	0.01	0.30	0.08	13.36
1956	1.12	0.19	0.84	1.10	0.88	0.41	3.03	1.42	0.59	0.14	0.91	0.30	10.93
1957	0.45	0.48	0.56	5.90	5.67	1.08	3.65	1.78	1.25	2.02	2.21	0.02	25.07
1958	0.09	0.28	1.29	0.99	4.79	3.01	4.42	1.20	1.38	0.58	0.22	0.20	18.45
1959	0.43	0.47	1.19	2.03	3.48	1.61	0.94	2.63	3.58	0.97	0.05	0.03	17.41
1960	0.11	0.73	0.95	0.59	1.61	0.93	2.22	0.78	0.61	1.97	0.23	0.54	11.27
1961	0.14	0.65	1.21	0.56	0.84	3.86	2.14	2.26	1.91	0.98	0.44	0.43	15.42
1962	0.42	0.34	0.88	0.44	0.63	3.36	1.60	0.15	0.41	0.97	0.89	0.03	10.12
1963	0.53	0.20	0.62	0.02	0.77	1.22	1.35	5.22	1.84	0.39	0.46	0.62	13.24
1964	T	0.22	1.08	0.01	2.54	0.96	1.14	0.60	1.33	0.03	0.46	0.22	8.59
1965	0.14	0.72	1.12	1.61	1.81	8.00	5.02	3.83	2.24	0.49	T	0.45	25.43
1966	0.39	0.49	0.01	0.79	0.95	2.56	2.91	2.00	2.12	0.36	0.16	0.17	12.91
1967	0.31	0.15	0.18	2.04	2.18	2.74	5.26	3.09	0.73	1.68	0.25	0.67	19.28
1968	0.10	0.22	0.37	0.54	0.62	0.15	5.27	2.12	1.03	0.43	1.32	0.24	12.41
1969	0.11	0.12	0.77	1.83	4.46	2.72	3.90	2.38	1.13	2.86	0.39	0.32	20.99
1970	0.05	0.17	1.06	0.91	0.33	3.63	3.79	4.24	1.09	0.95	0.27	T	16.49
1971	0.34	0.53	0.34	1.36	2.24	0.39	2.82	1.99	1.36	0.23	0.03	0.23	11.86
1972	0.27	0.25	0.55	0.42	1.46	2.07	4.08	3.55	4.13	1.34	1.08	0.83	20.03
1973	0.06	0.06	1.16	1.72	4.27	0.47	3.31	0.89	1.03	0.35	0.15	0.64	14.11
1974	0.26	0.18	0.52	1.88	0.33	1.29	1.42	1.14	0.43	1.36	0.23	0.42	9.46
1975	0.13	0.29	0.24	0.68	1.00	2.97	2.65	2.06	0.16	0.52	1.00	0.07	11.77
RECORD MEAN	0.27	0.30	0.69	1.14	2.06	2.09	3.05	2.19	1.33	0.82	0.47	0.27	14.68

Aug	Sept	Oct	Nov	Dec	Total
177	18	0	0	0	449
209	22	0	0	0	535
138	41	0	0	0	464
124	17	0	0	0	407
180	13	0	0	0	442
109	26	0	0	0	524
180	41	5	0	0	480

Record mean values above are means through the current year for the period beginning in 1949. Data are from the Hagerman Hall location through 1946 and from Airport locations thereafter.

COLORADO SPRINGS, COLORADO

(Continued)

extremes, in either summer or winter, are comparatively rare. Relative humidity is normally low and wind movement moderately high. This is notably true of the west-to-east movement of the chinook winds, so important in moderating winter temperatures and reminding white men that the Indian meaning of "chinook" is "snow eater".

Colorado Springs is best known as a resort city, but the surrounding prairie is also important for cattle raising and a considerable amount of grazing land is used for sheep in the summer months. The growing season varies considerably in length, from a recorded shortest of 110 days to a longest of 194 days. The average is 149 days, from about May 8 to about October 4.

Normals, Means, and Extremes

Month	Normal Degree days Base 65 °F		Precipitation in inches												Relative humidity pct.			
			Water equivalent							Snow, Ice pellets					Hour 05	Hour 11	Hour 17	Hour 23
	Heating	Cooling	Normal	Maximum monthly	Year	Minimum monthly	Year	Maximum $ in 24 hrs.	Year	Maximum monthly	Year	Maximum in 24 hrs.	Year		(Local time)			
(a)				27		27		27		27		27			15	15	15	15
J	1128	0	0.31	1.12	1956	T	1964	0.73	1956	12.7	1956	8.4	1971		57	41	46	58
F	944	0	0.34	0.73	1960	0.03	1950	0.48	1957	11.5	1971	7.0	1971		60	39	39	59
M	921	0	0.77	1.29	1958	0.01	1966	0.86	1959	20.5	1964	13.3	1964		61	40	38	58
A	564	0	1.45	5.90	1957	0.01	1964	2.45	1957	42.7	1957	18.0	1957		61	34	32	54
M	301	6	2.12	5.67	1957	0.33	1974	2.57	1955	14.9	1957	14.9	1957		63	34	34	56
J	103	91	2.31	8.00	1965	0.15	1968	3.09	1954	1.1	1975	1.1	1975		66	35	34	57
J	9	186	3.10	5.27	1968	0.94	1959	3.00	1951	0.0		0.0			70	38	42	63
A	13	140	2.58	5.22	1963	0.15	1962	3.02	1970	0.0		0.0			70	39	41	63
S	155	32	1.11	4.13	1972	T	1953	1.73	1959	27.9	1959	17.1	1959		68	40	38	62
O	456	6	0.92	2.86	1969	0.01	1955	1.60	1960	21.7	1969	13.8	1972		58	35	36	55
N	825	0	0.45	2.21	1957	T	1965	0.94	1972	18.3	1957	14.5	1972		61	40	46	60
D	1054	0	0.27	0.83	1972	T	1970	0.67	1972	11.7	1967	8.2	1972		56	41	47	57
YR	6473	461	15.73	8.00	JUN 1965	T	DEC 1970	3.09	JUN 1954	42.7	APR 1957	18.0	APR 1957		63	38	39	59

(To better understand these tables. see full explanation of terms beginning on page 322)

Month	Wind					Pct. of possible sunshine	Mean sky cover, tenths, sunrise to sunset	Mean number of days											Average station pressure mb.
			Fastest mile					Sunrise to sunset							Temperatures °F Max.		Min.		
	Mean speed m.p.h.	Prevailing direction	Speed m.p.h.	Direction	Year			Clear	Partly cloudy	Cloudy	Precipitation .01 inch or more	Snow, Ice pellets 1.0 inch or more	Thunderstorms	Heavy fog, visibility ¼ mile or less	(b) 90° and above	32° and below	32° and below	0° and below	Elev. 6170 feet m.s.l.
(a)	27	14	25	25			27	27	27	27	27	27	27	27	15	15	15	15	3
J	10.0	NNE	55	29	1950		5.3	11	9	11	4	1	0	2	0	7	30	4	807.5
F	10.6	N	52	36	1954		5.5	9	8	11	5	2	*	2	0	5	27	1	808.7
M	11.5	N	60	29	1954		5.9	9	9	13	7	3	*	2	0	5	26	1	805.1
A	12.2	N	48	23	1963		5.8	8	10	12	7	2	2	2	0	1	14	0	806.9
M	11.7	NNW	52	27	1971		5.9	7	13	11	10	*	9	2	*	0	2	0	809.1
J	11.0	SSE	55	20	1954		4.8	11	12	7	9	*	11	1	3	0	0	0	811.7
J	9.6	NNW	47	35	1968		5.1	9	15	7	14	0	17	*	7	0	0	0	815.3
A	9.2	N	40	36	1972		4.9	10	14	7	11	0	13	1	4	0	0	0	814.8
S	9.7	SSE	40	27	1953		4.2	15	8	7	7	*	5	2	*	0	1	0	814.9
O	9.8	NNE	41	36	1975		4.2	16	7	8	5	1	1	2	0	*	7	0	813.1
N	9.8	NNE	50	32	1953		4.9	12	8	10	4	2	*	2	0	3	24	*	809.8
D	9.9	NNW	60	27	1953		5.0	12	9	10	4	1	0	2	0	7	29	2	809.0
YR	10.4	NNE	60	29	MAR 1954		5.1	129	122	114	86	12	59	21	15	28	161	7	810.5

FOOTNOTES Data for February - December 1960 considered in extracting temperature extremes above.
Data for April - December 1948 considered in extracting other extremes.
Means and extremes above are from existing and comparable exposures.
Annual extremes have been exceeded at other sites in the locality as follows:
Highest temperature 100 in June and July 1954; lowest temperature -32 in January 1883; maximum monthly precipitation 8.10 in May 1935.

Station: DENVER, COLORADO STAPLETON INT AP
Elevation (ground): 5283 feet

TEMPERATURES °F

Month	Normal			Extremes			
	Daily maximum	Daily minimum	Monthly	Record highest	Year	Record lowest	Year
(a)				16		16	
J	43.5	16.2	29.9	69	1971	-25	1963
F	46.2	19.4	32.8	76	1963	-18	1962
M	50.1	23.8	37.0	84	1971	-4	1962
A	61.0	33.9	47.5	84	1965	-2	1975
M	70.3	43.6	57.0	93	1974	26	1972
J	80.1	51.9	66.0	98	1971	36	1969
J	87.4	58.6	73.0	103	1973	43	1972
A	85.8	57.4	71.6	100	1969	41	1964
S	77.7	47.8	62.8	97	1960	20	1971
O	66.8	37.2	52.0	87	1975	3	1969
N	53.3	25.4	39.4	78	1973	-2	1961
D	46.2	18.9	32.6	73	1973	-18	1972
YR	64.0	36.2	50.1	103	JUL 1973	-25	JAN 1963

IMPORTANT:
The time-period covered by this record is limited: See footnotes on next page for explanation and for additional history of EXTREME HIGHS AND LOWS recorded in the general area.

Denver enjoys the mild, sunny, semi-arid climate that prevails over much of the central Rocky Mountain region, without the extremely cold mornings of the high elevations and restricted mountain valleys during the cold part of the year, or the hot afternoons of summer at lower altitudes. Wind is lessened by the proximity of the mountains. Extremely warm or cold weather is usually of short duration.

Airmasses from at least four different sources influence Denver's weather: polar air from Canada and the far northwest; moist air from the Gulf of Mexico; warm dry air from Mexico and the southwest; and Pacific air modified by its passage overland.

The good climate results largely from Denver's location on the east slope of the Rocky Mountains in the belt of the prevailing westerlies. During summer afternoons cumulus clouds so shade the City that temperatures of 90° or over are reached on an average of only thirty-five days of the year, and in only one year in five does the mercury very briefly reach the 100° mark. These short periods of high temperature occur when the winds aloft carry desert air from the southwest over Denver.

In the cold season the high altitude and the location of the mountains to the west combine to moderate temperatures. Invasions of cold air from the north, intensified by the high altitude, can be abrupt and severe. On the other hand, many of the cold airmasses that spread southward out of Canada over the plains are too shallow to reach Denver's altitude and move off over the lower plains to the east. Surges of cold air from the west are usually moderated in their descent down the east face of the mountains, and chinooks resulting from some of these westerly flows often raise the temperature far above that normally to be expected at this latitude in the cold season. These conditions result in a tempering of winter cold to an average temperature above that of other cities situated at the same latitude.

In the spring when the outbreaks of polar air are waning, they are met by moist currents from the Gulf of Mexico. The juxtaposition of these two currents produces the rainy season in Denver, which reached its peak in May.

Situated a long distance from any moisture source, and separated from the Pacific source by a high mountain barrier, Denver enjoys a low relative humidity, low average precipitation, and considerable clear-sky sunshine.

THE SEASONS

SPRING is the wettest, cloudiest, and windiest season. Much of the 39 percent of the annual total precipitation that occurs in spring falls as snow during the colder periods of the season. Stormy periods are often interspersed by stretches of mild sunny weather that remove previous snow cover. Severe storms usually arrive from the north with northeasterly winds.

SUMMER precipitation (about 31 percent of the annual total), particularly in July and August, usually falls from scattered local thundershowers during the afternoon and evening. Mornings are usually clear and sunny. Clouds often form during early afternoon and cut off the sunshine at what would otherwise be the hottest part of the day. Many afternoons have a cooling shower.

AUTUMN is the pleasantest season. Local summer thunderstorms are over and invasions of cold air and severe weather are still infrequent, so that there is less cloudiness and a greater percent of possible sunshine than at any other time of the year. Periods of unpleasant weather are generally brief. Precipitation amounts to about 19 percent of the annual total.

WINTER has less precipitation, only about 11 percent of the annual total and almost all of it snow. There is more cloudiness and the relative humidity averages higher than in the autumn. Weather can be quite severe, but as a general rule the severity doesn't last long.

DENVER, COLORADO

Normals, Means, and Extremes

(To better understand these tables, see full explanation of terms beginning on page 322)

Month	Normal Degree days Base 65 °F: Heating	Normal Degree days Base 65 °F: Cooling	Precipitation in inches, Water equivalent: Normal	Maximum monthly	Year	Minimum monthly	Year	Maximum in 24 hrs.	Year	Snow, Ice pellets: Maximum monthly	Year	Maximum in 24 hrs.	Year
(a)				41		41		41		41		41	
J	1088	0	0.61	1.44	1948	0.01	1952	1.02	1962	23.7	1948	12.4	1962
F	902	0	0.67	1.66	1960	0.01	1970	1.01	1953	18.3	1960	9.5	1953
M	868	0	1.21	2.89	1944	0.13	1945	1.48	1959	29.2	1961	16.3	1952
A	525	0	1.93	4.17	1942	0.03	1963	3.25	1967	28.3	1935	17.3	1957
M	253	0	2.64	7.31	1957	0.06	1974	3.55	1973	13.6	1950	10.7	1950
J	80	110	1.93	4.69	1967	0.10	1940	3.16	1970	0.3	1951	0.3	1951
J	0	248	1.78	6.41	1965	0.17	1939	2.42	1965	0.0		0.0	
A	0	208	1.29	4.47	1951	0.06	1960	3.43	1951	0.0		0.0	
S	120	54	1.13	4.67	1961	T	1944	2.44	1936	21.3	1936	19.4	1936
O	408	5	1.13	4.17	1969	0.05	1962	1.71	1947	31.2	1969	12.4	1969
N	768	0	0.76	2.97	1946	0.01	1949	1.29	1975	39.1	1946	15.5	1946
D	1004	0	0.43	2.84	1973	0.04	1946	1.38	1973	30.8	1973	11.8	1973
YR	6016	625	15.51	7.31	MAY 1957	T	SEP 1944	3.55	MAY 1973	39.1	NOV 1946	19.4	SEP 1936

Month	Relative humidity pct. Hour 05 (Local time)	Hour 11	Hour 17	Hour 23	Wind: Mean speed m.p.h.	Prevailing direction	Fastest mile: Speed m.p.h.	Direction	Year	Pct. of possible sunshine	Mean sky cover, tenths, sunrise to sunset	Mean number of days, Sunrise to sunset: Clear	Partly cloudy	Cloudy	Precipitation .01 inch or more	Snow, Ice pellets 1.0 inch or more	Thunderstorms	Heavy fog, visibility ¼ mile or less	Temperatures °F Max. (b) 90° and above	Max. 32° and below	Min. 32° and below	Min. 0° and below	Average station pressure mb. Elev. 5332 feet m.s.l.
(a)	15	15	15	15	27	15	26	26		26	27	41	41	41	41	41	41	35	15	15	15	15	3
J	62	45	48	62	9.3	S	46	SW	1969	72	5.5	10	10	11	6	2	0	1	0	6	30	5	833.2
F	67	44	43	66	9.3	S	49	NW	1953	71	5.8	8	9	11	6	3	*	2	0	4	27	1	834.4
M	69	42	41	65	10.0	S	53	NW	1952	69	6.1	8	10	13	9	4	*	1	0	4	26	1	830.4
A	69	38	34	59	10.4	S	56	NW	1960	66	6.1	7	10	13	9	3	1	1	0	*	14	*	832.0
M	70	38	37	61	9.5	S	43	SW	1964	64	6.1	6	13	12	10	*	6	1	*	0	2	0	834.0
J	72	38	37	62	9.1	S	47	S	1956	70	5.0	9	13	8	9	0	10	1	5	0	0	0	835.9
J	71	36	36	59	8.6	S	56	SW	1965	70	4.9	9	16	6	9	0	11	*	15	0	0	0	839.4
A	69	36	34	58	8.2	S	42	SW	1972	72	4.8	10	14	7	8	0	8	1	10	0	0	0	838.7
S	71	40	36	63	8.2	S	47	NW	1955	75	4.4	13	10	7	6	*	3	1	1	0	1	0	839.6
O	65	36	36	60	8.2	S	45	NW	1958	73	4.4	13	10	8	5	1	1	1	0	*	9	0	837.6
N	69	45	50	67	8.7	S	48	W	1962	65	5.3	11	9	10	5	2	*	1	0	2	26	*	835.1
D	66	45	52	65	9.0	S	51	NE	1953	68	5.3	11	10	10	5	2	0	1	0	5	30	3	834.6
YR	68	40	40	62	9.0	S	56	SW	JUL 1965	70	5.3	115	134	116	88	18	41	10	32	22	164	10	835.4

FOOTNOTES Means and extremes above are from existing and comparable exposures. Annual extremes have been exceeded at other sites in the locality as follows: Highest temperature 105 in August 1878; lowest temperature -30 in February 1936; maximum monthly precipitation 8.57 in May 1876; minimum monthly precipitation 0.00 in December 1881; maximum precipitation in 24 hours 6.53 in May 1876; maximum monthly snowfall 57.4 in December 1913; maximum snowfall in 24 hours 23.0 in April 1885; fastest mile of wind 65 from West in May 1933.

Snowfall

Season	July	Aug	Sept	Oct	Nov	Dec	Jan
1936-37	0.0	0.0	21.3	4.5	1.4	5.7	3.0
1937-38	0.0	0.0	T	0.2	3.0	8.1	5.4
1938-39	0.0	0.0	0.0	0.2	11.2	8.4	7.6
1939-40	0.0	0.0	0.0	7.6	0.5	4.9	13.7
1940-41	0.0	0.0	0.0	0.0	7.0	6.0	9.0
1941-42	0.0	0.0	T	T	2.2	8.7	8.0
1942-43	0.0	0.0	0.4	9.6	4.1	4.5	5.0
1943-44	0.0	0.0	0.0	1.0	2.3	3.0	12.1
1944-45	0.0	0.0	0.0	0.0	5.5	5.9	12.2
1945-46	0.0	0.0	T	2.3	3.8	0.8	10.2
#1946-47	0.0	0.0	0.4	3.8	39.1	0.7	7.3
1947-48	0.0	0.0	0.0	3.1	6.4	6.4	23.7
1948-49	0.0	0.0	0.0	0.8	6.7	4.8	20.5
1949-50	0.0	0.0	0.0	7.2	0.0	6.0	8.8
1950-51	0.0	0.0	0.0	0.0	11.9	5.9	15.7
1951-52	0.0	0.0	4.2	7.7	14.5	11.2	0.3
1952-53	0.0	0.0	0.0	1.2	14.5	3.1	7.4
1953-54	0.0	0.0	0.0	0.1	7.2	14.4	2.7
1954-55	0.0	0.0	0.0	0.4	3.9	8.6	3.5
1955-56	0.0	0.0	0.0	4.1	7.3	2.9	6.3
1956-57	0.0	0.0	0.0	0.6	21.3	6.3	5.3
1957-58	0.0	0.0	T	3.9	3.0	0.8	8.9
1958-59	0.0	0.0	T	2.6	9.7	7.7	17.4
1959-60	0.0	0.0	12.9	11.8	5.3	2.7	10.7
1960-61	0.0	0.0	0.0	4.6	5.1	17.8	1.0
1961-62	0.0	0.0	5.8	6.2	11.4	3.8	17.2
1962-63	0.0	0.0	0.7	0.0	5.0	1.2	9.1
1963-64	0.0	0.0	0.0	1.1	3.5	5.9	2.6
1964-65	0.0	0.0	0.0	T	6.0	4.4	13.2
1965-66	0.0	0.0	5.5	0.0	5.5	5.6	3.6
1966-67	0.0	0.0	T	8.3	3.0	1.9	9.9
1967-68	0.0	0.0	0.0	1.7	9.4	13.1	3.0
1968-69	0.0	0.0	0.0	0.4	5.8	6.9	2.8
1969-70	0.0	0.0	0.0	31.2	5.1	3.1	0.9
1970-71	0.0	0.0	4.6	5.9	9.2	0.9	8.6
1971-72	0.0	0.0	17.2	3.1	1.4	8.4	10.9
1972-73	0.0	0.0	0.0	9.7	19.4	9.8	12.1
1973-74	0.0	0.0	0.0	2.3	9.3	30.8	8.2
1974-75	0.0	0.0	1.8	1.0	11.9	2.1	3.6
1975-76	0.0	0.0	0.0	2.7	15.2	7.3	
RECORD MEAN	0.0	0.0	1.8	3.7	7.9	6.4	8.2

Heating Degree Days

Season	July	Aug	Sept	Oct	Nov	Dec	Jan
1955-56	0	2	126	336	858	911	955
1956-57	1	20	66	277	829	901	1206
1957-58	0	0	141	420	838	782	986
1958-59	14	4	106	342	724	898	1081
1959-60	0	6	191	518	815	876	1151
#1960-61	7	13	90	396	759	1187	1026
1961-62	14	0	273	459	902	1150	1411
1962-63	0	19	112	352	703	961	1417
1963-64	6	7	29	229	690	1125	1059
1964-65	0	16	123	375	743	981	921
1965-66	6	7	296	302	645	924	1122
1966-67	0	9	61	391	699	1018	954
1967-68	4	16	108	389	729	1186	1086
1968-69	10	35	145	399	871	1114	925
1969-70	2	0	56	801	769	998	1061
1970-71	0	0	198	584	770	977	1018
1971-72	24	0	273	479	771	1019	1063
1972-73	42	15	107	397	960	1239	1162
1973-74	8	0	166	321	758	1029	1277
1974-75	0	9	199	381	803	1043	1024
1975-76	0	4	195	363	840	843	

Cooling Degree Days

Year	Jan	Feb	Mar	Apr	May	June	July
1969	0	0	0	0	35	44	312
1970	0	0	0	0	16	93	222
1971	0	0	0	0	0	149	203
1972	0	0	0	0	6	110	210
1973	0	0	0	0	2	138	199
1974	0	0	0	0	36	176	307
1975	0	0	0	0	3	69	246

Feb	Mar	Apr	May	June	Total
6.7	7.5	9.2	0.0	T	59.3
2.6	10.3	5.0	0.5	0.0	35.1
13.3	7.6	6.9	T	0.0	55.2
6.1	11.7	T	0.0	0.0	44.5
1.9	10.2	8.3	0.0	0.0	42.4
11.5	7.6	8.5	1.7	0.0	48.2
1.4	7.3	T	4.5	0.0	36.8
3.3	28.1	23.6	7.7	0.0	81.1
6.2	3.0	23.0	T	0.0	55.8
4.6	3.2	T	0.8	0.0	25.7
12.3	12.0	4.7	1.3	T	61.6
7.3	22.0	5.5	T	0.0	74.4
0.4	14.2	12.7	T	0.0	60.1
2.9	5.4	9.0	13.6	0.0	52.9
10.5	17.6	12.9	0.0	0.3	74.8
10.2	25.2	11.2	T	0.0	84.5
16.5	11.8	12.0	1.7	0.0	68.2
0.6	6.3	7.6	2.6	0.0	41.5
12.2	19.5	4.9	0.0	0.0	53.0
10.5	13.0	3.7	T	0.0	47.8
1.6	8.9	25.5	8.8	0.0	78.3
12.0	14.4	14.1	0.0	0.0	57.1
17.5	26.8	17.6	T	0.0	99.3
18.3	9.0	9.3	T	0.0	80.0
7.9	29.2	8.6	6.4	0.0	80.6
11.3	6.8	10.0	0.0	0.0	72.5
2.1	18.0	0.2	0.0	0.0	36.3
12.7	18.4	12.1	1.0	0.0	57.3
17.1	14.9	0.3	T	0.0	55.9
14.6	2.8	6.4	2.9	0.0	46.9
4.4	6.6	3.6	3.0	0.0	40.7
7.3	9.2	15.1	T	0.0	58.8
4.2	13.2	T	0.0	0.0	33.3
0.3	20.5	4.7	T	0.0	65.8
11.9	9.6	6.0	T	0.0	56.7
9.1	7.1	17.2	0.0	0.0	74.4
3.0	15.1	24.8	1.0	0.0	94.9
10.3	12.8	17.8	0.0	T	91.5
4.0	14.3	10.9	6.1	0.0	55.7
7.9	12.7	9.9	1.6	T	60.1

DENVER, CO

Feb	Mar	Apr	May	June	Total
1072	764	581	143	0	5748
674	795	701	333	74	5877
765	990	606	138	36	5702
966	841	572	273	25	5848
1159	827	434	245	38	6260
828	804	560	299	65	6034
976	934	437	175	72	6803
768	848	442	156	50	5828
1082	982	545	230	72	6056
1044	1108	411	245	63	6030
1017	691	604	204	82	5900
832	679	498	388	135	5664
885	751	655	343	38	6190
821	1011	378	204	144	6057
734	969	632	200	78	6300
958	817	508	329	25	6184
832	621	486	246	4	5818
820	771	646	290	56	6505
831	671	507	137	67	5772
957	852	621	332	85	6306

Aug	Sept	Oct	Nov	Dec	Total
284	46	0	0	0	721
282	40	0	0	0	653
248	53	0	0	0	653
207	28	1	0	0	562
270	21	1	0	0	631
157	39	0	0	0	715
192	39	5	0	0	554

Average Temperature

Year	Jan	Feb	Mar	Apr	May	June	July	Aug	Sept	Oct	Nov	Dec	Annual
1936	30.3	25.0	39.4	49.2	60.4	70.4	77.0	73.4	62.3	48.8	40.1	34.2	50.9
1937	16.2	32.1	37.0	46.0	57.6	63.2	73.2	75.2	64.6	52.2	39.2	31.2	49.0
1938	32.4	35.0	41.6	47.4	54.4	66.7	71.0	73.4	64.6	54.8	35.0	31.4	50.6
1939	30.6	23.8	38.5	48.0	60.2	67.9	76.2	71.2	66.0	53.3	41.7	38.0	51.3
1940	21.4	33.8	41.2	47.4	58.4	69.2	73.9	70.9	64.7	54.6	35.5	33.3	50.3
1941	32.4	36.2	36.5	46.3	59.9	64.9	72.1	71.2	61.0	49.4	43.4	33.6	50.6
1942	27.7	21.8	36.1	50.6	55.4	64.7	72.6	71.2	61.4	51.0	42.4	36.4	49.3
1943	33.7	39.5	35.7	54.3	52.9	65.9	75.6	74.3	63.2	53.0	40.7	34.3	51.9
1944	30.7	32.4	33.4	42.3	58.0	67.0	71.5	72.8	63.0	54.3	40.7	30.7	49.7
1945	31.8	33.5	41.4	41.0	56.5	61.4	72.4	71.5	59.9	53.9	41.3	30.4	49.6
1946	31.4	35.7	44.6	55.1	51.4	68.2	74.6	71.2	63.4	48.2	33.6	37.6	51.2
#1947	30.8	28.8	36.3	45.8	55.6	62.0	72.5	72.8	66.2	55.6	33.0	33.1	49.4
1948	26.4	26.6	31.4	51.6	58.7	66.4	72.6	72.8	66.7	51.3	36.4	29.6	49.2
1949	16.3	30.6	39.5	49.2	57.0	65.0	72.4	71.4	63.2	49.5	48.6	32.5	49.6
1950	29.4	38.6	38.1	47.7	53.0	66.6	68.9	68.9	60.5	59.9	39.1	36.3	50.6
1951	26.9	33.9	35.8	43.8	57.3	60.9	73.5	70.7	61.5	48.2	38.1	29.0	48.3
1952	34.9	35.0	33.8	48.2	56.8	72.0	73.1	72.3	65.6	53.3	32.3	32.6	50.8
1953	39.6	32.7	43.6	42.8	53.4	69.7	74.0	71.2	66.0	54.4	43.1	31.4	51.8
1954	36.3	43.7	35.3	53.6	57.2	69.3	76.8	72.7	65.7	52.5	44.3	34.7	53.5
1955	27.2	27.1	36.5	50.1	59.0	64.0	75.5	73.1	63.9	54.0	36.2	35.4	50.2
1956	34.0	27.7	40.1	45.5	60.9	73.4	72.2	69.7	65.5	55.9	37.2	35.7	51.5
1957	25.8	40.7	39.1	41.4	53.9	65.9	73.5	72.6	61.4	51.4	36.8	39.6	50.2
1958	32.9	37.4	32.8	44.6	61.7	68.1	70.3	73.6	64.4	53.9	40.6	35.8	51.4
1959	30.0	30.2	37.6	45.6	56.2	70.9	72.6	73.0	61.1	48.1	37.6	36.5	50.0
#1960	27.6	24.8	38.1	50.5	57.2	68.3	73.2	73.4	65.0	52.0	39.5	26.5	49.7
1961	31.7	35.2	38.9	46.0	55.7	66.1	71.5	72.2	56.3	50.0	34.7	27.7	48.9
1962	19.5	29.9	34.6	50.3	59.8	65.5	72.9	72.5	62.4	53.4	41.3	33.8	49.7
1963	19.1	37.3	37.3	50.0	60.9	66.7	74.8	68.7	65.9	57.9	41.7	28.5	50.8
1964	30.6	27.4	33.0	46.6	58.8	65.0	75.8	70.4	62.5	52.7	40.0	33.2	49.7
1965	35.0	27.4	29.0	51.2	57.1	63.9	72.7	70.2	55.7	55.1	43.3	35.0	49.6
1966	28.6	28.4	42.5	44.6	58.7	64.6	76.9	70.8	65.0	52.2	41.5	31.9	50.5
1967	34.0	35.1	42.9	48.2	52.6	60.6	69.1	68.2	62.1	52.5	40.5	26.5	49.4
1968	29.7	34.2	40.6	43.0	53.9	67.8	71.7	68.1	60.9	51.9	35.7	28.9	48.9
1969	35.0	35.4	32.2	52.2	59.3	61.5	74.7	73.9	64.5	39.0	39.1	32.5	49.9
1970	30.6	38.6	33.5	43.7	58.8	65.2	72.0	73.9	59.5	45.9	39.1	33.3	49.5
1971	32.1	30.6	38.5	47.8	54.2	69.0	70.6	72.8	57.5	49.4	39.1	31.9	49.5
1972	30.5	36.2	44.8	48.5	57.0	68.3	70.2	71.0	62.1	52.1	32.9	24.9	49.9
1973	27.3	35.5	39.9	43.2	55.6	67.5	71.0	73.5	59.9	54.5	39.5	31.6	49.9
1974	23.7	35.2	43.2	47.9	61.6	68.4	74.7	69.5	59.4	52.4	38.0	31.2	50.5
1975	31.7	30.6	37.3	44.1	54.3	64.3	72.7	70.8	59.5	53.2	36.8	37.5	49.4
RECORD MEAN	30.1	32.8	38.7	47.4	56.7	66.6	72.6	71.3	62.6	51.6	39.6	32.3	50.2
MAX	42.8	45.2	51.2	60.1	69.5	80.5	86.4	85.0	76.8	65.4	52.6	44.9	63.4
MIN	17.4	20.3	26.1	34.7	43.9	52.7	58.8	57.6	48.4	37.7	26.6	19.7	37.0

# Indicates a station move or relocation of instruments.

Precipitation

Year	Jan	Feb	Mar	Apr	May	June	July	Aug	Sept	Oct	Nov	Dec	Annual
1936	0.23	0.15	1.36	0.41	2.23	1.65	2.69	2.21	3.49	1.83	0.13	0.42	16.80
1937	0.28	0.49	0.77	1.34	1.07	3.19	1.01	0.95	0.34	0.64	0.33	0.93	11.34
1938	0.43	0.25	1.76	3.18	3.94	1.73	1.00	2.25	3.34	0.14	1.48	0.93	20.43
1939	0.82	1.14	1.06	1.08	1.25	1.06	0.17	0.15	0.29	0.97	0.09	0.37	8.45
1940	1.01	0.67	2.26	1.46	1.99	0.10	1.24	0.25	4.05	0.35	0.76	0.36	14.50
1941	1.11	0.26	1.23	3.28	3.71	2.93	1.29	1.84	2.48	2.44	0.62	0.86	22.05
1942	0.66	0.91	0.68	4.17	1.12	3.08	1.02	0.77	0.81	2.94	0.28	0.15	16.59
1943	0.23	0.12	0.43	1.04	2.96	1.22	0.72	1.28	0.07	0.27	0.41	0.37	9.12
1944	1.08	0.25	2.89	3.92	1.73	0.92	3.34	0.46	T	0.06	0.52	0.37	15.54
1945	0.70	0.49	0.13	2.55	2.32	2.02	2.19	2.55	1.17	0.78	0.40	0.09	15.39
1946	0.64	0.27	0.52	2.09	1.95	0.82	1.60	1.38	1.18	0.88	2.97	0.04	14.34
#1947	0.37	0.87	1.04	1.30	4.61	2.76	1.52	1.27	0.91	3.41	0.73	0.27	19.06
1948	1.44	0.44	1.71	2.52	1.84	1.94	0.80	0.41	0.45	0.16	0.65	0.26	12.62
1949	1.17	0.03	2.29	1.46	3.31	4.27	1.35	0.92	0.28	1.36	0.01	0.33	16.78
1950	0.47	0.20	0.31	2.98	2.80	3.32	0.56	0.27	1.58	0.12	1.00	0.32	13.93
1951	0.83	0.78	1.47	2.01	1.78	2.27	0.83	4.47	0.97	2.16	1.17	0.69	19.43
1952	0.01	0.68	2.12	2.75	3.06	0.12	1.06	1.41	0.54	0.18	1.31	0.19	13.43
1953	0.39	1.39	1.15	1.29	2.66	1.46	1.98	1.25	0.20	0.44	1.00	1.02	14.23
1954	0.23	0.04	0.49	0.88	0.60	0.66	1.99	0.51	0.77	0.06	0.57	0.71	7.51
1955	0.23	0.85	1.14	0.48	2.47	1.39	2.99	2.41	2.72	0.66	0.56	0.15	16.05
1956	0.39	0.77	0.89	0.72	2.36	0.44	4.17	1.83	0.01	0.27	1.25	0.62	13.72
1957	0.32	0.73	1.09	4.13	7.31	1.09	1.29	2.03	0.42	2.62	0.49	0.06	21.58
1958	0.73	1.00	1.48	1.73	4.46	1.47	3.50	1.17	1.51	0.37	0.74	0.64	18.80
1959	1.24	1.31	2.85	1.35	3.33	0.44	0.83	0.25	1.82	2.46	0.40	0.26	16.54
1960	0.77	1.66	0.89	2.56	2.27	0.63	1.31	0.06	0.38	2.46	0.49	1.50	14.98
1961	0.07	0.66	2.51	1.06	4.12	1.11	1.60	1.21	4.67	0.77	0.93	0.30	19.01
1962	1.33	1.05	0.52	1.10	0.84	1.52	0.54	0.46	0.19	0.05	0.68	0.17	8.45
1963	0.71	0.21	1.42	0.03	0.68	3.59	0.55	2.52	1.25	0.31	0.45	0.51	12.23
1964	0.26	1.04	1.38	1.25	2.53	0.82	0.72	0.27	0.41	0.18	0.88	0.40	10.14
1965	1.00	1.27	1.20	1.05	1.82	4.14	6.41	1.06	2.58	0.45	0.36	0.53	21.87
1966	0.30	1.28	0.32	1.46	0.34	1.41	1.04	2.06	1.15	0.96	0.32	0.17	10.81
1967	0.84	0.39	0.79	3.95	4.77	4.69	3.25	0.83	0.60	1.13	1.01	1.06	23.31
1968	0.51	0.74	0.85	2.39	0.71	0.50	1.34	2.53	0.59	0.75	0.71	0.51	12.13
1969	0.17	0.43	1.10	1.33	6.12	2.99	1.81	0.79	1.67	4.17	0.62	0.32	21.52
1970	0.10	0.01	1.34	0.97	0.64	3.83	1.67	0.54	2.47	0.88	1.19	0.09	13.73
1971	0.35	0.78	0.53	1.98	1.34	0.23	1.20	0.85	2.85	0.44	0.16	0.25	10.96
1972	0.36	0.44	0.50	3.52	0.49	2.94	0.63	2.71	2.07	0.82	1.69	0.70	16.87
1973	1.31	0.16	1.76	3.73	5.06	0.20	2.47	1.28	2.85	0.47	0.83	2.84	22.96
1974	1.03	0.82	1.32	2.28	0.06	2.01	2.34	0.16	0.98	1.68	1.06	0.29	14.03
1975	0.23	0.37	1.19	1.14	2.80	2.11	2.78	2.00	0.24	0.30	1.88	0.47	15.51
RECORD MEAN	0.48	0.58	1.10	2.01	2.40	1.51	1.70	1.39	1.13	1.01	0.67	0.62	14.60

Record mean values above are means through the current year for the period beginning in 1872 for temperature and precipitation, 1935 for snowfall. Temperature and precipitation are from City Office locations through 1934. Heating degree days are from City Office locations through June 1939. Snowfall if from City Office locations through June 1934. Otherwise the data are from Airport locations.

Station: GRAND JUNCTION, COLORADO
WALKER FIELD

Elevation (ground): 4843 feet

TEMPERATURES °F

Month	Normal			Extremes			
	Daily maximum	Daily minimum	Monthly	Record highest	Year	Record lowest	Year
(a)				12		12	
J	36.7	16.5	26.6	60	1971	-15	1971
F	44.0	23.2	33.6	64	1972	-8	1974
M	52.8	29.6	41.2	81	1971	6	1971
A	64.6	38.8	51.7	85	1969	11	1975
M	75.8	48.5	62.2	94	1969	26	1970
J	85.9	56.6	71.3	103	1971	35	1974
J	93.1	64.2	78.7	105	1971	48	1968
A	89.1	61.6	75.4	103	1969	43	1968
S	81.3	53.0	67.2	96	1974	30	1971
O	67.9	41.9	54.9	88	1963	18	1975
N	50.9	28.6	39.8	71	1973	5	1975
D	39.4	19.6	29.5	64	1973	-9	1968
YR	65.1	40.2	52.7	105	JUL 1971	-15	JAN 1971

IMPORTANT:
The time-period covered by this record is limited: See footnotes following table of NORMALS, MEANS AND EXTREMES for explanation and for additional history of EXTREME HIGHS AND LOWS recorded in the general area.

Located in a large mountain valley, the junction of the Colorado and Gunnison rivers, on the west slope of the Rockies, Grand Junction has a climate marked by the wide seasonal range usual to interior localities at this latitude. Thanks, however, to the protective topography of the vicinity, sudden and severe weather changes are very infrequent. Elevation of the valley floor ranges from 4,400 to 4,800 feet above sea level, with mountains on all sides at distances of from 10 to 60 miles, reaching heights of 9,000 to over 12,000 feet.

This mountain valley location, with attendant "valley breezes" provides protection from spring and fall frosts, resulting in a growing season averaging 191 days in the city of Grand Junction. This value varies considerably in the outlying districts, is about the same in the upper valley around Palisade, and 3 to 4 weeks shorter near the river west of Grand Junction, where the "valley breeze" is less effective. Farming areas located on mesas also enjoy longer frost-free seasons than adjacent lower lying ground where cool air tends to collect at night; this effect is more noticeable in the west, or lower portion of the valley. The growing season is sufficiently long to permit growth commercially of almost all fruits except citrus varieties. Peaches are the leading fruit, with apricots, pears, cherries and apples important. A wide variety of vegetables, grain, feed crops and an important acreage of sugar beets are grown. Tomatoes are usually the leading vegetable. Summer grazing of cattle and sheep on nearby mountain ranges is extensive, foundation herds are wintered in the valley and there is some winter feeding of fat cattle and sheep.

The interior, continental location, ringed by mountains on all sides, results in quite low

(Continued page 390)

Snowfall

Season	July	Aug	Sept	Oct	Nov	Dec	Jan
1936-37	0.0	0.0	0.0	0.0	0.8	2.8	8.4
1937-38	0.0	0.0	0.0	0.0	T	5.9	4.0
1938-39	0.0	0.0	0.0	0.0	T	9.2	6.6
1939-40	0.0	0.0	0.0	0.0	0.0	1.4	7.7
1940-41	0.0	0.0	0.0	0.0	3.8	8.4	7.2
1941-42	0.0	0.0	0.0	0.0	2.2	3.2	2.0
1942-43	0.0	0.0	0.0	0.0	T	0.2	0.8
1943-44	0.0	0.0	0.0	T	T	3.3	3.0
1944-45	0.0	0.0	0.0	0.0	T	0.9	2.6
#1945-46	0.0	0.0	0.0	0.0	1.4	3.5	3.9
1946-47	0.0	0.0	0.0	0.0	2.5	4.1	5.2
1947-48	0.0	0.0	0.0	0.0	7.1	4.1	5.6
1948-49	0.0	0.0	0.0	T	7.2	9.6	18.2
1949-50	0.0	0.0	0.0	T	T	3.0	19.5
1950-51	0.0	0.0	0.0	0.0	T	2.6	10.1
1951-52	0.0	0.0	0.0	T	1.7	8.3	1.9
1952-53	0.0	0.0	0.0	0.0	3.8	7.2	4.2
1953-54	0.0	0.0	0.0	T	3.3	3.9	3.0
1954-55	0.0	0.0	0.0	0.0	8.7	1.5	4.3
1955-56	0.0	0.0	0.0	T	4.7	1.5	3.2
1956-57	0.0	0.0	0.0	1.8	2.3	6.4	33.7
1957-58	0.0	0.0	0.0	0.0	3.9	4.6	6.2
1958-59	0.0	0.0	0.0	0.0	3.2	1.8	4.5
1959-60	0.0	0.0	0.0	0.0	0.3	6.6	2.3
1960-61	0.0	0.0	0.0	0.0	2.2	1.1	T
1961-62	0.0	0.0	0.0	T	1.1	8.1	4.6
1962-63	0.0	0.0	0.0	0.0	3.3	4.9	17.7
1963-64	0.0	0.0	0.0	0.0	T	7.0	4.8
1964-65	0.0	0.0	0.0	0.0	12.1	3.0	5.9
1965-66	0.0	0.0	3.1	0.0	2.8	3.5	11.0
1966-67	0.0	0.0	0.0	1.9	4.2	6.3	2.8
1967-68	0.0	0.0	0.0	T	0.5	16.7	3.7
1968-69	0.0	0.0	0.0	0.0	0.2	7.8	3.4
1969-70	0.0	0.0	0.0	0.6	0.5	4.8	5.2
1970-71	0.0	0.0	0.0	3.1	T	4.1	3.2
1971-72	0.0	0.0	0.0	0.5	3.9	10.4	4.0
1972-73	0.0	0.0	0.0	5.7	1.3	9.7	12.8
1973-74	0.0	0.0	0.0	0.0	7.7	5.7	17.0
1974-75	0.0	0.0	0.0	T	0.1	4.6	7.9
1975-76	0.0	0.0	0.0	6.1	3.9	7.2	
RECORD MEAN	0.0	0.0	0.1	0.7	3.1	5.7	7.8

Heating Degree Days

Season	July	Aug	Sept	Oct	Nov	Dec	Jan
1955-56	0	0	33	279	888	900	870
1956-57	0	0	8	281	914	1235	1236
1957-58	0	11	55	340	854	1032	1084
1958-59	0	0	62	278	726	904	1096
1959-60	0	0	138	386	801	1007	1183
1960-61	0	4	17	338	696	1077	1099
1961-62	0	0	196	367	809	1290	1295
1962-63	0	0	39	255	620	1099	1633
#1963-64	0	2	4	145	624	1166	1220
1964-65	0	2	39	219	800	1067	1004
1965-66	0	0	138	209	496	960	1246
1966-67	0	2	16	256	628	1092	1268
1967-68	0	0	28	320	714	1442	1532
1968-69	0	12	86	346	804	1302	1125
1969-70	0	0	20	545	764	995	1100
1970-71	0	0	93	495	714	1019	1152
1971-72	0	0	134	389	792	1204	1076
1972-73	0	0	31	335	832	1303	1651
1973-74	0	0	72	266	708	1075	1487
1974-75	0	0	60	266	756	1167	1387
1975-76	0	0	35	358	858	1161	

Cooling Degree Days

Year	Jan	Feb	Mar	Apr	May	June	July
1969	0	0	0	3	104	124	481
1970	0	0	0	0	67	238	442
1971	0	0	0	0	36	264	479
1972	0	0	0	0	86	288	479
1973	0	0	0	0	35	222	410
1974	0	0	0	1	73	335	420
1975	0	0	0	0	9	133	419

Feb	Mar	Apr	May	June	Total
3.7	2.5	T	0.0	0.0	18.2
0.1	1.4	0.6	0.0	0.0	12.0
9.3	3.2	0.0	0.0	0.0	28.3
3.5	2.1	0.0	0.0	0.0	14.7
T	0.9	0.9	0.0	0.0	21.2
8.4	3.7	0.0	T	0.0	19.5
1.4	6.6	T	T	0.0	9.0
4.3	6.9	T	T	0.0	17.5
0.2	0.8	6.6	T	0.0	11.1
3.5	T	0.0	0.2	0.0	12.5
1.0	1.3	T	0.0	0.0	14.1
18.4	14.9	T	0.0	0.0	50.1
5.0	11.0	T	0.0	0.0	51.0
T	2.2	T	T	0.0	24.7
10.0	1.8	0.2	T	0.0	24.7
4.5	6.9	0.0	0.0	0.0	23.3
1.4	8.7	2.6	T	0.0	27.9
1.0	3.1	0.0	0.0	0.0	14.3
14.9	2.0	5.5	T	0.0	36.9
9.3	2.5	T	0.0	0.0	21.2
0.3	2.7	1.8	0.0	0.0	49.0
2.2	1.8	T	0.0	0.0	18.7
5.9	0.1	T	0.0	0.0	15.5
13.8	5.9	T	T	0.0	28.9
1.2	7.8	0.6	0.0	0.0	12.9
6.1	3.0	1.7	0.0	0.0	24.6
0.2	4.3	0.2	0.0	0.0	30.6
0.4	8.0	0.8	T	0.0	21.0
7.5	3.8	0.2	T	0.0	32.5
5.9	0.3	0.8	T	0.0	27.4
T	0.2	0.4	T	0.0	15.8
0.9	0.3	0.6	T	0.0	22.7
3.8	9.5	T	T	0.0	24.7
T	12.4	1.2	0.0	0.0	24.7
1.5	0.2	1.1	T	0.0	13.2
T	0.0	T	0.0	0.0	18.8
1.2	1.3	2.0	T	0.0	34.0
5.5	T	1.2	0.0	0.0	37.1
4.4	8.8	14.3	1.3	0.0	41.4
4.4	4.3	1.2	T	0.0	27.3

Average Temperature

Year	Jan	Feb	Mar	Apr	May	June	July	Aug	Sept	Oct	Nov	Dec	Annual
1936	27.4	36.6	44.9	55.2	65.9	75.8	79.8	77.4	66.6	55.0	39.0	30.8	54.5
1937	15.0	30.1	44.0	50.8	66.2	71.0	78.6	78.0	69.4	56.4	44.0	33.4	53.1
1938	32.4	38.2	43.0	53.2	60.1	73.2	77.7	77.0	68.2	56.4	33.4	29.2	53.5
1939	27.4	22.7	42.7	55.6	65.8	72.2	80.1	77.2	67.9	53.9	44.2	35.0	53.7
1940	28.6	37.9	47.3	54.4	67.4	76.6	80.8	77.6	67.9	56.0	38.0	31.0	55.3
1941	32.0	38.5	44.2	49.2	63.5	69.2	77.4	75.4	63.4	52.6	41.0	34.9	53.4
1942	28.4	28.6	39.2	54.3	60.4	72.0	79.4	76.9	67.1	55.1	42.4	34.7	53.2
1943	32.2	38.8	42.8	60.3	61.3	70.6	79.9	75.0	69.4	56.6	41.3	33.8	55.2
1944	25.8	34.8	40.4	48.0	62.2	69.5	77.6	76.6	69.3	58.6	41.5	32.2	53.0
1945	32.0	38.8	42.1	47.8	63.6	66.6	78.5	76.2	66.0	56.2	38.6	25.5	52.7
#1946	26.1	33.6	45.6	57.6	59.9	74.4	79.9	75.8	67.7	49.6	37.9	32.7	53.4
1947	22.0	36.0	44.2	51.0	64.3	66.6	78.4	74.0	70.0	56.5	34.5	28.6	52.2
1948	25.4	30.2	35.4	52.8	63.8	69.8	77.1	74.4	69.6	54.4	32.5	28.4	51.2
1949	18.9	20.3	42.8	54.1	61.0	69.0	77.2	75.5	67.6	51.1	44.4	29.4	50.9
1950	23.1	34.3	41.3	52.6	59.1	70.8	74.9	73.7	66.2	60.7	41.6	35.4	52.8
1951	25.3	30.7	41.0	51.7	62.1	68.0	79.4	73.9	66.3	52.4	36.2	23.0	50.8
1952	26.9	31.4	36.4	53.1	62.6	73.3	77.3	74.6	68.6	57.4	35.8	28.0	52.1
1953	33.5	33.1	43.1	49.3	56.5	74.0	79.5	72.6	69.2	54.9	42.6	27.1	52.9
1954	32.7	40.7	40.0	56.6	64.4	71.1	79.9	74.5	67.1	55.0	42.6	26.1	54.3
1955	23.9	21.5	38.5	48.9	60.4	69.6	79.4	76.0	69.9	55.9	35.1	35.8	51.2
1956	36.7	30.9	42.3	52.4	64.5	75.4	77.1	73.5	70.6	56.3	34.3	24.9	53.3
1957	25.0	31.0	43.2	48.9	56.8	69.9	76.1	72.9	65.2	54.3	36.3	31.5	50.9
1958	29.8	39.9	40.2	49.2	65.6	75.5	78.0	78.6	67.2	55.8	40.6	35.6	54.7
1959	29.4	35.7	41.3	52.6	62.9	75.7	79.5	75.3	64.6	52.4	38.1	32.2	53.3
1960	26.6	29.4	42.4	53.1	61.4	74.6	79.5	76.6	69.2	54.0	41.5	30.0	53.2
1961	29.4	37.1	42.4	50.3	63.0	76.2	78.4	76.2	58.9	52.9	37.9	23.1	52.2
1962	22.9	37.9	38.4	55.5	61.7	71.3	76.9	75.9	67.4	56.6	44.1	29.3	53.2
#1963	12.1	38.6	41.9	51.1	66.3	71.4	79.8	73.6	69.8	61.3	44.0	27.1	53.1
1964	25.5	29.5	37.0	50.3	62.3	70.2	81.3	74.1	66.6	58.0	38.1	30.4	51.9
1965	32.3	32.9	40.4	53.9	62.4	70.3	78.9	76.6	63.4	58.1	48.3	33.8	54.3
1966	24.5	30.6	46.1	53.6	65.4	72.0	80.9	77.0	69.1	56.5	43.9	29.5	54.1
1967	23.9	36.4	48.5	51.6	59.5	68.6	77.7	76.2	67.5	55.3	41.0	18.3	52.0
1968	15.4	37.0	43.8	46.3	59.1	72.8	78.0	70.3	64.2	53.8	38.0	22.7	50.1
1969	28.5	33.6	38.1	53.8	66.4	67.7	80.3	79.5	69.3	47.4	39.2	32.7	53.1
1970	29.3	40.9	39.8	45.9	63.3	71.4	79.1	78.7	64.1	48.8	41.0	31.9	52.9
1971	27.7	34.1	41.1	52.2	60.1	74.1	80.2	78.5	63.2	52.3	38.4	25.9	52.3
1972	30.0	36.6	46.6	53.3	63.1	74.3	80.2	77.1	68.1	54.0	37.1	22.7	53.6
1973	11.5	29.1	42.1	48.1	61.5	70.5	78.1	77.4	65.7	56.4	41.2	30.1	51.0
1974	16.9	19.9	48.2	51.0	65.0	74.9	78.3	75.6	66.4	56.2	39.6	27.1	51.6
1975	20.0	33.0	41.0	46.4	57.1	67.5	78.3	75.4	67.1	53.5	36.2	27.4	50.2
RECORD MEAN	25.7	33.3	42.7	52.2	61.9	71.8	78.3	75.6	66.8	54.2	39.9	28.5	52.6
MAX	36.1	43.9	54.4	65.0	75.3	86.4	92.3	89.0	80.4	67.2	51.4	38.7	65.0
MIN	15.2	22.7	31.0	39.4	48.4	57.2	64.3	62.1	53.1	41.2	28.3	18.3	40.1

# Indicates a station move or relocation of instruments.

GRAND JUNCTION, CO

Feb	Mar	Apr	May	June	Total
982	695	372	71	0	5090
948	670	478	252	45	6067
693	761	468	84	0	5382
814	728	369	104	0	5081
1026	697	359	156	0	5753
774	696	434	127	2	5264
752	819	286	148	18	5980
733	708	411	32	3	5533
1022	861	437	168	18	5667
893	758	334	158	8	5282
959	582	337	59	4	4990
795	508	396	213	21	5195
805	648	552	218	24	6283
874	826	332	52	34	5793
671	772	564	115	39	5585
858	734	378	182	4	5629
813	563	346	139	0	5456
999	705	499	139	49	6543
1260	513	415	66	32	5894
888	736	551	249	51	6111

Aug	Sept	Oct	Nov	Dec	Total
458	158	1	0	0	1329
430	72	0	0	0	1249
425	86	3	0	0	1313
381	130	3	0	0	1367
393	101	6	0	0	1167
335	109	0	0	0	1273
328	106	9	0	0	1004

Precipitation

Year	Jan	Feb	Mar	Apr	May	June	July	Aug	Sept	Oct	Nov	Dec	Annual
1936	0.22	1.02	0.57	0.45	0.24	0.74	1.60	1.13	0.72	0.52	0.21	0.57	7.99
1937	0.78	0.66	0.67	0.22	0.30	0.14	0.94	1.00	0.93	0.94	0.42	1.63	8.63
1938	0.58	0.31	1.10	0.74	0.81	0.98	0.14	0.69	2.41	0.30	0.07	1.12	9.25
1939	0.95	0.83	1.04	0.05	0.34	0.11	0.34	0.68	2.37	0.44	0.30	0.13	7.58
1940	1.43	1.04	0.88	0.98	T	0.07	0.64	0.28	2.35	1.41	0.83	1.07	10.98
1941	0.77	0.93	1.70	1.31	1.03	0.78	0.35	1.51	2.90	2.73	0.26	0.49	14.76
1942	0.19	1.17	0.56	1.26	0.15	0.01	1.15	0.84	0.41	0.53	0.13	0.08	6.48
1943	0.15	0.42	1.53	0.20	1.04	0.77	0.09	1.98	0.31	0.46	0.29	0.26	7.50
1944	0.27	0.61	0.88	1.67	0.59	0.59	0.75	0.10	T	0.50	0.98	0.24	7.18
1945	0.26	0.53	0.64	1.25	0.45	1.32	0.40	1.63	0.10	0.71	0.24	0.53	8.06
#1946	0.23	0.33	0.29	0.81	1.25	0.07	0.35	1.68	0.12	0.82	1.46	0.80	8.21
1947	0.40	0.11	0.60	0.59	0.41	1.38	0.09	1.27	0.26	1.98	0.69	0.49	8.27
1948	0.50	1.56	1.54	0.48	0.22	0.64	0.86	1.78	0.46	0.57	0.70	0.70	10.01
1949	1.33	0.40	1.75	0.74	0.74	0.53	0.91	0.32	1.72	0.72	0.15	0.31	9.62
1950	1.40	0.47	0.42	0.54	0.46	0.01	1.00	0.21	1.05	T	0.32	0.30	6.18
1951	0.78	0.83	0.25	0.56	0.64	0.28	0.19	1.16	0.32	1.27	0.25	1.89	8.42
1952	0.48	0.38	0.70	0.57	0.44	0.26	0.26	1.25	0.39	0.00	0.52	0.56	5.81
1953	0.53	0.16	1.20	0.71	0.42	0.17	0.19	2.81	T	1.48	1.22	0.34	9.23
1954	0.35	0.27	0.87	0.52	0.54	0.39	0.40	0.59	2.51	0.83	1.69	0.36	9.32
1955	0.61	1.05	0.17	1.13	1.30	0.24	0.48	0.85	0.38	0.02	0.34	0.18	6.75
1956	1.07	0.70	0.07	0.24	0.26	0.30	0.53	0.04	0.01	0.54	0.18	0.47	4.41
1957	2.46	0.63	0.73	1.51	1.79	0.61	0.57	3.48	0.09	2.24	1.15	0.43	15.69
1958	0.55	0.70	0.84	0.06	0.34	0.76	0.06	0.70	1.34	0.33	0.52	0.11	6.31
1959	0.36	0.90	0.10	0.45	0.39	0.09	0.08	0.98	0.82	0.66	0.50	0.88	6.21
1960	0.33	1.26	1.06	0.74	0.35	0.17	0.13	0.47	0.65	0.49	0.39	0.20	6.24
1961	T	0.18	1.47	0.85	1.11	T	0.03	1.63	2.22	0.70	0.66	0.63	9.48
1962	0.39	1.09	0.28	0.97	0.17	0.30	0.08	0.15	1.41	0.46	0.36	0.36	6.02
1963	0.99	0.47	0.55	0.12	0.01	0.61	0.93	1.75	0.48	0.60	0.36	0.45	7.32
1964	0.47	0.02	0.70	1.37	0.41	0.16	0.65	1.16	0.36	T	1.05	0.53	6.88
1965	0.66	0.94	0.87	1.95	1.35	1.33	0.89	0.67	2.52	1.40	0.82	0.76	14.16
1966	0.65	0.44	0.04	0.83	0.71	0.13	0.31	0.52	0.26	1.23	0.62	1.78	7.52
1967	0.25	0.22	0.18	0.08	1.52	1.34	1.03	0.59	0.37	0.63	0.33	1.14	7.68
1968	0.26	1.13	0.44	0.67	1.14	0.05	0.49	1.37	0.07	0.94	0.42	0.47	7.45
1969	1.03	0.40	0.67	0.33	0.45	2.07	0.21	0.88	1.45	2.01	0.45	0.36	10.31
1970	0.52	0.05	1.75	0.76	T	0.91	0.60	0.44	0.78	1.56	0.54	0.39	8.30
1971	0.19	0.13	0.02	0.42	1.10	0.03	0.15	1.02	0.58	1.13	0.56	0.67	6.00
1972	0.20	T	0.02	0.11	0.44	0.64	0.03	0.29	0.72	3.45	0.69	0.74	7.33
1973	0.79	0.12	0.65	0.86	1.45	0.87	0.52	0.62	0.33	0.20	0.91	0.62	7.94
1974	1.20	0.40	0.81	1.03	0.01	0.14	1.53	0.48	0.38	0.72	1.18	0.32	8.20
1975	0.53	0.49	1.74	1.38	1.23	0.43	1.39	0.09	0.16	0.85	0.39	0.50	9.18
RECORD MEAN	0.60	0.58	0.76	0.75	0.72	0.44	0.61	1.04	0.90	0.91	0.60	0.59	8.50

Record mean values above are means through the current year for the period beginning in 1892 for temperature and precipitation, 1947 for snowfall. Data are from Cooperative and City Office locations through March 16, 1946 and from Airport locations thereafter.

(Continued)

precipitation in all seasons. Consequently, agriculture is dependent on irrigation, for which an adequate supply of water has been available from mountain snows and rains. Summer rains occur chiefly as scattered light showers from thunderstorms which develop over nearby mountains. Winter snows are fairly frequent, but mostly light and quickly melt off. Even the infrequent snows of from 4 to 8 inches, which are heavy for this locality, seldom remain on the ground for prolonged periods. Blizzard conditions in the valley are extremely rare.

Temperatures at Grand Junction have ranged from 105° to -23°, but readings of 100° or higher are infrequent, and about one third of the winters have no readings below zero. Summer days with maximum temperatures in the middle and low 90's and minima in the low 60's are common. Relative humidity is very low during the summer, with values close to such other dry localities as the southern parts of New Mexico and Arizona. Spells of cold winter weather are sometimes prolonged due to cold air becoming trapped in the valley. Winds are usually very light during the coldest weather. Changes in winter are generally gradual, and abrupt changes are much less frequent than in eastern Colorado. "Cold Waves" are rare. Sunny days predominate in all seasons.

Flying weather conditions are generally favorable for operation of light airplanes, with visibilities of 20 miles or more and ceilings of 5,000 feet or higher prevailing approximately 95 percent of the time. Gusty surface winds are rather frequent in the spring and early summer. The prevailing wind is from the east-southeast due to the "valley breeze" effects, but the strongest winds are usually from the south and southwest, and are associated with thunderstorms or with pre-frontal weather.

Normals, Means, and Extremes

Month	Normal Degree days Base 65 °F		Precipitation in inches													Relative humidity pct.			
			Water equivalent							Snow, Ice pellets								
	Heating	Cooling	Normal	Maximum monthly	Year	Minimum monthly	Year	Maximum in 24 hrs.	Year	Maximum monthly	Year	Maximum in 24 hrs.	Year	Hour 05	Hour 11	Hour 17	Hour 23
														(Local time)			
(a)				29		29		29		29		29		12	12	12	12
J	1190	0	0.64	2.46	1957	T	1961	0.64	1956	33.7	1957	9.1	1957	77	67	63	75
F	879	0	0.61	1.56	1948	T	1972	0.53	1960	18.4	1948	8.6	1948	69	51	44	64
M	738	0	0.75	1.75	1970	0.02	1972	0.78	1949	14.9	1948	6.1	1948	59	39	32	50
A	404	0	0.79	1.95	1965	0.06	1958	1.33	1965	14.3	1975	8.9	1975	54	34	27	45
M	133	47	0.63	1.79	1957	T	1970	0.74	1973	1.3	1975	1.3	1975	49	28	22	37
J	20	209	0.55	2.07	1969	T	1961	1.57	1969	0.0		0.0		47	26	21	35
J	0	425	0.46	1.53	1974	0.03	1972	1.42	1974	0.0		0.0		48	29	22	36
A	0	322	1.05	3.48	1957	0.04	1956	1.21	1953	0.0		0.0		50	31	23	38
S	60	126	0.84	2.52	1965	T	1953	1.35	1965	3.1	1965	3.1	1965	52	33	25	40
O	324	11	0.93	3.45	1972	0.00	1952	1.24	1957	6.1	1975	6.1	1975	58	40	34	51
N	756	0	0.61	1.69	1954	0.15	1949	0.82	1974	12.1	1964	8.4	1954	69	51	47	65
D	1101	0	0.55	1.89	1951	0.11	1958	1.16	1951	16.7	1967	6.0	1967	77	64	62	75
YR	5605	1140	8.41	3.48	AUG 1957	0.00	OCT 1952	1.57	JUN 1969	33.7	JAN 1957	9.1	JAN 1957	59	41	35	51

(To better understand these tables, see full explanation of terms beginning on page 322)

Month	Wind					Pct. of possible sunshine	Mean sky cover, tenths, sunrise to sunset	Mean number of days												Average station pressure mb.
			Fastest mile					Sunrise to sunset							Temperatures °F				
															Max.		Min.		
	Mean speed m.p.h.	Prevailing direction	Speed m.p.h.	Direction	Year			Clear	Partly cloudy	Cloudy	Precipitation .01 inch or more	Snow, Ice pellets 1.0 inch or more	Thunderstorms	Heavy fog, visibility ¼ mile or less	(b) 90° and above	32° and below	32° and below	0° and below	Elev. 4839 feet m.s.l.
(a)	29	15	29	29		29	29	29	29	29	29	29	29	29	12	12	12	12	3
J	5.6	ESE	54	S	1950	59	6.1	9	8	14	7	3	*	3	0	14	30	5	854.4
F	6.8	ESE	56	W	1967	64	6.1	8	7	13	6	1	*	2	0	2	26	1	854.2
M	8.4	ESE	65	S	1954	64	6.1	9	8	14	7	1	1	1	0	*	19	0	847.4
A	9.7	ESE	59	W	1955	67	5.9	8	10	12	6	*	2	*	0	0	8	0	848.6
M	9.7	ESE	65	NW	1966	71	5.3	10	11	10	6	*	4	*	2	0	1	0	849.3
J	9.9	ESE	66	S	1951	78	4.0	15	9	6	4	0	5	0	12	0	0	0	850.9
J	9.3	ESE	56	SE	1955	77	4.2	14	12	5	5	0	8	0	26	0	0	0	853.1
A	9.0	ESE	56	W	1957	75	4.3	14	11	6	7	0	8	0	20	0	0	0	853.1
S	9.1	ESE	61	S	1947	79	3.4	17	8	5	5	*	5	0	4	0	*	0	853.7
O	8.1	ESE	61	NW	1954	73	4.2	15	8	8	6	*	1	*	0	0	4	0	854.1
N	6.7	ESE	54	NW	1954	63	5.3	11	8	11	6	1	*	1	0	*	20	0	853.6
D	5.9	ESE	48	NW	1951	60	5.8	10	7	14	7	2	*	2	0	8	29	1	855.2
YR	8.2	ESE	66	S	JUN 1951	70	5.1	140	107	118	71	9	35	8	64	25	138	7	852.3

FOOTNOTES

Means and extremes above are from existing and comparable exposures. Annual extremes have been exceeded at other sites in the locality as follows: Lowest temperature -23 in January 1963; maximum monthly precipitation 3.78 in September 1896; maximum precipitation in 24 hours 2.50 in October 1908; maximum snowfall in 24 hours 17.0 in November 1919.

Station: HARTFORD, CONNECTICUT
BRADLEY INTERNATIONAL AIRPORT
Elevation (ground): 169 feet

TEMPERATURES °F

Month	Normal			Extremes			
	Daily maximum	Daily minimum	Monthly	Record highest	Year	Record lowest	Year
(a)				16		16	
J	33.4	16.1	24.8	65	1967	-26	1961
F	35.7	17.9	26.8	59	1961	-21	1961
M	44.6	26.6	35.6	77	1968	-6	1967
A	58.9	36.5	47.7	94	1962	9	1970
M	70.3	46.2	58.3	96	1964	30	1964
J	79.5	56.0	67.8	100	1964	37	1964
J	84.1	61.2	72.7	102	1966	44	1962
A	81.9	58.9	70.4	101	1975	36	1965
S	74.5	51.0	62.8	96	1973	30	1974
O	64.3	40.8	52.6	91	1963	18	1974
N	50.6	31.9	41.3	81	1974	12	1972
D	36.8	19.6	28.2	65	1965	-9	1962
YR	59.6	38.6	49.1	102	JUL 1966	-26	JAN 1961

IMPORTANT:
The time-period covered by this record is limited: See footnotes on next page for explanation and for additional history of EXTREME HIGHS AND LOWS recorded in the general area.

Bradley Field is located about 3 miles west of the Connecticut River on a slight rise of ground in a broad portion of the Connecticut River Valley between North-South mountain ranges whose heights do not exceed 1,200 feet.

The station's latitude (41° 56' N) places it well inside the northern temperate climatic zone in a prevailing west to east movement of air carrying the majority of weather systems into Connecticut from the west. The average wintertime position of the "Polar Front" boundary between cold dry polar air and warm moist tropical air is just south of New England, which helps to explain the extensive winter storm activity and day to day variability of local weather. In summer, the "Polar Front" has an average position along the New England - Canada border with this station in a warm and pleasant atmosphere.

The location of Hartford, relative to continent and ocean, is also significant. Rapid weather changes result when storms move northward along the Mid-Atlantic coast, frequently producing strong and persistent northeast winds associated with storms known locally as coastals or northeasters. Seasonally, weather characteristics vary from the cold and dry continental-polar air of winter to the warm, maritime air of summer, the one from Canada, the other from the Gulf of Mexico, Caribbean Sea, or Atlantic Ocean.

Summer thunderstorms develop in the Berkshire Mountains to the west and northwest, move over the Connecticut Valley, and when accompanied by wind and hail, sometimes cause considerable damage to crops, particularly tobacco. During the winter, rain often falls through cold air trapped in the valley, creating extremely hazardous ice conditions. On clear nights in the late summer or early autumn, cool air drainage into the valley, and moisture from the Connecticut River, produce steam and/or ground fog which becomes quite dense throughout the valley, hampering ground and air transportation.

The mean date of the last springtime temperature of 32° or lower is April 22, and the mean date of the first autumn temperature of 32° is October 15.

HARTFORD, CONNECTICUT

Normals, Means, and Extremes

(To better understand these tables, see full explanation of terms beginning on page 322)

Month	Normal Degree days Base 65 °F: Heating	Normal Degree days Base 65 °F: Cooling	Precipitation in inches, Water equivalent: Normal	Maximum monthly	Year	Minimum monthly	Year	Maximum in 24 hrs.	Year	Snow, Ice pellets: Maximum monthly	Year	Maximum in 24 hrs.	Year
(a)				21		21		21		21		21	
J	1246	0	3.28	5.54	1964	0.39	1970	2.44	1962	30.6	1961	14.2	1961
F	1070	0	3.17	5.28	1960	1.14	1968	2.16	1965	32.2	1969	15.0	1969
M	911	0	3.82	6.71	1972	1.50	1965	2.31	1969	43.3	1956	14.0	1956
A	519	0	3.75	6.59	1973	1.38	1966	3.00	1969	5.5	1957	5.1	1958
M	226	18	3.50	7.49	1972	0.73	1959	2.71	1967	T	1967	T	1967
J	24	108	3.53	9.66	1972	0.71	1971	3.72	1960	0.0		0.0	
J	0	239	3.41	8.20	1960	1.49	1970	3.48	1960	0.0		0.0	
A	12	179	3.94	21.87	1955	1.09	1965	12.12	1955	0.0		0.0	
S	106	40	3.55	9.02	1975	1.22	1957	5.28	1960	0.0		0.0	
O	384	0	3.03	11.61	1955	0.35	1963	4.45	1959	0.4	1972	0.4	1972
N	711	0	4.33	8.53	1972	2.14	1973	2.39	1955	8.2	1971	8.0	1971
D	1141	0	4.06	8.36	1969	0.78	1955	3.12	1973	35.4	1969	13.9	1969
YR	6350	584	43.37	21.87	AUG 1955	0.35	OCT 1963	12.12	AUG 1955	43.3	MAR 1956	15.0	FEB 1969

Month	Relative humidity pct.: Hour 01	Hour 07	Hour 13	Hour 19 (Local time)	Wind: Mean speed m.p.h.	Prevailing direction	Fastest mile: Speed m.p.h.	Direction	Year	Pct. of possible sunshine	Mean sky cover, tenths, sunrise to sunset	Mean number of days, Sunrise to sunset: Clear	Partly cloudy	Cloudy	Precipitation .01 inch or more	Snow, Ice pellets 1.0 inch or more	Thunderstorms	Heavy fog, visibility ¼ mile or less	Temperatures °F Max.: 90° and above (b)	32° and below	Min.: 32° and below	0° and below	Average station pressure mb. Elev. 179 feet m.s.l.
(a)	16	16	16	16	21	9	21	21		21	21	21	21	21	21	21	21	21	16	16	16	16	3
J	70	72	57	63	9.6	NW	50	NW	1964	58	6.3	8	8	15	11	3	*	2	0	13	29	3	1011.6
F	70	73	56	61	9.9	NW	53	SW	1967	57	6.6	6	8	14	11	3	*	3	0	10	26	2	1010.2
M	69	72	53	58	10.5	NW	50	NE	1956	56	6.8	6	8	17	11	3	1	2	0	2	22	*	1008.5
A	68	69	44	52	10.7	S	47	NE	1956	57	6.7	6	9	15	11	1	1	2	*	0	10	0	1006.5
M	76	74	47	56	9.5	S	41	NW	1957	58	6.7	5	10	16	12	0	2	2	1	0	1	0	1007.5
J	82	79	53	62	8.5	S	45	W	1957	58	6.8	5	10	15	11	0	5	3	4	0	0	0	1009.3
J	83	80	51	62	7.9	S	36	NW	1966	61	6.6	5	12	14	10	0	5	2	8	0	0	0	1008.5
A	84	84	53	65	7.7	S	44	NW	1955	63	6.3	6	12	13	10	0	4	3	5	0	0	0	1010.8
S	87	87	55	71	7.8	S	43	NE	1960	59	6.2	8	9	13	10	0	2	4	2	0	*	0	1012.0
O	81	84	51	67	8.2	N	40	W	1955	58	5.9	9	9	13	8	0	1	4	*	0	6	0	1013.2
N	77	80	58	68	8.8	S	51	W	1955	46	7.0	5	9	16	12	*	*	2	0	*	16	0	1009.9
D	76	79	63	70	9.0	N	49	NW	1955	48	6.8	7	7	17	13	4	*	3	0	11	27	1	1011.5
YR	77	78	53	63	9.0	S	53	SW	FEB 1967	57	6.6	76	111	178	128	14	22	33	20	36	137	6	1010.0

FOOTNOTES

Means and extremes above are from existing and comparable exposures. Annual extremes have been exceeded at other sites in the locality as follows: Minimum monthly precipitation .18 in October 1924; maximum monthly snowfall 45.3 in December 1945; maximum snowfall in 24 hours 19.0 in February 1949; fastest mile wind 70 E in November 1950.

Snowfall

Season	July	Aug	Sept	Oct	Nov	Dec	Jan
1936-37	0.0	0.0	0.0	0.0	2.8	0.9	4.2
1937-38	0.0	0.0	0.0	0.0	1.8	2.1	23.6
1938-39	0.0	0.0	0.0	0.0	15.6	4.4	11.8
#1939-40	0.0	0.0	0.0	0.0	T	9.3	7.7
1940-41	0.0	0.0	0.0	T	5.0	4.1	10.3
1941-42	0.0	0.0	0.0	0.0	T	1.0	7.1
1942-43	0.0	0.0	0.0	0.0	T	10.2	19.6
1943-44	0.0	0.0	0.0	0.0	4.6	0.4	0.7
1944-45	0.0	0.0	0.0	0.0	6.6	12.9	20.1
1945-46	0.0	0.0	0.0	0.0	10.0	45.3	10.2
1946-47	0.0	0.0	0.0	0.0	0.2	5.1	6.3
1947-48	0.0	0.0	0.0	0.0	0.4	22.9	27.6
1948-49	0.0	0.0	0.0	0.0	1.7	13.2	16.4
1949-50	0.0	0.0	0.0	0.0	3.9	12.6	3.6
1950-51	0.0	0.0	0.0	0.0	T	7.4	12.3
1951-52	0.0	0.0	0.0	0.0	0.6	9.7	16.3
1952-53	0.0	0.0	0.0	T	0.3	2.2	16.4
1953-54	0.0	0.0	0.0	0.0	4.3	0.1	17.1
#1954-55	0.0	0.0	0.0	0.0	0.0	2.8	1.2
1955-56	0.0	0.0	0.0	T	3.0	3.2	6.8
1956-57	0.0	0.0	0.0	0.0	1.0	7.5	18.3
1957-58	0.0	0.0	0.0	T	T	5.5	13.3
1958-59	0.0	0.0	0.0	T	1.4	8.9	6.9
1959-60	0.0	0.0	0.0	0.0	0.6	9.1	13.4
1960-61	0.0	0.0	0.0	T	0.0	17.6	30.6
1961-62	0.0	0.0	0.0	0.0	5.0	11.3	1.6
1962-63	0.0	0.0	0.0	T	2.4	15.9	7.7
1963-64	0.0	0.0	0.0	T	T	16.1	13.8
1964-65	0.0	0.0	0.0	T	T	12.3	28.7
1965-66	0.0	0.0	0.0	0.0	T	4.5	18.4
1966-67	0.0	0.0	0.0	0.0	T	20.0	3.0
1967-68	0.0	0.0	0.0	0.0	3.7	21.7	7.5
1968-69	0.0	0.0	0.0	0.0	7.9	13.9	3.4
1969-70	0.0	0.0	0.0	T	T	35.4	3.2
1970-71	0.0	0.0	0.0	T	T	27.0	17.7
1971-72	0.0	0.0	0.0	0.0	8.2	6.6	2.9
1972-73	0.0	0.0	0.0	0.4	2.1	12.0	14.1
1973-74	0.0	0.0	0.0	0.0	T	3.1	14.3
1974-75	0.0	0.0	0.0	T	0.8	8.5	10.2
1975-76	0.0	0.0	0.0	0.0	0.3	13.4	
RECORD MEAN	0.0	0.0	0.0	T	1.7	13.0	11.3

Heating Degree Days

Season	July	Aug	Sept	Oct	Nov	Dec	Jan
#1955-56	0	8	129	354	754	1256	1113
1956-57	20	15	243	423	697	973	1360
1957-58	0	28	122	421	627	911	1210
1958-59	3	10	136	473	680	1326	1243
#1959-60	0	8	115	394	736	1041	1203
1960-61	4	13	130	438	653	1308	1487
1961-62	5	8	78	322	706	1110	1225
1962-63	3	20	179	428	819	1310	1277
1963-64	11	11	179	246	551	1342	1169
1964-65	2	16	128	419	644	1084	1311
1965-66	2	34	110	426	753	961	1186
1966-67	0	0	98	398	554	1019	993
1967-68	0	10	112	380	803	1013	1353
1968-69	0	16	56	326	775	1219	1262
1969-70	8	7	116	409	707	1175	1485
1970-71	0	0	89	322	619	1177	1410
1971-72	2	11	55	214	756	992	1140
1972-73	6	9	82	494	782	1054	1097
1973-74	0	0	102	322	635	988	1134
1974-75	2	1	121	542	725	1057	1040
1975-76	0	11	121	292	503	1125	

Cooling Degree Days

Year	Jan	Feb	Mar	Apr	May	June	July
1969	0	0	0	4	35	131	189
1970	0	0	0	8	58	129	322
1971	0	0	0	0	7	201	274
1972	0	0	0	3	30	83	286
1973	0	0	0	11	19	221	318
1974	0	0	0	11	34	110	282
1975	0	0	0	0	106	147	348

Feb	Mar	Apr	May	June	Total
0.9	5.0	0.9	0.0	0.0	14.7
7.9	1.6	3.3	0.0	0.0	40.3
8.6	15.2	1.0	0.0	0.0	56.6
16.9	5.9	1.7	0.0	0.0	41.5
1.9	18.7	0.0	0.0	0.0	40.0
5.7	2.3	0.5	0.0	0.0	16.6
8.5	9.6	0.1	0.0	0.0	48.0
8.9	12.2	T	0.0	0.0	26.8
24.3	2.9	0.0	0.0	0.0	66.8
13.5	0.0	0.9	0.0	0.0	79.9
18.7	2.9	0.7	0.0	0.0	33.9
15.0	11.8	T	0.0	0.0	77.7
13.4	15.8	0.0	0.0	0.0	60.5
18.9	5.6	4.7	0.0	0.0	49.3
6.1	11.3	0.0	0.0	0.0	37.1
16.1	4.2	0.0	0.0	0.0	46.9
6.5	T	T	0.0	0.0	25.4
1.1	T	0.3	0.0	0.0	22.9
5.3	11.3	3.6	0.0	0.0	24.2
14.5	43.3	5.3	0.0	0.0	76.1
3.5	8.3	5.5	0.0	0.0	44.1
17.1	12.4	5.1	0.0	0.0	53.4
6.9	19.1	0.0	0.0	0.0	43.2
4.6	16.9	T	0.0	0.0	44.6
14.9	15.7	1.4	0.0	0.0	80.2
22.9	0.7	T	0.0	0.0	41.5
14.5	13.8	T	0.0	0.0	54.3
22.0	4.1	T	0.0	0.0	56.0
6.0	7.8	1.7	0.0	0.0	56.5
19.1	10.6	T	0.0	0.0	52.6
25.2	33.2	1.4	T	0.0	82.8
1.6	6.8	0.0	0.0	0.0	41.3
32.2	4.4	0.0	0.0	0.0	61.8
6.7	14.7	2.0	0.0	0.0	62.0
8.4	12.8	4.0	0.0	0.0	69.9
24.9	13.2	2.7	0.0	0.0	58.5
5.9	0.4	0.3	0.0	0.0	35.2
5.8	4.8	2.1	0.0	0.0	30.1
16.0	2.5	0.3	0.0	0.0	38.3
13.2	12.2	1.7	T	0.0	53.1

HARTFORD, CT

Feb	Mar	Apr	May	June	Total
986	1066	653	340	37	6696
926	816	457	212	30	6172
1184	848	497	304	108	6260
1143	928	462	180	72	6656
919	1129	459	156	26	6186
1045	916	589	292	20	6895
1160	854	501	230	22	6221
1209	890	494	222	43	6894
1129	842	481	127	46	6134
1068	888	518	99	45	6222
1008	792	534	275	31	6112
1126	976	530	349	18	6061
1134	771	374	205	46	6201
1063	938	415	221	27	6318
1026	922	483	161	37	6536
1001	911	556	215	17	6317
1125	935	619	172	50	6071
1051	665	444	229	13	5926
1056	868	435	287	37	5864
986	894	567	111	43	6089

Aug	Sept	Oct	Nov	Dec	Total
273	88	5	0	0	725
280	108	16	0	0	921
243	142	11	4	0	882
203	70	1	0	0	676
362	99	8	0	0	1038
247	77	0	3	0	764
229	27	7	6	0	870

Average Temperature

Year	Jan	Feb	Mar	Apr	May	June	July	Aug	Sept	Oct	Nov	Dec	Annual
1936	27.2	21.8	43.4	45.8	61.2	67.8	73.0	71.6	64.2	53.2	39.0	35.0	50.3
1937	35.8	33.0	33.4	47.1	61.4	68.8	73.8	74.6	62.0	51.6	42.8	31.0	51.3
1938	26.6	31.6	40.8	51.0	57.6	68.1	73.5	74.2	61.7	56.6	44.2	32.4	51.6
1939	27.4	31.5	34.1	45.4	61.8	68.6	73.1	75.2	63.8	53.0	39.8	32.3	50.5
#1940	19.4	27.7	31.2	43.7	58.0	65.4	72.6	68.0	61.4	48.0	41.2	32.6	47.4
1941	23.5	28.0	31.6	52.7	59.6	68.2	72.7	69.1	64.4	54.7	45.2	33.2	50.2
1942	25.1	26.2	40.4	50.6	62.2	68.2	72.4	69.9	63.7	54.2	41.6	26.2	50.0
1943	24.5	27.9	34.8	42.8	59.6	72.3	73.6	70.6	63.0	52.0	39.8	26.9	49.0
1944	29.4	28.2	33.8	45.1	64.2	67.8	74.2	73.0	65.0	51.4	40.4	26.8	49.9
1945	20.2	27.6	46.2	53.2	55.6	67.8	72.5	69.6	66.6	51.0	42.4	24.0	49.7
1946	26.4	25.6	45.7	46.6	57.1	66.8	71.6	67.5	65.7	56.6	45.4	32.3	50.6
1947	30.8	26.5	35.6	46.4	57.1	65.4	73.3	73.2	63.7	57.8	39.8	27.8	49.8
1948	20.0	23.2	36.3	47.8	57.4	65.9	73.4	71.8	64.6	51.8	46.8	32.2	49.3
1949	34.0	33.0	38.5	50.4	59.7	71.3	76.8	73.4	61.8	57.9	40.8	32.1	52.6
1950	34.5	26.6	32.6	45.5	57.3	67.5	71.4	70.1	60.3	54.9	44.6	31.8	49.8
1951	31.0	32.4	39.0	50.0	59.8	66.7	73.5	70.9	63.2	54.3	38.9	32.2	51.0
1952	30.8	31.6	37.3	51.1	56.6	70.3	76.5	71.3	64.5	50.8	42.4	33.9	51.4
1953	32.3	34.5	39.7	49.1	60.4	69.5	73.3	71.3	65.2	54.9	44.3	37.0	52.6
#1954	24.5	36.2	38.9	50.1	57.0	68.6	71.9	67.7	61.2	57.2	41.7	31.5	50.5
1955	26.1	30.4	36.5	49.8	62.0	66.1	77.0	73.9	62.1	53.5	39.6	24.3	50.1
#1956	28.9	30.7	30.3	42.9	54.5	68.5	69.9	69.6	58.3	51.2	41.5	33.4	48.3
1957	20.8	31.8	38.4	50.1	58.9	71.6	72.0	67.5	63.7	51.2	43.9	35.3	50.4
1958	25.8	22.4	37.5	48.2	55.1	62.8	71.6	70.2	61.9	49.7	42.0	22.0	47.4
#1959	24.6	24.0	34.8	49.4	61.8	66.4	72.8	73.6	66.3	52.7	40.3	31.2	49.8
1960	26.0	33.0	28.3	49.5	60.0	67.6	70.3	70.7	62.0	50.8	43.0	22.7	48.7
1961	16.9	27.4	35.3	45.1	56.0	69.0	72.8	71.8	68.7	54.4	41.3	28.9	49.0
1962	25.3	23.4	37.2	48.4	58.9	68.4	69.0	69.2	60.0	50.9	37.4	22.5	47.6
1963	23.6	21.6	36.1	48.3	58.1	68.1	72.9	68.9	60.0	57.1	46.5	21.5	48.6
1964	27.1	25.9	37.7	48.8	62.6	68.3	75.0	68.1	63.0	51.3	43.3	29.7	50.1
1965	22.5	26.6	36.1	47.5	64.4	68.9	72.4	71.7	64.1	51.1	39.6	33.8	49.9
1966	26.4	28.8	39.1	46.9	56.4	70.7	75.8	73.4	63.4	51.9	46.2	31.8	50.9
1967	32.8	24.5	33.3	47.1	53.7	70.6	74.0	70.2	62.8	52.8	38.0	32.1	49.4
1968	21.1	25.8	39.9	52.4	58.2	67.4	75.1	70.8	65.0	54.7	38.9	25.4	49.6
1969	24.0	26.8	34.5	51.1	58.8	68.2	70.6	73.3	63.8	51.7	41.2	26.9	49.2
1970	16.8	28.2	35.1	49.0	61.5	67.8	75.2	73.8	65.4	54.9	44.1	26.8	49.9
1971	19.4	29.0	35.4	46.3	58.1	71.0	73.7	72.2	67.7	58.3	39.6	32.8	50.3
1972	27.9	26.0	34.6	44.3	60.1	65.9	73.8	71.1	64.3	48.9	38.7	30.8	48.9
1973	29.4	27.2	43.3	50.4	58.0	71.6	75.0	76.4	64.7	54.7	43.6	32.9	52.3
1974	28.2	27.0	36.8	50.7	56.6	67.3	73.7	72.7	63.3	47.3	40.7	30.7	49.6
1975	31.2	29.7	35.9	45.8	64.6	68.3	76.1	71.8	61.7	55.7	48.2	28.5	51.4
RECORD MEAN	27.1	27.7	36.9	47.9	59.0	67.9	73.1	70.9	63.7	53.3	42.1	30.4	50.0
MAX	35.2	36.1	45.6	58.1	69.9	78.4	83.4	81.2	74.1	64.0	50.5	38.0	59.5
MIN	19.0	19.2	28.2	37.7	48.0	57.3	62.8	60.6	53.2	42.6	33.6	22.8	40.4

# Indicates a station move or relocation of instruments.

Precipitation

Year	Jan	Feb	Mar	Apr	May	June	July	Aug	Sept	Oct	Nov	Dec	Annual
1936	6.95	3.21	6.10	3.21	2.39	3.05	2.33	4.22	3.87	3.69	1.21	6.88	47.11
1937	5.81	1.94	3.78	3.90	4.13	8.08	3.11	7.14	4.00	4.83	6.76	2.33	55.81
1938	5.62	2.20	1.93	3.14	4.66	6.18	11.24	3.21	14.59	1.56	3.44	3.86	61.63
1939	3.62	4.72	4.59	4.37	0.96	3.21	2.80	3.68	2.73	4.64	1.43	3.79	40.54
#1940	3.69	3.09	5.10	5.38	7.04	4.32	3.88	1.79	2.37	2.57	5.46	2.67	47.36
1941	1.95	2.19	2.10	1.04	3.14	4.00	6.53	3.27	0.70	1.95	3.05	3.08	33.00
1942	4.20	2.11	6.13	0.65	3.89	4.03	4.47	4.31	3.24	2.80	7.05	6.69	49.57
1943	3.75	2.02	4.54	2.99	5.31	3.48	3.27	1.18	0.65	4.82	4.32	0.91	37.24
1944	1.51	1.85	5.02	4.55	1.23	3.81	2.26	2.44	8.79	2.38	7.14	3.07	44.05
1945	3.75	4.55	2.52	4.67	6.01	4.53	3.31	3.83	1.59	2.09	5.81	6.85	49.51
1946	2.72	2.81	1.84	2.58	5.87	2.99	4.84	6.76	2.36	0.90	1.28	2.84	37.79
1947	3.18	2.61	2.09	5.20	3.10	4.76	6.32	3.31	2.97	2.10	5.23	3.55	44.42
1948	4.17	1.96	3.74	3.85	4.81	7.79	2.37	2.63	0.63	1.46	6.84	5.50	45.75
1949	4.99	3.32	2.37	3.78	5.63	0.87	3.23	3.02	3.03	2.06	2.74	3.40	38.44
1950	3.87	4.41	2.63	3.06	2.82	3.85	4.09	4.16	1.09	1.85	4.83	4.12	40.78
1951	4.09	5.09	6.08	2.34	4.23	3.49	1.35	3.13	2.00	4.13	7.36	5.36	48.65
1952	5.07	2.72	3.36	6.93	4.42	4.09	2.26	5.69	1.58	0.65	3.41	3.77	43.95
1953	7.23	2.88	9.21	5.60	4.63	3.08	4.24	1.71	1.34	4.77	2.95	4.73	52.37
#1954	2.06	1.89	3.50	3.68	3.90	2.05	3.11	4.54	5.13	1.63	4.87	3.81	40.17
1955	0.91	3.42	4.90	4.68	0.78	3.46	2.55	21.87	3.15	11.61	4.83	0.78	62.94
1956	2.71	4.01	6.61	3.58	1.83	3.63	3.51	1.13	4.25	1.70	3.75	4.64	41.55
1957	1.91	1.54	2.21	4.35	1.69	1.99	2.65	1.27	1.22	2.06	5.04	6.33	32.26
1958	5.36	2.27	2.80	5.94	3.13	3.54	2.73	3.41	6.49	3.61	3.46	1.42	44.16
1959	3.33	2.85	4.48	3.82	0.73	3.64	3.43	4.87	1.68	8.01	4.41	4.45	45.70
1960	3.08	5.28	2.50	3.71	3.02	4.62	8.20	3.00	8.37	2.30	3.88	2.53	50.49
1961	2.56	3.43	3.86	4.73	4.37	2.46	1.50	3.64	4.78	2.45	3.72	3.15	40.65
1962	3.87	4.04	1.89	3.33	2.25	3.04	1.64	6.27	4.63	4.24	2.59	2.61	40.40
1963	2.92	3.33	3.68	1.57	2.28	4.25	3.89	1.59	4.98	0.35	5.66	2.42	36.92
1964	5.54	3.43	3.63	3.76	0.87	1.68	3.07	2.46	1.42	1.98	2.20	4.51	34.55
1965	2.73	4.43	1.50	2.14	1.20	1.98	1.68	1.09	3.50	4.97	2.21	2.02	29.45
1966	3.05	4.40	3.15	1.38	3.01	2.72	3.96	1.90	6.05	4.23	3.82	3.60	41.27
1967	2.01	2.00	4.43	4.18	6.34	3.82	2.59	4.34	2.85	2.59	3.13	6.77	45.05
1968	1.92	1.14	4.55	2.74	3.93	6.65	1.58	2.53	2.88	2.03	5.46	5.22	40.63
1969	1.19	3.32	3.11	5.63	3.13	2.63	5.79	3.32	3.53	1.45	6.17	8.36	47.63
1970	0.39	5.15	4.28	4.12	3.59	2.49	1.49	3.18	3.20	2.08	4.31	4.15	38.43
1971	2.80	4.60	3.24	2.85	4.08	0.71	3.23	5.31	4.24	4.46	5.68	3.55	44.75
1972	2.02	5.12	6.71	4.61	7.49	9.66	3.84	3.45	1.84	4.20	8.53	7.08	64.55
1973	3.28	3.05	3.22	6.59	5.95	5.07	1.77	4.50	3.73	3.47	2.14	0.31	51.08
1974	4.10	1.95	4.49	3.64	3.03	2.38	2.39	3.36	8.57	2.34	2.62	4.52	43.39
1975	4.30	3.22	3.82	2.99	3.29	3.83	6.11	4.60	9.02	5.28	4.57	4.31	55.34
RECORD MEAN	3.44	3.26	3.72	3.68	3.53	3.51	3.58	3.88	3.67	3.08	3.82	3.83	43.00

Record mean values above are means through the current year for the period beginning in 1905 for temperature and precipitation, 1955 for snowfall. Data are from City Office locations through February 1940, from Brainerd Field through July 1954, and from Bradley Field thereafter.

Station: WILMINGTON, DELAWARE
GREATER WILMINGTON AIRPORT

Elevation (ground): 74 feet

TEMPERATURES °F

Month	Normal			Extremes			
	Daily maximum	Daily minimum	Monthly	Record highest	Year	Record lowest	Year
(a)				28		28	
J	40.2	23.8	32.0	75	1950	-4	1957
F	42.2	24.9	33.6	74	1954	-4	1961
M	51.1	32.0	41.6	86	1948	9	1960
A	63.0	41.5	52.3	91	1974	22	1965
M	73.1	51.6	62.4	95	1962	32	1966
J	81.6	61.1	71.4	99	1952	41	1972
J	85.5	66.1	75.8	102	1966	50	1952
A	83.9	64.3	74.1	101	1955	46	1965
S	78.2	57.6	67.9	100	1953	36	1974
O	67.8	46.5	57.2	91	1951	24	1969
N	55.2	36.2	45.7	85	1950	14	1955
D	43.0	26.3	34.7	72	1966	3	1962
YR	63.7	44.3	54.0	102	JUL 1966	-4	FEB 1961

IMPORTANT:
The time-period covered by this record is limited: See footnotes following table of **NORMALS, MEANS AND EXTREMES** for explanation and for additional history of **EXTREME HIGHS AND LOWS** recorded in the general area.

Delaware is part of the Atlantic Coastal Plain consisting mainly of the flat low land with many marshes. Small streams and tidal estuaries comprise the drainage of the state. Wilmington, at the northern end of the state, marks the beginning of low rolling hills extending northward and northwestward into Pennsylvania. The Delaware River, the Delaware Bay, and the Atlantic Ocean are along the eastern boundary of the state. The broad Chesapeake Bay lies 35 miles, or less, to the west of the western boundary of nearly the entire state. These large water areas influence to a considerable extent the climate of the Wilmington, Delaware, region.

Summers are warm and humid and winters are usually mild. During the summer maximum temperatures are usually in the eighties. The maximum temperature reaches 100° on the average of one year in six. During the coldest part of the year, mid-January, the normal daily average temperature is 32°. On the average, zero temperatures may be expected one year in four Most of the winter precipitation falls as rain. Seasonal snowfall has been as little as 1 inch, and there has been a season with nearly 50 inches snowfall. Snow is frequently mixed with rain and sleet. Snow seldom remains on the ground more than a few days.

The average date for the last occurrence in spring of temperature as low as 32° F. is mid-April. The average date for the first occurrence in fall of temperature as low as 32° F. is late October. The average freeze-free period is approximately 200 days.

The proximity of large water areas and the inflow of southerly winds cause the relative humidity to be quite high all year. During the summer months the average relative humidity is approximately 75 percent. Fog is relatively frequent and

(Continued page 396)

Snowfall

Season	July	Aug	Sept	Oct	Nov	Dec	Jan
1936-37	0.0	0.0	0.0	0.0	T	0.5	T
1937-38	0.0	0.0	0.0	T	T	T	1.0
1938-39	0.0	0.0	0.0	0.0	8.5	0.3	12.0
1939-40	0.0	0.0	0.0	0.0	T	1.5	4.7
1940-41	0.0	0.0	0.0	2.0	T	5.0	5.5
1941-42	0.0	0.0	0.0	0.0	0.0	T	3.5
1942-43	0.0	0.0	0.0	0.0	0.0	5.0	5.1
1943-44	0.0	0.0	0.0	0.0	T	0.0	2.5
1944-45	0.0	0.0	0.0	0.0	T	4.9	7.0
1945-46	0.0	0.0	0.0	0.0	T	10.5	1.0
1946-47	0.0	0.0	0.0	0.0	0.0	0.5	4.3
#1947-48	0.0	0.0	0.0	0.0	T	6.0	13.0
1948-49	0.0	0.0	0.0	0.0	0.0	6.4	4.2
1949-50	0.0	0.0	0.0	0.0	T	T	0.6
1950-51	0.0	0.0	0.0	0.0	0.8	0.7	2.6
1951-52	0.0	0.0	0.0	0.0	T	6.6	4.0
1952-53	0.0	0.0	0.0	0.0	2.0	2.8	5.2
1953-54	0.0	0.0	0.0	0.0	11.9	T	11.5
1954-55	0.0	0.0	0.0	0.0	T	0.9	3.8
1955-56	0.0	0.0	0.0	0.0	4.3	0.9	8.7
1956-57	0.0	0.0	0.0	0.0	T	T	6.5
1957-58	0.0	0.0	0.0	T	T	11.2	3.5
1958-59	0.0	0.0	0.0	0.0	T	0.6	3.3
1959-60	0.0	0.0	0.0	0.0	T	3.1	0.2
1960-61	0.0	0.0	0.0	T	T	13.2	16.5
1961-62	0.0	0.0	0.0	0.0	3.3	6.4	1.2
1962-63	0.0	0.0	0.0	0.3	T	8.6	5.2
1963-64	0.0	0.0	0.0	0.0	T	8.0	6.7
1964-65	0.0	0.0	0.0	0.0	T	1.6	8.4
1965-66	0.0	0.0	0.0	0.0	0.0	0.0	17.2
1966-67	0.0	0.0	0.0	0.0	T	21.5	0.6
1967-68	0.0	0.0	0.0	0.0	6.8	4.0	1.6
1968-69	0.0	0.0	0.0	0.0	T	0.6	2.9
1969-70	0.0	0.0	0.0	T	0.1	6.8	9.7
1970-71	0.0	0.0	0.0	0.0	0.0	3.2	5.8
1971-72	0.0	0.0	0.0	0.0	T	T	2.1
1972-73	0.0	0.0	0.0	T	T	T	T
1973-74	0.0	0.0	0.0	0.0	0.0	6.1	2.4
1974-75	0.0	0.0	0.0	0.0	T	T	5.1
1975-76	0.0	0.0	0.0	0.0	0.0	0.3	
RECORD MEAN	0.0	0.0	0.0	T	1.0	4.1	5.4

Heating Degree Days

Season	July	Aug	Sept	Oct	Nov	Dec	Jan
1955-56	0	0	45	226	645	1081	1021
1956-57	1	1	120	249	589	727	1120
1957-58	0	0	65	359	544	836	1056
1958-59	0	0	64	297	565	1123	1051
1959-60	0	0	44	256	605	831	920
1960-61	0	0	18	297	565	1130	1215
1961-62	0	0	36	250	553	976	1042
1962-63	0	4	113	266	672	1072	1130
1963-64	0	3	104	199	502	1128	982
1964-65	0	9	49	372	514	854	1108
1965-66	0	12	40	349	593	839	1103
1966-67	0	0	84	346	545	931	888
1967-68	0	0	80	327	722	866	1139
1968-69	0	0	7	205	532	949	1052
1969-70	0	0	41	288	606	993	1250
1970-71	0	0	25	175	487	895	1159
1971-72	0	2	23	93	585	702	889
1972-73	0	0	20	356	586	716	902
1973-74	0	0	15	179	469	839	886
1974-75	0	0	65	362	553	805	847
1975-76	0	0	56	177	418	888	

Cooling Degree Days

Year	Jan	Feb	Mar	Apr	May	June	July
1969	0	0	0	8	73	258	336
1970	0	0	0	2	97	211	365
1971	0	0	0	0	16	261	345
1972	0	0	2	0	35	143	376
1973	0	0	0	19	42	332	416
1974	0	0	0	24	64	175	370
1975	0	0	0	0	97	207	337

Feb	Mar	Apr	May	June	Total
5.0	7.5	T	0.0	0.0	13.0
3.5	3.0	T	0.0	0.0	7.5
T	2.5	T	0.0	0.0	23.3
8.1	2.8	2.5	0.0	0.0	19.6
6.6	9.0	0.0	0.0	0.0	28.1
2.3	2.2	0.0	0.0	0.0	8.0
1.0	8.0	T	0.0	0.0	19.1
3.7	9.5	1.0	0.0	0.0	16.7
6.5	0.0	0.0	0.0	0.0	18.4
2.0	0.0	0.0	0.0	0.0	13.5
13.5	2.2	0.0	0.0	0.0	20.5
14.8	1.6	0.0	0.0	0.0	35.4
10.1	T	0.0	0.0	0.0	20.7
0.4	T	T	0.0	0.0	1.0
0.7	T	0.0	0.0	0.0	4.8
T	6.8	0.0	0.0	0.0	17.4
1.0	5.5	T	0.0	0.0	16.5
0.6	0.3	T	0.0	0.0	24.3
8.5	2.0	0.0	0.0	0.0	15.2
1.1	12.3	T	0.0	0.0	27.3
1.3	1.2	T	0.0	0.0	9.0
14.5	20.3	T	0.0	0.0	49.5
0.4	1.9	1.1	0.0	0.0	7.3
5.1	13.4	T	0.0	0.0	21.8
13.3	1.1	T	0.0	0.0	44.1
8.0	5.2	T	0.0	0.0	24.1
4.6	0.3	0.0	T	0.0	19.0
14.9	9.5	T	0.0	0.0	39.1
1.7	5.8	0.6	0.0	0.0	18.1
10.0	T	T	0.0	0.0	27.2
18.7	2.7	T	0.0	0.0	43.5
0.9	1.3	0.0	0.0	0.0	14.6
5.5	7.8	0.0	0.0	0.0	16.8
1.5	0.4	0.0	0.0	0.0	18.5
0.2	2.4	0.6	0.0	0.0	12.2
7.0	0.3	0.1	0.0	0.0	9.5
1.2	T	T	0.0	0.0	1.2
11.5	T	T	0.0	0.0	20.0
4.8	1.1	T	0.0	0.0	11.0
5.8	3.7	0.1	T	0.0	20.1

WILMINGTON, DE

Feb	Mar	Apr	May	June	Total
790	810	456	199	13	5286
764	703	344	129	16	4763
1050	800	347	149	31	5237
890	734	325	103	22	5174
840	994	279	144	2	4915
843	687	486	203	6	5450
940	729	400	122	6	5054
1044	641	370	180	10	5502
962	669	467	91	21	5128
873	816	467	63	27	5152
921	676	507	186	24	5250
991	788	402	295	5	5275
994	626	319	171	6	5250
874	780	298	92	1	4790
876	803	389	95	1	5342
821	746	411	153	3	4875
935	732	443	105	27	4536
820	477	322	143	0	4342
887	635	300	137	7	4354
808	753	520	84	5	4802

Aug	Sept	Oct	Nov	Dec	Total
330	143	14	0	0	1162
371	244	38	0	0	1328
287	214	34	16	0	1173
334	165	8	0	0	1063
413	183	29	0	0	1434
355	113	2	6	0	1109
355	73	27	5	0	1101

Average Temperature

Year	Jan	Feb	Mar	Apr	May	June	July	Aug	Sept	Oct	Nov	Dec	Annual
1936	28.2	25.0	46.8	49.6	65.0	70.8	75.9	75.8	68.8	57.5	43.0	38.3	53.7
1937	41.0	35.2	37.6	51.0	63.8	72.0	75.7	75.8	65.1	54.4	44.6	34.2	54.2
1938	32.8	36.4	45.0	54.1	60.9	70.4	75.9	76.5	66.0	57.6	47.8	35.8	54.9
1939	32.6	38.6	42.2	50.2	64.2	72.4	74.6	76.0	68.4	57.0	42.8	36.8	54.6
1940	22.9	33.0	36.4	46.8	61.2	70.3	75.4	70.8	64.8	52.1	44.8	39.0	51.5
1941	30.8	30.2	35.6	56.3	64.9	70.7	75.0	73.0	70.2	61.4	48.0	38.8	54.6
1942	31.0	30.7	43.8	54.8	65.6	71.4	75.4	72.6	67.9	57.4	46.2	31.3	54.0
1943	31.9	34.8	42.6	47.4	63.4	75.4	75.0	75.2	67.0	54.5	44.3	33.6	53.8
1944	34.4	34.2	38.9	50.0	67.3	71.7	75.8	74.7	71.2	55.2	45.6	31.6	54.2
1945	26.1	33.4	51.6	55.4	60.2	71.0	74.2	71.6	70.2	54.7	47.3	30.0	53.8
1946	34.2	35.0	50.4	50.2	61.6	67.4	73.4	69.6	68.4	59.1	47.8	37.4	54.5
#1947	37.8	27.8	36.5	51.4	60.9	68.0	73.8	75.2	67.5	62.2	42.9	33.4	53.1
1948	25.5	31.0	43.4	51.0	61.4	70.6	75.7	73.6	66.8	54.2	49.4	36.3	53.2
1949	39.2	38.6	43.2	52.0	62.9	72.9	78.7	75.1	64.2	60.4	44.5	37.5	55.8
1950	42.7	33.6	37.6	48.3	60.1	69.7	74.0	72.5	63.4	57.6	45.0	32.4	53.1
1951	34.2	34.8	41.5	51.6	61.9	70.4	75.9	73.8	67.0	59.1	41.5	37.6	54.1
1952	37.0	37.6	40.5	54.6	61.0	73.4	78.4	74.3	67.4	52.4	45.5	37.4	55.0
1953	37.6	38.4	44.4	52.3	65.0	72.2	77.0	74.5	68.2	58.0	45.2	38.7	56.0
1954	31.3	40.4	41.5	55.6	60.6	72.0	76.2	72.9	68.3	59.6	43.8	35.1	54.8
1955	31.5	34.1	43.5	54.8	64.8	68.7	81.2	77.9	67.2	58.1	43.3	29.9	54.6
1956	31.8	37.5	38.6	49.9	59.9	71.7	73.4	73.4	64.6	56.8	45.2	41.3	53.7
1957	28.6	37.4	42.2	54.1	62.9	74.2	75.9	73.2	68.7	53.3	46.6	37.9	54.6
1958	30.8	27.3	39.0	53.4	60.7	67.4	76.5	73.0	65.8	55.4	45.8	28.6	52.0
1959	30.9	33.0	41.1	54.3	65.6	72.0	75.4	76.0	70.4	59.5	44.7	38.0	55.1
1960	35.1	35.9	32.8	56.4	60.6	71.0	73.1	74.9	68.0	55.3	45.9	28.4	53.1
1961	25.6	34.7	42.6	48.9	58.9	70.5	75.6	74.0	72.5	56.9	46.7	33.2	53.3
1962	31.2	31.3	41.2	52.2	64.2	71.5	72.6	72.9	63.6	56.7	42.5	30.3	52.5
1963	28.4	27.5	44.1	52.6	60.3	70.8	76.3	71.7	63.7	58.4	48.0	28.4	52.5
1964	33.2	31.6	43.1	49.4	64.3	72.1	75.8	71.5	67.2	52.8	47.6	37.3	53.8
1965	29.0	33.6	38.4	49.3	66.0	70.2	74.5	73.3	69.4	53.6	45.0	37.7	53.3
1966	29.3	31.9	42.9	47.9	60.3	72.5	77.2	74.8	65.3	53.6	46.6	34.8	53.1
1967	36.2	29.4	39.4	51.5	55.4	71.2	74.4	72.8	65.1	54.7	40.7	36.8	52.3
1968	28.0	30.5	44.6	54.1	59.6	71.4	76.7	77.1	69.7	59.0	47.0	34.2	54.3
1969	30.8	33.6	39.6	55.1	64.2	73.4	75.7	75.4	68.2	56.0	44.6	32.7	54.1
1970	24.5	33.5	38.9	51.9	64.8	71.7	76.6	76.7	72.1	60.4	48.5	35.9	54.6
1971	27.4	35.5	40.7	51.1	60.4	73.4	75.9	74.0	71.1	62.9	45.7	42.1	55.0
1972	36.1	32.6	41.3	50.0	62.5	68.6	76.9	75.5	69.6	53.5	45.2	41.6	54.4
1973	35.6	35.5	49.4	54.7	61.4	75.8	78.1	78.1	70.4	59.9	49.1	37.7	57.2
1974	36.2	33.1	44.3	55.5	62.4	70.4	76.7	76.1	66.5	53.2	46.6	38.9	55.0
1975	37.5	35.9	40.6	47.5	65.2	71.5	75.7	76.3	65.4	60.0	51.0	36.2	55.2
RECORD MEAN	32.6	33.1	41.9	52.2	62.7	71.4	76.0	74.1	67.9	56.8	45.7	35.2	54.2
MAX	40.4	41.3	51.3	62.7	73.3	81.6	85.7	83.6	77.6	66.7	54.3	42.9	63.5
MIN	24.8	24.8	32.5	41.6	52.0	61.1	66.3	64.6	58.1	46.9	37.0	27.5	44.8

# Indicates a station move or relocation of instruments.

Precipitation

Year	Jan	Feb	Mar	Apr	May	June	July	Aug	Sept	Oct	Nov	Dec	Annual
1936	7.45	2.72	5.97	2.98	2.90	3.39	2.71	7.01	3.47	3.11	0.78	5.46	47.95
1937	6.36	2.30	2.09	4.41	2.37	5.48	2.58	6.57	2.69	5.29	3.19	1.38	44.71
1938	2.40	2.52	2.41	2.02	4.05	8.37	6.94	5.24	8.10	1.91	2.80	3.48	50.24
1939	3.57	5.90	3.85	6.47	0.35	5.59	1.67	6.78	0.87	5.68	0.72	1.90	43.35
1940	1.51	2.87	5.64	6.47	4.88	2.04	1.87	5.33	2.99	2.67	4.58	2.62	43.47
1941	3.17	1.88	1.99	2.90	1.42	3.61	5.66	3.21	0.73	1.94	2.91	3.78	33.20
1942	2.89	2.67	5.60	1.12	2.49	2.41	9.05	9.54	2.14	3.98	3.08	4.37	49.34
1943	2.73	1.88	2.76	3.56	6.18	4.05	3.87	1.12	0.45	6.20	3.54	1.45	37.79
1944	3.39	2.00	6.02	5.20	2.31	5.06	1.31	3.53	6.58	2.14	4.60	3.35	45.49
1945	4.27	3.15	2.73	4.32	5.17	4.80	9.94	10.67	4.41	1.85	5.70	4.04	61.05
1946	1.76	1.95	3.29	1.88	7.12	6.42	4.76	6.26	3.91	2.11	1.38	2.25	43.09
#1947	3.72	1.47	2.39	6.20	7.24	4.27	2.99	2.31	2.19	2.23	8.11	1.80	44.92
1948	4.05	2.66	3.76	3.07	7.35	5.25	1.15	4.58	1.87	1.25	4.82	5.25	45.06
1949	5.55	4.18	3.00	2.69	4.10	0.98	6.16	3.55	3.08	3.63	1.15	2.90	40.97
1950	1.97	3.11	4.74	1.81	3.32	2.45	4.35	3.05	7.06	2.46	4.22	1.95	40.49
1951	3.64	2.96	3.76	2.56	3.56	4.27	3.84	3.23	1.16	3.17	7.32	5.79	45.26
1952	5.09	2.73	5.35	5.57	4.61	2.52	7.40	3.09	3.12	0.46	5.40	3.61	48.95
1953	5.14	2.69	5.72	4.76	5.39	2.52	3.21	1.89	3.64	3.87	2.19	4.13	45.15
1954	1.71	1.82	4.03	2.84	2.38	0.44	1.93	5.82	3.39	2.08	4.14	3.14	33.72
1955	0.59	2.93	4.86	2.55	1.18	6.34	0.16	12.09	2.27	2.62	1.36	0.19	37.14
1956	2.61	4.21	5.18	2.80	2.12	3.58	7.39	3.58	2.77	3.58	5.94	4.09	47.85
1957	2.30	3.76	2.64	3.73	2.36	3.45	1.33	2.61	6.55	2.51	3.11	4.74	39.09
1958	3.63	4.14	5.39	4.62	3.89	5.17	7.51	7.00	2.91	3.99	2.37	1.25	51.87
1959	1.89	1.80	2.97	2.15	1.34	4.23	5.21	5.75	2.29	4.11	2.99	3.46	38.19
1960	2.86	3.69	1.71	2.93	5.12	1.37	6.18	5.08	9.53	2.85	2.04	2.67	46.03
1961	2.84	3.74	5.19	4.88	2.45	3.10	4.84	3.75	2.33	1.88	2.41	3.03	40.44
1962	2.51	3.26	4.30	3.50	1.61	3.05	1.78	1.87	3.65	1.51	4.87	2.50	34.41
1963	2.05	2.09	4.24	1.12	1.23	3.26	1.65	4.03	3.50	0.21	6.87	1.85	32.10
1964	4.13	3.37	2.20	5.97	0.22	1.02	3.70	1.83	2.77	1.29	1.62	4.70	32.82
1965	2.38	2.17	3.20	1.76	1.41	1.62	3.84	2.04	2.41	1.59	0.94	1.54	24.90
1966	2.82	4.90	0.81	3.16	3.35	0.70	3.09	1.42	8.53	5.17	1.75	3.81	39.51
1967	1.67	1.90	5.45	2.69	3.79	3.01	4.45	11.16	1.16	2.05	2.08	5.24	44.65
1968	2.29	1.52	4.75	1.57	4.78	2.81	1.83	1.17	1.50	3.28	3.92	2.33	31.75
1969	1.68	1.76	1.71	1.58	3.21	3.62	6.48	2.34	6.84	1.47	1.79	7.90	40.38
1970	1.00	2.13	3.61	5.56	0.94	6.16	6.03	2.31	0.82	2.64	4.09	3.02	38.31
1971	2.22	6.29	2.29	2.15	4.51	2.50	3.65	8.38	6.99	6.41	5.52	1.33	52.24
1972	2.50	5.43	2.40	4.47	3.85	7.49	2.07	0.25	1.64	4.20	7.84	5.99	48.13
1973	3.81	3.42	4.02	6.57	5.56	5.19	2.82	2.44	3.02	2.22	0.67	7.31	47.05
1974	2.92	1.73	4.56	3.08	3.96	3.97	1.49	5.11	5.65	1.77	1.19	4.18	39.61
1975	4.23	2.95	4.63	3.03	5.65	6.16	5.53	2.55	6.19	3.06	2.63	3.00	49.61
RECORD MEAN	3.28	3.14	3.70	3.53	3.53	3.81	4.49	4.74	3.69	3.00	3.24	3.48	43.63

Record mean values above are means through the current year for the period beginning in 1895 for temperature, 1894 for precipitation, and 1948 for snowfall. Data are from Co-operative locations through 1947; temperatures through February 1912 and precipitation through July 11, 1912, from 6th and King Streets, otherwise from Porter Reservoir. Data are from Airport locations beginning January 1948.

(Continued)

may occur in any month. Light southeast winds blowing up the Delaware Bay favor the formation of fog. Light north-northeast winds bring in smoke from Philadelphia and from the heavy industry area located along the Delaware River north of Wilmington.

Rainfall distribution throughout the year is fairly uniform; however, the greatest amounts normally come during the summer months. Mostly, the summer rainfall comes in the form of thunderstorms. Moisture deficiencies for crops occur occasionally, but severe droughts are rare. During the fall, winter, and spring seasons, much of the rainfall comes as a result of storms forming over the southern states, or the south Atlantic and then moving northward along the Atlantic Coast. During the late summer and early fall, hurricanes occasionally cause heavy rainfall, but winds seldom reach hurricane force in Wilmington. Heavy rains occasionally cause minor flash flooding, but the streams and rivers of northern Delaware are not subject to major flooding. Strong easterly and southeasterly winds sometimes cause high tides in the Delaware Bay and the Delaware River, resulting in the flooding of lowlands and damage to bay front and river front properties.

Normals, Means, and Extremes

	Normal Degree days Base 65 °F		Precipitation in inches												Relative humidity pct.			
			Water equivalent							Snow, Ice pellets					Hour 01	Hour 07	Hour 13	Hour 19
Month	Heating	Cooling	Normal	Maximum monthly	Year	Minimum monthly	Year	Maximum in 24 hrs.	Year	Maximum monthly	Year	Maximum in 24 hrs.	Year		(Local time)			
(a)				28		28		28		28		28			28	28	28	28
J	1023	0	2.85	5.55	1949	0.59	1955	1.61	1968	17.2	1966	11.2	1966		74	75	61	69
F	879	0	2.75	6.29	1971	1.52	1968	2.29	1966	18.7	1967	9.9	1967		72	75	58	66
M	725	0	3.74	5.72	1953	0.81	1966	2.75	1958	20.3	1958	15.6	1958		72	74	53	63
A	381	0	3.20	6.57	1973	1.12	1963	2.56	1961	1.1	1959	1.1	1959		74	73	50	61
M	128	48	3.35	7.35	1948	0.22	1964	2.35	1968	T	1963	T	1963		79	76	53	64
J	0	196	3.24	7.49	1972	0.44	1954	4.35	1972	0.0		0.0			83	79	54	66
J	0	335	4.31	7.51	1958	0.16	1955	6.24	1952	0.0		0.0			84	80	54	67
A	0	282	3.98	12.09	1955	0.25	1972	4.11	1971	0.0		0.0			85	84	56	70
S	32	119	3.42	9.53	1960	0.82	1970	5.62	1960	0.0		0.0			85	85	55	72
O	254	12	2.60	6.41	1971	0.21	1963	3.88	1966	0.3	1962	0.3	1962		83	84	53	71
N	579	0	3.49	7.84	1972	0.67	1973	3.83	1956	11.9	1953	11.9	1953		78	80	56	70
D	939	0	3.32	7.90	1969	0.19	1955	2.22	1969	21.5	1966	12.4	1966		75	77	60	70
YR	4940	992	40.25	12.09	AUG 1955	0.16	JUL 1955	6.24	JUL 1952	21.5	DEC 1966	15.6	MAR 1958		79	79	55	67

(To better understand these tables, see full explanation of terms beginning on page 322)

	Wind							Mean number of days											Average station pressure mb.
			Fastest mile					Sunrise to sunset							Temperatures °F Max.		Min.		
Month	Mean speed m.p.h.	Prevailing direction	Speed m.p.h.	Direction	Year	Pct. of possible sunshine	Mean sky cover, tenths, sunrise to sunset	Clear	Partly cloudy	Cloudy	Precipitation .01 inch or more	Snow, Ice pellets 1.0 inch or more	Thunderstorms	Heavy fog, visibility ¼ mile or less	(b) 90° and above	32° and below	32° and below	0° and below	Elev. 80 feet m.s.l.
(a)	27	16	27	27			28	28	28	28	28	28	28	28	28	28	28	28	3
J	9.7	WNW	46	29	1957		6.6	7	7	17	11	2	*	5	0	7	25	*	1017.0
F	10.5	NW	46	29	1956		6.5	7	7	14	10	2	*	4	0	4	22	*	1014.9
M	11.2	WNW	43	29	1971		6.5	7	9	15	11	1	1	3	0	1	16	0	1012.8
A	10.5	WNW	45	29	1963		6.5	7	8	15	11	*	2	3	*	0	3	0	1011.9
M	9.0	S	45	27	1957		6.6	6	11	14	12	0	4	3	1	0	*	0	1011.3
J	8.4	S	40	23	1960		6.0	7	11	12	9	0	6	2	4	0	0	0	1012.7
J	7.7	NW	48	27	1963		6.1	7	12	12	9	0	6	2	8	0	0	0	1012.8
A	7.4	S	46	35	1971		5.8	9	10	12	9	0	6	3	5	0	0	0	1014.7
S	7.8	S	40	07	1956		5.7	10	8	12	8	0	2	3	2	0	0	0	1015.7
O	8.1	NW	58	20	1954		5.3	12	7	12	7	0	1	4	*	0	2	0	1017.6
N	9.1	NW	46	16	1950		6.2	8	9	13	9	*	1	4	0	*	11	0	1015.5
D	9.3	WNW	44	29	1962		6.5	7	8	16	10	1	*	4	0	4	22	0	1015.8
YR	9.1	NW	58	20	OCT 1954		6.2	94	107	164	116	6	31	39	19	15	102	*	1014.4

FOOTNOTES

Means and extremes above are from existing and comparable exposures. Annual extremes have been exceeded at other sites in the locality as follows: Highest temperature 107 in August 1918; lowest temperature -15 in February 1934; maximum monthly precipitation 14.91 in August 1911; minimum monthly precipitation 0.06 in October 1924; maximum precipitation in 24 hours 6.53 in August 1945; maximum monthly snowfall 27.0 in January 1935; maximum snowfall in 24 hours 22.0 in December 1909.

Station: WASHINGTON, D. C.
WASHINGTON NATIONAL AIRPORT
Elevation (ground): 10 feet

TEMPERATURES °F

Month	Normal			Extremes			
	Daily maximum	Daily minimum	Monthly	Record highest	Year	Record lowest	Year
(a)				15		15	
J	43.5	27.7	35.6	76	1975	3	1972
F	46.0	28.6	37.3	77	1972	4	1961
M	55.0	35.2	45.1	86	1963	16	1962
A	67.1	45.7	56.4	91	1974	27	1969
M	76.6	55.7	66.2	97	1969	36	1966
J	84.6	64.6	74.6	100	1969	47	1972
J	88.2	69.1	78.7	101	1966	56	1963
A	86.6	67.6	77.1	99	1962	51	1963
S	80.2	61.0	70.6	96	1973	39	1963
O	69.8	49.7	59.8	91	1967	29	1969
N	57.2	38.8	48.0	86	1974	20	1970
D	45.2	29.5	37.4	74	1971	10	1963
YR	66.7	47.8	57.3	101	JUL 1966	3	JAN 1972

IMPORTANT:
The time-period covered by this record is limited: See footnotes on next page for explanation and for additional history of EXTREME HIGHS AND LOWS recorded in the general area.

Washington lies at the western edge of the middle Atlantic coastal plain, about 50 miles east of the Blue Ridge Mountains and 35 miles west of Chesapeake Bay at the junction of the Potomac and Anacostia Rivers. Elevations range from a few feet above sea level to about 400 feet in parts of the northwest section of the city.

Observational records have been kept continuously since November 1870. Since June 1941, the official observations have been taken at Washington National Airport. Significant temperature differences within the metropolitan area are not unusual. Average minimum temperatures at some locations are 8 degrees lower than official airport readings. Minimum temperatures for the airport are highest for the area since the airport is located near the center of the urban heat island. Variations in the average maximum temperatures over the metropolitan area are usually less than 5 degrees. Rainfall and snow fall amounts at the airport are less than an average for the area; some locations average 5 inches more precipitation than the airport per annum.

Summers are warm and humid and winters mild; generally pleasant weather prevails in the spring and autumn. The coldest weather occurs in late January and early February. The warmest weather occurs late in July. There are no well pronounced wet and dry seasons. Thunderstorms, during the summer months, often bring sudden and heavy rain showers and may be attended by damaging winds, hail, or lightning. On June 9, 1929, a violent local thunderstorm was accompanied by wind gusts up to 100 m.p.h. Two severe hailstorms with resultant damage of $100,000 or more are recorded, one in April 1938 and the other in May 1953. Tornadoes rarely occur, but three rather destructive ones have been recorded — one in April 1923 and one in November 1927; the resulting damage was $100,000 or more in each case. In April 1973 a tornado struck in the vicinity of suburban Fairfax, Virginia causing an estimated $15,000,000 damage.

Tropical disturbances occasionally, during their northward passage, influence Washington's weather mainly with high winds and heavy rainfall, but extensive damage from wind and tidal flooding is rare.

With the passage of Hurricane Hazel on October 15, 1954, the peak gust of wind reached 98 m.p.h., but only 1.73 inches of rainfall was recorded. Hurricane Connie, August 12-13, 1955, produced 6.60 inches of rainfall but the peak wind was only 58 m.p.h. During June 21-22, 1972, Hurricane Agnes produced 7.52 inches of rain at Washington National Airport. Flooding from the rains of Agnes caused 16 deaths in the greater metrpolitan area and damage totaled $300,000,000 in Virginia, Maryland, Delaware and the District of Columbia.

(Continued page 400)

WASHINGTON, DISTRICT OF COLUMBIA

Normals, Means, and Extremes

(To better understand these tables, see full explanation of terms beginning on page 322)

Month	Normal Degree days Base 65 °F: Heating	Cooling	Precipitation in inches — Water equivalent: Normal	Maximum monthly	Year	Minimum monthly	Year	Maximum in 24 hrs.	Year	Snow, Ice pellets: Maximum monthly	Year	Maximum in 24 hrs.	Year
(a)				34		34		32		32		32	
J	911	0	2.62	5.08	1949	0.31	1955	1.73	1948	21.3	1966	13.8	1966
F	776	0	2.45	5.71	1961	0.80	1968	1.77	1971	19.0	1967	14.4	1958
M	617	0	3.33	7.43	1953	0.64	1945	3.43	1958	17.1	1960	7.9	1960
A	265	7	2.86	5.97	1952	0.26	1942	3.08	1970	0.6	1972	0.6	1972
M	72	109	3.68	10.69	1953	1.06	1963	4.32	1953	T	1963	T	1963
J	0	288	3.48	11.53	1972	1.24	1954	7.19	1972	0.0		0.0	
J	0	425	4.12	11.06	1945	0.93	1966	4.69	1970	0.0		0.0	
A	0	375	4.67	14.31	1955	0.55	1962	6.39	1955	0.0		0.0	
S	14	182	3.08	12.36	1975	0.20	1967	5.31	1975	0.0		0.0	
O	190	29	2.66	8.18	1942	T	1963	4.98	1955	T	1974	T	1974
N	510	0	2.90	6.70	1963	0.37	1965	2.63	1971	6.9	1967	6.9	1967
D	856	0	3.04	6.54	1969	0.22	1955	2.08	1974	16.2	1962	11.4	1957
YR	4211	1415	38.89	14.31	AUG 1955	T	OCT 1963	7.19	JUN 1972	21.3	JAN 1966	14.4	FEB 1958

Month	Relative humidity pct.: Hour 01	Hour 07	Hour 13	Hour 19 (Local time)	Wind: Mean speed m.p.h.	Prevailing direction	Fastest mile: Speed m.p.h.	Direction	Year	Pct. of possible sunshine	Mean sky cover, tenths, sunrise to sunset	Mean number of days — Sunrise to sunset: Clear	Partly cloudy	Cloudy	Precipitation .01 inch or more	Snow, Ice pellets 1.0 inch or more	Thunderstorms	Heavy fog, visibility ¼ mile or less	Temperatures °F Max.: 90° and above (b)	Max.: 32° and below	Min.: 32° and below	Min.: 0° and below	Average station pressure mb. Elev. 65 feet m.s.l.
(a)	15	15	15	15	27	13	27	27		27	27	27	27	27	34	32	27	27	15	15	15	15	3
J	66	69	54	59	9.9	NW	56	NW	1957	48	6.6	8	7	16	11	2	*	2	0	5	23	0	1018.1
F	64	68	53	56	10.4	S	57	SW	1961	51	6.4	7	7	14	9	1	*	2	0	2	19	0	1016.0
M	63	68	49	53	10.9	NW	60	E	1951	55	6.4	7	9	15	11	1	1	1	0	*	9	0	1013.8
A	65	68	48	50	10.5	S	56	N	1952	56	6.4	7	9	14	10	0	3	1	*	0	1	0	1013.2
M	71	72	51	57	9.2	S	48	S	1952	58	6.3	7	11	13	11	0	5	*	2	0	0	0	1012.1
J	76	76	53	60	8.7	S	57	NW	1954	64	5.9	8	11	11	9	0	5	*	8	0	0	0	1013.7
J	75	75	52	60	8.1	S	54	E	1951	62	6.0	7	13	11	10	0	6	*	13	0	0	0	1013.9
A	77	78	53	62	8.0	S	49	NE	1955	62	5.7	10	9	12	9	0	5	*	10	0	0	0	1015.6
S	78	79	55	65	8.2	S	56	SE	1952	62	5.5	11	8	11	8	0	2	*	4	0	0	0	1016.4
O	76	79	51	62	8.5	SSW	78	SE	1954	60	5.2	12	7	12	7	0	1	2	*	0	1	0	1018.4
N	70	73	52	60	9.2	S	60	E	1952	53	6.0	9	8	13	8	*	*	1	0	0	5	0	1016.7
D	68	71	57	62	9.4	NW	62	SW	1957	47	6.5	9	6	16	9	1	*	2	0	2	17	0	1016.9
YR	71	73	52	59	9.2	S	78	SE	OCT 1954	57	6.1	102	105	158	112	5	29	13	37	9	74	0	1015.4

FOOTNOTES Means and extremes above are from existing and comparable exposures. Annual extremes have been exceeded at other sites in the locality as follows: Highest temperature 106 in July 1930+; lowest temperature -15 in February 1899; maximum monthly precipitation 17.45 in September 1934; maximum precipitation in 24 hours 7.31 in August 1928; maximum monthly snowfall 35.2 in February 1899; maximum snowfall in 24 hours 25.0 in January 1922.

Snowfall

Season	July	Aug	Sept	Oct	Nov	Dec	Jan
1936-37	0.0	0.0	0.0	0.0	T	1.5	T
1937-38	0.0	0.0	0.0	0.0	T	T	1.5
1938-39	0.0	0.0	0.0	0.0	7.0	T	7.8
1939-40	0.0	0.0	0.0	0.0	0.4	4.4	15.3
1940-41	0.0	0.0	0.0	1.5	T	T	3.2
1941-42	0.0	0.0	0.0	0.0	0.0	0.2	1.8
1942-43	0.0	0.0	0.0	0.0	0.0	5.7	6.2
#1943-44	0.0	0.0	0.0	0.0	T	0.1	2.0
1944-45	0.0	0.0	0.0	0.0	T	1.5	2.8
1945-46	0.0	0.0	0.0	0.0	T	10.3	6.8
1946-47	0.0	0.0	0.0	0.0	0.0	2.2	4.1
1947-48	0.0	0.0	0.0	0.0	T	3.6	12.1
1948-49	0.0	0.0	0.0	0.0	T	4.4	7.4
1949-50	0.0	0.0	0.0	0.0	T	T	0.3
1950-51	0.0	0.0	0.0	0.0	1.6	3.8	0.8
1951-52	0.0	0.0	0.0	0.0	T	4.8	1.6
1952-53	0.0	0.0	0.0	0.0	1.7	2.0	1.3
1953-54	0.0	0.0	0.0	0.0	6.7	T	11.3
1954-55	0.0	0.0	0.0	T	0.0	0.1	2.3
1955-56	0.0	0.0	0.0	0.0	2.3	0.5	4.5
1956-57	0.0	0.0	0.0	0.0	T	0.2	10.1
1957-58	0.0	0.0	0.0	T	0.3	12.0	0.3
1958-59	0.0	0.0	0.0	0.0	T	0.9	4.0
1959-60	0.0	0.0	0.0	0.0	T	T	T
1960-61	0.0	0.0	0.0	0.0	T	8.7	13.6
1961-62	0.0	0.0	0.0	0.0	1.3	1.2	2.0
1962-63	0.0	0.0	0.0	0.0	T	16.2	2.1
1963-64	0.0	0.0	0.0	0.0	T	6.4	8.9
1964-65	0.0	0.0	0.0	0.0	0.2	0.5	9.1
1965-66	0.0	0.0	0.0	0.0	0.0	0.2	21.3
1966-67	0.0	0.0	0.0	0.0	T	16.1	1.3
1967-68	0.0	0.0	0.0	0.0	6.9	6.3	2.8
1968-69	0.0	0.0	0.0	0.0	T	T	0.2
1969-70	0.0	0.0	0.0	0.0	T	6.8	3.6
1970-71	0.0	0.0	0.0	0.0	T	5.2	4.8
1971-72	0.0	0.0	0.0	0.0	1.4	0.1	0.3
1972-73	0.0	0.0	0.0	T	T	0.0	T
1973-74	0.0	0.0	0.0	0.0	0.0	11.0	1.5
1974-75	0.0	0.0	0.0	T	T	0.1	6.6
1975-76	0.0	0.0	0.0	0.0	0.0	0.4	
RECORD MEAN	0.0	0.0	0.0	T	0.7	3.9	4.7

Heating Degree Days

Season	July	Aug	Sept	Oct	Nov	Dec	Jan
1955-56	0	0	15	182	578	968	937
1956-57	0	1	88	188	560	638	988
1957-58	0	0	40	292	458	725	943
1958-59	0	0	22	203	447	987	926
1959-60	0	0	28	195	545	704	824
#1960-61	0	0	7	212	489	1048	1081
1961-62	0	0	16	181	459	882	932
1962-63	0	0	59	182	599	981	1034
1963-64	0	0	70	129	449	1042	882
1964-65	0	0	29	300	415	771	974
1965-66	0	1	18	236	458	723	1001
1966-67	0	0	41	246	462	843	735
1967-68	0	0	34	240	592	773	1033
1968-69	0	0	0	162	445	875	949
1969-70	0	0	18	226	525	883	1077
1970-71	0	0	17	131	464	777	1034
1971-72	0	0	12	61	518	597	815
1972-73	0	0	8	278	543	654	843
1973-74	0	0	4	103	399	708	677
1974-75	0	0	26	250	446	674	740
1975-76	0	0	20	102	328	752	

Cooling Degree Days

Year	Jan	Feb	Mar	Apr	May	June	July
1969	0	0	0	24	151	367	458
1970	0	0	0	10	166	311	449
1971	0	0	0	0	52	337	422
1972	0	0	3	5	50	184	393
1973	0	0	2	21	47	371	448
1974	0	0	4	33	96	205	441
1975	1	0	0	12	177	344	448

Feb	Mar	Apr	May	June	Total
7.7	11.0	T	0.0	0.0	20.2
1.4	2.5	T	0.0	0.0	5.4
0.3	T	T	0.0	0.0	15.1
4.3	0.4	0.5	0.0	0.0	25.3
2.0	11.2	0.0	0.0	0.0	17.9
0.1	11.5	0.0	0.0	0.0	13.6
0.7	7.9	T	0.0	0.0	20.5
2.5	T	T	0.0	0.0	4.6
3.0	T	0.0	0.0	0.0	7.3
4.5	T	0.0	0.0	0.0	21.6
10.3	3.4	0.0	0.0	0.0	20.0
7.7	T	0.0	0.0	0.0	23.4
4.0	T	0.0	0.0	0.0	15.8
T	3.1	T	0.0	0.0	3.4
3.0	1.0	0.0	0.0	0.0	10.2
T	3.8	0.0	0.0	0.0	10.2
0.2	3.1	T	0.0	0.0	8.3
T	T	T	0.0	0.0	18.0
4.2	T	0.0	0.0	0.0	6.6
T	4.0	0.0	0.0	0.0	11.3
1.6	2.2	0.1	0.0	0.0	14.2
17.2	10.6	0.0	0.0	0.0	40.4
T	T	T	0.0	0.0	4.9
7.2	17.1	0.0	0.0	0.0	24.3
18.0	T	T	0.0	0.0	40.3
6.5	4.0	0.0	0.0	0.0	15.0
2.0	1.1	0.0	T	0.0	21.4
11.7	6.2	0.4	0.0	0.0	33.6
1.9	5.4	0.0	0.0	0.0	17.1
6.9	T	0.0	0.0	0.0	28.4
19.0	0.7	0.0	0.0	0.0	37.1
2.4	3.0	0.0	0.0	0.0	21.4
2.2	6.7	0.0	0.0	0.0	9.1
3.6	T	0.0	0.0	0.0	14.0
0.3	1.4	T	0.0	0.0	11.7
14.4	T	0.6	0.0	0.0	16.8
0.1	T	T	0.0	0.0	0.1
4.2	T	T	0.0	0.0	16.7
5.8	0.3	T	0.0	0.0	12.8
5.1	2.4	T	T	0.0	16.8

Average Temp.

Year	Jan	Feb	Mar	Apr	May	June	July	Aug	Sept	Oct	Nov	Dec	Annual
1936	30.6	29.6	50.3	52.2	67.4	72.8	78.4	77.9	71.4	59.7	45.0	39.8	56.3
1937	43.8	36.6	42.1	53.4	65.8	75.1	77.2	77.8	65.9	55.3	46.6	37.0	56.4
1938	35.7	40.9	49.8	57.1	63.4	72.8	78.4	78.6	67.4	58.8	49.8	38.4	57.6
1939	37.8	42.3	46.4	53.4	68.0	75.4	76.2	78.8	71.0	58.4	46.0	40.1	57.8
1940	24.9	37.1	40.7	50.8	64.4	74.8	77.5	73.4	66.8	55.7	48.2	42.8	54.8
#1941	34.8	33.8	39.8	60.6	66.8	73.2	77.0	75.4	72.4	64.4	50.1	41.4	57.5
1942	34.4	34.1	46.8	58.2	68.4	74.0	78.6	74.8	70.3	59.8	47.6	34.4	56.8
1943	35.8	38.2	44.6	51.1	66.9	78.8	78.0	78.6	67.6	56.4	46.8	36.6	56.6
1944	37.2	37.8	42.6	53.4	70.8	74.6	78.2	75.8	70.6	56.6	47.4	34.2	56.6
#1945	30.8	38.4	55.5	59.4	63.0	74.4	76.4	74.8	72.8	57.6	49.3	32.9	57.1
#1946	36.8	39.2	53.0	56.0	65.2	72.4	76.2	72.6	70.0	61.4	51.8	41.4	58.0
#1947	41.7	31.4	40.0	57.2	64.6	71.6	75.5	79.0	69.8	64.5	46.2	36.6	56.5
#1948	28.8	36.8	48.0	55.9	64.6	74.0	78.0	75.8	69.4	56.2	51.4	40.2	56.6
1949	42.6	43.8	46.6	55.0	66.0	75.1	81.0	77.6	67.1	63.4	48.1	41.9	59.0
1950	48.0	38.7	41.7	52.4	64.5	73.9	76.2	75.6	66.9	61.0	47.9	35.6	56.9
1951	39.3	38.6	45.6	55.9	64.9	73.4	78.7	76.8	70.3	62.1	44.1	40.9	57.6
1952	40.7	41.1	43.3	57.0	64.2	76.9	80.5	76.2	68.9	55.3	48.2	38.9	57.6
1953	40.7	42.6	47.5	56.1	70.1	74.6	79.6	76.3	69.7	60.5	48.1	40.9	58.9
1954	35.9	43.5	44.5	59.6	62.6	74.4	78.8	75.2	73.3	62.0	45.2	37.1	57.7
1955	35.4	37.8	47.1	58.2	67.1	70.2	82.1	78.3	69.9	59.6	45.5	33.6	57.1
1956	34.5	41.1	43.2	53.6	63.6	73.3	75.6	75.0	66.6	59.0	46.1	44.2	56.3
1957	32.9	41.4	45.8	59.2	67.2	76.6	79.2	75.7	71.9	55.4	49.6	41.4	58.0
1958	34.4	31.2	41.4	57.1	65.2	71.3	79.1	75.4	69.1	59.1	49.9	32.9	55.5
1959	34.9	39.0	45.4	58.5	69.8	76.0	78.5	80.3	73.2	62.2	46.8	42.0	58.9
#1960	38.2	38.3	35.6	61.2	63.7	74.1	77.0	78.5	71.3	58.7	48.5	31.0	56.3
1961	29.8	38.3	47.6	52.0	62.2	73.2	78.6	77.6	74.8	59.5	50.2	36.4	56.7
1962	34.6	34.6	44.2	56.3	68.7	73.8	75.3	76.8	67.0	60.3	44.9	33.2	55.8
1963	31.4	31.0	48.5	57.8	64.9	73.7	77.6	75.4	66.5	61.2	49.8	31.1	55.7
1964	36.3	36.9	47.5	54.1	68.1	76.0	79.1	75.5	69.9	55.1	51.0	39.9	57.5
1965	33.4	36.8	41.4	51.8	69.1	72.6	78.2	77.2	72.6	57.5	49.5	41.5	56.8
1966	32.4	36.2	47.5	52.7	65.0	76.0	80.9	78.7	68.6	57.0	49.5	37.6	56.8
1967	41.0	34.0	45.0	57.6	60.0	74.7	77.2	76.2	68.0	57.9	45.0	39.9	56.4
1968	31.4	34.3	49.7	58.0	63.7	74.1	79.9	79.2	72.0	61.3	50.0	36.6	57.5
1969	34.2	36.9	43.0	58.7	68.4	77.1	79.5	76.3	70.1	58.8	47.2	36.3	57.2
1970	30.0	37.1	41.9	55.3	68.3	75.2	79.2	79.0	75.0	62.5	49.3	39.7	57.7
1971	31.3	39.1	43.2	55.0	63.7	75.9	78.3	76.7	73.0	64.7	48.2	45.5	57.9
1972	38.5	36.5	45.6	54.1	64.6	70.2	77.5	75.9	71.0	56.0	46.8	43.6	56.7
1973	37.6	37.0	51.1	56.0	62.8	77.1	79.2	79.9	74.3	63.3	51.6	41.9	59.3
1974	42.9	39.2	49.2	58.3	65.1	71.5	79.0	78.4	70.2	57.3	50.9	43.1	58.8
1975	40.9	40.6	45.2	53.6	69.7	76.4	79.3	80.1	68.5	63.2	54.4	40.5	59.4
RECORD MEAN	36.1	37.7	45.7	56.1	65.8	74.3	78.4	76.9	70.3	59.6	48.4	38.4	57.3
MAX	43.8	46.0	54.8	66.4	75.7	83.6	87.4	85.7	79.3	69.2	57.2	45.9	66.3
MIN	28.4	29.3	36.5	45.7	55.9	65.0	69.4	68.1	61.3	50.0	39.6	30.8	48.3

# Indicates a station move or relocation of instruments.

WASHINGTON, DC
WASHINGTON NATIONAL AIRPORT

Feb	Mar	Apr	May	June	Total
685	668	360	121	15	4529
657	587	240	66	4	4017
941	723	255	66	0	4443
721	601	222	39	8	4176
766	905	200	103	0	4270
740	536	399	123	6	4641
848	642	302	60	0	4322
946	505	245	87	1	4639
810	536	339	54	4	4315
785	724	395	27	24	4444
800	535	374	99	11	4256
859	611	249	178	3	4227
886	471	216	87	0	4332
780	671	208	40	0	4130
773	713	294	56	0	4565
722	670	294	85	2	4196
817	599	326	56	21	3322
777	423	286	109	0	3921
716	490	228	85	4	3414
677	608	345	24	0	3790

Aug	Sept	Oct	Nov	Dec	Total
360	180	39	1	0	1580
442	324	60	0	0	1762
372	258	60	22	0	1523
346	195	8	2	0	1186
469	288	57	3	0	1706
422	192	17	27	0	1437
475	132	50	15	0	1654

Precipitation

Year	Jan	Feb	Mar	Apr	May	June	July	Aug	Sept	Oct	Nov	Dec	Annual
1936	5.87	3.83	4.47	1.98	5.32	2.29	4.07	3.61	1.98	1.70	0.76	5.23	41.11
1937	7.83	3.33	1.50	6.85	4.02	5.23	3.67	6.70	1.76	8.81	3.88	0.71	54.29
1938	2.64	2.37	2.23	1.67	3.51	2.26	5.06	4.64	4.27	1.15	2.60	2.69	35.09
1939	3.41	5.71	2.89	3.78	0.41	4.55	2.01	3.22	6.90	4.06	1.40	2.20	40.54
1940	2.12	2.77	3.42	6.19	3.10	0.86	5.73	5.00	1.34	2.15	5.26	2.27	40.21
#1941	3.04	0.92	2.57	2.73	1.58	4.38	3.57	2.30	0.93	0.99	0.58	3.28	26.87
1942	2.19	1.55	3.87	0.26	3.51	3.73	4.31	11.61	2.64	8.18	1.92	4.25	48.02
1943	2.37	2.02	3.86	2.88	5.30	2.30	1.79	0.57	1.88	3.13	4.21	1.25	31.56
1944	2.36	2.31	4.83	2.98	1.11	2.77	5.62	6.01	4.97	2.39	3.14	2.97	41.46
1945	2.69	2.80	0.64	3.13	3.06	3.31	11.06	2.62	3.93	1.34	4.24	4.71	43.53
1946	1.88	2.32	1.67	1.93	6.99	1.40	3.14	5.75	2.72	2.77	1.33	1.72	33.62
1947	3.81	1.27	1.02	2.48	4.44	6.86	3.47	1.81	4.70	1.23	4.20	1.36	36.65
1948	4.57	1.67	3.66	3.05	8.87	5.44	4.31	9.00	3.19	3.09	6.00	4.69	57.54
1949	5.08	2.68	3.42	1.94	6.33	2.42	4.22	4.09	3.49	3.27	0.94	1.98	39.86
1950	1.91	2.72	4.17	1.86	5.76	3.14	5.11	7.32	6.73	3.59	2.87	2.72	47.90
1951	2.18	2.65	2.92	3.49	2.74	6.69	5.25	1.75	2.67	1.67	4.79	4.54	41.34
1952	4.48	1.77	3.76	5.97	4.73	3.06	4.46	5.20	4.06	0.66	6.33	2.95	47.43
1953	4.13	2.35	7.43	4.77	10.69	2.98	2.72	3.48	4.07	3.73	1.50	3.32	51.17
1954	2.30	0.85	3.47	3.30	2.98	1.24	1.70	3.15	0.63	4.06	1.78	2.82	28.28
1955	0.31	3.13	3.70	2.57	3.38	2.76	2.32	14.31	0.65	6.46	1.63	0.22	41.44
1956	1.99	2.82	3.53	2.06	2.17	2.66	5.88	1.94	3.70	2.62	2.81	3.02	35.20
1957	2.61	2.75	2.23	2.73	1.40	3.02	1.05	2.44	3.57	2.49	2.87	5.62	32.78
1958	2.51	4.14	5.85	4.92	2.77	3.21	7.15	6.49	2.57	2.35	2.04	1.62	45.62
1959	2.21	1.51	2.20	4.01	2.89	5.35	4.38	2.87	2.05	2.43	2.22	3.26	35.38
1960	2.66	3.33	2.08	3.15	4.35	2.55	4.61	4.13	4.17	2.54	0.99	2.43	36.99
1961	3.12	5.71	4.18	3.24	2.57	4.84	3.95	6.31	1.02	2.37	1.75	2.88	41.94
1962	1.59	3.65	3.83	2.90	3.46	2.44	1.63	0.55	2.64	1.93	5.12	3.33	33.07
1963	1.86	1.94	5.43	0.99	1.06	6.87	1.95	7.21	3.61	T	6.70	1.72	39.34
1964	3.98	3.38	2.53	4.37	1.46	1.30	1.87	1.89	3.07	1.34	1.42	2.87	29.48
1965	2.73	1.89	4.37	1.65	1.72	1.88	2.98	4.44	2.12	2.32	0.37	0.47	26.94
1966	3.95	3.57	1.44	3.33	2.74	2.02	0.93	1.67	6.87	4.72	1.50	3.28	36.02
1967	1.35	2.32	3.49	0.80	4.27	1.51	5.24	9.17	0.20	1.77	2.10	5.93	38.15
1968	1.97	0.80	3.66	1.53	4.23	7.40	1.31	3.95	2.97	3.17	3.62	2.22	36.83
1969	1.69	2.08	1.60	1.71	1.20	3.46	9.44	6.98	5.07	1.14	2.39	6.54	43.30
1970	1.24	2.69	2.82	5.35	2.79	2.80	8.12	1.09	1.57	2.05	5.77	3.33	39.62
1971	1.86	5.44	1.93	2.10	6.80	1.72	4.97	7.18	2.48	6.12	3.76	1.66	46.02
1972	2.45	5.27	2.27	3.99	4.78	11.53	3.43	2.82	1.27	3.56	6.05	4.55	51.97
1973	2.26	2.68	2.97	4.19	3.39	2.11	2.68	4.41	1.58	1.71	0.97	6.03	34.98
1974	2.66	0.95	4.21	2.26	4.37	3.40	1.15	5.77	4.39	1.13	1.24	4.43	35.96
1975	3.09	1.56	5.33	2.13	4.71	2.15	7.16	3.54	12.36	2.38	2.05	4.04	50.50
RECORD MEAN	2.59	2.61	3.36	2.88	3.91	3.54	4.10	4.75	3.34	2.76	2.96	3.20	40.00

Record mean values above are means through the current year for the period beginning in 1872 for temperature, 1871 for precipitation, and 1944 for snowfall. Temperature, precipitation, and heating degree day data are from City Office sites through June 1941 and from Airport sites thereafter. Snowfall data are from City Office sites through 1943 and from Airport sites thereafter.

(Continued)

In recent years, urban flooding caused by locally heavy rains has become a major problem. The most critical flooding is associated with the Alexandria portion of Four Mile Run in nearby Virginia but other streams in the Metropolitan Area are flooding with increasing frequency.

Occasional overflows from the Potomac River result from heavy rain over the basin, at times augmented by melting snow. In a few cases during cold winters ice forms on the river and in spring flooding is caused by ice gorges when the ice breaks up. The river is in tidewater and above normal tides associated with hurricane or severe storms along the coast cause flooding at times. Major floods occurred in June 1972, October 1954 and 1942, April 1937, March 1936 and August 1933. In 1954 and 1933 the flooding resulted mainly from high tides caused by hurricane winds. In 1942 the flooding was a combination of heavy rain and tidal flooding. In the other cases the flooding resulted mainly from heavy rain in the Potomac basin.

Snow accumulations of more than 10 inches are relatively rare. Usually the melt-off is rapid, but snow depths of 3 or more inches make driving hazardous, and slows or halts traffic. Schools may be closed and community activities may be temporarily disorganized, but usually conditions improve within a day or two. The first significant snow accumulation of a season is often the most disruptive.

The greatest recorded snowfall from a single storm was 28 inches. this is known as the Knickerbocker Storm and occurred in two days of January 1922. The snowfall accumulation collapsed the roof of the Knickerbocker Theater and resulted in the loss of many lives. Snowfalls of this magnitude are rare.

Records of the past 20 years show the average date of the last freezing temperature in the spring to be March 29 and the latest April 16. The average date of the first freezing temperature in the fall is November 10 and the earliest October 20.

The weather ship, **RESEARCHER** *is operated by NOAA's National Ocean Survey, gathering data for processing by the Enviornmental Research Labratories.*

DAYTONA BEACH, FLORIDA

Station: DAYTONA BEACH, FLORIDA
REGIONAL AIRPORT
Elevation (ground): 31 feet

TEMPERATURES °F

Month	Normal			Extremes			
	Daily maximum	Daily minimum	Monthly	Record highest	Year	Record lowest	Year
(a)				32		32	
J	69.1	47.6	58.4	85	1957	23	1971
F	70.4	48.7	59.6	88	1962	24	1958
M	74.5	53.3	63.9	90	1975	31	1968
A	80.2	59.2	69.7	96	1968	35	1950
M	85.2	64.8	75.0	100	1953	44	1971
J	88.4	70.4	79.4	102	1944	54	1975
J	89.6	72.3	81.0	99	1952	65	1965
A	89.4	72.8	81.1	99	1956	65	1957
S	87.0	72.0	79.5	99	1944	52	1956
O	81.4	65.2	73.3	95	1959	41	1954
N	75.1	55.1	65.1	89	1948	27	1950
D	70.2	49.0	59.6	85	1972	21	1962
YR	80.0	60.9	70.5	102	JUN 1944	21	DEC 1962

IMPORTANT:
The time-period covered by this record is limited: See footnotes following table of NORMALS, MEANS AND EXTREMES for explanation and for additional history of EXTREME HIGHS AND LOWS recorded in the general area.

Daytona Beach is located on the Atlantic Ocean, with the Halifax River, part of Florida's Inland Waterway, running through the City. Terrain in the area is flat, soil is mostly sandy, and elevations in the area range from 3 to 15 feet above m.s.l. near the ocean to near 31 feet at the airport and along a ridge running along the western city limits.

Nearness to the ocean results in a climate tempered by the effect of land and sea breezes. In the summer, while maximum temperatures reach 90° or above during the late morning or early afternoon, the number of hours of 90° or above is relatively small due to the beginning of the sea breeze near midday and the occurrence of local afternoon convective thundershowers which lower the temperature to the comfortable eighties. Winters, although subject to invasions of cold air, are relatively mild due to the nearness of the ocean and latitudinal location.

The "rainy season" from June through mid-October produces 60 percent of the annual rainfall. The major portion of the summer rainfall occurs in the form of local convective thundershowers. These showers are occasionally heavy and produce as much as 2 or 3 inches of rain. The more severe showers may be attended by strong gusty winds. Almost all rainfall during the winter months is associated with frontal passages.

Long periods of cloudiness and rain are infrequent, usually not lasting over 2 or 3 days. These

(Continued page 404)

Snowfall

Season	July	Aug	Sept	Oct	Nov	Dec	Jan
1970-71	0.0	0.0	0.0	0.0	0.0	0.0	0.0
1971-72	0.0	0.0	0.0	0.0	0.0	0.0	0.0
1972-73	0.0	0.0	0.0	0.0	0.0	0.0	0.0
1973-74	0.0	0.0	0.0	0.0	0.0	0.0	0.0
1974-75	0.0	0.0	0.0	0.0	0.0	0.0	0.0
1975-76	0.0	0.0	0.0	0.0	0.0	0.0	
RECORD MEAN	0.0	0.0	0.0	0.0	0.0	T	0.0

Heating Degree Days

Season	July	Aug	Sept	Oct	Nov	Dec	Jan
1955-56	0	0	0	21	87	193	381
1956-57	0	0	0	0	165	169	127
1957-58	0	0	0	31	37	260	398
1958-59	0	0	0	9	18	182	276
#1959-60	0	0	0	2	82	196	244
1960-61	0	0	0	0	22	336	336
1961-62	0	0	0	8	33	192	259
1962-63	0	0	0	16	117	320	264
1963-64	0	0	0	15	91	322	279
1964-65	0	0	0	18	22	126	246
1965-66	0	0	0	10	57	173	263
1966-67	0	0	0	3	88	217	168
1967-68	0	0	0	6	72	108	227
1968-69	0	0	0	27	152	301	216
1969-70	0	0	0	0	105	272	330
1970-71	0	0	0	0	164	143	230
1971-72	0	0	0	0	71	19	85
1972-73	0	0	0	0	62	139	226
1973-74	0	0	0	10	15	239	0
1974-75	0	0	0	0	69	201	108
1975-76	0	0	0	0	102	222	

Cooling Degree Days

Year	Jan	Feb	Mar	Apr	May	June	July
1969	7	4	17	173	300	473	559
1970	13	9	101	253	351	478	557
1971	39	65	45	150	270	420	484
1972	107	16	67	193	299	447	494
1973	45	14	148	148	324	450	527
1974	147	50	145	159	349	414	447
1975	71	95	118	191	386	441	488

Feb	Mar	Apr	May	June	Total
0.0	0.0	0.0	0.0	0.0	0.0
0.0	0.0	0.0	0.0	0.0	0.0
0.0	0.0	0.0	0.0	0.0	0.0
0.0	0.0	0.0	0.0	0.0	0.0
0.0	0.0	0.0	0.0	0.0	0.0
T	0.0	0.0	0.0	0.0	T

Average Temperature

Year	Jan	Feb	Mar	Apr	May	June	July	Aug	Sept	Oct	Nov	Dec	Annual
1936	59.0	58.3	65.4	70.0	74.2	78.0	81.0	79.6	78.8	75.8	64.6	62.4	70.6
1937	70.6	61.8	62.0	69.0	73.1	79.2	79.8	79.6	77.8	71.1	63.6	57.1	70.4
1938	58.4	63.7	68.0	68.8	74.0	76.2	78.9	80.2	77.1	69.6	67.0	57.8	70.0
1939	59.4	66.4	67.0	68.2	72.2	78.4	79.9	78.8	79.0	74.0	62.8	56.7	70.2
1940	48.6	56.6	61.2	65.8	69.7	77.0	78.5	79.4	76.2	68.6	64.4	63.4	67.4
1941	57.0	52.6	58.3	69.2	70.6	79.8	80.4	82.4	79.8	77.6	66.7	63.2	69.8
1942	54.9	53.6	61.2	66.5	73.0	78.8	82.5	80.6	78.6	72.0	66.4	61.8	69.2
#1943	59.8	55.4	63.6	67.3	76.2	80.2	80.4	81.0	78.8	69.4	63.3	60.0	69.6
1944	56.7	65.6	67.2	71.0	74.8	81.4	81.0	81.0	81.4	71.6	64.2	50.4	71.0
1945	57.4	64.4	70.1	72.6	73.8	80.6	80.8	81.0	81.3	74.3	64.6	57.8	71.6
1946	61.6	61.2	66.7	70.6	76.0	78.0	81.4	81.2	79.2	75.7	72.0	65.2	72.4
#1947	67.7	52.8	60.3	74.4	76.3	79.4	79.6	81.4	79.8	75.0	67.7	62.0	71.4
1948	56.0	63.3	69.0	72.0	76.6	79.8	80.4	80.6	79.8	71.4	72.1	65.9	72.2
1949	64.4	67.6	64.0	69.9	74.6	79.0	80.8	80.0	79.1	75.8	60.6	63.1	71.6
1950	66.8	62.5	63.4	63.7	75.5	80.5	80.3	80.2	78.6	75.5	60.8	54.6	70.2
1951	58.0	57.1	64.5	66.2	74.4	78.8	80.8	82.1	79.8	75.2	63.3	64.0	70.3
1952	61.1	59.3	65.5	65.8	74.9	81.3	81.7	80.9	79.3	72.9	63.7	56.7	70.3
1953	58.7	62.3	68.3	69.0	78.3	79.7	81.5	80.6	79.3	71.0	65.0	61.7	71.3
1954	60.8	61.2	62.1	71.9	73.7	80.1	80.8	82.3	80.5	70.9	61.6	55.7	70.1
1955	56.1	60.2	64.8	70.1	75.7	77.2	80.0	81.5	80.1	71.1	64.0	59.4	70.0
1956	52.5	62.9	62.8	67.1	75.4	78.1	80.7	81.3	77.5	72.8	62.1	61.7	69.6
1957	63.1	65.1	62.5	70.5	74.8	79.0	80.8	80.5	80.0	71.1	68.5	57.1	71.1
1958	52.0	50.7	61.7	69.6	73.9	80.1	81.5	81.2	80.2	72.2	69.4	59.2	69.3
#1959	56.7	65.9	61.9	68.9	76.7	79.2	80.9	80.6	80.1	77.9	65.8	59.2	71.1
1960	57.8	57.8	58.4	69.6	72.9	77.1	81.0	80.2	79.1	74.4	67.1	54.1	69.1
1961	54.0	60.5	67.1	65.6	73.5	76.8	79.9	80.5	78.7	71.9	67.4	61.1	69.8
1962	57.2	64.8	60.6	66.9	76.7	78.6	81.3	80.8	79.3	73.0	62.0	55.0	69.7
1963	57.4	54.7	66.5	71.6	75.8	81.2	80.6	81.3	78.7	71.8	63.3	54.8	69.8
1964	56.7	56.4	64.2	71.1	74.8	80.6	81.0	80.8	78.3	70.4	67.9	62.9	70.4
1965	57.5	61.3	63.6	70.8	72.3	77.3	78.7	79.9	79.1	71.6	65.5	59.7	69.8
1966	57.0	59.2	61.9	68.2	75.6	77.6	81.6	81.2	79.1	74.2	64.1	58.4	69.8
1967	60.6	58.5	67.0	72.4	75.5	78.0	79.4	78.7	76.0	71.3	64.5	63.2	70.5
1968	58.2	52.9	60.0	72.2	75.1	78.6	80.7	80.8	79.1	73.2	61.6	56.2	69.0
1969	58.0	55.2	57.9	70.5	74.4	80.5	82.8	80.4	79.7	77.1	63.5	56.5	69.7
1970	54.5	56.1	65.5	73.1	76.1	80.8	82.7	83.5	82.4	76.9	60.6	61.5	71.1
1971	58.6	59.9	60.0	68.0	73.3	78.7	80.5	80.7	79.6	76.1	65.9	67.8	70.7
1972	65.5	59.0	64.7	70.8	74.4	79.6	80.7	80.2	78.7	75.0	67.3	63.5	71.6
1973	58.9	56.3	68.2	68.7	75.2	79.8	81.9	80.3	80.8	75.0	69.6	58.4	71.1
1974	69.5	59.5	68.5	69.3	76.0	78.6	79.2	80.3	80.5	72.0	65.5	59.5	71.5
1975	63.6	65.7	65.6	70.1	77.2	79.5	80.5	80.5	79.6	75.2	66.8	58.6	71.9
RECORD MEAN	59.1	59.7	64.2	69.5	74.7	79.0	80.6	80.7	79.3	73.3	65.2	59.6	70.4
MAX	69.7	70.5	75.0	80.1	84.9	88.2	89.5	89.2	86.9	81.4	75.0	70.1	80.0
MIN	48.4	48.9	53.3	58.8	64.5	69.8	71.7	72.2	71.6	65.2	55.3	49.1	60.7

# Indicates a station move or relocation of instruments.

DAYTONA BEACH, FL

Feb	Mar	Apr	May	June	Total
128	137	40	0	0	987
72	124	8	3	0	668
402	129	21	2	0	1280
58	125	25	0	0	693
216	240	21	4	0	1005
165	62	47	0	0	968
88	179	55	0	0	814
288	73	15	0	0	1093
251	106	13	0	0	1077
138	136	9	1	0	696
192	120	26	0	0	841
192	37	5	0	0	710
344	185	0	0	0	942
275	228	2	0	0	1201
252	80	2	0	0	1041
199	194	55	7	0	992
182	69	15	0	0	441
251	38	29	0	0	745
197	30	24	0	0	515
69	91	30	0	0	568

Aug	Sept	Oct	Nov	Dec	Total
483	447	383	66	13	2925
580	532	373	37	40	3324
495	445	348	106	113	2980
477	415	317	138	98	3068
482	483	326	156	40	3143
480	469	223	90	40	3013
487	445	325	163	29	3239

Precipitation

Year	Jan	Feb	Mar	Apr	May	June	July	Aug	Sept	Oct	Nov	Dec	Annual
1936	3.88	8.89	2.42	1.21	4.51	7.06	2.83	4.35	2.99	6.37	2.71	3.36	50.58
1937	2.22	4.73	4.14	2.69	2.59	2.96	5.64	7.72	7.96	5.69	7.43	1.52	55.29
1938	0.73	3.18	1.69	1.04	1.96	2.84	8.36	2.82	8.14	3.23	3.93	1.37	39.29
1939	1.09	0.45	1.48	5.29	2.40	6.96	9.53	5.78	7.67	2.83	0.45	1.19	45.12
1940	1.65	2.24	1.98	2.45	0.97	5.21	8.53	4.44	8.59	0.04	0.16	4.30	40.56
1941	3.42	4.40	2.01	3.11	1.32	7.29	11.46	6.56	2.86	13.68	7.47	3.72	67.30
1942	2.15	2.52	5.68	0.98	2.35	10.12	2.38	3.73	6.54	2.67	1.06	2.22	42.40
#1943	1.51	0.18	6.57	2.86	3.09	4.35	11.01	10.47	11.71	7.14	0.55	0.67	60.11
1944	1.28	0.29	7.21	2.87	0.45	8.27	14.58	9.33	6.46	4.40	0.55	0.12	55.81
1945	3.62	0.88	0.41	1.53	1.56	7.00	7.45	6.83	9.65	5.14	0.79	4.50	49.36
1946	1.62	2.98	1.76	0.49	2.80	4.23	8.17	10.21	10.75	3.87	2.81	0.61	50.30
#1947	0.78	6.04	5.29	5.31	4.82	13.43	8.65	6.97	5.75	5.72	1.98	0.90	65.64
1948	4.07	1.22	5.14	2.36	0.49	2.40	10.43	7.33	9.82	8.29	1.07	1.93	54.55
1949	0.37	1.95	2.01	7.12	1.40	4.24	5.97	11.46	6.26	3.65	1.86	3.93	50.22
1950	0.15	0.59	3.53	2.79	2.13	6.45	5.56	3.88	5.86	13.00	0.74	2.54	47.22
1951	0.77	2.46	1.18	3.28	2.53	2.66	3.80	4.19	14.02	8.54	3.15	2.88	49.46
1952	0.66	6.76	3.01	1.66	4.39	1.35	1.25	9.02	11.92	5.41	1.96	0.71	48.10
1953	1.75	3.35	7.75	4.97	1.46	1.37	8.67	19.89	10.00	12.93	2.30	4.85	79.29
1954	0.37	0.86	2.33	6.29	3.21	2.35	3.50	3.04	1.88	4.91	3.98	1.24	33.96
1955	2.47	1.43	1.84	1.78	1.55	7.76	5.67	2.64	6.66	3.17	2.61	1.22	38.80
1956	2.55	0.90	0.25	2.42	2.48	7.41	3.01	4.06	1.94	5.82	0.46	0.06	31.36
1957	0.97	1.62	3.13	1.73	5.65	4.23	10.53	4.01	10.65	1.80	0.82	1.34	46.48
1958	3.94	4.73	5.52	2.24	2.27	6.06	1.96	4.00	2.19	8.52	1.77	1.95	45.15
1959	4.53	2.13	7.70	3.17	2.40	8.13	5.68	3.60	5.26	7.12	4.26	2.26	56.24
1960	1.16	9.13	7.52	0.76	0.62	10.75	8.70	6.84	10.96	0.97	0.53	1.24	59.18
1961	1.96	3.70	1.17	2.16	2.39	6.81	5.16	7.68	3.20	2.25	2.85	0.73	40.06
1962	0.90	0.82	1.82	0.78	0.16	7.96	10.04	8.50	8.84	3.57	2.49	0.71	46.59
1963	2.91	5.83	1.46	1.40	6.82	7.42	6.89	2.01	5.43	2.71	7.98	2.17	53.03
1964	5.29	2.65	4.84	3.61	2.58	4.73	7.67	10.81	11.39	3.54	3.13	2.52	62.76
1965	2.22	3.00	3.05	1.00	0.08	9.00	3.72	2.97	4.33	3.65	0.97	2.14	36.13
1966	2.89	5.58	0.36	2.56	6.77	15.19	7.09	7.93	4.49	4.60	1.19	1.60	60.25
1967	1.26	3.98	0.31	T	0.73	7.51	9.04	3.02	5.56	0.19	T	2.98	34.58
1968	0.42	1.73	1.79	0.40	4.79	14.38	6.25	11.09	6.07	7.44	2.43	1.38	58.17
1969	1.53	2.03	2.74	0.12	6.47	2.47	2.61	9.40	8.89	6.97	1.96	5.03	50.22
1970	3.94	3.79	3.59	2.08	1.68	2.62	3.65	3.61	3.54	3.87	0.31	0.72	33.40
1971	0.61	5.48	2.00	2.57	3.12	4.73	3.20	3.97	7.20	9.53	1.33	2.49	46.23
1972	2.37	3.97	6.66	1.41	4.02	7.06	3.22	8.29	0.42	3.08	10.96	2.48	53.94
1973	4.66	2.02	2.63	3.09	2.41	4.32	4.69	7.58	5.14	4.40	0.75	2.54	44.23
1974	0.30	1.10	3.19	0.44	2.66	8.65	6.31	9.96	10.50	1.42	0.48	2.20	47.21
1975	1.66	2.27	1.52	2.96	2.99	9.00	6.89	3.16	6.61	5.84	1.46	0.83	45.19
RECORD MEAN	2.00	3.02	3.15	2.39	2.79	6.37	6.57	6.53	6.95	5.25	2.32	2.02	49.36

Record mean values above are means through the current year for the period beginning in 1935 for temperature and precipitation, 1944 for snowfall.

(Continued)

periods are usually associated with a stationary front with waves, a so-called "northeaster", or a tropical disturbance.

Tropical disturbances or hurricanes are not considered a great threat to this area of the state. While not outside the hurricane belt, past history indicates the chance of having hurricane force winds in any given year to be about 1 in 30. Generally hurricanes in this latitude tend to pass well offshore or lose much of their intensity while crossing the state before reaching this area. Only in gusts have hurricane force winds ever been recorded at this station.

Heavy fog occurs mostly during the winter and early spring. These fogs usually form by radiational cooling at night and dissipate soon after sunrise. On rare occasions sea fog moves in from the ocean and persists for two or three days.

There is no significant source in the area for air pollution.

Normals, Means and Extremes

Month	Normal Degree days Base 65 °F: Heating	Cooling	Precipitation in inches: Water equivalent: Normal	Maximum monthly	Year	Minimum monthly	Year	Maximum in 24 hrs.	Year	Snow, Ice pellets: Maximum monthly	Year	Maximum in 24 hrs.	Year	Relative humidity pct.: Hour 01 (Local time)	Hour 07	Hour 13	Hour 19
(a)				32		32		32		32		32		31	31	31	31
J	241	37	2.05	5.29	1964	0.15	1950	2.21	1945	0.0		0.0		87	89	60	78
F	210	62	2.92	9.13	1960	0.29	1944	4.39	1971	T	1951	T	1951	84	87	57	73
M	120	83	3.37	7.75	1953	0.25	1956	5.74	1953	0.0		0.0		84	86	56	71
A	17	158	2.39	7.12	1949	T	1967	4.00	1949	0.0		0.0		84	85	54	70
M	0	310	2.65	6.82	1963	0.08	1965	4.22	1947	0.0		0.0		86	85	57	72
J	0	432	6.60	15.19	1966	1.35	1952	6.28	1966	0.0		0.0		88	87	63	76
J	0	496	6.69	14.58	1944	1.25	1952	3.90	1967	0.0		0.0		90	88	66	79
A	0	499	6.84	19.89	1953	2.01	1963	4.76	1974	0.0		0.0		91	91	68	81
S	0	435	7.10	14.02	1951	0.42	1972	6.34	1964	0.0		0.0		88	89	67	81
O	5	262	5.52	13.00	1950	0.19	1967	9.29	1953	0.0		0.0		85	87	64	78
N	97	100	2.13	10.96	1972	T	1967	5.15	1972	0.0		0.0		86	88	60	78
D	212	45	1.96	5.03	1969	0.06	1956	4.01	1969	T	1962	T	1962	86	88	61	80
YR	902	2919	50.22	19.89	AUG 1953	T	NOV 1967	9.29	OCT 1953	T	DEC 1962	T	DEC 1962	87	87	61	76

(To better understand these tables, see full explanation of terms beginning on page 322)

Month	Wind: Mean speed m.p.h.	Prevailing direction	Fastest mile: Speed m.p.h.	Direction	Year	Pct. of possible sunshine	Mean sky cover, tenths, sunrise to sunset	Mean number of days: Sunrise to sunset: Clear	Partly cloudy	Cloudy	Precipitation .01 inch or more	Snow, Ice pellets 1.0 inch or more	Thunderstorms	Heavy fog, visibility ¼ mile or less	Temperatures °F Max. (b) 90° and above	32° and below	Min. 32° and below	0° and below	Average station pressure mb. Elev. 41 feet m.s.l.
(a)	30	18	27	27			27	32	32	32	32	32	31	31	32	32	32	32	3
J	9.1	NW	40	27	1959		5.8	9	10	12	7	0	1	6	0	0	2	0	1019.9
F	10.0	NNW	44	20	1960		5.7	9	8	11	8	0	2	3	0	0	1	0	1018.1
M	10.2	SSW	44	23	1957		5.7	9	10	12	8	0	3	4	*	0	*	0	1016.5
A	10.0	E	46	18	1953		5.2	10	11	9	6	0	4	2	2	0	0	0	1017.6
M	9.3	E	40	25	1961		5.4	9	12	10	8	0	8	2	6	0	0	0	1014.5
J	8.5	SW	40	26	1965		6.4	6	12	12	12	0	13	1	11	0	0	0	1015.0
J	7.7	SSW	40	25	1963		6.5	4	14	13	14	0	18	1	15	0	0	0	1016.3
A	7.4	E	50	11	1949		6.4	4	15	12	14	0	16	2	14	0	0	0	1017.2
S	8.9	E	58	11	1960		6.5	4	14	12	13	0	8	1	6	0	0	0	1015.0
O	9.6	NE	53	05	1950		5.7	9	11	11	11	0	4	2	1	0	0	0	1016.9
N	8.9	NW	37	27	1963		5.0	10	11	9	7	0	1	3	0	0	*	0	1019.0
D	8.8	NW	40	34	1954		5.7	10	9	12	7	0	1	5	0	0	2	0	1019.3
YR	9.0	E	58	11	SEP 1960		5.8	93	137	135	115	0	80	32	54	0	5	0	1017.1

FOOTNOTES

Means and extremes above are from existing and comparable exposures. Annual extremes have been exceeded at other sites in the locality as follows: Lowest temperature 18 in January 1940; maximum monthly precipitation 24.82 in October 1924; maximum precipitation in 24 hours 12.85 in October 1924.

Station: MIAMI, FLORIDA
INTERNATIONAL AIRPORT

Elevation (ground): 7 feet

TEMPERATURES °F

Month	Normal			Extremes			
	Daily maximum	Daily minimum	Monthly	Record highest	Year	Record lowest	Year
(a)				11		11	
J	75.6	58.7	67.2	86	1967	35	1971
F	76.6	59.0	67.8	88	1974	36	1967
M	79.5	63.0	71.3	90	1974	37	1968
A	82.7	67.3	75.0	96	1971	46	1971
M	85.3	70.7	78.0	93	1974	61	1971
J	88.0	73.9	81.0	94	1967	67	1972
J	89.1	75.5	82.3	96	1969	70	1965
A	89.9	75.8	82.9	96	1970	70	1967
S	88.3	75.0	81.7	93	1968	70	1966
O	84.6	71.0	77.8	90	1969	56	1968
N	79.9	64.5	72.2	87	1973	40	1970
D	76.6	60.0	68.3	85	1968	34	1968
YR	83.0	67.9	75.5	96	APR 1971	34	DEC 1968

IMPORTANT:
The time-period covered by this record is limited: See footnotes on next page for explanation and for additional history of EXTREME HIGHS AND LOWS recorded in the general area.

Miami is located in Latitude 25° 47' North, Longitude 80° 11' West, on the lower east coast of Florida. To the east of the City lies Biscayne Bay, an arm of the ocean, about 15 miles long and 3 miles wide. East of the bay is the island of Miami Beach, a mile or less wide and about ten long, and beyond Miami Beach is the Atlantic Ocean. The surrounding countryside is level and sparsely wooded.

The climate of Miami is essentially subtropical marine, featured by a long, warm summer, with abundant rainfall, followed by a mild, dry winter. The marine influence is evidenced by the low daily range of temperature and the rapid warming of cold airmasses which pass to the east of the State. Located as it is, the Miami area is subject to winds from the east or southeast about half the time, and in several specific respects has a climate whose features differ from those prevailing farther inland.

One of these features is the annual precipitation for the area. The cooperative station on Miami Beach, at the water's edge, has a normal annual rainfall of about 46 inches. The Weather Service Office at the airport has a normal of over 59 inches. The daily rainfall is somewhat different at the two locations. During the early morning hours more rainfall occurs at Miami Beach than at the airport, while during the afternoon the reverse is true. The airport office is about 9 miles inland.

The average daily range of temperature (difference between the maximum and the minimum) is only 10° at Miami Beach, while well inland the average daily range is near 18°. An even more striking difference appears in the annual number of days with temperatures reaching 90° or higher. At the Miami Beach station the figure is less than 15 per year and at inland stations above 60. Minimum temperature contrasts also are particularly marked under proper conditions, the difference between inland locations and the Miami Beach station frequently amounting to 15° or more, especially in winter.

Freezing temperatures occur occasionally in the farming districts southwest, west, and northwest of the City, but almost never near the ocean. Noteworthy past cold periods occurred in February 1917, December - January 1917 - 1918, December 1934, January 1940, and January - February 1958. More detailed information about frost in the agricultural regions near the City appears in publications of the Federal - State Frost Warning Service, Lakeland, Florida. No snow has ever been reported.

Tropical hurricanes occasionally affect the area, the months of greatest frequency being September and October. Noteworthy hurricanes were those of September 17 - 18, 1926, November 4, 1935, September 15, 1945, October 17 - 18, 1950; Donna, September 10, 1960, Cleo, August 27, 1964, and Betsy, September 8, 1965.

Destructive tornadoes are very rare, although funnel clouds occasionally touch the ground, and waterspouts are sighted quite often along the beaches during the summer months; however, significant damage is seldom reported. Some of the more important tornadoes occurred in April 1925, June 1959, February 1968, and June 1968. In the April 1925 tornado 5 people were killed, and these were the only deaths ever reported in the Miami area from tornadoes.

MIAMI, FLORIDA

Normals, Means, and Extremes

(To better understand these tables, see full explanation of terms beginning on page 322)

Month	Normal Degree days Base 65 °F: Heating	Normal Degree days: Cooling	Precipitation in inches: Water equivalent: Normal	Water equivalent: Maximum monthly	Year	Minimum monthly	Year	Maximum in 24 hrs.	Year	Snow, Ice pellets: Maximum monthly	Year	Maximum in 24 hrs.	Year	Relative humidity pct.: Hour 01 (Local time)	Hour 07	Hour 13	Hour 19	Wind: Mean speed m.p.h.	Prevailing direction	Fastest mile: Speed m.p.h.	Direction	Year	Pct. of possible sunshine	Mean sky cover, tenths, sunrise to sunset	Mean number of days: Sunrise to sunset: Clear	Partly cloudy	Cloudy	Precipitation .01 inch or more	Snow, Ice pellets 1.0 inch or more	Thunderstorms	Heavy fog, visibility ¼ mile or less	Temperatures °F: Max. (b) 90° and above	Max. 32° and below	Min. 32° and below	Min. 0° and below	Average station pressure mb. Elev. 12 feet m.s.l.
(a)				33		33		33		33		33		11	11	11	11	26	15	18	18			27	26	26	26	33	26	26	27	11	11	11	11	3
J	53	121	2.15	6.66	1969	0.04	1951	2.68	1973	0.0		0.0		80	84	61	70	9.3	NNW	37	31	1966		5.3	10	13	8	7	0	1	2	0	0	0	0	1019.9
F	67	151	1.95	6.56	1966	0.01	1944	5.73	1966	0.0		0.0		78	82	56	65	10.0	ESE	38	30	1964		5.2	9	11	8	6	0	1	1	0	0	0	0	1018.5
M	17	206	2.07	7.22	1949	0.02	1956	7.07	1949	0.0		0.0		77	82	56	65	10.3	SE	46	04	1966		5.3	9	14	8	6	0	2	1	*	0	0	0	1017.4
A	0	300	3.60	10.21	1960	0.07	1971	5.18	1960	0.0		0.0		75	80	54	64	10.6	ESE	32	23	1958		5.3	8	15	7	6	0	2	1	1	0	0	0	1017.9
M	0	403	6.12	18.54	1968	0.44	1965	8.42	1958	0.0		0.0		80	83	60	70	9.4	ESE	37	32	1961		5.8	6	15	10	10	0	7	*	2	0	0	0	1015.5
J	0	480	9.00	22.36	1968	1.81	1945	7.63	1966	0.0		0.0		84	87	67	76	8.2	SE	37	13	1967		6.9	3	14	13	15	0	13	0	6	0	0	0	1016.0
J	0	536	6.91	13.51	1947	1.77	1963	4.55	1952	0.0		0.0		83	86	65	73	7.8	SE	38	18	1962		6.6	3	16	12	16	0	16	*	8	0	0	0	1017.3
A	0	555	6.72	16.88	1943	1.65	1954	6.92	1964	0.0		0.0		83	87	66	74	7.7	SE	74	36	1964		6.5	2	19	10	17	0	16	*	8	0	0	0	1017.3
S	0	501	8.74	24.40	1960	2.63	1951	7.58	1960	0.0		0.0		85	89	67	77	8.2	ESE	69	06	1965		6.8	2	15	13	18	0	11	*	6	0	0	0	1015.0
O	0	397	8.18	21.08	1952	1.50	1962	9.95	1948	0.0		0.0		83	87	65	74	9.3	ENE	41	05	1966		6.1	6	14	11	15	0	5	*	*	0	0	0	1015.7
N	13	229	2.72	13.15	1959	0.09	1970	7.93	1959	0.0		0.0		80	84	60	70	9.4	N	32	08	1966		5.3	8	14	8	8	0	1	1	0	0	0	0	1018.4
D	56	159	1.64	6.39	1958	0.13	1966	4.38	1964	0.0		0.0		78	83	58	68	9.0	N	38	32	1967		5.2	10	12	9	6	0	1	1	0	0	0	0	1019.6
YR	206	4038	59.80	24.40	SEP 1960	0.01	FEB 1944	9.95	OCT 1948	0.0		0.0		81	84	61	70	9.1	ESE	74	36	AUG 1964		5.8	76	172	117	129	0	75	7	32	0	0	0	1017.4

FOOTNOTES

Means and extremes above are from existing and comparable exposures. Annual extremes have been exceeded at other sites in the locality as follows: Airport locations: Highest temperature 100 in July 1942; lowest temperature 26 in December 1934 (28 in January 1940); maximum precipitation in 24 hours 12.58 in April 1942. City locations: Lowest temperature 27 in February 1917; maximum precipitation in 24 hours 15.10 in November 1925; fastest mile of wind 122 from the South in October 1950. Miami Beach (Allison Hospital): Fastest mile of wind 132 from the East, September 18, 1926.

Snowfall

Season	July	Aug	Sept	Oct	Nov	Dec	Jan
1970-71	0.0	0.0	0.0	0.0	0.0	0.0	0.0
1971-72	0.0	0.0	0.0	0.0	0.0	0.0	0.0
1972-73	0.0	0.0	0.0	0.0	0.0	0.0	0.0
1973-74	0.0	0.0	0.0	0.0	0.0	0.0	0.0
1974-75	0.0	0.0	0.0	0.0	0.0	0.0	0.0
1975-76	0.0	0.0	0.0	0.0	0.0	0.0	
RECORD MEAN	0.0	0.0	0.0	0.0	0.0	0.0	0.0

Heating Degree Days

Season	July	Aug	Sept	Oct	Nov	Dec	Jan
1955-56	0	0	0	0	7	17	132
#1956-57	0	0	0	0	37	46	18
1957-58	0	0	0	1	0	76	137
1958-59	0	0	0	0	0	26	82
1959-60	0	0	0	0	25	31	85
1960-61	0	0	0	0	0	63	77
1961-62	0	0	0	0	0	64	58
1962-63	0	0	0	0	26	120	48
1963-64	0	0	0	0	25	85	67
#1964-65	0	0	0	0	0	4	63
1965-66	0	0	0	0	0	16	70
1966-67	0	0	0	0	27	41	28
1967-68	0	0	0	0	0	25	56
1968-69	0	0	0	0	32	80	18
1969-70	0	0	0	0	21	53	117
1970-71	0	0	0	0	42	23	67
1971-72	0	0	0	0	0	0	2
1972-73	0	0	0	0	3	30	41
1973-74	0	0	0	0	1	93	0
1974-75	0	0	0	0	2	32	14
1975-76	0	0	0	0	33	49	

Cooling Degree Days

Year	Jan	Feb	Mar	Apr	May	June	July
1969	104	66	145	375	459	526	597
1970	85	59	239	425	446	518	558
1971	176	219	202	315	444	488	558
1972	262	144	227	307	398	454	498
1973	212	81	301	324	459	499	531
1974	294	150	335	342	471	518	551
1975	261	233	276	382	456	501	508

Feb	Mar	Apr	May	June	Total
0.0	0.0	0.0	0.0	0.0	0.0
0.0	0.0	0.0	0.0	0.0	0.0
0.0	0.0	0.0	0.0	0.0	0.0
0.0	0.0	0.0	0.0	0.0	0.0
0.0	0.0	0.0	0.0	0.0	0.0
0.0	0.0	0.0	0.0	0.0	0.0

Average Temperature

Year	Jan	Feb	Mar	Apr	May	June	July	Aug	Sept	Oct	Nov	Dec	Annual
1940	59.2	62.5	67.2	69.6	74.1	80.6	82.0	81.9	79.8	75.0	71.5	71.5	72.9
1941	65.1	63.1	65.8	72.9	74.4	80.4	81.5	83.5	81.3	80.2	73.4	71.7	74.4
#1942	64.8	61.2	68.8	71.6	76.6	80.9	83.3	81.9	81.4	76.7	72.2	69.4	74.1
1943	68.5	63.6	70.4	71.9	78.0	80.1	81.1	82.1	81.2	75.3	70.6	66.2	74.1
1944	64.5	69.8	73.4	75.9	75.6	81.8	82.3	82.7	81.8	75.5	68.8	64.2	74.8
1945	65.1	68.7	73.1	77.0	75.9	81.2	81.6	82.2	81.3	77.9	70.4	67.0	75.1
1946	68.5	69.7	72.2	74.9	79.4	81.1	81.3	82.7	81.3	78.3	76.0	72.4	76.5
1947	73.1	62.5	67.5	77.9	78.3	80.6	81.0	82.0	81.5	78.3	76.0	70.1	75.8
1948	66.9	71.0	76.3	75.7	77.9	81.5	82.1	82.3	81.3	77.2	76.8	72.9	76.8
1949	70.2	73.5	70.8	75.8	77.6	80.3	82.3	82.1	81.6	79.0	68.7	71.8	76.2
1950	73.1	69.9	71.6	70.4	78.3	81.7	81.4	81.7	81.0	78.9	69.0	65.2	75.2
1951	65.2	65.1	70.5	73.5	77.7	81.0	81.8	83.6	83.3	78.1	71.0	72.5	75.3
1952	69.2	68.0	74.5	73.0	78.9	82.9	83.4	83.3	82.9	78.2	73.3	66.6	76.2
1953	67.6	71.2	74.7	75.7	80.5	81.3	82.5	83.5	82.0	76.0	72.4	69.5	76.4
1954	69.1	67.9	69.5	76.6	79.2	81.2	82.9	84.9	82.4	77.2	70.8	64.2	75.5
1955	64.9	67.7	71.4	75.6	78.0	80.3	81.0	83.2	82.1	77.1	72.6	69.4	75.3
1956	62.7	71.0	70.3	73.9	79.3	80.7	82.7	83.8	80.7	78.2	69.8	69.4	75.2
#1957	70.1	72.7	70.5	76.2	78.5	81.3	81.7	81.7	81.4	76.4	75.0	65.6	75.9
1958	61.4	59.4	69.9	74.5	77.3	81.7	82.5	83.5	82.4	77.2	76.7	69.0	74.6
1959	66.4	74.9	71.3	75.0	77.8	80.3	80.7	81.0	80.6	80.4	73.8	67.1	75.8
1960	66.7	67.4	67.6	74.4	77.0	81.1	83.7	83.3	81.7	79.5	74.7	65.5	75.2
1961	64.9	69.6	73.8	74.1	78.0	81.1	83.5	83.4	82.0	77.7	73.6	68.9	75.9
1962	68.1	71.4	70.2	73.1	77.0	80.0	83.3	82.9	81.1	77.5	68.1	63.7	74.7
1963	67.1	65.8	73.4	74.7	77.0	80.6	83.2	83.0	81.3	76.2	71.2	63.5	74.8
#1964	67.4	65.7	74.6	77.1	77.6	81.2	82.8	83.6	82.3	76.9	74.9	72.2	76.4
1965	67.0	70.9	73.1	76.7	78.5	80.7	81.3	81.7	79.9	78.1	74.2	69.3	76.0
1966	66.0	68.9	69.2	72.8	77.6	78.2	81.1	81.7	81.2	77.9	70.2	66.6	74.3
1967	71.4	68.9	72.8	74.7	79.3	79.9	82.4	81.8	81.3	76.2	71.2	70.3	75.8
1968	66.1	62.7	67.0	75.9	77.6	79.6	81.6	83.9	82.2	77.8	71.0	66.6	74.3
1969	67.6	65.2	67.8	77.3	79.6	82.3	84.1	83.5	82.5	80.3	70.4	65.9	75.5
1970	63.8	64.7	71.8	79.0	79.1	82.0	82.7	84.0	82.2	79.5	69.6	70.9	75.8
1971	68.2	70.9	70.3	75.0	79.1	81.0	82.7	81.9	80.7	78.9	73.9	74.2	76.4
1972	73.0	68.4	72.1	75.0	77.6	79.9	80.9	81.7	80.4	77.9	73.3	70.8	75.9
1973	70.3	65.3	74.5	75.6	79.6	81.3	81.8	81.3	81.8	77.6	76.2	67.0	76.1
1974	74.3	68.9	75.6	76.2	80.0	82.1	82.6	84.0	84.1	78.1	72.9	69.0	77.3
1975	72.7	73.1	73.4	77.5	79.4	81.5	81.1	82.6	82.0	79.2	72.3	69.0	77.0
RECORD													
MEAN	67.5	68.0	71.3	74.9	78.0	80.9	82.2	82.7	81.6	77.8	72.3	68.5	75.5
MAX	75.8	76.7	79.6	82.7	85.4	87.9	89.1	89.7	88.2	84.5	79.8	76.6	83.0
MIN	59.2	59.2	62.9	67.1	70.5	73.8	75.2	75.6	75.0	71.1	64.8	60.3	67.9

# Indicates a station move or relocation of instruments.

MIAMI, FL

Feb	Mar	Apr	May	June	Total
9	23	0	0	0	188
0	17	0	0	0	118
193	28	0	0	0	435
0	16	2	0	0	126
55	59	0	0	0	255
29	11	1	0	0	181
7	30	2	0	0	161
46	6	0	0	0	246
67	4	0	0	0	248
25	18	0	0	0	110
41	16	0	0	0	143
41	0	0	0	0	137
101	57	0	0	0	239
54	49	0	0	0	233
58	19	0	0	0	268
45	31	5	0	0	213
39	0	0	0	0	41
64	0	0	0	0	138
37	0	0	0	0	131
1	10	0	0	0	59

Aug	Sept	Oct	Nov	Dec	Total
581	532	478	191	88	4142
596	522	457	185	213	4303
531	476	443	274	292	4418
523	471	408	261	217	4170
516	511	394	343	163	4334
596	578	414	245	163	4657
553	517	448	257	178	4570

Precipitation

Year	Jan	Feb	Mar	Apr	May	June	July	Aug	Sept	Oct	Nov	Dec	Annual
1940	3.52	2.26	5.40	0.86	3.34	11.55	6.08	8.71	17.53	4.18	0.49	3.20	67.12
1941	2.83	3.89	3.89	5.96	1.12	7.09	15.33	5.01	8.01	2.22	6.44	1.55	63.34
#1942	2.37	2.31	1.81	20.40	4.26	19.54	1.23	3.63	7.05	3.46	1.57	1.24	68.87
1943	1.50	0.50	1.14	2.07	9.99	4.96	7.57	16.88	8.30	4.20	4.83	0.51	62.45
1944	3.03	0.01	1.25	3.01	6.08	2.37	7.95	3.17	5.69	6.76	0.30	0.57	40.19
1945	1.70	0.30	0.74	2.86	1.92	1.81	7.35	4.27	8.94	9.07	1.40	1.92	42.28
1946	1.11	1.28	1.70	1.27	8.18	7.72	11.78	5.13	5.24	3.83	5.15	2.54	54.93
1947	1.87	2.79	1.99	4.45	6.20	9.95	13.51	6.66	10.70	14.75	4.56	0.96	78.39
1948	3.99	1.02	0.53	6.78	6.65	5.53	6.62	9.35	23.02	13.94	0.71	1.51	79.65
1949	0.11	0.37	7.22	5.72	6.07	10.37	3.96	7.57	9.07	7.15	1.23	3.30	62.14
1950	0.50	1.85	0.63	2.57	3.27	3.80	7.99	8.65	3.86	12.48	2.66	1.20	49.46
1951	0.04	2.09	0.47	4.79	1.66	5.08	8.64	5.13	2.63	6.54	0.54	1.06	38.67
1952	0.59	2.30	2.01	1.44	0.68	2.05	7.14	4.93	4.44	21.08	0.25	1.99	48.90
1953	6.08	1.63	0.81	4.17	3.15	5.40	6.66	9.07	13.10	10.26	2.44	2.38	65.15
1954	0.49	2.18	1.96	5.45	13.43	10.14	9.21	1.65	8.28	4.24	4.77	0.46	62.26
1955	0.71	0.76	0.23	1.36	3.74	9.69	7.89	4.27	5.52	4.36	0.98	1.84	41.35
1956	1.74	0.91	0.02	2.28	5.44	3.93	2.34	4.59	9.59	5.56	0.34	0.26	37.00
#1957	0.08	4.68	2.68	5.04	10.11	5.82	9.54	16.58	3.32	7.64	2.54	2.84	70.87
1958	5.67	1.54	5.16	0.85	18.14	6.54	6.58	8.40	4.82	4.15	3.68	6.39	71.92
1959	2.21	2.32	4.85	2.00	6.16	20.56	8.20	8.18	12.98	7.62	13.15	1.10	89.33
1960	0.19	2.20	0.67	10.21	3.46	6.31	5.27	4.15	24.40	10.54	2.36	0.50	70.26
1961	5.12	0.63	1.91	0.56	6.81	10.48	1.91	4.68	3.40	3.92	2.15	0.13	41.70
1962	1.46	0.13	2.78	1.19	0.92	10.36	3.74	8.02	7.82	1.50	4.15	0.20	42.27
1963	0.65	3.45	0.73	0.33	6.34	6.80	1.77	4.77	11.12	4.43	1.43	4.26	46.08
1964	0.45	2.21	0.50	3.31	4.67	10.48	5.51	9.84	4.22	9.77	3.00	6.24	60.20
1965	1.98	2.98	3.97	1.20	0.44	6.55	6.56	4.97	11.38	16.79	0.96	0.62	58.40
1966	3.97	6.56	3.25	1.80	5.53	21.37	8.50	7.62	8.00	10.88	3.84	0.74	82.06
1967	2.75	1.14	3.60	0.15	1.68	15.98	5.55	8.13	9.18	12.88	3.81	1.37	66.22
1968	1.92	2.77	0.88	1.27	18.54	22.36	6.15	8.34	11.11	8.71	1.21	0.13	83.39
1969	6.66	2.02	1.98	4.63	8.02	11.42	8.48	4.31	8.24	13.57	1.01	1.15	71.49
1970	2.64	1.77	2.61	0.95	10.98	5.53	4.48	3.60	8.89	3.01	0.09	0.17	44.72
1971	0.51	0.80	0.40	0.07	4.13	11.65	4.72	6.02	9.63	7.48	0.98	4.33	50.72
1972	1.60	2.71	3.01	2.67	13.71	10.90	7.13	6.49	5.08	2.86	2.77	4.18	63.11
1973	3.41	2.21	1.76	2.24	1.08	8.93	6.14	14.60	6.59	3.36	0.46	2.46	53.24
1974	2.54	0.10	2.27	2.11	2.63	8.12	6.09	9.29	6.38	3.68	4.62	1.17	49.00
1975	1.39	0.90	0.61	0.53	4.94	6.37	4.99	5.19	4.69	6.25	2.80	0.44	39.10
RECORD													
MEAN	2.15	1.83	2.08	3.18	6.07	9.06	6.93	7.11	8.62	7.77	2.61	1.80	59.21

Record mean values above are means through the current year for the period beginning in 1940. Data are from airport locations.

ORLANDO, FLORIDA

Station: ORLANDO, FLORIDA
ORLANDO JETPORT AT MC COY
Elevation (ground): 96 feet

TEMPERATURES °F

Month	Normal: Daily maximum	Normal: Daily minimum	Normal: Monthly	Extremes: Record highest	Extremes: Year	Extremes: Record lowest	Extremes: Year
(a)				12		12	
J	70.5	50.0	60.3	86	1972	24	1966
F	71.8	51.2	61.5	89	1971	28	1970
M	76.0	55.7	65.9	92	1970	31	1968
A	81.5	61.1	71.3	96	1968	44	1971
M	86.7	66.1	76.4	99	1973	54	1971
J	89.3	71.1	80.2	97	1970	63	1965
J	89.8	72.9	81.4	98	1972	68	1965
A	90.0	73.5	81.8	98	1972	69	1975
S	87.9	72.3	80.1	96	1970	64	1964
O	82.5	66.0	74.3	94	1971	47	1973
N	76.2	56.9	66.6	88	1972	30	1970
D	71.5	51.5	61.5	86	1972	29	1968
YR	81.1	62.4	71.8	99	MAY 1973	24	JAN 19[illegible]

IMPORTANT:
The time-period covered by this record is limited: See footnotes following table of **NORMALS, MEANS AND EXTREMES** for explanation and for additional history of **EXTREME HIGHS AND LOWS** recorded in the general area.

Snowfall

Season	July	Aug	Sept	Oct	Nov	Dec	Jan
1970-71	0.0	0.0	0.0	0.0	0.0	0.0	0.0
1971-72	0.0	0.0	0.0	0.0	0.0	0.0	0.0
1972-73	0.0	0.0	0.0	0.0	0.0	0.0	0.0
1973-74	0.0	0.0	0.0	0.0	0.0	0.0	0.0
# 1974-75	0.0	0.0	0.0	0.0	0.0	0.0	0.0
1975-76	0.0	0.0	0.0	0.0	0.0	0.0	
RECORD MEAN	0.0	0.0	0.0	0.0	0.0	0.0	T

Heating Degree Days

Season	July	Aug	Sept	Oct	Nov	Dec	Jan
1955-56	0	0	0	11	62	152	305
1956-57	0	0	0	0	137	113	91
1957-58	0	0	0	23	23	203	371
1958-59	0	0	0	6	9	150	236
#1959-60	0	0	0	0	69	154	175
1960-61	0	0	0	0	14	250	250
1961-62	0	0	0	5	16	149	176
1962-63	0	0	0	4	98	255	209
#1963-64	0	0	0	3	72	272	235
1964-65	0	0	0	7	14	84	178
1965-66	0	0	0	1	19	112	215
1966-67	0	0	0	2	70	169	119
1967-68	0	0	0	0	29	80	191
1968-69	0	0	0	19	120	237	168
1969-70	0	0	0	0	93	204	316
1970-71	0	0	0	0	120	79	165
1971-72	0	0	0	0	26	9	51
1972-73	0	0	0	0	54	105	160
#1973-74	0	0	0	6	13	193	0
1974-75	0	0	0	0	40	163	73
1975-76	0	0	0	0	85	174	

Cooling Degree Days

Year	Jan	Feb	Mar	Apr	May	June	July
1969	12	10	32	232	376	544	608
1970	19	14	128	330	399	511	586
1971	77	97	90	238	411	505	569
1972	181	44	146	243	391	524	570
1973	88	28	207	198	421	548	602
# 1974	213	51	183	207	410	463	492
1975	105	121	141	237	442	481	489

Orlando, by virtue of its location in the central section of the Florida peninsula (which is abounding with lakes) is almost surrounded by water and, therefore, relative humidities remain high here the year round, with values hovering near 90 percent at night and dipping to 40 to 50 percent in the afternoon (sometimes to 20 percent in the winter).

The rainy season extends from June through September (sometimes through October when tropical storms are near). During this period scattered afternoon thundershowers are an almost daily occurrence, and these bring a drop in temperature to make the climate bearable (although, most summers, temperatures above 95° are rather rare). Too, a breeze is usually present, and this also contributes towards general comfort.

During the winter months rainfall is light. While temperatures, on infrequent occasion, may drop at night to near freezing, they rise rapidly during the day and, in the brilliant sunshine, afternoons are pleasant.

Frozen precipitation in the form of snowflakes, snow pellets, or sleet is rare. However, hail is occasionally reported during thunderstorms.

Hurricanes are usually not considered a great threat to Orlando, since, to reach this area, they must pass over a substantial stretch of land and, in so doing, lose much of their punch.

(Continued page 410)

Average Temperature

Year	Jan	Feb	Mar	Apr	May	June	July	Aug	Sept	Oct	Nov	Dec	Annual
#1936	58.6	56.9	63.9	69.8	74.5	77.8	81.6	81.0	79.4	76.8	64.4	62.8	70.6
1937	69.4	62.2	64.6	69.7	75.6	80.5	81.2	81.4	78.8	72.0	63.8	58.4	71.5
1938	59.3	65.2	70.2	70.4	77.0	77.8	79.6	81.2	78.3	70.2	66.6	57.8	71.1
1939	60.3	67.0	69.0	72.2	76.2	81.0	82.0	80.4	81.2	75.4	63.6	59.0	72.3
1940	50.4	57.8	64.8	68.4	73.8	80.0	82.0	82.3	78.2	70.9	64.6	63.8	69.8
1941	57.0	55.8	60.2	70.0	72.9	81.4	80.6	82.8	79.2	76.2	65.4	62.3	70.3
#1942	56.6	57.0	65.1	70.6	76.6	80.8	84.5	82.4	81.3	74.1	68.2	63.2	71.7
1943	62.8	59.4	66.4	70.6	78.2	82.3	82.8	88.0	80.4	70.6	65.2	62.0	71.9
1944	58.8	68.2	69.6	72.9	75.2	82.8	82.1	83.0	82.5	72.6	65.4	58.3	72.6
1945	59.8	66.2	72.8	75.7	76.8	82.0	81.8	82.1	81.0	75.0	65.4	59.4	73.2
1946	62.3	63.3	68.3	72.5	78.4	79.8	82.6	82.8	80.9	76.0	73.8	66.8	74.0
1947	69.0	54.2	62.2	76.4	77.8	80.4	80.0	82.0	80.2	76.0	68.8	64.0	72.6
1948	58.0	66.0	71.5	74.1	79.0	82.6	82.0	82.0	80.6	73.2	73.7	67.4	74.2
1949	66.4	69.6	67.4	72.5	77.8	80.6	82.6	81.8	81.1	77.8	62.7	65.2	73.8
1950	68.2	65.1	66.5	67.1	78.0	83.0	81.5	82.3	80.2	77.0	63.5	57.7	72.5
1951	60.0	59.8	66.1	68.5	75.7	80.5	81.8	83.8	81.4	76.1	63.7	65.1	71.9
1952	62.5	61.1	67.3	67.8	77.4	83.0	82.5	82.5	80.5	73.3	65.6	58.0	71.8
1953	60.2	63.5	70.0	71.0	79.7	81.1	82.8	81.5	80.0	71.7	66.1	62.7	72.5
1954	61.9	62.2	64.1	74.1	75.3	81.1	81.4	83.5	80.9	72.1	63.2	57.3	71.4
1955	58.4	62.2	67.4	72.3	77.8	79.3	81.2	82.1	81.4	72.4	65.6	60.8	71.7
1956	55.1	65.5	65.7	70.2	77.8	79.9	82.1	82.5	78.3	73.4	63.8	64.5	71.6
1957	64.7	67.5	65.8	72.3	76.9	80.7	82.6	81.3	81.0	72.1	69.4	59.1	72.8
1958	52.9	52.4	63.7	71.4	75.6	82.0	82.6	82.7	81.9	72.7	71.3	60.6	70.8
1959	58.3	67.6	63.7	70.9	78.0	81.0	81.3	81.7	79.7	78.5	66.9	60.7	72.3
#1960	60.5	59.7	60.9	72.0	76.0	79.5	83.1	83.3	80.3	77.2	69.9	57.6	71.7
1961	56.9	64.7	70.6	69.4	77.0	80.6	83.3	82.9	81.1	73.6	69.4	63.9	72.8
1962	60.9	68.4	63.7	70.3	79.8	81.6	83.9	82.8	80.6	75.0	63.0	57.7	72.3
#1963	59.5	57.2	69.5	73.6	77.9	82.4	82.9	83.9	80.5	73.8	65.4	56.5	71.9
1964	58.5	58.3	68.1	74.1	77.1	82.4	81.6	82.8	79.8	72.5	70.5	64.4	72.5
1965	60.0	64.1	67.0	74.8	77.1	79.0	80.5	82.2	80.8	74.2	69.5	62.6	72.7
1966	58.7	62.3	64.4	70.5	77.4	78.0	82.3	82.3	80.1	75.8	65.8	60.1	71.5
1967	63.2	60.0	68.3	74.3	78.3	80.2	82.4	82.0	79.7	74.0	67.5	65.9	73.0
1968	59.6	54.8	61.4	73.5	76.7	78.8	81.3	82.3	80.3	74.3	63.4	58.7	70.4
1969	59.8	57.8	60.4	72.5	76.9	82.9	84.4	82.2	81.2	77.9	64.0	58.7	71.6
1970	55.1	58.7	67.0	75.8	77.7	81.8	83.8	82.3	83.6	77.0	63.4	64.6	72.6
1971	62.0	64.1	64.8	72.1	78.2	81.7	83.1	83.3	81.8	79.0	69.5	71.4	74.2
1972	68.9	62.0	68.7	72.7	77.4	82.2	83.2	82.8	81.8	76.8	68.9	66.1	74.3
1973	62.4	59.7	71.1	71.1	78.3	83.1	84.2	81.8	81.4	75.6	70.9	60.4	73.3
#1974	71.6	60.5	70.2	71.4	78.0	80.3	80.7	82.0	81.8	72.6	67.6	60.9	73.1
1975	65.8	67.6	67.4	72.4	79.1	80.8	80.5	82.3	80.7	76.6	67.4	60.2	73.4
RECORD MEAN	61.3	62.2	66.7	72.2	77.5	81.1	82.3	82.5	80.8	74.7	67.0	61.8	72.5
MAX	72.2	73.4	78.0	83.4	88.4	90.9	91.7	91.6	89.4	83.7	77.3	72.7	82.7
MIN	50.3	51.0	55.4	60.9	66.6	71.3	72.8	73.3	72.2	65.7	56.6	50.9	62.3

# Indicates a station move or relocation of instruments.

Precipitation

Year	Jan	Feb	Mar	Apr	May	June	July	Aug	Sept	Oct	Nov	Dec	Annual
#1936	4.11	6.29	2.90	1.58	3.58	11.28	2.63	4.95	5.81	5.07	2.21	1.77	52.18
1937	0.97	5.00	2.97	3.78	4.47	5.22	5.14	13.14	9.37	4.55	3.67	0.82	59.10
1938	0.73	0.81	1.74	0.34	6.30	4.49	4.81	4.36	5.30	3.88	1.49	0.30	34.55
1939	1.21	0.35	1.75	4.97	4.87	15.64	6.34	8.90	5.24	1.67	0.39	1.09	52.42
1940	2.14	2.89	4.23	4.44	1.72	6.67	10.14	8.04	7.35	0.37	0.22	5.81	54.02
1941	4.69	4.16	2.47	5.53	2.73	8.18	9.44	6.46	4.76	5.33	3.61	2.29	59.65
#1942	2.32	3.03	5.83	2.32	1.17	10.57	2.01	6.71	4.17	0.24	0.12	2.80	41.29
1943	1.19	0.50	3.92	1.53	5.42	3.66	5.17	5.85	7.18	3.04	0.87	1.28	39.61
1944	2.14	0.10	3.69	4.07	2.83	6.43	11.04	5.39	4.52	8.53	0.11	T	48.85
1945	3.86	0.11	0.54	1.47	2.93	13.70	7.06	5.28	15.87	1.61	1.00	2.52	55.95
1946	2.24	2.96	1.15	0.81	4.24	7.78	8.57	10.06	7.75	3.32	0.97	0.28	50.13
1947	0.87	4.78	5.55	4.98	2.81	11.61	13.90	6.71	8.87	4.83	1.90	0.66	67.47
1948	6.44	1.84	4.05	1.08	0.97	1.97	8.76	12.30	10.81	2.55	0.45	1.31	52.53
1949	0.31	0.47	0.29	3.02	2.54	7.97	6.05	8.83	8.25	1.51	1.22	3.82	44.28
1950	0.15	0.48	3.44	4.82	2.93	5.55	8.27	3.48	7.93	14.51	0.09	4.30	55.95
1951	0.52	2.28	0.96	5.99	1.40	5.08	14.51	7.84	9.34	3.08	4.86	2.06	57.92
1952	0.70	5.47	6.67	2.88	2.45	2.32	4.43	6.51	4.94	3.69	0.74	0.65	41.45
1953	2.86	2.89	3.03	6.18	1.87	6.28	6.85	15.19	8.84	3.50	4.78	3.58	65.85
1954	0.45	1.16	0.99	4.44	3.55	5.81	13.64	4.39	3.99	5.07	2.68	1.80	47.97
1955	2.00	1.12	1.59	1.36	3.13	4.73	6.88	6.65	6.97	4.10	2.17	1.56	42.26
1957	0.91	1.93	3.76	4.74	8.58	4.39	4.35	9.45	7.47	1.68	0.82	2.85	50.93
1958	4.49	2.83	6.16	3.79	2.68	3.83	9.93	3.40	1.65	7.27	2.48	2.69	51.20
1959	2.78	4.55	7.69	4.91	4.44	7.95	8.02	6.77	8.33	5.97	0.99	1.37	63.77
#1960	1.49	5.64	10.54	2.55	0.50	9.50	19.57	3.20	11.21	3.17	0.30	1.07	68.74
1961	1.75	2.82	2.21	0.28	0.43	8.08	9.93	6.99	4.84	2.87	0.92	0.66	41.78
1962	1.11	2.08	3.55	1.58	2.74	3.11	12.77	5.11	12.24	1.90	2.46	1.70	50.35
1963	3.17	4.76	2.69	1.23	3.56	6.67	3.83	3.54	6.72	0.46	6.39	2.26	45.?8
1964	6.18	3.42	4.65	2.14	2.74	6.11	6.68	9.00	9.47	1.64	0.45	1.91	54.39
1965	1.79	3.67	3.02	0.66	0.52	7.36	11.55	5.49	5.99	4.06	1.06	2.23	47.40
1966	4.45	6.31	2.57	1.92	6.57	9.77	6.73	7.76	6.25	1.98	0.09	0.99	55.39
1967	0.84	5.49	1.31	0.28	1.69	11.16	4.63	6.83	5.88	0.35	0.03	2.42	40.91
1968	0.65	2.76	2.27	0.30	3.72	18.28	5.60	3.44	5.91	5.47	2.82	0.88	52.10
1969	2.22	3.30	5.52	2.38	1.40	5.04	6.73	7.17	6.44	9.45	0.87	4.66	55.18
1970	4.05	6.77	3.66	0.45	4.08	4.92	5.97	5.91	3.25	2.60	0.24	2.06	43.96
1971	0.45	2.98	1.46	1.52	4.31	4.39	8.29	7.51	2.98	3.06	1.21	1.93	40.09
1972	0.99	4.96	5.06	1.39	3.76	6.33	3.98	16.11	0.43	2.34	4.11	1.89	51.35
1973	4.82	2.73	4.13	2.82	4.74	6.63	6.24	7.33	11.53	1.10	0.74	2.56	55.37
# 1974	0.18	0.63	3.67	1.17	2.69	15.28	6.01	6.56	5.78	0.48	0.31	1.62	44.38
1975	0.98	1.49	1.10	1.36	7.52	9.70	9.26	4.75	4.97	4.74	0.66	0.51	47.04
RECORD MEAN	2.08	2.85	3.37	2.49	3.26	7.18	8.21	7.00	7.06	3.88	1.52	1.83	50.73

Record mean values above are means through the current year for the period beginning in 1943.

Feb	Mar	Apr	May	June	Total
0.0	0.0	0.0	0.0	0.0	0.0
0.0	0.0	0.0	0.0	0.0	0.0
0.0	0.0	0.0	0.0	0.0	0.0
0.0	0.0	0.0	0.0	0.0	0.0
0.0	0.0	0.0	0.0	0.0	0.0
0.0	0.0	0.0	0.0	0.0	T

ORLANDO, FL

Feb	Mar	Apr	May	June	Total
80	85	7	0	0	702
40	62	0	0	0	443
362	92	6	0	0	1080
36	98	15	0	0	550
171	175	11	0	0	755
97	25	9	0	0	645
46	111	21	0	0	524
232	33	2	0	0	833
199	39	4	0	0	824
89	82	0	0	0	454
122	72	5	0	0	546
157	25	0	0	0	542
293	149	0	0	0	742
206	169	0	0	0	919
187	58	0	0	0	858
115	92	20	0	0	591
124	24	6	0	0	240
169	12	9	0	0	509
173	15	8	0	0	408
44	57	10	0	0	387

Aug	Sept	Oct	Nov	Dec	Total
540	495	406	68	16	3339
544	565	380	77	72	3625
573	510	440	167	214	3891
561	509	374	179	148	3870
529	501	341	199	58	3720
536	510	241	125	43	3474
541	479	366	167	32	3601

(Continued)

For example, although the eye of hurricane Donna, in 1960, passed over the western environs of Orlando, highest sustained wind speeds noted at the Weather Bureau observatory (eastern section of Orlando) were only 46 m.p.h. and peak gusts 69 m.p.h. This is not to imply that sustained hurricane speeds (75 m.p.h. or higher) never occur here, but that they occur only rarely. Also, Orlando, being inland, is relatively safe from high water (which does the major portion of hurricane damage), although heavy rains sometimes briefly flood sections of the City.

Normals, Means, and Extremes

Month	Normal Degree days Base 65 °F		Precipitation in inches												Relative humidity pct.			
			Water equivalent							Snow, Ice pellets					Hour 01	Hour 07	Hour 13	Hour 19
	Heating	Cooling	Normal	Maximum monthly	Year	Minimum monthly	Year	Maximum in 24 hrs.	Year	Maximum monthly	Year	Maximum in 24 hrs.	Year	(Local time)			
(a)				33		33		33		33		33		11	12	12	12
J	197	52	2.28	6.44	1948	0.15	1950	3.35	1964	T	1958	T	1958	85	88	57	70
F	184	90	2.95	6.77	1970	0.10	1944	4.38	1970	0.0		0.0		81	85	52	62
M	94	118	3.46	10.54	1960	0.16	1956	5.03	1960	0.0		0.0		83	86	50	60
A	13	202	2.72	6.18	1953	0.28	1967	2.79	1953	0.0		0.0		82	87	46	57
M	0	353	2.94	8.58	1957	0.43	1961	3.14	1957	0.0		0.0		83	87	49	61
J	0	456	7.11	18.28	1968	1.97	1948	8.40	1945	0.0		0.0		87	87	56	71
J	0	508	8.29	19.57	1960	3.83	1963	8.19	1960	0.0		0.0		88	89	59	74
A	0	521	6.73	16.11	1972	3.20	1960	5.29	1949	0.0		0.0		89	91	60	77
S	0	453	7.20	15.87	1945	0.43	1972	9.67	1945	0.0		0.0		88	90	60	76
O	0	288	4.07	14.51	1950	0.35	1967	7.74	1950	0.0		0.0		85	87	56	74
N	75	123	1.56	6.39	1963	0.03	1967	4.03	1951	0.0		0.0		84	87	53	70
D	170	62	1.90	4.66	1959	T	1944	3.61	1969	0.0		0.0		85	86	56	71
YR	733	3226	51.21	19.57	JUL 1960	T	DEC 1944	9.67	SEP 1945	T	JAN 1958	T	JAN 1958	85	87	55	68

(To better understand these tables, see full explanation of terms beginning on page 322)

Month	Wind					Pct. of possible sunshine	Mean sky cover, tenths, sunrise to sunset	Mean number of days											Average station pressure mb.
			Fastest mile					Sunrise to sunset							Temperatures °F				
															Max.		Min.		Elev. 106 feet m.s.l.
	Mean speed m.p.h.	Prevailing direction	Speed m.p.h.	Direction	Year			Clear	Partly cloudy	Cloudy	Precipitation .01 inch or more	Snow, Ice pellets 1.0 inch or more	Thunderstorms	Heavy fog, visibility ¼ mile or less	(b) 90° and above	32° and below	32° and below	0° and below	
(a)	27	15	26	26			27	27	27	27	33	33	31	27	12	12	12	12	3
J	9.0	NNE	42	25	1953		5.6	9	11	11	6	0	1	6	0	0	1	0	1017.1
F	9.8	S	46	25	1969		5.5	9	9	10	7	0	1	3	0	0	*	0	1015.3
M	10.0	S	45	29	1955		5.5	10	10	11	8	0	3	3	1	0	*	0	1013.7
A	9.6	SE	50	02	1956		5.1	10	12	8	5	0	3	1	6	0	0	0	1014.7
M	8.9	SE	43	20	1955		5.3	10	12	9	8	0	8	2	12	0	0	0	1011.7
J	8.3	SW	64	32	1970		6.4	5	14	11	14	0	14	1	18	0	0	0	1012.2
J	7.5	S	46	14	1961		6.5	3	17	11	18	0	19	1	24	0	0	0	1013.7
A	7.3	S	50	32	1957		6.4	3	17	11	16	0	17	1	25	0	0	0	1014.5
S	8.0	ENE	46	24	1969		6.5	4	14	12	14	0	9	1	17	0	0	0	1012.4
O	8.8	N	48	05	1950		5.4	10	11	10	9	0	3	2	2	0	0	0	1014.2
N	8.7	N	46	26	1968		4.7	12	10	8	5	0	1	3	0	0	*	0	1016.5
D	8.6	NNE	32	07	1959		5.3	11	9	11	6	0	1	5	0	0	1	0	1016.7
YR	8.7	S	64	32	JUN 1970		5.7	96	146	123	115	0	80	29	105	0	2	0	1014.4

FOOTNOTES

Means and extremes above are from existing and comparable exposures. Annual extremes have been exceeded at other sites in the locality as follows: Highest temperature 103 in September 1921; lowest temperature 20 in December 1962.

Station: TAMPA, FLORIDA INTERNATIONAL AIRPORT
Elevation (ground): 19 feet

TEMPERATURES °F

Month	Normal: Daily maximum	Normal: Daily minimum	Normal: Monthly	Extremes: Record highest	Year	Extremes: Record lowest	Year
(a)				12		12	
J	70.6	50.1	60.4	84	1975	23	1971
F	71.9	51.7	61.8	88	1971	27	1967
M	76.1	55.9	66.0	88	1974	35	1971
A	82.4	61.6	72.0	93	1975	40	1971
M	87.5	66.9	77.2	98	1975	49	1971
J	89.9	72.0	81.0	97	1964	61	1972
J	90.1	73.7	81.9	97	1964	63	1970
A	90.4	74.0	82.2	98	1975	67	1973
S	89.0	72.6	80.8	96	1972	64	1972
O	83.9	65.5	74.7	93	1971	40	1964
N	77.1	56.4	66.8	90	1971	23	1970
D	72.0	51.2	61.6	86	1972	27	1968
YR	81.7	62.6	72.2	98	AUG 1975	23	JAN 1971

IMPORTANT:
The time-period covered by this record is limited: See footnotes on next page for explanation and for additional history of EXTREME HIGHS AND LOWS recorded in the general area.

An outstanding feature of Tampa's climate is the summer thundershower season. On the average, the station has 91 days with thundershowers occurring mostly in the late afternoons of June, July, August, and September. The resulting sudden drop in temperature from about 90° to 70° induces an agreeable physiological reaction. Between a dry spring and a dry fall, some 30 inches (about 60 percent of the annual) of rain falls during the four summer months.

Because of the flat terrain, night ground fogs occur frequently during the cool-weather season. Temperature throughout the year is modified by the waters of the Gulf and bays.

Snowfall is negligible and freezing temperatures rare. The annual temperature ranges about 22° from a mean of 60° in January to 82.0° in August. The cool-weather season is favorable for citrus, strawberries, and winter truck crops. Damaging freezes may occur once or twice in a season, although many winters have none. The winter of 1957-58 was the coldest on record. The cold weather started early in December and was very noticeable on the 12th and 13th when the mercury fell to 27° and 26°, respectively. Five more freeze periods occurred during the winter of 1957-58, and the month of February was the coldest February on record with a mean temperature of 52.9°.

The risk of a hurricane moving in from the Gulf of Mexico has been greatest in June and October. A tropical storm of July 28-29, 1960, brought Tampa's heaviest rain, 12.11 inches, in 24 hours. The Gulf hurricane of October 25, 1921, brought Tampa Bay's most destructive and highest tide, 10.5 feet above mean low water. Highest wind velocity, SE 75 m.p.h. for a 5-minute period, occurred during the passage of the Labor Day hurricane of September 3-5, 1935. Worst damage along local west coast beaches resulted from the small but prolonged Gulf hurricane of Septemper 3-6, 1950. The Florida citrus belt took its worst beating in the great hurricane of October 19, 1944, which brought Tampa's lowest recorded sea level pressures, 28.55 inches. Many hurricanes, by replenishing soil moisture and raising the water table, do far more good than harm. The year 1959 was the wettest on record when 76.57 inches of rainfall was measured. In contrast, the driest year on record occurred in 1956 when 28.89 inches were recorded.

Normals, Means, and Extremes

(To better understand these tables. see full explanation of terms beginning on page 322)

Month	Normal Degree days Base 65 °F: Heating	Normal Degree days Base 65 °F: Cooling	Precipitation in inches, Water equivalent: Normal	Maximum monthly	Year	Minimum monthly	Year	Maximum in 24 hrs.	Year	Snow, Ice pellets: Maximum monthly	Year	Maximum in 24 hrs.	Year	Relative humidity pct. Hour 01 (Local time)	Hour 07	Hour 13	Hour 19
(a)				29		29		29		29		29		12	12	12	12
J	203	60	2.33	8.02	1948	T	1950	3.29	1953	T	1965	T	1965	85	87	60	74
F	176	90	2.86	7.95	1963	0.21	1950	3.25	1963	T	1951	T	1951	81	84	55	69
M	90	118	3.89	12.64	1959	0.06	1956	5.20	1960	0.0		0.0		81	85	54	66
A	9	219	2.10	6.59	1957	T	1967	3.70	1951	0.0		0.0		81	86	49	61
M	0	378	2.41	7.55	1959	0.17	1973	3.97	1971	0.0		0.0		80	84	50	60
J	0	480	6.49	13.75	1974	1.86	1951	5.53	1974	0.0		0.0		82	85	59	67
J	0	524	8.43	20.59	1960	2.31	1962	12.11	1960	0.0		0.0		84	87	62	72
A	0	533	8.00	18.59	1949	2.35	1952	5.37	1949	0.0		0.0		86	90	64	75
S	0	474	6.35	13.04	1947	1.28	1972	4.67	1950	0.0		0.0		85	89	60	74
O	0	301	2.54	7.36	1952	0.23	1974	2.54	1968	0.0		0.0		84	88	56	71
N	71	125	1.79	6.12	1963	T	1960	4.22	1963	0.0		0.0		84	87	54	73
D	169	64	2.19	6.66	1950	0.21	1956	3.28	1969	0.0		0.0		83	86	56	73
YR	718	3366	49.38	20.59	JUL 1960	T	APR 1967	12.11	JUL 1960	T	JAN 1965	T	JAN 1965	83	86	57	69

Month	Wind: Mean speed m.p.h.	Prevailing direction	Fastest mile: Speed m.p.h.	Direction	Year	Pct. of possible sunshine	Mean sky cover, tenths, sunrise to sunset	Mean number of days, Sunrise to sunset: Clear	Partly cloudy	Cloudy	Precipitation .01 inch or more	Snow, Ice pellets 1.0 inch or more	Thunderstorms	Heavy fog, visibility ¼ mile or less	Temperatures °F Max. (b) 90° and above	Max. 32° and below	Min. 32° and below	Min. 0° and below	Average station pressure mb. Elev. 11 feet m.s.l.
(a)	29	14	23	23		29	29	29	29	29	29	29	29	29	12	12	12	12	3
J	8.9	N	35	29	1959	65	5.5	10	10	11	6	0	1	6	0	0	2	0	1020.8
F	9.6	E	50	32	1954	67	5.4	9	9	10	7	0	1	3	0	0	1	0	1019.3
M	9.9	S	43	29	1956	71	5.5	10	10	11	7	0	2	3	0	0	0	0	1017.4
A	9.7	ENE	37	29	1961	74	5.0	11	11	8	5	0	3	2	1	0	0	0	1018.3
M	9.2	E	46	36	1958	75	5.2	10	12	9	6	0	6	1	10	0	0	0	1015.4
J	8.4	E	67	31	1964	66	6.3	5	14	11	12	0	14	*	16	0	0	0	1015.8
J	7.6	E	58	32	1963	61	6.8	2	16	13	16	0	22	*	20	0	0	0	1017.0
A	7.4	ENE	38	11	1961	59	6.7	3	16	12	17	0	21	*	20	0	0	0	1017.4
S	8.4	ENE	56	34	1960	60	6.5	4	14	12	13	0	12	*	16	0	0	0	1015.1
O	9.1	NNE	38	02	1953	64	5.2	11	11	9	7	0	3	1	2	0	0	0	1017.4
N	8.8	NNE	40	29	1963	66	4.8	12	10	8	5	0	1	3	*	0	*	0	1019.5
D	8.9	N	45	36	1953	63	5.3	11	9	11	6	0	1	5	0	0	1	0	1020.2
YR	8.8	E	67	31	JUN 1964	66	5.7	98	142	125	107	0	88	24	85	0	4	0	1017.8

FOOTNOTES

Means and extremes above are from existing and comparable exposures. Annual extremes have been exceeded at other sites in the locality as follows: Highest temperature 98 in June 1952+; lowest temperature 18 in December 1962; maximum monthly snowfall 0.1 in February 1889; fastest mile wind 84 in September 1935.

Snowfall

Season	July	Aug	Sept	Oct	Nov	Dec	Jan
1970-71	0.0	0.0	0.0	0.0	0.0	0.0	0.0
1971-72	0.0	0.0	0.0	0.0	0.0	0.0	0.0
1972-73	0.0	0.0	0.0	0.0	0.0	0.0	0.0
1973-74	0.0	0.0	0.0	0.0	0.0	0.0	0.0
1974-75	0.0	0.0	0.0	0.0	0.0	0.0	0.0
1975-76	0.0	0.0	0.0	0.0	0.0	0.0	
RECORD MEAN	0.0	0.0	0.0	0.0	0.0	0.0	T

Heating Degree Days

Season	July	Aug	Sept	Oct	Nov	Dec	Jan
1955-56	0	0	0	6	63	154	298
1956-57	0	0	0	0	120	95	82
1957-58	0	0	0	25	21	193	356
1958-59	0	0	0	3	2	135	213
1959-60	0	0	0	0	59	144	170
1960-61	0	0	0	0	16	240	231
1961-62	0	0	0	5	15	137	175
1962-63	0	0	0	2	98	240	212
#1963-64	0	0	0	15	75	316	216
1964-65	0	0	0	27	24	114	204
1965-66	0	0	0	5	37	160	267
1966-67	0	0	0	7	85	198	129
1967-68	0	0	0	0	69	95	193
1968-69	0	0	0	27	138	264	201
1969-70	0	0	0	0	111	218	343
1970-71	0	0	0	0	145	115	201
1971-72	0	0	0	0	41	13	62
1972-73	0	0	0	0	65	130	166
1973-74	0	0	0	6	24	200	0
1974-75	0	0	0	0	39	138	84
1975-76	0	0	0	0	88	183	

Cooling Degree Days

Year	Jan	Feb	Mar	Apr	May	June	July
1969	8	2	14	224	353	521	568
1970	12	10	85	255	352	464	557
1971	54	86	58	174	342	490	541
1972	131	20	90	204	365	487	528
1973	75	15	188	158	374	510	574
1974	196	55	204	197	413	460	506
1975	93	115	151	282	521	536	572

Feb	Mar	Apr	May	June	Total
0.0	0.0	0.0	0.0	0.0	0.0
0.0	0.0	0.0	0.0	0.0	0.0
0.0	0.0	0.0	0.0	0.0	0.0
0.0	0.0	0.0	0.0	0.0	0.0
0.0	0.0	0.0	0.0	0.0	0.0
T	0.0	0.0	0.0	0.0	T

Average Temperature

Year	Jan	Feb	Mar	Apr	May	June	July	Aug	Sept	Oct	Nov	Dec	Annual
1936	61.8	61.0	66.8	72.0	77.2	80.0	82.4	82.2	81.4	77.4	66.5	64.8	72.8
1937	72.4	62.4	64.7	70.5	77.2	81.4	82.0	81.8	80.6	73.8	64.4	59.8	72.6
1938	61.0	66.4	71.8	71.6	78.6	79.6	80.9	83.1	79.8	72.0	68.6	61.2	72.9
1939	62.6	68.4	70.2	73.0	76.0	80.8	81.6	80.7	80.9	76.6	64.9	61.8	73.1
#1940	52.0	58.0	64.6	69.4	74.6	81.3	83.2	82.5	78.6	72.6	67.2	67.2	70.9
1941	59.4	57.3	61.7	71.6	76.2	81.7	82.2	85.0	82.0	79.4	69.2	65.6	72.6
1942	58.2	56.7	64.1	70.6	77.6	81.4	84.6	83.6	82.0	75.4	69.4	64.4	72.3
1943	62.8	59.8	66.2	71.6	79.2	82.2	81.7	82.8	80.8	71.8	65.8	62.0	72.2
1944	59.5	67.6	69.1	73.6	77.4	83.1	82.6	82.8	83.1	73.2	66.5	58.8	73.1
1945	59.8	65.8	73.2	76.0	77.0	82.6	81.7	82.0	81.6	75.2	66.2	59.4	73.4
#1946	62.8	63.6	68.0	72.6	78.9	80.2	82.1	82.4	80.6	76.1	73.6	66.1	73.9
1947	69.0	54.8	62.0	76.6	77.6	80.8	80.4	81.6	79.6	76.0	68.9	64.1	72.6
1948	58.2	66.4	71.8	74.0	78.2	82.2	82.0	81.9	81.2	74.2	73.6	68.0	74.3
1949	67.2	70.0	68.0	73.4	78.8	80.6	82.4	81.4	81.0	77.9	63.6	66.0	74.2
1950	69.6	65.3	66.6	67.7	78.5	82.5	81.4	81.9	80.2	76.9	64.1	58.3	72.8
1951	61.3	60.9	67.3	69.6	77.4	82.6	82.5	84.4	82.4	76.4	64.6	66.0	73.0
1952	63.5	61.9	67.8	69.1	76.9	83.1	82.3	82.6	80.6	72.4	66.0	58.4	72.1
1953	61.3	64.0	69.9	70.4	79.2	81.2	82.1	81.1	79.8	72.5	67.0	63.8	72.7
1954	62.4	62.8	63.8	74.9	75.3	80.4	80.7	82.5	81.0	73.1	63.9	57.7	71.6
1955	58.9	62.3	66.0	72.0	76.8	78.6	80.3	81.8	80.7	73.2	65.6	61.1	71.5
1956	55.3	66.2	65.1	69.9	78.5	79.6	81.0	82.1	78.5	74.0	64.8	65.5	71.7
1957	64.8	67.4	65.6	72.7	77.4	80.3	81.8	80.9	80.5	71.8	68.6	59.3	72.6
1958	53.3	52.9	64.1	71.6	76.7	82.1	83.1	82.9	82.9	74.2	72.7	61.8	71.5
1959	59.0	69.0	64.9	71.9	78.6	81.4	82.9	82.1	81.5	79.6	67.9	61.3	73.3
1960	60.3	60.3	62.1	73.3	75.6	80.0	82.6	83.0	81.7	77.0	70.2	58.1	72.0
1961	57.7	65.0	70.4	68.6	76.7	80.9	82.9	82.7	81.8	74.4	69.8	64.2	73.0
1962	60.5	66.8	63.8	69.4	77.9	79.6	83.0	81.9	79.7	74.8	62.5	58.2	71.5
#1963	58.6	56.8	68.4	72.3	76.5	80.7	81.7	82.8	80.1	73.7	65.6	54.9	71.0
1964	58.6	57.1	68.0	74.0	76.7	81.8	82.0	81.5	79.3	70.9	67.7	63.2	71.7
1965	58.6	63.8	66.4	72.7	76.3	79.5	80.3	81.5	80.5	72.5	67.0	60.6	71.7
1966	57.0	59.9	63.1	69.2	78.5	79.2	81.7	82.5	80.6	75.3	65.1	59.2	70.9
1967	62.3	59.5	67.8	73.2	77.3	79.9	80.8	80.3	79.2	73.5	65.3	64.8	72.0
1968	59.4	54.3	60.9	72.5	75.7	79.6	80.2	82.0	79.6	73.2	62.3	57.6	69.8
1969	58.5	55.8	58.2	72.3	76.2	82.1	83.1	80.9	80.5	76.9	62.9	58.1	70.5
1970	54.0	57.6	64.9	73.2	76.2	80.1	82.8	82.9	81.9	76.1	61.9	62.4	71.2
1971	60.0	63.1	62.2	69.4	75.8	81.2	82.3	81.8	80.3	77.5	67.7	69.4	72.6
1972	67.0	60.7	66.8	71.4	76.6	81.0	81.9	82.1	81.3	76.1	68.2	65.1	73.2
1973	61.9	57.4	70.2	69.3	76.8	81.8	83.2	81.8	81.7	75.8	70.8	60.1	72.6
1974	71.1	61.1	70.9	70.9	78.2	80.1	81.1	82.8	82.8	72.9	67.9	61.9	73.5
1975	65.1	66.6	67.6	74.0	81.5	82.6	83.2	83.7	81.9	77.9	68.3	60.2	74.4
RECORD MEAN	61.1	62.3	66.7	71.5	76.9	80.6	81.8	82.0	80.6	74.7	67.0	62.0	72.3
MAX	70.4	71.6	76.1	81.1	86.3	89.1	89.6	89.9	88.5	83.2	76.4	71.3	81.1
MIN	51.8	52.9	57.2	61.9	67.5	72.1	73.9	74.0	72.6	66.1	57.6	52.6	63.4

# Indicates a station move or relocation of instruments.

TAMPA, FL

Feb	Mar	Apr	May	June	Total
56	76	5	0	0	658
38	57	0	0	0	392
343	77	2	0	0	1017
11	78	10	0	0	452
164	147	5	0	0	689
92	22	15	0	0	616
55	106	19	0	0	512
229	37	2	0	0	820
227	37	4	0	0	890
96	84	2	0	0	546
172	93	18	0	0	752
175	23	0	0	0	617
306	157	0	0	0	820
252	220	0	0	0	1102
209	81	0	0	0	962
134	139	36	0	0	770
139	26	5	0	0	286
223	18	21	0	0	623
159	17	12	0	0	418
64	61	5	0	0	391

Aug	Sept	Oct	Nov	Dec	Total
498	471	377	55	10	3101
563	514	353	58	40	3263
526	463	396	128	155	3413
536	497	352	168	141	3519
529	510	348	205	55	3541
562	540	250	130	48	3561
585	512	407	191	39	4004

Precipitation

Year	Jan	Feb	Mar	Apr	May	June	July	Aug	Sept	Oct	Nov	Dec	Annual
1936	3.45	7.43	2.53	0.93	3.61	4.69	8.85	7.59	4.68	2.67	0.70	2.22	49.35
1937	1.72	10.92	2.83	3.75	4.98	5.91	8.32	8.08	1.05	2.88	3.44	1.12	55.00
1938	1.20	0.85	1.32	0.35	5.06	8.85	10.11	0.78	5.48	6.94	0.70	0.29	41.93
1939	1.35	0.90	1.00	1.17	6.57	9.48	9.21	14.29	4.01	2.38	0.33	1.02	51.71
#1940	3.20	4.69	2.04	3.27	0.31	8.17	4.63	9.34	4.04	0.02	0.15	3.12	42.98
1941	3.54	3.61	4.40	5.19	0.16	7.06	5.89	3.87	6.40	2.34	4.75	7.04	54.25
1942	3.21	3.52	5.68	1.64	1.23	6.80	5.28	4.34	3.93	0.03	0.10	2.90	38.66
1943	0.35	1.24	3.75	0.75	2.05	12.54	10.80	6.35	5.07	1.04	0.59	0.36	44.89
1944	1.84	0.56	3.78	0.81	3.20	6.20	4.04	5.49	2.38	5.67	0.70	0.20	34.87
1945	4.05	0.75	0.20	1.55	0.42	18.52	12.23	12.28	8.19	4.01	0.75	3.70	66.65
#1946	2.32	5.76	2.28	0.37	3.55	11.41	13.68	6.50	7.88	4.86	0.42	0.09	59.12
1947	1.12	4.02	6.98	3.54	1.19	6.15	11.10	11.59	13.04	3.54	2.49	1.19	65.95
1948	8.02	1.00	3.37	4.28	0.51	5.07	8.33	8.43	3.36	1.02	1.57	1.63	46.59
1949	0.18	0.34	0.22	2.70	1.52	7.59	3.97	18.59	10.47	1.32	1.04	0.30	48.24
1950	T	0.21	3.83	2.13	1.91	6.81	13.77	8.04	9.79	2.84	0.23	6.66	56.22
1951	0.54	2.06	1.99	5.19	1.83	1.86	6.72	7.37	9.60	0.84	3.68	2.15	43.83
1952	0.89	3.74	6.49	1.25	2.07	2.83	10.70	2.35	5.26	7.36	1.73	0.70	45.37
1953	4.04	3.51	3.75	2.95	0.47	7.90	6.80	5.33	11.56	1.70	4.89	4.28	57.18
1954	0.99	1.58	2.01	2.48	5.90	4.57	6.73	4.73	6.35	0.63	5.38	1.85	43.20
1955	2.59	2.73	2.65	1.23	0.72	2.55	11.90	9.57	8.82	3.23	2.15	0.67	48.81
1956	2.02	1.37	0.06	2.08	2.15	2.86	3.69	6.60	3.90	3.50	0.45	0.21	28.89
1957	1.53	3.25	6.98	6.59	7.21	11.11	10.61	11.74	5.95	2.28	1.44	1.74	70.43
1958	5.41	4.17	5.21	3.61	3.15	5.78	4.83	9.59	6.75	3.38	1.99	4.16	58.03
1959	3.66	2.36	12.64	5.48	7.55	9.13	7.29	10.44	8.49	6.26	1.02	2.25	76.57
1960	1.32	3.70	11.00	1.66	1.07	6.36	20.59	7.72	8.17	2.28	T	1.57	65.44
1961	1.45	3.81	2.23	1.44	2.14	2.64	7.69	6.22	2.43	0.25	0.94	3.80	35.04
1962	1.40	1.46	4.26	1.43	2.76	6.34	2.31	10.14	7.57	1.28	2.21	0.46	41.62
1963	2.25	7.95	2.31	0.21	1.56	4.34	8.11	4.10	3.87	0.29	6.12	2.31	43.42
1964	5.08	5.37	3.92	0.53	3.58	6.64	9.75	10.73	5.89	2.86	0.38	3.19	57.92
1965	1.56	2.57	2.28	1.10	0.67	7.30	9.70	5.59	7.36	1.43	0.88	2.34	42.78
1966	4.05	3.08	1.16	1.57	0.71	6.44	7.62	4.75	4.12	1.22	0.39	0.94	36.05
1967	1.32	4.30	0.66	T	0.63	4.70	10.30	10.34	2.20	2.42	0.45	2.04	39.36
1968	0.41	1.52	1.23	0.74	2.08	6.72	8.39	6.79	3.58	4.16	3.14	0.59	39.35
1969	1.78	2.11	5.33	0.05	6.23	4.39	7.39	11.88	4.09	3.12	2.68	5.17	54.22
1970	3.10	4.02	6.12	0.49	4.12	2.05	2.77	8.43	3.95	0.89	1.08	1.25	38.27
1971	0.86	4.25	0.54	1.80	4.09	2.54	7.74	7.46	10.16	4.70	1.40	0.79	46.33
1972	0.54	4.44	3.01	0.38	1.88	5.24	6.65	9.78	1.28	3.29	3.53	2.16	42.18
1973	3.75	2.54	4.21	2.42	0.17	4.19	4.77	9.43	8.91	0.98	2.82	5.52	49.71
1974	0.17	0.89	2.35	0.38	1.11	13.75	3.43	4.67	4.00	0.23	0.12	2.80	33.90
1975	0.91	1.56	1.09	0.91	2.07	8.73	6.65	4.24	11.25	4.94	0.22	0.87	43.44
RECORD MEAN	2.24	2.78	2.98	2.10	2.89	7.10	7.94	8.01	6.54	2.74	1.62	2.05	48.99

Record mean values above are means through the current year for the period beginning in 1890 for temperature and precipitation, 1947 for snowfall. Data are from City Office locations through 1940.

ATLANTA, GEORGIA

Atlanta is located in the foothills of the southern Appalachians in north-central Georgia. The terrain is rolling to hilly and slopes downward toward the east, west, and south so that drainage of the major river systems is generally into the Gulf of Mexico from the western and southern sections of the City and to the Atlantic from the eastern portions of the City. Atlanta has a mean elevation about 1,000 feet above sea level.

The Gulf of Mexico and the Atlantic Ocean are approximately 250 miles south and southeast of the City, respectively. Both the Appalachian chain of mountains and the two nearby maritime bodies exert an important influence on Atlanta's climate. Temperatures are moderated throughout the year while abundant precipitation fosters natural vegetation and growth of crops. Summer temperatures in Atlanta are moderated somewhat by elevation but are still rather warm. However, prolonged periods of hot weather are rare. Afternoon high temperatures equal or exceed 90 degrees less than one day in five, while 100 degree heat is rarely experienced. The highest temperature ever recorded was 103 degrees on July 12, 1930, and on July 29, 1952.

With the mountains to the north tending to retard the southward movement of Polar air masses, Atlanta's winters are rather mild. Cold spells are not unusual but they are rather short lived and seldom disrupt outdoor activities for an extended period of time. The lowest temperature ever recorded in Atlanta was 9 degrees below zero over a snow cover on February 13, 1899. March 24 is the average date of the last freezing temperature in the spring and November 12 the average date of the first freezing temperature in the fall which gives an average growing season of 233 days.

Monthly rainfall ranges from a mean of about 2-1/2 inches in October to nearly 6 inches in March with an annual precipitation average of about 48 inches. Dry periods occur mainly during the late summer and early autumn with a maximum of thundershower activity during July. Severe local thunderstorms occur most frequently in March, April, and May, some spawning highly damaging tornadoes.

The average annual snowfall is about 1-1/2 inches. However, a snow of 4 inches or more occurs about once every 5 years. The record snowfall of 8.3 inches occurred January 23, 1940, and 1-1/2 inches has fallen as late as April 25 in 1910. Most snows melt in a short period of time due to the rapid warming which often follows the storm. Ice storms (freezing rain or glaze) occur about every 2 years, causing hazardous travel and disruption of utilities. Severe ice storms occur about once in ten years, causing major disruption of utilities and significant property damage.

Station: ATLANTA, GEORGIA
HARTSFIELD ATLANTA INTL AP
Elevation (ground): 1010 feet

TEMPERATURES °F

	Normal			Extremes			
Month	Daily maximum	Daily minimum	Monthly	Record highest	Year	Record lowest	Year
(a)				15		15	
J	51.4	33.4	42.4	77	1975	-3	1966
F	54.5	35.5	45.0	79	1962	8	1970
M	61.1	41.1	51.1	85	1974	20	1975
A	71.4	50.7	61.1	88	1970	26	1973
M	79.0	59.2	69.1	93	1962	37	1971
J	84.6	66.6	75.6	98	1969	48	1972
J	86.5	69.4	78.0	98	1970	53	1967
A	86.4	68.6	77.5	98	1968	56	1964
S	81.2	63.4	72.3	96	1975	36	1967
O	72.5	52.3	62.4	88	1971	29	1968
N	61.9	40.8	51.4	84	1961	14	1970
D	52.7	34.3	43.5	77	1971	1	1962
YR	70.3	51.3	60.8	98	JUL 1970	-3	JAN 1966

IMPORTANT:
The time-period covered by this record is limited: See footnotes following table of **NORMALS, MEANS AND EXTREMES** for explanation and for additional history of **EXTREME HIGHS AND LOWS** recorded in the general area.

(Continued)

The Bermuda High pressure area has a dominant effect on Atlanta's weather, particularly in the summer months. Winds average only about 9 m.p.h. during the year with relatively small fluctuations of the barometric pressure. East or northeast winds produce the most unpleasant weather although southerly winds are quite humid during the summer. The generally light wind conditions contribute to the formation of an occasional early morning fog. However, the number of clear to partly cloudy days far exceed the number of cloudy days, making Atlanta a sunny place to live.

Normals, Means, and Extremes

(To better understand these tables, see full explanation of terms beginning on page 322)

Month	Normal Degree days Base 65 °F: Heating	Cooling	Precipitation in inches — Water equivalent: Normal	Maximum monthly	Year	Minimum monthly	Year	Maximum in 24 hrs.	Year	Snow, Ice pellets: Maximum monthly	Year	Maximum in 24 hrs.	Year
(a)				41		41		41		41		41	
J	701	0	4.34	10.82	1936	1.42	1941	3.91	1973	8.3	1940	8.3	1940
F	560	0	4.41	12.77	1961	0.99	1943	5.67	1961	3.9	1952	3.9	1952
M	443	12	5.84	11.51	1942	2.44	1974	5.08	1970	4.8	1960	4.0	1960
A	144	27	4.61	9.86	1936	1.45	1950	4.26	1936	T	1971	T	1971
M	27	154	3.71	7.83	1948	0.32	1936	5.13	1948	0.0		0.0	
J	0	321	3.67	7.52	1939	0.74	1944	3.41	1943	0.0		0.0	
J	0	403	4.90	11.26	1948	1.20	1952	5.44	1948	0.0		0.0	
A	0	388	3.54	8.69	1967	0.88	1963	5.05	1940	0.0		0.0	
S	8	227	3.15	7.32	1953	0.26	1954	5.46	1956	0.0		0.0	
O	137	57	2.50	7.53	1966	T	1963	3.27	1937	0.0		0.0	
N	408	0	3.43	15.72	1948	0.41	1939	4.11	1935	1.0	1968	1.0	1968
D	667	0	4.24	9.92	1961	1.08	1955	3.85	1961	2.5	1963	2.2	1963
YR	3095	1589	48.34	15.72	NOV 1948	T	OCT 1963	5.67	FEB 1961	8.3	JAN 1940	8.3	JAN 1940

Month	Relative humidity pct. Hour 01	Hour 07	Hour 13	Hour 19 (Local time)	Wind: Mean speed m.p.h.	Prevailing direction	Fastest mile: Speed m.p.h.	Direction	Year	Pct. of possible sunshine	Mean sky cover, tenths, sunrise to sunset	Mean number of days — Sunrise to sunset: Clear	Partly cloudy	Cloudy	Precipitation .01 inch or more	Snow, Ice pellets 1.0 inch or more	Thunderstorms	Heavy fog, visibility ¼ mile or less	Temperatures °F Max. (b) 90° and above	Max. 32° and below	Min. 32° and below	Min. 0° and below	Average station pressure mb. Elev. 1034 feet m.s.l.
(a)	15	15	15	15	37	14	33	33		41	41	41	41	41	41	41	41	41	15	15	15	15	3
J	77	80	61	66	10.5	NW	54	NW	1945	47	6.5	8	7	16	12	*	1	5	0	2	16	*	983.2
F	70	76	55	58	11.0	NW	59	W	1946	52	6.2	8	6	14	10	*	2	3	0	*	14	0	980.9
M	70	79	52	55	11.0	NW	69	SE	1969	57	6.1	9	7	15	12	*	4	3	0	0	6	0	979.1
A	72	80	52	53	10.1	NW	68	SW	1956	65	5.5	10	8	12	9	0	4	2	0	0	1	0	980.6
M	79	83	55	59	8.6	NW	65	SW	1971	69	5.6	9	11	11	9	0	6	1	1	0	0	0	978.0
J	84	86	59	65	7.9	NW	70	NE	1953	67	5.9	7	13	10	10	0	9	1	5	0	0	0	979.7
J	88	90	64	71	7.4	SW	56	SE	1954	61	6.4	5	14	12	12	0	11	2	6	0	0	0	980.2
A	87	91	62	70	7.1	NW	49	NW	1941	65	5.8	7	14	10	9	0	8	2	6	0	0	0	981.8
S	84	89	61	69	8.0	ENE	49	[illegible]	[illegible]	63	5.5	10	10	10	7	0	3	2	2	0	0	0	980.8
O	78	84	53	65	8.3	NW	47	NW	1954	67	4.5	14	8	9	6	0	1	2	0	0	*	0	983.6
N	76	82	54	63	9.1	NW	46	NE	1947	60	5.2	12	6	12	8	*	1	3	0	*	6	0	983.4
D	76	80	60	67	9.8	NW	63	W	1942	50	6.2	9	7	15	10	*	1	5	0	*	14	0	982.2
YR	78	83	57	63	9.1	NW	70	NE	JUN 1953	61	5.8	108	111	146	116	1	50	30	19	2	58	*	981.1

FOOTNOTES

Means and extremes are from existing and comparable exposures. Annual extremes have been exceeded at other sites in the locality as follows: Highest temperature 103 in July 1952; lowest temperature -9 (-8.5) in February 1899; maximum monthly precipitation 15.82 in January 1883; maximum precipitation in 24 hours 7.36 in March 1886; maximum monthly snowfall 11.6 in February 1895.

Snowfall

Season	July	Aug	Sept	Oct	Nov	Dec	Jan
1936-37	0.0	0.0	0.0	0.0	T	0.0	0.0
1937-38	0.0	0.0	0.0	0.0	T	0.7	0.3
1938-39	0.0	0.0	0.0	0.0	T	T	0.0
1939-40	0.0	0.0	0.0	0.0	0.0	T	8.3
1940-41	0.0	0.0	0.0	0.0	0.0	0.0	0.0
1941-42	0.0	0.0	0.0	0.0	T	0.0	0.1
1942-43	0.0	0.0	0.0	0.0	0.0	0.0	T
1943-44	0.0	0.0	0.0	0.0	0.0	T	T
1944-45	0.0	0.0	0.0	0.0	T	T	T
1945-46	0.0	0.0	0.0	0.0	0.0	0.5	0.1
1946-47	0.0	0.0	0.0	0.0	0.0	0.0	0.0
#1947-48	0.0	0.0	0.0	0.0	0.0	0.0	0.9
1948-49	0.0	0.0	0.0	0.0	0.0	0.0	T
1949-50	0.0	0.0	0.0	0.0	0.0	0.0	0.0
1950-51	0.0	0.0	0.0	0.0	T	T	0.0
1951-52	0.0	0.0	0.0	0.0	T	T	0.0
1952-53	0.0	0.0	0.0	0.0	T	0.0	1.3
1953-54	0.0	0.0	0.0	0.0	0.0	0.1	T
1954-55	0.0	0.0	0.0	0.0	T	0.1	T
1955-56	0.0	0.0	0.0	0.0	0.0	0.0	T
1956-57	0.0	0.0	0.0	0.0	0.0	T	T
1957-58	0.0	0.0	0.0	0.0	0.0	T	T
1958-59	0.0	0.0	0.0	0.0	0.0	2.4	T
1959-60	0.0	0.0	0.0	0.0	0.0	T	T
1960-61	0.0	0.0	0.0	0.0	0.0	T	0.1
1961-62	0.0	0.0	0.0	0.0	0.0	1.0	3.5
1962-63	0.0	0.0	0.0	0.0	0.0	T	T
1963-64	0.0	0.0	0.0	0.0	T	2.5	0.8
1964-65	0.0	0.0	0.0	0.0	0.0	T	2.4
1965-66	0.0	0.0	0.0	0.0	0.0	0.0	0.7
1966-67	0.0	0.0	0.0	0.0	T	0.0	0.0
1967-68	0.0	0.0	0.0	0.0	0.0	0.0	0.7
1968-69	0.0	0.0	0.0	0.0	1.0	T	T
1969-70	0.0	0.0	0.0	0.0	T	T	0.6
1970-71	0.0	0.0	0.0	0.0	0.0	T	T
1971-72	0.0	0.0	0.0	0.0	T	1.0	T
1972-73	0.0	0.0	0.0	0.0	0.0	0.0	1.0
1973-74	0.0	0.0	0.0	0.0	0.0	T	0.0
1974-75	0.0	0.0	0.0	0.0	0.0	T	T
1975-76	0.0	0.0	0.0	0.0	0.6	0.0	
RECORD MEAN	0.0	0.0	0.0	0.0	T	0.2	0.7

Heating Degree Days

Season	July	Aug	Sept	Oct	Nov	Dec	Jan
1955-56	0	0	0	138	433	664	724
1956-57	0	0	5	49	436	324	585
1957-58	0	0	36	207	340	560	801
1958-59	0	0	0	117	268	681	701
1959-60	0	0	8	121	396	575	636
#1960-61	0	0	5	84	362	744	814
1961-62	0	0	12	150	310	658	736
1962-63	0	0	40	132	471	759	857
1963-64	0	0	19	55	398	907	743
1964-65	0	0	2	201	288	567	669
1965-66	0	0	3	176	332	619	874
1966-67	0	0	5	177	379	663	645
1967-68	0	0	52	193	490	530	792
1968-69	0	2	0	157	441	760	761
1969-70	0	0	13	125	445	719	895
1970-71	0	0	3	64	457	537	681
1971-72	0	0	0	36	436	390	559
1972-73	0	0	3	136	465	511	725
1973-74	0	0	1	86	295	639	357
1974-75	0	0	26	148	381	833	547
1975-76	0	0	28	113	342	665	

Cooling Degree Days

Year	Jan	Feb	Mar	Apr	May	June	July
1969	0	0	1	31	162	379	494
1970	0	0	0	80	178	292	430
1971	0	0	0	38	115	374	358
1972	0	0	3	56	72	227	370
1973	0	0	11	15	78	322	438
1974	0	1	24	42	198	229	405
1975	0	0	6	44	195	313	359

ATLANTA, GEORGIA

Feb	Mar	Apr	May	June	Total
0.0	0.0	0.0	0.0	0.0	T
0.0	0.0	0.0	0.0	0.0	1.0
0.0	0.0	0.0	0.0	0.0	T
T	T	0.0	0.0	0.0	8.3
T	0.0	0.0	0.0	0.0	T
T	3.7	0.0	0.0	0.0	3.8
T	0.4	0.0	0.0	0.0	0.4
0.0	T	0.0	0.0	0.0	T
0.0	0.0	0.0	0.0	0.0	T
0.0	0.0	0.0	0.0	0.0	0.6
0.5	T	0.0	0.0	0.0	0.5
0.5	0.0	0.0	0.0	0.0	1.4
0.0	0.0	0.0	0.0	0.0	T
0.0	T	0.0	0.0	0.0	T
T	T	0.0	0.0	0.0	T
3.9	0.0	0.0	0.0	0.0	3.9
T	0.0	0.0	0.0	0.0	1.3
T	0.0	0.0	0.0	0.0	0.1
T	0.0	0.0	0.0	0.0	0.1
T	0.0	0.0	0.0	0.0	T
0.0	T	0.0	0.0	0.0	T
2.7	T	0.0	0.0	0.0	2.7
T	T	0.0	0.0	0.0	2.4
T	4.8	0.0	0.0	0.0	4.8
T	T	0.0	0.0	0.0	0.1
0.0	T	0.0	0.0	0.0	4.5
T	0.0	0.0	0.0	0.0	T
0.3	0.0	0.0	0.0	0.0	3.6
0.1	0.5	0.0	0.0	0.0	3.0
T	T	0.0	0.0	0.0	0.7
2.0	0.0	0.0	0.0	0.0	2.0
3.5	T	0.0	0.0	0.0	4.2
1.2	0.0	0.0	0.0	0.0	2.2
T	0.0	0.0	0.0	0.0	0.6
1.0	T	T	0.0	0.0	1.0
T	T	0.0	0.0	0.0	1.0
T	0.0	0.0	0.0	0.0	1.0
T	T	0.0	0.0	0.0	T
T	T	0.0	0.0	0.0	T
0.4	0.2	T	0.0	0.0	1.5

ATLANTA, GA

Feb	Mar	Apr	May	June	Total
396	348	164	9	6	2882
291	410	109	31	0	2240
756	466	128	29	0	3323
480	422	108	10	0	2787
611	713	96	71	0	3227
429	322	276	66	5	3107
410	525	235	4	0	3040
724	272	100	42	0	3397
713	423	160	32	0	3450
586	500	110	0	3	2926
605	451	171	26	5	3262
642	270	67	78	20	2946
769	389	154	31	0	3400
620	555	93	28	0	3417
586	371	95	15	0	3264
572	533	156	56	0	3059
643	387	161	21	5	2638
617	240	230	72	0	2999
531	241	155	5	0	2310
493	451	192	2	0	2873

Aug	Sept	Oct	Nov	Dec	Total
348	197	51	0	0	1663
442	371	77	0	0	1870
371	265	95	13	5	1634
396	297	25	7	0	1453
388	323	79	20	0	1674
368	187	41	11	0	1506
406	193	63	21	0	1600

Average Temperature

Year	Jan	Feb	Mar	Apr	May	June	July	Aug	Sept	Oct	Nov	Dec	Annual
1936	39.0	41.6	56.6	58.8	73.0	79.4	81.2	79.8	76.0	64.4	50.1	46.6	62.2
1937	53.0	44.4	50.5	59.7	70.9	79.6	69.6	79.5	71.2	58.8	47.4	43.1	61.5
1938	43.0	51.4	58.4	61.4	71.2	75.2	79.2	81.2	73.8	64.2	54.0	43.6	63.0
1939	45.2	49.7	55.8	60.1	69.3	78.8	80.2	77.8	76.2	64.7	50.2	45.6	62.8
1940	29.6	42.0	49.8	59.3	67.9	77.4	77.2	78.5	71.6	64.4	51.3	47.6	59.7
1941	44.2	39.8	46.6	63.6	72.6	77.4	80.0	80.0	76.6	69.6	52.6	47.8	62.6
#1942	42.6	40.3	52.0	63.8	69.9	77.8	80.4	77.7	72.4	63.6	54.4	43.8	61.6
1943	46.3	46.8	50.6	61.4	72.0	81.2	79.9	80.9	70.7	60.9	51.0	44.5	62.2
1944	44.4	50.4	52.9	60.2	72.6	80.2	78.3	77.2	73.5	62.8	51.0	41.2	62.0
1945	43.2	48.7	61.8	63.7	66.6	78.0	79.2	78.2	76.2	61.4	53.2	38.4	62.4
1946	44.7	48.0	59.2	64.1	68.4	75.4	77.8	77.2	71.2	62.2	57.4	48.3	62.8
1947	45.8	38.7	45.3	63.7	68.9	75.5	77.0	79.2	75.0	66.4	48.8	45.4	60.8
#1948	37.4	48.2	55.6	65.6	70.7	78.9	80.0	77.3	71.5	60.4	55.0	47.8	62.4
1949	51.8	51.6	53.2	59.8	71.7	76.2	79.8	77.9	70.8	67.2	51.1	45.6	63.1
1950	55.5	50.8	50.2	58.8	72.8	77.5	77.5	76.2	71.4	65.9	47.6	40.6	62.1
1951	45.3	47.5	53.1	60.1	70.1	77.5	79.1	80.9	73.9	65.1	47.5	47.2	62.3
1952	49.4	48.5	51.5	61.6	71.9	82.3	82.0	78.2	71.5	59.0	52.8	43.6	62.7
1953	47.1	47.4	54.6	59.5	73.3	78.2	78.7	78.9	72.3	64.0	52.7	43.8	62.5
1954	45.2	50.1	53.1	65.5	64.2	78.0	82.1	82.5	77.8	64.5	49.5	43.7	63.0
1955	43.6	47.6	56.1	65.9	72.7	72.9	79.1	80.1	75.4	61.9	50.7	43.4	62.5
1956	41.5	51.2	53.9	61.0	72.4	76.8	79.3	80.4	72.0	64.8	50.5	54.3	63.2
1957	45.9	54.7	51.5	64.3	70.8	77.8	79.0	79.5	73.3	58.4	53.7	46.7	63.0
1958	38.9	37.8	49.8	62.4	70.7	77.0	78.8	78.9	74.0	62.0	56.5	42.7	60.8
1959	42.2	47.7	51.2	63.0	72.2	76.6	79.1	80.6	73.3	64.8	51.8	46.3	62.4
#1960	44.2	43.8	41.8	63.7	68.5	76.9	80.3	78.9	74.0	65.7	52.6	40.7	60.9
1961	38.5	49.5	54.7	56.4	65.2	72.7	76.3	75.6	73.0	61.1	55.3	43.5	60.1
1962	41.0	50.1	47.8	57.7	74.1	75.5	78.6	76.6	70.0	62.7	49.1	40.3	60.3
1963	37.2	38.9	56.4	62.9	68.8	74.3	75.8	77.7	70.9	65.1	51.5	35.5	59.6
1964	40.8	40.3	51.2	60.6	68.9	77.8	76.5	76.0	72.6	58.8	55.6	46.5	60.4
1965	43.2	43.9	48.8	63.3	71.8	71.7	76.6	77.3	72.9	60.3	53.8	44.8	60.7
1966	36.6	43.2	50.2	60.6	67.6	73.4	78.2	75.4	70.6	59.4	52.1	43.4	59.2
1967	43.9	41.8	56.7	65.0	66.2	72.5	74.1	74.0	66.5	59.4	48.5	47.7	59.7
1968	39.2	38.3	52.3	60.9	67.4	75.7	77.7	79.0	71.5	61.7	50.1	40.2	59.5
1969	40.2	42.7	46.9	62.8	69.2	77.4	80.8	76.1	70.9	62.5	50.1	41.7	60.1
1970	35.9	43.9	52.9	64.4	70.1	74.6	78.7	79.1	77.0	65.2	49.5	47.4	61.6
1971	42.9	44.3	47.5	60.8	66.7	77.2	76.3	76.7	73.7	66.8	50.7	52.3	61.3
1972	46.8	42.6	52.4	61.3	66.5	72.2	76.8	77.7	74.6	61.1	49.6	48.3	60.8
1973	41.4	42.8	57.4	57.6	65.0	75.6	78.9	77.4	75.6	64.7	55.6	44.2	61.3
1974	53.2	45.8	57.8	61.1	71.0	72.5	77.9	76.7	70.2	61.3	52.4	44.3	62.0
1975	47.2	47.1	50.5	59.8	71.0	75.3	76.4	77.9	70.3	63.3	54.0	43.4	61.4
RECORD MEAN	43.5	45.6	52.6	61.3	69.6	76.4	78.5	77.8	73.1	62.9	52.0	44.7	61.5
MAX	51.8	54.6	62.3	71.3	79.4	85.8	87.4	86.6	82.0	72.3	61.1	52.9	70.6
MIN	35.1	36.6	42.8	51.2	59.7	66.9	69.5	68.9	64.2	53.4	42.8	36.4	52.3

# Indicates a station move or relocation of instruments.

Precipitation

Year	Jan	Feb	Mar	Apr	May	June	July	Aug	Sept	Oct	Nov	Dec	Annual
1936	10.82	8.42	4.22	9.86	0.32	3.17	4.03	5.95	5.44	3.61	2.33	7.98	66.15
1937	8.88	4.52	2.73	8.61	2.32	6.06	2.30	5.50	0.95	6.30	0.85	1.49	50.51
1938	1.86	1.18	5.98	8.27	1.88	7.39	3.88	1.83	3.47	0.20	4.76	2.94	43.64
1939	4.05	9.34	4.48	2.36	3.82	7.52	3.35	5.91	2.62	0.12	0.41	3.10	47.08
1940	5.62	3.83	5.27	2.77	2.03	3.41	8.82	8.16	3.07	0.43	3.29	4.39	51.09
1941	1.42	1.91	4.05	3.12	0.47	4.99	4.99	4.30	1.35	0.57	1.79	6.98	35.94
#1942	3.47	3.84	11.51	1.47	5.29	3.61	4.60	5.53	5.73	3.86	1.38	5.32	55.61
1943	6.09	0.99	8.02	5.70	3.75	6.63	2.70	2.68	2.37	0.47	2.61	2.38	44.39
1944	3.87	7.18	5.93	6.62	1.65	0.74	2.30	1.46	3.45	1.09	2.60	2.61	39.50
1945	2.98	6.17	2.87	8.10	3.92	3.15	7.97	1.33	3.05	4.73	3.24	6.74	54.25
1946	7.20	4.67	7.09	2.98	6.39	6.54	2.26	2.60	2.72	3.02	1.79	1.44	48.70
1947	8.09	2.20	8.09	5.24	4.99	5.83	1.47	5.67	1.35	3.50	9.05	4.21	59.69
#1948	3.47	6.20	10.19	2.82	7.83	1.32	11.26	4.20	3.60	0.73	15.72	4.11	71.45
1949	4.57	4.11	4.32	6.99	1.87	4.80	2.81	6.47	2.91	3.10	0.86	2.80	45.61
1950	2.06	3.02	4.01	1.45	3.73	4.08	7.39	5.51	3.61	2.57	0.81	2.94	41.18
1951	2.25	3.78	4.60	4.88	0.47	4.86	7.41	1.17	5.58	2.78	2.63	8.36	48.77
1952	3.46	4.49	8.61	1.92	3.94	3.11	1.20	7.05	1.61	0.75	2.12	5.93	44.19
1953	5.39	5.95	3.41	6.86	3.58	2.09	4.38	1.67	7.32	0.09	1.35	7.75	49.84
1954	3.73	2.70	3.07	1.91	3.31	2.08	6.31	1.14	0.26	0.17	4.12	3.00	31.80
1955	4.93	3.98	3.27	4.31	2.43	3.53	6.52	1.54	0.96	1.17	2.71	1.08	36.43
1956	1.88	6.57	5.93	5.18	2.60	2.21	7.26	1.10	6.19	2.00	1.55	3.12	45.59
1957	5.35	1.91	4.69	6.04	3.40	3.06	3.16	3.52	5.30	2.69	6.70	3.05	48.87
1958	3.88	5.91	5.19	4.50	4.11	4.09	8.85	3.56	3.14	1.69	2.14	2.58	49.64
1959	3.38	3.61	6.61	2.83	5.35	1.50	3.27	1.42	3.46	7.14	1.35	2.31	42.23
1960	10.16	5.27	5.26	4.59	0.96	1.26	2.25	5.60	4.84	2.57	0.89	2.46	46.11
1961	1.74	12.77	7.33	5.01	3.18	7.38	2.19	4.94	1.68	0.07	2.39	9.92	58.60
1962	5.24	5.09	6.72	5.96	0.38	4.39	5.25	1.21	3.51	1.53	6.19	2.34	47.81
1963	5.10	3.24	5.92	5.85	4.66	6.68	8.12	0.88	5.19	T	3.81	5.86	55.31
1964	6.01	4.17	9.51	8.68	2.59	2.88	7.14	4.10	1.38	5.63	3.11	4.93	60.13
1965	3.74	4.31	5.94	3.10	2.51	7.15	4.59	1.53	3.02	2.35	2.32	1.70	42.26
1966	5.94	7.04	4.02	4.19	5.84	2.95	3.32	3.94	2.15	7.53	4.82	4.60	56.34
1967	4.85	3.75	3.63	2.81	4.95	3.06	6.46	8.69	1.90	2.51	5.52	6.71	54.84
1968	4.07	1.40	4.54	6.33	6.42	2.65	5.34	4.13	1.29	2.99	4.81	4.89	48.86
1969	2.85	3.20	4.00	5.70	7.68	1.00	2.64	6.12	3.74	1.53	2.67	3.27	44.40
1970	2.95	2.99	6.94	3.24	3.01	2.62	3.59	3.26	1.82	6.29	1.86	3.66	42.25
1971	4.40	5.77	8.65	4.09	2.12	3.33	8.22	2.76	3.32	0.31	3.42	2.79	49.18
1972	9.26	3.16	4.49	2.31	4.28	4.04	3.81	2.78	1.86	3.04	3.96	7.62	50.61
1973	8.89	3.44	9.53	4.03	7.14	3.35	2.10	1.35	4.16	0.75	2.31	8.11	55.16
1974	5.36	6.37	2.44	3.72	3.83	3.20	4.64	6.26	1.06	1.22	3.89	5.31	47.30
1975	6.19	8.98	8.31	4.28	4.62	5.52	8.52	3.30	2.99	5.31	4.62	3.36	66.00
RECORD MEAN	4.79	4.73	5.57	4.06	3.58	3.81	4.76	3.99	3.12	2.56	3.14	4.55	48.66

Record mean values above are means through the current year for the period beginning in 1879 for temperature and precipitation, 1935 for snowfall. Data are from City Office locations through 1934 and from Airport locations thereafter.

SAVANNAH, GEORGIA

Station: SAVANNAH, GEORGIA MUNICIPAL AIRPORT   Elevation (ground): 46 feet

TEMPERATURES °F

Month	Normal: Daily maximum	Normal: Daily minimum	Normal: Monthly	Extremes: Record highest	Year	Record lowest	Year
(a)				11		11	
J	61.1	38.7	49.9	83	1975	9	1966
F	63.6	40.5	52.1	84	1966	16	1967
M	69.5	46.4	58.0	91	1974	26	1971
A	77.8	54.3	66.1	95	1967	33	1966
M	84.8	61.8	73.3	98	1967	40	1971
J	89.3	68.8	79.1	102	1971	53	1966
J	90.8	71.3	81.1	99	1968	61	1972
A	90.3	70.9	80.6	100	1968	61	1966
S	85.4	66.9	76.2	97	1972	43	1967
O	78.2	55.9	67.1	93	1971	33	1965
N	69.3	44.9	57.1	85	1973	15	1970
D	62.1	38.7	50.4	83	1971	19	1975
YR	76.8	54.9	65.9	102	JUN 1971	9	JAN 1966

IMPORTANT:
The time-period covered by this record is limited: See footnotes following table of NORMALS, MEANS AND EXTREMES for explanation and for additional history of EXTREME HIGHS AND LOWS recorded in the general area.

Savannah is surrounded by flat terrain, low and marshy to the north and east, rising to several feet above sea level to the west and south. About half the land to the west and south is cleared and the other half in woods, much of the latter lying in swamp.

The area has a temperate climate, with a seasonal mean temperature of 51° F. in winter, 64° F. in spring, 80° F. in summer, and 66° F. in autumn. The growing season averages 273 days, from an average date of last freeze in spring of February 26, to a first in autumn on November 26. Killing frost has occurred as late as April 16 and as early in autumn as October 25. During the history of the station, the lowest recorded was 8° F., and the highest 105° F. Summer temperatures are moderated almost every afternoon by thundershower activity.

Of the normal 51.15 inches of rain, about half falls in the thunderstorm season of June 15 through September 15. The remainder, produced principally by squall-line and frontal showers, is spread over the other 9 months with a minor peak in March. Considerable periods of fair, mild weather are experienced in October, November, April, and to a less extent, in May. Snow is a rarity and even a trace does not occur on an average of once a year. The greatest recorded fall was 3.6 inches in February 1968. Severe tropical storms affect this area about once in 10 years. Rainfall from these storms constitute our heaviest sustained precipitation. Instances of this are the 22.79 inches in August 1898, and 22.88 inches in September 1924, most of which was from tropical storms.

The present exposure of the thermometers gives readings more nearly commensurate with those of suburban street levels of Savannah than was the case of previous locations atop various buildings.

(Continued page 420)

Snowfall

Season	July	Aug	Sept	Oct	Nov	Dec	Jan
1970-71	0.0	0.0	0.0	0.0	0.0	0.0	T
1971-72	0.0	0.0	0.0	0.0	0.0	0.0	0.0
1972-73	0.0	0.0	0.0	0.0	0.0	0.0	T
1973-74	0.0	0.0	0.0	0.0	0.0	0.0	0.0
1974-75	0.0	0.0	0.0	0.0	0.0	0.0	0.0
1975-76	0.0	0.0	0.0	0.0	0.0	0.0	
RECORD MEAN	0.0	0.0	0.0	0.0	0.0	T	T

Heating Degree Days

Season	July	Aug	Sept	Oct	Nov	Dec	Jan
1955-56	0	0	0	87	283	507	568
1956-57	0	0	8	20	302	232	391
1957-58	0	0	3	107	209	442	644
1958-59	0	0	0	84	144	517	537
1959-60	0	0	0	30	261	463	473
1960-61	0	0	0	44	183	607	593
1961-62	0	0	3	66	217	414	502
1962-63	0	0	5	79	317	543	557
1963-64	0	0	1	42	232	653	514
#1964-65	0	0	0	116	157	355	463
1965-66	0	0	0	92	204	454	612
1966-67	0	0	0	50	259	480	413
1967-68	0	0	12	82	269	306	592
1968-69	0	0	0	73	309	533	539
1969-70	0	0	0	38	332	530	698
1970-71	0	0	1	20	303	340	458
1971-72	0	0	0	10	236	187	256
1972-73	0	0	0	25	239	261	462
1973-74	0	0	0	47	148	435	107
1974-75	0	0	2	79	243	368	315
1975-76	0	0	0	25	228	446	

Cooling Degree Days

Year	Jan	Feb	Mar	Apr	May	June	July
1969	0	4	8	86	194	450	539
1970	4	0	26	163	262	403	521
1971	1	13	18	92	210	474	502
1972	28	8	14	130	214	328	505
1973	0	0	63	63	275	434	540
1974	52	9	96	99	302	360	448
1975	20	33	48	104	374	439	423

Feb	Mar	Apr	May	June	Total
0.0	0.0	0.0	0.0	0.0	T
0.0	0.0	0.0	0.0	0.0	0.0
3.2	0.0	0.0	0.0	0.0	3.2
0.0	0.0	0.0	0.0	0.0	0.0
0.0	0.0	0.0	0.0	0.0	0.0
0.3	T	0.0	0.0	0.0	0.3

Average Temperature

Year	Jan	Feb	Mar	Apr	May	June	July	Aug	Sept	Oct	Nov	Dec	Annual
1936	50.5	50.8	62.8	66.2	74.6	80.0	82.8	83.0	80.0	71.7	58.2	53.8	67.9
1937	64.0	53.8	59.0	66.0	74.4	81.4	81.3	81.4	76.8	66.4	57.2	51.0	67.7
1938	52.2	58.2	65.7	67.8	76.8	78.8	80.4	84.4	78.1	67.4	62.3	52.5	68.7
1939	55.8	60.3	63.7	67.4	73.2	82.2	82.8	81.2	80.4	71.0	57.3	54.1	69.1
1940	41.8	51.4	58.2	64.2	72.2	80.6	81.8	81.8	76.7	69.0	61.0	57.3	66.3
1941	52.7	48.1	54.2	69.0	74.5	80.5	82.7	84.0	80.0	75.8	61.8	56.2	68.3
1942	51.6	48.0	60.4	68.1	74.7	81.1	84.7	81.8	78.6	70.3	62.3	52.8	67.9
1943	53.6	54.1	58.9	65.6	75.6	83.0	83.0	83.2	76.4	66.2	58.4	52.8	67.6
1944	52.2	58.9	62.0	66.4	75.8	83.4	80.2	80.8	79.8	68.2	58.1	49.0	67.9
#1945	51.8	57.8	68.4	70.2	72.2	81.8	81.1	80.4	80.1	67.3	60.0	47.4	68.2
1946	53.4	55.1	63.7	67.8	74.0	78.4	81.2	80.2	76.0	68.4	64.4	55.7	68.2
1947	57.9	47.0	52.2	69.2	73.6	78.3	79.6	80.7	77.4	70.8	57.4	52.2	66.4
1948	46.2	54.0	62.0	68.6	74.7	81.0	81.6	80.2	76.0	64.0	64.6	56.8	67.5
1949	59.9	60.2	59.2	66.0	73.6	79.0	81.7	81.3	76.0	72.6	56.4	54.9	68.4
#1950	62.6	57.5	56.7	62.8	75.1	81.1	79.9	80.0	76.1	69.2	53.9	46.0	66.7
1951	50.6	52.3	58.9	64.4	72.3	80.2	81.2	82.3	77.0	70.1	54.1	55.7	66.6
1952	56.8	53.9	59.4	64.0	74.7	83.6	82.1	80.6	75.4	63.3	57.3	48.8	66.7
1953	53.4	54.0	62.0	64.2	78.5	78.7	80.9	79.5	75.2	67.1	55.5	51.4	66.7
1954	53.1	55.3	57.6	68.7	68.9	80.1	82.4	83.8	77.8	66.0	54.1	48.4	66.3
1955	47.8	53.3	61.7	67.6	74.9	75.7	80.1	81.2	76.7	65.8	56.1	46.6	65.8
1956	46.5	58.6	57.8	64.7	74.2	77.9	81.0	81.2	73.9	56.8	55.6	58.5	66.5
1957	52.9	59.0	57.3	65.8	72.8	78.8	79.3	80.0	77.3	63.1	59.0	50.6	66.3
1958	43.9	44.2	54.0	65.9	72.4	78.9	81.9	81.0	77.7	63.9	61.2	48.1	64.4
1959	47.5	55.5	56.7	66.7	75.4	78.7	80.4	80.5	76.4	70.3	57.2	49.8	66.2
1960	49.6	49.6	47.8	66.5	72.3	78.2	81.2	80.6	76.4	69.3	59.3	45.2	64.7
1961	45.6	54.7	63.2	61.4	71.3	77.5	81.8	79.1	77.1	65.2	60.6	52.1	65.8
1962	49.0	57.8	55.0	63.3	77.0	77.6	81.9	80.2	75.3	68.3	54.4	47.2	65.6
1963	46.8	47.1	61.2	66.9	72.6	79.1	80.1	81.7	74.3	66.7	57.3	43.7	64.8
#1964	48.2	47.8	58.4	66.8	73.2	81.4	79.1	79.6	74.7	63.1	60.1	53.7	65.5
1965	49.9	52.4	56.8	66.4	74.8	76.4	79.8	80.6	76.7	66.2	58.0	50.1	65.7
1966	44.9	51.2	55.6	64.7	71.6	74.6	80.9	79.6	76.4	67.3	57.1	49.5	64.4
1967	51.4	49.6	61.7	69.0	73.2	77.2	79.9	79.4	71.6	64.4	56.4	55.3	65.7
1968	45.7	44.6	57.0	68.0	72.5	79.1	81.6	82.1	76.5	68.7	54.8	47.6	64.8
1969	47.4	47.1	52.4	66.1	71.0	79.7	82.2	78.9	75.4	69.9	53.9	47.7	64.3
1970	42.4	49.2	59.2	68.3	73.0	78.2	81.6	81.8	78.9	70.2	54.8	54.1	66.0
1971	50.1	52.4	54.5	64.6	71.1	80.5	80.9	80.8	78.6	72.4	58.0	60.6	67.0
1972	57.5	51.3	59.3	66.7	71.6	75.7	81.0	81.0	77.3	68.1	58.1	57.1	67.1
1973	49.8	49.6	63.6	64.0	73.5	79.3	82.2	80.0	79.0	68.9	61.6	51.2	66.9
1974	62.9	53.0	63.8	65.6	74.5	76.8	79.2	79.6	76.3	64.6	57.7	53.1	67.3
1975	55.3	57.7	59.5	65.4	76.7	79.5	78.4	81.7	76.5	70.0	59.3	50.5	67.5
RECORD MEAN	51.8	53.5	59.4	66.2	73.6	79.3	81.4	80.9	77.0	67.9	58.6	52.4	66.8
MAX	61.2	63.0	69.1	75.9	82.9	88.2	90.0	89.2	85.0	77.0	68.5	62.0	76.0
MIN	42.4	43.9	49.6	56.4	64.2	70.4	72.8	72.6	68.9	58.8	48.7	42.8	57.6

# Indicates a station move or relocation of instruments.

SAVANNAH, GA

Feb	Mar	Apr	May	June	Total
205	253	97	1	0	2001
193	254	65	20	0	1485
584	333	73	14	0	2409
285	257	60	0	0	1884
441	535	58	15	0	2276
295	119	143	7	4	1995
223	316	122	0	0	1863
494	168	44	21	0	2228
493	221	50	4	0	2210
359	282	66	0	0	1798
387	294	88	11	0	2142
428	159	26	12	1	1828
582	270	34	3	0	2150
498	395	48	3	0	2398
437	199	57	8	0	2299
359	338	100	15	0	1934
400	183	74	1	0	1347
423	98	85	4	0	1597
340	124	73	1	0	1275
232	212	86	0	0	1537

Aug	Sept	Oct	Nov	Dec	Total
438	320	199	8	1	2247
528	423	188	4	9	2531
495	414	248	34	56	2557
503	379	125	38	23	2295
473	429	177	52	13	2519
462	347	74	32	8	2289
528	351	187	65	2	2574

Precipitation

Year	Jan	Feb	Mar	Apr	May	June	July	Aug	Sept	Oct	Nov	Dec	Annual
1936	3.27	3.74	3.67	1.67	1.85	3.57	6.68	3.23	5.05	2.43	1.25	3.34	39.75
1937	1.84	4.38	2.50	4.15	1.97	7.83	8.91	7.33	4.73	3.76	2.98	1.09	51.47
1938	0.68	0.54	1.25	2.30	6.21	4.57	3.84	1.81	4.25	1.67	1.09	1.60	29.81
1939	1.17	5.81	1.58	1.90	2.22	6.00	5.50	5.37	2.90	1.10	0.67	1.74	35.96
1940	3.31	4.67	2.65	1.39	0.92	4.35	5.43	6.84	1.31	0.35	1.12	4.20	36.54
1941	0.53	2.04	2.54	1.89	0.43	12.28	10.83	4.43	1.26	2.36	1.82	4.89	45.30
1942	3.41	3.44	5.67	0.28	1.71	5.21	9.09	2.48	2.37	0.46	1.08	3.49	38.69
1943	2.63	0.69	4.73	2.03	2.33	3.89	13.19	5.66	0.76	0.06	0.81	4.05	40.83
1944	3.23	4.37	9.96	3.27	1.11	3.64	7.14	13.60	4.56	7.96	1.67	0.50	61.01
#1945	1.88	2.81	0.76	3.91	2.06	5.35	9.92	5.79	15.72	1.72	0.57	5.42	55.91
1946	2.00	1.27	3.69	1.96	5.92	4.47	9.31	5.00	1.65	5.10	2.28	0.49	43.14
1947	1.25	0.56	6.17	4.29	2.28	11.74	4.60	4.68	14.00	4.65	5.51	7.52	67.25
1948	4.49	1.17	9.70	5.32	5.77	2.69	11.33	6.76	6.45	2.54	4.45	3.67	64.34
1949	0.48	3.79	0.92	2.96	2.73	7.60	1.33	11.20	6.67	1.23	0.45	1.80	41.16
#1950	0.48	0.52	4.96	3.36	4.67	3.71	6.71	6.01	17.30	4.83	0.87	2.52	55.94
1951	0.85	1.16	4.58	1.90	0.74	3.04	10.17	9.69	6.06	3.47	3.25	3.75	48.66
1952	1.33	3.30	3.90	2.00	7.68	4.36	1.92	6.87	1.77	2.11	1.31	1.92	38.47
1953	2.19	4.54	3.68	3.71	0.51	5.38	7.56	6.87	13.47	0.27	1.57	5.50	55.25
1954	1.10	1.41	1.42	2.40	4.45	0.84	3.73	1.33	6.56	4.06	2.15	3.38	32.83
1955	5.95	1.53	0.18	4.16	1.88	6.57	7.25	2.86	5.61	1.18	0.95	0.40	38.52
1956	1.66	2.96	1.76	3.62	4.30	9.01	5.86	4.21	5.71	2.90	0.28	0.89	43.16
1957	0.51	2.18	4.66	2.96	10.08	5.60	13.93	5.82	10.15	1.77	4.57	1.73	63.96
1958	3.17	2.78	5.99	6.44	4.19	5.56	6.52	6.19	3.02	1.71	0.59	1.85	48.01
1959	3.39	5.17	9.57	2.27	7.53	3.07	5.86	11.39	8.37	8.54	1.38	1.46	68.00
1960	3.13	6.59	2.69	3.68	4.01	5.51	15.70	2.94	5.84	1.44	0.42	1.78	53.73
1961	2.15	3.76	4.69	7.74	3.50	3.74	4.08	12.80	2.61	0.09	0.99	2.85	49.00
1962	5.11	1.73	5.90	3.02	1.36	10.19	8.05	7.69	6.56	0.92	1.85	1.70	54.08
1963	3.32	5.06	1.68	4.55	3.85	14.39	7.94	2.36	3.61	0.02	2.28	1.77	50.83
1964	6.29	7.92	2.71	2.64	4.66	2.55	20.10	8.37	3.93	6.94	2.90	4.16	73.17
1965	0.83	4.34	7.75	1.39	2.62	5.63	7.46	4.56	4.82	1.33	2.09	2.99	45.81
1966	6.05	3.66	3.79	1.88	6.73	6.61	7.89	3.73	1.78	1.19	0.15	1.93	45.39
1967	7.18	2.80	0.50	1.38	2.94	4.38	6.23	8.57	2.12	1.36	0.84	2.97	41.27
1968	1.79	1.16	0.89	2.09	4.80	5.86	6.35	3.83	0.48	3.53	2.59	3.97	37.34
1969	1.77	1.59	5.11	0.71	8.74	9.99	7.57	10.33	3.74	4.04	3.82	3.43	60.84
1970	3.11	2.32	8.51	0.95	5.41	5.21	5.76	10.61	5.88	2.29	0.42	3.37	53.84
1971	3.40	2.60	2.63	3.53	3.56	6.98	9.07	14.94	1.67	8.01	1.26	3.69	61.34
1972	3.99	4.61	3.84	1.20	5.84	6.54	1.35	12.62	0.36	0.54	4.91	2.77	48.57
1973	3.61	4.46	5.36	4.43	1.23	9.19	2.89	6.45	3.65	0.19	0.68	3.26	45.40
1974	1.37	2.79	1.87	2.75	7.25	6.00	6.48	7.90	2.61	0.10	0.96	1.85	41.93
1975	3.17	3.01	3.99	4.71	6.00	2.08	11.55	3.13	8.01	1.25	1.09	3.19	51.18
RECORD MEAN	2.77	3.19	3.54	2.84	3.37	5.61	6.84	7.09	5.61	2.80	1.94	2.79	48.39

Record mean values above are means through the current year for the period beginning in 1874 for temperature, 1871 for precipitation, and 1951 for snowfall. Data are from City Office locations through April 1945 and from Airport locations thereafter.

(Continued)

Then, especially on still, clear radiation nights, temperatures near the ground and in lower inland places were as much as 15° lower than official minima. Present differences on comparable nights range from 3° to 8°. The extreme minima for the winter months are considered representative of the area, because they occurred at times with considerable wind. Extreme maxima also are representative of the area.

Sunshine is adequate at all seasons and seldom are there two or more days in succession without it. Sea-and land-breeze effect is usually not felt in Savannah, though it is a daily feature on the nearby islands. Dry, continental airmasses reach this area in summer mostly by sliding down the Atlantic coast and giving cooler northeast winds. Such masses reaching this area from the northwest or west in summer bring mostly clear skies and our highest temperatures.

Normals, Means, and Extremes

Month	Normal Degree days Base 65 °F		Precipitation in inches												Relative humidity pct.			
			Water equivalent							Snow, Ice pellets					Hour 01	Hour 07	Hour 13	Hour 19
	Heating	Cooling	Normal	Maximum monthly	Year	Minimum monthly	Year	Maximum in 24 hrs.	Year	Maximum monthly	Year	Maximum in 24 hrs.	Year	(Local time)				
(a)				25		25		25		25		25		11	11	11	11	
J	483	15	2.92	7.18	1967	0.51	1957	2.80	1967	T	1973	T	1973	82	85	57	70	
F	379	19	2.86	7.92	1964	1.16	1968	3.46	1964	3.6	1968	3.6	1968	77	82	51	62	
M	256	38	4.41	9.57	1959	0.18	1955	4.65	1959	T	1968	T	1968	79	83	47	60	
A	63	96	2.93	7.74	1961	0.71	1969	3.66	1961	0.0		0.0		81	85	47	60	
M	0	260	4.20	10.08	1957	0.51	1953	4.23	1969	0.0		0.0		85	86	52	66	
J	0	423	5.89	14.39	1963	0.84	1954	4.06	1963	0.0		0.0		88	88	57	70	
J	0	499	7.87	20.10	1964	1.35	1972	6.36	1957	0.0		0.0		89	90	61	74	
A	0	484	6.47	14.94	1971	1.33	1954	7.04	1971	0.0		0.0		91	92	63	78	
S	0	336	5.57	13.47	1953	0.36	1972	5.87	1954	0.0		0.0		89	91	61	77	
O	60	125	2.81	8.54	1959	0.02	1963	3.57	1959	0.0		0.0		86	88	53	75	
N	253	16	1.94	4.91	1972	0.15	1966	5.02	1969	0.0		0.0		84	87	49	72	
D	458	6	3.28	5.50	1953	0.40	1955	3.47	1964	T	1962	T	1962	83	85	54	72	
YR	1952	2317	51.15	20.10	JUL 1964	0.02	OCT 1963	7.04	AUG 1971	3.6	FEB 1968	3.6	FEB 1968	85	87	54	70	

(To better understand these tables, see full explanation of terms beginning on page 322)

Month	Wind					Pct. of possible sunshine	Mean sky cover, tenths, sunrise to sunset	Mean number of days												Average station pressure mb.
			Fastest mile					Sunrise to sunset							Temperatures °F					
															Max.		Min.			
	Mean speed m.p.h.	Prevailing direction	Speed m.p.h.	Direction	Year			Clear	Partly cloudy	Cloudy	Precipitation .01 inch or more	Snow, Ice pellets 1.0 inch or more	Thunderstorms	Heavy fog, visibility ¼ mile or less	(b) 90° and above	32° and below	32° and below	0° and below	Elev. 51 feet m.s.l.
(a)	25	13	25	25		25	25	25	25	25	25	25	25	25	11	11	11	11	3
J	8.6	WNW	46	NW	1955	53	6.2	9	7	15	9	0	1	5	0	*	10	0	1019.8
F	9.5	NE	44	WNW	1960	57	6.0	9	6	13	9	*	1	3	0	0	9	0	1017.6
M	9.6	WNW	40	W	1973	64	5.9	9	9	13	10	0	3	3	*	0	3	0	1015.7
A	9.2	SSE	40	N	1963	70	5.5	10	9	11	7	0	4	2	1	0	0	0	1016.7
M	8.1	SW	42	N	1965	68	5.7	9	11	11	9	0	8	3	4	0	0	0	1013.5
J	7.7	SW	66	E	1953	65	6.1	7	11	12	11	0	10	3	11	0	0	0	1014.7
J	7.3	SW	51	SE	1951	63	6.5	5	14	12	15	0	16	1	18	0	0	0	1015.6
A	6.9	SW	58	N	1954	63	6.2	6	14	11	13	0	13	2	15	0	0	0	1016.9
S	7.7	NE	56	NW	1959	59	6.3	6	11	13	10	0	6	4	5	0	0	0	1015.6
O	7.7	NNE	37	NE	1952	64	5.0	12	9	10	6	0	1	4	1	0	0	0	1018.6
N	7.8	NNE	34	W	1957	63	5.1	12	7	11	6	0	*	5	0	0	4	0	1019.5
D	8.2	NE	37	NW	1962	55	5.9	9	8	14	8	0	*	4	0	0	9	0	1018.9
YR	8.2	SW	66	E	JUN 1953	62	5.9	103	116	146	112	*	64	40	56	*	35	0	1016.9

FOOTNOTES

Means and extremes above are from existing and comparable exposures. Annual extremes have been exceeded at other sites in the locality as follows: Highest temperature 105 in July 1879; lowest temperature 8 in February 1899; maximum monthly precipitation 22.88 in September 1924; minimum monthly precipitation T in December 1889; maximum precipitation in 24 hours 11.44 in September 1928; fastest mile wind 90 in August 1940.

Station: HILO, HAWAII
GENERAL LYMAN FIELD
Elevation (ground): 27 feet

TEMPERATURES °F

Month	Normal: Daily maximum	Normal: Daily minimum	Normal: Monthly	Extremes: Record highest	Year	Extremes: Record lowest	Year
(a)				29		29	
J	79.6	62.8	71.2	89	1967	54	1969
F	79.4	62.6	71.0	92	1968	53	1962
M	78.8	63.3	71.1	93	1972	54	1971
A	79.8	64.6	72.2	89	1963	56	1949
M	81.3	65.6	73.5	94	1966	58	1947
J	82.7	66.5	74.6	90	1969	60	1946
J	83.0	67.5	75.3	88	1974	62	1970
A	83.5	68.2	75.9	93	1950	63	1955
S	83.6	67.6	75.6	92	1951	61	1970
O	83.2	66.7	75.0	91	1972	62	1970
N	81.3	65.6	73.5	88	1965	58	1948
D	79.4	63.7	71.6	90	1964	56	1947
YR	81.3	65.4	73.4	94	MAY 1966	53	FEB 1962

IMPORTANT:
The time-period covered by this record is limited: See footnotes on next page for explanation and for additional history of EXTREME HIGHS AND LOWS recorded in the general area.

The city of Hilo is located near the midpoint of the eastern shore of the Island of Hawaii. This island is by far the largest of the Hawaiian group, with an area of 4,038 square miles, more than twice that of all the other islands combined. Its topography is dominated by the great volcanic masses of Mauna Loa and Mauna Kea, both of which exceed 13,600 feet in elevation, and of Hualalai (8,271 feet), the Kohala Mountains (5,480 feet), and Kilauea (4,090 feet). In fact the island consists entirely of the slopes of these mountains and of the broad saddles between them.

Hawaii is diamond-shaped, about 93 miles long, from north to south, and 76 miles wide. Its highest point is the summit of Mauna Kea at 13,796 feet. Mauna Loa and Kilauea, which occupy the southern half of the island, are still active volcanoes and hence smooth-sloped, in contrast to the deeply eroded valleys that indent portions of Mauna Kea and the Kohala Mountains.

Hawaii lies well within the belt of northeasterly trade winds generated by the semi-permanent Pacific high pressure cell to the north and east. The climate of the island is greatly influenced by terrain. Its outstanding features are the marked variations in rainfall with elevation and from place to place, the persistent northeasterly trade winds in areas exposed to them, and the equable temperatures from day to day and season to season in localities near sea level.

Over the island's windward slopes, rainfall occurs principally in the form of showers within the ascending moist trade winds. Mean annual rainfall, except for the semi-sheltered Hamakua district increases from 100 inches or more along the coasts to a maximum of over 300 inches at elevations of 2,000 to 3,000 feet, and then declines to about 15 inches at the summits of Mauna Kea and Mauna Loa. In general, leeward (southern and western) areas are topographically sheltered from the trades -- hence from trade-wind showers -- and are therefore drier; although sea breezes created by daytime heating of the land move onshore and upslope, causing afternoon and evening cloudiness and showers. Where mountain slopes are steeper, mean annual rainfall may range from 30 inches along the coast to 120 inches at elevations of 2,500 to 3,000 feet. The driest locality on the island -- and in the State -- with an average annual rainfall of less than 10 inches, is the coastal strip just leeward of the southern portion of the Kohala Mountains and of the saddle between the Kohalas and Mauna Kea.

These marked contrasts in rainfall are reflected in soil and vegetation, with frequent abrupt transitions from lush tropical growth to near-desert conditions, such as occurs between Kilauea's wet windward slopes and the Kau Desert just to the south.

Within the city of Hilo itself, average rainfall varies from about 130 inches a year near the shore to as much as 200 inches in mountain sections. The wettest part of the island, with a mean annual rainfall exceeding 300 inches, lies about 6 miles upslope from the city limits. Rain falls on about 280 days a year in the Hilo area.

Hawaii's equable temperatures are associated with its mid-ocean location and the small seasonal variation in the amount of energy received from the sun. At Hilo, the range in average temperature from February and

(Continued page 424)

HILO, HAWAII

Normals, Means, and Extremes

(To better understand these tables, see full explanation of terms beginning on page 322)

Month	Normal Degree days Base 65 °F: Heating	Normal Degree days Base 65 °F: Cooling	Precipitation, Water equivalent: Normal	Water equivalent: Maximum monthly	Year	Water equivalent: Minimum monthly	Year	Water equivalent: Maximum in 24 hrs.	Year	Snow, Ice pellets: Maximum monthly	Year	Snow, Ice pellets: Maximum in 24 hrs.	Year	Relative humidity pct. Hour 02 (Local time)	Hour 08	Hour 14	Hour 20	Wind: Mean speed m.p.h.	Wind: Prevailing direction	Fastest mile: Speed m.p.h.	Fastest mile: Direction	Fastest mile: Year	Pct. of possible sunshine	Mean sky cover, tenths, sunrise to sunset	Mean number of days, Sunrise to sunset: Clear	Partly cloudy	Cloudy	Precipitation .01 inch or more	Snow, Ice pellets 1.0 inch or more	Thunderstorms	Heavy fog, visibility ¼ mile or less	Temperatures °F Max. (b) 90° and above	Max. 32° and below	Min. 32° and below	Min. 0° and below	Average station pressure mb. Elev. 36 feet m.s.l.
(a)				33		33		33		33		33		26	26	26	26	26	14	9	9		25	29	29	29	29	33	33	30	30	30	30	30	30	3
J	0	192	9.07	29.11	1949	0.36	1953	9.94	1949	0.0		0.0		84	80	67	83	7.5	SW	30	SE	1968	44	6.7	5	12	14	18	0	1	0	0	0	0	0	1014.1
F	0	176	12.90	43.66	1969	1.70	1963	15.70	1969	0.0		0.0		85	80	67	82	7.9	SW	26	SE	1975	42	6.9	4	10	14	18	0	1	0	*	0	0	0	1016.7
M	0	185	13.69	31.91	1948	0.88	1972	9.18	1953	0.0		0.0		87	81	67	83	7.7	SW	29	SE	1972	38	7.7	2	10	19	24	0	2	0	*	0	0	0	1017.6
A	0	216	12.88	31.94	1963	2.93	1962	11.07	1971	0.0		0.0		88	82	69	84	7.5	WSW	23	SE	1968	33	8.2	1	8	21	25	0	1	0	0	0	0	0	1017.2
M	0	264	10.07	25.01	1964	1.18	1945	10.26	1965	0.0		0.0		88	80	68	83	7.3	WSW	22	E	1969	34	8.0	1	10	20	25	0	1	0	*	0	0	0	1017.0
J	0	288	6.61	15.50	1943	2.68	1949	2.83	1963	0.0		0.0		87	78	65	82	7.2	WSW	21	E	1968	41	7.6	2	10	18	24	0	*	0	*	0	0	0	1016.8
J	0	319	9.54	14.89	1958	3.83	1975	5.42	1951	0.0		0.0		88	81	67	82	6.9	WSW	26	SE	1974	41	7.7	1	12	18	27	0	*	0	0	0	0	0	1016.5
A	0	338	10.88	26.42	1957	2.66	1971	9.65	1970	0.0		0.0		88	81	68	83	6.9	WSW	25	NW	1972	40	7.6	1	11	19	27	0	*	0	*	0	0	0	1015.8
S	0	318	7.44	13.63	1947	1.59	1974	6.02	1960	0.0		0.0		87	79	67	83	6.8	WSW	20	E	1972	41	7.1	3	12	15	23	0	*	0	*	0	0	0	1015.3
O	0	310	10.96	26.10	1951	2.40	1962	8.88	1951	0.0		0.0		87	80	68	85	6.7	SW	24	SE	1972	39	7.2	3	12	16	24	0	1	0	*	0	0	0	1015.6
N	0	255	13.77	27.03	1959	3.74	1943	15.59	1959	0.0		0.0		87	82	70	86	6.8	WSW	22	SE	1975	33	7.4	3	10	17	24	0	1	0	0	0	0	0	1014.7
D	0	205	15.76	50.82	1954	0.77	1963	10.50	1946	0.0		0.0		86	82	70	85	7.3	SW	30	NW	1973	35	7.1	4	11	16	22	0	1	0	*	0	0	0	1015.7
YR	0	3066	133.57	50.82	DEC 1954	0.36	JAN 1953	15.70	FEB 1969	0.0		0.0		87	81	68	83	7.2	WSW	30	NW	DEC 1973	39	7.4	30	128	207	282	0	9	0	1	0	0	0	1016.1

FOOTNOTES Means and extremes above are from existing and comparable exposures. Annual extremes have been exceeded at other sites in the locality as follows: Lowest temperature 51 in May 1910; maximum monthly precipitation 66.96 in March 1922; minimum monthly precipitation 0.14 in January 1953; maximum precipitation in 24 hours 19.20 in March 1922; highest wind (fastest observed 1-minute speed) for period 1954-1966 was 46 from 70° in February 1963.

Snowfall

Season	July	Aug	Sept	Oct	Nov	Dec	Jan

Heating Degree Days

Season	July	Aug	Sept	Oct	Nov	Dec	Jan

Cooling Degree Days

Year	Jan	Feb	Mar	Apr	May	June	July
1969	207	209	240	239	298	341	344
1970	223	173	195	229	273	270	290
1971	203	201	142	185	232	306	366
1972	163	171	281	236	256	316	330
1973	233	180	239	222	253	294	341
1974	299	219	261	263	276	315	351
1975	192	201	197	232	257	288	311

Feb	Mar	Apr	May	June	Total

Average Temperature

Year	Jan	Feb	Mar	Apr	May	June	July	Aug	Sept	Oct	Nov	Dec	Annual
1936	72.2	72.6	71.0	72.7	72.4	75.0	75.4	75.6	75.7	76.2	73.2	70.6	73.6
1937	69.8	70.3	70.0	72.4	74.3	76.0	75.8	76.8	76.6	76.5	74.6	73.6	73.9
1938	73.0	74.2	72.6	72.6	73.4	75.8	76.2	77.0	76.1	76.2	73.6	71.8	74.4
1939	71.0	73.4		72.2	73.0	73.0	74.2	75.2	74.6	74.3	71.8	71.6	
1940	72.2	71.4	72.1	73.9	75.2	75.4	76.0	76.4	76.2	76.3	74.2	72.4	74.2
1941	72.1	70.9	70.0	71.3	72.1	74.6	75.2	77.2	75.9	75.2	73.4	70.1	73.2
1942	70.6	70.6	68.2	69.6	73.0	74.2	75.7	76.0	75.8	74.6	75.0	73.9	73.2
1943	71.4	70.0	70.0	72.0	74.4	74.3		75.2	75.4	74.8	72.8	72.4	
1944	71.4	70.4	72.6	72.7	73.0	73.5	74.4	74.3	74.2	73.7	72.4	71.2	72.8
1945	72.1	72.0	71.4	73.7	75.2	75.6	75.6	75.8	75.4	74.4	73.4	72.0	73.9
#1946	71.1	71.8	71.3	70.9	72.9	74.5	75.0	75.7	75.9	75.0	73.1	70.7	73.2
#1947	69.5	71.0	70.5	71.9	72.5	73.9	74.0	74.5	75.1	74.4	72.7	70.5	72.5
1948	69.5	70.3	70.0	72.3	73.0	74.1	74.9	75.8	75.0	74.0	72.0	69.6	72.5
#1949	69.2	69.6	68.6	69.3	71.8	73.3	73.4	74.2	73.8	73.3	70.7	70.5	71.5
1950	72.1	71.8	71.8	70.9	72.3	73.3	74.3	75.8	75.2	74.3	73.7	70.8	73.0
1951	70.8	70.1	71.8	71.5	73.2	74.8	75.8	75.5	76.1	74.8	72.4	70.9	73.2
1952	69.9	70.5	69.9	70.1	71.4	72.8	73.8	74.3	74.0	74.7	73.0	70.8	72.1
1953	71.3	69.9	69.8	71.3	72.6	73.7	74.6	75.3	74.9	73.7	71.9	70.6	72.5
#1954	70.6	70.6	69.8	72.7	72.8	74.8	75.0	76.3	75.5	74.7	73.9	69.5	73.0
1955	69.3	68.8	69.2	70.6	71.5	72.2	72.5	73.5	73.1	72.7	72.1	71.2	71.4
1956	72.0	69.4	70.9	71.9	72.1	73.5	74.5	75.2	74.6	74.1	72.6	71.8	72.7
1957	70.7	68.9	69.9	71.0	72.5	75.0	75.4	75.9	76.5	75.8	73.7	71.6	73.0
1958	70.9	70.6	69.9	71.6	72.2	74.2	75.5	76.7	75.6	74.7	73.2	70.8	73.0
1959	71.9	70.8	71.5	72.5	73.4	75.1	75.8	76.6	75.1	74.9	73.1	70.7	73.5
1960	69.1	70.2	71.1	72.0	73.4	74.6	75.7	75.6	75.7	75.3	72.4	71.6	73.1
1961	71.7	71.7	71.9	72.5	73.7	74.9	75.2	76.1	75.4	75.6	73.4	70.7	73.6
1962	72.1	70.7	70.7	73.2	73.0	74.3	74.3	75.6	74.6	74.5	72.6	70.8	73.0
1963	71.1	72.9	72.0	73.6	73.3	74.5	75.4	75.7	76.0	75.0	73.7	73.1	73.9
1964	72.1	70.2	70.8	71.7	72.0	75.0	75.2	75.4	75.0	73.7	72.7	73.2	73.1
1965	71.7	68.4	69.7	72.4	74.5	74.1	75.2	75.8	76.8	75.4	73.7	69.9	73.1
1966	69.7	69.9	71.6	71.8	75.0	75.1	76.6	77.1	77.4	77.0	75.6	74.3	74.3
1967	71.9	73.9	74.1	74.3	77.1	77.5	77.8	77.1	77.0	77.2	75.4	73.3	75.6
1968	72.9	74.9	74.5	73.8	75.7	76.6	76.8	76.5	76.8	77.1	76.2	73.7	75.5
1969	71.4	72.2	72.5	72.8	74.5	76.2	75.8	76.2	75.0	74.5	73.3	71.5	73.8
1970	72.0	71.1	71.1	72.4	73.7	73.7	74.2	74.9	74.8	75.3	73.9	72.7	73.3
1971	71.3	71.9	69.4	70.9	72.2	75.0	76.6	76.6	76.6	75.4	73.8	70.9	73.4
1972	70.1	70.7	73.8	72.7	73.0	75.3	75.4	76.5	76.4	76.0	73.3	71.4	73.7
1973	72.2	71.1	72.5	72.2	72.9	74.6	75.7	76.3	76.3	75.8	75.4	73.8	74.1
1974	74.5	72.6	73.1	73.5	73.8	75.3	76.1	76.9	77.3	76.9	73.6	72.3	74.6
1975	71.0	71.9	71.2	72.4	73.1	74.4	74.8	75.7	75.5	74.7	73.5	72.2	73.4
RECORD MEAN	71.1	70.9	71.1	72.1	73.2	74.5	75.2	75.8	75.6	75.0	73.4	71.6	73.3
MAX	79.0	78.8	78.7	79.3	80.6	82.2	82.5	83.1	83.3	82.8	80.6	78.9	80.8
MIN	63.2	63.0	63.5	64.8	65.7	66.8	67.8	68.4	67.8	67.2	66.1	64.2	65.7

# Indicates a station move or relocation of instruments.

HILO, HI

Feb	Mar	Apr	May	June	Total

Precipitation

Year	Jan	Feb	Mar	Apr	May	June	July	Aug	Sept	Oct	Nov	Dec	Annual
1936	5.39	2.37	18.43	12.31	14.18	5.80	13.09	28.57	20.19	14.83	6.05	39.68	180.89
1937	28.52	14.00	30.48	13.20	14.51	5.44	15.20	18.81	8.49	8.70	17.08	11.85	186.28
1938	24.38	12.03	28.12	35.04	17.67	7.52	7.84	8.45	7.49	6.76	16.33	16.89	188.52
1939	22.14	18.65	40.29	20.91	5.49	10.03	13.38	6.67	5.29	9.64	12.60	3.02	168.11
1940	0.78	3.27	3.79	3.99	5.49	6.25	11.38	23.46	12.51	14.95	12.81	3.03	101.71
1941	6.41	0.73	9.76	4.23	18.37	9.67	8.85	15.44	18.02	28.54	10.37	13.47	143.86
#1942	1.61	5.43	46.25	19.60	7.72	7.01	4.93	10.39	8.49	9.21	5.63	12.72	138.99
1943	12.22	10.00	8.95	7.71	7.00	15.50	12.72	8.46	6.37	3.00	3.74	11.04	106.71
1944	4.44	21.88	2.97	12.37	10.71	6.04	14.75	9.96	8.34	11.20	15.81	18.47	136.94
1945	2.98	6.30	21.36	12.29	1.18	9.08	4.57	14.96	4.96	7.38	12.72	16.87	114.65
1946	21.83	10.21	13.27	13.13	3.60	5.42	13.78	5.69	4.63	9.10	4.82	42.08	147.56
#1947	4.80	3.25	16.88	8.93	9.05	5.63	11.15	11.13	13.63	15.29	19.70	21.49	140.93
1948	5.72	11.26	31.91	11.03	11.12	4.68	5.80	7.50	7.61	15.10	20.78	19.33	151.84
#1949	29.11	8.51	10.14	6.08	2.71	2.68	8.33	5.73	4.90	9.09	11.66	14.11	113.05
1950	9.16	18.19	6.97	30.34	15.90	5.03	8.96	5.35	6.01	7.17	10.17	15.90	139.15
1951	9.33	26.12	16.42	4.38	3.76	3.46	11.97	10.21	2.45	26.10	14.89	20.97	150.06
1952	14.54	7.76	21.24	11.39	6.57	9.71	6.52	6.88	5.86	9.61	13.54	7.03	120.65
1953	0.36	13.01	21.83	4.15	10.97	5.62	4.25	5.39	3.63	4.41	7.57	8.49	89.68
#1954	5.73	15.87	13.37	3.07	9.72	6.33	11.28	13.62	8.22	8.26	16.04	50.82	162.33
1955	12.17	20.52	9.16	16.80	10.69	4.80	11.13	8.03	3.99	5.64	15.62	4.90	123.45
1956	7.95	39.32	15.08	6.04	14.45	9.78	5.74	18.40	4.03	14.44	22.76	10.37	168.36
1957	8.80	8.95	3.90	17.50	6.32	4.74	13.27	26.42	4.20	13.23	12.30	19.71	139.34
1958	2.91	5.41	5.04	4.99	7.84	6.53	14.89	16.56	7.41	14.64	16.87	2.86	105.95
1959	8.44	13.09	7.83	8.06	6.70	3.12	5.57	7.48	7.27	9.26	27.03	13.97	117.82
1960	25.95	15.97	7.13	15.04	11.70	6.73	9.68	12.86	12.00	10.69	14.93	4.12	146.80
1961	2.34	20.50	5.75	5.52	8.12	5.78	5.47	7.63	6.76	22.95	12.84	16.04	119.70
1962	2.51	5.31	10.88	2.93	13.58	3.25	8.01	4.15	9.49	2.40	6.63	2.31	71.45
1963	1.14	1.70	15.85	31.94	12.60	10.91	12.40	7.66	10.18	11.36	8.24	0.77	124.75
1964	14.65	18.22	19.58	11.03	25.01	7.01	6.39	7.33	12.62	11.56	23.39	9.65	166.44
1965	9.28	3.71	8.33	18.49	21.05	8.85	7.15	4.79	5.72	5.80	19.18	14.94	127.29
1966	12.56	7.63	5.59	5.24	5.04	7.49	13.26	7.22	8.37	15.69	20.83	15.09	124.01
1967	8.04	10.35	9.46	21.26	9.84	6.26	14.03	19.55	6.78	10.08	21.25	17.10	154.00
1968	4.77	11.46	10.21	29.68	2.71	8.72	7.43	9.62	8.53	5.97	10.22	24.82	134.14
1969	19.66	43.66	30.64	14.57	7.83	2.76	11.75	17.50	7.24	3.19	6.33	8.10	173.23
1970	2.76	2.56	4.89	28.60	20.26	5.60	12.27	20.53	5.61	8.44	7.21	35.25	153.98
1971	13.47	5.31	12.04	27.82	6.49	2.79	4.13	2.66	8.63	7.28	17.88	32.19	140.69
1972	10.96	10.13	0.88	17.79	4.71	4.58	9.07	8.77	5.20	9.52	13.23	4.01	98.85
1973	3.45	5.51	18.84	7.34	8.34	3.69	4.40	3.54	8.07	9.72	26.88	8.19	107.97
1974	5.88	7.57	13.47	19.11	8.07	4.76	7.81	4.25	1.59	6.65	14.56	19.20	112.92
1975	19.62	9.28	10.40	10.23	3.01	4.20	3.83	8.13	2.73	8.88	11.15	8.47	99.93
RECORD MEAN	9.62	12.68	12.43	13.48	9.29	6.11	9.14	9.94	6.76	10.09	14.57	15.72	129.83

Aug	Sept	Oct	Nov	Dec	Total
351	308	300	253	208	3298
313	303	325	276	246	3116
367	354	328	271	188	3143
365	349	348	256	207	3278
358	345	340	321	278	3404
375	375	376	262	235	3607
339	323	309	262	233	3144

Record mean values above are means through the current year for the period beginning in 1947 for temperature and 1943 for precipitation. Average temperature from the Federal Building through February 1946, Total Precipitation from the Federal Building through April 1942, and for January 1945 - - January-February 1946; all other data from the General Lyman Airport.

(Continued)

March, the coldest months, to August, the warmest, is only 5.2° F. and the average daily range, 15.1° F. The highest temperature of record at Hilo Airport is 94° F; the lowest 53° F. Greater variations occur in localities with less rain and cloud, but temperatures in the mid-90's and low 50's are uncommon anywhere on the island near sea level.

The trade winds prevail throughout the year (although they may be absent for days or even weeks at a time) and profoundly influence the climate. However, the island's entire western coast is sheltered from the trades by high mountains, except that unusually strong trade winds may sweep through the relatively low (2,600-foot) saddle between the Kohala Mountains and Mauna Kea and reach the areas to the lee. But even places exposed to the trades may be affected by local mountain circulations. For example, the prevailing wind at Hilo Airport is not the northeasterly trade, but the southwesterly wind that drifts downslope off Mauna Loa during the night and early morning hours.

Except for heavy rain, really bad weather seldom occurs. Thunderstorms average only 8 per year, and are rarely severe. During the winter, cold fronts or the cyclonic storms of subtropical origin (the so-called Kona storms) may bring blizzards to the upper slopes of Mauna Loa and Mauna Kea, with snow extending at times to 9,000 feet or below and icing nearer the summit.

Storms crossing the Pacific a thousand miles to the north, or Kona storms closer by, may generate seas that cause heavy swell and surf along the northern, eastern, and southwestern shores of the island.

Station: HONOLULU, HAWAII
HONOLULU INT AIRPORT
Elevation (ground): 7 feet

TEMPERATURES °F

Month	Normal			Extremes			
	Daily maximum	Daily minimum	Monthly	Record highest	Year	Record lowest	Year
(a)				6		6	
J	79.3	65.3	72.3	85	1973	53	1972
F	79.2	65.3	72.3	85	1974	54	1972
M	79.7	66.3	73.0	87	1974	58	1975
A	81.4	68.1	74.8	87	1974	59	1973
M	83.6	70.2	76.9	88	1974	63	1975
J	85.6	72.2	78.9	90	1973	65	1964
J	86.8	73.4	80.1	90	1974	67	1974
A	87.4	74.0	80.7	91	1974	67	1974
S	87.4	73.4	80.4	92	1974	66	1975
O	85.8	72.0	78.9	91	1973	64	1975
N	83.2	69.8	76.5	89	1963	58	1972
D	80.3	67.1	73.7	85	1974	54	1962
YR	83.3	69.8	76.6	92	SEP 1974	53	JAN 1972

IMPORTANT:
The time-period covered by this record is limited: See footnotes on next page for explanation and for additional history of EXTREME HIGHS AND LOWS recorded in the general area.

Oahu, on which Honolulu is located, is the third largest of the Hawaiian Islands, and is marked by two important mountain systems. The Koolau Range, at an average elevation of 2,000 feet parallels the northeastern coast. The Waianae Mountains, somewhat higher in elevation, parallel the west coast. Honolulu Airport, the business and Waikiki districts, and a number of the City's residential areas lie along the coastal plain leeward (relative to the trade winds) of the Koolaus.

The climate of Hawaii is unusually pleasant for the tropics. Its oustanding features are (1) the persistence of the trade winds, where not disrupted by high mountains; (2) the remarkable variability in rainfall over short distances; (3) the sunniness of the leeward lowlands, in contrast to the persistent cloudiness over nearby mountain crests; (4) the equable temperature from day to day and season to season; and (5) the infrequency of severe storms.

The prevailing wind throughout the year is the northeasterly trade wind, although its average frequency varies from more than 90 percent during the summer to only 50 percent in January.

Annual rainfall in the Honolulu area averages 24 inches along the coast but increases to about 35 inches a mile inland and to about 60 to 70 inches 2 miles inland. Parts of the Koolau Range average 300 inches or more a year. This heavy mountain rainfall sustains extensive irrigation of cane fields and the water supply for Honolulu. East (windward) of the Koolaus, coastal areas receive 30 to 50 inches annually; cane and pineapple fields in central Oahu get about 35 to 40 inches. Oahu is driest along the coast west of the Waianaes where rainfall drops to about 20 inches a year. However, variations from month to month and year to year are considerable; more so during the cooler season, when occasional major storms provide much of the rain, than in the summer, when rain occurs primarily as showers that form within the moist trade winds as they override the mountains. Thus, March rainfall at Honolulu Airport has ranged from more than 20 inches to as little as one one-hundredth of an inch. In the mean, about half of the Airport's annual total occurs during its three wettest months, December through February. Trade wind rainfall is more frequent at night. Daytime showers, usually light, often occur while the sun continues to shine — a phenomenon referred to locally as "liquid sunshine".

Hawaii's equable temperatures are associated with the small seasonal variation in the amount of energy received from the sun and the tempering effect of the surrounding ocean. The range in temperature averages only 7 degrees between the warmest months (August and September) and the coolest months (January and February) and about 12 degrees between day and night. Daily maximums run from the high 70's in winter to the mid-80's in summer, and daily minimums from the mid-60's to the low 70's. However, the Honolulu Airport area has recorded as high as 93 degrees and as low as 52 degrees.

Average water temperatures at Waikiki Beach vary from 75 degrees in the morning to 77 degrees in the afternoon during March, and from 77 degrees in the morning to 82 degrees in the afternoon during August.

Because of the persistence and moderate humidity of the northeasterly trade winds, even the warmest months are usually comfortable. But when the trades diminish or give way to southerly winds, a situation known locally as "kona weather" ("kona storms" when stormy), the humidity may become oppressively high.

Weather severe enough to interfere with shipping or travel is uncommon. Intense rains of the the October to April "winter" season sometimes cause serious, but local, flash flooding. Thunderstorms are infrequent and usually mild, as compared with those of the midwestern United States. Hail seldom occurs and when it does is small and rarely damaging to crops. Infrequently a small tornado or a waterspout moving onshore may do some damage. Only a few tropical cyclones have struck Hawaii since 1950 but a small number, most of them drifting westward from their breeding grounds off the Mexican coast or forming to the east of the Islands, have approached near enough for their outlying winds, clouds and rain to effect the Islands.

Normals, Means, and Extremes

(To better understand these tables, see full explanation of terms beginning on page 322)

Month	Normal Degree days Base 65 °F: Heating	Normal Degree days Base 65 °F: Cooling	Precipitation in inches, Water equivalent: Normal	Maximum monthly	Year	Minimum monthly	Year	Maximum in 24 hrs.	Year	Snow, Ice pellets: Maximum monthly	Year	Maximum in 24 hrs.	Year
(a)				29		29		26		29		29	
J	0	226	4.40	14.74	1949	0.48	1960	6.72	1963	0.0		0.0	
F	0	212	2.46	13.68	1955	0.48	1969	6.88	1955	0.0		0.0	
M	0	240	3.18	20.79	1951	0.01	1957	17.07	1958	0.0		0.0	
A	0	294	1.36	8.92	1963	0.01	1960	4.21	1972	0.0		0.0	
M	0	369	0.96	7.23	1965	0.05	1949	3.44	1965	0.0		0.0	
J	0	417	0.32	2.46	1971	T	1959	2.28	1967	0.0		0.0	
J	0	468	0.60	2.01	1970	0.03	1950	1.03	1967	0.0		0.0	
A	0	487	0.76	3.08	1959	T	1974	2.35	1959	0.0		0.0	
S	0	462	0.67	2.74	1947	0.07	1957	1.40	1963	0.0		0.0	
O	0	431	1.51	5.83	1951	0.11	1957	2.81	1951	0.0		0.0	
N	0	345	2.99	14.72	1965	0.03	1962	9.15	1954	0.0		0.0	
D	0	270	3.69	12.09	1955	0.39	1959	8.14	1955	0.0		0.0	
YR	0	4221	22.90	20.79	MAR 1951	T	AUG 1974	17.07	MAR 1958	0.0		0.0	

Month	Relative humidity pct.: Hour 02 (Local time)	Hour 08	Hour 14	Hour 20	Wind: Mean speed m.p.h.	Prevailing direction	Fastest mile: Speed m.p.h.	Direction	Year	Pct. of possible sunshine	Mean sky cover, tenths, sunrise to sunset
(a)	6	6	6	6	26	14	24	24		23	29
J	81	80	64	74	10.0	ENE	67	SW	1959	63	5.5
F	78	77	60	70	10.8	ENE	63	W	1957	65	5.7
M	77	75	61	71	11.4	ENE	59	SE	1951	69	6.0
A	74	70	59	69	12.1	ENE	40	NE	1961	67	6.3
M	73	67	55	67	12.2	ENE	35	E	1953	70	6.0
J	72	66	54	66	12.9	ENE	39	E	1954	71	5.6
J	70	65	51	65	13.6	ENE	34	E	1959	74	5.3
A	71	67	54	68	13.6	ENE	52	SE	1959	75	5.3
S	71	66	52	66	11.7	ENE	36	SE	1963	75	5.1
O	72	68	55	68	10.9	ENE	40	SE	1961	67	5.6
N	79	74	60	71	11.2	ENE	65	NE	1957	60	5.7
D	80	78	61	72	11.1	ENE	59	NE	1957	59	5.6
YR	75	71	57	69	11.8	ENE	67	SW	JAN 1959	68	5.6

Month	Mean number of days, Sunrise to sunset: Clear	Partly cloudy	Cloudy	Precipitation .01 inch or more	Snow, Ice pellets 1.0 inch or more	Thunderstorms	Heavy fog, visibility ¼ mile or less	Temperatures °F Max.: (b) 90° and above	32° and below	Min.: 32° and below	0° and below	Average station pressure mb. Elev. 15 feet m.s.l.
(a)	26	26	26	26	26	26	26	6	6	6	6	3
J	9	12	10	10	0	1	0	0	0	0	0	1014.3
F	8	11	9	10	0	1	0	0	0	0	0	1017.2
M	8	13	10	9	0	1	0	0	0	0	0	1017.7
A	6	13	11	9	0	1	0	0	0	0	0	1017.4
M	7	14	10	7	0	*	0	0	0	0	0	1017.2
J	6	17	7	6	0	*	0	*	0	0	0	1017.1
J	8	17	6	8	0	*	0	*	0	0	0	1016.7
A	8	17	6	7	0	*	0	4	0	0	0	1016.1
S	9	15	6	7	0	*	0	4	0	0	0	1015.7
O	8	15	8	10	0	1	0	*	0	0	0	1015.7
N	7	14	9	10	0	1	0	0	0	0	0	1014.9
D	8	13	10	11	0	1	0	0	0	0	0	1015.9
YR	92	171	102	102	0	8	0	9	0	0	0	1016.3

FOOTNOTES

Means and extremes above are from existing and comparable exposures. Annual extremes have been exceeded at other sites in the locality as follows: Maximum precipitation in 24 hours 17.41 in March 1958 at the City Office. Temperature extremes for period January 1965 through August 1970 excluded as non-representative due to poor exposure of hygrothermometer. See Station Location table on back page.

Snowfall

Season	July	Aug	Sept	Oct	Nov	Dec	Jan

Heating Degree Days

Season	July	Aug	Sept	Oct	Nov	Dec	Jan

Cooling Degree Days

Year	Jan	Feb	Mar	Apr	May	June	July
1969	133	255	269	295	369	428	500
1970	293	239	378	409	485	490	540
1971	216	269	284	326	355	376	435
1972	178	170	249	307	386	425	484
1973	252	219	353	322	382	432	485
1974	300	270	285	378	415	434	468
1975	235	224	256	292	337	400	438

Feb	Mar	Apr	May	June	Total

Average Temperature

Year	Jan	Feb	Mar	Apr	May	June	July	Aug	Sept	Oct	Nov	Dec	Annual
1947	70.7	72.1	73.5	75.3	75.8	78.8	79.5	79.7	79.4	79.1	76.3	73.2	76.1
1948	70.3	71.1	73.2	73.9	76.5	78.3	79.0	79.9	79.5	77.6	75.0	72.6	75.6
1949	70.3	71.7	72.4	73.3	75.4	76.9	77.8	78.4	78.6	77.4	74.1	73.7	75.0
1950	72.3	74.3	73.7	73.8	76.0	77.2	78.0	79.0	78.7	78.5	75.4	72.0	75.7
1951	73.0	72.1	72.6	74.4	76.5	77.8	79.6	79.7	79.7	78.6	76.9	74.1	76.3
1952	72.6	72.9	72.9	73.3	73.7	76.5	78.1	79.1	78.4	77.1	76.1	73.7	75.4
1953	72.5	73.3	73.7	74.8	76.8	77.7	78.3	79.4	78.8	77.6	75.2	72.8	75.9
1954	71.8	73.0	71.5	74.6	75.0	78.3	78.2	79.5	79.3	78.1	76.9	73.0	75.8
1955	72.5	70.5	70.5	74.1	74.9	75.8	76.9	76.8	77.0	76.0	74.9	73.5	74.5
1956	73.3	72.1	73.8	73.9	75.8	76.7	78.4	79.3	79.5	77.9	75.4	74.2	75.9
1957	72.7	70.6	71.7	73.0	75.7	78.5	79.5	79.6	79.8	79.2	77.4	74.0	76.0
1958	71.6	[illegible]	71.0	73.8	75.1	77.7	78.1	79.4	79.7	77.4	74.7	72.0	75.3
1959	72.5	71.9	75.2	74.4	76.7	79.0	79.8	80.1	80.9	78.8	76.9	74.3	76.7
1960	72.8	72.4	73.7	74.9	77.1	79.1	79.8	80.4	79.8	79.3	76.9	74.4	76.7
1961	73.6	74.6	75.7	75.9	78.0	78.4	79.1	80.4	79.8	79.2	76.3	75.0	77.2
#1962	74.6	72.3	73.2	76.4	77.2	78.6	79.2	80.0	79.1	77.2	77.5	72.7	76.5
1963	71.1	72.2	72.3	75.3	76.4	79.2	80.7	81.5	81.0	79.7	77.1	74.0	76.7
1964	75.1	74.7	74.7	75.7	76.4	77.9	79.3	80.4	80.2	78.3	76.4	74.9	77.0
1965	71.9	69.8	72.1	75.0	77.0	79.1	79.9	79.7	80.0	78.2	77.1	73.3	76.1
1966	72.6	72.0	75.2	75.1	77.1	80.6	80.8	82.0	82.4	80.9	77.2	74.6	77.6
1967	72.5	73.9	73.8	74.7	78.2	79.7	81.5	82.1	82.4	80.6	77.6	74.0	77.6
1968	73.0	73.4	74.8	76.7	78.4	80.4	81.5	82.9	82.0	80.6	78.8	72.7	77.9
1969	69.1	73.9	73.6	74.7	76.7	79.1	80.9	83.2	82.0	80.5	78.7	76.5	77.4
#1970	74.2	73.3	76.9	78.3	80.4	81.1	82.2	83.8	79.0	78.5	75.8	74.7	78.2
#1971	71.7	74.4	73.9	75.6	76.2	77.3	78.9	79.5	79.1	78.0	75.7	73.3	76.1
1972	70.4	70.6	72.8	75.0	77.3	78.9	80.4	81.1	80.5	79.3	76.7	71.6	76.2
1973	72.9	72.6	76.1	75.5	77.1	79.2	80.5	81.2	81.0	79.4	77.0	73.8	77.2
1974	74.5	74.4	74.0	77.4	78.2	79.3	79.9	81.2	80.0	79.5	75.7	75.8	77.5
1975	72.4	72.8	73.0	74.5	75.7	78.1	79.0	80.1	79.4	79.1	77.1	73.0	76.2
RECORD MEAN	72.4	72.6	73.3	74.7	76.2	78.0	79.1	79.8	79.5	78.4	76.1	73.7	76.1
MAX	79.1	79.3	79.8	81.0	82.5	84.3	85.2	85.9	86.0	84.8	82.4	79.8	82.5
MIN	65.6	65.8	66.7	68.4	69.9	71.7	72.9	73.6	73.0	72.0	69.7	67.5	69.7

# Indicates a station move or relocation of instruments.

HONOLULU, HI

Feb	Mar	Apr	May	June	Total

Precipitation

Year	Jan	Feb	Mar	Apr	May	June	July	Aug	Sept	Oct	Nov	Dec	Annual
1947	1.27	0.51	0.60	0.23	0.53	0.42	0.15	0.79	2.74	0.53	1.55	1.36	10.68
1948	6.39	3.48	0.67	1.69	0.17	0.14	0.19	1.07	1.17	0.32	3.24	1.23	19.76
1949	14.74	5.49	0.64	0.14	0.05	0.27	0.32	0.08	0.15	0.35	0.69	2.28	25.20
1950	13.24	1.04	0.63	5.74	0.32	0.07	0.03	1.00	0.49	0.67	1.92	6.53	31.68
1951	1.21	2.98	20.79	0.49	0.23	0.38	0.24	1.14	0.91	5.83	0.23	5.30	39.73
1952	4.45	0.48	0.56	0.35	0.15	0.13	0.07	0.09	0.27	2.50	1.21	0.39	10.65
1953	1.25	2.87	1.54	0.24	0.14	0.02	0.25	0.03	0.71	0.60	0.42	1.90	9.97
1954	1.49	3.98	2.54	1.98	0.16	0.20	1.73	0.19	0.54	1.04	9.39	4.06	27.30
1955	2.74	13.68	4.36	0.85	0.76	0.08	0.23	0.59	0.22	0.37	1.89	12.09	37.86
1956	3.58	3.30	0.53	0.51	1.01	0.14	0.12	0.53	0.14	1.81	7.24	2.32	21.23
1957	13.33	1.68	0.01	1.56	1.12	0.12	0.39	0.37	0.07	0.11	2.62	2.84	24.22
1958	0.50	5.15	18.51	0.40	0.24	0.21	0.88	3.07	0.48	2.88	0.06	2.64	35.02
1959	3.76	2.23	0.16	0.54	0.69	T	0.28	3.08	0.88	0.64	1.49	0.39	14.14
1960	0.48	0.51	1.48	0.01	3.85	0.18	0.73	0.40	0.81	1.16	0.22	2.24	12.07
1961	4.17	0.93	0.43	0.71	0.23	0.87	0.28	0.47	0.48	2.40	2.05	1.24	14.26
1962	2.20	2.62	2.10	1.07	0.32	0.11	0.13	0.32	0.66	0.70	0.03	3.32	13.58
1963	10.58	1.11	8.39	8.92	3.36	0.33	1.01	0.03	1.47	1.08	0.20	1.43	37.91
1964	2.18	0.52	5.21	0.88	0.21	0.08	1.34	0.46	0.97	0.34	2.36	5.57	20.12
1965	3.02	0.80	0.99	1.48	7.23	0.25	1.37	0.87	0.52	3.56	14.72	7.97	42.78
1966	1.39	3.71	0.39	0.46	0.41	0.04	0.43	0.82	0.16	2.95	9.44	2.98	23.18
1967	0.79	2.53	6.78	1.29	2.12	2.43	1.21	2.53	0.42	1.53	2.78	9.93	34.34
1968	8.17	2.91	2.49	3.14	1.22	0.24	0.29	0.10	1.30	2.13	5.64	9.63	37.26
1969	8.20	0.48	3.00	0.10	0.81	0.23	0.63	0.11	0.87	0.96	5.77	1.34	22.50
1970	1.81	0.77	0.07	0.74	0.21	0.23	2.01	0.21	0.39	1.88	5.94	1.23	15.49
1971	6.19	2.37	5.57	2.19	0.43	2.46	0.04	0.26	1.03	2.27	0.95	2.88	26.64
1972	5.28	5.00	2.45	5.15	0.12	0.79	0.20	0.46	0.92	2.39	0.59	3.59	26.94
1973	0.67	0.60	0.40	0.72	0.89	0.09	0.46	0.32	0.64	1.78	3.73	3.94	14.24
1974	4.21	1.28	3.49	4.13	0.82	1.52	0.44	T	2.08	2.77	2.69	0.59	24.02
1975	6.42	2.36	2.02	0.51	0.19	0.03	0.40	0.03	0.11	0.18	11.54	0.60	24.39
RECORD MEAN	4.61	2.60	3.34	1.59	0.97	0.42	0.55	0.67	0.74	1.58	3.47	3.51	24.05

Aug	Sept	Oct	Nov	Dec	Total
572	517	488	419	365	4610
586	429	426	332	306	4913
456	431	408	328	265	4149
506	470	450	357	209	4191
512	484	455	367	279	4542
509	458	457	328	341	4643
475	438	442	372	257	4166

Record mean values above are means through the current year for the period beginning in 1947 through 1964 and September 1970 to date for temperature. Precipitation record means are for the period 1947 to date.

BOISE, IDAHO

Boise is situated in the valley of the river from which it takes its name–about 8 miles below the mouth of a mountain canyon where the valley proper begins. Sheltered by large shade trees and averaging 2,710 feet in elevation the denser part of the City covers a gentle alluvial slope of about 2 miles width stretching southwest from the foothills of the Boise Mountains to the river. The Boise mountains rise to 5,000 - 6,000 feet above sea level in about 8 miles, the slopes partly mantled with sagebrush and then chaparral giving way near the summit to ridges of fir, spruce, and pine. Across the river, the land rises in 2 irregular steps, or benches, for several miles, finally reaching the low divide between the Boise and Snake Rivers. Downstream the valley widens, merging with the valley of the Snake about 40 miles to the northwest; once semiarid, the entire area is now irrigated from the Arrowrock and Anderson Reservoirs upstream.

Although airmasses from the Pacific are considerably modified by the time they reach Boise, their influence, particularly in winter, alternates with that of atmospheric developments from other directions. The result is almost a typical upland continental type of climate in summer, but one tempered by periods of cloudy or stormy and mild weather during the course of nearly every winter. From year to year, average monthly, or even seasonal, temperatures may vary through a wide range, yet day-to-day changes are comparatively small for an inland middle-latitude station. The Boise climate in general may be described as dry and temperature, with sufficient variation to be stimulating.

Following are details not included in the accompanying tables:

TEMPERATURE

Summer hot periods rarely last longer than a few days, but maximum temperatures of 100° or higher occur nearly every year -- the average number of such days is: 2 in July and 1 in August. Summer maxima generally are reached in late afternoon, followed by rapidly falling temperature after sunset. The average 5 p.m. wet bulb temperature for July is 62°, indicating relatively comfortable conditions despite the high temperatures.

Winter cold spells, when they occur, average longer in duration than the summer hot ones; the record cold month of January 1949 had 16 days with minimum temperatures of 0° or lower. During cold weather, there is ordinarily little wind to add to the discomfort.

PRECIPITATION

The normal precipitation pattern in the Boise area shows a winter maximum and a very pronounced summer minimum. Total amount and intensity are generally greatest near the foothills, dwindling to westward. Since the beginning of records in 1884, the

Station: BOISE, IDAHO MUNICIPAL AIRPORT
Elevation (ground): 2838 feet

TEMPERATURES °F

Month	Normal			Extremes			
	Daily maximum	Daily minimum	Monthly	Record highest	Year	Record lowest	Year
(a)				36		36	
J	36.5	21.4	29.0	63	1953	-17	1950
F	43.8	27.2	35.5	67	1958	-10	1950
M	51.6	30.5	41.1	78	1966	6	1971
A	61.4	36.5	49.0	92	1946	19	1968
M	70.6	44.1	57.4	98	1966	26	1974
J	78.3	51.2	64.8	109	1940	33	1962
J	90.5	58.5	74.5	111	1960	41	1955
A	87.6	56.7	72.2	110	1961	37	1965
S	77.6	48.5	63.1	102	1945	23	1970
O	64.7	39.4	52.1	91	1963	11	1971
N	48.9	30.7	39.8	73	1975	-3	1955
D	39.1	25.0	32.1	65	1964	-23	1972
YR	62.6	39.1	50.9	111	JUL 1960	-23	DEC 1972

IMPORTANT:
The time-period covered by this record is limited: See footnotes following table of NORMALS, MEANS AND EXTREMES for explanation and for additional history of EXTREME HIGHS AND LOWS recorded in the general area.

(Continued)

greatest 24-hour precipitation has been 2.72 inches (March 5-6, 1871); at the present Air Terminal location, occupied since 1940, the greatest has been 2.24 inches (June 11-12, 1958). Since the beginning of more detailed records on December 1, 1898, the greatest 1-hour precipitation has been 0.98 inch (July 30, 1912). Greatest depth of snow on the ground during the same period has been 18 inches on February 2, 1916.

WINDS

Tornadoes have never been reported at Boise, and winds approaching destructive force are rare; the fastest mile, 61 m.p.h. from the west on July 29, 1944, which did some damage to trees and powerlines, was the highest since Weather Bureau records began in 1899. Northwesterly winds, drying and rather "raw" in character, although of moderate velocity, are common from March through May.

descending from the nearby foothills at night, frequently have a moderating effect on winter temperatures. There is an occasional, but moderate, duststorm during the warmer months, usually occurring at times of cold frontal passage.

MISCELLANEOUS

Relative humidity, by eastern U.S. standards, is low, but widespread irrigation maintains humidity several percent above the general dryness of western arid conditions in summer. Damage or bodily injury by lightning is rare, character of thunderstorms being predominately mild. An average of 4 hailstorms per year is reported, and there is occasional damage over small areas. December and January are the months of maximum fog or low stratus cloud conditions. Only a moderate amount of sunshine is received in the average winter, but protracted periods of clear, sunny weather are the rule in summer. "Ice storms" are practically unknown.

FREEZE DATA
(Based on records for 1940-65)

Last Occurrence in Spring	32°	28°	24°
Average date	May 6	April 21	March 29
Latest date	5/31/55	5/22/60	4/24/50

First Occurrence in Fall	32°	28°	24°
Average date	Oct. 12	Oct. 23	Nov. 5
Earliest date	9/9/46	9/9/46	9/17/65

BOISE, IDAHO

Normals, Means, and Extremes

(To better understand these tables, see full explanation of terms beginning on page 322)

Month	Normal Degree days Base 65 °F: Heating	Normal Degree days Base 65 °F: Cooling	Precipitation in inches, Water equivalent: Normal	Maximum monthly	Year	Minimum monthly	Year	Maximum in 24 hrs.	Year	Snow, Ice pellets: Maximum monthly	Year	Maximum in 24 hrs.	Year
(a)				36		36		36		36		36	
J	1116	0	1.47	3.87	1970	0.12	1949	1.48	1953	21.4	1964	8.5	1950
F	826	0	1.16	2.62	1975	0.19	1964	1.00	1951	25.2	1949	13.0	1949
M	741	0	1.01	2.27	1957	0.18	1944	1.12	1943	11.9	1951	6.4	1952
A	480	0	1.14	3.04	1955	0.09	1949	1.27	1969	8.0	1967	7.2	1969
M	252	17	1.32	4.00	1942	0.09	1940	1.51	1942	4.0	1964	4.0	1964
J	97	91	1.06	3.41	1941	0.01	1966	2.24	1958	T	1954	T	1954
J	0	295	0.15	0.95	1960	0.00	1947	0.94	1960	T	1970	T	1970
A	12	235	0.30	2.37	1968	T	1969	0.79	1960	0.0		0.0	
S	127	70	0.41	2.54	1959	T	1974	0.87	1959	0.0		0.0	
O	406	6	0.80	2.25	1956	T	1952	0.76	1947	2.7	1971	1.7	1971
N	756	0	1.32	2.44	1973	0.35	1952	0.88	1971	8.8	1973	6.5	1964
D	1020	0	1.36	3.19	1964	0.25	1962	1.16	1955	15.6	1951	6.6	1953
YR	5833	714	11.50	4.00	MAY 1942	0.00	JUL 1947	2.24	JUN 1958	25.2	FEB 1949	13.0	FEB 1949

Month	Relative humidity pct. Hour 05 (Local time)	Hour 11	Hour 17	Hour 23	Wind: Mean speed m.p.h.	Prevailing direction	Fastest mile: Speed m.p.h.	Direction	Year	Pct. of possible sunshine	Mean sky cover, tenths, sunrise to sunset
(a)	36	36	36	36	36	24	36	36		35	36
J	80	73	71	79	8.6	SE	50	SE	1941	41	7.7
F	80	68	61	78	9.4	SE	56	W	1954	52	7.2
M	74	55	45	68	10.4	SE	52	W	1957	63	6.8
A	71	47	36	60	10.3	SE	50	W	1942	68	6.4
M	69	45	34	59	9.6	NW	50	W	1954	71	5.7
J	68	42	31	54	9.2	NW	50	SW	1948	75	4.8
J	53	33	21	38	8.5	NW	61	W	1944	89	2.6
A	51	34	23	39	8.3	NW	56	SE	1963	85	3.1
S	58	39	30	48	8.3	SE	50	SE	1960	82	3.5
O	67	49	41	61	8.6	SE	56	SE	1950	67	5.1
N	78	66	61	75	8.7	SE	57	NW	1953	45	6.9
D	82	74	73	81	8.5	SE	56	NW	1950	39	7.6
YR	69	52	44	62	9.0	SE	61	W	JUL 1944	67	5.6

Month	Mean number of days, Sunrise to sunset: Clear	Partly cloudy	Cloudy	Precipitation .01 inch or more	Snow, Ice pellets 1.0 inch or more	Thunderstorms	Heavy fog, visibility ¼ mile or less	Temperatures °F Max. (b) 90° and above	Max. 32° and below	Min. 32° and below	Min. 0° and below	Average station pressure mb. Elev. 2868 feet m.s.l.
(a)	36	36	36	36	36	36	36	36	36	36	36	3
J	5	5	21	12	3	*	5	0	10	26	2	918.1
F	5	6	17	10	1	*	3	0	2	21	*	917.6
M	6	8	17	9	1	1	1	0	*	18	0	912.3
A	7	9	14	8	*	1	*	*	0	8	0	914.3
M	9	10	12	8	*	3	*	1	0	2	0	914.2
J	12	10	8	7	0	3	*	5	0	0	0	913.5
J	21	7	3	2	0	3	0	19	0	0	0	914.1
A	19	8	4	2	0	2	0	15	0	0	0	914.3
S	17	7	6	3	0	1	*	3	0	*	0	917.0
O	12	8	11	7	*	1	1	*	0	5	0	917.2
N	6	7	17	10	1	*	3	0	1	18	*	916.8
D	5	5	21	12	2	*	6	0	6	25	*	920.2
YR	124	90	151	91	8	15	19	43	19	124	2	915.8

FOOTNOTES Means and extremes above are from existing and comparable exposures. Annual extremes have been exceeded at other sites in the locality as follows: Maximum monthly precipitation 7.66 in March 1871; maximum precipitation in 24 hours 2.72 in March 1871; maximum monthly snowfall 36.6 in December 1884; maximum snowfall in 24 hours 17.0 in December 1884.

Snowfall

Season	July	Aug	Sept	Oct	Nov	Dec	Jan
1936-37	0.0	0.0	0.0	0.0	T	2.6	25.5
1937-38	0.0	0.0	0.0	0.0	T	0.1	0.6
#1938-39	0.0	0.0	0.0	T	5.0	0.1	5.0
#1939-40	0.0	0.0	0.0	T	0.0	1.5	3.5
1940-41	0.0	0.0	0.0	0.0	4.7	T	4.1
1941-42	0.0	0.0	0.0	0.0	0.0	11.0	11.5
1942-43	0.0	0.0	0.0	T	0.5	1.0	7.3
1943-44	0.0	0.0	0.0	T	T	1.0	3.5
1944-45	0.0	0.0	0.0	0.0	T	1.3	3.4
1945-46	0.0	0.0	0.0	T	1.8	8.3	5.9
1946-47	0.0	0.0	0.0	0.6	3.6	T	9.1
1947-48	0.0	0.0	0.0	0.0	6.2	5.5	0.5
1948-49	0.0	0.0	0.0	0.0	5.5	13.8	4.2
1949-50	0.0	0.0	0.0	T	0.0	6.8	19.7
1950-51	0.0	0.0	0.0	0.0	T	2.9	10.3
1951-52	0.0	0.0	0.0	T	T	15.6	11.0
1952-53	0.0	0.0	0.0	0.0	T	2.5	1.1
1953-54	0.0	0.0	0.0	0.0	T	10.7	2.2
1954-55	0.0	0.0	0.0	0.0	0.0	3.1	14.6
1955-56	0.0	0.0	0.0	T	6.9	4.3	10.0
1956-57	0.0	0.0	0.0	T	1.2	3.2	12.4
1957-58	0.0	0.0	0.0	0.0	T	5.1	7.1
1958-59	0.0	0.0	0.0	0.0	T	0.1	6.3
1959-60	0.0	0.0	0.0	0.0	T	1.6	11.5
1960-61	0.0	0.0	0.0	T	2.1	1.1	T
1961-62	0.0	0.0	0.0	T	3.4	6.5	9.2
1962-63	0.0	0.0	0.0	0.0	0.3	T	10.1
1963-64	0.0	0.0	0.0	T	1.0	5.5	21.4
1964-65	0.0	0.0	0.0	0.0	7.3	8.7	18.4
1965-66	0.0	0.0	0.0	T	0.7	4.5	3.6
1966-67	0.0	0.0	0.0	0.1	T	9.0	2.0
1967-68	0.0	0.0	0.0	0.0	1.3	4.3	3.3
1968-69	0.0	0.0	0.0	0.0	1.3	11.4	14.4
1969-70	0.0	0.0	0.0	1.2	0.3	4.8	2.9
1970-71	T	0.0	0.0	0.3	0.1	4.4	4.0
1971-72	0.0	0.0	0.0	2.7	0.4	14.8	5.0
1972-73	0.0	0.0	0.0	T	T	12.6	7.3
1973-74	0.0	0.0	0.0	0.0	8.8	4.5	6.0
1974-75	0.0	0.0	0.0	0.0	0.9	4.6	5.4
1975-76	0.0	0.0	0.0	T	3.9	4.2	
RECORD MEAN	T	0.0	0.0	0.1	1.7	5.5	7.6

Heating Degree Days

Season	July	Aug	Sept	Oct	Nov	Dec	Jan
1955-56	44	0	192	363	875	912	970
1956-57	11	33	97	458	883	1059	1343
1957-58	5	5	75	470	850	942	1032
1958-59	2	3	143	299	735	870	896
#1959-60	12	15	212	470	901	1142	1266
1960-61	0	67	63	377	727	1063	989
1961-62	0	0	239	485	833	1052	1354
1962-63	8	32	56	369	703	908	1286
1963-64	2	2	21	252	631	1138	1202
1964-65	0	62	166	370	835	916	951
1965-66	7	30	234	266	613	1075	1004
1966-67	7	18	68	476	654	1039	885
1967-68	0	0	49	434	723	1146	1092
1968-69	0	59	119	382	684	918	945
1969-70	3	13	91	585	751	935	886
1970-71	0	0	240	537	650	969	958
1971-72	10	6	210	492	753	1069	1047
1972-73	11	0	222	406	727	1270	1056
1973-74	4	13	103	382	692	817	1099
1974-75	10	11	53	391	689	983	1132
1975-76	6	21	74	399	759	1035	

Cooling Degree Days

Year	Jan	Feb	Mar	Apr	May	June	July
1969	0	0	0	0	32	121	256
1970	0	0	0	0	24	201	357
1971	0	0	0	0	31	81	320
1972	0	0	0	0	62	129	283
1973	0	0	0	0	51	177	341
1974	0	0	0	0	13	252	289
1975	0	0	0	0	10	64	426

Feb	Mar	Apr	May	June	Total
9.3	T	0.6	0.0	0.0	38.0
4.8	6.6	0.0	0.4	0.0	12.5
13.9	3.6	T	0.0	0.0	27.6
1.5	T	0.0	0.0	0.0	6.5
T	0.0	T	0.0	0.0	8.8
5.0	3.5	T	0.0	0.0	31.0
8.2	1.0	0.0	T	0.0	18.0
5.3	T	T	T	0.0	9.8
0.3	1.7	T	T	0.0	6.7
2.2	T	T	0.0	0.0	18.2
T	T	T	0.0	0.0	13.3
12.0	6.9	T	T	0.0	31.1
25.2	0.0	0.0	0.0	0.0	48.7
3.4	T	T	T	T	29.9
3.6	11.9	T	0.0	0.0	28.7
5.9	9.2	0.0	0.0	0.0	41.7
1.0	4.9	0.9	T	0.0	10.4
T	1.2	0.2	0.0	T	14.3
4.1	0.1	4.4	T	0.0	26.3
7.7	2.6	T	T	0.0	31.5
7.2	0.2	T	0.0	0.0	24.2
0.2	0.5	T	T	0.0	12.9
3.0	0.3	T	0.0	0.0	9.7
4.0	3.5	T	T	0.0	20.6
3.2	0.8	0.0	T	0.0	7.2
1.6	3.7	T	0.0	0.0	24.4
T	0.4	1.7	0.0	0.0	12.5
2.1	2.6	0.4	4.0	0.0	37.0
0.4	0.4	1.3	T	0.0	36.5
7.1	0.2	0.1	0.0	0.0	16.2
1.9	0.3	8.0	T	0.0	21.3
0.1	0.8	0.3	T	0.0	10.1
5.5	1.3	7.2	0.0	0.0	41.1
0.1	2.3	1.1	0.5	0.0	13.2
2.1	1.6	T	0.0	0.0	12.5
3.5	0.6	1.6	0.0	0.0	28.6
0.3	0.6	T	0.0	0.0	20.8
2.4	5.7	T	0.0	0.0	27.4
6.3	2.2	2.6	0.9	0.0	22.9
3.8	2.0	0.8	0.2	T	21.7

BOISE, ID

Feb	Mar	Apr	May	June	Total
1085	710	424	225	92	5892
848	699	483	224	81	6219
632	745	510	119	69	5454
771	737	421	382	43	5302
905	681	475	327	23	6429
661	631	500	234	13	5325
912	812	377	275	85	6424
600	636	498	164	124	5384
1113	843	583	323	127	6237
781	793	435	317	82	5708
884	668	467	172	97	5517
742	707	627	279	79	5581
688	586	555	235	58	5566
797	689	432	147	75	5247
659	724	631	249	79	5606
765	763	465	176	78	5601
818	598	543	194	45	5785
708	673	470	182	91	5816
728	687	452	304	42	5323
782	721	607	275	76	5730

Aug	Sept	Oct	Nov	Dec	Total
251	75	0	0	0	735
341	30	0	0	0	953
435	42	2	0	0	911
303	40	0	0	0	817
269	51	1	0	0	890
226	71	0	0	0	851
182	96	11	0	0	789

Average Temperature

Year	Jan	Feb	Mar	Apr	May	June	July	Aug	Sept	Oct	Nov	Dec	Annual
1936	31.6	28.4	40.2	54.1	62.8	69.2	78.3	75.0	62.0	55.0	37.4	35.2	52.4
1937	15.4	32.4	44.4	48.2	60.4	66.0	76.9	71.2	65.6	55.2	45.7	37.5	51.6
1938	35.9	40.6	41.8	51.8	56.2	67.0	75.0	71.8	68.6	54.0	35.6	34.2	52.7
#1939	34.0	30.4	44.4	53.6	61.8	63.1	75.9	74.7	64.3	52.3	42.4	40.2	53.1
1940	33.0	38.9	45.6	50.0	61.3	69.6	74.9	74.2	63.2	54.4	35.5	35.3	53.0
1941	33.2	39.4	45.4	50.1	58.4	62.9	75.4	70.9	57.9	50.9	42.0	35.0	51.8
1942	20.7	31.6	40.2	51.8	53.0	60.8	75.7	72.9	63.2	52.6	39.6	33.4	49.6
1943	28.2	35.9	39.9	54.0	54.0	61.6	73.2	70.9	66.6	53.9	40.0	32.8	50.9
1944	25.0	34.0	38.4	48.9	58.6	60.8	72.2	70.7	63.8	58.0	38.7	29.0	49.8
1945	32.2	37.6	40.0	46.0	56.6	61.1	74.9	73.4	59.9	55.2	39.6	30.8	50.6
1946	29.0	33.8	43.8	51.8	57.6	65.4	74.8	73.2	61.0	45.2	37.7	36.2	50.8
1947	23.2	38.0	44.9	49.4	62.2	61.8	75.1	72.3	62.8	55.2	36.1	31.4	51.0
1948	33.0	32.0	37.9	48.0	56.3	66.5	70.4	70.4	61.8	52.3	37.0	25.4	49.2
1949	10.3	30.7	43.2	53.4	61.5	65.6	74.4	73.6	65.6	46.4	44.6	31.1	50.1
1950	25.4	35.3	39.8	47.6	54.1	63.6	73.3	72.7	63.2	56.9	42.6	36.3	50.9
1951	29.1	36.9	37.1	50.7	56.8	62.3	75.7	72.2	63.6	49.2	38.7	27.5	50.0
1952	26.6	30.4	36.8	52.5	57.6	64.2	73.5	72.9	65.4	56.9	35.0	34.1	50.5
1953	41.0	36.4	42.4	46.1	52.2	59.4	74.1	71.5	66.0	52.9	45.3	31.3	51.5
1954	36.5	38.8	39.3	49.9	59.9	61.3	75.4	68.2	61.6	50.9	43.5	30.6	51.3
1955	23.5	27.2	36.2	44.0	53.6	66.7	71.3	74.6	62.5	53.3	35.6	35.4	48.6
1956	33.5	27.4	41.9	50.6	59.5	64.5	75.2	69.7	64.2	50.1	35.3	30.7	50.2
1957	21.5	34.5	42.2	48.7	58.2	66.0	73.2	70.7	65.3	49.5	36.4	34.4	50.0
1958	31.5	42.2	40.7	47.8	64.3	66.0	74.0	75.9	62.0	55.3	40.2	36.6	53.1
#1959	35.8	37.2	41.0	50.7	52.7	68.6	76.0	70.0	59.7	49.6	34.7	27.9	50.4
1960	24.0	33.6	42.9	49.0	54.5	68.9	80.7	69.0	66.0	52.7	40.6	30.5	51.0
1961	32.9	41.2	44.4	48.1	57.9	72.9	76.3	77.8	57.2	49.1	37.0	30.9	52.1
1962	21.1	32.2	38.6	52.4	56.0	65.5	72.2	70.7	65.2	53.1	41.4	35.4	50.3
1963	23.3	43.3	44.3	48.3	60.9	63.9	72.2	73.5	70.9	57.8	43.7	28.1	52.5
1964	26.0	26.3	37.6	45.3	55.1	62.5	74.9	69.2	59.6	52.9	36.9	35.2	48.5
1965	34.1	36.9	39.2	50.2	54.9	64.7	73.3	71.1	57.1	56.4	44.3	30.1	51.0
1966	32.4	33.3	43.2	49.2	61.5	65.0	73.2	72.1	66.2	49.4	43.0	31.3	51.6
1967	36.2	38.3	42.0	43.9	56.5	66.1	78.5	78.0	68.6	50.7	40.7	27.8	52.3
1968	29.5	41.1	45.9	46.3	57.8	67.9	77.3	68.7	63.0	52.4	42.0	35.1	52.2
1969	34.3	36.2	42.5	50.5	61.1	66.3	72.9	72.4	64.2	45.9	39.7	34.6	51.7
1970	36.2	41.2	41.4	43.8	57.5	68.9	76.3	75.8	57.8	47.5	43.2	33.5	51.9
1971	33.9	37.5	40.2	49.2	60.0	64.9	74.7	78.6	59.2	49.0	39.7	30.2	51.4
1972	30.9	36.5	45.5	46.7	60.6	67.6	73.5	74.5	58.8	51.7	40.5	23.8	50.9
1973	30.7	39.4	43.0	49.1	60.5	67.6	75.6	73.0	63.1	52.4	41.7	38.4	52.9
1974	29.4	38.7	42.6	49.7	55.4	71.7	73.8	71.7	65.3	52.2	41.7	33.2	52.1
1975	28.2	36.9	41.5	44.5	56.2	64.4	78.3	70.0	65.5	52.3	39.5	31.4	50.7
RECORD MEAN	29.9	35.5	42.3	49.6	57.8	65.4	74.5	72.5	62.7	52.3	40.6	32.1	51.3
MAX	37.1	43.5	52.2	61.5	70.7	79.0	90.1	87.8	76.8	64.5	49.6	39.1	62.7
MIN	22.7	27.5	32.3	37.7	44.8	51.8	58.9	57.1	48.5	40.1	31.6	25.1	39.8

# Indicates a station move or relocation of instruments.

Precipitation

Year	Jan	Feb	Mar	Apr	May	June	July	Aug	Sept	Oct	Nov	Dec	Annual
1936	2.13	2.26	0.73	0.70	0.69	1.59	0.41	0.38	0.07	0.04	0.01	0.78	9.79
1937	1.60	1.44	1.80	1.50	0.37	0.44	0.07	0.00	0.39	1.18	1.71	2.10	12.60
1938	1.51	0.82	3.16	1.09	2.55	1.29	0.85	0.03	0.34	1.68	2.51	0.57	16.40
#1939	1.19	1.38	0.76	0.36	0.11	0.38	0.15	T	1.53	0.70	0.13	1.39	8.08
1940	1.84	1.78	2.26	1.80	0.09	0.08	0.36	0.01	1.87	1.82	1.32	0.54	13.77
1941	1.23	1.51	0.18	1.35	1.65	3.41	0.11	0.61	0.22	1.00	0.77	1.77	13.81
1942	0.98	1.41	0.52	1.28	4.00	0.62	T	0.02	0.01	0.58	2.31	2.75	14.48
1943	1.27	0.88	2.08	1.39	0.72	1.09	0.16	T	T	1.42	0.50	0.41	9.92
1944	0.41	1.20	0.18	2.92	0.36	2.04	0.06	T	0.16	0.43	1.60	1.09	10.45
1945	1.09	2.17	1.76	0.47	2.21	0.78	0.07	0.08	0.44	0.62	1.51	2.24	13.44
1946	1.37	1.31	1.67	0.35	0.55	0.13	0.04	0.26	0.16	1.11	2.05	0.86	9.86
1947	0.50	0.44	1.84	0.52	1.02	0.80	0.00	0.05	0.80	2.18	1.27	0.66	10.08
1948	0.81	1.58	1.42	1.37	0.91	1.57	0.08	0.05	0.31	0.68	1.02	2.11	11.91
1949	0.12	2.05	0.48	0.09	0.73	0.37	T	0.12	0.19	1.20	1.40	0.68	7.43
1950	2.53	1.09	2.01	0.55	1.27	0.92	0.04	0.52	0.92	0.42	1.53	2.19	13.99
1951	1.66	2.16	1.05	0.94	0.94	0.70	0.29	0.07	0.01	1.60	1.80	2.47	13.69
1952	1.24	1.12	2.05	1.08	1.08	1.10	0.15	T	0.05	T	0.35	1.00	9.22
1953	3.35	1.49	0.92	1.52	2.59	1.22	T	0.12	0.02	0.11	1.31	1.15	13.80
1954	1.09	0.55	1.20	0.42	0.95	1.10	0.06	0.24	0.08	0.44	0.94	1.09	8.16
1955	1.32	0.43	0.39	3.04	1.48	0.63	0.39	T	0.12	0.74	1.43	2.22	12.19
1956	2.17	0.91	0.39	1.62	2.18	0.80	0.15	0.08	0.02	2.25	0.41	0.84	11.82
1957	1.04	1.72	2.27	1.15	2.79	0.25	T	T	0.06	0.42	0.81	2.08	12.59
1958	1.37	1.91	0.57	1.94	2.05	2.94	0.48	0.53	0.12	0.09	1.04	1.28	14.32
1959	1.33	0.63	1.08	0.19	1.68	0.27	T	0.64	2.54	0.76	0.36	0.53	10.01
1960	1.33	1.74	1.39	0.43	1.21	0.01	0.95	0.83	0.29	0.49	1.82	0.43	10.92
1961	0.42	1.20	1.39	0.22	0.54	0.55	0.25	0.21	0.79	1.76	0.95	0.90	9.18
1962	1.00	0.77	1.27	0.92	2.90	0.12	0.04	0.12	0.40	1.22	1.67	0.25	10.68
1963	1.13	1.70	0.21	1.65	0.85	1.90	T	0.64	0.75	0.99	2.41	1.02	13.25
1964	2.46	0.19	0.64	1.35	1.76	2.00	0.41	0.53	0.70	0.21	2.33	3.19	15.77
1965	2.89	0.31	0.43	2.81	0.80	1.20	0.25	0.88	0.55	0.28	1.51	0.61	12.52
1966	0.81	0.73	0.60	0.61	0.32	0.01	0.06	0.01	0.19	0.29	1.60	1.41	6.64
1967	1.49	0.35	0.37	1.47	0.49	1.07	0.05	T	0.58	0.42	0.89	0.50	7.68
1968	0.43	1.86	0.71	0.35	0.40	0.60	T	2.37	0.10	0.70	1.50	1.95	10.97
1969	3.50	1.00	0.26	1.35	0.50	2.00	0.02	T	0.68	0.64	0.59	1.77	12.31
1970	3.87	0.30	1.04	0.93	0.73	1.72	0.28	0.10	1.00	0.81	2.03	1.37	14.18
1971	2.04	0.65	1.50	0.40	0.25	1.58	0.12	0.18	0.64	0.53	2.32	1.63	11.84
1972	2.15	0.91	1.50	0.62	0.32	0.90	0.21	0.05	1.11	0.64	1.11	1.79	11.31
1973	1.14	0.42	0.65	1.49	0.74	0.19	0.07	0.03	0.82	1.15	2.44	2.23	11.37
1974	1.35	0.66	1.50	0.67	0.10	0.60	0.53	0.22	T	1.45	0.67	1.71	9.46
1975	0.59	2.62	1.92	1.53	0.88	0.78	0.82	0.48	0.01	1.99	0.78	1.29	13.69
RECORD MEAN	1.51	1.27	1.27	1.16	1.18	0.92	0.25	0.23	0.50	0.99	1.34	1.35	11.97

Record mean values above are means through the current year for the period beginning in 1900 for temperature and precipitation, 1940 for snowfall. Data are from City Office locations through June 1939 and from Airport locations thereafter.

CHICAGO, ILLINOIS

Chicago is along the southwest shore of Lake Michigan and occupies a plain which, for the most part, is only some tens of feet above the lake. Lake Michigan averages 579 feet above m.s.l. Natural water drainage over most of the City would be into Lake Michigan, and from areas west of the City is into the Mississippi River system. But actual drainage over most of the City is artificially channeled also into the Mississippi system.

Topography does not significantly affect air flow in or near the City except that lesser frictional drag over Lake Michigan causes winds to be frequently stronger along the lake shore, and often permits air-masses moving from the north to reach shore areas an hour or more before affecting western parts of the City.

Chicago is in a region of frequently changeable weather. The climate is predominantly continental, ranging from relatively warm in summer to relatively cold in winter. However, the continentality is partially modified by Lake Michigan, and to a lesser extent by other Great Lakes. In late autumn and winter, airmasses that are initially very cold often reach the City only after being tempered by passage over one or more of the lakes. Similarly, in late spring and summer, airmasses reaching the City from the north, northeast, or east are cooler because of movement over the Great Lakes. Very low winter temperatures most often occur in air that flows southward to the west of Lake Superior before reaching the Chicago area. In summer the higher temperatures are with south or southwest flow and are therefore not influenced by the lakes, the only modifying effect being a local lake breeze. Strong south or southwest flow may overcome the lake breeze and cause high temperatures to extend over the entire City.

During the warm season, when the lake is cold relative to land, there is frequently a lake breeze that reduces daytime temperature near the shore, sometimes by 10° or more below temperatures farther inland. When the breeze off the lake is light this effect usually reaches inland only a mile or two, but with stronger on-shore winds the whole City is cooled. On the other hand, temperatures at night are warmer near the lake so that 24-hour averages on the whole are only slightly different in various parts of the City and suburbs.

In summer a combination of high temperature and humidity may develop, usually building up progressively over a period of several days when winds continue out of the south or southwest, becoming oppressive for one or perhaps several days, then ending abruptly with a shift of winds into northwest or northerly. The change may be preceded or accompanied by thundershowers. High relative humidity often results from wind flow off the lake, but the air is then cooler and not oppressive.

In about half the summers a temperature of 99° or higher has been recorded at Midway Airport (less often downtown), while half the winters have had a minimum as low as -10°. There is a 50 percent likelihood that the temperature will fall to 32° or lower by October 26, and that the last temperature of 32° or lower in spring will have occurred by April 20. However, temperatures this low have been recorded as early as September 25 in autumn, and as late in spring as May 14. Normal daily mean temperatures are below 32° for 87 days during winter. The normal heating season is from mid-September to early June. Ninety-four percent of the normal heating load is between October 1 and April 30, and 55 percent during the winter months of December through February. The normal air-conditioning season lasts from about mid-June to early September.

Precipitation falls mostly from air that has passed over the Gulf of Mexico. But in winter there is sometimes snowfall, light inland but locally heavy near the lake shore, with Lake Michigan as the principal moisture source. The heavy lake-shore snow occurs when initially colder air moves from the north with a long trajectory over Lake Michigan and impinges on the Chicago lake shore. In this situation the airmass is warmed and its moisture content increased up to a height of several thousand feet. Snowfall is produced by upward currents that become stronger, because of frictional effects, when the air moves from the lake onto land. This type of snowfall therefore tends to be heavier and to extend fartner inland in south-shore areas of the City and in Indiana suburbs, where the angle between wind-flow and shoreline is greatest. The effect of Lake Michigan, both on winter temperatures and lake-produced snowfall, is enhanced by non-freezing of much of the lake during winter, even though shore areas and harbors are often ice-choked. This type of local heavy snowfall may occur once or a few times in a normal season.

Station: CHICAGO, ILLINOIS
MIDWAY AIRPORT
Elevation (ground): 607 feet

TEMPERATURES °F

Month	Normal			Extremes			
	Daily maximum	Daily minimum	Monthly	Record highest	Year	Record lowest	Year
(a)				12		12	
J	31.5	17.0	24.3	65	1967	-16	1966
F	34.6	20.2	27.4	65	1972	-9	1971
M	44.6	29.0	36.8	80	1974	5	1974
A	59.3	40.4	49.9	88	1970	16	1975
M	70.3	49.7	60.0	94	1975	29	1966
J	80.6	60.3	70.5	101	1971	41	1972
J	84.4	65.0	74.7	99	1974	46	1972
A	83.3	64.1	73.7	98	1964	43	1965
S	75.8	56.0	65.9	95	1971	34	1974
O	65.1	45.6	55.4	94	1963	26	1972
N	48.1	32.6	40.4	78	1974	7	1964
D	35.3	21.6	28.5	71	1970	-10	1967
YR	59.4	41.8	50.6	101	JUN 1971	-16	JAN 1966

IMPORTANT:
The time-period covered by this record is limited: See footnotes following table of NORMALS, MEANS AND EXTREMES for explanation and for additional history of EXTREME HIGHS AND LOWS recorded in the general area.

(Continued)

Summer thundershowers are often locally heavy and variable; parts of the City may receive substantial rainfall and other parts none. Longer periods of continuous precipitation are mostly in autumn, winter, and spring. About one-half the precipitation in winter, and about 10 percent of the yearly total precipitation falls as snow. Snowfall from month to month and year to year is greatly variable. There is a 50 percent likelihood that the first and last 1-inch snowfall of a season will occur by December 5 and March 20, respectively. The corresponding dates for the first and last 3-inch snowfall are December 24 and March 2. Freezing rain sometimes occurs but is usually light. During the cold season slight melting and refreezing of precipitation is a fairly common hazard to highway traffic.

Channeling of winds between tall buildings often causes locally stronger gusts in the central business area. Also winds are often locally more brisk along the shoreline; otherwise the nickname "windy city" is a misnomer, because the average wind speed is not greater than in many other parts of the United States.

Fog is infrequent. Visibility is much more often restricted by local air pollution, a condition that is worst during the heating season, but which continues throughout the year because of extensive industrial activity. For much of the time in autumn, winter, and spring, smoke and other air pollution is carried away by winds, sometimes rapidly, but on some occasions when there is little or no wind the pollution accumulates, especially during night and early morning hours. Summertime air pollution is less, partly because of lesser output, but also because of better vertical dispersal; on the other hand, on many summer days surface wind flow converges into the City, preventing or lessening horizontal outflow at the ground.

The amount of sunshine is moderate in summer and quite low in winter. A considerable amount of cloudiness, especially in winter, is locally produced by lake effect. Days in summer with no sunshine are rare. The total sunshine in December, partly because of shorter days, is only a little over one-third the July total

CHICAGO, ILLINOIS

Normals, Means, and Extremes

(To better understand these tables, see full explanation of terms beginning on page 322)

Month	Normal Degree days Base 65 °F: Heating	Cooling	Precipitation in inches, Water equivalent: Normal	Maximum monthly	Year	Minimum monthly	Year	Maximum in 24 hrs.	Year	Snow, Ice pellets: Maximum monthly	Year	Maximum in 24 hrs.	Year
(a)				33		33		33		33		33	
J	1262	0	1.85	4.09	1965	0.26	1961	2.86	1960	28.9	1967	19.8	1967
F	1053	0	1.59	3.35	1950	0.25	1969	1.54	1960	22.5	1967	8.3	1956
M	874	0	2.73	5.00	1954	0.33	1958	2.50	1948	22.3	1965	14.3	1970
A	453	0	3.75	8.33	1947	0.45	1971	4.08	1947	10.7	1970	10.7	1970
M	208	53	3.41	7.59	1945	0.78	1950	3.63	1966	0.2	1966	0.2	1966
J	26	191	3.95	8.89	1950	0.78	1956	4.58	1959	0.0		0.0	
J	0	301	4.09	8.98	1957	1.33	1945	6.24	1957	0.0		0.0	
A	8	277	3.14	6.79	1965	0.85	1973	3.83	1968	0.0		0.0	
S	57	84	3.00	14.17	1961	0.46	1956	3.68	1972	0.0		0.0	
O	316	19	2.62	12.06	1954	0.20	1964	5.63	1954	4.4	1967	4.4	1967
N	738	0	2.20	5.05	1966	0.89	1949	2.93	1966	14.3	1951	8.6	1975
D	1132	0	2.11	6.67	1949	0.30	1962	2.79	1965	33.3	1951	12.5	1960
YR	6127	925	34.44	14.17	SEP 1961	0.20	OCT 1964	6.24	JUL 1957	33.3	DEC 1951	19.8	JAN 1967

Month	Relative humidity pct. Hour 00 (Local time)	Hour 06	Hour 12	Hour 18	Wind: Mean speed m.p.h.	Prevailing direction	Fastest mile: Speed m.p.h.	Direction	Year	Pct. of possible sunshine	Mean sky cover, tenths, sunrise to sunset	Mean number of days, Sunrise to sunset: Clear	Partly cloudy	Cloudy	Precipitation .01 inch or more	Snow, Ice pellets 1.0 inch or more	Thunderstorms	Heavy fog, visibility ¼ mile or less	Temperatures °F Max. (b) 90° and above	Max. 32° and below	Min. 32° and below	Min. 0° and below	Average station pressure mb. Elev. 623 feet m.s.l.
(a)	12	12	12	12	33	19	33	33		33	33	33	33	33	33	33	33	33	12	12	12	12	3
J	71	73	65	68	11.4	W	50	W	1950	44	7.0	7	6	18	11	3	*	2	0	16	27	4	995.2
F	69	72	62	65	11.6	W	51	SW	1967	47	6.9	6	6	16	10	3	*	1	0	11	25	2	994.9
M	70	74	59	61	11.9	W	54	NW	1955	51	7.0	5	9	17	13	2	3	1	0	4	20	0	992.2
A	68	74	56	58	11.8	W	50	NW	1951	53	6.7	6	8	16	13	*	5	1	0	*	5	0	992.4
M	69	73	53	53	10.4	SSW	54	S	1950	61	6.3	7	10	14	12	0	5	1	1	0	*	0	990.1
J	69	75	54	55	9.4	SW	50	W	1953	67	5.9	7	11	12	11	0	7	*	5	0	0	0	990.9
J	71	77	55	55	8.3	SW	46	NW	1959	70	5.3	10	12	9	9	0	6	*	8	0	0	0	993.2
A	75	80	56	59	8.1	SW	54	NW	1949	68	5.3	10	12	9	8	0	5	1	5	0	0	0	994.7
S	75	81	56	60	9.0	S	48	SW	1959	63	5.4	10	10	10	9	0	4	*	2	0	0	0	995.9
O	71	78	54	59	9.8	S	45	S	1949	62	5.4	11	9	11	8	*	2	1	*	0	2	0	996.7
N	74	79	65	69	11.3	SSW	60	SW	1952	41	7.1	6	7	17	10	1	1	1	0	2	13	0	997.3
D	77	80	72	74	11.1	W	50	SW	1948	38	7.2	6	6	19	11	3	1	2	0	10	25	1	995.4
YR	72	76	59	61	10.3	W	60	SW	NOV 1952	57	6.3	91	106	168	123	12	39	13	21	42	118	7	994.1

FOOTNOTES Means and extremes above are from existing and comparable exposures. Annual extremes have been exceeded at other sites in the locality as follows: Highest temperature 105 in July 1934; lowest temperature -23 in December 1872; minimum monthly precipitation 0.06 in February 1877; maximum monthly snowfall 42.5 in January 1918; fastest mile of wind 87 from Northeast in February 1894.

Snowfall

Season	July	Aug	Sept	Oct	Nov	Dec	Jan
1936-37	0.0	0.0	0.0	T	0.6	0.8	2.4
1937-38	0.0	0.0	0.0	T	2.7	3.4	6.3
1938-39	0.0	0.0	0.0	T	0.2	3.5	24.7
1939-40	0.0	0.0	0.0	0.0	0.4	0.5	8.6
1940-41	0.0	0.0	0.0	0.0	14.8	4.1	10.7
#1941-42	0.0	0.0	0.0	0.0	5.2	1.7	4.6
1942-43	0.0	0.0	T	T	3.3	10.1	20.8
1943-44	0.0	0.0	0.0	T	0.2	0.1	3.3
1944-45	0.0	0.0	0.0	0.0	1.0	15.8	12.8
1945-46	0.0	0.0	0.0	0.0	0.7	11.1	3.9
1946-47	0.0	0.0	0.0	0.0	T	8.3	7.4
1947-48	0.0	0.0	0.0	0.0	6.2	6.1	9.9
1948-49	0.0	0.0	0.0	0.0	T	6.8	0.5
1949-50	0.0	0.0	0.0	0.0	2.6	5.3	3.0
1950-51	0.0	0.0	0.0	0.0	7.0	27.1	6.2
1951-52	0.0	0.0	0.0	T	14.3	33.3	8.3
1952-53	0.0	0.0	0.0	3.0	T	5.0	5.1
1953-54	0.0	0.0	0.0	0.0	7.6	5.4	1.9
1954-55	0.0	0.0	0.0	0.1	5.7	8.2	6.5
1955-56	0.0	0.0	0.0	T	5.9	2.1	1.2
1956-57	0.0	0.0	0.0	0.0	1.5	8.5	12.9
1957-58	0.0	0.0	0.0	1.9	0.5	6.0	9.2
1958-59	0.0	0.0	0.0	0.0	0.7	13.2	18.4
1959-60	0.0	0.0	0.0	T	6.6	10.4	3.5
1960-61	0.0	0.0	0.0	T	0.7	14.0	6.3
1961-62	0.0	0.0	0.0	T	1.6	16.6	20.1
1962-63	0.0	0.0	0.0	0.3	0.4	4.3	21.1
1963-64	0.0	0.0	0.0	0.0	T	7.9	2.5
1964-65	0.0	0.0	0.0	0.0	0.8	13.3	10.0
1965-66	0.0	0.0	0.0	0.0	T	5.8	9.1
1966-67	0.0	0.0	0.0	0.0	1.5	6.7	28.9
1967-68	0.0	0.0	0.0	4.4	1.2	2.7	12.7
1968-69	0.0	0.0	0.0	0.0	0.8	11.9	6.8
1969-70	0.0	0.0	0.0	0.0	3.8	20.2	15.5
1970-71	0.0	0.0	0.0	0.0	0.3	4.2	12.8
1971-72	0.0	0.0	0.0	0.0	1.2	0.3	11.7
1972-73	0.0	0.0	0.0	0.8	5.5	10.3	0.8
1973-74	0.0	0.0	0.0	0.0	T	26.0	10.1
1974-75	0.0	0.0	0.0	T	5.1	16.3	7.2
1975-76	0.0	0.0	0.0	0.0	10.8	11.7	
RECORD MEAN	0.0	0.0	0.0	0.3	2.9	10.5	9.4

Heating Degree Days

Season	July	Aug	Sept	Oct	Nov	Dec	Jan
1955-56	0	0	43	300	864	1205	1123
1956-57	3	3	86	153	724	993	1425
1957-58	0	0	89	397	736	941	1192
1958-59	0	4	67	255	659	1315	1437
1959-60	0	0	62	406	939	898	1137
1960-61	0	0	26	301	657	1225	1284
1961-62	3	2	77	293	718	1204	1450
1962-63	1	1	112	276	674	1234	1600
#1963-64	2	6	50	98	579	1454	1090
1964-65	1	17	101	423	633	1160	1250
1965-66	0	26	99	350	683	879	1437
1966-67	0	4	83	363	653	1116	1113
1967-68	26	16	104	381	803	1027	1243
1968-69	4	9	41	331	691	1116	1336
1969-70	2	0	56	390	777	1118	1475
1970-71	4	0	79	293	723	1032	1413
1971-72	5	2	56	146	683	871	1311
1972-73	15	12	93	454	818	1224	1118
1973-74	0	1	70	232	685	1158	1230
1974-75	0	2	157	360	715	1041	1144
1975-76	2	0	155	279	532	1029	

Cooling Degree Days

Year	Jan	Feb	Mar	Apr	May	June	July
1969	0	0	0	1	88	125	316
1970	0	0	0	32	104	221	349
1971	0	0	0	2	29	341	246
1972	0	0	0	1	83	120	312
1973	0	0	0	5	2	243	357
1974	0	0	0	18	26	105	329
1975	0	0	0	0	89	242	354

Feb	Mar	Apr	May	June	Total
3.1	4.8	0.3	0.0	0.0	12.0
5.4	2.8	13.6	0.0	0.0	34.2
5.1	0.3	0.1	0.0	0.0	33.9
12.9	6.3	0.1	2.2	0.0	31.0
11.2	11.7	0.0	0.0	0.0	52.5
9.2	9.1	T	0.0	0.0	29.8
2.9	7.8	0.3	0.0	0.0	45.2
12.5	7.9	T	T	0.0	24.0
4.3	1.0	T	T	0.0	34.9
7.8	0.4	0.0	0.0	0.0	23.9
5.0	13.3	0.1	T	0.0	34.1
5.6	10.3	T	0.0	0.0	38.1
5.9	0.6	0.5	0.0	0.0	14.3
16.6	5.3	1.0	0.0	0.0	33.8
6.8	4.9	2.4	0.0	0.0	54.4
2.0	7.5	1.0	0.0	0.0	66.4
5.5	4.8	T	T	0.0	23.4
8.2	19.9	T	0.2	0.0	43.2
6.5	5.2	0.0	0.0	0.0	32.2
13.2	3.9	T	0.0	0.0	26.3
2.9	3.2	2.3	0.0	0.0	31.3
1.0	1.4	T	0.0	0.0	20.0
4.0	4.6	0.1	0.0	0.0	41.0
16.4	14.0	T	T	0.0	50.9
7.1	3.8	8.8	0.0	0.0	40.7
13.3	7.0	0.3	T	0.0	58.9
11.2	5.4	T	0.0	0.0	42.7
6.4	18.4	T	0.0	0.0	35.2
13.1	22.3	T	0.0	0.0	59.5
6.0	3.8	T	0.2	0.0	24.9
22.5	5.7	3.1	0.0	0.0	68.4
4.9	2.5	T	0.0	0.0	28.4
3.2	6.7	0.0	T	0.0	29.4
9.0	17.8	10.7	0.0	0.0	77.0
5.0	14.8	0.8	T	0.0	37.9
14.7	15.6	3.3	0.0	0.0	46.8
8.9	3.8	2.8	T	0.0	32.9
18.1	3.3	0.8	0.0	0.0	58.3
9.1	4.5	10.0	0.0	0.0	52.2
8.5	7.6	1.5	T	0.0	40.7

Average Temperature

Year	Jan	Feb	Mar	Apr	May	June	July	Aug	Sept	Oct	Nov	Dec	Annual
1936	19.0	15.2	39.6	43.6	64.4	64.6	76.8	75.0	68.2	53.6	38.0	34.0	49.3
1937	26.9	26.4	32.8	46.5	57.9	65.9	74.4	75.7	65.1	51.2	37.4	26.6	48.9
1938	25.4	34.6	45.0	50.2	58.3	67.6	73.8	75.0	65.0	58.8	43.6	29.2	52.2
1939	31.6	27.6	38.2	45.2	61.4	70.8	74.0	72.6	70.0	56.0	41.6	35.0	52.0
1940	16.2	29.2	32.2	44.6	54.1	67.4	74.2	72.0	64.6	57.4	38.6	33.5	48.7
1941	28.1	25.6	32.0	52.7	62.4	69.4	73.7	73.6	68.8	56.9	43.2	36.4	51.9
#1942	25.6	26.5	39.6	53.9	59.5	68.2	75.2	72.3	62.4	53.3	40.9	23.0	50.0
1943	22.6	27.8	32.2	45.6	56.6	72.2	75.7	75.0	61.6	53.7	36.2	27.6	48.9
1944	31.4	29.0	32.3	45.3	64.4	72.8	74.2	74.1	66.2	53.4	42.7	22.0	50.6
1945	19.2	28.8	48.6	49.8	54.1	65.4	72.0	72.0	64.0	51.4	39.8	22.2	48.9
1946	26.7	28.6	47.2	51.1	56.9	68.3	74.6	69.9	65.6	58.5	42.4	31.9	51.8
1947	28.7	20.4	31.8	46.6	53.8	66.0	71.1	80.2	66.7	62.1	34.6	30.0	49.3
1948	18.0	26.3	36.1	53.1	55.0	67.6	74.8	73.6	67.8	51.5	43.0	30.4	49.8
1949	28.4	27.8	37.5	47.8	61.5	74.0	77.8	74.7	60.4	57.2	40.1	31.8	51.6
1950	29.4	26.3	32.9	41.5	60.5	69.1	72.3	70.0	64.9	59.0	34.3	19.6	48.3
1951	23.5	27.3	35.3	46.9	62.1	66.9	72.6	70.0	62.9	54.9	32.9	26.2	48.4
1952	27.3	32.3	35.2	51.2	58.7	74.3	77.4	72.7	65.5	48.8	42.8	32.4	51.6
1953	29.2	31.7	39.2	46.7	61.0	73.6	76.4	75.8	67.6	59.7	44.4	31.8	53.1
1954	27.7	37.6	35.0	53.3	57.1	75.7	76.5	73.3	69.4	55.3	42.5	31.9	52.9
1955	24.9	28.8	37.2	57.0	63.8	69.1	81.3	78.7	67.9	55.5	36.0	25.8	52.2
1956	28.5	29.4	36.4	47.2	60.5	73.9	72.9	74.1	65.0	60.8	40.6	32.8	51.9
1957	18.8	33.4	37.6	49.6	58.8	71.2	76.4	73.4	64.2	52.0	40.2	34.5	50.9
1958	26.3	20.0	36.1	51.4	61.7	64.7	73.5	73.8	66.2	57.5	42.8	22.4	49.7
1959	18.5	26.1	37.3	49.2	65.8	72.9	74.8	78.7	69.0	51.9	33.4	35.9	51.1
1960	28.1	25.8	26.4	53.4	58.6	68.2	73.7	75.7	70.6	55.6	42.8	25.3	50.4
1961	23.3	34.3	40.8	44.3	57.2	69.6	74.0	74.4	69.2	56.1	40.9	26.0	50.9
1962	18.1	25.8	34.6	49.9	67.1	70.9	72.1	74.7	64.2	57.3	42.4	25.0	50.2
#1963	13.3	19.2	41.5	52.4	58.7	73.4	75.0	72.6	67.6	64.3	45.4	17.9	50.1
1964	29.5	28.8	35.9	51.1	66.0	73.1	75.7	71.7	65.9	51.1	43.7	27.4	51.7
1965	24.5	27.4	30.2	47.7	64.0	68.9	72.7	70.3	65.0	54.0	42.0	36.3	50.3
1966	18.4	27.9	40.2	47.7	55.5	71.5	78.3	71.7	65.0	53.3	43.0	28.7	50.1
1967	28.8	22.0	38.6	50.4	54.8	71.4	70.6	69.2	64.8	53.4	38.0	31.7	49.5
1968	24.8	25.1	43.4	52.9	58.3	72.3	74.3	74.7	66.7	55.7	41.7	28.7	51.5
1969	21.7	30.3	34.4	51.2	61.2	65.6	74.9	75.3	66.4	53.3	38.8	28.7	50.2
1970	17.3	26.6	35.2	52.2	63.3	71.2	75.9	75.2	66.2	55.8	40.7	31.4	50.9
1971	19.2	28.2	35.7	48.7	57.6	75.8	72.7	72.4	70.4	62.2	42.0	36.7	51.8
1972	22.5	25.5	34.8	46.9	61.7	66.1	74.4	73.4	64.8	50.2	37.5	25.2	48.6
1973	28.7	30.2	45.1	48.6	55.7	72.8	76.3	76.7	67.0	58.5	41.9	27.5	52.4
1974	25.1	27.0	38.8	52.1	56.9	66.6	75.4	72.0	61.5	53.5	40.9	31.2	50.1
1975	27.9	26.9	34.2	43.5	63.0	72.1	76.1	76.4	61.4	56.6	47.1	31.5	51.4
RECORD MEAN	24.7	27.1	36.4	47.8	58.2	68.4	73.8	72.5	65.6	54.5	40.4	29.4	49.9
MAX	31.7	34.0	43.5	55.7	66.8	76.8	81.7	80.0	73.5	62.4	47.3	35.7	57.4
MIN	17.7	20.1	29.2	39.8	49.6	59.9	65.8	65.0	57.7	46.6	33.5	23.1	42.3

# Indicates a station move or relocation of instruments.

CHICAGO, IL
MIDWAY AIRPORT

Feb	Mar	Apr	May	June	Total
1025	878	532	212	35	6217
877	842	473	228	23	5830
1253	890	406	149	61	6114
1083	853	466	114	12	6265
1132	1192	374	221	39	6400
853	741	612	265	31	5995
1091	935	480	117	28	6398
1277	720	383	225	26	6529
1043	894	419	83	23	5741
1048	1069	515	105	32	6354
1031	761	511	314	33	6124
1198	814	437	330	10	6121
1152	666	360	218	14	6010
966	941	406	197	101	6139
1071	919	406	149	27	6390
1023	903	482	257	10	6219
1139	929	539	177	78	5936
967	609	489	284	0	6083
1058	803	397	272	51	5957
1059	947	638	142	22	6227

Aug	Sept	Oct	Nov	Dec	Total
329	107	35	0	0	1001
322	123	12	0	0	1163
237	226	64	0	0	1145
278	94	0	0	0	888
368	137	39	0	0	1151
222	60	10	0	0	770
358	52	25	4	0	1124

Precipitation

Year	Jan	Feb	Mar	Apr	May	June	July	Aug	Sept	Oct	Nov	Dec	Annual
1936	1.64	1.33	1.00	2.54	2.08	1.03	0.22	4.29	8.97	3.00	0.90	2.58	29.58
1937	2.29	0.63	1.20	4.61	1.64	5.02	1.41	2.68	1.89	3.09	1.25	1.27	26.98
1938	2.02	2.11	3.51	2.20	3.98	6.78	3.90	2.12	5.29	0.77	0.95	1.18	34.81
1939	2.22	1.98	2.96	3.22	3.66	5.13	2.74	1.47	0.49	1.79	0.95	0.90	27.51
1940	1.25	0.89	2.41	3.17	5.16	1.31	1.29	3.95	0.31	3.26	2.36	1.38	26.74
1941	2.26	1.01	2.60	2.63	3.42	3.43	1.10	2.16	5.20	8.44	2.07	0.97	35.29
#1942	1.39	3.03	2.68	1.59	4.50	1.87	4.01	3.61	5.12	1.44	3.71	2.71	35.66
1943	2.12	1.34	2.47	3.37	7.08	1.47	5.14	5.20	0.92	1.49	1.39	0.34	32.33
1944	0.89	1.70	4.51	3.33	4.36	3.18	1.93	1.89	1.56	0.59	1.31	1.10	26.35
# 1945	0.80	1.18	2.29	4.20	7.59	4.12	1.33	4.23	6.01	1.18	2.88	1.65	37.46
1946	1.94	0.98	3.57	1.28	3.54	5.22	2.49	1.93	2.01	2.82	3.17	2.43	31.38
1947	2.06	0.38	2.69	8.33	3.97	4.40	4.10	3.16	3.26	2.60	2.63	1.63	39.21
1948	1.71	1.62	4.65	1.44	4.80	3.21	3.18	2.50	2.38	0.62	2.41	3.04	31.56
1949	3.32	2.42	3.32	2.14	2.46	3.65	3.59	1.31	1.24	2.73	0.89	6.67	33.74
1950	3.77	3.35	2.01	4.67	0.78	8.89	6.78	1.78	2.00	1.29	1.63	2.70	39.65
1951	1.81	2.62	2.81	4.62	4.90	2.05	4.96	4.86	5.29	2.73	3.74	2.76	43.15
1952	2.18	0.44	3.64	2.54	3.18	3.63	2.27	3.69	1.61	0.90	2.25	1.96	28.29
1953	1.47	1.58	3.92	2.82	2.43	4.63	4.16	1.00	2.02	1.25	1.77	3.10	30.15
1954	1.10	2.40	5.00	4.43	1.75	4.27	4.58	5.91	0.83	12.06	1.80	1.79	45.92
1955	1.49	1.83	1.72	2.01	3.86	3.04	2.84	5.35	1.47	5.37	1.46	0.52	30.96
1956	0.38	2.26	1.10	4.65	3.06	0.78	2.49	4.18	0.46	0.30	1.31	1.26	22.23
1957	2.06	1.77	1.98	6.09	3.21	5.94	8.98	5.36	1.08	3.15	2.72	1.95	44.29
1958	1.12	0.33	0.33	1.64	3.12	6.43	4.74	2.51	1.86	2.12	1.58	0.57	26.35
1959	2.13	2.39	3.91	4.00	3.87	5.94	4.77	1.63	2.17	2.86	3.01	2.00	38.68
1960	3.73	3.16	1.15	3.14	2.83	3.77	3.58	1.02	1.40	1.71	1.28	1.07	27.84
1961	0.26	0.90	2.96	3.28	1.53	3.70	2.99	6.07	14.17	3.49	1.66	1.89	42.90
1962	2.53	1.81	1.82	1.56	2.90	2.56	4.65	0.85	0.77	1.38	1.09	0.30	22.22
1963	1.01	0.54	2.44	4.79	2.17	2.39	7.31	2.15	2.63	0.62	1.21	0.76	28.02
1964	1.08	0.57	3.81	4.96	1.74	1.94	4.83	2.19	2.50	0.20	1.26	1.87	26.95
1965	4.09	1.76	3.44	4.21	1.47	2.89	4.61	6.79	6.21	1.06	1.10	4.42	42.05
1966	1.12	1.78	2.58	5.13	5.78	1.57	6.60	1.41	0.92	2.17	5.05	2.65	36.76
1967	3.22	1.86	2.32	5.37	1.39	8.75	2.36	2.07	3.17	4.67	2.27	3.65	41.10
1968	1.69	1.10	1.04	2.18	2.06	2.15	1.55	5.31	3.68	0.71	4.34	3.92	29.73
1969	2.16	0.25	1.96	5.32	4.04	5.77	7.58	1.11	1.31	3.95	1.55	1.78	36.78
1970	1.03	1.05	2.69	7.07	4.18	7.09	2.58	3.47	6.71	4.94	3.57	1.71	46.09
1971	1.11	2.39	3.30	0.45	1.98	2.18	5.00	1.96	3.47	0.85	0.96	5.93	29.58
1972	1.11	0.92	3.51	3.66	2.88	2.77	2.86	6.19	5.75	3.62	3.18	4.74	41.19
1973	1.51	1.27	4.60	5.46	4.17	2.69	3.98	0.85	4.23	3.47	1.44	4.32	37.99
1974	3.28	2.07	2.85	4.33	5.98	6.25	3.96	0.90	1.53	1.21	2.82	2.35	37.53
1975	3.68	2.29	2.44	7.84	5.31	4.63	1.53	5.51	1.09	2.26	2.94	2.53	42.05
RECORD MEAN	1.93	1.80	2.70	3.14	3.49	3.69	3.43	3.15	3.13	2.59	2.32	2.10	33.47

Record mean values above are means through the current year for the period beginning in 1873 for temperature, 1871 for precipitation and 1943 for snowfall. Data are from City Office locations through 1925, University of Chicago location 1-1-26 through 6-30-42, and from Airport locations 7-1-42 to date.

Station: PEORIA, ILLINOIS
GREATER PEORIA AIRPORT
Elevation (ground): 652 feet

TEMPERATURES °F

Month	Normal Daily maximum	Normal Daily minimum	Normal Monthly	Extremes Record highest	Year	Record lowest	Year
(a)				16		16	
J	31.9	15.7	23.8	66	1967	-20	1963
F	36.0	19.3	27.7	70	1972	-14	1975
M	46.5	28.1	37.3	81	1967	-10	1960
A	61.7	40.8	51.3	87	1970	17	1975
M	72.3	50.7	61.5	92	1975	25	1966
J	81.7	60.9	71.3	100	1971	40	1969
J	85.5	64.6	75.1	102	1966	47	1972
A	84.0	62.9	73.5	99	1964	44	1967
S	76.4	54.6	65.5	94	1960	31	1974
O	65.9	44.0	55.0	90	1963	19	1972
N	48.7	31.1	39.9	77	1964	4	1964
D	35.7	20.3	28.0	71	1970	-18	1963
YR	60.5	41.1	50.8	102	JUL 1966	-20	JAN 1963

IMPORTANT:
The time-period covered by this record is limited: See footnotes following table of **NORMALS, MEANS AND EXTREMES** for explanation and for additional history of **EXTREME HIGHS AND LOWS** recorded in the general area.

The climate of this area is typically continental as shown by its changeable weather and the wide range of temperature extremes.

The Airport Station is situated on a rather level tableland surrounded by well-drained and gently rolling terrain. It is set back a mile from the rim of the Illinois River Valley and is almost 200 feet above the river bed. Exposures of all instruments are good.

Monthly mean temperatures range from 24° during January to 75° during July with an annual average of 51°. Illustrating the extreme conditions that have occurred, the single year of 1936 had 17 days with temperatures 100° or higher in July while the early part of that same year had 26 zero days in a 31-day period. 1936 also had the absolute maximum record of 113° set on July 15, but the absolute minimum of -27° dates back to January of 1884. June and September are usually the most pleasant months of the year. Then during October or first of November, "Indian Summer" is often experienced with an extended period of warm dry weather.

The average date for the last occurrence in the spring of temperatures as low as 32° is April 16 with the latest date occurring on May 12 in 1960. The average date for the first occurrence in the fall of temperatures as low as 32° is October 21 with the earliest date occurring on September 26 in 1928. The average growing season is 189 days with the longest growing season of record of 214 days occurring in 1931, while the shortest was 151 days in 1928.

(Continued page 438)

Snowfall

Season	July	Aug	Sept	Oct	Nov	Dec	Jan
1936-37	0.0	0.0	0.0	T	0.1	0.6	4.7
1937-38	0.0	0.0	0.0	T	4.1	0.8	6.3
1938-39	0.0	0.0	0.0	T	0.6	0.9	13.6
1939-40	0.0	0.0	0.0	0.0	T	8.0	4.3
1940-41	0.0	0.0	0.0	0.0	1.3	0.3	9.1
1941-42	0.0	0.0	0.0	0.0	3.5	3.6	3.5
#1942-43	0.0	0.0	1.0	0.0	3.2	9.5	14.2
1943-44	0.0	0.0	0.0	0.0	0.4	3.0	T
1944-45	0.0	0.0	0.0	0.0	0.3	8.3	7.0
1945-46	0.0	0.0	0.0	0.0	0.5	7.0	1.8
1946-47	0.0	0.0	0.0	0.0	0.0	5.1	5.1
1947-48	0.0	0.0	0.0	0.0	3.6	1.8	4.3
1948-49	0.0	0.0	0.0	0.0	T	2.0	3.2
1949-50	0.0	0.0	0.0	0.0	0.3	3.6	2.1
1950-51	0.0	0.0	0.0	T	4.8	8.3	4.8
1951-52	0.0	0.0	0.0	0.0	8.9	9.8	2.3
1952-53	0.0	0.0	0.0	0.0	T	2.4	5.2
1953-54	0.0	0.0	0.0	0.0	1.8	4.3	0.1
1954-55	0.0	0.0	0.0	T	4.0	8.2	12.0
1955-56	0.0	0.0	0.0	T	2.2	2.3	1.8
1956-57	0.0	0.0	0.0	0.0	2.8	9.1	10.0
1957-58	0.0	0.0	0.0	T	0.4	5.4	11.0
1958-59	0.0	0.0	0.0	0 0	1.0	5.0	11.6
1959-60	0.0	0.0	0.0	0.0	7.0	2.4	3.3
1960-61	0.0	0.0	0.0	0.0	0.3	4.6	3.5
1961-62	0.0	0.0	0.0	0.0	0.7	10.5	10.5
1962-63	0.0	0.0	0.0	T	T	2.1	7.0
1963-64	0.0	0.0	0.0	0.0	0.4	6.1	4.8
1964-65	0.0	0.0	0.0	0.0	1.0	7.2	5.5
1965-66	0.0	0.0	0.0	0.0	0.1	4.2	0.6
1966-67	0.0	0.0	0.0	0.0	T	3.8	10.0
1967-68	0.0	0.0	0.0	1.8	2.5	2.2	8.4
1968-69	0.0	0.0	0.0	0.0	1.5	4.6	4.6
1969-70	0.0	0.0	0.0	0.0	0.6	11.0	7.3
1970-71	0.0	0.0	0.0	0.0	T	3.4	5.4
1971-72	0.0	0.0	0.0	0.0	4.0	T	10.2
1972-73	0.0	0.0	0.0	0.3	7.3	4.7	0.8
1973-74	0.0	0.0	0.0	0.0	0.1	18.9	6.7
1974-75	0.0	0.0	0.0	0.0	9.1	6.2	8.8
1975-76	0.0	0.0	0.0	0.0	8.1	1.4	
RECORD MEAN	0.0	0.0	0.0	0.1	2.3	5.5	5.6

Heating Degree Days

Season	July	Aug	Sept	Oct	Nov	Dec	Jan
1955-56	0	0	41	331	874	1194	1208
1956-57	0	6	74	129	747	1026	1434
1957-58	0	0	70	408	758	949	1233
1958-59	1	11	72	274	652	1296	1435
#1959-60	1	0	66	421	954	930	1171
1960-61	2	0	53	342	724	1278	1351
1961-62	2	5	120	347	752	1262	1501
1962-63	4	0	137	341	717	1279	1613
1963-64	2	22	64	93	652	1534	1118
1964-65	2	8	108	435	637	1212	1254
1965-66	0	18	100	391	707	914	1406
1966-67	0	10	106	419	666	1103	1151
1967-68	10	30	113	394	841	1083	1323
1968-69	5	7	68	377	732	1150	1377
1969-70	0	0	77	443	818	1211	1545
1970-71	2	3	84	353	774	1080	1418
1971-72	17	5	85	186	728	945	1402
1972-73	9	19	87	461	855	1271	1161
1973-74	0	0	54	253	671	1237	1292
1974-75	0	1	157	354	756	1081	1156
1975-76	13	1	171	306	596	1069	

Cooling Degree Days

Year	Jan	Feb	Mar	Apr	May	June	July
1969	0	0	0	0	67	122	334
1970	0	0	0	24	99	178	317
1971	0	0	0	14	22	359	217
1972	0	0	0	0	103	140	273
1973	0	0	0	7	3	211	315
1974	0	0	0	12	43	99	377
1975	0	0	0	0	83	237	292

Feb	Mar	Apr	May	June	Total
2.0	1.2	T	0.0	0.0	8.6
7.0	T	6.2	0.0	0.0	24.4
3.3	T	T	0.0	0.0	18.4
8.2	2.3	T	T	0.0	22.8
3.3	5.1	0.0	0.0	0.0	19.1
8.9	0.7	T	0.0	0.0	20.2
6.5	7.7	0.2	0.0	0.0	42.3
11.0	2.8	0.0	T	0.0	17.2
3.0	2.7	T	0.0	0.0	21.3
3.2	9.9	T	0.0	0.0	22.4
5.3	6.8	T	0.0	0.0	22.3
4.0	3.0	0.0	0.0	0.0	16.7
3.8	0.1	1.2	0.0	0.0	10.3
10.7	2.0	T	T	0.0	18.7
5.4	10.2	2.1	0.0	0.0	35.6
6.5	4.8	T	0.0	0.0	32.3
0.4	3.2	2.6	0.0	0.0	13.8
2.8	4.3	0.0	T	0.0	13.3
3.1	5.6	0.0	0.0	0.0	32.9
5.2	4.5	T	0.0	0.0	16.0
0.5	8.2	1.6	0.0	0.0	32.2
1.5	0.4	T	0.0	0.0	18.7
2.6	4.2	T	0.0	0.0	24.4
12.0	16.9	T	T	0.0	41.6
5.3	0.7	1.2	0.0	0.0	15.6
7.5	2.0	1.1	0.0	0.0	32.3
6.2	T	0.0	0.0	0.0	15.3
6.2	7.9	T	0.0	0.0	25.4
5.8	13.5	0.0	0.0	0.0	33.0
2.0	0.8	T	0.1	0.0	7.8
3.6	2.7	1.4	0.0	0.0	21.5
1.6	1.1	T	0.0	0.0	17.6
2.2	4.1	0.0	0.0	0.0	17.0
5.9	8.3	4.6	0.0	0.0	37.7
0.6	5.8	0.0	0.0	0.0	15.2
6.2	8.0	0.9	0.0	0.0	29.3
2.7	1.2	0.7	0.0	0.0	17.7
1.9	0.9	1.2	0.0	0.0	29.7
12.8	3.8	1.6	0.0	0.0	42.3
4.7	4.7	0.6	T	0.0	23.5

Average Temperature

Year	Jan	Feb	Mar	Apr	May	June	July	Aug	Sept	Oct	Nov	Dec	Annual
1936	17.2	14.8	41.9	48.2	67.0	72.0	84.3	80.3	70.5	54.2	37.8	33.8	51.8
1937	23.8	27.8	36.2	49.7	63.2	70.8	75.8	78.3	65.8	52.2	36.7	26.8	50.6
1938	26.2	36.2	47.4	53.3	62.2	69.9	76.5	77.2	68.1	60.3	43.0	30.0	54.2
1939	32.2	27.5	41.0	47.7	66.2	73.0	76.2	73.2	71.7	57.1	41.2	33.9	53.4
1940	13.3	29.4	35.9	49.8	58.9	73.6	77.4	74.8	66.6	59.0	38.2	34.0	50.9
1941	28.4	25.7	35.4	56.0	66.8	73.4	77.0	76.2	69.7	58.0	43.3	36.4	53.9
1942	25.6	26.8	42.0	56.1	61.9	71.9	76.3	73.4	64.8	55.2	41.4	24.6	51.7
#1943	24.3	30.6	35.4	48.8	58.8	73.2	76.1	75.6	61.9	53.8	36.4	26.2	49.9
1944	31.0	29.4	34.4	47.4	66.4	74.2	74.8	73.8	66.2	54.4	43.0	22.2	51.4
1945	19.8	29.6	49.4	51.6	55.6	66.4	72.4	74.0	65.4	51.5	39.6	21.6	49.8
1946	27.2	30.8	50.1	54.2	58.2	70.4	76.1	69.9	65.8	59.0	42.8	33.0	53.1
1947	28.5	21.5	32.7	49.8	56.8	68.0	72.4	82.0	68.2	63.2	35.0	31.3	50.8
1948	20.2	27.6	37.5	55.0	59.6	70.6	74.8	74.3	69.0	52.2	42.8	31.4	51.2
1949	26.5	27.5	39.0	50.6	64.4	74.7	78.4	74.5	60.4	57.4	42.3	33.3	52.4
1950	29.2	26.9	34.6	44.3	63.6	69.9	72.4	69.0	65.8	60.1	34.0	20.8	49.2
1951	24.3	27.9	34.7	47.9	63.9	68.4	73.8	71.7	62.3	55.2	33.3	26.1	49.1
1952	27.2	33.0	36.1	52.4	60.9	76.7	77.0	72.6	65.7	48.4	42.5	32.3	52.1
1953	28.4	32.9	39.9	47.0	61.7	75.8	77.0	75.1	67.2	59.0	43.0	31.1	53.2
1954	27.4	37.5	35.4	55.6	57.5	75.5	77.8	73.8	69.1	55.4	41.8	31.1	53.1
1955	24.5	28.1	37.8	58.7	64.3	68.4	80.9	77.8	67.6	54.3	35.6	26.3	52.0
1956	25.9	29.8	38.9	48.8	64.3	74.1	73.7	74.1	65.5	61.6	39.9	31.8	52.4
1957	18.6	34.5	38.3	51.1	61.1	71.7	77.6	75.2	64.8	51.6	39.5	34.1	51.5
1958	25.0	19.5	36.8	52.2	62.7	66.4	72.8	73.9	65.8	56.5	43.1	23.0	49.8
#1959	18.5	27.0	38.9	51.0	66.1	73.6	75.0	77.8	68.1	51.3	32.9	34.7	51.3
1960	26.9	24.0	22.6	53.0	57.8	68.1	72.0	73.4	68.3	54.0	40.7	23.6	48.7
1961	21.3	31.8	40.6	44.4	56.5	69.4	73.3	72.3	66.2	53.7	39.6	24.1	49.4
1962	16.5	25.9	33.7	50.2	68.2	71.0	72.0	73.6	62.6	54.9	40.8	23.6	49.4
1963	12.8	18.6	41.5	52.9	59.0	73.0	74.3	70.4	65.2	64.2	43.0	15.5	49.2
1964	28.7	28.1	36.0	52.2	66.3	72.7	76.2	72.4	65.4	50.8	43.5	25.7	51.5
1965	24.3	27.0	28.0	50.9	66.7	71.3	73.7	71.2	64.7	52.5	41.2	35.4	50.6
1966	19.5	27.8	40.7	48.1	57.1	70.4	78.4	70.3	63.8	51.3	42.6	29.2	49.9
1967	27.6	21.8	40.2	52.7	56.4	72.3	72.0	68.1	63.3	52.6	36.8	29.8	49.5
1968	22.1	23.7	43.0	52.4	57.7	72.4	73.2	73.8	64.3	53.9	40.4	27.6	50.4
1969	20.3	30.4	33.0	52.6	61.4	66.4	75.6	73.1	64.8	51.5	37.5	25.8	49.4
1970	15.1	25.9	35.3	52.2	64.2	69.8	74.9	72.3	65.8	53.6	39.1	29.9	49.8
1971	19.2	27.7	35.5	51.9	57.7	76.8	71.2	71.6	68.9	60.0	40.5	34.3	51.3
1972	19.7	24.5	36.9	48.9	63.2	68.0	73.2	72.4	66.2	50.0	36.2	23.8	48.6
1973	27.4	28.9	46.5	50.9	57.9	71.8	75.0	74.7	67.0	57.7	42.4	24.8	52.1
1974	23.1	29.4	41.1	53.6	59.3	66.7	76.9	72.2	61.1	53.6	39.6	29.9	50.5
1975	27.5	26.1	33.8	47.0	64.6	72.1	73.8	74.7	60.9	55.3	44.9	30.2	50.9
RECORD MEAN	24.4	28.0	38.5	50.9	61.6	71.3	75.6	73.7	66.2	54.7	40.4	28.6	51.1
MAX	32.5	36.2	47.8	61.3	72.4	82.1	86.5	84.5	77.2	65.6	49.1	36.1	60.9
MIN	16.3	19.7	29.1	40.5	50.7	60.5	64.6	62.9	55.2	43.8	31.6	21.1	41.3

\# Indicates a station move or relocation of instruments.

PEORIA, IL

Feb	Mar	Apr	May	June	Total
1014	801	491	124	26	6104
847	824	431	158	9	5685
1271	868	381	114	35	6087
1057	800	418	103	5	6124
1183	1308	374	233	18	6659
922	750	612	277	29	6340
1088	960	455	63	14	6569
1292	723	367	200	14	6687
1066	891	384	66	17	5909
1058	1139	416	72	1	6342
1037	746	502	260	22	6103
1205	766	371	291	7	6095
1192	673	371	229	13	6272
962	984	367	172	73	6274
1088	914	402	115	28	6641
1035	906	402	241	0	6298
1167	866	475	150	42	6068
1005	566	423	216	0	6073
991	736	348	214	42	5838
1085	959	534	92	17	6192

Aug	Sept	Oct	Nov	Dec	Total
260	80	30	0	0	893
239	109	6	0	0	972
214	210	37	0	0	1073
253	130	3	0	0	902
306	121	35	0	0	998
233	47	6	0	0	817
307	55	14	0	0	988

Precipitation

Year	Jan	Feb	Mar	Apr	May	June	July	Aug	Sept	Oct	Nov	Dec	Annual
1936	1.79	1.63	1.80	1.64	1.72	0.45	1.24	2.27	10.58	3.35	1.18	3.26	30.91
1937	2.86	2.46	1.02	4.42	3.22	4.87	2.32	1.55	1.14	2.69	1.28	2.06	29.89
1938	4.32	2.21	4.42	3.80	5.72	6.76	6.34	3.01	2.12	0.84	1.65	1.43	42.62
1939	3.40	2.88	3.24	5.16	4.48	5.53	4.80	2.38	0.85	3.80	1.14	0.61	38.27
1940	0.58	0.61	2.01	3.83	3.30	1.24	0.84	3.60	0.92	3.25	2.06	1.75	23.99
1941	3.11	1.01	1.48	5.04	6.52	3.38	1.66	2.79	5.32	10.80	2.00	1.46	44.57
1942	1.39	5.18	2.18	3.71	3.48	5.56	4.73	2.24	2.55	0.96	4.58	2.58	39.14
#1943	1.68	1.04	2.43	5.79	7.35	3.49	2.56	4.63	0.88	1.60	1.23	0.58	33.26
1944	0.57	1.74	5.92	8.32	4.12	2.72	1.73	2.86	4.49	1.23	1.33	0.90	35.93
1945	0.49	1.24	3.90	5.58	4.90	5.66	0.57	1.11	7.36	0.74	2.19	2.39	36.13
1946	2.63	0.58	4.22	1.55	5.06	7.41	0.79	3.40	2.32	3.88	5.29	1.76	38.89
1947	1.47	0.33	2.25	8.66	4.63	7.13	1.64	1.33	2.49	3.57	2.54	3.13	39.17
1948	1.25	1.70	3.94	1.81	2.55	3.25	8.18	0.81	1.72	1.18	1.13	2.61	30.13
1949	4.43	1.63	2.57	2.75	1.17	3.25	4.93	1.28	1.62	2.71	0.65	6.34	33.33
1950	4.09	2.75	1.73	8.49	1.45	5.90	4.13	1.67	3.49	0.61	2.04	0.95	37.30
1951	1.58	3.44	3.35	4.09	2.56	4.04	5.81	3.30	2.50	2.97	2.43	1.16	37.23
1952	1.51	1.59	4.10	3.88	3.90	5.68	2.44	4.73	1.77	0.85	3.09	1.89	35.43
1953	1.28	0.77	4.80	2.81	2.16	3.47	6.32	1.61	2.11	0.74	0.43	2.33	28.83
1954	0.89	2.68	3.41	5.47	2.59	6.35	3.82	8.56	0.93	3.27	2.19	1.80	41.96
1955	2.56	2.44	1.76	3.69	3.54	3.20	0.65	4.72	2.62	3.73	0.72	0.36	29.99
1956	0.25	1.11	0.54	3.12	5.20	0.98	4.67	4.47	0.41	0.67	2.30	1.90	25.62
1957	1.70	0.83	2.63	5.61	7.96	3.04	2.00	1.57	1.21	4.34	2.55	3.55	36.99
1958	1.30	0.57	0.39	2.65	3.32	4.86	8.42	3.35	3.15	0.93	2.02	0.49	31.45
1959	1.71	1.84	3.46	2.50	5.09	1.03	2.83	2.25	3.51	3.56	0.96	1.89	30.63
1960	1.93	1.98	3.24	3.55	6.33	5.42	3.51	5.32	2.82	1.43	1.57	0.53	37.63
1961	0.32	1.07	3.26	2.38	2.19	3.39	5.56	1.94	13.09	1.77	2.79	1.69	39.45
1962	1.97	1.23	2.15	0.89	5.67	2.11	2.77	1.80	1.29	3.56	1.05	0.33	24.82
1963	0.56	0.48	5.32	4.08	1.24	1.53	3.56	2.99	1.76	1.42	1.94	0.78	25.66
1964	1.02	0.54	3.77	6.92	1.04	4.22	1.59	2.06	3.63	0.03	3.01	1.12	28.95
1965	8.11	0.93	3.40	5.58	3.85	1.04	3.31	8.61	8.17	0.69	1.22	3.35	48.26
1966	1.49	2.60	1.78	3.98	4.50	2.29	3.66	2.56	3.06	1.80	2.42	3.00	33.14
1967	1.08	1.07	2.33	5.47	2.80	2.03	5.74	2.34	2.72	5.56	2.18	2.63	35.95
1968	1.12	1.55	0.93	2.20	4.70	6.16	4.32	1.71	4.83	0.58	2.99	2.80	33.89
1969	2.43	0.56	1.20	2.94	2.37	4.93	5.55	2.82	3.31	5.67	0.79	1.13	33.70
1970	0.56	0.64	1.60	7.18	3.89	3.92	5.46	3.21	11.49	4.36	1.11	1.30	44.72
1971	0.59	1.64	1.09	0.71	2.80	0.98	5.21	2.19	3.07	1.71	1.43	4.96	26.38
1972	0.81	0.74	2.48	4.38	1.30	5.97	3.54	4.26	5.21	2.50	2.56	2.48	36.23
1973	1.76	0.99	6.95	4.26	4.51	6.46	6.04	0.90	7.58	5.18	1.48	4.11	50.22
1974	3.09	1.65	2.69	4.11	6.26	11.69	2.63	0.81	1.45	2.07	4.13	1.93	42.51
1975	2.59	2.85	1.73	3.92	5.19	3.90	4.26	5.62	2.74	3.63	2.75	2.04	41.22
RECORD MEAN	1.82	1.80	2.77	3.52	3.92	3.89	3.78	3.06	3.75	2.46	2.27	2.00	35.04

Record mean values above are means through the current year for the period beginning in 1905 for temperature, 1856 for precipitation and 1944 for snowfall. Data are from cooperative and city locations through May 4, 1943.

PEORIA, ILLINOIS

(Continued)

The normal annual precipitation is 35.06 inches with individual years ranging from 23.18 inches in 1910 to 53.26 inches in 1858. Precipitation is normally heaviest during the growing season and at a minimum during midwinter. However, the wettest month on record was September in 1961 with 13.09 inches; and the driest was October of 1964 with only 0.03 of an inch. The maximum amount of rainfall occurring in any 24-hour period was 5.52 inches in May of 1927. Maximum amounts recorded for shorter periods are: for 5 minutes, 0.75 of an inch; for 15 minutes, 1.26 inches; for 30 minutes, 2.10 inches; and for 60 minutes, 2.60 inches.

Annual snowfall has ranged from only 6.0 inches in 1928 to 45.7 inches in 1926. The earliest snow of record occurred on September 25, 1942, when 1.0 inch fell; while traces have occurred as late in the spring as May 9. The heaviest single storm of record brought 18 inches during the last 2 days of February in 1900.

Normals, Means, and Extremes

Month	Normal Degree days Base 65 °F		Precipitation in inches: Water equivalent							Snow, Ice pellets				Relative humidity pct.			
	Heating	Cooling	Normal	Maximum monthly	Year	Minimum monthly	Year	Maximum in 24 hrs.	Year	Maximum monthly	Year	Maximum in 24 hrs.	Year	Hour 00 (Local time)	Hour 06	Hour 12	Hour 18
(a)				36		36		32		32		32		16	16	16	16
J	1277	0	1.82	8.11	1965	0.25	1956	4.45	1965	12.0	1955	9.0	1967	77	78	69	72
F	1044	0	1.50	5.18	1942	0.33	1947	1.92	1954	12.8	1975	7.6	1944	78	79	66	70
M	859	0	2.80	6.95	1973	0.39	1958	3.39	1944	16.9	1960	9.0	1946	77	82	64	66
A	416	5	4.36	8.66	1947	0.71	1971	5.06	1950	4.6	1970	3.6	1970	72	78	57	56
M	180	71	3.87	7.96	1957	1.04	1964	3.62	1956	0.1	1966	0.1	1966	76	81	57	57
J	17	206	3.91	11.69	1974	0.98	1971	4.44	1974	0.0		0.0		76	82	57	57
J	0	313	3.76	8.42	1958	0.57	1945	3.56	1953	0.0		0.0		81	86	59	60
A	8	271	3.07	8.61	1965	0.81	1974	4.32	1955	0.0		0.0		82	88	59	63
S	70	85	3.55	13.09	1961	0.41	1956	4.15	1961	0.0		0.0		82	88	60	65
O	327	17	2.51	10.80	1941	0.03	1964	3.70	1969	1.8	1967	1.8	1967	77	85	58	62
N	753	0	2.02	5.29	1946	0.43	1953	2.45	1946	9.1	1974	7.2	1951	79	83	67	71
D	1147	0	1.89	6.34	1949	0.33	1962	3.38	1949	18.9	1973	10.2	1973	82	84	73	77
YR	6098	968	35.06	13.09	SEP 1961	0.03	OCT 1964	5.06	APR 1950	18.9	DEC 1973	10.2	DEC 1973	78	83	62	65

(To better understand these tables, see full explanation of terms beginning on page 322)

Month	Wind: Mean speed m.p.h.	Prevailing direction	Fastest mile: Speed m.p.h.	Direction	Year	Pct. of possible sunshine	Mean sky cover, tenths, sunrise to sunset	Mean number of days: Sunrise to sunset: Clear	Partly cloudy	Cloudy	Precipitation .01 inch or more	Snow, Ice pellets 1.0 inch or more	Thunderstorms	Heavy fog, visibility ¼ mile or less	Temperatures °F Max. (b) 90° and above	Max. 32° and below	Min. 32° and below	Min. 0° and below	Average station pressure mb. Elev. 662 feet m.s.l.
(a)	32	9	32	32		32	32	32	32	32	36	32	32	32	16	16	16	16	3
J	11.2	S	54	S	1950	45	6.8	7	6	18	9	2	1	3	0	17	29	6	994.4
F	11.6	WNW	52	W	1953	50	6.7	7	5	16	8	2	1	3	0	11	27	2	993.7
M	12.3	WNW	56	W	1959	52	6.9	6	8	17	11	2	3	2	0	5	21	*	990.3
A	12.3	S	66	SW	1947	55	6.8	6	8	16	12	*	5	1	0	*	6	0	990.6
M	10.4	S	61	SW	1950	59	6.3	7	10	14	12	0	7	1	*	0	1	0	988.6
J	9.1	S	66	N	1953	66	6.1	7	11	12	10	0	9	1	5	0	0	0	989.6
J	8.0	S	75	NW	1953	68	5.4	9	13	9	8	0	8	1	6	0	0	0	992.1
A	7.8	S	65	W	1956	67	5.3	11	10	10	8	0	7	1	4	0	0	0	993.3
S	8.8	S	73	W	1965	64	5.1	11	9	10	9	0	5	1	2	0	*	0	994.5
O	9.5	S	60	SW	1958	63	5.1	12	8	11	7	*	2	2	*	0	4	0	995.5
N	11.2	S	56	W	1964	44	6.7	7	6	17	9	1	1	2	0	1	17	0	993.2
D	10.9	S	58	SW	1948	39	7.0	7	5	19	10	2	1	3	0	14	27	2	994.0
YR	10.3	S	75	NW	JUL 1953	57	6.2	97	99	169	112	8	49	21	17	49	131	11	992.5

FOOTNOTES

Means and extremes above are from existing and comparable exposures. Annual extremes have been exceeded at other sites in the locality as follows: Highest temperature 113 in July 1936; lowest temperature -27 in January 1884: maximum precipitation in 24 hours 5.52 in May 1927; maximum monthly snowfall 26.5 in February 1900; maximum snowfall in 24 hours 18.0 in February 1900.

Station: SPRINGFIELD, ILLINOIS
CAPITAL AIRPORT
Elevation (ground): 588 feet

TEMPERATURES °F

	Normal			Extremes			
Month	Daily maximum	Daily minimum	Monthly	Record highest	Year	Record lowest	Year
(a)				16		16	
J	34.8	18.6	26.7	67	1970	-18	1974
F	38.9	21.8	30.4	74	1972	-22	1963
M	48.7	30.1	39.4	82	1972	-12	1960
A	63.6	42.6	53.1	88	1963	21	1961
M	74.1	52.6	63.4	95	1967	28	1966
J	83.3	62.5	72.9	100	1971	40	1966
J	86.6	65.6	76.1	106	1966	48	1975
A	85.0	63.7	74.4	103	1964	43	1964
S	78.7	55.6	67.2	99	1960	33	1974
O	68.1	45.0	56.6	91	1963	21	1972
N	51.0	32.7	41.9	80	1961	-3	1964
D	38.2	22.7	30.5	74	1970	-17	1973
YR	62.6	42.8	52.7	106	JUL 1966	-22	FEB 1963

IMPORTANT:
The time-period covered by this record is limited: See footnotes on next page for explanation and for additional history of EXTREME HIGHS AND LOWS recorded in the general area.

The location of Springfield near the center of North America gives it a typical continental climate with warm summers and fairly cold winters. The surrounding country is nearly level. There are no large hills in the vicinity, but rolling terrain is found near the Sangamon River and Spring Creek.

The absolute temperature range is from 112° to -24°. Monthly average temperatures range from the upper twenties for January to the upper seventies for July. Considerable variation may take place within the seasons. Temperatures of 70° or higher may occur in the winter and temperatures near 50° are sometimes recorded during the summer months.

There are no wet and dry seasons. Mean monthly precipitation ranges from well above 4 inches in May and June to slightly more than 2 inches in January. There is some variation in rainfall totals from year to year, with the absolute range extending from 23 inches in 1940 to 58 inches in 1882. The average annual snowfall is 22 inches, but snow tends to disappear within a few days after it falls. Thunderstorms are common during hot weather, and these are sometimes locally severe with brief but heavy showers. The average year has about fifty thunderstorms of which two-thirds occur during the months of May through August. Damaging hail accompanies only a few of the thunderstorms and the areas affected are usually small.

Sunshine is particularly abundant during the summer months when days are long and cloudiness is at a minimum. January is the darkest month, with only about a third as much sunshine as July or August. March is the windiest month, and August the month with the least wind. Velocities of more than 40 m.p.h. are not unusual for brief periods in most months of the year. The prevailing wind direction is southerly during most of the year with northwesterly winds during the late fall and early spring months.

An overall description of the climate of Springfield would be one indicating pleasant conditions with sharp seasonal changes, but no extended periods of severely cold weather. Summer weather is often uncomfortably warm and humid.

SPRINGFIELD, ILLINOIS

Normals, Means, and Extremes

(To better understand these tables, see full explanation of terms beginning on page 322)

Month	Normal Degree days Base 65 °F: Heating	Normal Degree days Base 65 °F: Cooling	Precipitation in inches, Water equivalent: Normal	Maximum monthly	Year	Minimum monthly	Year	Maximum in 24 hrs.	Year	Snow, Ice pellets: Maximum monthly	Year	Maximum in 24 hrs.	Year
(a)				28		28		28		28		28	
J	187	0	1.75	5.67	1949	0.35	1961	2.78	1975	13.0	1968	8.8	1964
F	969	0	1.77	4.43	1951	0.51	1958	1.52	1974	14.9	1960	10.3	1965
M	794	0	2.70	7.89	1973	0.63	1956	2.84	1972	20.3	1960	7.3	1953
A	363	6	4.14	9.91	1964	0.73	1971	3.90	1970	4.9	1957	4.2	1957
M	132	82	3.54	6.37	1974	0.96	1969	2.48	1975	T	1966	T	1966
J	12	249	4.16	8.87	1960	0.23	1959	4.73	1958	0.0		0.0	
J	0	344	3.81	6.97	1963	0.91	1974	3.54	1950	0.0		0.0	
A	8	300	2.74	7.70	1974	0.65	1953	4.79	1956	0.0		0.0	
S	48	114	3.27	7.73	1970	0.62	1952	5.12	1959	0.0		0.0	
O	282	21	3.08	6.15	1955	0.16	1964	3.51	1973	0.1	1967	0.1	1967
N	693	0	2.14	4.19	1964	0.43	1949	2.46	1964	9.2	1951	8.0	1951
D	1070	0	1.92	6.00	1967	0.15	1955	2.40	1949	22.7	1973	10.9	1973
YR	5558	1116	35.02	9.91	APR 1964	0.15	DEC 1955	5.12	SEP 1959	22.7	DEC 1973	10.9	DFC 1973

Month	Relative humidity pct. Hour 00 (Local time)	Hour 06	Hour 12	Hour 18	Wind: Mean speed m.p.h.	Prevailing direction	Fastest mile: Speed m.p.h.	Direction	Year	Pct. of possible sunshine	Mean sky cover, tenths, sunrise to sunset	Mean number of days, Sunrise to sunset: Clear	Partly cloudy	Cloudy	Precipitation .01 inch or more	Snow, Ice pellets 1.0 inch or more	Thunderstorms	Heavy fog, visibility ¼ mile or less	Temperatures °F Max. (b) 90° and above	Max. 32° and below	Min. 32° and below	Min. 0° and below	Average station pressure mb. Elev. 613 feet m.s.l.
(a)	16	16	16	16	28	15	28	28		28	28	28	28	28	28	28	28	28	16	16	16	16	3
J	76	78	68	72	12.9	NW	65	SW	1949	46	6.8	7	6	18	9	2	1	3	0	14	27	5	996.8
F	78	79	67	70	13.1	NW	63	SE	1948	50	6.5	8	5	15	9	2	1	3	0	8	25	2	995.6
M	77	81	64	65	14.1	NW	66	SW	1948	51	6.9	7	7	17	12	2	3	2	0	3	18	*	992.1
A	71	77	56	56	13.7	S	60	W	1962	56	6.6	7	8	15	12	*	6	1	0	0	5	0	992.3
M	75	79	54	55	11.7	SSW	58	W	1960	64	6.1	8	9	14	11	0	7	1	1	0	*	0	990.3
J	76	81	53	55	10.1	SSW	75	SW	1957	69	5.8	9	9	12	10	0	9	*	8	0	0	0	991.3
J	79	83	56	57	8.4	SSW	73	SW	1962	73	5.4	10	11	10	9	0	9	1	9	0	0	0	993.6
A	83	88	59	64	8.0	SSW	58	W	1951	73	5.1	12	9	10	8	0	7	1	6	0	0	0	994.7
S	82	87	56	64	9.2	SSW	52	SW	1960	70	5.0	12	8	10	9	0	5	1	3	0	0	0	996.2
O	76	83	53	61	10.6	S	45	W	1962	65	4.9	13	7	11	7	0	2	1	*	0	3	0	997.5
N	79	83	65	70	12.9	S	57	S	1951	49	6.4	8	7	15	9	1	1	2	0	1	15	*	995.4
D	81	83	73	77	12.7	S	66	SW	1948	41	7.0	7	6	18	10	2	1	3	0	11	25	1	996.1
YR	78	82	60	64	11.4	S	75	SW	JUN 1957	60	6.0	108	92	165	113	8	50	18	28	37	118	8	994.3

FOOTNOTES

Means and extremes above are from existing and comparable exposures. Annual extremes have been exceeded at other sites in the locality as follows: Highest temperature 112 in July 1954; lowest temperature -24 in February 1905; maximum monthly precipitation 15.16 in September 1926; minimum monthly precipitation 0.02 in November 1904; maximum precipitation in 24 hours 5.94 in June 1917; maximum monthly snowfall 24.4 in February 1900; maximum snowfall in 24 hours 15.0 in February 1900.

Snowfall

Season	July	Aug	Sept	Oct	Nov	Dec	Jan
1936-37	0.0	0.0	0.0	T	0.8	1.1	4.7
1937-38	0.0	0.0	0.0	T	2.6	T	1.7
1938-39	0.0	0.0	0.0	0.0	0.3	0.5	16.3
1939-40	0.0	0.0	0.0	0.0	T	6.9	8.2
1940-41	0.0	0.0	0.0	0.0	T	1.5	8.4
1941-42	0.0	0.0	0.0	0.0	4.8	1.7	2.4
1942-43	0.0	0.0	0.0	T	4.0	8.1	3.1
1943-44	0.0	0.0	0.0	T	T	11.7	T
1944-45	0.0	0.0	0.0	T	0.5	14.5	9.7
1945-46	0.0	0.0	0.0	0.0	0.3	10.7	1.2
1946-47	0.0	0.0	0.0	0.0	0.0	0.7	5.0
1947-48	0.0	0.0	0.0	0.0	0.3	0.8	0.6
1948-49	0.0	0.0	0.0	0.0	T	3.9	0.7
1949-50	0.0	0.0	0.0	0.0	0.2	0.4	0.7
1950-51	0.0	0.0	0.0	0.0	1.1	7.2	2.9
1951-52	0.0	0.0	0.0	T	9.2	8.4	2.9
1952-53	0.0	0.0	0.0	0.0	0.5	2.9	0.9
#1953-54	0.0	0.0	0.0	0.0	0.8	2.3	T
1954-55	0.0	0.0	0.0	T	0.9	2.9	3.8
1955-56	0.0	0.0	0.0	T	2.0	1.7	6.6
1956-57	0.0	0.0	0.0	0.0	2.0	1.9	5.7
1957-58	0.0	0.0	0.0	T	0.1	5.0	2.1
1958-59	0.0	0.0	0.0	0.0	2.5	1.6	4.6
1959-60	0.0	0.0	0.0	0.0	0.3	3.2	3.4
1960-61	0.0	0.0	0.0	0.0	0.1	9.0	3.4
1961-62	0.0	0.0	0.0	0.0	5.5	9.5	12.7
1962-63	0.0	0.0	0.0	0.0	T	4.7	5.2
1963-64	0.0	0.0	0.0	0.0	T	5.2	10.8
1964-65	0.0	0.0	0.0	0.0	4.4	1.6	9.1
1965-66	0.0	0.0	0.0	0.0	T	1.7	0.4
1966-67	0.0	0.0	0.0	0.0	0.3	2.0	6.4
1967-68	0.0	0.0	0.0	0.1	2.8	6.4	13.0
1968-69	0.0	0.0	0.0	0.0	0.7	4.7	5.0
1969-70	0.0	0.0	0.0	0.0	0.5	10.2	7.0
1970-71	0.0	0.0	0.0	0.0	T	0.9	4.2
1971-72	0.0	0.0	0.0	0.0	4.4	T	8.1
1972-73	0.0	0.0	0.0	0.0	5.4	3.1	0.6
1973-74	0.0	0.0	0.0	0.0	1.3	22.7	7.3
1974-75	0.0	0.0	0.0	0.0	6.8	2.5	4.5
1975-76	0.0	0.0	0.0	0.0	8.5	4.3	
RECORD MEAN	0.0	0.0	0.0	T	2.2	4.6	4.8

Heating Degree Days

Season	July	Aug	Sept	Oct	Nov	Dec	Jan
1955-56	0	0	35	310	806	1121	1204
1956-57	0	6	65	116	706	937	1324
1957-58	0	0	72	392	721	874	1119
1958-59	2	5	59	276	602	1187	1309
#1959-60	0	0	56	339	871	865	1082
1960-61	0	0	13	263	639	1209	1248
1961-62	0	4	75	275	669	1150	1381
1962-63	2	2	90	268	653	1186	1486
1963-64	2	18	45	80	589	1420	1055
1964-65	0	10	66	356	554	1100	1158
1965-66	0	13	54	321	575	822	1329
1966-67	0	5	100	388	618	1065	1091
1967-68	9	34	104	337	789	1032	1271
1968-69	1	2	31	353	703	1107	1282
1969-70	0	0	59	370	748	1135	1457
1970-71	0	1	41	281	690	952	1275
1971-72	9	1	65	130	633	820	1253
1972-73	3	11	58	375	795	1181	1089
1973-74	0	0	30	191	578	1140	1200
1974-75	0	2	135	299	680	996	1044
1975-76	10	0	125	253	528	973	

Cooling Degree Days

Year	Jan	Feb	Mar	Apr	May	June	July
1969	0	0	0	6	110	205	407
1970	0	0	0	31	136	229	361
1971	0	0	0	32	33	425	248
1972	0	0	0	6	114	199	347
1973	0	0	0	12	12	251	350
1974	0	0	7	14	70	136	437
1975	0	0	0	2	115	271	315

Feb	Mar	Apr	May	June	Total
4.5	3.9	T	0.0	0.0	15.0
2.4	0.0	0.1	0.0	0.0	6.8
2.9	T	0.1	0.0	0.0	20.1
1.6	0.1	1.4	0.2	0.0	18.4
4.5	4.7	0.0	0.0	0.0	19.1
9.4	1.2	T	0.0	0.0	19.5
0.6	4.0	T	0.0	0.0	19.8
8.9	6.3	T	0.0	0.0	26.9
3.7	2.0	T	T	0.0	30.4
4.8	0.2	1.0	0.0	0.0	18.2
4.5	10.7	0.0	0.0	0.0	20.9
8.5	4.8	0.0	0.0	0.0	15.0
3.3	0.6	T	0.0	0.0	8.5
3.8	3.3	T	0.0	0.0	8.4
7.0	7.4	1.9	0.0	0.0	27.5
3.6	2.4	T	0.0	0.0	26.5
0.2	9.2	1.6	0.0	0.0	15.3
0.7	2.0	0.0	T	0.0	5.8
2.4	4.4	0.0	0.0	0.0	14.4
7.3	4.6	T	0.0	0.0	22.2
T	1.7	4.9	0.0	0.0	16.2
1.2	1.7	T	0.0	0.0	10.1
1.7	0.9	0.0	0.0	0.0	11.3
14.9	20.3	0.0	0.0	0.0	42.1
6.5	0.7	1.8	0.0	0.0	21.5
9.6	2.6	0.3	0.0	0.0	40.2
11.9	0.2	T	0.0	0.0	22.0
13.6	6.3	T	0.0	0.0	35.9
14.2	11.1	T	0.0	0.0	40.4
8.6	3.5	T	T	0.0	14.2
3.7	2.4	0.1	0.0	0.0	14.9
1.7	4.5	T	0.0	0.0	28.5
6.8	7.0	0.0	0.0	0.0	24.2
3.9	4.3	1.1	0.0	0.0	27.0
3.4	0.7	3.8	0.0	0.0	13.0
6.0	3.6	T	0.0	0.0	22.1
3.1	0.3	0.9	0.0	0.0	13.4
5.3	4.4	0.4	0.0	0.0	41.4
14.2	4.5	0.4	0.0	0.0	32.9
5.9	4.3	0.6	T	0.0	22.4

Average Temperature

Year	Jan	Feb	Mar	Apr	May	June	July	Aug	Sept	Oct	Nov	Dec	Annual
1936	21.2	19.7	45.0	50.4	69.2	74.2	86.2	82.5	72.8	56.6	40.0	35.8	54.5
1937	27.3	30.4	39.0	52.6	65.4	73.4	78.0	79.5	67.6	54.4	38.8	29.2	53.0
1938	29.2	39.1	50.5	55.4	64.0	72.8	80.2	79.4	71.9	62.6	45.4	32.7	56.9
1939	35.4	30.6	44.2	50.7	68.0	75.3	79.0	75.3	74.3	59.6	43.4	36.2	56.0
1940	14.5	31.0	39.5	51.4	61.4	75.7	78.8	76.7	68.8	62.6	41.1	36.4	53.2
1941	30.9	29.1	38.0	58.3	69.4	76.1	78.8	78.0	71.4	60.9	44.8	38.6	56.2
1942	29.0	29.9	44.4	58.4	64.5	73.9	78.8	75.5	67.6	57.4	45.3	28.0	54.4
1943	27.6	35.4	38.0	51.9	62.2	76.8	79.8	79.0	65.2	56.8	40.4	28.6	53.5
1944	33.6	33.8	39.1	50.8	69.8	78.3	79.0	77.0	69.2	58.4	45.2	25.6	54.9
1945	24.4	33.3	52.3	54.7	59.4	69.5	76.0	76.0	67.8	55.8	43.0	25.2	53.1
1946	31.2	35.4	54.6	57.4	61.2	74.6	78.2	72.2	68.6	62.0	46.1	36.9	56.5
1947	33.4	25.8	35.7	52.5	61.1	71.2	75.6	84.4	70.3	65.6	39.0	34.9	54.1
1948	24.4	31.8	41.6	58.4	63.7	74.6	77.8	77.0	71.0	55.7	45.8	35.0	54.7
1949	30.4	32.9	42.2	52.7	67.6	76.8	80.4	76.8	63.6	59.6	46.0	37.0	55.5
1950	33.7	32.3	38.2	48.2	66.9	73.3	75.0	71.6	67.6	63.1	36.5	24.5	52.6
1951	29.3	32.0	37.6	50.3	67.0	70.6	76.6	74.9	65.2	58.0	36.5	30.4	52.4
1952	31.7	37.0	39.5	54.2	64.4	80.4	79.9	75.5	69.6	52.8	45.5	35.4	55.5
#1953	32.7	37.0	43.9	50.2	65.7	79.2	79.7	77.2	70.4	61.6	46.2	35.1	56.6
1954	29.7	39.3	37.8	57.5	59.0	77.0	80.4	75.2	71.6	56.5	42.9	33.5	55.0
1955	27.9	31.5	40.2	59.8	65.1	69.5	81.0	77.9	69.7	55.4	37.9	28.6	53.7
1956	25.9	31.9	41.3	49.8	65.0	74.6	74.5	74.8	67.1	62.4	41.3	34.5	53.6
1957	22.0	36.3	40.3	52.9	62.9	73.0	78.2	75.9	65.2	52.2	40.7	36.6	53.0
1958	28.7	23.0	36.7	53.3	63.8	68.1	73.7	75.2	67.2	56.9	44.9	26.4	51.5
1959	22.5	30.4	41.7	53.0	67.1	75.1	75.6	78.3	69.0	54.1	35.8	37.0	53.3
#1960	30.0	26.5	24.2	56.2	59.6	69.7	74.4	75.7	72.7	56.9	43.5	25.8	51.3
1961	24.5	33.5	43.8	47.7	58.4	71.0	75.8	73.6	69.4	56.8	42.5	27.8	52.1
1962	20.2	30.4	37.1	52.7	72.3	74.0	73.8	73.4	65.1	58.4	43.0	26.6	52.2
1963	16.9	22.0	44.6	55.7	62.2	75.3	74.6	70.6	66.9	66.4	45.2	18.9	51.6
1964	30.7	29.1	38.3	55.1	68.7	75.1	77.9	74.5	69.0	53.3	46.5	29.4	53.9
1965	27.3	30.0	31.1	54.6	70.3	73.2	74.2	72.4	68.6	55.1	45.6	38.2	52.4
1966	21.9	29.5	43.1	49.5	57.7	71.5	80.8	72.0	64.0	52.3	44.1	30.5	51.4
1967	29.5	26.4	43.8	56.5	59.3	73.8	72.9	68.6	63.7	54.9	38.5	31.4	51.6
1968	23.8	25.6	42.8	52.9	59.0	74.5	75.8	75.2	66.7	54.8	41.3	29.1	51.8
1969	23.4	31.5	32.6	54.6	64.2	70.7	77.9	74.0	66.4	54.0	39.7	28.2	51.5
1970	17.9	28.7	37.9	54.7	66.5	71.5	76.4	74.0	69.2	56.2	41.7	34.0	52.4
1971	23.7	30.7	39.1	54.4	60.4	79.0	72.4	72.5	71.2	62.9	43.8	38.5	54.1
1972	24.4	29.0	40.8	52.5	64.7	70.5	75.9	73.8	68.7	52.9	38.3	26.7	51.5
1973	29.7	30.7	48.3	51.9	59.6	73.2	76.0	76.0	69.8	60.7	45.5	28.0	54.1
1974	26.1	32.6	44.2	54.8	61.6	68.3	78.8	72.9	61.9	55.8	42.2	32.7	52.7
1975	31.1	29.4	37.4	50.4	66.5	73.6	74.7	76.6	63.8	57.7	47.1	33.4	53.5
RECORD MEAN	27.4	30.5	40.7	53.2	63.6	73.2	77.2	75.1	68.0	56.7	42.5	31.6	53.3
MAX	35.1	38.5	49.6	63.1	73.8	83.3	87.5	85.2	78.4	66.9	50.8	38.7	62.6
MIN	19.6	22.4	31.8	43.2	53.4	63.1	66.9	64.9	57.5	46.5	34.1	24.4	44.0

# Indicates a station move or relocation of instruments.

SPRINGFIELD, IL

Feb	Mar	Apr	May	June	Total
953	730	464	120	23	5766
799	761	386	125	6	5231
1170	872	354	98	23	5695
961	719	364	89	2	5575
1114	1257	301	190	14	6089
877	650	521	227	22	5669
963	855	397	30	4	5803
1198	630	291	126	6	5938
1034	822	307	47	6	5425
973	1041	320	36	0	5614
987	670	459	242	15	5487
1074	662	289	230	10	5532
1134	684	358	203	8	5963
934	995	314	130	31	5883
1013	830	332	83	26	6053
952	793	342	168	0	5495
1040	745	375	114	27	5212
957	512	398	174	0	5553
901	642	316	167	29	5194
992	848	435	63	7	5501

Aug	Sept	Oct	Nov	Dec	Total
288	108	37	0	0	1162
284	174	17	0	0	1232
241	254	69	2	0	1304
291	178	10	0	0	1145
348	184	64	0	0	1221
252	49	17	2	0	984
367	94	36	0	0	1200

Precipitation

Year	Jan	Feb	Mar	Apr	May	June	July	Aug	Sept	Oct	Nov	Dec	Annual
1936	1.77	1.74	3.61	2.20	1.88	1.14	1.36	1.61	6.06	2.54	2.30	2.71	28.92
1937	4.95	1.67	0.69	3.64	2.42	4.72	6.70	0.94	2.16	2.81	1.62	2.31	34.63
1938	1.53	2.12	4.45	3.32	7.34	4.23	2.83	2.49	1.98	3.36	1.48	1.85	36.98
1939	2.89	3.21	4.56	5.37	1.62	3.90	1.07	5.75	0.14	1.99	1.46	1.09	33.05
1940	1.21	0.80	2.80	3.68	3.37	1.53	1.31	2.47	0.38	1.14	2.46	1.73	22.88
1941	2.67	0.58	1.34	5.37	3.03	2.25	2.23	2.05	6.97	13.39	3.37	1.47	44.72
1942	1.59	4.82	1.82	2.34	3.43	5.44	7.06	0.91	4.45	3.07	5.82	2.61	43.36
1943	1.01	0.72	2.37	3.44	10.60	2.78	3.03	0.10	2.45	2.76	1.28	1.82	32.36
1944	0.38	2.76	3.72	8.52	4.26	0.58	0.81	4.11	3.84	1.22	1.37	1.71	33.28
1945	1.06	1.32	4.77	4.62	4.20	7.34	1.00	3.36	8.38	1.95	3.18	2.22	43.40
1946	1.22	1.80	2.58	2.54	5.59	5.27	4.15	3.17	3.06	3.65	5.33	1.55	39.91
1947	1.93	0.36	2.54	5.18	5.11	6.86	1.26	1.85	5.03	2.64	1.03	2.69	36.48
1948	0.56	1.53	4.86	1.29	2.52	7.65	4.42	2.03	0.90	1.27	1.93	1.90	30.86
1949	5.67	2.65	2.01	1.95	2.52	3.10	3.43	4.21	2.21	4.60	0.43	4.74	37.52
1950	5.22	2.25	1.75	2.81	1.75	4.25	5.63	2.81	1.35	0.97	2.48	0.78	32.05
1951	1.77	4.43	3.86	5.09	2.49	8.80	1.66	1.96	2.76	2.89	2.25	1.55	39.51
1952	1.65	2.20	2.81	5.19	3.08	4.20	4.01	0.94	0.62	1.14	2.75	1.80	30.39
1953	1.30	1.34	5.08	1.85	1.33	3.30	3.88	0.65	1.92	1.18	0.78	1.37	23.98
1954	0.85	1.15	1.54	3.59	1.95	3.95	2.25	4.54	0.91	3.25	0.82	1.87	26.67
1955	2.32	2.76	1.43	3.37	5.11	2.50	4.01	3.06	2.60	6.15	0.69	0.15	34.15
1956	0.57	1.73	0.63	3.22	3.56	3.09	6.88	5.20	0.81	0.45	2.44	2.63	31.21
1957	1.59	1.76	2.00	8.86	4.61	5.65	4.60	3.07	1.31	2.85	2.25	3.42	41.97
1958	1.23	0.51	1.08	3.07	2.95	8.14	6.85	0.67	1.73	0.64	3.26	0.43	30.56
1959	1.83	2.04	2.91	2.23	3.15	0.23	3.64	5.39	6.47	5.41	1.35	1.33	35.98
1960	1.31	2.15	4.09	4.43	4.07	8.87	3.73	2.55	1.64	2.54	2.13	1.40	38.91
1961	0.35	1.79	3.47	3.95	4.22	2.43	6.38	3.08	6.35	2.01	2.60	1.28	37.91
1962	3.04	1.48	3.54	1.31	3.16	3.62	3.82	1.11	1.42	5.68	1.91	0.53	30.62
1963	0.41	0.89	5.05	2.25	2.65	1.30	6.97	5.46	0.74	1.07	1.51	0.59	28.89
1964	1.64	1.27	4.00	9.91	1.82	2.26	1.32	2.20	1.24	0.16	4.19	1.01	31.02
1965	3.17	1.88	2.62	4.59	1.67	6.54	2.05	5.90	6.43	0.85	0.89	2.49	39.08
1966	0.36	2.20	1.04	5.75	3.54	1.35	0.96	2.71	4.72	2.37	3.08	2.62	30.70
1967	2.41	0.91	2.61	2.11	4.42	2.54	3.39	2.51	4.03	4.20	1.18	6.00	36.31
1968	1.79	1.15	1.25	2.44	5.69	3.25	4.67	0.99	3.29	1.43	3.08	2.64	31.67
1969	2.50	1.96	2.00	5.35	0.96	2.68	4.60	2.34	3.97	5.80	1.13	1.39	34.68
1970	0.54	0.67	1.99	9.10	2.26	4.68	2.55	4.20	7.73	2.50	0.70	1.33	38.25
1971	1.24	2.36	1.18	0.73	3.59	0.96	5.96	1.06	3.76	0.99	1.41	4.38	27.62
1972	1.03	0.82	4.03	3.35	1.88	2.72	1.70	4.52	3.95	1.40	3.27	3.36	32.03
1973	1.31	0.84	7.89	5.29	2.62	7.29	3.36	1.66	3.28	5.46	1.43	3.86	44.29
1974	2.61	3.15	3.39	3.11	6.37	5.00	0.91	7.70	2.17	1.39	3.58	1.44	40.82
1975	4.28	3.63	1.91	2.89	5.90	4.38	2.71	3.34	2.84	1.37	2.50	1.91	37.66
RECORD MEAN	2.02	2.06	3.04	3.58	4.09	4.05	3.13	2.98	3.42	..64	2.40	2.07	35.48

Record mean values above are means through the current year for the period beginning in 1879 for temperature and precipitation, 1948 for snowfall. Temperature, degree days, and snowfall data are from City locations through 1953, precipitation amounts are from City locations through 1947; otherwise data are from Airport locations.

Station: INDIANAPOLIS, INDIANA
WEIR COOK AIRPORT
Elevation (ground): 792 feet

TEMPERATURES °F

Month	Normal: Daily maximum	Normal: Daily minimum	Normal: Monthly	Extremes: Record highest	Extremes: Year	Extremes: Record lowest	Extremes: Year
(a)				17		17	
J	36.0	19.7	27.9	70	1967	-20	1972
F	39.3	22.1	30.7	74	1972	-10	1965
M	49.0	30.3	39.7	80	1974	-6	1960
A	62.8	41.8	52.3	89	1970	18	1972
M	72.9	51.5	62.2	93	1965	28	1966
J	82.3	61.1	71.7	96	1962	42	1969
J	85.4	64.6	75.0	99	1970	48	1975
A	84.0	62.4	73.2	97	1964	41	1965
S	77.7	54.9	66.3	96	1964	34	1974
O	67.0	44.3	55.7	88	1971	20	1962
N	50.5	32.8	41.7	78	1961	4	1959
D	38.7	23.1	30.9	70	1970	-14	1963
YR	62.2	42.4	52.3	99	JUL 1970	-20	JAN 1972

IMPORTANT:
The time-period covered by this record is limited: See footnotes following table of **NORMALS, MEANS AND EXTREMES** for explanation and for additional history of **EXTREME HIGHS AND LOWS** recorded in the general area.

Snowfall

Season	July	Aug	Sept	Oct	Nov	Dec	Jan
1936-37	0.0	0.0	0.0	0.0	T	3.8	3.4
#1937-38	0.0	0.0	0.0	0.0	3.1	4.6	3.0
1938-39	0.0	0.0	0.0	0.0	6.4	1.9	15.0
1939-40	0.0	0.0	0.0	0.0	0.3	6.6	3.9
1940-41	0.0	0.0	0.0	0.0	T	T	2.7
1941-42	0.0	0.0	0.0	0.0	2.3	0.3	0.2
1942-43	0.0	0.0	0.0	0.0	4.1	7.8	4.1
1943-44	0.0	0.0	0.0	0.0	0.2	5.0	T
1944-45	0.0	0.0	0.0	0.0	0.4	5.1	9.2
1945-46	0.0	0.0	0.0	0.0	1.0	8.2	3.9
1946-47	0.0	0.0	0.0	0.0	0.0	3.3	0.9
1947-48	0.0	0.0	0.0	0.0	0.2	4.7	4.1
1948-49	0.0	0.0	0.0	0.0	0.5	5.6	1.2
1949-50	0.0	0.0	0.0	0.0	T	0.6	1.3
1950-51	0.0	0.0	0.0	0.0	3.8	7.0	10.8
1951-52	0.0	0.0	0.0	T	4.0	6.8	0.7
1952-53	0.0	0.0	0.0	0.0	1.3	6.9	4.5
1953-54	0.0	0.0	0.0	0.0	3.9	4.2	5.7
1954-55	0.0	0.0	0.0	T	5.0	2.4	4.4
1955-56	0.0	0.0	0.0	T	3.9	3.3	11.6
1956-57	0.0	0.0	0.0	0.0	2.7	3.2	7.6
1957-58	0.0	0.0	0.0	T	T	3.4	4.0
1958-59	0.0	0.0	0.0	0.0	4.6	1.4	5.2
1959-60	0.0	0.0	0.0	0.0	3.3	2.8	T
1960-61	0.0	0.0	0.0	0.0	T	6.2	3.6
1961-62	0.0	0.0	0.0	0.0	0.5	6.2	5.1
1962-63	0.0	0.0	0.0	1.2	0.2	6.1	9.0
1963-64	0.0	0.0	0.0	0.0	0.3	7.8	9.2
1964-65	0.0	0.0	0.0	0.0	2.6	1.1	12.2
1965-66	0.0	0.0	0.0	0.0	T	2.9	2.5
1966-67	0.0	0.0	0.0	0.0	8.3	3.3	2.4
1967-68	0.0	0.0	0.0	T	6.3	3.5	17.0
1968-69	0.0	0.0	0.0	0.0	0.6	1.6	9.3
1969-70	0.0	0.0	0.0	0.0	2.5	12.9	7.8
1970-71	0.0	0.0	0.0	0.0	0.2	0.4	1.5
1971-72	0.0	0.0	0.0	0.0	4.4	0.4	7.9
1972-73	0.0	0.0	0.0	T	1.9	1.1	0.4
1973-74	0.0	0.0	0.0	0.0	0.4	27.5	3.8
1974-75	0.0	0.0	0.0	0.0	3.8	5.8	6.8
1975-76	0.0	0.0	0.0	0.0	4.5	8.1	
RECORD MEAN	0.0	0.0	0.0	T	2.2	4.8	4.9

Heating Degree Days

Season	July	Aug	Sept	Oct	Nov	Dec	Jan
1955-56	0	0	29	322	820	1119	1164
1956-57	0	7	104	143	711	808	1280
1957-58	0	2	90	415	721	888	1136
1958-59	2	6	77	318	640	1257	1239
#1959-60	0	0	54	371	878	895	1020
1960-61	0	0	28	316	674	1245	1275
1961-62	0	3	60	276	684	1108	1272
1962-63	3	2	142	286	673	1221	1406
1963-64	0	20	71	117	590	1437	1056
1964-65	2	16	73	405	581	1009	1155
1965-66	0	18	66	355	603	811	1312
1966-67	0	0	77	402	631	995	997
1967-68	3	9	83	327	761	964	1232
1968-69	4	13	49	354	656	1057	1211
1969-70	0	0	85	358	816	1137	1458
1970-71	4	0	51	301	715	930	1281
1971-72	3	1	49	129	648	813	1186
1972-73	8	4	36	413	746	1018	1059
1973-74	0	0	20	211	552	1052	1028
1974-75	0	5	163	380	671	988	1016
1975-76	8	0	137	288	551	992	

Cooling Degree Days

Year	Jan	Feb	Mar	Apr	May	June	July
1969	0	0	0	5	78	190	344
1970	0	0	0	26	122	213	327
1971	0	0	0	2	17	324	237
1972	0	0	0	8	95	156	313
1973	0	0	0	11	20	256	349
1974	0	0	11	19	73	131	346
1975	0	0	0	3	100	222	281

Indianapolis is located in the central part of the State and is situated on mostly level or slightly rolling terrain. The greater part of the City lies east of White River, which flows in a general north to south direction. The National Weather Service Office is located at Weir Cook Airport approximatley 7 miles southwest of the central part of the City. From Weir Cook Airport, elevation 793 feet, the terrain slopes gradually downward to a little below 700 feet m.s.l. at the White River, then upward again to just over 800 feet m.s.l. to the north ana east. Street elevation at former City Office location is 718 feet.

The climate is continental, with rather warm summers, moderately cold winters, and occasional wide variations in temperature, particularly during the colder seasons. Periods of humid, muggy weather occur during the summer although usually these Gulf airmasses either do not push so far north or are soon replaced by cooler less humid air from northerly latitudes. Occasionally, hot, dry winds prevail from the west or southwest for several days. The longest and most severe heat was in July 1936 when the temperature climbed to 100 degrees or more for 9 consecutive days. Late spring and the fall season are usually very pleasant. Periods of 2 to 3 weeks of sunny days and mild temperatures are common during the fall.

(Continued page 444)

Feb	Mar	Apr	May	June	Total
2.2	6.1	0.2	0.0	0.0	15.7
1.9	T	1.2	0.0	0.0	13.8
7.1	0.2	T	0.0	0.0	30.6
10.3	0.4	4.0	T	0.0	25.5
3.7	1.0	0.0	0.0	0.0	7.4
3.4	3.3	T	0.0	0.0	9.5
2.1	3.1	T	0.0	0.0	21.2
8.8	3.3	T	0.0	0.0	17.3
2.6	T	T	0.0	0.0	17.3
1.7	1.5	T	0.0	0.0	16.3
5.5	9.5	T	0.0	0.0	19.2
5.9	5.6	0.0	0.0	0.0	20.5
T	5.1	T	0.0	0.0	12.4
3.9	0.4	T	0.0	0.0	6.2
4.0	7.0	0.1	0.0	0.0	32.7
2.1	2.0	0.1	0.0	0.0	15.7
0.3	7.5	3.1	0.0	0.0	23.6
1.6	1.4	T	0.0	0.0	16.8
4.5	3.7	T	0.0	0.0	20.0
3.8	9.0	0.8	0.0	0.0	32.4
1.1	T	3.7	0.0	0.0	18.3
0.6	1.3	T	T	0.0	9.3
1.0	10.1	0.0	0.0	0.0	22.3
9.2	9.3	T	T	0.0	24.6
14.3	0.4	2.7	0.0	0.0	27.2
14.0	1.7	T	0.0	0.0	27.5
6.8	6.1	0.0	0.0	0.0	29.4
12.7	4.1	0.2	0.0	0.0	34.3
15.3	5.3	T	0.0	0.0	36.5
6.3	0.8	T	T	0.0	12.5
8.1	3.0	0.0	0.0	0.0	25.1
1.1	8.8	T	0.0	0.0	36.7
0.8	6.4	T	0.0	0.0	18.7
9.2	5.6	0.2	0.0	0.0	38.2
8.2	2.8	T	0.0	0.0	13.1
6.3	0.3	0.6	0.0	0.0	19.9
1.4	2.0	1.1	0.0	0.0	7.9
8.0	3.0	2.1	0.0	0.0	44.8
4.8	10.5	0.1	0.0	0.0	31.8
5.1	3.8	0.5	T	0.0	21.3

Average Temperature

Year	Jan	Feb	Mar	Apr	May	June	July	Aug	Sept	Oct	Nov	Dec	Annual
1936	21.4	21.2	43.8	47.0	65.0	71.2	82.0	79.5	69.8	54.8	38.4	34.7	52.4
#1937	32.6	29.8	36.2	49.8	61.8	70.4	74.0	76.0	63.6	51.6	37.7	28.2	51.0
1938	28.2	37.6	46.0	52.8	61.6	69.0	75.4	75.4	67.7	57.0	42.4	31.6	53.8
1939	33.2	31.0	41.8	47.2	64.8	72.9	74.7	72.8	70.7	56.7	40.0	33.4	53.3
1940	14.2	30.8	36.8	47.5	57.8	71.2	75.6	75.6	64.9	58.6	39.8	36.4	50.8
1941	29.4	26.3	35.2	56.8	63.6	71.5	76.0	74.3	69.8	58.2	43.0	36.6	53.4
1942	27.7	27.4	42.0	55.3	62.2	71.4	75.1	72.1	64.4	54.8	44.0	26.2	51.9
1943	28.2	31.7	35.8	47.7	61.2	74.8	75.8	74.5	61.8	53.4	37.9	28.6	51.0
1944	32.6	33.0	36.8	49.8	67.4	74.0	75.8	74.2	66.0	54.0	43.0	25.3	52.6
1945	22.8	32.0	51.2	52.6	56.4	68.1	72.4	72.1	67.4	52.2	42.2	23.9	51.1
1946	29.0	33.0	51.9	53.0	59.2	70.5	74.8	69.0	66.2	59.0	45.2	35.4	53.8
1947	33.7	22.5	32.8	50.6	58.3	68.0	70.6	79.0	66.4	62.4	37.8	31.6	51.1
1948	21.0	31.0	41.2	54.0	60.8	71.3	74.5	73.6	67.4	51.2	44.6	34.3	52.0
1949	34.0	35.0	41.0	50.2	63.1	73.4	78.2	73.8	60.6	59.2	42.3	35.8	53.9
1950	37.4	31.6	36.8	45.9	63.6	68.6	72.3	70.2	64.6	59.2	36.4	23.4	50.8
1951	29.1	30.7	37.8	48.4	63.9	69.9	74.1	72.0	62.6	57.0	35.6	30.6	51.0
1952	33.1	35.3	39.8	52.0	61.1	76.6	76.7	73.0	66.0	49.8	42.9	34.9	53.4
1953	32.9	35.6	42.1	47.7	64.6	75.9	75.9	74.3	67.2	58.4	43.6	32.8	54.3
1954	30.8	40.1	37.6	57.4	57.9	75.5	77.8	73.6	69.6	55.9	42.1	32.2	54.2
1955	27.5	32.2	40.6	57.1	63.6	67.1	79.4	75.9	68.9	54.7	37.6	28.7	52.8
1956	27.2	33.5	40.2	48.9	62.5	72.1	72.9	73.0	63.8	60.7	41.1	38.8	52.9
1957	23.5	36.5	40.8	53.3	62.1	72.1	75.4	73.4	64.6	51.4	40.7	36.2	52.5
1958	28.1	23.7	35.9	52.2	61.3	66.8	73.5	71.9	65.5	54.9	43.6	24.2	50.2
#1959	24.9	31.7	38.8	51.7	65.7	73.0	75.2	77.3	68.4	53.8	35.5	35.9	52.7
1960	31.8	28.1	26.2	54.8	58.8	68.5	71.6	74.1	69.8	54.7	42.3	24:6	50.4
1961	23.6	34.0	43.6	45.6	56.4	67.9	73.4	71.4	70.9	56.2	42.0	29.1	51.2
1962	23.7	30.7	37.7	51.1	69.2	73.2	73.3	72.4	62.6	56.7	42.4	25.5	51.5
1963	19.5	21.1	42.4	53.3	59.7	71.3	73.4	68.9	65.4	62.1	45.1	18.5	50.0
1964	30.7	29.0	40.6	54.7	65.6	73.4	74.6	72.5	67.2	51.7	45.3	32.2	53.1
1965	27.5	29.5	33.7	54.4	68.3	71.7	72.9	71.1	67.5	53.7	44.7	38.6	52.8
1966	22.4	30.4	43.3	51.3	58.4	72.4	79.2	73.2	65.2	51.9	43.8	32.7	52.0
1967	32.6	27.7	44.0	53.6	59.3	73.9	73.8	71.1	65.9	55.2	39.4	33.7	52.5
1968	25.1	26.4	42.8	53.7	58.6	72.3	75.3	74.5	65.8	54.4	42.9	30.6	51.9
1969	25.7	31.7	35.7	54.0	63.4	69.8	75.8	72.7	65.2	53.8	37.5	28.2	51.1
1970	17.9	28.6	38.1	55.1	65.6	71.5	75.2	74.2	69.1	55.2	40.9	34.7	52.2
1971	23.4	28.9	37.3	51.0	58.9	75.6	72.3	71.3	69.4	62.0	43.1	38.4	52.7
1972	26.5	28.4	39.8	52.1	65.0	68.8	74.6	73.1	68.3	51.5	39.9	31.9	51.7
1973	30.7	31.5	49.4	51.3	59.5	73.3	76.0	74.4	69.9	59.4	46.4	30.9	54.4
1974	31.6	32.4	45.3	55.0	62.1	68.6	76.0	71.8	60.6	52.5	42.5	32.9	52.6
1975	32.0	32.0	36.9	48.9	65.5	71.5	73.5	76.1	62.6	55.9	46.4	32.8	52.8
RECORD MEAN	28.5	30.8	40.1	52.0	62.5	71.8	75.7	73.7	66.9	55.5	42.0	31.9	52.6
MAX	36.2	38.8	48.9	61.6	72.4	81.6	85.6	83.6	77.1	65.5	50.1	39.0	61.7
MIN	20.7	22.8	31.3	42.3	52.5	61.9	65.7	63.7	56.7	45.4	33.8	24.7	43.5

# Indicates a station move or relocation of instruments.

INDIANAPOLIS, IN

Feb	Mar	Apr	May	June	Total
906	763	483	162	42	5810
793	742	396	131	9	5124
1150	897	386	141	28	5854
925	803	397	104	6	5774
1064	1198	333	214	24	6051
861	657	580	268	35	5939
957	839	441	41	2	5683
1222	691	352	185	16	6199
1037	750	308	64	11	5461
989	964	323	39	0	5556
962	668	412	223	11	5441
1040	652	353	219	2	5368
1112	680	333	205	11	5720
925	904	329	121	38	5661
1012	829	316	95	11	6117
1006	852	417	198	0	5755
1054	774	389	89	35	5170
937	477	416	184	0	5298
905	617	314	158	18	4875
918	866	481	78	22	5588

Aug	Sept	Oct	Nov	Dec	Total
245	95	18	0	0	975
292	182	5	0	0	1167
202	189	40	0	0	1011
266	141	0	0	0	979
302	172	44	1	0	1155
225	40	3	2	0	850
355	71	14	0	0	1046

Precipitation

Year	Jan	Feb	Mar	Apr	May	June	July	Aug	Sept	Oct	Nov	Dec	Annual
1936	1.29	2.83	2.31	4.19	1.49	3.41	0.61	2.88	5.12	3.62	4.85	3.10	35.70
#1937	8.76	1.69	1.53	4.86	2.17	4.32	4.70	3.84	3.46	6.52	1.86	3.83	47.54
1938	0.99	2.75	8.11	3.68	6.07	7.53	7.30	4.70	1.98	1.06	3.59	1.47	49.23
1939	6.72	3.16	3.22	5.85	0.48	5.49	5.09	1.75	1.13	2.91	1.57	1.43	38.80
1940	1.52	2.31	1.11	6.14	3.45	1.77	1.28	2.45	1.49	0.94	3.29	2.66	28.41
1941	1.72	0.56	1.03	2.01	1.93	5.13	0.99	1.67	1.78	8.36	2.19	1.59	28.96
1942	1.05	3.58	3.85	2.49	4.80	9.74	2.95	3.43	2.68	0.98	5.22	1.71	42.48
1943	0.65	1.01	3.30	1.74	10.10	3.29	3.02	2.42	3.26	1.37	1.94	1.05	33.15
1944	0.21	2.82	4.20	7.90	3.33	2.32	1.99	1.98	2.31	0.61	2.19	1.11	30.97
1945	0.57	2.59	7.76	5.11	4.15	8.12	4.06	2.80	5.61	2.04	3.19	2.49	48.49
1946	1.44	2.51	3.62	1.07	7.13	2.37	1.58	2.52	1.00	1.54	3.27	3.03	31.08
1947	4.06	0.37	1.95	5.82	3.91	5.67	2.33	5.22	3.45	2.44	1.44	1.61	38.27
1948	2.52	1.82	6.32	3.44	3.26	4.24	3.36	1.04	3.03	2.12	4.93	3.18	39.26
1949	7.41	2.38	3.16	1.62	2.75	4.18	2.95	6.64	2.52	4.25	0.89	4.32	43.07
1950	12.69	5.32	3.88	3.44	2.68	6.55	2.15	4.08	4.96	0.98	5.52	3.00	55.25
1951	2.95	3.76	3.16	3.26	2.78	5.77	3.12	2.43	2.39	3.28	5.21	4.68	42.79
1952	3.69	2.71	5.77	3.99	3.90	6.17	2.45	2.46	4.62	0.64	3.87	3.01	43.28
1953	2.57	1.93	5.41	3.18	4.50	4.86	6.19	1.76	1.44	1.70	2.29	2.42	38.25
1954	3.40	2.64	2.99	2.34	1.98	1.15	2.40	2.73	0.96	3.92	1.32	2.10	27.93
1955	2.09	2.34	2.26	3.31	3.37	1.79	5.24	1.21	6.01	4.27	5.32	0.70	37.91
1956	1.05	3.99	1.90	4.50	4.91	3.48	3.93	2.55	1.07	1.09	2.31	3.86	34.64
1957	2.98	1.85	1.92	7.83	9.15	6.91	5.91	3.89	2.22	2.94	3.40	6.70	55.70
1958	1.48	0.41	1.49	2.51	3.65	6.09	8.11	3.12	3.35	2.72	4.71	0.47	38.11
1959	4.68	3.22	2.58	3.52	3.67	2.30	2.97	2.56	2.33	5.66	3.21	2.91	39.61
1960	2.35	3.28	1.62	2.05	4.04	7.28	3.27	1.78	2.43	1.61	1.68	1.88	33.27
1961	1.22	3.15	7.91	6.68	6.46	3.47	2.61	2.70	4.40	1.27	3.72	3.05	46.64
1962	4.58	2.27	4.01	1.69	5.14	1.45	6.87	5.78	4.13	2.83	1.42	1.09	41.26
1963	1.15	0.58	10.74	2.58	2.10	5.30	4.66	2.22	0.24	0.17	2.18	0.86	32.78
1964	2.04	2.01	7.20	8.09	1.42	2.73	4.09	0.68	1.27	0.64	3.13	3.05	36.35
1965	3.86	4.33	2.17	5.80	1.44	3.49	3.18	3.25	5.16	1.05	1.41	2.97	38.11
1966	1.13	2.91	1.31	3.32	1.47	1.28	2.71	1.31	5.73	1.60	4.72	5.23	32.72
1967	1.81	1.84	3.33	3.00	5.00	1.07	2.34	2.38	0.80	5.72	2.54	4.92	34.75
1968	2.96	1.51	3.73	2.86	9.25	2.51	2.19	4.45	1.54	1.13	4.74	4.18	41.05
1969	6.19	1.23	1.33	4.42	1.82	4.16	8.02	2.98	2.89	4.83	2.86	2.04	42.77
1970	1.17	1.86	2.51	6.53	2.43	1.97	4.43	1.87	2.41	3.66	2.12	2.07	32.98
1971	1.98	5.35	1.49	1.16	4.25	3.39	5.68	1.93	3.10	1.84	1.29	6.02	37.48
1972	1.57	1.15	2.48	5.81	1.89	6.04	2.01	2.94	5.65	2.25	5.65	2.83	40.27
1973	2.27	1.11	5.63	2.76	1.79	5.91	6.67	2.74	2.43	3.11	3.62	4.27	42.31
1974	3.39	2.58	3.60	3.45	6.27	5.15	1.20	5.63	3.25	0.99	2.99	2.81	41.31
1975	4.37	4.13	4.16	4.14	2.42	5.73	4.63	4.68	2.32	2.80	3.63	3.71	46.72
RECORD MEAN	2.99	2.54	3.82	3.72	3.88	4.11	3.78	3.18	3.19	2.66	3.19	2.92	39.98

Record mean values above are means through the current year for the period beginning in 1871 for temperature and precipitation, 1932 for snowfall. Data are from city locations through July 1931.

(Continued)

Precipitation is normally adequate for good crops and is well distributed throughout the year. Rainfall of an inch or more in 24 hours occurs on an average of about once a month and lesser measurable amounts on about 10 or 12 days. Snowfalls of 3 inches or more occur on an average of about 2 or 3 times during the winter.

The average freeze free period extends from April 23 to October 22. However, freezing has occurred as late as May 27 and as early as September 27.

Several flood controlling reservoirs and local levee and/or channel improvements now protect most formerly flood-prone areas.

Normals, Means, and Extremes

Month	Normal Degree days Base 65 °F: Heating	Normal Degree days Base 65 °F: Cooling	Precipitation in inches, Water equivalent: Normal	Maximum monthly	Year	Minimum monthly	Year	Maximum in 24 hrs.	Year	Snow, Ice pellets: Maximum monthly	Year	Maximum in 24 hrs.	Year	Relative humidity pct.: Hour 01 (Local time)	Hour 07	Hour 13	Hour 19
(a)				36		36		33		44		33		16	16	16	16
J	1150	0	2.86	12.69	1950	0.21	1944	3.47	1950	17.0	1968	10.3	1965	77	80	69	71
F	960	0	2.36	5.35	1971	0.37	1947	2.38	1975	15.3	1965	12.5	1965	76	79	66	69
M	784	0	3.75	10.74	1963	1.03	1941	3.05	1963	10.5	1975	5.6	1948	75	79	63	65
A	387	6	3.87	8.09	1964	1.07	1946	2.56	1961	4.0	1940	3.1	1953	72	77	55	57
M	159	72	4.08	10.10	1943	1.42	1964	3.53	1961	T	1966	T	1966	78	82	57	58
J	11	212	4.16	9.74	1942	1.07	1967	3.80	1963	0.0		0.0		80	82	58	59
J	0	310	3.67	8.11	1958	0.99	1941	4.18	1973	0.0		0.0		83	87	60	62
A	5	259	2.80	6.64	1949	0.68	1964	2.72	1949	0.0		0.0		86	90	61	65
S	63	102	2.87	6.01	1955	0.24	1963	3.07	1961	0.0		0.0		84	90	59	66
O	302	13	2.51	8.36	1941	0.17	1963	3.90	1959	1.2	1962	1.2	1962	80	87	57	64
N	699	0	3.10	5.65	1972	0.89	1949	3.02	1955	8.3	1966	8.2	1966	81	85	67	73
D	1057	0	2.71	6.70	1957	0.47	1958	2.21	1971	27.5	1973	11.5	1973	81	83	73	77
YR	5577	974	38.74	12.69	JAN 1950	0.17	OCT 1963	4.18	JUL 1973	27.5	DEC 1973	12.5	FEB 1965	79	83	62	65

(To better understand these tables, see full explanation of terms beginning on page 322)

Month	Wind: Mean speed m.p.h.	Prevailing direction	Fastest mile ∅: Speed m.p.h.	Direction	Year	Pct. of possible sunshine	Mean sky cover, tenths, sunrise to sunset	Mean number of days, Sunrise to sunset: Clear	Partly cloudy	Cloudy	Precipitation .01 inch or more	Snow, Ice pellets 1.0 inch or more	Thunderstorms	Heavy fog, visibility ¼ mile or less	Temperatures °F Max.: 90° and above (b)	32° and below	Min.: 32° and below	0° and below	Average station pressure mb. Elev. 808 feet m.s.l.
(a)	27	14	31	31		32	33	44	44	44	36	34	33	33	16	16	16	16	3
J	11.1	NW	90	W	1950	41	7.2	6	6	19	11	2	1	4	0	13	27	4	989.6
F	11.2	WNW	65	SW	1948	51	6.9	6	6	16	10	2	1	2	0	8	25	1	988.1
M	11.9	WNW	68	NW	1947	51	7.1	5	8	18	13	1	3	2	0	3	18	*	985.3
A	11.5	SW	60	W	1956	55	7.0	6	7	17	12	*	5	1	0	0	6	0	986.4
M	9.7	SW	68	W	1951	61	6.5	7	9	15	12	0	7	1	1	0	1	0	984.3
J	8.5	SW	77	N	1946	68	6.1	7	11	12	10	0	8	1	4	0	0	0	985.8
J	7.4	SW	57	W	1957	70	5.8	8	13	10	9	0	8	1	6	0	0	0	987.5
A	7.2	SW	54	NW	1946	71	5.4	10	12	9	8	0	6	2	3	0	0	0	988.9
S	8.1	SW	61	NW	1952	66	5.4	11	8	11	8	0	4	1	2	0	0	0	989.6
O	8.9	SW	56	NW	1952	64	5.2	12	8	11	8	*	2	1	0	0	4	0	991.3
N	10.7	SW	59	SW	1948	42	6.9	7	7	16	10	1	1	2	0	1	15	0	989.0
D	10.5	SW	56	SW	1971	39	7.3	5	6	20	12	2	*	3	0	10	25	1	989.0
YR	9.7	SW	90	W	JAN 1950	58	6.4	90	101	174	123	7	45	21	15	35	120	7	987.9

FOOTNOTES

Means and extremes above are from existing and comparable exposures. Annual extremes have been exceeded at other sites in the locality as follows: Highest temperature 107 in July 1934; lowest temperature -25 in January 1884; maximum monthly precipitation 13.12 in July 1875; minimum monthly precipitation 0.07 in March 1910; maximum precipitation in 24 hours 6.80 in September 1895; maximim monthly snowfall 30.4 in March 1906; fastest mile of wind 111 from Northwest in June 1929.

Station: SOUTH BEND, INDIANA
ST. JOSEPH COUNTY AIRPORT

Elevation (ground): 773 feet

TEMPERATURES °F

Month	Normal			Extremes			
	Daily maximum	Daily minimum	Monthly	Record highest	Year	Record lowest	Year
(a)				12		12	
J	31.5	16.5	24.0	63	1967	-19	1972
F	34.1	18.5	26.3	60	1972	-11	1975
M	43.9	26.6	35.3	77	1967	-2	1967
A	58.4	37.8	48.1	83	1964	11	1972
M	69.4	47.3	58.4	91	1975	24	1968
J	79.4	57.7	68.6	98	1971	35	1972
J	82.8	61.7	72.3	99	1974	44	1972
A	81.8	60.2	71.0	97	1964	40	1965
S	74.7	52.8	63.8	94	1973	33	1964
O	63.7	43.0	53.4	92	1963	25	1972
N	47.2	31.9	39.6	78	1975	8	1964
D	35.1	21.2	28.2	67	1975	-12	1963
YR	58.5	39.6	49.1	99	JUL 1974	-19	JAN 1972

IMPORTANT:
The time-period covered by this record is limited: See footnotes on next page for explanation and for additional history of EXTREME HIGHS AND LOWS recorded in the general area.

The drainage for Saint Joseph County, Indiana, is through the Saint Joseph River into Lake Michigan; also, through the Kankakee River to the Illinois River, and then into the Mississippi River. The land is a mixture of level prairie, some of which is former marshland, interspersed with some moraines and hills. Several small natural lakes are in the area, but they have little, if any, general effect on the climate. The nearest shore of Lake Michigan is located 20 miles to the northwest to 35 miles to the west of South Bend. This Lake greatly affects the temperature and snowfall during the winter months. The Lake tends to give warmer temperatures to the area during the winter, but also gives considerable cloudiness and a greater snowfall whenever there is a passage of northwest winds over the Lake. The extent of the snow area due to the Lake effect extends from the Lake to about 30 miles southeast and south of the Lake, with the greatest falls southeastward from the Lake for about 25 miles. Severe cold is occasionally experienced for short periods in the winter, although the mean temperatures during the winter months are only a few degrees below the freezing point. Summertime temperatures will average near 71°, but there are brief humid hot periods. Precipitation is fairly evenly distributed with the greatest amounts generally during the growing season. There are occasional droughts, but the diversity of crops grown prevents a complete failure. The predominant snow season is from November through March, although there are also generally lighter amounts in October and April. Based on records beginning in 1940, the average date for the last occurrence in the spring of temperatures as low as 32° F. is May 2, and the first in autumn is around October 18. The latest date of freezing temperature in the spring is May 30, and the earliest in autumn is September 18. The average length of the growing season is 165 days.

Normals, Means, and Extremes

(To better understand these tables, see full explanation of terms beginning on page 322)

Month	Normal Degree days Base 65 °F: Heating	Cooling	Precipitation in inches – Water equivalent: Normal	Maximum monthly	Year	Minimum monthly	Year	Maximum in 24 hrs.	Year	Snow, Ice pellets: Maximum monthly	Year	Maximum in 24 hrs.	Year
(a)				36		36		36		36		36	
J	1271	0	2.37	5.28	1959	0.44	1945	2.81	1960	45.3	1959	15.6	1967
F	1084	0	1.94	4.53	1960	0.54	1969	2.64	1954	35.1	1958	10.3	1967
M	921	0	2.75	5.56	1944	0.54	1958	2.33	1972	33.9	1960	14.8	1960
A	507	0	4.01	9.20	1947	0.50	1971	3.14	1947	13.1	1961	8.1	1961
M	245	40	3.17	6.28	1943	1.19	1961	2.34	1966	0.6	1966	0.6	1966
J	35	143	3.72	9.09	1968	1.13	1971	4.70	1968	0.0		0.0	
J	6	232	3.67	7.18	1958	0.02	1946	3.31	1962	0.0		0.0	
A	24	210	3.26	7.55	1975	0.32	1950	3.70	1966	0.0		0.0	
S	98	62	3.07	7.67	1972	0.59	1939	2.40	1943	1.2	1942	1.0	1942
O	368	8	3.06	9.75	1954	0.42	1950	3.18	1954	8.6	1962	5.4	1962
N	762	0	2.71	4.89	1966	1.37	1962	1.91	1950	23.4	1951	10.3	1951
D	1141	0	2.47	5.50	1965	0.60	1943	3.33	1965	41.9	1962	12.5	1954
YR	6462	695	36.20	9.75	OCT 1954	0.02	JUL 1946	4.70	JUN 1968	45.3	JAN 1959	15.6	JAN 1967

Month	Relative humidity pct. Hour 01 (Local time)	Hour 07	Hour 13	Hour 19	Wind: Mean speed m.p.h.	Prevailing direction	Fastest mile: Speed m.p.h.	Direction	Year	Pct. of possible sunshine	Mean sky cover, tenths, sunrise to sunset	Mean number of days – Sunrise to sunset: Clear	Partly cloudy	Cloudy	Precipitation .01 inch or more	Snow, Ice pellets 1.0 inch or more	Thunderstorms	Heavy fog, visibility ¼ mile or less	Temperatures °F Max. (b) 90° and above	Max. 32° and below	Min. 32° and below	Min. 0° and below	Average station pressure mb. Elev. 773 feet m.s.l.
(a)	12	12	12	12	27	14	26	26			30	36	36	36	36	36	36	36	12	12	12	12	3
J	79	81	74	75	12.0	SW	52	22	1975		8.0	3	7	21	15	5	*	3	0	15	27	4	989.1
F	78	80	69	71	11.9	SW	47	20	1953		7.8	4	5	19	13	5	*	2	0	12	26	2	988.4
M	77	80	64	67	12.4	NNW	51	20	1961		7.6	4	8	19	14	3	2	2	0	5	21	*	986.1
A	73	78	58	60	12.2	NNW	55	27	1962		6.9	6	8	16	13	1	5	1	0	0	8	0	986.6
M	75	77	54	55	10.9	SSW	44	24	1964		6.4	6	10	15	12	0	5	2	*	0	1	0	984.4
J	78	81	57	59	9.5	SSW	50	27	1950		6.2	7	10	13	11	0	8	1	3	0	0	0	985.3
J	81	84	56	59	8.3	SSW	45	34	1951		5.6	8	14	9	9	0	7	1	4	0	0	0	987.7
A	84	87	58	63	8.1	SSW	63	32	1953		5.5	9	13	9	9	0	6	2	3	0	0	0	989.2
S	84	89	61	68	9.0	SSW	35	31	1972		5.8	9	9	12	9	*	4	2	1	0	0	0	990.1
O	79	84	61	68	9.9	SSW	38	25	1955		5.8	9	9	13	9	*	2	2	0	0	3	0	991.2
N	81	84	70	75	11.4	SSW	45	18	1952		7.8	4	6	20	13	3	1	2	0	2	13	0	988.3
D	82	84	77	80	11.5	SW	43	23	1953		8.2	3	6	22	15	5	*	3	0	10	24	*	989.1
YR	79	82	63	67	10.6	SSW	63	32	AUG 1953		6.8	72	105	188	142	22	43	24	11	44	124	6	988.0

FOOTNOTES

Means and extremes above are from existing and comparable exposures. Annual extremes have been exceeded at other sites in the locality as follows: Highest temperature 109 in July 1934; lowest temperature -22 in January 1943.

Snowfall

Season	July	Aug	Sept	Oct	Nov	Dec	Jan
1936-37	0.0	0.0	0.0	0.0	1.7	0.7	3.3
#1937-38	0.0	0.0	0.0	2.5	12.1	7.5	19.0
1938-39	0.0	0.0	0.0	0.0	2.3	4.2	20.8
#1939-40	0.0	0.0	0.0	0.0	2.2	6.1	19.9
1940-41	0.0	0.0	0.0	0.0	8.3	4.7	11.2
1941-42	0.0	0.0	0.0	0.0	3.0	2.3	9.9
1942-43	0.0	0.0	1.2	T	5.9	18.9	23.8
1943-44	0.0	0.0	0.0	T	3.5	11.3	1.0
1944-45	0.0	0.0	0.0	0.0	3.2	16.7	11.3
1945-46	0.0	0.0	0.0	0.0	5.0	15.7	8.4
1946-47	0.0	0.0	0.0	0.0	T	10.1	9.8
1947-48	0.0	0.0	0.0	0.0	8.9	11.5	10.6
1948-49	0.0	0.0	0.0	T	T	7.3	1.7
1949-50	0.0	0.0	0.0	T	9.3	8.8	2.8
1950-51	0.0	0.0	0.0	0.0	12.6	23.8	12.8
1951-52	0.0	0.0	0.0	T	23.4	30.7	12.7
1952-53	0.0	0.0	0.0	2.0	2.3	10.0	11.4
1953-54	0.0	0.0	0.0	0.0	12.8	16.3	14.5
1954-55	0.0	0.0	0.0	6.5	4.9	23.9	12.7
1955-56	0.0	0.0	0.0	T	11.4	8.4	12.7
1956-57	0.0	0.0	0.0	0.0	11.1	13.7	25.4
1957-58	0.0	0.0	0.0	T	3.5	17.0	19.9
1958-59	0.0	0.0	0.0	0.0	4.7	19.0	45.3
1959-60	0.0	0.0	0.0	0.0	11.1	8.7	12.4
1960-61	0.0	0.0	0.0	T	10.1	14.4	20.7
1961-62	0.0	0.0	0.0	T	0.7	9.5	18.7
1962-63	0.0	0.0	0.0	8.6	3.0	41.9	16.4
1963-64	0.0	0.0	0.0	0.0	7.2	25.0	10.0
1964-65	0.0	0.0	0.0	T	13.5	18.5	14.7
1965-66	0.0	0.0	0.0	2.4	7.3	8.6	26.9
1966-67	0.0	0.0	T	T	16.2	18.2	30.4
1967-68	0.0	0.0	0.0	5.0	7.0	12.5	12.6
1968-69	0.0	0.0	0.0	T	8.8	27.9	24.1
1969-70	0.0	0.0	0.0	T	10.5	17.1	24.8
1970-71	0.0	0.0	0.0	0.0	11.0	20.0	22.5
1971-72	0.0	0.0	0.0	0.0	16.3	4.4	19.2
1972-73	0.0	0.0	0.0	1.5	12.6	19.7	5.5
1973-74	0.0	0.0	0.0	0.0	1.0	22.6	14.4
1974-75	0.0	0.0	0.0	0.6	7.9	19.9	9.2
1975-76	0.0	0.0	0.0	0.0	10.7	14.0	
RECORD MEAN	0.0	0.0	T	0.7	8.0	15.9	15.6

Heating Degree Days

Season	July	Aug	Sept	Oct	Nov	Dec	Jan
1955-56	0	2	92	338	877	1206	1214
1956-57	2	23	149	214	749	966	1406
1957-58	0	7	154	469	742	977	1241
1958-59	1	16	121	325	683	1370	1428
1959-60	1	0	87	430	953	931	1160
1960-61	9	0	51	371	690	1239	1333
1961-62	7	5	79	342	740	1178	1413
1962-63	10	8	181	340	741	1264	1598
#1963-64	9	38	79	144	592	1407	1100
1964-65	5	40	155	493	648	1157	1244
1965-66	3	56	121	411	727	879	1377
1966-67	4	31	128	412	658	1079	1109
1967-68	31	30	137	429	861	1064	1317
1968-69	11	27	69	372	724	1171	1316
1969-70	0	0	110	421	826	1158	1485
1970-71	18	11	93	327	766	1066	1387
1971-72	16	13	86	171	716	892	1269
1972-73	24	35	112	468	801	1115	1080
1973-74	0	4	60	229	611	1102	1142
1974-75	0	3	144	378	672	985	1077
1975-76	13	1	175	300	503	992	

Cooling Degree Days

Year	Jan	Feb	Mar	Apr	May	June	July
1969	0	0	0	0	59	109	257
1970	0	0	0	19	63	158	240
1971	0	0	0	3	17	283	163
1972	0	0	0	0	47	74	226
1973	0	0	0	7	1	226	297
1974	0	0	0	10	17	114	321
1975	0	0	0	0	86	203	232

Feb	Mar	Apr	May	June	Total
5.3	5.4	T	0.0	0.0	16.4
11.7	0.5	8.0	0.0	0.0	61.3
9.0	2.3	2.0	0.0	0.0	40.6
10.6	10.7	0.5	0.6	0.0	50.6
10.9	5.3	0.0	0.0	0.0	40.4
16.6	9.5	T	0.0	0.0	41.3
16.2	6.6	0.4	0.0	0.0	73.0
9.5	12.0	1.7	0.0	0.0	39.0
3.6	2.8	T	T	0.0	37.6
11.7	0.3	0.0	0.0	0.0	41.1
12.2	7.6	0.4	T	0.0	40.1
4.0	3.0	T	0.0	0.0	38.0
11.2	3.0	T	0.0	0.0	23.2
16.2	6.2	5.7	0.0	0.0	49.0
6.3	3.5	1.7	0.0	0.0	60.7
2.4	5.9	3.7	0.0	0.0	78.8
6.1	2.4	2.0	0.0	0.0	36.2
12.9	14.2	T	0.5	0.0	71.2
14.8	8.7	T	0.0	0.0	71.5
13.4	4.2	3.0	0.0	0.0	53.1
4.3	3.8	6.5	0.0	0.0	64.8
35.1	4.8	T	0.0	0.0	80.3
8.5	12.3	T	0.0	0.0	89.8
28.3	33.9	0.7	T	0.0	95.1
12.1	1.4	13.1	T	0.0	71.8
17.4	9.2	1.8	0.0	0.0	57.3
21.7	10.4	0.5	0.0	0.0	102.5
14.4	22.7	0.3	0.0	0.0	79.6
20.1	20.5	0.4	0.0	0.0	87.7
10.7	11.4	5.4	0.6	0.0	73.3
31.6	11.3	2.9	0.0	0.0	110.6
20.1	8.7	1.5	T	0.0	67.4
10.0	6.8	T	0.0	0.0	77.6
11.2	16.7	7.9	0.0	0.0	88.2
7.5	19.1	2.6	0.0	0.0	82.7
21.2	16.1	7.1	0.0	0.0	84.3
10.6	4.7	1.7	0.0	0.0	56.3
11.9	9.4	1.2	0.0	0.0	60.5
13.9	17.8	5.4	0.0	0.0	74.7
13.6	9.6	2.2	T	0.0	65.6

SOUTH BEND, IN

Feb	Mar	Apr	May	June	Total
1090	931	584	272	53	6659
927	885	515	228	28	6092
1231	925	458	212	98	6514
1099	897	512	158	36	6646
1150	1272	441	259	58	6742
961	806	666	342	52	6520
1140	955	539	133	29	6560
1312	813	475	278	59	7079
1085	898	437	119	38	5946
1058	1120	535	99	36	6590
1028	796	584	402	47	6431
1220	880	474	337	8	6340
1233	779	444	311	35	6671
1034	988	433	226	105	6476
1094	1007	497	181	68	6847
1012	959	562	280	7	6488
1110	972	582	197	109	6133
977	561	446	268	0	5887
1028	780	403	250	51	5660
1035	944	634	136	37	6045

Aug	Sept	Oct	Nov	Dec	Total
256	73	3	0	0	757
185	82	5	0	0	752
114	155	34	0	0	769
180	55	0	0	0	582
292	126	29	0	0	978
222	60	11	0	0	755
274	32	25	1	0	853

Average Temperature

Year	Jan	Feb	Mar	Apr	May	June	July	Aug	Sept	Oct	Nov	Dec	Annual
1936	19.0	15.6	39.3	43.7	62.7	67.4	78.6	75.6	67.1	52.5	36.4	32.6	49.2
1937	28.1	27.1	32.0	47.4	59.2	66.6	72.8	73.4	62.6	50.0	37.8	25.8	48.6
#1938	25.2	33.8	44.0	49.8	60.1	67.9	73.9	74.8	64.8	57.5	44.4	30.2	52.2
#1939	31.0	29.6	38.6	43.6	62.1	71.2	72.8	74.4	67.5	53.4	38.7	34.0	51.2
1940	14.7	26.8	30.2	44.2	55.0	68.5	74.2	72.2	62.2	54.7	37.0	32.9	47.7
1941	26.4	23.3	31.0	53.7	62.1	69.8	73.6	72.4	67.9	54.4	41.9	35.4	51.0
1942	24.2	22.4	38.1	52.2	60.4	69.6	73.2	70.0	61.2	51.6	41.1	23.4	49.0
1943	20.8	26.9	32.8	43.2	56.4	71.8	73.2	71.7	59.5	50.4	35.6	26.0	47.4
1944	30.6	28.3	30.4	44.7	63.6	71.6	73.0	73.0	64.0	51.0	41.7	23.0	49.6
1945	19.0	28.9	47.2	44.7	52.4	64.5	70.8	70.2	63.2	49.8	40.0	21.6	47.4
1946	26.4	27.8	47.4	48.6	56.4	67.4	73.6	67.6	65.0	57.2	42.6	32.2	51.0
1947	27.2	19.6	29.8	46.0	52.6	65.2	69.0	78.8	65.0	59.8	34.6	28.7	48.0
1948	16.7	24.8	35.5	51.4	54.7	66.4	73.2	71.6	66.4	49.5	42.8	29.4	48.6
1949	30.0	28.7	36.3	46.1	59.8	72.0	76.0	72.0	58.6	56.0	39.3	32.6	50.4
1950	31.2	25.4	31.4	41.0	59.9	66.5	69.3	69.2	63.0	57.0	34.6	20.8	47.5
1951	25.8	27.3	35.1	45.7	60.1	66.1	70.9	67.6	60.7	53.9	32.0	26.3	47.6
1952	27.7	31.1	35.1	48.5	56.1	72.1	74.2	69.9	63.8	47.1	41.2	31.9	49.9
1953	28.9	31.5	37.8	44.4	60.5	71.6	74.0	72.4	64.0	56.3	42.5	31.2	51.3
1954	26.6	34.8	33.3	51.6	54.3	71.7	72.5	69.3	66.2	52.8	40.7	29.4	50.3
1955	23.9	26.8	35.9	54.0	60.4	66.3	78.3	75.7	64.6	54.2	35.6	25.8	50.1
1956	25.1	27.2	34.7	45.4	58.0	71.4	71.6	71.0	61.8	58.4	39.8	33.6	49.9
1957	19.4	31.8	36.2	48.3	58.4	68.9	73.7	70.6	61.5	49.6	40.0	33.2	49.3
1958	24.7	20.9	35.0	49.6	58.9	63.0	71.2	70.5	63.2	54.9	42.1	20.6	47.9
1959	18.6	25.6	35.8	47.7	63.6	69.9	71.7	76.8	67.4	51.1	33.0	34.6	49.7
1960	27.3	25.1	23.7	50.8	56.9	65.7	70.4	72.3	68.1	53.0	41.8	24.8	48.4
1961	21.8	30.5	38.8	42.5	54.2	67.7	71.7	71.2	68.2	54.1	40.1	26.7	49.0
1962	19.1	24.1	34.0	47.6	64.9	69.0	69.3	71.3	61.0	54.4	40.1	24.0	48.2
#1963	13.3	18.0	38.5	49.2	56.6	69.5	71.7	67.6	64.6	61.8	45.1	19.4	47.9
1964	29.3	27.3	35.8	50.4	63.5	71.1	74.0	69.0	63.0	48.9	43.2	27.5	50.2
1965	24.7	27.0	28.7	46.9	64.2	67.5	69.9	68.1	63.7	51.6	40.6	36.4	49.1
1966	20.3	28.1	39.1	45.3	52.2	68.8	72.9	67.2	62.3	51.7	42.8	29.9	48.4
1967	29.0	21.1	36.5	48.9	54.3	70.6	69.8	67.9	62.5	51.7	36.0	30.5	48.2
1968	22.3	22.3	39.7	50.0	55.2	68.9	71.0	71.6	64.6	53.7	40.7	27.0	48.9
1969	22.3	27.8	32.9	50.3	59.5	64.9	73.1	73.0	63.6	51.4	37.2	27.5	48.6
1970	16.8	25.7	32.3	48.8	61.0	67.8	72.0	70.4	64.4	54.4	39.4	30.4	48.6
1971	20.0	28.6	33.9	46.2	56.3	73.9	69.5	68.1	67.1	60.4	40.9	36.0	50.1
1972	23.9	26.5	33.4	45.4	60.0	63.6	71.4	69.4	62.9	49.7	38.1	28.8	47.8
1973	29.9	30.0	46.7	50.1	56.1	72.3	74.4	74.1	67.0	58.3	44.4	29.2	52.7
1974	27.9	28.1	39.6	51.7	57.3	66.8	75.0	71.9	62.0	53.0	42.4	32.9	50.7
1975	30.0	27.8	34.4	43.6	63.2	70.3	71.8	73.6	60.1	55.9	48.1	32.7	51.0
RECORD MEAN	24.7	25.9	36.1	47.9	59.0	68.8	73.1	71.4	64.7	53.6	40.0	28.5	49.5
MAX	32.2	33.8	44.9	58.3	70.1	79.9	84.1	82.5	75.5	63.7	47.9	35.3	59.0
MIN	17.1	17.9	27.2	37.5	47.9	57.7	62.1	60.3	53.8	43.4	32.1	21.6	39.9

# Indicates a station move or relocation of instruments.

Precipitation

Year	Jan	Feb	Mar	Apr	May	June	July	Aug	Sept	Oct	Nov	Dec	Annual
1936	1.14	1.48	1.47	3.41	1.88	1.40	1.49	4.11	4.68	3.47	2.37	2.52	29.42
1937	2.70	1.57	1.31	5.08	3.07	2.85	5.97	5.40	2.59	3.07	2.02	1.91	37.54
#1938	1.80	3.13	3.58	1.99	5.34	5.19	4.29	2.05	3.92	0.76	1.24	1.91	35.20
#1939	2.74	1.44	3.05	4.50	0.94	6.98	5.40	4.85	0.59	3.27	2.01	1.43	37.20
1940	1.57	1.27	2.11	3.84	4.73	5.61	1.08	4.78	1.93	2.88	2.35	2.22	34.37
1941	1.72	0.99	1.65	3.64	2.43	2.85	2.47	1.78	2.87	9.35	2.89	1.37	34.01
1942	2.31	1.98	2.52	2.89	3.11	1.94	3.91	4.20	2.56	2.19	3.88	2.57	34.06
1943	1.61	1.43	2.64	3.37	6.28	2.84	5.96	5.15	5.20	2.10	2.87	0.60	40.05
1944	0.96	1.34	5.56	4.26	4.26	2.39	1.30	2.31	2.84	3.35	2.10	1.24	31.91
1945	0.44	1.09	2.83	4.33	5.55	3.26	6.20	2.70	4.59	1.69	2.29	1.11	36.08
1946	2.05	2.09	3.89	1.61	4.06	4.95	0.02	1.59	2.14	2.88	2.47	3.66	31.41
1947	2.61	0.87	2.16	9.20	5.94	3.46	2.80	2.53	7.02	0.98	2.28	1.93	41.78
1948	1.91	2.31	4.79	1.90	5.29	3.95	2.39	1.16	3.02	0.93	2.27	3.26	33.18
1949	3.96	2.89	2.12	1.27	3.24	4.55	3.53	3.40	3.98	3.03	2.04	5.01	39.02
1950	4.62	3.72	3.47	5.32	2.41	8.20	6.15	0.32	3.07	0.42	4.27	2.97	44.94
1951	2.17	1.33	1.88	4.75	3.67	4.07	5.01	5.05	4.49	4.75	4.00	3.69	44.86
1952	2.08	0.88	2.50	2.84	4.09	3.85	2.82	3.47	0.71	1.31	2.27	1.97	28.79
1953	2.39	1.28	2.52	3.57	2.75	3.32	1.89	3.39	1.99	1.20	1.64	1.36	27.30
1954	1.63	4.01	4.03	5.55	2.47	1.69	5.82	5.10	1.63	9.75	2.23	2.80	46.71
1955	2.20	1.93	2.38	2.23	2.20	2.17	4.23	6.45	2.90	6.01	2.61	0.70	36.01
1956	1.05	2.67	1.59	4.47	4.73	1.41	1.59	3.68	0.62	0.57	2.04	1.43	25.85
1957	2.52	1.52	2.51	6.05	2.37	3.21	2.39	5.72	1.59	5.25	3.26	4.47	40.86
1958	1.48	1.99	0.54	2.12	1.76	3.58	7.18	3.82	2.40	1.10	2.87	1.15	29.99
1959	5.28	2.65	3.58	4.25	2.28	1.40	4.12	0.97	2.90	5.44	3.62	1.98	38.47
1960	4.23	4.53	2.15	2.70	1.83	5.75	1.92	3.26	3.40	2.44	1.86	0.87	34.94
1961	0.95	1.55	3.80	4.93	1.19	3.66	3.76	2.82	5.78	1.82	1.49	2.03	33.78
1962	3.36	1.74	1.82	2.34	2.19	5.02	4.87	3.49	1.28	4.39	1.37	2.64	34.51
1963	1.28	1.11	3.03	2.42	2.48	1.81	5.11	1.30	1.18	1.21	2.32	1.90	25.15
1964	1.57	1.03	5.01	5.37	1.32	4.45	4.80	3.42	3.39	0.89	2.33	2.54	36.12
1965	4.74	2.70	3.35	4.87	1.67	2.24	2.22	5.43	5.55	2.53	1.65	5.50	42.45
1966	1.54	1.73	2.58	5.72	3.89	1.90	4.40	5.48	1.10	1.32	4.89	4.73	39.28
1967	3.56	2.26	1.73	4.96	1.57	5.49	2.11	2.77	2.59	5.01	3.34	4.08	39.47
1968	2.06	3.21	1.24	2.40	2.44	9.09	2.06	3.17	4.38	1.43	4.42	3.42	39.32
1969	3.61	0.54	1.92	5.51	4.26	5.17	4.88	0.44	1.42	4.70	2.29	1.25	35.99
1970	1.34	0.76	2.81	5.43	3.35	3.92	4.14	3.37	5.37	3.68	3.57	1.78	39.52
1971	1.55	2.12	2.10	0.50	1.64	1.13	4.16	2.80	5.16	2.23	1.83	4.58	29.80
1972	1.82	1.39	3.63	3.23	3.01	2.72	4.52	3.85	7.67	3.76	2.90	4.78	43.28
1973	1.64	1.02	3.85	3.88	3.61	4.85	3.33	1.29	2.11	3.49	1.45	4.30	34.82
1974	3.24	2.20	2.81	4.17	4.82	4.08	1.17	1.70	4.65	2.46	3.21	3.00	37.51
1975	4.58	3.26	2.96	6.02	2.08	5.46	2.58	7.55	1.15	1.31	4.73	3.72	45.40
RECORD MEAN	2.32	1.79	2.79	3.39	3.53	3.56	3.27	3.34	3.27	2.93	2.71	2.54	35.44

Record mean values above are means through the current year for the period beginning in 1894 for temperature and precipitation, 1940 for snowfall. Temperature and degree day data are from Cooperative locations through March 1939 and from Airport locations thereafter. Precipitation and snowfall data are from Cooperative locations through July 1939 and from Airport locations thereafter.

DES MOINES, IOWA

Located in the heart of the North American landmass, Des Moines enjoys a climate which is continental in character. In winter the mean pressure of the heart region is higher than that of the surrounding areas, and is accompanied by an outflow of cold, dry air. In summer the mean pressure of the heart region is relatively low, and is accompanied by a general inflow of warm, moist air. There results a marked seasonal contrast in both temperature and precipitation which is characteristic of continental climates.

The average temperature for the year is 50°, but the average temperature for the individual months varies from 21° in January to 76° in July. The variation in extremes is 140°, from an extreme low of -30° in midwinter to an extreme high of 110° in midsummer. Precipitation averages about 31.5 inches annually, but the variation is large, from a minimum of 17.1 inches in 1956 to a maximum of 56.8 inches in 1881. The variation in monthly amounts is even more remarkable, from the very dry month of October 1952, with only .03 inch precipitation, to the very wet month of June 1881, with 15.79 inches rainfall. The average seasonal snowfall is 32 inches, but here, also, there has been great variability from a minimum of 8.3 inches in the winter of 1965-66 to a maximum of 72.0 inches in the winter of 1911-12.

Since agriculture is the mainstay of the area, it is convenient to separate the year into arbitrary seasons, corresponding to the growing seasons of the staple crops of the section. There is the winter season when most plant life is dormant, based on normal mean temperatures less than 40°, lasting about 19 weeks from mid-November to late March. The summer season, when corn and soybeans can be grown, with mean daily temperatures 60° and above, lasts about 21 weeks from early May to the beginning of October. The spring growing season, including part of the growing season of oats and forage crops, and the fall harvest season with mean daily temperatures within the range from 40° to 59°, each lasts about 6 weeks.

The winter season is a season of dry cold, occasionally broken by storms of short duration. The prevailing winds are from the northwest. The average precipitation for the 19 weeks is about 6 inches, or approximately 20 percent of the annual amount. At the beginning, and again at the close of the season, the precipitation may occur as rain, but during the major portion of the season it falls as snow, sometimes drifting badly when occasional cold waves sweep across the state. Bitterly cold days, with both maximum and minimum temperatures below zero, occur on an average of only 3 days in 4 years.

Beginning with the spring growing season, the frequency and intensity of precipitation increases

Station: DES MOINES, IOWA
MUNICIPAL AIRPORT
Elevation (ground): 938 feet

TEMPERATURES °F

	Normal			Extremes			
Month	Daily maximum	Daily minimum	Monthly	Record highest	Year	Record lowest	Year
(a)				15		15	
J	27.5	11.3	19.4	62	1967	-24	1970
F	32.5	15.8	24.2	73	1972	-18	1972
M	42.5	25.2	33.9	83	1968	-22	1962
A	59.7	39.2	49.5	90	1970	9	1975
M	70.9	50.9	60.9	98	1967	30	1967
J	79.8	61.1	70.5	99	1970	42	1969
J	84.9	65.3	75.1	104	1974	47	1971
A	83.2	63.4	73.3	100	1964	45	1967
S	74.6	54.0	64.3	95	1971	31	1972
O	64.9	43.6	54.3	95	1963	14	1972
N	46.4	29.2	37.8	76	1965	-3	1964
D	32.8	17.2	25.0	67	1975	-16	1963
YR	58.3	39.7	49.0	104	JUL 1974	-24	JAN 1970

IMPORTANT:
The time-period covered by this record is limited: See footnotes following table of **NORMALS, MEANS AND EXTREMES** for explanation and for additional history of **EXTREME HIGHS AND LOWS** recorded in the general area.

(Continued)

very markedly to a maximum in June. The total for the growing seasons averages about 25 inches, or approximately 80 percent of the annual total. The total for the 21 weeks of summer is about 18 inches, or slightly under 60 percent of the annual amount. The importance of this fact is evident in the large amounts of moisture required by the staple crops of the area during the first half of the growing season. By summer the winds are generally from a southerly quadrant, bringing into the state the ample supplies of moisture from the Gulf of Mexico. The rain falls mainly in the form of thundershowers, occasionally accompanied by damaging winds or hail.

The fall, or harvest season, is a period of ample sunshine and diminishing precipitation. It is a season favorable for the drying and harvesting of the corn and soybean crops, and completes the climatic regime so favorable for the growing of those crops. More interest is shown in the first killing frost of the season (in reference to the corn crop) than to any other seasonal threshold. Damaging frosts result in a harvest of 'soft' corn with light weight and poor keeping qualities. The average date of first 32° freeze in this area is October 10.

DES MOINES, IOWA

Normals, Means, and Extremes

(To better understand these tables, see full explanation of terms beginning on page 322)

Month	Normal Degree days Base 65 °F: Heating	Cooling	Precipitation in inches, Water equivalent: Normal	Maximum monthly	Year	Minimum monthly	Year	Maximum in 24 hrs.	Year	Snow, Ice pellets: Maximum monthly	Year	Maximum in 24 hrs.	Year
(a)				36		36		36		36		36	
J	1414	0	1.14	4.38	1960	0.07	1954	2.97	1960	19.8	1942	19.8	1942
F	1142	0	1.05	2.99	1951	0.13	1968	1.77	1961	21.3	1962	12.1	1950
M	964	0	2.31	5.37	1961	0.41	1971	2.42	1945	18.8	1948	8.5	1957
A	465	0	2.94	6.31	1974	1.05	1942	3.80	1974	15.1	1973	10.4	1973
M	186	59	4.21	7.53	1960	1.23	1949	2.79	1954	0.2	1944	0.2	1944
J	26	191	4.90	14.19	1947	1.13	1963	5.50	1947	0.0		0.0	
J	0	317	3.28	10.51	1958	0.04	1975	5.14	1958	0.0		0.0	
A	13	270	3.30	10.47	1954	0.71	1953	6.18	1975	0.0		0.0	
S	94	73	3.07	10.19	1961	0.41	1950	4.47	1961	T	1942	T	1942
O	350	18	2.14	7.29	1941	0.03	1952	2.81	1947	2.4	1967	2.4	1967
N	816	0	1.42	4.60	1952	0.03	1969	3.35	1952	13.5	1968	11.8	1968
D	1240	0	1.09	2.90	1941	0.22	1946	1.46	1973	23.9	1961	11.0	1961
YR	6710	928	30.85	14.19	JUN 1947	0.03	NOV 1969	6.18	AUG 1975	23.9	DEC 1961	19.8	JAN 1942

Month	Relative humidity pct. Hour 00 (Local time)	Hour 06	Hour 12	Hour 18	Wind: Mean speed m.p.h.	Prevailing direction	Fastest mile: Speed m.p.h.	Direction	Year	Pct. of possible sunshine	Mean sky cover, tenths, sunrise to sunset
(a)	14	14	14	14	26	19	25	25		25	26
J	77	78	71	72	11.7	NW	66	NW	1953	51	6.6
F	78	80	69	68	11.8	NW	56	W	1952	54	6.4
M	75	80	64	61	13.1	NW	66	S	1953	54	6.9
A	71	79	58	55	13.4	NW	76	W	1965	55	6.7
M	72	79	57	53	11.6	SE	70	W	1955	60	6.5
J	75	82	58	55	10.5	S	76	NW	1953	67	5.9
J	76	82	57	56	9.0	S	73	W	1968	71	5.3
A	79	85	58	58	8.8	S	60	SSE	1960	70	5.2
S	80	85	61	62	9.6	S	55	NW	1953	64	5.3
O	72	78	55	57	10.6	S	56	W	1952	64	5.1
N	76	80	65	67	11.7	NW	72	W	1952	49	6.5
D	79	81	72	73	11.5	NW	61	SW	1951	45	6.9
YR	76	81	62	61	11.1	NW	76	W	APR 1965	59	6.1

Month	Mean number of days, Sunrise to sunset: Clear	Partly cloudy	Cloudy	Precipitation .01 inch or more	Snow, Ice pellets 1.0 inch or more	Thunderstorms	Heavy fog, visibility ¼ mile or less	Temperatures °F Max. (b) 90° and above	Max. 32° and below	Min. 32° and below	Min. 0° and below	Average station pressure mb. Elev. 963 feet m.s.l.
(a)	26	26	26	36	36	36	26	14	14	14	14	3
J	8	6	17	7	2	*	2	0	19	30	9	986.2
F	8	5	15	7	2	*	2	0	14	27	4	983.0
M	6	8	17	10	2	2	2	0	6	22	*	979.2
A	7	7	16	10	*	4	1	*	*	7	0	978.8
M	7	9	15	11	0	7	1	1	0	*	0	977.1
J	7	12	11	11	0	10	1	4	0	0	0	977.9
J	10	12	9	9	0	8	1	9	0	0	0	980.9
A	11	10	10	9	0	7	1	6	0	0	0	981.7
S	12	6	12	9	0	5	1	1	0	*	0	983.6
O	12	7	12	7	*	3	1	*	0	4	0	983.4
N	7	7	16	6	1	1	2	0	3	17	*	981.7
D	7	6	18	7	2	*	3	0	15	29	3	982.8
YR	102	95	168	106	10	50	18	21	57	137	16	981.4

FOOTNOTES

Means and extremes above are from existing and comparable exposures. Annual extremes have been exceeded at other sites in the locality as follows: Highest temperature 110 in July 1936 and earlier; lowest temperature -30 in January 1884; maximum monthly precipitation 15.79 in June 1881; maximum monthly snowfall 37.0 in January 1886.

Snowfall

Season	July	Aug	Sept	Oct	Nov	Dec	Jan
1936-37	0.0	0.0	0.0	0.0	1.4	4.2	4.0
1937-38	0.0	0.0	0.0	0.2	5.3	4.1	9.0
1938-39	0.0	0.0	0.0	0.8	2.0	4.8	5.6
1939-40	0.0	0.0	0.0	0.0	0.0	4.2	6.9
1940-41	0.0	0.0	0.0	0.0	1.8	11.0	16.4
1941-42	0.0	0.0	0.0	T	0.1	10.1	19.8
1942-43	0.0	0.0	T	T	4.4	2.9	5.8
1943-44	0.0	0.0	0.0	0.0	0.6	1.6	1.4
1944-45	0.0	0.0	0.0	0.0	2.7	11.0	9.5
1945-46	0.0	0.0	0.0	0.0	1.1	10.2	6.0
1946-47	0.0	0.0	0.0	0.0	T	2.3	18.8
1947-48	0.0	0.0	0.0	0.0	4.3	1.0	1.7
1948-49	0.0	0.0	0.0	0.0	T	7.3	18.1
1949-50	0.0	0.0	0.0	0.0	0.1	1.9	5.5
#1950-51	0.0	0.0	0.0	0.0	0.8	2.9	4.3
1951-52	0.0	0.0	0.0	0.0	0.6	12.0	4.3
1952-53	0.0	0.0	0.0	0.0	5.6	6.2	7.3
1953-54	0.0	0.0	0.0	0.0	T	3.9	0.4
1954-55	0.0	0.0	0.0	0.1	T	5.4	10.7
1955-56	0.0	0.0	0.0	0.2	1.2	4.4	4.8
1956-57	0.0	0.0	0.0	0.0	4.8	5.7	13.1
1957-58	0.0	0.0	0.0	T	6.8	9.1	9.7
1958-59	0.0	0.0	0.0	0.0	0.8	4.4	10.6
1959-60	0.0	0.0	0.0	T	6.1	4.4	11.2
1960-61	0.0	0.0	0.0	T	T	2.8	5.5
1961-62	0.0	0.0	0.0	0.0	2.7	23.9	4.2
1962-63	0.0	0.0	0.0	1.4	1.5	3.1	15.9
1963-64	0.0	0.0	0.0	0.0	T	7.6	6.4
1964-65	0.0	0.0	0.0	T	0.5	2.6	7.4
1965-66	0.0	0.0	0.0	0.0	T	2.4	3.6
1966-67	0.0	0.0	0.0	T	T	7.1	4.0
1967-68	0.0	0.0	0.0	2.4	0.7	2.6	8.5
1968-69	0.0	0.0	0.0	T	13.5	5.2	6.8
1969-70	0.0	0.0	0.0	T	T	12.0	3.2
1970-71	0.0	0.0	0.0	0.0	0.2	1.4	15.9
1971-72	0.0	0.0	0.0	0.0	10.3	2.9	5.8
1972-73	0.0	0.0	0.0	T	10.2	9.5	15.3
1973-74	0.0	0.0	0.0	0.0	T	9.6	10.6
1974-75	0.0	0.0	0.0	0.0	9.3	9.1	13.3
1975-76	0.0	0.0	0.0	0.0	7.0	0.5	
RECORD MEAN	0.0	0.0	T	0.1	2.7	6.1	8.7

Heating Degree Days

Season	July	Aug	Sept	Oct	Nov	Dec	Jan
1955-56	0	1	70	347	1008	1343	1392
1956-57	0	14	103	162	807	1111	1518
1957-58	0	2	113	449	877	1018	1238
1958-59	4	27	78	304	694	1294	1503
1959-60	6	2	131	471	1034	957	1352
#1960-61	0	0	82	339	715	1202	1328
1961-62	0	0	167	311	841	1434	1609
1962-63	0	0	110	289	728	1266	1751
1963-64	0	18	54	95	649	1542	1145
1964-65	0	28	124	433	707	1286	1465
1965-66	0	14	154	310	715	915	1568
1966-67	0	13	136	375	789	1239	1276
1967-68	14	18	109	440	850	1112	1317
1968-69	2	11	92	378	898	1351	1508
1969-70	0	0	45	478	773	1270	1617
1970-71	0	0	100	352	748	1114	1521
1971-72	8	4	96	184	756	1132	1495
1972-73	7	10	112	523	925	1442	1326
1973-74	0	0	68	209	719	1325	1406
1974-75	0	12	168	307	755	1131	1308
1975-76	0	0	148	267	637	1085	

Cooling Degree Days

Year	Jan	Feb	Mar	Apr	May	June	July
1969	0	0	0	0	99	129	349
1970	0	0	0	31	131	238	368
1971	0	0	0	13	26	362	234
1972	0	0	0	3	77	184	289
1973	0	0	0	2	19	267	358
1974	0	0	0	0	52	149	499
1975	0	0	0	3	116	237	408

[illegible]	Feb	Mar	Apr	May	June	Total
8.2	5.4	0.6	0.0	0.0	23.8	
2.0	T	1.9	T	0.0	22.5	
20.4	7.9	1.0	0.0	0.0	42.5	
16.3	7.9	0.0	T	0.0	35.3	
1.0	6.8	0.0	0.0	0.0	37.0	
11.8	1.6	0.0	0.0	0.0	43.4	
0.9	10.9	T	0.0	0.0	24.9	
4.6	13.0	T	0.2	0.0	21.4	
10.8	0.4	1.2	T	0.0	35.6	
0.3	3.7	1.7	0.0	0.0	23.0	
3.1	3.2	3.9	T	0.0	31.3	
6.7	18.8	0.0	0.0	0.0	32.5	
5.8	0.7	2.0	0.0	0.0	33.9	
15.3	8.1	5.1	0.0	0.0	36.0	
2.8	16.7	T	0.0	0.0	27.5	
3.2	9.4	3.3	0.0	0.0	32.8	
9.9	2.4	T	0.0	0.0	31.4	
3.9	5.4	0.0	T	0.0	13.6	
6.8	2.6	0.0	0.0	0.0	25.6	
6.1	2.5	0.3	0.0	0.0	19.5	
0.7	11.2	1.3	0.0	0.0	36.8	
3.0	4.5	T	0.0	0.0	33.1	
4.1	15.6	6.2	0.0	0.0	41.7	
18.5	15.8	2.2	0.0	0.0	58.2	
6.9	16.4	2.7	0.0	0.0	34.3	
21.3	11.1	0.9	0.0	0.0	64.1	
6.5	6.2	0.0	0.0	0.0	34.6	
4.1	10.1	T	0.0	0.0	28.2	
7.6	17.3	0.0	0.0	0.0	35.4	
0.5	1.8	T	T	0.0	8.3	
2.3	0.5	0.9	T	0.0	14.8	
2.1	T	0.1	T	0.0	16.4	
12.3	2.8	0.0	0.0	0.0	40.6	
1.2	9.8	3.9	0.0	0.0	30.1	
13.7	5.3	0.4	0.0	0.0	36.9	
9.0	1.6	0.6	0.0	0.0	30.2	
4.6	T	15.1	0.0	0.0	54.7	
6.1	1.9	1.2	0.0	0.0	29.4	
17.9	5.6	4.5	0.0	0.0	59.7	
7.0	7.0	1.6	T	0.0	33.2	

Average Temperature

Year	Jan	Feb	Mar	Apr	May	June	July	Aug	Sept	Oct	Nov	Dec	Annual
1936	11.2	8.0	41.3	47.8	68.2	71.4	85.8	80.4	69.5	52.2	36.6	30.6	50.2
1937	14.6	21.4	34.2	49.0	63.4	70.8	77.6	78.8	67.5	52.2	35.1	24.5	49.1
1938	22.6	31.8	45.8	51.6	61.0	71.2	78.9	77.6	69.0	61.6	39.2	28.5	53.2
1939	30.8	21.4	37.6	49.5	68.4	72.8	78.5	71.7	70.5	54.8	41.6	34.0	52.6
1940	10.4	25.4	33.6	48.2	59.4	73.7	78.7	72.2	67.6	60.0	35.6	30.2	49.6
1941	25.6	24.2	36.1	55.6	67.8	71.6	77.2	77.4	67.2	55.8	42.0	33.4	52.8
1942	23.5	24.7	39.4	56.2	61.0	71.5	76.1	73.9	63.0	55.2	40.4	22.6	50.6
1943	19.0	29.4	32.2	49.8	58.3	72.4	77.0	75.2	61.2	53.0	35.7	27.4	49.2
1944	31.5	28.8	31.6	46.0	65.6	72.9	75.0	73.3	66.1	55.8	41.7	21.6	50.8
1945	21.3	27.4	47.2	50.2	56.5	65.2	74.4	74.2	64.6	53.8	39.4	19.4	49.5
1946	24.3	31.5	48.5	56.0	58.2	71.8	75.8	70.3	65.0	57.2	40.2	31.6	52.5
1947	27.7	19.0	32.8	48.6	56.5	70.6	75.2	82.7	69.4	62.8	34.6	29.2	50.5
1948	20.6	24.1	33.0	56.0	61.2	70.7	77.0	76.3	70.4	53.2	41.4	28.3	51.0
1949	19.2	21.0	36.2	50.8	65.4	74.8	77.8	74.5	60.8	57.1	43.5	29.0	50.8
#1950	20.4	23.9	32.5	44.2	61.7	70.1	71.6	69.2	65.9	60.1	34.7	20.8	47.9
1951	20.4	25.5	28.6	45.8	63.2	66.4	73.6	72.3	60.8	52.6	32.2	20.5	46.8
1952	21.4	32.3	33.2	50.5	60.4	75.6	75.5	71.1	66.1	48.7	38.9	27.3	50.1
1953	24.1	29.6	38.1	44.8	60.4	74.2	76.3	75.0	66.2	58.9	42.6	29.2	51.6
1954	19.6	37.7	33.2	53.8	56.8	74.5	79.4	73.5	67.8	52.4	42.5	29.4	57.7
1955	21.6	22.1	35.7	57.5	64.7	68.6	81.0	78.1	68.1	54.1	31.1	21.5	50.4
1956	19.9	25.6	35.2	47.6	63.4	76.0	74.6	74.5	65.0	60.7	37.9	28.9	50.8
1957	15.8	30.8	36.8	50.0	59.9	70.4	79.7	74.5	62.0	50.2	35.5	32.0	49.8
1958	24.8	16.9	34.8	50.2	63.9	67.0	71.2	74.4	65.2	55.9	41.7	23.1	49.1
1959	16.4	23.8	36.4	49.4	62.9	72.8	74.1	77.9	64.3	49.6	30.3	33.9	49.3
1960	21.2	19.4	21.4	51.9	61.0	68.9	74.4	74.9	66.6	54.2	40.9	25.9	48.4
#1961	22.0	30.1	37.5	44.7	58.7	70.6	74.1	73.2	62.4	55.0	36.7	18.5	48.6
1962	13.0	20.5	29.8	49.3	69.2	71.3	74.3	74.2	63.3	57.2	40.5	24.0	48.9
1963	8.5	18.9	39.4	51.7	59.7	74.0	75.9	71.4	65.9	64.5	43.2	15.2	49.0
1964	27.8	26.3	30.4	48.0	64.3	69.9	77.2	70.4	63.6	50.8	41.2	23.3	49.4
1965	17.6	20.2	22.7	48.1	66.2	70.3	74.8	72.9	61.0	55.3	41.0	35.3	48.8
1966	14.2	24.7	41.0	46.0	57.7	70.4	78.6	70.8	62.4	52.9	38.4	24.8	48.5
1967	23.7	22.2	40.3	51.1	57.1	69.0	72.1	70.3	62.3	51.5	36.5	28.9	48.8
1968	22.3	23.9	42.6	51.1	57.0	72.4	74.2	73.0	63.3	53.8	34.8	21.3	49.2
1969	16.2	25.9	28.2	52.5	62.9	67.3	76.0	74.7	66.1	50.0	39.0	23.8	48.5
1970	12.7	27.1	32.9	51.7	65.8	72.4	76.6	73.9	65.5	54.1	39.8	28.8	50.1
1971	15.7	23.1	35.2	52.1	58.7	76.8	72.1	73.2	68.1	60.5	39.6	28.2	50.3
1972	16.6	19.9	37.1	48.9	62.5	70.2	73.9	72.4	64.6	48.0	33.9	18.4	47.2
1973	22.0	27.7	45.6	49.2	59.8	73.6	76.4	76.9	65.7	59.0	40.7	22.1	51.6
1974	19.5	28.0	39.8	53.0	60.3	69.1	80.9	71.1	60.9	55.0	39.6	28.2	50.4
1975	22.7	22.4	29.7	46.9	65.9	72.3	77.9	77.1	61.8	57.2	43.5	29.9	50.6
RECORD MEAN	20.8	24.7	36.3	50.4	61.5	71.1	76.1	73.7	65.3	54.2	38.5	26.1	49.9
MAX	29.5	33.6	45.4	60.6	71.6	81.0	86.5	84.0	75.9	64.8	47.6	34.2	59.6
MIN	12.0	15.8	27.1	40.1	51.3	61.1	65.6	63.4	54.7	43.6	29.3	18.0	40.2

# Indicates a station move or relocation of instruments.

DES MOINES, IA

	Feb	Mar	Apr	May	June	Total
1137	916	523	149	11	6897	
952	867	457	179	13	6183	
1341	933	445	98	37	6551	
1148	877	467	140	15	6551	
1316	1344	415	153	13	7194	
970	845	600	221	10	6312	
1239	1086	474	32	17	7210	
1285	787	400	195	3	6814	
1116	1069	504	91	25	6308	
1247	1305	509	86	1	7191	
1122	737	565	256	16	6372	
1192	767	421	308	22	6538	
1184	685	411	260	24	6424	
1086	1135	368	159	50	7038	
1055	987	422	99	9	6755	
1167	915	393	211	0	6521	
1303	857	478	149	23	6485	
1039	594	470	173	0	6621	
1033	775	363	189	20	6107	
1185	1090	539	81	11	6587	

	Aug	Sept	Oct	Nov	Dec	Total
	308	84	20	0	0	989
	280	123	20	0	0	1191
	263	194	52	0	0	1144
	247	109	C	0	0	909
	378	98	30	0	0	1152
	209	52	4	0	0	974
	383	58	32	0	C	1237

Precipitation

Year	Jan	Feb	Mar	Apr	May	June	July	Aug	Sept	Oct	Nov	Dec	Annual
1936	1.86	0.95	1.57	1.33	1.45	3.81	0.41	2.53	8.50	0.93	0.76	1.54	25.64
1937	1.85	0.80	1.99	3.29	7.13	3.95	0.58	2.72	1.41	1.38	0.65	0.68	26.43
1938	0.83	0.46	2.24	4.21	5.21	2.33	2.49	3.08	2.55	1.33	2.14	0.74	27.61
1939	1.10	2.33	1.80	1.26	1.79	7.45	4.11	5.58	1.20	1.16	0.47	0.44	28.69
1940	0.61	1.89	1.59	3.19	2.09	2.03	3.90	9.63	0.53	1.65	2.08	1.28	30.47
1941	2.51	0.38	0.84	1.56	2.32	6.50	1.33	2.36	8.63	7.29	1.34	2.90	37.96
1942	1.56	1.38	2.07	1.05	6.60	7.36	6.50	2.20	2.72	2.35	2.15	1.14	37.08
1943	0.51	0.66	1.96	2.98	4.17	7.10	5.58	6.42	2.02	0.49	0.50	0.62	33.01
1944	1.31	0.66	2.48	5.07	6.76	6.24	1.64	4.42	2.46	0.58	1.22	1.70	34.54
1945	0.76	1.60	5.13	5.00	6.32	3.75	2.24	1.82	6.51	0.15	1.24	2.87	37.39
1946	2.31	0.15	4.63	1.40	2.97	5.82	1.66	6.14	3.09	4.04	0.78	0.22	33.21
1947	1.98	0.29	2.08	6.11	5.35	14.19	0.42	0.93	0.72	6.86	1.67	1.47	42.07
1948	0.18	2.39	3.49	1.91	1.98	3.36	6.98	1.37	1.27	1.43	3.61	1.90	29.87
1949	3.12	1.07	2.38	1.07	1.23	4.53	3.13	1.76	2.21	1.59	0.57	0.72	23.38
#1950	1.40	2.23	0.81	3.12	5.60	4.82	2.93	2.05	0.41	0.77	0.38	0.27	24.79
1951	0.59	2.99	3.86	5.20	5.56	3.86	4.46	4.74	1.39	2.64	1.81	0.93	38.03
1952	1.03	0.77	4.03	1.52	4.15	5.74	2.57	5.70	0.53	0.03	4.60	1.15	31.82
1953	0.76	2.00	2.37	3.22	2.22	4.03	1.71	0.71	0.66	0.13	1.22	0.97	20.00
1954	0.07	1.35	1.86	3.48	5.90	5.30	1.01	10.47	1.98	3.95	0.06	0.78	36.21
1955	1.35	1.52	0.89	2.63	2.93	1.71	3.69	1.77	4.42	0.52	0.11	0.44	21.98
1956	0.51	0.46	0.51	1.24	1.71	1.29	2.76	3.47	1.21	1.66	1.79	0.46	17.07
1957	0.79	0.13	1.74	2.84	5.36	3.67	2.47	2.93	1.79	3.29	1.94	1.33	28.28
1958	0.71	0.61	0.61	1.31	3.59	3.34	10.51	1.78	4.06	0.07	2.00	0.25	28.84
1959	0.79	1.07	3.94	3.51	6.63	5.71	1.63	2.44	3.13	2.64	2.91	1.91	36.31
1960	4.38	1.58	1.46	2.40	7.53	3.46	1.99	6.78	2.54	2.11	0.52	0.45	35.20
1961	0.33	2.68	5.37	2.39	1.58	2.92	7.05	2.77	10.19	3.00	2.78	1.82	42.88
1962	0.54	1.60	1.42	2.51	6.02	3.96	2.94	1.60	1.93	3.22	0.80	0.50	27.04
1963	0.83	0.72	2.39	4.18	3.94	1.13	4.01	4.83	1.83	2.56	1.36	0.54	28.32
1964	0.51	0.28	1.25	3.29	2.90	6.49	3.37	3.94	4.28	0.29	0.95	0.87	28.42
1965	1.62	1.14	3.02	4.18	3.89	4.80	1.93	1.93	7.23	0.79	1.79	1.64	33.96
1966	0.96	0.25	1.56	1.74	5.37	5.22	2.43	2.09	0.75	0.29	0.70	0.49	21.85
1967	0.77	0.28	1.64	2.25	2.22	7.39	0.81	0.79	2.54	1.93	0.47	0.73	21.82
1968	0.78	0.13	0.93	4.19	2.62	3.42	4.48	4.05	2.63	1.47	1.90	1.71	28.31
1969	1.01	0.97	1.41	4.46	4.75	7.32	4.34	1.83	2.43	2.87	0.03	1.01	32.43
1970	0.26	0.24	3.28	2.28	4.21	2.45	1.96	4.95	6.51	5.20	1.46	0.83	33.63
1971	1.75	2.34	0.41	1.54	3.87	4.31	2.16	1.83	2.19	3.51	3.29	1.12	28.32
1972	0.44	0.63	1.05	3.56	3.05	2.58	5.86	6.65	5.45	2.36	2.43	1.96	36.02
1973	2.09	2.21	4.15	4.67	5.01	2.04	9.17	1.37	7.07	3.26	1.49	2.65	45.18
1974	1.51	0.84	1.99	6.31	7.19	4.62	1.33	2.81	2.08	3.96	1.20	1.83	35.67
1975	1.41	1.48	1.90	2.65	3.41	5.98	0.04	9.73	1.70	0.63	2.20	0.48	31.61
RECORD MEAN	1.14	1.13	1.92	2.85	4.28	4.67	3.36	3.59	3.41	2.37	1.58	1.19	31.49

Record mean values above are means through the current year for the period beginning in 1878 for temperature, 1877 for precipitation and 1940 for snowfall. Data are from city locations through 1950.

TOPEKA, KANSAS

Topeka, located near the geographical center of the United States, close to the western edge of the prairie-lands corn belt, the southern edge of the glacial drift, and about the middle of the temperate zone, offers all the variety in weather generally found in an inland locality separated by mountains or great distances from the modifying influence of the ocean. The City straddles the Kansas River nearly 60 miles above its junction with the Missouri. The Kansas River flows in an easterly direction through northeastern Kansas, and in the Topeka reach the valley ranges from 2 to 4 miles wide, and is bordered by rolling prairie uplands of some 200 to 300 feet higher elevation on both sides.

Averages and extremes of Topeka's climate are given in the tables. Other significant climatic aspects are:

Normally more than 70 percent of the annual precipitation falls during the six crop-growing months, April through September. The rains of this period are usually of short duration, predominantly of the thundershower type and occur more frequently during the nighttime and early morning hours than at other times of the day.

With much of the precipitation occurring in connection with warm-season thunderstorms, falls at excessive rates are not uncommon. The greatest 24-hour amount of record is 8.08 inches on September 6-7, 1909. Twenty-four-hour falls of 5 inches or more occur about once in 9 years; 4 inches or more four times in 10 years; 3 inches or more eight times in 10 years; and 2 inches or more five times every 2 years. Rainfall, amounting to an inch in an hour, occurs with a frequency of five times every 2 years, and falls of 2 inches in two hours can be expected one year out of two. Maximum falls observed in various time periods are: 5 minutes, 0.90; 10 minutes, 1.40; 15 minutes, 1.55; 20 minutes, 2.08; 30 minutes, 2.92; 60 minutes. 4.16; and 120 minutes, 4.77.

Individual summers show wide departure from average conditions. Hottest summer of record was 1936 when temperature of 100° or higher was recorded on 59 days. On the other hand, 25 percent of the summers pass with two or fewer 100° temperature days. Similarly, precipitation has shown a wide range for June, July, and August -- from 2.60 inches in 1936 to 27.67 inches in 1951. Dry summers are hot with low relative humidity and persistent southerly winds; years with more moisture are cooler. Oppressively warm periods with high relative humidity are usually of short duration.

Winters average about 50° cooler than summers, but are not unpleasant as long as the weather remains near normal. Cold spells are seldom prolonged; only on rare occasions do daytime temperatures fail to rise above the zero mark. January and February of 1936 produced 17 days with minimum temperatures of zero or lower, in contrast to a number of winters with no zero readings. Cold air invasions are usually ushered in by strong north or northwesterly winds, but less than half of these are accompanied by precipitation. Winter precipitation is often in the form of snow, sleet, or glaze, but storms of such severity as to prevent normal movement of traffic or to interfere with scheduled activity are not common. The longest period with snow on the ground was 51 days in the winter of 1939-1940. Blizzards are infrequent.

Station: TOPEKA, KANSAS
MUNICIPAL-PHILIP BILLARD-AP
Elevation (ground): 877 feet

TEMPERATURES °F

Month	Normal			Extremes			
	Daily maximum	Daily minimum	Monthly	Record highest	Year	Record lowest	Year
(a)				11		11	
J	38.3	17.7	28.0	73	1967	-20	1974
F	44.1	22.7	33.4	84	1972	-20	1971
M	52.6	29.7	41.2	88	1966	-4	1967
A	66.3	42.6	54.5	91	1975	10	1975
M	75.8	53.2	64.5	97	1975	30	1971
J	84.0	63.0	73.5	97	1973	45	1969
J	89.2	67.2	78.2	105	1974	43	1972
A	88.5	65.9	77.2	105	1970	47	1967
S	80.4	56.0	68.2	103	1975	30	1972
O	70.3	44.8	57.6	94	1975	20	1972
N	54.3	31.5	42.9	82	1964	4	1975
D	41.8	21.8	31.8	69	1973	-8	1973
YR	65.5	43.0	54.3	105	JUL 1974	-20	JAN 1974

IMPORTANT:
The time-period covered by this record is limited: See footnotes following table of **NORMALS, MEANS AND EXTREMES** for explanation and for additional history of **EXTREME HIGHS AND LOWS** recorded in the general area.

(Continued)

In the transitional spring and fall seasons, the numerous days of fair weather are interspersed with short intervals of stormy weather. Winter weather continues to make occasional appearances well into the spring season and moderate to heavy snows occur occasionally in late March or even early April. Spring snows melt rapidly, with a quick reaction to warmer weather. Strong, blustery winds are quite common in late winter and spring. Autumn is characteristically a season of warm dry, cool nights, and infrequent precipitation, with cold air invasions gradually increasing in intensity as the season progresses. Winter's first major storm usually strikes before the close of November and severe weather sometimes occurs during the early part of that month.

Of the twelve tornadoes recorded within present City boundaries, the only major storm was on June 8, 1966. It was one of the most damaging single tornadoes in nationwide records. This tornado entered Topeka city limits at 7:15 p.m. with almost total destruction occurring along an 8-mile-long by 4-block-wide path from southwest to northeast through the heart of the City. Approximately 820 dwellings were destroyed, with 1,010 sustaining major damage and 1,925 having minor damage. Along the 22-mile path which began about 12 miles southwest of the City, there were 16 fatalities, 406 injuries, and property losses in excess of $100 million.

Smoke and fog are of rather infrequent consequence in visibility and health consideration.

With the City built on both banks of the Kansas River and along two tributaries -- Soldier Creek in North Topeka and the Shunganunga in the south and east part of town -- flooding is always a possibility following periods of heavy rain. Several overflows of the Kansas have caused serious property damage, but the greatest flood since incorporation of the City was in 1951, when the river crested at 36.34 feet on July 13, inundating all of North Topeka, most of Oakland, extensive farmlands, and business and residential areas immediately along the south side of the river within the City limits. Credible accounts indicate a flood nearly 6 feet higher in 1844.

Nearly all crops of the temperate zone can be produced in the vicinity of Topeka with its growing season of almost 200 days. In the fertile Kaw Valley excellent corn is raised, and potatoes, alfalfa, and truck gardens flourish. Wheat and other small grains, clover, soybeans, and fruit and berries do well, and the area supports an extensive dairy industry.

TOPEKA, KANSAS

Normals, Means, and Extremes

(To better understand these tables, see full explanation of terms beginning on page 322)

Month	Normal Degree days Base 65 °F: Heating	Cooling	Precipitation in inches — Water equivalent: Normal	Maximum monthly	Year	Minimum monthly	Year	Maximum in 24 hrs.	Year	Snow, Ice pellets: Maximum monthly	Year	Maximum in 24 hrs.	Year	Relative humidity pct. Hour 00 (Local time)	Hour 06	Hour 12	Hour 18	Wind: Mean speed m.p.h.	Prevailing direction	Fastest mile: Speed m.p.h.	Direction	Year	Pct. of possible sunshine	Mean sky cover, tenths, sunrise to sunset	Mean number of days — Sunrise to sunset: Clear	Partly cloudy	Cloudy	Precipitation .01 inch or more	Snow, Ice pellets 1.0 inch or more	Thunderstorms	Heavy fog, visibility ¼ mile or less	Temperatures °F Max. (b) 90° and above	32° and below	Min. 32° and below	0° and below	Average station pressure mb. Elev. 885 feet m.s.l.
(a)				29		29		29		29		29		11	11	11	11	26	14	26	26		26	29	29	29	29	29	29	29	29	11	11	11	11	3
J	1147	0	0.97	5.24	1949	0.06	1954	1.17	1973	18.0	1962	8.3	1947	77	78	65	67	10.5	N	52	S	1962	54	6.2	9	6	16	6	2	*	2	0	11	29	3	987.0
F	885	0	0.98	3.49	1971	0.14	1963	2.33	1971	22.4	1971	15.2	1971	74	77	61	60	10.9	N	47	NW	1967	54	6.4	8	6	14	6	1	1	2	0	6	24	1	986.4
M	745	8	2.17	8.44	1973	0.10	1966	2.56	1947	22.1	1960	8.4	1960	72	78	56	53	12.7	E	66	SW	1950	54	6.7	7	8	16	8	1	2	1	0	2	18	*	981.4
A	329	14	3.62	8.12	1967	0.65	1963	3.59	1967	6.8	1970	7.6	1970	72	80	55	52	12.7	S	63	SE	1957	56	6.4	7	9	14	9	*	6	1	*	*	5	0	981.5
M	118	103	4.01	6.12	1950	0.41	1966	2.83	1962	0.0		0.0		77	83	56	54	11.3	S	72	N	1963	60	6.3	8	9	14	11	0	10	1	1	0	*	0	980.0
J	13	268	5.80	15.20	1967	0.92	1952	5.52	1967	0.0		0.0		80	86	61	59	10.4	S	72	SW	1966	64	6.0	8	10	12	10	0	10	*	6	0	0	0	981.0
J	0	409	4.21	12.02	1950	0.68	1975	4.19	1951	0.0		0.0		78	85	58	56	8.8	S	81	N	1958	68	5.3	10	11	10	9	0	9	1	14	0	0	0	983.7
A	0	378	4.18	8.24	1964	0.26	1971	4.48	1962	0.0		0.0		78	86	58	57	8.9	S	57	N	1959	69	4.9	12	10	9	8	0	8	1	12	0	0	0	984.1
S	55	151	3.28	12.71	1973	0.66	1952	3.77	1970	0.0		0.0		83	88	60	62	9.3	S	57	N	1952	64	5.0	12	7	11	7	0	6	1	3	0	*	0	986.2
O	259	30	2.65	6.01	1967	0.04	1952	4.04	1973	0.8	1970	0.8	1970	77	82	54	58	9.7	S	63	NE	1954	65	4.8	13	7	11	6	0	4	1	*	0	3	0	986.4
N	663	0	1.26	6.27	1964	T	1954	4.66	1964	9.4	1972	7.4	1975	79	82	61	65	10.4	S	56	SW	1963	54	5.8	10	7	13	6	*	1	1	0	1	16	0	985.1
D	1029	0	1.53	4.30	1973	0.07	1950	2.54	1973	15.2	1973	9.0	1973	79	81	67	70	10.4	S	61	NW	1963	50	6.3	8	7	16	6	2	*	2	0	7	27	1	985.9
YR	5243	1361	34.66	15.20	JUN 1967	T	NOV 1954	5.52	JUN 1967	22.4	FEB 1971	15.2	FEB 1971	77	82	60	59	10.5	S	81	N	JUL 1958	60	5.8	112	97	156	95	7	58	14	36	28	122	5	984.1

FOOTNOTES

Note: Fastest mile, 81 mph from north on July 11, 1958, estimated from 5-minute wind speed. Recorder inoperative.
Means and extremes above are from existing and comparable exposures. Annual extremes have been exceeded at other sites in the locality as follows: Highest temperature 114 in July 1936; lowest temperature -25 in February 1899; greatest precipitation in 24 hours 8.08 September 6-7, 1909; maximum monthly snowfall 27.1 in February 1900; greatest snowfall in 24 hours 18.7, February 27-28, 1900.

Snowfall

Season	July	Aug	Sept	Oct	Nov	Dec	Jan
1936-37	0.0	0.0	0.0	0.0	T	1.2	T
1937-38	0.0	0.0	0.0	T	6.3	0.5	0.1
1938-39	0.0	0.0	0.0	0.0	T	T	6.5
1939-40	0.0	0.0	0.0	0.0	T	4.5	14.7
1940-41	0.0	0.0	0.0	0.0	1.0	5.4	8.7
1941-42	0.0	0.0	0.0	1.0	1.9	3.4	0.9
1942-43	0.0	0.0	0.0	0.0	1.1	12.1	4.2
1943-44	0.0	0.0	0.0	0.0	0.7	12.6	3.2
1944-45	0.0	0.0	0.0	0.0	0.2	5.7	1.6
1945-46	0.0	0.0	0.0	0.0	1.8	14.5	2.5
#1946-47	0.0	0.0	0.0	0.0	T	0.3	8.6
1947-48	0.0	0.0	0.0	0.0	1.2	5.3	6.6
1948-49	0.0	0.0	0.0	0.0	T	6.2	12.4
1949-50	0.0	0.0	0.0	0.0	0.0	3.8	2.5
1950-51	0.0	0.0	0.0	0.0	0.4	0.5	2.4
1951-52	0.0	0.0	0.0	T	T	4.9	2.7
1952-53	0.0	0.0	0.0	0.0	2.4	6.9	0.9
1953-54	0.0	0.0	0.0	0.0	4.0	5.4	0.4
1954-55	0.0	0.0	0.0	0.0	T	1.8	4.1
1955-56	0.0	0.0	0.0	0.0	0.9	3.7	9.3
1956-57	0.0	0.0	0.0	0.0	0.2	2.6	4.9
1957-58	0.0	0.0	0.0	T	T	2.2	11.0
1958-59	0.0	0.0	0.0	0.0	5.0	7.7	10.3
1959-60	0.0	0.0	0.0	T	1.0	0.4	3.6
1960-61	0.0	0.0	0.0	0.0	T	5.6	0.9
1961-62	0.0	0.0	0.0	0.0	1.2	11.2	18.0
1962-63	0.0	0.0	0.0	T	T	2.3	5.5
1963-64	0.0	0.0	0.0	0.0	T	3.6	2.3
1964-65	0.0	0.0	0.0	0.0	1.3	4.3	2.9
1965-66	0.0	0.0	0.0	0.0	T	3.6	0.5
1966-67	0.0	0.0	0.0	0.0	T	8.3	3.4
1967-68	0.0	0.0	0.0	0.0	T	11.1	4.7
1968-69	0.0	0.0	0.0	0.0	T	0.8	6.2
1969-70	0.0	0.0	0.0	0.0	0.8	9.4	2.1
1970-71	0.0	0.0	0.0	0.8	T	7.9	2.1
1971-72	0.0	0.0	0.0	0.0	2.4	1.2	3.0
1972-73	0.0	0.0	0.0	0.0	9.4	4.0	13.5
1973-74	0.0	0.0	0.0	0.0	T	15.2	7.8
1974-75	0.0	0.0	0.0	0.0	1.3	1.4	5.0
1975-76	0.0	0.0	0.0	0.0	8.3	2.7	
RECORD MEAN	0.0	0.0	0.0	T	1.4	5.0	5.4

Heating Degree Days

Season	July	Aug	Sept	Oct	Nov	Dec	Jan
1955-56	0	0	26	241	791	1074	1214
1956-57	0	8	34	109	674	925	1291
1957-58	0	0	55	355	702	844	1062
1958-59	0	5	49	244	553	1078	1265
1959-60	0	0	63	375	838	840	1136
1960-61	0	0	31	216	611	1044	1113
1961-62	0	5	116	257	714	1234	1352
1962-63	0	0	92	225	620	1018	1452
1963-64	0	2	16	64	521	1286	945
#1964-65	0	9	67	316	572	1087	1044
1965-66	0	0	74	253	572	770	1202
1966-67	0	2	64	316	620	1053	1032
1967-68	1	7	87	356	690	985	1184
1968-69	0	1	35	282	745	1108	1210
1969-70	0	0	17	408	666	1083	1284
1970-71	0	0	57	344	706	945	1262
1971-72	4	0	69	143	580	927	1216
1972-73	10	0	59	337	764	1152	1158
1973-74	0	0	58	191	603	1082	1317
1974-75	0	3	134	213	649	991	1056
1975-76	2	0	137	230	581	941	

Cooling Degree Days

Year	Jan	Feb	Mar	Apr	May	June	July
1969	0	0	0	4	107	158	456
1970	0	0	0	35	149	239	407
1971	0	0	3	21	42	381	309
1972	0	0	5	22	74	297	308
1973	0	0	0	13	21	304	394
1974	0	0	6	21	140	165	490
1975	0	0	0	38	129	289	390

Feb	Mar	Apr	May	June	Total
5.3	5.1	2.0	0.0	0.0	13.6
6.6	0.1	6.5	0.0	0.0	20.1
9.3	0.2	T	0.0	0.0	16.0
3.2	0.5	0.6	0.0	0.0	23.5
1.7	9.2	0.0	0.0	0.0	26.0
4.0	T	0.0	0.0	0.0	11.2
0.9	7.4	0.0	0.0	0.0	25.7
5.8	8.1	T	T	0.0	30.4
6.7	1.8	T	0.0	0.0	16.0
0.9	1.4	0.0	0.0	0.0	21.1
6.5	5.4	T	0.0	0.0	20.8
4.6	8.0	0.0	0.0	0.0	25.7
3.9	2.3	T	0.0	0.0	24.8
0.4	2.2	0.8	0.0	0.0	9.7
4.3	0.5	T	0.0	0.0	8.1
0.9	11.6	0.0	0.0	0.0	20.1
T	11.3	T	0.0	0.0	21.5
T	T	0.0	0.0	0.0	9.8
13.8	4.4	0.0	0.0	0.0	24.1
6.3	2.9	1.0	0.0	0.0	24.1
1.5	5.8	1.4	0.0	0.0	16.4
1.9	8.1	0.0	0.0	0.0	23.2
0.2	3.1	3.4	0.0	0.0	29.7
17.3	22.1	T	0.0	0.0	44.4
3.1	8.5	0.6	0.0	0.0	18.7
2.4	0.1	T	0.0	0.0	32.9
2.2	0.2	0.0	0.0	0.0	10.2
2.0	2.9	0.0	0.0	0.0	10.8
7.3	5.0	0.0	0.0	0.0	20.8
0.6	T	T	0.0	0.0	4.7
1.9	0.8	0.0	0.0	0.0	14.4
5.7	T	T	0.0	0.0	21.5
3.4	2.0	0.0	0.0	0.0	12.4
T	4.9	6.8	0.0	0.0	24.0
22.4	7.5	T	0.0	0.0	40.7
6.7	3.0	T	0.0	0.0	16.3
1.7	0.0	0.1	0.0	0.0	28.7
2.1	1.5	1.3	0.0	0.0	27.9
6.7	7.8	3.6	0.0	0.0	25.8
4.5	4.5	0.7	0.0	0.0	21.5

TOPEKA, KS

Feb	Mar	Apr	May	June	Total
925	655	425	59	10	5420
796	705	388	110	8	5048
1077	874	350	76	10	5405
926	622	361	92	4	5199
1113	1145	288	115	3	5916
816	663	460	197	3	5154
896	803	393	10	4	5784
903	544	244	91	0	5189
882	765	264	51	25	4821
955	984	263	30	0	5327
922	552	423	107	6	4881
875	570	247	205	15	4999
965	572	338	202	5	5392
866	857	282	94	42	5522
811	785	376	45	29	5504
1065	735	274	144	0	5532
958	567	324	109	10	4907
864	537	378	129	0	5388
807	558	258	64	7	4945
1008	839	352	46	7	5298

Aug	Sept	Oct	Nov	Dec	Total
330	146	32	0	0	1233
490	188	16	0	0	1524
345	273	42	0	0	1416
309	169	20	0	0	1204
384	115	52	0	0	1283
292	47	12	0	0	1173
448	116	61	3	0	1474

Average Temperature

Year	Jan	Feb	Mar	Apr	May	June	July	Aug	Sept	Oct	Nov	Dec	Annual
1936	21.2	19.4	49.0	54.4	69.8	78.4	88.4	87.4	73.2	56.0	43.1	37.8	56.5
1937	22.2	30.4	39.4	54.4	67.8	76.2	82.6	84.3	72.0	57.3	40.1	30.7	54.8
1938	32.1	37.2	51.6	56.3	64.8	74.8	82.2	83.9	72.8	66.2	44.0	36.4	58.5
1939	38.5	28.8	45.6	54.2	70.6	76.2	85.8	77.8	77.0	62.2	44.9	39.7	58.4
1940	13.8	31.8	43.2	54.3	64.4	75.2	82.6	76.4	70.2	65.2	40.1	36.2	54.4
1941	31.8	32.2	40.4	58.6	70.4	74.6	81.2	79.8	71.3	59.5	45.7	39.0	57.0
1942	31.0	32.4	44.4	60.2	63.7	74.2	82.1	77.2	67.5	59.3	46.2	30.4	55.7
1943	28.1	39.2	38.8	57.9	62.2	76.7	81.6	82.6	66.7	56.4	41.9	30.2	55.2
1944	36.2	36.4	38.6	50.2	69.1	77.0	79.0	77.6	70.5	60.8	46.4	29.0	55.9
1945	31.4	34.8	51.8	53.6	61.0	68.9	78.0	79.6	69.9	57.6	46.1	25.4	54.8
#1946	33.4	42.7	55.4	59.8	62.0	76.5	81.6	77.4	67.2	59.2	44.4	37.4	58.1
1947	31.4	27.4	36.8	53.0	60.4	71.6	76.1	84.4	72.6	65.4	38.6	34.4	54.3
1948	23.8	28.6	37.2	60.5	63.6	73.0	78.1	77.9	70.8	54.8	43.4	33.6	53.8
1949	23.4	30.0	41.2	52.8	67.6	75.8	79.2	75.8	63.4	58.6	47.6	33.8	54.1
1950	28.5	34.9	39.7	50.3	65.6	73.8	71.5	71.7	66.7	62.6	39.4	29.9	52.9
1951	29.0	34.1	37.8	50.5	64.7	69.1	76.5	77.3	64.6	56.2	38.2	29.5	52.3
1952	32.0	38.6	38.4	53.0	64.6	82.1	80.1	78.0	70.6	53.0	41.6	31.4	55.3
1953	33.8	39.8	45.0	49.7	63.7	81.7	79.3	77.5	71.8	61.3	45.5	34.9	57.0
1954	27.6	44.4	41.0	60.5	60.0	77.1	85.3	80.9	75.2	59.1	47.3	34.8	57.8
1955	31.1	28.2	42.0	61.6	66.7	70.9	84.3	79.8	72.4	58.1	38.4	30.1	55.3
1956	25.7	32.9	43.6	51.6	69.3	76.8	80.0	79.6	70.9	62.8	42.3	34.9	55.9
1957	23.1	36.4	42.0	52.3	62.8	72.2	80.5	78.4	65.0	53.4	41.4	37.6	53.8
1958	30.5	26.2	36.6	53.1	65.8	71.6	75.1	76.2	69.5	58.4	46.5	29.9	53.3
1959	24.0	31.7	44.7	53.0	65.8	74.5	74.4	80.2	67.8	52.6	36.9	37.8	53.6
1960	28.2	26.4	27.8	56.1	63.3	72.2	75.0	78.2	70.2	58.4	44.5	31.0	52.6
1961	28.8	35.6	43.3	50.2	59.8	72.0	76.7	74.4	65.0	57.0	41.0	25.0	52.4
1962	21.2	32.8	38.9	52.2	72.7	72.5	76.2	76.7	65.4	60.0	44.0	31.9	53.7
1963	18.0	32.5	47.3	57.4	65.3	77.3	80.3	78.4	71.9	67.6	47.4	23.4	55.6
#1964	34.2	34.3	40.0	56.4	68.9	72.1	81.2	74.5	68.1	54.6	46.2	29.8	55.0
1965	31.0	30.8	33.0	57.2	68.6	73.1	77.0	74.9	66.9	57.3	45.7	39.9	54.6
1966	26.0	31.9	47.0	50.8	63.8	72.7	83.1	74.8	65.8	55.4	44.1	30.7	53.8
1967	31.5	33.4	47.0	57.4	60.8	72.1	75.0	72.1	63.6	54.7	41.7	33.0	53.5
1968	26.6	31.6	46.4	53.5	59.1	74.1	76.4	75.5	66.6	57.3	40.0	29.0	53.0
1969	25.8	33.9	37.1	55.5	65.3	68.7	79.4	75.5	69.0	52.7	42.5	29.9	52.9
1970	23.3	35.9	39.5	53.5	68.1	71.8	77.8	80.6	69.1	54.2	41.2	34.3	54.1
1971	24.1	26.8	41.1	56.3	61.4	77.5	74.5	75.9	71.6	61.6	45.4	34.8	54.2
1972	25.6	31.8	46.7	54.7	63.6	74.3	74.4	74.7	68.5	54.6	39.4	27.7	53.0
1973	27.5	33.9	47.5	52.6	61.3	74.9	77.4	77.1	66.6	60.4	44.8	29.9	54.5
1974	22.3	35.9	46.9	56.8	67.2	70.0	80.6	74.1	61.9	58.4	43.1	32.7	54.2
1975	30.7	28.8	37.8	54.4	67.3	74.2	77.3	79.3	64.0	59.3	45.5	34.5	54.4
RECORD MEAN	28.5	32.5	42.7	54.9	64.5	74.0	78.9	77.4	69.1	58.0	43.6	32.7	54.7
MAX	38.1	42.6	53.7	66.2	75.3	84.6	89.9	88.5	80.5	69.7	54.1	41.9	65.4
MIN	18.9	22.3	31.6	43.6	53.6	63.4	67.9	66.3	57.7	46.2	33.0	23.4	44.0

# Indicates a station move or relocation of instruments.

Precipitation

Year	Jan	Feb	Mar	Apr	May	June	July	Aug	Sept	Oct	Nov	Dec	Annual
1936	1.73	0.42	0.25	3.02	4.79	0.92	1.11	0.57	7.32	0.86	0.09	1.55	22.63
1937	1.82	0.61	2.05	1.76	3.12	1.14	1.65	3.35	0.43	1.40	1.34	0.76	19.43
1938	1.14	0.92	2.20	2.01	11.16	2.58	3.97	2.15	0.37	0.35	1.92	0.24	29.01
1939	0.70	1.52	1.27	3.72	1.33	5.63	1.26	3.51	0.40	0.83	1.42	0.74	22.33
1940	1.32	1.00	1.38	3.58	4.01	2.76	0.08	6.40	1.20	2.09	3.34	1.31	28.47
1941	3.79	0.33	1.43	3.32	3.78	5.45	1.38	7.79	3.81	10.65	0.65	2.07	44.45
1942	0.11	1.85	1.01	4.16	5.29	4.83	1.92	7.72	6.86	2.75	1.33	2.74	40.57
1943	0.15	0.64	0.68	1.40	4.93	11.46	4.29	2.10	4.00	2.43	0.44	1.78	34.30
1944	0.54	0.97	4.90	8.65	2.81	3.41	3.43	6.93	3.03	2.33	2.24	5.08	44.32
1945	0.44	1.27	4.31	8.58	6.68	5.32	2.75	0.87	6.20	0.46	0.16	1.31	38.35
#1946	1.98	0.52	2.85	3.19	3.37	6.24	0.89	6.30	3.33	1.49	1.02	1.87	33.05
1947	0.63	0.45	3.74	6.01	2.68	5.09	3.53	5.37	1.13	3.04	1.37	3.94	36.98
1948	0.49	1.10	4.23	1.74	4.85	4.54	5.50	2.71	1.32	1.82	1.64	0.78	30.72
1949	5.24	1.79	2.23	5.43	5.16	6.89	4.34	7.01	1.77	3.27	0.68	1.92	45.73
1950	0.84	0.68	0.63	2.03	6.12	5.81	12.02	5.87	2.35	2.25	0.24	0.07	38.91
1951	1.00	1.53	1.80	3.08	4.12	10.59	11.57	5.07	4.99	3.07	1.35	0.43	48.60
1952	0.24	0.46	2.76	3.84	3.78	0.92	0.85	4.21	0.66	0.04	2.29	1.28	21.33
1953	0.10	1.57	3.10	1.32	4.53	1.07	4.17	3.13	2.77	0.99	2.31	1.25	26.31
1954	0.06	2.06	0.63	2.22	4.38	3.78	5.21	6.58	0.70	3.20	T	1.21	30.03
1955	1.34	2.52	0.67	2.55	4.62	5.06	2.21	3.75	3.51	1.73	0.19	0.33	28.48
1956	0.75	0.70	0.42	3.94	2.36	5.32	4.44	2.35	1.02	1.33	1.96	0.76	25.35
1957	0.35	0.36	3.96	5.01	4.18	5.10	5.21	1.48	5.11	4.30	1.92	1.16	38.14
1958	1.32	1.13	2.69	1.78	2.29	7.52	8.58	3.71	3.78	1.97	3.27	0.69	38.73
1959	0.77	0.58	2.30	1.76	4.70	2.87	2.92	2.65	2.68	4.04	0.13	1.70	27.10
1960	1.09	2.14	2.23	2.23	1.70	3.43	3.16	3.70	1.38	3.03	0.13	1.42	25.64
1961	0.07	1.59	6.32	2.65	5.29	2.43	7.25	1.92	5.69	4.88	2.50	1.07	41.66
1962	1.99	1.28	1.43	1.23	4.23	4.46	3.68	6.64	4.50	1.36	1.04	0.42	32.26
1963	0.56	0.14	2.53	0.65	4.91	2.71	3.13	1.30	1.00	0.96	0.96	0.22	19.07
1964	0.54	0.29	1.73	4.70	2.09	8.10	1.81	8.24	1.13	0.14	6.27	0.94	35.98
1965	1.60	1.27	1.58	2.31	3.41	10.14	3.33	3.53	7.22	0.92	0.20	2.46	37.97
1966	0.16	0.54	0.10	1.98	0.41	8.83	0.75	3.62	1.46	0.42	0.24	0.79	19.30
1967	1.06	0.21	1.91	8.12	5.07	15.20	3.06	1.84	4.64	6.01	0.41	3.11	50.64
1968	0.89	0.56	0.46	4.20	3.37	3.18	10.17	7.40	2.50	4.19	1.56	2.10	40.58
1969	0.84	0.42	1.37	7.14	3.77	8.46	3.26	0.87	2.03	3.98	0.10	1.24	33.48
1970	0.19	0.34	1.03	3.49	5.46	5.82	1.39	0.83	7.70	2.49	1.23	1.65	31.62
1971	1.20	3.49	0.64	1.08	4.83	3.10	4.07	0.26	1.35	3.87	3.03	1.83	28.75
1972	0.47	0.56	1.37	3.93	2.90	1.14	4.81	3.26	4.89	2.11	3.99	1.78	31.21
1973	2.67	1.71	8.44	4.03	4.37	2.96	10.16	2.83	12.71	4.57	2.14	4.30	60.89
1974	0.99	1.20	1.22	2.78	3.59	3.72	2.90	4.89	1.40	5.16	2.19	1.18	31.22
1975	1.50	1.67	1.66	3.26	3.88	4.85	0.68	1.69	4.35	0.05	4.44	1.12	29.15
RECORD MEAN	0.98	1.29	2.04	3.08	4.34	4.76	3.96	4.00	3.60	2.50	1.64	1.19	33.38

Record mean values above are means through the current year for the period beginning in 1887 for temperature, 1878 for precipitation and 1947 for snowfall. Data are from City Office locations through August 1946 and from Airport locations thereafter.

WICHITA, KANSAS

Wichita lies in the path of alternate masses of warm, moist air moving northward from the Gulf of Mexico and cold, dry air moving southward from the Polar Regions. Consequently, weather in this area is subject to frequent and often abrupt changes. Summer months are usually warm and occasionally the term "hot" is a better description. Winters are usually mild. The temperature extremes for the period of weather records at Wichita are 114° on August 12, 1936, and -22° on February 12, 1899. On the average, temperatures of 90° or above occur on 60 to 65 days per year, while readings of zero or lower occur on about two days per year.

Wichita has an elevation of a little more than 1,300 feet above sea level. This elevation is conducive to a greater night and day temperature range than would be expected at lower altitudes. The surrounding terrain is of a gentle, sloping character with no large bodies of water which affect the climatic conditions in the vicinity. The average freeze-free period has a duration of about six and one-half months, extending from mid-April to late October.

It is of significance to agriculture that a large portion of the precipitation falls during the growing season. The six months, April through September, account for about 70 percent of the annual precipitation. The highest monthly averages are in the spring and summer while January is usually the driest month. The wettest year of record was 1951 with 50.48 inches. The driest year was 1966 with 12.15 inches; however, the driest 12-month period was May 1966, through April 1967, with only 10.25 inches. Thunderstorms occur on about 56 days per year with the greatest frequency during spring and early summer. Hail accompanying thunderstorms is not uncommon; however, hail damage is infrequent.

Brief flooding occasionally results from very heavy thunderstorm rainfall; but, with the completion of the Wichita-Valley Center Flood Control Project Works, in 1959, Wichita is now protected against floods from the Arkansas River, Little Arkansas River, Cowskin Creek, Chisholm Creeks, and the Big Slough. This project, a series of floodways and diversion canals, was designed to protect against floods up to the 75-100 year frequency class. No flooding from major streams has occurred since October 2, 1955.

Snow is light, averaging about 15 inches per year. The heaviest amounts of snow occur in the months of December through March. January has the highest monthly average; however, the greatest monthly fall on record was 20.5 inches in February 1913, and heaviest 24-hour fall was 13.5 inches on March 15-16, 1970.

The prevailing wind direction is southerly and the

Station: WICHITA, KANSAS
1321 feet
Elevation (ground): MID-CONTINENT AIRPORT

TEMPERATURES °F

Month	Normal			Extremes			
	Daily maximum	Daily minimum	Monthly	Record highest	Year	Record lowest	Year
(a)				23		23	
J	41.4	21.2	31.3	75	1967	-12	1962
F	47.1	25.4	36.3	82	1972	-6	1971
M	55.0	32.1	43.6	89	1956	-2	1960
A	68.1	45.1	56.6	96	1972	15	1975
M	77.1	55.0	66.1	100	1967	32	1966
J	86.5	65.0	75.8	106	1956	43	1969
J	91.7	69.6	80.7	113	1954	51	1975
A	91.0	68.3	79.7	110	1964	48	1967
S	81.9	59.2	70.6	103	1954	35	1967
O	71.3	47.9	59.6	95	1954	23	1957
N	55.8	33.8	44.8	80	1956	1	1975
D	44.3	24.6	34.5	83	1955	-5	1968
YR	67.6	45.6	56.6	113	JUL 1954	-12	JAN 1962

IMPORTANT:
The time-period covered by this record is limited: See footnotes following table of **NORMALS, MEANS AND EXTREMES** for explanation and for additional history of **EXTREME HIGHS AND LOWS** recorded in the general area.

(Continued)

average velocity compares with other midwestern areas. The windiest months of the year are March and April with averages of 14.8 miles per hour for both months. July has the least wind with an average of 11.3 m.p.h. while the annual average is 12.8 m.p.h. There is often a marked variation in wind velocity through the day, increasing during the warmest hours of the afternoon and diminishing during the nighttime hours. Strong northerly winds often follow the passage of the occasionally severe cold fronts characteristic of Great Plains weather. On rare occasions during the summer, strong, hot, dry southwesterly winds do considerable damage to growing crops in just a few hours. The fastest wind ever recorded was 100 m.p.h., from the north, during a passing squall. Tornadoes have been observed in the vicinity on occasions.

Flying weather conditions are generally favorable for operation of light airplanes with the visibility 7 miles or more and the ceiling 1,000 feet or higher 95 percent of the time. Gusty surface winds are rather frequent, especially in the spring and summer. The strongest winds are associated with thunderstorms and frontal weather.

WICHITA, KANSAS

Normals, Means, and Extremes

(To better understand these tables, see full explanation of terms beginning on page 322)

Month	Normal Degree days Base 65 °F: Heating	Cooling	Precipitation in inches — Water equivalent: Normal	Maximum monthly	Year	Minimum monthly	Year	Maximum in 24 hrs.	Year	Snow, Ice pellets: Maximum monthly	Year	Maximum in 24 hrs.	Year	Relative humidity pct. (Local time): Hour 00	Hour 06	Hour 12	Hour 18
(a)				22		22		22		22		22		22	22	22	22
J	1045	0	0.85	2.73	1973	0.02	1961	0.98	1971	18.5	1962	13.0	1962	77	80	64	67
F	804	0	0.98	2.12	1975	0.02	1963	1.53	1973	16.7	1971	11.9	1971	75	79	60	60
M	671	8	1.78	9.17	1973	0.01	1971	2.65	1961	16.5	1970	13.5	1970	69	76	54	51
A	275	23	2.95	4.49	1970	0.22	1963	2.40	1969	2.3	1973	2.3	1973	70	77	52	49
M	90	124	3.60	8.60	1975	0.52	1973	4.70	1963	0.0		0.0		75	83	55	53
J	7	331	4.49	10.46	1957	0.94	1954	4.98	1965	0.0		0.0		74	83	53	49
J	0	487	4.35	9.22	1962	0.05	1975	3.74	1969	0.0		0.0		68	79	49	45
A	0	456	3.10	7.91	1960	0.59	1957	3.75	1959	0.0		0.0		68	79	49	45
S	32	200	3.69	9.46	1973	0.03	1956	3.03	1968	0.0		0.0		74	82	56	53
O	211	44	2.50	6.13	1959	T	1958	4.24	1955	0.1	1960	0.1	1960	74	81	53	56
N	606	0	1.17	5.88	1964	T	1954	4.33	1964	7.1	1972	5.5	1975	74	79	57	62
D	946	0	1.12	2.80	1973	0.03	1955	1.35	1973	9.7	1967	5.1	1964	77	80	63	67
YR	4687	1673	30.58	10.46	JUN 1957	T	OCT 1958	4.98	JUN 1965	18.5	JAN 1962	13.5	MAR 1970	73	80	55	55

Month	Wind: Mean speed m.p.h.	Prevailing direction	Fastest mile: Speed m.p.h.	Direction	Year	Pct. of possible sunshine	Mean sky cover, tenths, sunrise to sunset	Mean number of days — Sunrise to sunset: Clear	Partly cloudy	Cloudy	Precipitation .01 inch or more	Snow, Ice pellets 1.0 inch or more	Thunderstorms	Heavy fog, visibility ¼ mile or less	Temperatures °F Max.: (b) 90° and above	32° and below	Min.: 32° and below	0° and below	Average station pressure mb. Elev. 1340 feet m.s.l.
(a)	22	10	22	22		22	22	22	22	22	22	22	22	22	22	22	22	22	3
J	12.5	S	57	N	1965	59	6.1	10	6	15	5	1	*	3	0	9	28	2	970.0
F	13.1	N	54	N	1965	59	6.0	8	7	13	5	1	1	3	0	5	24	*	969.4
M	14.5	S	60	N	1965	60	6.3	9	7	15	7	1	2	1	0	2	16	*	964.3
A	14.7	S	63	W	1964	62	6.1	8	8	14	7	*	6	1	*	*	3	0	965.1
M	13.1	S	58	S	1962	64	5.9	9	10	12	10	0	9	1	3	0	*	0	963.9
J	12.6	S	64	NW	1957	69	5.4	9	11	10	9	0	10	*	12	0	0	0	965.1
J	11.3	S	66	NW	1956	74	4.9	12	11	8	8	0	8	*	21	0	0	0	967.7
A	11.3	S	47	NW	1964	73	4.5	14	10	7	7	0	7	*	19	0	0	0	967.8
S	11.7	S	56	N	1956	65	5.0	13	6	11	8	0	6	1	6	0	0	0	969.6
O	12.3	S	52	S	1961	66	4.8	13	8	10	6	0	3	1	1	*	1	0	970.0
N	12.4	S	51	N	1964	59	5.6	11	6	13	5	*	1	2	0	1	14	0	968.6
D	12.2	S	54	NW	1963	56	6.1	9	8	14	6	1	*	3	0	5	27	*	969.2
YR	12.6	S	66	NW	JUL 1956	65	5.5	125	98	142	84	5	55	18	62	21	113	2	967.6

FOOTNOTES

Means and extremes above are from existing and comparable exposures. Annual extremes have been exceeded at other sites in the locality as follows: Highest temperature 114 in August 1936; lowest temperature -22 in February 1899; maximum monthly precipitation 14.43 in June 1923; minimum monthly precipitation 0.00 in October 1952; maximum precipitation in 24 hours 7.99 in September 1911; maximum monthly snowfall 20.5 in February 1913; fastest mile of wind 100 from North in July 1948.

Snowfall

Season	July	Aug	Sept	Oct	Nov	Dec	Jan
1936-37	0.0	0.0	0.0	0.0	T	2.1	0.3
1937-38	0.0	0.0	0.0	0.0	4.9	T	T
1938-39	0.0	0.0	0.0	0.0	0.2	T	3.0
1939-40	0.0	0.0	0.0	0.0	0.0	5.0	11.8
#1940-41	0.0	0.0	0.0	0.0	1.7	0.7	3.8
1941-42	0.0	0.0	0.0	0.2	0.2	3.6	2.2
1942-43	0.0	0.0	T	0.0	1.3	14.8	2.5
1943-44	0.0	0.0	0.0	0.0	0.2	8.5	0.4
#1944-45	0.0	0.0	0.0	0.0	T	2.6	1.5
1945-46	0.0	0.0	0.0	0.0	T	5.4	0.8
1946-47	0.0	0.0	0.0	0.0	0.1	T	9.0
1947-48	0.0	0.0	0.0	0.0	T	3.5	12.0
1948-49	0.0	0.0	0.0	0.0	3.6	1.0	19.6
1949-50	0.0	0.0	0.0	0.0	0.0	3.8	0.5
1950-51	0.0	0.0	0.0	0.0	T	0.3	0.4
1951-52	0.0	0.0	0.0	0.6	8.1	2.2	3.2
1952-53	0.0	0.0	0.0	0.0	6.8	0.5	1.7
#1953-54	0.0	0.0	0.0	T	1.4	2.4	0.8
1954-55	0.0	0.0	0.0	0.0	0.0	0.2	2.0
1955-56	0.0	0.0	0.0	0.0	0.2	0.1	6.6
1956-57	0.0	0.0	0.0	0.0	T	0.8	2.3
1957-58	0.0	0.0	0.0	T	T	T	3.9
1958-59	0.0	0.0	0.0	0.0	2.4	7.5	8.6
1959-60	0.0	0.0	0.0	0.0	2.7	2.0	6.1
1960-61	0.0	0.0	0.0	0.1	T	2.6	0.3
1961-62	0.0	0.0	0.0	0.0	0.1	4.9	18.5
1962-63	0.0	0.0	0.0	0.0	T	4.2	3.7
1963-64	0.0	0.0	0.0	0.0	0.0	4.7	0.2
1964-65	0.0	0.0	0.0	0.0	0.1	5.4	3.3
1965-66	0.0	0.0	0.0	0.0	0.0	0.9	4.7
1966-67	0.0	0.0	0.0	0.0	T	5.0	2.1
1967-68	0.0	0.0	0.0	0.0	2.2	9.7	0.6
1968-69	0.0	0.0	0.0	0.0	0.3	2.8	T
1969-70	0.0	0.0	0.0	0.0	T	3.5	2.8
1970-71	0.0	0.0	0.0	T	T	T	T
1971-72	0.0	0.0	0.0	0.0	2.3	2.4	1.7
1972-73	0.0	0.0	0.0	0.0	7.1	2.7	17.7
1973-74	0.0	0.0	0.0	0.0	T	8.7	4.1
1974-75	0.0	0.0	0.0	0.0	1.8	2.2	7.6
1975-76	0.0	0.0	0.0	0.0	5.5	T	
RECORD MEAN	0.0	0.0	0.0	T	1.1	3.2	4.4

Heating Degree Days

Season	July	Aug	Sept	Oct	Nov	Dec	Jan
1955-56	0	0	17	198	716	980	1094
1956-57	0	5	12	94	628	856	1189
1957-58	0	0	36	323	687	757	932
1958-59	0	0	35	206	491	984	1187
1959-60	0	0	41	300	748	747	1050
1960-61	0	0	13	171	545	990	1036
1961-62	0	2	86	184	688	1097	1213
1962-63	0	0	40	172	581	927	1323
1963-64	0	0	9	50	523	1184	867
1964-65	0	1	34	200	531	1038	918
1965-66	0	1	73	179	428	733	1131
1966-67	0	0	33	247	499	996	945
1967-68	2	1	63	280	645	936	998
1968-69	0	5	22	224	691	1054	1076
1969-70	0	0	2	361	610	939	1163
1970-71	1	0	64	358	696	866	1118
1971-72	4	0	77	165	628	897	1171
1972-73	2	0	46	319	750	1123	1159
1973-74	0	0	58	159	541	1021	1237
1974-75	0	0	92	156	596	920	974
1975-76	0	0	98	201	596	892	

Cooling Degree Days

Year	Jan	Feb	Mar	Apr	May	June	July
1969	0	0	0	1	90	208	563
1970	0	0	2	24	187	315	513
1971	0	0	0	19	65	425	414
1972	0	0	2	26	88	358	385
1973	0	0	0	7	39	360	482
1974	0	0	4	12	149	233	608
1975	0	0	0	32	49	275	450

Feb	Mar	Apr	May	June	Total
4.7	4.9	0.0	0.0	0.0	12.0
9.3	T	6.2	0.0	0.0	20.4
7.7	1.5	T	0.0	0.0	12.4
6.1	0.1	0.2	0.0	0.0	23.2
4.5	8.9	0.0	0.0	0.0	19.6
4.3	T	0.0	0.0	0.0	10.5
0.1	10.1	0.0	0.0	0.0	28.8
0.3	0.4	T	0.0	0.0	9.8
4.3	1.2	0.5	0.0	0.0	10.1
0.8	0.2	0.0	0.0	0.0	7.2
7.8	5.2	T	0.0	0.0	22.1
6.1	4.8	0.0	0.0	0.0	26.4
2.1	0.8	1.5	0.0	0.0	28.6
0.1	0.9	T	0.0	0.0	5.3
3.8	T	T	0.0	0.0	4.5
0.5	5.9	T	0.0	0.0	20.5
1.0	0.7	T	0.0	0.0	10.7
T	T	0.0	0.0	0.0	4.6
5.5	1.1	0.0	0.0	0.0	8.8
3.2	2.9	0.1	0.0	0.0	13.1
1.9	1.0	1.3	0.0	0.0	7.3
3.3	16.4	0.0	0.0	0.0	23.6
0.3	0.9	0.8	0.0	0.0	20.5
14.5	10.3	T	0.0	0.0	35.6
10.4	7.5	T	0.0	0.0	20.9
T	T	0.0	0.0	0.0	23.5
0.2	T	0.0	0.0	0.0	8.1
1.5	T	0.0	0.0	0.0	6.4
2.7	T	0.0	0.0	0.0	11.5
0.8	T	0.0	0.0	0.0	6.4
T	0.7	0.0	0.0	0.0	7.8
1.0	T	0.0	0.0	0.0	13.5
8.3	5.1	0.0	0.0	0.0	16.5
T	16.5	0.1	0.0	0.0	22.9
16.7	T	0.0	0.0	0.0	16.7
4.4	0.8	0.0	0.0	0.0	11.6
0.2	T	2.3	0.0	0.0	30.0
0.7	2.0	0.3	0.0	0.0	15.8
15.2	7.6	T	0.0	0.0	34.4
4.1	3.3	0.2	0.0	0.0	16.3

Average Temperature

Year	Jan	Feb	Mar	Apr	May	June	July	Aug	Sept	Oct	Nov	Dec	Annual
1936	28.0	25.0	51.0	56.5	69.6	79.0	87.8	89.0	74.2	56.1	44.8	39.8	58.4
1937	24.3	33.7	40.6	56.0	67.6	76.4	81.8	84.0	72.0	58.4	42.0	33.6	55.9
1938	35.6	38.9	51.9	56.7	64.6	74.6	82.2	84.2	74.2	67.0	43.9	38.0	59.3
1939	40.5	30.3	48.0	55.1	69.4	76.4	84.4	80.0	77.6	64.0	46.2	41.1	59.4
#1940	16.2	34.8	46.2	54.6	65.6	75.4	81.4	77.4	71.0	65.8	40.7	37.5	55.6
1941	34.4	34.6	40.6	57.0	69.1	72.7	80.0	79.6	72.2	59.4	45.4	39.6	57.0
1942	32.0	33.8	45.7	59.0	63.6	73.6	80.8	77.2	67.5	58.9	46.8	32.4	55.9
1943	30.0	40.4	39.0	59.6	61.2	76.6	80.9	84.4	68.7	57.6	44.1	31.6	56.2
#1944	36.6	38.8	41.0	51.4	67.8	78.4	79.6	79.6	70.4	60.8	47.5	31.5	57.0
1945	34.1	35.2	51.4	53.0	62.2	70.4	78.6	79.1	69.8	58.0	48.0	28.0	55.6
1946	35.2	44.0	54.0	60.8	61.9	76.3	83.4	79.6	71.0	61.0	44.9	40.0	59.4
1947	34.0	31.8	39.6	53.6	62.6	74.0	79.0	85.0	75.4	68.4	41.6	36.4	56.8
1948	27.8	32.0	39.9	63.0	66.0	75.2	78.2	78.0	73.3	59.4	44.0	36.8	56.1
1949	23.6	32.8	43.7	56.0	67.2	76.5	80.3	76.6	66.2	60.0	50.8	37.2	55.9
1950	30.4	39.4	42.2	52.6	65.5	75.7	73.5	72.8	68.3	65.0	42.3	34.5	55.2
1951	32.2	37.7	39.9	51.9	65.3	71.0	78.7	79.7	66.2	56.8	39.5	33.7	54.4
1952	36.5	40.5	40.7	53.9	66.0	82.5	81.0	81.1	72.8	56.6	43.5	33.0	57.4
#1953	37.4	40.9	49.4	51.8	65.6	83.1	78.7	78.8	75.1	62.6	46.7	36.5	58.9
1954	30.7	45.8	42.6	62.4	61.4	78.5	89.3	85.6	77.6	61.0	49.2	37.3	60.1
1955	34.7	32.3	43.8	62.5	68.3	71.6	84.0	80.6	74.1	59.2	40.8	33.1	57.1
1956	29.5	35.5	45.4	53.1	70.1	79.3	82.4	83.6	74.6	64.3	43.8	37.2	58.2
1957	26.4	39.6	43.9	53.3	63.6	72.7	82.8	80.2	66.1	55.2	41.8	40.4	55.5
1958	34.7	29.7	36.0	53.6	68.9	76.3	78.4	78.6	71.3	60.2	48.5	33.1	55.8
1959	26.5	33.7	46.9	55.4	67.7	76.3	76.4	81.4	71.0	55.2	39.9	40.6	55.9
1960	30.9	28.7	33.8	59.1	64.6	75.4	76.7	79.3	72.4	61.0	46.5	33.0	55.1
1961	31.4	37.2	46.6	53.8	63.3	74.2	78.8	76.8	66.8	59.6	41.8	29.4	55.0
1962	25.6	37.1	43.4	55.1	75.4	75.1	80.0	80.6	68.6	62.3	45.4	34.9	56.9
1963	22.2	36.9	50.0	60.5	68.3	78.8	82.6	81.2	72.5	67.7	47.3	26.6	57.9
1964	36.8	36.1	42.1	59.2	70.2	76.9	85.0	76.8	70.8	58.7	47.2	31.2	57.6
1965	35.2	34.4	36.8	60.4	68.8	76.3	81.9	78.2	68.5	60.4	50.5	41.2	57.7
1966	28.3	33.6	49.1	53.5	65.7	76.2	84.9	76.1	68.6	58.0	48.3	32.7	56.2
1967	34.3	36.3	50.5	61.5	64.0	74.5	76.2	74.7	65.9	57.7	43.2	34.6	56.1
1968	32.5	33.8	48.0	55.5	61.0	76.1	80.3	77.9	67.9	59.3	41.7	30.7	55.4
1969	30.1	36.1	36.1	56.4	65.2	71.0	82.9	78.9	71.9	54.6	44.5	34.6	55.2
1970	27.3	38.5	39.7	55.1	69.3	74.5	81.3	83.2	69.7	53.9	41.5	36.9	55.9
1971	28.8	28.8	44.0	57.0	63.9	78.9	78.0	76.8	70.8	60.6	43.9	35.8	55.6
1972	27.0	34.8	47.9	55.3	64.1	76.7	77.1	78.4	71.0	55.6	39.8	28.5	54.7
1973	27.4	35.6	48.4	52.2	61.9	76.8	80.3	79.8	67.8	61.1	46.7	31.9	55.8
1974	24.9	38.7	47.9	56.4	68.3	72.5	84.4	76.7	64.1	60.5	44.9	35.1	56.2
1975	33.4	28.5	40.4	54.7	64.0	73.6	79.2	81.4	65.8	60.3	44.8	36.0	55.2
RECORD MEAN	31.6	35.2	44.7	56.3	65.4	75.3	80.3	79.3	70.9	59.6	45.2	35.0	56.5
MAX	41.1	45.5	55.7	67.3	75.7	85.8	91.1	90.4	81.8	70.5	55.3	44.2	67.0
MIN	22.0	24.9	33.6	45.3	55.1	64.7	69.4	68.2	60.0	48.6	35.0	25.7	46.0

# Indicates a station move or relocation of instruments.

WICHITA, KS

Feb	Mar	Apr	May	June	Total
848	602	379	52	4	4890
705	646	359	103	8	4607
982	891	334	44	8	4994
870	555	300	62	0	4690
1048	961	203	97	1	5196
771	562	376	129	0	4593
776	665	315	8	4	5038
780	463	170	72	0	4528
831	702	200	41	10	4417
851	868	176	23	0	4640
871	490	342	100	2	4350
798	463	160	143	5	4289
899	525	285	153	1	4788
804	887	254	77	20	5114
738	778	312	43	26	4972
1005	643	253	95	0	5099
871	524	310	109	0	4756
816	506	386	125	0	5232
732	529	263	42	1	4583
1016	757	333	72	9	4925

Aug	Sept	Oct	Nov	Dec	Total
437	214	45	0	0	1558
573	212	22	0	0	1848
372	259	34	0	0	1588
421	234	34	0	0	1548
468	149	47	0	0	1552
368	69	23	0	0	1466
515	128	63	0	0	1512

Precipitation

Year	Jan	Feb	Mar	Apr	May	June	July	Aug	Sept	Oct	Nov	Dec	Annual
1936	0.94	0.02	T	0.58	3.30	1.04	0.21	0.04	4.84	3.77	0.01	0.83	15.58
1937	1.54	0.73	2.80	0.57	4.13	3.99	4.77	2.86	1.80	1.12	0.75	0.58	25.64
1938	0.12	2.48	1.91	2.85	8.14	4.49	2.24	5.60	2.62	0.16	2.05	0.15	32.81
1939	1.09	1.93	1.57	2.14	3.25	8.90	0.72	5.84	0.30	1.14	0.81	0.95	28.64
#1940	1.40	1.43	0.74	6.15	5.82	4.85	0.94	2.87	6.14	1.05	3.82	1.56	36.77
1941	1.53	1.09	1.11	2.83	2.89	7.05	2.41	3.54	4.29	4.81	0.78	0.92	33.25
1942	0.23	1.93	0.88	7.08	1.67	8.69	2.34	4.51	7.21	3.77	0.68	3.14	42.13
1943	0.27	0.67	1.21	1.94	6.59	3.43	6.51	1.95	3.14	1.83	0.07	2.33	29.94
#1944	1.01	1.34	4.55	12.42	2.04	1.60	5.49	4.77	2.20	2.20	1.93	3.98	43.53
1945	1.07	0.84	1.85	6.79	1.28	4.00	5.01	4.11	10.58	0.51	0.05	0.62	36.71
1946	2.21	1.23	1.81	1.87	2.11	2.71	0.32	2.90	1.27	4.32	2.14	0.78	23.67
1947	0.71	0.52	2.91	5.20	4.69	2.57	2.89	0.82	0.25	1.50	0.89	2.98	25.93
1948	1.00	1.19	1.51	1.65	1.86	9.76	6.39	2.72	1.05	0.67	3.30	0.25	31.35
1949	6.29	1.80	2.01	3.85	6.15	3.16	6.97	1.13	3.62	1.91	0.06	1.22	38.17
1950	0.52	1.61	0.50	0.88	2.24	4.02	13.37	5.93	1.04	0.48	0.26	0.02	30.87
1951	1.03	2.58	2.69	6.33	7.60	10.07	4.45	5.38	6.59	2.05	1.47	0.24	50.48
1952	0.41	0.35	2.68	1.97	2.31	1.08	4.94	2.52	0.28	0.00	2.40	1.09	20.03
#1953	0.15	0.82	3.35	0.57	2.02	2.17	2.39	0.82	0.53	3.77	1.46	1.06	19.11
1954	0.09	0.57	1.30	1.54	4.84	0.94	0.19	0.96	1.09	2.83	T	0.18	14.53
1955	0.61	1.71	0.68	0.72	4.02	3.98	1.30	1.06	3.79	5.84	0.03	0.03	23.77
1956	0.43	0.45	0.91	1.46	1.40	1.28	2.51	0.70	0.03	2.69	0.48	0.39	12.73
1957	0.19	0.77	2.60	3.31	7.57	10.46	1.99	0.59	5.05	2.72	1.45	0.45	37.15
1958	0.81	1.03	4.07	1.23	2.44	3.00	7.19	2.93	6.11	T	2.39	0.46	31.66
1959	0.53	0.23	0.85	2.17	5.53	2.35	7.38	4.20	2.31	6.13	0.30	1.60	33.58
1960	1.37	1.41	1.18	1.28	4.10	4.59	5.57	7.91	2.25	5.03	0.37	1.73	36.79
1961	0.02	1.51	4.83	2.00	4.02	2.61	6.56	3.80	5.24	4.87	2.80	1.01	39.27
1962	1.07	0.47	0.26	1.02	0.99	4.80	9.22	2.95	8.23	1.32	1.62	0.60	32.55
1963	1.22	0.02	1.67	0.22	6.15	4.51	2.70	2.86	4.90	2.47	1.04	0.34	28.10
1964	0.71	0.53	0.89	2.97	5.84	3.73	2.23	6.10	2.66	1.64	5.88	1.03	34.21
1965	0.56	1.39	0.48	2.63	6.26	8.00	3.62	4.91	8.44	0.32	0.11	2.25	38.97
1966	0.23	1.44	0.26	2.21	0.76	2.67	1.78	1.09	0.72	0.47	0.09	0.43	12.15
1967	0.28	0.09	0.57	1.30	1.42	5.62	4.28	1.91	3.19	2.98	0.39	1.41	23.44
1968	0.14	0.20	1.36	2.16	4.37	2.38	3.65	6.41	5.91	3.06	2.47	1.31	33.42
1969	0.45	1.35	1.73	4.30	3.28	6.82	6.23	1.07	4.77	2.80	0.01	1.36	34.17
1970	0.28	0.21	2.70	4.49	1.58	6.72	0.47	2.37	4.04	1.88	0.05	0.49	25.28
1971	0.98	1.70	0.01	2.35	3.02	2.70	6.65	1.49	1.73	5.54	2.49	0.95	29.61
1972	0.15	0.28	0.56	3.32	2.47	2.02	3.86	3.31	1.31	2.00	3.06	0.97	23.31
1973	2.73	1.20	9.17	3.78	0.52	1.21	6.07	0.68	9.46	3.43	0.91	2.80	41.96
1974	0.56	0.25	2.36	4.29	4.65	2.79	0.09	4.11	1.08	3.44	2.69	2.22	28.53
1975	1.28	2.12	1.72	1.57	8.60	6.88	0.05	2.77	1.19	0.08	2.89	0.48	29.63
RECORD MEAN	0.81	1.13	1.81	2.87	4.21	4.45	3.44	3.03	3.31	2.41	1.53	1.06	30.06

Record mean values above are means through the current year for the period beginning in 1889 for temperature and precipitation, 1954 for snowfall.

Station: LEXINGTON, KENTUCKY
BLUE GRASS FIELD
Elevation (ground): 966 feet

TEMPERATURES °F

Month	Normal: Daily maximum	Normal: Daily minimum	Normal: Monthly	Extremes: Record highest	Year	Extremes: Record lowest	Year
(a)				12		12	
J	41.3	24.5	32.9	71	1972	-11	1972
F	44.3	26.2	35.3	75	1972	-6	1970
M	53.4	33.7	43.6	81	1973	12	1970
A	66.0	44.6	55.3	84	1970	22	1972
M	75.5	53.8	64.7	90	1964	26	1966
J	83.5	62.5	73.0	97	1966	39	1966
J	86.4	65.9	76.2	98	1966	47	1972
A	85.5	64.4	75.0	98	1964	42	1965
S	79.6	57.6	68.6	96	1964	35	1965
O	68.8	46.8	57.8	87	1971	25	1972
N	53.9	35.3	44.6	80	1971	9	1964
D	43.7	27.2	35.5	72	1971	-4	1963
YR	65.2	45.2	55.2	98	JUL 1966	-11	JAN 1972

IMPORTANT:
The time-period covered by this record is limited: See footnotes following table of **NORMALS, MEANS AND EXTREMES** for explanation and for additional history of **EXTREME HIGHS AND LOWS** recorded in the general area.

Lexington, County Seat of Fayette County, is located in the heart of the famed Kentucky Blue Grass Region. Fayette County is a gently rolling plateau with the elevation varying between 900 and 1,050 feet above mean sea level. It is noted for its beauty, the fertility of its soil, excellent grass, stock farms, and burley tobacco. The soil has a high phosphorus content and this is very valuable in growing pasture grasses for the grazing of cattle and horses. Lexington has a decided continental climate with a rather large diurnal temperature range. The climate is temperate and well suited to a varied plant and animal life. There are no bodies of water close enough to have any effect on the climate. The closest river is the Kentucky which makes an arc about 15 to 20 miles to the southeast, south, and southwest on its course to the Ohio River. There are numerous small creeks that rise in the county and flow into the river. The reservoirs of the Lexington Water Company are about 5 miles southeast of the City and are the largest bodies of water in the area.

Lexington is subject to rather sudden and large changes in temperature with the spells generally of rather short duration. Temperatures above 100 degrees and below zero degrees are relatively rare. The average temperature for the winter is 35 degrees, spring 62 degrees, fall 50 degrees and for the summer season 74 degrees.

In the spring there is a 10% chance of a temperature below 24 degrees occurring after April 7, 28 degrees after April 16, and 32 degrees after

(Continued page 462)

Snowfall

Season	July	Aug	Sept	Oct	Nov	Dec	Jan
1936-37	0.0	0.0	0.0	T	6.1	4.6	0.2
1937-38	0.0	0.0	0.0	0.0	2.9	3.6	2.8
1938-39	0.0	0.0	0.0	0.0	5.0	0.1	5.7
1939-40	0.0	0.0	0.0	0.0	0.1	11.7	17.8
1940-41	0.0	0.0	0.0	0.0	1.4	0.0	0.3
1941-42	0.0	0.0	0.0	0.0	0.3	T	9.3
1942-43	0.0	0.0	0.0	T	0.0	6.6	16.4
#1943-44	0.0	0.0	0.0	0.0	0.2	4.2	2.6
1944-45	0.0	0.0	0.0	0.0	T	5.4	5.7
1945-46	0.0	0.0	0.0	0.0	T	9.0	T
1946-47	0.0	0.0	0.0	0.0	0.0	1.0	3.1
1947-48	0.0	0.0	0.0	0.0	T	T	21.1
1948-49	0.0	0.0	0.0	0.0	T	4.5	2.6
1949-50	0.0	0.0	0.0	0.0	0.6	0.4	T
1950-51	0.0	0.0	0.0	0.0	9.7	5.5	8.0
1951-52	0.0	0.0	0.0	0.0	2.8	4.2	1.5
1952-53	0.0	0.0	0.0	T	2.1	2.1	5.1
1953-54	0.0	0.0	0.0	0.0	1.2	3.6	4.8
1954-55	0.0	0.0	0.0	0.1	2.2	1.6	8.1
1955-56	0.0	0.0	0.0	0.0	0.2	2.5	5.3
1956-57	0.0	0.0	0.0	0.0	1.3	0.1	1.3
1957-58	0.0	0.0	0.0	T	0.6	1.5	2.3
1958-59	0.0	0.0	0.0	0.0	3.4	T	3.3
1959-60	0.0	0.0	0.0	0.0	0.8	1.8	0.3
1960-61	0.0	0.0	0.0	0.0	T	5.0	6.2
1961-62	0.0	0.0	0.0	0.0	1.2	5.1	6.1
1962-63	0.0	0.0	0.0	T	T	2.4	6.8
1963-64	0.0	0.0	0.0	0.0	1.0	8.2	10.8
1964-65	0.0	0.0	0.0	0.0	0.7	0.7	9.9
1965-66	0.0	0.0	0.0	0.0	T	1.3	12.4
1966-67	0.0	0.0	0.0	0.0	8.4	0.3	1.5
1967-68	0.0	0.0	0.0	0.0	T	10.7	12.1
1968-69	0.0	0.0	0.0	0.0	1.0	1.5	1.9
1969-70	0.0	0.0	0.0	0.0	1.4	5.2	8.4
1970-71	0.0	0.0	0.0	0.0	T	1.2	4.0
1971-72	0.0	0.0	0.0	0.0	0.7	T	1.4
1972-73	0.0	0.0	0.0	0.2	1.7	0.4	1.0
1973-74	0.0	0.0	0.0	0.0	0.0	4.3	T
1974-75	0.0	0.0	0.0	T	1.4	2.8	4.6
1975-76	0.0	0.0	0.0	0.0	T	0.9	
RECORD MEAN	0.0	0.0	0.0	T	0.6	1.8	5.1

Heating Degree Days

Season	July	Aug	Sept	Oct	Nov	Dec	Jan
1955-56	0	0	4	264	696	968	1031
1956-57	0	8	78	138	650	630	1034
1957-58	0	0	39	370	608	774	1065
1958-59	0	1	39	272	538	1082	1043
1959-60	0	0	24	253	672	813	893
1960-61	0	0	6	212	575	1081	1144
1961-62	0	0	32	226	588	907	1081
1962-63	0	0	94	243	621	1054	1183
#1963-64	0	1	55	84	540	1217	924
1964-65	0	11	61	375	502	850	1010
1965-66	0	9	52	346	558	777	1225
1966-67	0	3	62	340	570	908	851
1967-68	1	4	83	289	722	800	1090
1968-69	0	5	20	296	552	938	1011
1969-70	0	0	44	274	657	996	1209
1970-71	6	0	31	229	637	821	1087
1971-72	0	0	8	69	536	591	909
1972-73	10	1	20	366	612	739	920
1973-74	0	1	21	172	490	880	744
1974-75	0	0	125	338	578	836	852
1975-76	0	0	128	249	488	895	

Cooling Degree Days

Year	Jan	Feb	Mar	Apr	May	June	July
1969	0	0	0	7	97	260	404
1970	0	0	0	26	137	199	295
1971	0	0	0	0	25	266	281
1972	0	0	0	11	47	130	287
1973	0	0	12	18	21	266	342
1974	0	0	10	21	94	108	296
1975	0	0	0	11	130	267	357

Feb	Mar	Apr	May	June	Total
6.7	1.0	0.0	0.0	0.0	18.6
1.4	0.0	0.1	0.0	0.0	10.8
4.4	T	0.3	0.0	0.0	15.5
5.3	2.7	0.8	T	0.0	38.4
3.5	1.2	0.0	0.0	0.0	6.4
3.8	1.5	T	0.0	0.0	14.9
2.3	8.9	0.3	0.0	0.0	34.5
5.8	0.6	0.2	0.0	0.0	13.6
0.8	0.0	0.0	0.0	0.0	11.9
2.2	T	0.0	0.0	0.0	11.2
11.1	11.7	0.0	0.0	0.0	26.9
9.1	T	0.0	0.0	0.0	30.2
T	3.9	0.0	0.0	0.0	11.0
T	1.0	0.3	0.0	0.0	2.3
7.9	9.6	1.0	0.0	0.0	41.7
1.8	0.1	T	0.0	0.0	10.4
T	2.2	0.1	0.0	0.0	11.6
1.7	T	0.0	0.0	0.0	11.3
4.6	0.3	0.0	0.0	0.0	16.9
0.3	1.2	0.2	0.0	0.0	9.7
T	4.6	T	0.0	0.0	7.3
6.9	2.3	0.0	0.0	0.0	13.6
T	0.4	0.4	0.0	0.0	7.5
16.4	17.7	T	0.0	0.0	37.0
4.6	T	2.9	0.0	0.0	18.7
0.8	2.4	0.8	0.0	0.0	16.4
8.2	T	0.0	0.0	0.0	17.4
12.0	0.3	0.0	0.0	0.0	32.3
1.8	2.8	0.0	0.0	0.0	15.9
6.5	1.2	T	0.0	0.0	21.4
11.1	4.3	0.0	0.0	0.0	25.6
3.1	8.6	0.0	0.0	0.0	34.5
6.1	1.7	0.0	0.0	0.0	12.2
9.9	6.2	T	0.0	0.0	31.1
9.1	5.3	0.0	0.0	0.0	19.6
6.3	2.4	T	0.0	0.0	10.8
1.4	0.4	0.2	0.0	0.0	5.3
3.6	0.7	T	0.0	0.0	8.6
1.5	5.6	T	0.0	0.0	15.9
4.8	3.1	0.2	0.0	0.0	15.6

Average Temperature

Year	Jan	Feb	Mar	Apr	May	June	July	Aug	Sept	Oct	Nov	Dec	Annual
1936	25.8	29.6	48.0	50.2	67.8	76.0	81.1	81.5	72.8	57.7	41.1	38.6	55.9
1937	41.7	35.5	39.5	54.0	64.1	75.4	76.2	78.5	67.5	53.9	41.4	34.2	55.3
1938	33.6	43.3	50.6	57.5	65.0	68.6	77.5	77.5	69.8	59.4	46.8	37.2	57.2
1939	38.0	39.3	47.2	52.0	66.6	74.8	76.0	75.0	74.6	59.9	42.4	36.6	56.9
1940	20.0	34.0	40.9	51.6	60.0	73.2	76.4	76.7	66.6	61.0	44.5	41.4	53.9
1941	34.4	31.2	38.5	59.0	67.1	74.6	78.0	76.9	73.6	63.0	45.7	41.0	56.9
1942	31.5	31.5	56.4	57.6	64.6	74.4	78.4	74.8	67.4	58.0	47.6	33.9	55.0
1943	36.2	37.0	41.0	50.8	66.4	78.0	77.6	78.5	67.2	56.9	43.4	33.9	55.6
#1944	37.0	40.6	42.1	52.6	70.8	77.4	77.7	75.0	67.4	56.0	43.8	30.6	56.0
1945	28.6	36.2	54.4	57.1	60.2	69.6	74.0	74.6	71.8	56.2	46.4	29.1	54.9
1946	34.2	37.5	54.6	56.9	62.2	72.3	74.8	69.3	68.4	59.6	49.8	40.1	56.6
1947	37.8	25.9	34.8	55.2	60.3	70.4	70.0	79.0	68.2	63.6	41.8	36.3	53.6
1948	23.4	35.8	47.6	57.8	62.3	73.7	76.6	74.2	69.0	53.8	48.0	38.0	55.0
1949	41.2	40.6	44.2	51.8	65.7	75.3	79.6	74.9	64.0	61.4	44.2	40.0	56.9
1950	43.7	37.9	40.8	50.4	65.3	71.4	72.4	71.6	65.7	61.5	38.5	29.7	54.1
1951	34.9	35.4	41.9	51.7	65.3	73.4	77.4	76.1	67.4	59.1	38.4	37.6	54.9
1952	38.5	38.9	44.6	54.7	65.2	78.8	79.7	76.0	68.4	51.1	45.9	38.3	56.7
1953	39.7	39.4	46.7	51.1	67.9	77.1	77.3	76.3	69.9	61.8	46.3	35.0	57.4
1954	35.3	42.9	42.8	60.8	60.1	75.2	79.7	76.4	73.6	58.0	44.6	35.2	57.1
1955	32.1	36.4	46.5	59.0	66.2	67.9	78.8	77.7	72.6	56.9	41.7	33.6	55.8
1956	31.5	40.6	43.6	51.7	64.6	72.5	75.2	74.4	65.9	61.0	43.2	44.4	55.7
1957	31.4	40.3	43.1	57.9	64.9	73.8	76.9	75.4	69.4	52.9	44.5	39.8	55.9
1958	30.5	25.8	38.6	54.2	63.8	69.4	76.4	74.1	67.9	56.5	47.2	29.8	52.8
1959	31.1	37.4	42.4	55.8	68.5	72.7	77.3	78.1	71.5	58.6	42.3	38.5	56.2
1960	35.9	31.0	29.7	58.1	61.6	71.4	74.7	76.7	70.5	58.7	45.5	29.8	53.6
1961	27.8	40.7	47.0	48.7	59.3	70.1	75.6	74.1	71.9	58.1	45.3	35.5	54.5
1962	29.9	38.8	41.7	52.3	71.6	72.9	75.4	75.6	65.0	58.8	44.1	30.8	54.7
#1963	26.6	28.6	48.9	57.3	62.8	72.0	73.6	72.5	66.6	63.9	46.8	25.5	53.8
1964	35.0	32.0	45.3	58.3	66.9	74.3	75.2	75.0	68.2	52.7	48.0	37.4	55.7
1965	32.2	34.3	37.9	55.9	68.9	71.3	73.7	74.5	68.8	53.9	46.2	39.6	54.8
1966	25.3	33.3	44.6	52.6	60.5	71.6	77.4	72.6	65.3	54.2	45.7	35.5	53.2
1967	37.3	30.2	50.0	58.8	62.0	72.1	72.5	70.6	64.9	56.1	40.7	39.0	54.5
1968	29.6	28.0	46.0	55.1	62.1	72.0	75.9	75.5	67.8	56.6	46.4	34.6	54.1
1969	32.1	36.2	38.9	56.3	65.5	72.8	77.8	74.7	67.8	57.9	42.8	32.7	54.6
1970	25.8	32.4	40.5	57.2	66.5	71.3	74.1	74.6	72.7	57.7	43.6	38.3	54.5
1971	29.7	34.8	40.3	52.0	59.2	73.7	73.9	73.9	72.5	64.7	47.2	45.7	55.6
1972	35.4	33.2	42.2	53.7	63.2	67.6	73.8	72.9	69.8	53.0	44.5	40.9	54.2
1973	35.1	35.2	53.8	52.9	60.1	73.6	75.8	74.9	72.2	60.9	48.5	36.4	56.6
1974	40.7	37.4	48.5	55.8	63.6	67.2	74.4	73.3	62.6	54.3	45.7	37.8	55.1
1975	37.3	39.5	41.4	52.2	67.4	73.5	76.4	77.5	63.4	57.4	48.5	35.8	55.9
RECORD MEAN	33.6	35.1	43.9	54.2	64.1	72.7	76.2	74.9	69.1	57.5	44.8	36.1	55.2
MAX	41.6	43.7	53.3	64.3	74.2	82.6	85.9	84.7	79.3	67.8	53.5	43.8	64.6
MIN	25.6	26.5	34.4	44.1	54.0	62.8	66.4	65.0	58.8	47.2	36.0	28.3	45.8

\# indicates a station move or relocation of instruments.

LEXINGTON, KY

Feb	Mar	Apr	May	June	Total
703	660	410	114	33	4883
683	670	288	105	2	4286
1091	811	324	92	16	5190
766	692	284	63	5	4785
980	1089	243	174	6	5147
672	554	490	188	21	4943
726	718	411	21	3	4713
014	495	268	126	2	5100
952	606	222	55	16	4672
851	834	277	26	8	4805
883	631	373	167	21	5042
967	468	223	138	23	4553
1065	581	298	124	8	5065
799	800	261	77	17	4776
908	750	251	84	1	5174
838	759	382	198	0	4988
917	700	343	96	47	4216
827	353	371	167	0	4386
767	514	289	128	37	4043
705	726	387	51	4	4602

Aug	Sept	Oct	Nov	Dec	Total
309	134	57	0	0	1268
306	266	11	0	0	1240
285	239	65	10	0	1171
250	171	0	4	0	900
314	245	51	0	0	1269
264	60	11	4	0	868
394	86	18	0	0	1263

Precipitation

Year	Jan	Feb	Mar	Apr	May	June	July	Aug	Sept	Oct	Nov	Dec	Annual
1936	4.00	2.07	4.43	5.76	1.46	1.18	2.85	1.26	2.55	2.80	2.65	5.20	36.21
1937	15.10	2.77	1.59	5.32	3.28	5.80	3.17	3.52	0.87	3.96	1.74	3.51	50.63
1938	3.77	2.49	5.56	3.25	4.75	3.06	6.81	3.70	2.29	0.38	3.60	1.69	41.35
1939	5.94	8.48	5.39	6.46	2.00	7.66	3.30	1.80	1.59	2.58	1.15	2.35	48.70
1940	2.31	4.68	6.07	4.81	5.36	2.98	3.42	3.32	2.59	0.55	3.59	3.24	42.92
1941	2.32	0.84	2.27	2.22	1.72	4.18	7.34	1.89	0.67	4.22	3.17	2.28	33.12
1942	3.38	2.82	4.11	3.11	3.38	5.72	8.16	7.26	2.96	3.54	5.72	6.59	56.75
1943	3.31	1.98	7.47	4.00	6.73	3.09	7.68	1.06	1.86	1.61	0.55	2.48	41.82
#1944	1.95	3.67	5.29	4.21	2.49	1.58	2.77	6.22	2.41	1.88	1.60	5.00	39.07
1945	3.05	6.25	5.56	4.16	4.76	7.03	4.63	1.55	1.61	1.67	5.15	2.28	47.70
1946	2.87	4.26	4.44	0.79	6.71	5.33	5.84	3.60	3.14	1.84	2.03	3.31	44.16
1947	6.62	0.85	1.82	4.83	4.75	5.15	3.01	2.88	2.65	2.79	3.32	1.70	40.37
1948	2.58	4.93	7.06	7.50	3.56	2.26	3.57	2.61	2.14	3.29	6.19	4.73	50.42
1949	5.55	5.86	5.06	3.34	1.87	4.97	4.56	4.37	1.32	1.85	2.53	7.26	48.54
1950	16.65	3.64	3.61	3.34	5.06	4.17	6.84	2.70	4.28	1.51	5.04	1.83	58.67
1951	11.15	3.64	4.96	2.49	2.16	4.38	1.83	2.98	3.60	3.10	6.87	7.30	54.46
1952	5.62	2.72	7.36	2.06	3.15	4.43	3.01	2.80	1.58	1.17	3.51	3.58	40.99
1953	4.10	1.44	7.84	3.88	5.47	3.71	3.67	2.44	1.58	1.12	1.46	2.44	39.15
1954	4.16	1.68	2.38	3.79	2.23	2.14	3.82	3.29	4.97	1.33	2.36	3.38	35.53
1955	1.57	7.69	7.03	1.71	6.43	4.06	5.73	3.95	2.43	2.29	2.56	1.86	47.31
1956	3.25	7.06	6.47	4.79	3.70	6.80	6.10	3.59	1.77	1.78	2.32	4.52	52.15
1957	4.45	3.48	2.15	7.66	4.22	5.74	0.76	3.02	3.18	2.70	5.57	5.69	48.62
1958	3.29	1.77	2.26	4.16	5.29	4.61	10.64	4.02	2.60	0.86	3.31	1.15	43.96
1959	4.86	3.18	1.82	2.99	3.20	3.21	4.05	2.19	0.24	3.91	4.49	4.43	38.57
1960	2.50	4.55	1.49	1.65	4.03	11.69	1.94	4.14	5.20	2.50	3.61	1.79	45.09
1961	1.71	3.89	6.18	6.04	6.14	5.12	5.98	2.62	1.50	0.88	3.04	3.89	46.99
1962	4.29	7.24	5.16	2.61	5.68	4.68	4.24	2.71	2.66	4.46	3.92	2.36	50.01
1963	1.47	1.81	6.82	1.61	3.48	3.27	7.18	4.14	0.37	0.33	1.81	0.81	33.10
1964	2.83	2.52	10.06	2.86	1.68	3.55	3.99	1.96	4.91	0.57	2.37	6.18	43.48
1965	2.83	2.92	5.45	3.24	1.20	3.28	3.64	1.92	3.55	2.44	1.02	0.61	32.10
1966	3.99	3.64	0.99	7.16	4.65	1.36	5.74	4.55	4.03	1.44	4.01	4.60	46.36
1967	1.35	2.29	6.03	3.61	6.94	2.65	5.87	3.63	2.97	2.11	4.15	3.99	45.59
1968	1.44	0.71	6.76	3.23	6.87	2.83	4.54	5.27	2.98	2.57	3.23	2.89	43.32
1969	4.26	1.60	1.50	3.83	3.78	4.61	4.37	5.96	0.49	1.53	3.42	4.15	39.50
1970	0.95	3.60	4.72	9.30	3.18	3.81	3.39	2.61	5.71	2.37	2.35	5.51	47.50
1971	3.29	4.72	2.02	2.10	6.14	7.84	7.64	0.88	3.51	0.52	1.71	4.30	44.67
1972	4.10	5.60	4.04	8.75	3.84	3.61	5.58	3.95	4.30	2.71	4.21	6.92	57.61
1973	1.53	1.58	5.08	5.67	8.22	6.06	5.15	3.58	1.40	2.65	6.58	3.42	50.92
1974	6.39	2.24	5.89	3.33	5.52	7.21	4.82	11.18	4.18	1.53	4.08	3.72	60.09
1975	3.66	5.70	10.38	6.17	2.69	2.23	5.60	3.96	6.46	5.09	2.93	4.24	59.11
RECORD MEAN	4.16	3.26	4.60	3.74	3.85	4.20	4.44	3.45	2.65	2.34	3.22	3.64	43.75

Record mean values above are means through the current year for the period beginning in 1871 for temperature and precipitation, 1945 for snowfall.

(Continued)

April 28. In the fall there is a 10% chance of 32 degrees occurring before October 13, 28 degrees before October 23, and 24 degrees before November 4. these percentages are based on 74 years of record.

Precipitation is evenly distributed throughout the winter, spring, and summer, with near 12 inches recorded on the average for each of these seasons. The fall season averages near 8-1/2 inches. Snowfall amounts are variable and the ground does not retain snow cover more than a few days at a time.

The months of September and October are the most pleasant of the year. They have the least amount of precipitation, the greatest number of clear days, and generally comfortable temperatures are the rule during these months.

Normals, Means, and Extremes

Month	Normal Degree days Base 65 °F		Precipitation in inches												Relative humidity pct.			
			Water equivalent								Snow, Ice pellets				Hour 01	Hour 07	Hour 13	Hour 19
	Heating	Cooling	Normal	Maximum monthly	Year	Minimum monthly	Year	Maximum in 24 hrs.	Year		Maximum monthly	Year	Maximum in 24 hrs.	Year	(Local time)			
(a)				31		31		31			31		31		11	12	12	12
J	995	0	3.95	16.65	1950	0.95	1970	2.98	1951		21.1	1948	9.4	1966	75	79	67	69
F	832	0	3.42	7.69	1955	0.71	1968	3.21	1975		16.4	1960	7.3	1971	74	78	63	65
M	673	10	4.80	10.38	1975	0.99	1966	3.85	1952		17.7	1960	9.5	1947	71	77	58	59
A	302	11	3.87	9.30	1970	0.79	1946	4.39	1948		2.9	1961	2.9	1961	69	74	55	56
M	106	97	4.16	8.22	1973	1.20	1965	2.89	1973		0.0		0.0		75	79	56	58
J	8	248	4.31	11.69	1960	1.36	1966	5.88	1960		0.0		0.0		79	82	57	60
J	0	347	4.83	10.64	1958	1.83	1951	3.11	1974		0.0		0.0		82	85	58	63
A	0	313	3.40	11.18	1974	0.88	1971	3.56	1968		0.0		0.0		82	86	58	64
S	40	148	2.65	6.46	1975	0.24	1959	3.50	1964		0.0		0.0		82	87	58	67
O	246	23	2.12	5.09	1975	0.33	1963	3.21	1962		0.2	1972	0.2	1972	76	83	55	64
N	612	0	3.36	6.87	1951	1.02	1965	2.58	1957		9.7	1950	7.5	1966	76	79	61	68
D	915	0	3.62	7.30	1951	0.61	1965	2.97	1949		10.7	1967	7.8	1967	76	80	68	72
YR	4729	1197	44.49	16.65	JAN 1950	0.24	SEP 1959	5.88	JUN 1960		21.1	JAN 1948	9.5	MAR 1947	76	81	59	64

(To better understand these tables, see full explanation of terms beginning on page 322)

Wind					Pct. of possible sunshine	Mean sky cover, tenths, sunrise to sunset	Mean number of days												Average station pressure mb.
		Fastest mile					Sunrise to sunset							Temperatures °F Max.		Min.			Elev. 989 feet m.s.l.
Mean speed m.p.h.	Prevailing direction	Speed m.p.h.	Direction	Year			Clear	Partly cloudy	Cloudy	Precipitation .01 inch or more	Snow, Ice pellets 1.0 inch or more	Thunderstorms	Heavy fog, visibility ¼ mile or less	(b) 90° and above	32° and below	32° and below	0° and below		
28	17	14	14			31	31	31	31	31	31	31	31	12	12	12	12		3
11.6	S	39	25	1962		7.3	6	6	19	13	2	1	3	0	9	22	2		984.1
11.7	SSW	46	32	1962		6.9	6	6	16	11	1	1	2	0	5	22	1		982.3
11.9	SSW	36	27	1962		7.0	6	7	18	13	1	3	1	0	1	15	0		979.8
11.5	SSW	46	32	1963		6.6	6	9	15	13	*	4	1	0	0	4	0		981.0
9.2	S	35	22	1965		6.2	7	11	13	12	0	7	1	*	0	*	0		979.0
8.3	S	35	22	1968		5.8	8	11	11	11	0	8	1	4	0	0	0		980.8
7.4	SSW	37	29	1966		5.7	8	13	10	11	0	10	1	5	0	0	0		981.9
7.0	S	39	22	1964		5.2	10	12	9	9	0	7	2	5	0	0	0		983.4
8.0	S	29	22	1968		5.2	11	9	10	8	0	3	2	2	0	0	0		983.6
8.6	S	32	26	1965		4.9	13	7	11	8	0	2	2	0	0	3	0		985.7
10.6	S	32	23	1973		6.5	7	7	16	11	1	1	1	0	1	11	0		984.0
11.2	S	37	19	1971		7.2	6	6	19	12	1	*	2	0	4	19	0		983.1
9.7	S	46	32	APR 1963		6.2	94	104	167	131	5	47	19	17	19	95	2		982.4

FOOTNOTES

Means and extremes above are from existing and comparable exposures.
Annual extremes have been exceeded at other sites in the locality as follows:
Highest temperature 108 in July 1936; lowest temperature -21 in January 1963;
minimum monthly precipitation .11 in October 1924; maximum precipitation in 24 hours 8.06 in August 1932;
maximum snowfall 21.7 in January 1918; maximum snowfall in 24 hours 13.4 in January 1943.

Station: LOUISVILLE, KENTUCKY
STANDIFORD FIELD
Elevation (ground): 477 feet

TEMPERATURES °F

Month	Normal			Extremes			
	Daily maximum	Daily minimum	Monthly	Record highest	Year	Record lowest	Year
(a)				15		15	
J	42.0	24.5	33.3	73	1975	-20	1963
F	45.0	26.5	35.8	77	1972	-4	1966
M	54.0	34.0	44.0	83	1967	15	1969
A	66.9	44.8	55.9	88	1962	24	1972
M	75.6	53.9	64.8	91	1962	31	1966
J	83.7	62.9	73.3	97	1971	42	1966
J	87.3	66.4	76.9	101	1966	50	1972
A	86.8	64.9	75.9	101	1964	49	1965
S	80.5	57.7	69.1	96	1964	37	1965
O	70.3	45.9	58.1	89	1963	25	1962
N	54.9	35.1	45.0	82	1968	10	1964
D	44.1	27.1	35.6	73	1975	-3	1962
YR	65.9	45.3	55.6	101	JUL 1966	-20	JAN 1963

IMPORTANT:
The time-period covered by this record is limited: See footnotes on next page for explanation and for additional history of EXTREME HIGHS AND LOWS recorded in the general area.

Louisville is located on the left bank of the Ohio River, 604 miles below Pittsburgh, Pennsylvania, and 377 miles above the mouth of the river at Cairo, Illinois. The City is divided by Beargrass Creek and its South Fork into two portions with entirely different types of topography. The eastern portion is rolling, containing several creeks and consists of plateaus and rolling hillsides. The highest elevation in this area is 565 feet. The western portion is mostly flat and is of lower elevation with an average height about 100 feet lower than that of the eastern part. A large part of this westerly section lies in the flood plain of the Ohio River. With few exceptions, the industries of the City are located in the western portion, while the eastern portion is almost entirely residential. A range of low hills about 5 miles northwest of Louisville, on the Indiana side of the Ohio River, present a partial barrier to arctic blasts in the winter months. During colder months, snow is frequently observed on the summits of these hills when there is no snow in the city of Louisville or in riverside communities on the Indiana side of the Ohio River.

The climate of Louisville, while continental in type, is of a variable nature because of its position in midlatitudes, in the belt of the westerly winds, in the path of cyclonic and anticyclonic storms, and its location in the interior of the continent, but still not shut off from a great source of moisture, the Gulf of Mexico. Since highs and lows pass through this area, the temperature generally varies with the systems. Thus, in winter and summer, there are occasional cold and hot spells of short duration with quick moderation as the high pressure ridge moves off. As a whole, winters are moderately cold and summers are normally warm. In the spring and fall, when high pressure systems have a smaller frequency, temperatures are more consistent and fewer extremes are experienced. Temperatures of 100° or more in summer and 0° or less in winter are rare. January is the coldest month of the year and July the warmest. The City is so situated geographically as to receive rainfall from cyclonic storms which, particularly in the winter and spring, move along a path extending from Texas to New England. It is also situated so as to receive rainfall from storms which move across the continent from west to east. Thunderstorms with high intensities of rainfall are common during the spring and summer months. As a result, precipitation in Louisville is nonseasonal and varies from year to year, and month to month with the fall months usually the driest. Generally March is the month of greatest monthly rainfall and October of least monthly rainfall. Snowfall, while seldom heavy, is a usual occurrence during the months of November through March. As with rainfall, amounts vary from year to year and month to month. Some snow has also been recorded in the months of October and April. Mean total amounts for the months of December, January, and February are about the same with January showing a slight edge in total amount. Relative humidity remains rather high throughout the summer months. Cloud cover is about equally distributed throughout the year with the winter months showing somewhat of an increase in amount. The percentage of possible sunshine at Louisville varies from month to month with the greatest amount during the summer months as a result of the decreasing sky cover during that season. Heavy fog is unusual and there is only an average of 10 days during the year with heavy fog and these occur only in the months of September through March. The average date for the last occurrence in the spring of temperatures as low as 32° F. is at the end of the first decade in April; the occurrence of the first 32° F. reading in the autumn is generally at the beginning of the last week in October. The prevailing direction of the wind has a southerly component and the velocity averages under 10 m.p.h. The strongest winds are usually associated with thunderstorm activity.

LOUISVILLE, KENTUCKY

Normals, Means, and Extremes

(To better understand these tables, see full explanation of terms beginning on page 322)

Month	Normal Degree days Base 65 °F: Heating	Cooling	Precipitation in inches: Water equivalent: Normal	Maximum monthly	Year	Minimum monthly	Year	Maximum in 24 hrs.	Year	Snow, Ice pellets: Maximum monthly	Year	Maximum in 24 hrs.	Year
(a)				28		28		28		28		28	
J	983	0	3.53	11.38	1950	1.11	1967	2.78	1966	15.1	1964	7.2	1964
F	818	0	3.47	8.34	1956	0.80	1968	2.82	1975	13.1	1948	11.0	1966
M	661	10	5.05	14.91	1964	1.02	1966	6.97	1964	22.9	1960	12.1	1968
A	286	13	4.10	11.10	1970	1.01	1962	4.85	1970	1.6	1973	1.6	1973
M	105	99	4.20	9.04	1950	1.60	1965	4.60	1961	0.0		0.0	
J	5	254	4.05	10.11	1960	0.75	1966	5.14	1960	0.0		0.0	
J	0	369	3.76	9.38	1973	1.18	1954	5.37	1973	0.0		0.0	
A	0	338	2.99	8.79	1974	0.23	1953	3.05	1970	0.0		0.0	
S	35	158	2.94	8.41	1965	0.27	1953	4.22	1954	0.0		0.0	
O	241	27	2.35	6.12	1975	0.62	1964	2.78	1962	T	1962	T	1962
N	600	0	3.33	9.12	1957	1.16	1954	3.58	1948	13.2	1966	13.0	1966
D	911	0	3.34	6.85	1951	1.06	1963	2.21	1964	9.3	1961	5.0	1961
YR	4645	1268	43.11	14.91	MAR 1964	0.23	AUG 1953	6.97	MAR 1964	22.9	MAR 1960	13.0	NOV 1966

Month	Relative humidity pct. (Local time): Hour 01	Hour 07	Hour 13	Hour 19	Wind: Mean speed m.p.h.	Prevailing direction	Fastest mile: Speed m.p.h.	Direction	Year	Pct. of possible sunshine	Mean sky cover, tenths, sunrise to sunset	Mean number of days: Sunrise to sunset: Clear	Partly cloudy	Cloudy	Precipitation .01 inch or more	Snow, Ice pellets 1.0 inch or more	Thunderstorms	Heavy fog, visibility ¼ mile or less	Temperatures °F Max. (b) 90° and above	Max. 32° and below	Min. 32° and below	Min. 0° and below	Average station pressure mb. Elev. 488 feet m.s.l.
(a)	15	15	15	15	28	15	28	28		28	28	28	28	28	28	28	28	28	15	15	15	15	3
J	72	76	64	64	9.6	S	50	S	1950	41	7.4	6	6	19	12	2	1	1	0	9	23	1	1002.0
F	72	76	62	62	9.8	NW	61	NW	1967	47	6.9	6	6	16	11	1	1	1	0	5	21	*	1000.1
M	71	76	59	58	10.4	NW	56	W	1952	50	7.0	6	8	17	13	1	3	1	0	1	13	0	997.2
A	69	75	53	53	10.1	SW	57	W	1953	55	6.7	6	9	15	12	*	5	*	0	0	3	0	998.2
M	77	83	56	56	8.1	SE	57	W	1957	62	6.2	8	9	14	11	0	7	*	*	0	*	0	995.7
J	81	84	57	59	7.4	S	58	W	1957	67	5.8	8	11	11	10	0	7	*	5	0	0	0	997.1
J	81	86	58	60	6.7	S	60	NW	1966	66	5.8	7	14	10	11	0	8	1	9	0	0	0	998.3
A	82	87	57	60	6.4	N	52	NW	1956	68	5.2	11	11	9	8	0	6	1	8	0	0	0	999.9
S	83	89	60	64	6.8	SE	57	NW	1954	65	5.4	10	9	11	8	0	3	1	3	0	0	0	1000.6
O	79	85	55	61	7.1	SE	38	SE	1955	63	5.0	12	8	11	7	0	2	2	0	0	2	0	1002.8
N	75	79	61	65	9.0	S	60	SE	1952	47	6.6	8	6	16	10	*	1	1	0	*	9	0	1001.3
D	74	77	66	68	9.3	S	61	SW	1953	39	7.2	6	6	19	12	1	1	1	0	4	20	*	1000.8
YR	76	81	59	61	8.4	S	61	NW	FEB 1967	57	6.3	94	103	168	125	5	45	9	25	19	91	2	999.5

FOOTNOTES

Means and extremes above are from existing and comparable exposures. Annual extremes have been ex :r sites in the locality as follows:
Highest temperature 107 in July 1901; maximum monthly precipitation 19.17 in January 1937; minim :cipitation 0.07 in October 1908;
maximum monthly snowfall 24.6 in December 1918+; maximum snowfall in 24 hours 15.0 in December mile wind 68 in May 1915.

Snowfall

Season	July	Aug	Sept	Oct	Nov	Dec	Jan
1936-37	0.0	0.0	0.0	0.0	7.6	1.6	T
1937-38	0.0	0.0	0.0	1.2	T	0.4	0.6
#1938-39	0.0	0.0	0.0	0.0	1.5	T	2.0
1939-40	0.0	0.0	0.0	0.0	T	15.0	8.2
1940-41	0.0	0.0	0.0	0.0	T	0.0	0.3
1941-42	0.0	0.0	0.0	0.0	T	T	5.2
1942-43	0.0	0.0	0.0	T	0.0	7.1	1.5
1943-44	0.0	0.0	0.0	0.0	T	1.0	1.2
#1944-45	0.0	0.0	0.0	0.0	T	2.7	7.2
1945-46	0.0	0.0	0.0	0.0	0.5	6.3	0.3
1946-47	0.0	0.0	0.0	0.0	0.0	2.6	1.7
#1947-48	0.0	0.0	0.0	0.0	T	T	9.0
1948-49	0.0	0.0	0.0	0.0	T	4.0	2.7
1949-50	0.0	0.0	0.0	0.0	T	1.4	T
#1950-51	0.0	0.0	0.0	0.0	4.8	4.8	7.0
1951-52	0.0	0.0	0.0	0.0	0.7	2.3	2.1
1952-53	0.0	0.0	0.0	T	2.3	3.7	4.8
1953-54	0.0	0.0	0.0	0.0	T	2.2	5.3
1954-55	0.0	0.0	0.0	T	T	0.1	6.0
1955-56	0.0	0.0	0.0	0.0	0.3	0.7	9.8
1956-57	0.0	0.0	0.0	0.0	1.2	T	3.2
1957-58	0.0	0.0	0.0	T	T	0.4	3.1
1958-59	0.0	0.0	0.0	0.0	5.5	0.6	1.5
1959-60	0.0	0.0	0.0	0.0	0.6	0.3	0.3
1960-61	0.0	0.0	0.0	0.0	T	9.0	3.8
1961-62	0.0	0.0	0.0	0.0	0.9	9.3	4.8
1962-63	0.0	0.0	0.0	T	T	1.8	6.0
1963-64	0.0	0.0	0.0	0.0	T	7.1	15.1
1964-65	0.0	0.0	0.0	0.0	0.9	0.2	11.8
1965-66	0.0	0.0	0.0	0.0	0.0	T	7.0
1966-67	0.0	0.0	0.0	0.0	13.2	0.5	0.4
1967-68	0.0	0.0	0.0	0.0	T	2.7	13.8
1968-69	0.0	0.0	0.0	0.0	0.3	1.1	3.2
1969-70	0.0	0.0	0.0	0.0	0.7	7.7	7.9
1970-71	0.0	0.0	0.0	0.0	0.3	0.8	3.2
1971-72	0.0	0.0	0.0	0.0	5.4	T	1.6
1972-73	0.0	0.0	0.0	0.0	2.0	2.2	1.1
1973-74	0.0	0.0	0.0	0.0	0.0	4.5	1.0
1974-75	0.0	0.0	0.0	0.0	1.0	1.2	3.0
1975-76	0.0	0.0	0.0	0.0	0.1	0.7	
RECORD MEAN	0.0	0.0	0.0	T	1.4	2.5	4.9

Heating Degree Days

Season	July	Aug	Sept	Oct	Nov	Dec	Jan
1955-56	0	0	4	230	653	919	999
1956-57	0	4	63	131	624	624	1016
1957-58	0	0	22	316	577	712	999
1958-59	0	0	23	229	492	1040	1001
#1959-60	0	0	11	241	642	771	830
1960-61	0	0	10	240	596	1078	1115
1961-62	0	0	30	232	593	877	1065
1962-63	0	0	95	224	617	1071	1200
1963-64	0	1	71	86	493	1178	895
1964-65	0	5	44	349	502	829	943
1965-66	0	2	45	304	526	697	1170
1966-67	0	0	35	324	531	907	882
1967-68	0	0	68	259	660	788	1069
1968-69	0	1	10	276	511	903	987
1969-70	0	0	42	282	645	971	1141
1970-71	0	0	23	220	582	781	1052
1971-72	0	0	13	65	537	610	914
1972-73	0	0	16	298	628	793	927
1973-74	0	0	13	144	450	860	772
1974-75	0	0	122	314	543	794	830
1975-76	0	0	73	205	431	801	

Cooling Degree Days

Year	Jan	Feb	Mar	Apr	May	June	July
1969	0	0	0	9	106	277	431
1970	0	0	0	36	147	244	343
1971	0	0	0	2	35	351	310
1972	0	0	3	25	81	193	386
1973	0	0	7	29	28	325	422
1974	0	0	22	31	109	136	345
1975	0	0	0	24	152	320	402

Feb	Mar	Apr	May	June	Total
6.8	3.8	0.0	0.0	0.0	19.8
T	T	T	0.0	0.0	2.2
6.4	T	T	0.0	0.0	9.9
9.3	T	T	T	0.0	32.5
1.0	0.1	0.0	0.0	0.0	1.4
0.1	T	T	0.0	0.0	5.3
0.7	1.5	0.2	0.0	0.0	11.0
2.0	0.5	T	0.0	0.0	4.7
2.1	0.0	0.0	0.0	0.0	12.0
2.4	T	0.0	0.0	0.0	9.5
5.1	10.8	0.0	T	0.0	20.2
13.1	T	0.0	0.0	0.0	22.1
T	2.6	T	0.0	0.0	9.3
T	0.1	T	0.0	0.0	1.5
7.1	10.7	T	0.0	0.0	34.4
3.3	0.8	T	0.0	0.0	9.2
T	3.1	0.4	0.0	0.0	14.3
T	T	T	0.0	0.0	7.5
1.9	T	T	0.0	0.0	8.0
1.2	1.6	T	0.0	0.0	13.6
T	0.4	0.2	0.0	0.0	5.0
3.4	8.0	0.0	0.0	0.0	14.9
T	T	0.0	0.0	0.0	7.6
10.7	22.9	T	0.0	0.0	34.8
12.5	0.4	0.2	0.0	0.0	25.9
2.5	1.6	1.0	0.0	0.0	20.1
3.4	0.3	0.0	0.0	0.0	11.5
7.7	0.2	0.0	0.0	0.0	30.1
3.9	4.6	0.0	0.0	0.0	21.4
11.4	1.3	0.4	0.0	0.0	20.1
7.8	9.3	0.0	0.0	0.0	31.2
1.8	12.7	0.0	0.0	0.0	31.0
6.3	2.2	0.0	0.0	0.0	13.1
7.4	10.7	T	0.0	0.0	34.4
11.9	5.2	0.1	0.0	0.0	21.5
3.4	1.2	T	0.0	0.0	11.6
1.1	0.5	1.6	0.0	0.0	8.5
0.9	2.8	T	0.0	0.0	9.2
1.3	10.0	T	0.0	0.0	16.5
4.4	4.0	0.1	0.0	0.0	17.3

Average Temperature

Year	Jan	Feb	Mar	Apr	May	June	July	Aug	Sept	Oct	Nov	Dec	Annual
1936	27.8	29.6	50.0	52.0	69.4	76.6	83.3	83.0	73.9	58.4	42.0	39.6	57.1
1937	40.2	35.8	41.6	55.3	65.8	75.1	77.2	79.2	67.9	56.0	43.3	34.4	56.0
1938	34.3	44.2	52.4	59.2	66.2	72.6	78.6	78.4	71.2	60.8	48.6	38.0	58.7
#1939	40.6	38.2	48.6	53.2	67.9	75.8	77.9	76.4	75.6	61.6	44.6	38.6	58.2
1940	20.4	35.3	43.1	53.8	62.6	74.8	78.2	78.6	68.2	63.2	46.6	42.4	55.6
1941	36.1	32.8	40.4	61.0	68.6	75.6	79.0	78.3	74.2	63.8	47.6	42.0	58.3
1942	32.8	33.2	48.6	59.5	65.5	74.4	79.7	76.2	68.6	59.1	49.1	34.2	56.7
1943	36.1	39.2	42.2	53.0	68.0	77.6	78.3	79.0	67.4	58.2	44.5	35.0	56.6
1944	38.4	41.2	43.2	56.2	72.2	79.7	79.0	76.8	69.4	58.9	47.2	32.0	57.8
#1945	30.4	34.7	57.0	58.2	62.2	72.0	75.0	75.6	72.2	56.4	47.0	30.2	56.1
1946	35.0	38.7	56.3	58.0	63.0	74.0	76.1	70.7	69.0	60.1	49.7	41.6	57.7
#1947	39.0	28.1	37.1	57.0	62.4	72.5	72.4	81.0	69.8	65.0	42.7	38.0	55.4
1948	25.5	37.2	48.8	59.8	65.1	75.2	78.0	76.2	70.4	55.5	49.0	40.1	56.7
1949	41.6	41.4	46.2	54.4	67.8	75.6	81.1	76.4	64.6	62.2	46.6	41.5	58.3
#1950	44.6	39.0	42.5	52.3	67.0	73.1	74.7	73.1	67.6	62.3	40.5	30.5	55.6
1951	35.7	36.5	43.0	53.4	66.6	74.3	77.7	77.1	67.4	59.4	39.4	38.2	55.7
1952	39.2	40.7	45.4	55.7	65.7	80.6	80.7	77.4	68.8	51.9	46.8	39.2	57.7
1953	40.0	41.0	47.7	53.1	69.0	78.7	78.8	77.3	70.4	60.4	46.4	36.4	58.3
1954	36.0	44.6	43.7	62.1	61.1	77.3	81.4	77.8	74.2	59.3	46.1	37.0	58.4
1955	33.6	37.6	47.4	61.8	67.7	69.7	81.3	80.1	73.4	58.3	43.3	35.2	57.5
1956	32.5	41.3	46.1	54.0	65.7	73.9	76.9	75.2	66.2	61.1	44.0	44.7	56.8
1957	32.0	41.7	44.9	59.1	66.2	74.8	77.6	75.5	69.9	54.6	45.6	41.8	57.0
1958	32.5	27.6	40.5	57.1	66.3	72.4	78.2	76.4	70.2	58.3	48.8	31.1	54.9
1959	32.5	38.9	44.7	58.7	70.8	75.9	79.8	80.6	73.7	59.1	43.3	39.9	58.2
#1960	38.0	33.8	32.5	60.6	63.9	71.0	74.2	76.9	70.5	57.5	45.0	29.9	54.5
1961	28.8	39.1	47.6	49.2	59.0	68.9	76.5	75.1	73.0	57.9	45.2	36.4	54.7
1962	30.5	39.1	42.3	53.1	71.4	73.4	76.2	76.4	65.0	59.3	44.2	30.3	55.1
1963	26.1	30.2	49.5	59.0	63.3	73.0	74.8	73.4	66.8	63.5	48.4	26.7	54.6
1964	35.9	33.4	45.3	58.4	66.8	75.1	76.4	76.2	69.1	53.4	48.0	38.0	56.3
1965	34.3	35.9	38.9	58.3	70.0	73.4	76.3	75.2	70.5	55.7	47.3	42.3	56.5
1966	27.1	34.1	46.1	53.4	62.3	73.1	81.1	75.6	67.4	54.6	47.2	35.6	54.8
1967	36.3	30.9	50.6	59.7	62.4	73.4	74.5	72.2	65.7	57.2	42.7	39.4	55.4
1968	30.3	30.1	45.7	56.8	63.4	74.0	77.7	77.9	69.0	57.4	48.0	35.7	55.5
1969	33.1	36.9	39.9	58.0	66.2	73.5	78.7	74.7	67.5	57.3	43.3	33.5	55.2
1970	27.9	33.6	42.3	59.3	67.2	72.9	75.8	76.0	73.4	58.1	45.3	39.6	56.0
1971	30.9	35.0	42.0	54.7	61.5	76.5	74.8	74.1	72.2	64.4	47.0	45.1	56.5
1972	35.2	34.9	44.8	56.2	65.5	70.6	77.1	76.1	72.3	55.3	44.0	39.1	55.9
1973	35.0	36.4	53.7	54.4	61.5	75.6	78.4	77.0	73.6	62.3	49.8	37.1	57.9
1974	39.8	39.3	49.8	57.2	65.1	68.7	75.9	75.0	63.2	54.9	47.0	39.1	56.3
1975	38.1	40.2	43.3	54.4	69.0	75.4	77.7	79.3	66.2	59.4	50.6	38.9	57.7
RECORD MEAN	34.7	36.8	45.6	56.3	66.0	74.6	78.3	76.8	70.4	58.9	46.4	37.2	56.9
MAX	42.6	45.2	54.8	66.2	76.1	84.4	88.1	86.6	80.5	69.3	55.0	45.0	66.2
MIN	26.7	28.3	36.3	46.4	55.9	64.8	68.5	66.9	60.2	48.5	37.8	29.4	47.5

# Indicates a station move or relocation of instruments.

LOUISVILLE, KY

Feb	Mar	Apr	May	June	Total
680	584	348	90	30	4537
644	618	264	86	0	4074
1041	754	247	59	2	4729
723	627	222	51	0	4408
897	1002	197	151	6	4748
721	536	477	193	23	4989
720	694	385	16	0	4612
968	476	231	109	1	4992
910	603	215	55	7	4514
808	802	223	20	0	4525
857	580	353	127	8	4669
949	453	209	139	13	4442
1007	590	247	98	4	4790
778	771	213	61	14	4525
875	697	200	70	0	4923
833	707	303	137	0	4638
866	623	282	61	19	3990
796	349	343	129	0	4279
714	487	257	99	19	3815
688	665	333	22	0	4311

Aug	Sept	Oct	Nov	Dec	Total
308	127	49	0	0	1307
346	283	15	0	0	1414
291	237	58	3	0	1287
351	242	2	4	0	1287
380	280	71	2	0	1544
319	75	8	10	0	1055
451	116	36	5	0	1506

Precipitation

Year	Jan	Feb	Mar	Apr	May	June	July	Aug	Sept	Oct	Nov	Dec	Annual
1936	1.59	2.10	2.99	4.10	1.09	0.35	1.81	2.21	3.50	3.25	4.11	2.77	29.87
1937	19.17	1.65	0.76	4.06	3.84	4.14	0.93	4.27	1.09	4.48	1.66	3.58	49.63
1938	2.47	2.16	6.76	2.01	4.66	2.23	6.95	3.79	2.99	0.49	3.13	1.38	39.02
#1939	4.42	6.95	7.11	4.96	0.96	7.00	5.91	2.98	1.20	1.38	1.16	2.43	46.46
1940	1.56	5.23	5.34	7.21	2.48	1.59	1.36	1.59	0.97	0.54	3.98	3.10	34.95
1941	2.32	0.45	1.20	2.77	1.25	6.82	2.36	1.91	0.64	5.80	1.84	3.41	30.77
1942	2.58	2.58	4.48	3.73	3.43	8.48	1.96	6.10	3.55	1.80	5.99	4.80	49.48
1943	1.35	1.27	10.02	3.04	4.91	3.81	2.35	0.50	1.92	1.12	0.73	1.75	32.77
1944	1.13	3.34	4.72	6.47	4.34	0.49	3.80	5.69	4.94	0.44	1.51	3.91	40.78
#1945	1.88	5.68	10.23	3.93	4.46	5.80	2.51	1.68	3.49	2.13	5.23	2.34	49.36
1946	2.52	6.17	4.91	2.39	5.11	4.75	3.11	4.26	1.34	2.16	4.33	2.94	43.99
#1947	5.31	0.40	2.20	6.26	6.04	4.03	4.22	1.75	2.86	2.74	2.30	1.86	39.97
1948	2.54	4.61	7.15	6.39	2.63	2.03	3.74	1.34	1.47	2.19	8.13	3.05	45.27
1949	7.10	4.06	5.65	3.07	3.14	6.78	2.78	3.47	0.91	3.33	1.56	4.84	46.69
#1950	11.38	5.72	2.80	3.17	9.04	7.01	5.51	3.02	3.06	0.99	5.03	2.66	59.39
1951	7.83	3.36	5.75	2.88	3.89	4.45	2.89	2.66	3.15	3.27	4.17	6.85	51.15
1952	5.11	2.90	5.99	1.85	2.73	4.18	1.21	2.39	1.75	2.01	2.79	4.67	37.58
1953	3.68	0.87	4.71	4.30	4.32	1.68	5.40	0.23	0.27	0.80	1.90	2.22	30.38
1954	4.21	2.02	1.25	3.05	1.86	0.81	1.18	4.51	5.16	3.86	1.16	3.87	32.94
1955	1.80	6.93	5.96	4.40	5.77	3.38	3.30	0.26	4.47	4.44	3.73	1.11	45.55
1956	2.87	8.34	4.50	2.63	3.98	2.38	2.59	4.03	3.70	1.74	1.52	2.74	41.02
1957	2.83	2.83	1.66	6.09	5.78	6.57	4.28	1.01	2.80	2.26	9.12	4.88	50.11
1958	2.91	1.36	3.13	5.38	3.03	3.84	7.05	3.45	4.07	1.65	2.77	1.19	39.83
1959	5.51	2.76	2.13	1.68	4.42	1.11	2.61	5.20	0.48	3.26	4.15	3.77	37.08
1960	2.55	4.31	2.42	1.17	3.52	10.11	1.99	1.79	3.00	1.58	3.35	2.88	38.67
1961	1.57	5.24	7.63	4.83	9.00	3.59	5.16	1.56	1.48	2.00	4.23	3.75	50.04
1962	4.03	6.58	3.58	1.01	3.33	4.75	1.84	2.20	3.56	4.70	1.59	2.74	39.91
1963	1.18	1.11	9.04	1.87	4.56	4.18	7.33	2.13	3.48	0.81	1.69	1.06	38.44
1964	2.45	2.45	14.91	3.06	1.85	2.24	3.03	2.63	4.16	0.62	3.32	5.86	46.58
1965	2.76	4.67	4.82	3.28	1.60	2.27	4.86	2.12	8.41	2.54	1.33	1.14	39.80
1966	5.73	5.01	1.02	9.56	3.91	0.75	2.13	5.18	2.59	1.04	3.67	4.33	44.92
1967	1.11	2.01	4.37	4.39	4.62	4.41	7.33	4.30	1.73	3.06	3.08	3.51	43.92
1968	2.13	0.80	6.23	3.94	5.16	1.70	3.07	3.68	2.61	1.00	3.34	3.62	37.28
1969	5.31	1.65	1.94	3.77	3.91	2.97	4.05	3.65	1.08	1.69	3.08	3.69	36.79
1970	1.40	2.87	4.52	11.10	1.85	5.20	3.33	7.65	3.57	4.79	1.75	4.18	52.21
1971	2.64	6.28	2.12	2.16	6.15	2.64	6.74	1.83	4.72	1.96	2.06	2.98	42.28
1972	2.87	3.94	4.07	8.48	4.46	1.08	3.64	2.45	4.24	2.55	6.31	5.29	49.38
1973	1.96	1.60	6.26	5.77	7.04	6.20	9.38	0.91	2.34	2.28	7.59	2.64	53.97
1974	4.38	1.64	5.41	2.74	3.86	2.58	2.04	8.79	3.52	2.09	3.03	2.85	42.93
1975	4.87	4.53	9.65	6.47	4.50	3.15	1.91	3.89	2.64	6.12	3.69	4.89	56.31
RECORD MEAN	3.91	3.41	4.61	3.98	3.88	3.85	3.71	3.25	2.76	2.56	3.45	3.57	42.94

Record mean values above are means through the current year for the period beginning in 1873 for temperature and precipitation, 1948 for snowfall. Data are from City Office locations through June 1945.

NEW ORLEANS, LOUISIANA

The New Orleans metropolitan area is virtually surrounded by water. Lake Pontchartrain, some 610 square miles in area, borders the city on the north and is connected to the Gulf of Mexico through Lake Borgne on the east. In other directions there are bayous, lakes and marshy delta land. The proximity of the Gulf of Mexico also has a great influence on the climate. Elevations in the city vary from a few feet below to a few feet above mean sea level. A massive levee system surrounding the city and along the Mississippi River offers protection against flooding from the river and tidal surges. The New Orleans International Airport is located 12 miles west of downtown New Orleans, between the Mississippi River and Lake Pontchartrain.

The climate of the city can best be described as humid with the surrounding water modifying the temperature and decreasing the range between the extremes. Almost daily sporadic afternoon thunderstorms from mid-June through September keep the temperature from rising much above 90 degrees F. There is only an average of about seven days per year when the temperature reaches 95 degrees F. or higher, while 102 degrees F is the warmest, occurring most recently on June 30, 1954. From about mid-November to mid-March, the area is subjected alternately to the southerly flow of warm tropical air and to the northerly flow of cold continental air in periods of varying lengths. The usual track of winter storms is to the north of New Orleans; but occasionally one moves this far south, bringing large and rather sudden drops in temperature. However, the cold spells seldom last over three or four days. The lowest temperature of record was 7 degrees F on February 13, 1899. In about two-thirds of the years, the annual lowest temperature is 24 degrees F or warmer, with some years entirely above freezing.

During the winter and spring, the cold Mississippi River water enhances the formation of river fogs, particularly when light southerly winds bring warm moist air into the area from the Gulf of Mexico. The nearby lakes and marshes also contribute to fog formation. Even so, the fog usually does not seriously affect automobile traffic except for brief periods. However, air travel will be suspended for several hours and river traffic, at times, will be unable to move between New Orleans and the Gulf for several days.

Rather frequent and sometimes very heavy rains are typical for this area. During the past 100 years, an average of 120 days of measurable rain per year occurred at the official observation site in the city with the annual amount averaging 60.44 inches.

A fairly definite rainy period is from mid-December to mid-March. Precipitation during this period is most likely to be steady rain of two to three days duration, instead of showery type. April,

Station: NEW ORLEANS, LOUISIANA
NEW ORLEANS INT'L AP
Elevation (ground): 4 feet

TEMPERATURES °F

Month	Normal			Extremes			
	Daily maximum	Daily minimum	Monthly	Record highest	Year	Record lowest	Year
(a)				29		29	
J	62.3	43.5	52.9	83	1957	14	1963
F	65.1	46.0	55.6	85	1972	19	1970
M	70.4	50.9	60.7	87	1963	26	1968
A	78.4	58.8	68.6	91	1948	32	1971
M	84.9	65.3	75.1	96	1953	41	1960
J	89.6	71.2	80.4	100	1954	55	1972
J	90.4	73.3	81.9	99	1951	60	1967
A	90.6	73.1	81.9	100	1951	60	1968
S	86.6	69.7	78.2	97	1954	42	1967
O	79.9	59.6	69.8	92	1962	35	1968
N	70.3	49.8	60.1	86	1973	24	1970
D	64.2	45.3	54.8	84	1971	17	1962
YR	77.7	58.9	68.3	100	JUN 1954	14	JAN 1963

IMPORTANT:
The time-period covered by this record is limited: See footnotes following table of **NORMALS, MEANS AND EXTREMES** for explanation and for additional history of **EXTREME HIGHS AND LOWS** recorded in the general area.

(Continued)

May, October and November are generally dry; but there have been some extremely heavy showers in those months. The greatest 24-hour amount of precipitation since 1871 was 14.01 inches April 15-16, 1972 while 13.68 inches fell October 1-2, 1937. The heaviest recorded rate of rainfall in New Orleans was 1 inch in 5 minutes measured during a thunderstorm February 5, 1955. Snowfall is rather infrequent and light. However, 8.2 inches fell February 14-15, 1895; and 4.5 inches fell on December 31, 1963.

While thunder occurs with most of the showers in the area, thunderstorms with damaging winds are infrequent. hail of a damaging nature seldom occurs, and tornadoes are extremely rare. However, waterspouts are observed quite often on nearby lakes.

The city has been hard hit by three hurricanes since 1900. On September 29, 1915; September 19, 1945 and September 9, 1965, intense hurricanes moved over the area and caused loss of life and tremendous property damage. The most recent one, Hurricane Betsy, 1965, brought destruction from wind and water to the New Orleans metropolitan area. Fifty deaths from drowning were attributable to the storm surge. A sustained wind of 125 mph with higher gusts were estimated atop of the Federal Building. Several other tropical storms and hurricanes have affected the area this century, but to a much lesser extent.

The lower Mississippi River floods result from runoff upstream. If the water level in the river becomes dangerously high, the spillways upriver can be opened to divert the floodwaters. Rainfall in the New Orleans area is pumped into the surrounding lakes and bayous. Local street and minor urban flooding of short duration result from occasional downpours.

Air pollution is not a serious problem. The area is not highly industrialized, and long periods of air stagnation are rare.

Normals, Means, and Extremes

(To better understand these tables, see full explanation of terms beginning on page 322)

Month	Normal Degree days Base 65 °F: Heating	Normal Degree days Base 65 °F: Cooling	Precipitation in inches — Water equivalent: Normal	Maximum monthly	Year	Minimum monthly	Year	Maximum in 24 hrs.	Year	Snow, Ice pellets: Maximum monthly	Year	Maximum in 24 hrs.	Year
(a)				29		29		29		29		29	
J	403	28	4.53	12.62	1966	0.54	1968	4.77	1955	0.1	1973	0.1	1973
F	299	37	4.82	10.56	1959	1.02	1962	5.60	1961	2.0	1958	2.0	1958
M	188	53	5.49	19.09	1948	0.24	1955	7.87	1948	T	1959	T	1959
A	29	137	4.15	10.47	1973	0.33	1965	4.35	1953	0.0		0.0	
M	0	313	4.20	14.33	1959	0.99	1949	9.86	1959	0.0		0.0	
J	0	462	4.74	12.28	1975	1.12	1952	4.19	1953	0.0		0.0	
J	0	524	6.72	11.46	1954	3.45	1951	4.30	1966	0.0		0.0	
A	0	524	5.27	11.77	1955	2.00	1952	4.82	1975	0.0		0.0	
S	0	396	5.58	16.74	1971	0.24	1953	6.50	1971	0.0		0.0	
O	40	189	2.26	6.45	1959	0.00	1952	3.44	1975	0.0		0.0	
N	179	32	3.88	14.58	1947	0.21	1949	8.72	1975	T	1950	T	1950
D	327	11	5.13	10.77	1967	1.46	1958	4.85	1973	2.7	1963	2.7	1963
YR	1465	2706	56.77	19.09	MAR 1948	0.00	OCT 1952	9.86	MAY 1959	2.7	DEC 1963	2.7	DEC 1963

Month	Relative humidity pct. Hour 00	Hour 06	Hour 12	Hour 18 (Local time)	Wind: Mean speed m.p.h.	Prevailing direction	Fastest mile: Speed m.p.h.	Direction	Year	Pct. of possible sunshine	Mean sky cover, tenths, sunrise to sunset	Mean number of days — Sunrise to sunset: Clear	Partly cloudy	Cloudy	Precipitation .01 inch or more	Snow, Ice pellets 1.0 inch or more	Thunderstorms	Heavy fog, visibility ¼ mile or less	Temperatures °F Max. (b) 90° and above	Max. 32° and below	Min. 32° and below	Min. 0° and below	Average station pressure mb. Elev. 30 feet m.s.l.
(a)	27	27	27	27	27		16	16		2	27	27	27	27	27	27	27	27	29	29	29	29	3
J	84	86	67	73	9.5		46	21	1975	38	6.7	7	7	17	10	0	2	7	0	*	5	0	1018.9
F	82	85	63	68	10.1		43	26	1970	60	6.2	8	6	14	10	*	3	4	0	0	3	0	1018.3
M	83	85	61	65	10.3		37	18	1969	56	6.2	8	9	14	9	0	4	4	0	0	1	0	1014.3
A	85	88	61	66	9.8		35	07	1960	61	5.7	8	11	11	7	0	4	2	*	0	*	0	1016.1
M	86	89	60	65	8.3		55	36	1973	53	5.2	10	12	9	7	0	6	1	3	0	0	0	1013.0
J	87	89	62	67	7.0		48	05	1971	60	5.1	10	13	7	10	0	9	*	16	0	0	0	1014.3
J	89	91	66	73	6.3		36	24	1973	52	6.2	5	15	11	15	0	16	*	20	0	0	0	1015.3
A	89	91	66	73	6.1		42	33	1969	51	5.5	8	14	9	13	0	13	*	19	0	0	0	1016.0
S	87	89	66	75	7.5		69	09	1965	62	5.3	10	11	9	10	0	7	*	8	0	0	0	1014.3
O	85	88	59	73	7.6		40	17	1964	71	4.1	16	7	8	6	0	2	2	1	0	0	0	1018.2
N	84	86	60	74	8.9		30	31	1969	60	5.0	11	9	10	7	0	2	4	0	0	1	0	1019.0
D	84	86	67	75	9.2		46	28	1973	53	6.2	8	8	15	10	*	2	6	0	*	4	0	1019.1
YR	85	88	63	71	8.4		69	09	SEP 1965	57	5.6	109	122	134	114	*	69	31	67	*	13	0	1016.4

FOOTNOTES

Means and extremes above are from existing and comparable exposures. Annual extremes have been exceeded at other sites in the locality as follows: Highest temperature 102 in June 1954 and earlier (City Office); lowest temperature 7 in February 1899; maximum monthly precipitation 25.11 in October 1937; maximum precipitation in 24 hours 14.01 in April 1927; maximum monthly snowfall 8.2 in February 1895; maximum snowfall in 24 hours 8.2 in February 1895.

Snowfall

Season	July	Aug	Sept	Oct	Nov	Dec	Jan
1970-71	0.0	0.0	0.0	0.0	0.0	0.0	0.0
1971-72	0.0	0.0	0.0	0.0	0.0	0.0	0.0
1972-73	0.0	0.0	0.0	0.0	0.0	0.0	0.1
1973-74	0.0	0.0	0.0	0.0	0.0	T	0.0
1974-75	0.0	0.0	0.0	0.0	0.0	0.0	0.0
1975-76	0.0	0.0	0.0	0.0	0.0	0.0	
RECORD MEAN	0.0	0.0	0.0	0.0	T	0.1	T

Heating Degree Days

Season	July	Aug	Sept	Oct	Nov	Dec	Jan
1955-56	0	0	0	50	207	314	414
1956-57	0	0	0	0	215	158	218
1957-58	0	0	5	72	149	302	502
1958-59	0	0	0	28	119	378	454
1959-60	0	0	0	13	244	295	419
1960-61	0	0	0	30	132	406	539
1961-62	0	0	0	26	173	306	467
1962-63	0	0	0	24	211	427	540
1963-64	0	0	0	9	170	583	459
1964-65	0	0	0	73	163	297	315
1965-66	0	0	0	54	84	339	560
1966-67	0	0	0	33	150	376	390
1967-68	0	0	20	56	187	265	407
1968-69	0	0	0	55	303	435	353
1969-70	0	0	0	19	224	330	561
1970-71	0	0	0	24	284	248	329
1971-72	0	0	0	10	208	137	245
1972-73	0	0	0	28	293	314	447
1973-74	0	0	0	18	80	355	117
1974-75	0	0	0	24	194	341	270
1975-76	0	0	6	16	222	417	

Cooling Degree Days

Year	Jan	Feb	Mar	Apr	May	June	July
1969	28	17	1	133	266	462	537
1970	20	0	25	200	297	442	520
1971	29	25	44	151	252	456	514
1972	50	26	38	175	281	479	453
1973	0	9	96	99	247	507	607
1974	71	27	147	144	345	402	484
1975	34	45	80	132	321	440	479

Feb	Mar	Apr	May	June	Total
0.0	0.0	0.0	0.0	0.0	0.0
0.0	0.0	0.0	0.0	0.0	0.0
0.6	0.0	0.0	0.0	0.0	0.7
0.0	0.0	0.0	0.0	0.0	T
0.0	0.0	0.0	0.0	0.0	0.0
0.1	T	0.0	0.0	0.0	0.2

Average Temperature

Year	Jan	Feb	Mar	Apr	May	June	July	Aug	Sept	Oct	Nov	Dec	Annual
1936	54.5	54.1	65.8	67.8	76.2	83.8	83.6	83.2	82.7	72.8	60.4	56.2	70.1
1937	65.5	56.2	58.7	69.2	77.5	81.6	83.8	83.0	79.6	69.7	57.7	54.4	69.7
1938	55.0	60.8	70.4	68.6	76.6	82.4	82.8	84.6	79.4	72.8	62.1	55.6	70.9
#1939	59.0	60.2	66.0	68.4	74.9	81.9	82.8	82.2	80.6	72.2	59.4	56.9	70.4
1940	42.2	52.2	62.0	67.4	74.4	80.0	81.4	81.6	77.4	71.5	60.8	58.6	67.5
1941	54.6	52.4	56.4	70.4	76.0	80.4	82.6	83.9	80.6	77.6	59.8	57.8	69.4
1942	50.0	51.9	60.4	68.4	74.9	80.6	82.8	81.6	77.4	72.9	63.6	56.8	68.4
1943	54.7	57.0	59.7	69.8	78.8	82.9	83.0	83.8	76.2	68.1	59.0	54.6	69.0
1944	53.4	63.8	63.8	68.8	75.7	83.8	83.2	83.4	81.0	71.0	63.1	54.1	70.4
1945	53.4	60.8	69.5	70.8	74.4	81.8	81.0	82.9	80.8	70.6	64.9	51.2	70.2
#1946	54.2	57.8	65.2	71.4	74.6	78.4	81.8	82.4	77.2	71.4	65.2	56.9	69.7
1947	55.4	49.4	55.8	70.0	75.3	81.6	81.2	82.3	80.2	75.4	59.6	55.3	68.5
1948	46.0	58.2	64.6	72.0	76.6	82.4	83.0	81.7	75.8	68.8	62.8	59.8	69.3
1949	59.8	61.9	61.8	67.3	76.4	81.4	82.2	82.2	78.7	74.6	59.2	59.0	70.4
1950	67.1	60.8	59.3	64.8	76.3	81.4	80.7	81.5	79.2	71.2	57.1	52.5	69.3
1951	55.6	56.6	62.5	66.5	74.7	81.4	83.2	85.8	80.0	72.6	56.8	59.8	69.6
1952	62.3	58.8	60.2	65.6	75.0	82.1	81.6	82.5	77.7	63.7	58.1	54.3	68.5
1953	56.8	56.4	67.1	68.1	77.9	83.5	82.2	82.0	79.2	70.4	59.7	52.3	70.3
1954	55.4	59.8	60.2	71.3	71.2	80.9	82.4	82.8	80.7	71.1	58.7	54.6	69.1
1955	53.2	58.0	65.3	71.4	78.3	78.8	81.2	82.7	80.7	69.3	60.1	55.5	69.5
1956	51.7	61.2	62.5	67.7	77.1	78.7	81.9	81.6	77.8	72.0	60.2	61.1	69.5
1957	60.0	63.7	61.3	69.4	76.9	80.6	84.2	81.8	76.7	66.8	61.8	55.2	69.9
1958	48.6	48.5	58.7	69.3	75.7	81.4	81.8	81.8	80.1	69.6	63.2	52.7	67.6
1959	50.3	57.2	60.0	67.9	77.1	81.3	82.0	82.7	79.9	73.1	58.5	55.6	68.8
1960	51.8	49.6	56.2	67.5	71.4	80.1	83.9	81.3	78.2	70.5	61.4	52.1	67.0
1961	47.4	58.1	64.6	64.7	72.7	77.3	79.7	79.7	78.1	68.0	61.1	56.2	67.3
1962	50.5	63.9	57.9	65.8	76.1	79.3	83.7	82.3	78.5	71.6	57.9	51.0	68.2
1963	47.5	48.2	65.6	72.6	75.2	79.5	81.2	81.6	77.7	70.0	60.3	46.1	67.1
1964	50.0	49.8	60.5	70.6	74.6	78.9	80.6	81.7	77.0	64.8	61.8	56.4	67.2
1965	54.9	54.4	58.9	70.9	75.5	78.5	81.0	77.7	76.2	66.7	64.5	54.0	67.8
1966	46.9	52.0	59.0	68.7	75.0	77.1	82.2	80.4	77.0	68.9	61.6	53.3	66.9
1967	52.5	52.5	63.2	72.2	73.8	81.6	80.5	80.0	75.1	65.6	60.3	58.2	68.0
1968	51.6	47.2	55.9	68.1	74.1	80.4	82.4	81.0	75.4	68.5	55.5	50.8	65.9
1969	54.2	54.6	53.8	68.8	73.3	80.3	82.1	80.1	76.7	71.1	58.5	54.5	67.3
1970	47.3	51.7	60.1	70.7	74.2	79.6	81.6	81.5	80.1	68.7	55.4	57.9	67.4
1971	55.1	53.9	59.2	66.9	72.9	80.0	81.4	81.1	78.9	71.7	59.2	63.4	68.6
1972	58.6	56.1	61.9	69.8	73.9	80.8	79.4	81.1	79.6	70.4	56.6	55.3	68.6
1973	50.3	52.6	65.5	64.2	72.5	81.7	84.4	81.7	79.7	73.4	66.6	54.1	68.9
1974	63.3	55.9	67.3	69.0	75.8	78.1	80.3	80.4	77.0	66.9	59.8	55.3	69.1
1975	57.2	58.9	61.4	66.8	75.1	79.4	80.2	80.5	75.1	69.9	61.2	51.9	68.2
RECORD MEAN	54.3	56.5	61.7	68.9	75.4	80.8	82.2	82.0	78.8	70.7	60.7	55.6	69.0
MAX	62.9	65.6	70.8	77.9	84.3	89.5	90.4	90.1	86.6	79.8	70.0	64.4	77.7
MIN	45.6	47.3	52.5	59.8	66.4	72.1	74.0	73.9	70.9	61.6	51.4	46.7	60.2

# Indicates a station move or relocation of instruments.

NEW ORLEANS, LA

Feb	Mar	Apr	May	June	Total
170	124	40	0	0	1319
109	136	37	1	0	874
459	199	23	0	0	1711
241	162	29	0	0	1411
440	292	35	26	0	1764
216	97	88	2	0	1510
98	250	87	0	0	1407
469	91	6	0	0	1768
432	180	29	0	0	1862
316	231	11	1	0	1407
361	201	31	0	0	1630
353	129	2	3	0	1436
511	303	29	2	0	1780
304	339	12	0	0	1801
367	171	24	5	0	1701
328	216	88	2	0	1519
278	126	25	0	0	1029
351	72	114	9	0	1628
274	71	16	0	0	931
210	183	73	0	0	1295

Aug	Sept	Oct	Nov	Dec	Total
474	360	213	34	9	2534
520	460	148	2	32	2666
508	424	221	40	92	2756
507	446	200	48	19	2722
524	448	289	136	24	2986
484	368	93	45	45	2655
491	314	171	114	16	2637

Precipitation

Year	Jan	Feb	Mar	Apr	May	June	July	Aug	Sept	Oct	Nov	Dec	Annual
1936	8.78	5.46	2.25	6.55	3.97	0.71	8.43	7.48	6.75	3.49	3.06	3.86	60.79
1937	3.93	2.15	5.58	7.42	3.36	8.87	3.38	7.94	6.24	25.11	1.45	3.97	79.40
1938	5.27	1.50	0.91	2.93	3.60	2.57	7.85	3.35	4.54	0.96	2.10	4.59	40.17
#1939	2.24	4.20	1.20	3.05	12.72	6.38	4.39	4.66	2.16	0.88	2.24	1.82	45.94
1940	3.28	7.51	4.09	7.01	1.04	7.27	15.21	7.57	4.79	0.70	1.31	7.31	67.09
1941	3.03	2.64	2.74	1.93	1.17	6.58	6.23	5.76	4.73	4.08	1.78	2.55	43.22
1942	0.63	10.10	6.64	1.53	4.33	10.95	4.16	7.79	5.48	2.09	2.29	4.66	60.65
1943	2.28	1.51	7.34	2.26	2.06	3.71	6.84	1.28	10.26	2.12	1.73	4.63	46.02
1944	7.16	3.66	6.23	7.90	3.24	1.80	2.71	3.33	3.62	1.30	12.82	2.87	56.64
1945	3.88	4.86	1.81	4.53	2.12	4.06	16.87	3.74	7.37	3.21	2.48	5.94	60.87
#1946	5.06	3.59	15.76	3.32	13.53	11.29	4.58	7.33	8.35	0.31	3.79	3.24	80.15
1947	8.30	2.84	6.24	7.38	4.11	3.65	4.18	4.23	3.40	1.66	14.58	9.59	70.16
1948	5.72	1.96	19.09	1.49	1.74	1.28	4.48	5.79	13.53	1.07	13.72	5.31	75.18
1949	2.78	2.85	8.13	8.78	0.99	4.37	6.01	3.63	5.19	4.27	0.21	5.36	52.57
1950	3.93	4.08	5.63	7.30	2.76	5.97	7.20	4.34	0.98	1.18	0.91	6.12	50.40
1951	5.49	1.98	7.74	7.79	1.66	2.98	3.45	4.93	7.04	1.11	3.00	3.17	50.34
1952	2.70	8.06	5.06	4.82	5.79	1.12	6.23	2.00	2.81	0.00	3.00	6.86	48.45
1953	2.56	7.10	3.53	5.94	1.39	7.22	10.44	4.88	0.24	0.51	10.39	8.93	63.13
1954	3.96	1.34	2.22	2.29	4.45	3.16	11.46	5.40	6.66	5.46	2.04	6.04	54.48
1955	7.13	5.16	0.24	4.81	5.38	4.42	9.96	11.77	4.53	0.90	2.74	2.81	59.85
1956	2.37	7.27	3.66	4.16	2.37	6.68	6.65	4.99	8.02	1.90	1.78	6.49	56.34
1957	1.55	2.88	8.19	6.79	1.24	7.41	5.12	7.57	10.21	2.15	4.15	3.09	60.35
1958	6.78	3.96	6.98	2.00	6.70	2.81	9.12	3.19	6.57	0.89	1.10	1.46	51.56
1959	3.71	10.56	3.82	3.18	14.33	6.76	7.96	4.53	3.47	6.45	1.14	2.58	68.49
1960	3.34	4.77	3.68	5.69	3.30	1.68	4.26	6.51	4.11	4.90	0.60	4.17	47.01
1961	6.94	9.00	8.53	2.88	6.46	8.01	10.38	7.26	8.90	0.51	8.66	6.01	83.54
1962	4.19	1.02	1.60	2.66	1.31	8.87	4.70	2.41	2.52	3.29	1.96	4.47	39.00
1963	5.21	5.90	1.00	1.84	3.17	4.16	6.40	2.12	7.35	T	7.85	5.25	50.25
1964	9.60	5.35	5.45	5.66	1.69	5.52	5.90	3.88	4.93	3.50	3.51	3.10	58.09
1965	4.48	5.25	1.95	0.33	3.62	2.21	5.26	6.34	10.03	1.03	1.49	7.35	49.34
1966	12.62	10.11	1.90	4.92	9.31	2.10	9.42	2.84	5.55	3.15	0.72	5.44	68.08
1967	4.22	6.80	1.60	2.18	3.56	2.40	6.42	7.51	3.73	3.79	0.45	10.77	53.43
1968	0.54	3.02	3.49	3.59	4.13	3.69	4.96	4.78	2.44	1.40	4.97	6.14	43.15
1969	3.12	4.80	7.08	6.04	5.51	2.47	6.64	7.80	1.08	0.51	1.73	5.26	52.04
1970	2.53	2.28	7.22	0.43	4.68	4.97	3.70	10.21	4.25	4.94	0.85	4.28	50.34
1971	1.13	4.87	3.61	1.53	1.38	8.02	4.55	5.75	16.74	0.58	2.63	6.64	57.43
1972	6.98	6.03	6.07	1.64	6.31	3.10	3.90	4.92	3.29	4.64	8.45	8.65	63.98
1973	2.68	5.40	12.17	10.47	4.68	6.08	5.94	3.37	11.07	5.07	4.04	8.31	79.28
1974	8.46	5.53	6.64	5.52	9.84	3.83	5.66	6.70	7.58	2.26	5.88	4.89	72.79
1975	2.95	3.64	5.32	6.69	8.03	12.28	8.35	10.11	3.97	4.00	11.35	3.81	80.50
RECORD MEAN	4.58	4.63	5.38	4.54	4.80	4.74	6.81	5.79	5.58	2.99	4.03	5.06	58.93

Record mean values above are means through the current year for the period beginning in 1947. Data are from the City Office through June 1939 and from the Airport Office thereafter.

SHREVEPORT, LOUISIANA

Shreveport is located on the west side of the Red River, opposite Bossier City, in the northwestern section of Louisiana, some 30 miles south of Arkansas and 15 miles east of Texas. A portion of the city is situated in the Red River bottom lands and the remainder in gently rolling hills that begin about one mile west of the river. The NOAA National Weather service Office is at the Shreveport Regional Airport, about seven miles southwest of the downtown area. Elevations in the Shreveport area range from about 170 to 280 feet above sea level.

The climate of Shreveport is transitional between the subtropical humid type prevalent to the south and the continental climates of the Great Plains and Middle West to the north. During winter, masses of moderate to severely cold air move periodically through the area. Rainfall is abundant with the normal annual total more than 46 inches. Amounts are substantial from late autumn to spring and there is a summer-early autumn minimum, with monthly averages less than three inches in August, September, and October.

The majority of rainfall is of convective and airmass types — showery and brief — except during winter when nearly continuous frontal rains may persist for a few days. Extremes of precipitation occur at all seasons; and, although torrential rainfall is exceptional in the Shreveport area, 12.44 inches fell in 24-hour period on July 24/25, 1933, and 19.08 inches fell over a three-day period on July 23, 24, and 25th, 1933. The July 1933 monthly total was a substantial 25.45 inches. The greatest annual rainfall of record was in 1957, when 67.23 inches was recorded, and the driest year of record was 1899, when only 23.10 inches fell.

The winter months are normally mild with cold spells generally of short duration. The typical pattern is turning cold one day, reaching the lowest temperature on the second day, and a beginning of warming on the third day. Freezing temperatures are recorded on an average of 34 days during the year. The average date of the first 32 degree F in the autumn is November 13 and the average date of the last freeze in the spring is March 5. These dates produce a mean freeze-free period of 252 days. Temperatures of freezing or below occur each winter but drop below 16 degrees F only about one-half of the winter seasons. Freezing temperatures have been recorded as early as October 20 and as late as April 13. Temperatures recorded at the NWS Office at the airport on clear, calm nights are normally 2 degrees to 5 degrees F warmer than those in the low-lying river bottom lands in the area.

Snow fall averages less than two inches per year; measurable amounts occur on an average of only once every other year; many consecutive years may pass with no measurable snow. The heaviest

Station: SHREVEPORT, LOUISIANA
SHREVEPORT REGIONAL AIRPORT
Elevation (ground): 254 feet

TEMPERATURES °F

Month	Normal			Extremes			
	Daily maximum	Daily minimum	Monthly	Record highest	Year	Record lowest	Year
(a)				23		23	
J	56.6	37.8	47.2	84	1972	3	1962
F	60.4	40.6	50.5	83	1956	18	1958
M	67.3	46.2	56.8	92	1974	22	1971
A	76.9	55.9	66.4	91	1955	32	1975
M	83.6	63.1	73.4	95	1953	42	1960
J	90.1	70.2	80.2	101	1953	54	1970
J	93.5	72.8	83.2	106	1954	58	1972
A	93.8	72.5	83.2	107	1962	58	1956
S	87.9	66.8	77.4	103	1956	42	1967
O	79.3	55.7	67.5	97	1954	31	1957
N	67.2	45.2	56.2	88	1955	22	1975
D	58.9	39.4	49.2	84	1955	9	1963
YR	76.3	55.5	65.9	107	AUG 1962	3	JAN 1962

IMPORTANT:
The time-period covered by this record is limited: See footnotes following table of **NORMALS, MEANS AND EXTREMES** for explanation and for additional history of **EXTREME HIGHS AND LOWS** recorded in the general area.

(Continued)

snowstorm in the Shreveport area was 11.0 inches in December of 1929. This fell on the 21st and 22nd, and one-half inch remained on the ground December 25th, making this the only Christmas Day of record with snow on the ground. In 1948, 12.4 inches of snow was measured in January for the greatest monthly amount of record. Almost as troublesome as snowfall are the occasional ice and sleet storms which may do considerable damage to trees, power and telephone lines, as well as making travel very difficult.

The summer months are consistently quite warm, with maximum temperatures exceeding 100 degrees F about 10 days per year and exceeding 95 degrees F about 45 days per year. Showers fall at any one place in the area on about eight days during each of the summer months. The resulting point rainfall totals are usually less than one-half inch except on two or three days per month when heavier amounts are recorded.

The average relative humidity is rather high in all seasons. These high humidities may be experienced at any hour but occur mainly during the early morning hours, with two-thirds of the hours shortly before sunrise having relative humidity of 90 percent or higher. In contrast, more than half of the mid-afternoon hours have had relative humidity of less than 50 percent.

Temperatures in spring, especially in April and May, are usually mild and pleasant and those in autumn from late September until December are generally delightful for outdoor activities.

By March, trees and grass are becoming green and early spring planting is generally well under way before the end of the month. Subtropical vegetation and flowers such as Magnolia, Camellia, and Gardenia need only occasional protection to survive. Roses often bloom into December and begin blooming again by late March.

Thunderstorms occur each month, but are most frequent in spring and summer months. The fewest days with rain are in October although the smallest normal rainfalls are in August and September. The October showers — some produced by squall lines and cold fronts — are generally heavier than the airmass showers which occur in the summer months. Severe local storms, including hailstorms, tornadoes, and local wind storms have occurred over small areas in all seasons, but are most frequent during the spring months. Large hail of a damaging nature rarely occurs, although hail as large as grapefruit fell in March, 1961.

Tropical cyclones are in the dissipating stages by the time they reach this portion of the state and winds from them are usually not a destructive factor. Associated heavy rainfall can contribute to local flooding, however, as was the case in July, 1933.

Normals, Means, and Extremes

(To better understand these tables, see full explanation of terms beginning on page 322)

Month	Normal Degree days Base 65 °F: Heating	Cooling	Precipitation in inches: Water equivalent: Normal	Maximum monthly	Year	Minimum monthly	Year	Maximum in 24 hrs.	Year	Snow, Ice pellets: Maximum monthly	Year	Maximum in 24 hrs.	Year	Relative humidity pct.: Hour 00 (Local time)	Hour 06	Hour 12	Hour 18	Wind: Mean speed m.p.h.	Prevailing direction	Fastest mile: Speed m.p.h.	Direction	Year	Pct. of possible sunshine	Mean sky cover, tenths, sunrise to sunset	Mean number of days: Sunrise to sunset: Clear	Partly cloudy	Cloudy	Precipitation .01 inch or more	Snow, Ice pellets 1.0 inch or more	Thunderstorms	Heavy fog, visibility ¼ mile or less	Temperatures °F: Max. (b) 90° and above	Max. 32° and below	Min. 32° and below	Min. 0° and below	Average station pressure mb. Elev. 259 feet m.s.l.
(a)				23		23		23		23		23		23	23	23	23	23	11	13	13		23	23	23	23	23	23	23	23	23	23	23	23	23	3
J	552	0	4.04	10.09	1974	0.27	1971	2.85	1968	3.5	1962	3.5	1962	77	83	64	65	9.9	S	37	22	1967	49	6.7	8	5	18	10	*	2	4	0	1	11	0	1010.0
F	416	11	3.71	6.51	1965	0.90	1954	3.53	1965	2.0	1965	2.0	1965	74	82	59	57	10.3	S	40	27	1965	54	6.2	8	5	15	8	*	3	2	0	0	7	0	1009.5
M	291	36	4.10	7.23	1969	0.56	1966	2.77	1960	4.0	1965	4.0	1965	74	82	57	55	10.7	S	41	29	1964	56	6.3	8	7	16	9	*	5	2	*	0	3	0	1004.4
A	65	107	5.19	11.19	1957	1.06	1971	7.17	1953	0.0		0.0		78	86	58	57	10.4	S	52	28	1975	55	6.4	7	8	15	9	0	6	1	*	0	*	0	1006.2
M	5	266	5.04	11.78	1967	1.22	1962	4.66	1955	0.0		0.0		82	89	58	59	8.8	S	37	13	1970	64	6.0	9	9	13	8	0	7	1	4	0	0	0	1003.5
J	0	456	3.34	12.39	1961	0.89	1967	4.10	1961	0.0		0.0		82	89	57	58	7.9	S	37	16	1963	71	5.3	9	13	8	8	0	7	1	18	0	0	0	1005.2
J	0	564	2.89	9.46	1972	0.15	1964	4.30	1972	0.0		0.0		81	89	56	57	7.6	S	32	16	1963	74	5.3	10	12	9	8	0	7	*	25	0	0	0	1006.5
A	0	564	2.68	6.83	1955	0.50	1969	4.64	1955	0.0		0.0		81	90	55	57	7.3	S	37	25	1963	72	5.0	11	12	8	7	0	6	1	24	0	0	0	1007.3
S	0	372	3.07	9.59	1968	0.17	1956	5.39	1961	0.0		0.0		81	90	57	61	7.7	ENE	44	19	1965	68	5.0	12	8	10	7	0	4	1	14	0	0	0	1006.9
O	70	148	2.90	7.44	1970	0.00	1963	3.88	1957	0.0		0.0		79	87	53	61	7.8	SSE	35	31	1966	71	4.5	14	8	9	6	0	2	2	3	0	*	0	1010.2
N	278	14	3.57	9.49	1957	0.71	1967	5.94	1969	T	1975	T	1975	78	85	56	64	9.1	S	38	29	1975	62	5.2	12	6	12	8	0	3	3	0	0	3	0	1009.9
D	490	0	4.19	8.10	1960	0.68	1958	3.35	1965	3.2	1963	3.0	1963	79	85	63	68	9.4	S	37	14	1965	53	6.2	9	7	15	9	*	2	4	0	*	9	0	1010.1
YR	2167	2538	44.72	12.39	JUN 1961	0.00	OCT 1963	7.17	APR 1953	4.0	MAR 1965	4.0	MAR 1965	79	86	58	60	8.9	S	52	28	APR 1975	64	5.7	117	100	148	97	*	54	21	89	1	34	0	1007.5

FOOTNOTES Means and extremes above are from existing and comparable exposures. Annual extremes have been exceeded at other sites in the locality as follows: Highest temperature 110 in August 1909; lowest temperature -5 in February 1899.

Snowfall

Season	July	Aug	Sept	Oct	Nov	Dec	Jan
1970-71	0.0	0.0	0.0	0.0	0.0	0.0	0.8
1971-72	0.0	0.0	0.0	0.0	T	0.0	T
1972-73	0.0	0.0	0.0	0.0	0.0	0.0	0.6
1973-74	0.0	0.0	0.0	0.0	0.0	T	0.0
1974-75	0.0	0.0	0.0	0.0	0.0	0.0	3.4
1975-76	0.0	0.0	0.0	0.0	T	0.0	
RECORD MEAN	0.0	0.0	0.0	0.0	T	0.2	0.5

Heating Degree Days

Season	July	Aug	Sept	Oct	Nov	Dec	Jan
1955-56	0	0	0	79	351	493	569
1956-57	0	0	0	23	334	344	548
1957-58	0	0	0	115	310	384	616
1958-59	0	0	0	85	261	621	609
1959-60	0	0	0	61	462	443	598
1960-61	0	0	0	43	251	626	661
1961-62	0	0	1	71	320	518	690
1962-63	0	0	0	47	294	502	785
1963-64	0	0	0	12	234	772	568
1964-65	0	0	6	93	216	479	446
1965-66	0	0	3	78	103	400	703
1966-67	0	0	0	99	181	570	553
1967-68	0	0	15	72	244	500	604
1968-69	0	0	0	57	346	560	495
1969-70	0	0	0	86	314	510	713
1970-71	0	0	0	97	324	351	459
1971-72	0	0	4	7	282	304	499
1972-73	0	0	6	92	419	597	621
1973-74	0	0	0	40	164	557	533
1974-75	0	0	14	32	312	541	473
1975-76	0	0	4	39	286	492	

Cooling Degree Days

Year	Jan	Feb	Mar	Apr	May	June	July
1969	15	0	0	57	241	470	675
1970	9	0	5	138	259	420	528
1971	22	1	24	82	203	510	576
1972	22	10	31	128	235	480	501
1973	0	2	16	64	223	412	504
1974	7	6	115	63	288	355	541
1975	23	0	21	91	238	403	501

Feb	Mar	Apr	May	June	Total
0.6	0.3	0.0	0.0	0.0	1.7
0.0	0.0	0.0	0.0	0.0	T
T	0.0	0.0	0.0	0.0	0.6
0.0	0.0	0.0	0.0	0.0	T
T	T	0.0	0.0	0.0	3.4
0.4	0.3	0.0	0.0	0.0	1.4

SHREVEPORT, LA

Feb	Mar	Apr	May	June	Total
319	267	111	0	0	2189
249	308	91	15	0	1912
564	391	87	4	0	2471
402	287	127	0	0	2392
608	511	37	23	0	2743
342	167	148	15	5	2258
227	356	104	1	0	2288
512	162	30	11	0	2343
556	254	35	0	0	2431
432	473	28	0	0	2173
485	238	62	8	0	2080
511	140	13	13	0	2080
614	308	49	0	0	2406
438	455	44	2	0	2397
429	344	58	14	0	2468
398	316	94	15	0	2054
382	185	62	0	0	1725
429	135	145	9	0	2453
386	152	78	2	0	1912
457	305	124	0	0	2258

Aug	Sept	Oct	Nov	Dec	Total
604	402	177	11	0	2652
606	492	106	23	28	2614
488	403	191	28	9	2537
553	467	167	1	0	2595
417	305	145	66	0	2154
477	200	77	35	0	2164
493	271	141	34	12	2228

SHREVEPORT, LOUISIANA

Average Temperature

Year	Jan	Feb	Mar	Apr	May	June	July	Aug	Sept	Oct	Nov	Dec	Annual
1936	44.6	44.6	63.7	64.8	74.4	83.8	83.4	86.6	82.2	65.5	54.3	52.0	66.7
1937	50.2	51.1	54.4	66.6	76.0	82.4	83.6	84.4	77.9	66.2	53.6	50.6	66.4
1938	50.2	57.9	66.3	65.5	74.8	80.6	83.6	85.0	79.4	72.0	55.8	50.2	68.5
1939	52.2	51.2	62.0	65.0	74.7	82.4	86.0	85.3	82.4	69.2	54.5	54.4	68.3
1940	35.8	49.2	59.0	64.8	71.9	78.4	81.8	79.8	74.7	70.1	55.4	52.8	64.5
#1941	51.2	47.3	53.1	67.8	75.0	79.6	83.8	84.6	79.6	73.1	53.6	50.4	66.6
1942	44.9	47.4	57.2	67.2	72.6	81.3	83.9	82.6	74.8	66.8	60.6	48.4	65.6
1943	48.2	53.4	53.4	68.0	76.4	83.6	85.0	86.8	75.2	65.6	53.2	47.0	66.3
1944	46.2	54.6	58.0	65.3	72.6	83.0	85.2	83.9	77.5	67.2	57.6	44.8	66.3
1945	45.7	52.6	64.0	66.8	71.4	80.6	81.3	81.8	79.0	65.0	59.8	44.4	66.0
1946	46.4	53.0	61.7	69.5	71.5	78.5	82.8	81.4	75.4	67.4	58.6	54.1	66.7
1947	47.4	43.4	51.2	67.1	71.8	81.0	82.4	85.6	78.9	72.7	53.0	49.7	65.3
1948	39.1	48.4	57.2	70.4	73.8	82.6	85.3	84.6	76.9	65.7	55.7	52.2	66.0
1949	48.2	53.0	57.4	64.2	77.0	81.8	83.6	81.1	75.4	67.4	58.3	51.2	66.6
1950	56.2	55.0	55.9	62.9	75.7	79.9	81.4	81.0	74.6	69.8	54.2	45.9	66.0
1951	48.2	50.6	57.9	63.5	73.6	81.3	84.6	87.5	77.5	68.1	52.0	51.6	66.3
#1952	55.6	54.1	55.5	62.0	72.7	83.6	83.8	84.1	76.8	60.6	54.6	48.1	66.0
1953	51.4	50.7	63.2	63.6	74.7	84.6	82.0	82.3	78.0	69.7	54.2	45.9	66.7
1954	49.3	56.7	56.7	70.2	68.8	81.7	87.0	86.9	80.7	69.3	55.3	50.8	67.8
1955	47.9	49.9	59.7	69.3	75.7	77.5	82.5	81.2	79.6	66.7	55.3	49.4	66.2
1956	46.6	54.5	57.3	63.5	76.2	79.3	84.8	84.1	78.3	69.6	54.1	54.6	66.9
1957	47.4	56.8	54.8	65.1	74.5	79.8	83.8	82.3	74.6	63.5	55.5	52.6	65.9
1958	44.9	44.6	52.2	63.8	73.4	80.8	82.9	82.1	77.3	65.2	57.0	44.7	64.1
1959	45.2	50.5	55.8	62.6	75.5	78.4	81.6	81.9	78.2	67.3	50.2	50.4	64.8
1960	45.9	44.0	48.5	67.3	71.3	80.0	82.9	82.1	77.5	68.4	57.1	44.6	64.2
1961	43.4	52.7	61.2	62.7	71.7	75.5	79.5	79.0	76.5	66.7	54.7	48.1	64.3
1962	42.4	57.2	53.3	64.0	75.4	78.6	84.0	84.8	77.5	70.7	55.2	48.5	66.0
1963	39.6	46.4	62.2	68.7	74.8	82.1	83.7	85.0	78.4	71.9	58.0	39.9	66.0
1964	46.5	45.6	56.8	68.7	75.1	81.0	84.2	84.0	78.5	64.2	59.3	50.1	66.2
1965	50.8	49.4	49.6	70.1	73.7	78.4	83.0	82.1	77.2	66.1	63.2	52.0	66.3
1966	42.3	47.5	58.1	66.2	72.7	79.0	85.0	81.0	75.3	64.0	60.4	46.9	64.9
1967	47.6	46.5	63.5	71.0	71.1	80.9	79.8	80.0	73.2	66.5	57.1	48.9	65.5
1968	45.4	43.6	55.9	66.5	72.7	80.1	81.0	82.0	73.6	66.6	53.7	46.6	64.0
1969	49.3	49.2	50.1	65.1	72.4	80.5	86.6	84.3	78.2	67.8	54.7	48.3	65.5
1970	42.0	49.4	53.8	67.4	72.7	78.8	81.7	84.3	81.1	65.1	54.7	54.3	65.5
1971	50.6	50.6	55.4	64.3	70.8	81.7	83.3	80.6	78.1	70.7	56.4	55.4	66.5
1972	49.4	51.9	59.8	66.9	72.3	80.8	81.0	82.6	80.2	67.2	50.9	45.5	65.7
1973	44.7	49.5	60.9	62.0	71.7	78.5	81.1	78.2	74.9	68.2	61.5	46.8	64.8
1974	47.8	51.2	63.6	64.3	74.0	76.6	82.1	80.1	71.0	66.2	55.6	47.3	65.0
1975	50.2	48.4	55.6	63.7	72.4	78.2	80.9	80.7	73.7	68.0	56.3	49.3	64.8
RECORD MEAN	47.5	50.7	58.0	66.1	73.3	80.5	83.1	82.7	77.2	67.2	56.2	49.2	65.9
MAX	56.4	60.2	68.0	76.2	83.1	90.3	92.9	92.8	87.3	78.1	66.4	58.3	75.8
MIN	38.5	41.1	47.9	55.9	63.4	70.6	73.2	72.6	67.0	56.3	45.9	40.1	56.0

# Indicates a station move or relocation of instruments.

Precipitation

Year	Jan	Feb	Mar	Apr	May	June	July	Aug	Sept	Oct	Nov	Dec	Annual
1936	1.77	1.40	2.65	2.18	2.69	0.39	3.27	0.39	0.84	4.09	2.34	4.43	26.44
1937	8.39	2.28	5.26	2.43	0.98	3.47	1.42	3.02	3.34	4.96	7.41	7.63	50.59
1938	2.25	2.38	4.95	6.51	3.31	4.04	4.00	2.05	1.33	0.37	5.82	3.15	40.16
1939	6.79	8.96	0.85	1.11	3.06	2.58	1.82	2.66	0.69	0.70	6.10	4.91	40.23
1940	2.24	4.77	2.22	8.58	4.46	5.53	5.06	8.61	0.36	2.33	10.09	7.91	62.16
#1941	3.57	3.84	3.69	2.49	8.52	4.26	4.00	1.90	2.77	8.83	4.10	3.37	51.34
1942	1.12	1.34	3.02	10.34	8.00	6.04	0.56	7.99	2.80	1.34	0.62	2.06	45.23
1943	2.57	1.54	5.94	2.63	2.41	0.87	0.99	0.53	2.57	2.07	2.83	5.69	30.64
1944	6.35	5.57	7.37	5.52	9.21	0.94	1.35	5.05	1.22	0.03	4.47	8.98	56.06
1945	4.05	5.02	11.99	6.47	3.45	3.55	5.68	1.26	2.81	6.90	2.83	3.66	57.67
1946	11.53	5.39	5.55	5.32	9.47	5.18	4.58	3.44	1.54	2.47	6.37	3.69	64.53
1947	3.57	3.60	6.19	6.40	2.84	2.02	0.84	2.77	3.52	1.76	4.93	5.84	44.28
1948	4.39	4.14	3.39	2.80	6.92	1.16	2.58	1.06	0.41	1.47	7.03	2.75	38.10
1949	7.81	3.72	2.94	2.86	1.63	2.16	4.37	1.06	3.74	14.02	0.37	5.20	49.88
1950	5.69	4.30	2.18	5.95	6.85	2.72	6.45	4.11	3.84	3.08	1.91	0.80	47.88
1951	5.43	2.72	3.28	1.82	1.10	2.81	3.30	0.47	5.52	1.64	2.43	7.23	37.75
#1952	4.22	5.76	4.44	5.34	6.71	0.74	4.26	1.11	0.80	0.04	3.98	5.24	42.64
1953	4.26	3.98	4.61	9.82	8.35	1.30	3.03	1.22	1.06	1.57	2.16	5.20	46.56
1954	3.82	0.90	1.49	3.93	7.94	1.88	1.01	0.92	2.27	2.88	4.24	3.66	34.94
1955	3.44	4.43	3.00	4.78	9.64	2.67	6.17	6.83	1.09	1.93	0.83	2.42	47.23
1956	3.68	4.58	4.47	4.51	3.85	3.11	0.30	2.25	0.17	2.05	3.50	1.54	34.01
1957	5.07	4.05	6.55	11.19	3.45	8.37	3.26	1.75	4.17	6.78	9.49	3.10	67.23
1958	4.18	1.98	3.15	7.78	2.89	6.86	4.13	2.22	8.58	0.55	3.75	0.68	46.75
1959	1.17	4.79	2.82	3.58	3.23	3.35	3.29	2.13	1.64	3.90	2.94	6.18	39.02
1960	3.08	4.49	4.04	1.39	1.88	7.35	2.88	4.99	4.98	2.34	2.99	8.10	48.51
1961	3.79	3.88	6.15	1.70	1.46	12.39	3.95	2.26	5.75	3.51	5.16	7.50	57.50
1962	4.26	2.12	3.28	5.78	1.22	4.70	0.60	3.96	2.57	1.26	3.52	2.35	35.62
1963	1.46	2.42	0.91	3.53	2.25	2.65	1.00	3.74	2.36	0.00	6.72	2.99	30.03
1964	2.57	2.74	4.24	7.27	1.41	1.87	0.15	4.71	2.51	0.64	1.65	2.55	32.31
1965	3.77	6.51	3.39	1.16	5.40	3.18	1.49	1.82	6.55	0.36	1.20	6.29	41.12
1966	4.22	3.45	0.56	8.02	3.78	2.05	0.58	1.71	3.27	1.62	0.97	3.63	33.86
1967	1.36	2.91	1.02	2.11	11.78	0.89	6.15	4.67	1.27	1.34	0.71	3.92	38.13
1968	8.33	2.22	1.89	9.38	6.05	2.78	4.68	1.89	9.59	1.90	5.85	3.27	57.83
1969	1.14	4.32	7.23	6.63	5.18	1.16	1.06	0.50	0.97	3.16	7.50	3.95	42.80
1970	1.23	4.70	4.30	5.12	4.36	1.14	3.94	2.04	1.64	7.44	2.09	3.80	41.80
1971	0.27	4.13	2.11	1.06	5.26	0.97	6.15	2.99	1.30	3.86	3.75	3.65	35.50
1972	5.97	0.94	2.45	2.06	4.13	2.76	9.46	1.27	2.10	6.32	5.32	4.18	46.96
1973	5.65	1.52	5.01	6.44	2.00	5.84	7.63	0.77	6.39	5.38	5.16	6.37	58.16
1974	10.09	3.67	3.60	3.09	4.58	6.29	7.73	3.84	6.64	3.79	5.80	2.34	61.46
1975	4.55	4.51	5.84	3.91	5.31	3.48	3.45	1.65	0.98	3.87	4.44	1.88	43.87
RECORD MEAN	4.16	3.57	4.20	4.72	4.41	3.29	3.54	2.59	2.91	2.94	3.84	4.48	44.65

Record mean values above are means through the current year for the period beginning in 1875 for temperature, 1872 for precipitation, and 1953 for snowfall.

Station: CARIBOU, MAINE
MUNICIPAL AIRPORT
Elevation (ground): 624 feet

TEMPERATURES °F

Month	Normal			Extremes			
	Daily maximum	Daily minimum	Monthly	Record highest	Year	Record lowest	Year
(a)				36		36	
J	19.8	1.5	10.7	51	1950	-32	1974
F	23.0	2.7	12.9	48	1970	-41	1955
M	32.8	14.4	23.6	73	1962	-20	1967
A	45.5	27.9	36.7	80	1942	-2	1964
M	60.3	39.0	49.7	91	1960	18	1974
J	70.3	48.8	59.6	96	1944	30	1958
J	75.6	54.1	64.9	95	1955	36	1969
A	73.1	51.5	62.3	95	1975	34	1965
S	64.7	43.4	54.1	91	1945	23	1950
O	52.8	34.8	43.8	79	1968	14	1972
N	38.2	24.6	31.4	68	1956	-3	1969
D	23.9	8.2	16.1	58	1950	-26	1975
YR	48.3	29.2	38.8	96	JUN 1944	-41	FEB 1955

IMPORTANT:
The time-period covered by this record is limited: See footnotes following table of NORMALS, MEANS AND EXTREMES for explanation and for additional history of EXTREME HIGHS AND LOWS recorded in the general area.

Snowfall

Season	July	Aug	Sept	Oct	Nov	Dec	Jan
1939-40							19.4
1940-41	0.0	0.0	T	5.1	18.7	25.2	29.3
1941-42	0.0	0.0	T	4.0	11.4	13.5	13.9
1942-43	0.0	0.0	0.0	T	8.7	19.1	12.3
1943-44	0.0	0.0	0.0	T	8.2	10.2	2.2
1944-45	0.0	0.0	0.0	1.7	10.3	21.4	39.5
1945-46	0.0	0.0	0.0	2.0	20.3	11.7	22.7
1946-47	0.0	0.0	0.0	0.5	5.8	27.4	14.3
1947-48	0.0	0.0	T	0.0	9.1	9.9	24.6
1948-49	0.0	0.0	0.0	0.8	12.7	16.1	20.0
1949-50	0.0	0.0	0.0	T	32.2	10.5	22.1
1950-51	0.0	0.0	T	1.8	2.2	12.0	23.4
1951-52	0.0	0.0	0.0	0.6	24.7	29.9	21.2
1952-53	0.0	0.0	0.0	6.5	4.8	16.7	19.1
1953-54	0.0	0.0	0.0	3.5	3.7	18.5	23.8
1954-55	0.0	0.0	0.0	0.1	7.2	49.4	38.5
1955-56	0.0	0.0	T	0.4	6.5	15.4	17.1
1956-57	0.0	0.0	0.0	0.7	9.8	29.0	14.0
1957-58	0.0	0.0	0.0	0.3	7.8	22.5	35.6
1958-59	0.0	0.0	0.0	1.9	20.5	14.6	17.4
1959-60	0.0	0.0	T	9.9	10.7	12.2	29.1
1960-61	0.0	0.0	0.0	T	1.5	17.8	31.6
1961-62	0.0	0.0	0.0	4.1	7.1	8.9	12.7
1962-63	0.0	0.0	0.0	11.0	3.9	37.4	30.7
1963-64	0.0	0.0	T	12.1	16.8	6.5	20.2
1964-65	0.0	0.0	0.0	0.9	12.9	37.2	18.7
1965-66	0.0	0.0	0.0	1.2	27.0	17.8	30.3
1966-67	0.0	0.0	0.0	0.4	7.1	24.2	27.8
1967-68	0.0	0.0	0.0	T	9.3	31.3	33.5
1968-69	0.0	0.0	0.0	T	28.0	31.2	29.5
1969-70	0.0	0.0	0.0	2.3	4.6	28.6	6.0
1970-71	0.0	0.0	0.0	7.6	11.0	32.4	16.6
1971-72	0.0	0.0	0.0	T	18.9	26.3	15.7
1972-73	0.0	0.0	0.0	1.7	13.3	59.9	20.3
1973-74	0.0	0.0	T	T	14.5	23.4	20.7
1974-75	0.0	0.0	T	0.4	34.9	12.6	31.2
1975-76	0.0	0.0	0.0	T	10.4	36.4	
RECORD MEAN	0.0	0.0	T	2.3	12.7	22.7	22.4

Heating Degree Days

Season	July	Aug	Sept	Oct	Nov	Dec	Jan
1955-56	50	85	379	649	1022	1667	1348
1956-57	125	204	438	620	1000	1554	1973
1957-58	102	192	283	592	895	1356	1423
1958-59	88	109	339	727	1054	1841	1648
1959-60	26	87	281	700	1041	1434	1640
1960-61	76	91	292	711	929	1497	1897
1961-62	61	104	188	580	905	1343	1713
1962-63	151	115	400	695	1062	1497	1597
1963-64	42	189	417	535	905	1741	1595
1964-65	46	199	419	737	1063	1484	1743
1965-66	115	161	351	737	1191	1514	1489
1966-67	64	106	393	683	899	1354	1567
1967-68	14	55	276	636	1000	1471	1823
1968-69	48	191	199	515	1097	1452	1534
1969-70	109	86	364	732	895	1331	1861
1970-71	17	80	328	540	905	1697	1833
1971-72	59	141	274	569	1106	1648	1759
1972-73	55	145	326	818	1130	1775	1711
1973-74	9	44	373	649	1117	1270	1810
1974-75	40	66	369	789	998	1433	1717
1975-76	19	93	310	700	960	1674	

Cooling Degree Days

Year	Jan	Feb	Mar	Apr	May	June	July
1969	0	0	0	0	0	45	48
1970	0	0	0	0	2	47	164
1971	0	0	0	0	2	36	38
1972	0	0	0	0	21	35	51
1973	0	0	0	0	0	67	126
1974	0	0	0	0	2	21	38
1975	0	0	0	0	0	54	137

The Caribou Municipal Airport is located in Aroostook County, the largest and northernmost County in the State. The airport lies on top of high land which is about on the same level as most of the surrounding gently rolling hills. The Aroostook River, which runs about one mile to the east and southeast of the station, has little effect on the local weather. Even though Caribou is located only 150 miles from the Atlantic coast, its climate can be justly classed as a severe typical continental type. Winters are particularly long and windy, with snowfall averaging about 110 inches per season. While the extreme low temperatures may be less severe than one might expect, temperatures of zero or lower normally occur over 40 times per year. A study of heating degree day data will show the outstanding part that cold weather plays here.

Summers are cool and generally favored with abundant rainfall, which is one of the most important factors in the high yield of the potato and grain crops throughout the County. Our location high up in the St. Lawrence Valley allows Aroostook County to come under the influence of the Summer Polar Front, resulting in practically no dry periods of more than 3 or 4 days in the growing season. The growing season at Caribou averages more than 120 days, with the average last freeze in the Spring near May 18th and the average first freeze in Autumn near September 22nd. (Continued page 476)

Feb	Mar	Apr	May	June	Total
14.7	32.7	9.6	T	0.0	
7.7	20.5	0.2	4.4	0.0	111.1
31.4	25.5	7.8	0.0	0.0	107.5
12.0	10.1	17.6	1.0	0.0	80.8
18.0	15.0	6.0	0.0	0.0	59.6
12.0	12.1	4.1	2.0	T	103.1
25.0	8.3	8.4	T	0.0	98.4
30.8	17.6	12.4	T	0.0	108.8
9.7	14.3	3.6	T	0.0	71.2
31.5	14.4	7.1	T	0.0	102.6
35.6	13.8	3.2	T	0.0	117.4
23.0	9.4	0.8	T	0.0	72.6
41.0	11.4	3.3	T	0.0	132.1
16.5	33.1	16.2	0.0	0.0	112.9
31.9	11.7	3.7	T	0.0	96.8
38.8	47.1	T	T	0.0	181.1
20.5	18.9	5.2	T	0.0	84.0
22.2	13.4	4.2	0.5	0.0	93.8
39.5	17.0	5.6	0.0	0.0	128.3
18.8	37.7	2.3	T	0.0	113.2
41.0	18.9	11.0	0.0	0.0	132.8
28.8	39.7	24.4	1.0	0.0	144.8
16.3	7.7	11.7	T	0.0	68.5
30.6	23.0	10.9	T	0.0	147.5
10.1	24.7	11.5	0.0	T	101.9
14.8	6.1	4.0	0.0	0.0	94.6
20.9	10.7	2.8	8.2	0.0	118.9
26.0	10.5	2.2	10.9	0.0	109.1
5.3	26.3	T	0.0	0.0	105.7
29.7	19.5	14.1	0.0	0.0	152.0
15.0	19.8	11.7	T	0.0	88.0
16.3	38.6	12.2	0.0	T	134.7
25.1	41.4	9.4	T	0.0	136.8
27.8	7.8	22.2	0.0	0.0	153.0
11.9	21.6	13.1	4.2	0.0	109.4
9.8	18.2	15.1	0.0	0.0	122.2
22.5	20.0	8.3	0.9	T	111.8

Average Temperature

Year	Jan	Feb	Mar	Apr	May	June	July	Aug	Sept	Oct	Nov	Dec	Annual
1939		10.3	15.2	32.9	48.8	58.0	66.6	66.0	52.0	41.6	28.0	17.5	
1940	9.0	13.4	22.4	34.5	51.6	56.8	64.4	61.9	53.6	38.6	28.1	11.9	37.2
1941	6.5	16.4	20.6	38.4	50.4	59.0	65.6	58.6	53.0	40.4	29.4	17.6	38.0
1942	7.6	12.4	28.3	37.6	53.6	62.1	63.6	62.5	55.4	45.2	28.8	10.0	38.9
1943	4.3	13.8	17.5	30.6	48.3	57.8	64.2	61.2	52.8	45.0	29.7	10.0	36.3
1944	14.0	9.1	18.8	32.5	54.4	59.0	65.0	67.2	56.2	41.2	33.8	13.0	38.7
1945	7.8	13.6	28.2	41.9	47.2	58.0	65.8	64.6	55.6	41.1	28.8	13.7	38.9
1946	8.4	7.8	28.4	34.3	48.6	59.2	62.0	62.0	57.5	46.5	29.8	13.2	38.1
1947	8.5	16.7	26.1	29.1	46.4	57.6	69.0	65.1	53.7	48.8	30.8	13.2	38.8
1948	7.4	4.7	17.9	35.6	49.6	56.7	64.8	64.9	55.6	43.2	36.4	19.9	38.1
1949	13.0	10.7	22.6	40.1	49.6	62.8	66.8	63.4	53.4	46.7	25.2	19.6	39.5
1950	14.0	8.1	19.8	36.1	52.8	57.6	63.5	61.4	50.2	42.6	36.1	22.3	38.7
1951	13.6	15.2	25.0	41.1	50.5	57.8	63.7	61.8	55.1	44.0	28.0	14.3	39.2
1952	10.6	16.8	25.9	37.6	49.5	60.3	69.6	64.0	54.4	39.6	29.8	18.9	39.7
1953	15.8	17.4	25.2	39.9	51.1	60.2	64.1	61.1	54.9	44.0	36.5	22.4	41.1
1954	6.5	21.2	22.4	35.5	48.7	59.4	61.5	59.4	52.1	44.2	32.7	18.9	38.5
1955	11.3	15.1	20.0	37.6	50.1	60.6	65.9	64.8	52.1	43.9	30.6	11.1	38.6
1956	21.4	13.3	18.8	35.9	43.7	59.0	61.1	58.8	50.3	44.8	31.4	14.6	37.8
1957	1.3	15.5	26.3	36.3	49.3	60.3	62.3	58.9	55.5	45.7	34.9	21.0	38.9
1958	18.8	12.5	31.8	40.5	48.0	54.5	63.1	62.1	53.6	41.3	29.6	5.5	38.4
1959	11.6	6.8	20.6	37.7	56.3	57.0	69.5	63.7	56.4	42.3	30.1	18.5	39.0
1960	12.0	22.9	21.5	34.9	57.1	61.0	63.5	63.9	55.5	41.8	33.8	16.5	40.4
1961	3.8	12.6	21.0	35.7	47.3	60.2	64.7	63.2	59.5	46.0	34.5	21.4	39.2
1962	9.7	7.4	30.7	36.2	49.1	60.6	60.3	62.2	51.6	42.3	29.4	16.6	38.0
1963	13.4	6.0	19.9	35.3	49.8	61.9	67.5	59.0	50.9	47.6	34.5	8.7	37.9
1964	13.4	15.9	24.1	37.1	51.8	58.8	65.8	58.6	50.8	41.0	29.3	16.9	38.6
1965	8.7	11.5	25.6	37.0	49.1	61.1	61.5	60.9	53.9	41.0	25.1	15.9	37.6
1966	16.7	15.3	28.2	37.6	49.0	60.4	64.1	62.0	51.7	42.7	34.8	21.1	40.3
1967	14.3	6.7	17.4	34.4	42.7	62.1	68.4	64.2	55.8	44.2	31.4	17.3	38.2
1968	6.1	9.9	25.7	41.0	49.7	59.1	66.3	59.1	58.5	48.4	28.2	18.0	39.2
1969	15.3	17.8	25.4	35.6	48.2	60.7	62.9	64.0	52.8	41.1	34.9	21.9	40.0
1970	4.9	13.1	25.3	38.2	50.6	61.7	69.7	66.0	53.9	47.4	34.6	10.1	39.6
1971	5.8	14.3	25.4	36.1	51.6	59.3	64.0	61.3	56.2	46.4	27.9	11.7	38.3
1972	8.2	6.4	18.3	34.7	52.4	61.5	64.7	60.5	54.2	38.3	27.1	7.6	36.2
1973	9.7	12.6	29.6	37.9	48.9	63.0	68.6	66.4	52.9	43.9	27.5	23.9	40.4
1974	6.7	10.8	21.0	36.8	45.2	62.7	64.7	64.3	52.7	39.3	31.4	18.5	37.9
1975	9.6	11.5	23.1	35.1	53.7	61.4	68.6	64.4	54.5	42.3	32.8	10.9	39.0
RECORD MEAN	10.2	12.6	23.3	36.5	49.8	59.7	65.1	62.6	54.0	43.4	31.0	15.8	38.7
MAX	19.5	22.8	32.7	45.1	60.4	70.4	75.7	73.4	64.5	52.3	37.8	23.9	48.2
MIN	0.9	2.4	13.9	27.8	39.2	49.0	54.4	51.7	43.5	34.4	24.1	7.6	29.1

# Indicates a station move or relocation of instruments.

CARIBOU, ME

Feb	Mar	Apr	May	June	Total
1492	1427	865	653	202	9839
1380	1194	856	482	178	10004
1464	1022	727	522	309	8887
1628	1372	813	360	240	10219
1213	1339	895	262	149	9067
1462	1356	872	540	161	9884
1613	1054	858	492	161	9072
1649	1390	884	461	134	10035
1417	1259	830	407	198	9535
1493	1213	831	485	164	9877
1388	1135	813	499	160	9553
1629	1468	912	682	121	9878
1594	1211	715	468	171	9434
1316	1219	876	512	167	9126
1449	1221	800	440	142	9430
1415	1224	860	411	199	9509
1698	1440	903	405	134	10136
1464	1092	807	491	122	9936
1512	1359	837	609	81	9670
1498	1295	890	343	158	9596

Aug	Sept	Oct	Nov	Dec	Total
62	4	0	0	0	159
117	1	0	0	0	331
33	16	0	0	0	125
11	9	0	0	0	127
97	17	0	0	0	307
50	5	0	0	0	116
80	0	0	0	0	271

Precipitation

Year	Jan	Feb	Mar	Apr	May	June	July	Aug	Sept	Oct	Nov	Dec	Annual
1939		2.22	1.81	2.94	2.15	2.58	3.42	2.28	4.24	4.14	0.45	3.17	
1940	1.81	1.58	4.35	3.94	2.44	7.11	4.51	2.20	3.89	2.02	4.97	3.48	42.30
1941	2.03	1.19	1.91	1.95	3.13	5.11	5.70	5.30	3.97	4.81	2.72	2.38	40.20
1942	1.44	2.05	3.23	1.05	2.27	4.85	1.97	3.39	3.04	3.02	1.87	2.42	30.60
1943	0.82	2.11	1.53	2.17	2.31	4.22	4.41	5.15	1.97	4.22	2.77	0.79	32.47
1944	0.12	1.47	2.55	0.92	1.01	3.94	3.22	1.52	3.71	6.20	2.48	2.10	29.24
1945	3.59	1.39	1.94	3.26	5.23	3.95	5.35	2.48	5.90	2.99	3.01	1.69	40.78
1946	1.53	2.43	2.29	2.43	3.36	2.99	3.69	4.13	1.54	3.50	4.38	2.72	34.99
1947	2.48	3.12	2.43	3.65	6.27	3.72	5.69	2.36	3.09	0.90	2.60	0.81	37.12
1948	1.19	1.14	2.34	2.30	5.91	3.12	2.73	3.45	3.27	4.63	4.14	2.92	37.14
1949	2.50	2.21	2.48	2.11	3.91	3.82	5.35	2.49	4.40	2.35	5.87	2.14	39.63
1950	2.94	2.31	2.29	2.60	0.67	4.55	2.47	4.23	1.26	1.99	6.53	4.98	36.82
1951	2.90	3.24	1.51	4.50	1.93	3.94	6.83	4.52	2.26	2.95	3.92	2.38	40.88
1952	2.27	2.61	1.11	2.49	2.92	5.68	2.65	2.22	2.18	4.80	1.51	2.23	32.67
1953	3.02	2.02	5.13	3.35	2.61	1.70	2.88	1.62	2.35	1.71	3.00	3.79	33.18
1954	1.59	2.63	1.28	3.80	3.85	5.62	5.17	6.30	8.14	4.70	3.02	5.01	51.11
1955	2.25	4.13	3.84	0.86	4.17	2.44	2.46	4.42	2.81	0.63	1.21	1.23	30.45
1956	2.49	1.93	1.36	2.37	2.42	3.35	2.86	4.26	2.57	2.24	2.77	2.13	30.75
1957	0.98	2.00	1.46	2.57	1.62	3.98	6.83	0.93	3.79	2.37	5.51	4.62	36.66
1958	3.36	2.62	1.52	3.42	1.96	4.51	4.26	8.45	2.01	2.63	2.15	0.93	37.82
1959	2.40	1.26	2.57	2.20	0.64	3.59	2.18	6.52	3.22	4.99	4.50	2.30	36.37
1960	2.24	3.69	2.38	2.96	3.36	4.95	3.39	2.82	2.60	3.41	2.81	3.19	37.80
1961	1.08	2.48	2.64	2.93	4.71	3.02	3.74	4.95	6.19	1.64	2.39	2.39	38.16
1962	1.84	1.16	0.70	2.94	2.91	2.36	6.72	3.05	3.84	3.33	4.35	3.18	36.38
1963	2.40	2.28	2.22	3.16	2.34	1.68	3.66	6.35	3.38	3.40	7.74	0.74	39.35
1964	2.64	0.56	3.12	2.07	2.81	1.80	3.58	3.38	1.33	4.19	2.28	2.98	30.74
1965	1.21	2.33	0.66	1.10	2.35	1.25	3.71	3.60	3.07	4.14	4.75	1.56	29.73
1966	2.06	1.49	2.61	0.73	1.73	2.06	3.27	1.54	3.19	3.47	3.60	2.17	27.92
1967	2.23	1.75	1.07	0.54	3.95	1.69	4.18	4.81	6.61	2.81	2.79	4.58	37.01
1968	2.31	1.46	4.01	2.15	1.33	1.65	4.24	2.01	0.86	3.51	3.98	4.16	31.67
1969	3.00	2.25	1.49	2.60	2.88	3.47	3.73	4.02	6.80	1.55	4.36	3.59	39.74
1970	0.31	2.09	2.25	3.56	4.26	3.25	2.54	3.18	5.46	6.35	1.85	2.58	37.68
1971	1.71	2.16	3.20	2.09	2.06	2.62	2.79	3.39	2.62	3.43	3.31	2.46	31.84
1972	1.32	2.38	4.72	1.09	3.69	4.97	4.21	5.07	3.88	4.03	2.76	5.28	43.40
1973	2.60	2.89	2.48	5.26	5.03	2.13	4.62	2.95	2.62	1.47	2.63	7.97	42.65
1974	1.89	1.37	3.56	3.81	3.61	2.82	3.39	3.98	3.40	1.15	4.16	2.05	35.19
1975	2.71	1.66	1.94	1.95	3.04	2.40	4.28	1.39	2.98	1.51	3.40	4.05	31.31
RECORD MEAN	2.04	2.10	2.37	2.54	3.00	3.43	3.96	3.68	3.45	3.17	3.42	2.89	36.05

Record mean values above are means through the current year for the period beginning in 1939.

(Continued)

Autumn climate is nearly ideal, with mostly golden warm days and crisp cool nights predominating. Aroostook County, even with its relatively short growing season, provides profitable farming. The principal crops are potatoes, peas, a variety of grains, and some hardy vegetables.

Probably unknown to many victims of hay fever and similar afflictions, the immediate Caribou area offers sparkling visibility and practically pollen-free air in the late Summer months. This latter condition is principally due to the extremely high degree of cultivation of all available land.

Normals, Means, and Extremes

Month	Normal Degree days Base 65 °F		Precipitation in inches											Relative humidity pct.			
			Water equivalent							Snow, Ice pellets				Ø Hour 01	Hour 07	Hour 13	Hour 19
	Heating	Cooling	Normal	Maximum monthly	Year	Minimum monthly	Year	Maximum in 24 hrs.	Year	Maximum monthly	Year	Maximum in 24 hrs.	Year	(Local time)			
(a)				36		36		36		36		36		19	31	31	31
J	1683	0	2.04	3.59	1945	0.12	1944	1.15	1945	39.5	1945	15.6	1961	74	74	67	72
F	1459	0	2.11	4.13	1955	0.56	1964	1.35	1955	41.0	1960	18.2	1952	75	74	64	70
M	1283	0	2.20	5.13	1953	0.66	1965	1.65	1940	47.1	1955	17.4	1940	76	75	62	68
A	849	0	2.42	5.26	1973	0.54	1967	2.11	1958	24.4	1961	10.9	1953	79	76	58	67
M	474	0	2.96	6.27	1947	0.64	1959	2.25	1948	10.9	1967	5.8	1967	79	74	53	62
J	170	8	3.41	7.11	1940	1.25	1965	2.37	1957	T	1971	T	1971	84	78	56	65
J	84	81	3.98	6.83	1957	1.97	1942	2.92	1957	0.0		0.0		84	82	58	70
A	122	39	3.78	8.45	1958	0.93	1957	4.14	1958	0.0		0.0		89	85	59	73
S	327	0	3.49	8.14	1954	0.86	1968	6.23	1954	T	1974	T	1974	89	87	60	76
O	657	0	3.31	6.35	1970	0.63	1955	4.07	1970	12.1	1963	9.4	1963	86	86	62	76
N	1008	0	3.50	7.74	1963	0.45	1939	1.77	1969	34.9	1974	15.5	1974	85	85	72	80
D	1516	0	2.62	7.97	1973	0.74	1963	2.80	1973	59.9	1972	14.7	1972	79	79	71	80
YR	9632	128	35.82	8.45	AUG 1958	0.12	JAN 1944	6.23	SEP 1954	59.9	DEC 1972	18.2	FEB 1952	82	80	62	72

(To better understand these tables, see full explanation of terms beginning on page 322)

Month	Wind					Pct. of possible sunshine	Mean sky cover, tenths, sunrise to sunset	Mean number of days											Average station pressure mb.
	Ø		Fastest mile					Sunrise to sunset					%	%	Temperatures °F Max.		Min.		
	Mean speed m.p.h.	Prevailing direction	Speed m.p.h.	Direction	Year			Clear	Partly cloudy	Cloudy	Precipitation .01 inch or more	Snow, Ice pellets 1.0 inch or more	Thunderstorms	Heavy fog, visibility ¼ mile or less	(b) 90° and above	32° and below	32° and below	0° and below	Elev. 628 feet m.s.l.
(a)	15	15					30	34	34	34	36	• 34	24	24	36	36	36	36	3
J	12.4	NW					6.9	7	7	17	14	6	*	2	0	26	31	16	990.1
F	12.0	NW					6.8	6	6	16	13	6	0	2	0	23	28	13	989.2
M	12.9	NW					6.9	7	7	17	13	5	*	2	0	14	29	4	988.4
A	11.7	NW					7.2	5	7	18	13	3	1	2	0	2	23	*	987.0
M	11.4	NW					7.4	4	9	18	13	*	2	1	*	*	6	0	989.6
J	10.4	WSW					7.3	3	10	17	13	0	4	2	1	0	*	0	991.0
J	9.8	WSW					7.1	3	13	15	14	0	7	3	1	0	0	0	989.0
A	9.3	WSW					6.8	4	12	15	13	0	4	2	1	0	0	0	992.1
S	10.4	WSW					6.8	6	8	16	13	0	1	3	*	0	3	0	992.5
O	10.9	NNW					7.1	5	8	18	12	1	1	2	0	*	14	0	993.2
N	11.1	WSW					8.1	2	7	21	14	3	*	4	0	9	25	*	989.3
D	11.5	WSW					7.4	5	7	19	14	6	0	3	0	24	30	10	992.4
YR	11.2	WSW					7.1	57	101	207	160	31	20	27	2	98	190	43	990.3

Ø Data accumulated through 1962.

% Through 1964. The station did not operate 24 hours daily. Fog and thunderstorm data may be incomplete.

Station: PORTLAND, MAINE
PORTLAND INTERNATIONAL AIRPORT
Elevation (ground): 43 feet

TEMPERATURES °F

Month	Normal Daily maximum	Normal Daily minimum	Normal Monthly	Extremes Record highest	Year	Record lowest	Year
(a)				35		35	
J	31.2	11.7	21.5	64	1950	-26	1971
F	33.3	12.5	22.9	64	1957	-39	1943
M	40.8	22.8	31.8	86	1946	-21	1950
A	52.8	32.5	42.7	85	1957	8	1954
M	63.6	41.7	52.7	92	1944	23	1956
J	73.2	51.1	62.2	97	1941	33	1944
J	79.1	56.9	68.0	98	1949	40	1965
A	77.6	55.2	66.4	103	1975	33	1965
S	69.9	47.4	58.7	95	1945	23	1941
O	60.2	38.0	49.1	88	1963	18	1974
N	47.5	29.7	38.6	74	1974	5	1940
D	34.9	16.4	25.7	62	1962	-21	1963
YR	55.3	34.7	45.0	103	AUG 1975	-39	FEB 1943

IMPORTANT:
The time-period covered by this record is limited: See footnotes on next page for explanation and for additional history of EXTREME HIGHS AND LOWS recorded in the general area.

As a rule, Portland has very pleasant summers and falls, cold winters with frequent thaws, and disagreeable springs. Very few summer nights are too warm and humid for comfortable sleeping. Autumn has the greatest number of sunny days and the least cloudiness. Winters are quite severe, but begin late and then extend deeply into the normal springtime.

Heavy seasonal snowfalls, over 100 inches, normally occur about each 10 years. True blizzards are very rare. The White Mountains, to the northwest, keep considerable snow from reaching the Portland area and also moderate the temperature.

Normal monthly precipitation is remarkably uniform throughout the year.

Winds are generally quite light with the highest velocities being confined mostly to March and November. Even in these months the occasional northeasterly gales have usually lost much of their severity before reaching the coast of Maine.

Temperatures well below zero are recorded frequently each winter. Cold waves sometimes come in on strong winds, but extremely low temperatures are generally accompanied by light winds.

The average freeze-free season at the airport station is 139 days. May 12 is the average date of the last freeze (32°) in spring, but this has been as early as April 22 and as late as May 31. The average date of the first freeze in fall is September 27, with the earliest and latest occurrences on September 17 and October 10. The freeze-free period is longer in the City proper, but may be even shorter at susceptible places further inland.

The Portland City Airport is located 2-3/4 miles west of the site of the former city office. The surrounding country is mostly open, rolling and sloping generally toward the Fore River, a body of brackish water about 1,000 feet wide at a distance of about 1/2 mile from the station and forming one boundary (north through east) of the field. The airport is about 5-1/2 miles west-northwest of the open ocean. A slight rise reaching an elevation of 100 feet, lying northwest of the field, cuts down the wind slightly from that direction. The older portion of the City is situated on a hill rising abruptly from sea level to 170 feet, 1-1/2 miles east of the airport and on the opposite side of the Fore River. A line of low hills southeast of the airport, near the ocean, which reach a maximum height of 160 feet, shuts off sight of the ocean from the airport. Sebago Lake with an area of 44 square miles is situated about 15 miles to the northwest and 45 miles farther are the White Mountains, averaging 3,000 to 5,000 feet in height.

Daily maximum temperatures at the present airport site agree closely with those near the former intown office, but minimum temperatures on clear, quiet mornings range as much as 15° lower at the airport.

PORTLAND, MAINE

Normals, Means, and Extremes

(To better understand these tables, see full explanation of terms beginning on page 322)

Month	Normal Degree days Base 65 °F: Heating	Cooling	Precipitation in inches – Water equivalent: Normal	Maximum monthly	Year	Minimum monthly	Year	Maximum in 24 hrs.	Year	Snow, Ice pellets: Maximum monthly	Year	Maximum in 24 hrs.	Year
(a)				35		35		35		35		35	
J	1349	0	3.38	9.41	1958	0.76	1970	2.04	1966	38.2	1966	14.2	1944
F	1179	0	3.57	6.76	1971	1.26	1968	3.21	1965	61.2	1969	21.5	1969
M	1029	0	3.60	9.97	1953	0.81	1965	3.47	1951	46.6	1956	11.7	1972
A	669	0	3.34	9.90	1973	0.71	1941	5.26	1973	15.7	1967	8.7	1971
M	381	0	3.33	7.74	1948	0.49	1965	2.33	1952	7.0	1945	7.0	1945
J	106	22	3.10	6.23	1967	0.70	1941	5.58	1967	0.0		0.0	
J	27	120	2.61	5.87	1951	0.61	1965	2.23	1947	0.0		0.0	
A	55	99	2.60	8.30	1946	0.27	1947	4.18	1946	0.0		0.0	
S	200	11	3.09	9.81	1954	0.30	1948	7.49	1954	T	1959	T	1959
O	493	0	3.31	12.27	1962	0.26	1947	7.71	1962	3.8	1969	3.6	1969
N	792	0	4.86	9.81	1963	2.10	1946	3.39	1951	15.6	1972	11.1	1972
D	1218	0	4.06	9.69	1969	0.98	1955	3.82	1969	54.8	1970	22.8	1970
YR	7498	252	40.80	12.27	OCT 1962	0.26	OCT 1947	7.71	OCT 1962	61.2	FEB 1969	22.8	DFC 1970

Month	Relative humidity pct. Hour 01	Hour 07	Hour 13	Hour 19 (Local time)	Wind: Mean speed m.p.h.	Prevailing direction	Fastest mile: Speed m.p.h.	Direction	Year	Pct. of possible sunshine	Mean sky cover, tenths, sunrise to sunset	Mean number of days – Sunrise to sunset: Clear	Partly cloudy	Cloudy	Precipitation .01 inch or more	Snow, Ice pellets 1.0 inch or more	Thunderstorms	Heavy fog, visibility ¼ mile or less	Temperatures °F Max. (b) 90° and above	Max. 32° and below	Min. 32° and below	Min. 0° and below	Average station pressure mb. Elev. 63 feet m.s.l.
(a)	35	35	35	35	35	15	35	35		35	32	35	35	35	35	35	35	35	35	35	35	35	3
J	76	77	62	71	9.2	N	50	SE	1951	55	6.1	10	7	14	11	4	0	2	0	16	30	6	1014.3
F	75	77	60	69	9.6	N	58	N	1952	59	6.0	9	7	12	10	4	*	2	0	12	27	5	1013.4
M	76	75	59	70	10.1	W	76	NE	1947	56	6.3	9	7	15	11	3	*	3	0	5	27	1	1011.9
A	80	74	55	70	10.0	S	57	S	1946	56	6.5	8	7	15	12	1	1	3	0	*	15	0	1009.7
M	85	75	58	72	9.2	S	49	NW	1950	56	6.6	7	9	15	13	*	2	6	*	0	3	0	1012.0
J	89	79	61	74	8.2	S	45	SW	1969	60	6.3	7	10	13	11	0	4	6	1	0	0	0	1013.4
J	90	81	60	75	7.7	S	44	W	1941	64	6.2	8	11	12	9	0	4	7	2	0	0	0	1011.7
A	90	84	59	78	7.6	S	69	E	1954	65	5.7	10	11	10	9	0	3	6	2	0	0	0	1014.5
S	90	86	61	81	7.8	S	62	SE	1960	61	5.7	11	7	12	8	0	2	6	*	0	1	0	1015.4
O	86	85	59	78	8.5	N	45	N	1963	58	5.6	11	8	12	9	*	1	5	0	0	9	0	1016.8
N	83	84	64	77	8.8	W	76	NE	1945	47	6.7	8	7	15	12	1	*	4	0	1	19	0	1012.7
D	79	80	63	74	9.0	N	62	SE	1957	53	6.2	9	8	14	12	4	*	2	0	12	29	3	1015.3
YR	83	80	60	74	8.8	S	76	NE	MAR 1947	58	6.2	107	99	159	127	18	18	52	5	46	160	15	1013.4

FOOTNOTES

Means and extremes are from existing and comparable exposures. Annual extremes have been exceeded at other sites in the locality as follows: Maximum monthly precipitation 12.29 in January 1935; minimum monthly precipitation 0.09 in October 1924; maximum snowfall in 24 hours 23.3 in January 1935.

Snowfall

Season	July	Aug	Sept	Oct	Nov	Dec	Jan
1936-37	0.0	0.0	0.0	0.0	2.9	2.4	5.6
1937-38	0.0	0.0	0.0	T	0.9	10.5	16.2
1938-39	0.0	0.0	0.0	0.0	16.5	2.3	14.5
1939-40	0.0	0.0	0.0	T	0.5	10.2	5.7
#1940-41	0.0	0.0	0.0	T	5.4	10.8	24.7
1941-42	0.0	0.0	0.0	T	T	1.5	3.6
1942-43	0.0	0.0	0.0	0.0	1.1	6.3	17.7
1943-44	0.0	0.0	0.0	T	13.4	3.6	17.6
1944-45	0.0	0.0	0.0	0.0	8.2	15.4	27.8
1945-46	0.0	0.0	0.0	T	11.0	10.8	21.2
1946-47	0.0	0.0	0.0	0.0	T	29.4	12.7
1947-48	0.0	0.0	0.0	0.0	1.0	18.9	30.5
1948-49	0.0	0.0	0.0	0.0	T	4.0	21.3
1949-50	0.0	0.0	0.0	0.0	2.0	5.3	17.4
1950-51	0.0	0.0	0.0	0.0	3.1	5.6	19.0
1951-52	0.0	0.0	0.0	0.0	2.6	29.1	27.5
1952-53	0.0	0.0	0.0	T	0.4	2.2	13.5
1953-54	0.0	0.0	0.0	0.0	0.7	0.6	27.4
1954-55	0.0	0.0	0.0	0.0	1.8	15.8	4.7
1955-56	0.0	0.0	0.0	T	1.4	9.6	12.4
1956-57	0.0	0.0	0.0	0.0	9.1	35.5	35.3
1957-58	0.0	0.0	0.0	0.0	T	0.9	30.1
1958-59	0.0	0.0	0.0	T	0.2	8.3	8.7
1959-60	0.0	0.0	T	0.1	4.8	17.6	21.4
1960-61	0.0	0.0	0.0	0.0	0.0	23.1	15.8
1961-62	0.0	0.0	0.0	0.8	9.7	19.1	9.9
1962-63	0.0	0.0	0.0	3.6	1.3	14.3	18.4
1963-64	0.0	0.0	0.0	1.7	T	19.8	17.4
1964-65	0.0	0.0	0.0	0.0	T	20.5	15.8
1965-66	0.0	0.0	0.0	T	0.6	9.1	38.2
1966-67	0.0	0.0	0.0	0.0	0.0	14.7	12.4
1967-68	0.0	0.0	0.0	0.0	3.6	18.9	20.0
1968-69	0.0	0.0	0.0	T	15.3	18.8	5.4
1969-70	0.0	0.0	0.0	3.8	T	24.7	6.2
1970-71	0.0	0.0	0.0	T	0.0	54.8	17.2
1971-72	0.0	0.0	0.0	0.0	6.2	12.5	7.0
1972-73	0.0	0.0	0.0	T	15.6	35.1	9.6
1973-74	0.0	0.0	0.0	0.0	0.0	7.2	15.0
1974-75	0.0	0.0	0.0	T	3.2	8.2	15.4
1975-76	0.0	0.0	0.0	T	3.6	25.3	
RECORD MEAN	0.0	0.0	T	0.3	3.4	15.6	17.6

Heating Degree Days

Season	July	Aug	Sept	Oct	Nov	Dec	Jan
1955-56	5	42	246	501	861	1448	1161
1956-57	62	63	307	519	806	1157	1580
1957-58	23	86	184	468	721	986	1183
1958-59	28	42	210	586	782	1449	1349
1959-60	2	38	181	522	785	1090	1273
1960-61	14	39	211	575	723	1317	1531
1961-62	66	47	104	433	751	1196	1369
1962-63	68	52	272	529	859	1266	1277
1963-64	31	94	299	395	691	1497	1251
1964-65	28	134	293	549	857	1222	1396
1965-66	41	61	242	532	845	1145	1315
1966-67	19	29	264	549	710	1181	1254
1967-68	15	27	155	467	900	1147	1496
1968-69	8	46	110	375	841	1228	1259
1969-70	30	7	179	494	710	1120	1491
1970-71	7	14	159	408	704	1400	1634
1971-72	3	20	147	381	878	1164	1322
1972-73	27	53	190	607	893	1264	1292
1973-74	0	9	231	480	813	970	1290
1974-75	15	17	206	624	762	1071	1177
1975-76	13	59	230	480	653	1258	

Cooling Degree Days

Year	Jan	Feb	Mar	Apr	May	June	July
1969	0	0	0	0	3	56	118
1970	0	0	0	0	4	55	172
1971	0	0	0	0	0	66	135
1972	0	0	0	0	0	3	114
1973	0	0	0	0	1	71	189
1974	0	0	0	2	4	26	121
1975	0	0	0	0	1	49	179

Feb	Mar	Apr	May	June	Total
1.5	11.3	5.7	0.0	0.0	29.4
12.1	2.9	2.5	0.0	0.0	45.1
9.8	30.9	6.5	T	0.0	80.5
20.9	11.1	9.5	T	0.0	57.9
0.3	19.8	0.0	0.0	0.0	61.0
16.2	14.3	6.3	0.0	0.0	41.9
15.2	13.2	2.7	0.0	0.0	56.2
19.6	13.9	1.0	0.0	0.0	69.1
27.6	3.3	0.0	7.0	0.0	89.3
27.9	0.0	4.3	0.0	0.0	75.2
19.4	4.0	1.1	0.0	0.0	66.6
12.3	15.5	T	0.0	0.0	78.2
11.5	7.5	0.4	0.0	0.0	44.7
29.2	16.9	T	0.0	0.0	70.8
9.8	10.9	T	T	0.0	48.4
34.8	11.0	T	0.0	0.0	105.0
9.4	3.7	2.1	0.0	0.0	31.3
8.0	12.1	0.9	0.0	0.0	49.7
18.6	14.7	T	0.0	0.0	55.6
35.3	46.6	11.2	T	0.0	116.5
1.5	3.1	5.5	0.0	0.0	90.0
30.5	21.1	6.3	0.0	0.0	88.9
22.1	21.0	T	0.0	0.0	60.3
28.4	21.1	T	0.0	0.0	93.4
10.7	21.0	9.8	T	0.0	80.4
32.3	12.1	7.7	0.0	0.0	91.6
22.6	19.1	0.8	T	0.0	80.1
17.8	21.2	1.7	0.0	0.0	79.6
13.2	3.4	2.6	0.0	0.0	55.5
21.3	2.8	0.7	2.0	0.0	74.7
45.8	17.5	15.7	0.1	0.0	106.2
4.5	11.9	0.0	0.0	0.0	58.9
61.2	9.3	T	0.0	0.0	110.0
9.8	20.7	2.9	0.0	0.0	68.1
35.6	24.7	9.2	0.0	0.0	141.5
38.0	21.7	6.3	0.0	0.0	91.7
6.6	0.5	2.3	0.0	0.0	69.7
4.3	6.2	8.3	0.0	0.0	41.0
11.6	6.3	1.7	0.0	0.0	46.4
20.4	13.5	3.2	0.3	0.0	74.3

Average Temperature

Year	Jan	Feb	Mar	Apr	May	June	July	Aug	Sept	Oct	Nov	Dec	Annual
1936	24.6	19.9	38.2	42.4	55.2	62.9	66.6	67.2	59.4	50.4	35.9	31.0	46.1
1937	31.6	30.4	31.3	43.4	56.2	63.8	70.6	72.4	61.0	49.4	40.5	26.8	48.1
1938	23.8	26.6	33.8	44.6	52.4	64.6	68.3	71.1	58.7	53.2	42.0	31.0	47.5
1939	23.6	24.8	29.2	40.6	53.2	61.1	67.9	69.7	60.2	49.7	37.0	29.0	45.5
#1940	19.0	27.1	30.4	40.4	52.7	60.4	68.5	65.8	60.0	48.0	37.4	24.4	44.5
1941	17.1	24.4	27.3	46.4	55.0	63.8	68.0	64.2	58.8	48.2	39.9	29.4	45.2
1942	20.8	22.1	36.0	44.6	54.8	62.4	66.8	66.3	58.9	49.2	36.2	23.0	45.1
1943	17.6	22.9	29.6	38.4	52.8	64.7	68.6	65.4	57.4	49.1	37.4	21.0	43.7
1944	22.7	21.1	29.1	38.9	55.7	61.2	68.5	70.6	59.5	47.6	38.2	23.6	44.7
1945	16.0	22.0	38.6	47.0	49.5	60.9	67.1	66.4	60.6	45.8	37.8	22.0	44.8
1946	19.8	19.2	39.5	40.4	51.6	61.8	65.5	64.3	60.8	51.0	40.6	26.6	45.1
1947	21.5	24.6	32.5	41.2	51.4	60.2	70.6	68.6	59.4	55.3	36.2	22.8	45.4
1948	15.6	18.2	30.8	41.4	50.0	59.5	70.2	69.4	60.3	47.8	42.2	29.8	44.6
1949	26.6	26.2	33.2	45.6	53.8	64.7	70.8	69.0	57.2	51.6	36.3	30.0	47.1
1950	26.9	18.3	26.4	40.9	52.8	62.4	68.0	65.7	54.5	49.2	41.5	29.4	44.7
1951	25.5	27.4	33.2	45.6	53.9	59.9	68.7	66.4	59.2	49.0	35.7	25.4	45.8
1952	23.4	26.0	31.7	43.8	51.6	65.0	71.7	67.3	59.4	46.6	37.7	30.1	46.2
1953	28.5	27.6	34.4	44.1	53.8	62.5	67.8	65.6	58.9	49.9	41.3	33.1	47.3
1954	17.9	29.2	31.6	43.0	51.2	61.3	65.9	63.9	56.4	51.7	38.6	27.4	44.9
1955	22.3	26.7	30.4	43.7	56.0	62.6	71.0	68.5	57.1	48.5	36.1	18.2	45.1
1956	27.4	24.6	25.6	40.0	48.2	62.0	65.1	65.5	55.1	48.0	38.0	27.5	43.9
1957	13.9	26.8	33.6	44.6	54.5	64.1	67.1	63.3	60.3	49.6	40.7	32.9	45.9
1958	26.6	19.0	36.2	43.8	50.9	58.1	67.0	66.5	58.6	45.8	38.6	18.0	44.1
1959	21.3	18.1	30.7	43.0	56.2	59.1	69.8	68.5	60.9	48.0	38.6	29.7	45.3
1960	23.7	28.8	27.4	42.4	54.4	63.7	66.7	66.2	58.8	46.2	40.7	22.2	45.1
1961	15.3	24.2	30.1	41.9	51.1	62.6	65.8	66.3	64.1	50.8	39.7	26.1	44.8
1962	20.6	18.1	33.4	42.0	51.1	62.3	64.0	64.8	56.1	47.6	36.1	23.8	43.3
1963	23.6	17.4	31.9	42.4	52.5	63.1	68.9	62.9	54.8	52.3	41.7	16.6	44.0
1964	24.4	23.0	31.9	40.9	54.8	62.6	67.6	61.1	55.6	47.1	36.2	25.3	44.2
1965	19.8	21.6	33.3	41.1	54.8	63.1	66.3	66.5	58.0	47.6	36.6	27.9	44.7
1966	22.3	22.6	32.7	39.9	50.4	63.1	67.7	66.2	56.2	47.1	41.1	26.7	44.7
1967	24.4	17.2	26.5	41.5	47.3	63.3	67.5	66.8	59.9	49.7	34.8	27.8	43.9
1968	16.6	19.2	33.2	45.1	51.0	60.0	70.0	66.4	61.7	52.8	36.7	25.2	44.8
1969	24.2	25.0	31.1	43.0	52.8	62.6	67.6	71.3	60.9	48.9	41.1	28.7	46.5
1970	16.7	25.4	32.4	43.6	55.7	63.5	70.1	68.8	61.0	51.7	41.3	19.6	45.8
1971	12.2	21.9	31.6	41.6	52.7	64.3	69.0	68.9	61.3	52.5	35.4	27.3	44.9
1972	22.2	21.1	28.9	40.6	52.6	59.6	67.5	65.3	58.7	45.2	35.0	24.0	43.4
1973	23.1	23.4	37.7	45.5	51.3	63.8	70.8	70.9	58.4	49.2	37.7	33.5	47.1
1974	23.2	24.5	33.9	45.1	50.6	61.3	68.2	67.9	58.8	44.7	39.3	30.2	45.6
1975	26.7	25.0	29.8	40.0	55.6	61.5	70.1	66.8	57.2	49.3	43.0	24.3	45.8
RECORD MEAN	22.4	23.4	32.3	42.8	53.2	62.4	68.2	66.6	59.6	49.6	38.6	26.9	45.5
MAX	30.8	32.0	40.0	51.1	62.0	71.5	77.2	75.4	68.4	58.2	46.1	34.5	53.9
MIN	14.0	14.8	24.5	34.5	44.3	53.2	59.2	57.8	50.7	40.9	31.1	19.2	37.0

# Indicates a station move or relocation of instruments.

PORTLAND, ME

Feb	Mar	Apr	May	June	Total
1166	1213	743	516	141	8043
1062	965	610	331	109	7571
1283	889	630	430	206	7089
1305	1053	653	295	187	7939
1040	1159	674	321	89	7174
1140	1075	688	427	95	7835
1307	976	686	438	107	7480
1327	1019	673	379	108	7829
1214	1020	718	324	111	7645
1212	975	710	320	125	7821
1183	994	745	449	108	7660
1330	1187	699	544	92	7858
1320	981	590	424	164	7686
1112	1043	652	377	118	7169
1104	1005	637	283	93	7153
1202	1028	695	373	81	7705
1265	1112	725	379	155	7551
1157	842	575	419	99	7418
1126	958	595	444	131	7047
1112	1086	746	286	146	7248

Aug	Sept	Oct	Nov	Dec	Total
211	59	0	0	0	447
136	41	0	0	0	408
149	43	1	0	0	394
71	8	0	0	0	196
201	40	0	0	0	502
115	28	0	0	0	296
120	2	0	0	0	351

Precipitation

Year	Jan	Feb	Mar	Apr	May	June	July	Aug	Sept	Oct	Nov	Dec	Annual
1936	10.01	5.30	7.48	4.54	1.41	2.68	0.76	2.05	2.02	2.94	1.75	8.09	49.03
1937	4.64	3.17	5.68	5.75	5.58	3.95	0.95	0.95	3.99	5.16	5.77	4.18	49.77
1938	4.13	4.11	3.17	2.57	4.00	3.71	5.67	1.69	6.47	2.74	3.60	4.29	46.15
1939	3.19	3.52	8.00	5.79	1.52	2.08	5.94	2.87	1.62	3.34	0.56	4.16	42.59
#1940	3.69	4.57	5.34	7.12	5.82	3.13	3.18	1.15	3.92	0.32	5.52	3.11	46.87
1941	2.79	3.07	2.24	0.71	1.46	0.70	2.35	2.61	1.42	2.13	2.89	2.90	25.27
1942	3.20	3.92	7.55	2.17	1.77	5.94	5.01	1.06	1.28	2.55	4.71	4.99	44.15
1943	2.14	2.81	2.43	3.34	6.09	2.42	3.78	3.27	1.64	6.55	5.56	1.00	41.03
1944	2.28	3.98	5.12	3.90	1.00	5.42	3.03	0.59	6.79	2.36	6.59	3.74	44.80
1945	3.88	3.92	1.86	3.28	6.77	5.84	2.56	1.25	3.84	5.52	5.10	5.95	49.77
1946	3.74	2.61	1.07	2.71	3.50	1.67	2.22	8.30	2.90	1.49	2.10	4.49	36.80
1947	4.02	2.34	2.72	2.69	4.37	3.92	3.06	0.27	1.73	0.26	4.87	1.96	32.21
1948	2.39	1.64	2.63	2.90	7.74	3.91	1.24	1.06	0.30	3.34	6.48	3.83	37.46
1949	4.65	3.14	2.04	3.72	3.50	2.05	1.71	1.22	6.27	2.26	4.26	1.75	36.57
1950	4.43	2.45	4.14	2.38	1.55	1.63	0.80	4.54	1.82	2.11	5.73	4.09	35.67
1951	2.94	3.71	9.19	5.26	2.67	2.97	5.87	2.48	2.38	4.01	8.00	6.56	56.04
1952	5.39	5.66	3.20	4.15	5.04	5.46	0.75	3.51	2.67	1.85	2.24	5.28	45.20
1953	5.15	3.30	9.97	5.21	3.66	0.81	2.57	3.27	2.60	3.83	3.92	4.02	48.31
1954	2.63	4.18	3.97	4.31	6.73	3.52	2.63	4.79	9.81	2.01	5.36	5.32	55.26
1955	0.76	5.01	4.10	2.50	2.33	2.31	2.05	3.02	1.66	6.71	3.73	0.98	35.16
1956	5.82	3.87	3.75	3.38	3.06	1.51	3.03	1.58	3.61	2.52	3.93	3.35	39.41
1957	2.07	1.56	1.91	1.91	2.28	2.38	1.34	0.80	1.02	2.13	5.85	3.10	26.35
1958	9.41	1.72	2.06	5.28	2.05	1.91	5.27	2.21	2.77	4.36	4.19	1.19	42.42
1959	3.00	2.70	4.50	1.71	1.57	4.72	2.06	2.13	3.19	5.28	4.95	4.92	40.73
1960	2.65	6.38	3.27	3.23	6.34	2.17	3.06	1.32	5.01	2.92	3.15	3.71	43.21
1961	1.46	3.58	2.48	6.48	2.97	3.11	2.87	2.25	4.21	1.69	4.69	2.96	38.75
1962	2.68	2.25	2.15	4.51	1.84	2.65	2.89	2.87	2.53	12.27	4.25	5.47	46.36
1963	2.73	2.95	3.38	2.19	3.52	1.95	2.51	3.25	2.29	1.85	9.81	2.16	38.59
1964	4.74	2.66	3.64	3.27	1.56	2.01	3.47	1.77	1.02	3.45	3.25	3.75	34.59
1965	1.68	6.36	0.81	2.93	0.49	2.27	0.61	1.84	2.31	2.49	3.96	2.40	28.15
1966	4.97	3.43	3.77	1.00	1.96	3.04	0.96	4.99	3.84	3.61	5.01	3.46	40.04
1967	2.52	4.63	2.16	4.74	5.34	6.23	3.46	2.57	2.68	1.31	2.52	6.00	44.16
1968	3.00	1.26	4.16	3.37	3.81	4.04	0.65	2.00	1.40	2.00	7.74	7.70	41.13
1969	3.63	6.28	3.36	2.86	1.67	3.53	5.45	2.20	5.28	2.51	8.54	9.69	55.00
1970	0.76	4.31	4.22	4.14	3.15	2.91	0.95	5.12	4.49	3.87	2.38	5.14	41.44
1971	2.25	6.76	4.74	1.86	4.09	1.09	3.14	3.24	3.55	3.95	4.13	2.85	41.65
1972	2.09	5.14	6.01	2.53	3.17	4.24	2.05	0.80	4.31	3.92	7.87	6.49	48.62
1973	2.58	2.57	3.33	9.90	6.28	4.87	1.70	3.48	2.23	3.38	2.40	9.57	52.29
1974	3.41	2.07	3.82	3.82	4.20	4.69	3.66	1.45	5.43	1.74	4.85	4.41	43.55
1975	4.40	2.51	3.20	3.71	1.09	4.87	2.06	3.89	4.34	4.50	6.01	8.14	48.72
RECORD MEAN	3.83	3.79	3.91	3.52	3.36	3.26	3.03	2.99	3.23	3.27	3.97	3.99	42.15

Record mean values above are means through the current year for the period beginning in 1874 for temperature, 1871 for precipitation, and 1941 for snowfall. Data are from city locations through November 1940.

BALTIMORE, MARYLAND

Baltimore-Washington International Airport lies in a region about midway between the rigorous climates of the North and the mild climates of the South, adjacent to the modifying influences of the Chesapeake Bay and Atlantic Ocean to the east and the Appalachian Mountains to the west. Since this region is near the average path of the low pressure systems which move across the country, changes in wind direction are frequent and contribute to the changeable character of the weather. The net effect of the mountains to the west and the Bay and Ocean to the east is to produce a more equable climate compared with other continental locations farther inland at the same latitude. While hot, humid, muggy periods of weather are not uncommon during the warmer months, they are frequently attended by afternoon or evening thundershowers or nighttime breezes which provide some relief from uncomfortable conditions.

Rainfall distribution throughout the year is rather uniform; however, the greatest intensities are confined to the summer and early fall months, the season for hurricanes and severe thunderstorms. Moisture deficiencies for crops occur occasionally during the growing season, but severe droughts are rare. Rainfall during the growing season occurs principally in the form of thundershowers, and rainfall totals during these months vary appreciably, depending on the number of thundershowers which occur largely by chance in a given locality.

The frictional effects of the land surfaces between Baltimore-Washington International Airport and the Atlantic Ocean decreases the intensity of hurricanes which move into this area to the extent that damaging hurricane winds rarely occur.

Hurricane force winds, 74 m.p.h., or more, however, may occur on rare occasions due to a severe cold front or a severe thunderstorm. The greatest damage by hurricanes is that produced along waterfronts and shores by the high tides and waves.

In summer, the area is under the influence of the large semi-permanent high pressure system commonly known as the Bermuda High and centered over the Atlantic Ocean near 30° North Latitude. This high pressure system brings a circulation of warm, humid airmasses over the area from the deep South. The proximity of large water areas and the inflow of southerly winds contribute to high relative humidities during much of the year.

January is the coldest month, and July, the warmest. Winter and spring months have the highest average windspeeds. Snowfall occurs on about 25 days per year on the average; however, an average of only 7 days annually produce snowfalls greater than 1.0 inch. Although heaviest amounts of snow generally fall in February, occasional heavy falls occur as late as March. The record-breaking snowstorm in the Baltimore

Station: BALTIMORE, MARYLAND
BALTIMORE-WASHINGTON INTL AP
Elevation (ground): 148 feet

TEMPERATURES °F

Month	Normal			Extremes			
	Daily maximum	Daily minimum	Monthly	Record highest	Year	Record lowest	Year
(a)				25		25	
J	41.9	24.9	33.4	75	1975	-7	1963
F	43.9	25.7	34.8	76	1954	-1	1967
M	53.0	32.5	42.8	85	1963	6	1960
A	65.2	42.4	53.8	94	1960	20	1965
M	74.8	52.5	63.7	98	1962	32	1966
J	83.2	61.6	72.4	100	1959	40	1972
J	86.7	66.5	76.6	102	1966	52	1962
A	85.1	64.7	74.9	102	1953	48	1952
S	79.0	57.9	68.5	99	1962	35	1963
O	68.3	46.4	57.4	92	1954	25	1969
N	56.1	36.0	46.1	83	1974	13	1955
D	43.9	26.6	35.3	74	1951	0	1960
YR	65.1	44.8	55.0	102	JUL 1966	-7	JAN 1963

IMPORTANT:
The time-period covered by this record is limited: See footnotes following table of NORMALS, MEANS AND EXTREMES for explanation and for additional history of EXTREME HIGHS AND LOWS recorded in the general area.

(Continued)

area occurred on January 27-29, 1922, when the snowfall totaled 26.5 inches.

Records at the Airport for the period, August 1950 through December 1973 indicate that the average date of the last temperature as low as 32° F. in the spring is April 15, while the average date of the first temperature as low as 32° F. in the autumn is October 26. The period between the last 32° F. temperature in the spring and the first in the autumn, commonly known as the growing season, averages 194 days.

Glaze or freezing rain which is hazardous to highway traffic occurs on an average of 2 to 3 times per year, generally in January or February. However, some occurrences have been noted in November and December. Some years pass without the occurrence of freezing rain, while in others it occurs on as many as 8 to 10 days. Sleet is observed on about 5 days annually. The sleet season begins as early as November in some years, and ends as late as March in some cases, with the greatest frequency of occurrence in January.

BALTIMORE, MARYLAND

Normals, Means, and Extremes

(To better understand these tables, see full explanation of terms beginning on page 322)

Month	Normal Degree days Base 65 °F: Heating	Normal Degree days: Cooling	Precipitation in inches, Water equivalent: Normal	Maximum monthly	Year	Minimum monthly	Year	Maximum in 24 hrs.	Year	Snow, Ice pellets: Maximum monthly	Year	Maximum in 24 hrs.	Year	Relative humidity pct. Hour 01 (Local time)	Hour 07	Hour 13	Hour 19	Wind: Mean speed m.p.h.	Prevailing direction	Fastest mile: Speed m.p.h.	Direction	Year	Pct. of possible sunshine	Mean sky cover, tenths, sunrise to sunset	Mean number of days, Sunrise to sunset: Clear	Partly cloudy	Cloudy	Precipitation .01 inch or more	Snow, Ice pellets 1.0 inch or more	Thunderstorms	Heavy fog, visibility ¼ mile or less	Temperatures °F Max.: (b) 90° and above	Max.: 32° and below	Min.: 32° and below	Min.: 0° and below	Average station pressure mb. Elev. 155 feet m.s.l.
(a)				25		25		25		25		25		22	22	22	22	25	13	25	25		25	25	25	25	25	25	25	25	25	25	25	25	25	3
J	980	0	2.91	5.27	1964	0.29	1955	2.54	1968	21.4	1966	12.1	1966	69	72	58	62	9.9	WNW	63	NE	1958	51	6.3	8	8	15	10	2	*	4	0	5	25	*	1014.7
F	846	0	2.81	6.21	1971	0.72	1968	2.18	1971	20.1	1967	15.5	1958	68	72	56	60	10.7	NW	68	W	1956	55	6.2	8	7	13	9	2	*	4	0	4	21	*	1012.8
M	688	0	3.69	6.80	1953	0.93	1966	3.18	1958	21.6	1960	13.0	1962	66	71	51	55	11.2	WNW	80	SE	1952	55	6.3	7	10	14	11	2	1	3	0	1	15	0	1010.6
A	340	0	3.07	8.15	1952	1.61	1968	2.80	1952	0.4	1964	0.4	1964	69	72	49	54	11.0	WNW	70	W	1954	55	6.2	7	9	14	11	*	2	2	*	0	3	0	1009.9
M	110	70	3.61	7.10	1960	0.43	1964	3.64	1960	T	1963	T	1963	77	77	52	60	9.6	W	65	SW	1961	57	6.2	7	11	13	11	0	4	2	1	0	*	0	1009.0
J	0	225	3.77	9.95	1972	0.15	1954	5.23	1972	0.0		0.0		82	80	53	63	8.7	WNW	80	SW	1952	62	5.7	8	12	10	9	0	6	1	7	0	0	0	1010.6
J	0	360	4.07	8.18	1960	0.30	1955	5.86	1952	0.0		0.0		81	81	53	64	8.2	W	57	NW	1962	65	5.6	9	12	10	8	0	6	1	11	0	0	0	1010.9
A	0	307	4.21	18.35	1955	0.77	1951	7.82	1955	0.0		0.0		83	84	55	67	8.2	W	54	NE	1955	62	5.6	10	10	11	10	0	5	1	8	0	0	0	1012.6
S	27	132	3.12	8.62	1975	0.21	1967	4.33	1960	0.0		0.0		83	85	55	69	8.4	S	56	W	1952	60	5.3	11	9	10	8	0	2	2	3	0	0	0	1013.5
O	250	14	2.81	6.88	1971	T	1963	3.49	1955	T	1972	T	1972	79	82	53	68	8.9	NW	73	SE	1954	59	5.0	13	7	11	7	0	1	3	*	0	2	0	1015.4
N	567	0	3.13	7.68	1952	0.68	1965	3.43	1952	8.4	1967	8.4	1967	74	77	54	64	9.5	WNW	58	E	1952	51	5.9	9	8	13	9	*	*	3	0	*	12	0	1013.6
D	921	0	3.26	7.44	1969	0.20	1955	2.37	1975	20.4	1966	14.1	1960	72	75	59	66	9.4	WNW	57	W	1953	48	6.4	8	7	16	9	1	*	4	0	4	21	*	1013.5
YR	4729	1108	40.46	18.35	AUG 1955	T	OCT 1963	7.82	AUG 1955	21.6	MAR 1960	15.5	FEB 1958	75	77	54	63	9.5	W	80	SW	JUN 1952	57	5.9	105	110	150	113	8	28	30	31	14	99	*	1012.3

FOOTNOTES

Means and extremes above are from existing and comparable exposures. Annual extremes have been exceeded at other sites in the locality as follows: Highest temperature 107 in July 1936; maximum monthly snowfall 33.9 in February 1899; maximum snowfall in 24 hours 24.5 in January 1922.

Snowfall

Season	July	Aug	Sept	Oct	Nov	Dec	Jan
1950-51	0.0	0.0	0.0	0.0	0.5	2.5	2.5
1951-52	0.0	0.0	0.0	0.0	T	5.4	1.7
1952-53	0.0	0.0	0.0	T	2.8	3.0	2.4
1953-54	0.0	0.0	0.0	0.0	5.9	T	13.7
1954-55	0.0	0.0	0.0	T	T	0.4	2.3
1955-56	0.0	0.0	0.0	0.0	2.0	0.5	8.4
1956-57	0.0	0.0	0.0	0.0	T	0.2	10.7
1957-58	0.0	0.0	0.0	0.0	T	9.5	1.5
1958-59	0.0	0.0	0.0	0.0	T	0.5	2.1
1959-60	0.0	0.0	0.0	0.0	0.0	1.5	0.3
1960-61	0.0	0.0	0.0	0.0	0.2	15.6	14.3
1961-62	0.0	0.0	0.0	0.0	3.2	7.2	2.0
1962-63	0.0	0.0	0.0	0.0	0.3	11.7	3.7
1963-64	0.0	0.0	0.0	0.0	T	9.7	10.3
1964-65	0.0	0.0	0.0	0.0	T	0.8	8.3
1965-66	0.0	0.0	0.0	0.0	0.0	T	21.4
1966-67	0.0	0.0	0.0	0.0	T	20.4	0.4
1967-68	0.0	0.0	0.0	0.0	8.4	4.6	2.5
1968-69	0.0	0.0	0.0	0.0	4.3	T	0.1
1969-70	0.0	0.0	0.0	0.0	T	9.0	6.1
1970-71	0.0	0.0	0.0	0.0	0.0	6.3	4.1
1971-72	0.0	0.0	0.0	0.0	1.0	T	1.1
1972-73	0.0	0.0	0.0	T	T	T	T
1973-74	0.0	0.0	0.0	0.0	0.0	8.3	1.2
1974-75	0.0	0.0	0.0	0.0	T	0.4	5.1
1975-76	0.0	0.0	0.0	0.0	0.0	0.7	
RECORD MEAN	0.0	0.0	0.0	T	1.1	4.6	5.1

Heating Degree Days

Season	July	Aug	Sept	Oct	Nov	Dec	Jan
1955-56	0	0	34	224	648	1037	994
1956-57	0	2	109	218	580	655	1069
1957-58	0	2	56	358	529	798	1001
1958-59	0	0	52	261	528	1081	1015
#1959-60	0	0	46	255	612	799	891
1960-61	0	0	18	266	536	1127	1153
1961-62	0	0	30	230	533	975	1004
1962-63	0	0	102	242	667	1048	1114
1963-64	0	2	95	197	524	1116	959
1964-65	0	0	41	358	448	797	1052
1965-66	0	5	34	336	576	819	1085
1966-67	0	0	68	353	555	905	846
1967-68	0	0	75	318	684	851	1100
1968-69	0	1	4	197	500	934	1028
1969-70	0	0	26	251	561	916	1148
1970-71	0	0	20	149	484	824	1080
1971-72	0	0	24	96	571	652	841
1972-73	2	0	16	357	649	759	935
1973-74	0	0	24	221	524	852	830
1974-75	0	0	49	303	509	759	818
1975-76	0	0	50	156	397	853	

Cooling Degree Days

Year	Jan	Feb	Mar	Apr	May	June	July
1969	0	0	0	16	93	304	392
1970	0	0	0	4	134	246	389
1971	0	0	0	0	24	278	363
1972	0	0	5	1	29	140	379
1973	0	0	0	15	29	263	344
1974	0	0	4	24	57	126	361
1975	0	0	0	4	112	252	351

Feb	Mar	Apr	May	June	Total
0.7	T	0.0	0.0	0.0	6.2
T	7.0	0.0	0.0	0.0	14.1
T	3.6	T	0.0	0.0	11.8
1.0	1.5	0.0	0.0	0.0	22.1
6.2	1.2	0.0	0.0	0.0	10.1
0.4	7.8	0.0	0.0	0.0	19.1
2.7	1.4	0.4	0.0	0.0	15.4
18.3	13.7	0.0	0.0	0.0	43.0
T	1.0	0.4	0.0	0.0	4.0
10.7	21.6	0.0	0.0	0.0	34.1
16.4	T	0.0	0.0	0.0	46.5
9.2	13.6	0.0	0.0	0.0	35.2
2.1	1.8	0.0	T	0.0	19.6
18.2	13.2	0.4	0.0	0.0	51.8
1.1	8.4	0.0	0.0	0.0	18.6
11.4	0.0	T	0.0	0.0	32.8
20.1	2.5	0.0	0.0	0.0	43.4
2.6	5.3	0.0	0.0	0.0	23.4
6.4	7.8	0.0	0.0	0.0	18.6
4.0	1.9	T	0.0	0.0	21.0
0.6	2.0	T	0.0	0.0	13.0
11.4	0.2	0.3	0.0	0.0	14.0
1.2	T	T	0.0	0.0	1.2
7.6	T	T	0.0	0.0	17.1
5.5	1.2	T	0.0	0.0	12.2
6.3	4.7	0.1	T	0.0	21.9

Average Temperature

Year	Jan	Feb	Mar	Apr	May	June	July	Aug	Sept	Oct	Nov	Dec	Annual
1950								73.9	65.1	58.0	45.1	32.3	
1951	36.8	36.0	42.9	52.9	62.2	71.2	76.9	74.4	68.1	59.9	41.2	37.8	55.0
1952	38.3	38.7	41.0	55.6	62.1	74.4	78.7	74.7	66.8	52.9	45.8	37.6	55.6
1953	38.8	39.6	44.7	53.0	65.8	72.5	76.7	74.3	67.7	57.7	45.9	39.1	56.3
1954	33.0	40.9	41.9	57.1	60.8	72.4	76.6	73.2	70.2	59.6	43.4	35.0	55.3
1955	32.3	34.4	44.9	55.9	65.2	68.4	81.2	78.1	68.2	58.3	43.1	31.3	55.1
1956	32.7	38.7	40.7	51.6	61.3	71.9	74.7	74.2	65.5	58.0	45.4	43.6	54.9
1957	30.3	39.0	43.5	56.2	64.9	74.8	76.4	73.1	69.6	53.2	47.2	39.1	55.6
1958	32.4	28.9	39.8	54.9	62.9	68.8	77.1	73.5	66.7	57.0	47.2	29.9	53.2
#1959	32.0	35.7	42.5	56.6	67.3	73.6	76.7	77.4	70.7	59.4	44.5	39.0	54.7
1960	36.0	36.2	33.4	58.4	61.6	72.1	74.6	76.9	69.1	56.6	46.9	28.4	54.2
1961	27.6	37.0	45.0	50.0	60.3	71.4	76.5	74.6	73.2	57.7	47.6	33.4	54.5
1962	32.4	32.3	42.2	53.9	66.2	72.3	73.6	74.6	64.8	57.7	41.5	30.9	53.5
1963	28.8	27.8	45.9	54.0	61.4	73.1	76.3	72.9	64.0	58.6	47.3	28.8	53.3
1964	33.8	33.2	44.4	50.9	65.3	72.7	77.0	73.5	68.1	53.3	49.8	39.1	55.1
1965	30.8	34.9	39.2	50.3	66.9	70.1	76.8	75.5	70.8	53.9	45.6	38.3	54.4
1966	29.8	30.5	43.3	49.5	61.7	72.9	78.9	76.5	66.7	53.4	46.4	35.6	53.8
1967	37.4	30.7	41.8	54.0	57.0	72.7	75.2	73.4	65.3	55.3	42.0	37.3	53.5
1968	29.2	32.2	46.6	54.0	59.7	72.6	78.2	78.7	70.3	59.7	48.2	34.6	55.3
1969	31.7	34.9	40.7	56.2	65.5	74.9	77.4	76.5	69.5	57.7	46.1	35.2	55.5
1970	27.8	35.4	40.4	53.3	66.6	73.0	77.2	77.4	73.7	61.5	48.6	38.2	56.1
1971	30.0	37.4	41.8	52.7	61.2	74.0	76.5	74.2	70.9	62.9	46.4	43.7	56.0
1972	37.6	34.3	43.6	51.6	62.7	68.1	76.9	75.4	69.8	53.5	43.2	40.4	54.8
1973	34.6	34.3	48.3	53.1	59.6	73.5	75.9	76.9	69.8	58.2	47.3	37.3	55.7
1974	37.9	33.8	45.2	55.3	61.9	68.5	76.5	75.0	67.5	55.3	48.2	40.3	55.4
1975	38.5	39.1	42.1	50.4	66.3	73.0	76.1	77.9	66.0	60.7	51.9	37.2	56.6
RECORD MEAN	33.2	35.0	42.6	53.6	63.1	72.1	76.8	75.3	68.5	57.3	46.0	36.4	55.0
MAX	41.8	43.9	52.3	64.6	73.9	82.7	87.0	85.2	78.7	68.1	55.7	44.8	64.9
MIN	24.6	26.1	32.9	42.6	52.2	61.5	66.5	65.3	58.3	46.4	36.3	28.0	45.1

# Indicates a station move or relocation of instruments.

BALTIMORE, MD

Feb	Mar	Apr	May	June	Total
758	749	414	172	18	5048
719	660	300	99	9	4420
1004	775	310	107	20	4960
815	691	276	67	16	4802
830	970	254	135	2	4794
780	612	457	173	11	5133
909	704	360	100	0	4845
1037	583	341	153	1	5288
916	631	425	87	14	4966
838	792	433	55	44	4858
961	665	460	157	23	5121
955	715	338	254	6	4995
943	566	324	173	1	5035
835	748	273	69	0	4589
822	752	346	77	0	4899
766	712	364	134	2	4535
884	663	396	94	42	4263
854	511	365	191	1	4640
868	613	309	148	14	4403
720	702	436	66	2	4364

Aug	Sept	Oct	Nov	Dec	Total
364	169	33	0	0	1371
390	291	45	0	0	1499
293	208	36	20	0	1222
331	166	7	0	0	1058
376	173	19	0	0	1219
317	130	8	11	0	1038
404	85	27	10	0	1245

Precipitation

Year	Jan	Feb	Mar	Apr	May	June	July	Aug	Sept	Oct	Nov	Dec	Annual
1950								2.66	5.93	2.67	2.05	3.74	
1951	2.88	3.36	3.70	3.69	3.92	8.80	1.84	0.77	4.13	2.02	6.20	4.49	45.80
1952	4.14	2.59	4.77	8.15	4.97	3.19	6.71	4.71	5.68	0.51	7.68	3.47	56.57
#1953	4.56	2.74	6.80	4.43	6.37	2.90	4.94	4.26	4.05	2.83	1.32	3.05	48.25
1954	2.02	1.21	3.96	3.07	2.07	0.15	1.77	4.10	1.16	3.24	2.42	2.72	27.89
1955	0.29	2.68	3.34	2.34	2.34	6.73	0.30	18.35	0.56	5.66	1.35	0.20	44.14
1956	2.49	3.38	4.11	2.18	2.38	2.11	7.06	1.81	3.42	4.65	2.69	3.22	39.50
1957	2.28	2.61	2.27	2.46	0.55	4.08	1.25	2.44	5.63	2.21	2.87	5.30	33.95
1958	3.45	3.51	6.18	4.29	2.75	3.65	7.73	6.26	1.27	2.51	2.15	1.39	45.14
1959	2.39	1.82	2.72	3.44	2.82	3.68	6.00	4.39	0.82	4.16	2.12	3.57	37.93
1960	2.31	4.95	2.82	3.40	7.10	1.27	8.18	4.30	6.38	2.12	1.08	2.92	46.83
1961	2.91	4.63	3.87	4.45	2.72	5.19	4.57	4.31	1.57	3.70	1.98	2.85	42.75
1962	2.02	4.41	4.85	4.25	2.43	3.16	2.09	2.26	2.39	2.96	6.50	2.92	40.24
1963	1.84	2.07	4.68	2.15	1.70	9.16	0.69	4.21	4.12	T	6.85	2.08	39.55
1964	5.27	4.36	2.98	4.37	0.43	2.40	2.66	1.96	2.61	1.19	2.51	3.94	34.68
1965	3.09	2.89	4.31	1.72	1.79	1.94	2.61	4.72	1.94	1.90	0.68	0.63	28.22
1966	4.15	4.24	0.93	4.39	4.53	1.18	1.48	1.87	8.50	4.80	2.78	3.53	42.38
1967	0.99	2.25	4.39	1.73	3.79	1.89	3.56	8.87	0.21	1.34	2.60	5.31	36.93
1968	3.42	0.72	4.41	1.61	5.41	3.35	2.75	4.16	4.39	3.13	3.85	2.60	39.80
1969	1.38	1.75	1.63	1.80	1.46	3.65	5.22	3.81	2.60	1.10	1.74	7.44	33.58
1970	0.94	3.34	3.07	4.53	1.69	4.10	4.32	1.33	0.46	3.04	5.11	3.50	35.43
1971	2.02	6.21	1.90	1.75	6.12	2.92	4.03	10.91	5.55	6.88	3.75	1.29	53.33
1972	2.82	6.01	2.38	5.30	4.11	9.95	2.81	2.22	1.15	3.51	7.05	5.02	52.33
1973	2.81	2.82	3.96	6.41	3.73	3.16	4.22	3.35	4.87	2.86	1.28	6.36	45.83
1974	2.92	0.94	4.12	2.59	3.58	2.84	0.85	5.85	5.45	1.53	1.39	5.70	37.76
1975	3.47	2.47	5.17	2.73	4.63	3.82	7.15	4.23	8.62	2.89	2.03	4.61	51.82
RECORD MEAN	2.67	3.12	3.73	3.49	3.34	3.81	3.79	4.62	3.50	2.83	3.20	3.52	41.62

Record mean values above are means through the current year for the period beginning in 1951.

Station: BOSTON, MASSACHUSETTS
GEN LOGAN INT AP
Elevation (ground): 15 feet

TEMPERATURES °F

Month	Normal: Daily maximum	Normal: Daily minimum	Normal: Monthly	Extremes: Record highest	Year	Record lowest	Year
(a)				11		11	
J	35.9	22.5	29.2	63	1974	-4	1968
F	37.5	23.3	30.4	58	1970	-3	1967
M	44.6	31.5	38.1	70	1974	6	1967
A	56.3	40.8	48.6	85	1974	22	1965
M	67.1	50.1	58.6	93	1964	37	1974
J	76.6	59.3	68.0	97	1973	46	1965
J	81.4	65.1	73.3	98	1968	54	1965
A	79.3	63.3	71.3	102	1975	47	1965
S	72.2	56.7	64.5	95	1969	38	1965
O	63.2	47.5	55.4	86	1971	30	1974
N	51.7	38.7	45.2	77	1974	17	1972
D	39.3	26.6	33.0	70	1966	-3	1968
YR	58.7	43.8	51.3	102	AUG 1975	-4	JAN 1968

IMPORTANT:
The time-period covered by this record is limited: See footnotes following table of NORMALS, MEANS AND EXTREMES for explanation and for additional history of EXTREME HIGHS AND LOWS recorded in the general area.

Snowfall

Season	July	Aug	Sept	Oct	Nov	Dec	Jan
1936-37	0.0	0.0	0.0	0.0	4.4	0.7	2.0
1937-38	0.0	0.0	0.0	0.0	0.3	4.6	29.6
1938-39	0.0	0.0	0.0	0.0	10.0	1.3	7.5
1939-40	0.0	0.0	0.0	0.0	1.0	6.5	4.6
1940-41	0.0	0.0	0.0	T	8.5	4.5	20.4
1941-42	0.0	0.0	0.0	T	T	0.2	8.2
1942-43	0.0	0.0	0.0	0.0	T	6.8	26.4
1943-44	0.0	0.0	0.0	0.0	T	0.3	5.1
1944-45	0.0	0.0	0.0	0.0	1.2	6.9	24.3
1945-46	0.0	0.0	0.0	0.0	4.9	24.6	9.8
1946-47	0.0	0.0	0.0	0.0	T	4.9	4.0
1947-48	0.0	0.0	0.0	0.0	1.1	26.8	32.5
1948-49	0.0	0.0	0.0	0.0	1.1	5.5	13.7
1949-50	0.0	0.0	0.0	0.0	1.4	2.3	7.9
1950-51	0.0	0.0	0.0	0.0	T	2.7	13.9
#1951-52	0.0	0.0	0.0	0.0	T	8.4	10.7
1952-53	0.0	0.0	0.0	T	T	2.4	13.6
1953-54	0.0	0.0	0.0	0.0	T	T	19.2
1954-55	0.0	0.0	0.0	0.0	T	10.3	0.9
1955-56	0.0	0.0	0.0	0.0	2.5	1.8	7.7
1956-57	0.0	0.0	0.0	0.0	0.6	15.4	20.6
1957-58	0.0	0.0	0.0	T	0.1	T	6.6
1958-59	0.0	0.0	0.0	0.0	0.1	4.6	4.1
1959-60	0.0	0.0	0.0	0.0	0.6	5.5	10.2
1960-61	0.0	0.0	0.0	T	T	16.9	18.7
1961-62	0.0	0.0	0.0	T	0.9	11.4	2.5
1962-63	0.0	0.0	0.0	T	0.9	5.3	6.5
1963-64	0.0	0.0	0.0	T	0.0	17.7	14.4
1964-65	0.0	0.0	0.0	T	T	12.2	22.2
1965-66	0.0	0.0	0.0	0.0	T	2.3	26.4
1966-67	0.0	0.0	0.0	0.0	0.0	9.9	0.5
1967-68	0.0	0.0	0.0	0.0	2.2	14.7	17.7
1968-69	0.0	0.0	0.0	0.0	0.4	5.1	0.9
1969-70	0.0	0.0	0.0	T	T	12.6	7.4
1970-71	0.0	0.0	0.0	T	T	27.9	12.0
1971-72	0.0	0.0	0.0	0.0	2.8	7.9	7.8
1972-73	0.0	0.0	0.0	T	0.6	3.3	3.6
1973-74	0.0	0.0	0.0	0.0	0.0	T	16.0
1974-75	0.0	0.0	0.0	0.0	2.0	3.6	2.2
1975-76	0.0	0.0	0.0	T	0.1	19.3	
RECORD MEAN	0.0	0.0	0.0	T	1.2	7.9	11.9

Heating Degree Days

Season	July	Aug	Sept	Oct	Nov	Dec	Jan
1955-56	0	5	85	307	685	1181	1057
1956-57	15	6	174	330	560	893	1284
1957-58	0	7	57	317	529	766	1046
1958-59	4	2	84	386	547	1190	1118
1959-60	1	7	79	319	611	885	1048
1960-61	0	5	103	335	503	1094	1231
1961-62	6	3	51	246	604	991	1118
1962-63	6	13	105	330	691	1078	1094
#1963-64	1	3	160	198	495	1207	1026
1964-65	14	26	140	380	620	1004	1220
1965-66	2	37	136	371	680	888	1115
1966-67	0	1	88	322	535	950	921
1967-68	0	4	110	347	739	923	1214
1968-69	1	9	46	247	630	1050	1099
1969-70	2	3	107	326	595	973	1295
1970-71	0	0	68	314	598	1113	1269
1971-72	0	2	37	169	651	882	985
1972-73	3	4	51	405	673	985	1033
1973-74	0	2	94	289	570	782	1023
1974-75	0	2	102	458	587	836	925
1975-76	0	8	70	239	395	941	

Cooling Degree Days

Year	Jan	Feb	Mar	Apr	May	June	July
1969	0	0	0	9	13	156	196
1970	0	0	0	0	25	118	294
1971	0	0	0	0	6	155	269
1972	0	0	0	0	26	74	279
1973	0	0	0	7	18	180	296
1974	0	0	0	10	22	81	235
1975	0	0	0	0	60	139	345

Climate is the composite of numerous weather elements. Three important influences are responsible for the main features of Boston's climate. First, the latitude (42° N) places the city in the zone of prevailing west to east atmospheric flow in which are encompassed the northward and southward movements of large bodies of air from tropical and polar regions. This results in variety and changeability of the weather elements. Secondly, Boston is situated on or near several tracks frequently followed by systems of low air pressure. The consequent fluctuations from fair to cloudy or stormy conditions reinforce the influence of the first factor, while also assuring a rather dependable precipitation supply. The third factor, Boston's east-coast location, is a moderating factor effecting temperature extremes of winter and summer.

Hot summer afternoons are frequently relieved by the locally celebrated "sea-breeze", as air flows inland from the cool water surface to displace the warm westerly current. This refreshing east wind is more commonly experienced along the shore than in the interior of the city or the western suburbs. In winter, under appropriate conditions, the severity of cold waves is reduced by the nearness of the then relatively warm water. The average date of the last occurrence of freezing temperature in spring is April 8; the latest is May 3, 1874 and 1882. The average date of the first occurrence of freezing temperature in autumn is November 7; the earliest on record is October 5, 1881. In suburban areas, especially away from the coast, these dates are later in spring and earlier in autumn by up to one month in the more susceptible localities.

(Continued page 486)

Feb	Mar	Apr	May	June	Total
T	1.9	T	0.0	0.0	9.0
10.0	0.3	0.9	0.0	0.0	45.7
4.7	16.5	0.2	0.0	0.0	40.2
23.8	0.3	1.5	0.0	0.0	37.7
1.3	13.1	0.0	T	0.0	47.8
6.2	7.9	1.5	0.0	0.0	24.0
4.5	8.0	T	0.0	0.0	45.7
9.6	12.7	T	0.0	0.0	27.7
26.3	0.5	0.0	T	0.0	59.2
9.8	0.2	1.5	0.0	0.0	50.8
9.0	0.9	0.6	0.0	0.0	19.4
17.0	11.8	0.0	0.0	0.0	89.2
6.9	9.9	0.0	0.0	0.0	37.1
15.2	5.1	T	0.0	0.0	31.9
9.2	3.9	0.0	0.0	0.0	29.7
19.1	1.4	0.0	0.0	0.0	39.6
11.4	0.2	2.2	T	0.0	29.8
1.9	0.4	2.1	0.0	0.0	23.6
6.5	7.0	0.4	0.0	0.0	25.1
14.5	31.2	3.2	0.0	0.0	60.9
2.8	11.5	1.1	0.0	0.0	52.0
23.9	12.0	2.1	T	0.0	44.7
10.7	14.6	T	0.0	0.0	34.1
2.3	22.3	T	0.0	0.0	40.9
14.9	9.0	2.0	0.0	0.0	61.5
28.7	1.1	0.1	0.0	0.0	44.7
4.6	13.6	T	0.0	0.0	30.9
23.2	7.7	T	0.0	0.0	63.0
4.7	9.7	1.6	0.0	0.0	50.4
12.1	3.3	T	T	0.0	44.1
23.5	22.9	3.3	T	0.0	60.1
3.4	6.8	0.0	0.0	0.0	44.8
41.3	6.1	T	0.0	0.0	53.8
10.5	18.2	0.1	0.0	0.0	48.8
8.1	7.4	1.9	0.0	0.0	57.3
16.5	12.1	0.4	0.0	0.0	47.5
2.5	0.3	T	0.0	0.0	10.3
17.8	0.1	3.0	0.0	0.0	36.9
17.0	1.8	1.0	0.0	0.0	27.6
12.2	7.9	0.8	T	0.0	41.9

Average Temperature

Year	Jan	Feb	Mar	Apr	May	June	July	Aug	Sept	Oct	Nov	Dec	Annual
1936	28.2	22.8	41.8	45.2	60.6	66.2	71.1	69.7	62.6	54.4	39.5	35.0	49.8
1937	37.4	33.2	34.1	45.2	59.1	66.4	73.2	74.6	63.0	52.6	44.0	31.2	51.2
1938	28.0	30.6	39.1	48.7	55.8	67.2	71.8	73.6	62.2	56.0	46.4	34.0	51.1
1939	27.8	32.2	33.2	43.6	56.4	65.6	72.3	73.8	64.5	54.2	40.8	33.4	49.8
1940	23.0	29.6	33.1	43.6	56.2	65.1	71.6	68.4	63.3	50.6	42.9	34.3	48.5
1941	25.2	29.4	33.4	51.6	59.8	68.2	71.4	70.6	66.0	55.9	48.0	35.2	51.2
1942	28.6	27.0	40.8	49.7	60.8	67.4	71.1	70.7	64.6	55.8	43.5	28.6	50.7
1943	25.5	30.6	36.0	43.4	57.6	71.2	74.1	71.0	63.0	53.8	43.3	29.6	49.9
1944	31.0	29.6	34.1	44.6	63.2	67.0	73.8	74.7	65.0	53.8	43.2	30.8	50.9
1945	23.8	30.5	46.3	52.5	55.2	66.6	71.9	70.8	67.1	53.1	45.5	28.5	51.0
1946	28.4	27.6	47.2	46.2	58.0	67.5	70.8	67.8	65.8	58.4	47.8	34.8	51.7
1947	32.6	29.6	37.7	47.2	56.9	65.4	74.4	73.2	64.8	61.6	41.2	30.4	51.2
1948	23.4	26.6	38.0	48.0	55.0	63.6	74.5	73.7	65.7	54.2	49.6	36.3	50.7
1949	34.6	34.4	39.2	50.8	60.4	71.6	76.2	74.4	63.2	58.4	43.5	36.8	53.6
1950	36.2	28.0	33.7	46.8	55.8	69.1	73.5	70.9	61.5	56.3	47.8	35.5	51.3
#1951	34.0	34.7	39.1	51.0	59.1	66.0	74.0	70.7	65.6	54.8	42.6	35.0	52.2
1952	32.6	32.5	37.2	50.5	57.2	70.7	77.5	72.3	66.3	53.0	44.9	35.7	52.6
1953	34.7	35.0	39.1	48.9	58.4	70.5	73.2	72.0	66.3	56.2	48.6	40.2	53.6
1954	26.0	36.4	38.8	50.1	56.3	66.6	72.2	70.1	63.2	58.6	44.4	34.4	51.4
1955	28.5	32.0	37.6	49.2	62.8	66.8	77.2	74.5	64.5	55.1	41.9	26.6	51.4
1956	30.6	32.5	33.6	45.6	55.4	68.9	71.7	71.9	61.1	54.4	46.1	36.0	50.7
1957	23.4	34.7	39.1	49.4	59.9	71.3	74.1	69.3	67.3	54.6	47.2	40.0	52.5
1958	31.0	25.5	39.1	48.8	56.6	63.9	72.4	72.4	64.6	52.6	46.6	26.4	50.0
1959	28.7	26.7	37.0	49.0	62.6	64.6	74.7	74.1	68.1	55.1	44.4	36.3	51.8
1960	30.9	35.3	32.7	48.3	59.7	69.6	73.1	72.1	63.7	53.9	48.0	29.5	51.4
1961	25.0	31.6	36.8	45.3	56.3	68.9	72.1	72.5	69.0	57.3	44.6	32.8	51.0
1962	28.7	26.7	38.5	49.4	57.2	68.4	70.4	70.0	62.9	54.1	41.7	30.0	49.8
#1963	29.5	25.9	39.1	48.9	59.4	69.5	74.7	70.4	60.8	60.0	48.3	25.9	51.0
#1964	31.7	29.1	38.7	46.1	60.3	67.1	71.5	66.4	62.0	52.5	44.1	32.4	50.2
1965	25.4	28.0	35.8	44.2	59.5	67.4	71.0	70.5	62.5	52.8	42.1	36.1	49.6
1966	28.8	31.3	39.8	45.9	57.3	69.4	74.9	71.3	63.5	54.5	46.9	34.2	51.5
1967	35.1	26.4	33.2	44.9	51.7	67.2	73.0	70.9	62.7	53.8	40.1	35.0	49.5
1968	25.6	26.1	39.1	49.6	56.1	64.9	75.2	70.7	65.0	57.9	43.8	30.9	50.4
1969	29.3	29.5	35.4	50.6	58.5	69.3	71.0	74.3	63.7	54.3	44.9	33.4	51.2
1970	23.0	32.3	37.4	49.0	59.6	67.0	74.3	73.6	65.6	54.9	44.8	28.9	50.9
1971	23.8	30.5	36.7	45.1	55.7	69.1	73.4	73.4	68.0	59.8	43.1	36.3	51.2
1972	33.0	29.6	36.3	44.9	57.6	65.4	73.8	71.5	65.7	51.8	42.3	33.0	50.4
1973	31.4	30.1	43.3	49.9	57.0	70.0	74.3	74.8	64.4	55.6	45.8	39.6	53.0
1974	31.7	29.1	38.7	50.9	54.7	64.8	72.4	72.0	63.7	50.1	45.3	37.8	50.9
1975	34.9	32.1	36.9	45.1	61.5	67.5	75.9	72.9	63.9	57.3	51.8	34.4	52.8
RECORD MEAN	28.9	29.1	36.9	46.9	57.7	67.0	72.6	70.7	64.0	54.2	43.5	32.6	50.3
MAX	36.4	36.8	44.3	55.0	66.3	75.7	80.9	78.7	72.0	62.1	50.6	39.6	58.2
MIN	21.3	21.4	29.4	38.8	49.0	58.2	64.2	62.7	56.0	46.2	36.3	25.6	42.4

# Indicates a station move or relocation of instruments.

BOSTON, MA

Feb	Mar	Apr	May	June	Total
936	966	575	304	54	6155
842	798	466	201	21	5590
1102	796	481	262	85	5448
1065	862	476	142	92	5968
855	992	493	166	33	5489
928	865	587	287	22	5960
1066	814	467	271	35	5672
1087	798	477	196	38	5913
1033	808	559	187	57	5734
1032	900	617	195	80	6228
936	776	566	258	46	5811
1075	977	596	403	58	5926
1122	797	454	270	76	6056
987	911	430	208	21	5639
909	846	473	184	52	5765
962	868	586	287	25	6090
1021	883	598	250	54	5532
971	666	450	258	24	5523
1000	809	429	335	77	5410
918	866	590	162	59	5505

Aug	Sept	Oct	Nov	Dec	Total
297	74	1	0	0	746
273	91	9	0	0	810
271	132	15	1	0	849
213	79	0	0	0	671
316	84	3	0	0	904
226	68	1	3	0	646
261	44	9	4	0	862

Precipitation

Year	Jan	Feb	Mar	Apr	May	June	July	Aug	Sept	Oct	Nov	Dec	Annual
1936	6.46	3.66	6.40	3.54	1.70	2.37	1.04	5.15	3.79	2.67	1.33	8.19	46.30
1937	3.93	1.31	3.57	5.34	2.52	3.47	1.17	4.97	3.69	3.95	4.66	5.09	43.67
1938	4.91	2.38	2.42	3.22	4.42	6.30	9.46	3.31	6.00	2.43	2.89	2.80	50.54
1939	2.18	3.79	5.23	4.54	1.29	2.70	0.75	2.14	1.01	4.77	1.14	2.91	32.45
1940	1.68	4.78	3.83	4.58	3.28	1.80	3.17	0.85	2.32	0.76	6.24	2.76	36.05
1941	4.21	1.70	3.40	1.70	2.43	4.29	2.90	1.55	1.18	1.92	2.40	3.19	30.87
1942	3.69	3.45	7.01	1.59	2.11	4.24	4.14	2.09	1.96	2.78	4.69	4.72	42.47
1943	3.74	1.23	4.02	2.64	4.56	1.49	3.91	1.28	1.41	4.82	2.16	0.99	32.25
1944	2.03	2.15	3.92	3.52	0.25	5.35	1.61	1.79	5.36	2.58	5.68	2.83	37.07
1945	3.67	4.09	1.90	2.02	4.47	6.44	2.12	4.27	1.81	2.23	6.86	7.42	47.30
1946	4.18	3.00	1.50	2.62	4.91	2.76	2.22	9.92	2.04	0.34	0.98	3.60	38.07
1947	2.45	1.44	2.30	4.15	4.36	2.88	3.98	2.19	3.95	1.13	5.13	3.95	37.91
1948	5.11	2.08	3.14	2.62	5.37	4.50	4.53	1.24	0.67	4.84	5.16	1.25	40.51
1949	3.21	3.25	1.66	3.23	2.53	0.93	1.10	2.12	6.47	1.60	3.71	1.64	31.45
1950	3.86	3.81	2.99	2.38	1.55	1.10	1.45	3.14	0.89	1.99	6.17	3.37	32.70
#1951	4.04	3.71	4.41	3.06	4.81	4.31	2.13	3.23	2.00	3.98	6.60	4.69	46.97
1952	4.31	4.71	4.41	4.41	3.57	3.26	0.52	6.86	1.13	1.61	1.72	4.09	40.60
1953	6.28	4.14	11.00	6.04	5.06	0.48	2.76	1.81	2.50	4.91	7.66	5.09	57.73
1954	3.26	3.37	3.33	5.25	13.38	2.78	2.50	5.64	8.31	3.58	5.52	5.40	62.32
1955	0.92	4.11	5.42	4.12	0.99	3.52	4.28	17.09	2.40	6.94	5.68	1.03	56.50
1956	6.99	4.36	5.39	2.94	1.85	2.03	3.32	1.46	5.07	4.39	3.46	6.13	47.39
1957	2.47	1.34	3.38	3.78	3.63	1.62	0.64	1.71	0.35	2.67	5.75	6.58	33.92
1958	9.54	5.87	4.48	7.82	4.45	2.96	3.91	5.37	7.50	4.62	3.35	1.78	61.65
1959	2.72	3.45	5.81	4.44	1.24	8.63	8.12	2.93	0.63	4.60	4.20	4.64	51.41
1960	3.04	4.84	3.23	3.51	3.80	3.46	5.18	1.64	5.97	2.48	2.49	4.82	44.46
1961	2.92	4.94	4.71	6.59	4.51	1.67	3.29	3.17	7.04	2.46	3.18	3.36	47.84
1962	3.11	4.16	1.48	3.85	1.86	2.33	1.61	3.72	4.10	8.68	3.80	4.53	43.23
1963	3.13	2.60	4.39	1.48	2.86	1.92	1.72	1.67	3.05	1.25	7.74	3.03	34.84
1964	4.56	4.67	3.48	3.69	0.53	1.91	3.12	1.78	2.65	2.82	2.18	5.08	36.47
1965	2.64	3.17	2.22	2.32	0.93	2.99	0.55	1.48	2.01	1.59	2.08	1.73	23.71
1966	5.29	3.48	1.98	1.24	2.66	3.40	3.21	1.25	3.42	2.62	4.43	3.03	36.01
1967	2.28	4.05	4.67	4.83	7.32	3.48	2.47	5.74	2.00	0.96	3.38	6.42	47.60
1968	3.85	1.15	7.86	1.72	3.26	5.65	0.55	1.63	1.79	1.85	6.74	6.23	42.28
1969	2.26	7.08	2.63	4.37	1.96	0.63	2.98	1.89	4.42	1.64	8.18	9.74	47.78
1970	0.89	4.65	4.32	2.79	3.01	4.62	1.27	4.12	2.60	2.63	4.09	6.92	41.91
1971	1.88	5.05	3.08	2.92	3.72	1.74	2.84	1.59	1.55	2.16	6.74	2.40	35.67
1972	2.05	5.29	5.37	3.34	5.26	6.76	2.19	0.83	5.94	2.98	7.02	6.08	53.11
1973	3.12	2.13	2.20	5.65	3.76	4.68	4.83	2.78	1.95	2.71	1.74	7.20	42.75
1974	3.22	3.24	4.01	3.86	2.87	2.29	1.54	3.41	7.03	3.12	1.73	3.92	40.24
1975	5.70	3.37	2.74	2.40	1.78	2.10	2.35	5.52	5.49	4.41	5.13	4.80	45.79
RECORD MEAN	3.58	3.40	3.84	3.57	3.25	3.16	3.15	3.57	3.25	3.22	3.89	3.67	41.55

Record mean values above are means through the current year for the period beginning in 1872 for temperature, 1871 for precipitation and 1936 for snowfall. Data are from City Office locations through 1935 and from Airport locations thereafter.

(Continued)

Boston has no dry season. For most years the longest run of days with no measurable precipitation does not extend much more than two weeks. This may occur at any time of year. Most growing seasons have several shorter dry spells during which irrigation for high-value crops may be useful.

Much of the rainfall from June to September comes from showers and thunderstorms. During the rest of the year, low pressure systems pass more or less regularly and produce precipitation on an average of roughly one day in three. Coastal storms, or "northeasters", are prolific producers of rain and snow. The main snow season extends from December through March. The average number of days with four inches or more of snowfall is four per season, and days with seven inches or more come about twice per season. Periods when the ground is bare or nearly bare of snow may occur at any time in the winter.

Relative humidity has been known to fall as **low as 5% (May 10, 1962)**, but such desert dryness is very rare. Heavy fog occurs on an average of about two days per month with its prevalence increasing eastward from the interior of Boston Bay to the open waters beyond.

The greatest number of hours of sunshine recorded in any month was 390, or 86% of possible, in June 1912, while the least was 60 hours, or 21%, in December 1972.

Although winds of 32 m.p.h. or higher may be expected on at least one day in every month of the year, gales are both more common and more severe in winter.

Normals, Means, and Extremes

Month	Normal Degree days Base 65 °F: Heating	Cooling	Precipitation in inches — Water equivalent: Normal	Maximum monthly	Year	Minimum monthly	Year	Maximum in 24 hrs.	Year	Snow, Ice pellets: Maximum monthly	Year	Maximum in 24 hrs.	Year	Relative humidity pct.: Hour 01	Hour 07	Hour 13	Hour 19 (Local time)
(a)				24		24		24		40		40		11	11	11	11
J	1110	0	3.69	9.54	1958	0.89	1970	2.07	1958	32.5	1948	12.8	1943	66	67	57	61
F	969	0	3.54	7.08	1969	1.15	1968	2.68	1969	41.3	1969	19.4	1958	65	68	58	61
M	834	0	4.01	11.00	1953	1.48	1962	4.13	1968	31.2	1956	17.7	1960	67	68	58	62
A	492	0	3.49	7.82	1958	1.24	1966	2.31	1973	3.3	1967	3.1	1956	67	67	54	60
M	218	20	3.47	13.38	1954	0.53	1964	5.74	1954	T	1967	T	1967	73	71	58	65
J	27	117	3.19	8.63	1959	0.48	1953	2.46	1960	0.0		0.0		78	74	60	68
J	0	260	2.74	8.12	1959	0.52	1952	2.42	1959	0.0		0.0		77	73	56	66
A	8	203	3.46	17.09	1955	0.83	1972	8.40	1955	0.0		0.0		77	74	56	67
S	76	61	3.16	8.31	1954	0.35	1957	5.64	1954	0.0		0.0		80	79	61	72
O	301	0	3.02	8.68	1962	0.96	1967	4.26	1962	T	1975	T	1975	74	75	57	66
N	594	0	4.51	8.18	1969	1.72	1952	3.33	1955	10.0	1938	8.0	1940	72	74	61	68
D	992	0	4.24	9.74	1969	1.03	1955	4.17	1969	27.9	1970	13.0	1960	69	72	62	66
YR	5621	661	42.52	17.09	AUG 1955	0.35	SEP 1957	8.40	AUG 1955	41.3	FEB 1969	19.4	FEB 1958	72	72	58	65

(To better understand these tables, see full explanation of terms beginning on page 322)

Month	Wind: Mean speed m.p.h.	Prevailing direction	Fastest mile: Speed m.p.h.	Direction	Year	Pct. of possible sunshine	Mean sky cover, tenths, sunrise to sunset	Mean number of days — Sunrise to sunset: Clear	Partly cloudy	Cloudy	Precipitation .01 inch or more	Snow, Ice pellets 1.0 inch or more	Thunderstorms	Heavy fog, visibility ¼ mile or less	Temperatures °F Max. (b): 90° and above	32° and below	Min.: 32° and below	0° and below	Average station pressure mb. Elev. 29 feet m.s.l.
(a)	18	15	17	17		40	40	40	40	40	24	40	40	40	11	11	11	11	3
J	14.2	NW	61	NW	1974	54	6.2	9	7	15	12	3	*	2	0	11	25	1	1016.7
F	14.2	WNW	57	S	1970	56	6.2	8	7	13	11	3	*	2	0	8	25	*	1015.4
M	14.0	NW	55	SW	1971	57	6.4	8	8	15	12	2	*	2	0	1	18	0	1013.7
A	13.4	WNW	52	NW	1963	56	6.5	7	9	14	12	*	1	2	0	0	3	0	1011.4
M	12.2	SW	50	NE	1967	58	6.5	6	11	14	12	0	2	3	*	0	0	0	1013.2
J	11.3	SW	40	NW	1959	63	6.2	7	10	13	11	0	4	2	2	0	0	0	1014.9
J	10.8	SW	45	N	1964	66	6.2	7	12	12	9	0	5	2	5	0	0	0	1013.9
A	10.8	SW	45	SW	1971	67	5.6	9	11	11	10	0	4	2	3	0	0	0	1016.0
S	11.4	SW	57	S	1960	63	5.5	10	8	12	9	0	2	2	1	0	0	0	1017.3
O	12.2	SW	45	NW	1963	61	5.5	11	8	12	9	0	1	2	0	0	1	0	1018.5
N	13.1	SW	54	NE	1968	51	6.4	8	7	15	12	*	*	2	0	*	6	0	1014.9
D	13.8	WNW	49	NW	1962	52	6.2	9	7	15	12	2	*	1	0	5	21	*	1016.8
YR	12.6	SW	61	NW	JAN 1974	59	6.1	99	105	161	128	11	19	23	11	26	98	1	1015.2

FOOTNOTES

Means and extremes above are from existing and comparable exposures. Annual extremes have been exceeded at other sites in the locality as follows: **Highest temperature** 104 in July 1911; lowest temperature -18 in February 1934; minimum monthly precipitation T in March 1915; **fastest** mile wind 87 S in September 1938.

Station: WORCESTER, MASSACHUSETTS MUNICIPAL AIRPORT

Elevation (ground): 986 feet

TEMPERATURES °F

Month	Normal			Extremes			
	Daily maximum	Daily minimum	Monthly	Record highest	Year	Record lowest	Year
(a)				20		20	
J	31.0	16.2	23.6	60	1974	-19	1957
F	33.1	17.0	25.1	63	1957	-12	1967
M	41.2	25.3	33.3	72	1968	-4	1967
A	54.9	35.6	45.3	88	1962	14	1969
M	66.1	45.4	55.8	92	1962	28	1970
J	75.0	55.1	65.1	93	1956	38	1972
J	79.4	60.8	70.1	94	1964	46	1963
A	77.2	59.0	68.1	96	1975	38	1965
S	70.1	51.9	61.0	89	1973	30	1957
O	60.6	42.5	51.6	85	1963	20	1969
N	47.3	32.5	39.9	70	1975	9	1972
D	34.3	20.1	27.2	66	1966	-13	1962
YR	55.8	38.4	47.1	96	AUG 1975	-19	JAN 1957

IMPORTANT:
The time-period covered by this record is limited: See footnotes on next page for explanation and for additional history of EXTREME HIGHS AND LOWS recorded in the general area.

Worcester Municipal Airport is located on the crest of a hill, 1,000 feet above mean sea level and about 500 feet above and 3 1/2 miles northwest of the City proper. It is surrounded by ridges and valleys with many of the latter containing reservoirs. However, of the ridges, only two of them are higher, one 400 feet higher and 2 1/2 miles northwest, and the other 1,000 feet higher and 15 miles north.

The proximity to the Atlantic Ocean, Long Island Sound, and the Berkshire Hills plays an important part in determining the weather and, hence, the climate of Worcester. Rapid weather changes occur when storms move up the east coast after developing through wave action off the Carolina Coast. In the majority of these cases, the waves pass to the south and east, resulting in northeast and easterly winds with rain or snow and fog. Storms developing in the Texas-Oklahoma area normally pass up the St. Lawrence River Valley, and, while much depends upon the movement and scope of these systems, usually deposit little precipitation over the area, however, they do bring an influx of warm air into the region. Wintertime cold wave snaps incidental to Canadian High Pressures Areas following cold front passages are quite frequent, but a tempering of the temperatures usually occurs before the full impact of the high reaches the county. Summertime thunderstorms develop over the hills to the west, with a majority moving towards the northeast. From the use of radar, we find many break up just before reaching Worcester, or pass either north or south of the City proper.

Airport site temperatures are moderate, as the normal mean for the warmest month, July, is 70.1°. Though winters are reasonably cold, prolonged periods of severe cold weather are extremely rare. The three coldest months, December through February, together have an average normal of over 25°. The coldest temperature since 1949 was -19° on January 15, 1957, while the warmest was 99° on September 2, 1953. A review of Worcester Cooperative records since 1901 shows an alltime high temperature of 102° on July 4, 1911, and an alltime low temperature of -24° on February 16, 1943. The average last freezing temperature in spring at the airport is April 26. The average first freezing temperature in fall is October 15. In this regard about two-thirds of both spring and fall dates fall within 10 days of the average. Airport temperatures produce an average season of 172 days without freezing. In comparison, the Worcester Cooperative records at Winter Hill show the average latest date in spring as May 7 and the average first freezing date in fall as October 3, resulting in a season of 149 days without freezing temperatures, which is 23 days less than the airport site. Some low-lying valleys are more frost prone than either Winter Hill or the airport. Local topography greatly affects this climatic factor.

Precipitation is usually plentiful and well distributed throughout the year. Monthly normals average 3.78 inches, ranging from slightly less than 3 inches in February, the driest month, to over 4 inches in August and November.

The snowfall for all Worcester sites since 1901 averages slightly less than 60 inches. Due partly to several unusually heavy March storms in recent years, the airport location now averages considerably higher

Normals, Means, and Extremes

(To better understand these tables, see full explanation of terms beginning on page 322)

Month	Normal Degree days Base 65 °F		Precipitation in inches: Water equivalent							Precipitation in inches: Snow, Ice pellets				Relative humidity pct.				Wind					Pct. of possible sunshine	Mean sky cover, tenths, sunrise to sunset	Mean number of days: Sunrise to sunset							Temperatures °F Max.		Temperatures °F Min.		Average station pressure mb.
	Heating	Cooling	Normal	Maximum monthly	Year	Minimum monthly	Year	Maximum in 24 hrs.	Year	Maximum monthly	Year	Maximum in 24 hrs.	Year	Hour 01 (Local time)	Hour 07	Hour 13	Hour 19	Mean speed m.p.h.	Prevailing direction	Fastest mile Speed m.p.h.	Fastest mile Direction	Fastest mile Year			Clear	Partly cloudy	Cloudy	Precipitation .01 inch or more	Snow, Ice pellets 1.0 inch or more	Thunderstorms	Heavy fog, visibility ¼ mile or less	(b) 90° and above	32° and below	32° and below	0° and below	Elev. 1017 feet m.s.l.
(a)				20		20		20		20		20		20	20	20	20	20	8	20	20			19	20	20	20	20	20	20	20	20	20	20	20	3
J	1283	0	3.35	8.11	1958	0.89	1970	2.32	1964	44.0	1966	18.7	1961	71	74	60	66	12.5	WSW	60	25	1959		6.0	9	9	13	11	4	*	6	0	17	30	4	978.9
F	1117	0	3.18	5.60	1971	1.26	1968	2.46	1973	45.2	1962	24.0	1962	70	73	59	64	12.2	WNW	76	32	1956		6.3	7	7	14	11	4	*	6	0	14	28	2	977.4
M	983	0	3.85	7.96	1972	1.62	1957	3.89	1968	36.5	1958	16.6	1960	69	71	55	61	11.8	W	76	29	1956		6.6	8	7	16	11	4	1	8	0	6	27	*	976.4
A	591	0	3.83	6.61	1958	1.62	1966	2.35	1959	11.3	1956	10.2	1956	68	66	49	55	11.5	W	54	05	1956		6.4	7	9	14	11	1	1	7	0	*	13	0	975.3
M	295	10	3.97	7.83	1972	0.86	1959	3.03	1967	T	1970	T	1970	72	67	49	58	10.5	SW	48	27	1956		6.5	6	10	15	12	0	3	7	*	0	1	0	977.2
J	61	64	3.60	9.25	1972	1.26	1969	3.19	1974	0.0		0.0		77	72	55	66	9.2	SW	39	25	1958		6.5	6	11	13	11	0	4	9	1	0	0	0	979.7
J	10	168	3.62	8.11	1959	1.00	1957	2.64	1959	0.0		0.0		77	74	56	67	8.7	SW	43	32	1957		6.4	6	12	13	10	0	5	7	1	0	0	0	979.1
A	24	121	4.19	5.86	1970	1.08	1956	3.17	1970	0.0		0.0		80	77	57	70	8.5	SW	34	27	1956		5.8	C	12	11	10	0	4	7	1	0	0	0	981.2
S	144	24	3.52	13.13	1974	0.83	1957	4.79	1960	0.0		0.0		83	81	61	75	9.0	SW	35	05	1961		5.8	9	9	12	9	0	2	8	0	0	*	0	981.6
O	415	0	3.54	8.56	1962	1.46	1963	3.77	1959	4.7	1962	4.7	1962	78	78	56	69	9.8	WSW	43	25	1958		5.6	11	8	12	8	*	1	7	0	0	5	0	982.2
N	753	0	4.66	10.40	1972	2.00	1973	2.98	1972	20.7	1971	14.8	1971	76	78	61	70	10.6	WSW	54	20	1956		6.7	7	7	16	12	1	*	8	0	2	17	0	978.1
D	1172	0	3.93	9.83	1973	1.86	1958	2.60	1973	32.1	1970	15.6	1961	75	77	64	71	11.3	WSW	51	23	1957		6.4	7	8	16	12	4	*	7	0	14	28	1	979.1
YR	6848	387	45.24	13.13	SEP 1974	0.83	SEP 1957	4.79	SEP 1960	45.2	FEB 1962	24.0	FEB 1962	75	74	57	66	10.5	W	76	29	MAR 1956		6.3	91	109	165	128	18	21	85	3	54	147	7	978.9

FOOTNOTES

Means and extremes above are from existing and comparable exposures. Annual extremes have been exceeded at other sites in the locality as follows: Highest temperature 102 in July 1911; lowest temperature -24 in February 1943; maximum monthly precipitation 18.68 in August 1955; minimum monthly precipitation 0.04 in March 1915; maximum precipitation in 24 hours 8.67 in August 1955.

Snowfall

Season	July	Aug	Sept	Oct	Nov	Dec	Jan
1936-37	0.0	0.0	0.0	0.0	3.9	1.8	6.9
1937-38	0.0	0.0	0.0	0.0	2.9	6.2	26.2
1938-39	0.0	0.0	0.0	0.0	11.7	5.7	8.1
1939-40	0.0	0.0	0.0	0.0	0.1	8.9	9.0
1940-41	0.0	0.0	0.0	T	12.2	4.7	25.4
1941-42	0.0	0.0	0.0	0.0	T	1.5	7.4
1942-43	0.0	0.0	0.0	0.0	0.6	11.1	25.1
1943-44	0.0	0.0	0.0	0.0	5.4	0.5	4.0
1944-45	0.0	0.0	0.0	0.0	5.0	9.2	21.7
1945-46	0.0	0.0	0.0	0.0	7.5	33.7	24.1
1946-47	0.0	0.0	0.0	0.0	T	11.8	5.1
#1947-48	0.0	0.0	0.0	0.0	3.5	26.2	37.7
1948-49	0.0	0.0	0.0	0.0	1.6	9.9	16.1
1949-50	0.0	0.0	0.0	0.0	3.2	9.7	7.6
1950-51	0.0	0.0	0.0	0.0	T	6.6	14.7
1951-52	0.0	0.0	0.0	0.0	2.5	12.8	17.9
1952-53	0.0	0.0	0.0	T	T	3.8	16.0
#1953-54	0.0	0.0	0.0	0.0	2.0	1.7	22.9
1954-55	0.0	0.0	0.0	0.0	1.0	6.2	T
1955-56	0.0	0.0	0.0	0.0	4.3	2.2	10.0
1956-57	0.0	0.0	0.0	0.0	0.2	18.2	21.7
1957-58	0.0	0.0	0.0	T	T	2.2	29.5
1958-59	0.0	0.0	0.0	T	1.4	10.2	8.9
1959-60	0.0	0.0	0.0	0.0	0.1	8.5	16.6
1960-61	0.0	0.0	0.0	3.6	T	20.8	32.4
1961-62	0.0	0.0	0.0	0.9	8.3	20.3	2.0
1962-63	0.0	0.0	0.0	4.7	3.6	18.1	11.7
1963-64	0.0	0.0	0.0	0.5	T	16.7	14.9
1964-65	0.0	0.0	0.0	2.1	T	11.7	18.7
1965-66	0.0	0.0	0.0	T	0.6	2.3	44.0
1966-67	0.0	0.0	0.0	0.0	0.7	13.6	2.5
1967-68	0.0	0.0	0.0	0.0	9.8	22.2	18.6
1968-69	0.0	0.0	0.0	0.0	15.3	12.2	1.8
1969-70	0.0	0.0	0.0	T	0.3	29.5	7.7
1970-71	0.0	0.0	0.0	T	T	32.1	16.6
1971-72	0.0	0.0	0.0	0.0	20.7	9.6	6.7
1972-73	0.0	0.0	0.0	T	6.1	13.8	17.9
1973-74	0.0	0.0	0.0	0.0	T	0.9	12.5
1974-75	0.0	0.0	0.0	T	1.2	13.1	22.6
1975-76	0.0	0.0	0.0	T	1.5	18.1	
RECORD MEAN	0.0	0.0	0.0	0.6	3.5	14.7	15.9

Heating Degree Days

Season	July	Aug	Sept	Oct	Nov	Dec	Jan
1955-56	0	18	165	419	843	1348	1203
1956-57	36	29	265	402	724	1071	1487
1957-58	17	50	129	460	708	959	1232
1958-59	18	21	182	542	722	1365	1297
1959-60	4	22	137	453	762	1067	1239
1960-61	19	31	186	495	688	1288	1426
1961-62	24	29	88	382	758	1175	1280
1962-63	35	48	217	483	825	1258	1310
1963-64	28	46	256	277	655	1383	1167
1964-65	36	80	189	472	704	1122	1362
1965-66	14	61	163	486	843	1076	1320
1966-67	4	19	218	489	649	1141	1097
1967-68	4	28	151	422	912	1087	1414
1968-69	8	31	79	375	830	1264	1286
1969-70	19	15	163	468	773	1224	1547
1970-71	2	12	174	410	738	1319	1461
1971-72	3	35	98	258	844	1061	1189
1972-73	16	41	171	622	897	1152	1200
1973-74	6	8	202	420	750	1017	1191
1974-75	6	9	190	592	760	1063	1158
1975-76	2	47	223	413	586	1161	

Cooling Degree Days

Year	Jan	Feb	Mar	Apr	May	June	July
1969	0	0	0	5	17	98	131
1970	0	0	0	0	16	70	197
1971	0	0	0	0	0	87	184
1972	0	0	0	0	9	41	215
1973	0	0	0	1	11	118	201
1974	0	0	0	4	8	59	159
1975	0	0	0	0	33	69	218

Feb	Mar	Apr	May	June	Total
T	8.2	3.8	0.0	0.0	24.6
8.7	1.9	T	0.0	0.0	45.9
8.9	17.0	0.4	0.0	0.0	51.8
26.8	4.3	0.0	0.0	0.0	49.1
2.0	19.1	0.0	0.0	0.0	63.4
9.2	11.0	6.4	0.0	0.0	35.5
5.5	12.3	1.7	0.0	0.0	56.3
7.3	13.9	0.2	0.0	0.0	31.3
23.2	3.9	0.0	1.5	0.0	64.5
18.1	T	1.3	0.0	0.0	84.7
9.3	6.6	5.3	T	0.0	38.1
17.0	14.0	T	0.0	0.0	98.4
12.8	15.8	T	0.0	0.0	56.2
29.4	11.8	2.7	0.0	0.0	64.4
7.9	7.4	0.0	0.0	0.0	36.6
20.3	9.5	T	0.0	0.0	63.0
11.3	1.3	5.8	T	0.0	38.2
4.6	T	T	0.0	0.0	31.2
4.0	8.0	2.0	0.0	0.0	21.2
21.6	35.4	11.3	0.0	0.0	84.8
6.2	11.3	8.0	0.0	0.0	65.6
20.1	36.5	9.2	T	0.0	97.5
11.3	32.9	T	0.0	0.0	64.7
13.2	26.6	1.5	0.0	0.0	66.5
20.4	17.6	9.5	0.0	0.0	104.3
45.2	4.5	1.8	T	0.0	83.0
22.2	15.3	0.1	T	0.0	75.7
27.3	6.0	1.2	0.0	0.0	66.6
5.9	17.7	6.7	0.0	0.0	62.8
19.7	5.8	0.8	T	0.0	73.2
35.5	34.6	7.3	T	0.0	94.2
6.4	9.2	T	0.0	0.0	66.2
39.5	6.9	T	0.0	0.0	75.7
11.4	19.9	3.3	T	0.0	72.1
11.4	12.1	7.8	0.0	0.0	80.0
35.0	20.1	7.2	0.0	0.0	99.3
5.8	0.4	0.4	0.0	0.0	44.4
15.0	1.7	3.7	0.0	0.0	33.8
21.9	4.9	1.4	0.0	0.0	65.1
19.8	16.0	4.1	T	0.0	74.6

Average Temp

Year	Jan	Feb	Mar	Apr	May	June	July	Aug	Sept	Oct	Nov	Dec	Annual
1936	24.0	19.3	40.6	43.1	59.3	65.4	69.3	69.4	61.5	51.0	35.7	32.1	47.6
1937	33.1	30.9	31.0	44.1	58.4	66.4	70.4	72.7	60.0	49.2	40.4	27.5	48.7
1938	23.6	28.9	37.5	48.2	54.7	66.4	70.8	71.7	59.5	54.9	42.7	29.3	49.0
1939	24.1	28.2	30.6	41.4	57.7	65.5	70.2	72.1	61.1	51.0	36.7	29.3	47.3
1940	19.3	27.0	29.8	41.4	55.1	64.0	70.6	66.1	60.3	46.9	39.0	35.4	46.2
1941	22.1	25.9	29.8	51.3	58.7	66.6	70.7	67.0	62.6	51.3	43.7	32.1	48.5
1942	24.2	23.3	37.9	49.6	60.6	66.6	69.4	68.2	62.6	52.6	39.8	24.2	48.2
1943	22.7	27.0	31.9	40.6	57.2	69.0	71.2	68.2	60.1	51.0	38.8	24.9	46.9
1944	26.8	25.7	31.6	42.2	62.5	65.6	71.8	72.0	62.7	50.6	39.6	26.2	48.1
1945	20.2	26.3	44.9	50.7	53.4	65.4	70.1	67.7	63.5	49.0	41.6	23.5	48.0
1946	24.3	22.8	44.4	43.9	55.2	64.4	69.0	64.4	63.2	54.7	43.8	29.9	48.3
1947	27.9	26.0	33.6	44.7	56.1	62.9	71.8	70.8	61.2	57.0	37.0	26.1	47.9
#1948	18.6	22.5	35.7	45.9	54.7	62.5	71.6	71.0	63.9	50.5	44.4	30.7	47.7
1949	29.8	29.2	35.0	47.4	57.6	69.6	74.2	71.8	59.5	55.5	37.7	31.2	49.9
1950	31.5	21.9	27.9	42.7	54.4	65.6	69.4	67.4	57.0	52.1	42.6	28.5	46.7
1951	27.9	29.2	33.9	46.8	56.6	63.1	70.2	67.3	61.2	51.2	36.2	29.1	47.7
1952	27.2	27.3	32.4	47.2	53.8	67.3	74.3	68.8	62.1	48.5	40.4	30.5	48.3
1953	29.6	29.7	35.7	45.2	56.8	67.3	69.7	68.8	63.0	53.4	43.8	34.7	49.8
#1954	21.4	32.4	34.0	47.2	53.3	64.5	68.2	65.1	58.4	54.5	39.7	28.8	47.3
1955	23.7	27.9	32.7	46.5	59.9	63.9	73.8	71.2	60.3	51.4	36.8	21.3	47.5
1956	26.3	27.1	28.5	40.5	52.1	66.7	67.6	68.5	57.2	52.3	40.7	30.3	46.5
1957	16.8	29.8	34.8	47.3	55.6	67.4	69.0	65.4	62.4	49.9	41.2	33.8	47.8
1958	25.1	19.1	34.3	46.4	52.7	59.9	68.7	67.4	59.6	47.4	40.8	20.9	45.2
1959	23.0	21.6	32.0	46.5	59.9	63.0	70.8	70.7	64.4	50.4	39.3	30.4	47.7
1960	24.8	28.3	26.1	46.0	57.4	64.5	67.7	67.3	59.5	48.8	41.9	23.2	46.3
1961	18.7	27.7	33.0	41.8	53.7	66.0	69.4	67.8	66.0	52.4	39.5	26.9	46.9
1962	23.5	22.1	34.3	45.0	55.0	65.0	66.0	66.1	58.2	49.2	37.3	24.2	45.5
1963	22.5	19.9	34.0	44.9	55.8	65.5	70.0	65.8	56.5	56.8	42.9	20.2	46.2
1964	27.2	23.9	35.2	43.7	58.9	64.3	68.6	63.4	59.3	49.6	41.2	28.4	47.0
1965	20.9	24.3	31.3	42.9	58.9	63.7	68.2	67.4	61.1	49.1	36.7	30.1	46.2
1966	22.2	25.8	34.2	42.0	52.9	65.4	70.7	68.1	58.2	49.0	43.1	28.0	46.7
1967	29.4	20.5	28.8	41.7	48.8	66.1	70.7	67.8	60.6	51.5	34.4	29.8	45.9
1968	19.2	20.0	35.6	48.5	53.8	62.2	71.2	68.0	63.5	53.0	37.1	24.0	46.3
1969	23.2	25.1	30.8	48.8	56.3	66.3	68.4	70.4	60.8	49.7	39.1	25.3	47.0
1970	14.9	24.2	30.4	44.6	56.9	63.7	71.1	70.1	60.6	51.7	40.2	22.2	45.9
1971	17.7	25.9	29.9	42.5	54.2	65.6	70.6	68.2	63.4	56.5	36.6	30.5	46.8
1972	26.4	23.3	30.4	40.4	55.7	62.2	71.1	66.9	59.7	44.7	34.9	27.6	45.3
1973	26.1	24.7	40.9	46.3	54.2	67.4	71.1	71.7	60.1	51.3	39.8	31.9	48.8
1974	26.4	23.9	33.5	47.5	52.4	64.0	69.7	69.7	59.7	45.8	39.4	30.4	46.9
1975	27.5	25.2	31.3	40.8	60.1	63.6	71.8	67.5	57.3	51.5	45.2	27.3	47.4
RECORD MEAN	24.2	25.2	32.6	44.9	55.5	65.0	70.1	68.1	60.4	51.0	39.6	27.8	47.0
MAX	31.9	33.3	40.5	54.5	65.8	74.8	79.3	77.2	69.3	60.1	47.1	35.0	55.7
MIN	16.5	17.0	24.7	35.2	45.1	55.1	60.8	58.9	51.4	41.9	32.1	20.5	38.3

# Indicates a station move or relocation of instruments.

WORCESTER, MA

Feb	Mar	Apr	May	June	Total
1090	1127	728	400	62	7403
979	927	528	302	51	6801
1280	941	553	378	167	6874
1208	1017	549	222	125	7268
1056	1198	564	231	70	6803
1036	985	685	363	41	7243
1195	943	596	329	70	6869
1257	953	599	290	85	7360
1187	921	632	224	92	6868
1136	1040	658	206	118	7123
1093	948	685	376	80	7145
1242	1115	691	493	73	7231
1300	904	490	343	126	7181
1111	1056	487	282	49	6858
1137	1068	604	261	99	7378
1087	1083	667	327	61	7341
1203	1065	733	290	116	6895
1120	738	555	338	37	6887
1145	969	520	391	82	6701
1110	1037	721	180	104	6930

Aug	Sept	Oct	Nov	Dec	Total
192	44	1	0	0	488
177	50	6	0	0	516
141	57	2	0	0	471
109	20	0	0	0	394
224	62	0	0	0	617
164	36	0	0	0	430
132	0	1	0	0	453

Precipitation

Year	Jan	Feb	Mar	Apr	May	June	July	Aug	Sept	Oct	Nov	Dec	Annual
1936	7.45	2.69	11.13	3.24	3.58	2.18	2.93	5.61	3.05	4.15	1.38	7.77	55.16
1937	4.85	2.22	3.38	4.74	3.81	3.63	1.61	4.22	3.98	4.20	8.87	2.81	48.32
1938	4.54	2.04	2.27	3.20	3.56	7.39	11.41	2.54	10.82	2.46	3.15	3.64	57.02
1939	2.61	3.73	4.46	3.42	1.78	4.60	2.61	4.29	1.99	4.87	0.98	3.52	38.86
1940	2.89	3.45	4.39	5.98	5.24	2.60	4.02	1.39	2.37	1.30	6.53	2.94	43.10
1941	2.81	2.28	1.94	0.85	2.02	3.21	2.40	2.22	1.11	2.42	3.35	3.31	27.92
1942	3.57	3.66	7.62	1.26	3.00	3.79	4.81	2.70	2.44	3.46	5.23	5.96	47.50
1943	2.53	1.52	3.30	4.27	5.15	3.40	5.16	1.93	0.58	5.35	3.50	0.84	37.53
1944	1.29	2.20	4.36	4.16	1.03	5.35	0.63	0.90	5.44	1.74	5.47	3.25	35.82
1945	3.38	3.73	2.35	4.40	6.22	6.79	3.65	3.78	1.78	2.03	5.43	5.21	48.75
1946	3.32	3.31	1.55	2.43	6.50	3.02	3.45	7.01	4.01	0.94	1.50	3.27	40.31
1947	2.85	1.65	3.36	4.72	4.16	3.33	4.98	1.07	3.33	1.17	4.76	2.36	37.74
#1948	3.15	2.05	3.30	3.44	7.38	6.27	6.35	2.21	0.98	3.33	6.23	2.65	47.34
1949	3.83	2.75	1.52	4.07	3.77	0.97	1.82	2.90	2.70	1.81	2.77	2.55	31.46
1950	4.21	3.36	3.62	3.85	3.16	2.45	2.63	4.76	1.97	2.32	6.13	3.65	42.11
1951	3.05	5.00	4.86	2.90	4.46	3.11	1.45	4.12	2.44	4.83	7.28	4.42	47.92
1952	4.43	2.35	3.59	4.94	4.20	5.49	1.54	6.67	2.44	1.59	2.47	4.22	43.93
1953	5.73	3.38	8.59	5.08	5.87	1.94	2.73	2.06	0.96	6.72	4.34	5.20	52.60
#1954	1.78	2.29	3.92	4.60	5.10	3.56	2.09	9.16	8.65	3.45	4.78	5.52	54.90
1955	0.59	3.04	4.06	3.41	2.82	3.08	3.07	18.68	2.61	10.98	4.54	0.68	57.56
1956	5.07	3.74	3.79	2.75	2.25	2.34	3.62	1.08	3.73	2.45	3.28	3.88	37.98
1957	1.60	1.42	1.62	3.91	2.82	3.23	1.00	2.49	0.83	3.00	5.78	6.92	34.62
1958	8.11	2.75	4.20	6.61	3.64	2.56	5.81	3.88	6.92	3.01	4.77	1.86	54.12
1959	3.92	2.75	5.56	5.93	0.86	5.28	8.11	4.32	2.42	8.25	5.30	4.74	57.44
1960	3.09	5.44	3.96	4.57	5.59	2.07	7.50	3.58	6.62	2.65	3.68	3.44	52.19
1961	3.02	3.28	4.05	5.72	3.40	2.29	4.42	4.90	5.66	2.68	3.41	3.35	46.18
1962	4.15	4.82	2.03	3.44	3.99	3.16	1.97	4.15	5.42	8.56	3.85	3.94	49.48
1963	3.10	3.03	4.63	1.89	3.00	2.48	1.88	2.65	4.38	1.46	8.20	2.38	39.08
1964	5.42	3.54	3.65	4.01	1.18	1.77	3.02	2.93	1.78	2.26	3.17	4.92	37.65
1965	1.71	4.30	2.37	3.56	1.51	3.14	1.03	3.40	2.83	3.02	2.90	2.21	31.98
1966	4.22	4.05	2.52	1.62	3.21	1.91	3.76	1.95	5.59	4.13	4.93	3.05	40.94
1967	2.38	3.15	3.73	5.10	7.01	3.72	5.91	3.47	5.06	1.83	3.65	5.72	50.73
1968	3.00	1.26	7.67	2.24	6.83	7.78	1.06	1.25	1.94	1.88	5.75	6.16	46.82
1969	1.29	3.04	2.53	5.30	3.09	1.26	3.81	3.34	6.16	1.78	6.81	7.69	46.10
1970	0.89	5.47	3.51	3.44	4.18	3.88	1.08	5.86	2.17	3.47	3.75	3.09	40.79
1971	1.97	5.60	1.93	1.71	5.22	1.88	5.27	4.67	4.23	3.66	5.01	2.68	43.83
1972	2.34	4.91	7.96	4.29	7.83	9.25	6.39	2.89	4.98	4.93	10.40	5.49	71.66
1973	4.04	3.30	3.50	6.33	4.73	6.98	3.82	4.29	3.80	4.63	2.00	9.83	57.25
1974	3.54	2.75	5.05	3.24	5.15	4.35	3.22	3.50	13.13	3.45	3.06	6.04	56.48
1975	5.35	3.52	3.37	2.66	2.07	3.32	3.92	4.59	7.21	6.06	5.28	4.61	51.96
RECORD MEAN	3.40	3.49	4.00	3.97	3.85	3.48	3.40	4.35	4.25	3.88	4.74	4.38	47.19

Record mean values above are means through the current year for the period beginning in 1948 for temperature and precipitation, 1956 for snowfall.

DETROIT, MICHIGAN

Detroit and the immediate suburbs, including nearby urban areas in Canada, occupy an area approximately 20 miles in radius. Complete weather records, made within a few miles of the urban center until 1966, are listed with subsequent temperature and precipitation records for Detroit City Airport. Complete data are now gathered at Metropolitan Airport, near the southwest edge of the urban area. These are listed with earlier partial records from that vicinity. Data for the Windsor Airport, near the southeast edge of the metropolitan complex, are published by the Atmospheric Environment Service of Canada.

The waterway, consisting of the Detroit and St. Clair Rivers, Lake St. Clair, and the west end of Lake Erie, lies at an elevation of 568 to 580 feet above sea level. Nearly flat land slopes up gently from the water's edge northwestward for about 10 miles and then gives way to increasingly rolling terrain. The Irish Hills, parallel to and about 40 miles northwest of the waterway, have tops 1,000 to 1,250 feet above sea level. On the Canadian side of the waterway the land is relatively level.

The slope of the land dries northwest winds and has an opposite effect on southeast winds. Northwest winds in winter bring snow flurries to all of Michigan. Flurries build up snow accumulations in many places, but in Detroit they rarely cause enough snow to be measured. Summer showers moving from the northwest also weaken and sometimes dissipate as they approach Detroit. On the other hand, much of the heaviest precipitation in winter comes with southeast winds, and this may be heavier in the Detroit area, especially to the northwest of the City, than in other places affected by the same storms.

Detroit's climate is controlled by (1) its location with respect to major storm tracks and (2) the influence of the Great Lakes. The normal wintertime storm track is south of the City, and most passing storms bring periods of snow or rain. In summer most storms pass to the north, often with brief showers in the area and occasionally with heavy thundershowers or damaging winds. The Great Lakes smooth out most climatic extremes. Precipitation is distributed evenly through all months of the year. The most pronounced lake effect occurs in the colder part of the winter. Arctic air moving across the lakes is warmed and moistened. Cold waves approaching from the northern plains are much reduced in intensity. But the price is an excess of cloudiness and very little sunshine in the winter.

Summers in Detroit are warm and sunny. Brief showers usually occur every few days, but often fall on only part of the metropolitan area. Extended periods of drought are unusual. Each year sees two or three series of days with temperatures in the nineties. The highest temperatures are often accompanied by high humidity. Most summer days are quite comfortable, and air conditioning is required only intermittently. In winter skies are cloudy and temperatures average near the freezing point. Day to day changes are not large. The mercury drops to near or a little below zero once or twice each year. Winter storms may bring rain, snow, or both. Freezing rain and sleet are not unusual. Most wintertime precipitation is more or less steady and continues for several hours. Snowstorms average about 3 inches, but heavier amounts accumulate several times each year.

Local climatic variations are due largely to (1) the immediate effect of Lake St. Clair and (2) the urban "heat island." On warm days in late spring or early summer,

Station: DETROIT, MICHIGAN
CITY AIRPORT
Elevation (ground): 619 feet

TEMPERATURES °F

Month	Normal			Extremes			
	Daily maximum	Daily minimum	Monthly	Record highest	Year	Record lowest	Year
(a)				41		41	
J	31.7	19.2	25.5	67	1950	-13	1963
F	33.7	20.1	26.9	68	1944	-16	1934
M	43.1	27.6	35.4	82	1945	-1	1943
A	57.6	38.6	48.1	87	1942	14	1954
M	68.5	48.3	58.4	93	1962	30	1966
J	79.1	59.1	69.1	104	1934	38	1969
J	83.1	63.4	73.3	105	1934	42	1972
A	81.6	62.1	71.9	101	1936	43	1934
S	74.2	54.8	64.5	100	1953	32	1942
O	63.4	45.2	54.3	92	1963	24	1972
N	47.7	34.4	41.1	81	1950	5	1958
D	35.4	23.8	29.6	66	1971	-5	1960
YR	58.3	41.4	49.9	105	JUL 1934	-16	FEB 1934

IMPORTANT:
The time-period covered by this record is limited: See footnotes following table of **NORMALS, MEANS AND EXTREMES** for explanation and for additional history of **EXTREME HIGHS AND LOWS** recorded in the general area.

(Continued)

lake breezes often lower afternoon temperatures by 10° to 15° in the eastern part of the City and the northeastern suburbs. Less pronounced local lake effects occur at other times of the year. The urban effect shows up mostly at night. Comparative readings show nearly uniform maximum temperatures over the metropolitan area. Minimum readings at Metropolitan Airport, in a semi-rural area, average 2.3° lower than those at City Airport, in a typical residential area, and 4.1° lower than those in downtown Detroit. On humid summer nights or on very cold winter nights, the difference can exceed 10°.

The growing season averages 180 days in length, and has ranged from 145 days to 205 days. Average date of the last freezing temperature is April 23; average date of the first freezing temperature is October 21. A freeze has occurred as late as May 12, and as early as September 29. Conditions are usually satisfactory for growth of all vegetation. The cold waters of the Great Lakes inhibit plant growth in the spring until all danger of frost is past, and warm waters delay autumn frosts, making the climate particularly favorable for orchards and small fruit growing.

Air pollution comes primarily from heavy industry spread along both shores of the waterway from Port Huron to Toledo. The most intense source of pollution is along the west bank of the Detroit River from just southwest of the downtown area to opposite Grosse Ile. Although the amount of contamination is very large, air motions both horizontal and vertical are usually sufficient to keep it from becoming a major hazard.

Normals, Means, and Extremes

(To better understand these tables, see full explanation of terms beginning on page 322)

Month	Normal Degree days Base 65 °F: Heating	Cooling	Precipitation in inches — Water equivalent: Normal	Maximum monthly %	Year	Minimum monthly %	Year	Maximum in 24 hrs. %	Year	Snow, Ice pellets: Maximum monthly ¢	Year	Maximum in 24 hrs. $	Year	Relative humidity pct. (Local time): Hour 01	Hour 07	Hour 13	Hour 19	Wind: Mean speed m.p.h.	Prevailing direction	Fastest mile: Speed m.p.h.	Direction	Year	Pct. of possible sunshine $	Mean sky cover, tenths, sunrise to sunset $	Mean number of days $ — Sunrise to sunset: Clear	Partly cloudy	Cloudy	Precipitation .01 inch or more %	Snow, Ice pellets 1.0 inch or more ¢	Thunderstorms	Heavy fog, visibility ¼ mile or less	Temperatures °F Max.: (b) 90° and above	32° and below	Min.: 32° and below	0° and below	Average station pressure mb. Elev. 626 feet m.s.l.
(a)				35		35		35		38		32		38	42	38	42	41	14	9	9		32	32	32	32	32	35	36	41	41	41	41	41	41	
J	1225	0	1.93	4.38	1950	0.23	1961	1.63	1960	21.1	1939	8.4	1957	75	78	69	73	11.6	W	40	22	1974	32	7.8	4	6	21	13	3	*	2	0	16	28	1	
F	1067	0	1.80	4.95	1938	0.10	1969	2.43	1950	15.8	1965	10.0	1965	75	78	65	71	11.5	NW	40	23	1971	43	7.3	4	7	17	12	3	1	1	0	13	26	1	
M	918	0	2.33	4.40	1938	0.47	1958	1.85	1949	15.5	1954	9.8	1934	74	77	60	66	11.5	NW	40	23	1972	49	7.0	5	8	18	13	2	2	1	0	5	22	*	
A	507	0	3.08	6.89	1947	0.74	1946	2.94	1947	6.8	1943	4.2	1942	70	73	53	58	11.1	NW	37	29	1967	52	6.8	6	8	16	12	*	3	1	0	*	8	0	
M	238	33	3.43	8.05	1943	0.58	1934	2.53	1948	0.1	1954	0.1	1954	71	71	51	56	9.9	S	33	35	1972	59	6.4	7	10	14	12	0	4	*	1	0	*	0	
J	26	149	3.04	6.58	1960	1.01	1959	3.53	1968	0.0		0.0		75	74	53	57	9.1	S	40	28	1971	65	6.0	7	12	11	11	0	6	*	3	0	0	0	
J	0	261	2.99	7.05	1969	0.81	1936	2.80	1957	0.0		0.0		75	75	51	55	8.3	S	40	28	1966	70	5.3	9	13	9	9	0	6	*	6	0	0	0	
A	11	225	3.04	7.51	1940	1.07	1936	3.65	1956	0.0		0.0		78	80	53	60	8.1	N	46	30	1968	65	5.4	10	12	9	9	0	5	1	4	0	0	0	
S	80	65	2.30	5.90	1936	0.53	1969	2.56	1959	0.0		0.0		79	83	54	64	8.9	S	36	14	1971	61	5.4	10	10	10	9	0	3	1	1	0	*	0	
O	342	10	2.52	7.80	1954	0.50	1964	3.72	1954	1.0	1943	1.0	1943	76	81	55	65	9.5	S	35	20	1973	56	5.6	10	9	12	9	0	1	1	*	0	2	0	
N	717	0	2.31	4.14	1948	0.57	1939	2.18	1951	9.2	1950	5.6	1951	76	79	64	70	11.3	SW	35	25	1975	35	7.5	4	7	19	11	1	*	1	0	2	13	0	
D	1097	0	2.19	4.60	1957	0.43	1943	2.45	1965	24.0	1951	6.8	1951	76	79	70	74	11.3	SW	43	21	1971	32	7.7	4	6	21	13	2	*	2	0	12	25	*	
YR	6228	743	30.96	8.05	MAY 1943	0.10	FEB 1969	3.72	OCT 1954	24.0	DEC 1951	10.0	FEB 1965	75	77	58	64	10.2	S	46	30	AUG 1968	54	6.5	80	108	177	131	11	32	11	15	48	124	2	

FOOTNOTES

Means and extremes above are from existing and comparable exposures. Annual extremes have been exceeded at other sites in the locality as follows: Lowest temperature -24 in December 1872; maximum monthly precipitation 8.76 in July 1878 (Smithsonian Institution records indicate 15.01 in July 1855); minimum monthly precipitation 0.04 in February 1877; maximum precipitation in 24 hours 4.75 in July 1925; maximum monthly snowfall 38.4 in February 1908; maximum snowfall in 24 hours 24.5 in April 1886; fastest mile of wind 95 from Northwest in June 1890.

$ Data accumulated through 1965.
% Through 1972.
¢ Through 1973.

Snowfall

Season	July	Aug	Sept	Oct	Nov	Dec	Jan
1936-37	0.0	0.0	0.0	0.3	2.0	1.6	4.4
1937-38	0.0	0.0	0.0	T	1.0	6.1	4.4
1938-39	0.0	0.0	0.0	0.0	2.7	6.1	21.1
1939-40	0.0	0.0	0.0	T	T	1.9	5.9
1940-41	0.0	0.0	0.0	0.0	9.1	4.3	6.4
1941-42	0.0	0.0	0.0	0.0	0.5	3.4	3.3
1942-43	0.0	0.0	0.0	T	4.4	9.2	18.4
1943-44	0.0	0.0	0.0	1.0	3.1	0.9	1.9
1944-45	0.0	0.0	0.0	0.0	T	11.8	5.8
1945-46	0.0	0.0	0.0	0.0	0.1	6.8	6.4
1946-47	0.0	0.0	0.0	0.0	0.3	5.3	7.6
1947-48	0.0	0.0	0.0	0.0	3.1	9.4	5.0
1948-49	0.0	0.0	0.0	0.0	T	3.6	4.6
1949-50	0.0	0.0	0.0	0.0	5.5	4.7	9.5
1950-51	0.0	0.0	0.0	0.0	9.2	6.5	15.4
1951-52	0.0	0.0	0.0	T	8.3	24.0	12.0
1952-53	0.0	0.0	0.0	T	T	4.3	9.4
1953-54	0.0	0.0	0.0	0.0	3.0	5.0	6.0
1954-55	0.0	0.0	0.0	T	0.7	6.6	2.9
1955-56	0.0	0.0	0.0	T	4.8	4.8	11.0
1956-57	0.0	0.0	0.0	0.0	6.7	5.4	17.9
1957-58	0.0	0.0	0.0	T	1.7	5.1	3.4
1958-59	0.0	0.0	0.0	0.0	4.5	6.4	15.4
1959-60	0.0	0.0	0.0	T	8.1	6.6	6.7
1960-61	0.0	0.0	0.0	T	1.0	4.5	3.3
1961-62	0.0	0.0	0.0	0.0	T	5.0	5.0
1962-63	0.0	0.0	0.0	T	0.2	11.2	7.5
1963-64	0.0	0.0	0.0	0.0	T	10.3	6.7
1964-65	0.0	0.0	0.0	T	2.6	8.4	7.1
1965-66	0.0	0.0	0.0	T	0.2	1.6	6.7
1966-67	0.0						
1967-68	0.0	0.0	0.0	T	0.4	3.4	11.4
1968-69	0.0	0.0	0.0	0.0	T	3.6	7.7
1969-70	0.0	0.0	0.0	T	3.0	12.1	10.1
1970-71	0.0	0.0	0.0		1.6	12.9	6.7
1971-72	0.0	0.0	0.0	0.0	4.3	2.0	10.8
1972-73	0.0	0.0	0.0	T	1.4	10.6	0.2
1973-74	0.0	0.0	0.0	0.0	T	17.5	
1974-75		0.0	0.0	T			
1975-76							
RECORD MEAN	0.0	0.0	0.0	T	2.5	7.1	7.9

Heating Degree Days

Season	July	Aug	Sept	Oct	Nov	Dec	Jan
1955-56	0	2	80	304	811	1165	1190
1956-57	0	11	172	240	716	929	1355
1957-58	0	7	130	432	713	952	1182
1958-59	1	8	98	323	657	1313	1349
1959-60	0	0	92	408	845	933	1110
1960-61	4	0	53	368	636	1229	1291
1961-62	4	2	64	276	705	1108	1318
1962-63	1	0	162	327	731	1226	1475
1963-64	2	9	100	131	562	1269	1066
1964-65	0	25	110	411	594	1066	1215
1965-66	10	24	85	419	663	894	1346
1966-67	0	0	112	390	703	1090	1077
1967-68	34	19	123	357	781	970	1274
1968-69	4	4	42	331	705	1123	1232
1969-70	0	1	84	401	748	1151	1442
1970-71	1	4	78	298	707	1077	1338
1971-72	0	4	56	148	698	896	1219
1972-73	21	18	91	486	770	1048	1085
1973-74	0	13	114	274	685	1054	1102
1974-75	0	0	126	394	654	1006	1046
1975-76	0	0		296	459	1037	

Cooling Degree Days

Year	Jan	Feb	Mar	Apr	May	June	July
1969	0	0	0	5	33	97	231
1970	0	0	0	18	71	188	328
1971	0	0	0	1	23	248	237
1972	0	0	0	0	41	83	288
1973	0	0	0	4	4	244	324
1974	0	0	0	14	18	150	321
1975	0	0	0	0	128	213	360

Feb	Mar	Apr	May	June	Total
1.8	2.8	T	0.0	0.0	12.9
4.8	2.4	3.9	0.0	0.0	22.6
10.8	1.4	0.7	0.0	0.0	42.8
11.7	9.3	3.4	T	0.0	32.2
4.2	2.8	0.0	0.0	0.0	26.8
9.3	2.2	4.7	0.0	0.0	23.4
2.7	2.9	6.8	0.0	0.0	44.4
11.1	3.9	0.9	0.0	0.0	22.8
7.7	0.3	0.2	T	0.0	25.8
8.7	T	0.0	0.0	0.0	22.0
4.1	9.4	3.3	T	0.0	30.0
4.6	4.5	T	0.0	0.0	26.6
3.1	2.1	0.3	0.0	0.0	13.7
13.0	9.6	0.5	0.0	0.0	42.8
4.4	6.5	0.2	0.0	0.0	42.2
7.3	7.0	T	0.0	0.0	58.6
0.7	1.0	1.2	0.0	0.0	16.6
10.4	15.5	T	0.1	0.0	40.0
10.9	6.2	T	0.0	0.0	27.3
10.6	13.3	0.7	0.0	0.0	45.2
8.9	3.9	2.8	0.0	0.0	45.6
4.1	3.5	0.2	0.0	0.0	18.0
4.3	6.6	T	0.0	0.0	37.2
14.8	11.5	T	T	0.0	47.7
5.1	0.4	3.7	T	0.0	18.0
15.7	2.3	0.1	0.0	0.0	28.1
7.6	3.2	T	T	0.0	29.7
5.1	9.2	1.2	0.0	0.0	32.5
15.8	12.9	2.4	0.0	0.0	49.2
2.5	2.6	0.7	T	0.0	14.3
	5.8	0.2	T		
2.7	8.0	T	0.0	0.0	25.9
1.1	1.5	T	0.0	0.0	13.9
7.9	5.9	2.2	0.0	0.0	41.2
7.4	6.4	0.7	0.0	0.0	
5.9	1.3	0.6	0.0	0.0	24.9
9.0	6.3	T	T	0.0	27.5
		0.0	0.0		
7.7	5.4	1.1	T	0.0	31.7

DETROIT, MI
CITY AIRPORT

Feb	Mar	Apr	May	June	Total
1061	1003	573	310	61	6560
958	867	497	281	52	6078
1173	883	457	228	76	6233
1093	945	486	159	34	6466
1081	1196	446	219	43	6373
950	795	638	295	47	6306
1157	922	486	134	26	6202
1287	838	470	245	26	6788
1040	886	469	113	52	5699
1070	1078	596	121	45	6331
1023	821	558	335	41	6219
1169	928	483	360	5	6317
1148	766	373	259	22	6126
1018	922	474	262	117	6234
1119	1020	494	183	38	6681
1025	990	573	238	27	6356
1141	993	596	165	89	6005
1101	670	484	267	1	6042
1109	874	430	283	27	5965
982	956	643	88	20	5915

Aug	Sept	Oct	Nov	Dec	Total
281	106	4	0	0	757
275	117	19	0	0	1016
224	133	26	0	0	892
190	81	1	0	0	684
275	115	13	0	0	979
277	69	4	1	0	854
306		18	0	0	

Average Temperature

Year	Jan	Feb	Mar	Apr	May	June	July	Aug	Sept	Oct	Nov	Dec	Annual
1936	21.6	16.0	37.6	42.3	62.8	65.8	74.7	73.1	66.2	51.2	35.4	32.2	48.2
1937	29.7	28.2	31.0	44.8	57.9	67.1	72.8	74.0	61.8	48.8	38.4	26.4	48.4
1938	24.3	31.2	41.6	48.2	58.4	67.6	74.0	74.8	61.8	55.0	42.6	30.2	50.8
1939	27.8	26.9	33.5	44.2	61.4	70.2	73.4	73.0	65.9	52.9	38.9	33.4	50.1
1940	19.0	26.7	28.6	42.8	55.7	67.6	73.4	70.4	62.8	52.2	38.0	32.0	47.4
1941	26.2	25.3	30.4	52.6	62.4	70.0	74.4	71.0	67.6	55.2	43.0	35.6	51.1
1942	25.8	22.6	39.5	52.9	59.5	69.0	73.6	70.6	62.6	53.4	41.2	25.6	49.6
1943	21.6	28.0	33.8	42.4	56.6	72.8	73.5	72.2	61.2	50.7	38.2	27.4	48.2
1944	30.8	28.6	31.2	42.9	63.3	71.5	73.6	74.4	65.6	52.8	42.6	24.8	50.2
1945	17.8	27.8	47.9	50.0	52.6	65.3	70.8	71.5	64.7	51.0	41.8	24.7	48.8
1946	28.1	26.6	46.0	47.8	56.6	67.4	73.3	68.4	65.2	58.2	43.9	32.2	51.1
1947	29.3	22.5	30.8	44.7	53.8	66.0	70.8	76.6	65.4	60.3	37.2	29.0	48.9
1948	19.6	24.4	34.8	51.2	55.5	67.3	73.7	72.1	66.1	50.1	45.6	31.7	49.3
1949	31.6	30.7	35.7	47.2	60.4	73.3	76.2	71.9	59.6	57.4	39.0	33.0	51.3
1950	32.6	26.5	30.2	41.5	58.3	68.2	71.1	70.2	63.1	56.4	36.7	25.4	48.4
1951	27.8	27.7	36.5	46.0	59.9	67.8	72.7	69.5	62.5	55.4	34.6	28.4	49.1
1952	29.3	29.3	34.3	49.6	57.3	72.7	76.5	71.5	64.8	48.1	42.8	34.1	50.9
1953	30.6	32.2	37.9	44.5	59.5	70.9	73.5	74.3	64.7	56.8	44.5	33.7	51.9
1954	26.1	33.5	33.5	50.2	54.7	71.3	71.8	70.3	65.6	54.5	41.2	29.7	50.2
1955	26.3	28.4	35.7	54.5	61.9	68.5	79.1	75.7	65.7	55.3	37.7	27.3	51.3
1956	26.4	28.1	32.4	45.7	56.0	69.8	71.8	71.2	60.4	57.5	40.9	34.9	49.6
1957	21.1	30.6	36.9	49.1	56.4	68.7	72.8	70.2	62.9	50.8	41.0	34.1	49.5
1958	26.6	22.8	36.4	49.6	58.4	63.9	72.4	71.0	63.8	55.0	42.9	22.4	48.8
1959	21.3	25.7	34.3	48.6	62.2	70.1	74.1	76.3	67.0	51.9	36.6	34.7	50.2
1960	29.0	27.5	26.3	50.6	58.4	66.9	70.8	71.9	66.9	53.2	43.6	25.2	49.2
1961	23.1	30.8	39.1	43.5	55.8	67.9	73.4	72.2	68.8	56.3	41.3	29.0	50.1
1962	22.3	23.5	35.0	49.6	65.2	69.1	71.0	71.0	61.4	54.6	40.3	25.1	49.0
1963	17.2	18.8	37.6	49.4	57.8	70.8	74.5	70.1	63.1	62.7	46.0	23.8	49.3
1964	30.4	28.9	36.1	49.3	63.7	69.6	76.0	69.1	64.4	51.4	44.9	30.4	51.2
1965	25.5	26.6	30.1	44.9	63.1	67.8	70.4	70.0	66.2	51.3	42.7	35.9	49.6
1966	21.4	28.3	38.3	46.3	54.4	71.2	75.6	71.3	63.4	52.2	41.4	29.5	49.5
1967	30.0	23.1	34.9	48.7	53.4	72.7	70.2	69.1	63.1	54.0	38.7	33.6	49.3
1968	23.7	25.2	40.2	52.5	56.8	70.1	73.7	75.3	68.5	55.6	41.3	28.5	51.0
1969	25.1	28.4	35.0	49.2	57.4	64.1	72.3	73.9	65.5	52.0	39.8	27.6	49.2
1970	18.3	24.8	31.9	48.9	61.2	69.8	75.3	73.5	66.1	55.8	41.3	30.1	49.8
1971	21.6	28.2	32.8	45.6	57.8	72.1	72.4	71.9	67.3	60.8	41.5	35.9	50.7
1972	25.5	25.4	32.8	44.9	60.9	64.6	73.4	70.3	64.4	49.1	39.1	31.0	48.4
1973	29.7	25.4	43.1	48.8	56.2	72.9	75.2	73.2	64.8	56.3	41.9	30.8	51.5
1974	29.2	25.2	36.6	50.9	56.3	68.9	75.1	73.8	62.9	52.2	43.0	32.3	50.5
1975	31.1	29.7	33.9	43.3	66.1	71.2	76.3	74.7		55.8	49.5	31.4	
RECORD MEAN	25.3	25.8	34.5	46.7	58.1	68.2	73.0	71.1	64.2	53.1	40.1	29.5	49.2
MAX	31.6	32.6	42.0	55.6	67.7	77.6	82.4	80.2	73.1	61.3	46.5	35.2	57.2
MIN	18.9	19.0	27.0	37.7	48.5	58.7	63.6	62.0	55.3	44.8	33.7	23.8	41.1

# Indicates a station move or relocation of instruments.

Precipitation

Year	Jan	Feb	Mar	Apr	May	June	July	Aug	Sept	Oct	Nov	Dec	Annual
1936	1.48	2.62	1.28	3.61	0.97	3.87	0.81	1.07	5.90	2.33	1.10	2.04	27.08
1937	3.64	1.64	0.59	5.03	3.07	4.14	7.03	2.51	1.80	2.35	0.97	1.70	34.47
1938	0.87	4.95	4.40	1.86	4.42	2.28	4.26	2.48	1.51	0.94	1.22	1.54	30.73
1939	2.54	4.70	2.38	4.04	0.97	4.70	2.54	1.39	2.70	1.66	0.57	1.02	29.21
1940	1.41	1.29	2.07	2.61	3.59	3.27	1.17	7.51	1.73	2.55	2.75	2.98	32.93
1941	1.46	0.55	1.59	1.55	2.29	2.94	2.14	3.94	0.81	3.09	1.78	1.31	23.45
1942	2.03	1.60	2.38	1.45	4.51	2.31	3.35	4.12	2.95	4.00	2.92	3.42	35.04
1943	2.25	1.52	2.18	4.11	8.05	1.65	6.01	1.12	2.35	1.30	2.07	0.43	33.04
1944	1.20	1.82	2.85	2.62	4.34	3.26	1.20	2.33	1.33	0.73	1.63	1.34	24.65
1945	0.45	1.89	3.50	3.37	6.11	4.47	3.18	1.54	4.40	3.14	1.27	2.08	35.40
1946	1.14	1.79	2.14	0.74	5.08	4.01	1.10	2.01	1.65	2.27	1.36	2.10	25.39
1947	2.63	0.38	2.45	6.89	6.97	3.49	2.42	2.85	3.96	1.31	1.80	1.85	37.00
1948	1.39	2.36	3.32	2.64	4.96	2.79	2.27	2.05	1.79	1.34	4.14	2.35	31.40
1949	2.74	2.68	2.60	2.03	3.96	1.85	4.85	4.40	1.90	5.50	1.23	3.51	37.25
1950	4.38	4.85	2.56	4.92	2.97	2.08	3.90	1.51	2.21	3.56	4.05	2.47	39.46
1951	1.91	3.13	2.60	2.71	3.30	3.13	4.10	2.99	1.97	4.96	3.48	3.50	37.78
1952	3.22	1.60	3.25	3.45	2.87	1.06	3.14	2.18	2.30	1.46	2.87	1.94	29.34
1953	1.90	0.82	2.96	3.32	2.99	3.09	2.65	1.52	1.80	0.63	0.83	1.35	23.86
1954	1.68	3.48	3.87	2.71	1.39	2.97	2.01	2.07	2.38	7.80	1.41	1.72	33.49
1955	1.69	2.49	2.11	2.00	1.16	1.87	1.10	3.75	1.82	4.45	2.38	1.41	26.23
1956	1.09	2.29	3.57	3.78	6.03	1.61	1.20	6.53	0.58	0.61	3.32	2.19	32.80
1957	1.99	1.85	1.76	4.44	2.97	3.23	5.98	1.99	2.91	4.83	3.28	4.60	39.83
1958	0.80	0.67	0.47	1.69	1.16	2.98	3.01	2.25	3.83	1.11	3.17	0.59	21.73
1959	2.81	2.24	2.65	4.73	3.62	1.01	1.27	7.07	4.69	4.61	3.24	2.86	40.80
1960	3.06	2.29	1.13	2.06	2.87	6.58	1.44	2.50	0.78	2.17	1.35	0.44	26.67
1961	0.23	2.20	2.68	5.23	2.54	2.74	2.99	5.12	5.55	1.49	2.96	1.29	35.02
1962	2.39	2.55	1.14	2.26	1.26	4.93	2.60	3.56	2.99	1.76	1.30	1.02	27.76
1963	0.64	0.70	2.47	2.25	2.28	3.10	2.91	1.71	1.28	0.51	1.27	1.37	20.49
1964	2.26	0.52	2.62	4.65	1.68	2.35	2.37	5.87	2.12	0.50	0.81	2.19	27.94
1965	3.74	2.49	3.02	3.04	2.16	2.11	2.99	3.24	4.15	2.88	1.20	3.93	34.95
1966	0.68	1.38	2.21	2.86	2.31	2.97	2.19						
1967			0.96	2.64	1.21				1.68	3.88	2.19	4.45	
1968	1.85	1.63	1.34	1.93	5.60	6.05	4.95	3.59	1.70	1.36	3.22	3.41	36.63
1969	2.52	0.10	1.45	3.67	3.49	3.93	7.05	2.46	0.53	1.02	2.27	1.42	29.91
1970	1.12	0.60	2.15	2.56	2.89	3.01	3.32	1.04	1.76			1.35	
1971	0.92	2.81	1.28		1.51		1.73	3.84	1.48	0.68	0.92	4.06	
1972	1.12	0.77	2.18	3.12	1.99	2.17	2.77	4.92	2.75	2.44	2.79	2.94	29.96
1973	1.41	0.91	4.09	1.38	2.80					1.72	3.20		
1974				2.41	2.28			3.66	1.93	0.71			
1975													
RECORD MEAN	2.08	2.05	2.42	2.72	3.29	3.32	3.16	2.86	2.65	2.39	2.31	2.24	31.49

Record mean values above are means through the current year for the period beginning in 1874 for temperature, 1871 for precipitation and 1936 for snowfall.

GRAND RAPIDS, MICHIGAN

Station: GRAND RAPIDS, MICHIGAN
KENT COUNTY AIRPORT
Elevation (ground): 784 feet

TEMPERATURES °F

Month	Normal			Extremes			
	Daily maximum	Daily minimum	Monthly	Record highest	Year	Record lowest	Year
(a)				12		12	
J	30.3	16.0	23.2	62	1967	-16	1972
F	32.6	16.4	24.5	54	1966	-19	1973
M	42.0	24.2	33.1	75	1967	-5	1967
A	57.3	35.6	46.5	88	1970	10	1965
M	68.8	45.4	57.1	90	1975	22	1966
J	79.1	55.6	67.4	96	1971	33	1972
J	83.3	59.6	71.5	97	1966	43	1972
A	81.9	58.1	70.0	100	1964	41	1964
S	73.9	50.8	62.4	93	1973	28	1974
O	63.1	40.8	52.0	87	1975	18	1974
N	46.2	31.1	38.7	77	1975	5	1975
D	33.9	20.8	27.4	65	1970	-11	1967
YR	57.7	37.9	47.8	100	AUG 1964	-19	FEB 1973

IMPORTANT:
The time-period covered by this record is limited: See footnotes following table of **NORMALS, MEANS AND EXTREMES** for explanation and for additional history of **EXTREME HIGHS AND LOWS** recorded in the general area.

Grand Rapids, Michigan, is located in the west-central part of Kent County, in the picturesque Grand River valley about 30 air miles east of Lake Michigan. The Grand River, the largest stream in Michigan flows through the City and bisects it into east and west sections. The valley has tall bluffs and high hills rising on all sides ranging in elevation from 602 feet on the valley floor to 1,020 feet in the extreme southern part of Kent County, south of the airport.

Grand Rapids is naturally under the climatic influence of Lake Michigan. In spring, the cooling effect of Lake Michigan retards the growth of vegetation until the danger of frost is past. The warming effect in the fall holds off frost until most of the crops are matured. Fall is a delightful time of year in western Michigan, compensating for the late spring. During the winter, excessive cloudiness and numerous snow flurries occur with strong westerly winds and the tempering effect of Lake Michigan on cold waves coming from the northwest is quite evident. The tempering effect of the lake promotes the growth of a great variety of tree fruits and berries, especially peaches and cherries. The intense cold of winter is modified to reduce winter kill of fruit trees. Summer days are pleasantly warm and most summer nights are quite comfortable. Prolonged severe cold waves, with below-zero temperatures, are of infrequent occurrence as the temperature usually rises to above zero during the day hours regardless of the readings of early morning.

The average growing season extends 170 days, with the average date of the last freezing temperature in spring, April 25, and the average date of the first freezing temperature in autumn, October 12. July is the sunniest month, and December the month with the least sunshine. November through January is usually the period of excessive cloudiness and the least sunshine.

(Continued page 496)

Snowfall

Season	July	Aug	Sept	Oct	Nov	Dec	Jan
1936-37	0.0	0.0	0.0	0.8	3.4	6.5	6.3
1937-38	0.0	0.0	0.0	T	4.4	14.9	10.2
1938-39	0.0	0.0	0.0	0.0	5.6	10.8	21.5
1939-40	0.0	0.0	0.0	T	0.8	7.3	16.1
1940-41	0.0	0.0	0.0	0.0	17.3	7.0	10.4
1941-42	0.0	0.0	0.0	0.0	5.4	5.4	31.2
1942-43	0.0	0.0	T	T	5.1	11.5	29.9
1943-44	0.0	0.0	0.0	T	8.8	1.5	3.1
1944-45	0.0	0.0	0.0	0.0	4.9	21.9	17.6
1945-46	0.0	0.0	0.0	T	9.2	19.9	19.4
1946-47	0.0	0.0	0.0	0.0	0.4	15.4	25.0
1947-48	0.0	0.0	0.0	0.0	17.2	9.8	22.8
#1948-49	0.0	0.0	0.0	T	T	5.3	8.1
1949-50	0.0	0.0	0.0	T	7.1	16.5	6.2
1950-51	0.0	0.0	0.0	0.0	17.5	24.0	18.4
1951-52	0.0	0.0	0.0	0.0	26.9	51.3	21.2
1952-53	0.0	0.0	T	T	6.4	9.5	11.0
1953-54	0.0	0.0	0.0	0.0	7.4	12.4	23.7
1954-55	0.0	0.0	0.0	0.4	3.2	12.3	25.1
1955-56	0.0	0.0	0.0	T	18.6	9.4	5.3
1956-57	0.0	0.0	T	0.0	6.1	6.3	25.4
1957-58	0.0	0.0	0.0	T	9.9	17.4	23.6
1958-59	0.0	0.0	0.0	0.0	8.6	26.6	32.6
1959-60	0.0	0.0	0.0	T	15.3	10.6	25.0
1960-61	0.0	0.0	0.0	T	5.9	13.5	30.0
1961-62	0.0	0.0	0.0	0.0	0.6	18.7	36.1
1962-63	0.0	0.0	0.0	2.6	0.8	26.2	42.6
#1963-64	0.0	0.0	0.0	0.0	0.9	21.6	18.6
1964-65	0.0	0.0	0.0	T	5.8	13.4	24.1
1965-66	0.0	0.0	T	0.0	9.1	9.6	25.9
1966-67	0.0	0.0	0.0	0.0	16.6	17.6	29.8
1967-68	0.0	0.0	T	8.4	11.0	9.6	11.8
1968-69	0.0	0.0	0.0	0.0	4.2	26.2	27.7
1969-70	0.0	0.0	0.0	T	14.3	11.8	23.2
1970-71	0.0	0.0	0.0	0.0	6.1	33.3	27.2
1971-72	0.0	0.0	0.0	0.0	14.9	3.7	22.6
1972-73	0.0	0.0	0.0	0.9	11.0	19.8	7.0
1973-74	0.0	0.0	0.0	0.0	0.4	20.0	13.3
1974-75	0.0	0.0	0.0	0.4	8.9	16.5	10.7
1975-76	0.0	0.0	0.0	0.0	6.6	23.3	
RECORD MEAN	0.0	0.0	T	0.8	9.1	17.1	20.2

Heating Degree Days

Season	July	Aug	Sept	Oct	Nov	Dec	Jan
#1955-56	0	4	108	292	847	1180	1255
1956-57	14	33	197	289	757	1018	1393
1957-58	1	19	196	511	794	1039	1290
1958-59	5	22	151	374	722	1373	1462
1959-60	4	0	109	492	937	987	1175
1960-61	17	3	90	413	688	1269	1359
1961-62	4	14	89	374	741	1158	1409
1962-63	10	7	184	372	763	1253	1513
#1963-64	8	36	135	203	620	1345	1157
1964-65	12	54	179	545	690	1202	1310
1965-66	5	50	145	462	743	968	1414
1966-67	0	12	146	426	680	1102	1120
1967-68	38	47	179	477	909	1080	1356
1968-69	30	36	90	434	805	1254	1360
1969-70	3	2	145	524	938	1232	1481
1970-71	13	17	150	397	798	1210	1441
1971-72	15	11	107	233	800	1016	1365
1972-73	28	41	126	577	867	1185	1162
1973-74	1	7	136	314	748	1196	1212
1974-75	5	22	275	555	816	1127	1227
1975-76	16	5	242	382	602	1161	

Cooling Degree Days

Year	Jan	Feb	Mar	Apr	May	June	July
1969	0	0	0	0	21	61	202
1970	0	0	0	19	49	122	242
1971	0	0	0	0	8	218	154
1972	0	0	0	0	37	61	200
1973	0	0	0	10	0	157	238
1974	0	0	0	4	6	60	201
1975	0	0	0	0	65	148	199

GRAND RAPIDS, MICHIGAN

Feb	Mar	Apr	May	June	Total
12.0	3.9	0.9	0.0	0.0	33.8
6.9	2.9	8.7	0.0	0.0	48.0
11.2	11.0	4.9	0.0	0.0	65.0
9.3	19.9	1.6	0.8	0.0	55.8
9.9	10.1	T	0.0	0.0	54.7
12.8	12.2	2.0	0.0	0.0	69.0
9.7	11.0	3.2	0.0	0.0	70.4
8.8	9.1	1.3	0.0	0.0	32.6
8.6	T	T	T	0.0	53.0
25.6	2.2	T	0.0	0.0	76.3
23.1	17.3	3.0	T	0.0	84.2
10.5	17.6	T	T	0.0	77.9
7.9	7.6	1.4	0.0	0.0	30.3
16.5	14.2	0.7	0.0	0.0	61.2
4.8	11.0	5.7	0.0	0.0	81.4
12.6	9.5	10.5	0.0	0.0	132.0
6.7	4.9	1.2	0.0	0.0	39.7
10.9	21.9	T	2.0	0.0	78.3
12.7	15.1	T	0.0	0.0	68.8
22.9	17.5	5.6	0.0	0.0	79.3
8.2	11.1	2.9	0.0	0.0	60.0
10.6	8.8	T	0.0	0.0	70.3
16.6	19.9	0.4	0.0	0.0	104.7
25.6	13.2	1.0	0.0	0.0	90.7
4.2	5.6	15.6	T	0.0	74.8
21.4	8.0	3.1	0.0	0.0	87.9
8.4	5.0	4.1	0.0	0.0	89.7
11.6	16.5	1.2	0.0	0.0	70.4
16.7	36.0	5.4	0.0	0.0	101.4
15.0	4.6	2.8	T	0.0	67.0
17.5	10.3	T	T	0.0	91.8
8.5	4.2	1.6	0.0	0.0	55.1
6.3	7.9	0.0	0.0	0.0	72.3
8.2	19.3	7.8	0.0	0.0	84.6
4.4	25.9	4.1	0.0	0.0	101.0
16.9	14.2	7.5	0.0	0.0	79.8
13.2	8.5	5.0	0.1	0.0	65.5
18.4	11.3	1.0	T	0.0	64.4
10.6	11.8	10.0	0.0	0.0	68.9
12.3	14.2	3.9	T	0.0	77.6

GRAND RAPIDS, MI

Feb	Mar	Apr	May	June	Total
1166	1076	627	316	62	6933
1025	932	539	300	42	6539
1248	929	518	252	122	6919
1187	1031	580	164	27	7098
1157	1268	488	254	65	6936
997	841	675	343	72	6767
1209	997	581	167	35	6778
1342	911	514	307	62	7238
1154	940	501	149	73	6321
1145	1197	657	142	57	7190
1102	860	632	400	47	6828
1242	950	554	410	9	6651
1255	827	482	342	70	7062
1132	1102	550	300	151	7244
1186	1117	559	216	61	7464
1140	1110	626	342	35	7279
1240	1089	675	204	102	6857
1178	708	552	341	4	6769
1225	967	532	364	113	6815
1133	1113	750	191	61	7275

Aug	Sept	Oct	Nov	Dec	Total
229	76	1	0	0	590
180	55	6	0	0	673
129	132	31	0	0	672
163	42	0	0	0	503
255	96	12	0	0	768
103	23	3	0	0	400
184	8	15	0	0	619

Average Temperature

Year	Jan	Feb	Mar	Apr	May	June	July	Aug	Sept	Oct	Nov	Dec	Annual
1936	21.4	15.0	37.2	42.2	62.8	67.2	77.3	73.9	65.8	50.2	36.0	32.4	48.4
1937	28.6	27.2	31.2	45.8	59.8	67.4	74.3	76.0	63.2	49.0	37.9	26.6	48.9
1938	23.8	30.6	42.1	48.2	58.7	67.6	73.4	74.4	61.7	56.6	43.0	30.4	50.9
1939	28.6	27.2	34.2	44.0	62.2	70.1	74.2	72.4	66.0	52.8	40.1	34.0	50.5
1940	20.0	27.1	28.8	44.3	55.8	68.2	74.2	70.6	63.2	53.0	37.8	31.9	47.9
1941	26.2	24.7	30.1	53.4	61.8	70.8	74.4	71.7	67.0	54.4	42.7	35.8	51.1
1942	25.6	22.9	38.0	53.6	59.8	69.4	73.0	71.0	62.0	52.6	41.0	26.4	49.6
1943	21.5	27.4	31.6	43.2	56.2	71.5	74.3	72.0	60.6	50.9	37.4	27.8	47.9
1944	31.0	28.4	30.8	44.2	63.0	70.6	73.4	74.0	65.2	51.8	42.0	25.6	50.0
1945	20.0	27.9	48.2	49.6	53.2	64.8	70.6	71.0	63.0	50.3	40.4	25.4	48.7
1946	27.0	25.7	46.0	49.0	56.4	67.8	73.8	69.2	65.4	57.8	43.0	31.9	51.1
1947	28.2	22.4	31.2	45.5	52.8	65.6	70.8	79.1	65.8	61.4	36.8	30.2	49.2
1948	19.9	25.0	34.8	51.8	55.4	67.2	74.0	73.2	67.4	50.7	44.1	30.9	49.5
1949	30.2	29.2	35.8	48.1	61.0	73.3	76.4	73.0	59.7	57.4	39.2	32.8	51.3
1950	30.1	26.2	30.2	40.9	59.7	67.3	70.7	68.4	62.5	56.9	35.9	25.4	47.8
1951	26.2	28.1	35.3	46.3	61.2	66.8	71.9	68.8	61.3	53.9	32.8	28.4	48.4
1952	28.0	30.1	33.6	49.5	57.6	71.4	74.7	70.6	64.3	46.9	42.0	33.2	50.2
1953	28.8	30.9	37.2	44.2	60.0	71.2	74.1	73.4	64.2	56.8	44.3	33.2	51.5
1954	25.1	34.3	32.6	50.0	55.0	71.7	71.5	69.8	64.7	53.1	42.0	30.0	50.0
#1955	25.8	27.4	34.5	54.7	61.1	68.0	78.9	76.7	64.1	55.7	36.5	26.7	50.9
1956	24.3	24.5	30.1	44.0	55.6	69.5	69.2	69.3	59.6	55.8	39.5	31.9	47.8
1957	19.7	28.2	34.7	47.1	55.9	67.5	72.2	68.8	59.6	48.3	38.3	31.3	47.6
1958	23.2	20.3	34.8	47.5	57.1	62.0	69.3	70.1	61.6	52.7	40.6	20.5	46.6
1959	17.7	22.3	31.5	45.5	62.8	69.7	71.7	75.5	65.4	48.9	33.5	32.9	48.1
1960	26.8	24.8	23.9	48.9	56.7	64.8	69.2	70.6	65.6	51.5	41.8	23.8	47.4
1961	20.9	29.2	37.7	42.3	54.3	65.9	71.4	70.0	67.0	52.9	40.1	27.4	48.3
1962	19.3	21.6	32.6	45.9	63.0	68.2	69.3	70.7	60.4	53.3	39.4	24.5	47.3
#1963	15.9	16.9	35.4	47.6	55.4	69.1	72.1	67.2	61.2	58.8	44.2	21.3	47.1
1964	27.5	25.0	34.5	48.2	62.0	68.9	73.1	67.3	61.4	47.2	41.8	26.0	48.6
1965	22.5	23.8	26.2	42.8	62.3	65.9	70.0	67.9	62.3	50.0	40.0	33.5	47.3
1966	19.1	25.5	37.1	43.8	52.0	69.2	73.6	68.5	61.4	51.2	42.1	29.2	47.7
1967	28.6	20.4	34.1	46.4	51.9	69.3	68.6	66.0	60.3	49.9	34.5	29.9	46.7
1968	21.0	21.4	38.0	48.8	54.0	66.7	69.8	70.6	63.7	51.8	37.9	24.3	47.3
1969	20.8	24.4	29.3	46.4	55.7	61.8	71.3	72.1	62.4	47.9	33.5	25.0	45.9
1970	17.0	22.4	28.8	46.8	59.4	66.8	72.1	70.1	61.7	52.2	38.3	25.7	46.8
1971	18.3	24.1	29.0	43.9	54.0	70.9	69.2	68.6	65.6	58.3	38.0	32.0	47.6
1972	20.8	21.9	29.7	42.3	59.3	63.5	70.3	68.7	62.0	46.1	35.9	26.6	45.6
1973	27.4	22.8	41.9	46.8	53.7	69.9	72.4	72.7	63.4	55.0	39.9	26.2	49.3
1974	25.7	21.1	33.6	47.2	53.2	63.0	71.1	67.3	56.4	46.9	37.6	28.4	46.0
1975	25.2	24.3	28.8	39.8	60.7	67.6	70.6	70.5	57.0	53.0	44.7	27.3	47.5
RECORD MEAN	24.4	24.4	33.9	46.5	57.9	68.0	72.6	70.6	63.2	52.1	39.3	28.5	48.5
MAX	30.8	31.5	41.9	56.3	68.5	78.8	83.3	81.2	73.3	61.3	46.0	34.2	57.3
MIN	18.0	17.2	25.8	36.7	47.2	57.1	61.9	60.0	53.1	42.8	32.5	22.7	39.6

# Indicates a station move or relocation of instruments.

Precipitation

Year	Jan	Feb	Mar	Apr	May	June	July	Aug	Sept	Oct	Nov	Dec	Annual
1936	2.13	2.18	0.73	2.27	0.72	2.35	0.79	3.91	7.67	2.77	0.43	3.72	29.67
1937	2.15	1.62	1.10	4.78	1.86	4.68	1.33	4.11	2.44	2.95	1.97	2.00	30.99
#1938	2.39	5.30	3.35	1.49	6.25	3.22	2.60	3.87	2.21	1.49	1.46	1.80	35.43
1939	2.48	3.29	1.21	4.16	1.12	7.08	0.32	5.80	1.68	2.85	0.77	1.07	31.83
1940	1.28	0.40	1.40	2.04	4.28	3.58	0.90	7.05	0.58	3.02	1.96	1.72	28.21
1941	1.38	0.52	2.03	1.45	3.13	2.03	2.62	4.21	5.00	6.18	3.00	1.61	33.16
1942	2.12	0.89	4.59	0.39	6.83	3.21	3.85	3.99	4.58	3.19	4.07	2.45	40.16
1943	1.92	1.49	2.98	2.36	5.50	3.68	2.46	1.98	1.97	1.31	1.61	0.36	27.62
1944	1.22	1.67	2.14	2.37	2.56	2.95	2.79	1.41	3.29	0.29	1.53	1.24	23.46
1945	0.35	1.19	1.61	3.60	5.32	4.07	1.17	2.05	7.46	2.19	2.55	1.87	33.43
1946	2.36	1.32	1.95	1.07	3.50	2.80	2.10	1.04	1.53	2.07	3.16	2.38	25.28
1947	2.30	0.98	1.91	6.33	4.99	2.41	2.11	1.95	5.75	1.08	2.85	2.31	34.97
1948	1.21	1.72	5.77	4.65	4.08	3.11	2.39	0.97	1.61	0.76	3.26	2.41	31.94
1949	2.54	2.07	2.28	1.95	1.51	3.11	4.67	0.99	2.11	1.61	1.07	4.53	28.44
1950	3.62	2.05	2.23	4.93	1.27	4.52	8.42	0.90	1.15	0.84	2.64	2.95	35.52
1951	2.25	2.22	2.02	4.25	2.05	5.45	0.56	3.18	4.71	3.21	3.83	3.65	37.38
1952	2.08	1.02	2.35	2.70	3.14	1.76	5.27	3.76	2.89	0.03	3.68	1.46	30.14
1953	1.62	1.61	1.90	2.42	2.02	3.97	1.34	2.22	2.55	1.83	1.06	1.57	24.11
1954	1.69	2.71	4.83	4.06	1.51	2.87	2.88	1.80	2.13	8.32	1.62	2.15	36.57
1955	1.70	1.52	2.07	1.96	1.83	2.20	2.03	4.35	0.94	2.77	2.59	1.18	25.14
1956	0.29	2.08	2.43	4.39	6.49	3.36	2.97	1.19	0.68	0.39	1.52	1.29	27.08
1957	2.19	2.31	1.93	4.55	5.05	6.42	4.35	1.62	3.43	3.29	3.74	2.38	41.26
1958	1.16	0.62	0.74	2.92	2.08	2.30	2.92	4.84	2.93	3.11	2.38	1.33	27.33
1959	2.32	2.56	2.99	4.80	2.97	0.59	2.08	3.48	1.96	5.58	3.02	2.52	34.87
1960	3.50	2.63	1.09	2.64	3.82	2.82	3.82	2.17	1.10	1.06	2.65	0.81	28.11
1961	1.35	0.90	3.26	3.98	1.03	1.29	1.90	2.06	9.15	1.62	1.55	1.54	29.63
1962	3.02	1.68	1.74	2.66	2.41	1.11	2.14	1.08	2.82	1.64	0.63	1.84	22.77
#1963	2.26	0.46	3.45	3.84	2.74	2.71	3.41	3.31	2.97	1.04	2.50	1.54	30.23
1964	1.42	0.73	3.54	5.28	3.96	4.12	2.14	3.19	3.16	0.60	2.13	2.01	32.28
1965	3.99	1.58	3.11	2.49	1.53	2.89	1.96	5.36	6.62	2.10	2.35	4.23	38.21
1966	1.22	2.28	2.65	4.62	2.16	2.36	1.95	3.82	1.92	2.33	7.81	4.01	37.13
1967	1.94	1.13	2.49	4.27	1.86	8.21	2.77	3.34	2.37	4.42	4.35	3.60	40.75
1968	1.55	2.12	1.08	2.40	2.67	5.02	2.74	2.86	4.21	4.05	4.28	3.16	36.14
1969	2.39	0.33	1.29	5.16	3.40	4.74	6.42	0.14	0.93	6.30	3.00	0.66	34.76
1970	1.18	0.51	2.43	3.27	4.24	6.53	6.32	2.89	7.18	3.65	3.42	1.89	43.51
1971	1.04	2.48	1.77	2.27	1.05	2.01	2.46	0.92	6.30	1.39	2.84	6.63	31.16
1972	1.26	0.90	2.11	3.85	1.99	4.64	3.72	5.01	3.96	2.92	2.06	4.96	37.38
1973	1.66	1.15	3.34	3.47	4.31	3.58	2.06	1.45	2.47	4.12	3.54	3.28	34.43
1974	3.23	2.09	5.12	2.93	4.01	4.43	0.97	4.61	2.05	2.44	3.11	1.83	36.82
1975	4.36	1.92	2.28	4.07	2.08	5.97	2.31	7.38	2.00	1.04	3.82	4.02	41.25
RECORD MEAN	2.25	1.89	2.46	2.93	3.28	3.59	2.84	2.67	3.38	2.75	2.70	2.44	33.18

Record mean values above are means through the current year for the period beginning in 1894 for temperature, 1870 for precipitation and 1964 for snowfall. Precipitation is from Airport records, beginning July 1938, snowfall from Airport records beginning January 1948, temperature and degree days from Airport records beginning January 1956.

GRAND RAPIDS, MICHIGAN

(Continued)

Precipitation is usually ample for the growth and development of all vegetation. About one-half of the annual precipitation falls during the growing season, May through September. Droughts occur occasionally, but are seldom of protracted length. The snowfall season extends from mid-November to mid-March, and some winters have had continuous snow cover throughout this period.

Violent windstorms are of infrequent occurrence, and these are usually associated with local thunderstorms. Tornadoes have struck the Grand Rapids area four times in the past 50 years with two very damaging tornadoes, one on April 3, 1956, and one on April 11, 1965.

The Grand River flows through the City, reaching critical heights in most years during quick spring thaws or ice jams, with local overflows in the lowlands north and south of the City.

Normals, Means, and Extremes

Month	Normal Degree days Base 65 °F		Precipitation in inches												Relative humidity pct.			
			Water equivalent							Snow, Ice pellets					Hour 01	Hour 07	Hour 13	Hour 19
	Heating	Cooling	Normal	Maximum monthly	Year	Minimum monthly	Year	Maximum in 24 hrs.	Year	Maximum monthly	Year	Maximum in 24 hrs.	Year		(Local time)			
(a)				12		12		12		12		12			12	12	12	12
J	1296	0	1.94	4.36	1975	1.04	1971	1.81	1975	29.8	1967	12.6	1967		80	81	73	77
F	1134	0	1.50	2.48	1971	0.33	1969	1.33	1968	18.4	1974	7.5	1966		77	78	67	71
M	989	0	2.50	5.12	1974	1.08	1968	1.51	1965	36.0	1965	13.2	1970		77	80	64	67
A	555	0	3.39	5.28	1964	2.27	1971	1.97	1972	10.0	1975	9.8	1975		75	79	59	60
M	270	25	3.19	4.31	1973	1.05	1971	1.98	1974	0.1	1973	0.1	1973		76	79	53	56
J	44	116	3.42	8.21	1967	2.01	1971	3.28	1972	0.0		0.0			80	81	56	59
J	8	210	3.09	6.42	1969	0.97	1974	2.53	1969	0.0		0.0			81	82	54	56
A	27	182	2.54	7.38	1975	0.14	1969	1.69	1975	0.0		0.0			83	86	56	60
S	114	36	3.30	7.18	1970	0.93	1969	1.71	1972	T	1967	T	1967		85	88	59	70
O	409	6	2.56	6.30	1969	0.60	1964	2.01	1969	8.4	1967	8.4	1967		81	85	62	72
N	789	0	2.80	7.81	1966	2.06	1972	2.66	1966	16.6	1966	8.3	1965		83	85	71	78
D	1166	0	2.16	6.63	1971	0.66	1969	2.13	1971	33.3	1970	15.1	1970		83	84	76	80
YR	6801	575	32.39	8.21	JUN 1967	0.14	AUG 1969	3.28	JUN 1972	36.0	MAR 1965	15.1	DEC 1970		80	82	62	67

(To better understand these tables, see full explanation of terms beginning on page 322)

Month	Wind					Pct. of possible sunshine	Mean sky cover, tenths, sunrise to sunset	Mean number of days												Average station pressure mb.
			Fastest mile					Sunrise to sunset							Temperatures °F					
															Max.		Min.			
	Mean speed m.p.h.	Prevailing direction	Speed m.p.h.	Direction	Year			Clear	Partly cloudy	Cloudy	Precipitation .01 inch or more	Snow, Ice pellets 1.0 inch or more	Thunderstorms	Heavy fog, visibility ¼ mile or less	(b) 90° and above	32° and below	32° and below	0° and below		Elev. 803 feet m.s.l.
(a)	12		12	12		12	12	12	12	12	12	12	12	12	12	12	12	12		3
J	11.7		60	SW	1972	34	8.3	3	4	24	16	6	1	3	0	18	29	4		987.2
F	11.1		58	SW	1971	41	7.6	4	6	18	12	5	*	2	0	15	27	3		987.6
M	11.2		50	SW	1974	47	7.6	4	7	20	13	4	2	3	0	7	25	1		985.4
A	11.3		54	N	1967	52	6.8	7	6	17	12	1	4	2	0	*	13	0		985.4
M	10.1		52	SW	1975	56	6.5	6	11	14	11	0	4	1	*	0	2	0		983.3
J	8.9		58	W	1964	61	6.3	6	11	13	11	0	7	1	2	0	0	0		984.0
J	8.4		44	W	1970	65	5.7	9	12	10	9	0	7	2	5	0	0	0		986.6
A	8.3		48	SW	1968	64	5.5	10	10	11	9	0	6	2	3	0	0	0		988.4
S	8.6		54	SW	1964	54	6.6	6	9	15	11	0	4	3	*	0	*	0		989.3
O	9.6		54	SW	1969	48	6.7	6	10	15	10	*	2	3	0	0	6	0		990.0
N	10.3		66	S	1975	27	8.3	2	6	22	14	3	2	3	0	3	17	0		986.9
D	10.5		60	SW	1971	24	8.6	2	4	25	17	6	1	4	0	14	28	1		987.8
YR	10.0		66	S	NOV 1975	50	7.0	65	96	204	145	25	38	28	10	57	148	8		986.8

FOOTNOTES

Means and extremes above are from existing and comparable exposures. Annual extremes have been exceeded at other sites in the locality as follows: Highest temperature 108 in July 1936; lowest temperature -24 in February 1899; maximum monthly precipitation 13.22 in June 1892; minimum monthly precipitation 0.02 inFebruary 1877; maximum precipitation in 24 hours 4.58 in June 1905; maximum monthly snowfall 54.0 at Weather Bureau Office (Post Office Building) in December 1951; fastest mile of wind 80 from Southwest in November 1940.

Station: HOUGHTON LAKE, MICH ROSCOMMON COUNTY AP
Elevation (ground): 1149 feet

TEMPERATURES °F

Month	Normal: Daily maximum	Normal: Daily minimum	Normal: Monthly	Extremes: Record highest	Year	Record lowest	Year
(a)				11		11	
J	25.8	9.0	17.4	53	1973	-21	1968
F	28.0	8.3	18.2	47	1971	-25	1970
M	36.9	16.4	26.7	67	1968	-23	1967
A	53.2	30.5	41.9	84	1970	5	1972
M	65.2	40.3	52.8	87	1975	21	1966
J	75.2	50.0	62.6	93	1971	29	1972
J	78.8	53.6	66.2	96	1966	33	1965
A	77.0	52.6	64.8	92	1975	35	1971
S	68.2	45.7	57.0	89	1973	24	1965
O	58.0	37.2	47.6	85	1971	16	1969
N	41.7	27.1	34.4	69	1975	1	1971
D	29.6	15.5	22.6	59	1970	-15	1970
YR	53.1	32.2	42.7	96	JUL 1966	-25	FEB 1970

IMPORTANT:
The time-period covered by this record is limited: See footnotes on next page for explanation and for additional history of EXTREME HIGHS AND LOWS recorded in the general area.

Houghton Lake, a resort community, is located in the north-central portion of Lower Michigan. The present station is situated on the northeast shore of Houghton Lake, the largest inland lake in Michigan, with a circumference of about 32 miles. The Muskegon River rises in Higgins Lake, 15 miles to the north, and flows through Houghton Lake, then southwestward to Lake Michigan. Streams emptying into Lake Huron rise a short distance to the east of this area. The station lies within the 1,000-foot plateau, which extends roughly 50 miles in the northern semicircle, 75 miles to the southwest, and about 20 miles to the southeast of Houghton Lake. In the immediate area, the land is level to rolling and gradually drops off to the east, dropping off more rapidly to the south, but there are hills and ridges from 100 to 300 feet higher in elevation to the north. Soils are generally quite sandy, or sandy loam supporting little agricultural production, but the area is rich in natural resources of forests, lakes, and streams. Thus, it is a prime resort area and tourist attraction.

The interior location diminishes the influence of the larger Great Lakes, which lie 70 to 80 miles east and west of Houghton Lake. Hence, the daily temperature range is larger, especially in summer, and temperature extremes are greater than are found nearer the shores of either Lake Michigan or Lake Huron. Temperatures reached the 100° mark about one summer out of ten and, at the other extreme, fell below zero an average of twenty-two times during the winter season at the cooperative station location on the southwest shore of the lake. The present site of the first order Weather Bureau station lies at the opposite side of the lake. The local tempering effect of the lake under prevailing southwesterly winds will likely result in somewhat lower maximums than shown by previous records.

Precipitation is normally a little heavier during the summer season. About 60 percent of the annual total falls in the 6-month period from April through September. The heaviest average monthly amounts, totalling about 3 inches each, are recorded in June and September. The driest month is February, with an average of about 1-1/4 inches. The heaviest intensity of precipitation occurs in connection with summertime thunderstorms.

The frequency and intensity of winter snow flurries are diminished by the greater distance the moist and unstable air must flow to reach this area. Much heavier snows, averaging over 100 inches a season, fall within a 30- to 60-mile radius to the north and west of Houghton Lake. Snowfall averages about 86 inches per year at Houghton Lake with considerable variation from year to year. Seasonal totals have ranged from 24.0 at Houghton Lake in 1936-37 to 124.1 inches for the 1970-71 season. Measurable amounts of snow have occurred in nine of the twelve months, but not in the same season, and the average number of months with measurable snowfall is six.

Cloudiness is greatest in the late fall and early winter, while sunshine percentage is highest in the spring and summer. Cloudiness is increased in the late fall due to the moisture and warmth picked up by the westerly and northwesterly winds while crossing Lake Michigan.

(Continued page 500)

HOUGHTON LAKE, MICHIGAN

Normals, Means, and Extremes

(To better understand these tables, see full explanation of terms beginning on page 322)

Month	Normal Degree days Base 65 °F: Heating	Cooling	Precipitation in inches: Water equivalent: Normal	Maximum monthly	Year	Minimum monthly	Year	Maximum in 24 hrs.	Year	Snow, Ice pellets: Maximum monthly	Year	Maximum in 24 hrs.	Year
(a)				11		11		11		11		11	
J	1476	0	1.46	3.13	1974	0.82	1972	1.39	1974	27.5	1971	9.2	1965
F	1310	0	1.20	3.36	1971	0.32	1969	1.43	1971	23.6	1971	8.5	1974
M	1187	0	1.72	2.36	1972	0.85	1968	0.74	1972	28.7	1971	11.7	1970
A	693	0	2.37	4.56	1967	1.28	1968	1.32	1971	10.8	1965	6.2	1973
M	389	11	2.78	4.88	1973	0.40	1966	1.94	1973	1.0	1974	1.0	1974
J	120	48	3.34	6.67	1969	0.95	1966	2.59	1969	0.0		0.0	
J	59	96	3.07	4.96	1975	1.26	1965	2.26	1974	T	1970	T	1970
A	94	87	2.35	7.18	1975	0.85	1969	2.42	1975	0.0		0.0	
S	248	8	3.17	5.85	1970	1.20	1971	1.55	1964	0.1	1967	0.1	1967
O	539	0	2.58	5.45	1969	0.47	1971	1.57	1970	4.1	1964	2.8	1967
N	918	0	2.53	4.81	1966	0.99	1972	1.81	1966	18.9	1968	11.5	1970
D	1314	0	1.82	4.48	1971	0.94	1969	1.70	1971	30.4	1968	9.9	1971
YR	8347	250	28.39	7.18	AUG 1975	0.32	FEB 1969	2.59	JUN 1969	30.4	DEC 1968	11.7	MAR 1970

Month	Relative humidity pct.: Hour 01	Hour 07	Hour 13	Hour 19 (Local time)	Wind: Mean speed m.p.h.	Prevailing direction	Fastest mile: Speed m.p.h.	Direction	Year	Pct. of possible sunshine	Mean sky cover, tenths, sunrise to sunset
(a)	11	11	11	11	11		11	11			11
J	83	83	73	78	10.3		40	26	1972		7.8
F	80	81	69	72	9.3		34	22	1971		7.3
M	80	83	64	67	9.3		31	25	1965		7.1
A	77	82	56	58	9.9		31	22	1975		6.7
M	78	78	51	54	9.2		35	27	1971		6.4
J	85	83	57	60	8.0		40	27	1969		6.3
J	85	85	55	59	7.6		32	32	1966		5.7
A	88	90	60	66	7.3		26	24	1969		5.6
S	89	92	62	73	8.0		32	23	1970		6.6
O	85	88	65	74	9.3		32	23	1968		7.1
N	86	88	74	81	9.9		40	27	1970		8.5
D	86	86	78	82	9.7		32	27	1970		8.4
YR	83	85	64	69	9.0		40	26	JAN 1972		6.9

Month	Mean number of days: Sunrise to sunset: Clear	Partly cloudy	Cloudy	Precipitation .01 inch or more	Snow, Ice pellets 1.0 inch or more	Thunderstorms	Heavy fog, visibility ½ mile or less	Temperatures °F: Max.: 90° and above (b)	32° and below	Min.: 32° and below	0° and below	Average station pressure mb. Elev. 1160 feet m.s.l.
(a)	11	11	11	11	11	11	11	11	11	11	11	3
J	3	7	21	15	6	*	2	0	23	31	8	972.6
F	5	6	17	12	6	*	2	0	20	28	9	973.9
M	6	6	19	12	5	1	3	0	11	28	3	972.4
A	7	7	16	12	1	3	2	0	1	19	0	972.7
M	8	9	14	11	0	5	1	0	0	6	0	970.6
J	6	11	13	12	0	8	1	1	0	*	0	971.5
J	8	13	10	9	0	8	2	1	0	0	0	973.8
A	9	12	10	9	0	7	4	*	0	0	0	975.7
S	6	10	14	12	0	5	4	0	0	2	0	976.0
O	5	8	18	12	*	2	4	0	0	9	0	976.4
N	2	5	23	14	4	1	4	0	5	21	0	972.8
D	3	5	23	15	6	*	3	0	20	30	3	974.1
YR	68	99	198	146	28	40	30	2	80	174	23	973.5

FOOTNOTES

Means and extremes above are from existing and comparable exposures. Annual extremes have been exceeded at other sites in the locality as follows: Highest temperature 107 in July 1936 and earlier; lowest temperature -48 in February 1918; maximum monthly precipitation 8.38 in October 1951; minimum monthly precipitation 0.18 in December 1960; maximum precipitation for one observational day 5.18 in July 1957; maximum monthly snowfall 43.5 in March 1923; maximum snowfall for one observational day 14.5 in March 1942.

Snowfall

Season	July	Aug	Sept	Oct	Nov	Dec	Jan
1936-37	0.0	0.0	0.0	2.0	2.3	4.0	2.8
1937-38	0.0	0.0	0.0	0.4	2.5	6.1	13.7
1938-39	0.0	0.0	0.0	0.0	1.2	8.5	11.7
1939-40	0.0	0.0	0.0	4.5	0.5	2.0	14.5
1940-41	0.0	0.0	0.0	2.0	16.2	16.4	19.9
1941-42	0.0	0.0	0.0	0.0	8.3	8.5	12.9
1942-43	0.0	0.0	3.0	T	4.4	18.0	24.6
1943-44	0.0	0.0	0.0	4.2	4.1	1.2	3.3
1944-45	0.0	0.0	0.0	0.0	8.4	10.9	10.1
1945-46	0.0	0.0	0.0	T	1.1	12.9	19.0
1946-47	0.0	0.0	0.0	0.0	T	8.2	22.2
1947-48	0.0	0.0	T	0.0	14.1	15.1	12.7
1948-49	0.0	0.0	0.0	T	T	10.5	13.2
1949-50	0.0	0.0	0.0	T	9.5	6.1	10.1
1950-51	0.0	0.0	0.0	0.0	8.8	6.7	22.7
#1951-52	0.0	0.0	0.0	T	17.0	25.0	25.0
1952-53	0.0	0.0	0.0	5.4	0.5	9.0	8.4
1953-54	0.0	0.0	0.0	T	1.5	11.5	10.9
1954-55	0.0	0.0	0.0	0.1	2.0	13.0	10.2
1955-56	0.0	0.0	0.0	0.3	12.5	24.7	4.5
1956-57	0.0	0.0	T	0.0	8.0	10.0	13.5
1957-58	0.0	0.0	0.0	T	5.5	9.8	14.9
1958-59	0.0	0.0	0.0	0.0	5.0	7.4	19.8
1959-60	0.0	0.0	0.0	T	12.0	12.3	18.6
1960-61	0.0	0.0	0.0	T	7.5	7.6	4.7
1961-62	0.0	0.0	0.0	0.0	5.0	7.0	25.1
1962-63	0.0	0.0	0.0	9.5	4.0	19.0	13.3
#1963-64	0.0	0.0	0.0	0.0	6.5	9.3	5.9
1964-65	0.0	0.0	0.0	4.1	3.8	12.5	26.5
1965-66	0.0	0.0	T	0.3	6.5	11.8	19.5
1966-67	0.0	0.0	0.0	T	15.1	15.4	22.6
1967-68	0.0	0.0	0.1	3.0	12.6	10.6	9.0
1968-69	0.0	0.0	0.0	1.0	18.9	30.4	25.8
1969-70	0.0	0.0	0.0	2.0	17.6	20.0	22.7
1970-71	T	0.0	0.0	T	17.7	23.1	27.5
1971-72	0.0	0.0	0.0	T	16.7	16.7	15.0
1972-73	0.0	0.0	0.0	0.6	4.1	29.2	8.3
1973-74	0.0	0.0	0.0	T	4.8	13.0	11.2
1974-75	0.0	0.0	T	T	6.0	18.0	11.8
1975-76	0.0	0.0	T	T	5.9	14.6	
RECORD MEAN	T	0.0	T	0.6	11.4	18.4	18.2

Heating Degree Days

Season	July	Aug	Sept	Oct	Nov	Dec	Jan
1955-56	2	20	211	434	985	1325	1409
1956-57	43	68	301	352	839	1178	1536
1957-58	31	68	264	588	839	1143	1325
1958-59	29	52	176	418	793	1512	1554
1959-60	18	6	162	572	1030	1111	1332
1960-61	48	28	166	503	753	1373	1476
1961-62	28	42	126	437	846	1233	1492
1962-63	50	54	254	452	859	1302	1640
#1963-64	37	63	211	238	699	1401	1274
1964-65	38	136	283	659	789	1331	1533
1965-66	109	123	266	593	883	1114	1607
1966-67	19	65	280	592	911	1295	1335
1967-68	69	116	288	579	1022	1260	1468
1968-69	71	100	159	510	903	1353	1444
1969-70	38	28	250	601	939	1342	1621
1970-71	30	54	225	478	878	1330	1556
1971-72	70	95	183	327	912	1197	1502
1972-73	77	92	242	716	933	1326	1324
1973-74	26	25	280	420	871	1298	1380
1974-75	27	56	337	633	856	1197	1327
1975-76	44	68	333	472	720	1272	

Cooling Degree Days

Year	Jan	Feb	Mar	Apr	May	June	July
1969	0	0	0	0	10	18	120
1970	0	0	0	6	15	74	167
1971	0	0	0	0	5	131	68
1972	0	0	0	0	11	19	131
1973	0	0	0	1	0	58	119
1974	0	0	0	1	6	41	120
1975	0	0	0	0	58	83	146

Feb	Mar	Apr	May	June	Total
2.1	9.6	1.2	0.0	0.0	24.0
7.3	2.5	T	T	0.0	32.5
7.7	12.0	8.8	0.0	0.0	49.9
11.5	15.0	0.7	1.0	0.0	49.7
11.1	11.2	T	0.0	0.0	76.8
7.8	29.6	0.4	0.0	0.0	67.5
20.0	18.7	6.1	T	0.0	94.8
6.0	13.9	4.5	0.0	0.0	37.2
11.7	0.8	1.5	T	0.0	43.4
23.8	5.0	T	T	0.0	61.8
12.7	10.6	T	T	0.0	53.7
15.3	14.0	T	0.0	0.0	71.2
13.2	4.4	T	0.0	0.0	41.3
10.4	11.0	3.7	0.0	0.0	50.8
11.9	17.8	2.4	0.0	0.0	70.3
5.9	8.0	1.6	0.0	0.0	82.5
7.9	3.8	1.5	0.0	0.0	36.5
9.2	7.4	1.2	0.5	0.0	42.2
9.2	10.0	T	0.0	0.0	44.5
15.5	12.2	1.5	0.0	0.0	71.2
5.2	12.0	4.2	0.0	0.0	52.9
5.8	6.3	T	0.0	0.0	42.3
25.3	12.0	4.2	0.0	0.0	73.7
15.3	10.8	T	T	0.0	69.0
10.0	9.9	1.1	T	0.0	40.8
20.6	7.4	T	0.0	0.0	65.1
9.4	11.8	9.0	T	0.0	76.0
6.3	12.0	1.0	0.0	0.0	41.0
12.9	17.9	10.8	0.0	0.0	88.5
7.3	9.2	7.1	0.1	0.0	61.8
14.3	9.4	4.5	T	0.0	81.3
15.6	4.9	0.7	0.0	0.0	56.5
8.7	9.5	0.4	0.3	0.0	95.0
12.8	24.5	3.8	T	0.0	103.4
23.6	28.7	3.5	T	0.0	124.1
18.7	26.8	2.9	0.0	0.0	96.8
15.2	5.3	7.9	0.8	0.0	71.4
17.5	12.3	3.1	1.0	0.0	62.9
12.4	14.0	4.5	0.0	0.0	66.7
14.5	14.8	4.5	0.2	0.0	82.6

Average Temperature

Year	Jan	Feb	Mar	Apr	May	June	July	Aug	Sept	Oct	Nov	Dec	Annual
1936	17.1	9.7	32.0	37.5	59.3	61.7	69.6	67.2	60.3	45.1	31.4	26.9	43.2
1937	22.3	22.6	25.3	41.2	56.4	62.9	68.8	70.0	57.9	44.5	34.2	21.6	44.0
1938	17.6	23.5	35.6	44.8	54.8	62.8	68.5	70.3	55.4	51.7	38.0	25.8	45.7
1939	21.7	19.0	26.3	39.9	58.6	64.7	68.7	66.5	59.4	45.9	33.8	29.4	44.5
1940	16.3	21.1	23.1	37.4	52.8	63.9	68.1	65.2	58.1	46.8	33.3	26.2	42.7
1941	20.1	20.2	22.2	49.1	57.8	65.8	69.8	65.1	61.5	49.1	38.4	30.4	45.8
1942	20.3	18.4	32.0	49.0	54.8	65.1	67.1	65.6	56.6	48.8	35.1	21.4	44.5
1943	15.7	21.3	23.7	39.0	52.4	67.1	67.6	66.1	54.8	45.8	33.1	23.1	42.5
1944	26.8	23.3	26.0	38.7	59.3	66.4	67.4	67.5	59.8	45.9	37.8	20.6	45.0
1945	14.1	22.0	42.0	46.2	49.5	59.6	64.7	65.5	57.7	45.2	36.7	20.0	43.6
1946	21.4	18.3	40.4	43.4	51.2	62.1	66.6	62.0	59.6	51.7	37.7	24.7	44.9
1947	22.9	17.6	24.3	39.0	48.7	61.5	66.1	72.5	60.2	57.0	31.5	23.9	43.8
1948	13.8	17.4	26.7	48.0	50.8	62.0	67.3	66.4	61.4	46.3	39.9	25.7	43.8
1949	24.7	23.5	28.4	42.6	55.5	67.5	70.1	67.1	54.6	52.4	32.5	26.3	45.4
1950	23.5	19.5	23.9	35.3	55.0	63.9	64.0	61.5	56.2	51.1	31.8	21.7	42.3
#1951	19.9	22.1	29.6	42.3	58.1	61.6	65.3	62.5	55.2	49.5	27.6	23.0	43.1
1952	22.8	23.4	26.7	45.0	54.0	67.1	70.7	66.6	59.5	43.7	37.6	29.7	45.6
1953	23.3	24.1	31.1	40.0	55.1	65.8	68.6	68.4	59.6	52.6	40.9	28.6	46.5
1954	18.2	28.6	27.1	44.8	49.7	66.7	66.6	64.6	59.3	49.7	37.4	24.0	44.7
1955	19.3	9.5	27.5	49.7	58.5	64.1	73.3	72.2	58.7	51.1	32.0	22.0	45.7
1956	19.3	20.4	24.2	40.1	52.4	65.6	65.2	65.2	55.3	53.5	36.8	26.9	43.7
1957	15.3	23.4	30.1	45.6	53.1	65.2	67.7	64.7	56.4	45.8	36.8	28.0	44.3
1958	22.0	17.0	31.1	44.8	53.8	58.5	66.7	66.6	59.7	51.2	38.4	16.1	43.8
1959	14.7	15.9	27.0	42.7	60.7	66.9	68.9	72.3	61.7	46.3	30.4	28.9	44.7
1960	21.9	20.3	20.5	45.0	56.0	61.9	66.7	67.6	61.5	48.6	39.7	20.5	44.2
1961	17.1	25.0	32.9	40.9	53.1	63.5	68.3	66.7	63.9	50.7	36.7	25.1	45.3
1962	16.7	16.0	29.9	43.3	60.5	64.0	65.4	66.3	56.9	50.4	36.1	22.8	44.0
1963	12.1	12.0	30.6	46.3	52.8	66.9	69.0	64.2	58.0	57.6	41.5	19.6	44.2
#1964	23.7	23.9	30.0	45.3	59.6	65.0	68.2	62.3	56.3	43.5	38.5	21.8	44.8
1965	15.5	18.3	22.5	37.9	57.9	61.4	63.0	63.0	56.7	45.7	35.4	28.9	42.1
1966	12.9	21.7	31.9	39.3	47.6	64.7	69.1	64.7	55.8	45.6	34.4	23.0	42.6
1967	21.7	11.9	27.0	42.1	48.4	66.4	65.2	62.1	55.4	46.2	30.7	24.2	41.8
1968	17.6	14.8	32.3	45.3	50.7	62.6	65.7	65.6	60.2	48.9	34.7	21.0	43.3
1969	18.3	19.4	23.2	43.1	52.9	56.9	67.5	68.4	57.2	45.4	33.4	21.6	42.3
1970	12.5	15.8	22.9	42.2	53.9	63.2	69.2	66.1	58.1	49.5	35.5	21.9	42.6
1971	14.7	18.7	23.4	38.8	51.6	67.0	64.7	63.4	60.8	54.7	34.4	26.2	43.2
1972	16.3	16.4	22.3	36.6	56.9	59.1	66.5	64.4	56.8	41.7	33.6	22.0	41.1
1973	22.1	18.1	38.1	43.1	50.6	64.9	67.7	68.9	57.4	51.3	35.8	22.9	45.1
1974	20.3	14.4	27.0	43.2	50.0	61.6	67.8	65.0	53.9	44.3	36.3	26.1	42.5
1975	22.0	20.7	24.3	37.0	59.7	64.1	68.1	65.0	53.7	49.6	40.8	23.8	44.1
RECORD MEAN	19.1	19.5	28.3	42.0	54.2	63.8	67.4	65.6	58.2	48.2	35.4	24.0	43.8
MAX	27.7	29.6	38.9	54.1	67.9	77.6	81.5	79.1	70.4	59.4	43.0	31.1	55.0
MIN	10.5	9.3	17.6	29.9	40.5	50.0	53.3	52.1	46.0	37.0	27.7	16.8	32.6

# Indicates a station move or relocation of instruments.

HOUGHTON LAKE, MI

Feb	Mar	Apr	May	June	Total
1286	1257	743	385	96	8153
1163	1073	580	365	69	7567
1339	1041	600	350	204	7792
1369	1171	659	189	58	7980
1288	1374	606	280	111	7890
1115	988	715	383	110	7658
1368	1082	655	220	71	7600
1481	1061	558	374	75	8160
1187	1078	586	208	122	7104
1303	1314	807	237	144	8574
1205	1020	763	535	91	8309
1484	1168	678	510	33	8370
1453	1005	582	438	137	8417
1272	1290	651	378	254	8385
1373	1296	682	348	122	8640
1289	1282	781	415	65	8383
1401	1320	847	254	191	8299
1307	829	653	442	54	7995
1411	1171	649	463	135	8129
1234	1254	836	215	101	8073

Precipitation

Year	Jan	Feb	Mar	Apr	May	June	July	Aug	Sept	Oct	Nov	Dec	Annual
1936	1.40	1.18	0.83	2.17	2.39	1.28	0.68	3.66	4.34	3.85	0.98	2.09	24.85
1937	1.64	0.96	0.34	3.60	2.35	2.19	3.20	2.30	4.09	2.54	2.54	0.84	26.59
1938	2.17	2.33	2.10	0.62	4.04	2.60	1.28	4.89	2.37	0.86	1.29	1.62	26.17
1939	1.13	1.52	0.81	2.09	3.98	3.57	1.39	5.36	3.07	1.90	0.52	0.89	26.23
1940	1.33	0.71	1.12	2.00	4.18	4.49	3.25	5.75	2.49	2.78	2.77	1.99	32.86
1941	1.57	0.89	1.15	1.78	2.60	1.84	1.60	1.46	5.06	6.56	2.89	1.19	28.59
1942	1.17	0.44	3.97	0.72	3.65	3.31	2.94	0.91	4.41	1.71	1.19	3.01	27.43
1943	1.56	1.92	2.21	1.68	2.08	6.72	1.36	2.52	1.27	1.96	1.95	0.54	25.77
1944	0.87	0.94	2.10	0.98	1.75	3.09	3.29	1.88	3.87	1.68	1.93	0.82	23.20
1945	0.39	1.12	0.94	2.33	4.10	5.63	2.23	3.20	4.43	3.27	3.37	1.14	32.15
1946	2.40	1.82	1.42	0.50	2.58	2.19	1.76	1.68	2.02	1.06	4.31	2.60	24.34
1947	1.89	0.67	1.33	4.03	5.08	1.90	5.33	0.80	4.22	0.75	2.77	2.02	30.79
1948	0.81	1.49	3.83	2.15	1.86	4.83	1.83	1.25	0.64	1.03	3.56	1.72	25.00
1949	2.03	1.87	1.40	1.36	1.93	5.69	1.47	1.89	1.57	1.70	1.69	1.88	24.48
1950	3.39	1.73	1.73	2.62	1.15	1.74	3.45	2.54	3.62	1.67	1.25	1.37	26.26
#1951	1.87	1.77	2.14	4.36	2.80	2.70	4.42	1.64	6.43	8.38	2.41	2.42	41.34
1952	2.41	0.66	1.67	1.74	1.63	1.54	8.34	3.02	1.61	0.55	2.73	3.09	28.99
1953	1.26	3.05	1.18	4.20	5.86	3.23	4.25	3.29	3.49	1.08	1.19	4.00	36.08
1954	1.36	1.13	0.91	4.57	1.98	5.42	1.30	0.35	3.31	6.24	0.93	1.34	28.84
1955	0.75	1.05	2.16	1.59	2.20	1.72	1.04	4.54	0.61	2.14	2.02	3.12	22.94
1956	0.19	1.38	2.04	2.76	4.27	1.76	4.29	5.08	1.84	0.51	2.30	1.65	28.07
1957	1.60	0.31	1.45	2.06	3.44	5.88	6.57	1.26	2.55	2.38	2.53	1.47	31.50
1958	1.06	0.32	0.36	1.87	0.85	2.46	1.88	2.16	3.38	2.27	4.16	0.52	21.29
1959	2.24	1.84	2.09	4.59	4.49	0.68	4.23	3.32	2.98	6.01	2.71	2.07	37.25
1960	1.32	1.66	1.56	3.01	4.49	3.14	4.02	2.14	1.95	2.00	2.97	0.18	28.44
1961	0.44	1.47	1.59	2.31	1.49	2.44	4.25	3.05	6.34	1.89	2.29	1.12	28.68
1962	1.86	1.77	0.87	1.17	2.56	2.82	2.86	4.56	2.61	2.62	0.96	1.07	25.73
1963	0.70	0.55	2.89	1.34	3.58	2.88	2.60	3.15	1.97	0.85	2.57	0.98	24.06
#1964	1.10	0.39	1.55	2.64	2.56	1.25	3.03	2.77	3.61	1.29	2.78	1.11	24.08
1965	2.47	1.40	1.83	2.85	2.81	2.43	1.26	5.05	5.76	1.97	2.41	2.73	32.97
1966	1.02	1.02	2.30	2.08	0.40	0.95	1.74	1.92	2.25	1.79	4.81	3.46	23.74
1967	2.02	0.88	1.32	4.56	2.41	5.65	1.28	1.66	1.73	2.73	2.82	2.41	29.47
1968	1.03	1.57	0.85	1.28	2.62	5.54	1.84	1.32	4.17	3.09	2.47	2.50	28.28
1969	1.87	0.32	0.86	2.59	3.57	6.67	3.57	0.85	1.63	5.45	2.19	0.94	30.51
1970	1.16	0.70	1.86	1.50	2.67	4.15	3.93	1.26	5.85	2.75	3.79	2.00	31.62
1971	1.30	3.36	1.79	2.19	1.52	2.84	3.14	1.76	1.20	0.47	1.96	4.48	26.01
1972	0.82	0.99	2.36	1.40	1.79	2.00	2.52	4.63	2.67	2.50	0.99	3.48	26.15
1973	1.22	1.33	1.95	1.66	4.88	2.84	2.34	2.29	1.95	3.11	1.34	1.81	26.72
1974	3.13	1.14	1.44	3.47	2.92	4.60	4.70	2.78	2.53	1.40	1.41	1.43	30.95
1975	1.97	1.14	1.50	2.63	2.79	3.79	4.96	7.18	1.52	0.85	2.20	1.33	31.86
RECORD MEAN	1.45	1.28	1.81	2.42	2.85	3.15	2.81	2.69	3.04	2.62	2.38	1.77	28.27

Aug	Sept	Oct	Nov	Dec	Total
138	24	0	0	0	310
95	24	1	0	0	382
50	62	17	0	0	333
78	4	0	0	0	243
155	60	2	0	0	395
62	11	0	0	0	241
78	2	2	0	0	369

Record mean values above are means through the current year for the period beginning in 1918 for temperature and precipitation, 1965 for snowfall. Data are from Cooperative locations through June 1964.

(Continued)

Degree-day data is provided as an index of heating requirements for buildings. For example: December averages 1314 degree days and April, 693 degree days, which means that under average conditions the amount of fuel necessary for heating in December will be nearly twice that required for April. Degree days for a single day are obtained by subtracting the mean temperature from 65. Only those days with averages below 65 are counted, for those above this value normally require no heating.

The growing season is normally quite short, averaging about 90 days between the spring and fall freezes. Freezing temperatures have been reported every month of the year, but occurrences in July and August are infrequent. Several years in succession may pass without freezing temperatures in July or August; such was the case for a period of 13 years, 1952 through 1964.

QUOTES FROM WEATHER FOLKLORE–

Evening red and morning gray
Will set the traveler on his way;
But evening gray and morning red
Will bring down rain upon his head.

Station: MARQUETTE, MICHIGAN
U. S. POST OFFICE
Elevation (ground): 677 feet

TEMPERATURES °F

Month	Normal			Extremes			
	Daily maximum	Daily minimum	Monthly	Record highest	Year	Record lowest	Year
(a)				39		39	
J	24.8	12.0	18.4	57	1944	-21	1963
F	26.5	12.6	19.6	56	1961	-13	1966
M	34.3	20.5	27.4	76	1946	-13	1962
A	47.9	32.4	40.2	86	1938	4	1954
M	58.9	40.8	49.9	100	1969	22	1954
J	69.6	50.3	60.0	101	1963	33	1972
J	75.3	57.3	66.3	99	1963	41	1969
A	73.9	57.0	65.5	102	1947	41	1971
S	65.3	49.5	57.4	98	1939	30	1965
O	56.3	41.0	48.7	86	1950	21	1942
N	39.8	28.8	34.3	73	1975	-1	1959
D	29.0	17.9	23.5	59	1962	-12	1968
YR	50.1	35.0	42.6	102	AUG 1947	-21	JAN 1963

IMPORTANT:
The time-period covered by this record is limited: See footnotes on next page for explanation and for additional history of EXTREME HIGHS AND LOWS recorded in the general area.

The city of Marquette is located on the south shore of Lake Superior, approximately midway between the eastern and western extremities of Michigan's Upper Peninsula. The terrain of the area near Marquette is quite hilly. Immediately to the south of the City, a range of hills rises abruptly several hundred feet above the elevation of the City. West of Marquette the elevation rises gradually to around 1,400 feet above m.s.l. in the vicinity of the Marquette County Airport, located about 8 miles from the downtown area.

The climate is influenced to a considerable extent by the proximity of Lake Superior. As a consequence of the cool expanse of water in summer, Marquette rarely is subject to the sweltering hot weather experienced in many inland areas. In winter, cold waves are tempered considerably by the waters of Lake Superior. However, winds blowing across these relatively warm waters pick up moisture to produce much cloudy weather throughout the winter, as well as frequent periods of snow flurries. Snowfall amounts caused by this lake effect vary greatly, but generally are heaviest from the lakeshore inland as far as the ridges of the hills to the south.

The average date of the last occurrence of freezing temperatures in spring is May 14 and the average date of the first freezing temperature in autumn is October 20. The length of the growing season ranges between 134 and 182 days and averages 159 days annually. The warmest year on record was 1931 with an average annual temperature of 46.8°, and the coldest year was 1885 with an average temperature of 36.6°.

Precipitation is rather evenly distributed throughout the year, there being no pronounced wet or dry periods. Total precipitation for the driest year on record, 1925, was 19.68 inches and for the wettest year, 1881, 42.70 inches. Snowfall is heavy, exceeding 100 inches in 7 out of every 10 winter seasons. The greatest snowfall on record for any winter was 189.1 inches during the 1890-91 season, followed closely by the winter of 1959-60 with 188.1 inches and that of 1949-50 with 188.0 inches. Least snowfall for any season was 53.4 inches in 1940-41. The greatest depth of snow on the ground was 48.6 inches and occurred on January 2, 1911.

MARQUETTE, MICHIGAN

Normals, Means, and Extremes

(To better understand these tables, see full explanation of terms beginning on page 322)

Month	Normal Degree days Base 65 °F: Heating	Cooling	Precipitation in inches – Water equivalent: Normal	Maximum monthly	Year	Minimum monthly	Year	Maximum in 24 hrs.	Year	Snow, Ice pellets: Maximum monthly	Year	Maximum in 24 hrs.	Year
(a)				38		38		38		38		38	
J	1445	0	1.54	3.93	1938	0.51	1956	1.39	1938	52.6	1971	13.3	1971
F	1271	0	1.52	3.29	1947	0.31	1956	1.18	1951	45.6	1960	16.1	1947
M	1166	0	1.88	4.46	1966	0.30	1941	1.56	1939	34.3	1972	16.0	1939
A	744	0	2.60	5.73	1960	0.64	1949	2.43	1947	32.8	1950	11.7	1951
M	473	0	2.93	7.70	1960	0.56	1948	2.39	1973	9.4	1960	7.8	1954
J	165	15	3.44	8.86	1939	1.37	1957	4.65	1939	T	1945	T	1945
J	57	97	3.07	10.20	1949	0.75	1957	3.94	1949	0.0		0.0	
A	82	97	3.01	5.40	1951	0.53	1969	2.51	1960	0.0		0.0	
S	235	7	3.45	7.22	1968	1.20	1967	2.77	1968	5.1	1974	5.1	1974
O	505	0	2.44	7.13	1959	0.21	1956	4.06	1959	9.1	1939	6.0	1939
N	921	0	2.99	5.08	1948	0.79	1939	2.29	1943	36.6	1959	12.5	1966
D	1287	0	1.97	3.96	1968	0.69	1943	1.23	1940	41.1	1968	14.2	1961
YR	8351	216	30.84	10.20	JUL 1949	0.21	OCT 1956	4.65	JUN 1939	52.6	JAN 1971	16.1	FEB 1947

Month	Relative humidity pct. Hour 01 ∅	Hour 07 $	Hour 13 $	Hour 19 $	Wind: Mean speed m.p.h.	Prevailing direction	Fastest mile: Speed m.p.h.	Direction	Year	Pct. of possible sunshine	Mean sky cover, tenths, sunrise to sunset	Mean number of days – Sunrise to sunset: Clear	Partly cloudy	Cloudy	Precipitation .01 inch or more	Snow, Ice pellets 1.0 inch or more	Thunderstorms %	Heavy fog, visibility ¼ mile or less %	Temperatures °F Max.: (b) 90° and above	32° and below	Min.: 32° and below	0° and below	Average station pressure mb. Elev. 734 feet m.s.l.
(a)	11	27	27	27	27	27	38	38		38	38	38	38	38	38	38	27	27	38	38	38	38	
J	74	75	68	72	8.9	W	52	INV	1938	34	8.1	3	6	22	17	6	0	1	0	24	31	5	
F	73	75	67	72	8.8	NW	42	SW	1959	43	7.7	3	6	19	14	6	*	1	0	21	28	4	
M	73	76	66	72	8.4	NW	57	SW	1938	51	7.3	5	8	18	13	4	1	1	0	14	28	1	
A	70	73	61	65	8.6	N	50	SW	1964	55	6.7	6	9	15	11	2	1	2	0	3	17	0	
M	72	73	62	63	8.2	NW	50	S	1943	57	6.6	6	10	15	12	*	3	3	*	*	4	0	
J	78	76	64	66	7.4	NW	59	SW	1958	60	6.4	6	11	13	12	0	6	4	1	0	0	0	
J	77	76	63	66	7.1	W	50	SW	1974	67	5.7	8	12	11	10	0	6	3	2	0	0	0	
A	79	80	64	69	7.5	W	52	SW	1960	61	5.9	8	12	11	11	0	5	1	1	0	0	0	
S	80	81	65	74	8.4	W	45	S	1943	52	6.6	6	9	15	13	*	3	1	1	0	*	0	
O	76	77	62	71	8.7	S	47	NW	1951	45	7.1	5	8	18	12	1	1	1	0	*	4	0	
N	79	79	70	75	9.0	W	50	SW	1958	27	8.4	2	5	23	15	5	*	1	0	6	19	*	
D	74	76	70	74	9.1	W	45	SW	1941	27	8.3	3	5	23	16	7	*	1	0	20	29	1	
YR	75	76	65	70	8.3	W	59	SW	JUN 1958	51	7.1	61	101	203	158	31	28	17	5	88	160	11	

(Local time)

FOOTNOTES

Means and extremes above are from existing and comparable exposures. Annual extremes have been exceeded at other sites in the locality as follows: Highest temperature 108 in July 1901; lowest temperature -27 in February 1888 and earlier; maximum monthly precipitation 12.73 in September 1881; minimum monthly precipitation 0.12 in February 1877; maximum precipitation in 24 hours 5.14 in June 1878; maximum monthly snowfall 54.3 in February 1890; maximum snowfall in 24 hours 17.0 in February 1890; fastest mile of wind 91 from South in May 1934.

% Through 1964. The station did not operate 24 hours daily. Fog and thunderstorm data may be incomplete. ∅ Through 1951. $ Through 1964.

Snowfall

Season	July	Aug	Sept	Oct	Nov	Dec	Jan
1936-37	0.0	0.0	0.0	1.5	25.2	5.3	23.9
1937-38	0.0	0.0	0.0	4.5	16.0	27.0	40.5
1938-39	0.0	0.0	0.0	6.0	21.4	19.7	14.6
1939-40	0.0	0.0	0.0	9.1	8.2	15.7	25.5
1940-41	0.0	0.0	0.0	T	10.4	15.0	12.6
1941-42	0.0	0.0	0.0	0.1	15.3	7.6	5.3
1942-43	0.0	0.0	2.0	2.0	15.4	38.6	16.9
1943-44	0.0	0.0	0.0	3.0	11.7	6.9	8.3
1944-45	0.0	0.0	0.0	0.0	11.8	24.4	15.2
1945-46	0.0	0.0	T	0.8	14.2	21.7	17.6
1946-47	0.0	0.0	0.0	T	9.1	21.6	13.4
1947-48	0.0	0.0	0.6	0.0	7.7	17.8	21.9
1948-49	0.0	0.0	0.0	0.1	17.0	6.1	20.8
1949-50	0.0	0.0	0.0	4.6	35.2	20.0	43.7
1950-51	0.0	0.0	T	T	23.8	39.2	19.1
1951-52	0.0	0.0	T	6.8	16.3	15.9	20.1
1952-53	0.0	0.0	0.0	5.1	6.3	26.0	17.8
1953-54	0.0	0.0	0.0	T	8.7	23.3	19.4
1954-55	0.0	0.0	0.0	3.0	8.0	8.6	18.1
1955-56	0.0	0.0	0.0	2.0	18.6	26.9	9.2
1956-57	0.0	0.0	0.2	T	31.0	28.6	13.4
1957-58	0.0	0.0	T	0.4	24.2	18.2	27.2
1958-59	0.0	0.0	0.4	0.5	11.8	29.8	14.7
1959-60	0.0	0.0	0.0	5.0	36.6	17.3	29.1
1960-61	0.0	0.0	0.0	5.5	20.4	21.5	18.6
1961-62	0.0	0.0	T	T	8.2	33.5	24.1
1962-63	0.0	0.0	0.0	4.5	4.5	23.2	16.5
1963-64	0.0	0.0	0.0	T	8.6	27.8	11.6
1964-65	0.0	0.0	0.0	1.7	14.9	27.9	17.0
1965-66	0.0	0.0	T	0.1	12.6	7.6	20.6
1966-67	0.0	0.0	0.0	1.1	28.0	32.6	29.8
1967-68	0.0	0.0	0.0	5.4	17.4	6.2	11.6
1968-69	0.0	0.0	0.0	2.0	15.6	41.1	29.5
1969-70	0.0	0.0	0.0	4.3	7.5	30.9	30.8
1970-71	0.0	0.0	T	0.1	11.0	26.6	52.6
1971-72	0.0	0.0	0.0	0.0	11.2	25.3	22.6
1972-73	0.0	0.0	0.0	2.2	6.5	37.7	14.8
1973-74	0.0	0.0	0.0	T	7.4	27.9	15.5
1974-75	0.0	0.0	5.1	5.8	10.3	10.6	34.7
1975-76	0.0	0.0	T	0.1	16.9	15.3	
RECORD MEAN	0.0	0.0	0.2	2.1	14.8	22.2	20.9

Heating Degree Days

Season	July	Aug	Sept	Oct	Nov	Dec	Jan
1955-56	22	29	260	476	1026	1381	1300
1956-57	161	89	362	363	920	1255	1607
1957-58	62	89	259	516	933	1218	1292
1958-59	91	95	208	477	843	1467	1617
1959-60	43	37	204	670	1161	1093	1349
1960-61	92	61	243	509	833	1388	1511
1961-62	55	41	224	494	873	1313	1568
1962-63	96	96	318	504	852	1338	1728
1963-64	51	112	242	222	763	1422	1225
1964-65	43	137	268	540	850	1355	1520
1965-66	105	131	355	547	929	1113	1533
1966-67	24	84	225	565	956	1267	1375
1967-68	85	118	203	598	1010	1243	1459
1968-69	81	106	166	465	890	1262	1349
1969-70	93	21	209	628	905	1215	1546
1970-71	49	44	224	443	887	1257	1563
1971-72	90	123	182	350	897	1218	1586
1972-73	103	121	305	653	950	1423	1323
1973-74	59	37	244	360	889	1296	1482
1974-75	27	77	360	563	843	1097	1376
1975-76	49	45	317	455	762	1290	

Cooling Degree Days

Year	Jan	Feb	Mar	Apr	May	June	July
1969	0	0	0	0	35	14	109
1970	0	0	0	0	6	66	176
1971	0	0	0	0	6	57	73
1972	0	0	0	0	14	26	76
1973	0	0	0	0	0	25	127
1974	0	0	0	0	5	40	162
1975	0	0	0	0	9	67	218

Feb	Mar	Apr	May	June	Total
26.7	4.7	13.9	T	0.0	101.2
12.2	7.9	3.6	T	T	111.7
25.5	29.0	4.7	0.0	0.0	120.9
16.9	8.8	19.2	2.4	0.0	105.8
11.1	3.0	1.3	0.0	0.0	53.4
8.1	17.3	6.2	T	0.0	59.9
9.0	29.3	12.2	T	0.0	125.4
16.1	23.6	7.7	3.6	0.0	80.9
21.0	4.0	9.0	T	T	85.4
12.6	2.8	2.6	T	0.0	72.3
39.1	8.7	12.2	2.9	0.0	107.0
10.4	9.4	5.3	T	0.0	73.1
24.8	5.7	1.4	T	0.0	75.9
28.0	21.5	32.8	2.2	0.0	188.0
18.1	14.1	23.5	T	0.0	137.8
12.6	11.6	7.7	T	0.0	91.0
28.4	14.0	22.2	T	0.0	119.8
7.4	21.2	0.9	8.7	0.0	89.6
12.2	29.6	T	T	0.0	79.5
6.2	16.0	8.4	T	0.0	87.3
12.2	5.3	17.8	0.2	0.0	108.7
33.8	12.9	4.9	T	0.0	121.6
14.1	29.6	3.1	T	0.0	104.0
45.6	30.9	14.2	9.4	0.0	188.1
20.2	24.8	5.4	1.7	0.0	118.1
35.9	12.0	2.0	1.1	0.0	116.8
12.2	15.0	0.7	0.7	0.0	77.3
21.7	18.2	3.6	0.0	0.0	91.5
20.1	22.4	2.9	T	0.0	106.9
13.0	31.5	12.4	0.3	0.0	98.1
23.5	10.4	2.4	4.5	0.0	132.3
44.4	4.1	5.5	T	0.0	94.6
12.2	17.7	1.0	0.1	0.0	119.2
18.3	11.1	0.9	1.6	0.0	105.4
22.7	15.9	2.7	3.9	0.0	135.5
23.2	34.3	14.4	0.0	0.0	131.0
12.8	0.4	2.5	3.1	0.0	80.0
18.2	5.2	13.2	2.3	0.0	89.7
28.7	29.0	0.2	0.0	0.0	124.4
19.8	16.0	7.7	1.3	T	105.0

MARQUETTE, MI

Feb	Mar	Apr	May	June	Total
1229	1227	852	560	159	8521
1241	1192	692	462	186	8530
1352	1070	672	507	253	8223
1378	1165	787	326	145	8599
1253	1353	746	507	199	8615
1119	1060	812	523	191	8342
1406	1128	801	372	259	8534
1487	1150	708	453	198	8928
1195	1221	717	286	230	7686
1370	1287	795	344	187	8696
1223	1026	809	559	149	8479
1448	1131	767	587	172	8601
1411	963	676	501	263	8530
1182	1214	692	436	297	8140
1323	1234	739	557	186	8658
1279	1189	754	513	162	8364
1447	1304	897	403	257	8754
1239	916	752	598	159	8542
1354	1180	747	535	192	8375
1165	1188	880	320	176	8072

Aug	Sept	Oct	Nov	Dec	Total
210	44	0	0	0	412
139	46	7	0	0	440
81	73	4	0	0	294
73	0	0	0	0	189
172	59	6	0	0	389
70	3	0	0	0	280
118	1	0	0	0	413

Average Temperature

Year	Jan	Feb	Mar	Apr	May	June	July	Aug	Sept	Oct	Nov	Dec	Annual
1936	16.2	6.7	27.6	34.0	52.0	56.8	69.7	64.7	59.0	42.8	28.9	26.2	40.4
#1937	16.0	20.8	23.0	37.8	51.8	61.4	67.2	70.3	56.6	43.4	33.0	21.0	41.8
1938	16.1	22.6	33.0	39.4	50.2	59.4	65.3	68.7	56.0	51.5	34.4	23.8	43.4
1939	21.2	15.3	23.2	34.8	51.0	59.9	67.4	65.8	58.1	44.4	36.3	30.2	42.3
1940	17.6	23.1	22.8	35.8	45.4	57.4	67.4	65.2	59.7	48.5	32.5	25.2	41.7
1941	21.0	21.6	25.7	45.3	55.5	61.4	67.6	63.5	59.9	47.4	35.6	28.8	44.4
1942	20.6	20.2	31.0	48.4	49.4	59.9	64.5	65.9	55.3	48.1	33.2	20.5	43.1
1943	15.0	19.8	21.5	36.8	49.8	58.7	69.2	65.7	54.3	47.2	32.1	23.5	41.1
1944	27.4	21.4	23.8	36.8	53.6	60.4	66.8	67.8	57.5	48.0	37.8	21.4	43.6
1945	14.6	20.7	38.1	40.1	44.1	58.0	64.2	66.6	57.2	45.2	33.5	21.0	41.9
1946	19.6	17.2	37.8	41.9	48.1	59.4	67.0	63.5	57.6	51.1	34.9	22.4	43.4
1947	21.0	17.9	26.6	34.2	44.2	56.2	65.0	70.9	58.3	56.2	30.5	23.0	42.0
1948	14.0	17.8	25.0	42.8	48.0	59.0	67.2	66.0	62.0	48.0	37.4	24.2	42.6
1949	22.4	19.4	26.8	43.7	50.6	64.6	69.0	67.7	55.3	51.2	33.4	24.1	44.0
1950	15.9	19.3	22.5	32.3	48.6	60.2	63.6	58.9	57.0	49.6	30.2	20.9	39.9
1951	17.9	19.6	25.7	38.7	53.6	56.7	66.0	60.8	54.4	45.6	28.3	21.3	40.7
1952	19.6	23.4	26.6	44.4	49.7	61.9	68.4	65.2	60.2	42.8	36.7	28.8	44.0
1953	22.2	21.4	30.4	36.2	50.3	61.3	67.0	68.7	57.9	53.1	39.4	26.3	44.5
1954	17.3	28.8	26.5	39.7	44.4	62.3	65.2	64.5	55.3	45.6	37.8	25.6	42.7
1955	20.8	20.2	24.8	46.8	54.0	63.5	71.1	69.6	57.6	49.6	30.7	20.3	44.1
1956	22.8	22.4	25.2	36.4	46.7	62.1	60.6	64.0	52.9	53.1	34.1	24.3	42.0
1957	13.0	20.5	26.3	41.6	50.1	60.0	66.9	64.3	56.8	48.2	33.7	25.4	42.2
1958	23.1	16.5	30.3	42.4	48.7	57.0	64.4	65.1	58.7	49.4	36.7	17.4	42.5
1959	12.6	15.6	27.1	38.6	54.6	63.1	69.0	68.2	59.3	43.2	26.1	29.5	42.2
1960	21.3	21.6	21.1	40.0	48.5	59.3	64.9	66.4	58.0	48.4	37.0	20.0	42.2
1961	16.0	24.8	30.6	37.6	48.0	59.9	65.1	67.4	59.8	49.0	35.6	22.4	43.0
1962	14.2	14.6	28.4	38.1	54.0	57.6	62.9	64.1	54.6	48.8	36.3	21.7	41.3
1963	9.2	11.7	27.7	41.2	50.5	61.3	68.6	63.9	57.2	58.8	39.3	18.9	42.4
1964	25.3	23.5	25.4	40.9	56.5	58.8	67.6	62.2	56.0	47.4	36.5	21.0	43.4
1965	15.8	15.8	23.3	38.2	54.2	60.1	63.1	62.6	53.1	47.4	33.9	28.9	41.4
1966	15.4	21.1	31.6	37.8	47.1	63.0	69.9	64.0	58.5	46.6	32.9	23.9	42.7
1967	20.4	13.1	28.3	39.2	45.8	60.5	64.6	63.6	59.0	45.5	31.0	24.7	41.3
1968	17.8	16.2	33.6	42.3	48.6	56.4	66.1	64.3	60.3	50.5	35.0	24.1	42.9
1969	21.3	22.6	25.6	41.7	51.9	55.4	65.3	70.8	59.3	44.5	34.6	25.6	43.2
1970	14.9	17.5	25.1	40.2	47.0	60.8	68.8	67.8	58.8	50.7	35.2	24.2	42.6
1971	14.4	19.2	26.3	39.7	48.4	61.3	64.2	63.4	61.1	53.6	34.9	25.4	42.7
1972	13.6	14.9	22.8	34.9	52.3	57.0	63.9	63.3	54.6	43.6	33.2	18.9	39.4
1973	22.1	20.5	35.2	39.8	45.4	60.3	67.0	69.1	58.6	53.4	35.1	23.0	44.1
1974	17.1	16.4	26.7	39.9	47.7	59.7	69.1	64.5	52.9	46.7	36.6	29.4	42.2
1975	20.4	23.2	26.5	35.4	54.7	61.1	70.3	67.1	54.2	50.1	39.4	23.1	43.8
RECORD MEAN	17.4	17.9	26.0	38.7	49.1	59.3	65.8	64.5	57.5	47.4	33.7	23.2	41.7
MAX	24.1	25.2	33.2	46.2	57.6	68.7	74.8	72.7	65.4	54.5	39.4	28.9	49.2
MIN	10.6	10.5	18.7	31.1	40.6	49.8	56.8	56.3	49.5	40.2	27.9	17.5	34.1

# Indicates a station move or relocation of instruments.

Precipitation

Year	Jan	Feb	Mar	Apr	May	June	July	Aug	Sept	Oct	Nov	Dec	Annual
1936	2.87	2.33	2.89	1.02	5.30	1.41	0.44	4.79	3.05	1.94	3.21	1.15	30.40
#1937	2.41	3.04	0.44	2.04	2.18	0.66	5.03	1.13	3.36	4.42	4.25	2.31	31.27
1938	3.93	1.52	1.95	3.31	2.66	3.99	1.54	4.72	1.87	3.43	2.96	2.97	34.85
1939	2.21	2.25	2.71	3.04	3.08	8.86	1.13	3.28	3.43	2.55	0.79	2.58	35.91
1940	2.48	1.55	1.02	2.98	4.37	4.54	1.91	1.69	3.05	1.79	3.96	1.64	30.98
1941	1.32	1.22	0.30	3.70	2.97	3.07	3.04	4.34	3.66	4.15	2.96	1.73	32.46
1942	0.52	0.76	3.14	2.01	3.90	2.91	3.30	3.22	5.73	2.55	3.49	3.58	35.11
1943	1.58	1.11	3.09	2.10	2.87	7.82	3.08	2.32	2.09	2.02	4.14	0.69	32.91
1944	1.18	1.90	2.53	2.46	1.97	4.78	5.17	2.87	3.34	1.23	4.41	2.06	33.90
1945	1.28	2.19	1.91	3.56	3.12	2.43	1.90	3.88	2.06	2.41	5.04	2.49	32.27
1946	2.21	1.43	1.12	0.65	2.89	2.85	0.93	4.98	2.78	1.82	2.50	1.82	25.98
1947	1.61	3.29	1.16	5.28	3.08	3.50	2.35	3.38	4.12	1.46	1.90	1.09	32.82
1948	1.83	1.06	1.47	2.35	0.56	3.40	2.14	2.10	1.21	0.54	5.08	0.72	22.46
1949	2.11	1.30	2.20	0.64	3.29	5.02	10.20	2.07	4.97	2.50	3.21	1.21	38.72
1950	3.51	1.75	2.55	4.05	3.31	2.22	3.21	2.73	2.01	0.60	4.56	2.91	33.41
1951	1.32	2.57	2.34	4.41	3.03	7.35	4.32	5.40	3.54	3.70	2.06	1.55	41.59
1952	1.76	0.75	1.18	1.31	2.18	2.68	4.73	3.18	1.62	0.88	2.29	2.67	25.23
1953	2.21	2.47	2.58	3.98	3.31	5.31	2.17	2.56	3.75	1.69	2.45	2.20	34.68
1954	1.69	0.78	2.20	3.31	4.20	3.23	1.17	2.28	5.61	3.68	1.32	0.90	30.37
1955	1.31	1.23	3.16	2.53	4.19	1.92	3.28	3.19	1.92	3.63	3.23	2.31	31.90
1956	0.51	0.31	1.14	2.16	3.60	3.20	5.11	2.76	1.98	0.21	3.71	2.11	26.80
1957	0.57	0.81	0.78	2.27	2.78	1.37	0.75	2.50	4.37	1.07	5.07	1.65	23.99
1958	1.71	2.39	0.85	0.88	0.98	3.35	4.25	2.98	2.00	1.82	2.53	1.67	25.41
1959	0.75	0.61	2.36	1.85	2.23	1.93	4.63	5.24	3.06	7.13	2.91	1.46	34.16
1960	1.58	2.30	1.58	5.73	7.70	4.14	4.24	3.61	3.58	2.73	3.02	1.15	41.36
1961	0.97	1.90	2.94	2.96	2.37	3.08	1.32	0.98	4.84	1.80	2.33	2.12	27.61
1962	1.38	2.47	1.33	1.38	2.17	2.16	1.43	3.37	4.66	1.91	1.16	2.57	25.99
1963	1.25	0.89	1.49	2.39	1.73	3.99	2.53	1.73	2.22	0.90	2.68	2.36	24.16
1964	1.31	1.42	1.74	2.91	3.13	2.50	2.95	5.04	3.91	1.79	2.65	2.13	31.48
1965	1.16	1.61	1.72	1.43	3.61	1.51	2.10	3.02	4.25	2.23	3.51	2.02	28.17
1966	1.33	0.72	4.46	1.58	1.10	2.46	1.80	3.90	3.10	3.18	3.62	2.79	30.04
1967	2.71	1.35	1.33	3.06	1.63	3.67	1.44	2.80	1.20	5.50	1.71	0.73	27.13
1968	1.24	3.08	0.76	3.11	2.86	7.07	1.81	2.44	7.22	2.47	1.68	3.96	37.70
1969	2.39	0.79	1.82	2.49	2.22	2.76	1.48	0.53	3.23	5.20	1.86	2.11	26.88
1970	1.90	1.20	1.17	1.55	4.86	1.46	5.36	0.94	5.47	2.29	2.68	1.75	30.63
1971	3.57	2.54	2.06	1.41	2.53	4.12	2.22	1.45	3.80	4.71	2.33	2.89	33.63
1972	1.53	1.43	3.25	2.62	2.50	1.70	2.85	4.12	5.32	1.96	3.39	3.03	33.70
1973	1.47	0.99	2.37	3.01	7.16	3.42	2.16	2.93	2.03	2.53	1.16	2.43	31.66
1974	1.31	1.42	0.61	3.28	2.49	3.57	1.80	3.87	4.01	3.05	2.87	0.81	29.09
1975	2.85	2.10	2.11	2.41	3.53	4.59	1.06	2.97	2.80	1.34	3.16	1.87	30.79
RECORD MEAN	2.02	1.69	2.02	2.43	2.94	3.43	3.03	2.78	3.47	2.72	2.88	2.26	31.67

Record mean values above are means through the current year for the period beginning in 1875 for temperature, 1872 for precipitation and 1938 for snowfall.

DULUTH, MINNESOTA

Duluth, Minnesota, is located at the western tip of Lake Superior. The City lies on and at the base of a range of hills that rise abruptly in the highest places from 600 to 800 feet above the level of Lake Superior. The range runs in a northeast and southwest direction. Two or three miles back from the waterfront the country assumes the character of a slightly rolling plateau.

Duluth extends along the west bank of the Saint Louis River, Spirit Lake, Saint Louis and Superior Bays, and Lake Superior, including Grassy, Rice's, and Minnesota Points. Directly opposite on the flats occupying the east banks of the Saint Louis Bay and the south banks of Superior and Allouez Bays lies the city of Superior, Wisconsin. The two Cities are frequently referred to as the Twin Ports.

Changes in weather are frequent and marked in the area, both summer and winter, making the climate invigorating. An important influence on the climate is the passage of a succession of high and low pressure systems that continually move across the United States from west to east.

The proximity of Lake Superior, which is the largest and coldest of the Great Lakes, materially influences the local climate too, especially in the spring and summer, and to a lesser degree in the fall and winter.

The prevailing winds are from the east and off the lake in May, June, and August, and from the west and northwest from September through April and in July. Summers are cool at the head of the Lakes. Afternoon temperatures of 90° or higher have occurred on an average of twice a year since the records began. Sometimes even in midsummer the local temperature attending the occasional strong easterly winds can be such that light overcoats may be necessary in those parts of the City adjacent to the lake, while 1 to 3 miles back of the range of hills the temperature may be fine and moderate and 10 miles farther inland the weather may be swelteringly warm. In Duluth proper the average number of days between the last occurrence of 32° in the spring and the first in autumn is 143 days. The average spring date is May 13, and the average fall date is October 3. At the Duluth Airport about 6 miles away from the lake, the average number of days between the 32° occurrences in spring and autumn is 125 days. The average spring date is May 22, and the average fall date is September 24. The latest a temperature of 32° or lower has occurred in the spring was June 13, 1962. The earliest in the autumn was September 2, 1946.

While the winters are cold, there is likewise the absence of many extremely low temperature readings. Occurrences of temperatures of 30° below zero or lower have averaged less than 1 per 2 years.

Precipitation is well distributed throughout the year and is adequate for vegetation. The heaviest rainfall is observed during the warm summer months, falling from showers and thundershowers. The average snowfall is 55 inches in downtown Duluth and near 75 inches at the airport. After the first general snow cover has fallen, it does not melt until late March or April. Snow falls frequently from December through March, making the Duluth area ideal for all winter sports. The heaviest 24-hour snowfall to date was 25.4 inches on December 5-6, 1950.

Station: DULUTH, MINNESOTA
INTERNATIONAL AIRPORT

Elevation (ground): 1428 feet

TEMPERATURES °F

Month	Normal			Extremes			
	Daily maximum	Daily minimum	Monthly	Record highest	Year	Record lowest	Year
(a)				15		15	
J	17.6	-.6	8.5	47	1973	-39	1972
F	22.1	2.0	12.1	44	1966	-32	1970
M	32.6	14.4	23.5	65	1968	-28	1962
A	47.8	29.3	38.6	83	1965	-5	1975
M	60.0	38.8	49.4	90	1969	17	1967
J	69.7	48.3	59.0	92	1963	27	1972
J	76.4	54.7	65.6	94	1964	36	1967
A	74.4	53.7	64.1	95	1961	33	1970
S	64.0	44.8	54.4	90	1961	23	1974
O	54.3	36.2	45.3	84	1963	12	1972
N	35.3	21.4	28.4	69	1975	-23	1964
D	22.5	6.3	14.4	55	1962	-29	1967
YR	48.1	29.1	38.6	95	AUG 1961	-39	JAN 1972

IMPORTANT:

The time-period covered by this record is limited: See footnotes following table of **NORMALS, MEANS AND EXTREMES** for explanation and for additional history of **EXTREME HIGHS AND LOWS** recorded in the general area.

(Continued)

Heavy fog is reported on an average of over 50 days of the year in Duluth. The nearness of Lake Superior and the abruptly rising terrain causes the condition when warm, moist air has a trajectory over the lake. On occasion the fog lasts into the second day.

Harbor ice begins to form about November 15, attains its maximum thickness the last of February, and usually disappears the middle of April. In the lake the average date of any considerable formation is in January; the average date of disappearance the middle of April. While the dates of formation are fairly uniform, the dates of disappearance vary considerably. After the lake ice breaks up, it drifts to and fro in the wind. With a southwest wind the whole field is moved lakeward or with a northwest wind shoved against the south shore. A northeast wind returns the ice to the harbor entrances. Sometimes during strong northeasters it packs to such depths that navigation is impeded and boats become fast in the ice.

Relative humidity, which is an important factor in individual comfort, is relatively high in Duluth. However, the high humidities are experienced when temperatures are modified by winds off the lake. Extremes of temperature are usually accompanied by dry air. In the summer the warm southwest winds are accompanied by dry air, while in the winter the cold north and northwest winds are likewise relatively dry.

DULUTH, MINNESOTA

Normals, Means, and Extremes

(To better understand these tables, see full explanation of terms beginning on page 322)

Month	Normal Degree days Base 65 °F: Heating	Normal Degree days Base 65 °F: Cooling	Precipitation in inches, Water equivalent: Normal	Maximum monthly	Year	Minimum monthly	Year	Maximum in 24 hrs.	Year	Snow, Ice pellets: Maximum monthly	Year	Maximum in 24 hrs.	Year	Relative humidity pct. Hour 00 (Local time)	Hour 06	Hour 12	Hour 18	Wind: Mean speed m.p.h.	Prevailing direction	Fastest mile: Speed m.p.h.	Direction	Year	Pct. of possible sunshine	Mean sky cover, tenths, sunrise to sunset	Mean number of days, Sunrise to sunset: Clear	Partly cloudy	Cloudy	Precipitation .01 inch or more	Snow, Ice pellets 1.0 inch or more	Thunderstorms	Heavy fog, visibility ¼ mile or less	Temperatures °F Max. (b) 90° and above	Max. 32° and below	Min. 32° and below	Min. 0° and below	Average station pressure mb. Elev. 1417 feet m.s.l.
(a)				34		34		26		32		32		14	14	14	14	26	14	25	25		25	27	27	27	27	34	32	33	27	14	14	14	14	3
J	1751	0	1.16	4.70	1969	0.14	1961	1.74	1975	46.8	1969	13.4	1972	74	76	69	69	12.1	NW	63	W	1958	49	6.8	7	7	17	12	5	*	3	0	28	31	18	962.1
F	1481	0	0.85	2.37	1971	0.22	1968	1.38	1965	31.5	1955	17.0	1948	71	75	64	64	11.9	NW	67	E	1958	54	6.4	8	6	14	10	4	*	2	0	24	28	15	965.0
M	1287	0	1.76	5.12	1965	0.22	1959	1.94	1965	45.5	1965	19.4	1965	73	78	63	62	12.1	WNW	57	NE	1966	56	6.7	7	7	17	11	4	1	3	0	17	30	6	962.9
A	792	0	2.55	5.84	1948	0.59	1959	2.27	1954	31.5	1950	11.2	1961	71	77	58	57	13.3	NW	75	NE	1958	54	7.0	5	8	17	11	2	1	3	0	3	22	*	963.7
M	484	0	3.41	7.67	1962	0.80	1967	2.28	1962	8.1	1954	4.3	1954	72	76	55	54	12.3	E	61	W	1959	55	6.8	5	10	16	13	*	4	6	*	0	6	0	961.0
J	194	14	4.44	7.51	1944	1.19	1956	4.05	1958	0.2	1945	0.2	1945	80	82	61	60	10.8	E	47	W	1952	58	6.7	5	11	14	13	0	7	7	*	0	1	0	960.5
J	67	86	3.73	8.48	1949	0.97	1947	3.40	1974	0.0		0.0		81	84	58	59	9.9	WNW	72	W	1952	67	5.9	7	14	10	11	0	8	5	1	0	0	0	963.4
A	104	76	3.79	10.31	1972	0.71	1970	3.43	1972	T	1949	T	1949	84	88	63	64	9.8	E	56	W	1952	61	6.0	8	12	11	11	0	8	7	1	0	0	0	964.6
S	318	0	3.06	6.58	1964	0.19	1952	3.77	1972	0.3	1974	0.2	1974	84	87	64	69	10.7	WNW	53	NW	1960	52	6.6	6	9	15	11	0	4	6	0	0	3	0	965.7
O	611	0	2.30	7.53	1949	0.13	1944	2.90	1973	8.1	1966	7.9	1966	77	82	63	67	11.5	WNW	61	S	1956	48	6.7	7	8	16	9	*	2	5	0	*	11	0	964.6
N	1098	0	1.73	4.19	1975	0.28	1962	2.64	1968	28.9	1947	15.7	1968	79	81	71	73	12.2	WNW	68	E	1960	34	7.8	4	6	20	11	3	*	4	0	12	25	1	963.4
D	1569	0	1.40	3.70	1968	0.16	1952	2.12	1950	44.3	1950	25.4	1950	79	80	75	76	11.4	NW	65	NW	1957	39	7.4	6	6	19	12	4	*	3	0	27	31	11	964.6
YR	9756	176	30.18	10.31	AUG 1972	0.13	OCT 1944	4.05	JUN 1958	46.8	JAN 1969	25.4	DEC 1950	77	80	64	64	11.5	WNW	75	NE	APR 1958	54	6.7	75	104	186	135	22	35	54	2	111	187	51	963.5

FOOTNOTES

Means and extremes above are from existing and comparable exposures. Annual extremes have been exceeded at other sites in the locality as follows: Highest temperature 106 in July 1936; lowest temperature -41 in January 1885; maximum monthly precipitation 11.52 in September 1881; minimum monthly precipitation 0.07 in December 1905; maximum precipitation in 24 hours 5.35 in July 1909; maximum monthly snowfall 48.2 in March 1917.

Snowfall

Season	July	Aug	Sept	Oct	Nov	Dec	Jan
1936-37	0.0	0.0	0.0	7.0	14.8	14.9	21.4
1937-38	0.0	0.0	0.0	T	0.8	9.2	19.5
1938-39	0.0	0.0	0.0	0.3	6.7	12.3	13.7
1939-40	0.0	0.0	0.0	1.2	1.5	1.3	3.6
1940-41	0.0	0.0	0.0	0.0	14.7	5.7	10.5
1941-42	0.0	0.0	T	T	0.2	4.6	3.1
#1942-43	0.0	0.0	T	2.2	0.5	16.8	9.3
1943-44	0.0	0.0	0.0	T	16.8	2.7	5.2
1944-45	0.0	0.0	0.0	0.0	6.0	5.0	11.1
1945-46	0.0	0.0	0.0	T	5.9	11.0	20.3
1946-47	0.0	0.0	0.0	T	8.5	15.2	12.9
1947-48	0.0	0.0	0.0	0.0	28.9	8.9	19.5
1948-49	0.0	0.0	0.0	T	5.3	13.0	26.7
1949-50	0.0	T	T	1.1	10.7	6.2	39.3
1950-51	0.0	0.0	0.0	0.4	10.6	44.3	7.2
1951-52	0.0	0.0	T	5.8	2.9	19.0	15.4
1952-53	0.0	0.0	0.0	0.5	7.3	1.8	19.8
1953-54	0.0	0.0	0.0	T	4.4	23.0	23.0
1954-55	0.0	0.0	T	2.9	7.4	4.2	16.4
1955-56	0.0	0.0	0.0	6.5	22.4	24.1	12.9
1956-57	0.0	0.0	0.0	0.0	17.0	21.0	4.6
1957-58	0.0	0.0	0.0	0.3	12.6	5.8	14.8
1958-59	0.0	0.0	T	0.4	3.6	13.7	8.6
1959-60	0.0	0.0	T	3.3	7.4	22.4	20.4
1960-61	0.0	0.0	0.0	T	14.8	7.4	2.8
1961-62	0.0	0.0	T	T	2.8	14.4	14.2
1962-63	0.0	0.0	0.0	0.7	1.8	8.4	3.6
1963-64	0.0	0.0	0.0	0.0	1.6	15.9	10.8
1964-65	0.0	0.0	T	T	8.6	24.3	10.6
1965-66	0.0	0.0	T	T	25.9	8.6	11.8
1966-67	0.0	0.0	T	8.1	7.6	15.4	36.7
1967-68	0.0	0.0	0.0	0.8	4.2	4.3	10.8
1968-69	0.0	0.0	0.0	T	21.8	37.7	46.8
1969-70	0.0	0.0	0.0	4.3	9.1	38.8	7.5
1970-71	0.0	0.0	0.0	0.2	16.8	20.9	31.8
1971-72	0.0	0.0	0.0	0.2	6.4	17.5	30.9
1972-73	0.0	0.0	T	0.5	6.7	20.0	9.2
1973-74	0.0	0.0	0.0	T	7.6	15.7	13.4
1974-75	0.0	0.0	0.3	0.8	4.5	19.1	32.7
1975-76	0.0	0.0	0.0	0.1	25.7	7.8	
RECORD MEAN	0.0	T	T	1.2	10.2	16.1	17.2

Heating Degree Days

Season	July	Aug	Sept	Oct	Nov	Dec	Jan
1955-56	24	29	313	609	1314	1751	1625
1956-57	122	112	426	477	1100	1532	1978
1957-58	35	79	372	669	1102	1466	1522
1958-59	98	114	285	607	1070	1822	1947
1959-60	46	63	311	790	1378	1278	1695
#1960-61	65	62	299	607	998	1626	1769
1961-62	58	32	343	597	1070	1612	1912
1962-63	132	121	388	611	930	1560	1989
1963-64	50	107	216	280	874	1715	1487
1964-65	50	215	377	631	1037	1751	1854
1965-66	127	158	506	617	1109	1355	2053
1966-67	36	145	304	670	1187	1589	1662
1967-68	80	144	269	694	1147	1504	1730
1968-69	90	140	254	576	1073	1644	1780
1969-70	99	20	258	746	1075	1466	1939
1970-71	38	67	311	630	1107	1616	1996
1971-72	111	133	273	531	1099	1553	2012
1972-73	134	146	440	802	1167	1792	1654
1973-74	72	66	354	513	1106	1651	1843
1974-75	45	160	507	684	1069	1404	1713
1975-76	46	129	418	561	1003	1642	

Cooling Degree Days

Year	Jan	Feb	Mar	Apr	May	June	July
1969	0	0	0	0	11	4	76
1970	0	0	0	0	8	42	162
1971	0	0	0	0	0	32	24
1972	0	0	0	0	8	22	24
1973	0	0	0	0	0	1	72
1974	0	0	0	0	0	19	115
1975	0	0	0	0	2	18	168

Feb	Mar	Apr	May	June	Total
17.0	3.8	5.4	0.0	0.0	84.3
5.6	6.1	T	0.6	0.0	41.8
33.9	13.7	8.0	0.0	0.0	88.6
13.2	14.6	2.1	0.7	0.0	38.2
7.4	9.1	2.6	0.0	0.0	50.0
6.4	21.5	2.4	T	0.0	38.2
5.4	15.5	1.1	T	0.0	50.8
7.8	15.1	0.1	T	0.0	47.7
11.2	3.1	5.8	T	0.2	42.4
9.5	1.6	3.0	T	0.0	51.3
12.6	9.0	11.2	T	0.0	69.4
26.6	16.3	1.0	T	0.0	101.2
12.1	15.3	6.7	T	0.0	79.1
10.8	26.0	31.5	6.0	0.0	131.6
16.5	21.8	8.0	0.5	0.0	109.3
4.3	21.6	3.2	T	0.0	72.2
12.8	11.9	14.2	T	0.0	68.3
11.8	12.4	0.9	8.1	0.0	83.6
31.5	23.6	5.0	T	T	91.0
8.4	17.5	9.9	1.8	0.0	103.5
20.6	10.9	6.7	0.0	0.0	80.8
3.1	11.7	0.1	T	0.0	48.4
9.2	3.7	3.5	T	0.0	42.7
11.8	2.2	1.8	T	0.0	69.3
7.7	8.8	24.4	2.5	0.0	68.4
18.3	7.7	5.7	0.2	0.0	63.3
14.4	19.1	0.2	0.2	0.0	48.4
6.8	13.5	5.6	0.0	0.0	54.2
19.3	45.5	1.6	1.0	0.0	110.9
4.3	24.5	10.2	1.7	0.0	87.0
2.7	6.9	1.6	1.3	0.0	80.3
2.7	4.1	8.7	3.7	0.0	39.3
3.0	3.0	8.7	T	0.0	121.0
8.9	9.9	14.8	1.6	0.0	94.9
27.4	12.7	6.5	0.6	0.0	116.9
20.7	11.0	20.4	T	0.0	107.1
3.0	2.1	2.8	1.5	0.0	45.8
15.3	15.1	5.2	1.0	0.0	73.3
12.3	30.3	0.4	T	0.0	100.4
12.1	13.7	7.2	1.0	T	78.7

DULUTH, MN

Feb	Mar	Apr	May	June	Total
1560	1406	930	526	156	10243
1504	1328	769	475	224	10047
1524	1175	707	450	297	9398
1552	1223	813	439	161	10131
1488	1475	786	446	204	9950
1261	1100	883	468	160	9298
1609	1255	917	468	263	10136
1620	1159	711	471	160	9852
1407	1396	783	338	238	8891
1650	1519	802	397	209	10492
1473	1166	903	546	165	10178
1714	1243	832	592	210	10184
1611	1017	729	507	227	9659
1411	1346	725	449	332	9820
1581	1355	781	573	162	10055
1464	1332	794	518	124	9997
1698	1458	946	357	211	10382
1429	1022	793	526	171	10076
1508	1373	806	565	206	10063
1479	1447	1013	358	226	10105

Aug	Sept	Oct	Nov	Dec	Total
135	16	0	0	0	242
102	30	0	0	0	344
60	47	1	0	0	164
59	0	0	0	0	113
84	18	0	0	0	175
15	0	0	0	0	149
41	0	0	0	0	229

Average Temperature

Year	Jan	Feb	Mar	Apr	May	June	July	Aug	Sept	Oct	Nov	Dec	Annual
1936	2.6	-1.9	24.0	33.4	52.7	57.6	70.6	66.6	58.8	39.2	23.6	17.1	37.0
1937	3.3	12.0	22.3	37.0	51.0	60.4	66.0	69.7	56.2	41.2	27.6	13.7	38.4
1938	8.6	18.2	32.8	39.0	47.3	60.2	64.4	68.0	57.9	49.4	27.0	15.8	40.7
1939	15.2	6.2	22.6	35.1	50.4	57.2	67.0	65.6	56.6	43.0	35.6	26.5	40.1
1940	8.1	18.6	20.6	37.1	47.9	57.6	66.3	63.8	60.0	48.8	25.8	18.9	39.5
1941	13.5	14.4	24.3	44.0	52.8	60.0	68.6	65.0	56.9	46.0	31.6	22.4	41.6
1942	17.0	16.0	31.4	44.5	47.8	56.8	63.3	64.4	53.3	46.2	28.8	12.3	40.2
1943	5.6	14.6	18.0	38.1	50.0	57.8	69.0	65.8	52.6	47.0	25.6	18.0	38.5
1944	21.9	14.4	21.7	37.0	51.3	58.4	64.8	65.0	55.9	47.4	34.1	15.2	40.6
1945	9.2	14.6	34.6	36.2	45.4	55.3	64.1	65.7	54.3	44.0	27.2	11.8	38.5
1946	11.4	10.2	35.7	42.8	47.2	58.0	65.9	64.2	55.0	45.4	29.6	14.0	40.0
1947	15.2	11.1	24.5	36.1	47.4	55.4	67.8	66.8	55.3	52.3	24.2	15.6	39.3
1948	6.6	10.8	23.2	41.0	51.7	59.9	65.8	66.8	63.2	48.1	32.5	16.8	40.5
1949	14.0	11.0	24.1	44.4	50.0	62.4	67.0	67.2	54.6	47.0	32.6	14.5	40.8
1950	3.6	15.2	18.8	31.2	45.8	57.6	62.0	59.2	56.4	46.5	23.8	10.0	35.8
1951	6.8	14.6	19.6	38.2	51.7	56.3	64.5	58.7	51.5	41.9	22.4	12.2	36.5
1952	8.6	21.2	23.3	44.6	50.9	59.5	65.9	62.2	55.9	39.8	30.3	22.2	40.4
1953	12.5	13.5	26.6	35.9	48.7	57.9	64.2	66.6	55.0	49.7	33.7	16.8	40.1
1954	5.8	25.2	22.4	37.0	43.9	59.7	64.4	63.6	54.1	42.2	32.7	20.3	39.3
1955	11.3	11.6	17.3	44.9	51.5	60.7	69.0	67.9	55.6	45.2	22.3	9.6	38.9
1956	13.5	12.0	21.0	34.3	47.1	60.2	60.7	62.0	51.1	48.8	28.2	15.9	37.9
1957	2.0	11.8	23.1	38.5	48.6	55.5	65.3	64.3	53.0	43.9	28.3	18.0	37.7
#1958	16.1	10.7	28.1	40.8	49.5	54.9	62.4	63.4	55.7	45.3	29.1	6.7	38.6
1959	2.2	9.5	25.3	37.7	50.7	60.9	67.0	65.4	54.9	39.3	18.8	23.6	37.9
1960	10.5	13.5	17.1	38.6	50.4	58.4	65.9	64.8	55.5	45.3	31.5	12.4	38.7
#1961	7.9	19.7	29.4	35.3	49.8	61.3	65.1	67.6	54.7	45.6	29.1	12.9	39.9
1962	3.4	7.5	24.3	34.2	50.0	56.8	60.8	61.9	51.9	45.1	33.8	14.6	37.0
1963	0.9	7.1	27.5	41.0	49.6	61.3	66.9	62.9	57.9	56.0	35.7	9.6	39.7
1964	16.9	16.4	19.8	38.7	54.3	58.4	66.3	59.1	52.4	44.4	30.2	8.4	38.8
1965	5.2	6.0	15.8	38.0	52.0	58.0	61.9	61.1	48.0	44.8	27.8	21.1	36.6
1966	-1.3	12.3	27.1	34.7	47.3	61.1	68.0	61.5	54.8	43.2	25.2	13.5	37.3
1967	11.2	3.7	24.8	37.0	45.6	58.2	64.1	61.7	56.0	42.4	26.6	16.3	37.3
1968	9.1	9.3	32.0	40.5	48.4	57.4	64.2	61.7	56.6	46.2	28.9	11.9	38.8
1969	7.5	14.4	21.4	40.6	50.6	53.8	64.0	68.5	56.7	40.7	28.9	17.5	38.7
1970	2.4	8.4	21.1	38.7	46.6	60.8	68.8	66.0	55.5	44.4	27.8	12.7	37.8
1971	0.6	12.6	21.8	38.3	48.1	61.7	62.0	62.4	57.3	47.7	28.1	14.7	37.9
1972	0.2	6.4	17.9	33.3	53.5	58.4	61.2	61.9	50.0	38.9	25.9	7.2	34.6
1973	11.6	13.7	31.8	38.3	47.8	59.1	64.8	65.5	53.6	48.2	27.9	11.7	39.5
1974	5.6	11.0	20.6	37.9	46.6	58.6	67.1	60.1	47.9	42.8	29.2	19.5	37.2
1975	9.6	12.0	18.2	31.0	53.3	57.9	68.7	62.0	50.9	46.7	31.3	11.8	37.8
RECORD MEAN	8.5	12.1	23.9	37.9	48.8	58.4	65.1	63.8	55.1	44.7	29.0	15.0	38.5
MAX	17.2	21.2	32.3	46.6	58.7	68.7	75.3	73.3	64.1	52.9	35.8	22.6	47.4
MIN	-0.2	3.0	15.5	29.2	38.9	48.0	54.9	54.2	46.1	36.4	22.1	7.3	29.6

# Indicates a station move or relocation of instruments.

Precipitation

Year	Jan	Feb	Mar	Apr	May	June	July	Aug	Sept	Oct	Nov	Dec	Annual
1936	1.53	1.57	2.36	2.65	2.76	0.93	0.63	1.93	1.48	1.28	1.58	2.29	20.99
1937	1.99	1.79	0.40	3.17	3.92	3.51	2.73	3.87	4.30	1.50	1.29	0.89	29.36
1938	1.55	0.63	2.91	4.48	5.60	3.21	2.23	1.56	2.85	0.64	2.25	1.10	29.01
1939	1.75	3.20	1.42	1.28	1.93	4.34	2.03	5.66	0.72	2.09	0.16	0.22	24.80
1940	0.27	1.07	1.58	2.56	3.52	1.84	3.05	2.14	3.47	2.19	3.40	0.51	25.60
#1941	1.08	0.72	0.85	2.74	2.67	3.67	2.86	6.53	6.28	1.62	0.34	0.41	29.77
1942	0.25	0.29	2.36	2.75	4.90	3.33	3.54	3.54	2.05	1.00	0.83	0.98	25.82
1943	1.31	1.03	1.87	1.25	3.69	6.80	2.97	4.97	1.98	2.49	0.83	0.28	29.47
1944	0.50	0.57	1.15	1.53	6.17	7.51	3.60	6.43	1.99	0.13	2.27	0.34	32.19
1945	0.74	0.77	3.68	2.81	1.48	4.47	4.75	3.39	4.02	0.77	1.34	1.92	30.14
1946	1.82	0.71	1.71	1.49	3.42	7.23	1.79	1.33	5.16	6.24	2.60	1.33	34.83
1947	0.97	1.04	0.82	2.57	1.74	6.84	0.97	5.90	2.11	1.46	3.10	0.56	28.08
1948	1.14	1.67	2.01	5.84	0.86	4.58	3.77	2.79	0.37	0.84	2.55	1.69	28.11
1949	1.84	0.87	2.42	1.08	4.05	5.32	8.48	1.84	2.22	7.53	1.11	1.50	38.26
1950	3.12	0.80	3.84	4.25	6.45	3.51	4.07	3.17	1.43	3.87	1.88	3.69	40.08
1951	0.49	1.79	2.30	2.11	2.88	5.04	3.68	6.64	6.25	2.57	1.37	1.71	36.83
1952	0.88	0.25	2.06	0.77	0.90	7.13	6.44	4.55	0.19	0.57	1.21	0.16	25.11
1953	1.24	1.12	1.88	3.57	5.60	4.07	5.68	6.43	0.88	0.35	1.91	1.90	34.63
1954	1.45	1.03	1.83	4.05	4.47	4.10	2.70	1.38	2.92	1.32	0.79	0.26	26.30
1955	0.95	1.64	1.26	1.48	2.97	3.98	6.81	3.96	4.83	1.75	1.97	1.89	33.49
1956	0.93	0.46	1.07	1.87	2.08	1.19	1.78	4.72	1.92	2.43	1.47	1.43	21.35
1957	0.19	1.52	0.99	1.84	2.47	6.84	5.56	1.72	2.98	1.75	2.59	0.37	28.82
1958	1.08	0.36	0.85	1.26	1.59	5.67	3.82	3.85	4.33	1.22	2.47	0.86	27.36
1959	0.46	0.28	0.22	0.59	5.63	4.06	4.29	4.48	4.83	2.62	0.69	2.48	30.63
1960	0.88	0.52	0.23	3.80	4.37	2.98	2.81	4.10	1.66	2.19	2.65	0.74	26.93
1961	0.14	0.65	2.53	4.72	3.26	1.33	2.47	0.71	3.01	1.79	1.61	1.26	23.48
1962	0.88	1.82	1.08	2.67	7.67	3.01	2.97	4.40	3.03	0.86	0.28	0.90	29.57
1963	0.32	0.87	1.50	2.21	2.28	4.04	1.82	2.96	2.80	1.01	1.51	1.08	22.40
1964	1.10	0.57	1.10	4.10	5.74	3.50	1.47	6.57	6.58	0.59	1.84	1.79	34.95
1965	0.89	1.73	5.12	1.64	2.96	4.51	3.57	3.76	5.56	3.30	3.33	1.67	38.04
1966	0.98	1.31	3.84	1.99	1.53	4.14	6.13	6.42	1.52	3.56	1.17	1.56	34.15
1967	3.12	0.24	0.66	1.99	0.80	5.21	2.91	2.31	1.34	1.44	0.50	0.91	21.43
1968	0.77	0.22	1.89	4.83	4.02	5.39	3.60	2.07	3.42	5.28	3.10	3.70	38.29
1969	4.70	0.26	0.39	1.46	2.82	2.18	3.03	2.18	4.13	2.42	1.25	2.67	27.49
1970	0.51	0.43	1.15	3.16	2.81	1.68	3.58	0.71	2.01	6.07	3.39	1.97	27.47
1971	1.56	2.37	2.02	1.29	3.45	3.25	3.91	4.50	2.67	6.09	2.07	1.22	34.40
1972	2.28	1.47	1.45	2.17	2.00	3.70	6.71	10.31	5.30	0.83	1.37	2.02	39.61
1973	0.67	0.29	1.54	1.35	3.81	2.43	2.36	8.46	4.28	4.56	1.61	0.69	32.05
1974	0.97	0.82	0.78	2.07	3.09	4.07	4.85	3.79	0.98	1.57	1.36	1.15	25.50
1975	3.69	0.76	2.59	2.21	1.44	5.59	2.26	2.52	2.32	1.20	4.19	0.64	29.41
RECORD MEAN	1.15	0.96	1.61	2.20	3.12	3.95	3.67	3.48	3.18	2.22	1.67	1.16	28.37

Record mean values above are means through the current year for the period beginning in 1904 for temperature and precipitation, 1944 for snowfall. City office locations were sources of data as follows: Average temperature through 1958; total degree days and total precipitation through 1941; and total snowfall through June 1943.

MINNEAPOLIS-ST. PAUL, MINNESOTA

The Twin Cities of Minneapolis and St. Paul are located at the confluence of the Mississippi and Minnesota Rivers over the heart of an artesian water basin. Its terrain varies little in elevation from that of the official observation station at International Airport. However, to the east and south some hills are about 1,100 feet above mean sea level. Numerous lakes dot the Cities. Minneapolis alone boasts of 22 lakes and lakelets within its city park system. The largest body of water is Lake Minnetonka about 15 miles west of the Airport. These bodies of water are relatively shallow and ice-covered during winter months and therefore provide almost no moisture source. During the warmer part of the year the water area provided by these lakes is too small to have any noticeable modifying influence upon the migratory airmasses that pass over Minneapolis-St. Paul.

The climate of Minneapolis-St. Paul is predominantly the continental type for the Cities are situated very close to the geographical center of the North American continent. There are wide variations in temperature, ample summer rainfall, and scanty winter precipitation. In general, there exists a tendency to extremes in all climatic features. Disturbances originating in the northwestern United States and many which have their origin in the southwest migrate eastward near the Twin Cities to be followed by cooler, sometimes much colder, polar airmasses from the northwest and north. This cyclonic control of climate gives the Twin Cities changeable weather that is stimulating and invigorating.

The temperature variation from season to season is quite large. It ranges from very warm though comfortable due to low daytime humidity in summer to very cold in winter. The normal mean temprature for the winter months of December, January, and February is about 16° F., and for the summer months of June, July, and August, about 70°F. Recorded temperature extremes cover a range of 142° from 34° below zero in January 1936, to 108° in July of that same year, 1936. There were 36 consecutive days during January-February 1936 when the temperature was below zero, and 11 straight days in July 1948 when it was 90° or higher. Cold winters are accepted, but more attention is given the warmer months, the length of the growing season, and the rainfall. The average date of the last occurrence of a temperature 32° F. or lower is April 29. The latest date recorded was May 24, 1925. The average date of the first temperature occurrence of 32° F. or lower in autumn is October 13. The earliest date recorded was September 3, 1974 The shortest growing season was 119 days in 1929 and the longest was 207 days in 1894 and 1900. The average growing season is 166 days. Because of this favorable growing season, all crops generally mature before the autumn freeze occurs.

Although the total annual precipitation is important, its proper distribution during the growing season is even more significant. For the most part, vegetation is dormant for seven months. During the remaining five months, May through September, the major crops of

Station: MINNEAPOLIS, MINNESOTA
INTERNATIONAL AIRPORT
Elevation (ground): 834 feet

TEMPERATURES °F

Month	Normal			Extremes			
	Daily maximum	Daily minimum	Monthly	Record highest	Year	Record lowest	Year
(a)				16		16	
J	21.2	3.2	12.2	46	1973	-34	1970
F	25.9	7.1	16.5	54	1964	-28	1965
M	36.9	19.6	28.3	83	1968	-32	1962
A	55.5	34.7	45.1	91	1962	2	1962
M	67.9	46.3	57.1	95	1969	18	1967
J	77.1	56.7	66.9	99	1963	37	1969
J	82.4	61.4	71.9	101	1974	43	1972
A	80.8	59.6	70.2	98	1964	39	1967
S	70.7	49.3	60.0	95	1960	26	1974
O	60.7	39.2	50.0	87	1975	15	1972
N	40.6	24.2	32.4	74	1975	-17	1964
D	26.6	10.6	18.6	62	1962	-24	1973
YR	53.8	34.3	44.1	101	JUL 1974	-34	JAN 1970

IMPORTANT:
The time-period covered by this record is limited: See footnotes following table of **NORMALS, MEANS AND EXTREMES** for explanation and for additional history of **EXTREME HIGHS AND LOWS** recorded in the general area.

(Continued)

corn, soybeans, hay, and small grains are produced. During this period, the normal rainfall is 16.78 inches, approximately 65 percent of the normal annual precipitation. Winter snowfall can be heavy and averages more than 40 inches a season. The heaviest snowfall observed in any single month was 40.0 inches in March 1951. Snow has occurred in all months except June, July, and August.

Thunderstorms are the principal source of pricipitation during the crop season. Although some damage can, and does, result from the more severe thunderstorms, any losses brought about the excessive rains, high winds, lightning, and hail, or by any combination of these phenomena are greatly offset by the benefits gained from the rainfall.

During the winter months humidities are high and sunshine is at a minimum. During the months of December and January frequently less than 40 percent of possible sunshine has been observed. Fog does occur, but not too frequently. During the late fall, winter, and early spring when the ground is cold or covered with snow, advective cooling or maritime moist air from the south will cause either fog or very low cloudiness, usually the latter.

Severe storms such as tornadoes, freezing rain (glaze), and hail are not numerous. The Twin Cities lie along the northern edge of the region of maximum tornado frequency in the United States. Four severe tornadoes have struck Minneapolis-St. Paul, one each on August 20, 1904, and July 20, 1951, and two separate tornadoes during the evening of May 6, 1965, within a 1-hour and 45-minute period. During each of them, lives were lost, many persons were injured, and millions of dollars of property damage occurred.

Minneapolis and St. Paul river terminals mark the end of upstream navigation and the beginning of downstream navigation on the Mississippi River. The river mileage from the St. Paul terminal to the Gulf of Mexico is 1,793.1 miles. The Mississippi River itself begins with flow from Lake Itasca in northern Minnesota, 512.3 miles upstream from St. Anthony Falls in Minneapolis, or about 2,320 miles from the Gulf of Mexico. Since the winter season is long with daily mean temperatures below freezing from mid-November to late March, the Mississippi River is frozen over at the Cities from approximately December 10 until March 20.

Floods occur along the Mississippi River both at Minneapolis and St. Paul. They are due to spring snow melt, or to excessive rainfall, or to a combination of both. Occasionally an ice jam forms and creates a local flood condition. The flood problem at St. Paul is complicated because the Minnesota river empties into the Mississippi River between the two Cities. Consequently, high water or flooding on the Minnesota River creates a greater flood potential at St. Paul. Flood stage at St. Paul is 14.0 feet and at Minneapolis, 16.0 feet. Flood stage at St. Paul can be expected on the average once in every eight years.

Normals, Means, and Extremes

(To better understand these tables, see full explanation of terms beginning on page 322)

Month	Normal Degree days Base 65 °F: Heating	Normal Degree days: Cooling	Precipitation in inches, Water equivalent: Normal	Maximum monthly	Year	Minimum monthly	Year	Maximum in 24 hrs.	Year	Snow, Ice pellets: Maximum monthly	Year	Maximum in 24 hrs.	Year
(a)				37		37		37		37		37	
J	1637	0	0.73	3.63	1967	0.11	1959	1.21	1967	35.3	1967	7.6	1950
F	1358	0	0.84	2.07	1962	0.06	1964	1.10	1966	26.5	1962	9.3	1939
M	1138	0	1.68	4.75	1965	0.32	1958	1.66	1965	40.0	1951	13.7	1952
A	597	0	2.04	5.40	1975	0.59	1952	2.23	1975	9.6	1957	9.3	1949
M	271	26	3.37	8.03	1962	0.61	1967	3.03	1965	3.0	1946	3.0	1946
J	65	122	3.94	7.99	1975	1.06	1973	2.65	1975	0.0		0.0	
J	11	225	3.69	7.10	1955	0.58	1975	4.12	1949	0.0		0.0	
A	21	182	3.05	6.60	1959	0.43	1946	3.22	1956	0.0		0.0	
S	173	23	2.73	7.53	1942	0.41	1940	3.55	1942	1.7	1942	1.7	1942
O	472	7	1.78	5.68	1971	0.01	1952	2.95	1966	3.7	1959	2.5	1955
N	978	0	1.20	5.15	1940	0.02	1939	2.91	1940	26.3	1940	16.2	1940
D	1438	0	0.89	2.21	1968	T	1943	1.11	1953	33.2	1969	9.8	1945
YR	8159	585	25.94	8.03	MAY 1962	T	DEC 1943	4.12	JUL 1949	40.0	MAR 1951	16.2	NOV 1940

Month	Relative humidity pct. Hour 00 (Local time)	Hour 06	Hour 12	Hour 18	Wind: Mean speed m.p.h.	Prevailing direction	Fastest mile: Speed m.p.h.	Direction	Year	Pct. of possible sunshine	Mean sky cover, tenths, sunrise to sunset	Mean number of days, Sunrise to sunset: Clear	Partly cloudy	Cloudy	Precipitation .01 inch or more	Snow, Ice pellets 1.0 inch or more	Thunderstorms	Heavy fog, visibility ¼ mile or less	Temperatures °F Max. (b) 90° and above	Max. 32° and below	Min. 32° and below	Min. 0° and below	Average station pressure mb. Elev. 838 feet m.s.l.
(a)	16	16	16	16	37	14	37	37		37	37	37	37	37	37	37	37	37	16	16	16	16	3
J	73	74	67	69	10.4	NW	40	SE	1956	51	6.4	8	7	16	9	3	*	1	0	24	31	15	985.8
F	73	74	65	65	10.6	NW	52	NW	1952	57	6.2	8	7	13	7	3	*	1	0	20	28	9	987.9
M	74	77	64	63	11.3	NW	47	E	1951	54	6.7	7	8	16	10	3	1	1	0	11	27	2	984.3
A	70	76	55	54	12.4	NW	52	WSW	1964	55	6.6	7	8	15	10	1	2	1	*	*	13	0	984.1
M	69	77	54	52	11.4	SE	61	NW	1964	58	6.5	7	9	15	12	*	5	1	1	0	2	0	981.5
J	74	80	55	54	10.5	SE	63	NW	1939	63	6.1	7	10	13	12	0	8	1	3	0	0	0	981.3
J	76	82	55	54	9.3	S	92	W	1951	70	5.1	11	11	9	10	0	8	*	6	0	0	0	984.4
A	78	85	56	56	9.1	SE	63	N	1967	67	5.2	11	11	9	10	0	6	1	4	0	0	0	985.2
S	81	87	60	62	9.9	S	47	N	1951	61	5.5	10	9	11	9	*	4	1	1	0	1	0	987.3
O	75	83	59	63	10.5	SE	73	S	1949	57	5.5	11	7	13	8	*	2	1	0	0	7	0	986.4
N	79	82	67	71	11.0	NW	60	SW	1958	39	7.1	5	7	18	8	2	1	1	0	6	22	*	985.8
D	77	79	71	73	10.3	NW	52	W	1946	40	7.0	6	7	18	9	3	*	1	0	22	29	8	987.3
YR	75	80	61	61	10.6	NW	92	W	JUL 1951	58	6.2	98	101	166	113	14	36	11	14	83	158	34	985.1

FOOTNOTES

Means and extremes above are from existing and comparable exposures. Annual extremes have been exceeded at other sites in the locality as follows: Highest temperature 108 in July 1936; maximum monthly precipitation 11.87 in July 1892; maximum precipitation in 24 hours 7.80 in July 1892.

Snowfall

Season	July	Aug	Sept	Oct	Nov	Dec	Jan
1936-37	0.0	0.0	0.0	0.1	1.7	11.2	12.2
#1937-38	0.0	0.0	0.0	T	1.2	5.4	9.3
1938-39	0.0	0.0	0.0	1.9	0.5	9.1	7.4
1939-40	0.0	0.0	0.0	0.6	T	4.8	5.0
1940-41	0.0	0.0	0.0	0.0	26.3	10.6	3.3
1941-42	0.0	0.0	0.0	T	3.8	8.6	1.7
1942-43	0.0	0.0	1.7	0.3	0.9	7.0	10.1
1943-44	0.0	0.0	0.0	T	10.3	T	1.0
1944-45	0.0	0.0	0.0	0.0	2.5	1.1	8.2
1945-46	0.0	0.0	T	0.0	4.5	14.6	4.3
1946-47	0.0	0.0	0.0	T	4.1	5.9	7.6
1947-48	0.0	0.0	0.0	0.0	21.8	6.7	3.5
1948-49	0.0	0.0	0.0	T	2.5	2.3	12.5
1949-50	0.0	0.0	0.0	T	2.7	6.5	17.0
1950-51	0.0	0.0	0.0	0.0	5.6	25.0	7.1
1951-52	0.0	0.0	T	0.8	10.8	16.5	9.9
1952-53	0.0	0.0	0.0	T	10.1	6.0	6.0
1953-54	0.0	0.0	0.0	0.0	1.9	5.9	3.6
1954-55	0.0	0.0	0.0	0.4	6.4	4.0	7.8
1955-56	0.0	0.0	0.0	2.5	6.0	14.6	4.6
1956-57	0.0	0.0	0.0	0.0	6.8	2.1	4.9
1957-58	0.0	0.0	0.0	T	10.3	2.2	2.4
1958-59	0.0	0.0	T	T	3.3	2.4	1.4
1959-60	0.0	0.0	0.0	3.7	6.9	3.5	9.5
1960-61	0.0	0.0	0.0	T	2.4	1.7	4.6
1961-62	0.0	0.0	0.1	0.0	2.5	18.1	5.9
1962-63	0.0	0.0	0.0	T	5.6	3.2	5.0
1963-64	0.0	0.0	0.0	0.0	T	7.6	5.0
1964-65	0.0	0.0	0.0	T	4.3	8.1	10.5
1965-66	0.0	0.0	0.0	0.0	1.6	1.2	11.9
1966-67	0.0	0.0	0.0	0.2	3.4	12.7	35.3
1967-68	0.0	0.0	0.0	0.3	0.8	2.4	10.6
1968-69	0.0	0.0	0.0	T	4.9	28.7	21.6
1969-70	0.0	0.0	0.0	2.4	3.8	33.2	9.8
1970-71	0.0	0.0	0.0	T	6.3	5.5	19.9
1971-72	0.0	0.0	0.0	0.0	13.2	12.8	12.2
1972-73	0.0	0.0	T	T	1.1	15.3	11.6
1973-74	0.0	0.0	0.0	0.0	0.1	17.9	2.5
1974-75	0.0	0.0	0.0	0.0	1.2	6.1	27.4
1975-76	0.0	0.0	0.0	0.0	16.2	5.6	
RECORD MEAN	0.0	0.0	T	0.3	5.8	8.9	9.0

Heating Degree Days

Season	July	Aug	Sept	Oct	Nov	Dec	Jan
1955-56	0	2	136	423	1173	1631	1615
1956-57	9	22	202	271	920	1267	1698
1957-58	0	13	184	500	963	1226	1311
1958-59	12	37	108	370	871	1519	1686
#1959-60	5	4	152	634	1181	1073	1467
1960-61	8	11	202	503	943	1490	1641
1961-62	0	10	239	396	938	1536	1794
1962-63	27	15	262	461	891	1422	1927
1963-64	1	32	129	216	793	1703	1390
1964-65	0	63	224	515	894	1551	1702
1965-66	7	40	368	447	950	1140	1909
1966-67	0	40	185	536	1042	1446	1556
1967-68	36	65	166	577	1024	1335	1567
1968-69	10	28	143	451	922	1486	1723
1969-70	5	0	131	580	933	1379	1842
1970-71	3	5	190	476	959	1443	1811
1971-72	16	22	164	413	962	1438	1844
1972-73	34	52	218	651	974	1664	1474
1973-74	1	3	185	350	915	1493	1642
1974-75	0	48	289	467	933	1252	1561
1975-76	15	7	231	387	818	1346	

Cooling Degree Days

Year	Jan	Feb	Mar	Apr	May	June	July
1969	0	0	0	0	76	49	276
1970	0	0	0	17	54	213	323
1971	0	0	0	2	5	218	141
1972	0	0	0	0	94	109	148
1973	0	0	0	1	4	158	280
1974	0	0	0	5	18	93	369
1975	0	0	0	0	66	159	371

Feb	Mar	Apr	May	June	Total
7.6	8.2	3.6	0.0	0.0	44.6
7.4	6.2	T	T	0.0	29.5
11.9	6.0	4.8	0.0	0.0	41.6
9.1	25.6	T	T	0.0	45.1
5.5	6.8	T	0.0	0.0	52.5
5.2	4.6	T	0.0	0.0	23.9
4.6	9.8	T	T	0.0	34.4
4.2	11.1	0.3	T	0.0	26.9
15.4	0.7	6.0	T	0.0	33.9
11.9	1.5	0.1	3.0	0.0	39.9
1.9	3.3	2.0	0.2	0.0	25.0
11.6	5.2	0.3	T	0.0	49.1
3.4	8.3	9.3	0.0	0.0	38.3
7.9	11.1	6.4	T	0.0	51.6
8.6	40.0	2.6	T	0.0	88.9
15.0	25.4	0.6	0.0	0.0	79.0
13.4	6.7	0.7	T	0.0	42.9
1.0	10.7	0.2	2.4	0.0	25.7
11.0	4.3	T	0.0	0.0	33.9
2.4	14.0	1.1	0.0	0.0	45.2
8.7	7.0	9.6	0.0	0.0	39.1
1.2	3.5	1.6	0.0	0.0	21.2
6.3	5.7	T	0.0	0.0	19.1
2.7	5.5	T	T	0.0	31.8
8.7	15.1	7.7	0.0	0.0	40.2
26.5	21.8	6.4	0.0	0.0	81.3
5.4	9.8	5.5	T	0.0	34.5
1.0	9.7	5.6	0.0	0.0	28.9
11.7	37.1	2.0	T	0.0	73.7
6.8	14.2	0.4	T	0.0	36.1
23.7	2.6	0.2	0.3	0.0	78.4
2.2	0.8	0.4	0.0	0.0	17.5
5.3	7.3	0.3	0.0	0.0	68.1
4.3	8.6	1.3	T	0.0	63.4
13.9	7.0	1.9	0.2	0.0	54.7
7.6	10.4	8.0	0.0	0.0	64.2
11.3	0.4	2.0	0.0	0.0	41.7
15.7	7.7	7.3	0.0	0.0	51.2
9.0	18.3	2.2	0.0	0.0	64.2
8.5	10.5	2.6	0.2	0.0	45.8

MINNEAPOLIS, MN

Feb	Mar	Apr	May	June	Total
1444	1205	686	246	12	8573
1241	1065	545	263	33	7536
1383	980	507	169	106	7342
1334	956	530	192	28	7643
1364	1395	574	247	82	8178
1184	1013	788	335	43	8161
1488	1248	691	198	68	8606
1478	946	526	319	46	8320
1186	1209	543	154	49	7405
1486	1405	690	211	19	8760
1358	899	678	357	41	8194
1572	1086	600	404	30	8497
1440	808	491	358	62	7929
1274	1261	461	204	136	8099
1382	1204	577	249	20	8302
1341	1139	537	297	18	8219
1576	1188	687	204	73	8587
1208	761	611	299	13	7959
1344	1092	535	338	72	7970
1379	1324	775	188	39	8255

Aug	Sept	Oct	Nov	Dec	Total
298	77	12	0	0	788
225	83	5	0	0	920
168	106	3	0	0	643
208	13	0	0	0	572
271	47	8	0	0	769
127	6	1	0	0	619
220	18	16	0	0	850

MINNEAPOLIS-ST. PAUL, MINNESOTA

Average Temperature

Year	Jan	Feb	Mar	Apr	May	June	July	Aug	Sept	Oct	Nov	Dec	Annual
1936	3.8	0.0	29.9	39.8	64.2	66.4	81.4	74.7	66.7	46.4	30.1	22.6	43.8
1937	5.4	13.4	27.0	44.5	59.8	67.2	77.0	77.7	63.5	46.7	31.9	17.9	44.3
#1938	13.5	21.8	38.0	46.0	56.8	67.9	73.4	73.8	62.2	55.4	31.5	20.4	46.7
1939	19.6	9.2	29.4	42.4	64.0	68.6	74.6	71.2	64.2	47.5	37.6	27.6	46.3
1940	6.5	19.4	24.2	43.6	56.0	68.0	75.8	68.8	65.3	54.0	27.8	22.0	44.3
1941	17.4	14.8	28.1	52.8	63.3	69.1	74.7	72.6	63.2	50.8	36.5	26.2	47.5
1942	20.5	20.8	35.8	52.2	56.0	66.8	71.4	70.5	57.2	50.3	33.6	15.4	45.9
1943	7.8	17.4	23.6	44.4	55.6	70.4	74.6	71.9	58.2	49.4	29.5	23.4	43.8
1944	26.6	20.6	25.8	43.0	62.4	69.7	71.4	71.6	61.6	51.2	37.8	19.3	46.8
1945	12.7	17.7	39.8	43.9	52.1	61.4	70.4	71.0	60.2	48.6	31.8	13.4	43.6
1946	15.2	16.8	42.4	51.1	55.2	67.0	73.6	68.8	59.8	51.2	33.0	20.6	46.2
1947	21.6	14.8	28.9	42.1	53.5	64.6	72.8	78.2	63.1	59.2	26.6	17.7	45.3
1948	10.0	15.6	27.3	50.0	58.5	67.3	75.2	72.7	67.8	51.2	35.1	20.0	45.9
1949	14.0	13.4	29.5	47.1	62.0	72.2	76.4	74.2	58.4	52.9	37.2	20.4	46.4
1950	6.8	16.4	24.0	36.9	56.1	67.8	70.5	67.7	62.6	53.7	27.8	12.4	41.9
1951	9.3	17.5	21.1	42.3	61.8	64.7	71.8	68.1	56.9	48.9	25.6	16.4	42.1
1952	12.4	23.7	26.1	50.1	58.7	69.6	73.2	69.1	63.1	44.4	35.3	23.4	45.7
1953	16.7	17.9	31.2	40.9	58.6	70.9	72.5	73.3	62.1	57.4	39.3	22.0	46.9
1954	10.3	31.8	27.9	46.5	53.1	71.2	74.4	70.4	60.5	47.7	38.3	23.4	46.3
1955	14.1	14.4	25.6	53.9	63.3	68.2	78.0	76.1	63.0	51.4	25.6	12.2	45.5
1956	12.7	15.0	25.9	41.8	58.1	73.4	70.1	71.2	58.7	56.5	34.1	23.9	45.1
1957	10.1	20.6	30.4	46.9	57.0	67.3	76.5	70.9	59.4	48.7	32.7	25.3	45.5
1958	22.4	15.5	33.2	47.9	60.8	63.3	70.3	71.4	62.7	53.1	35.7	15.9	46.0
#1959	10.6	17.2	34.0	47.1	60.6	70.8	74.5	75.2	63.1	44.4	25.4	30.1	46.1
1960	17.5	17.8	19.8	45.9	57.0	63.8	71.7	72.1	61.8	48.7	33.3	16.8	43.8
1961	12.0	22.5	32.0	38.5	54.7	68.1	70.8	71.3	59.1	52.2	33.5	15.3	44.2
1962	7.1	11.7	24.5	42.2	60.6	66.2	67.5	68.3	56.4	50.2	35.0	19.0	42.4
1963	2.9	12.1	34.2	47.3	55.4	69.8	73.5	68.9	62.2	58.1	38.3	10.0	44.4
1964	20.0	23.9	25.8	46.8	61.5	68.7	76.0	68.5	58.9	48.2	35.0	14.8	45.7
1965	10.0	11.8	19.5	41.8	58.7	66.5	70.5	68.6	52.8	50.7	33.1	28.0	42.7
1966	3.3	16.3	35.8	42.2	53.6	68.4	76.8	68.2	60.3	47.5	30.1	18.1	43.4
1967	14.6	8.7	29.8	44.7	52.3	66.9	68.8	66.2	60.3	46.3	30.7	21.8	42.6
1968	14.3	15.2	38.8	48.5	53.4	67.2	71.1	70.7	61.1	50.7	34.0	16.9	45.2
1969	9.4	19.3	24.1	49.3	60.6	61.8	73.6	74.4	63.0	46.5	33.6	20.3	44.7
1970	5.6	15.4	26.0	46.1	58.5	71.2	75.2	71.9	61.2	49.6	32.7	18.2	44.3
1971	6.5	17.0	28.0	47.0	55.4	71.5	68.8	69.6	62.8	51.4	32.7	18.4	44.1
1972	5.5	10.5	26.5	41.9	61.3	66.0	68.5	69.8	57.9	43.7	32.2	11.3	41.3
1973	17.4	21.6	40.2	44.4	55.2	69.5	73.8	73.4	60.1	53.8	34.3	16.7	46.7
1974	11.9	16.9	29.5	47.1	54.4	65.5	76.6	67.3	55.3	49.8	33.7	24.4	44.4
1975	14.5	15.5	22.1	38.9	60.9	68.8	76.3	71.7	57.7	52.8	37.5	21.3	44.8
RECORD MEAN	13.2	16.7	29.6	45.7	57.9	67.8	73.1	70.7	61.5	50.0	33.0	19.5	44.9
MAX	21.7	25.4	37.9	55.3	68.0	77.6	83.1	80.6	71.3	59.4	40.5	26.9	54.0
MIN	4.6	8.0	21.3	36.1	47.7	58.0	63.0	60.7	51.6	40.6	25.5	12.0	35.8

\# Indicates a station move or relocation of instruments.

Precipitation

Year	Jan	Feb	Mar	Apr	May	June	July	Aug	Sept	Oct	Nov	Dec	Annual
1936	0.77	1.55	2.66	1.48	2.25	2.29	0.11	3.48	0.78	0.66	0.66	1.78	18.47
1937	1.24	0.48	1.07	2.62	5.42	3.11	0.48	4.10	1.67	1.36	0.51	0.53	22.59
#1938	0.87	0.62	2.11	3.27	6.97	2.96	3.36	3.45	3.24	0.84	1.29	0.77	29.75
1939	1.06	0.88	0.61	2.19	3.55	4.95	2.75	3.65	2.31	1.56	0.02	0.97	24.50
1940	0.37	0.91	2.16	1.21	1.64	7.10	2.46	4.54	0.41	1.57	5.15	1.02	28.54
1941	0.74	0.89	0.77	1.87	2.91	3.29	1.98	3.66	3.47	5.52	1.05	0.85	27.00
1942	0.15	0.45	1.74	3.41	6.78	2.69	3.80	2.11	7.53	0.78	0.27	0.85	30.56
1943	0.91	0.57	0.81	0.98	4.27	4.23	3.78	1.75	2.47	1.30	1.64	T	22.71
1944	0.24	1.10	1.20	2.24	6.15	6.69	4.39	3.65	0.97	0.26	2.10	0.09	29.08
1945	0.63	1.84	1.95	2.95	3.09	5.57	4.13	2.27	2.13	0.30	0.93	1.41	27.20
1946	0.94	1.15	1.20	0.66	3.04	7.80	2.76	0.43	6.58	2.51	1.22	0.63	28.97
1947	0.71	0.20	0.47	2.44	2.57	5.30	0.96	2.41	1.48	1.10	2.85	0.60	21.09
1948	0.15	1.37	1.43	1.77	0.74	2.58	1.34	3.37	1.04	0.60	1.89	0.67	16.95
1949	1.65	0.14	3.37	1.89	0.90	2.74	6.01	2.64	2.67	1.72	0.42	0.99	25.14
1950	1.27	0.68	2.20	2.19	2.87	1.26	3.74	1.84	1.46	1.22	0.89	1.99	21.61
1951	0.44	1.71	3.00	1.86	4.14	5.50	5.44	1.94	5.80	1.44	2.12	1.21	34.60
1952	1.05	1.20	3.09	0.59	2.86	3.98	4.56	4.18	0.42	0.01	1.28	0.45	23.67
1953	0.55	1.23	1.51	2.04	1.92	7.10	6.81	2.75	0.55	0.15	1.54	1.76	27.91
1954	0.25	0.32	2.10	3.53	2.54	4.71	1.33	3.08	3.65	1.23	0.61	0.33	23.68
1955	0.47	1.54	0.52	0.92	0.69	1.53	7.10	2.84	0.99	2.21	1.04	1.26	21.11
1956	0.48	0.20	1.62	0.67	2.37	6.58	5.32	5.22	0.79	1.95	1.35	0.20	26.75
1957	0.32	0.83	1.31	1.23	3.13	4.12	6.31	5.75	1.65	1.40	1.56	0.24	27.85
1958	0.21	0.24	0.32	1.99	1.39	2.01	3.15	3.03	1.09	1.55	1.01	0.21	16.20
1959	0.11	0.61	0.59	0.64	5.03	4.07	2.60	6.60	2.29	2.43	0.63	1.28	26.88
1960	0.68	0.22	0.81	2.04	3.19	3.08	1.93	3.99	3.79	0.31	0.87	0.55	21.46
1961	0.28	0.89	2.81	2.39	3.48	1.87	2.94	2.38	3.01	3.03	1.06	1.60	25.74
1962	0.55	2.07	1.87	1.31	8.03	1.48	5.12	3.47	2.46	1.69	0.52	0.26	28.83
1963	0.46	0.41	1.18	2.07	5.06	1.91	1.53	1.55	3.47	0.81	0.52	0.60	19.57
1964	0.47	0.06	1.35	2.98	3.44	2.18	2.02	5.42	5.21	0.57	1.19	1.08	25.97
1965	0.47	1.59	4.75	3.52	7.86	4.01	4.69	4.04	4.90	0.90	1.98	1.23	39.94
1966	0.95	1.55	2.48	0.89	1.46	3.51	2.47	4.40	1.69	3.53	0.39	1.02	24.34
1967	3.63	1.59	0.96	4.07	0.61	7.53	1.36	2.79	0.63	1.73	0.09	0.45	25.44
1968	0.71	0.13	1.89	2.94	3.74	6.78	6.46	0.75	6.16	5.62	0.54	2.21	37.93
1969	2.05	0.31	0.90	1.55	1.98	2.93	2.95	0.99	0.49	2.53	0.65	2.06	19.39
1970	0.47	0.16	2.05	3.55	4.77	1.27	3.66	2.19	3.19	4.97	3.82	0.43	30.53
1971	1.22	1.74	1.21	1.11	3.14	3.52	3.94	1.78	2.73	5.68	2.67	0.70	29.44
1972	0.84	0.49	1.25	1.69	2.18	3.31	5.12	2.48	1.96	1.77	1.11	1.57	23.77
1973	0.92	0.84	1.12	2.32	2.48	1.06	2.90	3.05	2.08	1.29	1.97	1.10	21.13
1974	0.17	1.06	1.00	2.42	2.08	5.21	1.14	2.75	0.58	1.69	0.66	0.35	19.11
1975	2.82	0.79	1.67	5.40	3.81	7.99	0.58	4.92	1.31	0.27	4.80	0.79	35.15
RECORD MEAN	0.83	0.86	1.51	2.12	3.40	4.11	3.45	3.18	2.87	2.02	1.36	0.91	26.62

Record mean values above are means through the current year for the period beginning in 1891 for temperature and precipitation, 1939 for snowfall. Data are from city locations through March 1938.

JACKSON, MISSISSIPPI

Jackson is about 45 miles east of the Mississippi River on the west bank of Pearl River about 150 miles north of the Gulf of Mexico. The nearby terrain is gently rolling with no local topographic features that appreciably influence the weather. The Weather Bureau Office is nearly 7 miles east-northeast of the Jackson Post Office and over 5 miles southwest of the Ross Barnett Reservoir, which has approximately 50 square miles of water surface. Alluvial plains up to 3 miles wide extend along the river near Jackson where some levees have been built on both sides of the river. The largest floods produced crest stages of 37.2 feet (19.2 feet above flood stage) on December 21, 1961, and April 1, 1902.

Jackson's climate is significantly humid during most of the year, with a relatively short cold season and a rather long warm season. The proximity of the Gulf of Mexico and the prevalence of southerly winds amount to a maritime characteristic during the warm season that shifts the time of maximum daily mean temperature to near the end of July. In the cold season polar and arctic airmasses cover the area a significant portion of the time providing a continental modification of the climate to the extent of shifting the time of the minimum daily mean temperature to early January. Temperatures as high as 80° occasionally occur in midwinter and drop as low as 55° in midsummer. Subzero temperatures have been recorded twice in the 20th century (January 1940 and 1962).

Station: JACKSON, MISSISSIPPI
ALLEN C THOMPSON FIELD
Elevation (ground): 310 feet

TEMPERATURES °F

Month	Normal			Extremes			
	Daily maximum	Daily minimum	Monthly	Record highest	Year	Record lowest	Year
(a)				12		12	
J	58.4	35.8	47.1	82	1972	7	1966
F	61.7	37.8	49.8	82	1972	11	1970
M	68.7	43.4	56.1	88	1974	18	1968
A	78.2	53.1	65.7	92	1970	30	1971
M	85.0	60.4	72.7	99	1964	38	1971
J	91.0	67.7	79.4	103	1969	49	1972
J	92.7	70.6	81.7	102	1970	51	1967
A	92.6	69.8	81.2	99	1972	55	1966
S	88.0	64.0	76.0	98	1972	35	1967
O	80.1	51.5	65.8	91	1972	30	1968
N	68.5	42.0	55.3	88	1971	17	1966
D	60.5	37.3	48.9	81	1971	14	1966
YR	77.1	52.8	65.0	103	JUN 1969	7	JAN 1966

IMPORTANT:
The time-period covered by this record is limited: See footnotes following table of NORMALS, MEANS AND EXTREMES for explanation and for additional history of EXTREME HIGHS AND LOWS recorded in the general area.

Mean monthly precipitation ranges from about 4 inches to over 5 inches for the months of December through July while the relatively dry fall season provides significantly less precipitation with a minimum of a little over 2 inches for October. Although infrequent, tropical disturbances, including hurricanes and their remnants, that pass near or visit the Mississippi Coast in the summer and early fall, may bring several days of heavy rain. Occasionally during the summer the pressure distribution alters to bring westerly or northerly winds with hot, dry weather as the result. If these periods are prolonged, drought conditions may develop and the danger of fires increases. Snowfall averages less than 2 inches per season and the total is a trace or none in almost two-thirds of the seasons. Single storms frequently account for the significant portion of a season's snowfall. Severe ice storms, freezing rain and sleet with a destructive accretion of ice, occasionally cause major damage to wire lines and trees in the winter or early spring season.

Usually thunderstorms occur in each month, but at times one or more months in the October to March period have none. Generally the more intense rainfalls are associated with thunderstorms. The heaviest recorded rate of rainfall in the Jackson area was 0.77 inch in 5 minutes during a thunderstorm the night of March 3, 1964. Excessive rainfalls may occur in any season. In the late fall, winter, and early spring, thunderstorms may occur at any time of the night or day. They are usually associated with passing weather systems and are likely to be attended by higher winds than in the summer. In the winter about one-fifth of the days with rain have thunder; in the summer, nearly all. Thunderstorms are only occasionally accompanied by hail; most of that which falls is less than 5/8 inch in diameter. Hail of a damaging nature seldom occurs and usually then only in a small area.

Humidities of 90 percent or higher have occurred at any hour in the year. They are most frequent in the early morning hours. In the summer, at times there develops

(Continued)

a combination of high temperatures together with high humidity; this usually builds up progressively for several days, and becomes oppressive for one or more days. Summer nights are frequently uncomfortable, partly because of the humid conditions, but more so because the wind becomes very light or calm in the late afternoon and at night. Relief is at times afforded by afternoon or evening thunderstorms that lower the temperature. Humidities of less than 50 percent occur on some days each month, usually in the early afternoon hours. Humidities drop under 30 percent on about one-quarter of the October and November days; the number of days with such low humidities diminishes in the other months. In July and August there may be none.

In the annual course of the normal mean daily temperatures, the greatest rise is early in April, and the greatest drop is in October. The average date for the last occurrence in the spring of temperatures as low as 32° is March 18 and the average date for the first such occurrence in the fall is November 8. Some low-lying or frost-susceptible places average later dates in the spring and earlier in the fall. On April 25, 1910, a temperature of 31° was recorded at Jackson, while on October 9, 1917, a temperature of 32° was noted. The mean freeze-free season is 235 days; in 1944 it lasted 287 days; in 1910, 187 days. The highest temperatures for the year range from the middle 90's to over 100° and the lowest temperature for the year is below 20° in about four-fifths of the years. The nights at times can remain uncomfortably warm. There have been occasions when the temperatures did not drop below 75° for 4 consecutive days. Minimum temperatures of 76° or higher have occurred between early June and late September; the lowest temperature, September 1, 1905, was 82°.

Over a year's time about half of the hourly winds range from 4 to 12 m.p.h. and nearly a third are 3 m.p.h. or less. For construction design purposes sustained winds around 70-75 m.p.h. have a 50-year mean recurrence interval 30 feet above ground. Each year there is some wind damage in the area mostly from the more severe gusts or sustained "straight-line" winds of severe local thunderstorms or windstorms. The most recent major tornado that damaged part of Jackson was in the late afternoon March 3, 1966, while the previous major one occurred in the early morning June 6, 1916.

Normals, Means, and Extremes

(To better understand these tables, see full explanation of terms beginning on page 322)

Month	Normal Degree days Base 65 °F: Heating	Cooling	Precipitation in inches – Water equivalent: Normal	Maximum monthly	Year	Minimum monthly	Year	Maximum in 24 hrs.	Year	Snow, Ice pellets: Maximum monthly	Year	Maximum in 24 hrs.	Year	Relative humidity pct. Hour 00 (Local time)	Hour 06	Hour 12	Hour 18	Wind: Mean speed m.p.h.	Prevailing direction	Fastest mile: Speed m.p.h.	Direction	Year	Pct. of possible sunshine	Mean sky cover, tenths, sunrise to sunset	Mean number of days – Sunrise to sunset: Clear	Partly cloudy	Cloudy	Precipitation .01 inch or more	Snow, Ice pellets 1.0 inch or more	Thunderstorms	Heavy fog, visibility ¼ mile or less	Temperatures °F Max. (b) 90° and above	Max. 32° and below	Min. 32° and below	Min. 0° and below	Average station pressure mb. Elev. 331 feet m.s.l.
(a)				12		12		12		12		12		12	12	12	12	12		11	11		11	12	12	12	12	12	12	12	12	12	12	12	12	3
J	569	14	4.53	11.00	1974	0.86	1969	1.86	1966	1.5	1964	1.5	1964	84	87	66	72	9.1		38	N	1968	48	6.7	8	6	17	12	*	2	4	0	*	12	0	1008.2
F	442	18	4.62	7.90	1965	2.32	1964	3.46	1974	3.6	1968	3.6	1968	82	86	59	63	9.0		39	S	1974	55	6.0	9	5	14	9	*	3	3	0	*	13	0	1007.1
M	313	36	5.63	10.92	1964	2.05	1966	3.87	1964	5.3	1968	5.3	1968	82	87	57	58	9.6		45	NW	1966	61	6.2	9	7	15	11	*	6	2	0	0	5	0	1003.3
A	74	95	4.65	11.88	1964	1.25	1965	4.98	1973	T	1971	T	1971	84	90	57	60	9.1		38	SE	1973	60	6.0	8	8	14	9	0	5	2	*	0	*	0	1005.2
M	6	245	4.38	10.82	1967	1.36	1965	3.27	1966	0.0		0.0		87	91	56	61	7.3		40	NW	1967	63	5.6	9	10	12	10	0	7	1	5	0	0	0	1002.2
J	0	432	3.40	7.44	1975	0.32	1973	2.54	1974	0.0		0.0		86	90	55	60	6.4		40	SE	1969	67	5.4	9	12	9	7	0	8	1	18	0	0	0	1004.0
J	0	518	4.27	9.81	1975	1.54	1974	4.93	1975	0.0		0.0		89	93	59	66	6.1		36	S	1970	61	6.1	6	14	11	11	0	12	1	24	0	0	0	1004.5
A	0	502	3.59	6.65	1966	1.65	1963	3.45	1966	0.0		0.0		90	94	60	70	5.8		40	NE	1969	62	5.7	7	14	10	11	0	11	2	21	0	0	0	1005.5
S	0	330	2.99	9.61	1965	0.56	1969	5.86	1965	0.0		0.0		90	94	60	72	6.7		43	SE	1965	58	5.6	9	10	11	9	0	5	2	11	0	0	0	1004.7
O	91	116	2.22	9.13	1970	0.00	1963	6.99	1975	0.0		0.0		89	93	54	73	6.5		36	N	1964	65	4.4	15	7	9	6	0	1	2	1	0	*	0	1008.1
N	301	10	3.87	6.44	1964	0.93	1967	4.21	1964	T	1975	T	1975	87	91	58	74	7.9		42	NW	1973	54	5.3	11	7	12	8	0	2	3	0	0	5	0	1008.2
D	504	5	5.04	9.82	1971	3.65	1965	4.61	1971	3.1	1963	1.8	1963	85	89	66	77	8.7		39	S	1966	45	6.5	8	6	17	11	0	3	4	0	0	10	0	1007.9
YR	2300	2321	49.19	11.88	APR 1964	0.00	OCT 1963	6.99	OCT 1975	5.3	MAR 1968	5.3	MAR 1968	86	90	59	67	7.7		45	NW	MAR 1966	59	5.8	108	106	151	113	*	65	26	80	*	46	0	1005.7

FOOTNOTES Means and extremes above are from existing and comparable exposures. Annual extremes have been exceeded at other sites in the locality as follows: Highest temperature 107 in July 1930; lowest temperature -5 in January 1940; maximum monthly precipitation 15.76 in November 1948; maximum precipitation in 24 hours 7.50 in December 1942; maximum monthly snowfall 10.6 in January 1940; maximum snowfall in 24 hours 10.6 in January 1940; Fastest mile wind 68 S in March 1952.

Snowfall

Season	July	Aug	Sept	Oct	Nov	Dec	Jan
1936-37	0.0	0.0	0.0	0.0	0.0	0.0	0.0
1937-38	0.0	0.0	0.0	0.0	0.0	T	0.0
1938-39	0.0	0.0	0.0	0.0	0.2	0.0	0.0
1939-40	0.0	0.0	0.0	0.0	0.0	0.0	10.6
1940-41	0.0	0.0	0.0	0.0	0.0	0.0	0.0
1941-42	0.0	0.0	0.0	0.0	0.0	0.0	T
1942-43	0.0	0.0	0.0	0.0	0.0	0.0	0.0
1943-44	0.0	0.0	0.0	0.0	0.0	T	1.0
1944-45	0.0	0.0	0.0	0.0	0.0	T	T
1945-46	0.0	0.0	0.0	0.0	0.0	T	T
1946-47	0.0	0.0	0.0	0.0	0.0	T	0.0
#1947-48	0.0	0.0	0.0	0.0	0.0	T	5.2
1948-49	0.0	0.0	0.0	0.0	0.0	0.0	4.0
1949-50	0.0	0.0	0.0	0.0	0.0	T	0.0
1950-51	0.0	0.0	0.0	0.0	T	T	2.4
1951-52	0.0	0.0	0.0	0.0	T	0.0	0.0
1952-53	0.0	0.0	0.0	0.0	T	0.0	T
#1953-54	0.0	0.0	0.0	0.0	0.0	T	T
1954-55	0.0	0.0	0.0	0.0	0.0	T	0.0
1955-56	0.0	0.0	0.0	0.0	0.0	0.0	0.0
1956-57	0.0	0.0	0.0	0.0	0.0	0.0	0.0
1957-58	0.0	0.0	0.0	0.0	T	0.0	T
1958-59	0.0	0.0	0.0	0.0	0.0	T	T
1959-60	0.0	0.0	0.0	0.0	0.0	T	T
1960-61	0.0	0.0	0.0	0.0	0.0	T	T
1961-62	0.0	0.0	0.0	0.0	0.0	0.0	4.0
#1962-63	0.0	0.0	0.0	0.0	0.0	0.0	T
1963-64	0.0	0.0	0.0	0.0	0.0	3.1	1.5
1964-65	0.0	0.0	0.0	0.0	T	T	T
1965-66	0.0	0.0	0.0	0.0	0.0	0.0	T
1966-67	0.0	0.0	0.0	0.0	T	T	0.0
1967-68	0.0	0.0	0.0	0.0	0.0	T	T
1968-69	0.0	0.0	0.0	0.0	0.0	0.0	0.0
1969-70	0.0	0.0	0.0	0.0	0.0	T	T
1970-71	0.0	0.0	0.0	0.0	0.0	0.0	T
1971-72	0.0	0.0	0.0	0.0	T	0.0	0.0
1972-73	0.0	0.0	0.0	0.0	0.0	0.0	T
1973-74	0.0	0.0	0.0	0.0	0.0	0.3	0.0
1974-75	0.0	0.0	0.0	0.0	T	0.0	T
1975-76	0.0	0.0	0.0	0.0	T	T	
RECORD MEAN	0.0	0.0	0.0	0.0	T	T	0.1

Heating Degree Days

Season	July	Aug	Sept	Oct	Nov	Dec	Jan
1955-56	0	0	0	135	385	517	635
1956-57	0	0	0	30	377	298	481
1957-58	0	0	17	148	301	449	707
1958-59	0	0	0	83	276	632	663
1959-60	0	0	0	71	412	498	606
1960-61	0	0	0	71	276	626	748
1961-62	0	0	5	109	308	516	690
#1962-63	0	0	0	73	340	567	752
#1963-64	0	0	3	27	265	810	602
1964-65	0	0	0	124	219	465	512
1965-66	0	0	9	129	173	481	747
1966-67	0	0	0	155	270	581	570
1967-68	0	0	35	141	368	461	662
1968-69	0	0	0	93	369	592	523
1969-70	0	0	0	95	372	550	741
1970-71	0	0	0	85	367	388	507
1971-72	0	0	0	19	328	235	431
1972-73	0	0	4	71	400	466	634
1973-74	0	0	0	61	173	486	327
1974-75	0	0	6	79	308	465	429
1975-76	0	0	26	59	304	543	

Cooling Degree Days

Year	Jan	Feb	Mar	Apr	May	June	July
1969	3	0	0	75	235	465	577
1970	7	0	5	173	274	431	496
1971	9	7	10	69	138	453	503
1972	20	17	30	126	221	445	487
1973	1	0	51	77	210	498	583
1974	25	8	91	64	279	298	487
1975	26	17	46	96	290	407	509

Feb	Mar	Apr	May	June	Total
0.0	0.0	0.0	0.0	0.0	0.0
0.0	0.0	0.0	0.0	0.0	T
0.0	0.0	0.0	0.0	0.0	0.2
1.0	0.0	0.0	0.0	0.0	11.6
0.0	T	0.0	0.0	0.0	T
T	T	0.0	0.0	0.0	T
0.0	T	0.0	0.0	0.0	T
0.0	0.0	0.0	0.0	0.0	1.0
0.0	0.0	0.0	0.0	0.0	T
0.0	0.0	0.0	0.0	0.0	T
T	T	0.0	0.0	0.0	T
T	0.0	0.0	0.0	0.0	5.2
0.0	T	0.0	0.0	0.0	4.0
0.0	0.0	0.0	0.0	0.0	T
1.8	T	0.0	0.0	0.0	4.2
0.0	0.0	0.0	0.0	0.0	T
0.0	0.0	0.0	0.0	0.0	T
0.0	T	0.0	0.0	0.0	T
0.0	0.0	0.0	0.0	0.0	T
0.0	0.0	0.0	0.0	0.0	0.0
0.0	T	0.0	0.0	0.0	T
2.5	0.0	0.0	0.0	0.0	2.5
T	0.0	0.0	0.0	0.0	T
9.1	T	0.0	0.0	0.0	9.1
T	0.0	0.0	0.0	0.0	T
0.0	0.0	0.0	0.0	0.0	4.0
1.0	0.0	0.0	0.0	0.0	1.0
T	T	0.0	0.0	0.0	4.6
T	T	0.0	0.0	0.0	T
0.0	0.0	0.0	0.0	0.0	T
T	0.0	0.0	0.0	0.0	T
3.6	5.3	0.0	0.0	0.0	8.9
0.0	0.0	0.0	0.0	0.0	0.0
0.0	T	0.0	0.0	0.0	T
T	T	T	0.0	0.0	T
T	0.0	0.0	0.0	0.0	T
T	0.0	0.0	0.0	0.0	T
0.0	0.0	0.0	0.0	0.0	0.3
0.0	T	0.0	0.0	0.0	T
0.3	0.4	T	0.0	0.0	0.8

JACKSON, MS

Feb	Mar	Apr	May	June	Total
314	310	133	0	3	2432
241	328	114	24	0	1893
682	429	89	16	0	2838
395	321	127	3	0	2500
620	550	57	49	0	2863
336	169	172	37	2	2437
236	387	151	2	0	2404
597	179	45	8	0	2561
592	280	44	0	0	2623
500	459	48	2	0	2329
520	326	98	13	0	2496
574	192	20	26	0	2388
721	362	64	12	0	2826
470	476	65	3	0	2591
516	340	72	23	0	2709
444	394	147	40	0	2372
410	216	76	1	0	1716
503	135	146	19	0	2378
419	165	115	1	0	1747
348	293	138	0	0	2066

Aug	Sept	Oct	Nov	Dec	Total
460	312	137	3	0	2267
522	460	81	7	18	2474
487	406	181	29	20	2312
561	506	169	15	16	2613
477	382	181	81	5	2546
451	223	57	34	19	2036
487	255	101	59	7	2300

Average Temperature

Year	Jan	Feb	Mar	Apr	May	June	July	Aug	Sept	Oct	Nov	Dec	Annual
1936	46.2	47.0	62.0	61.8	72.4	80.2	81.6	82.4	80.3	65.8	52.6	50.4	65.2
1937	57.2	51.2	53.3	63.6	73.4	79.8	80.4	81.6	74.8	62.0	51.4	47.2	64.6
1938	49.7	56.8	66.1	63.6	72.6	77.5	81.2	82.1	75.8	66.0	55.3	48.0	66.2
#1939	52.0	52.4	61.0	62.9	72.5	80.8	84.1	81.9	80.2	67.2	52.4	51.2	66.5
1940	31.9	46.3	57.2	62.7	70.6	78.6	81.0	80.8	73.4	66.4	54.8	52.4	63.0
1941	49.6	45.4	50.8	66.9	73.8	80.2	83.2	82.1	79.0	72.9	52.5	51.2	65.6
1942	43.3	45.7	56.5	66.3	71.9	80.6	82.6	81.1	74.2	67.2	59.3	50.1	64.9
1943	48.6	52.1	54.6	66.6	76.8	83.2	83.2	85.6	74.1	63.2	52.4	48.4	65.7
1944	47.8	56.4	59.0	64.1	73.4	82.4	83.2	82.0	78.8	66.2	56.6	45.8	66.3
1945	46.4	52.8	64.2	66.4	69.6	79.4	80.8	81.0	78.2	64.4	58.8	43.7	65.5
1946	47.8	52.0	61.4	68.2	71.4	78.2	80.8	80.2	76.2	67.1	60.8	52.8	66.4
#1947	49.2	42.5	51.0	66.1	71.2	79.8	80.1	84.3	78.6	71.4	53.8	50.0	64.9
1948	39.6	51.3	60.0	69.0	73.8	82.0	84.5	81.4	73.8	64.4	57.4	52.4	65.8
1949	53.8	54.4	57.2	64.0	75.1	80.2	82.4	81.4	75.6	70.1	55.4	52.2	66.8
1950	59.8	55.6	55.0	61.5	75.9	79.7	79.9	80.0	75.1	68.8	52.3	44.4	65.7
1951	49.1	51.8	58.8	62.8	73.9	81.0	83.7	85.7	78.3	68.7	51.3	52.8	66.5
1952	55.1	54.5	55.5	62.0	72.8	84.6	84.9	84.0	74.8	58.9	53.6	48.5	65.8
1953	52.1	50.8	62.5	62.8	75.4	84.6	82.4	81.6	77.1	68.0	54.5	45.9	66.5
1954	49.6	54.9	56.1	70.4	67.8	82.1	84.5	86.0	79.4	67.5	54.0	48.5	66.7
#1955	46.1	49.9	60.0	68.6	76.1	75.5	80.5	80.2	78.4	63.7	53.4	48.5	65.1
1956	44.4	54.6	55.3	62.4	74.7	76.6	81.9	80.8	74.1	66.7	53.1	55.9	65.1
1957	49.5	57.6	54.3	65.8	73.0	79.4	81.5	80.2	73.3	61.3	55.6	50.3	65.1
1958	42.0	40.4	51.0	64.6	72.1	78.9	81.3	79.7	77.3	63.8	56.8	44.3	62.7
1959	43.5	50.9	54.6	63.0	74.9	78.1	80.8	81.4	76.4	68.3	51.6	48.7	64.4
1960	45.5	43.5	47.5	66.1	69.9	80.0	83.9	80.5	76.2	66.7	55.8	44.5	63.3
1961	40.6	52.9	60.5	61.0	70.4	75.5	79.1	79.1	75.9	64.1	55.5	48.2	68.6
1962	42.7	57.2	52.5	62.6	75.3	78.5	84.3	83.2	77.2	68.3	53.6	46.5	65.1
#1963	40.5	43.5	61.5	68.1	74.4	80.7	81.1	81.9	75.0	70.0	56.4	38.6	64.3
#1964	45.3	44.4	56.3	68.1	74.7	80.7	81.3	81.7	77.1	62.5	59.4	50.5	65.2
1965	48.5	47.2	50.2	67.8	74.0	77.7	81.5	79.5	76.3	62.6	60.1	49.4	64.6
1966	40.8	46.3	54.7	64.8	70.9	76.1	82.4	78.3	74.4	61.1	56.2	46.5	62.7
1967	46.4	44.2	60.5	69.3	69.6	78.3	77.3	77.0	69.8	61.4	52.7	50.1	63.1
1968	43.4	39.9	53.9	65.9	71.2	79.6	80.7	80.9	73.3	66.2	52.7	45.7	62.8
1969	48.0	48.1	49.3	65.1	72.3	80.3	83.5	79.6	75.2	66.2	52.4	47.1	63.9
1970	41.2	46.3	54.0	68.1	72.9	79.1	80.8	81.6	80.1	64.7	52.8	52.7	64.5
1971	48.7	49.1	52.4	62.2	67.9	79.9	81.0	80.5	78.3	70.1	54.7	57.9	65.2
1972	51.5	51.2	58.8	66.4	71.9	79.6	80.4	82.8	81.5	68.0	52.0	50.1	66.2
1973	44.3	46.9	62.1	62.5	70.9	81.3	83.7	80.1	77.6	68.6	61.7	49.3	65.7
1974	55.1	50.1	62.4	63.1	73.8	74.8	80.4	79.3	72.0	64.1	55.6	50.4	65.1
1975	51.8	52.9	56.8	63.5	74.1	78.3	81.2	80.6	72.3	66.2	56.6	47.4	65.1
RECORD MEAN	48.4	50.9	57.3	65.3	72.6	79.6	81.8	81.5	76.9	66.5	55.7	49.5	65.5
MAX	58.8	61.8	68.8	76.9	84.1	90.9	92.6	92.5	88.6	79.8	68.2	60.0	76.9
MIN	37.9	39.9	45.8	53.7	61.0	68.3	71.0	70.4	65.2	53.2	43.2	38.9	54.0

# Indicates a station move or relocation of instruments.

Precipitation

Year	Jan	Feb	Mar	Apr	May	June	July	Aug	Sept	Oct	Nov	Dec	Annual
1936	5.17	6.66	3.68	5.27	2.52	3.37	3.64	3.68	0.95	0.39	3.00	8.04	46.37
1937	11.48	4.35	2.92	4.43	2.61	3.90	2.46	5.92	2.07	3.53	3.05	3.70	50.42
1938	5.54	3.86	6.13	10.13	1.71	5.11	7.82	3.36	0.52	0.98	2.36	3.30	50.82
#1939	5.35	9.48	5.39	1.76	3.95	4.75	1.81	2.45	1.60	0.69	0.85	5.26	43.34
1940	3.04	4.91	3.67	7.29	1.37	4.09	10.68	1.83	1.08	1.17	5.72	9.46	54.31
1941	2.42	2.80	6.85	4.05	2.03	2.73	3.45	3.38	2.31	5.35	2.20	5.52	43.09
1942	2.29	2.84	4.91	0.80	2.22	2.31	4.34	11.39	3.73	3.32	0.86	10.24	49.25
1943	1.31	3.73	6.42	5.40	1.55	5.01	3.56	0.68	2.45	0.82	2.47	3.80	37.20
1944	3.77	6.61	9.97	7.73	6.02	0.52	1.58	4.65	1.03	0.28	5.62	6.08	53.86
1945	2.50	8.33	9.87	3.15	3.76	9.27	5.9[illegible]	4.02	1.68	4.79	1.99	3.94	59.21
1946	7.88	8.40	7.57	1.17	10.19	4.11	7.63	0.23	0.79	1.18	8.40	3.62	61.17
#1947	12.01	1.15	4.71	9.73	4.27	2.54	0.98	2.37	3.16	1.04	7.81	4.42	54.19
1948	3.28	5.68	5.37	4.13	4.46	1.42	1.54	6.25	3.87	0.80	15.76	3.77	56.33
1949	8.13	5.25	11.26	2.81	4.16	5.48	6.24	1.14	5.37	3.52	0.01	2.53	55.90
1950	8.26	9.28	5.46	2.98	4.12	3.47	8.12	3.18	1.53	1.30	2.94	3.82	54.46
1951	8.63	3.39	5.54	5.46	0.16	2.63	3.30	2.19	3.08	0.33	1.59	5.95	42.25
1952	2.08	2.24	3.58	2.21	6.22	1.59	1.46	1.51	2.10	T	2.61	6.06	31.66
1953	4.61	7.85	4.88	8.44	7.12	1.36	3.40	2.27	0.26	0.77	0.84	4.53	46.33
1954	4.87	1.48	2.91	2.68	8.30	2.10	2.65	2.17	2.98	1.48	2.47	3.61	37.70
#1955	3.91	5.43	2.14	7.16	5.18	0.92	13.13	0.52	0.22	0.53	3.37	2.90	45.41
1956	2.13	7.44	6.52	4.67	3.58	7.37	1.71	3.27	0.04	3.46	1.55	5.03	46.77
1957	3.85	2.60	6.14	4.75	3.70	8.92	3.22	0.93	8.29	2.79	9.78	3.03	58.00
1958	3.92	3.61	5.19	6.83	4.78	8.77	5.33	2.87	8.30	0.95	2.40	2.27	55.22
1959	3.73	4.09	4.86	3.86	4.69	2.16	8.81	2.76	3.03	4.18	2.33	5.96	50.46
1960	5.29	4.56	5.22	1.46	3.95	2.18	1.09	10.23	2.10	2.39	2.45	4.21	45.13
1961	3.07	6.59	8.90	2.00	2.96	7.49	8.55	3.96	1.22	0.84	8.33	11.16	65.07
1962	7.06	2.75	3.61	8.55	2.59	1.36	1.49	2.91	2.34	1.70	2.88	3.25	40.49
#1963	5.33	2.82	1.93	2.44	1.47	3.29	6.28	1.65	0.88	0.00	4.55	4.39	35.03
1964	5.21	2.32	10.92	11.88	2.18	2.45	5.17	6.43	3.67	7.83	6.44	6.95	71.45
1965	2.86	7.90	6.66	1.25	1.36	2.54	1.92	3.61	9.61	0.84	1.79	3.65	43.99
1966	8.23	7.84	2.05	5.76	7.96	1.45	3.14	6.65	4.87	1.63	3.66	4.83	58.07
1967	1.86	3.56	2.32	1.66	10.82	3.76	4.05	3.49	1.80	2.78	0.93	8.68	45.71
1968	4.56	2.54	2.83	7.20	7.54	1.02	2.24	3.90	1.95	0.28	5.55	5.58	45.19
1969	0.86	3.02	4.90	6.59	1.52	1.29	5.46	3.35	0.56	2.26	1.87	7.22	38.90
1970	2.09	2.63	5.40	2.75	2.43	2.54	2.34	5.64	6.48	9.13	2.70	4.23	48.36
1971	3.02	5.68	7.68	6.86	8.05	3.40	6.28	2.64	6.00	0.09	2.54	9.82	62.06
1972	5.94	3.09	5.57	2.44	4.52	2.01	3.31	2.84	5.04	2.08	3.52	9.67	50.03
1973	4.59	4.23	6.12	9.44	5.96	0.32	1.99	2.38	4.44	2.72	6.15	6.71	55.05
1974	11.00	6.72	3.50	6.74	3.01	3.39	1.54	6.17	5.06	1.74	4.12	7.22	60.21
1975	4.57	6.18	4.86	5.07	6.53	7.44	9.81	6.21	2.68	8.25	4.34	4.29	70.23
RECORD MEAN	4.85	4.81	5.45	5.22	4.44	3.84	4.44	3.61	2.78	2.27	3.67	5.58	50.96

Record mean values above are means through the current year for the period beginning in 1909 for temperature and precipitation, 1964 for snowfall.

Station: KANSAS CITY, MISSOURI INTERNATIONAL AIRPORT
Elevation (ground) 1014 feet

TEMPERATURES °F

Month	Normal			Extremes			
	Daily maximum	Daily minimum	Monthly	Record highest	Year	Record lowest	Year
(a)				3		3	
J	36.2	19.3	27.8	61	1973	-13	1974
F	41.9	24.2	33.1	66	1974	-4	1973
M	50.5	31.8	41.2	82	1974	-1	1973
A	64.8	45.1	55.0	85	1975	12	1975
M	74.3	55.7	65.0	91	1975	34	1973
J	82.6	65.2	73.9	98	1974	47	1973
J	88.0	69.6	78.8	107	1974	52	1973
A	86.7	68.1	77.4	103	1975	50	1973
S	78.8	58.8	68.8	98	1975	39	1975
O	68.9	48.3	58.6	89	1975	28	1973
N	52.7	34.5	43.6	73	1973	7	1973
D	40.4	24.1	32.3	67	1973	-7	1973
YR	63.7	45.3	54.5	107	JUL 1974	-13	JAN 1974

IMPORTANT:
The time-period covered by this record is limited: See footnotes following table of NORMALS, MEANS AND EXTREMES for explanation and for additional history of EXTREME HIGHS AND LOWS recorded in the general area.

Climatic averages and extremes and definite seasons of spring, summer, fall, and winter have an important influence on a locality's population, business, and agriculture.

The National Weather Service Office at Kansas City is very near the geographical center of the United States at latitude 39° 07' north and longitude 94° 35' west. The surrounding terrain is gently rolling. Its modified continental climate follows from the fact that there are no natural obstructions in the vicinity to prevent the free sweep of air currents from all directions. It is, therefore, not surprising that some of the features which might ordinarily prevail at this latitude are almost obscured by the importation of warm or cold air from source regions many hundreds of miles away. Moist air currents from the Gulf of Mexico sometimes vie with the desiccating winds from the semiarid regions of the southwest to determine whether flood or drought shall prevail, and there is often conflict between the warm, moist gulf currents and the cold polar continental currents from the north in this area. In short, the factors contributing to rapid changes of weather in Kansas City, located in the "Heart of America", are so many and varied as to defy enumeration here.

Early spring brings a period of frequent and rapid fluctuations in weather, with the fluctuations generally less frequent as spring progresses. The last freezing temperatures in the spring usually occur around April 7, though they have occurred as late as May 6.

The summer season is characterized by warm days and mild nights, with moderate humidities. July is the warmest month.

The fall season is normally mild and usually includes a period near the middle of the season characterized by mild sunny days and cool nights. The first freezing temperatures of fall usually occur around October 26, but have occurred as early as September 30. (Continued page 518)

Snowfall

Season	July	Aug	Sept	Oct	Nov	Dec	Jan
1936-37	0.0	0.0	0.0	0.0	T	4.2	3.6
1937-38	0.0	0.0	0.0	T	3.4	0.5	0.2
1938-39	0.0	0.0	0.0	0.0	2.0	T	6.1
#1939-40	0.0	0.0	0.0	0.0	0.0	4.1	12.8
1940-41	0.0	0.0	0.0	0.0	2.6	1.2	11.8
1941-42	0.0	0.0	0.0	0.0	2.0	3.9	0.6
1942-43	0.0	0.0	0.0	0.0	0.1	10.0	3.4
1943-44	0.0	0.0	0.0	0.0	1.4	9.7	0.8
1944-45	0.0	0.0	0.0	0.0	T	7.5	1.0
1945-46	0.0	0.0	0.0	0.0	0.5	14.8	0.8
1946-47	0.0	0.0	0.0	0.0	0.0	0.3	6.6
1947-48	0.0	0.0	0.0	0.0	T	0.2	5.7
1948-49	0.0	0.0	0.0	0.0	T	6.9	13.7
#1949-50	0.0	0.0	0.0	0.0	0.0	3.4	1.4
1950-51	0.0	0.0	0.0	0.0	0.2	1.0	3.5
1951-52	0.0	0.0	0.0	0.1	0.3	3.5	4.4
1952-53	0.0	0.0	0.0	T	4.6	4.2	2.7
1953-54	0.0	0.0	0.0	0.0	1.8	8.8	1.1
1954-55	0.0	0.0	0.0	T	T	T	5.7
1955-56	0.0	0.0	0.0	0.0	0.8	3.8	8.2
1956-57	0.0	0.0	0.0	0.0	T	3.9	6.9
1957-58	0.0	0.0	0.0	T	T	5.5	16.5
1958-59	0.0	0.0	0.0	0.0	4.9	4.7	13.2
1959-60	0.0	0.0	0.0	0.0	0.9	0.8	5.1
1960-61	0.0	0.0	0.0	0.0	0.1	6.1	0.7
1961-62	0.0	0.0	0.0	0.0	0.2	16.6	30.5
1962-63	0.0	0.0	0.0	0.0	T	5.1	5.9
1963-64	0.0	0.0	0.0	0.0	0.0	4.3	7.5
1964-65	0.0	0.0	0.0	0.0	2.1	6.2	4.2
1965-66	0.0	0.0	0.0	0.0	T	2.5	T
1966-67	0.0	0.0	0.0	0.0	T	7.2	7.6
1967-68	0.0	0.0	0.0	T	0.2	7.0	2.8
1968-69	0.0	0.0	0.0	0.0	3.2	0.8	6.0
1969-70	0.0	0.0	0.0	0.0	0.6	3.8	2.5
1970-71	0.0	0.0	0.0	T	T	3.6	1.3
1971-72	0.0	0.0	0.0	0.0	0.2	1.0	3.0
#1972-73	0.0	0.0	0.0	0.0	3.6	3.1	10.9
1973-74	0.0	0.0	0.0	0.0	T	8.0	4.8
1974-75	0.0	0.0	0.0	0.0	1.4	1.2	5.4
1975-76	0.0	0.0	0.0	0.0	7.1	2.8	
RECORD MEAN	0.0	0.0	0.0	T	1.1	4.5	5.7

Heating Degree Days

Season	July	Aug	Sept	Oct	Nov	Dec	Jan
1955-56	0	0	18	182	740	1020	1143
1956-57	0	0	17	63	622	866	1215
1957-58	0	0	29	302	651	783	1020
1958-59	0	2	25	176	455	1017	1187
1959-60	0	0	44	289	776	756	1049
#1960-61	0	0	12	148	555	1046	1026
1961-62	0	1	100	196	626	1124	1280
1962-63	0	0	62	184	550	995	1394
1963-64	0	1	10	37	448	1225	857
1964-65	0	2	49	235	473	1004	1033
1965-66	0	0	44	175	497	646	1141
1966-67	0	2	29	207	478	931	956
1967-68	0	3	48	255	609	909	1125
1968-69	0	1	13	224	706	1090	1186
1969-70	0	0	3	330	562	984	1198
1970-71	0	0	25	231	610	801	1151
1971-72	4	0	57	87	538	863	1163
#1972-73	1	0	37	355	751	1155	1160
1973-74	0	0	53	173	578	1077	1272
1974-75	0	6	141	227	660	1009	1084
1975-76	0	0	142	224	567	954	

Cooling Degree Days

Year	Jan	Feb	Mar	Apr	May	June	July
#1969	0	0	0	4	126	188	513
1970	0	0	0	59	250	317	493
1971	0	0	5	54	81	437	366
1972	0	3	7	41	146	368	386
1973	0	0	0	4	30	291	368
1974	0	0	4	13	109	176	538
1975	0	0	0	22	117	284	498

Feb	Mar	Apr	May	June	Total
3.9	4.2	T	0.0	0.0	15.9
4.9	0.1	7.0	0.0	0.0	16.1
5.8	0.3	0.1	0.0	0.0	14.3
4.0	0.6	0.8	0.0	0.0	22.3
0.5	5.6	0.0	0.0	0.0	21.7
5.1	T	0.0	0.0	0.0	11.6
T	6.0	T	0.0	0.0	19.5
8.0	1.5	T	T	0.0	21.4
3.6	3.2	T	0.0	0.0	15.3
2.7	T	0.0	0.0	0.0	18.8
5.4	8.6	T	0.0	0.0	20.9
4.4	7.4	0.0	0.0	0.0	17.7
2.2	4.0	T	0.0	0.0	26.8
0.5	0.2	T	0.0	0.0	5.5
3.1	0.2	1.0	0.0	0.0	9.0
1.8	11.1	T	0.0	0.0	21.2
T	10.8	T	0.0	0.0	22.3
0.2	T	0.0	0.0	0.0	11.9
7.5	7.0	0.0	0.0	0.0	20.2
8.4	4.4	T	0.0	0.0	25.6
T	T	2.9	0.0	0.0	13.7
0.9	8.3	0.0	0.0	0.0	31.2
0.6	6.1	0.9	0.0	0.0	30.4
20.7	29.3	1.7	0.0	0.0	58.5
1.4	0.7	3.7	0.0	0.0	12.7
6.2	0.4	1.1	0.0	0.0	55.0
3.3	0.3	0.0	0.0	0.0	14.6
8.5	5.3	0.0	0.0	0.0	25.6
7.7	9.6	0.0	0.0	0.0	29.8
3.7	3.5	T	T	0.0	9.7
0.9	1.1	T	0.0	0.0	16.8
2.7	T	T	0.0	0.0	12.7
1.6	2.8	0.0	0.0	0.0	14.4
2.2	1.0	4.6	0.0	0.0	14.7
8.2	7.4	0.0	0.0	0.0	20.5
2.9	3.3	T	0.0	0.0	10.4
0.3	0.0	1.3	0.0	0.0	19.2
0.3	0.5	0.3	0.0	0.0	13.9
4.6	5.9	2.3	0.0	0.0	20.8
3.8	3.9	0.7	T	0.0	19.7

KANSAS CITY, MO

Feb	Mar	Apr	May	June	Total
877	613	377	52	5	5027
719	649	342	69	0	4562
1053	828	288	52	4	5010
856	569	273	56	0	4616
1056	1067	238	86	2	5363
732	649	457	179	5	4809
835	766	339	5	3	5275
908	490	204	71	0	4858
830	714	239	41	12	4412
911	955	237	15	0	4914
869	492	365	95	9	4333
874	548	213	193	11	4438
941	528	245	131	3	4797
857	845	258	86	24	5290
785	707	280	26	22	4897
931	659	208	92	0	4708
920	557	263	71	0	4523
868	529	394	127	0	5377
823	559	270	84	6	4895
1036	878	381	42	5	5469

Aug	Sept	Oct	Nov	Dec	Total
435	216	52	0	0	1534
546	232	39	0	0	1935
421	295	64	3	0	1726
389	219	16	0	0	1575
382	110	46	0	0	1231
264	47	8	0	0	1159
464	105	43	1	0	1534

Average Temperature

Year	Jan	Feb	Mar	Apr	May	June	July	Aug	Sept	Oct	Nov	Dec	Annual
1936	21.7	19.6	48.9	54.3	70.9	78.4	87.8	87.0	73.6	57.2	42.4	38.8	56.7
1937	23.0	31.2	39.8	54.0	67.2	75.8	81.4	83.8	72.0	57.0	39.8	31.2	54.7
1938	32.0	38.1	52.1	56.4	65.2	74.0	82.4	83.0	72.3	66.4	45.2	36.1	58.6
#1939	38.5	29.4	45.9	53.9	70.1	76.0	84.7	77.0	76.7	62.1	43.8	39.4	58.1
1940	12.8	32.8	42.7	54.0	63.6	74.7	81.6	76.3	70.0	65.4	40.8	37.2	54.3
1941	32.2	31.8	40.6	59.0	70.5	74.8	80.0	79.5	72.4	60.4	46.2	40.0	57.3
1942	31.5	32.2	44.9	60.5	64.2	74.2	81.5	76.8	67.7	59.0	46.8	30.9	55.8
1943	28.3	38.6	39.0	57.2	62.6	76.6	81.4	81.0	66.3	56.6	41.6	30.6	55.0
1944	36.0	35.6	39.	50.3	69.5	77.0	78.8	76.5	70.4	61.2	46.9	28.2	55.8
1945	30.6	35.0	51.8	54.4	60.8	68.9	77.4	79.7	69.8	57.2	46.2	25.8	54.8
1946	33.0	41.8	55.6	60.5	62.2	76.2	81.2	77.0	69.3	62.7	46.4	38.6	58.7
1947	33.2	28.9	37.6	54.0	61.9	73.4	78.8	86.2	73.8	68.0	40.0	37.2	56.1
1948	25.1	31.0	39.6	61.8	65.5	74.8	79.5	79.2	72.6	57.3	46.2	35.8	55.7
1949	25.8	32.4	42.9	55.1	68.9	77.0	80.6	77.2	64.4	60.6	49.8	37.1	56.0
1950	30.3	35.5	40.0	50.9	67.0	75.2	72.5	72.1	67.9	64.9	40.8	30.9	54.0
1951	30.7	34.8	38.7	51.3	66.6	69.7	77.5	78.1	66.0	57.6	39.7	30.7	53.5
1952	33.9	39.4	39.6	54.6	65.9	83.7	80.4	77.3	72.1	55.4	44.7	34.1	56.7
1953	34.5	40.3	46.1	50.9	64.4	82.6	81.2	80.0	74.1	63.4	47.3	36.1	58.4
1954	29.3	45.4	41.7	60.7	61.8	79.2	87.1	81.5	76.5	59.4	48.9	36.9	59.1
1955	32.5	31.5	43.7	63.3	67.6	71.3	85.4	80.9	73.6	60.0	40.1	31.8	56.8
1956	27.9	34.5	45.2	53.6	69.7	77.8	80.8	81.4	74.0	66.1	44.1	36.8	57.6
1957	25.6	39.1	43.8	54.6	65.6	75.1	83.3	81.2	67.9	55.4	43.1	39.5	56.2
1958	31.9	27.3	38.0	55.6	68.2	73.6	77.0	79.4	71.4	61.7	49.9	32.0	55.5
1959	26.6	34.1	46.4	56.5	69.0	77.2	78.0	82.2	70.8	55.6	38.9	40.4	56.3
#1960	30.9	28.3	30.4	58.2	65.6	74.4	77.8	80.2	73.9	61.6	46.4	31.1	54.9
1961	31.7	38.6	43.8	50.1	60.6	72.3	77.3	75.4	66.0	59.0	43.8	28.5	54.0
1962	23.5	34.9	40.1	54.5	74.7	74.7	78.0	79.3	66.8	61.8	46.5	32.8	55.7
1963	19.8	32.3	49.2	59.2	67.5	79.3	81.7	79.0	74.1	72.0	49.8	25.2	57.4
1964	37.2	36.2	41.8	57.4	70.1	73.7	82.5	76.0	69.4	57.6	49.9	32.3	57.0
1965	31.4	32.3	34.0	58.5	71.6	74.6	78.5	77.1	69.9	60.5	48.2	44.0	56.7
1966	28.0	33.7	49.1	52.8	65.6	73.3	83.4	74.9	68.8	59.7	49.1	34.8	56.1
1967	33.9	33.6	47.8	58.9	61.7	72.9	76.5	75.1	67.9	58.6	44.4	35.4	55.6
1968	28.4	32.3	48.1	57.0	62.2	77.6	79.4	77.8	69.5	59.6	41.2	29.7	55.3
1969	26.5	34.2	37.6	56.3	66.1	70.2	81.4	78.9	71.8	55.7	46.1	33.1	54.8
1970	26.1	36.7	42.0	57.4	72.1	74.5	80.8	82.4	71.6	58.6	44.4	38.9	57.1
1971	27.7	31.5	43.7	59.7	64.4	79.4	76.4	78.3	72.6	64.0	46.9	37.0	56.8
#1972	27.3	33.2	47.1	57.4	67.1	76.9	77.2	77.3	70.9	53.9	39.6	27.5	54.6
1973	27.3	33.8	47.7	51.8	61.5	74.5	76.6	77.1	66.7	60.7	45.5	30.1	54.5
1974	23.8	35.3	46.9	56.2	65.6	70.5	82.1	73.0	61.6	57.7	42.8	32.2	54.0
1975	29.9	27.8	36.5	52.8	67.1	74.2	80.9	79.8	63.5	58.9	45.9	34.1	54.3
RECORD MEAN	29.7	33.1	43.2	55.5	65.3	74.7	79.5	78.0	70.0	59.1	44.7	33.6	55.6
MAX	38.2	41.9	52.8	65.2	74.7	83.9	88.9	87.5	79.7	69.1	53.6	41.5	64.8
MIN	21.2	24.2	33.5	45.7	55.8	65.4	70.0	68.4	60.2	49.1	35.8	25.7	46.3

Precipitation

# Indicates a station move or relocation of instruments.

Year	Jan	Feb	Mar	Apr	May	June	July	Aug	Sept	Oct	Nov	Dec	Annual
1936	1.17	0.55	0.08	1.89	4.16	0.51	0.36	0.25	7.99	2.01	0.19	2.35	21.51
1937	3.37	0.86	1.73	2.51	3.63	3.73	3.11	2.26	0.21	1.15	1.33	0.95	24.84
1938	1.89	0.90	3.06	1.87	7.64	5.22	3.82	6.78	1.84	0.70	2.70	0.55	36.97
#1939	1.28	0.98	1.14	7.04	2.85	10.99	1.18	4.64	0.54	0.95	2.45	0.68	34.72
1940	1.26	1.07	1.95	4.21	4.33	3.84	0.80	6.48	1.30	1.68	3.95	1.68	32.55
1941	4.91	0.58	0.87	4.03	3.18	6.79	2.34	4.66	4.62	11.94	0.94	1.76	46.62
1942	0.14	3.16	2.62	4.58	3.68	7.35	2.69	5.80	3.15	2.68	2.74	2.43	41.02
1943	0.31	0.61	1.17	1.75	4.71	7.66	3.39	1.90	2.28	1.93	0.20	1.47	27.38
1944	0.68	1.78	5.09	10.57	4.14	3.78	3.54	7.97	4.38	1.03	2.94	3.74	49.64
1945	0.38	0.85	4.32	6.63	5.55	6.05	1.73	0.26	6.55	0.92	0.60	1.42	35.26
1946	3.40	0.94	2.48	4.57	2.87	4.37	0.94	3.70	2.45	3.83	0.58	1.43	31.56
1947	0.83	0.45	5.03	7.76	4.26	8.19	1.07	4.35	4.01	5.25	1.60	3.61	46.41
1948	0.53	0.94	4.84	0.80	1.72	5.45	7.29	2.71	1.88	1.89	1.69	1.20	30.94
#1949	5.22	1.36	2.92	2.03	5.31	6.41	3.30	3.15	4.37	5.70	0.21	1.95	41.93
1950	0.69	1.22	0.71	2.39	3.26	2.63	9.90	5.77	2.48	0.50	0.22	0.22	29.99
1951	1.07	1.84	2.33	2.87	3.92	8.42	7.54	6.87	5.67	3.99	1.00	0.70	46.22
1952	0.57	1.16	4.05	4.26	4.09	3.66	4.73	6.51	2.12	0.17	2.22	1.07	34.61
1953	0.19	1.51	3.84	3.29	2.98	1.48	0.96	0.55	1.56	1.64	1.10	1.83	20.93
1954	0.05	1.75	1.62	4.51	3.57	3.64	0.93	5.01	0.63	5.10	0.04	0.67	27.52
1955	2.19	3.27	0.71	1.60	7.44	4.71	0.93	3.27	3.41	2.78	0.05	0.30	30.66
1956	0.67	1.35	0.54	2.77	4.36	3.61	4.58	3.29	0.22	0.75	2.18	1.60	25.92
1957	1.31	0.36	3.07	3.72	5.04	7.11	2.27	0.41	5.26	3.97	1.98	2.21	36.71
1958	2.54	1.32	2.75	2.78	2.73	4.84	10.70	1.23	7.16	1.38	1.86	0.56	39.85
1959	1.74	0.85	4.29	2.93	5.14	1.38	5.29	5.95	2.68	6.27	0.19	1.78	38.49
1960	1.43	2.62	3.11	3.78	2.83	4.49	2.49	3.12	0.40	5.91	0.33	2.12	32.63
1961	0.05	2.44	6.66	4.20	5.20	6.55	9.02	3.81	11.58	3.24	5.54	1.96	60.25
1962	2.95	2.02	1.94	1.10	5.29	2.93	6.17	3.10	7.32	1.89	1.24	1.04	36.99
1963	0.59	0.41	1.94	0.80	4.17	3.21	4.40	4.08	1.44	0.94	2.30	0.37	24.65
1964	1.20	1.50	3.20	5.40	5.50	5.40	2.94	3.79	3.07	0.36	4.73	1.73	38.82
1965	2.35	1.81	3.51	2.21	2.19	7.50	9.83	6.27	7.75	1.83	0.24	2.25	47.74
1966	0.21	0.76	1.88	3.04	2.48	8.63	0.89	4.24	2.67	0.45	1.05	0.91	27.21
1967	2.09	0.35	2.85	6.86	6.04	9.71	1.81	0.31	7.87	8.63	0.45	1.72	48.69
1968	0.27	1.20	0.73	3.91	5.19	2.33	5.13	4.32	1.04	3.52	3.03	1.29	31.96
1969	1.31	0.49	1.36	4.77	3.89	10.57	10.29	8.70	3.67	6.50	0.08	0.72	52.35
1970	0.21	0.46	1.02	3.95	4.75	5.32	0.62	4.02	10.79	2.30	0.94	1.74	36.12
1971	1.48	0.89	0.87	1.29	3.02	3.20	3.13	1.04	2.70	3.47	1.68	3.82	26.59
#1972	0.56	0.41	2.13	3.98	2.18	2.71	3.43	2.90	2.69	2.29	3.00	1.47	27.75
1973	2.05	1.35	9.08	2.91	5.65	2.84	8.71	1.60	10.32	5.80	2.36	2.59	55.26
1974	1.05	1.12	1.19	2.94	10.07	2.16	1.13	4.98	1.13	7.22	1.62	1.52	36.12
1975	2.14	1.59	1.49	6.61	3.45	2.46	0.25	4.85	6.10	0.35	2.75	2.03	34.07
RECORD MEAN	1.35	1.46	2.59	3.40	4.70	4.82	3.85	3.95	4.30	2.91	1.87	1.46	36.66

Record mean values above are means through the current year for the period beginning in 1889 for temperature and precipitation, 1936 for snowfall. Data are from City Office locations through March 1935 and from Airport locations thereafter.

(Continued)

Winters are not severely cold. January is the coldest month. Falls of snow to a depth of 10 inches or more are comparatively rare. The distribution of measurable snow normally extends from October to March.

Precipitation is distributed throughout the seasons in the following order: spring, 29 percent, summer, 35 percent, fall, 24 percent, winter, 12 percent. Nearly 70 percent of the annual precipitation occurs during the 6 months, April to September. From an agricultural standpoint, it is interesting to note that more than 75 percent of the annual moisture normally falls during the vegetal period or growing season. The frequency and distribution of precipitation over a normal day is also an important factor in crop growth as well as a matter of importance to the man in the street. In the vegetal period, April to October, the maximum frequency of precipitation occurs during the 6 hours following midnight and the minimum frequency during the 6 hours following noon.

Normals, Means, and Extremes

Month	Normal Degree days Base 65 °F: Heating	Cooling	Precipitation in inches — Water equivalent: Normal	Maximum monthly	Year	Minimum monthly	Year	Maximum in 24 hrs.	Year	Snow, Ice pellets: Maximum monthly	Year	Maximum in 24 hrs.	Year	Relative humidity pct. Hour 00 (Local time)	Hour 06	Hour 12	Hour 18
(a)				3		3		3		3		3		3	3	3	3
J	1153	0	1.25	2.14	1975	1.05	1974	0.93	1975	5.4	1975	5.0	1973	73	75	65	67
F	893	0	1.25	1.59	1975	1.12	1974	0.78	1974	4.6	1975	1.0	1975	74	75	65	64
M	745	7	2.55	9.08	1973	1.18	1974	1.78	1973	5.9	1975	5.0	1975	72	78	62	61
A	314	14	3.50	6.61	1975	2.91	1973	4.69	1975	2.3	1975	2.3	1975	67	74	54	53
M	111	111	4.28	10.07	1974	3.45	1975	4.26	1974	0.0		0.0		72	80	56	53
J	12	279	5.55	2.84	1973	2.16	1974	1.03	1973	0.0		0.0		75	81	54	55
J	0	428	4.37	8.71	1973	0.25	1975	2.67	1973	0.0		0.0		68	77	48	46
A	0	388	3.81	4.98	1974	1.60	1973	3.88	1975	0.0		0.0		76	85	58	57
S	42	156	4.21	10.32	1973	1.13	1974	4.04	1973	0.0		0.0		83	89	66	68
O	235	37	3.24	7.22	1974	0.35	1975	4.92	1973	0.0		0.0		73	81	58	61
N	642	0	1.47	2.75	1975	1.62	1974	2.03	1973	7.1	1975	6.1	1975	76	80	65	67
D	1014	0	1.52	2.59	1973	1.52	1974	1.66	1975	3.1	1972	5.0	1973	77	79	70	71
YR	5161	1420	37.00	10.32	SEP 1973	0.25	JUL 1975	4.92	OCT 1973	7.1	NOV 1975	6.1	NOV 1975	74	80	60	60

(To better understand these tables, see full explanation of terms beginning on page 322)

Month	Wind: Mean speed m.p.h.	Prevailing direction	Fastest mile: Speed m.p.h.	Direction	Year	Pct. of possible sunshine	Mean sky cover, tenths, sunrise to sunset	Mean number of days — Sunrise to sunset: Clear	Partly cloudy	Cloudy	Precipitation .01 inch or more	Snow, Ice pellets 1.0 inch or more	Thunderstorms	Heavy fog, visibility ¼ mile or less	Temperatures °F Max. (b): 90° and above	32° and below	Min.: 32° and below	0° and below	Average station pressure mb. Elev. 1025 feet m.s.l.
(a)	3		3	3		3	3	3	3	3	3	3	3	3	3	3	3	3	3
J	10.7		37	SW	1975	64	6.4	8	6	17	9	2	*	2	0	11	25	4	980.9
F	11.7		36	NW	1974	54	6.5	8	4	16	7	*	*	3	0	8	24	*	980.6
M	11.7		42	E	1974	61	7.2	6	6	19	12	*	2	4	0	3	11	0	976.0
A	11.8		40	SE	1974	65	5.9	9	8	13	10	1	6	1	0	1	4	0	976.3
M	9.6		42	SW	1974	67	5.6	11	9	11	10	0	9	2	1	0	0	0	974.7
J	9.4		32	S	1973	72	5.0	12	8	10	9	0	9	1	6	0	0	0	976.0
J	7.9		70	NW	1973	84	3.8	16	11	4	5	0	6	*	19	0	0	0	978.8
A	8.6		30	W	1974	69	4.6	14	8	9	8	0	5	*	11	0	0	0	979.2
S	8.3		33	NW	1975	51	6.2	10	4	16	11	0	6	4	1	0	0	0	980.9
O	10.0		35	S	1974	62	4.1	16	7	8	6	0	3	1	0	0	*	0	981.5
N	11.6		34	NE	1972	46	6.5	7	6	17	7	1	2	4	0	2	11	0	979.5
D	10.9		49	SW	1972	54	6.5	9	5	17	9	2	1	4	0	7	27	1	980.0
YR	10.2		70	NW	JUL 1973	64	5.7	126	82	157	104	6	49	26	38	32	102	5	978.7

FOOTNOTES

Means and extremes above are from existing and comparable exposures.
Annual extremes have been exceeded at other sites in the locality as follows:
Highest temperature 113 in August 1936; lowest temperature -22 in February 1899;
maximum monthly precipitation 16.17 in September 1914; mimimum monthly precipitation 0.04 in November 1954;
maximum precipitation in 24 hours 7.46 in August 1969; maximum monthly snowfall 40.2 in March 1912;
maximum snowfall in 24 hours 25.0 in March 1912; fastest mile 72 mph in August 1971.

Station: ST. LOUIS, MISSOURI
INTERNATIONAL AIRPORT
Elevation (ground): 535 feet

TEMPERATURES °F

Month	Normal			Extremes			
	Daily maximum	Daily minimum	Monthly	Record highest	Year	Record lowest	Year
(a)				15		15	
J	39.9	22.6	31.3	76	1970	-11	1963
F	44.2	26.0	35.1	85	1972	-2	1965
M	53.0	33.5	43.3	88	1963	3	1974
A	67.0	46.0	56.5	92	1970	22	1975
M	76.0	55.5	65.8	92	1972	31	1966
J	84.9	64.8	74.9	98	1971	43	1969
J	88.4	68.8	78.6	106	1966	51	1972
A	87.2	67.1	77.2	105	1962	47	1965
S	80.1	59.1	69.6	100	1971	36	1974
O	69.8	48.4	59.1	94	1963	25	1972
N	54.1	35.9	45.0	81	1971	1	1964
D	42.7	26.5	34.6	76	1970	-6	1973
YR	65.6	46.2	55.9	106	JUL 1966	-11	JAN 1963

IMPORTANT:
The time-period covered by this record is limited: See footnotes on next page for explanation and for additional history of EXTREME HIGHS AND LOWS recorded in the general area.

Saint Louis is located at the confluence of the nation's two major rivers and near the geographical center of the United States. Thus, with a somewhat modified continental climate, it is in the enviable position of being able to enjoy the vicissitude of a four-season climate without the undue hardship of prolonged periods of extreme cold, extreme heat, or high humidity. To the south is the warm, moist air of the Gulf of Mexico, and to the north in Canada is a favored region of cold air-masses. The alternate invasion of Saint Louis by air-masses from these sources, and the conflict along the frontal zones where they come together, produce a variety of weather conditions, none of which are likely to persist to the point of monotony.

Winters are brisk and stimulating, seldom severe. Records, since 1871, show that temperatures drop to zero or below an average of two or three days per year. Maximum temperatures remain as cold as 32° or lower less than 20 to 25 days in most years. The record low temperature recorded by the National Weather Service was -22° on January 5, 1884, but the alltime record low for Saint Louis was a -23° back in 1864.

Snowfall has averaged less than 20 inches per winter season since 1930 and has varied from a mere 0.7 inch in 1931-32 to 42.4 inches in 1973-74. Snowfall of one inch or more is received between 5 to 10 days in most winters, but there have been seasons when less than an inch fell, as in 1931-32 and other years when there were 15 days or more with one inch or more snowfall. Snowfall of an inch or more has occurred as late as May 2 (1929 3 inches), and as early as November 5. It was at this early date, November 5-6, 1951, that the fourth heaviest snowfall of record occurred at the airport, with a fall of 10.3 inches. The greatest snowfall at the airport was 12.0 inches received on December 19, 1973. The greatest snowfall of record at Saint Louis was 20.4 inches, and this occurred March 30-31, 1890. The winter of 1911-12 had the greatest total snowfall of record with 67.6 inches.

The long term record for Saint Louis (since 1871) indicates that maximum temperatures of 90° or higher occur an average of 35 to 40 days per year. Extremely hot days of 100° or more are expected on no more than about 5 days per year. The highest temperature on record is 115° read at the airport on July 14, 1954. On the same days 112° was recorded at the city office location on top of the ten-story Federal Building.

The last temperature as low as 32° in the spring has occurred as early as March 8, and as late as May 10, while the first occurrence of a freezing temperature in the fall has been as early as September 28, and as late as November 27. There is an average of approximately 190 days between the last freezing temperature in the spring and first such temperature in the fall, but this can vary from 150 days to around 230 days. The average date of the last freeze in the spring is April 15, and the average date of the first freeze in the fall is October 20.

Normal annual precipitation for the Saint Louis area, based on the average for the period 1941-1970, is a little over 35 inches, but 68.83 inches was recorded in 1858, and as little as 20.59 inches in 1953. The three winter months are the driest, with an average total of about 6 inches of precipitation. The spring months of April to June are normally the wettest with normal total precipitation of nearly 12 inches. From the middle of summer in July into the fall, it is not unusual to have extended periods of 1 to 2 weeks or more without appreciable rainfall.

Thunderstorms occur on the average between 40 to 50 days per year. During any year there are usually a few of these that can be classified as severe storms with hail and damaging winds. During the entire period of record there have been only four tornadoes which produced extensive damage and loss of life in Saint Louis: May 27, 1896, September 29, 1927, February 10, 1959, and January 24, 1967

Normals, Means, and Extremes

(To better understand these tables, see full explanation of terms beginning on page 322)

Month	Normal Degree days Base 65 °F: Heating	Normal Degree days: Cooling	Precipitation in inches, Water equivalent: Normal	Maximum monthly	Year	Minimum monthly	Year	Maximum in 24 hrs.	Year	Snow, Ice pellets: Maximum monthly	Year	Maximum in 24 hrs.	Year
(a)				18		18		18		39		39	
J	1045	0	1.85	5.38	1975	0.22	1970	2.43	1975	13.2	1962	11.2	1958
F	837	0	2.06	4.17	1974	0.25	1963	2.56	1959	12.9	1961	8.3	1966
M	682	9	3.03	5.81	1973	1.09	1966	1.84	1962	22.3	1960	10.0	1958
A	272	17	3.92	9.09	1970	1.37	1959	2.33	1970	6.5	1971	6.1	1971
M	103	128	3.86	7.25	1961	1.02	1972	2.94	1974	T	1944	T	1944
J	10	307	4.42	8.65	1969	0.47	1959	3.29	1960	0.0		0.0	
J	0	422	3.69	7.81	1958	0.60	1970	3.16	1958	0.0		0.0	
A	0	378	2.87	6.44	1970	0.08	1971	2.66	1974	0.0		0.0	
S	35	173	2.89	6.21	1972	0.76	1960	2.85	1969	0.0		0.0	
O	224	41	2.79	5.77	1969	0.21	1975	2.14	1969	T	1967	T	1967
N	600	0	2.47	5.74	1968	0.44	1969	2.87	1972	11.3	1951	10.3	1951
D	942	0	2.04	6.50	1971	0.32	1958	2.57	1971	26.3	1973	12.0	1973
YR	4750	1475	35.89	9.09	APR 1970	0.08	AUG 1971	3.29	JUN 1960	26.3	DEC 1973	12.0	DEC 1973

Month	Relative humidity pct. Hour 00 (Local time)	Hour 06	Hour 12	Hour 18	Wind: Mean speed m.p.h.	Prevailing direction	Fastest mile: Speed m.p.h.	Direction	Year	Pct. of possible sunshine	Mean sky cover, tenths, sunrise to sunset	Mean number of days, Sunrise to sunset: Clear	Partly cloudy	Cloudy	Precipitation .01 inch or more	Snow, Ice pellets 1.0 inch or more	Thunderstorms	Heavy fog, visibility ¼ mile or less	Temperatures °F Max. (b) 90° and above	Max. 32° and below	Min. 32° and below	Min. 0° and below	Average station pressure mb. Elev. 564 feet m.s.l.
(a)	15	15	15	15	26	14	17	17		16	27	27	27	27	18	18	18	18	15	15	15	15	3
J	77	82	64	69	10.3	NW	39	W	1970	52	6.8	7	7	17	8	2	1	2	0	11	26	2	999.0
F	76	80	61	64	10.8	NW	46	NW	1967	51	6.5	7	6	15	8	2	1	1	0	6	23	*	997.6
M	73	81	57	58	11.8	WNW	45	NE	1968	54	6.8	6	9	16	11	1	3	2	0	1	15	0	994.0
A	70	78	54	53	11.4	WNW	45	W	1964	56	6.5	7	8	15	11	*	6	1	*	0	3	0	994.6
M	76	82	56	55	9.4	S	42	SE	1970	62	6.2	8	9	14	11	0	6	*	1	0	*	0	992.6
J	78	84	57	56	8.6	S	60	SE	1964	69	5.9	7	12	11	9	0	7	*	8	0	0	0	993.8
J	78	86	57	56	7.6	S	40	NW	1969	71	5.6	9	12	10	9	0	7	*	13	0	0	0	995.7
A	81	89	57	58	7.4	S	48	NW	1966	66	5.3	10	12	9	8	0	6	*	11	0	0	0	997.0
S	83	91	61	64	7.9	S	39	SW	1974	63	5.1	11	8	11	9	0	4	1	4	0	0	0	998.2
O	76	84	55	60	8.5	S	48	SW	1967	62	4.9	13	8	10	8	0	2	1	*	0	2	0	999.8
N	78	84	62	68	9.9	S	41	S	1961	49	6.1	9	7	14	8	1	1	1	0	1	12	0	997.8
D	81	85	70	75	10.2	WNW	44	W	1968	41	6.9	7	6	18	10	1	1	2	0	7	24	1	998.1
YR	77	84	59	61	9.5	S	60	SE	JUN 1964	58	6.1	101	104	160	110	6	45	11	37	26	106	3	996.5

FOOTNOTES Means and extremes above are from existing and comparable exposures. Annual extremes have been exceeded at other sites in the locality as follows: Highest temperature 115 in July 1954; lowest temperature -23 in January 1864; maximum monthly precipitation 20.45 in August 1946; minimum monthly precipitation 0.00 in November 1865; maximum precipitation in 24 hours 8.78 in August 1946; maximum monthly snowfall 28.8 in March 1912; maximum snowfall in 24 hours 20.4 in March 1890; fastest mile of wind 91 from Northwest in May 1896.

Snowfall

Season	July	Aug	Sept	Oct	Nov	Dec	Jan
#1936-37	0.0	0.0	0.0	T	1.1	4.6	4.3
1937-38	0.0	0.0	0.0	T	1.0	3.5	0.5
#1938-39	0.0	0.0	0.0	0.0	3.7	T	10.1
1939-40	0.0	0.0	0.0	T	0.0	11.1	10.4
1940-41	0.0	0.0	0.0	0.0	T	T	1.8
1941-42	0.0	0.0	0.0	0.0	5.3	2.7	0.5
1942-43	0.0	0.0	0.0	0.0	T	8.8	2.0
#1943-44	0.0	0.0	0.0	T	T	6.1	0.6
1944-45	0.0	0.0	0.0	0.0	T	6.7	3.2
1945-46	0.0	0.0	0.0	0.0	T	10.2	6.3
1946-47	0.0	0.0	0.0	0.0	T	T	2.9
1947-48	0.0	0.0	0.0	0.0	0.2	1.0	7.4
1948-49	0.0	0.0	0.0	0.0	T	6.2	0.4
1949-50	0.0	0.0	0.0	0.0	0.1	T	1.4
1950-51	0.0	0.0	0.0	0.0	0.8	7.2	5.9
1951-52	0.0	0.0	0.0	T	11.3	0.9	1.7
1952-53	0.0	0.0	0.0	0.0	1.4	2.5	1.6
1953-54	0.0	0.0	0.0	0.0	T	T	0.5
1954-55	0.0	0.0	0.0	T	T	T	1.4
1955-56	0.0	0.0	0.0	T	T	T	8.1
1956-57	0.0	0.0	0.0	0.0	0.4	1.2	2.7
#1957-58	0.0	0.0	0.0	0.0	T	0.6	11.6
1958-59	0.0	0.0	0.0	0.0	4.5	1.0	4.7
1959-60	0.0	0.0	0.0	0.0	T	0.2	2.9
1960-61	0.0	0.0	0.0	0.0	T	5.6	5.3
1961-62	0.0	0.0	0.0	0.0	4.7	3.7	13.2
1962-63	0.0	0.0	0.0	0.0	0.0	0.8	3.5
1963-64	0.0	0.0	0.0	0.0	T	6.4	8.1
1964-65	0.0	0.0	0.0	0.0	3.1	0.3	7.3
1965-66	0.0	0.0	0.0	0.0	T	0.1	2.5
1966-67	0.0	0.0	0.0	0.0	T	0.1	1.4
1967-68	0.0	0.0	0.0	T	1.6	4.2	6.9
1968-69	0.0	0.0	0.0	0.0	T	1.3	2.3
1969-70	0.0	0.0	0.0	0.0	T	10.2	2.1
1970-71	0.0	0.0	0.0	0.0	T	0.9	0.4
1971-72	0.0	0.0	0.0	0.0	1.3	0.0	4.1
1972-73	0.0	0.0	0.0	0.0	5.2	1.0	2.2
1973-74	0.0	0.0	0.0	0.0	0.0	26.3	4.2
1974-75	0.0	0.0	0.0	0.0	1.2	1.5	4.1
1975-76	0.0	0.0	0.0	0.0	7.6	3.9	
RECORD MEAN	0.0	0.0	0.0	T	1.4	3.5	4.1

Heating Degree Days

Season	July	Aug	Sept	Oct	Nov	Dec	Jan
1955-56	0	0	9	230	692	979	1101
1956-57	0	0	27	75	600	816	1175
#1957-58	0	0	30	310	638	745	1042
1958-59	0	2	41	214	482	1072	1190
1959-60	0	0	30	258	777	792	970
#1960-61	0	0	7	213	551	1048	1132
1961-62	0	0	52	211	623	1015	1242
1962-63	0	0	62	194	595	1041	1347
1963-64	0	11	33	74	574	1320	932
1964-65	0	2	55	333	526	1019	1016
1965-66	0	7	49	286	489	717	1233
1966-67	0	0	78	336	534	931	932
1967-68	3	7	67	268	682	928	1121
1968-69	0	2	14	293	640	1008	1106
1969-70	0	0	27	313	644	1013	1241
1970-71	0	0	24	287	635	863	1159
1971-72	0	0	47	97	574	751	1081
1972-73	2	0	29	317	751	1069	997
1973-74	0	0	31	182	538	1077	1083
1974-75	0	0	127	242	625	954	979
1975-76	2	0	110	228	498	910	

Cooling Degree Days

Year	Jan	Feb	Mar	Apr	May	June	July
1969	0	0	0	9	113	246	486
1970	0	0	0	54	195	247	410
1971	0	0	2	35	45	427	326
1972	0	0	5	35	129	268	394
1973	0	0	1	17	25	294	435
1974	0	0	24	36	109	164	463
1975	0	0	2	12	133	308	405

Feb	Mar	Apr	May	June	Total
1.6	10.3	0.0	0.0	0.0	21.9
2.5	0.0	0.3	0.0	0.0	7.8
7.1	0.1	T	0.0	0.0	21.0
3.2	0.4	0.3	0.0	0.0	25.4
3.3	2.5	0.0	0.0	0.0	7.6
9.1	3.5	T	0.0	0.0	21.1
1.0	4.4	T	0.0	0.0	16.2
5.4	2.2	0.0	T	0.0	14.3
9.4	T	T	0.0	0.0	19.3
5.0	0.0	0.0	0.0	0.0	21.5
4.5	14.8	0.0	0.0	0.0	22.2
7.5	4.8	0.0	0.0	0.0	20.9
1.2	14.9	T	0.0	0.0	22.7
0.3	1.5	T	0.0	0.0	3.3
2.0	7.1	T	0.0	0.0	23.0
1.8	2.7	T	0.0	0.0	18.4
T	5.3	T	0.0	0.0	10.8
T	1.0	0.0	0.0	0.0	1.5
0.4	3.7	0.0	0.0	0.0	5.5
8.1	5.6	T	0.0	0.0	21.8
T	3.2	1.8	0.0	0.0	9.3
0.6	12.3	0.0	0.0	0.0	25.1
T	0.4	0.0	0.0	0.0	10.6
9.8	22.3	0.0	0.0	0.0	35.2
12.9	T	T	0.0	0.0	23.8
3.6	0.6	T	0.0	0.0	25.8
1.8	1.2	T	0.0	0.0	7.3
8.8	8.2	T	0.0	0.0	31.5
5.7	8.7	0.0	0.0	0.0	25.1
7.1	0.9	T	0.0	0.0	10.6
0.9	1.2	0.0	0.0	0.0	3.6
0.4	7.7	0.0	0.0	0.0	20.8
5.8	2.7	0.0	0.0	0.0	12.1
3.7	5.0	1.0	0.0	0.0	22.0
1.4	0.2	6.5	0.0	0.0	9.4
1.9	0.3	T	0.0	0.0	7.6
3.0	0.2	0.2	0.0	0.0	11.8
4.5	7.4	0.0	0.0	0.0	42.4
12.1	6.3	T	0.0	0.0	25.2
4.0	4.5	0.3	T	0.0	17.8

ST LOUIS, MO

Feb	Mar	Apr	May	June	Total
811	615	368	74	12	4891
686	664	317	72	0	4432
1100	828	284	69	10	5056
813	594	273	63	0	4744
985	1072	241	129	1	5255
810	597	455	232	25	5070
792	783	370	25	1	5114
1016	507	247	103	3	5115
884	696	216	41	6	4787
869	938	250	19	0	5027
915	570	397	156	4	4823
940	530	257	188	12	4738
1031	587	290	137	2	5123
826	834	247	85	15	5070
893	751	257	55	20	5214
866	718	303	122	0	4977
884	619	295	80	10	4438
849	430	348	121	0	4913
804	539	253	101	21	4629
919	803	353	48	1	5051

Aug	Sept	Oct	Nov	Dec	Total
381	162	43	0	0	1440
360	236	17	0	0	1519
340	279	62	10	0	1526
358	219	9	0	0	1417
375	187	57	4	0	1395
300	52	25	2	0	1175
406	110	51	4	0	1431

Average Temperature

Year	Jan	Feb	Mar	Apr	May	June	July	Aug	Sept	Oct	Nov	Dec	Annual
#1936	25.4	24.4	49.2	52.4	71.2	77.2	87.4	85.6	74.2	58.8	43.4	39.4	57.4
1937	30.1	33.1	40.6	55.5	66.4	74.8	78.6	81.3	69.1	56.2	41.8	31.4	54.9
1938	33.2	42.6	54.0	56.8	65.2	73.3	80.8	81.2	72.2	63.2	46.8	34.8	58.7
#1939	38.4	33.2	47.2	52.3	68.6	75.7	80.0	75.2	75.4	60.8	43.4	36.2	57.2
1940	14.6	32.6	42.4	53.2	62.4	75.4	78.2	77.0	68.7	63.0	42.2	38.6	54.0
1941	33.9	31.6	39.4	58.8	69.0	75.7	79.8	79.7	71.6	61.6	45.4	39.7	57.2
1942	31.4	33.0	45.8	59.4	64.6	74.0	79.4	75.2	68.3	58.2	47.5	31.2	55.7
#1943	30.6	38.8	39.4	54.2	64.1	76.8	80.6	79.8	65.6	56.5	41.6	30.6	54.9
1944	36.0	37.0	40.4	52.6	70.1	78.4	78.4	77.1	69.4	59.4	46.2	28.0	56.1
1945	27.7	35.0	53.4	56.1	60.2	69.8	76.0	76.9	69.0	57.2	45.4	27.6	54.5
1946	33.8	40.0	56.3	60.0	62.0	75.8	79.2	72.7	68.6	61.7	47.5	39.8	58.1
1947	36.6	28.2	36.4	54.8	63.0	73.1	76.0	84.9	71.2	65.5	40.4	38.0	55.7
1948	25.5	33.2	43.2	59.8	64.0	74.7	78.4	77.5	71.2	55.8	47.0	37.6	55.7
1949	32.4	36.1	43.6	53.6	68.8	76.9	80.4	76.6	63.9	59.9	48.7	39.7	56.7
1950	37.7	36.6	40.7	50.7	67.0	74.1	75.2	72.3	67.3	64.2	38.4	28.9	54.4
1951	32.6	35.4	40.1	52.1	67.5	72.2	78.2	76.6	66.3	59.3	38.8	33.6	54.4
1952	35.9	39.8	42.4	54.8	65.9	83.1	81.4	76.7	70.0	53.7	46.0	37.0	57.2
1953	35.3	39.9	46.8	52.1	67.2	81.5	81.4	78.3	72.4	62.0	47.6	37.7	58.5
1954	32.7	43.8	42.1	62.1	61.6	79.4	84.9	80.0	74.6	58.9	45.9	36.7	58.6
1955	33.0	35.9	44.9	62.9	68.3	71.5	83.4	80.2	73.6	58.3	41.7	33.1	57.2
1956	29.2	36.9	45.1	53.4	67.8	76.2	77.8	79.3	70.8	64.5	45.0	38.5	57.0
#1957	26.9	40.4	43.4	56.4	66.2	75.6	80.1	79.3	68.4	54.9	43.5	40.8	56.3
1958	31.3	25.4	38.0	55.7	66.1	71.5	76.5	77.5	69.1	59.1	48.9	30.3	54.1
1959	26.3	35.7	45.7	56.8	69.6	76.4	78.0	80.8	71.3	57.1	39.0	39.3	56.3
#1960	33.5	30.8	30.3	58.9	62.7	73.9	76.2	79.1	74.2	59.0	46.5	30.9	54.7
1961	28.3	35.9	45.5	50.0	58.3	70.1	76.2	75.4	71.1	59.2	44.1	32.0	53.8
1962	24.7	36.6	39.6	53.1	72.1	74.0	75.8	75.6	66.4	61.0	44.9	31.2	54.6
1963	21.3	28.5	48.8	58.2	63.9	75.4	77.3	74.9	68.5	66.9	45.7	22.2	54.3
1964	34.7	34.3	42.3	58.7	69.6	74.8	78.5	76.5	69.3	54.0	47.3	31.9	56.0
1965	31.9	33.8	34.5	58.4	70.5	75.1	76.8	75.8	69.1	56.4	48.5	41.7	56.1
1966	25.0	32.1	46.7	51.7	61.7	73.7	82.9	74.2	65.6	54.2	47.1	34.8	54.1
1967	34.7	31.3	48.3	58.5	60.8	74.0	74.9	72.4	66.5	57.5	42.0	34.8	54.7
1968	28.6	29.3	46.1	55.6	61.9	77.0	77.6	77.5	68.0	56.9	43.5	32.3	54.5
1969	29.2	35.3	37.8	56.9	65.7	72.5	80.5	77.0	69.3	56.1	43.4	32.1	54.7
1970	24.8	33.0	40.6	58.0	69.3	72.3	77.9	76.3	71.8	56.1	43.6	37.0	55.1
1971	27.4	33.9	41.7	55.9	62.3	78.9	75.4	75.7	72.5	63.7	46.0	40.6	56.2
1972	29.9	34.3	45.0	56.1	66.4	73.4	77.5	76.3	71.1	54.8	39.8	30.4	54.6
1973	32.6	34.5	50.9	53.7	61.7	74.6	78.7	76.9	70.0	60.7	47.0	30.0	55.9
1974	29.8	36.1	48.1	57.5	65.0	69.5	79.8	74.5	62.3	57.8	44.0	34.0	54.9
1975	33.2	32.0	39.0	53.4	67.6	74.9	77.8	77.9	64.7	59.0	48.3	35.5	55.3
RECORD MEAN	31.7	34.8	44.3	56.1	65.9	75.1	79.3	77.5	70.1	59.0	45.3	35.3	56.2
MAX	39.9	43.3	53.5	65.7	75.4	84.4	88.6	86.9	79.7	68.7	53.8	42.9	65.2
MIN	23.4	26.2	35.0	46.4	56.4	65.8	70.0	68.0	60.4	49.2	36.8	27.6	47.1

# Indicates a station move or relocation of instruments.

Precipitation

Year	Jan	Feb	Mar	Apr	May	June	July	Aug	Sept	Oct	Nov	Dec	Annual
#1936	1.32	1.97	1.67	2.80	0.85	3.07	0.60	0.85	5.94	2.79	2.20	2.08	26.14
1937	5.40	1.34	2.14	4.79	4.08	6.78	1.10	1.38	2.21	3.39	1.19	3.05	36.85
1938	1.29	3.34	6.59	3.06	4.27	6.46	2.86	1.04	1.00	1.12	3.90	2.56	37.49
#1939	3.93	2.82	1.63	5.71	1.97	4.75	1.70	7.62	1.11	1.65	2.42	1.25	36.56
1940	0.90	1.46	2.27	3.49	2.27	2.17	1.30	2.83	T	2.41	2.94	2.69	24.73
1941	2.27	0.48	0.72	5.45	2.32	2.54	0.52	2.17	4.45	6.67	2.78	1.00	31.37
1942	0.90	2.53	1.75	2.05	3.97	8.32	5.41	3.75	1.46	3.19	5.07	3.24	41.64
#1943	0.60	0.76	3.20	2.54	11.20	5.91	2.91	1.35	3.46	2.71	1.12	1.77	37.53
1944	0.20	2.65	2.71	9.54	4.46	2.19	2.97	3.25	2.96	1.07	1.15	1.75	34.90
1945	1.10	2.49	7.63	6.18	2.71	7.87	1.38	3.58	10.04	1.22	1.63	1.72	47.55
1946	1.38	2.03	3.22	2.40	5.14	2.31	1.63	14.78	2.22	4.14	8.71	2.35	50.31
1947	2.08	0.27	2.58	7.25	3.23	7.44	1.06	0.55	3.03	4.05	1.80	2.44	35.78
1948	0.85	1.73	6.40	1.32	2.44	5.12	12.69	2.08	1.71	3.88	2.55	1.49	42.26
1949	5.74	2.65	2.57	1.60	5.40	4.91	5.96	2.32	3.32	6.66	0.11	4.52	45.76
1950	8.00	2.74	3.60	4.48	3.13	3.26	1.26	3.72	2.62	1.48	2.76	0.58	37.63
1951	1.67	4.98	2.75	2.46	2.57	6.16	2.95	2.78	3.15	2.48	2.60	1.82	36.37
1952	1.41	2.50	3.52	3.85	1.18	0.99	4.61	3.13	0.56	0.24	2.30	1.38	25.67
1953	1.53	1.38	4.06	3.43	1.77	2.04	1.31	0.86	0.40	2.50	0.83	0.48	20.59
1954	1.23	0.67	1.14	2.41	2.50	2.71	2.08	4.56	3.29	3.93	1.19	1.90	27.61
1955	2.14	3.45	2.15	3.57	2.45	4.78	2.97	2.33	3.19	2.73	1.54	0.03	31.33
1956	0.73	3.69	0.84	2.85	4.84	3.07	7.03	1.53	1.21	0.65	4.19	3.80	34.43
#1957	0.97	3.74	2.87	8.18	6.70	10.48	4.65	0.61	0.88	2.34	2.96	2.78	47.16
1958	2.13	0.47	3.87	2.81	2.73	5.31	7.81	3.32	2.16	2.77	3.68	0.32	37.38
1959	1.42	3.39	2.40	1.37	3.56	0.47	2.08	2.13	2.85	3.81	2.90	1.93	28.31
1960	1.11	1.19	2.77	3.11	4.72	7.97	2.27	0.98	0.76	3.36	1.41	2.13	31.78
1961	0.39	2.06	4.75	3.47	7.25	3.67	6.20	1.88	4.01	2.67	2.90	1.95	41.20
1962	3.56	2.53	3.00	2.52	2.44	4.75	5.49	2.29	2.63	2.70	0.71	1.99	34.61
1963	0.74	0.25	5.54	1.98	4.77	3.87	1.37	2.55	1.13	2.85	2.90	0.67	28.62
1964	1.70	2.30	3.84	4.99	2.68	2.73	4.25	2.39	1.47	0.73	3.84	1.24	32.16
1965	2.51	1.16	2.34	3.67	1.38	3.03	3.17	3.59	3.00	0.46	0.78	3.17	28.26
1966	0.65	4.12	1.09	6.03	4.59	1.59	1.26	3.72	2.15	2.18	2.47	2.49	32.34
1967	2.89	1.72	2.77	3.40	4.73	4.46	3.84	1.36	4.33	3.45	2.15	6.20	41.30
1968	1.86	1.09	2.06	1.48	6.78	0.90	3.92	1.60	3.74	0.69	5.74	2.63	32.49
1969	3.61	2.04	2.47	4.01	2.11	8.65	7.08	0.52	5.03	5.77	0.44	1.99	43.72
1970	0.22	0.64	2.17	9.09	2.04	5.08	0.60	6.44	5.54	2.21	0.77	1.40	36.20
1971	0.66	3.08	1.81	1.65	5.66	2.43	4.70	0.08	3.98	1.51	1.67	6.50	33.73
1972	0.77	0.74	2.93	4.49	1.02	1.19	3.10	2.69	6.21	1.47	5.59	3.54	33.74
1973	1.40	1.04	5.81	4.25	3.92	4.23	2.85	2.46	3.52	2.33	3.65	4.36	39.82
1974	3.51	4.17	2.58	2.40	5.90	3.45	0.90	5.05	2.50	1.51	3.15	1.71	36.83
1975	5.38	3.59	4.08	4.56	3.23	3.78	2.56	5.44	2.48	0.21	2.62	2.28	40.21
RECORD MEAN	2.21	2.31	3.26	3.74	4.12	4.10	3.29	2.96	3.20	2.64	2.64	2.23	36.70

Record mean values above are means through the current year for the period beginning in 1873 for temperature, 1871 for precipitation and 1937 for snowfall. Degree Days are from Airport locations. Other data from City Office locations through 1936 and from Airport locations thereafter.

HELENA, MONTANA

Helena is located on the south side of an intermountain valley bounded on the north and east by the Big Belt Mountains and on the west and south by the main chain of the Continental Divide. The valley is approximately 25 miles in width from north to south and 35 miles long from east to west. The average height of the mountains above the valley floor is about 3,000 feet.

The climate of Helena may be described as modified continental. Several factors enter into modifying continental climate characteristics. Some of these are invasion by Pacific Ocean airmasses, drainage of cool air into the valley from the surrounding mountains, and the protecting mountain shield in all directions which makes temperature changes somewhat smaller than those expected of a true continental climate.

The mountains to the north and east sometimes deflect shallow masses of invading cold arctic air to the east. Following periods of extreme cold, when the return circulation of maritime air has brought warming to most of the eastern part of the state, cold air may remain trapped in the valley for several days before being replaced by warmer air. During these periods of transition from cold-to-warm temperatures, inversions are often quite pronounced. Occasionally, temperatures in the center of the City, 200 feet higher, may be several degrees warmer than at the airport. This is noted mostly just before the invading warmer air reaches the valley floor, although there are times when the warm air will not reach the airport even after having reached the City.

As may be expected in a northern latitude, cold waves may occur from November through February, with temperatures occasionally dropping to zero or lower. The greatest number of days with zero or colder temperature can be expected during January. The greatest drop in temperature during a cold wave occurred on December 14-15, 1924, when the temperature fell 79° from a high of 63° at 2:00 p.m. on the 14th to -16° 24 hours later, finally reaching a low of -25° at midnight on the 15th. Generally the protection afforded by the mountains helps to prevent such extreme falls. Twenty-four hour changes seldom exceed 40°. There are about 161 days, on the average, between the last date of a minimum of 28° in the spring and the first in the fall. The average dates of these occurrences are April 27 and October 5. The same dates for 32° occurrences are May 12 and September 23.

Summertime temperatures are moderate, with maximum readings generally under 90° and very seldom reaching 100°. The highest ever observed was 105° on August 24, 1969. Like all mountain stations, there is usually a marked change in temperature from day to night. During the summer this tends to produce an agreeable combination of fairly warm days and cool nights.

Total precipitation varies widely throughout the valley, from a semiarid total of 9 to 10 inches in the drier northern and eastern portions of the valley to a subhumid 30 inches along the Continental Divide to the southwest. Most of the precipitation falls from April through July from frequent showers or thundershowers, but usually with some steady rains in June, the wettest month of the year. Late summer, fall, and winter months are relatively dry. April-September growing season precipitation varies considerably, but the average is about 8 inches.

Station: HELENA, MONTANA
HELENA AIRPORT
Elevation (ground): 3828 feet

TEMPERATURES °F

Month	Normal			Extremes			
	Daily maximum	Daily minimum	Monthly	Record highest	Year	Record lowest	Year
(a)				12		12	
J	28.3	7.8	18.1	58	1974	-35	1969
F	35.8	14.9	25.4	61	1967	-24	1975
M	41.7	19.4	30.6	74	1966	-16	1969
A	55.2	30.2	42.7	81	1969	5	1975
M	64.8	39.5	52.2	90	1966	23	1969
J	71.6	46.7	59.2	96	1974	30	1969
J	83.7	52.1	67.9	102	1973	36	1971
A	82.0	50.4	66.2	105	1969	36	1971
S	70.0	40.9	55.5	99	1967	18	1970
O	58.7	31.9	45.3	85	1963	-3	1972
N	42.6	20.8	31.7	67	1965	-14	1975
D	33.2	13.3	23.3	62	1975	-38	1964
YR	55.6	30.7	43.2	105	AUG 1969	-38	DEC 1964

IMPORTANT:
The time-period covered by this record is limited: See footnotes following table of **NORMALS, MEANS AND EXTREMES** for explanation and for additional history of **EXTREME HIGHS AND LOWS** recorded in the general area.

(Continued)

Thunderstorms are rather frequent from May through August with the maximum occurrence in July. Snow can be expected from September through May, but amounts during the spring and fall are usually light, and snow on the ground ordinarily lasts only a day or two. During the winter months snow may remain on the ground for several weeks at a time. There is little drifting of snow in the valley, and blizzard conditions are very infrequent.

Severe ice, sleet, and hailstorms are very seldom observed. Since 1880, only one hailstorm (on July 19, 1948) caused extensive damage in the city of Helena.

In winter, hours of sunshine are more than would be expected at a mountain location. Considering the entire period of record, the average percent of possible sunshine December through February is 48 percent, and 100 percent of possible on the coldest days is rather common.

Due to the sheltering influence of the mountains, Foehn (Chinook) winds are not as pronounced as might be expected for a location on the eastern slopes of the Rocky Mountains. Strong winds can occur at any time throughout the year, but generally don't last more than a few hours at a time.

HELENA, MONTANA

Normals, Means, and Extremes

(To better understand these tables, see full explanation of terms beginning on page 322)

Month	Normal Degree days Base 65 °F: Heating	Normal Degree days: Cooling	Precipitation in inches, Water equivalent: Normal	Maximum monthly	Year	Minimum monthly	Year	Maximum in 24 hrs.	Year	Snow, Ice pellets: Maximum monthly	Year	Maximum in 24 hrs.	Year
(a)				35		35		35		35		35	
J	1454	0	0.55	2.78	1969	0.03	1944	0.77	1969	35.6	1969	11.5	1969
F	1109	0	0.38	1.13	1959	0.06	1961	0.58	1953	19.7	1959	8.6	1959
M	1066	0	0.69	1.43	1967	0.02	1959	1.01	1957	21.6	1955	8.7	1955
A	669	0	0.93	3.00	1975	0.33	1946	1.25	1951	20.6	1967	12.9	1960
M	401	0	1.76	3.77	1962	0.43	1966	2.06	1964	12.7	1967	12.5	1967
J	194	20	2.38	4.74	1944	0.25	1960	1.70	1947	2.7	1969	2.7	1969
J	33	123	0.96	3.89	1975	0.08	1973	1.63	1975	T	1972	T	1972
A	57	94	0.98	4.23	1974	0.24	1955	1.86	1974	0.0		0.0	
S	304	19	0.97	3.37	1965	0.08	1972	1.42	1957	13.7	1965	13.3	1957
O	611	0	0.59	2.68	1975	0.04	1964	0.85	1954	11.0	1969	7.4	1969
N	999	0	0.61	1.50	1950	0.04	1969	0.82	1959	32.9	1959	21.5	1959
D	1293	0	0.58	1.39	1967	0.13	1954	0.50	1971	22.8	1967	10.7	1941
YR	8190	256	11.38	4.74	JUN 1944	0.02	MAR 1959	2.06	MAY 1964	35.6	JAN 1969	21.5	NOV 1959

Month	Relative humidity pct. Hour 05 (Local time)	Hour 11	Hour 17	Hour 23	Wind: Mean speed m.p.h.	Prevailing direction	Fastest mile: Speed m.p.h.	Direction	Year	Pct. of possible sunshine	Mean sky cover, tenths, sunrise to sunset
(a)	12	12	12	12	35	15	35	35		35	35
J	68	64	63	67	7.1	W	73	SW	1944	47	7.5
F	71	63	56	68	7.7	W	73	W	1949	54	7.4
M	69	54	46	64	8.6	W	61	SW	1955	60	7.3
A	71	49	40	61	9.4	W	52	W	1950	57	7.4
M	70	44	37	58	8.9	W	56	SW	1975	61	6.9
J	72	46	39	60	8.7	W	56	W	1970	62	6.4
J	66	39	28	50	7.9	W	65	SW	1975	79	3.9
A	65	40	30	50	7.6	W	65	S	1947	75	4.4
S	72	48	36	59	7.6	W	54	NW	1943	67	5.4
O	72	52	43	64	7.4	W	62	W	1948	60	6.1
N	75	63	58	71	7.2	W	56	SW	1962	45	7.2
D	71	67	64	70	7.1	W	59	NW	1946	43	7.5
YR	70	52	45	62	7.9	W	73	W	FEB 1949	61	6.4

Month	Mean number of days, Sunrise to sunset: Clear	Partly cloudy	Cloudy	Precipitation .01 inch or more	Snow, Ice pellets 1.0 inch or more	Thunderstorms	Heavy fog, visibility ¼ mile or less	Temperatures °F Max. (b) 90° and above	Max. 32° and below	Min. 32° and below	Min. 0° and below	Average station pressure mb. Elev. 3898 feet m.s.l.
(a)	35	35	35	35	35	35	35	12	12	12	12	3
J	5	6	20	8	3	*	2	0	14	29	9	879.6
F	4	6	18	6	2	*	1	0	9	27	4	880.8
M	4	8	19	8	2	*	1	0	6	28	2	876.3
A	3	9	18	8	1	1	*	0	1	21	0	879.4
M	5	10	16	11	*	4	*	*	0	5	0	879.8
J	6	10	14	12	*	8	*	1	0	*	0	879.4
J	15	11	5	7	0	10	*	7	0	0	0	882.0
A	14	10	7	8	0	8	*	8	0	0	0	881.6
S	10	9	11	6	*	2	*	1	0	5	0	884.6
O	8	9	14	6	1	*	*	0	1	18	*	881.9
N	4	8	18	7	2	*	1	0	5	28	1	879.9
D	4	7	20	8	3	*	2	0	14	30	5	880.9
YR	82	103	180	96	14	34	8	18	48	189	21	880.5

FOOTNOTES Means and extremes above are from existing and comparable exposures. Annual extremes have been exceeded at other sites in the locality as follows: Lowest temperature -42 in January 1957; maximum monthly precipitation 6.67 in May 1927; minimum monthly precipitation T in August 1940 and earlier; maximum precipitation in 24 hours 3.67 in June 1908; maximum monthly snowfall 46.4 in December 1880.

Snowfall

Season	July	Aug	Sept	Oct	Nov	Dec	Jan
1936-37	0.0	0.0	T	5.2	8.0	11.7	15.0
1937-38	0.0	0.0	0.3	T	5.2	14.0	11.1
1938-39	0.0	0.0	0.0	11.7	1.4	4.4	4.5
#1939-40	0.0	0.0	0.7	4.5	T	2.7	9.7
1940-41	0.0	0.0	0.0	T	8.3	0.5	4.8
1941-42	0.0	0.0	1.9	0.5	1.9	14.6	10.6
1942-43	0.0	0.0	0.1	T	11.5	3.1	24.6
1943-44	0.0	0.0	T	T	3.0	3.2	0.6
1944-45	0.0	0.0	0.0	0.0	3.3	12.4	3.3
1945-46	0.0	0.0	1.2	T	2.5	9.0	4.1
1946-47	0.0	0.0	0.0	4.3	14.5	12.5	4.6
1947-48	0.0	0.0	5.3	0.4	13.4	2.8	5.2
1948-49	0.0	0.0	0.0	0.5	1.6	13.2	13.8
1949-50	0.0	0.0	7.5	3.6	T	9.3	12.9
1950-51	0.0	0.0	0.9	0.2	19.9	9.9	5.8
1951-52	0.0	0.0	0.4	5.6	4.1	22.6	3.7
1952-53	0.0	0.0	0.0	T	13.6	4.3	3.2
1953-54	0.0	0.0	0.0	T	T	4.6	24.2
1954-55	0.0	0.0	1.6	1.3	9.7	0.3	3.4
1955-56	0.0	0.0	1.2	3.0	17.7	15.3	9.4
1956-57	0.0	0.0	0.0	1.9	0.7	5.4	18.7
1957-58	0.0	0.0	13.4	8.2	10.3	2.8	1.0
1958-59	0.0	0.0	0.0	0.3	7.4	15.3	7.4
1959-60	0.0	0.0	T	3.4	32.9	4.5	4.9
1960-61	0.0	0.0	0.0	4.1	2.0	2.9	1.8
1961-62	0.0	0.0	T	1.3	6.4	4.2	10.1
1962-63	0.0	0.0	0.4	0.0	1.2	1.5	9.8
1963-64	0.0	0.0	0.0	T	2.7	21.2	6.2
1964-65	0.0	0.0	0.0	0.0	6.3	13.2	2.3
1965-66	0.0	0.0	13.7	0.0	2.1	1.4	6.3
1966-67	0.0	0.0	0.0	T	9.5	5.7	7.3
1967-68	0.0	0.0	0.0	T	2.7	22.8	8.7
1968-69	0.0	0.0	3.0	0.4	7.4	11.0	35.6
1969-70	0.0	0.0	0.0	11.0	0.1	6.1	7.0
1970-71	0.0	0.0	T	1.4	5.4	7.5	16.2
1971-72	0.0	0.0	T	0.8	4.6	14.5	14.9
1972-73	T	0.0	0.3	4.7	0.7	7.8	3.2
1973-74	0.0	0.0	1.3	7.2	12.5	7.2	9.9
1974-75	0.0	0.0	T	1.5	0.8	2.7	15.2
1975-76	0.0	0.0	0.0	6.3	4.9	3.9	
RECORD MEAN	T	0.0	1.5	2.1	6.8	8.5	9.2

Heating Degree Days

Season	July	Aug	Sept	Oct	Nov	Dec	Jan
1955-56	93	7	330	532	1355	1427	1495
1956-57	49	85	216	608	967	1145	1962
1957-58	7	57	264	738	976	998	1129
1958-59	99	14	263	561	1018	1253	1367
1959-60	41	69	351	652	1219	1112	1522
1960-61	7	114	242	572	934	1266	1158
1961-62	1	7	476	652	1109	1311	1528
1962-63	58	77	295	515	837	1106	1687
#1963-64	32	32	131	427	897	1484	1328
1964-65	1	101	332	542	1028	1420	1090
1965-66	14	69	578	478	903	1153	1370
1966-67	8	51	117	570	930	1157	1120
1967-68	0	1	130	539	954	1422	1525
1968-69	23	102	294	633	937	1493	1788
1969-70	35	14	219	826	938	1207	1427
1970-71	22	12	413	763	1063	1372	1422
1971-72	91	22	454	707	936	1524	1628
1972-73	136	49	418	798	1010	1588	1465
1973-74	23	47	317	588	1208	1136	1452
1974-75	16	130	338	588	905	1149	1355
1975-76	14	119	322	666	1045	1199	

Cooling Degree Days

Year	Jan	Feb	Mar	Apr	May	June	July
1969	0	0	0	0	1	18	128
1970	0	0	0	0	0	76	130
1971	0	0	0	0	0	14	42
1972	0	0	0	0	2	30	42
1973	0	0	0	0	4	45	151
1974	0	0	0	0	0	102	190
1975	0	0	0	0	0	1	154

Feb	Mar	Apr	May	June	Total
4.2	12.2	1.8	0.0	0.0	58.1
7.8	14.0	4.0	4.9	0.0	61.3
13.1	9.7	0.3	T	T	45.1
9.6	5.2	1.3	T	0.0	33.7
1.3	2.0	3.1	T	0.0	20.0
11.8	7.5	0.8	2.5	0.0	52.1
8.0	9.2	2.3	T	T	58.8
12.7	9.7	T	T	0.0	29.2
1.3	2.5	3.7	0.0	0.0	26.5
4.0	1.3	T	T	0.0	22.1
3.6	7.0	1.3	0.0	0.0	47.8
4.0	7.3	2.0	3.2	0.0	43.6
11.2	12.1	T	0.6	T	53.0
2.7	9.2	8.5	8.4	1.5	63.6
2.9	11.4	3.5	4.4	0.9	59.8
8.1	11.8	0.1	0.0	0.0	56.4
14.5	1.4	0.6	0.4	0.0	38.0
0.2	8.9	8.9	T	0.0	46.8
3.3	21.6	10.9	2.2	0.0	54.3
1.9	5.5	4.7	3.3	0.0	62.0
5.8	12.9	6.3	0.0	0.0	51.7
16.4	8.6	3.4	0.0	0.0	64.1
19.7	0.4	1.5	T	0.0	52.0
3.7	4.5	20.0	T	0.0	73.9
0.4	9.1	8.3	T	0.0	28.6
7.3	7.3	8.7	0.0	0.0	45.3
2.0	5.9	2.3	T	0.0	23.1
6.3	7.4	6.6	10.1	0.0	60.5
9.4	12.9	6.3	5.0	0.0	55.4
5.1	2.3	1.9	T	0.0	32.8
10.5	14.9	20.6	12.7	0.0	81.2
0.9	0.8	10.0	T	0.0	45.9
3.6	7.0	2.6	0.7	2.7	74.0
9.5	9.0	7.9	1.4	0.0	52.0
3.5	2.5	0.7	T	0.0	37.2
3.3	4.5	3.8	T	0.0	46.4
1.8	0.1	6.5	T	0.0	25.1
5.9	2.2	1.5	0.2	0.0	47.9
10.7	12.3	15.4	0.2	0.0	58.8
6.2	7.2	5.3	1.6	0.1	48.5

Average Temperature

Year	Jan	Feb	Mar	Apr	May	June	July	Aug	Sept	Oct	Nov	Dec	Annual
1936	23.2	2.0	31.8	43.8	58.9	62.6	74.7	67.7	56.4	47.6	27.8	27.2	43.6
1937	-2.4	22.8	32.2	43.6	54.7	58.7	70.8	66.8	58.6	50.0	35.2	28.2	43.3
1938	26.6	19.2	33.0	44.0	50.2	60.8	67.2	66.1	64.2	45.2	30.8	28.5	44.6
1939	31.6	19.0	34.6	46.2	56.0	55.6	70.2	67.8	57.4	46.7	39.2	33.6	46.5
#1940	15.4	26.6	39.6	42.4	57.1	63.9	70.4	69.9	60.4	49.4	23.0	28.7	45.6
1941	22.6	27.8	36.6	44.2	54.6	61.6	69.2	67.0	50.4	42.4	35.6	24.5	44.7
1942	9.8	15.5	32.6	45.6	48.6	55.9	68.4	65.8	56.0	46.7	30.8	27.7	42.0
1943	6.4	21.6	21.0	47.3	49.0	56.2	67.6	66.4	57.6	47.4	32.8	23.2	41.4
1944	23.4	23.2	26.7	44.3	53.6	55.6	64.6	62.4	56.2	48.8	30.8	16.0	42.1
1945	26.5	26.7	33.4	39.2	51.2	56.1	69.0	67.8	53.2	49.2	31.6	21.3	43.8
1946	28.3	30.6	40.0	48.0	50.2	59.4	68.6	66.0	54.8	38.7	27.4	26.2	44.8
1947	19.9	27.2	32.4	44.3	54.1	55.9	68.8	65.4	56.0	48.6	27.8	26.8	43.9
1948	25.1	20.5	26.2	43.2	52.4	60.8	64.0	65.6	56.8	44.1	33.8	12.8	42.1
1949	0.6	14.4	28.8	47.8	54.7	59.6	66.6	68.3	55.0	39.6	39.8	20.0	41.3
1950	0.6	30.8	30.4	40.6	48.4	56.9	64.8	64.3	54.0	47.7	25.7	26.5	40.9
1951	16.9	25.2	21.1	40.6	52.1	53.9	67.5	62.5	51.9	41.2	30.7	14.5	39.8
1952	12.6	22.8	27.4	47.3	52.9	60.0	65.7	66.1	59.0	46.6	26.2	22.6	42.4
1953	34.5	29.8	35.6	39.8	48.2	57.7	69.6	67.0	59.2	49.3	38.6	31.4	46.7
1954	16.2	34.7	27.4	39.9	52.7	55.7	70.2	64.0	55.4	42.6	39.1	23.0	43.4
1955	20.3	20.7	21.1	39.1	49.3	58.8	65.6	68.0	54.6	47.7	19.7	18.8	40.3
1956	16.5	18.6	33.4	41.8	54.2	62.2	67.8	63.7	57.6	45.2	32.6	27.9	43.5
1957	1.7	21.9	32.1	42.1	55.0	60.5	69.0	66.2	56.2	41.0	32.3	32.6	42.6
1958	28.4	25.1	30.1	42.2	60.7	58.8	62.9	69.4	56.5	46.7	30.9	24.4	44.7
1959	20.7	14.7	36.3	43.1	47.4	61.9	68.1	64.2	53.7	43.7	24.3	28.9	42.3
1960	15.7	23.8	32.6	42.1	50.5	60.8	71.5	63.4	57.0	46.4	33.6	23.9	43.5
1961	27.4	36.6	37.0	40.6	53.7	68.5	70.9	71.3	48.9	43.7	27.8	22.6	45.8
1962	15.7	24.5	29.1	47.2	51.7	60.9	65.2	64.9	55.0	48.1	36.9	29.2	44.0
#1963	10.5	34.8	37.6	42.6	53.4	60.0	68.2	68.0	61.2	50.9	34.8	16.9	44.9
1964	22.0	27.2	29.9	41.8	51.7	59.0	70.2	63.4	53.8	47.4	30.5	19.1	43.0
1965	29.6	26.6	24.6	44.4	50.1	59.5	67.7	65.8	45.6	49.3	34.7	27.5	43.8
1966	20.6	27.0	36.5	42.5	56.5	59.3	71.5	66.7	62.7	46.4	33.8	27.4	45.9
1967	28.7	32.7	29.0	37.8	52.1	59.9	70.5	71.4	61.9	47.4	33.0	19.0	45.3
1968	15.7	28.9	39.6	39.7	49.6	58.3	68.2	63.2	55.0	44.4	33.5	16.7	42.8
1969	7.2	14.5	21.3	46.7	55.2	57.8	67.9	70.1	58.0	38.1	33.5	25.9	41.4
1970	18.8	32.5	28.2	36.5	51.5	62.3	68.2	67.9	51.1	40.2	29.3	20.6	42.2
1971	19.0	28.5	31.9	41.5	51.4	57.0	63.2	69.0	49.7	42.0	33.6	15.6	41.9
1972	12.4	26.8	39.1	39.8	50.9	61.8	61.7	66.0	50.9	39.0	31.1	13.6	41.1
1973	17.7	22.8	36.0	40.3	52.9	61.2	68.9	66.8	54.4	45.8	24.5	28.2	43.3
1974	18.1	32.8	33.9	46.0	48.6	64.9	70.4	61.5	53.5	45.8	34.7	27.7	44.8
1975	21.1	13.7	28.8	32.9	48.6	56.9	69.2	61.2	54.1	43.3	29.9	26.0	40.5
RECORD MEAN	19.7	24.2	32.2	43.3	52.0	59.7	67.8	66.3	55.6	45.4	32.6	24.4	43.6
MAX	28.6	33.4	42.0	54.4	63.5	71.5	81.9	80.3	68.3	56.6	41.9	32.8	54.6
MIN	10.8	15.0	22.3	32.1	40.5	47.8	53.7	52.2	42.9	34.2	23.3	16.0	32.6

# Indicates a station move or relocation of instruments.

HELENA, MT

Feb	Mar	Apr	May	June	Total
1344	971	687	331	113	8685
1202	1013	679	302	145	8373
1113	1073	679	167	189	7390
1405	886	651	540	126	8183
1192	996	682	446	134	8416
789	863	726	354	21	7046
1133	1104	527	404	147	8399
842	842	665	358	172	7454
1089	1080	690	411	192	7793
1070	1250	612	454	169	8069
1058	874	670	267	188	7622
898	1107	807	396	171	7332
1042	780	751	472	206	7822
1407	1348	543	301	226	9095
904	1132	849	409	153	8113
1013	1020	699	414	251	8464
1102	796	747	430	120	8557
1174	892	732	374	155	8791
897	956	564	500	99	7787
1429	1114	954	501	235	8714

Aug	Sept	Oct	Nov	Dec	Total
178	20	0	0	0	345
109	5	0	0	0	320
154	0	0	0	0	210
89	0	0	0	0	163
108	3	0	0	0	311
31	0	0	0	0	323
12	0	0	0	0	167

Precipitation

Year	Jan	Feb	Mar	Apr	May	June	July	Aug	Sept	Oct	Nov	Dec	Annual
1936	0.57	1.51	0.45	0.99	0.89	2.28	0.69	0.69	0.90	0.84	0.39	0.69	10.89
1937	0.84	0.18	0.98	0.57	0.29	2.27	1.38	0.65	2.25	0.38	0.31	1.50	11.60
1938	0.54	0.37	0.94	0.61	3.65	3.36	1.91	1.24	0.72	2.27	0.25	0.23	16.09
1939	0.20	0.70	0.47	0.56	1.59	2.63	0.44	0.48	0.89	1.24	0.05	0.34	9.59
#1940	0.55	0.66	0.65	1.14	1.37	1.46	1.79	T	2.00	0.42	0.36	0.04	10.44
1941	0.25	0.15	0.31	1.74	1.67	2.86	2.29	0.61	2.27	0.88	0.40	0.77	14.20
1942	0.60	0.49	0.51	0.55	2.35	1.96	0.48	0.60	0.66	0.58	0.87	0.29	9.94
1943	1.09	0.38	0.39	1.45	0.67	2.49	0.18	0.89	0.78	0.51	0.23	0.19	9.25
1944	0.03	0.47	0.51	0.55	1.79	4.74	1.42	1.62	0.82	0.04	0.47	0.37	12.83
1945	0.08	0.07	0.90	0.58	1.94	2.79	0.29	0.46	1.46	0.23	0.25	0.60	9.65
1946	0.20	0.21	0.56	0.33	2.40	1.27	1.41	0.48	2.51	1.24	0.89	0.94	12.44
1947	0.34	0.37	1.10	0.81	0.48	4.34	0.95	0.50	3.05	0.55	1.40	0.27	14.16
1948	0.51	0.22	0.49	0.58	2.58	3.40	1.85	1.02	0.31	0.05	0.61	0.80	12.42
1949	0.66	0.59	0.69	0.61	2.18	1.56	0.33	0.66	1.08	0.28	0.15	0.37	9.16
1950	1.05	0.14	0.82	1.25	1.36	2.18	0.72	1.35	0.99	0.43	1.50	0.61	12.40
1951	0.38	0.24	0.84	1.58	1.00	1.61	1.81	1.58	0.81	0.79	0.31	1.08	12.03
1952	0.15	0.56	1.27	0.37	2.16	1.34	0.62	0.66	0.18	0.35	1.05	0.28	8.99
1953	0.51	1.02	0.22	0.83	2.72	1.76	0.14	0.59	0.34	0.13	0.20	0.42	8.88
1954	1.26	0.10	0.46	0.73	1.17	2.15	1.14	1.35	0.65	0.86	0.48	0.13	10.48
1955	0.19	0.20	1.28	1.32	1.02	2.19	2.70	0.24	0.24	0.19	1.22	1.13	11.92
1956	0.64	0.09	0.42	0.67	1.28	1.80	1.04	1.43	0.16	1.02	0.12	0.46	9.13
1957	0.95	0.30	1.19	0.67	3.25	2.23	0.79	1.23	1.85	1.27	0.61	0.31	14.65
1958	0.16	0.95	1.13	0.83	1.34	4.28	1.26	0.59	0.42	0.20	0.74	1.01	12.91
1959	0.43	1.13	0.02	0.35	1.93	1.90	0.11	0.36	0.46	0.95	1.45	0.28	9.37
1960	0.23	0.25	0.22	1.56	0.94	0.25	1.02	2.12	0.13	0.26	0.19	0.34	7.51
1961	0.12	0.06	1.03	0.90	1.36	0.78	1.05	0.62	1.16	0.16	0.37	0.55	8.16
1962	0.67	0.51	0.69	0.90	3.77	2.50	1.27	1.80	0.31	0.95	0.57	0.14	14.08
1963	0.50	0.25	0.44	0.81	1.34	2.59	0.80	0.80	1.10	1.39	0.29	1.27	11.58
1964	0.31	0.27	0.51	1.56	3.52	2.98	0.83	1.91	0.16	0.04	0.53	0.99	13.61
1965	0.36	0.49	0.85	0.98	2.20	3.85	0.60	1.92	3.37	0.13	0.62	0.15	15.52
1966	0.46	0.33	0.28	0.51	0.43	0.96	0.32	0.42	0.34	0.75	1.04	0.62	6.46
1967	0.61	0.62	1.43	2.38	2.08	2.36	0.46	0.58	0.68	1.50	0.31	1.39	14.40
1968	0.59	0.16	0.53	1.21	1.62	2.68	0.26	2.00	2.22	0.23	0.92	0.75	13.17
1969	2.78	0.22	0.57	0.60	1.13	3.50	1.77	0.38	0.33	1.06	0.04	0.31	12.69
1970	0.51	0.67	0.96	0.81	1.20	2.11	0.93	0.63	0.36	0.58	0.44	0.54	9.74
1971	1.38	0.63	0.41	0.58	1.77	0.93	0.56	1.22	0.89	0.39	0.34	1.02	10.12
1972	1.12	0.54	0.63	0.41	0.77	1.12	0.56	1.63	0.08	0.57	0.33	0.46	8.22
1973	0.22	0.13	0.05	0.66	1.08	0.73	0.08	0.56	0.43	0.66	1.03	0.63	6.26
1974	0.66	0.23	0.38	0.76	2.07	0.34	0.49	4.23	0.22	0.51	0.30	0.26	10.45
1975	1.26	0.72	0.88	3.00	1.95	2.83	3.89	2.47	0.47	2.68	0.48	0.31	20.94
RECORD MEAN	0.74	0.53	0.73	0.99	1.90	2.23	1.07	0.91	1.09	0.79	0.64	0.64	12.26

Record mean values above are means through the current year for the period beginning in 1881 for temperature and precipitation, 1941 for snowfall. Data are from City Office locations through 1940 and from Airport locations thereafter.

Station: NORTH PLATTE, NEBRASKA
LEE BIRD FIELD
Elevation (ground): 2775 feet

TEMPERATURES °F

Month	Normal: Daily maximum	Normal: Daily minimum	Normal: Monthly	Extremes: Record highest	Year	Record lowest	Year
(a)				11		11	
J	36.6	10.1	23.4	68	1967	-23	1974
F	40.9	15.2	28.1	76	1972	-14	1975
M	47.2	21.3	34.3	86	1968	-6	1965
A	61.4	34.2	47.8	90	1965	7	1975
M	71.4	45.2	58.3	96	1967	21	1967
J	80.6	55.3	68.0	100	1974	29	1969
J	87.6	61.0	74.3	105	1973	41	1971
A	86.7	59.3	73.0	103	1970	38	1974
S	77.0	47.6	62.3	100	1971	22	1974
O	67.0	35.0	51.0	91	1968	11	1969
N	50.5	21.8	36.2	77	1965	-8	1975
D	39.8	13.8	26.8	74	1964	-25	1967
YR	62.2	35.0	48.6	105	JUL 1973	-25	DEC 1967

IMPORTANT:
The time-period covered by this record is limited: See footnotes following table of **NORMALS, MEANS AND EXTREMES** for explanation and for additional history of **EXTREME HIGHS AND LOWS** recorded in the general area.

Snowfall

Season	July	Aug	Sept	Oct	Nov	Dec	Jan
1936-37	0.0	0.0	0.0	3.0	0.3	4.2	7.7
1937-38	0.0	0.0	0.0	T	0.6	3.3	1.1
1938-39	0.0	0.0	0.0	T	2.0	1.8	4.1
1939-40	0.0	0.0	0.0	T	T	7.9	5.6
1940-41	0.0	0.0	0.0	0.0	2.3	5.3	2.9
1941-42	0.0	0.0	0.0	0.0	0.2	5.1	2.0
1942-43	0.0	0.0	0.0	T	1.7	0.9	3.1
1943-44	0.0	0.0	0.0	1.0	0.2	0.6	5.2
1944-45	0.0	0.0	0.0	0.0	4.0	3.9	5.4
1945-46	0.0	0.0	1.0	T	0.4	9.9	1.0
1946-47	0.0	0.0	0.0	0.3	7.9	1.6	4.9
1947-48	0.0	0.0	0.0	0.0	5.2	8.6	1.3
#1948-49	0.0	0.0	0.0	T	4.6	9.4	21.2
1949-50	0.0	0.0	0.0	T	T	2.4	3.5
1950-51	0.0	0.0	0.0	0.0	4.1	2.7	2.1
#1951-52	0.0	0.0	0.0	2.0	3.2	6.3	3.0
1952-53	0.0	0.0	0.0	T	4.4	2.9	1.2
1953-54	0.0	0.0	0.0	0.0	9.1	5.7	1.8
1954-55	0.0	0.0	0.0	T	0.8	1.5	10.4
1955-56	0.0	0.0	0.0	T	4.9	6.5	5.2
1956-57	0.0	0.0	0.0	0.5	5.2	1.3	2.8
1957-58	0.0	0.0	0.0	0.9	3.0	6.4	2.2
•1958-59	0.0	0.0	0.0	0.7	5.8	4.7	5.2
1959-60	0.0	0.0	0.0	7.3	0.7	0.3	12.4
1960-61	0.0	0.0	0.0	T	2.9	4.4	T
1961-62	0.0	0.0	T	0.0	4.0	7.3	1.7
1962-63	0.0	0.0	0.0	0.0	1.5	6.1	8.7
1963-64	0.0	0.0	0.0	0.0	T	5.3	T
1964-65	0.0	0.0	0.0	0.0	T	1.8	9.2
1965-66	0.0	0.0	T	0.0	0.5	6.3	10.5
1966-67	0.0	0.0	0.0	1.4	0.5	8.5	9.3
1967-68	0.0	0.0	0.0	T	2.9	3.4	1.6
1968-69	0.0	0.0	0.0	0.0	0.3	10.3	12.4
1969-70	0.0	0.0	0.0	15.7	0.8	1.8	3.6
1970-71	0.0	0.0	0.0	9.0	3.6	1.8	5.6
1971-72	0.0	0.0	0.0	2.0	2.5	2.1	2.6
1972-73	0.0	0.0	0.0	0.8	8.0	8.7	3.8
1973-74	0.0	0.0	0.0	T	4.3	14.1	4.2
1974-75	0.0	0.0	0.0	0.0	T	4.5	2.2
1975-76	0.0	0.0	0.0	0.8	10.9	1.2	
RECORD MEAN	0.0	0.0	T	1.6	3.2	4.9	5.1

Heating Degree Days

Season	July	Aug	Sept	Oct	Nov	Dec	Jan
1955-56	0	4	152	437	1063	1354	1288
1956-57	0	31	120	315	891	1040	1512
1957-58	0	0	182	482	882	968	1175
1958-59	3	6	110	416	840	1183	1292
1959-60	6	1	198	594	1034	1000	1400
1960-61	0	4	124	389	844	1162	1182
1961-62	0	0	278	479	926	1312	1333
1962-63	3	4	171	363	755	1152	1607
1963-64	0	1	65	219	780	1329	1140
#1964-65	0	43	143	450	870	1229	1189
1965-66	0	11	345	335	718	1113	1530
1966-67	0	34	135	442	863	1250	1240
1967-68	19	29	132	479	926	1305	1321
1968-69	17	18	150	428	911	1421	1509
1969-70	1	0	45	716	795	1129	1315
1970-71	2	1	214	600	899	1177	1320
1971-72	12	0	210	472	829	1157	1368
1972-73	24	15	169	567	1047	1479	1343
1973-74	10	0	219	407	892	1290	1518
1974-75	0	40	256	373	900	1262	1216
1975-76	6	0	228	437	1035	1191	

Cooling Degree Days

Year	Jan	Feb	Mar	Apr	May	June	July
1969	0	0	0	0	58	63	257
1970	0	0	0	4	48	155	300
1971	0	0	0	0	1	177	167
1972	0	0	0	0	43	137	199
1973	0	0	0	0	11	121	260
1974	0	0	0	5	24	117	394
1975	0	0	0	10	11	89	311

The climate of North Platte is characterized throughout the year by frequent and rapid changes in the weather. During the winter, most of the North Pacific Lows cross the country to the north. The passage usually brings little or no snowfall, and only a moderate drop in temperature. Generally only when there is a major outbreak of cold air from western Canada does the temperature fall to zero or below. The duration of below-zero minimum temperature is hardly ever more than two mornings, and by the third or fourth day the temperature is ordinarily rising to the forties or higher. Snowfall at the onset of a cold outbreak is usually less than 2 inches. Only when a low moved from the middle Rockies slowly through Nebraska, allowing continuing easterly winds long enough to draw moist air from the southeast into the low circulation, do snowfalls of any appreciable amount occur. Few of these storms move slowly enough, or are intense enough to deposit much precipitation in the North Platte area. However, during some winters the cold outbreak and the intense low from the mid-Rockies combine to produce severe cold and snow several inches in depth, with blizzard conditions following. During and after these snowfalls and blizzards, rail and highway traffic may be stalled until the snow is cleared. Widespread loss of unsheltered liverstock resulted from a series of such conditions in January 1949.

The sudden and frequent weather changes of the winter continue through spring with decreasing

(Continued page 528)

Feb	Mar	Apr	May	June	Total
4.8	4.1	4.0	0.0	0.0	28.1
3.6	0.7	3.3	T	0.0	12.6
2.1	9.5	2.4	0.0	0.0	21.9
3.0	3.4	1.0	0.0	0.0	20.9
4.6	5.7	0.8	0.0	0.0	21.6
15.3	6.2	0.0	T	0.0	28.8
0.9	7.0	T	0.0	0.0	13.6
7.4	10.1	4.2	0.0	0.0	28.7
3.3	3.5	7.4	T	0.0	27.5
1.0	11.5	0.3	T	0.0	25.1
2.8	3.1	5.4	0.5	0.0	26.5
5.2	8.2	0.0	0.0	0.0	28.5
2.0	19.9	0.5	0.0	0.0	57.6
7.1	9.0	2.4	6.0	0.0	30.4
1.6	0.7	T	0.0	0.0	11.2
9.1	8.3	0.7	0.0	0.0	32.6
7.7	3.9	1.0	T	0.0	21.1
0.3	7.9	0.1	2.1	0.0	27.0
15.7	5.2	T	0.0	0.0	33.6
3.0	2.8	9.9	T	0.0	32.3
2.0	7.2	13.1	0.0	0.0	32.1
15.5	16.9	3.5	0.0	0.0	48.4
9.3	10.2	1.4	0.0	0.0	37.3
7.3	10.6	2.2	0.0	0.0	40.8
0.7	20.0	13.0	0.0	0.0	41.0
10.7	7.1	T	0.0	0.0	30.8
0.9	9.5	0.2	0.0	0.0	26.9
8.6	5.4	5.6	0.0	0.0	24.9
7.2	5.0	T	0.0	0.0	23.2
1.7	9.6	5.0	0.2	0.0	33.8
0.8	0.7	4.5	3.6	0.0	29.3
3.0	0.8	2.2	0.0	0.0	13.9
3.2	1.8	T	T	0.0	28.0
4.0	18.4	0.4	0.0	0.0	44.7
2.7	19.0	0.8	T	0.0	42.5
1.9	0.1	0.1	0.0	0.0	11.3
0.4	1.6	1.7	0.0	0.0	25.0
1.0	2.3	0.7	0.0	0.0	-26.6
2.6	3.9	3.0	0.0	0.0	16.2
5.0	7.4	2.9	0.2	0.0	30.3

Average Temperature

Year	Jan	Feb	Mar	Apr	May	June	July	Aug	Sept	Oct	Nov	Dec	Annual
1936	21.7	11.4	40.2	47.2	63.8	73.0	82.8	78.7	67.9	49.5	38.6	30.8	50.5
1937	10.2	26.5	35.4	48.4	62.8	68.2	79.0	79.6	66.8	52.0	36.6	28.0	49.5
1938	30.2	30.9	43.3	50.2	58.8	71.0	77.1	78.2	67.7	58.7	35.3	30.0	52.6
1939	32.6	23.6	40.5	49.2	65.2	69.6	79.6	73.4	68.8	53.0	40.9	35.0	52.6
1940	13.4	30.8	39.0	48.4	60.5	72.1	79.6	73.4	69.2	57.2	34.8	30.8	50.8
1941	27.8	30.2	35.5	50.6	64.6	69.0	75.1	75.1	64.8	52.0	41.0	31.0	51.4
1942	26.0	24.6	37.9	53.4	57.2	67.9	76.6	73.8	60.8	52.7	39.0	31.2	50.1
1943	25.9	36.8	32.8	53.4	55.7	68.8	77.7	77.8	63.0	51.8	38.9	31.2	51.2
1944	29.2	26.6	31.0	44.4	63.0	69.0	73.6	74.6	64.1	54.2	37.6	27.7	49.6
1945	29.7	31.6	43.6	45.8	56.2	62.2	74.6	73.4	61.6	54.8	40.4	22.0	49.7
1946	31.7	36.6	45.0	56.7	55.0	70.4	76.9	72.0	64.5	49.6	36.1	32.6	52.3
1947	30.0	26.6	34.8	47.1	57.0	64.6	74.2	79.2	66.4	59.6	34.0	26.9	50.2
#1948	26.8	28.0	32.0	56.2	61.0	68.0	74.9	73.9	68.0	52.0	36.2	27.4	50.4
1949	10.6	23.0	35.4	49.3	61.2	69.0	75.3	72.8	60.9	50.4	45.1	28.6	48.5
1950	18.7	31.4	32.6	43.1	55.9	68.4	69.6	68.3	61.5	55.8	34.3	30.5	47.5
#1951	24.5	31.6	31.6	44.0	58.2	61.8	70.7	71.4	58.9	48.2	34.7	21.3	46.4
1952	27.9	31.5	30.8	47.4	58.1	75.0	74.8	73.9	64.9	47.9	31.0	25.5	49.1
1953	32.6	29.6	40.2	43.1	56.6	72.8	75.2	73.6	64.0	54.2	37.5	27.7	50.6
1954	24.5	40.3	32.2	51.1	54.5	71.3	79.4	73.6	66.4	48.8	40.3	30.5	51.1
1955	20.3	20.0	34.1	52.8	61.6	63.7	79.3	77.0	64.0	50.8	29.3	21.2	47.8
1956	23.3	25.3	37.1	41.9	60.2	74.0	73.2	71.6	63.5	55.0	35.1	31.2	49.3
1957	16.1	32.5	34.7	44.3	55.6	66.2	76.5	74.2	59.2	49.4	35.3	33.7	48.1
1958	26.9	25.3	23.7	45.0	61.3	66.8	71.0	73.7	64.5	51.3	36.8	26.6	47.7
1959	23.2	24.2	36.6	46.4	58.0	72.5	71.8	75.3	60.6	45.7	30.3	32.6	48.1
1960	19.6	19.7	28.0	49.7	57.5	66.5	74.2	74.1	65.2	52.3	36.7	27.3	47.6
1961	26.6	32.2	37.9	42.8	55.2	69.0	73.4	74.8	57.5	49.3	33.9	22.5	47.9
1962	21.9	26.9	32.0	49.6	63.9	66.8	72.0	72.7	60.2	53.2	39.7	27.6	48.9
1963	13.1	32.3	40.8	50.8	60.5	72.9	77.5	73.4	65.9	58.1	38.8	21.9	50.5
#1964	28.1	24.9	32.3	47.0	60.9	67.2	77.5	69.8	63.1	50.3	35.8	25.2	48.5
1965	26.3	23.4	25.5	51.4	60.1	67.1	73.1	70.5	53.8	54.0	40.9	28.9	47.9
1966	15.6	21.4	38.5	43.8	60.0	68.8	77.6	67.8	62.1	50.5	36.0	24.5	47.2
1967	24.9	30.8	39.9	49.3	51.9	64.6	70.3	68.8	61.2	49.8	33.9	22.8	47.3
1968	22.2	27.1	39.9	46.2	53.3	69.5	72.6	71.6	61.1	51.1	34.4	19.0	47.4
1969	16.2	24.2	29.0	51.4	61.0	62.8	73.0	73.6	65.8	41.7	38.3	28.4	47.1
1970	22.3	31.8	31.3	45.6	61.9	68.1	74.3	75.6	60.8	45.4	34.8	26.8	48.2
1971	22.1	24.5	33.4	48.0	54.7	70.2	69.8	72.2	59.7	49.5	37.1	27.6	47.4
1972	20.7	29.9	40.7	46.6	58.1	68.4	70.4	70.8	61.2	46.4	29.8	17.2	46.7
1973	21.5	30.3	40.4	45.8	56.0	67.7	72.8	73.7	58.4	51.7	35.0	23.2	48.0
1974	16.0	33.0	40.1	50.0	59.5	66.5	77.5	67.1	57.5	52.9	34.8	24.2	48.3
1975	25.7	23.4	31.5	46.6	57.1	65.7	74.6	73.2	58.5	50.9	30.2	26.4	47.0
RECORD MEAN	23.6	27.8	36.3	48.6	58.8	68.6	74.7	73.0	63.4	51.4	36.9	27.3	49.2
MAX	35.9	40.2	49.1	61.6	71.1	80.9	87.5	86.1	77.4	66.2	50.3	39.4	62.1
MIN	11.2	15.3	23.4	35.6	46.4	56.2	61.9	59.9	49.3	36.5	23.4	15.1	36.2

# Indicates a station move or relocation of instruments.

NORTH PLATTE, NE

Feb	Mar	Apr	May	June	Total
1147	855	687	183	5	7175
903	935	615	290	50	6702
1106	1272	594	137	56	6854
1137	871	550	224	22	6654
1310	1143	457	242	48	7433
914	833	660	314	37	6463
1062	1017	463	90	57	7017
911	745	423	165	10	6309
1157	1006	534	190	63	6484
1158	1217	405	173	26	6903
1213	815	628	199	48	6955
950	771	465	427	70	6648
1096	770	558	363	26	7024
1133	1106	399	178	122	7392
923	1041	582	136	55	6738
1127	974	501	311	13	7139
1013	745	549	250	32	6637
967	756	567	283	34	7251
889	765	445	190	62	6687
1160	1032	558	247	62	7106

Aug	Sept	Oct	Nov	Dec	Total
276	76	0	0	0	730
341	96	0	0	0	944
229	59	1	0	0	634
202	64	0	0	0	645
278	29	3	0	0	702
115	40	3	0	0	698
260	39	7	0	0	727

Precipitation

Year	Jan	Feb	Mar	Apr	May	June	July	Aug	Sept	Oct	Nov	Dec	Annual
1936	0.48	0.40	0.57	1.59	3.17	1.64	0.96	1.23	0.35	0.41	0.03	0.43	11.26
1937	0.62	0.30	1.09	1.09	0.64	3.15	2.21	0.76	0.89	1.27	0.06	0.29	12.37
1938	0.07	0.25	0.79	3.60	3.70	2.62	3.15	1.80	5.41	0.03	0.23	0.16	21.81
1939	0.70	0.15	0.88	1.26	2.51	3.51	0.35	1.17	0.20	0.56	T	0.64	11.93
1940	0.31	0.23	1.12	0.88	0.66	2.84	0.66	0.71	0.88	1.56	0.45	0.68	10.98
1941	0.30	0.36	0.65	3.64	1.55	2.30	5.35	0.81	3.31	1.07	0.23	0.42	19.99
1942	0.25	1.32	1.41	6.83	3.70	5.06	1.82	1.40	7.54	0.01	0.25	0.15	29.74
1943	0.21	0.08	0.50	2.33	2.04	3.45	2.10	1.79	0.21	1.35	0.24	0.04	14.34
1944	1.84	0.70	0.98	3.61	2.60	2.56	3.67	0.78	0.13	0.30	1.08	0.24	18.49
1945	0.41	0.29	0.29	2.01	2.43	4.10	2.92	3.90	3.40	0.03	0.10	0.83	20.71
1946	0.07	0.07	2.29	0.63	3.63	2.34	1.11	1.13	2.21	5.80	1.28	0.18	20.74
1947	0.36	0.18	0.34	1.94	2.40	4.87	2.67	1.05	1.77	0.45	1.60	0.84	18.47
#1948	0.08	0.37	0.60	0.08	2.37	2.28	3.12	4.25	0.89	0.27	0.70	0.82	15.83
1949	2.19	0.15	4.37	1.15	5.10	3.84	3.74	0.95	1.97	1.42	0.76	0.45	26.09
1950	0.31	0.65	0.86	1.43	3.86	1.17	4.56	7.16	1.83	0.17	0.61	0.19	22.80
#1951	0.20	1.41	0.23	2.18	7.11	10.47	5.47	2.28	2.13	1.02	0.32	0.62	33.44
1952	0.74	0.80	0.98	1.20	3.20	0.33	1.53	4.03	0.67	0.24	0.40	0.24	14.36
1953	0.08	1.15	0.77	1.39	0.98	2.05	1.80	2.16	T	1.65	1.10	0.52	13.65
1954	0.10	0.01	0.60	0.12	2.13	1.57	1.59	2.06	0.94	1.18	0.06	0.10	10.46
1955	0.84	1.17	0.36	2.22	4.70	5.02	0.42	0.32	1.51	0.08	0.78	0.68	18.10
1956	0.47	0.22	0.24	1.60	1.20	5.25	3.16	2.04	0.03	1.79	0.78	0.12	16.90
1957	0.14	0.29	1.27	3.07	7.21	3.59	3.20	5.36	2.68	1.45	0.96	0.50	29.72
1958	0.13	1.51	1.35	2.28	3.42	1.72	5.83	2.06	1.91	0.35	0.90	0.31	21.77
1959	0.31	0.59	2.61	1.35	3.51	3.91	1.27	2.43	1.89	2.12	0.15	0.23	20.37
1960	1.12	1.28	0.92	1.77	2.29	4.05	1.33	1.14	0.35	0.26	0.32	0.49	15.32
1961	T	0.07	2.24	2.49	5.15	2.58	1.23	1.08	2.78	0.15	0.50	0.44	18.71
1962	0.07	0.72	1.15	0.51	8.01	5.30	5.33	0.10	2.38	0.43	0.09	0.66	24.75
1963	0.48	0.15	0.71	1.09	3.98	1.82	1.60	2.18	6.03	0.67	0.39	0.24	19.34
1964	T	0.62	1.26	3.76	2.06	4.78	4.52	2.63	1.02	0.17	0.04	0.10	20.96
1965	0.61	0.35	0.25	1.42	4.18	6.81	6.68	1.82	5.69	0.73	0.05	1.02	29.61
1966	0.30	0.15	1.12	1.05	0.77	5.14	3.35	2.74	2.09	0.31	0.04	0.51	17.57
1967	0.47	0.03	0.09	1.03	3.94	6.05	3.74	0.06	1.12	0.58	0.19	0.15	17.45
1968	0.12	0.36	0.11	3.04	1.72	2.25	1.82	3.97	0.82	1.50	0.46	0.87	17.04
1969	0.94	0.26	0.17	0.15	1.35	4.20	2.52	1.61	0.80	2.91	0.18	0.10	15.19
1970	0.23	0.28	0.97	2.46	1.31	4.33	1.68	0.28	2.27	1.27	0.91	0.22	16.21
1971	0.47	1.28	0.97	3.94	2.54	5.84	3.48	0.91	2.01	1.75	0.90	0.16	24.25
1972	0.16	0.08	0.65	1.19	3.18	2.96	3.58	0.95	1.46	0.62	1.12	0.42	16.37
1973	0.40	0.10	2.45	1.45	3.85	0.88	2.87	2.82	3.98	1.26	0.54	1.13	21.73
1974	0.27	0.08	0.42	1.17	1.64	3.86	2.27	1.15	0.24	0.61	0.04	0.42	12.17
1975	0.26	0.17	0.92	1.77	2.12	6.12	2.51	0.25	0.56	0.14	1.15	0.22	16.19
RECORD MEAN	0.40	0.48	0.89	2.04	2.89	3.32	2.69	2.20	1.61	1.03	0.49	0.50	18.54

Record mean values above are means through the current year for the period beginning in 1875 for temperature and precipitation, 1953 for snowfall. Data are from City Office locations through 1948 and from Airport locations thereafter.

(Continued)

intensity of temperature changes but increasing precipitation. The summer and fall months experience frequent changes from hot to cool weather. Most summer and fall precipitation is associated with thunderstorm activity, so the amounts are extremely variable. The surrounding area is frequently damaged by locally severe hailstorms, one of these having caused a million dollars worth of damage in the city of North Platte in August 1950.

Summer temperatures may run in the upper nineties and lower hundreds many days during the summer months, but the elevation and good radiation brings rapid cooling after nightfall to lows generally in the sixties or below by daybreak. Since the humidity is generally low, the extremely hot days of the summer are not uncomfortable.

Normals, Means, and Extremes

Month	Normal Degree days Base 65 °F: Heating	Cooling	Precipitation in inches, Water equivalent: Normal	Maximum monthly	Year	Minimum monthly	Year	Maximum in 24 hrs.	Year	Snow, Ice pellets: Maximum monthly	Year	Maximum in 24 hrs.	Year	Relative humidity pct. Hour 00 (Local time)	Hour 06	Hour 12	Hour 18
(a)				24		24		24		24		24		11	11	11	11
J	1290	0	0.45	1.12	1960	T	1964	0.69	1960	12.4	1969	9.0	1965	77	78	64	64
F	1033	0	0.52	1.51	1958	0.01	1954	1.15	1971	15.7	1955	9.7	1955	76	78	59	56
M	952	0	0.99	2.61	1959	0.09	1967	2.26	1959	20.0	1961	9.7	1971	72	78	52	48
A	522	6	1.93	3.94	1971	0.12	1954	2.42	1971	13.1	1957	7.7	1961	72	79	47	43
M	238	30	3.26	8.01	1962	0.77	1966	2.95	1962	3.6	1967	2.3	1967	72	82	48	46
J	65	155	3.77	6.81	1965	0.33	1952	3.80	1965	0.0		0.0		76	85	53	49
J	7	295	2.98	6.68	1965	0.42	1955	3.15	1964	0.0		0.0		75	84	52	49
A	8	256	2.07	5.36	1957	0.06	1967	2.93	1957	0.0		0.0		74	84	50	46
S	141	60	2.01	6.03	1963	T	1953	2.53	1963	T	1965	T	1965	76	83	50	47
O	439	0	0.99	2.91	1969	0.08	1955	1.37	1953	15.7	1969	8.8	1969	73	80	46	47
N	864	0	0.52	1.15	1975	0.04	1974	0.92	1975	10.9	1975	6.5	1975	77	81	56	59
D	1184	0	0.41	1.13	1973	0.10	1969	0.70	1968	14.1	1973	8.6	1968	78	81	63	65
YR	6743	802	19.90	8.01	MAY 1962	T	JAN 1964	3.80	JUN 1965	20.0	MAR 1961	9.7	MAR 1971	75	81	53	51

(To better understand these tables, see full explanation of terms beginning on page 322)

Month	Wind: Mean speed m.p.h.	Prevailing direction	Fastest mile: Speed m.p.h.	Direction	Year	Pct. of possible sunshine	Mean sky cover, tenths, sunrise to sunset	Mean number of days, Sunrise to sunset: Clear	Partly cloudy	Cloudy	Precipitation .01 inch or more	Snow, Ice pellets 1.0 inch or more	Thunderstorms	Heavy fog, visibility ¼ mile or less	Temperatures °F Max. (b) 90° and above	32° and below	Min. 32° and below	0° and below	Average station pressure mb. Elev. 2787 feet m.s.l.
(a)	23	12	24	24		23	23	23	23	23	23	23	23	23	11	11	11	11	3
J	9.3	NW	52	NW	1962	60	6.3	8	9	14	5	2	0	1	0	13	31	9	917.4
F	10.1	NW	68	N	1953	57	6.4	7	7	14	5	2	*	2	0	8	28	2	918.1
M	11.8	N	67	NW	1956	59	6.5	8	7	16	7	2	1	2	0	5	28	1	913.6
A	12.9	N	69	SE	1975	62	6.3	7	9	14	8	1	3	1	*	*	13	0	913.8
M	12.1	SE	70	S	1955	62	6.3	7	10	14	10	*	7	1	1	*	3	0	914.3
J	10.8	SE	72	N	1960	69	5.1	10	12	8	10	0	11	1	5	0	*	0	915.3
J	9.6	SE	66	SE	1969	75	4.5	13	12	6	10	0	11	1	12	0	0	0	918.3
A	9.5	SSE	56	SW	1952	73	4.6	13	11	7	7	0	8	2	11	0	0	0	917.8
S	9.9	SSE	53	N	1953	69	4.7	13	9	8	6	0	4	2	3	0	3	0	920.1
O	9.6	SSE	72	SW	1956	70	4.6	14	8	9	5	*	1	2	*	*	15	0	918.7
N	9.6	NW	64	NW	1959	60	5.8	9	9	12	4	1	*	2	0	3	28	1	917.8
D	9.1	NW	59	NW	1959	59	5.9	9	8	14	4	1	0	2	0	11	31	5	917.7
YR	10.4	NW	72	N	JUN 1960	65	5.6	118	111	136	83	10	48	19	31	42	180	17	916.9

FOOTNOTES

Means and extremes above are from existing and comparable exposures. Annual extremes have been exceeded at other sites in the locality as follows: Highest temperature 112 in July 1954; lowest temperature -35 in February 1899 and earlier; maximum monthly precipitation 10.47 in June 1951; maximum precipitation in 24 hours 6.23 in September 1942; maximum monthly snowfall 27.8 in March 1912; maximum snowfall in 24 hours 13.0 in March 1949 and earlier.

Station: OMAHA, NEBRASKA
EPPLEY AIRFIELD

Elevation (ground): 977 feet

TEMPERATURES °F

Month	Normal			Extremes			
	Daily maximum	Daily minimum	Monthly	Record highest	Year	Record lowest	Year
(a)				12		12	
J	32.7	12.4	22.6	64	1964	-22	1974
F	38.5	17.4	28.0	78	1972	-19	1975
M	47.7	26.4	37.1	89	1968	-1	1975
A	64.4	40.1	52.3	93	1965	5	1975
M	74.4	51.5	63.0	97	1967	31	1967
J	83.1	61.3	72.2	103	1974	40	1969
J	88.6	65.8	77.2	110	1974	44	1972
A	87.2	64.0	75.6	107	1964	43	1967
S	78.6	54.0	66.3	103	1975	31	1974
O	69.1	42.6	55.9	95	1975	13	1972
N	50.9	29.1	40.0	80	1964	-9	1964
D	37.8	18.1	28.0	67	1973	-13	1968
YR	62.8	40.2	51.5	110	JUL 1974	-22	JAN 1974

IMPORTANT:
The time-period covered by this record is limited: See footnotes on next page for explanation and for additional history of EXTREME HIGHS AND LOWS recorded in the general area.

Omaha, Nebraska, is situated on the west bank of the Missouri River. The river level at Omaha is normally about 965 feet above sea level and the rolling hills in and around Omaha rise to about 1,300 feet above sea level. The climate is typical continental with relatively warm summers and cold, dry winters. It is situated midway between two distinctive climatic zones, the humid east and the dry west. Fluctuations between these two zones produce weather conditions for periods that are characteristic of either zone, or combinations of both. Omaha is also affected by most storms or "lows" that cross the country. This causes periodic and rapid changes in weather, especially during the winter months.

Most of the precipitation in Omaha falls during sharp showers or thunderstorms, and these occur mostly during the growing season, April to September. Of the total precipitation, about 75 percent falls during the 6-month period, April to September, mostly as evening or nighttime showers and thunderstorms. Although winters are relatively cold, precipitation is light, with only 10 percent of the total annual precipitation falling during the winter months.

Sunshine is fairly abundant, ranging around 50 percent of the possible in the winter to 75 percent of the possible in the summer.

The average date for the last occurrence in the spring of temperatures as low as 32° F. is April 14, and for the first occurrence of 32° F. or lower in autumn is October 20. The longest freeze free period on record is 219 days in 1924, and the shortest period 152 days in 1885. The average length of the freeze free period is 188 days.

OMAHA, NEBRASKA

Normals, Means, and Extremes

(To better understand these tables, see full explanation of terms beginning on page 322)

Month	Normal Degree days Base 65 °F: Heating	Cooling	Precipitation in inches — Water equivalent: Normal	Maximum monthly	Year	Minimum monthly	Year	Maximum in 24 hrs.	Year	Snow, Ice pellets: Maximum monthly	Year	Maximum in 24 hrs.	Year
(a)				40		40		40		40		40	
J	1314	0	0.76	3.70	1949	0.05	1943	1.52	1967	25.7	1936	13.1	1949
F	1036	0	0.98	2.97	1965	0.10	1968	2.24	1954	25.4	1965	18.3	1965
M	865	0	1.59	5.96	1973	0.12	1956	1.45	1959	27.2	1948	13.0	1948
A	391	10	2.97	6.45	1951	0.23	1936	2.56	1938	8.6	1945	8.6	1945
M	148	86	4.11	10.33	1959	0.56	1948	3.58	1964	2.0	1945	2.0	1945
J	20	236	4.94	10.81	1947	1.03	1972	3.48	1942	0.0		0.0	
J	0	378	3.71	9.60	1958	0.46	1975	3.37	1958	0.0		0.0	
A	6	334	3.97	9.12	1959	0.73	1941	3.40	1959	0.0		0.0	
S	71	110	3.27	13.75	1965	0.41	1953	6.47	1965	T	1961	T	1961
O	301	19	1.93	4.99	1961	T	1952	3.13	1968	7.2	1941	7.2	1941
N	750	0	1.11	4.05	1948	0.04	1955	2.53	1948	12.0	1957	8.7	1957
D	1147	0	0.84	3.30	1941	T	1943	1.79	1941	19.9	1969	10.2	1969
YR	6049	1173	30.18	13.75	SEP 1965	T	OCT 1952	6.47	SEP 1965	27.2	MAR 1948	18.3	FEB 1965

Month	Relative humidity pct. Hour 00 (Local time)	Hour 06	Hour 12	Hour 18	Wind: Mean speed m.p.h.	Prevailing direction	Fastest mile: Speed m.p.h.	Direction	Year	Pct. of possible sunshine	Mean sky cover, tenths, sunrise to sunset	Mean number of days — Sunrise to sunset: Clear	Partly cloudy	Cloudy	Precipitation .01 inch or more	Snow, Ice pellets 1.0 inch or more	Thunderstorms	Heavy fog, visibility ¼ mile or less	Temperatures °F Max. (b) 90° and above	Max. 32° and below	Min. 32° and below	Min. 0° and below	Average station pressure mb. Elev. 982 feet m.s.l.
(a)	12	12	12	12	40	15	40	40		40	40	40	40	40	40	40	40	40	12	12	12	12	3
J	74	76	66	68	11.1	NNW	57	NW	1938	55	6.1	9	8	14	7	3	*	2	0	14	30	8	982.2
F	74	77	62	62	11.5	NNW	57	NW	1947	55	6.3	7	8	13	7	2	*	2	0	10	27	3	982.4
M	71	76	57	54	12.7	NNW	73	NW	1950	55	6.6	7	8	16	9	2	1	1	0	4	22	*	977.8
A	68	76	53	48	13.2	NNW	65	NW	1937	59	6.4	7	9	14	9	*	4	1	*	*	6	0	977.4
M	71	79	54	50	11.4	SSE	73	NW	1936	62	6.2	7	10	14	12	*	8	1	2	0	*	0	976.2
J	75	81	56	53	10.5	SSE	72	N	1942	68	5.6	8	11	11	11	0	10	*	8	0	0	0	976.6
J	77	82	56	55	9.1	SSE	109	N	1936	76	4.7	12	12	7	9	0	8	1	14	0	0	0	979.7
A	80	86	59	57	9.2	SSE	66	N	1944	72	4.7	13	10	8	9	0	8	1	9	0	0	0	980.0
S	83	88	61	61	9.7	SSE	47	E	1948	67	4.8	13	7	10	8	0	5	1	2	0	*	0	982.3
O	76	82	55	57	10.1	SSE	62	NW	1966	67	4.7	13	8	10	6	*	3	2	*	0	5	0	982.0
N	77	81	63	66	11.2	SSE	56	NW	1951	52	6.0	9	7	14	5	1	1	2	0	2	19	*	980.9
D	78	80	68	71	10.8	SSE	52	NW	1938	48	6.4	8	7	16	7	2	*	2	0	10	29	2	981.8
YR	75	80	59	59	10.9	SSE	109	N	JUL 1936	62	5.7	113	105	147	100	10	48	15	36	41	138	13	979.9

FOOTNOTES

Means and extremes above are from existing and comparable exposures. Annual extremes have been exceeded at other sites in the locality as follows: Highest temperature 114 in July 1936; lowest temperature -32 in January 1884; maximum precipitation in 24 hours 7.03 in August 1903; maximum monthly snowfall 29.2 in March 1912.

Snowfall

Season	July	Aug	Sept	Oct	Nov	Dec	Jan
1936-37	0.0	0.0	0.0	0.0	0.1	6.3	14.1
1937-38	0.0	0.0	0.0	T	1.7	0.8	8.7
1938-39	0.0	0.0	0.0	0.0	0.3	0.6	4.4
1939-40	0.0	0.0	0.0	T	T	8.4	10.8
1940-41	0.0	0.0	0.0	0.0	2.0	11.0	12.2
1941-42	0.0	0.0	0.0	7.2	2.5	10.8	6.4
1942-43	0.0	0.0	0.0	0.0	1.0	7.0	1.3
1943-44	0.0	0.0	0.0	0.0	1.0	T	0.1
1944-45	0.0	0.0	0.0	0.0	5.0	4.9	8.1
1945-46	0.0	0.0	0.0	0.0	0.2	12.0	4.0
1946-47	0.0	0.0	0.0	0.0	1.8	2.3	10.6
1947-48	0.0	0.0	0.0	0.0	7.9	2.2	7.5
1948-49	0.0	0.0	0.0	0.0	2.0	12.4	17.5
1949-50	0.0	0.0	0.0	T	T	1.2	10.0
1950-51	0.0	0.0	0.0	0.0	0.9	1.6	6.1
1951-52	0.0	0.0	0.0	0.0	1.1	16.7	4.1
1952-53	0.0	0.0	0.0	0.0	8.3	8.6	7.3
1953-54	0.0	0.0	0.0	0.0	T	0.4	2.8
1954-55	0.0	0.0	0.0	T	T	0.7	7.9
1955-56	0.0	0.0	0.0	0.0	0.5	0.9	8.5
1956-57	0.0	0.0	0.0	0.0	5.2	2.5	6.8
1957-58	0.0	0.0	0.0	T	12.0	5.5	8.8
1958-59	0.0	0.0	0.0	0.0	1.0	1.5	6.0
1959-60	0.0	0.0	0.0	0.0	1.5	5.1	14.0
1960-61	0.0	0.0	0.0	0.0	T	1.1	4.7
1961-62	0.0	0.0	T	0.0	4.0	19.6	5.0
1962-63	0.0	0.0	0.0	T	0.8	8.1	14.5
1963-64	0.0	0.0	0.0	0.0	0.0	6.6	4.9
1964-65	0.0	0.0	0.0	0.0	2.6	5.4	6.8
1965-66	0.0	0.0	0.0	0.0	0.1	1.7	2.8
1966-67	0.0	0.0	0.0	T	0.1	6.8	7.2
1967-68	0.0	0.0	0.0	1.5	T	5.7	4.6
1968-69	0.0	0.0	0.0	0.0	4.7	8.6	8.3
1969-70	0.0	0.0	0.0	T	0.5	19.9	3.2
1970-71	0.0	0.0	0.0	3.5	T	0.5	13.1
1971-72	0.0	0.0	0.0	0.0	9.0	4.4	1.9
1972-73	0.0	0.0	0.0	T	9.7	5.9	15.8
1973-74	0.0	0.0	0.0	0.0	4.1	10.7	11.5
1974-75	0.0	0.0	0.0	0.0	5.4	8.1	22.7
1975-76	0.0	0.0	0.0	0.0	6.3	0.6	
RECORD MEAN	0.0	0.0	T	0.3	2.6	5.9	8.5

Heating Degree Days

Season	July	Aug	Sept	Oct	Nov	Dec	Jan
1955-56	0	0	65	305	964	1284	1354
1956-57	0	5	78	161	752	1004	1463
1957-58	0	0	91	404	828	921	1181
1958-59	0	9	52	272	678	1164	1431
1959-60	3	0	115	433	948	923	1370
1960-61	0	0	63	282	704	1110	1245
1961-62	0	4	174	283	805	1384	1444
1962-63	0	0	117	284	685	1134	1590
#1963-64	0	5	35	96	623	1458	1117
1964-65	0	24	93	353	676	1227	1298
1965-66	0	5	169	257	670	864	1440
1966-67	0	13	107	354	741	1132	1216
1967-68	8	15	109	417	791	1129	1307
1968-69	2	1	60	313	824	1268	1430
1969-70	0	0	25	478	714	1242	1507
1970-71	0	0	105	426	799	1085	1458
1971-72	5	1	95	228	707	1113	1392
1972-73	6	7	106	488	831	1357	1307
1973-74	0	0	90	254	750	1302	1427
1974-75	0	15	191	300	726	1115	1311
1975-76	0	0	141	251	695	1051	

Cooling Degree Days

Year	Jan	Feb	Mar	Apr	May	June	July
1969	0	0	0	2	95	149	416
1970	0	0	0	32	172	286	386
1971	0	0	0	12	34	393	295
1972	0	0	0	3	74	249	314
1973	0	0	0	3	23	257	332
1974	0	0	0	11	52	182	540
1975	0	0	0	7	115	242	441

Feb	Mar	Apr	May	June	Total
2.1	3.5	0.2	0.0	0.0	26.3
5.1	T	T	T	0.0	16.3
17.8	5.9	1.4	0.0	0.0	30.4
9.7	8.1	T	0.0	0.0	37.0
3.7	3.4	0.0	0.0	0.0	32.3
21.9	3.7	0.0	0.0	0.0	52.5
0.1	10.5	0.0	0.0	0.0	19.9
8.4	13.4	1.7	T	0.0	24.6
16.2	1.1	8.6	2.0	0.0	45.9
0.1	2.6	0.0	T	0.0	18.9
4.1	5.1	T	T	0.0	23.9
13.7	27.2	0.0	0.0	0.0	58.5
11.9	1.5	2.1	0.0	0.0	47.4
9.2	5.5	1.7	0.0	0.0	27.6
1.3	9.3	1.1	0.0	0.0	20.3
2.2	13.8	1.6	0.0	0.0	39.5
6.7	2.7	0.5	0.0	0.0	34.1
1.9	2.9	0.0	T	0.0	8.0
7.2	7.2	0.0	0.0	0.0	23.0
3.2	0.4	0.2	0.0	0.0	13.7
1.8	11.6	2.8	0.0	0.0	30.7
3.7	7.8	T	0.0	0.0	37.8
5.3	13.2	0.7	0.0	0.0	27.7
13.4	22.7	T	0.0	0.0	56.7
6.3	6.4	1.3	0.0	0.0	19.8
13.2	8.9	0.9	0.0	0.0	51.6
3.2	13.0	0.0	0.0	0.0	39.6
3.5	10.5	T	0.0	0.0	25.5
25.4	16.1	0.0	0.0	0.0	56.3
1.3	8.3	T	T	0.0	14.2
0.8	0.3	0.7	1.0	0.0	16.9
1.1	T	T	T	0.0	12.9
14.0	3.2	0.0	0.0	0.0	38.8
1.1	5.8	T	0.0	0.0	30.5
17.4	4.3	0.5	0.0	0.0	39.3
5.0	3.1	1.5	0.0	0.0	24.9
4.6	T	2.3	0.0	0.0	38.3
2.4	4.2	0.8	0.0	0.0	33.7
11.9	5.1	4.6	0.0	0.0	57.8
7.4	6.8	0.9	0.1	0.0	32.5

Average Temperature

Year	Jan	Feb	Mar	Apr	May	June	July	Aug	Sept	Oct	Nov	Dec	Annual
1936	10.4	6.5	42.4	49.1	68.0	73.8	86.7	81.8	70.0	52.2	37.6	29.4	50.7
1937	11.0	22.2	35.4	49.9	64.2	72.2	79.6	81.6	68.8	52.8	36.2	26.9	50.1
1938	24.5	28.5	45.0	53.4	61.4	72.8	80.4	78.5	70.4	63.0	38.8	30.6	53.9
1939	33.0	20.1	39.2	51.1	69.4	74.0	80.6	74.6	71.8	55.4	41.6	34.2	53.8
1940	8.2	25.0	35.6	49.5	61.3	73.3	80.3	72.8	69.0	61.2	34.8	30.5	50.1
1941	25.9	26.2	37.0	55.2	68.0	71.8	77.2	77.8	68.6	55.2	40.3	33.0	53.0
1942	25.2	24.5	38.8	57.0	60.8	72.4	78.0	75.4	63.0	55.4	40.8	24.2	51.3
1943	19.9	32.4	33.5	53.4	58.9	72.8	78.3	77.4	63.6	52.9	35.8	28.0	50.6
1944	31.6	28.2	36.1	46.2	66.8	73.4	76.1	74.3	66.6	56.8	40.4	23.5	51.7
1945	24.8	28.8	46.0	50.0	57.6	66.0	75.8	76.2	66.1	55.1	40.0	19.2	50.5
1946	26.6	33.7	50.2	57.7	59.2	73.4	77.2	73.0	65.8	56.8	39.8	31.6	53.8
1947	28.6	21.8	34.2	48.6	58.4	69.1	77.0	83.2	69.7	63.3	35.4	28.8	51.5
1948	20.1	25.2	32.0	57.0	62.7	71.9	78.1	76.9	70.0	54.0	39.8	27.6	51.3
1949	17.4	20.4	36.6	52.8	66.0	73.8	78.0	75.0	61.4	56.7	45.2	29.9	51.2
1950	18.4	25.4	34.1	46.5	61.7	71.5	71.9	70.1	64.5	59.1	35.5	24.4	48.6
1951	20.3	28.7	30.7	46.1	63.7	66.8	74.7	74.7	62.0	53.2	34.5	20.1	47.9
1952	22.2	34.2	33.4	51.1	62.6	78.9	77.6	72.9	68.0	50.4	38.9	26.7	51.4
1953	24.6	31.9	40.5	46.5	61.5	77.6	78.5	76.4	68.0	60.1	44.1	32.1	53.5
#1954	19.6	40.8	35.1	55.3	58.8	76.2	82.6	76.3	70.4	53.9	45.7	31.6	53.9
1955	24.7	20.8	36.5	59.9	66.4	69.2	82.7	80.0	69.4	55.4	32.6	23.4	51.8
1956	21.1	26.1	37.6	48.4	65.5	77.6	76.2	76.8	66.8	61.1	39.7	32.4	52.5
1957	17.6	32.5	38.3	50.8	61.3	71.0	81.5	76.3	63.4	51.8	37.1	35.0	51.4
1958	26.7	20.3	35.7	51.0	65.7	69.7	73.1	75.8	67.5	57.1	42.2	26.6	51.0
1959	18.7	25.0	39.4	50.8	63.1	74.0	74.7	78.9	65.0	50.8	33.1	34.9	50.7
1960	20.5	19.2	23.1	53.2	62.2	70.0	75.8	75.6	67.7	56.2	41.3	28.9	49.5
1961	24.6	31.1	39.5	47.5	60.1	71.6	77.0	75.1	62.3	55.8	38.0	20.1	50.2
1962	18.2	25.0	31.9	50.9	70.1	72.3	75.6	75.0	63.2	57.0	42.0	28.2	50.8
#1963	13.7	27.1	42.7	54.7	63.1	76.3	79.0	74.3	67.8	64.4	44.1	17.8	52.1
1964	28.6	30.5	33.7	52.8	68.0	71.9	80.1	70.5	65.3	53.7	42.2	25.2	51.9
1965	23.0	22.2	27.1	53.2	68.1	71.8	75.7	74.1	61.0	57.2	42.4	36.9	51.1
1966	18.4	28.8	44.1	48.2	61.0	72.6	79.4	71.0	63.7	53.9	40.1	28.3	50.8
1967	25.5	28.4	45.5	55.6	59.1	70.8	74.4	71.7	62.5	52.1	38.4	28.4	51.1
1968	22.6	27.3	44.6	52.5	58.0	74.0	76.4	75.0	65.4	55.8	37.4	24.0	51.1
1969	18.7	26.7	31.5	53.1	63.2	67.9	78.2	75.6	67.7	50.1	41.0	24.8	49.9
1970	16.3	32.0	35.9	53.0	68.1	74.3	77.3	76.3	66.2	51.7	38.2	29.8	51.6
1971	17.8	25.3	37.2	54.4	60.4	77.8	74.2	74.7	67.8	58.8	41.2	28.9	51.5
1972	20.0	25.4	40.8	51.2	62.4	72.6	74.6	73.6	65.4	49.1	37.1	21.1	49.5
1973	22.6	28.6	44.3	50.4	59.4	73.3	75.5	77.6	64.2	57.3	39.8	22.7	51.3
1974	18.8	30.6	42.1	52.6	61.9	69.8	82.2	70.5	59.7	55.3	40.7	28.9	51.1
1975	22.5	22.4	31.7	49.4	66.2	72.5	78.9	79.7	62.6	58.2	41.6	30.9	51.4
RECORD MEAN	22.0	26.5	37.5	51.7	62.7	72.3	77.4	75.1	66.3	55.0	39.3	27.5	51.1
MAX	31.0	35.7	47.1	62.1	72.8	82.3	87.6	85.2	76.8	65.8	48.7	35.9	60.9
MIN	12.9	17.3	27.8	41.2	52.5	62.2	67.2	65.0	55.8	44.2	29.9	19.0	41.3

# Indicates a station move or relocation of instruments.

OMAHA, NE

Feb	Mar	Apr	May	June	Total
1121	841	502	114	7	6557
904	821	431	159	5	5783
1250	904	419	63	15	6076
1114	790	426	135	14	6105
1319	1290	379	119	12	6911
942	784	528	188	4	5850
1116	1020	431	22	19	6702
1058	681	314	120	0	5983
994	964	364	55	19	5730
1191	1168	361	55	0	6446
1008	642	501	185	13	5754
1020	615	295	249	17	5759
1085	631	380	228	11	6111
1066	1028	353	140	56	6541
917	894	388	68	2	6235
1106	853	319	172	1	6324
1143	741	408	147	12	5992
1014	636	437	191	0	6380
955	702	379	140	31	6030
1189	1024	469	72	11	6423

Aug	Sept	Oct	Nov	Dec	Total
338	113	25	0	0	1138
361	148	20	0	0	1405
308	188	42	0	0	1272
280	124	1	0	0	1045
395	74	22	0	0	1106
193	39	4	0	0	1021
464	76	44	0	0	1389

Precipitation

Year	Jan	Feb	Mar	Apr	May	June	July	Aug	Sept	Oct	Nov	Dec	Annual
1936	1.50	0.69	0.84	0.23	4.37	3.28	0.52	2.43	4.54	1.07	0.14	1.12	20.73
1937	1.15	0.22	1.60	1.67	2.45	4.77	5.04	0.97	0.80	1.43	0.26	0.15	20.51
1938	0.68	0.91	0.51	5.19	2.68	2.03	6.84	3.99	4.84	1.52	1.53	0.15	30.87
1939	0.50	1.55	0.89	0.64	1.65	5.42	4.05	2.03	0.41	1.09	0.35	0.62	19.20
1940	0.56	1.17	1.71	3.46	1.26	3.06	1.56	5.00	0.56	2.53	2.24	1.39	24.50
1941	1.03	0.59	0.36	3.07	1.05	6.69	2.70	0.73	5.27	3.57	1.01	3.30	29.37
1942	0.09	1.93	1.50	0.52	3.93	5.40	4.49	3.25	3.84	1.01	0.18	0.56	26.70
1943	0.05	0.50	0.98	2.45	4.27	6.30	3.90	1.68	0.74	0.55	0.61	T	22.03
1944	0.75	0.94	1.67	6.38	4.21	5.93	2.37	4.93	0.92	0.85	1.47	0.47	30.89
1945	0.47	1.26	1.53	5.35	5.83	4.18	4.31	1.34	4.30	0.02	0.15	1.79	30.53
1946	0.59	0.19	2.71	0.58	3.53	6.78	1.84	3.92	3.73	4.02	1.87	0.12	29.88
1947	0.71	0.19	0.87	6.31	4.65	10.81	2.90	1.06	0.79	2.58	1.23	1.09	33.19
1948	0.29	1.92	1.74	2.57	0.56	2.21	5.91	3.48	4.86	1.67	4.05	1.03	30.29
1949	3.70	1.44	1.40	1.20	3.94	6.73	2.04	3.43	3.17	3.22	0.04	0.19	30.50
1950	0.95	1.40	0.60	1.71	4.94	1.69	6.65	6.00	0.47	2.95	0.48	0.19	28.03
1951	0.66	2.02	3.18	6.45	7.09	4.88	4.08	7.03	2.71	1.02	0.51	0.97	40.60
1952	0.73	0.68	2.35	2.94	4.09	4.84	2.85	6.75	1.59	T	3.35	1.02	31.19
1953	0.46	0.80	1.77	2.71	2.00	3.72	1.03	1.45	0.41	0.76	2.13	1.19	18.43
1954	0.24	2.59	0.71	2.89	3.32	3.20	0.72	6.84	1.28	3.12	0.04	0.07	25.02
1955	0.75	1.06	0.78	3.52	1.21	4.31	4.06	1.31	3.68	0.40	0.04	0.22	21.34
1956	0.71	0.32	0.12	1.19	1.31	2.67	7.44	3.52	2.07	1.93	1.81	0.18	23.27
1957	0.38	0.13	2.44	2.37	5.01	6.27	1.74	7.25	2.44	3.81	2.19	0.42	34.45
1958	1.18	0.85	0.83	4.18	1.87	1.29	9.60	3.07	4.18	0.08	1.07	0.06	28.26
1959	0.56	0.92	3.35	2.63	10.33	5.53	0.90	9.12	2.20	2.15	0.65	1.13	39.47
1960	1.17	1.17	2.07	1.99	6.53	5.69	1.85	7.12	4.04	1.05	0.11	0.40	33.19
1961	0.23	0.79	3.59	1.64	5.98	4.44	3.12	4.56	4.77	4.99	2.23	1.50	37.84
1962	0.41	1.94	1.53	0.64	5.26	2.56	7.55	3.80	3.79	1.74	0.68	0.80	30.70
1963	1.09	0.36	3.05	3.43	1.29	4.67	2.25	4.82	2.18	1.05	0.39	0.48	25.06
1964	0.54	0.36	1.58	4.40	7.46	6.39	4.61	4.13	2.60	0.50	2.34	0.84	35.75
1965	0.60	2.97	2.63	3.71	6.19	5.15	4.39	2.06	13.75	0.76	1.24	1.40	44.85
1966	0.81	0.41	0.88	0.83	3.67	5.93	4.70	1.85	2.16	0.64	0.22	0.62	22.72
1967	2.00	0.16	0.82	2.61	2.26	9.86	4.33	1.53	4.15	1.69	0.28	0.79	30.48
1968	0.49	0.10	0.57	3.93	4.35	4.44	2.61	3.30	5.74	4.62	1.50	2.04	33.69
1969	1.10	1.33	1.25	3.95	4.48	3.27	4.27	5.06	1.33	2.24	0.11	1.80	30.19
1970	0.20	0.14	0.85	2.84	2.64	2.48	1.98	4.66	4.93	4.88	1.23	0.42	27.25
1971	0.95	2.43	0.49	0.90	7.21	3.30	1.77	1.60	0.57	4.20	3.12	1.05	27.59
1972	0.38	0.36	1.14	4.63	5.13	1.03	7.28	2.60	4.93	3.21	3.25	1.62	35.56
1973	1.44	0.87	5.96	3.60	4.94	1.56	4.98	1.27	8.04	2.60	1.43	1.65	38.34
1974	0.63	0.16	0.80	1.72	2.65	1.79	0.79	4.17	2.54	2.74	1.41	0.31	20.21
1975	2.01	1.06	1.78	3.37	3.72	4.30	0.46	1.80	2.16	0.01	2.85	0.46	23.98
RECORD MEAN	0.75	0.90	1.43	2.64	3.79	4.54	3.67	3.38	3.17	2.09	1.23	0.89	28.48

Record mean values above are means through the current year for the period beginning in 1873 for temperature, 1871 for precipitation and 1936 for snowfall.

Station: LAS VEGAS, NEVADA
MCCARRAN INTERNATIONAL AIRPORT
Elevation (ground) : 2162

TEMPERATURES °F

Month	Normal			Extremes			
	Daily maximum	Daily minimum	Monthly	Record highest	Year	Record lowest	Year
(a)				16		16	
J	55.7	32.6	44.2	77	1975	8	1963
F	61.3	36.9	49.1	82	1972	19	1972
M	67.8	41.7	54.8	91	1966	23	1971
A	77.5	50.0	63.8	96	1962	31	1975
M	87.5	59.0	73.3	108	1974	40	1964
J	97.2	67.4	82.3	115	1970	51	1971
J	103.9	75.3	89.6	116	1973	62	1970
A	101.5	73.3	87.4	113	1969	56	1968
S	94.8	65.4	80.1	107	1971	46	1965
O	81.0	53.1	67.1	99	1963	26	1971
N	65.7	40.8	53.3	85	1973	26	1975
D	56.7	33.7	45.2	74	1975	15	1968
YR	79.2	52.4	65.8	116	JUL 1973	8	JAN 1963

IMPORTANT:
The time-period covered by this record is limited: See footnotes following table of **NORMALS, MEANS AND EXTREMES** for explanation and for additional history of **EXTREME HIGHS AND LOWS** recorded in the general area.

Las Vegas is situated near the center of a broad desert valley, which is almost surrounded by mountains ranging from 2,000 to 10,000 feet higher than the floor of the valley. This Vegas Valley, comprising about 600 square miles, runs from northwest to southeast, and slopes gradually upward on each side towards the surrounding mountains. Weather observations are taken at McCarran Airport, 7 miles south of downtown Las Vegas, and about 5 miles southwest and 300 feet higher than the lower portions of the valley. Since mountains encircle the valley, drainage winds are usually downslope toward the center, or lowest portion of the valley. This condition also affects minimum temperatures, which in lower portions of the valley can be from 15 degrees to 25 degrees colder than recorded at the airport on clear, calm nights. The four seasons are well defined. Summers are typically "desert" with maximum temperatures usually in the 100 degree plus bracket. The proximity of the mountains contributes materially to the relatively cool summer nights, with the majority of the minimums being between 70 degrees

(Continued)

and 75 degrees. There is a period of about two weeks almost every summer when warm, moist, tropical air predominates weather conditions in this area, and causes scattered thundershowers, occasionally quite severe, together with higher than average humidity. Although maximum temperatures are much lower during this humid period, minimum temperatures are higher than usual and many natives consider this the most unpleasant weather of the year. Soil erosion, especially near the mountains and foothills surrounding the valley, is evidence that these summer thundershowers have in the past on occasion developed into "cloudburst" proportions. Aside from this short humid period, summers are not as uncomfortable as indicated by the daytime maxima, because of the prevailing low humidity. Winters, on the whole, are mild and pleasant. Daytime temperatures average near 60 degrees, and with mostly clear skies and warm sunshine, there is little decrease in outdoor activities. Winter minimum temperatures average 3 degrees above freezing. The spring and fall seasons are generally considered most ideal, although rather sharp temperature transients occur during these months. There are but few days during the spring and fall months when outdoor activities are affected in any degree by the weather.

The Sierra Nevada Mountains of California and the Spring Mountains immediately west of the Vegas Valley, the latter rising to elevations over 10,000 feet above the valley floor, act as effective barriers to moisture laden storms moving eastward from the Pacific Ocean. It is mainly these barriers that result in a minimum of dark overcast and rainy days. Rainy days average less than one in June to three per month in the winter months. Snow rarely falls in this valley and it usually melts as it falls, or shortly thereafter. Two notable exceptions occurred. During January 1949 16.7 inches of snow fall was recorded and in January 1974 13.4 inches fell and the maximum depth on the ground was 8 inches. January 1949 will be remembered because of relatively heavy snows over the far southwest, which extended to the southern California coastline.

Strong winds, associated with major storms, usually reach this valley from the southwest or through the pass from the northwest. Winds over 50 m.p.h. are infrequent but, when they do occur, are probably the most provoking of the elements experienced in the Vegas Valley, because of the blowing dust and sand associated with these stronger winds.

LAS VEGAS, NEVADA

Normals, Means, and Extremes

(To better understand these tables, see full explanation of terms beginning on page 322)

Month	Normal Degree days Base 65 °F: Heating	Normal Degree days Base 65 °F: Cooling	Precipitation in inches, Water equivalent: Normal	Maximum monthly	Year	Minimum monthly	Year	Maximum in 24 hrs.	Year	Snow, Ice pellets: Maximum monthly	Year	Maximum in 24 hrs.	Year
(a)				27		27		27		27		27	
JAN	645	0	0.45	2.41	1949	T	1971	1.01	1952	16.7	1949	9.0	1974
FEB	451	6	0.30	1.64	1973	0.00	1967	0.63	1958	T	1975	T	1975
MAR	324	8	0.33	1.83	1973	0.00	1972	1.14	1952	T	1975	T	1975
APR	126	90	0.27	2.44	1965	0.00	1962	0.97	1965	T	1970	T	1970
MAY	10	268	0.10	0.96	1969	0.00	1970	0.80	1969	0.0		0.0	
JUN	0	519	0.09	0.82	1967	0.00	1974	0.75	1967	0.0		0.0	
JUL	0	763	0.44	1.64	1956	0.00	1963	1.32	1956	0.0		0.0	
AUG	0	694	0.49	2.59	1957	0.00	1956	2.59	1957	0.0		0.0	
SEP	0	453	0.27	1.58	1963	0.00	1971	1.07	1963	0.0		0.0	
OCT	74	139	0.22	1.12	1972	0.00	1967	0.65	1972	T	1956	T	1956
NOV	357	6	0.43	2.22	1965	0.00	1956	1.78	1960	4.0	1964	4.0	1964
DEC	614	0	0.37	1.38	1959	0.00	1963	0.83	1959	2.0	1967	2.0	1967
YEAR	2601	2946	3.76	2.59	AUG 1957	0.00	JUN 1974	2.59	AUG 1957	16.7	JAN 1949	9.0	JAN 1974

Month	Relative humidity pct. Hour 04 (Local time)	Hour 10	Hour 16	Hour 22	Wind: Mean speed m.p.h.	Prevailing direction	Fastest mile: Speed m.p.h.	Direction	Year	Pct. of possible sunshine	Mean sky cover, tenths, sunrise to sunset	Mean number of days, Sunrise to sunset: Clear	Partly cloudy	Cloudy	Precipitation .01 inch or more	Snow, Ice pellets 1.0 inch or more	Thunderstorms	Heavy fog, visibility ¼ mile or less	Temperatures °F Max. (b) 90° and above	Max. 32° and below	Min. 32° and below	Min. 0° and below	Average station pressure mb. Elev. 2180 feet m.s.l.
(a)	15	15	15	15	27	15	11	11		27	27	27	27	27	27	27	27	27	15	15	15	15	3
JAN	52	39	29	46	7.1	W	52	SW	1965	78	4.8	14	6	11	3	*	0	*	0	*	17	0	942.1
FEB	47	34	25	40	8.2	SW	54	NW	1965	81	4.5	13	7	8	2	0	*	*	0	0	6	0	941.2
MAR	41	28	20	33	9.7	SW	52	SW	1966	83	4.5	14	9	8	3	0	*	*	*	0	2	0	935.8
APR	34	21	15	26	10.9	SW	48	N	1969	86	3.6	17	7	6	2	0	1	0	2	0	*	0	936.1
MAY	31	18	12	22	10.8	SW	52	SW	1971	88	3.2	19	8	4	1	0	1	0	16	0	0	0	934.0
JUN	26	16	11	17	10.7	SW	46	SW	1965	93	2.0	23	5	2	1	0	1	0	25	0	0	0	933.5
JUL	29	19	14	22	9.9	SW	64	SW	1971	87	2.9	19	9	3	3	0	5	0	31	0	0	0	934.9
AUG	35	23	17	26	9.3	SW	55	NE	1971	88	2.5	21	8	2	3	0	5	0	30	0	0	0	935.4
SEP	32	22	16	25	8.7	SW	54	NW	1971	92	1.7	24	4	2	1	0	2	0	22	0	0	0	936.5
OCT	37	25	19	31	7.9	WSW	52	NW	1970	86	2.7	21	6	4	2	0	1	*	5	0	*	0	938.7
NOV	48	34	28	42	7.1	W	46	SW	1973	81	3.8	16	7	7	2	*	*	*	0	0	2	0	940.5
DEC	55	41	33	49	7.0	W	54	SW	1964	78	4.4	15	7	9	2	*	*	*	0	*	13	0	943.3
YEAR	39	27	20	32	8.9	SW	64	SW	JUL 1971	86	3.4	216	83	66	24	1	15	1	132	*	41	0	937.7

FOOTNOTES Means and extremes above are from existing and comparable exposures. Annual extremes have been exceeded at other sites in the locality as follows: Highest temperature 117 in July 1942; maximum monthly precipitation 3.39 in September 1939.

Snowfall

Season	July	Aug	Sept	Oct	Nov	Dec	Jan
1970-71	0.0	0.0	0.0	0.0	0.0	T	T
1971-72	0.0	0.0	0.0	0.0	0.0	T	0.0
1972-73	0.0	0.0	0.0	0.0	0.0	0.0	0.3
1973-74	0.0	0.0	0.0	0.0	0.0	0.0	13.4
1974-75	0.0	0.0	0.0	0.0	0.0	T	0.0
1975-76	0.0	0.0	0.0	0.0	T	0.0	
RECORD MEAN	0.0	0.0	0.0	T	0.2	0.1	1.2

Heating Degree Days

Season	July	Aug	Sept	Oct	Nov	Dec	Jan
1955-56	0	0	0	17	350	520	497
1956-57	0	0	0	85	427	590	657
1957-58	0	0	0	89	475	556	580
1958-59	0	0	0	42	338	497	571
#1959-60	0	0	2	48	340	534	736
1960-61	0	0	0	63	351	636	611
1961-62	0	0	0	136	438	693	635
1962-63	0	0	0	28	229	588	733
1963-64	0	0	0	17	295	626	703
1964-65	0	0	0	12	444	606	551
1965-66	0	0	15	17	266	615	685
1966-67	0	0	0	47	286	578	606
1967-68	0	0	0	18	244	716	638
1968-69	0	0	1	28	304	743	536
1969-70	0	0	0	112	341	589	643
1970-71	0	0	0	111	295	631	630
1971-72	0	0	4	207	417	724	697
1972-73	0	0	0	108	453	727	744
1973-74	0	0	0	42	349	576	738
1974-75	0	0	0	55	300	634	607
1975-76	0	0	0	73	354	516	

Cooling Degree Days

Year	Jan	Feb	Mar	Apr	May	June	July
1969	0	0	13	62	390	500	7723
1970	0	0	0	21	334	560	818
1971	0	0	24	53	148	556	8715
1972	0	2	66	80	308	597	8763
1973	0	0	0	54	382	612	8334
1974	0	0	24	43	394	731	744
1975	0	0	2	2	276	570	792

Feb	Mar	Apr	May	June	Total
0.0	0.0	0.0	0.0	0.0	T
0.0	0.0	0.0	0.0	0.0	T
0.0	T	0.0	0.0	0.0	0.3
0.0	0.0	0.0	0.0	0.0	13.4
T	T	0.0	0.0	0.0	T
T	T	T	0.0	0.0	1.5

Average Temperature

Year	Jan	Feb	Mar	Apr	May	June	July	Aug	Sept	Oct	Nov	Dec	Annual
1937	31.2	44.8	53.4	61.6	74.2	82.1	87.8	87.6	80.3	67.0	54.0	47.5	64.3
1938	46.0	47.7	53.2	64.4	70.2	81.0	87.0	86.0	79.9	63.4	46.0	46.8	64.3
1939	44.2	41.2	55.8	65.0	74.2	81.6	88.5	87.8	75.6	63.7	55.1	48.5	65.1
1940	46.5	50.2	58.4	65.2	78.0	86.4	88.3	89.0	76.3	66.4	50.1	46.2	66.8
1941	46.9	52.8	55.4	59.2	73.4	78.8	87.2	83.0	73.0	60.7	52.8	46.1	64.1
1942	45.8	46.3	53.7	64.6	71.0	83.3	91.7	86.8	77.4	67.7	54.4	47.7	65.9
1943	46.4	51.8	58.5	68.0	75.4	80.2	88.6	87.2	80.9	67.8	52.7	47.8	67.1
1944	44.8	46.9	55.0	62.1	73.5	77.6	87.1	87.4	81.1	70.2	53.2	46.6	65.5
1945	45.4	51.0	53.0	63.2	74.8	80.8	89.8	86.4	80.4	67.5	51.6	43.2	65.6
1946	43.8	46.8	56.0	69.1	74.6	85.8	89.3	88.3	80.0	61.6	50.6	48.6	66.2
1947	42.6	53.4	59.9	66.2	78.8	82.2	88.6	87.0	83.3	67.8	50.3	44.0	67.0
#1948	45.6	46.4	50.4	65.0	72.0	82.6	88.6	86.7	79.8	67.3	49.6	41.1	64.6
1949	32.4	41.8	53.6	67.1	70.8	83.3	89.3	85.0	82.2	63.3	58.9	43.3	64.2
1950	41.2	51.7	56.7	67.1	72.5	81.3	88.7	87.3	78.2	71.8	56.6	51.2	67.0
1951	43.8	47.5	54.6	64.1	72.8	82.0	90.1	85.5	81.4	64.9	50.9	42.3	65.0
1952	41.8	48.4	50.4	64.1	76.2	80.3	88.2	90.8	80.7	71.9	49.5	45.4	65.6
1953	50.4	48.7	56.4	63.9	66.2	81.7	90.6	87.1	81.8	65.3	55.1	44.0	65.9
1954	45.3	54.1	52.2	69.6	77.8	81.2	90.7	86.0	80.6	68.4	57.2	43.8	67.3
1955	41.1	43.7	54.1	60.3	70.2	81.6	87.2	86.7	80.8	69.8	53.1	48.1	64.8
1956	48.8	45.6	56.5	63.4	74.3	85.5	88.2	86.2	83.4	65.3	50.6	45.8	66.2
1957	43.6	55.0	56.9	63.5	69.3	85.8	88.9	86.3	80.1	63.7	49.0	46.8	65.8
1958	46.0	52.2	52.1	62.4	78.0	84.0	88.8	90.5	81.0	69.9	53.5	48.8	67.3
1959	46.4	47.7	57.2	68.7	72.2	86.8	93.4	87.1	77.8	68.2	53.4	47.4	67.2
#1960	41.0	46.0	59.7	66.0	73.4	87.4	91.0	88.3	82.0	66.1	53.0	44.3	66.5
1961	45.1	51.0	56.2	65.1	72.9	87.0	91.0	87.7	75.6	64.1	50.3	42.5	65.7
1962	44.3	49.9	51.3	70.3	70.6	82.3	88.3	89.8	81.4	68.7	57.3	45.9	66.7
1963	41.1	55.8	54.0	58.5	75.9	78.6	90.4	87.9	80.5	70.1	55.0	44.6	66.0
1964	42.0	45.6	52.3	61.8	70.9	80.9	90.7	87.6	78.4	72.0	50.0	45.3	64.8
1965	47.1	49.5	53.2	61.2	69.6	78.0	88.7	87.9	74.8	69.8	55.9	45.0	65.1
1966	42.7	45.8	57.9	66.4	77.5	83.9	89.3	89.6	80.1	66.5	55.4	46.1	66.8
1967	45.3	50.6	59.3	56.2	72.5	79.6	91.7	90.3	80.0	69.1	56.7	41.6	66.1
1968	44.2	55.7	57.5	62.0	73.5	84.0	89.0	83.5	79.7	67.0	54.5	40.8	66.0
1969	47.5	46.3	53.0	64.4	76.8	81.4	89.7	92.2	82.5	62.8	53.5	45.8	66.3
1970	44.0	52.5	54.9	58.6	75.3	83.4	91.1	88.8	77.2	63.8	55.0	44.5	65.8
1971	44.4	49.7	55.8	63.0	68.0	83.3	92.8	89.0	77.6	61.7	50.9	41.4	64.8
1972	42.3	52.0	63.7	65.1	74.5	84.7	93.1	86.5	78.0	63.5	49.7	41.3	66.2
1973	40.9	49.6	50.7	62.2	76.7	85.2	91.7	87.6	78.9	67.7	53.4	46.2	65.9
1974	41.0	48.9	59.5	63.4	77.0	89.1	88.8	87.7	83.4	69.3	54.8	44.4	67.3
1975	45.3	48.8	53.9	56.6	72.5	83.8	90.3	87.5	81.7	66.1	53.0	48.2	65.6
RECORD													
MEAN	43.8	49.1	55.3	63.9	73.6	82.8	89.6	87.5	79.7	66.7	53.0	45.4	65.9
MAX	56.2	61.9	69.0	78.2	88.6	98.4	104.9	102.5	95.3	81.6	66.7	57.8	80.1
MIN	31.4	36.2	41.6	49.5	58.5	67.2	74.3	72.5	64.1	51.8	39.3	32.9	51.6

LAS VEGAS, NV

Feb	Mar	Apr	May	June	Total
553	268	105	8	0	2318
276	243	93	32	0	2403
350	394	154	3	0	2601
477	239	21	19	0	2204
544	177	77	4	0	2462
384	268	63	5	0	2381
418	420	13	30	0	2783
254	337	109	7	0	2285
557	394	141	72	0	2805
427	358	220	49	0	2667
529	235	54	0	0	2416
397	189	261	25	0	2389
265	231	110	8	0	2230
518	381	74	16	0	2601
344	304	208	8	0	2549
421	306	105	47	0	2546
373	99	69	6	0	2596
428	437	132	12	0	3041
443	188	82	13	0	2431
446	340	249	37	0	2668

Aug	Sept	Oct	Nov	Dec	Total
852	532	54	0	0	3175
748	371	81	1	0	2934
752	390	112	0	0	2906
675	398	69	0	0	3071
708	424	134	8	0	3155
713	559	195	0	0	3403
704	508	117	2	0	2973

Precipitation

# Indicates a station move or relocation of instruments.

Year	Jan	Feb	Mar	Apr	May	June	July	Aug	Sept	Oct	Nov	Dec	Annual
1937	0.66	0.06	0.91	T	T	T	0.70	T	0.01	0.00	T	0.11	2.45
1938	0.14	0.89	1.17	0.13	0.13	0.23	0.46	0.10	0.37	0.21	T	0.63	4.46
1939	1.55	0.28	0.40	0.55	0.11	0.00	0.25	0.17	3.39	0.07	0.35	0.18	7.30
1940	0.34	1.18	0.23	0.39	0.13	0.01	T	0.07	0.88	0.05	0.30	1.78	5.36
1941	1.14	1.58	1.63	1.68	0.21	T	0.93	1.75	T	1.13	0.33	0.34	10.72
1942	0.00	0.06	0.36	0.06	T	0.00	T	1.77	0.00	0.09	0.00	0.05	2.39
1943	1.01	0.14	0.52	0.85	T	0.00	T	0.04	0.31	0.03	T	1.34	4.24
1944	0.40	1.08	0.06	T	0.18	0.00	T	0.00	0.00	0.01	0.42	0.05	2.20
1945	0.41	0.10	1.58	T	0.03	T	1.68	0.40	0.00	0.43	T	0.65	5.28
1946	0.01	0.04	0.14	0.07	0.11	0.00	0.08	0.38	0.51	0.66	1.04	0.25	3.29
1947	T	T	T	T	0.11	0.00	0.13	0.16	0.01	1.13	0.22	0.96	2.72
#1948	T	0.33	0.03	T	0.00	T	0.00	0.06	T	0.01	0.00	0.33	0.76
1949	2.41	0.62	0.31	0.08	0.29	0.07	0.23	0.25	T	0.02	0.01	0.13	4.42
1950	0.02	0.07	T	T	T	T	1.34	0.29	0.62	T	T	T	2.34
1951	0.19	0.02	0.03	0.04	0.10	0.00	0.57	0.16	0.98	0.05	0.44	0.23	2.81
1952	1.07	T	1.50	0.57	T	0.01	0.47	0.49	0.87	0.00	0.16	0.41	5.55
1953	0.01	0.00	0.03	T	0.03	T	0.23	0.10	0.02	0.12	0.02	T	0.56
1954	0.91	0.02	0.81	T	0.00	0.01	1.61	0.28	0.45	0.02	0.36	0.24	4.71
1955	1.40	0.13	T	0.11	0.03	0.39	1.55	1.74	0.00	T	0.03	0.02	5.40
1956	0.23	0.00	0.00	0.08	T	0.00	1.64	0.00	0.00	0.09	0.00	0.00	2.04
1957	0.26	0.16	0.10	0.55	0.15	T	0.41	2.59	T	0.49	0.26	0.01	4.98
1958	0.43	0.73	0.55	0.64	0.18	0.00	0.01	0.18	0.21	0.63	0.96	0.00	4.52
1959	0.11	0.72	T	T	T	T	0.02	0.33	0.01	0.51	1.09	1.38	4.17
1960	0.56	0.42	0.05	0.10	T	T	0.41	T	0.23	0.49	1.88	0.26	4.40
1961	0.22	0.01	0.51	0.02	T	T	0.53	0.80	0.26	0.26	0.10	0.46	3.17
1962	0.10	0.39	0.17	0.00	0.06	0.01	T	T	0.03	0.45	T	0.24	1.45
1963	0.12	0.33	0.23	0.10	T	0.15	0.00	0.42	1.58	0.61	0.33	0.00	3.87
1964	0.05	0.02	0.02	0.03	0.05	0.03	0.24	0.05	T	T	0.63	T	1.12
1965	0.05	0.45	0.74	2.44	0.40	T	0.28	0.38	T	T	2.22	1.00	7.96
1966	T	0.07	0.04	0.01	T	0.15	0.30	0.09	0.35	0.09	0.33	0.48	1.91
1967	0.47	0.00	T	0.09	0.21	0.82	0.20	0.38	1.03	0.00	1.52	0.82	5.54
1968	0.01	0.22	0.22	0.10	T	0.31	0.11	0.04	0.01	T	0.02	0.07	1.11
1969	1.57	0.96	0.57	T	0.96	0.23	0.06	0.33	0.08	0.27	0.06	T	5.09
1970	0.01	0.86	0.28	0.04	0.00	0.18	0.58	1.79	0.00	0.02	0.38	0.15	4.29
1971	T	0.03	T	T	0.84	T	0.08	0.90	0.00	0.06	0.12	0.51	2.54
1972	0.00	T	0.00	0.07	0.46	0.32	0.13	0.84	0.63	1.12	1.09	0.19	4.85
1973	0.49	1.64	1.83	0.35	0.09	0.03	T	0.08	T	0.02	0.14	0.01	4.68
1974	2.00	0.11	0.16	T	T	0.00	0.58	0.08	0.16	0.61	0.23	0.59	4.52
1975	0.01	0.05	1.07	0.42	0.35	T	0.26	0.06	1.17	0.03	T	0.05	3.47
RECORD													
MEAN	0.47	0.35	0.42	0.25	0.13	0.08	0.41	0.45	0.36	0.25	0.39	0.36	3.92

Record mean values above are means through the current year for the period beginning in 1937 for temperature and precipitation, 1949 for snowfall.

Satellites specially developed for meteorological observation of the earth have given forecasters an effective new tool. This sketch shows NOAA-1, operated by NOAA's National Enviornmental Satellite Service.

Station: CONCORD, NEW HAMPSHIRE
MUNICIPAL AIRPORT
Elevation (ground): 342 feet

TEMPERATURES °F

Month	Normal			Extremes			
	Daily maximum	Daily minimum	Monthly	Record highest	Year	Record lowest	Year
(a)				10		10	
J	31.3	9.9	20.6	60	1974	-29	1971
F	33.8	11.3	22.6	57	1966	-27	1971
M	42.4	22.1	32.3	68	1968	-16	1967
A	56.7	31.7	44.2	88	1969	8	1969
M	68.6	41.5	55.1	96	1975	21	1966
J	77.7	51.6	64.7	97	1966	30	1972
J	82.6	56.7	69.7	102	1966	35	1965
A	80.1	54.2	67.2	101	1975	29	1965
S	72.4	46.5	59.5	93	1973	22	1965
O	62.3	36.3	49.3	84	1971	10	1972
N	47.9	28.1	38.0	78	1974	-1	1972
D	34.6	14.9	24.8	61	1970	-18	1975
YR	57.5	33.7	45.6	102	JUL 1966	-29	JAN 1971

IMPORTANT:
The time-period covered by this record is limited: See footnotes on next page for explanation and for additional history of EXTREME HIGHS AND LOWS recorded in the general area.

Concord, the Capital of New Hampshire, is situated near the geographical center of New England at an altitude of approximately 300 feet above sea level on the Merrimack River. Its surroundings are hilly with many lakes and ponds. The countryside is generously wooded, mostly on land reclaimed from fields which were formerly cleared for farming. From sea level nearly 50 miles away in a southeasterly direction, the terrain slopes gently upward to the City, then rises some 2,000 feet higher in only half that distance westward to a ridge that extends to lofty Mount Washington in the White Mountains 75 miles north of town.

Northwesterly winds are prevalent. They bring cold, dry air during the winter and pleasantly cool, dry air in the summer. Further study of the general circulation, using resultant winds which consider both direction and speed, uncovers a seasonal variation. The greater strength of the southerly winds during the warmest months results in a flow of air from the southwest or west-southwest in July and August. The overall movement is from the west or west-northwest during the transitional months of June and September and is northwesterly the rest of the year. The speed of the wind varies but little from month to month. The early afternoon wind, for example, averages 8 m.p.h. in July, 9 m.p.h. for the 6-month period from June to November, inclusive, 10 m.p.h. December through February, and maintains its maximum average speed of 11 m.p.h. March through May. The breezes are somewhat lighter, and it is frequently calm during the night and early morning so the winter low temperatures, as a rule, do not interrupt normal out-of-doors activity, or feel too severe. Easterly winds usually accompany the rains of summer and the snows of winter.

The daily temperature ranges from an average minimum of 10 degrees to an average maximum of 31 degrees F. in the middle of January, the coldest part of winter. Near the end of July, the warmest period of the year, the average range is from daily lows of about 57 degrees to high temperatures near 83 degrees F., which makes comfortably warm days and cool nights. Very hot summer weather is infrequent. During any month, temperatures considerably above the average maxima and much below the normal minima are observed. The average date for experiencing the last freezing temperature in the spring is May 17, and the average date for the first temperature of 32 degrees or less in autumn is September 24 at the present observation point. Freezing temperatures have occurred as late as June and as early as August. The lowest temperature of a winter can be expected to be in the range of 10 degrees to 25 degrees below zero and to occur between December 31 and February 11 most seasons.

The average amount of precipitation for the warmer half of the year differs little from that for the colder

(Continued page 540)

CONCORD, NEW HAMPSHIRE

Normals, Means, and Extremes

(To better understand these tables, see full explanation of terms beginning on page 322)

Month	Normal Degree days Base 65 °F: Heating	Cooling	Precipitation in inches, Water equivalent: Normal	Maximum monthly	Year	Minimum monthly	Year	Maximum in 24 hrs.	Year	Snow, Ice pellets: Maximum monthly	Year	Maximum in 24 hrs.	Year	Relative humidity pct. Hour 01 (Local time)	Hour 07	Hour 13	Hour 19	Wind: Mean speed m.p.h.	Prevailing direction	Fastest mile: Speed m.p.h.	Direction	Year	Pct. of possible sunshine	Mean sky cover, tenths, sunrise to sunset	Mean number of days, Sunrise to sunset: Clear	Partly cloudy	Cloudy	Precipitation .01 inch or more	Snow, Ice pellets 1.0 inch or more	Thunderstorms	Heavy fog, visibility ¼ mile or less	Temperatures °F Max. (b) 90° and above	Max. 32° and below	Min. 32° and below	Min. 0° and below	Average station pressure mb. Elev. 346 feet m.s.l.
(a)				34		34		34		34		34		10	10	10	10	34	22	33	33		34	34	34	34	34	34	34	34	34	10	10	10	10	3
J	1376	0	2.67	5.83	1958	0.40	1970	1.66	1964	33.2	1945	19.0	1944	74	74	59	66	7.3	NW	44	NW	1972	52	6.1	9	8	14	11	4	*	2	0	16	30	10	1004.4
F	1187	0	2.45	5.54	1951	0.93	1968	2.10	1951	49.8	1969	14.2	1972	72	75	59	63	7.9	NW	42	N	1950	54	6.1	8	7	13	10	4	*	2	0	14	27	8	1003.3
M	1014	0	2.77	7.81	1953	0.93	1965	2.27	1974	38.3	1956	13.6	1959	75	78	57	63	8.2	NW	71	NE	1950	52	6.4	8	8	15	11	3	*	3	0	5	27	1	1001.8
A	624	0	2.92	5.10	1951	1.16	1966	2.10	1945	10.0	1972	6.8	1956	76	77	47	55	7.9	NW	52	NW	1945	53	6.4	7	9	14	11	1	1	2	0	*	19	0	999.8
M	315	8	3.02	8.26	1954	0.60	1965	2.19	1954	5.0	1945	5.0	1945	83	80	49	60	7.0	NW	48	NW	1945	54	6.6	7	9	15	12	*	2	3	1	0	6	0	1001.4
J	58	49	3.35	10.10	1944	0.81	1964	4.47	1944	0.0		0.0		92	88	57	69	6.3	NW	38	W	1971	57	6.3	6	12	12	11	0	5	4	2	0	1	0	1003.3
J	16	162	3.14	5.91	1967	0.96	1955	2.54	1971	0.0		0.0		93	89	54	68	5.6	NW	45	SW	1971	62	6.1	7	12	12	10	0	6	6	5	0	0	0	1002.1
A	45	113	2.89	6.88	1973	0.95	1944	3.71	1973	0.0		0.0		92	90	54	71	5.3	NW	56	E	1934	60	5.8	8	13	10	10	0	4	7	3	0	0	0	1004.8
S	182	17	3.06	7.78	1960	0.41	1948	4.12	1960	0.0		0.0		93	93	59	80	5.4	NW	42	E	1960	54	5.9	9	9	12	9	0	2	9	1	0	2	0	1005.6
O	487	0	2.68	8.78	1962	0.59	1947	4.24	1962	2.1	1969	2.1	1969	87	89	54	75	5.9	NW	39	NW	1944	54	5.7	10	9	12	8	*	1	7	0	*	13	0	1006.9
N	810	0	3.96	6.78	1963	1.27	1946	2.89	1947	18.4	1971	9.5	1961	83	85	63	75	6.5	NW	72	NE	1950	42	6.8	6	8	16	12	1	*	4	0	2	21	*	1002.7
D	1246	0	3.26	7.52	1973	0.58	1943	3.31	1969	38.1	1956	14.6	1946	79	81	66	72	7.0	NW	52	NW	1962	47	6.4	8	8	15	11	4	*	3	0	14	29	5	1005.0
YR	7360	349	36.17	10.10	JUN 1944	0.40	JAN 1970	4.47	JUN 1944	49.8	FEB 1969	19.0	JAN 1944	83	83	56	68	6.7	NW	72	NE	NOV 1950	54	6.2	93	112	160	125	18	21	52	11	51	175	25	1003.4

FOOTNOTES

Ø For period April 1965 through current year.
Means and extremes above are from existing and comparable exposures. Annual extremes have been exceeded at other sites in the locality as follows: Lowest temperature -37 in February 1943; maximum monthly precipitation 10.97 in September 1888; minimum monthly precipitation T in March 1915; maximum precipitation in 24 hours 5.97 in September 1932; maximum monthly snowfall 59.0 in February 1893.

Snowfall

Season	July	Aug	Sept	Oct	Nov	Dec	Jan
1936-37	0.0	0.0	0.0	0.0	3.5	9.0	12.6
#1937-38	0.0	0.0	0.0	0.0	5.1	9.7	20.4
1938-39	0.0	0.0	0.0	0.0	18.4	6.8	18.1
1939-40	0.0	0.0	0.0	0.0	1.0	9.2	9.1
#1940-41	0.0	0.0	0.0	0.5	10.2	8.9	23.8
1941-42	0.0	0.0	0.0	T	1.3	7.4	8.9
1942-43	0.0	0.0	0.0	T	3.9	6.2	22.4
1943-44	0.0	0.0	0.0	0.0	14.9	1.7	23.6
1944-45	0.0	0.0	0.0	0.0	10.3	13.0	33.2
1945-46	0.0	0.0	0.0	T	4.8	10.5	28.1
1946-47	0.0	0.0	0.0	0.0	T	23.4	7.3
1947-48	0.0	0.0	0.0	0.0	2.9	22.5	32.6
1948-49	0.0	0.0	0.0	0.0	T	2.5	20.1
1949-50	0.0	0.0	0.0	0.0	1.4	6.5	14.8
1950-51	0.0	0.0	0.0	0.0	T	7.9	12.9
1951-52	0.0	0.0	0.0	0.0	5.2	21.8	27.6
1952-53	0.0	0.0	0.0	0.7	1.2	5.0	16.9
1953-54	0.0	0.0	0.0	0.0	0.2	3.5	20.2
1954-55	0.0	0.0	0.0	0.0	0.5	11.3	0.9
1955-56	0.0	0.0	0.0	T	3.5	5.6	8.0
1956-57	0.0	0.0	0.0	0.0	10.3	38.1	20.5
1957-58	0.0	0.0	0.0	0.0	T	4.6	30.9
1958-59	0.0	0.0	0.0	T	1.6	11.1	9.8
1959-60	0.0	0.0	0.0	0.0	1.4	15.3	16.5
1960-61	0.0	0.0	0.0	T	T	23.1	11.4
1961-62	0.0	0.0	0.0	T	10.0	19.7	6.7
1962-63	0.0	0.0	0.0	T	0.4	12.7	15.3
1963-64	0.0	0.0	0.0	T	T	16.9	24.3
1964-65	0.0	0.0	0.0	T	T	12.4	13.2
1965-66	0.0	0.0	0.0	T	1.0	4.6	32.9
1966-67	0.0	0.0	0.0	0.0	T	14.3	8.3
1967-68	0.0	0.0	0.0	0.0	15.0	15.0	15.8
1968-69	0.0	0.0	0.0	0.0	11.6	13.4	4.7
1969-70	0.0	0.0	0.0	2.1	T	20.7	5.0
1970-71	0.0	0.0	0.0	0.0	T	30.1	15.6
1971-72	0.0	0.0	0.0	0.0	18.4	17.4	10.8
1972-73	0.0	0.0	0.0	0.0	12.9	23.2	13.1
1973-74	0.0	0.0	0.0	0.0	T	6.6	15.4
1974-75	0.0	0.0	0.0	0.0	2.9	18.3	19.5
1975-76	0.0	0.0	0.0	0.0	2.2	25.1	
RECORD MEAN	0.0	0.0	0.0	0.1	4.0	14.2	16.7

Heating Degree Days

Season	July	Aug	Sept	Oct	Nov	Dec	Jan
1955-56	0	23	210	502	857	1446	1216
1956-57	50	50	323	532	799	1170	1592
1957-58	17	67	167	482	714	990	1269
1958-59	21	24	182	544	811	1459	1353
1959-60	0	28	174	484	790	1100	1287
1960-61	8	22	180	560	745	1363	1562
1961-62	21	25	86	389	756	1172	1369
1962-63	31	30	234	519	860	1312	1363
1963-64	20	57	267	342	675	1472	1295
#1964-65	8	106	246	539	831	1230	1418
1965-66	50	78	227	556	899	1163	1376
1966-67	6	5	244	520	697	1196	1241
1967-68	8	34	208	482	965	1144	1520
1968-69	18	92	133	424	899	1311	1330
1969-70	64	40	193	534	777	1275	1668
1970-71	4	25	181	431	760	1379	1622
1971-72	26	49	165	396	970	1185	1327
1972-73	27	82	223	695	1007	1284	1357
1973-74	15	9	244	518	860	1112	1345
1974-75	34	26	213	694	865	1182	1339
1975-76	10	78	260	532	747	1330	

Cooling Degree Days

Year	Jan	Feb	Mar	Apr	May	June	July
1969	0	0	0	0	4	65	82
1970	0	0	0	1	27	58	196
1971	0	0	0	0	0	95	135
1972	0	0	0	0	17	52	167
1973	0	0	0	3	2	145	184
1974	0	0	0	3	9	40	118
1975	0	0	0	0	48	108	263

Feb	Mar	Apr	May	June	Total
1.8	19.2	9.4	0.0	0.0	55.5
9.5	4.1	1.8	0.0	0.0	50.6
8.3	20.0	5.3	0.0	0.0	76.9
22.4	14.6	7.2	0.0	0.0	63.5
1.4	17.2	0.0	0.2	0.0	62.2
10.5	14.3	5.8	0.0	0.0	48.2
8.8	7.2	3.0	0.0	0.0	51.5
20.7	13.4	0.3	0.0	0.0	74.6
17.9	2.1	0.0	5.0	0.0	81.5
15.8	T	2.5	0.0	0.0	61.7
12.4	8.0	5.8	0.0	0.0	56.9
13.7	16.2	0.2	0.0	0.0	88.1
5.4	5.5	T	0.0	0.0	33.5
19.2	8.6	0.7	0.0	0.0	51.2
5.8	8.0	T	0.0	0.0	34.6
25.3	12.7	0.0	0.0	0.0	92.6
7.3	2.5	1.5	T	0.0	35.1
5.5	6.3	0.2	0.0	0.0	35.9
13.7	12.9	0.3	0.0	0.0	39.6
23.8	38.3	9.9	0.0	0.0	89.1
2.8	2.7	2.8	0.0	0.0	77.2
14.2	16.2	2.7	0.0	0.0	68.6
16.1	30.3	T	0.0	0.0	68.9
12.6	12.1	T	0.0	0.0	57.9
10.8	14.7	3.9	0.0	0.0	63.9
29.8	4.5	0.4	0.0	0.0	71.1
14.8	13.9	0.5	T	0.0	57.6
19.1	15.8	T	0.0	0.0	76.1
6.5	5.2	1.3	0.0	0.0	38.6
17.7	3.7	T	1.1	0.0	61.0
32.6	19.6	6.0	T	0.0	80.8
6.7	7.4	0.0	0.0	0.0	59.9
49.8	5.7	T	0.0	0.0	85.2
13.8	14.2	2.8	0.0	0.0	58.6
19.8	24.0	6.3	0.0	0.0	95.8
29.8	13.6	10.0	0.0	0.0	100.0
5.6	0.1	3.4	0.0	0.0	58.3
7.0	6.5	3.9	0.0	0.0	39.4
17.1	4.7	5.5	0.0	0.0	68.0
15.7	10.9	2.3	0.2	0.0	64.1

CONCORD, NH

Feb	Mar	Apr	May	June	Total
1144	1218	748	443	71	7878
1062	942	517	284	66	7387
1272	900	574	386	169	7007
1279	1044	577	235	107	7636
1032	1151	591	201	69	6907
1121	1002	665	383	54	7565
1316	956	585	341	33	7049
1287	966	639	291	70	7602
1231	964	636	221	70	7250
1191	1015	704	257	133	7678
1184	935	681	362	73	7584
1323	1164	683	496	57	7632
1358	928	598	424	118	7787
1165	1128	613	389	119	7621
1179	1055	572	256	108	7721
1165	1064	682	332	73	7718
1267	1142	736	262	112	7637
1250	905	596	370	78	7874
1223	1025	573	432	99	7455
1218	1075	730	152	98	7626

Aug	Sept	Oct	Nov	Dec	Total
168	44	0	0	0	363
145	56	6	0	0	489
118	55	0	0	0	403
60	5	0	0	0	301
242	67	2	0	0	645
92	40	0	0	0	302
134	0	0	0	0	553

Average Temperature

Year	Jan	Feb	Mar	Apr	May	June	July	Aug	Sept	Oct	Nov	Dec	Annual
1936	21.6	17.6	39.4	43.2	59.0	65.2	68.4	67.0	60.6	49.4	33.5	29.6	46.2
#1937	29.6	28.9	29.2	43.1	57.6	65.6	71.2	72.8	59.8	47.6	38.7	24.7	47.4
1938	21.0	26.8	35.6	47.6	54.4	67.4	71.1	71.5	58.4	53.9	41.2	28.5	48.1
1939	21.8	25.4	28.2	40.8	56.8	65.2	70.8	72.0	60.6	49.6	36.4	27.4	46.2
1940	18.0	25.2	30.1	41.0	55.9	64.0	70.7	67.2	59.4	46.6	38.5	27.2	45.3
#1941	20.2	25.2	29.8	51.4	55.2	65.3	69.8	63.6	59.9	47.8	39.8	28.3	46.4
1942	20.3	21.0	36.8	46.6	58.8	64.9	68.0	66.4	60.0	50.0	36.7	21.4	45.9
1943	17.0	22.6	29.2	38.4	54.8	67.4	70.5	65.5	57.8	49.2	36.7	21.1	44.2
1944	22.5	20.7	28.2	39.8	60.2	64.0	70.3	70.2	60.6	47.3	37.0	22.2	45.2
1945	15.4	23.0	40.6	49.1	52.0	64.8	69.2	66.6	61.4	47.0	38.0	20.2	45.6
1946	19.2	18.0	41.1	42.2	54.0	63.6	67.9	64.0	61.0	51.0	40.7	25.2	45.7
1947	21.8	22.2	31.5	41.5	54.0	61.8	71.8	70.3	59.6	55.2	34.6	21.4	45.5
1948	14.1	16.4	31.0	43.8	52.8	61.6	70.0	69.1	60.2	47.4	42.5	29.0	44.8
1949	27.7	27.0	34.8	46.4	55.6	68.4	72.3	69.5	57.8	51.6	35.0	28.0	47.8
1950	27.5	18.6	27.5	41.8	55.6	65.3	69.1	67.1	55.6	50.6	41.2	28.2	45.7
1951	25.2	27.3	33.5	45.7	55.8	62.9	69.4	66.4	59.3	50.0	34.0	24.7	46.2
1952	23.4	24.7	31.9	46.8	53.1	67.3	72.9	67.9	61.1	46.9	38.0	28.7	46.9
1953	27.6	27.7	35.3	45.0	57.2	65.8	69.8	66.4	61.1	50.1	41.1	32.3	48.3
1954	18.6	29.7	32.7	45.5	53.7	64.4	67.5	64.4	57.5	52.1	38.0	26.3	45.9
1955	20.9	25.9	31.5	45.6	59.2	64.5	74.1	71.2	58.6	48.6	36.2	18.2	46.2
1956	25.6	25.3	25.6	39.8	50.8	65.4	66.2	66.3	54.9	47.5	38.3	27.0	44.4
1957	13.5	26.8	34.4	47.6	56.2	67.4	68.2	64.1	61.4	49.3	40.9	32.9	46.9
1958	23.9	19.3	35.7	45.6	52.5	60.0	68.9	68.0	59.8	47.2	37.8	17.8	44.7
1959	21.2	19.1	31.1	45.5	59.4	63.4	72.1	70.2	62.6	49.2	38.3	29.3	46.8
1960	23.2	29.2	27.6	45.2	58.3	65.1	68.5	68.0	59.7	46.8	39.9	20.8	46.0
1961	14.5	24.8	32.4	42.6	53.2	65.4	69.5	68.5	67.1	52.4	39.5	27.0	46.4
1962	20.6	17.8	34.0	45.3	54.6	66.3	66.6	67.8	57.7	48.1	36.1	22.6	44.8
1963	20.8	18.8	33.5	43.4	55.5	66.4	72.1	65.6	56.5	53.8	42.3	17.3	45.5
1964	22.9	22.4	33.6	43.6	58.8	65.6	70.8	62.7	57.4	47.4	37.1	25.1	45.6
#1965	18.9	22.2	31.9	41.3	57.1	62.5	65.9	66.6	58.8	46.8	34.8	27.3	44.5
1966	20.4	22.5	34.6	42.2	53.4	66.8	72.2	69.6	57.0	48.0	41.5	26.2	46.2
1967	24.8	17.5	27.1	42.0	48.8	66.1	70.2	67.2	58.4	49.3	32.7	27.8	44.3
1968	15.8	18.0	34.8	44.8	51.1	62.0	69.3	64.6	61.0	51.2	34.8	22.5	44.2
1969	21.9	23.2	28.3	44.3	52.3	63.0	65.4	68.9	59.7	47.5	38.9	23.7	44.8
1970	11.0	22.6	30.7	45.8	57.3	63.1	70.9	68.7	60.6	51.0	39.3	20.3	45.1
1971	12.5	23.3	30.4	42.1	54.1	65.5	68.3	67.0	61.1	51.9	32.4	26.6	44.6
1972	22.0	21.2	27.9	40.2	56.8	62.8	69.3	64.1	57.5	42.3	31.2	23.4	43.2
1973	21.0	20.2	35.5	45.0	52.9	66.9	70.3	72.3	58.8	48.2	36.1	28.9	46.3
1974	21.4	21.1	31.8	45.8	51.1	62.8	67.5	67.0	58.9	42.5	35.9	26.7	44.4
1975	21.6	21.5	30.1	40.4	61.3	65.0	72.9	66.5	56.1	47.6	39.9	21.9	45.4
RECORD MEAN	21.3	22.8	31.9	44.4	56.2	64.9	70.0	67.3	59.7	49.2	37.5	25.6	45.9
MAX	31.6	33.5	41.4	55.8	68.7	77.0	82.0	78.9	71.3	60.7	46.8	34.7	56.9
MIN	11.0	12.1	22.4	32.9	43.6	52.7	58.0	55.6	48.1	37.6	28.2	16.4	34.9

# Indicates a station move or relocation of instruments.

Precipitation

Year	Jan	Feb	Mar	Apr	May	June	July	Aug	Sept	Oct	Nov	Dec	Annual
1936	5.67	2.82	9.80	3.59	1.03	1.99	3.76	3.75	1.77	4.72	2.25	7.64	48.79
#1937	3.44	3.28	3.08	3.86	5.21	3.48	2.76	4.62	2.66	4.51	7.59	3.56	48.05
1938	3.94	2.11	2.07	2.18	3.11	5.12	7.57	2.58	10.68	2.07	2.96	4.04	48.43
1939	3.06	2.70	3.16	4.22	1.98	3.61	1.41	5.04	2.25	2.77	0.50	2.58	33.28
1940	2.33	2.77	3.40	4.95	6.24	1.48	7.18	1.13	3.73	0.65	5.93	3.42	43.21
#1941	2.23	1.87	1.44	0.42	2.38	2.25	3.92	1.87	0.91	1.66	3.34	2.66	24.95
1942	2.81	1.81	5.67	1.45	2.00	5.36	5.02	0.95	5.23	2.23	4.80	4.72	42.05
1943	2.12	1.57	2.47	2.82	3.89	2.35	5.18	3.19	0.73	4.33	4.38	0.58	33.61
1944	1.79	2.56	3.92	3.14	1.58	10.10	2.35	0.95	7.11	1.74	3.17	2.26	40.67
1945	3.61	3.00	1.60	4.38	5.89	6.04	4.07	1.40	1.69	2.68	3.92	5.66	43.94
1946	3.05	2.36	1.37	2.99	4.80	1.78	3.05	5.28	4.29	0.93	1.27	3.62	34.79
1947	2.92	1.93	2.98	2.98	3.37	5.03	3.82	1.18	2.50	0.59	6.68	2.10	36.08
1948	2.41	1.53	2.25	3.41	5.04	4.56	2.41	1.73	0.41	1.44	5.56	2.11	32.86
1949	4.24	1.83	1.20	2.77	3.68	1.51	3.50	2.04	4.75	2.07	2.11	1.39	31.09
1950	4.29	2.31	3.35	2.85	1.61	2.94	0.96	5.37	0.96	1.92	4.55	3.42	34.53
1951	2.43	5.54	4.29	5.10	3.38	3.29	5.62	2.39	2.93	3.44	6.45	4.41	49.27
1952	4.59	2.33	3.13	4.45	3.33	3.80	2.36	2.34	3.04	1.14	1.48	5.46	37.45
1953	4.99	2.41	7.81	4.27	3.46	2.64	2.89	4.49	1.34	4.90	3.11	3.99	46.30
1954	2.35	2.65	2.95	3.73	8.26	3.82	2.14	4.81	5.42	2.62	4.45	3.38	46.58
1955	0.73	3.74	3.28	2.03	2.84	2.18	0.96	3.95	2.18	4.34	4.06	0.87	31.16
1956	4.40	2.70	3.67	3.34	1.75	1.69	3.27	2.08	5.57	1.60	2.12	4.56	36.75
1957	1.65	1.13	1.22	1.56	1.95	2.95	2.87	1.37	2.56	3.21	6.59	4.95	32.01
1958	5.83	1.51	1.43	3.95	1.92	2.50	3.58	2.61	3.60	1.96	4.40	1.40	34.69
1959	3.27	2.28	4.45	2.60	0.60	3.68	1.93	5.90	1.66	6.79	4.60	3.44	41.20
1960	2.46	2.82	2.48	4.59	4.00	3.47	3.62	2.57	7.78	2.09	2.58	2.47	40.93
1961	1.07	2.33	1.48	3.35	2.85	2.15	3.13	3.55	3.44	2.06	3.70	2.88	31.99
1962	2.66	2.59	1.64	2.13	2.58	3.30	2.99	2.59	1.76	8.78	2.65	3.15	36.82
1963	2.05	2.37	2.12	1.23	2.17	1.22	2.94	2.74	2.12	1.22	6.78	1.57	28.53
1964	3.64	1.93	3.01	2.05	1.15	0.81	3.37	2.74	0.42	2.24	3.47	3.07	27.90
1965	0.97	3.06	0.93	2.49	0.60	2.72	1.73	3.12	1.87	2.71	2.45	1.52	24.17
1966	2.69	2.13	2.19	1.16	2.16	1.78	2.30	4.05	5.40	3.31	3.01	2.42	32.60
1967	1.23	2.36	1.75	3.52	3.92	3.82	5.91	1.97	2.04	0.99	2.86	3.82	34.19
1968	1.79	0.93	3.80	2.85	5.20	5.90	1.62	3.60	2.34	2.23	5.24	5.82	41.32
1969	1.34	3.69	2.36	2.75	1.26	4.70	4.40	2.84	4.43	1.56	5.87	7.10	42.30
1970	0.40	4.27	2.78	3.38	3.04	2.26	2.33	3.06	3.40	3.64	3.03	3.08	34.67
1971	1.63	3.87	2.28	2.19	3.36	1.67	5.14	2.79	1.91	2.69	2.91	2.36	32.80
1972	1.44	2.60	4.16	2.71	4.20	3.54	5.40	2.12	2.55	2.23	6.57	4.55	42.07
1973	2.44	1.91	2.58	4.55	4.20	4.86	1.05	6.88	1.77	2.46	1.82	7.52	42.04
1974	2.80	2.32	3.98	2.58	3.74	1.82	1.41	2.20	4.74	1.64	3.20	4.02	34.45
1975	4.12	2.36	3.12	2.47	1.22	3.87	3.71	3.94	5.15	4.29	4.91	3.12	42.28
RECORD MEAN	2.89	2.62	3.08	2.98	3.13	3.31	3.58	3.42	3.43	3.13	3.46	3.10	38.13

Record mean values above are means through the current year for the period beginning in 1871 for temperature, 1855 for precipitation and 1942 for snowfall. Data are from Cooperative and City Office locations through April 1941.

(Continued)

half. Precipitation occurrences average approximately one day of three for the year, with a somewhat higher frequency for the April-May period offsetting the lower frequency of August-October. The more significant rains and heavier snowfalls are associated with easterly winds, especially northeasterly winds. The seasonal snowfall ordinarily amounts to a total of 40 to 80 inches. The first snowfall of an inch or more is likely to come between the middle of November and the middle of December. As a rule the first snowstorm with 3 or more inches can be expected before the end of December. The snow cover normally lasts from mid-December until the last week of March, but bare ground is not rare in the winter, nor is a snowscape rare earlier or later in the season. Rain, sleet, or freezing rain may come instead of the usual snow sometimes during winter.

A few humid days may be expected each summer, and humidifying the air often adds to indoor comfort during the winter, but the humidity is generally in a range that promotes comfort during all four seasons.

Agriculture is neither intensive nor large scale in vicinity of the station. Potatoes and other frost-resistant vegetables, hardy fruits such as apples, forage for the dairy industry, and maple sugar are the principal crops.

The climate is excellent for recreational activities through the greater part of the year. The combination of warm, sunny days and cool nights in summer and early fall provides the basic requirements for all types of mild-season recreation. Likewise, in winter and early spring, the abundant snowfall and cold weather provide excellent skiing, snowshoeing, tobogganing, skating, and ice-fishing.

Station: ATLANTIC CITY, NEW JERSEY
AVIATION FACILITIES EXPER CNTR
Elevation (ground): 64 feet

TEMPERATURES °F

Month	Normal			Extremes			
	Daily maximum	Daily minimum	Monthly	Record highest	Year	Record lowest	Year
(a)				11		11	
J	41.4	24.0	32.7	78	1967	-8	1965
F	42.9	24.9	33.9	70	1971	-7	1967
M	50.7	31.5	41.1	81	1968	7	1967
A	62.3	41.0	51.7	94	1969	12	1969
M	72.4	50.7	61.6	99	1969	25	1966
J	80.8	59.7	70.3	106	1969	37	1967
J	84.7	65.4	75.1	104	1966	46	1965
A	83.0	63.8	73.4	97	1975	40	1965
S	77.3	56.8	67.1	93	1973	32	1969
O	67.5	45.9	56.7	87	1967	23	1969
N	55.9	36.1	46.0	81	1974	11	1964
D	44.2	26.0	35.1	72	1966	0	1968
YR	63.6	43.8	53.7	106	JUN 1969	-8	JAN 1965

IMPORTANT:
The time-period covered by this record is limited: See footnotes on next page for explanation and for additional history of EXTREME HIGHS AND LOWS recorded in the general area.

The Atlantic City Weather Bureau Airport Station is located at the National Aviation Facilities Experimental Center, Pomona, which is about ten miles west-northwest of Atlantic City and the Atlantic Ocean. The surrounding terrain is fairly flat at an elevation of 50 - 60 feet above mean sea level. Vegetation in the area consists of scrub pine and low underbrush, but clearing for the air facility has been quite extensive. Bays and salt marshes are as near as six miles east of the airport. Atlantic City is located on Absecon Island on the southeast coast of New Jersey. Surrounding terrain, composed of tidal marshes and beach sand, is flat and lies slightly above sea level. The climate is principally continental in character; however, the moderating influence of the Atlantic Ocean is apparent throughout the year, being more marked in the City than at the airport. As a result, summers are relatively cooler and winters milder than elsewhere at the same latitude.

Land and sea breezes, local circulations resulting from the differential heating and cooling of the land and sea, often prevail. These winds occur when moderate or intense storms are not present in the area, thus enabling the local circulation to overcome the general wind pattern. During the warm season sea breezes in the late morning and afternoon hours prevent excessive heating. Frequently, the temperature at Atlantic City during the afternoon hours during the summer averages several degrees lower than at the airport and the airport averages several degrees lower than localities farther inland. On occasions, sea breezes have lowered the temperature as much as 15° to 20° within a half hour. However, the major effect of the sea breeze at the airport is to prevent the temperature from rising above the eighties. Consequently, temperatures of 90° or higher normally are recorded about three times per year at Atlantic City, 18 times per year at the airport, and about twice the latter figure at more inland locations. Because the change in ocean temperature lags behind the air temperature from season to season, the weather tends to remain comparatively mild late into the fall, but on the other hand, warming is retarded in the spring. Normal ocean temperatures (Coast and Geodetic Survey figures) range from an average near 37° in January to near 72° in August. With respect to normal air temperatures, February is the coldest month, with January a close second, and warmest temperatures are normally experienced in July.

Precipitation, on the average, is moderate and well distributed throughout the year, with June the driest month and August the wettest. However, great year to year variation in amounts is evidenced in August, September, and October, with some greater amounts and higher averages resulting from storms of tropical origin passing northward near or offshore. Thunderstorms are mostly a warm season phenomena. The bulk of winter precipitation results from storms which move northeastward along, or in close proximity to, the east coast of the United States. Snowfall, at about 15 inches per year, is considerably less than elsewhere at the same latitude and does not remain long on the ground. Here again the moderating influence of the ocean plays an important role. Precipitation, often beginning as snow, will frequently become mixed with or change to rain while continuing as snow over more interior sections. In addition, ice storms and resultant glaze are relatively infrequent.

ATLANTIC CITY, NEW JERSEY

Normals, Means, and Extremes

(To better understand these tables, see full explanation of terms beginning on page 322)

Month	Normal Degree days Base 65 °F: Heating	Normal Degree days Base 65 °F: Cooling	Precipitation in inches %, Water equivalent: Normal	Water equivalent: Maximum monthly	Year	Water equivalent: Minimum monthly	Year	Water equivalent: Maximum in 24 hrs.	Year	Snow, Ice pellets: Maximum monthly	Year	Snow, Ice pellets: Maximum in 24 hrs.	Year
(a)				32		32		32		31		31	
J	1001	0	3.56	7.71	1948	0.26	1955	2.86	1944	15.9	1961	14.4	1964
F	871	0	3.37	5.98	1958	1.46	1946	2.59	1966	35.2	1967	13.1	1967
M	741	0	4.31	6.80	1953	0.62	1945	2.27	1968	17.6	1969	11.5	1969
A	399	0	3.37	7.95	1952	1.24	1945	3.37	1952	3.2	1965	3.2	1965
M	131	25	3.54	11.51	1948	0.40	1957	4.15	1959	0.0		0.0	
J	9	168	3.38	6.36	1970	0.10	1954	2.91	1952	0.0		0.0	
J	0	313	4.36	13.09	1959	1.30	1957	6.46	1959	0.0		0.0	
A	0	260	4.90	11.98	1967	0.34	1943	6.40	1966	0.0		0.0	
S	35	98	2.99	6.27	1966	0.41	1970	3.98	1954	0.0		0.0	
O	262	0	3.46	7.50	1943	0.15	1963	2.95	1958	T	1972	T	1972
N	570	0	4.21	9.65	1972	0.72	1946	3.93	1953	7.8	1967	7.8	1967
D	927	0	4.01	7.33	1969	0.62	1955	2.75	1951	8.6	1960	7.5	1960
YR	4946	864	45.46	13.09	JUL 1959	0.10	JUN 1954	6.46	JUL 1959	35.2	FEB 1967	14.4	JAN 1964

Month	Relative humidity pct. Hour 01 (Local time)	Hour 07	Hour 13	Hour 19	Wind: Mean speed m.p.h.	Wind: Prevailing direction	Fastest mile: Speed m.p.h.	Fastest mile: Direction	Fastest mile: Year	Pct. of possible sunshine	Mean sky cover, tenths, sunrise to sunset	Mean number of days, Sunrise to sunset: Clear	Partly cloudy	Cloudy	Precipitation .01 inch or more	Snow, Ice pellets 1.0 inch or more	Thunderstorms	Heavy fog, visibility ¼ mile or less	Temperatures °F Max. (b) 90° and above	Max. 32° and below	Min. 32° and below	Min. 0° and below	Average station pressure mb. Elev. 67 feet m.s.l.
(a)	11	11	11	11	17	5	16	16		15	17	17	17	17	32	31	17	17	11	11	11	11	3
J	73	75	57	69	11.8	WNW	47	29	1971	49	6.3	9	7	15	11	1	*	4	0	7	24	1	1017.4
F	74	77	57	67	12.2	W	43	27	1960	48	6.5	7	7	14	10	2	*	4	0	5	22	1	1015.4
M	76	77	55	66	12.5	WNW	46	24	1973	51	6.3	8	8	15	11	1	1	4	0	1	18	0	1013.3
A	77	76	51	65	12.3	S	46	07	1961	53	6.3	7	10	13	11	*	2	3	*	0	7	0	1012.4
M	84	79	57	70	10.8	S	35	31	1973	54	6.4	6	12	13	10	0	3	4	1	0	*	0	1012.2
J	89	85	60	74	9.7	S	37	29	1964	58	6.2	7	11	12	9	0	5	5	4	0	0	0	1013.7
J	89	85	59	74	9.1	S	37	26	1970	60	6.3	7	10	14	9	0	6	4	5	0	0	0	1013.8
A	90	87	57	76	8.7	S	35	12	1971	62	6.0	8	10	13	9	0	5	4	5	0	0	0	1015.5
S	89	88	58	80	9.3	ENE	60	32	1960	59	5.7	10	8	12	8	0	2	4	2	0	*	0	1016.4
O	86	87	56	78	9.7	W	41	29	1961	57	5.3	11	8	12	7	0	1	5	0	0	4	0	1018.0
N	80	82	57	74	11.1	W	40	27	1960	50	6.1	8	9	13	9	*	1	3	0	*	13	0	1016.0
D	76	77	59	72	11.3	WNW	55	36	1960	42	6.5	8	7	16	9	1	*	4	0	2	21	*	1016.2
YR	82	81	57	72	10.7	S	60	32	SEP 1960	54	6.1	96	107	162	113	4	26	48	16	15	110	1	1015.0

FOOTNOTES

Means and extremes above are from existing and comparable exposures. Annual extremes have been exceeded at other sites in the locality as follows: Lowest temperature -9 in February 1934; maximum monthly precipitation 14.87 in August 1882; minimum monthly precipitation .01 in September 1941; maximum precipitation in 24 hours 9.21 in October 1903; maximum snowfall in 24 hours 18.0 in February 1902.

% Based on U.S. Naval Air Station and Weather Bureau Airport Station records.

Snowfall

Season	July	Aug	Sept	Oct	Nov	Dec	Jan
1936-37	0.0	0.0	0.0	0.0	0.1	T	0.0
1937-38	0.0	0.0	0.0	0.0	0.0	0.5	T
1938-39	0.0	0.0	0.0	0.0	5.9	T	4.8
1939-40	0.0	0.0	0.0	0.0	T	5.6	13.8
1940-41	0.0	0.0	0.0	T	0.0	0.8	0.2
1941-42	0.0	0.0	0.0	0.0	0.0	T	3.3
1942-43	0.0	0.0	0.0	0.0	T	3.0	0.2
1943-44	0.0	0.0	0.0	0.0	T	T	3.2
1944-45	0.0	0.0	0.0	0.0	T	0.8	0.1
1945-46	0.0	0.0	0.0	0.0	1.1	12.4	5.1
1946-47	0.0	0.0	0.0	0.0	0.0	0.3	2.9
1947-48	0.0	0.0	0.0	0.0	0.0	6.5	8.5
1948-49	0.0	0.0	0.0	0.0	0.0	0.6	T
1949-50	0.0	0.0	0.0	0.0	T	0.0	0.5
1950-51	0.0	0.0	0.0	0.0	T	T	0.7
1951-52	0.0	0.0	0.0	0.0	T	1.6	T
1952-53	0.0	0.0	0.0	0.0	2.6	T	0.1
1953-54	0.0	0.0	0.0	0.0	T	T	11.8
1954-55	0.0	0.0	0.0	0.0	0.0	0.7	1.0
1955-56	0.0	0.0	0.0	0.0	T	T	6.6
1956-57	0.0	0.0	0.0	0.0	0.0	T	7.9
#1957-58	0.0	0.0	0.0	0.0	T	4.6	12.7
1958-59	0.0	0.0	0.0	0.0	0.0	5.1	2.7
1959-60	0.0	0.0	0.0	0.0	T	1.5	0.6
1960-61	0.0	0.0	0.0	T	0.0	8.6	15.9
1961-62	0.0	0.0	0.0	0.0	0.0	1.0	7.1
1962-63	0.0	0.0	0.0	T	T	5.1	4.4
1963-64	0.0	0.0	0.0	0.0	0.0	7.6	15.1
1964-65	0.0	0.0	0.0	0.0	T	1.0	8.2
1965-66	0.0	0.0	0.0	0.0	0.0	0.0	15.1
1966-67	0.0	0.0	0.0	0.0	T	8.5	1.1
1967-68	0.0	0.0	0.0	0.0	7.8	3.9	0.8
1968-69	0.0	0.0	0.0	0.0	T	4.3	0.5
1969-70	0.0	0.0	0.0	0.0	T	0.6	10.3
1970-71	0.0	0.0	0.0	0.0	0.0	1.4	7.2
1971-72	0.0	0.0	0.0	0.0	0.0	0.1	2.9
1972-73	0.0	0.0	0.0	T	T	T	0.0
1973-74	0.0	0.0	0.0	0.0	0.1	T	0.4
1974-75	0.0	0.0	0.0	0.0	0.2	T	3.3
1975-76	0.0	0.0	0.0	0.0	0.0	0.8	
RECORD MEAN	0.0	0.0	0.0	T	0.4	2.4	4.8

Heating Degree Days

Season	July	Aug	Sept	Oct	Nov	Dec	Jan
1955-56	0	0	25	157	563	992	978
1956-57	1	0	70	183	524	605	1019
#1957-58	0	1	40	258	427	699	962
1958-59	0	1	62	306	510	1132	1029
1959-60	0	0	48	254	586	800	914
1960-61	0	0	20	267	505	1074	1174
1961-62	0	0	29	226	525	920	977
1962-63	0	2	83	250	630	1007	1040
1963-64	0	1	102	170	438	1059	916
#1964-65	0	1	42	351	532	869	1152
1965-66	3	24	70	368	596	879	1125
1966-67	0	0	85	373	513	888	801
1967-68	0	1	149	399	757	922	1195
1968-69	0	18	45	314	629	1031	1068
1969-70	4	16	108	356	626	939	1174
1970-71	0	0	49	224	515	876	1117
1971-72	4	15	47	143	620	736	958
1972-73	5	8	28	410	612	691	885
1973-74	0	0	64	245	519	773	788
1974-75	0	0	68	393	557	800	857
1975-76	0	2	108	251	505	904	

Cooling Degree Days

Year	Jan	Feb	Mar	Apr	May	June	July
1969	0	0	0	17	65	170	264
1970	0	0	0	0	63	136	279
1971	0	0	0	0	6	178	228
1972	0	0	0	0	11	83	341
1973	0	0	0	10	21	233	321
1974	0	0	0	19	44	121	319
1975	0	0	0	0	74	164	305

Feb	Mar	Apr	May	June	Total
7.0	0.1	0.0	0.0	0.0	7.2
0.3	1.6	0.0	0.0	0.0	2.4
T	1.3	T	0.0	0.0	12.0
4.6	0.5	0.9	0.0	0.0	25.4
14.3	5.7	0.0	0.0	0.0	21.0
T	T	0.0	0.0	0.0	3.3
1.3	3.8	0.0	0.0	0.0	8.3
1.1	4.9	T	0.0	0.0	9.2
2.9	T	0.0	0.0	0.0	3.8
3.7	0.0	0.0	0.0	0.0	22.3
10.1	2.3	0.0	0.0	0.0	15.6
7.1	T	0.0	0.0	0.0	22.1
2.4	T	T	0.0	0.0	3.0
T	0.2	T	0.0	0.0	0.7
2.0	T	0.0	0.0	0.0	2.7
T	7.7	0.0	0.0	0.0	9.3
1.6	3.5	0.0	0.0	0.0	7.8
T	T	T	0.0	0.0	11.8
7.4	T	0.0	0.0	0.0	9.1
0.6	10.2	0.4	0.0	0.0	17.8
1.0	0.2	1.0	0.0	0.0	10.1
13.3	2.9	0.0	0.0	0.0	33.5
T	T	2.0	0.0	0.0	9.8
3.6	13.4	T	0.0	0.0	19.1
7.6	0.2	0.0	0.0	0.0	32.3
4.6	3.9	T	0.0	0.0	16.6
0.3	T	0.0	0.0	0.0	9.8
12.0	3.4	T	0.0	0.0	38.1
3.3	2.8	3.2	0.0	0.0	18.5
8.0	T	0.0	0.0	0.0	23.1
35.2	2.1	T	0.0	0.0	46.9
4.2	1.8	0.0	0.0	0.0	18.5
7.0	17.6	0.0	0.0	0.0	29.4
5.9	T	0.0	0.0	0.0	16.8
1.9	0.9	T	0.0	0.0	11.4
5.9	T	T	0.0	0.0	8.9
0.4	T	T	0.0	0.0	0.4
9.9	T	T	0.0	0.0	10.4
1.6	2.0	T	0.0	0.0	7.1
5.1	3.1	0.3	0.0	0.0	16.1

ATLANTIC CITY, NJ

Feb	Mar	Apr	May	June	Total
741	768	533	284	37	5078
721	701	394	173	29	4420
981	757	408	221	41	4795
852	740	367	131	23	5153
816	1009	311	140	12	4890
804	677	478	198	14	5211
860	743	392	134	12	4818
986	596	375	178	13	5160
913	674	461	121	33	4888
890	838	485	109	77	5346
971	726	529	275	43	5609
996	813	411	341	23	5244
1094	674	417	196	13	5817
926	847	354	150	29	5411
867	820	453	166	13	5542
814	798	514	228	29	5164
936	816	550	187	44	5056
842	523	414	207	3	4628
885	632	329	184	27	4446
790	763	566	121	17	4932

Aug	Sept	Oct	Nov	Dec	Total
282	129	18	0	0	945
285	187	20	0	0	970
191	129	17	12	0	761
282	132	4	0	0	853
345	113	20	0	0	1063
292	103	2	6	0	906
282	48	10	0	0	883

Average Temperature

Year	Jan	Feb	Mar	Apr	May	June	July	Aug	Sept	Oct	Nov	Dec	Annual
1936	31.2	28.8	43.8	47.6	60.4	67.2	73.8	74.2	68.1	59.4	45.1	41.2	53.4
1937	43.4	36.0	40.0	49.6	60.8	69.5	75.8	74.0	65.8	56.0	47.0	37.2	54.6
1938	35.8	38.8	44.0	52.0	59.4	67.1	73.0	75.0	67.0	57.8	50.0	39.4	54.9
1939	36.0	39.6	42.0	49.0	60.8	69.9	72.5	76.4	68.6	58.6	45.5	39.1	54.8
1940	25.0	34.5	37.2	45.4	57.4	69.2	73.4	71.8	66.6	53.8	47.4	41.6	51.9
1941	34.3	32.3	36.8	52.6	62.8	68.4	72.8	73.0	69.1	62.2	51.0	41.0	54.7
1942	33.7	32.2	43.4	51.7	62.4	70.4	76.3	73.4	69.4	59.8	49.6	35.2	54.8
1943	34.4	36.0	41.0	46.4	59.6	73.4	73.0	72.2	65.8	56.4	46.2	36.0	53.4
1944	36.0	35.9	39.6	47.8	61.2	69.8	73.3	72.9	68.7	57.2	46.6	35.2	53.7
1945	29.2	35.4	49.2	52.9	58.6	69.8	74.6	72.6	70.2	57.6	49.6	33.4	54.4
1946	35.5	36.2	47.3	50.6	60.3	66.4	72.5	71.9	68.6	61.2	51.8	41.7	55.3
1947	41.2	31.0	37.6	48.8	57.8	66.0	72.8	74.6	69.4	63.0	45.9	36.2	53.7
1948	29.4	34.4	42.0	49.0	57.9	68.0	74.0	73.7	68.2	56.6	52.6	40.8	53.8
1949	41.7	41.0	41.9	51.4	59.2	71.0	77.4	76.1	66.0	62.6	48.2	40.6	56.5
1950	44.3	37.1	38.4	47.3	56.3	67.7	73.5	72.2	65.2	59.9	49.2	36.7	54.0
1951	38.2	37.3	42.3	51.5	61.0	68.2	74.7	73.6	69.1	60.7	45.2	41.1	55.2
1952	38.8	38.7	40.9	52.8	60.0	71.6	77.5	74.6	69.1	55.6	48.8	40.2	55.7
1953	40.5	40.2	44.9	51.5	61.6	68.2	75.8	74.5	69.6	59.4	50.1	42.6	56.6
1954	34.9	40.7	42.0	51.5	58.9	69.0	73.9	72.5	69.0	61.8	46.8	37.1	54.8
1955	33.2	34.4	43.6	51.4	60.4	67.3	76.0	76.3	68.6	60.5	46.1	32.7	54.2
1956	33.2	39.2	40.0	47.1	56.0	68.8	72.4	73.5	66.3	58.9	47.3	45.2	54.0
1957	31.9	38.9	42.1	51.7	60.0	69.9	73.8	70.6	69.6	56.5	50.6	42.3	54.8
#1958	33.8	29.8	40.3	51.2	57.8	65.8	76.9	72.8	66.0	55.5	47.8	28.3	52.2
1959	31.5	34.3	40.9	52.6	64.1	71.4	74.6	76.1	69.7	59.5	45.3	39.0	54.9
1960	35.3	36.7	32.3	55.2	61.0	70.7	73.7	74.8	67.9	56.5	47.9	30.1	53.5
1961	26.9	36.1	43.0	49.1	59.2	69.4	76.6	74.9	73.4	58.1	47.7	35.1	54.6
1962	33.2	34.1	40.8	52.2	63.2	70.6	72.9	73.0	64.6	57.1	43.7	32.3	53.1
1963	31.3	29.5	45.5	52.5	60.3	70.5	76.1	72.4	63.9	59.9	50.2	30.5	53.5
#1964	35.3	33.2	43.1	49.7	64.0	70.9	76.3	72.2	67.6	53.5	47.0	36.8	54.1
1965	27.6	33.0	37.8	48.7	64.1	67.6	72.8	72.1	68.0	53.1	44.9	36.4	52.2
1966	28.5	30.1	41.4	47.2	56.6	70.2	75.2	73.4	65.2	52.7	47.7	36.2	52.0
1967	38.9	29.2	38.6	51.4	54.1	69.0	73.4	71.5	61.2	52.4	39.5	35.1	51.2
1968	26.1	27.1	43.0	51.0	58.9	70.1	74.2	73.9	66.5	55.0	43.8	31.5	51.8
1969	30.3	31.8	37.4	53.6	62.0	69.5	73.2	73.3	65.5	53.9	43.9	34.5	52.4
1970	26.9	33.8	38.2	49.6	61.5	68.9	73.7	73.9	69.4	58.2	47.6	36.5	53.2
1971	28.8	35.7	39.0	47.6	57.6	69.7	72.0	70.4	67.5	60.7	44.5	41.1	52.9
1972	33.9	32.5	38.4	46.5	59.1	66.1	75.6	73.5	68.2	51.6	44.3	42.5	52.7
1973	36.2	34.7	48.0	51.3	58.8	72.5	75.1	75.9	66.4	57.4	47.4	39.9	55.3
1974	39.3	33.2	44.4	54.5	60.3	68.0	75.0	74.2	65.9	52.2	46.3	39.0	54.3
1975	37.2	36.5	40.1	45.9	63.3	69.6	74.5	73.8	62.8	57.0	47.9	35.5	53.7
RECORD MEAN	32.2	33.0	40.7	50.5	60.5	69.7	74.5	73.5	66.6	55.8	46.0	35.6	53.2
MAX	41.2	42.0	50.1	61.0	71.0	79.9	83.8	82.9	76.6	66.4	55.6	44.5	62.9
MIN	23.1	24.0	31.3	39.9	49.9	59.4	65.2	64.0	56.6	45.2	36.3	26.6	43.5

# Indicates a station move or relocation of instruments.

Precipitation

Year	Jan	Feb	Mar	Apr	May	June	July	Aug	Sept	Oct	Nov	Dec	Annual
1936	5.92	4.71	3.87	3.32	2.47	4.50	3.74	3.01	5.74	2.30	0.67	7.65	47.90
1937	6.88	3.05	3.00	4.22	1.85	3.45	0.96	6.13	1.07	5.43	5.07	1.28	42.39
1938	3.26	2.19	1.97	2.20	3.56	4.61	7.08	3.91	11.76	3.19	3.59	1.82	49.14
1939	5.65	6.01	6.04	5.78	0.89	1.60	1.60	8.95	1.50	5.11	2.17	1.33	46.63
1940	1.78	3.51	4.60	5.84	4.69	1.55	4.89	4.18	1.55	1.48	4.82	2.53	41.42
1941	4.31	3.09	2.86	2.99	1.47	4.12	3.97	2.93	0.01	1.57	1.31	3.43	32.06
1942	2.92	2.22	5.22	1.28	1.45	1.46	5.45	9.95	3.62	6.59	2.21	3.96	46.23
1943	3.55	2.32	4.43	4.00	2.42	2.75	1.64	0.44	3.61	7.93	2.95	1.89	37.93
1944	4.45	2.64	5.32	5.79	1.01	4.21	1.50	2.91	5.76	4.01	9.06	2.36	49.02
1945	2.83	3.64	0.99	2.79	3.09	2.52	10.22	4.08	2.28	2.69	3.28	7.86	46.27
1946	2.77	1.97	3.58	1.89	4.74	3.41	3.87	2.92	1.93	1.44	1.37	1.98	31.87
1947	4.30	1.71	2.10	4.16	4.10	1.77	1.71	3.51	2.57	2.29	3.14	2.34	33.70
1948	8.14	3.36	3.48	3.13	8.80	4.21	4.08	8.23	0.64	3.19	8.87	6.07	62.20
1949	6.28	4.99	3.91	2.58	4.01	0.36	3.02	3.37	1.67	5.57	3.45	2.15	41.36
1950	2.48	3.81	3.74	1.89	2.52	3.11	3.28	3.77	5.83	1.32	3.67	3.04	38.46
1951	2.57	4.60	3.29	1.80	1.99	4.90	1.86	1.15	1.40	2.69	7.55	4.83	38.63
1952	5.46	1.87	5.48	6.94	6.01	1.29	1.64	7.44	1.20	0.90	4.21	4.51	46.95
1953	5.12	4.00	5.60	3.92	6.72	2.76	3.60	9.67	0.54	2.81	7.88	3.29	55.91
1954	3.04	1.38	2.72	3.33	2.44	0.28	1.65	4.73	5.06	1.67	4.04	3.68	34.02
1955	0.38	2.99	4.39	2.77	0.62	6.29	2.29	5.90	1.99	3.70	2.50	0.90	34.72
1956	2.87	3.58	4.40	2.71	2.36	4.12	4.79	3.25	3.03	5.88	2.44	4.15	43.58
1957	1.86	4.01	4.30	2.28	0.54	2.76	0.31	3.38	2.14	1.62	4.54	6.78	34.52
#1958	5.24	6.86	7.57	4.33	4.42	4.38	9.72	9.48	3.71	6.11	2.71	2.64	67.17
1959	1.59	1.86	3.84	3.33	5.03	1.29	13.09	3.57	1.48	4.37	5.15	3.15	47.75
1960	2.69	5.71	3.67	2.34	2.21	0.77	5.84	2.36	4.03	3.08	1.74	3.46	37.90
1961	4.06	4.51	6.36	3.12	3.17	3.00	3.40	1.73	3.36	4.73	2.83	3.38	43.65
1962	4.21	3.47	5.42	3.50	1.77	4.20	1.72	5.29	3.09	2.04	4.88	3.84	43.43
1963	2.94	2.50	5.21	1.39	2.95	3.07	2.60	2.93	4.35	0.15	6.46	2.35	36.90
1964	6.35	4.32	2.80	7.59	1.46	0.84	2.79	1.63	5.91	2.67	1.18	3.47	41.01
1965	3.58	2.44	3.75	2.00	2.59	1.24	2.61	2.40	1.60	1.18	0.79	1.09	25.27
1966	3.45	5.17	0.70	2.58	3.17	1.87	2.59	9.04	6.27	3.73	1.91	4.81	45.29
1967	1.16	3.24	3.78	2.76	3.68	1.37	4.19	11.98	1.50	2.86	1.72	5.57	43.81
1968	2.77	1.69	4.99	1.50	5.55	2.86	1.75	2.20	0.43	2.73	3.10	3.89	33.46
1969	1.68	2.38	3.19	3.55	1.68	1.42	12.64	2.56	1.65	2.09	4.28	7.33	44.45
1970	1.50	3.08	3.11	4.66	1.81	6.36	2.83	2.70	0.41	3.73	5.73	3.04	38.96
1971	2.67	5.26	1.64	1.29	1.88	0.69	3.65	10.40	4.39	4.20	5.02	2.08	43.17
1972	2.93	4.31	3.59	4.62	3.51	4.82	2.81	0.44	3.66	5.11	9.65	3.63	49.08
1973	3.26	3.63	3.08	4.39	3.08	4.32	3.28	2.05	4.73	2.74	1.43	5.48	41.47
1974	3.47	2.40	4.62	2.66	2.61	2.52	1.99	5.50	2.95	1.90	1.08	4.76	36.46
1975	5.94	3.08	3.84	3.90	5.44	3.86	6.02	5.01	5.16	1.76	3.76	2.53	50.30
RECORD MEAN	3.19	3.47	3.74	3.25	3.03	2.62	4.64	4.52	3.26	3.07	3.52	3.69	42.00

Record mean values above are means through the current year for the period beginning in June 1958 for temperature and precipitation, 1945 for snowfall. Data are from City Office locations through June 1958.

Station: NEWARK, NEW JERSEY INTERNATIONAL AIRPORT
Elevation (ground): 7 feet

TEMPERATURES °F

Month	Normal: Daily maximum	Normal: Daily minimum	Normal: Monthly	Extremes: Record highest	Extremes: Year	Extremes: Record lowest	Extremes: Year
(a)				10		10	
J	38.5	24.3	31.4	69	1974	1	1968
F	40.2	24.9	32.6	66	1974	4	1967
M	48.8	32.4	40.6	79	1968	8	1967
A	61.2	42.2	51.7	91	1974	26	1975
M	71.6	52.1	61.9	96	1969	35	1966
J	81.1	61.6	71.4	101	1966	46	1972
J	85.6	67.2	76.4	105	1966	59	1973
A	83.7	65.5	74.6	100	1973	50	1965
S	77.0	58.6	67.8	95	1973	41	1974
O	66.9	48.1	57.5	87	1967	28	1969
N	54.2	38.2	46.2	81	1974	20	1967
D	41.5	27.4	34.5	68	1966	8	1968
YR	62.5	45.2	53.9	105	JUL 1966	1	JAN 1968

IMPORTANT:
The time-period covered by this record is limited: See footnotes following table of NORMALS, MEANS AND EXTREMES for explanation and for additional history of EXTREME HIGHS AND LOWS recorded in the general area.

Terrain in vicinity of the station is flat and rather marshy. To the northwest are ridges oriented roughly in a SSW to NNE direction. They rise to an elevation of about 200 feet at four and one-half to five miles and to 500 to 600 feet at seven to eight miles. All winds between WNW and NNW are downslope and therefore are subject to some adiabatic temperature increase. This effect is evident in the rapid improvement which normally occurs with shift of wind to westerly following a coastal storm or front passage. The drying effect of the downslope winds accounts for the relatively few local convectional thunderstorms occurring at the station. Easterly winds, particularly SE, bring into play the ocean influence on the temperature. Temperature falls of from 5 to 15 degrees, depending on the season, are not uncommon when the wind backs from southwesterly to southeasterly. Periods of very hot weather, lasting as long as a week, are associated with a WSW flow of air which has a long trajectory over land on the left of the Bermuda high pressure system. Extremes of cold are related to rapidly moving outbreaks of cold air which travel southeastward from the Hudson Bay region. Temperatures of zero or below are experienced in one winter out of four. Average dates of the last occurrence in spring and the first occurrence in autumn, of temperatures as low as 32° are April 7 and November 2, respectively. A considerable amount of the annual precipitation is realized from the Northeasters of the Atlantic coast. These storms, more typi-

(Continued page 546)

Snowfall

Season	July	Aug	Sept	Oct	Nov	Dec	Jan
1936-37	0.0	0.0	0.0	0.0	2.0	0.5	3.0
1937-38	0.0	0.0	0.0	0.0	T	T	5.6
1938-39	0.0	0.0	0.0	0.0	14.2	0.7	10.9
1939-40	0.0	0.0	0.0	0.0	T	2.1	3.5
1940-41	0.0	0.0	0.0	T	1.5	3.6	13.2
#1941-42	0.0	0.0	0.0	0.0	T	1.0	5.7
1942-43	0.0	0.0	0.0	0.0	T	6.7	10.7
1943-44	0.0	0.0	0.0	0.0	T	T	6.3
1944-45	0.0	0.0	0.0	0.0	T	6.8	15.3
1945-46	0.0	0.0	0.0	0.0	2.9	16.5	3.5
1946-47	0.0	0.0	0.0	0.0	0.0	2.3	5.9
1947-48	0.0	0.0	0.0	0.0	T	29.1	16.4
1948-49	0.0	0.0	0.0	0.0	T	20.7	6.1
1949-50	0.0	0.0	0.0	0.0	0.4	1.5	0.5
1950-51	0.0	0.0	0.0	0.0	T	3.4	5.1
1951-52	0.0	0.0	0.0	0.0	T	4.9	3.7
1952-53	0.0	0.0	0.0	0.3	0.9	8.2	3.7
1953-54	0.0	0.0	0.0	0.0	2.4	T	10.6
1954-55	0.0	0.0	0.0	0.0	T	T	3.1
1955-56	0.0	0.0	0.0	0.0	2.2	3.8	2.4
1956-57	0.0	0.0	0.0	0.0	T	1.3	7.8
1957-58	0.0	0.0	0.0	T	T	16.2	6.3
1958-59	0.0	0.0	0.0	0.0	T	5.3	2.2
1959-60	0.0	0.0	0.0	0.0	0.4	9.1	3.6
1960-61	0.0	0.0	0.0	T	0.0	24.0	22.2
1961-62	0.0	0.0	0.0	0.0	0.8	13.2	1.0
1962-63	0.0	0.0	0.0	T	0.3	7.8	7.5
1963-64	0.0	0.0	0.0	0.0	T	10.7	13.5
1964-65	0.0	0.0	0.0	0.0	0.0	3.9	16.1
1965-66	0.0	0.0	0.0	T	0.0	T	10.2
1966-67	0.0	0.0	0.0	0.0	0.0	12.6	1.3
1967-68	0.0	0.0	0.0	0.0	3.1	3.9	4.6
1968-69	0.0	0.0	0.0	0.0	0.4	4.7	1.1
1969-70	0.0	0.0	0.0	0.0	T	8.5	9.1
1970-71	0.0	0.0	0.0	0.0	0.0	2.9	13.2
1971-72	0.0	0.0	0.0	0.0	T	0.4	3.1
1972-73	0.0	0.0	0.0	T	T	T	0.7
1973-74	0.0	0.0	0.0	0.0	0.0	2.1	6.8
1974-75	0.0	0.0	0.0	0.0	T	1.2	1.4
1975-76	0.0	0.0	0.0	0.0	T	2.4	
RECORD MEAN	0.0	0.0	0.0	T	0.4	6.9	6.8

Heating Degree Days

Season	July	Aug	Sept	Oct	Nov	Dec	Jan
1955-56	0	0	45	204	639	1101	1013
1956-57	9	2	117	244	565	767	1140
1957-58	0	0	54	289	495	796	1025
1958-59	0	0	37	323	520	1103	1036
1959-60	0	0	39	233	578	832	940
1960-61	0	0	14	247	485	1079	1185
1961-62	0	0	21	200	526	960	1052
1962-63	0	7	81	250	640	1046	1091
1963-64	0	0	108	139	454	1100	946
#1964-65	1	0	40	278	461	895	1133
1965-66	0	11	50	339	610	807	1066
1966-67	0	0	63	286	480	876	864
1967-68	0	1	58	285	677	823	1148
1968-69	0	0	6	193	573	1003	1039
1969-70	0	0	49	284	575	984	1255
1970-71	0	0	24	199	472	914	1160
1971-72	0	1	12	95	569	724	909
1972-73	0	0	22	356	599	776	906
1973-74	0	0	18	166	479	787	909
1974-75	0	0	62	341	521	802	864
1975-76	0	1	59	195	400	913	

Cooling Degree Days

Year	Jan	Feb	Mar	Apr	May	June	July
1969	0	0	0	15	80	243	293
1970	0	0	0	4	94	187	384
1971	0	0	0	0	25	307	403
1972	0	0	3	4	41	142	406
1973	0	0	0	20	26	296	432
1974	0	0	0	28	64	172	381
1975	0	0	0	0	117	211	375

Feb	Mar	Apr	May	June	Total
2.1	3.4	T	0.0	0.0	11.0
T	0.3	5.2	0.0	0.0	11.1
2.9	5.3	T	0.0	0.0	34.0
10.3	4.3	1.4	0.0	0.0	21.6
6.2	14.5	0.0	0.0	0.0	39.0
0.6	3.1	3.5	0.0	0.0	13.9
4.1	5.1	T	0.0	0.0	26.6
10.5	4.9	1.5	0.0	0.0	23.2
7.5	T	T	0.0	0.0	29.6
6.4	T	0.0	0.0	0.0	29.3
20.5	4.3	T	0.0	0.0	33.0
13.0	4.0	0.0	0.0	0.0	62.5
8.0	6.4	0.0	0.0	0.0	41.2
7.2	0.4	0.7	0.0	0.0	10.7
0.9	1.5	0.0	0.0	0.0	10.9
2.1	6.0	T	0.0	0.0	16.7
0.4	0.8	0.0	0.0	0.0	14.3
0.6	T	0.4	0.0	0.0	14.0
7.1	3.5	T	0.0	0.0	13.7
2.4	26.0	3.4	T	0.0	40.2
8.8	2.1	4.1	0.0	0.0	24.1
16.3	19.5	T	0.0	0.0	58.3
1.0	8.2	1.1	0.0	0.0	17.8
5.2	19.0	T	0.0	0.0	37.3
23.3	4.0	T	0.0	0.0	73.5
13.1	1.5	T	0.0	0.0	29.6
3.6	2.5	T	0.0	0.0	21.7
15.0	4.0	T	0.0	0.0	43.2
1.8	4.6	0.7	0.0	0.0	27.1
8.6	T	0.0	0.0	0.0	18.8
25.4	18.0	T	0.0	0.0	57.2
0.6	1.7	0.0	0.0	0.0	13.9
16.5	5.9	0.0	0.0	0.0	28.6
5.5	4.3	T	0.0	0.0	27.4
1.1	4.2	2.2	0.0	0.0	23.6
12.3	1.0	T	0.0	0.0	16.8
0.6	0.6	T	0.0	0.0	1.9
8.1	3.1	0.3	0.0	0.0	20.4
12.7	1.1	T	0.0	0.0	16.4
8.0	5.0	0.5	T	0.0	27.6

NEWARK, NJ

Feb	Mar	Apr	May	June	Total
833	864	516	218	19	5452
795	705	367	132	17	4860
1036	752	355	188	25	5015
928	761	343	101	27	5179
827	959	322	114	0	4844
814	729	487	169	3	5212
963	705	393	120	7	4947
1041	691	368	164	4	5383
955	687	473	88	21	4971
905	799	442	55	17	5026
882	717	500	212	14	5208
991	842	425	331	5	5163
1012	676	325	167	12	5184
938	804	317	101	2	4976
892	796	390	97	5	5327
827	732	402	155	7	4892
969	757	444	93	19	4592
882	504	339	163	1	4548
921	661	273	127	12	4353
832	775	524	84	6	4811

Aug	Sept	Oct	Nov	Dec	Total
390	131	17	0	0	1169
387	201	33	0	0	1290
350	222	46	12	0	1365
347	175	3	0	0	1121
459	205	28	0	0	1466
361	115	1	3	0	1125
321	46	20	10	0	1100

Average Temperature

Year	Jan	Feb	Mar	Apr	May	June	July	Aug	Sept	Oct	Nov	Dec	Annual
1936	27.7	24.4	44.4	47.4	63.5	69.2	74.9	74.2	66.6	55.8	41.4	38.0	52.3
1937	39.0	34.2	36.0	49.4	63.2	70.8	75.4	75.8	64.0	53.6	44.4	34.1	53.3
1938	31.0	35.0	43.6	53.2	59.7	69.4	75.5	76.6	63.8	57.4	46.4	35.7	53.9
1939	31.4	36.4	39.2	47.8	64.0	72.1	74.8	76.5	66.8	55.5	42.0	35.1	53.5
1940	23.7	32.2	34.4	45.8	59.9	68.4	74.3	70.0	64.0	51.8	43.6	37.1	50.4
#1941	29.0	30.6	35.4	56.2	63.0	70.6	75.0	71.9	68.0	58.8	47.4	36.9	53.6
1942	29.2	29.4	42.5	53.0	64.8	70.4	75.7	72.6	66.6	56.8	45.0	30.0	53.0
1943	29.8	32.3	38.8	45.9	61.9	75.4	75.8	74.5	65.7	53.6	43.2	31.2	52.3
1944	32.6	32.0	36.7	48.2	65.6	71.4	77.8	76.2	68.2	54.5	44.3	30.6	53.2
1945	24.0	32.9	50.6	55.2	58.8	70.8	74.1	72.4	69.6	54.2	46.0	29.0	53.1
1946	32.4	31.0	48.8	50.2	61.4	69.4	75.0	70.8	69.2	60.0	49.2	37.0	54.5
1947	36.5	28.2	37.6	50.2	59.9	67.8	75.5	75.6	67.6	61.0	43.2	32.9	53.0
1948	24.4	29.3	41.8	50.3	60.0	69.4	76.7	74.7	68.4	55.0	50.8	35.8	53.0
1949	37.6	38.2	42.5	53.2	62.4	73.6	79.6	76.2	65.0	61.6	44.2	38.3	56.0
1950	40.3	31.5	36.2	48.4	58.7	70.5	75.2	72.8	64.1	58.5	47.0	33.5	53.1
1951	35.4	35.5	41.7	52.6	62.8	69.6	76.1	74.2	67.1	57.9	42.1	37.2	54.4
1952	35.8	35.7	39.9	53.9	60.1	73.4	79.2	74.1	68.2	53.2	46.5	37.1	54.8
1953	36.6	37.5	42.9	51.4	62.8	72.7	77.2	74.8	69.0	58.8	47.3	39.2	55.9
1954	29.7	39.5	41.3	53.1	59.6	71.1	76.2	72.3	66.9	60.4	44.8	35.2	54.2
1955	30.7	34.2	41.4	53.3	64.7	68.9	80.5	77.7	67.1	58.8	43.5	29.3	54.2
1956	32.0	36.0	36.9	47.8	58.9	71.9	73.1	73.7	64.0	57.2	46.1	39.9	53.1
1957	28.0	36.4	42.0	53.3	62.9	73.8	77.3	73.0	69.5	55.6	48.3	39.1	54.9
1958	31.7	27.8	40.4	53.0	59.2	67.5	76.7	74.9	67.4	55.0	47.4	29.2	52.5
1959	31.4	31.6	40.3	53.5	65.7	71.6	76.7	77.6	71.5	59.9	45.5	38.0	55.3
1960	34.4	36.3	33.9	54.8	62.2	72.3	74.9	75.1	67.9	57.3	48.5	30.0	54.0
1961	26.6	35.8	41.2	48.6	59.7	71.9	77.3	75.8	74.5	59.5	47.4	33.8	54.4
1962	30.8	30.3	42.0	52.5	64.3	72.5	73.9	72.9	64.7	57.3	43.5	31.1	53.0
1963	29.6	27.6	42.5	52.6	61.1	72.0	77.0	74.0	64.0	61.2	49.7	29.3	53.4
1964	34.3	31.9	42.6	49.1	65.4	71.2	76.0	73.9	68.9	55.9	49.4	35.9	54.6
#1965	28.3	32.4	39.0	50.0	67.3	71.6	75.7	74.5	68.4	54.0	44.4	38.8	53.7
1966	30.4	33.2	41.7	48.2	59.3	73.8	79.6	76.5	66.6	55.5	48.9	36.5	54.2
1967	36.9	29.4	37.6	50.9	54.3	72.0	74.2	73.5	66.6	56.4	42.2	38.3	52.7
1968	27.8	29.9	43.1	54.0	59.6	69.7	78.2	76.9	70.7	59.7	45.7	32.5	54.0
1969	31.3	31.3	38.8	54.6	64.1	72.8	74.2	77.3	67.5	56.2	45.5	33.1	53.9
1970	24.2	33.0	39.0	51.9	64.6	70.9	77.2	77.3	70.6	59.5	49.1	35.3	54.4
1971	27.3	35.2	41.2	51.4	60.6	74.8	77.8	76.0	71.8	63.2	46.2	41.4	55.6
1972	35.4	31.3	40.5	50.0	63.0	68.8	77.9	75.9	69.8	53.3	44.8	39.7	54.2
1973	35.5	33.3	48.6	54.2	60.4	74.6	78.7	79.6	71.0	60.3	48.8	39.4	57.0
1974	35.4	31.9	43.4	56.5	62.7	70.1	77.1	76.5	66.6	53.9	47.5	38.9	55.0
1975	36.9	35.1	39.7	47.3	65.8	71.6	76.9	75.1	64.3	59.1	51.7	35.4	54.9
RECORD MEAN	32.0	32.4	40.6	51.1	61.9	71.2	76.3	74.6	67.6	57.0	46.0	35.1	53.8
MAX	39.0	40.0	48.7	60.5	71.6	80.7	85.5	83.6	76.7	66.3	53.9	42.1	62.4
MIN	24.9	24.8	32.4	41.7	52.1	61.6	67.0	65.6	58.4	47.6	38.1	28.0	45.2

# Indicates a station move or relocation of instruments.

Precipitation

Year	Jan	Feb	Mar	Apr	May	June	July	Aug	Sept	Oct	Nov	Dec	Annual
1936	6.28	2.50	4.24	2.63	2.02	5.74	2.40	3.52	4.05	4.30	0.94	6.63	45.25
1937	6.25	1.88	2.78	5.17	2.35	3.62	2.60	6.72	3.21	4.56	4.01	1.72	44.87
1938	3.48	1.78	2.11	2.91	2.63	5.49	7.96	1.92	6.29	1.77	3.69	2.73	42.76
1939	3.53	5.88	4.55	4.00	0.78	4.06	1.71	3.83	1.14	4.20	1.41	1.45	36.54
1940	2.52	2.77	4.77	5.95	8.10	3.60	2.63	4.36	3.51	2.32	3.76	3.11	47.40
#1941	3.15	2.82	2.59	2.93	0.98	4.59	4.08	6.20	0.14	2.03	2.87	3.92	36.30
1942	3.27	2.49	5.54	1.15	2.43	3.39	5.86	8.46	5.55	2.43	4.33	4.37	49.27
1943	2.80	1.98	3.61	2.50	6.16	3.12	4.64	3.89	2.65	8.20	2.36	1.47	43.38
1944	4.45	2.46	6.45	4.85	1.55	3.52	2.43	2.29	10.28	2.35	7.41	2.96	51.00
1945	2.94	2.96	2.63	2.89	5.53	4.17	6.15	2.62	5.98	3.35	5.01	4.33	48.56
1946	1.68	1.46	3.16	1.20	7.28	5.25	5.85	5.21	4.13	1.03	1.57	2.38	40.20
1947	3.32	2.59	2.18	5.31	5.38	3.69	2.25	4.82	3.98	2.20	7.37	3.78	46.87
1948	4.58	2.25	3.74	3.33	8.12	6.19	6.88	4.35	1.14	1.89	2.96	5.84	51.27
1949	6.33	3.69	1.95	4.13	4.01	0.07	2.95	2.66	3.06	1.59	1.15	2.47	34.06
1950	2.42	3.92	3.98	1.96	2.58	2.35	5.41	6.05	1.75	1.42	5.07	4.66	41.57
1951	4.06	3.62	5.83	3.12	5.16	2.65	4.83	2.56	0.95	4.21	6.75	4.85	48.59
1952	4.92	2.35	4.94	6.01	5.96	6.01	4.11	6.68	3.62	0.89	3.41	4.40	53.30
1953	5.57	2.75	8.49	6.07	4.21	1.79	2.77	1.91	1.25	3.50	1.56	3.85	43.72
1954	1.36	2.07	3.38	2.58	3.66	0.85	1.45	6.37	5.80	1.75	4.79	2.89	36.95
1955	0.81	2.89	4.06	2.25	2.30	2.94	1.14	11.84	2.29	6.70	3.06	0.27	40.55
1956	1.50	4.47	6.29	3.04	2.45	3.31	4.99	3.08	2.10	3.83	3.98	3.22	42.26
1957	1.77	2.77	2.73	5.45	1.87	1.54	1.51	2.64	3.80	2.13	3.13	5.74	35.08
1958	3.55	4.36	4.31	6.41	3.76	3.66	4.53	2.39	3.60	5.48	1.97	1.45	45.47
1959	2.40	1.89	4.09	2.05	1.47	3.60	2.49	6.94	2.45	4.22	3.94	4.17	39.71
1960	2.79	4.11	2.98	3.09	4.11	1.07	6.39	4.61	6.23	2.79	2.41	3.89	44.47
1961	3.34	3.97	4.96	5.28	3.35	2.46	7.95	4.22	1.49	2.06	2.64	3.65	45.37
1962	2.56	4.25	3.35	3.44	1.46	3.89	2.34	5.73	3.33	3.72	4.39	2.39	40.85
1963	2.19	2.16	3.92	0.90	2.37	2.01	2.24	1.93	3.94	0.21	5.68	1.97	29.52
1964	5.12	2.59	2.27	5.56	0.52	3.09	4.74	0.50	1.30	1.55	2.08	4.10	33.42
1965	2.86	2.91	2.81	2.60	1.23	1.23	1.73	2.87	2.20	2.31	1.48	1.86	26.09
1966	2.29	4.41	1.12	3.01	4.86	0.49	0.89	3.08	7.86	3.78	3.06	3.01	37.86
1967	1.15	3.00	5.86	2.84	3.57	3.31	7.53	5.53	1.35	2.87	2.35	4.65	44.01
1968	1.71	1.22	3.59	2.24	6.28	4.37	1.87	2.41	2.48	2.02	4.38	4.32	36.89
1969	1.47	2.68	3.53	3.51	2.73	2.53	7.11	2.24	6.63	1.75	2.80	4.97	41.95
1970	0.87	3.29	3.42	3.52	2.64	2.41	3.68	3.91	1.83	2.36	4.41	2.05	34.39
1971	2.74	4.44	3.29	1.35	3.65	1.48	6.98	10.63	7.88	2.96	3.86	1.51	50.77
1972	2.26	4.01	3.09	3.08	6.02	6.02	4.70	2.30	1.03	4.83	8.42	4.10	49.86
1973	3.65	3.39	3.63	5.77	3.56	4.03	3.63	3.36	3.39	3.35	1.29	7.24	46.29
1974	2.84	1.44	4.11	2.37	3.49	3.60	1.31	7.17	5.76	1.85	0.80	4.02	38.76
1975	3.99	2.56	2.94	2.29	3.27	6.40	8.02	4.36	9.00	3.24	3.67	2.91	52.65
RECORD MEAN	3.10	2.90	3.88	3.40	3.53	3.35	3.89	4.29	3.83	2.94	3.39	3.32	41.82

Record mean values above are means through the current year for the period beginning in 1931 for temperature and precipitation, 1942 for snowfall.

(Continued)

cal of the fall and winter, generally last for a minimum of two days and commonly produce between one and two inches of precipitation. Storms producing 4 inches or more of snow occur on the average of twice a winter with a maximum frequency of five. Snowstorms producing falls of eight inches or more have occurred in one-half the winters. As many as three such storms have been experienced in one winter. The average sea level pressure is 30.02 inches with extremes of 31.02 inches and 28.69 inches.

Normals, Means, and Extremes

Month	Normal Degree days Base 65 °F		Precipitation in inches												Relative humidity pct.			
			Water equivalent							Snow, Ice pellets					Hour 01	Hour 07	Hour 13	Hour 19
	Heating	Cooling	Normal	Maximum monthly	Year	Minimum monthly	Year	Maximum in 24 hrs.	Year	Maximum monthly	Year	Maximum in 24 hrs.	Year	(Local time)				
(a)				22		22		22		34		34		10	10	10	10
J	1042	0	2.91	5.12	1964	0.81	1955	1.78	1962	22.2	1961	13.7	1961	70	73	58	63
F	907	0	2.95	4.47	1956	1.22	1968	2.45	1961	25.4	1967	20.0	1961	67	71	56	60
M	756	0	3.93	6.29	1954	1.12	1966	2.58	1969	26.0	1956	17.6	1956	66	69	52	57
A	399	0	3.44	6.41	1958	0.90	1963	2.01	1958	4.1	1957	4.1	1957	64	64	46	52
M	143	47	3.60	6.28	1968	0.52	1964	4.11	1968	T	1956	T	1956	71	69	52	58
J	5	197	2.99	6.40	1975	0.49	1966	2.31	1973	0.0		0.0		75	73	55	62
J	0	353	4.03	8.02	1975	0.89	1966	3.40	1971	0.0		0.0		72	71	52	59
A	0	298	4.27	11.84	1955	0.50	1964	7.84	1971	0.0		0.0		74	74	52	60
S	34	118	3.44	9.00	1975	1.03	1972	5.27	1971	0.0		0.0		76	77	55	64
O	243	11	2.82	6.70	1955	0.21	1963	3.04	1973	0.3	1952	0.3	1952	75	77	53	64
N	564	0	3.61	8.42	1972	0.80	1974	3.78	1972	3.1	1967	3.1	1967	72	76	57	65
D	946	0	3.46	7.24	1973	0.27	1955	2.14	1973	29.1	1947	26.0	1947	73	75	62	68
YR	5039	1024	41.45	11.84	AUG 1955	0.21	OCT 1963	7.84	AUG 1971	29.1	DEC 1947	26.0	DEC 1947	71	73	54	61

(To better understand these tables, see full explanation of terms beginning on page 322)

Month	Wind					Pct. of possible sunshine	Mean sky cover, tenths, sunrise to sunset	Mean number of days												Average station pressure mb.
	Mean speed m.p.h.	Prevailing direction	Fastest mile					Sunrise to sunset			Precipitation .01 inch or more	Snow, Ice pellets 1.0 inch or more	Thunderstorms	Heavy fog, visibility ¼ mile or less	Temperatures °F (b) Max.		Min.			Elev. 30 feet m.s.l.
			Speed m.p.h.	Direction	Year			Clear	Partly cloudy	Cloudy					90° and above	32° and below	32° and below	0° and below		
(a)	32	22	27	27			30	34	34	34	34	34	34	34	10	10	10	10		3
J	11.2	NE	45	25	1951		6.4	8	8	15	11	2	*	3	0	9	23	0		1018.2
F	11.6	NW	46	23	1965		6.4	7	8	13	10	2	*	2	0	5	22	0		1016.4
M	12.1	NW	43	27	1950		6.3	8	8	15	12	1	1	2	0	1	13	0		1014.4
A	11.4	WNW	50	27	1951		6.4	7	9	14	11	*	2	1	*	0	2	0		1013.0
M	10.0	SW	50	32	1963		6.4	7	11	13	12	0	4	2	1	0	0	0		1013.1
J	9.3	SW	55	07	1952		6.1	7	11	12	10	0	5	1	4	0	0	0		1014.8
J	8.8	SW	45	18	1950		6.2	7	12	12	10	0	6	1	8	0	0	0		1014.4
A	8.7	SW	46	09	1955		6.0	8	12	11	9	0	4	1	6	0	0	0		1016.3
S	9.0	SW	51	05	1960		5.6	10	9	11	8	0	2	1	2	0	0	0		1017.5
O	9.3	SW	48	11	1954		5.3	11	9	11	7	0	1	2	0	0	1	0		1019.2
N	10.1	SW	82	09	1950		6.3	8	8	14	10	*	*	2	0	0	6	0		1016.6
D	10.7	SW	55	32	1962		6.4	8	8	15	11	2	*	2	0	3	18	0		1017.5
YR	10.2	SW	82	09	NOV 1950		6.2	96	113	156	123	7	26	20	20	18	84	0		1016.0

FOOTNOTES

Means and extremes above are from existing and comparable exposures. Annual extremes have been exceeded at other sites in the locality as follows: Lowest temperature -14 in February 1934; maximum monthly precipitation 22.48 in August 1943; minimum monthly precipitation 0.07 in June 1949.

ALBUQUERQUE, NEW MEXICO

Station: ALBUQUERQUE, NEW MEXICO
INTL AIRPORT-KIRTLAND AFB
Elevation (ground): 5311 feet

TEMPERATURES °F

Month	Normal			Extremes			
	Daily maximum	Daily minimum	Monthly	Record highest	Year	Record lowest	Year
(a)				16		16	
J	46.9	23.5	35.2	69	1971	-17	1971
F	52.6	27.4	40.0	75	1972	1	1964
M	59.2	32.3	45.8	85	1971	9	1966
A	70.1	41.4	55.8	89	1965	22	1975
M	79.9	50.7	65.3	95	1974	28	1975
J	89.5	59.7	74.6	105	1974	42	1971
J	92.2	65.2	78.7	104	1971	54	1964
A	89.7	63.4	76.6	99	1972	52	1968
S	83.4	56.7	70.1	95	1975	37	1971
O	71.7	44.7	58.2	87	1972	25	1975
N	57.1	31.8	44.5	77	1975	10	1975
D	47.5	24.9	36.2	68	1966	3	1974
YR	70.0	43.5	56.8	105	JUN 1974	-17	JAN 1971

IMPORTANT:
The time-period covered by this record is limited: See footnotes on next page for explanation and for additional history of EXTREME HIGHS AND LOWS recorded in the general area.

Arid Continental' characterizes the climate of Albuquerque and vicinity in a minimum number of words. With an average annual rainfall of near eight inches there is generally insufficient natural moisture to maintain the growth of any but the most hardy desert vegetation. However, successful farming is carried on in the valley by irrigation and consid rable fruit and produce are raised. In the mountains east of the City precipitation is considerably heavier. At Tijeras Ranger Station, about 15 miles east of Albuquerque, the average annual rainfall is around 15 inches. Some dryland farming is carried on in this mountain area and native vegetation shows the effect of the heavier rainfall with good native grass cover and timbered mountains. The average monthly precipitation at Albuquerque varies from less than one-half inch during the winter months, November through March, to over an inch and a quarter during the months of July and August. With normally less than two inches of moisture, the winters are generally very dry. A considerable portion of this meager winter precipitation falls in the form of snow, but the monthly fall exceeds 3 inches infrequently and there are normally only four days a year when as much as one inch of snow occurs. Snow rarely remains on the ground in the valley for more than 24 hours but in the nearby mountains, snow cover is normal from the middle of December until early spring and a modern ski resort operates during the winter months just 25 miles from the City. The July-September period furnishes almost half of the annual moisture with most of the rain falling in the form of brief but at times rather heavy thundershowers. Prolonged rainy spells are practically unknown. These summer showers do not materially interfere with outdoor activities but do have a considerable moderating effect on summer daytime temperatures.

Temperatures in Albuquerque are those characteristic of high altitude, dry, continental climates. The average daily range of temperature is relatively high but extreme temperatures are rare as testified by the fact that there is normally less than one day a year when the temperature reaches 100° or drops to zero. Daytime temperatures during the winter average near 50° with only a few days on which the temperature does not rise above the freezing mark. In the summer, daytime maxima average less than 90° except in July and with the large daily range, the nights normally are comfortably cool. The air is normally dry with an average annual relative humidity of approximately 43%. "Muggy" days are unknown and the usual humidity during the warmer part of the day is about 30%, dropping down to less than 20% in June, the least humid month of the year.

Another feature of the climate is the large number of clear days and the high percentage of sunshine. Sunshine is recorded during more than three-fourths of the hours from sunrise to sunset and this high percentage carries through the winter months when clear, sunny weather predominates. Wind movement throughout the year averages around nine miles per hour, but during the late winter and spring months the average is somewhat higher and occasional windy and dusty days occur. These occasional dust storms are the most discomforting part of Albuquerque's climate. However there are on an average only 46 days during the year when the maximum wind speed reaches 32 miles per hour. Tornadoes rarely occur in the vicinity of Albuquerque.

ALBUQUERQUE, NEW MEXICO

Normals, Means, and Extremes

(To better understand these tables, see full explanation of terms beginning on page 322)

Month	Normal Degree days Base 65 °F: Heating	Normal Degree days Base 65 °F: Cooling	Precipitation in inches, Water equivalent: Normal	Maximum monthly	Year	Minimum monthly	Year	Maximum in 24 hrs.	Year	Snow, Ice pellets: Maximum monthly	Year	Maximum in 24 hrs.	Year	Relative humidity pct. Hour 05 (Local time)	Hour 11	Hour 17	Hour 23	Wind: Mean speed m.p.h.	Prevailing direction	Fastest mile: Speed m.p.h.	Direction	Year	Pct. of possible sunshine	Mean sky cover, tenths, sunrise to sunset	Mean number of days, Sunrise to sunset: Clear	Partly cloudy	Cloudy	Precipitation .01 inch or more	Snow, Ice pellets 1.0 inch or more	Thunderstorms	Heavy fog, visibility ¼ mile or less	Temperatures °F Max.: (b) 90° and above	32° and below	Min.: 32° and below	0° and below	Average station pressure mb. Elev. 5314 feet m.s.l.
(a)				36		36		36		36		36		15	15	15	15	36	15	36	36		36	36	36	36	36	36	36	36	36	15	15	15	15	3
J	924	0	0.30	1.17	1941	T	1970	0.87	1962	9.5	1973	5.1	1973	68	49	37	58	8.0	N	61	E	1949	73	4.8	13	8	10	4	1	*	1	0	3	29	1	837.9
F	700	0	0.39	1.42	1948	0.04	1959	0.48	1957	8.2	1964	4.2	1946	63	43	32	52	8.8	N	68	NW	1944	73	4.9	12	7	9	4	1	*	1	0	1	24	0	838.0
M	595	0	0.47	2.18	1973	T	1966	1.11	1973	13.9	1973	10.7	1973	54	32	23	42	10.0	SE	80	NW	1943	74	5.0	12	10	9	4	1	1	1	0	*	17	0	833.6
A	282	6	0.48	1.97	1942	T	1972	1.66	1969	8.1	1973	6.6	1973	45	25	17	33	10.9	S	72	S	1946	77	4.5	13	9	8	3	*	2	*	0	0	5	0	834.9
M	58	67	0.53	3.07	1941	T	1945	1.14	1969	T	1951	T	1951	43	22	16	30	10.5	S	72	W	1950	80	4.1	15	10	6	4	0	4	*	3	0	*	0	836.0
J	0	291	0.50	1.71	1967	T	1975	1.64	1952	0.0		0.0		44	23	17	31	10.0	S	82	SE	1946	83	3.2	18	9	3	4	0	5	*	16	0	0	0	837.5
J	0	425	1.39	3.33	1968	0.14	1958	1.77	1961	0.0		0.0		61	35	28	49	9.1	SE	68	E	1945	76	4.6	12	14	5	9	0	12	*	23	0	0	0	840.4
A	0	360	1.34	3.30	1967	T	1962	1.22	1967	0.0		0.0		65	39	30	52	8.1	SE	61	SE	1951	76	4.2	14	12	5	9	0	11	*	16	0	0	0	840.6
S	7	160	0.77	1.99	1940	T	1957	1.92	1955	T	1971	T	1971	59	40	31	52	8.5	SE	62	SE	1945	80	3.4	17	8	5	6	0	5	*	3	0	0	0	840.3
O	218	7	0.79	3.08	1972	0.00	1952	1.80	1969	0.5	1970	0.5	1970	59	37	29	48	8.3	SE	66	N	1959	79	3.4	18	7	6	5	0	3	*	0	0	2	0	840.4
N	615	0	0.29	1.45	1940	0.00	1949	0.76	1940	9.3	1940	5.5	1946	64	42	35	53	7.8	N	57	NW	1948	78	3.9	16	7	7	3	*	1	1	0	*	16	0	838.8
D	893	0	0.52	1.85	1959	0.00	1956	1.35	1958	14.7	1959	14.2	1958	70	51	43	61	7.7	N	90	SE	1943	72	4.6	14	8	9	4	1	*	1	0	2	29	0	839.0
YR	4292	1316	7.77	3.33	JUL 1968	0.00	DEC 1956	1.92	SEP 1955	14.7	DEC 1959	14.2	DEC 1958	58	37	28	47	9.0	SE	90	SE	DEC 1943	77	4.2	174	109	82	59	4	43	5	61	6	121	1	838.1

FOOTNOTES Means and extremes above are from existing and comparable exposures. Annual extremes have been exceeded at other sites in the locality as follows: Maximum monthly precipitation 8.15 in June 1852 (measured by Medical Officers of Army at Army Post near plaza).

Snowfall

Season	July	Aug	Sept	Oct	Nov	Dec	Jan
1936-37	0.0	0.0	T	0.0	0.0	1.5	4.0
1937-38	0.0	0.0	0.0	0.0	0.0	1.0	T
1938-39	0.0	0.0	0.0	T	0.1	0.1	1.0
#1939-40	0.0	0.0	0.0	0.0	T	0.3	T
1940-41	0.0	0.0	0.0	0.0	9.3	0.5	0.9
1941-42	0.0	0.0	0.0	0.0	0.4	2.0	2.1
1942-43	0.0	0.0	0.0	0.0	T	T	1.0
1943-44	0.0	0.0	0.0	0.0	T	4.0	4.9
1944-45	0.0	0.0	0.0	0.0	T	1.0	1.0
1945-46	0.0	0.0	T	0.0	0.0	2.6	3.8
1946-47	0.0	0.0	0.0	0.0	6.5	T	0.3
1947-48	0.0	0.0	0.0	0.0	5.7	5.1	3.1
1948-49	0.0	0.0	0.0	0.0	T	0.2	2.8
1949-50	0.0	0.0	0.0	T	0.0	5.0	T
1950-51	0.0	0.0	0.0	0.0	T	0.0	6.0
1951-52	0.0	0.0	0.0	0.0	T	3.0	T
1952-53	0.0	0.0	0.0	0.0	2.7	0.9	T
1953-54	0.0	0.0	0.0	0.0	7.5	3.7	2.9
1954-55	0.0	0.0	0.0	0.0	0.0	1.4	3.0
1955-56	0.0	0.0	0.0	0.0	T	1.0	2.9
1956-57	0.0	0.0	0.0	0.0	T	0.0	1.5
1957-58	0.0	0.0	0.0	T	T	2.9	2.3
1958-59	0.0	0.0	0.0	T	2.2	14.2	1.7
1959-60	0.0	0.0	0.0	T	0.0	14.7	1.8
1960-61	0.0	0.0	0.0	0.0	0.0	2.5	0.6
1961-62	0.0	0.0	0.0	T	3.4	2.4	4.0
1962-63	0.0	0.0	0.0	0.0	T	1.0	2.5
1963-64	0.0	0.0	0.0	0.0	T	T	0.5
1964-65	0.0	0.0	0.0	0.0	T	0.3	1.4
1965-66	0.0	0.0	0.0	0.0	T	3.0	5.4
1966-67	0.0	0.0	0.0	0.0	T	T	T
1967-68	0.0	0.0	0.0	0.2	1.0	2.8	T
1968-69	0.0	0.0	0.0	0.0	T	7.4	T
1969-70	0.0	0.0	0.0	0.0	T	1.1	T
1970-71	0.0	0.0	0.0	0.5	T	0.5	3.0
1971-72	0.0	0.0	T	T	T	6.8	1.2
1972-73	0.0	0.0	0.0	T	2.9	1.2	9.5
1973-74	0.0	0.0	0.0	0.3	0.6	0.1	9.3
1974-75	0.0	0.0	0.0	0.0	T	4.9	0.9
1975-76	0.0	0.0	0.0	0.0	0.2	2.9	
RECORD MEAN	0.0	0.0	T	T	1.2	2.8	2.2

Heating Degree Days

Season	July	Aug	Sept	Oct	Nov	Dec	Jan
1955-56	0	0	1	139	590	764	736
1956-57	0	0	0	195	715	880	771
#1957-58	0	0	3	269	739	817	914
1958-59	0	0	35	249	562	722	948
#1959-60	0	0	20	250	628	823	987
1960-61	0	0	3	256	548	956	956
1961-62	0	0	43	248	731	951	1030
1962-63	0	0	22	208	534	863	1098
1963-64	0	0	0	124	573	931	1076
1964-65	2	0	20	173	632	909	805
1965-66	0	0	56	217	492	895	1074
1966-67	0	0	15	247	541	942	980
1967-68	0	0	13	220	557	1003	870
1968-69	2	0	12	208	660	1080	831
1969-70	0	0	1	348	701	795	938
1970-71	0	0	58	380	605	878	968
1971-72	0	0	101	341	587	1022	889
1972-73	0	3	14	244	740	925	1020
1973-74	0	0	43	257	606	955	963
1974-75	0	2	68	212	593	1020	1051
1975-76	0	0	47	256	664	905	

Cooling Degree Days

Year	Jan	Feb	Mar	Apr	May	June	July
1969	0	0	0	6	127	263	478
1970	0	0	0	0	105	246	461
1971	0	0	5	0	26	277	414
1972	0	0	0	5	52	267	428
1973	0	0	0	0	48	267	422
1974	0	0	0	5	144	464	380
1975	0	0	0	0	25	256	372

Feb	Mar	Apr	May	June	Total
T	4.4	1.5	0.0	0.0	11.4
2.5	T	0.1	T	0.0	3.6
3.0	0.5	0.2	0.0	0.0	4.9
3.7	T	T	0.0	0.0	4.0
0.5	2.0	T	0.0	0.0	13.2
3.0	7.1	T	0.0	0.0	14.6
T	T	0.0	0.0	0.0	1.0
T	1.0	3.0	0.0	0.0	12.9
2.0	T	2.0	0.0	0.0	6.0
4.2	6.0	0.0	0.0	0.0	16.6
T	T	T	0.0	0.0	6.8
6.1	1.0	0.0	0.0	0.0	21.0
2.4	3.0	4.6	0.0	0.0	13.0
T	T	T	0.0	0.0	5.0
1.0	T	T	T	0.0	7.0
T	2.0	T	0.0	0.0	5.0
3.8	T	0.0	0.0	0.0	7.4
T	T	0.0	0.0	0.0	14.1
1.2	T	0.0	0.0	0.0	5.6
4.5	0.0	T	0.0	0.0	8.4
T	T	T	0.0	0.0	1.5
0.5	7.3	T	0.0	0.0	13.0
0.6	4.8	T	0.0	0.0	23.5
0.8	2.8	0.0	0.0	0.0	20.1
0.4	3.0	T	0.0	0.0	6.5
T	0.2	0.0	0.0	0.0	10.0
0.8	2.5	0.0	0.0	0.0	6.8
8.2	1.3	T	0.0	0.0	10.0
3.6	T	T	0.0	0.0	5.3
1.0	0.0	T	0.0	0.0	9.4
1.0	1.1	T	0.0	0.0	2.1
2.0	1.4	T	0.0	0.0	7.4
1.8	5.5	T	0.0	0.0	14.7
2.7	3.3	0.0	0.0	0.0	7.1
2.3	0.5	T	0.0	0.0	6.8
1.1	0.0	T	0.0	0.0	9.1
1.8	13.9	8.1	0.0	0.0	37.4
0.6	2.0	0.0	0.0	0.0	12.9
6.7	3.8	0.2	0.0	0.0	16.5
1.9	2.1	0.5	T	0.0	10.7

Average Temperature

Year	Jan	Feb	Mar	Apr	May	June	July	Aug	Sept	Oct	Nov	Dec	Annual
1936	32.6	39.9	47.1	55.4	65.0	74.3	77.0	76.4	66.2	55.2	42.0	35.2	55.5
1937	26.4	37.3	43.4	54.0	64.5	70.8	76.8	77.8	69.9	58.0	45.6	37.8	55.2
1938	36.0	40.4	46.2	54.4	62.8	73.2	75.9	76.7	67.4	57.6	38.0	37.7	55.5
#1939	34.4	30.0	46.2	56.0	65.5	74.3	76.2	75.7	70.6	56.0	44.2	40.0	55.8
1940	35.2	39.2	49.0	54.4	65.5	73.4	78.2	74.2	68.4	58.8	41.4	39.2	56.4
1941	36.0	42.8	45.0	50.6	63.8	70.2	76.0	75.1	67.3	56.6	45.5	37.7	55.6
1942	37.0	36.2	43.3	54.8	64.4	74.8	78.8	75.8	68.6	57.8	48.1	40.8	56.7
1943	38.6	43.6	48.2	60.9	65.8	74.0	79.0	78.4	70.2	56.8	44.3	32.1	57.7
1944	29.2	40.0	44.4	52.2	63.9	73.3	76.4	76.3	68.6	58.7	43.0	36.2	55.2
1945	36.8	43.0	45.0	52.3	66.2	72.6	78.4	78.2	70.6	58.6	45.2	33.4	56.7
1946	33.5	40.2	47.9	61.3	64.0	77.5	78.3	75.9	71.3	56.3	41.6	40.4	57.4
1947	33.0	42.2	47.4	54.5	67.0	72.8	80.2	76.0	72.6	60.4	40.4	34.6	56.8
1948	33.7	37.6	40.9	59.3	66.7	73.8	79.6	77.6	71.4	57.2	40.6	38.2	56.4
1949	30.3	37.2	47.9	55.5	64.8	73.7	77.7	76.3	71.8	56.2	50.7	34.1	56.4
1950	37.5	44.8	47.9	58.5	65.7	76.1	76.8	76.3	67.9	65.8	48.3	42.3	59.0
1951	36.6	39.8	46.3	54.8	66.5	74.7	82.6	76.6	71.9	58.8	42.2	36.2	57.2
1952	39.0	39.4	42.3	55.9	66.4	78.1	78.2	79.9	70.7	61.0	40.1	33.7	57.0
1953	42.2	38.7	48.8	55.1	61.5	78.1	80.0	77.7	73.0	59.2	46.3	32.8	57.8
1954	38.4	46.8	46.0	62.8	67.0	76.4	81.3	76.6	72.8	61.4	48.7	36.1	59.5
1955	33.8	34.8	47.4	55.1	63.9	73.9	77.0	76.9	72.5	61.1	45.1	40.0	56.8
1956	41.1	36.0	49.2	55.3	69.6	78.9	78.4	76.3	74.1	60.3	41.0	36.3	58.1
1957	39.9	48.1	47.3	54.2	61.9	74.8	79.1	76.0	70.3	56.6	40.3	38.5	57.3
#1958	35.3	43.5	42.8	53.0	68.6	78.5	79.6	78.9	69.2	56.9	46.0	41.5	57.8
1959	34.3	39.5	45.9	57.0	65.1	77.0	78.6	76.2	70.6	56.8	43.9	38.2	56.9
#1960	33.0	36.5	49.9	57.9	64.7	76.6	78.7	78.4	71.8	56.5	46.5	33.9	57.1
1961	33.9	40.6	47.0	54.5	65.9	75.8	76.7	75.2	65.6	56.8	40.3	34.1	55.5
1962	31.6	42.3	41.2	58.1	64.1	72.7	76.3	77.6	69.4	58.1	46.9	36.9	56.3
1963	29.4	40.5	45.2	57.7	68.0	74.6	81.4	75.9	72.5	61.5	45.7	34.8	57.3
1964	30.0	29.1	41.5	51.7	65.8	73.6	78.2	76.8	69.3	59.4	43.7	35.5	54.5
1965	38.8	39.4	44.6	54.8	61.7	69.4	77.9	75.4	66.6	58.0	48.4	35.8	55.9
1966	30.1	33.2	45.6	54.6	67.2	72.8	79.8	75.7	68.4	56.8	46.7	34.3	55.4
1967	33.2	40.5	52.0	57.8	63.8	71.5	79.2	74.5	68.4	58.2	46.1	32.4	56.5
1968	36.8	43.3	46.7	53.4	62.7	75.2	76.1	72.4	68.0	58.3	42.8	30.0	55.5
1969	38.0	38.5	41.1	57.4	66.2	73.6	80.2	79.0	70.0	53.8	41.4	39.1	56.6
1970	34.5	42.8	44.1	52.5	66.2	72.7	79.6	77.8	67.5	52.6	44.5	36.4	56.0
1971	33.6	38.9	47.7	53.3	61.7	73.8	78.1	73.9	66.4	53.8	45.2	31.9	54.8
1972	36.1	42.5	53.6	56.9	64.0	73.7	78.6	74.1	68.1	57.6	40.1	35.0	56.7
1973	31.8	35.9	45.1	50.2	62.7	73.5	78.4	78.0	67.5	56.4	44.6	34.0	54.8
1974	33.6	37.9	52.8	56.4	68.5	80.1	77.0	72.7	66.1	58.1	45.0	32.0	56.7
1975	30.8	38.0	45.0	49.9	61.0	73.0	76.8	76.1	66.3	56.5	42.6	35.6	54.3
RECORD MEAN	34.5	39.5	46.3	54.8	63.8	73.3	77.1	75.1	68.4	56.8	43.9	35.1	55.7
MAX	47.0	52.7	60.7	69.8	79.0	88.8	90.9	88.6	82.2	71.1	57.5	47.3	69.6
MIN	21.9	26.2	31.9	39.7	48.6	57.8	63.3	61.6	54.5	42.4	30.2	22.9	41.8

ALBUQUERQUE, NM

Feb	Mar	Apr	May	June	Total
836	483	288	20	0	3857
468	543	317	123	3	4015
596	679	354	24	0	4395
706	587	249	60	0	4118
819	462	211	82	0	4282
678	551	308	65	0	4321
629	730	214	78	2	4656
680	605	219	7	2	4238
1036	722	391	85	3	4941
709	624	300	128	24	4326
882	595	305	53	0	4569
682	396	211	109	0	4123
623	559	343	107	8	4303
735	735	228	84	0	4575
612	644	367	63	11	4480
725	533	343	122	5	4617
648	346	244	76	0	4254
811	607	440	113	3	4920
754	373	255	29	4	4239
748	614	449	143	6	4906

Precipitation

# Indicates a station move or relocation of instruments.

Year	Jan	Feb	Mar	Apr	May	June	July	Aug	Sept	Oct	Nov	Dec	Annual
1936	0.55	0.12	0.11	0.09	0.27	0.43	0.67	0.62	2.05	0.17	T	0.13	5.21
1937	0.21	0.11	0.63	0.42	2.78	1.91	1.02	0.22	0.67	0.79	0.01	0.48	9.45
1938	0.12	0.49	0.27	0.20	0.02	1.51	1.45	0.17	2.36	0.63	0.02	0.36	7.55
#1939	0.70	0.32	0.67	0.86	0.14	T	2.33	0.54	1.19	0.83	0.78	0.10	8.46
1940	0.52	0.58	0.48	0.21	1.71	1.32	0.62	3.25	1.99	0.36	1.45	0.87	13.36
1941	1.17	0.20	1.00	1.20	3.07	0.90	2.15	1.07	1.85	2.67	0.37	0.23	15.88
1942	0.13	0.54	0.39	1.97	T	0.22	0.20	1.42	1.55	0.73	T	1.10	8.25
1943	0.25	0.26	0.23	0.06	1.41	1.20	1.19	1.33	0.39	0.22	0.14	0.94	7.62
1944	0.46	0.42	0.49	0.91	0.57	0.85	1.58	1.44	0.65	0.86	0.56	0.76	9.55
1945	0.34	0.32	0.50	0.77	T	T	1.09	2.27	0.26	0.43	T	0.35	6.33
1946	0.25	0.33	1.03	0.26	0.31	0.07	2.28	1.49	0.57	1.02	0.54	0.12	8.27
1947	0.02	0.14	0.03	0.03	0.48	0.23	0.38	1.45	0.67	0.31	0.45	1.05	5.24
1948	0.18	1.42	0.41	0.33	0.94	0.57	0.46	0.51	0.80	0.60	0.11	0.11	6.44
1949	0.61	0.29	0.65	0.67	1.35	0.32	2.21	0.72	0.87	0.14	0.00	0.59	8.42
1950	0.02	0.38	0.04	0.27	0.06	0.23	2.00	0.08	1.01	0.01	T	0.00	4.10
1951	0.41	0.27	0.29	0.38	0.10	0.02	0.85	2.22	0.05	0.37	0.14	0.28	5.38
1952	0.20	0.17	0.59	0.76	0.65	1.64	1.91	1.10	0.34	0.00	0.53	0.20	8.09
1953	T	0.43	0.74	0.69	0.03	0.35	0.53	0.59	0.06	0.46	0.91	0.29	5.08
1954	0.20	0.07	0.24	T	0.51	0.01	1.45	0.65	0.77	0.25	0.22	0.14	4.51
1955	0.29	0.18	T	0.04	0.53	0.33	1.60	1.32	1.94	0.06	T	0.22	6.51
1956	0.46	0.49	T	T	0.18	0.43	1.49	0.62	0.02	0.34	0.03	0.00	4.06
1957	0.78	0.59	0.52	0.38	0.35	0.04	2.48	1.32	T	2.59	1.24	0.32	10.61
#1958	0.21	0.27	1.71	0.62	0.43	0.22	0.14	1.74	1.34	1.72	0.37	1.35	10.12
1959	0.17	0.04	0.42	0.43	0.80	0.78	0.73	2.79	0.36	1.70	0.07	1.85	10.14
1960	0.34	0.38	0.44	0.19	0.71	0.91	0.47	0.78	0.56	2.88	0.07	0.39	8.12
1961	0.23	0.10	0.61	0.73	0.01	0.11	2.70	1.69	1.09	0.47	0.48	0.65	8.87
1962	1.01	0.11	0.18	0.07	0.01	0.19	1.24	T	0.71	0.75	0.61	0.51	5.39
1963	0.29	0.24	0.55	0.14	0.03	0.11	1.43	3.00	0.63	0.76	0.29	T	7.47
1964	0.07	1.12	0.13	0.61	0.35	T	1.87	0.98	1.57	0.04	0.21	0.49	7.44
1965	0.47	0.60	0.49	0.49	0.19	0.99	1.65	0.61	1.18	0.89	0.33	1.42	9.31
1966	0.42	0.30	T	0.04	0.02	1.66	1.63	1.06	1.04	0.54	0.09	0.01	6.81
1967	0.01	0.44	0.25	T	0.04	1.71	0.61	3.30	0.79	0.18	0.15	0.56	8.04
1968	0.01	0.98	1.48	0.51	0.99	0.05	3.33	1.49	0.30	0.12	0.59	0.82	10.67
1969	0.08	0.34	0.41	1.76	1.31	0.59	0.94	0.95	1.08	2.37	0.01	0.72	10.56
1970	T	0.27	0.42	0.05	0.33	0.40	1.22	2.24	0.79	0.25	0.08	0.23	6.28
1971	0.27	0.21	0.03	0.78	0.16	0.02	1.05	0.87	1.44	1.15	0.67	1.40	8.05
1972	0.12	0.12	0.08	T	0.18	0.55	1.00	2.93	1.00	3.08	0.69	0.36	10.11
1973	0.85	0.33	2.18	0.91	0.66	1.37	1.80	1.19	1.13	0.35	0.08	0.03	10.88
1974	0.88	0.11	0.85	0.14	0.01	0.22	2.40	0.78	1.58	1.96	0.38	0.51	9.83
1975	0.26	0.99	0.95	0.10	0.66	T	1.43	1.40	1.66	T	0.28	0.28	8.01
RECORD MEAN	0.37	0.36	0.44	0.55	0.62	0.59	1.45	1.33	0.93	0.82	0.42	0.45	8.33

Aug	Sept	Oct	Nov	Dec	Total
442	158	7	0	0	1481
405	141	4	0	0	1362
282	149	0	0	0	1153
294	113	23	0	0	1182
409	124	0	0	0	1270
247	107	6	0	0	1353
351	96	0	0	0	1100

Record mean values above are means through the current year for the period beginning in 1893 for temperature and precipitation, 1940 for snowfall. Precipitation data are from Univ. of New Mexico location for 1/93-12/05, 7/06-9/06, 5/07-2/08, 4/08-8/08, 11/08, 1/09-2/09, 4/09-4/10, 9/18-3/31; 1216 W Central Avenue location for 1/06-6/06, 10/06-4/07, 8/07, 3/08, 9/08-10/08, 12/08, 3/09, 5/10-4/15, 7/15-9/15, 1/16; and Rio Grand Ind. School location for 5/15-6/15, 10/15-12/15 and 2/16-7/16. Temperature data are from Univ. of New Mexico location for 1/93-5/10; Rio Grande Ind. School location for 5-15-12/18; and Univ. of New Mexico location for 1/19-3/31.

ALBANY, NEW YORK

Albany is located on the west bank of the Hudson River some 150 miles north of New York City and the Atlantic Ocean, and about 8 miles south of the confluence of the Mohawk and Hudson Rivers. The river-front portion of the City is only a few feet above mean sea level, and there is a tidal effect in the Hudson River upstream beyond Albany to the Troy Dam. Some 11 miles west of Albany, the Helderberg escarpment rises to elevations ranging between 1400 and 1800 feet. Between the escarpment and the Hudson River the valley floor is gently rolling and lies some 200 to 500 feet above mean sea level. From the City eastward there is a more rugged valley floor some 5 or 6 miles in width with elevations of 300 to 600 feet. Farther to the east the terrain rises more sharply until about 12 miles east of Albany it reaches a north-south range of hills with elevations ranging from 1600 to 2000 feet.

The climate at Albany is primarily continental in character, but is subjected to some modification from the maritime climate which prevails in the extreme southeastern portion of New York State. The moderating effect on temperatures is more pronounced during the warmer months than in the cold winter season when outbursts of cold air sweep down from Canada with greater vigor than at other times of the year. In the warmer portion of the year temperatures rise rapidly during the daytime to moderate levels. As a rule, temperatures fall rapidly after sunset so that the nights are relatively cool. Very occasionally the area experiences extended periods of oppressive heat up to a week or more in duration. The highest temperature of record is 104°, but since 1874, 100° temperatures have been recorded on only 15 days.

Winters are usually cold and occasionally fairly severe. Maximum temperatures during the colder winter months often are below freezing and nighttime low temperatures frequently drop to 10° or lower. Subzero temperatures occur rather infrequently, about a dozen times a year. Snowfall in the area is quite variable and over some of the higher nearby areas ranges up to 75 inches or more for a season. Snow flurries are quite frequent during the cold months. Precipitation is sufficient to serve the economy of the region in most years, and only occasionally do periods of drought conditions become a threat. A considerable portion of the rainfall in the warmer months is from showers associated with thunderstorms, but hail is not usually of any consequence.

Station: ALBANY, NEW YORK
ALBANY COUNTY AIRPORT
Elevation (ground): 275 feet

TEMPERATURES °F

Month	Normal			Extremes			
	Daily maximum	Daily minimum	Monthly	Record highest	Year	Record lowest	Year
(a)				10		10	
J	30.4	12.5	21.5	62	1974	-28	1971
F	32.7	14.3	23.5	57	1974	-21	1973
M	42.6	24.2	33.4	77	1968	-10	1967
A	58.0	35.7	46.9	88	1970	10	1965
M	69.7	45.7	57.7	92	1970	26	1968
J	79.4	55.6	67.5	98	1968	36	1975
J	83.9	60.1	72.0	98	1966	43	1969
A	81.4	57.8	69.6	97	1975	37	1965
S	73.7	50.1	61.9	93	1973	28	1974
O	62.8	40.0	51.4	84	1968	16	1969
N	48.1	31.1	39.6	77	1974	5	1972
D	34.1	17.7	25.9	65	1970	-22	1969
YR	58.1	37.1	47.6	98	JUN 1968	-28	JAN 1971

IMPORTANT:
The time-period covered by this record is limited: See footnotes following table of NORMALS, MEANS AND EXTREMES for explanation and for additional history of EXTREME HIGHS AND LOWS recorded in the general area.

(Continued)

On the whole, wind velocities are moderate. The north-south Hudson River Valley has had a marked effect on the lighter winds and the warm months usually average out as a south wind. Destructive winds occur infrequently.

The area enjoys one of the highest percentages of sunshine that can be found in the State. This is true of the Hudson Valley area from Albany southward to the coast with slightly more sunshine progressively southward. Seldom does the area experience extended periods of cloudy days or extended periods of smog. Occasionally during the warm months there are short periods when high humidity associated with temperatures above 85° is rather uncomfortable.

The area enjoys a rather extensive growing season for northern latitudes. On the average the growing season is 160 days or more. Based on some 80 years or more of record the mean date of the last occurrence of 32° is April 27. The mean date of the first occurrence of 32° in the fall is October 13. Occasionally frost depth in the soil penetrates to around 4 feet, or slightly more in some locations. On the average a depth of about 3 feet can be expected.

Tornadoes are rather rare in the tri-county area of Albany, Rensselaer, and Schenectady Counties.

Normals, Means, and Extremes

(To better understand these tables, see full explanation of terms beginning on page 322)

Month	Normal Degree days Base 65 °F: Heating	Normal Degree days Base 65 °F: Cooling	Precipitation in inches, Water equivalent: Normal	Maximum monthly	Year	Minimum monthly	Year	Maximum in 24 hrs.	Year	Snow, Ice pellets: Maximum monthly	Year	Maximum in 24 hrs.	Year
(a)				29		29		29		29		29	
J	1349	0	2.20	4.12	1958	0.73	1955	1.68	1953	28.8	1966	15.4	1964
F	1162	0	2.11	4.14	1950	0.36	1968	1.50	1975	34.5	1962	17.9	1958
M	980	0	2.58	5.74	1953	1.07	1949	1.63	1975	34.7	1956	15.9	1956
A	543	0	2.70	4.71	1953	1.14	1963	2.20	1968	11.3	1974	10.7	1974
M	253	27	3.26	8.96	1953	1.22	1965	2.17	1968	1.4	1966	1.4	1966
J	39	114	3.00	7.36	1973	0.65	1964	3.48	1952	0.0		0.0	
J	9	226	3.12	6.96	1975	0.49	1968	2.70	1960	0.0		0.0	
A	22	165	2.87	7.33	1950	0.73	1947	4.52	1971	0.0		0.0	
S	135	42	3.12	7.89	1960	0.40	1964	3.66	1960	0.0		0.0	
O	422	0	2.63	8.83	1955	0.20	1963	2.66	1972	2.0	1952	2.0	1952
N	762	0	2.84	8.07	1972	1.17	1960	2.01	1959	24.6	1972	21.9	1971
D	1212	0	2.93	6.73	1973	0.64	1958	4.02	1948	57.5	1969	18.3	1966
YR	6888	574	33.36	8.96	MAY 1953	0.20	OCT 1963	4.52	AUG 1971	57.5	DEC 1969	21.9	NOV 1971

Month	Relative humidity pct. Hour 01 (Local time)	Hour 07	Hour 13	Hour 19	Wind: Mean speed m.p.h.	Prevailing direction	Fastest mile: Speed m.p.h.	Direction	Year	Pct. of possible sunshine	Mean sky cover, tenths, sunrise to sunset	Mean number of days, Sunrise to sunset: Clear	Partly cloudy	Cloudy	Precipitation .01 inch or more	Snow, Ice pellets 1.0 inch or more	Thunderstorms	Heavy fog, visibility ¼ mile or less	Temperatures °F Max. (b) 90° and above	Max. 32° and below	Min. 32° and below	Min. 0° and below	Average station pressure mb. Elev. 292 feet m.s.l.
(a)	10	10	10	10	37	15	37	37		37	37	37	37	37	29	29	37	37	10	10	10	10	3
J	79	80	63	73	9.8	WNW	57	W	1952	46	7.0	6	8	17	12	4	*	1	0	16	30	9	1008.3
F	74	77	58	67	10.3	WNW	71	NW	1953	51	6.9	5	8	15	11	4	*	1	0	13	27	6	1007.2
M	72	73	54	62	10.6	WNW	55	W	1941	52	7.0	6	8	17	12	3	1	1	0	4	26	*	1005.1
A	69	69	47	54	10.5	WNW	49	W	1954	53	6.9	6	8	16	12	1	1	1	0	*	16	0	1003.2
M	78	74	52	60	9.1	S	50	W	1950	55	6.9	5	9	17	13	*	4	2	*	0	2	0	1003.3
J	83	78	56	65	8.1	S	57	NW	1971	59	6.6	5	11	14	11	0	6	1	2	0	0	0	1005.2
J	83	79	54	63	7.3	S	43	NW	1938	64	6.3	6	13	12	11	0	7	1	4	0	0	0	1004.7
A	86	83	54	69	6.9	S	38	S	1950	61	6.1	7	12	12	10	0	5	3	2	0	0	0	1007.0
S	87	87	58	76	7.3	S	48	S	1961	56	6.0	8	10	12	9	0	2	4	1	0	1	0	1008.0
O	83	84	55	73	7.9	S	45	NW	1939	53	6.1	8	9	14	8	*	1	5	0	0	9	0	1009.6
N	80	82	63	75	8.9	S	70	E	1950	36	7.5	4	7	19	12	1	*	2	0	1	18	0	1006.4
D	81	82	68	76	9.1	S	54	W	1944	38	7.3	5	7	19	13	4	*	2	0	13	28	2	1008.2
YR	79	79	57	68	8.8	S	71	NW	FEB 1953	53	6.7	71	110	184	135	16	28	24	8	47	155	17	1006.4

FOOTNOTES

Means and extremes above are from existing and comparable exposures. Annual extremes have been exceeded at other sites in the locality as follows: Highest temperature 104 in July 1911; maximum monthly precipitation 13.48 in October 1869; minimum monthly precipitation 0.08 in January 1860; maximum precipitation in 24 hours 4.75 in October 1903; maximum snowfall in 24 hours 30.4 in March 1888.

Snowfall

Season	July	Aug	Sept	Oct	Nov	Dec	Jan
1936-37	0.0	0.0	0.0	T	4.1	3.8	5.4
#1937-38	0.0	0.0	0.0	0.0	1.1	5.1	17.2
1938-39	0.0	0.0	0.0	0.0	6.8	5.8	16.4
1939-40	0.0	0.0	0.0	0.0	1.0	4.8	11.5
1940-41	0.0	0.0	0.0	T	4.9	5.5	20.1
1941-42	0.0	0.0	0.0	0.0	T	6.5	11.5
1942-43	0.0	0.0	0.0	T	0.9	7.3	18.4
1943-44	0.0	0.0	0.0	0.0	16.9	0.6	11.4
1944-45	0.0	0.0	0.0	0.0	3.6	10.1	35.4
1945-46	0.0	0.0	0.0	0.0	7.7	16.2	10.0
#1946-47	0.0	0.0	0.0	T	0.1	9.2	5.7
1947-48	0.0	0.0	0.0	0.0	3.3	29.1	27.7
1948-49	0.0	0.0	0.0	T	0.7	7.3	20.6
1949-50	0.0	0.0	0.0	0.0	2.4	8.6	8.6
1950-51	0.0	0.0	0.0	0.0	4.0	17.4	9.9
1951-52	0.0	0.0	0.0	0.0	8.6	20.5	10.0
1952-53	0.0	0.0	0.0	2.0	1.0	4.0	21.7
1953-54	0.0	0.0	0.0	0.0	1.5	7.8	28.8
1954-55	0.0	0.0	0.0	0.0	1.8	1.7	2.1
1955-56	0.0	0.0	0.0	T	3.5	5.7	10.3
1956-57	0.0	0.0	0.0	0.0	7.6	28.1	16.7
1957-58	0.0	0.0	0.0	0.2	T	7.0	26.1
1958-59	0.0	0.0	0.0	T	4.6	6.4	12.2
1959-60	0.0	0.0	0.0	0.0	0.9	6.9	20.4
1960-61	0.0	0.0	0.0	T	0.1	16.6	17.2
1961-62	0.0	0.0	0.0	0.0	3.6	14.4	2.3
1962-63	0.0	0.0	0.0	T	1.6	11.3	24.5
1963-64	0.0	0.0	0.0	0.0	T	21.0	27.3
1964-65	0.0	0.0	0.0	T	T	11.2	20.4
1965-66	0.0	0.0	0.0	T	0.5	2.7	28.8
1966-67	0.0	0.0	0.0	0.0	T	29.4	5.7
1967-68	0.0	0.0	0.0	T	9.0	17.8	8.0
1968-69	0.0	0.0	0.0	0.0	13.5	18.1	6.3
1969-70	0.0	0.0	0.0	T	3.2	57.5	7.2
1970-71	0.0	0.0	0.0	T	T	43.8	15.2
1971-72	0.0	0.0	0.0	0.0	24.0	10.1	8.5
1972-73	0.0	0.0	0.0	T	24.6	22.5	11.2
1973-74	0.0	0.0	0.0	0.0	0.1	18.9	10.0
1974-75	0.0	0.0	0.0	T	2.2	12.5	14.0
1975-76	0.0	0.0	0.0	0.0	3.6	16.4	
RECORD MEAN	0.0	0.0	0.0	0.1	4.3	16.4	14.7

Heating Degree Days

Season	July	Aug	Sept	Oct	Nov	Dec	Jan
1955-56	0	12	174	387	821	1377	1279
1956-57	22	16	262	464	749	1066	1511
1957-58	3	30	152	450	691	981	1323
1958-59	8	8	142	499	745	1415	1354
1959-60	0	8	142	423	789	1080	1307
1960-61	12	11	100	480	696	1338	1530
1961-62	11	18	79	335	761	1152	1327
1962-63	6	23	207	451	894	1297	1381
1963-64	18	29	251	296	612	1446	1266
#1964-65	1	48	169	484	702	1141	1449
1965-66	11	49	120	421	817	1051	1342
1966-67	3	5	216	502	673	1163	1169
1967-68	0	19	153	429	899	1112	1557
1968-69	7	45	76	359	787	1281	1360
1969-70	13	22	137	491	749	1339	1708
1970-71	3	7	127	377	686	1336	1580
1971-72	20	45	109	311	838	1080	1298
1972-73	16	38	154	590	890	1113	1168
1973-74	2	3	200	431	750	1136	1285
1974-75	17	14	227	631	786	1113	1212
1975-76	0	19	173	357	580	1199	

Cooling Degree Days

Year	Jan	Feb	Mar	Apr	May	June	July
1969	0	0	0	2	23	95	165
1970	0	0	0	12	36	107	225
1971	0	0	0	0	9	98	132
1972	0	0	0	0	12	58	208
1973	0	0	0	7	6	164	248
1974	0	0	0	11	12	59	157
1975	0	0	0	0	58	97	248

Feb	Mar	Apr	May	June	Total
1.7	13.3	0.1	0.0	0.0	28.4
6.5	2.4	0.3	0.0	0.0	32.6
11.9	20.1	6.3	0.0	0.0	67.3
23.2	9.6	4.4	0.0	0.0	54.5
1.9	19.3	T	0.0	0.0	51.7
7.0	13.3	6.9	0.0	0.0	45.2
5.1	10.3	3.0	0.0	0.0	45.0
8.0	11.7	T	0.0	0.0	48.6
11.6	0.7	T	5.4	0.0	66.8
20.8	T	0.2	0.0	0.0	54.9
13.3	7.4	7.4	T	0.0	43.1
17.6	12.3	T	0.0	0.0	90.0
7.8	7.8	T	0.0	0.0	44.2
31.7	4.3	7.0	0.0	0.0	62.6
5.2	10.4	1.4	0.0	0.0	48.3
20.6	9.7	T	0.0	0.0	69.4
14.6	2.4	0.3	T	0.0	46.0
7.7	2.2	0.4	0.0	0.0	48.4
13.2	10.6	7.2	0.0	0.0	36.6
21.0	34.7	5.0	0.0	0.0	80.2
2.7	6.8	8.4	0.0	0.0	70.3
26.0	15.1	T	0.0	0.0	74.4
10.9	29.1	0.0	0.0	0.0	63.2
13.5	18.3	0.1	0.0	0.0	60.1
10.9	21.7	6.2	T	0.0	72.7
34.5	3.2	4.6	0.0	0.0	62.6
15.5	18.4	T	0.0	0.0	71.3
21.4	7.3	T	0.0	0.0	77.0
3.7	8.4	2.1	0.0	0.0	45.8
24.5	9.2	T	1.4	0.0	67.1
16.3	26.2	3.1	0.2	0.0	80.9
1.8	5.6	0.0	0.0	0.0	42.2
20.7	4.5	0.2	0.0	0.0	63.3
7.4	11.2	1.2	T	0.0	87.7
17.6	32.0	3.9	0.0	0.0	112.5
24.8	15.9	6.0	0.0	0.0	89.3
12.5	T	0.1	0.0	0.0	70.9
12.4	5.6	11.3	0.0	0.0	58.3
21.2	2.9	1.8	0.0	0.0	54.6
15.6	11.8	2.7	0.1	0.0	65.7

Average Temperature

Year	Jan	Feb	Mar	Apr	May	June	July	Aug	Sept	Oct	Nov	Dec	Annual
1936	23.6	18.3	42.3	45.0	62.1	69.2	74.4	71.4	63.4	52.2	37.2	32.0	49.3
1937	33.0	30.4	31.4	46.2	61.8	68.8	74.4	75.4	61.6	51.2	41.7	28.8	50.4
#1938	22.6	29.4	39.4	51.0	57.6	68.2	72.8	73.1	58.6	52.6	40.0	28.4	49.5
1939	22.0	24.6	28.2	42.1	60.6	67.2	71.8	73.8	61.7	49.0	35.2	27.0	46.9
1940	15.0	21.8	26.8	41.7	58.4	65.0	71.0	67.7	60.0	45.9	38.2	28.6	45.0
1941	18.4	23.4	27.9	52.2	59.3	68.7	73.4	68.0	63.2	51.4	42.4	29.8	48.2
1942	22.0	20.8	38.0	49.5	61.0	67.8	71.0	68.8	61.6	51.4	38.4	22.6	47.7
1943	17.8	24.0	31.4	39.7	57.8	72.0	72.7	69.1	60.6	50.0	36.0	23.2	46.2
1944	24.5	23.5	29.0	42.0	64.0	67.3	73.8	72.2	63.0	48.6	38.6	23.9	47.5
1945	14.0	24.8	43.8	50.8	53.4	65.6	70.0	69.2	64.8	48.8	39.6	21.4	47.2
#1946	24.2	22.0	43.8	44.8	55.2	64.8	71.0	66.0	63.9	54.2	42.6	28.4	48.4
1947	25.8	21.4	32.0	43.4	56.8	64.8	72.1	73.9	63.4	57.0	35.6	22.6	47.4
1948	15.3	18.2	31.9	46.9	56.2	65.2	71.0	70.9	63.0	48.6	45.0	29.2	46.8
1949	28.8	29.2	35.6	48.5	57.8	72.0	75.2	71.6	58.6	54.8	37.1	29.7	49.9
1950	31.0	20.5	27.2	43.1	57.5	66.1	69.9	68.5	58.2	52.6	41.3	25.4	46.8
1951	25.9	27.0	35.3	47.7	58.7	66.0	71.5	68.3	60.2	51.5	33.8	27.1	47.7
1952	26.3	27.1	32.5	50.3	54.4	68.1	74.8	70.0	62.1	46.6	39.8	30.2	48.5
1953	29.3	28.9	36.7	46.7	60.1	68.5	72.0	69.5	62.1	52.3	42.1	33.5	50.1
1954	18.5	31.4	34.4	48.5	55.3	67.7	70.4	67.0	60.4	54.8	39.7	27.9	48.0
1955	21.2	24.4	33.1	49.7	61.2	67.0	76.5	73.6	60.0	52.4	37.4	20.5	48.1
1956	23.5	26.1	27.9	42.6	53.5	67.3	69.0	69.0	57.7	49.8	39.9	30.4	46.4
1957	16.1	28.8	35.5	48.9	57.0	71.0	71.1	67.3	62.3	50.2	41.7	33.2	48.6
1958	22.1	18.9	36.0	49.1	54.4	62.1	71.7	70.2	61.5	48.9	39.9	19.2	46.2
1959	21.1	20.2	32.2	48.0	60.7	67.6	74.2	73.5	65.6	51.4	38.4	29.9	48.5
1960	22.7	28.0	26.5	49.6	60.4	67.1	69.5	69.9	62.8	49.4	41.5	21.6	47.4
1961	15.3	25.5	33.0	43.9	55.4	67.0	71.6	69.7	68.7	53.9	39.4	27.7	47.6
1962	21.9	20.5	34.7	47.0	59.8	68.1	69.0	69.0	58.7	50.2	35.0	23.0	46.4
1963	20.3	17.2	33.6	45.8	56.6	67.3	72.0	66.4	56.8	55.5	44.4	18.1	46.2
#1964	23.9	22.3	34.9	45.7	61.7	66.5	74.4	66.2	61.0	49.2	41.4	27.9	47.9
1965	18.1	22.3	31.2	42.2	59.6	66.9	68.9	69.4	63.6	51.2	37.6	30.8	46.8
1966	21.5	23.3	34.3	44.0	53.9	67.4	72.2	69.2	58.0	48.5	42.3	27.3	46.8
1967	27.0	18.0	29.0	43.5	50.4	69.9	71.6	69.3	61.3	51.0	34.8	28.9	46.2
1968	14.7	21.1	37.1	51.1	54.9	66.7	72.7	68.6	63.7	53.3	38.5	23.5	47.2
1969	20.9	24.7	31.1	47.6	56.3	66.0	69.7	70.6	62.4	49.0	39.7	21.6	46.6
1970	9.7	23.1	32.0	48.7	60.5	65.9	72.0	69.6	63.3	52.9	41.9	21.6	46.8
1971	13.9	25.4	30.6	42.3	54.9	66.3	68.4	66.8	64.8	54.7	36.9	30.0	46.3
1972	22.9	21.1	30.5	41.2	59.5	63.6	70.9	67.2	60.7	45.7	35.1	28.9	45.6
1973	27.0	22.0	41.9	48.8	55.3	68.7	72.8	72.9	60.5	51.0	39.9	28.2	49.1
1974	23.3	21.3	32.4	48.1	54.1	65.0	69.3	67.9	58.3	44.4	38.6	28.9	46.0
1975	25.7	24.9	30.8	40.7	61.9	65.1	72.8	70.0	59.4	53.3	45.5	26.1	48.0
RECORD MEAN	23.0	23.7	33.5	46.5	58.4	67.7	72.5	70.2	62.7	51.4	39.7	27.7	48.1
MAX	31.3	32.3	41.8	56.2	69.0	78.1	82.9	80.5	72.8	61.1	47.2	35.0	57.4
MIN	14.7	15.1	25.1	36.7	47.8	57.2	62.0	59.9	52.6	41.7	32.1	20.3	38.8

# Indicates a station move or relocation of instruments.

ALBANY, NY

Feb	Mar	Apr	May	June	Total
1123	1145	667	370	40	7395
1006	908	491	264	36	6795
1286	892	476	322	118	6724
1249	1010	502	220	68	7220
1067	1184	457	152	32	6641
1101	987	627	314	47	7243
1240	933	552	211	27	6646
1331	968	571	261	62	7452
1233	927	571	145	78	6872
1193	1041	679	197	68	7172
1162	948	623	347	57	6948
1312	1111	639	447	11	7251
1269	857	412	304	46	7057
1122	1043	518	284	55	6937
1168	1016	495	165	75	7378
1104	1059	672	315	50	7316
1269	1060	707	175	97	7009
1198	709	486	299	47	6708
1216	1005	511	343	54	6936
1115	1053	722	145	88	7123

Aug	Sept	Oct	Nov	Dec	Total
203	68	0	0	0	556
160	83	7	0	0	630
107	109	1	0	0	456
112	31	0	0	0	421
255	71	2	0	0	753
111	35	0	1	0	386
180	12	0	2	0	597

Precipitation

Year	Jan	Feb	Mar	Apr	May	June	July	Aug	Sept	Oct	Nov	Dec	Annual
1936	4.59	1.92	5.39	3.12	4.20	1.86	1.94	6.54	1.34	3.99	2.16	2.90	39.95
1937	2.61	2.08	2.40	1.89	4.13	5.31	4.35	4.16	5.08	2.61	1.83	2.05	38.50
#1938	3.49	1.60	1.63	2.59	3.42	3.52	5.11	3.18	8.76	1.18	2.36	3.33	40.17
1939	2.54	3.07	3.06	3.48	1.11	3.04	2.86	1.96	3.61	3.22	1.69	1.53	31.17
1940	1.13	2.83	4.53	3.93	3.68	2.83	4.23	1.78	4.31	0.89	3.13	2.64	35.91
1941	1.98	2.33	1.85	0.72	1.19	1.56	4.45	3.60	1.60	1.80	1.44	2.06	24.58
1942	1.71	0.95	4.01	1.85	2.46	2.52	6.58	0.66	4.52	2.85	3.34	4.24	35.69
1943	2.45	0.96	2.45	2.91	3.78	2.84	2.96	4.50	1.10	4.92	3.23	0.52	32.62
1944	1.11	1.24	2.45	3.27	1.35	6.78	1.82	2.80	3.70	2.69	2.53	1.84	31.58
1945	3.25	1.47	1.27	3.05	4.82	4.72	6.59	1.24	5.83	2.25	4.36	2.33	41.18
#1946	0.96	2.83	1.06	1.50	4.55	4.20	3.20	2.17	4.65	1.77	0.59	2.68	30.16
1947	2.38	0.89	1.73	3.33	5.13	4.15	3.66	0.73	1.60	2.30	3.94	2.36	32.20
1948	2.40	2.08	1.92	2.87	4.75	4.42	2.71	1.96	1.51	2.42	4.35	6.05	37.44
1949	2.78	1.52	1.07	2.35	3.20	1.69	3.30	2.92	2.10	1.95	1.20	1.65	25.73
1950	3.63	4.14	2.10	1.55	2.89	2.27	3.26	7.33	3.09	1.58	2.65	4.15	38.64
1951	2.36	3.32	4.30	2.38	2.79	4.19	4.29	4.40	5.44	4.48	3.68	3.58	45.21
1952	2.12	2.19	1.90	3.92	4.20	4.74	2.16	2.00	3.47	1.32	2.53	4.50	35.05
1953	3.39	2.17	5.74	4.71	8.96	1.92	1.69	2.88	2.78	3.54	1.54	2.76	42.08
1954	2.71	2.62	2.69	3.05	5.40	2.89	1.57	5.20	2.08	1.74	4.00	3.36	37.31
1955	0.73	3.08	3.44	2.49	1.51	2.05	0.86	5.28	3.36	8.83	3.14	0.88	35.65
1956	2.25	3.30	4.76	2.62	3.08	1.86	2.76	2.76	4.71	1.19	2.30	3.59	35.18
1957	1.16	1.02	1.54	2.25	4.94	2.36	2.17	1.66	1.61	2.57	2.24	4.12	27.64
1958	4.12	2.71	2.45	3.10	2.11	2.06	4.47	1.21	2.77	3.68	3.07	0.64	32.39
1959	2.75	1.59	3.20	2.46	2.09	1.75	1.67	2.10	1.88	5.60	4.44	2.86	32.39
1960	2.51	2.85	1.69	4.19	3.33	2.70	5.89	3.20	7.89	1.58	1.17	1.35	38.35
1961	1.47	2.47	3.11	3.09	4.44	2.97	4.78	4.76	2.47	1.22	2.98	1.96	35.72
1962	2.05	3.65	1.70	3.25	1.40	1.15	2.12	2.60	3.45	3.58	2.11	2.24	29.30
1963	2.38	1.84	3.45	1.14	1.90	2.94	1.20	2.49	2.69	0.20	4.15	1.86	26.24
1964	3.35	1.63	2.93	2.17	1.31	0.65	1.29	2.55	0.40	0.54	1.45	3.28	21.55
1965	1.95	1.92	1.73	2.38	1.22	1.91	3.52	4.32	3.76	2.37	1.89	0.97	27.94
1966	2.29	2.71	3.63	1.46	2.35	2.95	3.88	1.44	5.61	2.22	1.79	3.04	33.37
1967	1.22	1.76	2.56	3.69	3.36	2.85	3.38	2.17	2.23	3.48	2.68	3.90	33.28
1968	1.48	0.36	2.62	2.64	4.79	4.38	0.49	1.77	1.49	2.18	5.48	4.60	32.28
1969	2.13	1.66	1.32	3.51	2.64	5.30	5.08	2.18	2.06	1.55	5.56	6.51	39.50
1970	0.81	1.98	2.87	3.01	1.78	3.14	1.93	3.35	3.79	2.49	1.48	3.89	30.52
1971	1.78	4.10	3.11	2.00	3.48	2.81	3.89	7.04	2.40	2.09	3.78	3.09	39.57
1972	1.21	3.04	4.05	3.63	5.98	6.84	3.10	1.48	1.99	3.60	8.07	4.19	47.18
1973	2.16	1.34	1.99	4.47	5.45	7.36	1.68	2.89	1.33	2.07	1.27	6.73	38.74
1974	2.04	2.12	3.10	2.80	3.47	3.31	4.84	3.53	5.37	1.49	3.83	2.57	38.47
1975	2.75	3.58	2.72	2.18	2.96	3.80	6.96	5.98	4.57	5.88	2.89	2.78	47.05
RECORD MEAN	2.45	2.37	2.73	2.74	3.31	3.69	3.73	3.52	3.30	3.04	2.92	2.66	36.46

Record mean values above are means through the current year for the period beginning in 1874 for temperature, 1826 for precipitation and 1947 for snowfall. Data are from City Office locations through May 1938.

QUOTES FROM WEATHER FOLKLORE–

If three days old her face be bright and clear,
No rain or stormy gale the sailors fear;
But if she rise with bright and blushing cheek,
The blustering winds the bending mast will
shake,
If dull her face and blunt her horns appear,
On the fourth day a breeze or rain is near.
If on the third she moves with horns direct,
Not pointing downward or to heaven erect,
The western wind expect; and drenching rain,
If on the fourth her horns direct remain.
If to the earth her upper horn she bend,
Cold Boreas from the north his blast will send;
If upward she extend it to the sky,
Loud Notus with his blustering gale is nigh.
When the fourth day around her orb is spread
A circling ring of deep and murky red,
Soon from his cave the God of Storms will rise,
Dashing with foamy waves the lowering skies.
And when fair Cynthia her full orb displays,
Or when unveiled to sight are half her rays,
Then mark the various hues that paint her face,
And thus the fickle weather's changes trace.
If smile her pearly face benign and fair,
Calm and serene will breathe the balmy air;
If with deep blush her maiden cheek be red,
Then boisterous wind the caution sailors dread;
If sullen blackness hang upon her brow,
From clouds as black will rainy torrents flow.
Not through the month their power these
signs extend,
But all their influence with the quarter end.

– J. Lamb's "Aratus."

Station: BUFFALO, NEW YORK
GREATER BUFFALO INTL A
Elevation (ground): 705 feet

TEMPERATURES °F

Month	Normal			Extremes			
	Daily maximum	Daily minimum	Monthly	Record highest	Year	Record lowest	Year
(a)				15		15	
J	29.8	17.6	23.7	61	1967	-11	1968
F	31.0	17.7	24.4	61	1975	-20	1961
M	39.0	25.2	32.1	78	1966	-4	1967
A	53.3	36.4	44.9	83	1970	13	1972
M	64.3	45.9	55.1	88	1974	29	1970
J	75.1	56.3	65.7	94	1963	36	1972
J	79.5	60.7	70.1	94	1968	46	1965
A	77.6	59.1	68.4	93	1962	38	1965
S	70.8	52.3	61.6	90	1973	32	1963
O	60.2	42.7	51.5	82	1971	20	1965
N	46.1	33.5	39.8	80	1961	9	1971
D	33.6	22.2	27.9	66	1966	-4	1975
YR	55.0	39.1	47.1	94	JUL 1968	-20	FEB 1961

IMPORTANT:
The time-period covered by this record is limited: See footnotes on next page for explanation and for additional history of EXTREME HIGHS AND LOWS recorded in the general area.

For nearly 75 years the Weather Bureau Office at Buffalo was located downtown overlooking the waterfront. Instruments were exposed high above the ground level. On July 1, 1943, the office was moved to the Buffalo Airport. Roof exposures were maintained generally until August 1961 when radically lower levels were prescribed to meet aviation requirements. Vertical variability of many weather elements is much more pronounced than is the horizontal, hence, with the establishment of "ground" level exposures, discontinuity in the record has occurred.

The surrounding country is comparatively low and level to the west, gently rolling to the east and south, rising to pronounced hills within 12 to 18 miles, and to 1,000 feet above the level of Lake Erie at a point some 35 miles south-southeast of the City.

At the present location an escarpment of 50 to 100 feet lies east-west 1-1/2 miles to the north. The eastern end of Lake Erie is now 9 miles to the west-southwest, while Lake Ontario lies 25 miles to the north, the two being connected by the Niagara River, which flows north-northwestward from the end of Lake Erie.

Buffalo is located near the mean position of the polar front. Its weather is varied and changeable, characteristic of the latitude. Wide seasonal swings of temperature from hot to cold are tempered appreciably by the proximity of Lakes Erie and Ontario. Lake Erie lies to the southwest, the direction of the prevailing wind. Wind flow throughout the year is somewhat higher due to this exposure. The vigorous interplay of warm and cold airmasses during the winter and early spring months causes one or more windstorms. Precipitation is moderate and fairly evenly divided throughout the twelve months.

The spring season is cloudy and cooler than points not affected by the cold lake. Vegetation is retarded, a fact that protects it from late spring frosts. With heavy winter ice accumulations in the lake, typical spring conditions are delayed until late May or early June.

Summer comes suddenly in mid-June. Lake breezes temper the extreme heat of the summer season. Temperatures of 90° and above are infrequent. There is more summer sunshine here than in any other section of the state. Due to the stabilizing effects of Lake Erie, thunderstorms are relatively infrequent. Most of them are caused by frontal action. To the north and south of the City thunderstorms occur more often.

Autumn has long, dry periods and is frost free usually until mid-October. Cloudiness increases in November, continuing mostly cloudy throughout the winter and early spring. Snow flurries off the lake begin in mid-November or early December. Outbreaks of arctic air in December and on through the winter months produce locally heavy snowfalls from the lake. At the same time, temperatures of well below zero over Canada and the mid-west are raised 10° to 30° in crossing the lakes. Only on rare occasions do polar airmasses drop southward from eastern Hudson Bay across Lake Ontario without appreciable warming.

Normals, Means, and Extremes

(To better understand these tables, see full explanation of terms beginning on page 322)

Month	Normal Degree days Base 65 °F: Heating	Normal Degree days Base 65 °F: Cooling	Precipitation in inches, Water equivalent: Normal	Water equivalent: Maximum monthly	Year	Water equivalent: Minimum monthly	Year	Water equivalent: Maximum in 24 hrs.	Year	Snow, Ice pellets: Maximum monthly	Year	Snow, Ice pellets: Maximum in 24 hrs.	Year
(a)				32		32		32		32		32	
J	1280	0	2.90	6.47	1959	1.03	1946	2.40	1957	50.6	1945	18.2	1966
F	1137	0	2.55	5.80	1960	0.81	1968	2.31	1954	54.2	1958	14.5	1958
M	1020	0	2.85	5.25	1956	1.20	1967	2.14	1954	29.2	1959	15.8	1954
A	603	0	3.15	5.90	1961	1.27	1946	1.49	1944	15.0	1975	6.8	1975
M	321	14	2.97	6.39	1953	1.21	1965	2.03	1957	2.0	1945	2.0	1945
J	58	79	2.23	6.06	1972	0.11	1955	3.04	1968	0.0		0.0	
J	12	170	2.93	6.43	1963	0.99	1972	3.38	1963	0.0		0.0	
A	33	138	3.53	8.49	1975	1.10	1948	3.88	1963	0.0		0.0	
S	138	36	3.25	6.36	1967	0.77	1964	3.63	1967	T	1956	T	1956
O	419	0	3.01	9.13	1954	0.30	1963	3.49	1945	3.1	1972	2.5	1972
N	756	0	3.74	6.37	1949	1.44	1944	2.51	1949	28.6	1949	19.9	1955
D	1150	0	3.00	5.83	1954	0.69	1943	2.16	1945	51.1	1945	24.3	1945
YR	6927	437	36.11	9.13	OCT 1954	0.11	JUN 1955	3.88	AUG 1963	54.2	FEB 1958	24.3	DEC 1945

Month	Relative humidity pct. Hour 01	Hour 07	Hour 13	Hour 19 (Local time)	Wind: Mean speed m.p.h.	Wind: Prevailing direction	Fastest mile: Speed m.p.h.	Fastest mile: Direction	Fastest mile: Year	Pct. of possible sunshine	Mean sky cover, tenths, sunrise to sunset	Mean number of days, Sunrise to sunset: Clear	Partly cloudy	Cloudy	Precipitation .01 inch or more	Snow, Ice pellets 1.0 inch or more	Thunderstorms	Heavy fog, visibility ¼ mile or less	Temperatures °F Max. (b) 90° and above	Max. 32° and below	Min. 32° and below	Min. 0° and below	Average station pressure mb. Elev. 706 feet m.s.l.
(a)	15	15	15	15	36	14	32	32		32	32	32	32	32	32	32	32	32	15	15	15	15	3
J	76	78	72	76	14.5	WSW	91	SW	1950	34	8.4	2	6	23	20	7	*	2	0	17	29	2	991.5
F	78	79	70	75	14.1	SW	70	SW	1946	40	8.2	2	6	20	17	6	*	2	0	16	26	2	991.3
M	79	80	68	74	13.8	SW	68	W	1959	46	7.6	4	7	20	16	4	1	3	0	8	25	*	989.4
A	75	76	58	65	13.0	SW	67	W	1957	52	7.1	5	8	17	15	1	3	2	0	1	12	0	989.1
M	77	76	56	62	11.8	SW	63	SW	1950	58	6.8	6	9	16	13	*	3	2	0	0	1	0	987.6
J	79	78	57	62	11.3	SW	56	NW	1954	66	6.2	6	12	12	10	0	5	1	1	0	0	0	989.3
J	80	79	55	61	10.6	SW	59	NW	1953	69	5.9	7	14	10	10	0	6	1	1	0	0	0	990.2
A	83	83	59	67	10.1	SW	56	SW	1944	66	6.0	7	13	11	10	0	6	1	*	0	0	0	992.2
S	82	83	60	72	10.6	S	59	SW	1954	60	6.3	7	10	13	10	0	3	1	*	0	*	0	992.7
O	80	82	61	73	11.4	S	63	SW	1954	53	6.5	7	9	15	11	*	2	1	0	0	3	0	993.8
N	81	83	71	79	13.0	S	66	SW	1948	29	8.3	2	5	23	16	3	1	2	0	2	14	0	990.4
D	81	82	75	79	13.4	WSW	60	S	1945	27	8.5	1	6	24	20	6	1	1	0	13	26	*	991.6
YR	79	80	63	70	12.3	SW	91	SW	JAN 1950	53	7.1	56	105	204	168	26	30	20	2	56	136	4	990.8

FOOTNOTES Means and extremes above are from existing and comparable exposures. Annual extremes have been exceeded at other sites in the locality as follows: Highest temperature 99 in August 1948; lowest temperature -21 in February 1934; maximum monthly precipitation 10.63 in August 1885; minimum monthly precipitation .05 in August 1876; maximum precipitation in 24 hours 4.28 in August 1893.

Snowfall

Season	July	Aug	Sept	Oct	Nov	Dec	Jan
1936-37	0.0	0.0	0.0	T	9.7	6.2	9.7
1937-38	0.0	0.0	0.0	0.8	5.2	38.2	18.5
1938-39	0.0	0.0	0.0	0.0	11.1	14.2	29.4
1939-40	0.0	0.0	0.0	T	0.5	8.7	27.6
1940-41	0.0	0.0	0.0	T	17.5	12.1	17.3
1941-42	0.0	0.0	0.0	T	5.0	7.8	31.0
#1942-43	0.0	0.0	0.0	T	8.7	26.7	16.9
1943-44	0.0	0.0	0.0	1.5	13.6	1.7	3.4
1944-45	0.0	0.0	0.0	0.0	3.9	35.1	50.6
1945-46	0.0	0.0	0.0	T	25.2	51.1	10.7
1946-47	0.0	0.0	0.0	0.0	T	11.9	13.0
1947-48	0.0	0.0	0.0	0.0	9.9	4.3	14.5
1948-49	0.0	0.0	0.0	T	1.3	7.0	11.8
1949-50	0.0	0.0	0.0	0.0	28.6	9.5	14.8
1950-51	0.0	0.0	T	0.0	15.2	22.3	13.7
1951-52	0.0	0.0	0.0	T	17.7	31.6	16.8
1952-53	0.0	0.0	0.0	0.4	11.2	16.1	8.0
1953-54	0.0	0.0	0.0	0.0	22.7	10.9	16.2
1954-55	0.0	0.0	0.0	1.0	0.7	31.2	28.5
1955-56	0.0	0.0	0.0	T	26.0	20.3	17.7
1956-57	0.0	0.0	T	0.0	16.2	35.6	36.6
1957-58	0.0	0.0	0.0	T	19.2	4.8	31.1
1958-59	0.0	0.0	0.0	0.0	13.5	19.0	38.4
1959-60	0.0	0.0	0.0	T	12.2	14.2	18.3
1960-61	0.0	0.0	0.0	1.0	15.9	31.9	23.5
1961-62	0.0	0.0	0.0	T	5.6	30.2	26.2
1962-63	0.0	0.0	0.0	2.0	2.5	30.2	31.5
1963-64	0.0	0.0	0.0	0.0	3.1	24.0	13.7
1964-65	0.0	0.0	0.0	T	5.4	15.2	19.2
1965-66	0.0	0.0	0.0	1.2	12.2	7.0	48.0
1966-67	0.0	0.0	0.0	0.0	10.0	12.1	11.6
1967-68	0.0	0.0	0.0	T	19.7	10.4	19.1
1968-69	0.0	0.0	0.0	T	11.6	11.7	31.2
1969-70	0.0	0.0	0.0	1.0	22.1	23.4	38.0
1970-71	0.0	0.0	0.0	0.0	2.6	32.3	17.2
1971-72	0.0	0.0	0.0	0.0	18.7	12.9	27.6
1972-73	0.0	0.0	0.0	3.1	18.9	19.8	9.9
1973-74	0.0	0.0	0.0	0.0	3.0	23.1	19.7
1974-75	0.0	0.0	0.0	T	22.1	23.6	11.0
1975-76	0.0	0.0	0.0	T	5.5	27.3	
RECORD MEAN	0.0	0.0	T	0.3	12.6	20.6	21.6

Heating Degree Days

Season	July	Aug	Sept	Oct	Nov	Dec	Jan
1955-56	0	3	137	338	783	1229	1243
1956-57	12	13	218	300	687	947	1370
1957-58	13	26	140	456	717	930	1231
1958-59	2	19	124	395	687	1318	1317
1959-60	1	1	111	388	784	1004	1188
#1960-61	16	10	77	441	660	1339	1435
1961-62	30	17	76	323	722	1089	1310
1962-63	9	26	213	415	832	1231	1420
1963-64	20	72	240	241	635	1282	1099
1964-65	5	68	176	518	680	1097	1277
1965-66	23	46	122	525	742	942	1374
1966-67	7	19	199	495	700	1124	1086
1967-68	12	26	162	403	853	985	1393
1968-69	11	29	58	374	722	1180	1233
1969-70	13	16	147	433	769	1240	1459
1970-71	6	6	93	329	695	1161	1361
1971-72	11	29	87	202	771	971	1218
1972-73	16	33	113	574	860	1054	1152
1973-74	2	14	171	326	720	1107	1167
1974-75	2	0	187	483	738	1024	1077
1975-76	3	15	197	368	535	1134	

Cooling Degree Days

Year	Jan	Feb	Mar	Apr	May	June	July
1969	0	0	0	0	1	88	192
1970	0	0	0	16	21	108	197
1971	0	0	0	0	9	119	136
1972	0	0	0	0	12	48	210
1973	0	0	0	6	2	126	233
1974	0	0	0	0	7	71	163
1975	0	0	0	0	90	129	238

Feb	Mar	Apr	May	June	Total
10.9	14.6	0.5	0.0	0.0	51.6
9.8	3.0	6.9	T	0.0	82.4
15.3	10.2	3.4	0.0	0.0	83.6
20.2	15.7	5.1	0.0	0.0	77.8
23.1	9.3	T	0.0	0.0	79.3
28.0	13.7	4.1	0.0	0.0	89.6
17.7	10.4	5.1	T	0.0	85.5
24.6	10.5	2.7	0.0	0.0	58.0
23.3	5.8	T	2.0	0.0	120.7
23.5	T	T	0.0	0.0	110.5
22.2	13.5	4.0	0.8	0.0	65.4
7.0	4.2	T	T	0.0	39.9
5.2	14.3	0.5	0.0	0.0	40.1
19.3	13.7	2.8	0.0	0.0	88.7
12.3	7.9	T	0.0	0.0	71.4
8.9	7.4	0.6	0.0	0.0	83.0
11.9	5.5	2.8	0.0	0.0	55.9
12.6	26.3	1.2	T	0.0	89.9
12.0	11.1	0.3	0.0	0.0	84.8
14.3	23.1	3.8	T	0.0	105.2
3.1	10.2	12.0	0.0	0.0	113.7
54.2	11.2	4.2	0.0	0.0	124.7
14.0	29.2	0.4	T	0.0	114.5
49.5	19.5	1.9	T	0.0	115.6
11.9	5.1	13.1	T	0.0	102.4
28.2	6.7	4.5	0.0	0.0	101.4
15.5	7.7	0.3	0.1	0.0	89.8
14.6	12.8	3.3	0.0	0.0	71.5
9.4	17.5	4.2	0.0	0.0	70.9
15.2	11.4	3.2	0.1	0.0	98.3
19.8	10.8	0.6	1.2	0.0	66.1
11.7	10.6	0.1	0.0	0.0	71.6
12.8	8.0	3.1	0.0	0.0	78.4
21.9	12.6	1.5	T	0.0	120.5
19.4	22.6	2.9	0.0	0.0	97.0
31.4	14.1	5.2	0.0	0.0	109.9
16.1	8.5	2.4	0.1	0.0	78.8
22.8	12.9	7.1	0.1	0.0	88.7
16.3	7.6	15.0	0.0	0.0	95.6
18.3	11.9	3.2	0.1	0.0	88.6

BUFFALO, NY

Feb	Mar	Apr	May	June	Total
1061	1062	652	376	71	6955
951	894	508	321	38	6259
1242	940	498	343	111	6647
1134	1050	562	216	63	6887
1088	1258	494	235	48	6600
1072	952	749	385	90	7226
1216	1002	609	195	66	6655
1288	907	618	370	57	7386
1198	955	535	204	98	6579
1092	1080	706	186	100	6985
1114	931	648	401	68	6936
1239	1047	560	457	4	6937
1281	901	469	352	84	6921
1125	1052	540	325	102	6751
1121	1076	552	255	66	7147
1057	1085	691	327	36	6846
1237	1070	707	187	112	6602
1173	696	542	318	24	6555
1187	989	553	365	51	6652
1001	1053	764	175	32	6536

Aug	Sept	Oct	Nov	Dec	Total
212	69	6	0	0	568
173	72	12	0	0	599
122	107	15	0	0	508
123	57	0	0	0	450
230	78	3	0	0	678
158	29	0	0	0	428
171	3	3	0	0	634

Average Temperature

Year	Jan	Feb	Mar	Apr	May	June	July	Aug	Sept	Oct	Nov	Dec	Annual
1936	23.2	18.5	35.0	39.2	53.4	65.4	71.2	69.7	63.4	51.6	35.0	33.8	46.6
1937	32.4	28.6	27.8	43.0	55.1	65.2	71.0	73.3	61.4	48.1	39.4	27.9	47.8
1938	24.4	28.5	37.8	45.5	55.6	65.1	71.6	72.3	59.2	53.4	43.4	31.3	49.0
1939	26.3	27.4	30.3	39.0	55.6	65.7	70.5	72.0	62.8	52.0	38.0	32.3	47.7
1940	18.1	25.0	27.0	40.2	53.0	63.0	69.6	69.6	61.0	49.0	39.2	32.8	45.6
1941	24.5	23.6	26.2	48.2	54.6	66.0	72.1	67.8	65.1	52.8	43.8	33.8	48.2
1942	24.2	20.9	36.1	46.8	56.4	65.7	68.0	67.8	62.0	53.2	40.3	25.2	47.2
#1943	21.2	25.8	30.3	36.9	51.8	65.7	71.6	68.8	60.8	48.4	37.5	26.6	45.4
1944	29.7	25.1	30.0	41.1	63.4	67.1	72.4	71.8	63.6	50.2	42.0	25.4	48.5
1945	16.2	26.2	44.4	49.8	50.7	64.0	70.2	69.8	64.2	49.8	40.9	23.8	47.5
1946	27.4	24.7	44.5	44.4	55.0	63.9	71.2	66.0	64.4	56.6	44.4	31.5	49.5
1947	29.9	21.6	29.9	43.4	52.8	65.8	68.6	75.2	64.0	59.8	38.0	28.3	48.1
1948	18.6	25.2	35.0	48.8	53.2	65.2	72.0	70.2	64.9	49.6	47.1	32.4	48.5
1949	31.2	31.8	33.6	45.5	57.6	72.2	74.3	71.6	58.8	57.2	38.0	33.3	50.4
1950	35.0	24.8	28.3	39.9	57.3	65.0	69.0	68.6	60.7	54.7	39.0	27.1	47.5
1951	28.5	27.4	35.3	45.0	57.5	66.3	70.4	68.5	61.3	54.6	34.3	30.6	48.3
1952	28.5	29.1	33.5	48.2	53.9	67.3	74.3	70.1	63.1	46.5	42.9	33.3	49.2
1953	31.3	30.7	36.6	44.0	56.4	67.5	71.6	70.5	63.0	54.3	43.9	34.6	50.4
1954	23.5	33.1	32.9	47.3	54.5	68.2	69.6	66.9	62.3	53.9	41.7	28.7	48.5
1955	24.8	27.9	33.8	51.0	59.4	66.8	76.0	73.8	62.0	54.0	38.7	25.1	49.4
1956	24.6	28.3	30.6	43.0	53.1	66.4	68.9	69.0	58.9	55.3	42.0	34.2	47.9
1957	20.6	30.8	35.9	48.8	54.7	69.1	69.8	67.3	62.4	50.1	40.8	34.8	48.7
1958	25.1	20.4	34.5	48.2	54.0	61.9	71.3	68.9	62.1	52.2	41.8	22.3	46.9
1959	22.3	24.2	31.0	46.0	60.2	66.8	72.8	74.8	66.8	52.6	38.6	32.3	49.1
#1960	26.5	27.2	24.1	48.4	58.1	65.8	69.1	69.0	64.3	50.6	42.8	21.6	47.3
1961	18.5	26.5	34.2	39.8	53.1	63.4	69.7	69.6	68.6	54.5	40.8	29.7	47.4
1962	22.6	21.3	32.5	44.9	60.9	64.9	68.2	68.1	58.6	51.5	37.1	25.1	46.3
1963	18.9	18.8	35.4	44.2	52.9	66.7	70.2	64.3	57.1	57.1	43.6	23.4	46.1
1964	29.3	23.5	34.0	46.9	59.2	65.7	73.1	64.9	60.9	48.1	42.1	29.5	48.1
1965	23.6	25.8	30.0	41.2	59.6	64.3	67.6	67.8	63.5	47.8	40.0	34.3	47.1
1966	20.4	24.9	34.7	43.3	52.2	67.4	71.4	68.5	58.7	48.8	41.5	28.6	46.7
1967	29.8	20.6	30.9	46.1	50.1	72.5	71.2	68.1	60.7	51.9	36.3	33.0	47.6
1968	19.9	20.7	35.7	49.2	53.4	64.8	71.2	69.4	66.1	53.5	40.7	26.8	47.6
1969	25.0	24.6	30.9	46.8	54.4	64.4	70.5	71.2	62.2	51.0	39.1	24.8	47.1
1970	17.6	24.8	30.1	46.9	57.3	66.0	71.0	70.2	64.0	54.5	41.6	27.4	47.6
1971	20.9	27.0	29.8	41.8	54.5	67.6	68.7	67.8	65.4	58.7	39.1	33.5	47.9
1972	25.5	22.0	30.1	41.1	59.1	62.6	71.0	67.7	62.8	46.2	36.0	30.8	46.3
1973	27.6	22.9	42.4	46.9	54.5	68.2	72.3	71.8	61.7	54.3	40.8	29.0	49.4
1974	27.1	22.3	33.0	46.2	53.1	65.6	69.9	69.9	59.6	49.2	40.2	31.7	47.3
1975	30.1	29.1	30.8	39.3	62.1	68.0	72.3	69.7	58.3	53.1	46.9	28.3	49.0
RECORD MEAN	25.1	24.5	32.3	43.3	54.6	64.7	70.3	68.9	62.6	51.8	40.0	29.5	47.3
MAX	31.6	31.4	39.4	51.4	63.0	72.3	77.9	76.8	70.5	59.2	46.2	35.3	54.6
MIN	18.6	17.6	25.2	35.2	46.1	57.1	62.6	61.0	54.6	44.3	33.8	23.7	40.0

\# Indicates a station move or relocation of instruments.

Precipitation

Year	Jan	Feb	Mar	Apr	May	June	July	Aug	Sept	Oct	Nov	Dec	Annual
1936	2.26	2.37	7.03	1.78	0.92	1.08	1.08	1.94	2.91	2.90	1.76	1.74	27.77
1937	4.42	2.12	1.81	4.58	3.02	5.94	3.00	2.08	1.09	3.55	2.34	3.78	37.73
1938	1.99	4.23	1.84	2.02	2.06	2.28	2.06	3.24	3.57	0.37	3.79	2.27	29.72
1939	2.90	3.50	2.94	2.46	1.97	1.75	1.51	3.79	3.12	1.83	0.53	3.00	29.30
1940	2.47	3.71	2.35	2.31	3.51	4.44	1.48	3.12	3.72	1.15	4.38	3.37	36.01
1941	2.36	2.05	2.01	1.69	1.11	0.82	3.37	1.06	0.87	2.40	3.06	1.36	22.16
1942	3.25	4.26	3.79	2.16	3.75	0.76	2.42	2.45	3.40	3.12	4.26	5.01	38.63
#1943	1.98	2.30	2.44	3.72	3.52	2.77	1.73	2.59	3.45	4.01	2.57	0.69	31.77
1944	1.23	2.92	2.91	4.62	2.87	3.95	1.04	6.17	3.63	1.11	1.44	3.83	35.72
1945	3.71	3.04	4.26	3.15	2.84	2.55	3.97	1.18	4.88	5.87	3.95	5.07	44.47
1946	1.03	2.47	1.61	1.27	3.59	2.03	2.75	4.35	3.24	3.72	2.79	2.79	31.64
1947	4.65	1.59	2.05	3.95	4.83	4.01	3.54	1.80	2.11	0.66	4.01	1.96	35.16
1948	1.99	2.94	3.24	2.81	3.12	3.07	2.58	1.10	5.74	4.74	4.01	2.05	37.39
1949	2.71	2.64	2.52	2.42	2.09	1.17	3.15	5.27	3.10	1.67	6.37	3.68	36.79
1950	5.01	4.26	3.23	2.46	2.16	2.04	3.12	4.12	1.95	2.36	4.83	1.84	37.38
1951	2.63	2.96	4.57	4.03	2.01	4.48	3.50	1.36	2.52	1.87	4.47	3.35	37.75
1952	3.75	2.02	2.51	2.56	3.91	1.13	1.28	3.12	2.72	0.68	2.89	2.57	29.14
1953	2.81	1.46	3.76	2.24	6.39	0.98	3.60	3.21	3.09	0.32	4.94	3.08	35.88
1954	2.94	3.72	5.24	3.95	1.35	2.57	2.08	2.45	2.20	9.13	3.32	5.83	44.78
1955	2.61	2.42	4.60	3.35	1.65	0.11	2.13	4.81	2.97	8.12	4.20	2.82	39.79
1956	2.12	3.33	5.25	3.69	4.61	0.99	3.54	5.89	3.95	0.86	2.88	4.82	41.93
1957	4.92	1.65	2.23	4.86	4.03	2.92	2.97	1.11	3.84	1.12	5.30	3.74	38.69
1958	3.81	4.78	1.36	3.95	1.79	2.91	1.49	3.16	4.59	1.40	3.49	1.66	34.39
1959	6.47	3.45	3.87	3.21	2.10	1.94	1.98	4.78	2.52	4.93	3.58	3.98	42.81
1960	3.90	5.80	2.35	2.34	4.05	2.48	1.89	3.75	1.20	1.89	2.94	2.57	35.16
1961	1.41	2.63	2.59	5.90	3.01	3.66	3.02	4.03	2.53	2.41	3.30	2.62	37.11
1962	2.78	2.65	1.23	2.25	2.36	2.80	1.89	3.00	3.14	1.90	1.78	2.77	28.55
1963	1.51	1.03	2.19	2.77	2.22	0.61	6.43	8.04	1.20	0.30	5.07	1.83	33.20
1964	2.12	1.09	3.72	3.36	2.91	1.55	2.57	5.02	0.77	1.89	2.09	2.58	29.67
1965	3.27	2.99	1.97	1.99	1.21	1.50	3.69	4.12	2.37	5.07	4.69	2.60	35.47
1966	3.74	2.11	2.78	2.06	1.36	1.97	4.92	3.60	2.65	0.93	4.50	2.25	32.87
1967	1.18	1.39	1.20	2.60	3.69	2.50	1.57	4.04	6.36	4.78	3.13	2.16	34.60
1968	2.18	0.81	2.67	1.78	3.30	4.45	1.19	5.33	5.63	3.03	4.47	3.42	38.26
1969	3.85	0.97	1.62	4.16	3.75	3.51	3.83	2.48	2.04	2.77	4.09	3.09	36.16
1970	2.06	1.74	1.72	2.54	2.87	2.55	4.02	2.01	4.55	4.20	3.20	3.25	34.71
1971	1.46	3.03	2.07	1.48	1.56	4.25	4.50	4.43	1.88	1.57	3.07	3.61	32.91
1972	2.17	3.44	3.99	2.99	3.64	6.06	0.99	4.19	3.06	2.96	4.28	3.86	41.63
1973	2.03	1.98	3.27	3.56	2.99	1.68	3.68	2.98	1.44	4.27	4.07	4.89	36.84
1974	2.44	2.19	3.19	3.15	3.36	3.86	1.80	3.64	2.42	1.75	5.38	3.13	36.31
1975	2.11	2.93	2.92	1.86	3.31	3.65	2.34	8.49	2.44	1.13	2.77	4.58	38.53
RECORD MEAN	3.06	2.72	2.74	2.68	2.87	2.76	2.89	3.12	2.93	3.02	3.23	3.17	35.19

Record mean values above are means through the current year for the period beginning in 1874 for temperature, 1871 for precipitation and 1944 for snowfall. Data are from City Office locations through June 1943 and from Airport locations thereafter.

NEW YORK, NEW YORK

Station: NEW YORK, NEW YORK
CENTRAL PARK OBSERVATORY
Elevation (ground): 132 feet

TEMPERATURES °F

Month	Normal: Daily maximum	Normal: Daily minimum	Normal: Monthly	Extremes: Record highest	Year	Extremes: Record lowest	Year
(a)				107		107	
J	38.5	25.9	32.2	72	1950	-6	1882
F	40.2	26.5	33.4	75	1930	-15	1934
M	48.4	33.7	41.1	86	1945	3	1872
A	60.7	43.5	52.1	92	1915	12	1923
M	71.4	53.1	62.3	99	1962	32	1891
J	80.5	62.6	71.6	101	1966	44	1945
J	85.2	68.0	76.6	106	1936	52	1943
A	83.4	66.4	74.9	104	1918	50	1965
S	76.8	59.9	68.4	102	1953	39	1912
O	66.8	50.6	58.7	94	1941	28	1936
N	54.0	40.8	47.4	84	1950	5	1875
D	41.4	29.5	35.5	70	1946	-13	1917
YR	62.3	46.7	54.5	106	JUL 1936	-15	FEB 1934

IMPORTANT:
The time-period covered by this record is limited: See footnotes following table of NORMALS, MEANS AND EXTREMES for explanation and for additional history of EXTREME HIGHS AND LOWS recorded in the general area.

New York City, in area exceeding 300 square miles, is located on the Atlantic coastal plain at the mouth of the Hudson River. The terrain is diversified by numerous waterways; all but one of the City's five boroughs are situated on islands. Elevations range from less than 50 feet over most of Manhattan, Brooklyn and Queens to almost 300 feet in the northern Manhattan and the Bronx, and over 400 feet in Staten Island. Extensive suburban areas on Long Island, and Connecticut, New York State and New Jersey border the city on the east, north, and west. About 30 miles to the west and northwest, hills rise to about 1500 feet and to the north in upper Westchester County to 800 feet. To the southwest and to the east are the low-lying land areas of the New Jersey coastal plain and of Long Island, whose south shore borders on the Atlantic.

The New York Metropolitan area is close to the path of most storm and frontal systems which move across the North American continent. Therefore, weather conditions affecting the city most often approach from a westerly direction. New York City can thus experience higher temperatures in summer and lower ones in winter than would otherwise be expected in a coastal area. However, the frequent passage of weather systems often helps reduce the length of both warm and cold spells, and is also a major factor in keeping periods of prolonged air stagnation to a minimum.

Although continental influence predominates, oceanic influence is by no means absent. During the summer local sea breezes — winds blowing onshore from the cool water surface — often moderate the afternoon heat. As would be expected, the effect of the sea breeze diminishes inland. On winter mornings, ocean temperatures which are warm relative to the land reinforce the effect of the city heat island and minimum temperatures are often 10

(Continued page 560)

Snowfall

Season	July	Aug	Sept	Oct	Nov	Dec	Jan
1936-37	0.0	0.0	0.0	T	3.2	T	6.5
1937-38	0.0	0.0	0.0	T	0.8	0.7	6.5
1938-39	0.0	0.0	0.0	0.0	12.8	1.7	10.3
1939-40	0.0	0.0	0.0	0.0	T	3.1	3.5
1940-41	0.0	0.0	0.0	T	2.2	3.0	9.2
1941-42	0.0	0.0	0.0	0.0	0.0	0.3	6.4
1942-43	0.0	0.0	0.0	0.0	T	8.5	9.5
1943-44	0.0	0.0	0.0	0.0	T	T	4.8
1944-45	0.0	0.0	0.0	T	T	6.7	12.3
1945-46	0.0	0.0	0.0	0.0	3.7	15.6	4.2
1946-47	0.0	0.0	0.0	0.0	0.0	1.3	5.5
1947-48	0.0	0.0	0.0	0.0	T	29.6	15.3
1948-49	0.0	0.0	0.0	0.0	T	25.3	6.4
1949-50	0.0	0.0	0.0	0.0	0.5	1.1	0.4
1950-51	0.0	0.0	0.0	0.0	T	3.8	3.2
1951-52	0.0	0.0	0.0	0.0	T	3.3	6.2
1952-53	0.0	0.0	0.0	0.5	1.7	7.5	4.1
1953-54	0.0	0.0	0.0	0.0	2.2	T	12.7
1954-55	0.0	0.0	0.0	0.0	T	0.1	2.6
1955-56	0.0	0.0	0.0	0.0	1.0	3.3	1.2
1956-57	0.0	0.0	0.0	0.0	T	0.9	8.9
1957-58	0.0	0.0	0.0	0.0	T	8.7	9.2
1958-59	0.0	0.0	0.0	0.0	T	3.8	1.5
1959-60	0.0	0.0	0.0	0.0	0.5	15.8	2.5
1960-61	0.0	0.0	0.0	T	0.0	18.6	16.7
1961-62	0.0	0.0	0.0	0.0	T	7.7	0.6
1962-63	0.0	0.0	0.0	T	T	4.5	5.3
1963-64	0.0	0.0	0.0	0.0	T	11.3	13.3
1964-65	0.0	0.0	0.0	0.0	0.0	3.1	14.8
1965-66	0.0	0.0	0.0	T	0.0	T	11.6
1966-67	0.0	0.0	0.0	0.0	0.0	9.1	1.4
1967-68	0.0	0.0	0.0	0.0	3.2	5.5	3.6
1968-69	0.0	0.0	0.0	0.0	T	7.0	1.0
1969-70	0.0	0.0	0.0	0.0	T	6.8	8.4
1970-71	0.0	0.0	0.0	0.0	0.0	2.4	11.4
1971-72	0.0	0.0	0.0	0.0	T	T	2.8
1972-73	0.0	0.0	0.0	T	T	T	1.8
1973-74	0.0	0.0	0.0	0.0	0.0	2.8	7.8
1974-75	0.0	0.0	0.0	0.0	0.1	0.1	2.0
1975-76	0.0	0.0	0.0	0.0	T	2.3	
RECORD MEAN	0.0	0.0	0.0	T	1.0	5.9	7.5

Heating Degree Days

Season	July	Aug	Sept	Oct	Nov	Dec	Jan
1955-56	0	0	32	174	615	1085	1012
1956-57	11	3	98	225	545	739	1124
1957-58	0	0	48	268	461	761	1019
1958-59	0	0	38	313	507	1099	1040
1959-60	0	0	30	224	572	820	954
1960-61	0	0	10	229	452	1049	1149
1961-62	0	0	20	168	490	907	997
1962-63	1	10	78	243	646	1032	1074
1963-64	0	0	125	134	431	1040	902
1964-65	3	0	63	308	461	879	1088
1965-66	0	13	54	239	538	755	1007
1966-67	0	0	63	270	475	901	849
1967-68	0	4	55	264	671	825	1179
1968-69	0	0	3	183	538	944	1023
1969-70	0	0	28	240	551	974	1227
1970-71	0	0	27	210	490	940	1173
1971-72	0	0	14	106	596	743	920
1972-73	2	0	25	355	611	812	907
1973-74	0	0	29	162	493	800	913
1974-75	1	0	59	333	502	789	852
1975-76	0	3	62	193	387	898	

Cooling Degree Days

Year	Jan	Feb	Mar	Apr	May	June	July
1969	0	0	0	20	88	250	310
1970	0	0	0	8	86	190	385
1971	0	0	0	0	29	290	404
1972	0	0	0	5	47	118	384
1973	0	0	0	20	23	260	390
1974	0	0	0	19	47	155	385
1975	0	0	0	0	120	185	341

Feb	Mar	Apr	May	June	Total
3.4	2.5	T	0.0	0.0	15.6
T	0.7	6.4	0.0	0.0	15.1
5.5	7.0	T	0.0	0.0	37.3
12.0	5.3	1.8	0.0	0.0	25.7
5.4	19.2	0.0	0.0	0.0	39.0
1.9	0.5	2.2	0.0	0.0	11.3
4.4	7.1	T	0.0	0.0	29.5
7.7	4.8	6.5	0.0	0.0	23.8
8.1	T	0.0	0.0	0.0	27.1
7.9	T	T	T	0.0	31.4
17.7	6.1	T	0.0	0.0	30.6
13.6	4.7	0.0	0.0	0.0	63.2
10.7	4.2	0.0	0.0	0.0	46.6
8.5	1.4	1.9	0.0	0.0	13.8
1.9	2.7	0.0	0.0	0.0	11.6
2.8	7.4	0.0	0.0	0.0	19.7
0.4	0.9	T	0.0	0.0	15.1
0.5	0.1	0.3	0.0	0.0	15.8
5.2	3.6	0.0	0.0	0.0	11.5
2.7	21.1	4.2	0.0	0.0	33.5
7.0	2.6	2.5	0.0	0.0	21.9
10.7	15.9	0.2	0.0	0.0	44.7
0.4	6.7	0.6	0.0	0.0	13.0
1.9	18.5	0.0	0.0	0.0	39.2
18.2	1.2	T	0.0	0.0	54.7
9.6	0.2	T	0.0	0.0	18.1
3.7	2.8	T	0.0	0.0	16.3
14.1	6.0	T	0.0	0.0	44.7
2.5	2.8	1.2	0.0	0.0	24.4
9.8	T	0.0	0.0	0.0	21.4
23.6	17.4	T	0.0	0.0	51.5
1.1	6.1	0.0	0.0	0.0	19.5
16.6	5.6	0.0	0.0	0.0	30.2
6.4	4.0	T	0.0	0.0	25.6
T	1.3	0.4	0.0	0.0	15.5
17.8	2.3	T	0.0	0.0	22.9
0.8	0.2	T	0.0	0.0	2.8
9.4	3.2	0.3	0.0	0.0	23.5
10.6	0.3	T	0.0	0.0	13.1
8.6	5.2	0.9	T	0.0	29.1

NEW YORK, NY
CENTRAL PARK OBSERVATORY

Feb	Mar	Apr	May	June	Total
818	848	504	216	17	5321
771	708	367	126	7	4724
1045	759	358	193	29	4941
915	765	341	87	32	5137
827	975	336	101	0	4839
788	719	473	172	6	5047
921	675	370	123	12	4683
1021	653	337	161	9	5265
927	669	454	90	23	4795
867	765	426	64	30	4954
830	685	451	166	9	4747
999	843	462	305	5	5172
1042	668	292	170	15	5185
902	768	285	74	0	4720
890	809	387	109	6	5221
830	764	419	135	9	4997
965	775	445	94	26	4684
903	572	362	188	2	4739
925	704	309	165	27	4527
812	764	507	86	11	4716

Aug	Sept	Oct	Nov	Dec	Total
392	154	20	0	0	1234
398	207	30	0	0	1304
347	218	40	7	0	1335
338	169	3	0	0	1064
401	171	22	2	0	1289
360	115	1	6	0	1088
299	43	22	15	0	1025

Average Temperature

Year	Jan	Feb	Mar	Apr	May	June	July	Aug	Sept	Oct	Nov	Dec	Annual
1936	29.3	25.7	45.2	47.8	64.2	69.8	76.2	75.4	68.2	57.4	42.6	38.6	53.4
1937	40.2	34.8	36.5	49.6	64.2	71.8	76.5	76.6	66.0	55.1	46.4	35.4	54.4
1938	32.1	35.4	44.2	53.6	60.8	70.3	76.6	78.1	66.0	59.8	48.3	37.0	55.2
1939	32.2	37.0	39.2	48.2	64.9	73.0	76.6	78.1	68.6	57.2	43.6	36.9	54.6
1940	25.0	32.8	35.1	46.8	60.6	70.4	76.2	71.4	66.6	53.8	45.3	38.4	51.8
1941	29.4	31.1	35.9	56.8	64.6	71.9	75.8	74.0	70.0	60.7	50.0	38.3	54.9
1942	30.7	29.6	43.0	53.8	65.3	71.0	76.3	73.6	68.2	58.8	47.0	31.0	54.0
1943	30.8	34.6	40.2	46.0	62.6	76.2	76.8	75.9	67.4	55.7	45.4	33.0	53.7
1944	33.9	33.2	37.6	48.8	67.0	72.2	79.4	77.8	70.0	57.0	46.0	32.4	54.6
1945	25.0	33.9	51.1	55.6	59.2	70.8	74.6	73.4	70.3	56.2	47.6	31.0	54.0
1946	34.1	31.6	49.8	50.4	61.9	69.6	75.4	70.9	69.8	61.7	50.4	37.8	55.3
1947	37.2	29.2	37.8	50.4	59.9	68.4	75.5	76.0	68.6	63.6	44.2	34.0	53.7
1948	25.4	30.7	42.0	51.0	60.2	69.4	77.2	75.2	70.2	56.6	52.4	38.3	54.0
1949	38.6	38.6	42.8	53.8	63.1	74.2	79.6	76.7	66.2	63.1	46.2	39.4	56.8
1950	41.4	31.6	36.4	48.5	58.8	70.3	75.0	73.1	64.6	60.0	48.4	35.0	53.6
1951	36.5	36.2	41.5	53.0	63.3	69.8	76.8	74.5	68.2	58.6	43.5	38.6	55.0
1952	36.2	36.2	40.2	55.0	60.7	73.6	80.3	74.9	69.9	55.7	48.6	38.4	55.8
1953	37.6	38.4	43.4	52.3	63.4	73.6	77.8	75.8	70.4	60.7	49.7	41.3	57.0
1954	30.8	40.1	41.6	53.8	59.8	71.6	76.7	72.8	67.4	61.7	46.4	35.9	54.9
1955	31.0	35.0	41.7	53.5	65.4	68.9	80.9	78.1	67.8	59.8	44.3	29.7	54.7
1956	32.0	36.6	37.4	48.2	58.7	71.4	72.9	74.2	64.8	58.1	46.7	40.9	53.5
1957	28.5	37.3	41.9	53.2	63.1	74.3	77.7	73.6	69.7	56.2	49.4	40.2	55.5
1958	31.9	27.4	40.3	52.9	59.1	67.2	76.1	75.2	67.6	55.5	47.9	29.4	52.5
1959	31.1	32.1	40.1	53.8	66.4	71.2	76.3	77.5	72.3	59.8	45.8	38.4	55.4
1960	33.9	36.3	33.3	54.1	62.6	71.8	74.6	74.9	68.0	58.1	49.7	30.9	54.0
1961	27.7	36.7	41.5	49.0	59.9	72.3	78.1	76.4	73.6	61.1	48.8	35.5	55.1
1962	32.6	31.8	43.1	53.3	64.5	72.5	74.0	72.4	64.9	57.4	43.2	31.5	53.4
1963	30.1	28.3	43.7	53.7	61.1	70.9	76.4	72.1	63.1	61.8	50.4	31.2	53.6
1964	35.7	32.9	43.1	49.7	65.4	71.6	75.4	72.9	67.2	55.0	49.4	36.4	54.6
1965	29.7	33.9	40.0	50.6	66.4	70.1	74.3	73.2	67.5	57.3	46.8	40.5	54.2
1966	32.2	35.1	42.7	49.7	61.6	75.4	79.7	76.9	66.5	56.2	48.9	35.7	55.1
1967	37.4	29.2	37.6	49.6	55.2	72.8	75.3	73.9	66.7	57.2	42.5	38.2	53.0
1968	26.7	28.9	43.3	55.0	59.6	69.7	77.3	76.0	70.6	60.5	46.9	34.3	54.1
1969	31.8	32.6	40.1	55.9	65.3	73.1	74.8	77.4	69.0	57.7	46.4	33.4	54.8
1970	25.1	33.0	38.7	52.1	64.0	70.9	77.1	77.6	70.8	58.9	48.5	34.4	54.3
1971	27.0	35.1	40.1	50.8	61.4	74.2	77.8	75.9	71.6	62.7	45.1	40.8	55.2
1972	35.1	31.4	39.8	50.1	63.3	67.9	77.2	75.6	69.5	53.5	44.4	38.5	53.8
1973	35.5	32.5	46.4	53.4	59.5	73.4	77.4	77.6	69.5	60.2	48.3	39.0	56.1
1974	35.3	31.7	42.1	55.2	61.0	69.0	77.2	76.4	66.7	54.1	48.2	39.4	54.7
1975	37.3	35.8	40.2	47.9	65.8	70.5	75.8	74.4	64.2	59.2	52.3	35.9	54.9
RECORD MEAN	32.3	32.7	40.6	51.1	61.9	70.9	76.1	74.6	68.0	58.0	46.7	35.7	54.1
MAX	38.7	39.5	48.1	59.5	70.9	79.7	84.6	82.9	76.3	66.0	53.2	41.7	61.8
MIN	25.9	25.8	33.1	42.7	52.8	62.1	67.6	66.2	59.7	49.9	40.2	29.6	46.3

Precipitation

# Indicates a station move or relocation of instruments.

Year	Jan	Feb	Mar	Apr	May	June	July	Aug	Sept	Oct	Nov	Dec	Annual
1936	7.54	2.68	5.45	3.30	2.97	4.62	1.89	3.99	4.82	3.90	1.14	7.53	49.83
1937	5.97	2.48	2.90	5.09	2.91	4.36	5.54	7.32	5.05	4.56	4.73	2.06	52.97
1938	3.99	1.97	2.22	3.38	3.36	7.13	5.82	3.92	9.06	1.75	3.27	2.62	48.49
1939	3.80	6.20	4.78	4.26	0.89	3.80	0.99	4.83	1.90	4.31	1.40	1.39	38.55
1940	2.61	2.63	4.73	5.46	7.61	3.01	3.30	4.13	2.82	2.43	3.55	2.79	45.07
1941	3.23	3.53	3.05	2.40	2.25	4.77	4.07	5.92	0.51	1.87	3.39	4.05	39.04
1942	2.88	2.53	5.91	1.09	1.78	3.59	7.15	9.08	4.23	1.98	3.72	4.57	48.51
1943	2.46	1.87	3.68	1.72	5.04	2.17	3.38	3.80	1.71	7.60	2.11	1.20	36.74
1944	3.20	1.73	5.98	4.75	1.18	3.35	1.83	1.84	10.30	2.32	5.96	2.57	45.01
1945	2.24	2.94	2.23	3.66	5.34	4.01	5.16	2.75	5.50	2.03	4.56	4.56	44.98
1946	1.86	1.76	3.21	1.43	6.80	3.36	5.12	6.68	4.02	0.85	1.66	1.61	38.36
1947	2.74	2.24	2.30	5.08	4.25	3.44	2.72	2.40	3.15	1.73	6.82	3.92	40.79
1948	4.74	2.52	3.51	3.26	7.58	5.52	4.51	2.99	1.28	1.51	3.17	6.28	46.87
1949	6.04	3.58	1.66	4.42	3.41	0.02	4.21	4.29	3.43	1.92	0.96	2.30	36.24
1950	2.26	4.44	2.73	1.66	2.66	2.18	4.24	4.97	1.48	1.71	4.24	4.32	36.89
1951	3.95	3.05	5.62	2.44	4.93	2.97	3.67	2.53	0.70	3.77	6.49	4.28	44.40
1952	4.55	1.38	4.00	5.05	4.78	3.64	3.32	4.63	2.05	0.94	3.05	4.12	41.51
1953	4.90	2.37	8.76	5.20	4.35	1.82	3.86	2.10	1.10	4.30	2.02	4.42	45.20
1954	1.65	1.81	3.25	2.70	3.10	1.32	0.96	6.09	4.75	1.99	4.93	3.03	35.58
1955	0.77	3.01	3.71	1.97	2.64	2.52	0.51	10.86	2.67	6.87	4.12	0.25	39.90
1956	1.54	4.18	5.03	2.78	2.20	2.99	3.13	2.56	2.32	3.61	2.62	3.29	36.25
1957	1.70	2.43	1.99	4.51	3.67	1.85	1.47	2.87	3.01	3.27	4.46	5.26	36.49
1958	3.79	2.98	3.19	6.14	3.25	2.55	3.68	2.36	4.44	5.46	1.85	1.25	40.94
1959	2.34	1.69	3.77	1.91	1.33	4.20	4.28	4.45	1.11	4.83	4.22	4.64	38.77
1960	2.40	4.43	2.96	3.05	2.97	1.74	8.29	6.26	5.38	2.82	3.05	3.04	46.39
1961	1.88	3.96	4.23	5.08	3.60	2.86	4.92	3.13	1.70	2.21	2.71	3.04	39.32
1962	2.62	3.74	2.97	3.00	1.26	3.73	1.67	5.71	3.10	3.15	3.94	2.26	37.15
1963	1.93	2.55	3.61	1.27	2.16	2.72	2.19	3.21	3.95	0.14	8.24	2.31	34.28
1964	4.62	2.93	2.57	5.09	0.57	2.67	4.17	0.24	1.69	1.73	2.55	4.16	32.99
1965	3.09	3.66	2.49	2.90	1.58	1.27	1.33	2.73	1.70	2.16	1.46	1.72	26.09
1966	2.63	4.96	0.94	2.69	4.26	1.17	1.25	1.89	8.82	4.64	3.47	3.18	39.90
1967	1.39	2.68	5.97	3.45	4.08	4.64	6.99	5.94	1.84	3.47	2.59	6.08	49.12
1968	2.04	1.13	4.79	2.82	7.06	6.15	2.63	2.88	1.97	2.20	5.75	4.15	43.57
1969	1.10	3.05	3.73	3.99	2.67	3.16	7.37	2.53	8.32	1.97	3.58	7.07	48.54
1970	0.66	4.52	4.18	3.48	3.34	2.27	2.19	2.47	1.74	2.48	5.14	2.82	35.29
1971	2.67	5.33	3.80	2.95	4.24	2.31	7.20	9.37	7.36	4.14	5.64	1.76	56.77
1972	2.41	5.90	4.55	3.92	8.39	9.30	4.54	1.92	1.33	6.27	12.41	6.09	67.03
1973	4.53	4.55	3.60	8.05	4.51	4.55	5.89	3.08	2.75	3.92	1.82	9.98	57.23
1974	3.80	1.49	5.76	3.83	4.29	3.29	1.33	5.99	8.05	2.59	0.94	6.33	47.69
1975	4.76	3.33	3.32	3.04	3.38	7.58	11.77	3.05	9.32	3.70	4.33	3.63	61.21
RECORD MEAN	3.33	3.42	3.81	3.45	3.45	3.45	4.27	4.30	3.72	3.49	3.38	3.49	43.56

Record mean values above are means through the current year for the period beginning in 1912 for temperature and 1869 for precipitation and snowfall. Data are from Central Park locations.

(Continued)

to 20 degrees lower in the inland suburbs than in the central city. The relatively warm water temperatures also delay the advent of winter snows and make heavy snowfalls rare before late December. Conversely, the lag in warming of water temperatures keeps spring temperatures relatively cool. One year-round measure of the ocean's influence is the small average daily variation in temperature; another is the average length of the frost-free season — more than 200 days.

Precipitation is moderate and distributed fairly evenly throughout the year. Most of the rainfall from May through October comes from thunderstorms. It is therefore usually of brief duration and sometimes intense. Heavy rains of long duration associated with tropical storms occur infrequently in late summer or fall. For the other months of the year precipitation is more likely to be associated with widespread storm areas, so that day-long rain, snow or a mixture of both is more common. Precipitation accompanying winter storms sometimes starts as snow, later changes to rain and perhaps briefly back to snow before ending. Coastal storms, occurring most often in the fall and winter months, produce on occasion considerable amounts of precipitation and have been responsible for record rains, snows, and high winds.

The average annual precipitation is reasonably uniform within the city but is higher in the northern and western suburbs and less on eastern Long Island. Annual snowfall totals also show a consistent increase to the north and west of the city with lesser amounts along the south shores and the eastern end of Long Island, reflecting the influence of the ocean waters. Relative humidity averages about the same over the metropolitan area except again that the immediate coastal areas are more humid than inland locations.

Local Climatological Data is published for three locations in New York City: Central Park, La Guardia Airport and John F. Kennedy International Airport. Other nearby locations for which it is published are: Newark, New Jersey and Bridgeport, Connecticut.

Normals, Means, and Extremes

Month	Normal Degree days Base 65 °F		Precipitation in inches												Relative humidity pct.			
			Water equivalent							Snow, Ice pellets					Hour 01	Hour 07	Hour 13	Hour 19
	Heating	Cooling	Normal	Maximum monthly	Year	Minimum monthly	Year	Maximum in 24 hrs.	Year	Maximum monthly	Year	Maximum in 24 hrs.	Year		(Local time)			
(a)				107		107		64		107		107			43	55	55	55
J	1017	0	2.71	7.94	1915	0.66	1970	3.33	1915	27.4	1925	13.0	1935		65	68	60	61
F	885	0	2.92	6.87	1869	0.46	1895	3.04	1973	27.9	1934	17.4	1961		65	68	58	60
M	741	0	3.73	8.79	1876	0.90	1885	4.25	1876	30.5	1896	18.1	1941		64	67	55	58
A	387	0	3.30	8.77	1874	0.95	1881	2.67	1886	13.5	1875	10.2	1915		65	68	51	57
M	137	54	3.47	8.51	1908	0.30	1903	4.88	1968	T	1946	T	1946		71	71	53	60
J	0	202	2.96	9.78	1903	0.02	1949	4.74	1884	0.0		0.0			74	74	55	62
J	0	360	3.68	11.89	1889	0.49	1910	3.60	1971	0.0		0.0			75	75	55	63
A	0	307	4.01	10.86	1955	0.24	1964	5.78	1971	0.0		0.0			77	78	57	66
S	29	131	3.27	16.85	1882	0.21	1884	8.30	1882	0.0		0.0			77	79	57	67
O	209	14	2.85	13.31	1903	0.14	1963	11.17	1903	0.8	1925	0.8	1925		72	76	55	63
N	528	0	3.76	12.41	1972	0.60	1931	5.60	1972	19.0	1898	10.0	1898		69	73	59	63
D	915	0	3.53	9.98	1973	0.25	1955	3.21	1909	29.6	1947	26.4	1947		67	70	61	63
YR	4848	1068	40.19	16.85	SEP 1882	0.02	JUN 1949	11.17	OCT 1903	30.5	MAR 1896	26.4	DEC 1947		70	72	56	62

(To better understand these tables, see full explanation of terms beginning on page 322)

Month	Wind					Pct. of possible sunshine	Mean sky cover, tenths, sunrise to sunset	Mean number of days											Average station pressure mb.
			Fastest mile					Sunrise to sunset							Temperatures °F				
															Max. (b)		Min.		Elev. 87 feet m.s.l.
	Mean speed m.p.h.	Prevailing direction	Speed m.p.h.	Direction	Year			Clear	Partly cloudy	Cloudy	Precipitation .01 inch or more	Snow, Ice pellets 1.0 inch or more	Thunderstorms	Heavy fog, visibility ¼ mile or less	90° and above	32° and below	32° and below	0° and below	
(a)	56	45	29	29		99	42	42	42	42	107	105	15		62	62	62	62	3
J	10.7	NW	47	NW	1959	50	6.0	8	9	14	11	2	*		0	8	22	*	1015.8
F	10.9	NW	47	NE	1961	55	5.8	8	9	11	10	2	*		0	6	21	*	1013.7
M	11.1	NW	60	NW	1950	56	5.7	9	10	12	12	2	1		0	1	13	0	1012.0
A	10.5	NW	45	NE	1961	59	6.0	8	10	12	11	*	1		*	0	2	0	1010.5
M	8.8	SW	38	NE	1967	61	5.7	8	12	11	11	0	2		1	0	*	0	1010.8
J	8.1	SW	49	SW	1952	64	5.6	8	12	10	10	0	4		3	0	0	0	1012.4
J	7.7	SW	43	NW	1949	65	5.5	8	13	10	11	0	4		6	0	0	0	1012.5
A	7.7	SW	36	NE	1954	64	5.5	9	12	10	10	0	4		4	0	0	0	1014.6
S	8.1	SW	44	NE	1960	63	5.2	11	10	9	8	0	1		1	0	0	0	1015.5
O	9.0	SW	40	NE	1955	61	4.9	12	10	9	8	0	1		*	0	*	0	1017.0
N	9.9	NW	70	NE	1950	52	5.8	9	9	12	9	*	*		0	*	5	0	1014.3
D	10.4	NW	43	NW	1962	49	5.9	9	9	13	10	2	*		0	5	19	*	1015.1
YR	9.4	NW	70	NE	NOV 1950	59	5.6	107	125	133	121	8	20		16	20	81	*	1013.7

FOOTNOTES

Means and extremes above are from existing and comparable exposures. Annual extremes have been exceeded at other sites in the locality as follows: Maximum monthly snowfall 37.9 inches in February 1894; fastest mile of wind 113 from the SE in October 1954.

QUOTES FROM WEATHER FOLKLORE–

Above the rest, the sun who never lies,
Foretells the change of weather in the skies;
For if he rise unwilling to his race,
Clouds on his brow and spots upon his face,
Or if through mists he shoot his sullen beams,
Frugal of light in loose and straggling streams,
Suspect a drizzling day and southern rain,
Fatal to fruits and flocks, and promised grain.
– Virgil.

The sun reveals the secrets of the sky,
And who dares give the source of light
the lie. – Virgil.

Go plant the bean when the moon is light,
And you will find that this is right;
Plant the potatoes when the moon is dark,
And to this line you always hark;
But if you vary from this rule,
You will find you are a fool;
If you always follow this rule to the end,
You will always have money to spend.

Do business with men when the wind is
from the westerly;
for then the barometer is high.

Fishes in general, both in salt and
fresh waters, are observed to sport most
and bite more eagerly before rain than
at any other time.

Before rain the leaves of the lime,
sycamore, plane, and poplar trees show
a great deal more of their under surface
when trembling in the wind.

Pipes for smoking tobacco become
indicative of the state of the air.
When the scent is longer retained than
usual and seems denser and more
powerful it often forebodes a storm.

ROCHESTER, NEW YORK

Rochester is located approximately midway of Lake Ontario's southern shore and some 6 or 7 miles upstream from the mouth of the Genesee River. Roundabout the terrain is generally level or moderately undulating with a slight inclination toward the Lake which has a surface elevation of 246 feet above m.s.l. Some 5 miles south of Rochester, an elevation around 600 feet is attained while the 1,000-foot contour, following a general east-west course, is about 15 miles south of the City. The Genesee River rises in northwestern Pennsylvania and its valley approaches Rochester from a south-southwesterly direction with the stream flowing through the heart of the City.

Lake Ontario is deep and remains unfrozen in winter weather. In February 1934, during the coldest weather of record, thick ice formed only 10 miles into the Lake from the shore and Rochester harbor. As might be surmised, the Lake plays an important part in shaping the climate of the Rochester area. After storing up cold in the water during the winter, the Lake releases it in the spring, thus delaying the development of vegetation and reducing the losses from spring frosts. In the autumn, a reverse action takes place. Summer heat is stored and released in autumn to warm the air and so prolong the growing and harvest seasons. It is these factors that have so well adapted the region for the growth of fruits and vegetables. Apples, pears, peaches, sweet cherries and sour cherries are major crops in the area. The climate also favors the numerous fruit, ornamental and shrub nurseries of the area.

Both upper and lower extremes of temperature are moderated by the lake effect, so the long-term, as well as the daily, range is less than at strictly continental stations of comparable latitude. Rochester's summer temperature very rarely reaches 100° and the winter minimum falls to zero, or below, on an average of only about 6 days per year.

A further effect of the Lake is to promote cloudiness and the occurrence of precipitation, especially during cold weather when atmospheric circulatory processes gather moisture and heat in the lower layers, as airmasses move over the water surface from northerly directions. Upon striking the colder land surface south of the Lake clouds form and snow develops. Snowfalls so caused are frequent, but are in the main not heavy. This Lake phenomenon goes far to explain the winter deficiency of sunshine at Rochester - only about one-third of the amount possible is received. In comparison, more than two-thirds of that possible occurs on the average in June, July, and August.

Another important contributing element to the makeup of weather and climate in the Rochester area is its proximity to the so-called St. Lawrence storm track. Cyclonic systems progressing from the interior to the Atlantic Ocean through the St. Lawrence Valley transport moisture from the Gulf of Mexico which is precipitated enroute. This is the source of a large portion of the rainfall in the Rochester area, and practically all of its major snowstorms.

Although located in the humid section of the Northeastern United States, precipitation is relatively light, but it is notably uniform in its distribution - ranging in monthly averages from a little less than 2-1/2 inches to slightly more than 3 inches. Since the frequency of days with .01 of an inch, or more, ranges from an average of about 10 to around 15 per month, it is readily seen that as a rule amounts for individual storms must be relatively light.

Station: ROCHESTER, NEW YORK
ROCHESTER-MONROE COUNTY AP
Elevation (ground): 547 feet

TEMPERATURES °F

Month	Normal			Extremes			
	Daily maximum	Daily minimum	Monthly	Record highest	Year	Record lowest	Year
(a)				12		12	
J	31.3	16.7	24.0	68	1967	-11	1968
F	32.6	16.9	24.8	64	1965	-8	1970
M	41.1	24.9	33.0	79	1966	-2	1967
A	56.0	36.1	46.1	93	1970	14	1970
M	67.2	45.7	56.5	94	1974	26	1970
J	78.0	55.8	66.9	96	1964	36	1972
J	82.2	60.2	71.2	98	1966	42	1963
A	80.1	58.5	69.3	96	1965	36	1965
S	73.1	51.5	62.3	95	1973	30	1963
O	62.4	42.2	52.3	86	1971	20	1972
N	47.9	33.1	40.5	79	1971	5	1971
D	34.9	21.7	28.3	68	1966	-5	1969
YR	57.2	38.6	47.9	98	JUL 1966	-11	JAN 1968

IMPORTANT:
The time-period covered by this record is limited: See footnotes following table of **NORMALS, MEANS AND EXTREMES** for explanation and for additional history of **EXTREME HIGHS AND LOWS** recorded in the general area.

(Continued)

Snowfall occurrences in Rochester are likely to be spread over a period of about five months on the average. The average date of the first snowfall of measurable amount is near the end of the first decade in November, and that of last measurable snowfall in the spring is around mid-April. These first and last snows tend to melt rather rapidly until near the period when snow cover is more or less continuous, which is from about the fourth week in December to mid-March. The heaviest snowstorm of record at Rochester was an accumulation of 43.5 inches during a 63-hour period from February 28 to March 2, 1900.

Ground fogs are more frequent in the valleys to the south, but in the Rochester area serious restriction of visibility by fog is rather rare. For the entire year, the average number of days with heavy fog is not more than two in any one month.

The growing season in the immediate vicinity of Rochester averages between 175 and 180 days, beginning with the last week in April and terminating near the end of the third week in October. However, damaging frosts have occurred late in May and as early as late September.

ROCHESTER, NEW YORK

Normals, Means, and Extremes

(To better understand these tables, see full explanation of terms beginning on page 322)

Month	Normal Degree days Base 65 °F: Heating	Cooling	Precipitation in inches: Water equivalent: Normal	Maximum monthly	Year	Minimum monthly	Year	Maximum in 24 hrs.	Year	Snow, Ice pellets: Maximum monthly	Year	Maximum in 24 hrs.	Year	Relative humidity pct. Hour 01 (Local time)	Hour 07	Hour 13	Hour 19
(a)				35		35		35		35		35		12	12	12	12
J	1271	0	2.25	4.10	1966	0.81	1946	1.64	1966	60.2	1966	18.2	1966	74	75	67	72
F	1126	0	2.42	5.07	1950	0.74	1968	2.43	1950	64.8	1958	18.7	1960	75	76	66	71
M	992	0	2.57	5.42	1942	0.47	1958	2.21	1942	40.3	1959	17.6	1959	75	77	62	69
A	567	0	2.74	4.90	1944	1.28	1971	1.99	1943	14.9	1975	6.5	1975	75	76	53	60
M	285	22	2.80	6.62	1974	0.50	1965	3.85	1974	2.0	1945	2.0	1945	77	76	54	59
J	46	103	2.54	6.56	1972	0.22	1963	2.86	1950	0.0		0.0		81	78	55	61
J	9	202	2.89	9.70	1947	0.98	1955	2.94	1947	0.0		0.0		82	81	52	59
A	26	159	2.97	5.95	1968	0.76	1951	2.39	1968	T	1965	T	1965	86	87	56	66
S	126	45	2.35	5.21	1945	0.28	1960	2.61	1959	T	1956	T	1956	86	87	59	74
O	398	0	2.62	7.85	1955	0.23	1963	2.52	1945	1.4	1960	1.4	1960	81	83	60	73
N	735	0	2.83	5.51	1950	0.73	1960	3.13	1945	16.9	1972	11.2	1953	80	82	69	78
D	1138	0	2.35	5.05	1944	0.62	1958	1.59	1944	44.2	1970	17.8	1944	80	81	75	79
YR	6719	531	31.33	9.70	JUL 1947	0.22	JUN 1963	3.85	MAY 1974	64.8	FEB 1958	18.7	FEB 1960	79	80	61	68

Month	Wind: Mean speed m.p.h.	Prevailing direction	Fastest mile: Speed m.p.h.	Direction	Year	Pct. of possible sunshine	Mean sky cover, tenths, sunrise to sunset	Mean number of days: Sunrise to sunset: Clear	Partly cloudy	Cloudy	Precipitation .01 inch or more	Snow, Ice pellets 1.0 inch or more	Thunderstorms	Heavy fog, visibility ¼ mile or less	Temperatures °F Max. (b) 90° and above	32° and below	Min. 32° and below	0° and below	Average station pressure mb. Elev. 555 feet m.s.l.
(a)	35	23	35	35		35	35	35	35	35	35	35	35	35	12	12	12	12	3
J	11.7	WSW	73	W	1950	37	8.1	2	7	22	17	7	*	1	0	15	28	3	997.4
F	11.6	WSW	66	W	1956	42	7.9	2	7	19	16	7	*	1	0	14	26	2	997.3
M	11.1	WSW	65	W	1956	50	7.3	4	9	18	15	4	1	1	0	7	24	*	995.4
A	10.7	WSW	59	W	1946	55	6.7	6	8	16	13	1	2	1	*	1	12	0	994.6
M	9.3	WSW	63	SW	1950	60	6.6	6	10	15	12	*	4	1	*	0	1	0	993.3
J	8.4	SW	61	SW	1949	67	5.9	7	12	11	10	0	5	1	3	0	0	0	995.0
J	7.9	SW	56	W	1956	70	5.6	8	13	10	9	0	6	1	5	0	0	0	995.7
A	7.6	SW	59	NE	1955	68	5.8	8	13	10	10	0	6	1	2	0	0	0	997.6
S	8.0	SW	59	SW	1949	60	6.0	7	11	12	10	0	3	1	1	0	0	0	998.4
O	8.7	SW	50	NW	1941	51	6.5	7	9	15	11	*	1	2	0	0	4	0	999.8
N	10.2	WSW	59	E	1950	32	8.2	2	6	22	15	2	1	1	0	2	14	0	996.1
D	10.7	WSW	56	W	1949	31	8.4	2	5	24	17	6	*	1	0	11	25	1	997.6
YR	9.7	WSW	73	W	JAN 1950	54	6.9	61	110	194	154	27	29	13	11	50	135	6	996.5

FOOTNOTES

Means and extremes above are from existing and comparable exposures. Annual extremes have been exceeded at other sites in the locality as follows: Highest temperature 102 in July 1936; lowest temperature -22 in February 1934; minimum monthly precipitation 0.08 in October 1924; maximum precipitation in 24 hours 4.19 in August 1893; maximum snowfall in 24 hours 29.8 in March 1900.

Snowfall

Season	July	Aug	Sept	Oct	Nov	Dec	Jan
1936-37	0.0	0.0	0.0	T	9.2	12.2	7.4
1937-38	0.0	0.0	0.0	0.2	5.7	8.1	12.7
1938-39	0.0	0.0	0.0	0.0	7.2	8.3	34.4
1939-40	0.0	0.0	0.0	T	0.1	2.6	9.3
#1940-41	0.0	0.0	0.0	T	13.5	7.0	13.0
1941-42	0.0	0.0	0.0	T	0.2	5.9	5.0
1942-43	0.0	0.0	0.0	T	5.5	18.5	17.2
1943-44	0.0	0.0	0.0	T	5.2	5.1	4.0
1944-45	0.0	0.0	0.0	T	7.7	41.8	23.5
1945-46	0.0	0.0	0.0	0.0	10.9	11.0	6.7
1946-47	0.0	0.0	0.0	T	0.1	13.6	18.6
1947-48	0.0	0.0	0.0	0.0	2.0	15.3	18.8
1948-49	0.0	0.0	0.0	T	T	12.3	14.0
1949-50	0.0	0.0	0.0	0.0	6.1	9.4	14.2
1950-51	0.0	0.0	0.0	0.0	10.6	19.1	27.6
1951-52	0.0	0.0	0.0	T	16.3	23.6	13.9
1952-53	0.0	0.0	0.0	T	T	7.5	11.8
1953-54	0.0	0.0	0.0	0.0	11.9	10.2	19.8
1954-55	0.0	0.0	0.0	T	0.1	23.4	9.1
1955-56	0.0	0.0	0.0	T	10.1	24.8	21.1
1956-57	0.0	0.0	T	0.0	10.0	17.7	25.6
1957-58	0.0	0.0	0.0	1.4	9.9	6.9	37.9
1958-59	0.0	0.0	0.0	0.0	13.5	12.4	46.8
1959-60	0.0	0.0	0.0	T	11.6	25.4	32.7
1960-61	0.0	0.0	0.0	1.4	2.8	17.9	23.6
1961-62	0.0	0.0	0.0	0.0	7.5	6.0	11.7
1962-63	0.0	0.0	0.0	0.8	6.0	14.2	23.7
1963-64	0.0	0.0	0.0	0.0	4.4	34.6	20.2
1964-65	0.0	0.0	0.0	T	5.1	11.6	26.6
1965-66	0.0	T	0.0	0.9	8.0	6.0	60.2
1966-67	0.0	0.0	0.0	0.0	3.0	14.4	12.7
1967-68	0.0	0.0	0.0	T	10.0	6.9	24.2
1968-69	0.0	0.0	0.0	T	8.6	22.2	25.6
1969-70	0.0	0.0	0.0	T	5.8	42.0	37.9
1970-71	0.0	0.0	0.0	0.2	3.6	44.2	34.1
1971-72	0.0	0.0	0.0	0.0	11.2	13.8	18.1
1972-73	0.0	0.0	0.0	0.2	16.9	22.7	8.9
1973-74	0.0	0.0	0.0	0.0	4.2	23.4	14.4
1974-75	0.0	0.0	0.0	0.3	4.6	26.5	10.8
1975-76	0.0	0.0	0.0	T	1.8	28.3	
RECORD MEAN	0.0	T	T	0.1	6.7	18.2	21.0

Heating Degree Days

Season	July	Aug	Sept	Oct	Nov	Dec	Jan
1955-56	0	9	169	357	812	1251	1296
1956-57	19	27	239	342	715	993	1408
1957-58	17	49	158	477	721	948	1268
1958-59	5	31	139	428	700	1344	1327
1959-60	0	3	126	407	806	1052	1244
1960-61	22	24	83	452	647	1280	1410
1961-62	28	21	82	302	728	1092	1296
#1962-63	10	21	209	409	836	1202	1412
1963-64	24	52	253	247	615	1335	1132
1964-65	3	48	169	500	674	1090	1337
1965-66	24	53	122	496	748	937	1307
1966-67	0	16	190	458	639	1053	1046
1967-68	25	28	164	401	856	1005	1399
1968-69	15	36	67	369	710	1150	1229
1969-70	18	10	126	437	737	1231	1448
1970-71	3	11	126	349	699	1218	1405
1971-72	17	33	74	194	792	1048	1200
1972-73	7	24	92	534	833	982	1118
1973-74	2	14	162	305	653	1040	1167
1974-75	1	1	209	535	755	1034	1096
1975-76	4	14	194	365	525	1146	

Cooling Degree Days

Year	Jan	Feb	Mar	Apr	May	June	July
1969	0	0	0	0	18	94	202
1970	0	0	0	16	47	148	235
1971	0	0	0	0	10	133	143
1972	0	0	0	0	24	94	261
1973	0	0	0	15	6	194	267
1974	0	0	0	13	14	88	204
1975	0	0	0	0	89	121	257

Feb	Mar	Apr	May	June	Total
6.1	30.0	1.0	0.0	0.0	65.9
14.9	4.8	8.3	0.0	0.0	54.7
11.7	13.6	3.9	0.0	0.0	79.1
23.0	15.8	3.7	0.0	0.0	54.5
20.2	19.6	0.4	0.0	0.0	73.7
31.5	18.4	5.3	0.0	0.0	66.3
17.6	10.7	1.1	T	0.0	70.6
21.0	7.6	3.2	0.0	0.0	46.1
13.9	5.4	0.4	2.0	0.0	94.7
19.5	0.9	0.5	0.0	0.0	49.5
17.0	20.7	5.3	0.2	0.0	75.5
14.5	12.0	0.3	0.5	0.0	63.4
10.6	13.7	T	0.0	0.0	50.6
26.4	22.4	3.2	0.0	0.0	81.7
10.2	8.3	T	0.0	0.0	75.8
16.1	5.9	T	0.0	0.0	75.8
17.3	3.0	2.1	0.0	0.0	41.7
11.2	23.0	1.4	T	0.0	77.5
14.5	16.4	5.7	0.0	0.0	69.2
24.7	33.3	7.4	T	0.0	121.4
8.0	11.7	6.2	T	0.0	79.2
64.8	8.8	1.1	T	0.0	130.8
27.4	40.3	0.2	T	0.0	140.6
58.3	33.0	0.7	0.0	0.0	161.7
18.8	19.5	5.4	T	0.0	89.4
28.2	4.6	7.6	T	0.0	65.6
22.9	6.7	1.1	1.0	0.0	76.4
13.1	16.1	3.6	0.0	0.0	92.0
10.3	15.6	1.9	0.0	0.0	71.1
21.0	6.2	0.9	T	0.0	103.2
27.6	16.0	T	0.3	0.0	74.0
20.4	15.2	T	0.0	0.0	76.7
17.8	4.6	1.0	0.0	0.0	79.8
27.7	4.9	1.3	T	0.0	119.6
29.7	29.7	1.2	0.0	0.0	142.7
35.7	19.0	7.3	0.0	0.0	105.1
18.4	4.4	1.5	T	0.0	73.0
26.6	22.3	8.2	T	0.0	99.1
23.2	10.9	14.9	0.0	0.0	91.2
22.5	14.6	2.9	0.1	0.0	86.1

ROCHESTER, NY

Feb	Mar	Apr	May	June	Total
1101	1118	677	407	72	7269
979	944	520	311	48	6545
1269	965	509	337	131	6849
1182	1072	545	235	67	7075
1122	1313	491	212	56	6832
1045	945	692	366	64	7030
1215	969	589	181	52	6555
1309	902	556	332	51	7249
1181	939	526	187	98	6589
1096	1095	706	192	114	7024
1098	871	612	382	57	6707
1216	998	551	486	8	6661
1275	894	463	357	78	6945
1087	1013	517	302	86	6581
1149	1053	506	209	49	6973
1059	1122	707	342	49	7090
1199	1071	677	161	78	6544
1189	690	519	279	17	6284
1187	983	475	352	59	6399
1017	1031	764	139	52	6634

Aug	Sept	Oct	Nov	Dec	Total
233	92	7	0	0	646
176	69	13	0	0	704
159	155	15	0	0	615
179	79	0	0	0	637
269	96	4	0	0	851
181	40	0	0	0	540
178	5	6	0	0	656

Average Temperature

Year	Jan	Feb	Mar	Apr	May	June	July	Aug	Sept	Oct	Nov	Dec	Annual
1936	23.3	18.8	37.3	41.9	60.2	67.3	72.7	70.6	64.8	52.4	35.0	34.2	48.2
1937	33.2	29.2	29.4	44.8	58.1	66.8	72.8	74.2	61.2	48.9	40.2	28.2	48.8
1938	24.8	29.6	40.4	47.8	56.9	67.8	73.6	73.6	59.5	54.4	42.7	31.8	50.2
1939	26.0	27.1	31.2	42.0	59.8	67.6	72.2	73.4	64.6	52.0	37.9	31.8	48.8
#1940	18.4	24.8	27.4	42.4	57.8	66.0	72.0	70.0	61.6	47.3	38.9	30.8	46.4
1941	22.8	22.4	25.2	49.7	58.2	68.7	73.9	67.4	64.1	52.2	43.1	31.8	48.2
1942	24.4	20.4	35.6	50.1	59.8	67.8	71.0	69.2	62.9	52.4	39.4	24.4	48.1
1943	20.4	26.4	31.8	38.6	56.2	70.8	71.8	68.4	60.6	48.6	37.0	25.4	46.3
1944	28.6	24.0	29.7	40.2	63.2	67.0	72.6	72.5	62.6	49.4	40.7	23.2	47.8
1945	15.2	25.1	43.8	50.4	51.2	64.6	70.2	69.3	64.3	50.0	40.6	23.0	47.3
1946	26.2	23.4	43.2	44.4	55.6	65.2	70.5	65.8	64.0	56.8	43.7	30.6	49.1
1947	29.2	21.6	30.0	44.5	54.2	66.2	70.0	75.0	63.8	59.4	37.4	26.7	48.2
1948	18.4	23.1	34.1	49.0	53.4	65.3	72.2	70.2	64.1	49.0	46.2	31.2	48.0
1949	30.2	30.6	34.2	46.0	58.6	73.0	74.0	72.0	58.8	55.8	37.4	31.8	50.2
1950	33.3	24.4	27.8	40.8	57.1	65.9	69.6	68.6	59.9	54.0	39.6	26.5	47.3
1951	27.4	26.1	35.4	45.7	58.1	66.2	70.8	67.9	61.6	53.9	34.2	30.0	48.1
1952	27.7	28.6	33.3	48.8	54.3	68.1	75.8	70.7	64.3	47.1	42.8	33.4	49.6
1953	30.6	30.3	36.8	44.6	57.5	68.2	72.1	69.7	63.0	53.0	43.9	34.0	50.3
1954	22.6	32.1	32.1	47.0	54.9	68.1	69.9	66.9	61.3	54.1	41.3	27.7	48.2
1955	23.5	25.8	33.1	50.8	59.6	67.5	75.4	73.9	61.0	53.5	37.7	24.4	48.9
1956	23.1	26.9	28.7	42.2	52.4	66.6	68.2	68.2	58.0	53.8	41.0	32.7	46.8
1957	19.4	29.9	34.4	48.4	55.4	69.4	69.9	66.6	61.2	49.4	40.7	34.2	48.3
1958	23.9	19.4	33.6	47.9	54.3	61.4	70.4	68.2	61.5	51.2	41.5	21.4	46.2
1959	21.9	22.6	30.2	46.6	59.4	67.5	72.5	74.5	66.6	51.9	37.9	30.9	48.5
1960	24.6	26.1	22.4	48.6	58.7	65.6	68.5	67.7	64.5	50.2	43.2	23.5	47.0
1961	19.4	27.5	34.3	41.7	53.9	65.4	70.8	69.9	68.5	55.5	40.6	29.6	48.1
1962	22.9	21.4	33.5	45.7	62.4	66.0	67.6	68.9	58.9	51.8	36.9	26.0	46.8
#1963	19.3	17.9	35.7	46.2	54.3	67.1	70.9	65.5	56.7	57.3	44.3	21.7	46.4
1964	28.3	24.0	34.4	47.2	60.3	65.8	73.8	66.2	61.2	48.7	42.3	29.6	48.5
1965	21.6	25.7	29.5	41.3	60.1	64.4	67.5	68.4	63.8	48.8	39.8	34.6	47.1
1966	22.6	25.5	36.6	44.4	53.0	67.8	73.0	68.9	59.2	50.1	43.5	30.8	48.0
1967	31.1	21.4	32.5	46.4	49.1	70.4	69.4	67.6	60.4	52.1	36.3	32.3	47.4
1968	19.8	20.8	36.0	49.5	53.2	64.7	70.7	69.4	64.8	53.8	41.2	27.7	47.6
1969	25.2	26.0	32.0	47.6	55.6	65.0	70.7	72.0	63.6	50.9	40.1	25.1	47.8
1970	18.0	23.7	30.8	48.4	59.5	68.1	72.2	70.1	63.0	53.9	41.4	25.5	47.9
1971	19.5	26.9	28.5	41.1	54.0	67.5	68.8	68.8	67.4	59.0	38.4	30.9	47.6
1972	26.0	23.4	30.3	42.2	60.4	65.2	73.0	69.8	64.3	47.6	37.0	33.1	47.7
1973	28.7	22.2	42.5	48.0	56.1	70.7	73.4	73.0	62.5	55.0	43.0	31.2	50.5
1974	27.1	22.5	33.0	49.4	53.9	65.7	71.3	70.6	59.2	47.6	39.5	31.4	47.6
1975	29.5	28.4	31.6	39.3	63.2	67.1	73.0	70.0	58.4	53.1	47.2	27.8	49.0
RECORD MEAN	24.9	24.5	32.7	45.0	56.7	66.5	71.3	69.3	62.7	51.5	39.8	28.9	47.8
MAX	31.8	31.8	40.2	53.8	66.5	76.5	81.1	78.8	72.2	60.3	46.5	35.1	56.2
MIN	17.9	17.1	25.1	36.1	46.8	56.4	61.4	59.7	53.1	42.7	33.0	22.7	39.3

# Indicates a station move or relocation of instruments.

Precipitation

Year	Jan	Feb	Mar	Apr	May	June	July	Aug	Sept	Oct	Nov	Dec	Annual
1936	2.88	1.57	6.55	1.83	1.87	2.30	1.24	1.25	3.16	2.31	2.19	2.93	30.08
1937	3.13	1.38	2.83	3.42	2.37	3.76	1.92	4.71	0.50	4.21	2.65	2.15	33.03
1938	1.37	3.05	1.33	2.39	2.18	1.56	3.62	4.85	5.27	0.14	2.10	1.24	29.10
1939	3.39	2.67	2.56	2.59	0.64	3.28	1.91	1.65	2.54	1.53	0.46	1.97	25.19
#1940	1.26	3.08	2.92	3.30	2.75	2.52	1.82	1.28	2.33	1.52	2.98	2.84	28.60
1941	1.95	1.59	2.20	1.51	1.22	1.76	3.05	2.04	2.09	3.32	1.05	2.24	24.02
1942	1.28	4.51	5.42	2.60	3.51	1.03	2.84	1.66	2.72	3.22	3.40	4.48	36.67
1943	2.06	2.05	2.59	4.81	5.45	4.22	2.90	3.31	1.82	4.51	1.91	0.77	36.40
1944	1.18	2.91	2.12	4.90	2.64	3.42	1.78	2.71	1.90	1.17	2.29	5.05	32.07
1945	2.50	2.31	3.87	2.16	4.45	2.40	8.08	1.43	5.21	4.59	5.10	2.00	44.10
1946	0.81	2.70	0.77	1.41	2.82	3.21	2.81	3.62	2.71	3.79	2.36	2.61	29.62
1947	4.06	1.05	2.92	4.34	5.06	4.08	9.70	2.42	2.84	0.36	2.59	2.02	41.44
1948	2.37	2.50	2.91	3.26	3.39	2.76	2.36	1.82	1.54	2.66	2.92	1.63	30.12
1949	2.36	1.88	1.89	2.11	2.08	1.41	2.94	2.93	2.77	0.77	3.30	1.95	26.39
1950	3.71	5.07	4.28	1.87	2.81	4.00	3.53	2.30	1.81	3.68	5.51	1.97	40.54
1951	2.89	2.70	5.03	3.55	1.82	4.43	4.08	0.76	2.26	1.78	3.77	3.14	36.21
1952	2.47	2.53	2.70	2.60	3.43	0.81	2.69	1.43	2.90	1.37	2.39	1.82	27.14
1953	2.47	1.80	3.38	1.50	4.14	1.70	1.61	4.15	3.35	1.46	2.85	1.97	30.38
1954	1.53	2.47	4.09	2.75	1.59	2.03	1.41	3.74	1.93	4.53	2.51	3.38	31.96
1955	1.03	1.71	4.25	3.06	1.51	1.09	0.98	5.27	1.63	7.85	1.92	1.73	32.03
1956	2.09	3.23	3.41	4.14	3.83	0.97	[illegible].91	5.67	3.58	0.94	1.47	2.16	34.40
1957	2.62	1.56	1.75	2.77	2.98	3.63	2.24	0.96	2.46	0.97	1.81	1.92	25.67
1958	2.92	4.20	0.47	3.10	1.89	4.58	4.17	2.56	3.55	4.95	2.79	0.62	35.80
1959	3.87	2.70	2.28	1.91	2.21	2.06	1.63	2.30	2.72	4.07	1.84	4.64	32.23
1960	2.82	4.46	1.64	1.87	3.72	3.05	1.39	4.05	0.28	1.72	0.73	1.03	26.76
1961	1.10	3.21	2.70	4.07	2.96	3.78	2.41	3.09	0.39	1.58	3.99	1.23	30.51
1962	1.84	2.87	1.25	2.62	2.70	3.02	1.89	3.53	4.01	1.95	1.99	1.58	29.25
1963	1.24	1.43	2.53	2.74	2.33	0.22	2.72	3.26	1.17	0.23	4.32	1.90	24.09
1964	1.99	0.89	2.89	3.54	2.77	1.13	1.52	2.74	0.58	0.76	1.60	2.04	22.45
1965	3.05	2.24	2.07	1.85	0.50	0.64	1.46	2.94	1.98	2.82	3.40	2.21	25.16
1966	4.10	2.51	1.42	2.04	1.26	1.85	2.77	2.14	2.47	0.68	3.12	1.75	26.11
1967	0.94	1.67	1.31	1.69	2.74	1.57	2.68	4.64	3.84	4.35	2.89	1.52	29.84
1968	1.91	0.74	2.38	1.33	2.84	2.84	1.42	5.95	1.86	2.89	4.28	3.31	31.75
1969	2.46	0.91	1.16	3.48	2.25	4.69	1.83	1.82	1.77	1.69	3.42	3.66	29.14
1970	1.80	2.28	1.49	2.58	3.03	3.74	4.91	3.28	2.49	3.96	3.50	4.12	37.78
1971	2.66	4.21	3.43	1.28	1.71	3.52	5.59	3.18	1.79	1.34	1.96	3.49	34.16
1972	1.50	3.96	2.19	2.68	3.32	6.56	1.43	3.14	3.84	2.25	4.83	2.58	38.28
1973	1.28	1.70	2.92	3.21	2.68	2.84	1.14	1.94	1.41	2.67	3.82	3.62	29.23
1974	1.75	2.06	3.61	2.60	6.62	2.59	2.82	3.64	3.48	1.34	3.23	2.86	36.60
1975	1.83	2.82	2.74	1.43	2.85	5.35	1.18	2.31	3.15	1.83	1.35	3.76	30.60
RECORD MEAN	2.48	2.41	2.64	2.57	2.93	3.00	3.07	2.82	2.68	2.75	2.69	2.57	32.61

Record mean values above are means through the current year for the period beginning in 1872 for temperature, 1829 for precipitation and 1941 for snowfall. Data are from City Office locations through September 1940 except through October 1940 for Precipitation and Snowfall.

Station: SYRACUSE, NEW YORK
HANCOCK AIRPORT
Elevation (ground): 410 feet

TEMPERATURES °F

Month	Normal: Daily maximum	Normal: Daily minimum	Normal: Monthly	Extremes: Record highest	Year	Record lowest	Year
(a)				12		12	
J	31.4	15.8	23.6	70	1967	-26	1966
F	32.7	16.5	24.6	59	1974	-22	1967
M	41.5	24.8	33.2	77	1968	-5	1967
A	56.5	36.4	46.5	85	1974	9	1972
M	67.6	46.0	56.8	92	1971	25	1966
J	77.7	56.1	66.9	94	1974	35	1966
J	82.0	61.0	71.5	96	1966	45	1965
A	80.2	59.2	69.7	97	1965	40	1965
S	73.3	52.3	62.8	93	1973	28	1965
O	62.4	42.5	52.5	87	1963	20	1965
N	48.3	33.6	41.0	76	1971	10	1967
D	35.0	21.2	28.1	70	1966	-8	1975
YR	57.4	38.8	48.1	97	AUG 1965	-26	JAN 1966

IMPORTANT:
The time-period covered by this record is limited: See footnotes following table of NORMALS, MEANS AND EXTREMES for explanation and for additional history of EXTREME HIGHS AND LOWS recorded in the general area.

Syracuse is located approximately at the geographical center of the state. Gently rolling terrain stretches northward for about 30 miles to the eastern end of Lake Ontario. Oneida Lake is about 8 miles northeast of Syracuse. Approximately 5 miles south of the city hills rise to 1,500 feet. Immediately to the west terrain is gently rolling with elevations 500 to 800 feet above sea level.

The climate of Syracuse is primarily continental in character and comparatively humid. Nearly all cyclonic systems moving from the interior of the country through the St. Lawrence Valley will affect the Syracuse area. Seasonal and diurnal changes are marked and produce an invigorating climate.

In the summer and in portions of the transitional seasons temperatures usually rise rapidly during the daytime to moderate levels and as a rule fall rapidly after sunset so the nights are relatively cool and comfortable. There are only a few days in a year when atmospheric humidity causes great personal discomfort.

Winters are usually cold and are sometimes severe in part. Daytime temperatures average about 35° with nighttime lows about 18° above zero. Lowest ever recorded was minus 26°. Autumn, winter and spring seasons display marked variability.

Precipitation in the Syracuse area is derived principally from cyclonic storms which pass from the interior of the country through the St. Lawrence Valley. Lake Ontario provides the source of significant winter precipitation. The lake is quite deep and never freezes so cold air flowing over the lake is quickly saturated and produces the cloudiness and snow squalls

(Continued page 568)

Snowfall

Season	July	Aug	Sept	Oct	Nov	Dec	Jan
1936-37	0.0	0.0	0.0	T	14.3	10.8	10.9
1937-38	0.0	0.0	0.0	T	3.7	10.0	15.0
1938-39	0.0	0.0	0.0	0.0	9.8	27.1	30.9
1939-40	0.0	0.0	0.0	T	2.8	8.8	32.2
#1940-41	0.0	0.0	0.0	0.3	12.9	8.6	23.5
1941-42	0.0	0.0	0.0	T	0.5	19.0	9.5
1942-43	0.0	0.0	0.0	1.5	8.7	13.4	18.4
1943-44	0.0	0.0	0.0	0.0	7.4	10.1	16.3
1944-45	0.0	0.0	0.0	T	25.4	46.1	39.8
1945-46	0.0	0.0	0.0	T	7.8	7.7	26.3
1946-47	0.0	0.0	0.0	0.6	0.9	25.8	11.1
1947-48	0.0	0.0	0.0	0.0	6.6	21.1	21.3
1948-49	0.0	0.0	0.0	T	1.8	23.1	22.2
#1949-50	0.0	0.0	0.0	0.0	6.5	8.9	20.2
1950-51	0.0	0.0	0.0	0.0	8.1	33.8	21.2
1951-52	0.0	0.0	0.0	T	15.2	38.2	14.5
1952-53	0.0	0.0	0.0	4.4	4.2	11.1	17.5
1953-54	0.0	0.0	0.0	0.0	7.0	15.4	22.3
1954-55	0.0	0.0	0.0	0.1	6.9	20.0	20.0
1955-56	0.0	0.0	0.0	0.8	7.8	38.2	26.2
1956-57	0.0	0.0	0.0	0.0	7.7	16.8	25.2
1957-58	0.0	0.0	0.0	T	5.0	13.5	35.6
1958-59	0.0	0.0	0.0	T	22.1	22.5	48.8
1959-60	0.0	0.0	0.0	T	16.6	11.6	31.6
1960-61	0.0	0.0	0.0	2.0	2.7	27.8	37.3
1961-62	0.0	0.0	0.0	T	9.5	22.3	13.6
1962-63	0.0	0.0	0.0	2.8	11.0	33.8	22.2
1963-64	0.0	0.0	0.0	T	4.0	28.4	18.8
1964-65	0.0	0.0	0.0	0.3	4.0	18.3	31.8
1965-66	0.0	0.0	0.0	1.8	2.7	7.1	71.0
1966-67	0.0	0.0	0.0	0.0	T	33.0	18.3
1967-68	0.0	0.0	0.0	T	14.4	14.4	18.5
1968-69	0.0	0.0	0.0	0.8	16.5	25.4	24.5
1969-70	0.0	0.0	0.0	1.7	9.7	52.5	21.7
1970-71	0.0	0.0	0.0	0.8	7.0	51.9	30.3
1971-72	0.0	0.0	0.0	0.0	16.7	18.3	18.2
1972-73	0.0	0.0	0.0	0.3	15.8	29.8	11.9
1973-74	0.0	0.0	0.0	T	20.6	24.4	15.5
1974-75	0.0	0.0	0.0	2.8	4.8	26.2	11.8
1975-76	0.0	0.0	0.0	T	2.8	27.0	
RECORD MEAN	0.0	0.0	0.0	0.7	9.3	25.5	24.9

Heating Degree Days

Season	July	Aug	Sept	Oct	Nov	Dec	Jan
1955-56	0	6	141	341	790	1333	1307
1956-57	21	9	225	373	710	979	1428
1957-58	10	38	131	457	683	949	1345
1958-59	7	17	133	451	683	1408	1357
1959-60	0	4	115	393	786	1045	1241
1960-61	11	12	83	460	630	1273	1427
1961-62	14	13	70	292	724	1107	1262
#1962-63	6	16	185	422	875	1250	1364
1963-64	14	43	240	276	597	1365	1205
1964-65	2	30	154	475	636	1087	1370
1965-66	27	50	144	521	782	1011	1422
1966-67	6	7	186	473	652	1104	1059
1967-68	24	35	154	407	812	995	1438
1968-69	27	41	54	391	745	1163	1256
1969-70	22	20	134	425	730	1269	1508
1970-71	7	27	150	388	692	1222	1437
1971-72	13	51	96	256	840	980	1189
1972-73	9	23	98	567	833	1053	1128
1973-74	2	12	164	344	723	1094	1200
1974-75	16	3	202	565	726	1069	1100
1975-76	3	32	230	357	545	1154	

Cooling Degree Days

Year	Jan	Feb	Mar	Apr	May	June	July
1969	0	0	0	0	22	94	183
1970	0	0	0	8	22	74	160
1971	0	0	0	0	17	145	145
1972	0	0	0	0	9	78	262
1973	0	0	0	7	0	177	249
1974	0	0	0	14	6	77	148
1975	0	0	0	0	80	114	221

Feb	Mar	Apr	May	June	Total
12.4	25.0	6.4	0.0	0.0	79.8
11.7	9.1	11.2	0.0	0.0	60.7
12.5	16.8	5.4	0.0	0.0	102.5
34.3	29.3	5.3	0.0	0.0	112.7
15.6	32.4	0.4	0.0	0.0	93.7
33.2	14.8	7.7	0.0	0.0	84.7
19.3	8.6	6.1	0.5	0.0	76.5
18.6	12.6	1.5	0.0	0.0	66.5
14.7	1.5	0.2	1.0	0.0	128.7
22.2	1.4	2.4	0.0	0.0	67.8
26.6	38.6	5.3	1.7	0.0	110.6
13.4	12.5	0.6	T	0.0	75.5
12.5	17.0	T	0.0	0.0	76.6
44.1	33.9	4.4	0.0	0.0	118.0
17.5	12.2	T	0.0	0.0	92.8
21.0	11.6	T	0.0	0.0	100.5
31.0	9.2	0.1	0.0	0.0	77.5
19.2	18.4	3.6	0.0	0.0	85.9
26.8	27.5	0.1	0.0	0.0	101.4
31.6	36.0	6.2	T	0.0	146.8
6.7	12.7	7.0	T	0.0	76.1
72.6	12.5	1.9	0.0	0.0	141.1
17.8	26.0	T	0.0	0.0	137.2
50.5	22.9	1.6	0.0	0.0	134.8
25.8	26.5	8.4	T	0.0	130.5
25.0	1.2	5.7	0.0	0.0	77.3
28.3	15.8	1.8	0.8	0.0	116.5
16.1	15.2	1.3	0.0	0.0	83.8
24.9	13.3	4.7	0.0	0.0	97.3
27.0	7.8	0.5	0.9	0.0	118.8
21.0	10.4	0.3	T	0.0	83.0
23.2	10.7	T	0.0	0.0	81.2
21.3	9.4	T	0.0	0.0	97.9
25.8	12.7	1.2	0.2	0.0	125.5
25.2	37.2	4.8	0.0	0.0	157.2
50.0	22.7	7.8	0.0	0.0	133.7
13.3	3.6	5.3	1.2	0.0	81.2
23.7	31.2	7.8	T	0.0	123.2
27.3	20.6	12.0	0.0	0.0	105.5
27.6	17.7	3.3	0.1	0.0	109.1

SYRACUSE, NY

Feb	Mar	Apr	May	June	Total
1095	1123	656	386	49	7227
965	920	507	300	37	6474
1265	943	496	330	114	6761
1201	1045	516	222	66	7106
1096	1255	468	176	47	6626
1091	977	656	317	44	6981
1211	937	552	172	25	6379
1300	948	575	319	70	7330
1190	922	546	160	89	6647
1125	1069	676	215	132	6971
1168	945	665	429	80	7244
1275	1030	595	453	13	6853
1266	979	501	345	83	7039
1152	1063	536	306	103	6837
1139	1027	536	244	115	7169
1069	1040	658	295	50	7035
1216	1098	731	204	84	6758
1217	687	547	325	31	6518
1206	1004	493	339	52	6633
1026	1026	749	138	46	6666

Aug	Sept	Oct	Nov	Dec	Total
222	102	1	0	0	624
127	51	3	0	0	445
124	117	4	0	0	552
160	61	0	0	0	570
281	79	2	0	0	795
128	31	1	0	0	405
138	1	1	0	0	555

Average Temperature

Year	Jan	Feb	Mar	Apr	May	June	July	Aug	Sept	Oct	Nov	Dec	Annual
1936	23.3	19.2	39.0	43.5	61.0	68.2	73.0	71.4	64.2	53.2	36.2	33.2	48.8
1937	33.8	29.8	28.6	45.5	59.4	67.2	73.4	75.4	61.4	50.4	41.5	28.9	49.6
1938	25.0	29.6	40.2	48.8	57.3	68.2	74.0	74.2	58.9	54.2	43.0	31.4	50.4
1939	25.6	28.2	31.2	43.1	60.8	68.4	72.6	74.2	64.6	52.0	36.8	30.4	49.0
#1940	17.2	24.4	27.2	42.0	58.4	66.1	71.3	69.4	60.0	47.3	39.2	30.3	46.1
1941	22.6	21.7	26.3	50.6	57.8	68.7	73.0	67.0	63.6	52.7	43.3	31.0	48.2
1942	24.2	20.4	37.3	50.1	60.0	67.4	70.8	68.6	62.0	52.1	39.8	23.6	48.0
1943	19.2	25.6	32.0	38.5	56.8	70.6	72.3	68.6	60.0	48.6	37.2	24.8	46.2
1944	26.0	24.5	28.8	41.2	63.2	66.6	72.2	72.2	62.4	49.6	40.6	23.8	47.6
1945	14.4	26.3	44.4	50.8	52.6	64.8	70.6	69.4	64.7	49.9	40.5	22.6	47.6
1946	25.4	23.1	43.9	44.4	55.9	65.0	69.6	65.7	63.4	54.9	44.5	30.6	48.9
1947	27.9	20.4	30.8	44.7	55.5	65.6	71.2	74.2	63.4	57.8	37.2	25.8	47.9
1948	17.6	21.3	33.0	48.6	54.2	65.8	71.9	70.0	63.0	48.8	46.7	31.2	47.7
#1949	29.4	30.6	35.4	46.8	58.4	73.2	74.6	72.8	60.0	56.2	38.0	31.6	50.6
1950	33.2	22.4	27.1	42.5	57.9	65.7	70.3	69.2	58.8	53.3	40.9	24.8	47.2
1951	26.7	25.4	35.1	46.5	58.0	65.5	71.1	67.6	61.6	53.1	35.2	30.2	48.0
1952	26.8	27.5	33.2	49.5	54.2	67.3	74.7	69.9	63.8	48.2	42.5	31.8	49.1
1953	30.4	29.5	36.8	45.7	58.4	67.7	72.2	69.7	63.6	53.0	43.9	34.9	50.5
1954	20.4	33.0	33.3	48.1	56.2	68.4	70.9	67.7	61.9	55.4	40.9	27.6	48.7
1955	21.2	25.5	33.5	51.4	60.4	68.3	76.7	74.6	61.7	54.0	38.4	21.7	48.9
1956	22.6	27.0	28.5	42.9	53.4	67.0	68.2	69.2	58.8	52.7	41.2	33.3	47.1
1957	18.8	30.4	35.1	48.4	56.0	70.4	70.4	67.1	62.6	50.1	42.0	34.2	48.8
1958	21.4	19.5	34.3	48.3	54.5	62.5	70.5	69.1	61.9	50.4	41.9	19.4	46.1
1959	21.0	21.8	31.1	47.6	60.0	67.6	73.5	74.1	67.3	52.3	38.6	31.1	48.8
1960	24.7	27.0	24.4	49.5	59.8	66.6	69.4	68.7	63.8	50.0	43.8	23.7	47.6
1961	18.8	25.9	33.2	42.9	55.5	66.6	71.8	70.4	69.5	55.8	40.7	29.1	48.3
1962	24.1	21.5	34.6	47.3	62.3	68.3	69.2	69.1	59.7	51.2	35.5	24.5	47.3
#1963	20.8	18.4	34.2	45.6	54.7	66.6	71.7	66.1	57.2	56.3	44.9	20.8	46.4
1964	25.9	23.7	35.1	46.5	61.6	66.0	73.2	67.5	61.6	49.5	43.6	29.6	48.6
1965	20.5	24.6	30.3	42.3	59.4	63.7	67.5	69.1	62.8	47.9	38.7	32.1	46.6
1966	19.0	23.1	34.4	42.6	51.2	65.7	71.1	70.4	59.5	49.5	42.9	29.2	46.6
1967	30.6	19.2	31.6	44.9	50.2	69.5	67.7	66.6	60.7	51.8	37.6	32.7	46.9
1968	18.5	21.1	33.2	48.1	53.6	64.9	69.9	68.8	64.8	52.5	40.0	27.2	46.9
1969	24.3	23.6	30.4	46.9	55.7	64.5	69.9	71.3	63.8	51.1	40.4	23.8	47.1
1970	16.1	24.1	31.7	47.2	57.5	63.5	69.7	68.0	61.4	52.3	41.7	25.4	46.5
1971	18.5	26.5	31.2	42.8	55.8	67.9	69.0	67.1	65.6	56.6	36.9	33.2	47.6
1972	26.4	22.9	29.4	40.5	58.5	64.5	72.9	69.2	63.5	46.5	37.0	30.8	46.9
1973	28.4	21.4	42.6	46.8	54.3	69.6	72.7	73.5	62.0	53.7	40.7	29.5	49.6
1974	26.0	21.6	32.3	48.8	54.1	65.6	69.1	68.9	59.1	46.5	40.6	30.4	46.9
1975	29.4	28.1	31.7	39.9	62.9	67.1	71.7	68.2	57.1	53.2	46.6	27.6	48.6
RECORD MEAN	24.2	24.0	33.3	45.3	56.9	66.3	71.2	69.2	62.3	51.6	40.2	28.2	47.7
MAX	32.0	31.9	41.1	54.5	66.9	76.2	81.0	78.9	71.8	60.6	47.1	34.9	56.4
MIN	16.4	16.1	25.4	36.1	46.8	56.3	61.3	59.5	52.7	42.5	33.2	21.4	39.0

# Indicates a station move or relocation of instruments.

Precipitation

Year	Jan	Feb	Mar	Apr	May	June	July	Aug	Sept	Oct	Nov	Dec	Annual
1936	3.18	1.90	5.97	2.85	1.63	0.57	0.67	2.44	3.01	3.44	3.80	1.69	31.35
1937	3.68	3.14	2.68	3.51	3.23	6.59	2.85	5.83	1.39	6.83	2.66	2.74	45.13
1938	2.01	2.56	2.02	3.09	4.36	2.56	4.02	5.05	4.90	0.56	2.74	2.72	36.59
1939	2.74	2.86	2.87	2.59	0.55	2.21	3.08	1.40	1.58	2.79	1.16	3.15	26.98
#1940	1.72	5.22	5.42	3.98	4.08	3.27	2.32	1.23	1.91	1.89	3.32	3.78	38.14
1941	2.25	1.98	2.85	1.97	2.90	2.96	5.41	2.61	2.28	3.63	1.93	2.96	33.93
1942	1.59	3.55	4.52	2.43	3.71	2.09	2.72	2.40	3.32	2.99	3.44	6.55	39.31
1943	2.09	2.59	2.70	4.65	3.88	4.63	1.91	7.26	0.51	5.44	2.93	1.25	39.84
1944	1.75	2.55	2.90	3.65	3.19	5.89	1.43	2.65	2.18	1.92	4.23	5.00	37.34
1945	4.26	2.56	3.06	3.50	3.47	3.52	2.55	2.02	6.74	6.52	4.83	0.85	43.88
1946	2.58	2.72	1.52	2.14	2.43	3.85	3.24	2.61	2.83	4.78	2.20	3.14	34.04
1947	4.23	2.12	4.18	3.20	5.54	3.94	5.41	3.70	2.14	0.82	3.15	2.32	40.75
1948	1.93	2.19	2.63	4.10	3.87	3.89	2.05	2.53	1.02	1.87	4.34	3.28	33.70
#1949	3.25	2.04	2.34	3.60	2.37	3.08	3.10	3.92	4.38	1.36	2.32	2.32	34.08
1950	4.20	4.12	5.15	1.57	2.43	2.48	2.05	2.52	4.22	3.41	3.91	3.59	39.65
1951	2.73	5.38	4.65	3.79	1.97	4.21	5.22	3.33	3.17	1.86	3.76	4.34	44.41
1952	2.45	2.00	2.39	2.57	3.88	1.18	4.36	2.05	1.52	2.88	2.36	3.75	31.39
1953	2.91	2.71	3.75	2.07	4.35	1.51	1.93	2.39	2.11	1.64	1.74	2.61	29.72
1954	2.43	3.74	3.48	4.75	3.17	3.66	1.12	7.19	3.06	1.99	4.84	4.03	43.46
1955	1.61	3.32	6.84	1.81	1.90	2.43	2.85	3.80	1.87	8.29	2.69	2.53	39.94
1956	2.28	3.90	4.63	3.35	3.03	1.71	3.75	8.41	4.27	1.28	2.38	3.02	42.01
1957	2.19	1.76	2.01	2.60	2.88	4.18	6.13	3.45	2.28	0.93	1.86	2.90	33.17
1958	4.46	5.28	1.31	3.36	3.70	5.24	3.63	2.06	4.89	3.37	3.76	1.73	42.79
1959	4.59	2.22	2.93	2.51	1.97	2.53	2.54	4.48	0.93	7.15	4.34	5.01	41.20
1960	3.11	4.90	2.48	2.94	3.96	1.86	1.03	2.69	2.93	2.77	1.68	1.86	32.21
1961	2.30	4.14	4.22	3.74	2.40	3.68	5.08	1.78	1.21	3.59	2.99	2.45	37.58
1962	2.87	2.96	1.96	3.57	1.05	1.10	2.74	4.63	1.99	3.30	2.22	2.25	30.64
1963	1.85	2.05	2.79	2.22	2.84	2.49	1.21	3.59	0.85	0.21	5.65	2.06	27.81
1964	2.18	1.13	3.83	3.66	2.31	1.41	2.15	3.09	0.75	1.52	2.20	2.87	27.10
1965	2.28	2.82	1.63	3.53	1.61	2.04	1.34	1.95	3.60	2.70	2.97	1.92	28.39
1966	3.98	2.96	2.27	3.05	1.79	2.73	2.09	2.64	4.75	0.90	2.05	3.93	33.14
1967	1.47	1.49	1.34	2.11	3.33	1.56	6.33	5.00	2.73	3.52	4.48	2.66	36.02
1968	2.08	1.10	3.13	2.40	3.46	6.14	3.77	4.17	3.43	5.81	4.07	4.67	44.23
1969	3.37	1.49	1.08	3.95	4.34	3.74	0.90	1.77	1.13	2.30	4.56	3.42	32.05
1970	1.02	1.84	2.45	3.68	2.79	2.93	4.42	4.07	4.33	3.84	3.53	3.33	38.23
1971	1.90	4.07	2.90	2.19	3.40	3.26	6.49	4.01	2.56	1.62	3.52	3.26	39.18
1972	1.10	2.87	2.49	4.03	6.19	12.30	3.45	3.76	4.12	4.36	6.79	3.95	55.41
1973	1.85	1.71	3.45	6.91	5.58	7.07	3.62	2.97	4.57	3.81	6.73	4.38	52.65
1974	2.08	1.70	4.34	3.09	5.78	4.67	9.52	4.60	4.45	1.58	4.95	3.47	50.23
1975	2.54	3.05	2.67	2.01	2.74	4.08	9.32	5.35	8.81	3.69	3.54	4.10	51.90
RECORD MEAN	2.69	2.60	3.10	3.04	3.00	3.58	3.47	3.30	2.92	2.98	2.94	2.92	36.54

Record mean values above are means through the current year for the period beginning in 1902 for temperature and precipitation, 1950 for snowfall. Data are from City Office locations through 8-14-40.

(Continued)

which are a well-known feature of winter weather in the Syracuse area.

The area enjoys sufficient precipitation in most years to meet the needs of agriculture and water supplies. The precipitation is uncommonly well distributed, averaging about 3 inches per month throughout the year. Snowfall is moderately heavy with an annual average just over 100 inches. During the warmer months there are about 30 days per year with thunderstorms.

Wind velocities are moderate, but during the winter months there are numerous days with sufficient winds to cause blowing and drifting snow.

During December, January and February there is much cloudiness. Syracuse receives only about one-third of possible sunshine during winter months. Approximately two-thirds of possible sunshine is received during the warm months.

The growing season in the immediate vicinity of Syracuse is about 171 days. The average date of the last 32° temperature in the spring is April 28. The average date of the first 32° temperature in the fall is October 16.

Normals, Means, and Extremes

Month	Normal Degree days Base 65 °F: Heating	Cooling	Precipitation in inches — Water equivalent: Normal	Maximum monthly	Year	Minimum monthly	Year	Maximum in 24 hrs.	Year	Snow, Ice pellets: Maximum monthly	Year	Maximum in 24 hrs.	Year	Relative humidity pct. Hour 01	Hour 07	Hour 13	Hour 19 (Local time)
(a)				26		26		26		26		26		12	12	12	12
J	1283	0	2.68	4.59	1959	1.02	1970	1.47	1958	71.0	1966	24.5	1966	75	76	68	74
F	1131	0	2.79	5.38	1951	1.10	1968	1.99	1961	72.6	1958	21.4	1961	76	78	66	72
M	986	0	3.03	6.84	1955	1.08	1969	1.34	1974	37.2	1971	14.7	1971	77	78	62	69
A	555	0	3.08	6.91	1973	1.57	1950	2.42	1970	12.0	1975	7.1	1975	75	76	52	59
M	272	18	3.02	6.19	1972	1.05	1962	3.13	1969	1.2	1973	1.2	1973	78	75	55	60
J	46	103	3.09	12.30	1972	1.10	1962	3.88	1972	0.0		0.0		82	78	56	63
J	11	212	3.08	9.52	1974	0.90	1969	4.07	1974	0.0		0.0		83	79	55	63
A	18	164	3.50	8.41	1956	1.77	1969	4.27	1954	0.0		0.0		85	85	58	69
S	120	54	2.71	8.81	1975	0.75	1964	4.14	1975	0.0		0.0		85	87	62	76
O	392	0	3.09	8.29	1955	0.21	1963	3.60	1955	4.4	1952	2.4	1974	82	84	61	75
N	720	0	3.25	6.79	1972	1.68	1960	2.09	1967	22.1	1958	12.1	1973	80	81	68	77
D	1144	0	3.09	5.01	1959	1.73	1958	2.18	1952	52.5	1969	15.5	1969	80	81	74	79
YR	6678	551	36.41	12.30	JUN 1972	0.21	OCT 1963	4.27	AUG 1954	72.6	FEB 1958	24.5	JAN 1966	80	80	61	70

(To better understand these tables, see full explanation of terms beginning on page 322)

Month	Wind: Mean speed m.p.h.	Prevailing direction	Fastest mile: Speed m.p.h.	Direction	Year	Pct. of possible sunshine	Mean sky cover, tenths, sunrise to sunset	Mean number of days — Sunrise to sunset: Clear	Partly cloudy	Cloudy	Precipitation .01 inch or more	Snow, Ice pellets 1.0 inch or more	Thunderstorms	Heavy fog, visibility ¼ mile or less	Temperatures °F Max. (b) 90° and above	32° and below	Min. 32° and below	0° and below	Average station pressure mb. Elev. 408 feet m.s.l.
(a)	26	14	26	26		26	26	26	26	26	26	26	26	26	12	12	12	12	3
J	10.9	WSW	60	W	1974	35	7.9	3	7	21	18	8	*	1	0	16	28	5	1002.8
F	11.3	WNW	62	W	1967	40	7.8	3	6	19	16	8	*	1	0	15	26	3	1002.4
M	11.1	WNW	56	SE	1956	46	7.5	4	7	20	17	5	1	1	0	7	25	*	1000.2
A	11.0	WNW	52	NW	1957	51	6.8	6	7	17	14	1	2	1	0	*	14	0	999.1
M	9.5	WNW	50	NW	1964	56	6.5	6	10	15	13	*	3	1	*	0	1	0	998.3
J	8.6	WNW	49	NW	1961	61	6.1	8	10	12	11	0	6	1	1	0	0	0	999.9
J	8.4	WNW	47	NW	1951	67	5.7	8	13	10	11	0	7	1	3	0	0	0	1000.2
A	8.2	WSW	43	NW	1958	63	6.0	8	11	12	10	0	6	1	2	0	0	0	1002.5
S	8.6	S	52	W	1962	56	6.1	7	11	12	10	0	3	1	1	0	*	0	1003.3
O	9.2	WSW	63	SE	1954	46	6.6	7	8	16	11	*	1	1	0	0	4	0	1004.7
N	10.4	WSW	59	E	1950	26	8.3	2	6	22	16	3	1	1	0	2	14	0	1001.5
D	10.5	WSW	52	W	1962	25	8.4	2	5	24	19	8	*	1	0	12	26	1	1003.0
YR	9.8	WNW	63	SE	OCT 1954	50	7.0	64	101	200	167	32	29	9	7	50	138	9	1001.5

FOOTNOTES

Means and extremes above are from existing and comparable exposures. Annual extremes have been exceeded at other sites in the locality as follows: Highest temperature 102 in July 1936; maximum monthly precipitation 15.92 in June 1922; minimum monthly precipitation 0.19 in May 1920; maximum precipitation in 24 hours 4.79 in June 1922; maximum snowfall in 24 hours 27.2 in January 1925; fastest mile wind 69 SW in December 1921.

Station: ASHEVILLE, NORTH CAROLINA
ASHEVILLE AIRPORT
Elevation (ground): 2140 feet

TEMPERATURES °F

Month	Normal: Daily maximum	Normal: Daily minimum	Normal: Monthly	Extremes: Record highest	Extremes: Year	Extremes: Record lowest	Extremes: Year
(a)				11		11	
J	48.4	27.3	37.9	78	1975	-7	1966
F	50.6	28.2	39.4	77	1972	-2	1967
M	58.3	33.5	45.9	82	1974	14	1965
A	69.4	42.4	55.9	89	1972	24	1973
M	76.8	50.6	63.7	91	1969	29	1971
J	82.5	58.7	70.6	96	1969	35	1966
J	84.3	62.6	73.5	95	1970	46	1967
A	83.8	61.8	72.8	94	1968	43	1968
S	78.0	55.4	66.7	92	1975	30	1967
O	69.1	44.5	56.8	84	1971	24	1974
N	58.2	34.3	46.3	81	1974	8	1970
D	49.3	28.1	38.7	78	1971	8	1975
YR	67.4	44.0	55.7	96	JUN 1969	-7	JAN 1966

IMPORTANT:
The time-period covered by this record is limited: See footnotes on next page for explanation and for additional history of EXTREME HIGHS AND LOWS recorded in the general area.

The city of Asheville is located on both banks of the French Broad River, near the center of the French Broad Basin. Upstream from Asheville, the valley runs south for 18 miles and then curves toward the south-southwest; downstream from the City, the valley is oriented toward the north-northwest. Two miles upstream from the principal section of Asheville, the Swannanoa River joins the French Broad from the east. The entire valley is known as the "Asheville Plateau," having an average elevation near 2,200 feet above mean sea level, and is flanked by mountain ridges to the east and west, whose peaks range from 2,000 to 4,400 feet above the valley floor. At the Carolina-Tennessee border, about 25 miles north-northwest of Asheville, a relatively high ridge of mountains blocks the northern end of the valley.

Thirty miles south, the Blue Ridge Mountains form an escarpment, having a general elevation of about 2,700 feet m.s.l. The tallest peaks near Asheville are Mt. Mitchell, 6,684 feet m.s.l., 20 miles northeast of the City and Big Pisgah Mountain, 5,721 feet m.s.l., 16 miles to the southwest.

Asheville has a temperate, but invigorating climate. Considerable variation in temperature often occurs from day to day in summer, as well as during the other seasons. Temperature extremes at the City Office ranging from -7° to 99° have been recorded during the last 34 years of record, ending with 1964. The National Weather Service Office was relocated at the Asheville Airport on September 1, 1964. The warmest day of record, with an average temperature of 85°, was June 27, 1952, with a maximum temperature of 97°, and a minimum reading of 72°. The coldest day of record at the City Office, with an average temperature of 3°, was February 5, 1917, with a maximum temperature of 9°, and a minimum reading of -4°. Airport records indicate January 30, 1966, as the coldest day of record there with an average temperature of 2° as derived from a maximum of 11° and a minimum of -7°.

While the office was located in the City, the combination of roof exposure conditions and a smoke blanket, caused by inversions in temperature in the valley on quiet nights, resulted in higher early morning temperatures at City Office sites than were experienced nearer ground level in nearby rural areas. The growing season in this area is of sufficient length for commercial crops, the average length of freeze-free period being 195 days, based on City Office data. The average date of last occurrence in spring of a temperature 32° or lower is April 12; of 28°, March 29; of 20°, February 27. The average date of first occurrence in fall of 32° is October 24; of 28°, November 4; of 20°, December 4.

The orientation of the French Broad Valley appears to have a pronounced influence on the wind direction; prevailing winds are from the northwest during all months of the year. Also, the shielding effect of the nearby mountain barriers apparently has a direct bearing on the annual amount of precipitation received in this vicinity. Within the area roughly bounded by a line connecting Asheville, Weaverville, Marshall, Leicester, and Enka, the average annual precipitation is 38 inches, the lowest in North Carolina. Precipitation increases somewhat to the northwest of the Asheville-Marshall-Enka area and increases sharply in all other directions, especially to the south and southwest, where the average annual precipitation becomes more than 60 inches within 30 miles of Asheville.

Destructive events caused directly by meteorological conditions are infrequent. The most frequent, occurring approximately at 12-year intervals, are floods on the French Broad River. These floods are usually associated with heavy rains from decelerating tropical storms moving over or near this area. The outstanding floods since the beginning of records are: July 16, 1916; August 16, 1928; August 13 and 30, 1940; and September 29 and October 4-5, 1964. According to historical records, destructive floods also occurred in April 1791; August 1796 and 1810; May 1845; August 1850 and 1852; and June 1876. Snowstorms which have seriously disrupted normal life in this community occurred on January 26, 1906; March 18, 1936; March 2-3, 1942, and repeated heavy snows in March 1960. Only one hailstorm of record caused considerable property damage in Asheville, that of June 18, 1936.

ASHEVILLE, NORTH CAROLINA

Normals, Means, and Extremes

(To better understand these tables, see full explanation of terms beginning on page 322)

Month	Normal Degree days Base 65 °F: Heating	Normal Degree days Base 65 °F: Cooling	Precipitation in inches, Water equivalent: Normal	Water equivalent: Maximum monthly	Year	Water equivalent: Minimum monthly	Year	Water equivalent: Maximum in 24 hrs.	Year	Snow, Ice pellets: Maximum monthly	Year	Snow, Ice pellets: Maximum in 24 hrs.	Year	Relative humidity pct.: Hour 01 (Local time)	Hour 07	Hour 13	Hour 19	Wind: Mean speed m.p.h.	Wind: Prevailing direction	Fastest mile: Speed m.p.h.	Fastest mile: Direction	Fastest mile: Year	Pct. of possible sunshine	Mean sky cover, tenths, sunrise to sunset	Mean number of days, Sunrise to sunset: Clear	Partly cloudy	Cloudy	Precipitation .01 inch or more	Snow, Ice pellets 1.0 inch or more	Thunderstorms	Heavy fog, visibility ¼ mile or less	Temperatures °F Max. (b): 90° and above	Max.: 32° and below	Min.: 32° and below	Min.: 0° and below	Average station pressure mb. Elev. 2170 feet m.s.l.
(a)				11		11		11		11		11		11	11	11	11	11		11	11		11	11	11	11	11	11	11	11	11	11	11	11	11	3
J	840	0	3.39	4.26	1973	1.75	1970	1.54	1973	17.6	1966	7.6	1966	83	86	61	70	9.4		40	34	1975	56	6.2	9	7	15	11	1	1	5	0	3	22	*	942.9
F	717	0	3.60	6.56	1966	0.62	1968	3.17	1966	25.5	1969	11.7	1969	78	83	57	64	10.0		60	34	1972	63	5.8	10	5	13	10	2	*	3	0	2	22	*	940.5
M	592	0	4.66	9.86	1975	2.59	1966	5.13	1968	13.0	1969	10.9	1969	80	85	54	61	9.7		46	35	1969	68	5.9	9	9	13	12	1	3	2	0	*	15	0	939.7
A	279	6	3.53	5.71	1973	0.61	1975	3.06	1973	0.2	1971	0.2	1971	80	87	52	58	9.2		44	22	1970	67	5.7	9	10	11	9	0	3	3	0	0	5	0	940.8
M	100	60	3.31	8.83	1973	1.72	1970	4.95	1973	0.0		0.0		91	92	57	67	7.3		40	34	1971	63	6.2	8	9	14	12	0	8	5	*	0	*	0	939.8
J	14	182	3.97	6.54	1972	2.12	1975	3.54	1972	0.0		0.0		95	96	61	72	6.2		32	34	1974	66	6.3	6	11	13	12	0	8	9	1	0	0	0	942.2
J	0	264	4.87	7.53	1969	3.24	1966	4.02	1969	0.0		0.0		96	97	65	76	5.9		43	35	1966	60	6.8	3	13	15	14	0	11	12	2	0	0	0	943.1
A	0	244	4.50	11.28	1967	1.88	1972	4.12	1967	0.0		0.0		97	98	64	80	5.5		40	34	1973	55	6.5	5	13	13	13	0	10	16	2	0	0	0	944.7
S	50	101	3.57	7.53	1975	1.17	1970	3.41	1975	0.0		0.0		97	98	65	83	5.8		23	13	1975	57	6.4	6	11	13	10	0	3	13	*	0	*	0	943.6
O	269	15	3.25	7.05	1971	1.28	1974	2.95	1968	0.0		0.0		93	96	59	77	6.8		35	33	1972	63	5.1	13	7	11	9	0	1	9	0	0	5	0	945.4
N	561	0	2.94	4.89	1975	1.30	1965	1.79	1975	9.6	1968	5.7	1968	87	90	56	71	8.5		40	32	1974	64	5.3	11	8	11	9	*	1	4	0	*	15	0	943.8
D	815	0	3.59	8.48	1973	0.16	1965	2.66	1973	16.3	1971	16.3	1971	85	87	62	74	9.1		44	34	1965	57	6.1	10	6	15	10	1	*	5	0	1	20	0	941.7
YR	4237	872	45.18	11.28	AUG 1967	0.16	DEC 1965	5.13	MAR 1968	25.5	FEB 1969	16.3	DEC 1971	88	91	59	71	7.8		60	34	FEB 1972	62	6.0	99	109	157	129	5	50	86	5	6	105	1	942.4

FOOTNOTES

Means and extremes above are from existing and comparable exposures. Annual extremes have been exceeded at other sites in the locality as follows: Highest temperature 99 in July 1936; maximum monthly precipitation 13.75 in August 1940; minimum monthly precipitation T in October 1963; maximum precipitation in 24 hours 7.92 in October 1918; maximum monthly snowfall 28.9 in March 1960.

Snowfall

Season	July	Aug	Sept	Oct	Nov	Dec	Jan
1936-37	0.0	0.0	0.0	0.0	0.8	6.2	0.0
1937-38	0.0	0.0	0.0	0.1	0.1	0.7	1.5
1938-39	0.0	0.0	0.0	0.0	1.1	2.7	1.2
1939-40	0.0	0.0	0.0	0.0	T	4.4	7.7
1940-41	0.0	0.0	0.0	0.0	T	T	T
1941-42	0.0	0.0	0.0	0.0	T	0.0	3.1
1942-43	0.0	0.0	0.0	0.0	T	4.4	0.4
1943-44	0.0	0.0	0.0	0.0	0.0	T	9.0
1944-45	0.0	0.0	0.0	0.0	0.6	6.4	T
1945-46	0.0	0.0	0.0	0.0	T	11.0	4.2
1946-47	0.0	0.0	0.0	0.0	0.0	0.5	T
1947-48	0.0	0.0	0.0	0.0	0.0	3.4	7.7
1948-49	0.0	0.0	0.0	0.0	0.0	T	3.2
1949-50	0.0	0.0	0.0	0.0	0.8	0.2	0.0
1950-51	0.0	0.0	0.0	0.0	3.1	0.2	0.9
1951-52	0.0	0.0	0.0	0.0	1.0	1.2	0.1
1952-53	0.0	0.0	0.0	0.0	1.9	1.1	3.4
1953-54	0.0	0.0	0.0	0.0	0.3	0.5	3.6
1954-55	0.0	0.0	0.0	T	0.8	2.8	5.9
1955-56	0.0	0.0	0.0	0.0	1.0	0.6	3.4
1956-57	0.0	0.0	0.0	0.0	T	0.2	0.8
1957-58	0.0	0.0	0.0	T	0.5	1.5	1.1
1958-59	0.0	0.0	0.0	0.0	T	2.3	1.5
1959-60	0.0	0.0	0.0	0.0	T	1.0	2.0
1960-61	0.0	0.0	0.0	0.0	T	0.2	0.8
1961-62	0.0	0.0	0.0	T	T	1.2	13.3
1962-63	0.0	0.0	0.0	0.0	0.3	4.2	T
1963-64	0.0	0.0	0.0	0.0	1.2	8.9	1.7
#1964-65	0.0	0.0	0.0	0.0	T	T	5.5
1965-66	0.0	0.0	0.0	0.0	T	T	17.6
1966-67	0.0	0.0	0.0	0.0	1.3	0.8	1.5
1967-68	0.0	0.0	0.0	0.0	0.0	1.9	7.2
1968-69	0.0	0.0	0.0	0.0	9.6	T	0.1
1969-70	0.0	0.0	0.0	0.0	T	10.9	4.8
1970-71	0.0	0.0	0.0	0.0	T	6.1	0.1
1971-72	0.0	0.0	0.0	0.0	0.6	16.3	T
1972-73	0.0	0.0	0.0	0.0	0.6	T	7.1
1973-74	0.0	0.0	0.0	0.0	0.0	3.0	T
1974-75	0.0	0.0	0.0	0.0	3.1	3.0	0.4
1975-76	0.0	0.0	0.0	0.0	5.0	0.4	
RECORD MEAN	0.0	0.0	0.0	0.0	1.8	3.9	4.0

Heating Degree Days

Season	July	Aug	Sept	Oct	Nov	Dec	Jan
1955-56	0	0	11	272	605	845	937
1956-57	0	3	82	197	586	481	774
1957-58	0	0	60	398	509	731	1010
1958-59	0	0	41	292	449	860	877
1959-60	0	0	21	204	591	747	800
1960-61	0	0	32	194	522	931	971
1961-62	2	0	49	295	433	778	851
1962-63	0	0	91	224	565	941	943
1963-64	4	0	51	164	513	1038	826
#1964-65	0	20	46	372	399	679	863
1965-66	0	7	39	344	550	759	1075
1966-67	1	1	87	405	593	838	810
1967-68	7	2	158	351	660	713	947
1968-69	0	20	42	258	563	884	873
1969-70	0	8	59	280	623	875	1050
1970-71	0	0	29	194	565	682	875
1971-72	0	0	6	129	576	530	704
1972-73	3	0	8	304	578	605	846
1973-74	0	0	7	205	473	772	516
1974-75	0	0	65	316	519	760	715
1975-76	0	0	77	237	498	812	

Cooling Degree Days

Year	Jan	Feb	Mar	Apr	May	June	July
1969	0	0	0	4	85	262	343
1970	0	0	0	22	52	159	296
1971	0	0	0	3	25	232	238
1972	0	0	0	24	6	84	236
1973	0	0	0	1	16	190	288
1974	0	0	0	3	65	82	254
1975	0	0	0	11	82	124	237

Feb	Mar	Apr	May	June	Total
7.0	0.6	T	0.0	0.0	14.6
0.2	0.0	0.1	0.0	0.0	2.7
0.2	4.0	0.0	0.0	0.0	9.2
3.0	3.5	0.2	0.0	0.0	18.8
1.1	4.4	0.0	0.0	0.0	5.5
5.9	16.0	0.0	0.0	0.0	25.0
2.2	1.1	0.8	0.0	0.0	8.9
6.0	0.1	0.6	0.0	0.0	15.7
1.0	0.0	0.0	0.0	0.0	8.0
T	T	T	0.0	0.0	15.2
11.0	8.5	0.0	0.0	0.0	20.0
8.4	1.0	0.0	0.0	0.0	20.5
0.2	T	T	0.0	0.0	3.4
0.1	0.1	T	0.0	0.0	1.2
1.5	T	T	0.0	0.0	5.7
3.3	1.2	T	0.0	0.0	6.8
8.9	T	T	0.0	0.0	15.3
3.5	1.8	T	0.0	0.0	9.7
T	T	T	0.0	0.0	9.5
0.2	1.1	2.0	0.0	0.0	8.3
0.1	2.5	T	0.0	0.0	3.6
12.8	1.5	0.0	T	0.0	17.4
T	T	0.3	0.0	0.0	4.1
8.5	28.9	0.2	T	0.0	40.6
3.0	T	T	0.0	0.0	4.0
T	8.3	T	0.0	0.0	22.8
4.5	T	0.0	0.0	0.0	9.0
13.9	0.1	0.0	0.0	0.0	25.8
4.3	5.0	0.0	0.0	0.0	14.8
6.2	0.2	T	0.0	0.0	24.0
4.2	T	0.0	0.0	0.0	7.8
6.0	0.1	0.0	0.0	0.0	15.2
25.5	13.0	0.0	0.0	0.0	48.2
1.1	0.5	0.0	0.0	0.0	17.3
0.1	8.9	0.2	0.0	0.0	15.4
7.4	7.4	0.0	0.0	0.0	31.7
0.5	1.0	T	0.0	0.0	9.2
0.3	1.1	T	0.0	0.0	4.4
4.3	3.7	T	0.0	0.0	14.5
5.4	3.7	T	0.0	0.0	18.8

Average Temperature

Year	Jan	Feb	Mar	Apr	May	June	July	Aug	Sept	Oct	Nov	Dec	Annual
1936	33.4	36.6	49.0	53.3	66.5	72.4	75.6	74.8	70.2	58.5	44.9	42.4	56.5
1937	49.6	38.0	44.4	54.2	64.3	72.6	73.3	74.4	65.8	52.4	43.2	38.4	55.9
1938	38.2	44.8	52.4	55.8	64.2	69.6	73.8	75.1	67.4	57.2	48.8	39.4	57.2
1939	40.2	44.4	49.1	54.1	63.9	74.6	74.3	73.0	69.9	59.6	44.6	40.0	57.3
1940	26.4	38.8	43.4	53.7	62.2	71.6	72.8	72.3	65.2	57.2	46.4	43.6	54.5
1941	38.8	33.8	40.7	58.4	65.6	71.8	74.8	75.1	70.4	63.0	46.9	42.7	56.8
1942	37.4	33.5	47.2	58.5	63.9	73.0	74.6	71.8	67.0	57.5	48.0	38.5	55.9
1943	41.4	40.0	44.6	53.2	65.8	75.6	74.0	75.2	64.1	54.9	44.7	39.2	56.1
1944	39.6	43.4	46.4	54.4	66.8	73.0	72.6	72.0	68.2	56.4	45.1	35.9	56.2
1945	37.0	42.3	57.0	58.4	60.5	71.0	73.9	72.8	69.6	55.5	47.9	33.4	56.6
1946	39.4	41.6	54.0	58.0	62.5	70.3	73.8	71.0	66.2	58.4	52.6	42.6	57.5
1947	43.4	30.9	38.9	58.8	63.2	70.1	70.6	74.9	68.4	61.2	45.1	40.4	55.9
1948	32.4	44.0	50.0	60.3	63.8	71.8	75.4	72.2	66.4	54.4	50.8	42.1	57.0
1949	47.4	46.7	47.0	54.2	65.0	71.9	76.7	72.4	64.4	61.6	44.5	43.2	57.9
1950	51.6	44.0	43.8	52.9	67.1	71.3	72.3	71.5	66.4	61.2	42.1	34.8	56.6
1951	38.7	41.8	47.4	54.2	63.1	71.1	74.5	75.2	68.3	59.6	41.3	41.1	56.3
1952	44.3	43.6	46.0	55.9	65.0	76.8	75.8	72.7	66.2	53.4	46.1	39.2	57.1
1953	42.3	42.1	49.2	54.4	68.6	73.7	74.0	73.2	66.4	58.3	46.7	38.9	57.3
1954	40.4	43.9	45.7	61.2	58.5	71.2	76.3	74.5	70.2	57.4	43.2	37.1	56.7
1955	36.8	40.8	49.1	59.5	66.0	65.7	74.8	74.8	68.9	56.4	44.6	37.5	56.2
1956	34.6	44.7	47.2	54.0	65.7	70.0	73.6	73.5	64.9	59.0	45.2	49.3	56.8
1957	39.8	46.8	45.5	59.0	65.8	72.5	74.0	72.1	69.0	52.0	47.7	41.2	57.1
1958	32.2	29.7	42.9	55.5	64.8	71.2	74.4	73.4	66.4	55.5	50.1	37.0	54.4
1959	36.5	42.1	44.6	57.3	66.5	69.9	74.4	75.4	67.6	59.9	45.1	40.7	56.7
1960	39.0	36.6	33.5	58.2	61.1	71.1	73.4	74.1	68.1	58.9	47.4	34.7	54.7
1961	33.5	44.1	50.1	50.4	60.0	68.6	72.5	72.0	68.4	55.3	50.4	39.7	55.5
1962	37.4	45.8	43.4	52.9	69.4	70.2	73.7	72.3	65.4	58.3	46.0	34.4	55.7
1963	34.4	34.2	51.0	57.6	63.6	69.2	71.4	72.0	66.2	59.6	47.8	31.4	54.8
#1964	38.1	34.7	46.3	57.3	65.3	72.8	72.9	71.7	66.0	53.0	51.4	42.9	56.1
1965	37.0	37.9	42.4	57.4	65.8	66.8	72.2	71.1	66.8	53.8	46.4	40.3	54.8
1966	30.1	36.2	43.5	52.0	60.1	66.1	71.1	69.9	62.9	51.7	45.0	37.6	52.2
1967	38.7	35.0	49.8	57.6	59.7	66.8	68.7	68.5	60.2	53.5	42.7	41.8	53.6
1968	34.3	32.4	46.6	54.8	61.0	69.5	73.1	74.1	64.1	56.7	46.0	36.2	54.0
1969	36.7	37.8	41.3	56.7	65.2	73.1	75.9	70.7	65.8	56.2	44.0	36.5	55.0
1970	30.9	39.1	46.8	57.6	63.7	70.1	74.4	73.1	70.7	59.0	46.0	42.8	56.2
1971	36.5	39.5	43.1	55.2	61.1	72.4	72.5	72.2	69.5	61.8	45.8	47.7	56.5
1972	42.1	37.6	46.5	55.8	61.2	66.5	72.3	72.5	69.0	55.0	45.5	45.2	55.7
1973	37.5	38.5	52.7	52.8	60.3	71.0	74.1	74.2	70.0	58.8	49.1	39.8	56.5
1974	48.2	40.5	51.1	54.9	64.2	66.7	72.9	72.3	65.7	54.6	47.4	40.3	56.6
1975	41.7	42.5	44.8	54.1	66.0	68.8	72.4	72.9	65.2	57.3	48.2	38.6	56.1
RECORD MEAN	37.6	37.9	46.2	55.4	62.5	68.9	72.7	72.0	66.3	56.2	46.0	40.6	55.2
MAX	48.5	49.0	58.5	68.5	74.9	80.5	83.1	82.5	77.1	68.6	58.2	51.2	66.7
MIN	26.7	26.7	33.9	42.2	50.1	57.3	62.2	61.4	55.5	43.7	33.7	30.0	43.6

# Indicates a station move or relocation of instruments.

ASHEVILLE, NC

Feb	Mar	Apr	May	June	Total
584	550	346	58	40	4248
505	601	235	60	3	3527
981	679	288	70	4	4730
635	624	249	58	3	4088
818	969	226	181	2	4559
582	453	444	169	18	4316
531	664	371	27	1	4002
857	426	241	98	6	4392
873	572	251	59	8	4359
751	691	232	23	27	4103
800	660	383	149	42	4808
834	465	226	185	51	4496
939	566	306	150	7	4806
755	729	246	70	9	4449
720	557	236	86	3	4497
707	672	290	137	0	4151
790	569	294	116	35	3749
737	374	362	158	0	3975
680	423	299	83	24	3482
624	619	331	46	7	4002

Aug	Sept	Oct	Nov	Dec	Total
196	92	15	0	0	997
259	206	17	0	0	1011
231	149	37	8	0	923
237	134	0	1	0	722
292	163	19	0	0	969
234	92	1	0	0	731
252	89	0	0	0	795

Precipitation

Year	Jan	Feb	Mar	Apr	May	June	July	Aug	Sept	Oct	Nov	Dec	Annual
1936	7.15	3.78	6.42	4.38	1.44	2.58	6.77	3.40	5.30	3.85	1.15	4.84	51.06
1937	6.87	2.73	0.74	3.51	2.45	4.13	4.18	5.29	0.67	5.89	0.64	1.57	38.67
1938	2.59	1.04	4.20	1.47	3.29	3.24	4.90	2.67	4.72	0.22	4.85	2.22	35.41
1939	3.94	5.72	2.56	2.38	2.78	4.21	3.79	5.14	1.61	0.82	0.77	2.08	35.80
1940	2.13	2.61	2.85	3.26	1.99	3.10	4.03	13.75	0.35	1.12	1.36	2.79	39.34
1941	1.13	0.65	3.18	1.80	1.51	3.67	9.61	2.46	0.28	1.35	1.28	3.40	30.32
1942	2.18	3.49	4.69	1.08	4.63	2.07	3.95	3.89	5.39	1.72	0.51	5.43	39.03
1943	3.43	2.12	4.00	2.89	3.96	8.28	6.81	2.17	2.05	0.59	1.62	1.59	39.51
1944	2.52	6.46	5.30	2.73	2.85	1.97	6.24	2.76	3.42	2.06	1.95	2.27	40.53
1945	1.76	4.22	3.55	4.87	2.87	5.04	3.75	3.82	4.47	2.95	2.96	4.83	45.09
1946	4.40	4.29	4.85	3.09	3.87	1.08	6.49	1.78	1.31	5.69	1.21	1.86	39.92
1947	6.04	1.16	2.22	2.42	1.93	3.50	3.56	4.27	1.85	3.39	3.17	1.66	35.17
1948	2.55	3.45	4.41	1.34	2.64	4.96	4.10	4.75	1.60	0.93	7.15	3.92	41.80
1949	2.06	3.24	3.32	4.14	3.70	4.19	6.74	5.78	1.53	5.13	1.45	2.52	43.80
1950	3.14	2.06	3.91	1.78	4.03	3.06	4.10	2.65	2.25	1.84	1.03	4.11	33.96
1951	1.07	1.80	5.22	2.62	0.59	7.03	2.75	1.50	3.55	1.09	3.20	4.79	35.21
1952	3.09	2.40	7.15	3.72	0.94	3.18	3.17	5.53	0.84	1.23	2.53	2.28	36.06
1953	4.22	4.49	2.10	2.79	3.53	2.40	2.44	2.43	3.04	0.46	1.24	2.67	31.81
1954	6.31	3.64	5.11	1.81	2.78	3.08	3.10	1.98	1.12	2.98	2.84	2.58	37.33
1955	1.11	3.09	4.14	3.55	4.86	2.97	3.06	3.71	0.98	1.35	1.95	0.93	31.70
1956	1.02	4.87	3.53	4.33	1.65	2.21	5.11	1.38	7.31	2.67	1.34	2.96	38.38
1957	4.02	3.13	1.57	6.76	1.73	6.65	1.43	0.98	4.26	2.18	6.22	3.36	42.29
1958	2.89	3.03	3.05	4.04	4.02	1.15	3.91	1.56	1.94	1.83	1.88	3.93	33.23
1959	2.96	1.51	3.37	4.70	7.33	1.53	3.38	3.41	8.33	5.09	1.01	1.97	44.59
1960	2.79	4.19	3.97	2.76	2.11	3.05	2.85	7.24	2.21	4.26	0.68	1.49	37.60
1961	1.45	5.18	3.19	2.98	3.04	4.44	2.54	8.13	1.07	2.36	4.85	6.09	45.32
1962	4.46	3.58	4.13	3.25	2.83	6.20	3.24	3.47	2.40	2.40	2.40	1.66	40.02
1963	1.73	1.76	7.66	3.02	2.53	2.71	2.93	3.83	3.64	T	4.42	2.44	36.67
#1964	2.83	3.58	5.13	5.21	0.94	0.80	3.29	8.88	5.37	8.46	2.51	2.88	49.88
1965	2.16	4.60	5.10	2.62	3.33	4.12	4.47	4.03	4.69	2.92	1.30	0.16	39.50
1966	3.37	6.56	2.59	5.47	4.73	2.46	3.24	7.73	4.55	5.37	3.32	2.36	51.75
1967	2.02	2.20	2.86	1.11	6.79	4.45	6.90	11.28	2.53	3.30	2.54	6.13	52.11
1968	2.93	0.62	6.65	2.37	2.92	5.06	7.18	3.31	2.64	5.02	2.98	3.10	44.78
1969	2.64	5.08	4.01	3.53	3.32	3.82	7.53	6.47	3.04	2.63	1.91	4.63	48.61
1970	1.75	2.42	2.62	2.96	1.72	2.72	5.02	2.46	1.17	5.55	1.83	2.72	32.94
1971	2.53	4.93	3.48	2.06	3.54	5.00	5.47	3.03	3.80	7.05	2.84	4.32	48.05
1972	3.57	2.02	3.19	1.49	6.63	6.54	4.66	1.88	5.29	4.44	4.42	3.89	48.02
1973	4.26	4.23	8.91	5.71	8.83	3.87	6.95	4.57	3.12	2.41	3.57	8.48	64.91
1974	3.44	4.24	3.18	4.99	5.58	3.73	3.93	7.34	4.13	1.28	4.22	2.38	48.44
1975	3.86	4.56	9.86	0.61	8.17	2.12	3.31	3.63	7.53	3.94	4.89	4.44	56.92
RECORD MEAN	2.96	3.77	4.77	2.99	5.05	3.99	5.33	5.07	3.86	3.99	3.07	3.87	48.72

Record mean values above are means through the current year for the period beginning in 1965. Data are from City Office locations through 1964 and from Airport locations beginning January 1965.

RALEIGH, NORTH CAROLINA

Station: RALEIGH, NORTH CAROLINA
RALEIGH-DURHAM AIRPORT
Elevation (ground): 434 feet

TEMPERATURES °F

Month	Normal: Daily maximum	Normal: Daily minimum	Normal: Monthly	Extremes: Record highest	Extremes: Year	Extremes: Record lowest	Extremes: Year
(a)				11		11	
J	51.0	30.0	40.5	77	1967	0	1970
F	53.2	31.1	42.2	79	1965	5	1971
M	61.0	37.4	49.2	89	1968	17	1965
A	72.2	46.7	59.5	93	1967	23	1972
M	79.4	55.4	67.4	92	1975	33	1966
J	85.6	63.1	74.4	95	1973	43	1972
J	87.7	67.2	77.5	97	1966	48	1975
A	86.8	66.2	76.5	98	1968	46	1965
S	81.5	59.7	70.6	93	1975	39	1970
O	72.4	48.0	60.2	89	1968	24	1965
N	62.1	37.8	50.0	84	1974	11	1970
D	51.9	30.5	41.2	77	1971	9	1970
YR	70.4	47.8	59.1	98	AUG 1968	0	JAN 1970

IMPORTANT:
The time-period covered by this record is limited: See footnotes following table of **NORMALS, MEANS AND EXTREMES** for explanation and for additional history of **EXTREME HIGHS AND LOWS** recorded in the general area.

The Raleigh-Durham Airport is located in the zone of transition between the Coastal Plain and the Piedmont Plateau. The surrounding terrain is rolling, with an average elevation of around 400 feet; the range over a 10-mile radius is roughly between 200 and 550 feet. Being centrally located between the mountains on the west and the coast on the south and east, the Raleigh-Durham area enjoys a favorable climate. The mountains form a partial barrier to cold airmasses moving eastward from the interior of the Nation. As a result, there are very few days in the heart of the winter season when the temperature falls below the 20° mark. The average length of freeze-free growing season in the area is about 210 days, the average latest freeze in spring occurring around the first week in April and the first in fall about November 1. The average date of last occurrence in spring of a 28° temperature is around March 15; of 24°, March 1. In fall the average first occurrence of 28° is about November 20; of 24°, December 1. Topical air is present over the eastern and central sections of North Carolina during much of the summer season, bringing warm temperatures and rather high humidities to the Raleigh-Durham area frequently during the summer. Afternoon temperatures reach 90° or higher an average of about every third day in the middle of the summer, but reach 100° an average of less than once per year. Even in the hottest weather, early morning temperatures almost always drop into the lower seventies.

Rainfall is well distributed throughout the year as a whole. July has, on an average, the greatest amount of rainfall, and November the least. There are times in spring and summer when soil moisture is scanty. This usually results from too many days between rains rather than from a

(Continued page 574)

Snowfall

Season	July	Aug	Sept	Oct	Nov	Dec	Jan
1936-37	0.0	0.0	0.0	0.0	T	T	0.0
1937-38	0.0	0.0	0.0	0.0	0.0	2.0	1.1
1938-39	0.0	0.0	0.0	0.0	2.5	0.0	2.0
1939-40	0.0	0.0	0.0	0.0	0.0	1.0	5.7
#1940-41	0.0	0.0	0.0	0.0	0.0	0.0	0.0
1941-42	0.0	0.0	0.0	0.0	0.0	T	0.5
1942-43	0.0	0.0	0.0	0.0	0.0	5.6	0.7
#1943-44	0.0	0.0	0.0	0.0	T	2.0	3.5
1944-45	0.0	0.0	0.0	0.0	0.0	T	T
1945-46	0.0	0.0	0.0	0.0	0.0	4.9	5.4
1946-47	0.0	0.0	0.0	0.0	0.0	0.0	0.0
1947-48	0.0	0.0	0.0	0.0	T	0.4	2.5
1948-49	0.0	0.0	0.0	0.0	0.0	0.1	T
1949-50	0.0	0.0	0.0	0.0	0.0	T	T
1950-51	0.0	0.0	0.0	0.0	T	0.3	T
1951-52	0.0	0.0	0.0	0.0	0.0	T	T
1952-53	0.0	0.0	0.0	0.0	T	0.0	T
1953-54	0.0	0.0	0.0	0.0	0.6	T	6.5
1954-55	0.0	0.0	0.0	0.0	T	2.4	14.4
1955-56	0.0	0.0	0.0	0.0	0.0	T	2.0
1956-57	0.0	0.0	0.0	0.0	T	0.0	T
1957-58	0.0	0.0	0.0	0.0	0.0	1.0	3.0
1958-59	0.0	0.0	0.0	0.0	0.0	10.6	2.9
1959-60	0.0	0.0	0.0	0.0	T	T	T
1960-61	0.0	0.0	0.0	0.0	0.0	0.0	2.3
1961-62	0.0	0.0	0.0	0.0	0.0	T	10.1
1962-63	0.0	0.0	0.0	0.0	1.3	T	0.1
1963-64	0.0	0.0	0.0	0.0	0.0	T	0.4
1964-65	0.0	0.0	0.0	0.0	0.4	0.0	9.7
1965-66	0.0	0.0	0.0	0.0	0.0	0.0	12.3
1966-67	0.0	0.0	0.0	0.0	T	1.0	0.5
1967-68	0.0	0.0	0.0	0.0	T	1.4	3.0
1968-69	0.0	0.0	0.0	0.0	1.2	0.7	T
1969-70	0.0	0.0	0.0	0.0	0.0	0.0	2.0
1970-71	0.0	0.0	0.0	0.0	0.0	0.6	T
1971-72	0.0	0.0	0.0	0.0	T	3.7	0.0
1972-73	0.0	0.0	0.0	0.0	T	0.0	6.4
1973-74	0.0	0.0	0.0	0.0	0.0	2.8	0.0
1974-75	0.0	0.0	0.0	0.0	0.0	T	T
1975-76	0.0	0.0	0.0	0.0	2.6	T	
RECORD MEAN	0.0	0.0	0.0	0.0	0.2	1.0	2.7

Heating Degree Days

Season	July	Aug	Sept	Oct	Nov	Dec	Jan
1955-56	0	0	5	191	500	850	802
1956-57	0	0	58	129	489	428	748
1957-58	0	1	38	295	399	619	893
1958-59	0	0	23	217	355	864	780
1959-60	0	0	23	189	473	667	721
1960-61	0	0	11	170	422	874	878
1961-62	0	0	19	197	403	730	810
1962-63	0	0	61	166	510	832	870
1963-64	0	0	57	149	413	933	731
#1964-65	0	1	25	305	365	665	754
1965-66	0	5	7	208	416	650	898
1966-67	0	0	11	216	425	709	623
1967-68	0	0	35	199	539	574	855
1968-69	0	0	0	151	396	805	848
1969-70	0	0	45	222	561	841	989
1970-71	0	0	22	154	460	684	863
1971-72	0	0	3	61	496	456	623
1972-73	0	0	9	238	504	576	790
1973-74	0	0	2	126	312	690	481
1974-75	0	0	44	268	501	668	651
1975-76	0	0	17	117	351	705	

Cooling Degree Days

Year	Jan	Feb	Mar	Apr	May	June	July
1969	0	0	0	12	105	295	413
1970	0	0	0	41	113	236	350
1971	0	0	0	6	78	320	364
1972	0	0	5	37	36	170	382
1973	0	0	24	26	81	310	363
1974	0	0	25	51	130	210	363
1975	0	0	3	22	141	269	337

Feb	Mar	Apr	May	June	Total
7.8	T	0.0	0.0	0.0	7.8
T	0.0	0.0	0.0	0.0	3.1
0.0	T	0.0	T	0.0	4.5
T	7.0	0.0	0.0	0.0	13.7
0.8	1.0	0.0	0.0	0.0	1.8
T	0.6	0.0	0.0	0.0	1.1
T	0.3	0.0	0.0	0.0	6.6
0.0	0.0	0.0	0.0	0.0	5.5
0.0	0.0	0.0	0.0	0.0	T
0.0	0.0	0.0	0.0	0.0	10.3
T	3.5	0.0	0.0	0.0	3.5
13.5	T	0.0	0.0	0.0	16.4
0.0	0.0	0.0	0.0	0.0	0.1
T	T	T	0.0	0.0	T
1.2	T	0.0	0.0	0.0	1.5
3.5	1.2	0.0	0.0	0.0	4.7
T	0.0	0.0	0.0	0.0	T
0.0	0.0	0.0	0.0	0.0	7.1
T	0.0	0.0	0.0	0.0	16.8
0.0	T	0.0	0.0	0.0	2.0
T	T	0.0	0.0	0.0	T
3.9	T	0.0	0.0	0.0	7.9
T	T	0.0	0.0	0.0	13.5
4.7	14.0	0.0	0.0	0.0	18.7
1.5	0.0	0.0	0.0	0.0	3.8
0.4	4.3	0.0	0.0	0.0	14.8
6.9	0.0	0.0	0.0	0.0	8.3
3.1	T	0.0	0.0	0.0	3.5
3.4	T	0.0	0.0	0.0	13.5
T	0.0	0.0	0.0	0.0	12.3
9.1	0.0	0.0	0.0	0.0	10.6
1.3	T	0.0	0.0	0.0	5.7
0.8	9.3	0.0	0.0	0.0	12.0
T	T	0.0	0.0	0.0	2.0
T	5.3	0.0	0.0	0.0	5.9
1.4	2.6	0.0	0.0	0.0	7.7
4.5	0.4	0.0	0.0	0.0	11.3
T	2.9	0.0	0.0	0.0	5.7
T	0.6	0.0	0.0	0.0	0.6
1.9	1.4	T	0.0	0.0	7.2

RALEIGH, NC

Feb	Mar	Apr	May	June	Total
548	506	275	65	12	3754
494	499	162	59	5	3071
819	623	210	41	1	3939
591	504	179	26	4	3543
704	844	159	87	2	3869
559	393	367	83	8	3765
584	598	261	11	0	3613
803	354	193	86	4	3879
735	445	205	54	0	3722
616	628	232	0	15	3606
629	473	263	72	12	3633
723	361	151	105	13	3337
824	391	213	87	0	3717
667	667	195	61	0	3790
725	576	200	74	0	4233
636	611	258	87	0	3775
718	478	237	51	16	3139
692	334	231	88	0	3462
614	346	187	48	0	2806
589	553	293	34	0	3601

Aug	Sept	Oct	Nov	Dec	Total
283	128	28	0	0	1264
327	278	38	0	0	1383
329	222	61	17	5	1402
336	177	6	6	2	1157
365	254	48	7	0	1478
347	169	9	21	0	1325
421	209	38	12	0	1452

Average Temperature

Year	Jan	Feb	Mar	Apr	May	June	July	Aug	Sept	Oct	Nov	Dec	Annual
1936	38.2	39.7	55.2	57.2	71.4	75.4	79.9	79.4	74.0	63.6	50.2	45.2	60.8
1937	50.8	43.1	49.4	60.0	69.2	78.0	78.6	78.6	69.5	59.2	49.6	42.6	60.7
1938	42.0	49.1	57.2	62.0	69.3	74.0	77.6	80.7	71.6	61.3	54.6	44.0	62.0
1939	46.0	51.0	54.9	60.0	68.6	79.2	77.6	77.9	74.8	63.6	49.6	44.7	62.3
#1940	31.6	44.4	48.4	58.0	68.0	78.4	78.5	77.4	70.0	60.9	52.3	47.2	59.6
1941	40.6	38.7	44.8	63.6	70.2	75.6	80.2	78.7	75.1	68.2	53.4	46.2	61.3
1942	40.6	39.2	52.8	62.2	70.2	77.8	81.3	77.6	73.6	62.5	53.0	41.0	61.0
1943	43.4	45.4	49.9	58.0	71.0	80.4	79.2	79.1	69.2	60.1	49.5	41.6	60.6
#1944	41.4	44.9	49.4	59.2	73.4	77.6	77.3	75.7	72.4	59.5	49.0	37.5	59.8
1945	39.0	43.5	60.2	62.3	64.9	76.6	77.9	75.5	74.6	59.5	51.9	36.8	60.3
1946	41.3	44.6	46.4	59.2	66.3	74.3	76.1	73.9	70.8	61.4	54.7	45.6	60.4
1947	46.4	35.6	42.0	61.1	68.4	74.3	75.2	78.1	71.3	64.6	46.8	40.7	59.1
1948	34.5	41.8	53.8	61.5	67.6	75.9	79.9	76.4	70.1	57.1	54.8	44.9	59.8
1949	49.2	48.6	51.4	57.6	68.0	76.4	81.1	77.6	69.0	64.2	49.5	44.2	61.4
1950	52.2	44.8	47.6	57.8	68.6	75.2	77.1	76.0	70.1	63.4	48.0	37.6	59.9
1951	43.1	44.2	49.4	58.4	66.2	76.2	79.3	78.1	71.5	63.6	46.1	45.4	60.1
1952	46.8	44.6	49.0	59.3	68.2	80.0	80.5	76.8	70.3	55.8	50.7	41.6	60.3
1953	46.7	45.7	51.3	59.4	73.5	74.8	79.6	77.8	71.3	61.9	50.3	43.4	61.3
1954	41.6	47.2	49.1	63.6	63.3	75.4	78.8	77.4	74.9	62.7	47.1	40.0	60.1
1955	38.9	43.7	53.5	63.1	69.7	71.0	80.2	78.4	71.9	59.4	48.4	37.3	59.6
1956	38.9	45.9	48.8	57.2	67.5	74.9	77.8	77.2	69.1	61.9	48.8	51.0	59.9
1957	40.7	47.1	48.7	63.0	68.1	75.6	77.9	75.4	72.4	55.5	51.7	44.8	60.1
1958	35.9	35.5	44.6	59.1	67.3	72.9	79.4	76.8	69.0	58.3	53.3	36.9	57.4
1959	39.6	43.7	48.6	60.7	70.1	74.3	77.5	78.6	71.0	61.7	49.1	43.3	59.9
1960	41.6	40.5	37.6	62.1	66.1	75.0	76.1	77.6	70.8	60.5	50.8	36.6	57.9
1961	36.5	44.9	52.7	53.6	64.2	72.8	77.6	76.6	73.2	59.1	52.4	41.3	58.7
1962	38.8	43.9	45.5	57.4	72.0	73.5	75.7	75.8	68.2	61.8	47.7	38.0	58.2
1963	36.7	36.1	53.4	60.5	65.4	72.7	76.0	76.3	67.1	60.5	51.0	34.7	57.5
#1964	41.2	39.4	50.6	59.6	68.1	75.6	76.4	74.9	69.3	55.2	52.7	43.3	58.9
1965	40.5	42.9	44.6	58.3	71.9	71.9	76.2	77.2	72.7	58.8	50.9	43.8	59.1
1966	35.8	42.3	49.7	57.0	66.5	73.4	79.1	77.7	71.0	58.6	50.8	41.9	58.7
1967	44.8	38.9	53.7	62.5	63.9	72.0	76.9	76.3	67.5	59.4	46.8	46.3	59.1
1968	37.1	36.4	52.6	58.1	63.9	73.6	76.9	79.2	70.9	62.0	51.7	38.8	58.4
1969	37.4	40.9	43.4	58.7	66.2	74.7	78.0	73.8	67.5	58.6	46.1	37.7	56.9
1970	32.9	38.9	46.2	59.4	66.0	72.7	76.1	75.3	73.3	61.0	49.4	42.7	57.8
1971	37.0	42.1	45.1	56.4	64.4	75.4	76.6	75.3	72.0	64.8	48.7	50.3	59.0
1972	44.7	40.0	49.5	58.0	64.3	69.9	77.1	75.6	70.4	57.4	48.1	46.2	58.5
1973	39.3	40.0	54.8	57.9	64.5	75.1	76.5	76.6	73.2	62.2	54.6	42.5	59.8
1974	49.3	42.9	54.4	60.2	67.4	71.8	76.5	76.0	69.0	56.5	48.7	43.2	59.7
1975	43.8	43.7	47.1	55.8	68.2	73.7	75.6	78.3	71.1	62.2	53.5	42.0	59.6
RECORD MEAN	41.8	43.0	50.4	59.3	68.0	75.3	78.2	77.1	71.7	60.9	50.7	42.8	59.9
MAX	51.1	52.8	61.1	70.7	79.0	85.7	87.9	86.6	81.4	71.5	61.1	52.2	70.1
MIN	32.4	33.1	39.6	47.8	57.0	64.9	68.5	67.6	61.9	50.3	40.3	33.4	49.7

# Indicates a station move or relocation of instruments.

Precipitation

Year	Jan	Feb	Mar	Apr	May	June	July	Aug	Sept	Oct	Nov	Dec	Annual
1936	6.62	5.38	4.46	5.21	1.13	8.07	11.65	2.55	6.49	3.61	2.53	6.52	64.22
1937	7.14	3.40	1.93	6.26	0.94	3.81	4.33	5.65	1.85	3.54	1.61	2.38	42.84
1938	2.46	0.87	1.39	2.94	4.60	8.16	5.01	1.31	4.85	1.52	3.57	2.93	39.61
1939	2.75	9.73	2.61	3.57	6.26	3.84	8.31	9.99	2.35	3.03	1.75	2.24	56.43
#1940	2.58	2.52	3.35	3.16	3.51	1.81	2.51	7.19	1.71	0.44	4.02	1.66	34.46
1941	2.03	1.14	4.04	4.10	2.08	3.37	10.86	3.46	1.53	1.93	0.51	4.39	39.44
1942	1.29	2.51	5.04	1.68	3.36	4.34	3.15	7.03	5.30	6.26	1.56	3.81	45.33
1943	4.40	1.26	4.58	2.67	1.85	8.75	6.46	3.17	2.87	0.81	1.72	3.53	42.07
#1944	4.26	5.10	7.18	5.47	1.55	2.77	3.82	4.61	8.58	1.85	3.24	2.23	50.66
1945	1.65	5.39	1.83	2.96	2.82	1.90	10.05	5.25	12.94	2.16	1.89	6.20	55.04
1946	3.53	3.78	1.62	4.87	6.63	3.42	7.12	6.18	5.17	4.22	2.51	2.04	51.09
1947	4.90	1.20	2.74	3.12	1.62	5.34	2.68	4.68	6.29	6.28	5.92	1.18	45.95
1948	4.39	3.74	3.89	2.87	4.63	1.92	4.28	5.34	3.98	2.95	8.22	5.14	51.35
1949	2.83	3.14	1.48	2.45	4.18	2.80	5.35	8.87	5.87	2.59	2.31	1.65	43.52
1950	2.40	1.57	2.67	1.99	6.69	5.62	5.07	0.81	3.73	3.27	1.36	2.66	37.84
1951	1.57	1.86	2.47	4.49	1.77	3.43	4.69	4.03	1.38	2.90	2.71	3.24	34.54
1952	4.51	3.85	6.21	2.47	3.66	1.90	6.30	9.76	1.71	1.38	4.40	3.03	49.18
1953	4.10	3.68	4.43	4.57	1.37	3.99	0.80	2.70	3.46	0.44	1.65	4.84	36.03
1954	7.52	1.70	4.49	2.83	3.65	1.12	5.14	5.06	0.57	4.93	2.53	2.09	41.63
1955	2.52	3.93	1.56	2.70	1.95	2.13	6.38	10.49	4.33	1.96	2.34	0.59	40.88
1956	1.05	4.70	3.37	4.74	1.88	4.43	6.83	1.31	3.74	3.18	1.38	3.28	39.89
1957	2.82	4.40	2.25	1.66	5.86	6.03	2.15	4.85	4.58	1.71	6.53	3.42	46.26
1958	3.43	3.24	2.55	5.02	6.45	4.40	4.82	6.23	1.18	2.98	1.03	4.24	45.57
1959	1.77	3.38	3.22	5.83	2.53	2.59	8.83	5.92	3.52	6.53	2.58	2.25	48.95
1960	4.59	5.26	4.94	4.57	5.07	2.53	7.47	5.43	3.05	2.29	0.88	1.92	48.00
1961	2.88	5.75	4.37	2.23	2.94	4.05	3.10	6.52	1.25	1.16	2.10	4.76	41.11
1962	6.56	2.74	4.85	3.22	1.37	6.37	7.07	1.98	3.72	0.99	7.19	2.21	48.27
1963	2.96	3.45	3.80	1.77	4.05	1.72	3.51	2.10	2.77	0.44	7.06	3.28	36.91
1964	3.66	4.11	2.93	3.39	0.92	3.41	4.06	5.68	5.29	3.95	1.38	4.13	42.91
1965	1.47	2.40	4.08	1.51	2.20	8.32	5.54	3.00	2.65	1.77	1.23	0.25	34.42
1966	5.42	4.76	1.81	2.02	4.95	3.68	0.91	5.79	3.58	2.01	2.06	2.61	39.60
1967	1.64	3.80	1.62	3.02	4.15	4.57	3.49	6.22	1.74	2.26	2.14	4.93	39.58
1968	2.88	1.00	2.22	3.03	3.82	1.74	5.15	2.50	1.77	5.15	3.59	2.75	35.60
1969	1.55	3.60	3.95	1.43	2.85	4.81	4.40	6.31	6.21	2.09	1.01	3.31	41.52
1970	2.26	3.47	4.04	2.07	3.36	0.87	5.64	4.47	1.20	4.47	1.59	2.57	36.01
1971	3.28	3.85	3.69	2.59	4.68	2.79	4.56	6.26	2.91	7.53	1.81	1.69	45.64
1972	1.97	4.13	2.50	1.92	5.34	4.16	6.80	4.17	5.80	3.96	5.98	5.01	51.74
1973	2.67	5.50	4.06	4.40	3.99	9.38	3.12	4.60	1.13	0.60	0.61	6.38	46.44
1974	4.39	2.87	3.34	1.32	7.67	4.02	1.56	4.82	3.71	1.23	1.79	4.02	40.74
1975	6.09	2.85	6.26	1.64	3.84	1.66	6.74	2.11	5.77	1.23	4.60	4.04	46.83
RECORD MEAN	3.37	3.72	3.69	3.29	3.88	4.25	5.40	5.26	3.72	2.87	2.56	3.29	45.30

Record mean values above are means through the current year for the period beginning in 1887 for temperature and precipitation, 1945 for snowfall. Data are from the Raleigh Municipal Airport, 3.5 miles south of the Post Office, for the period December 12, 1940 through May 1944. Beginning with June 1944 data are from the Raleigh-Durham Airport.

(Continued)

shortage of total rainfall, but occasionally the accumulated total during the growing season falls short of plant needs. Most summer rain is produced by thundershowers, which may occasionally be accompanied by strong winds, intense rains, and hail. The Raleigh-Durham ares is far enough from the coast so that the bad weather effects of coastal storms are reduced. While snow and sleet usually occur each year, excessive accumulations of snow are rare.

From September 1887 to December 1950, the office was located in the downtown areas of Raleigh. The various buildings occupied were within an area of three blocks. All thermometers were exposed on the roof, and this, plus the smoke over the City, had an effect on the temperature record of that period. Lowest temperatures at the city office were frequently from 2° to 5° higher than those recorded in surrounding rural areas. Conversely, maximum temperatures in the City were generally a degree or two lower. Thus, the average daily temperatures at the old city office exposure were not very different from those in surrounding areas. These observations are supported by a period of simultaneous record from the Municipal Airport and the city office location between 1937 and 1940.

From September 1946 to May 1954, simultaneous records were kept at a surface location on North Carolina State College campus in Raleigh, and at the Raleigh-Durham Airport 10-1/2 air miles to the northwest. Minimum temperatures of this period are generally from 2° to 5° lower at the airport; these readings are believed to be representative of the surrounding countryside, and of suburban residential areas of Raleigh and Durham. Maximum temperatures recorded at the two stations were usually identical.

Normals, Means, and Extremes

	Normal Degree days Base 65 °F		Precipitation in inches												Relative humidity pct.			
			Water equivalent							Snow, Ice pellets					Hour 01	Hour 07	Hour 13	Hour 19
Month	Heating	Cooling	Normal	Maximum monthly	Year	Minimum monthly	Year	Maximum in 24 hrs.	Year	Maximum monthly	Year	Maximum in 24 hrs.	Year	(Local time)			
(a)				31		31		31		31		31		11	11	11	11
J	760	0	3.22	7.52	1954	1.05	1956	2.79	1954	14.4	1955	9.0	1966	73	78	56	64
F	638	0	3.32	5.75	1961	1.00	1968	3.22	1973	13.5	1948	9.1	1967	67	74	49	56
M	502	12	3.44	6.26	1975	1.48	1949	2.51	1952	14.0	1960	9.3	1969	70	79	49	56
A	180	15	3.07	5.83	1959	1.32	1974	2.09	1973	T	1950	T	1950	73	80	45	54
M	48	123	3.32	7.67	1974	0.92	1964	4.40	1957	0.0		0.0		84	86	55	67
J	0	282	3.67	9.38	1973	0.87	1970	3.44	1967	0.0		0.0		87	88	57	68
J	0	388	5.08	10.05	1945	0.80	1953	3.89	1952	0.0		0.0		89	91	61	74
A	0	357	4.93	10.49	1955	0.81	1950	5.20	1955	0.0		0.0		90	93	62	78
S	12	180	3.78	12.94	1945	0.57	1954	5.16	1944	0.0		0.0		89	93	60	79
O	186	37	2.81	7.53	1971	0.44	1963	4.10	1954	0.0		0.0		85	90	54	76
N	450	0	2.82	8.22	1948	0.61	1973	4.70	1963	2.6	1975	2.6	1975	76	83	49	65
D	738	0	3.08	6.38	1973	0.25	1965	3.18	1958	10.6	1958	9.1	1958	74	80	55	67
YR	3514	1394	42.54	12.94	SEP 1945	0.25	DEC 1965	5.20	AUG 1955	14.4	JAN 1955	9.3	MAR 1969	80	84	54	67

(To better understand these tables, see full explanation of terms beginning on page 322)

	Wind							Mean number of days											Average station pressure mb.
			Fastest mile					Sunrise to sunset							Temperatures °F Max.		Min.		
Month	Mean speed m.p.h.	Prevailing direction	Speed m.p.h.	Direction	Year	Pct. of possible sunshine	Mean sky cover, tenths, sunrise to sunset	Clear	Partly cloudy	Cloudy	Precipitation .01 inch or more	Snow, Ice pellets 1.0 inch or more	Thunderstorms	Heavy fog, visibility ¼ mile or less	(b) 90° and above	32° and below	32° and below	0° and below	Elev. 441 feet m.s.l.
(a)	26	14	22	22		21	26	27	27	27	31	31	31	26	11	11	11	11	3
J	8.7	SW	41	27	1971	55	6.2	9	7	15	10	1	*	4	0	3	19	*	1004.5
F	9.2	SW	40	22	1966	58	5.9	9	6	13	10	1	1	3	0	*	19	0	1002.2
M	9.6	SW	44	32	1967	63	5.9	10	7	14	11	*	2	2	0	0	11	0	1000.4
A	9.4	SW	40	14	1961	64	5.6	10	9	11	9	0	4	2	1	0	3	0	1000.7
M	7.9	SW	54	20	1972	60	6.0	8	10	13	10	0	6	3	1	0	0	0	998.9
J	7.1	SW	37	22	1971	61	5.8	8	12	10	9	0	7	2	5	0	0	0	1000.6
J	6.8	SW	69	23	1962	61	6.0	7	12	12	12	0	11	3	8	0	0	0	1001.2
A	6.5	NE	46	33	1969	61	6.0	8	12	11	10	0	8	4	7	0	0	0	1002.6
S	7.0	NE	35	23	1972	60	5.6	10	9	11	8	0	4	4	2	0	0	0	1002.5
O	7.3	NNE	73	29	1954	63	4.9	13	7	11	7	0	1	4	0	0	2	0	1004.8
N	7.9	SW	35	32	1969	63	5.1	12	8	10	8	*	1	3	0	0	11	0	1004.2
D	8.2	SW	35	21	1968	56	5.8	10	7	14	9	*	*	4	0	1	17	0	1003.4
YR	8.0	SW	73	29	OCT 1954	60	5.7	114	106	145	113	2	46	36	23	4	81	*	1002.2

FOOTNOTES

Means and extremes above are from existing and comparable exposures. Annual extremes have been exceeded at other sites in the locality as follows: Highest temperature 105° in July 1952; lowest temperature -2 in February 1899; maximum monthly precipitation 13.63 in August 1908; minimum monthly precipitation 0.06 in November 1931+; maximum precipitation in 24 hours 6.66 in September 1929; maximum monthly snowfall 20.0 in January 1893; maximum snowfall in 24 hours 17.8 in March 1927.

Station: FARGO, NORTH DAKOTA
HECTOR AIRPORT
Elevation (ground): 896 feet

TEMPERATURES °F

Month	Normal			Extremes			
	Daily maximum	Daily minimum	Monthly	Record highest	Year	Record lowest	Year
(a)				16		16	
J	15.4	-3.6	5.9	46	1964	-35	1965
F	20.6	.8	10.7	51	1963	-34	1962
M	33.5	14.9	24.2	78	1967	-23	1962
A	52.6	31.9	42.3	88	1962	-7	1975
M	66.8	42.3	54.6	98	1964	20	1966
J	75.9	53.4	64.7	98	1964	30	1969
J	82.8	58.6	70.7	100	1975	36	1967
A	81.6	56.8	69.2	100	1965	33	1964
S	69.6	46.2	57.9	99	1960	19	1965
O	58.4	35.5	47.0	93	1963	10	1972
N	37.2	20.0	28.6	70	1975	-22	1964
D	21.9	4.1	13.0	57	1962	-32	1967
YR	51.4	30.1	40.8	100	JUL 1975	-35	JAN 1965

IMPORTANT:
The time-period covered by this record is limited: See footnotes on next page for explanation and for additional history of EXTREME HIGHS AND LOWS recorded in the general area.

Moorhead, Minnesota, and Fargo are twin cities in the Red River Valley of the North. The Red River of the North flows northward between the two cities and is a part of the Hudson Bay drainage area. The Red River is approximately 2 miles east of the airport at its nearest point and has no significant effect on the weather. In recent years, spring floods due to melting snow have been common. Summer floods caused by heavy rains are infrequent.

The surrounding terrain is flat and open with northerly winds blowing up the Valley occasionally causing low cloudiness and fog; however, this upslope cloudiness is very infrequent. Aside from this, there are no pronounced climatic differences due to geographical features in the immediate area.

The summers are generally comfortable with very few days of hot and humid weather. Nights, with few exceptions, are comfortably cool. The winter months are cold and dry with maximum temperatures rising above freezing only on an average of 6 days each month, and nighttime lows dropping below zero approximately half of the time.

The average growing season is 136 days without freezing temperatures; the average date for freezing temperatures in the spring is May 12, and the average date for freezing temperatures in the fall is September 26. The latest date of freezing temperatures in the spring was June 9, 1915. The earliest date for the last freezing temperature in the spring was on April 21, 1939. The earliest date for the first freezing temperature in the fall was August 25, 1885; however, no freezing temperatures have occurred in August since 1886. The latest date in the fall for the first freezing temperatures was October 20, 1911.

Precipitation is the most important climatic factor in the area. The Red River Valley lies in an area where lighter amounts fall to the west and heavier amounts to the east. Seventy-five percent of the precipitation occurs during the growing season (April to September) and is often accompanied by electrical storms and heavy falls in a short time. Winter precipitation is light and indicates that heavy snowfall is the exception rather than the rule. The first light snow in the fall occasionally falls in September, but usually very little, if any, occurs until October or November. The latest fall is generally in April.

With the flat terrain, surface friction has little effect on the wind in the area and this fact has led to the legendary Dakota blizzards. Strong winds with even light snowfall cause much drifting and blowing snow, reducing visibilities to near zero. Fortunately, these conditions occur only several times during the winter months.

FARGO, NORTH DAKOTA

Normals, Means, and Extremes

(To better understand these tables, see full explanation of terms beginning on page 322)

Month	Normal Degree days Base 65 °F: Heating	Normal Degree days Base 65 °F: Cooling	Precipitation in inches, Water equivalent: Normal	Maximum monthly	Year	Minimum monthly	Year	Maximum in 24 hrs.	Year	Snow, Ice pellets: Maximum monthly	Year	Maximum in 24 hrs.	Year	Relative humidity pct. Hour 00	Hour 06	Hour 12	Hour 18 (Local time)	Wind: Mean speed m.p.h.	Prevailing direction	Fastest mile: Speed m.p.h.	Direction	Year	Pct. of possible sunshine	Mean sky cover, tenths, sunrise to sunset	Mean number of days, Sunrise to sunset: Clear	Partly cloudy	Cloudy	Precipitation .01 inch or more	Snow, Ice pellets 1.0 inch or more	Thunderstorms	Heavy fog, visibility ½ mile or less	Temperatures °F Max. (b) 90° and above	32° and below	Min. 32° and below	0° and below	Average station pressure mb. Elev. 899 feet m.s.l.
(a)				34		34		34		34		34		16	16	16	16	33	14	34	34		33	30	33	33	33	33	33	33	33	16	16	16	16	3
J	1832	0	0.50	1.36	1950	0.09	1961	0.68	1949	18.3	1975	7.0	1972	74	73	71	72	13.0	SSE	62	SE	1968	50	6.7	6	8	17	9	2	0	1	0	28	31	20	982.9
F	1520	0	0.44	1.60	1948	0.03	1954	1.22	1946	15.8	1948	11.2	1951	76	76	72	74	12.9	N	56	W	1957	58	6.6	6	8	14	7	2	0	2	0	23	28	14	985.9
M	1265	0	0.83	2.21	1950	0.03	1958	1.16	1950	18.7	1975	10.4	1975	81	83	71	72	13.5	N	56	N	1960	57	7.0	5	9	17	8	2	*	2	0	14	28	5	982.3
A	681	0	2.08	4.24	1942	0.02	1949	1.91	1963	12.8	1970	8.6	1970	78	82	63	60	14.6	N	68	NW	1964	57	6.7	6	9	15	8	1	1	1	0	1	17	*	981.9
M	334	11	2.29	5.95	1962	0.47	1952	2.35	1944	1.0	1950	1.0	1950	72	80	53	49	13.5	N	72	NW	1960	58	6.4	7	10	14	10	*	4	*	*	*	5	0	979.2
J	97	88	3.20	9.40	1975	0.58	1972	4.02	1975	0.0		0.0		78	83	58	54	12.0	SSE	115	NW	1959	59	6.2	6	12	12	11	0	8	*	2	0	*	0	977.8
J	13	190	3.16	8.42	1952	0.42	1950	3.93	1952	0.0		0.0		80	86	55	53	10.9	S	60	S	1965	71	4.9	11	13	7	10	0	9	1	5	0	0	0	980.8
A	33	163	2.85	8.52	1944	0.38	1969	4.72	1943	0.0		0.0		78	87	55	50	11.3	SSE	71	NW	1955	68	5.0	11	12	8	9	0	7	1	6	0	0	0	981.4
S	234	21	1.84	6.13	1957	0.13	1974	3.97	1957	0.6	1942	0.6	1942	80	87	59	57	12.4	SSE	88	N	1960	59	5.8	9	9	12	8	0	3	1	1	0	2	0	983.9
O	558	0	1.09	4.42	1971	0.08	1952	2.06	1971	8.1	1951	7.8	1951	78	83	61	62	13.0	SSE	57	NW	1960	56	6.0	9	8	14	6	*	1	1	*	*	12	0	982.3
N	1092	0	0.72	2.01	1947	0.04	1967	1.95	1974	19.0	1947	10.9	1960	81	84	71	74	13.4	S	66	N	1956	39	7.3	5	6	19	6	2	*	1	0	9	27	1	983.6
D	1612	0	0.62	2.19	1951	0.04	1958	0.87	1960	20.3	1951	8.0	1967	78	79	75	77	12.7	S	58	N	1957	43	7.0	6	8	17	8	2	*	2	0	26	31	13	984.5
YR	9271	473	19.62	9.40	JUN 1975	0.02	APR 1949	4.72	AUG 1943	20.3	DEC 1951	11.2	FEB 1951	78	82	64	63	12.7	N	115	NW	JUN 1959	57	6.3	87	112	166	103	11	34	13	14	101	181	54	982.2

FOOTNOTES Means and extremes above are from existing and comparable exposures. Annual extremes have been exceeded at other sites in the locality as follows: Highest temperature 114 in July 1936; lowest temperature -48 in January 1887; maximum monthly precipitation 9.58 in August 1900; minimum monthly precipitation T in November 1901; maximum precipitation in 24 hours 5.17 in July 1886; maximum monthly snowfall 30.4 in November 1896; maximum snowfall in 24 hours 19.2 in December 1927.

Snowfall

Season	July	Aug	Sept	Oct	Nov	Dec	Jan
1936-37	0.0	0.0	0.0	1.9	6.6	11.9	27.3
1937-38	0.0	0.0	0.0	T	2.8	16.6	5.8
1938-39	0.0	0.0	0.0	T	11.3	5.8	5.7
1939-40	0.0	0.0	0.0	1.4	0.1	2.2	2.6
1940-41	0.0	0.0	0.0	0.0	6.3	6.3	10.7
#1941-42	0.0	0.0	T	1.1	1.0	2.6	0.8
1942-43	0.0	0.0	0.6	2.2	2.7	9.2	3.3
1943-44	0.0	0.0	0.0	T	1.3	0.9	5.8
1944-45	0.0	0.0	0.0	0.0	5.3	3.1	4.2
1945-46	0.0	0.0	0.0	T	1.9	7.9	3.3
1946-47	0.0	0.0	0.0	T	4.9	7.1	2.7
1947-48	0.0	0.0	0.0	0.0	19.0	5.5	7.3
1948-49	0.0	0.0	0.0	T	10.2	3.8	12.4
1949-50	0.0	0.0	0.0	T	5.3	10.8	14.9
1950-51	0.0	0.0	0.0	1.0	4.9	7.2	5.7
1951-52	0.0	0.0	0.0	8.1	7.9	20.3	11.2
1952-53	0.0	0.0	0.0	T	0.8	6.3	3.3
#1953-54	0.0	0.0	0.0	T	6.5	8.6	7.0
1954-55	0.0	0.0	0.0	T	1.1	3.3	2.8
1955-56	0.0	0.0	0.0	T	6.0	4.9	7.9
1956-57	0.0	0.0	T	0.0	0.5	3.2	3.3
1957-58	0.0	0.0	T	T	1.6	1.2	2.8
1958-59	0.0	0.0	0.0	T	6.5	0.9	2.0
1959-60	0.0	0.0	0.0	0.7	3.6	1.5	6.2
1960-61	0.0	0.0	0.0	T	11.0	3.6	1.6
1961-62	0.0	0.0	0.0	T	0.5	6.5	10.9
1962-63	0.0	0.0	0.0	0.2	3.1	2.5	1.3
1963-64	0.0	0.0	0.0	0.0	0.4	4.3	8.4
1964-65	0.0	0.0	0.0	T	2.7	11.9	1.2
1965-66	0.0	0.0	T	0.0	6.1	6.1	5.0
1966-67	0.0	0.0	0.0	1.2	1.3	3.4	15.1
1967-68	0.0	0.0	0.0	0.7	0.7	10.3	4.0
1968-69	0.0	0.0	0.0	0.8	3.9	11.4	14.5
1969-70	0.0	0.0	0.0	2.0	1.9	9.5	2.3
1970-71	0.0	0.0	0.0	0.9	6.4	8.3	15.1
1971-72	0.0	0.0	0.0	3.8	2.3	10.0	16.5
1972-73	0.0	0.0	T	3.8	1.7	18.5	1.7
1973-74	0.0	0.0	0.0	T	3.9	12.3	6.1
1974-75	0.0	0.0	0.0	0.4	1.0	5.1	18.3
1975-76	0.0	0.0	0.0	0.4	3.8	1.9	
RECORD MEAN	0.0	0.0	T	0.8	4.1	6.8	6.9

Heating Degree Days

Season	July	Aug	Sept	Oct	Nov	Dec	Jan
1955-56	3	10	231	534	1376	1845	1826
1956-57	14	39	291	404	1025	1494	1935
1957-58	0	35	274	568	1074	1343	1470
1958-59	38	56	174	498	1054	1684	1903
#1959-60	8	8	226	746	1329	1205	1762
1960-61	23	9	223	539	1046	1701	1803
1961-62	2	9	301	527	1039	1681	1880
1962-63	11	5	232	439	892	1492	1957
1963-64	5	14	127	262	901	1748	1528
1964-65	5	94	304	604	1065	1902	2051
1965-66	19	59	477	544	1161	1415	2216
1966-67	0	84	230	644	1253	1642	1723
1967-68	65	49	158	645	1073	1544	1773
1968-69	31	66	201	565	1015	1736	2066
1969-70	20	10	229	757	1028	1522	1996
1970-71	16	26	251	560	1109	1723	2035
1971-72	57	36	241	535	1052	1630	1931
1972-73	25	41	261	695	1089	1897	1638
1973-74	32	3	309	451	1187	1698	1963
1974-75	3	91	345	537	1066	1362	1630
1975-76	14	22	284	492	1012	1550	

Cooling Degree Days

Year	Jan	Feb	Mar	Apr	May	June	July
1969	0	0	0	0	39	5	131
1970	0	0	0	0	2	146	233
1971	0	0	0	0	3	109	65
1972	0	0	0	0	74	125	135
1973	0	0	0	0	0	76	140
1974	0	0	0	0	9	75	281
1975	0	0	0	0	11	92	308

Feb	Mar	Apr	May	June	Total
15.7	2.1	16.7	0.0	0.0	82.2
8.5	0.7	0.1	0.5	0.0	35.0
13.0	3.5	1.3	0.0	0.0	40.6
6.3	14.6	0.7	0.0	0.0	27.9
3.3	5.2	0.5	0.0	0.0	32.3
3.3	3.6	4.9	T	0.0	17.3
8.6	10.5	T	T	0.0	37.1
1.9	13.6	T	0.3	0.0	23.8
8.4	1.0	4.1	0.4	0.0	26.5
13.0	4.3	7.4	0.5	0.0	38.3
2.9	5.2	7.5	0.0	0.0	30.3
15.8	7.2	1.2	0.0	0.0	56.0
5.6	2.1	T	T	0.0	34.1
2.7	10.2	12.4	1.0	0.0	57.3
12.1	11.5	2.0	0.0	0.0	44.4
3.2	9.9	1.8	0.0	0.0	62.4
6.4	4.6	0.9	T	0.0	22.3
0.3	4.9	0.5	0.9	0.0	28.7
12.0	7.4	0.3	0.0	0.0	26.9
1.8	9.2	4.7	0.0	0.0	34.5
4.4	0.7	2.8	0.0	0.0	14.9
1.9	1.8	T	0.0	0.0	9.3
3.5	0.2	1.1	T	0.0	14.2
1.2	2.4	7.9	0.2	0.0	23.7
2.3	T	2.8	T	0.0	21.3
10.1	10.7	2.0	0.0	0.0	40.7
3.9	5.3	6.0	0.1	0.0	22.4
6.2	8.4	9.2	0.0	0.0	36.9
1.7	13.1	2.5	T	0.0	33.1
1.1	15.4	5.0	0.0	0.0	38.7
2.6	4.9	5.0	T	0.0	33.5
2.4	2.0	11.6	0.4	0.0	32.1
7.8	3.0	T	T	0.0	41.4
3.6	9.1	12.8	T	0.0	41.2
4.8	1.8	1.0	T	0.0	38.3
10.9	7.1	3.1	0.0	0.0	53.7
1.4	1.4	2.4	0.0	0.0	30.9
7.1	10.5	2.7	0.0	0.0	42.6
5.9	18.7	3.7	T	0.0	53.1
5.3	6.5	3.8	0.1	0.0	34.3

FARGO, ND

Feb	Mar	Apr	May	June	Total
1714	1406	895	361	13	10214
1465	1159	668	286	88	8868
1471	1049	587	237	182	8290
1555	1051	649	342	63	9067
1550	1526	708	276	87	9431
1292	936	811	375	41	8798
1660	1304	749	258	61	9471
1535	1112	640	339	45	8699
1331	1364	553	177	68	8078
1618	1582	695	324	66	10310
1649	1089	829	430	86	9974
1716	1178	795	480	96	9841
1592	952	628	375	79	8933
1460	1536	582	348	230	9836
1511	1431	773	407	55	9739
1461	1153	609	333	30	9306
1763	1269	718	231	60	9523
1361	893	701	328	79	9058
1550	1298	676	431	86	9684
1535	1438	867	265	79	9218

Aug	Sept	Oct	Nov	Dec	Total
249	59	0	0	0	483
180	95	3	0	0	659
142	56	0	0	0	375
217	23	0	0	0	574
219	13	0	0	0	448
75	3	1	0	0	444
126	1	15	0	0	553

Average Temperature

Year	Jan	Feb	Mar	Apr	May	June	July	Aug	Sept	Oct	Nov	Dec	Annual
1936	-6.2	-9.8	24.0	35.9	62.2	65.6	80.2	71.6	62.2	41.6	25.2	14.2	38.9
1937	-6.1	5.6	22.4	40.8	58.0	63.6	72.1	74.2	59.0	44.1	26.2	10.7	39.2
1938	6.3	9.8	34.8	43.6	52.5	64.8	71.2	72.5	61.1	52.1	24.2	16.1	42.4
1939	11.3	-0.8	22.5	40.3	62.2	64.4	72.8	70.5	61.0	42.6	34.9	25.2	42.2
1940	4.0	15.2	20.4	39.8	55.0	63.3	72.6	66.8	63.8	52.0	24.3	18.0	41.3
1941	10.6	9.3	24.4	47.0	59.6	66.3	72.4	69.6	58.3	46.4	31.4	21.0	43.0
#1942	18.0	13.4	33.8	47.8	52.0	62.6	68.8	68.4	54.2	47.2	27.5	7.6	41.8
1943	-1.3	10.9	17.6	43.8	51.2	63.8	73.0	69.6	55.9	48.4	29.6	19.8	40.2
1944	21.1	11.8	20.2	41.0	58.5	65.4	69.3	67.4	58.1	47.8	32.9	14.6	42.3
1945	10.8	13.6	35.0	39.2	48.4	60.3	68.6	68.3	56.2	44.6	26.0	6.8	39.8
1946	8.0	6.7	34.7	47.4	51.8	64.6	71.2	66.4	57.2	43.4	27.4	12.2	40.9
1947	16.1	9.3	24.6	39.5	50.0	61.4	71.5	73.9	57.7	53.2	22.2	10.0	40.8
1948	3.0	5.6	17.7	44.2	56.0	63.8	71.2	70.0	64.7	48.1	29.0	11.8	40.4
1949	3.6	2.4	22.1	46.8	57.6	65.6	71.3	72.6	56.8	45.9	34.1	10.4	40.8
1950	-7.1	5.8	20.7	33.5	51.2	65.6	67.9	65.5	60.4	47.5	22.3	6.7	36.7
1951	1.1	13.4	15.8	40.3	58.8	60.7	68.5	64.8	54.6	43.4	21.0	7.1	37.5
1952	1.4	16.5	20.4	48.0	56.1	67.3	69.7	67.9	62.4	41.8	30.8	18.7	41.8
#1953	10.4	16.3	28.0	37.5	54.8	64.9	69.9	71.8	59.0	53.5	35.1	14.7	43.0
1954	-1.4	26.5	25.5	41.2	50.4	65.3	71.8	68.8	57.0	44.7	34.5	19.7	42.0
1955	9.5	5.8	16.8	50.8	60.8	65.4	74.5	72.6	58.7	47.7	18.9	5.4	40.6
1956	6.1	5.8	19.5	35.0	53.3	70.7	68.0	68.5	55.7	51.7	30.6	16.7	40.1
1957	2.5	12.5	27.5	42.6	56.1	62.7	75.4	69.0	56.1	46.5	29.0	21.5	41.8
1958	17.4	12.4	30.9	45.2	58.2	59.7	67.4	68.9	59.9	48.8	29.7	10.5	42.4
#1959	3.7	9.5	30.9	43.2	55.2	68.2	72.2	72.5	58.9	40.7	20.5	25.9	41.8
1960	8.1	11.3	15.5	41.2	56.6	63.3	71.4	70.6	59.9	47.5	29.9	10.0	40.5
1961	6.8	18.7	34.5	37.8	53.2	68.7	70.5	73.5	56.0	47.9	30.1	10.7	42.4
1962	4.4	5.6	22.7	39.9	56.6	66.2	68.8	71.6	57.6	51.1	35.0	16.6	41.3
1963	2.0	10.1	29.0	43.5	54.3	68.8	73.6	70.3	62.2	57.3	34.7	8.6	42.9
1964	15.6	18.9	20.8	46.4	61.1	67.2	74.0	64.9	55.4	45.2	29.2	3.8	41.9
1965	-1.2	7.1	13.7	41.6	54.4	63.9	68.5	66.5	48.9	47.3	26.0	19.2	38.0
1966	-6.4	6.2	29.7	37.2	51.4	66.1	73.8	65.5	58.2	44.0	23.1	11.9	38.4
1967	9.3	3.8	26.8	38.3	49.7	62.6	67.9	66.7	60.8	44.0	29.0	15.1	39.5
1968	7.7	9.9	34.1	43.9	52.9	64.1	69.6	68.1	59.3	46.7	31.0	8.9	41.4
1969	-1.6	12.8	15.3	45.4	54.8	57.3	68.4	72.4	59.0	40.3	30.5	15.6	39.2
1970	0.6	10.9	18.6	39.1	51.7	67.9	71.8	69.7	59.7	46.8	27.8	9.3	39.5
1971	-0.7	12.7	27.6	44.5	54.2	67.5	65.1	68.3	58.5	47.4	29.6	12.2	40.6
1972	2.7	4.1	23.9	41.0	59.8	66.9	68.4	70.5	56.9	42.4	28.6	3.8	39.1
1973	10.3	16.3	36.0	41.4	54.2	64.7	68.3	71.7	54.8	50.2	25.1	10.1	41.9
1974	1.7	9.6	22.9	42.2	51.1	64.4	73.7	64.3	53.4	47.5	29.2	20.9	40.1
1975	12.3	10.1	18.4	35.9	56.6	65.2	74.3	68.1	55.4	49.4	31.1	14.8	41.0
RECORD MEAN	5.0	9.4	24.1	42.1	54.7	64.6	70.0	68.0	57.9	45.8	27.5	12.9	40.2
MAX	14.6	19.1	33.3	52.6	66.7	75.9	81.8	80.1	69.7	56.6	36.2	21.7	50.7
MIN	-4.6	-0.3	14.8	31.6	42.6	53.3	58.1	55.8	46.1	34.9	18.8	4.0	29.6

# Indicates a station move or relocation of instruments.

Precipitation

Year	Jan	Feb	Mar	Apr	May	June	July	Aug	Sept	Oct	Nov	Dec	Annual
1936	0.39	1.38	1.31	0.74	1.22	0.48	0.42	0.96	0.26	0.36	0.58	0.77	8.87
1937	1.55	0.77	0.30	4.69	1.37	1.89	2.68	3.59	1.56	0.11	0.44	0.94	19.89
1938	0.48	0.51	0.46	2.07	3.60	1.04	1.96	2.59	1.97	0.15	0.86	0.52	16.21
1939	0.58	0.69	0.23	0.91	0.48	3.92	0.43	1.49	0.59	1.43	0.09	0.39	11.23
1940	0.13	0.48	1.33	1.07	1.40	1.75	3.66	3.33	0.22	2.22	0.52	0.53	16.64
1941	0.66	0.17	0.54	3.51	1.35	5.45	1.34	2.85	3.57	1.93	0.09	0.22	21.68
#1942	0.07	0.22	1.88	4.24	2.19	2.32	0.87	6.71	1.27	0.81	0.28	0.65	21.51
1943	0.33	0.69	0.85	1.05	3.65	5.64	2.52	6.81	0.79	1.64	0.15	0.10	24.22
1944	0.60	0.16	1.26	1.17	4.70	3.41	6.95	8.52	1.40	0.17	1.85	0.19	30.38
1945	0.33	0.87	1.20	2.03	2.22	0.76	1.22	3.28	2.98	0.35	0.26	0.66	16.16
1946	0.32	1.44	0.88	1.10	2.04	4.03	0.98	1.76	3.35	2.12	1.04	0.66	19.72
1947	0.32	0.41	0.48	3.69	1.33	3.23	0.80	2.49	2.28	1.13	2.01	0.46	18.63
1948	0.77	1.60	0.87	2.44	1.05	4.57	4.10	0.79	0.87	0.53	0.87	0.37	18.83
1949	1.24	0.53	0.36	0.02	3.54	2.71	4.95	1.19	0.36	2.76	0.79	1.31	19.76
1950	1.36	0.26	2.21	1.79	4.99	2.29	0.42	0.42	1.54	0.99	0.50	0.60	17.37
1951	0.45	0.72	0.85	0.46	1.63	2.36	3.77	5.64	0.79	1.69	0.70	2.19	21.25
1952	1.07	0.30	0.68	0.24	0.47	2.03	8.42	2.69	0.15	0.08	1.67	0.47	18.27
#1953	0.37	0.57	0.46	2.94	3.44	5.23	1.08	2.94	0.75	0.32	0.77	0.70	19.57
1954	0.47	0.03	0.65	1.13	0.81	1.46	2.34	2.60	2.68	0.59	0.17	0.25	13.18
1955	0.18	0.97	0.63	0.48	1.81	2.62	6.86	1.11	1.27	0.34	0.70	0.47	17.44
1956	0.72	0.18	0.91	1.45	1.63	2.85	3.58	1.75	0.83	1.14	1.60	0.31	16.95
1957	0.31	0.23	0.08	1.90	2.00	5.47	4.72	1.68	6.13	1.64	0.82	0.05	25.03
1958	0.16	0.15	0.03	1.39	1.41	5.08	5.74	3.93	0.71	0.72	1.58	0.04	20.94
1959	0.13	0.20	0.08	0.66	1.88	4.78	4.26	3.02	0.77	1.61	0.31	0.53	18.23
1960	0.17	0.06	0.11	3.62	1.71	1.82	2.40	3.91	1.26	1.34	1.63	1.01	19.04
1961	0.09	0.18	0.38	2.27	2.71	1.36	3.00	1.02	4.44	1.70	0.06	0.57	17.78
1962	1.07	0.97	1.08	1.51	5.95	2.78	5.92	3.25	2.42	0.86	0.54	0.30	26.65
1963	0.13	0.33	0.51	2.67	2.61	1.69	0.66	4.41	1.19	0.23	0.12	0.39	14.94
1964	0.54	0.27	0.92	3.76	0.87	4.85	0.77	2.85	1.70	0.10	0.72	0.91	18.26
1965	0.10	0.14	1.36	3.04	3.06	3.10	4.81	2.55	3.50	0.55	0.79	1.01	24.01
1966	0.40	0.26	1.92	1.78	1.27	2.91	4.01	3.80	0.54	1.40	0.18	0.50	18.97
1967	1.03	0.21	0.34	4.14	1.00	2.54	0.60	0.41	0.31	1.06	0.04	1.36	13.04
1968	0.37	0.27	1.29	4.09	2.08	3.94	1.49	1.61	2.23	1.75	0.37	1.11	20.60
1969	1.27	0.46	0.54	1.55	2.36	2.03	5.92	0.38	1.55	1.51	0.14	0.81	18.52
1970	0.10	0.20	1.52	2.30	2.83	2.63	0.43	1.24	3.61	1.61	0.96	0.47	17.90
1971	0.81	0.34	0.56	1.10	2.68	3.51	2.80	0.92	4.30	4.42	0.83	0.59	22.86
1972	0.94	0.61	0.74	0.96	3.52	0.58	2.78	3.45	1.22	1.25	0.22	1.51	17.78
1973	0.12	0.13	1.25	0.70	1.65	1.78	3.60	3.85	4.98	1.54	0.90	1.02	21.52
1974	0.35	0.36	0.71	3.40	4.03	0.90	4.75	6.46	0.13	3.10	0.48	0.32	24.99
1975	1.32	0.27	1.48	3.24	1.45	9.40	2.42	2.90	1.24	1.76	0.64	0.18	26.30
RECORD MEAN	0.62	0.60	0.88	2.04	2.47	3.46	3.18	2.84	1.98	1.48	0.83	0.67	21.05

Record mean values above are means through the current year for the period beginning in 1881 for temperature and precipitation, 1943 for snowfall. Data are from city locations through January 1942.

Station: CINCINNATI, OHIO
ABBE OBSERVATORY
Elevation (ground): 761 feet

TEMPERATURES °F

Month	Normal Daily maximum	Normal Daily minimum	Normal Monthly	Extremes Record highest	Year	Record lowest	Year
(a)				59		59	
J	39.8	24.3	32.1	77	1950	-17	1936
F	42.9	25.8	34.4	77	1972	-9	1951
M	52.2	33.5	42.9	88	1929	3	1943
A	65.5	44.6	55.1	90	1925	18	1923
M	75.2	53.6	64.4	95	1937	28	1966
J	83.6	62.5	73.1	102	1944	40	1972
J	86.6	65.8	76.2	109	1934	48	1972
A	86.0	64.1	75.1	103	1936	43	1915
S	79.8	57.0	68.4	101	1954	32	1942
O	68.8	46.7	57.8	92	1951	20	1925
N	53.0	36.2	44.6	83	1950	1	1929
D	41.8	27.1	34.4	71	1956	-13	1917
YR	64.6	45.1	54.9	109	JUL 1934	-17	JAN 1936

IMPORTANT:
The time-period covered by this record is limited: See footnotes following table of **NORMALS, MEANS AND EXTREMES** for explanation and for additional history of **EXTREME HIGHS AND LOWS** recorded in the general area.

Snowfall

Season	July	Aug	Sept	Oct	Nov	Dec	Jan
1935-36	0.0	0.0	0.0	0.0	T	9.7	9.9
1936-37	0.0	0.0	0.0	0.0	8.9	1.2	6.0
1937-38	0.0	0.0	0.0	T	2.7	4.6	3.6
1938-39	0.0	0.0	0.0	0.0	3.5	0.2	6.5
1939-40	0.0	0.0	0.0	0.0	T	6.2	7.6
1940-41	0.0	0.0	0.0	0.0	0.4	T	4.0
1941-42	0.0	0.0	0.0	0.0	T	T	5.3
1942-43	0.0	0.0	0.0	0.0	0.0	15.5	2.9
1943-44	0.0	0.0	0.0	0.0	0.2	8.8	T
1944-45	0.0	0.0	0.0	0.0	3.0	8.2	9.9
1945-46	0.0	0.0	0.0	0.0	1.7	8.5	1.1
1946-47	0.0	0.0	0.0	0.0	0.0	4.0	3.4
1947-48	0.0	0.0	0.0	0.0	T	0.7	9.1
1948-49	0.0	0.0	0.0	0.0	T	2.3	3.3
1949-50	0.0	0.0	0.0	0.0	0.4	0.3	0.9
1950-51	0.0	0.0	0.0	0.0	8.9	6.0	12.1
1951-52	0.0	0.0	0.0	T	3.7	8.4	1.2
1952-53	0.0	0.0	0.0	T	2.9	5.0	3.7
1953-54	0.0	0.0	0.0	0.0	1.7	3.6	3.2
1954-55	0.0	0.0	0.0	T	0.3	3.9	11.2
1955-56	0.0	0.0	0.0	0.0	5.1	1.8	15.5
1956-57	0.0	0.0	0.0	0.0	4.0	1.5	5.5
1957-58	0.0	0.0	0.0	0.3	0.3	4.0	4.6
1958-59	0.0	0.0	0.0	0.0	8.8	3.1	7.3
1959-60	0.0	0.0	0.0	0.0	1.3	2.4	0.3
1960-61	0.0	0.0	0.0	0.0	T	11.6	7.0
1961-62	0.0	0.0	0.0	0.0	1.5	8.1	4.4
1962-63	0.0	0.0	0.0	T	0.4	2.1	9.3
1963-64	0.0	0.0	0.0	0.0	0.4	7.4	15.4
1964-65	0.0	0.0	0.0	0.0	1.3	T	8.1
1965-66	0.0	0.0	0.0	0.0	T	1.2	5.0
1966-67	0.0	0.0	0.0	0.0	10.2	1.0	2.0
1967-68	0.0	0.0	0.0	0.0	1.0	1.6	7.6
1968-69	0.0	0.0	0.0	0.0	T	1.1	0.5
1969-70	0.0	0.0	0.0	0.0	0.8	5.5	4.5
1970-71	0.0	0.0	0.0	0.0	0.2	T	2.1
1971-72	0.0	0.0	0.0	0.0	1.0	0.0	1.4
1972-73	0.0	0.0	0.0	0.0	5.8	1.2	T
1973-74	0.0	0.0	0.0	0.0	0.0		
RECORD MEAN	0.0	0.0	0.0	0.1	1.6	3.9	5.1

Heating Degree Days

Season	July	Aug	Sept	Oct	Nov	Dec	Jan
1955-56	0	0	15	258	702	993	1077
1956-57	0	3	79	131	633	678	1123
1957-58	0	0	41	358	603	784	1080
1958-59	2	1	41	259	527	1157	1088
1959-60	0	0	35	283	714	808	916
1960-61	0	0	14	242	551	1112	1135
1961-62	0	0	40	225	612	973	1123
1962-63	0	2	102	239	612	1098	1239
1963-64	0	1	43	76	519	1257	929
1964-65	0	12	60	339	510	903	1026
1965-66	0	8	48	299	551	742	1228
1966-67	0	1	74	359	600	947	894
1967-68	3	3	91	317	743	858	1153
1968-69	1	6	31	300	580	993	1100
1969-70	0	0	61	289	723	1066	1227
1970-71	5	0	27	213	621	853	1150
1971-72	0	0	29	80	602	729	1044
1972-73	11	1	27	361	696	878	969
1973-74	0	0	17	151	500	935	868
1974-75	0	0	111	286	554	862	878
1975-76	0	0	92	237	451	853	

Cooling Degree Days

Year	Jan	Feb	Mar	Apr	May	June	July
1969	0	0	0	11	108	234	392
1970	0	0	0	32	158	225	320
1971	0	0	0	0	41	334	296
1972	0	0	1	12	83	129	330
1973	0	0	5	19	17	279	336
1974	0	0	13	32	89	140	348
1975	0	0	0	7	166	275	349

The city of Cincinnati is located on the bank of the Ohio River in extreme southwestern Ohio. It extends over two ranges of hills bisected by the Mill Creek Valley, with hilltops extending some 400 feet above the valley floor. The City incorporates the lower portion of the Little Miami Valley to the east and extends to within 5 or 6 miles of the Greater Miami Valley to the west.

The climate is basically continental, with a wide range in temperature. Cincinnati is subjected to frequent changes in the weather due to the passage of numerous cyclonic storms in the winter and spring, and thunderstorms during the summer. The fall season of the year is very pleasant, with the least rainfall, an abundance of sunshine, and comfortable temperatures.

The length of the freeze-free period is 198 days on the average, with the average date of the last spring occurrence of 32° temperatures being on April 10, and the average date of the first occurrence in the fall on October 25.

The prevailing south to southwest winds on the western side of the Bermuda high during the summer months carry warm, moist air from the Gulf of Mexico up the Mississippi and Ohio valleys into the Cincinnati area, giving a high frequency of thunderstorms. Nearly one-third of the yearly precipitation occurs during these same months.

(Continued page 580)

Feb	Mar	Apr	May	June	Total
7.5	1.2	0.4	0.0	0.0	28.7
4.7	13.0	0.0	0.0	0.0	33.8
1.1	T	0.4	0.0	0.0	12.4
11.4	T	0.2	0.0	0.0	21.8
10.1	3.5	T	0.0	0.0	27.4
2.9	0.4	0.0	0.0	0.0	7.7
2.9	1.2	T	0.0	0.0	9.4
0.8	5.7	0.3	0.0	0.0	25.2
5.8	1.4	T	0.0	0.0	16.2
6.1	T	T	0.0	0.0	27.2
2.4	0.6	T	0.0	0.0	14.3
5.5	5.6	0.0	T	0.0	18.5
11.6	0.4	0.0	0.0	0.0	21.8
T	4.0	T	0.0	0.0	9.6
2.8	1.0	0.3	0.0	0.0	5.7
6.4	6.3	T	0.0	0.0	39.7
2.8	1.2	T	T	0.0	17.3
T	6.3	3.4	0.0	0.0	21.3
2.5	0.4	T	0.0	0.0	11.4
2.2	2.1	0.0	0.0	0.0	19.7
0.6	6.1	1.6	0.0	0.0	30.7
0.8	0.5	T	0.0	0.0	12.3
2.1	6.2	T	0.0	0.0	17.5
0.5	9.2	0.7	0.0	0.0	29.6
9.8	12.5	T	0.0	0.0	26.3
10.7	1.4	1.5	0.0	0.0	32.2
8.0	3.3	2.0	0.0	0.0	27.3
2.3	0.3	0.0	0.0	0.0	14.4
5.6	0.7	T	0.0	0.0	29.5
6.3	6.3	T	0.0	0.0	22.0
7.8	0.5	T	T	0.0	14.5
5.0	9.0	0.0	0.0	0.0	27.2
2.6	11.4	0.0	0.0	0.0	24.2
0.2	2.0	0.0	0.0	0.0	3.8
2.1	12.1	T	0.0	0.0	25.0
14.6	6.4	0.0	0.0	0.0	23.3
6.8	T	0.1	0.0	0.0	9.3
1.4	2.8	0.4	0.0	0.0	11.6
4.3	3.4	0.5	T	0.0	18.9

CINCINNATI, OH
ABBE OBSERVATORY

Feb	Mar	Apr	May	June	Total
765	680	430	126	29	5075
725	669	320	111	1	4473
1060	828	316	87	9	5166
798	702	272	70	5	4922
964	1056	245	183	1	5205
719	558	497	194	20	5042
853	744	376	33	5	4984
1053	546	288	131	7	5317
940	636	242	49	11	4703
867	850	296	22	0	4885
892	624	388	188	14	4982
1002	581	289	195	12	4954
1072	619	277	139	7	5282
858	815	293	82	29	5088
938	795	251	79	5	5434
890	756	370	153	0	5038
954	730	349	98	64	4679
834	407	397	152	0	4733
847	588	283	136	27	4352
748	736	437	42	5	4659

Aug	Sept	Oct	Nov	Dec	Total
286	108	26	0	0	1165
304	263	13	0	0	1315
253	200	49	1	0	1174
296	145	0	0	0	996
326	225	58	0	0	1265
326	63	10	3	0	1024
436	101	24	6	0	1364

Average Temperature

Year	Jan	Feb	Mar	Apr	May	June	July	Aug	Sept	Oct	Nov	Dec	Annual
1936	25.2	26.8	46.8	49.2	66.8	74.2	81.7	80.1	71.4	56.6	40.1	37.7	54.7
1937	38.6	33.4	38.3	52.7	63.2	72.7	75.3	76.8	65.4	53.7	41.6	32.0	53.6
1938	32.4	40.5	49.1	56.4	63.6	70.7	76.2	76.2	68.6	58.0	47.3	36.4	56.3
1939	37.7	35.4	45.2	50.7	66.5	74.0	75.0	74.6	73.5	59.0	42.8	37.4	56.0
1940	19.0	32.9	40.1	50.1	60.4	73.0	76.2	76.2	65.8	59.9	43.9	39.8	53.1
1941	32.8	30.4	37.2	59.2	66.9	73.0	77.4	75.5	71.8	61.6	46.2	39.3	55.9
1942	31.3	30.4	45.8	57.0	64.4	73.0	77.0	73.5	66.4	57.3	46.8	31.2	54.5
1943	34.4	35.6	39.8	49.8	64.8	77.0	77.4	76.2	65.9	56.1	42.5	32.2	54.3
1944	36.2	37.9	40.4	53.6	70.8	76.9	78.0	76.6	67.9	56.6	44.8	29.2	55.7
1945	26.1	34.4	54.6	56.3	60.0	70.2	74.0	74.4	71.0	55.8	45.9	28.5	54.3
1946	34.4	37.4	54.7	55.6	61.8	72.5	74.9	70.2	68.9	59.8	49.9	39.2	56.6
1947	38.2	26.6	36.3	54.1	61.4	70.9	71.9	80.2	69.1	64.5	41.5	36.1	54.2
1948	24.9	35.0	46.5	58.0	62.4	73.5	76.8	75.1	70.5	54.2	48.8	38.3	55.3
1949	39.4	40.2	45.0	52.5	65.9	75.7	80.0	76.0	63.3	62.0	45.9	39.9	57.3
1950	41.9	36.5	40.1	50.1	65.5	71.0	73.9	72.5	66.4	61.5	39.2	28.9	54.0
1951	34.3	34.9	42.2	52.5	66.0	72.7	76.5	75.8	66.8	59.2	38.7	35.5	54.6
1952	37.7	37.7	43.3	54.7	63.5	77.8	78.7	74.8	67.9	52.1	46.5	37.6	56.0
1953	37.6	39.6	45.9	50.8	67.0	76.0	76.7	76.4	69.9	60.0	46.1	36.1	56.8
1954	35.2	42.7	41.0	60.9	59.8	74.7	77.9	74.6	71.9	58.0	44.3	34.8	56.3
1955	31.3	35.6	45.0	59.6	65.7	68.5	79.6	78.0	70.7	56.8	41.6	32.7	55.4
1956	30.0	38.4	42.9	50.9	64.1	72.6	75.0	74.6	65.2	61.1	43.7	43.0	55.1
1957	28.6	38.9	43.2	56.9	64.5	73.9	76.8	74.8	68.2	53.3	44.7	39.5	55.3
1958	29.9	26.9	38.2	54.8	63.9	69.8	75.2	74.0	67.9	57.3	47.5	27.4	52.7
1959	29.7	36.3	42.1	56.4	68.4	73.5	77.3	80.0	71.9	57.5	41.0	38.7	56.1
1960	35.3	31.4	30.8	58.8	61.4	71.3	74.4	76.7	70.7	57.5	46.4	28.9	53.7
1961	28.1	39.1	46.8	48.5	59.3	70.0	75.5	74.5	72.1	58.1	44.6	33.4	54.2
1962	28.6	34.3	40.8	53.9	70.8	73.0	75.1	75.5	64.7	59.1	44.3	29.4	54.1
1963	24.7	27.2	47.2	56.6	62.4	72.5	75.4	72.6	67.6	64.3	47.5	24.4	53.5
1964	34.9	32.4	44.2	57.3	67.4	74.0	76.3	75.0	68.6	53.9	47.8	35.7	55.6
1965	31.8	33.8	37.3	55.3	70.4	73.5	74.8	74.4	69.1	55.7	46.5	40.9	55.3
1966	25.2	32.9	44.9	52.1	60.2	73.1	78.7	74.1	65.5	53.3	44.7	34.2	53.2
1967	36.0	29.0	46.5	56.7	60.0	73.2	73.1	71.9	64.9	55.5	40.1	37.1	53.7
1968	27.6	27.8	44.9	55.8	61.3	73.3	76.1	75.5	67.5	56.5	45.6	32.8	53.7
1969	29.3	34.2	38.5	55.5	65.5	71.6	77.4	74.0	66.3	56.3	40.7	30.4	53.3
1970	25.1	31.4	39.1	57.5	67.3	72.2	74.9	74.6	72.7	58.3	44.1	37.3	54.6
1971	27.7	33.0	40.4	52.4	61.2	75.9	74.3	72.9	70.5	63.8	44.8	41.3	54.9
1972	31.2	31.9	41.3	53.6	64.4	66.9	75.1	74.3	68.8	53.1	41.6	36.5	53.2
1973	33.5	34.9	51.8	52.2	60.4	74.1	75.7	75.3	71.8	61.9	48.1	34.6	56.2
1974	36.8	34.6	46.2	56.4	63.3	68.5	76.0	75.3	63.2	55.9	46.3	36.9	55.0
1975	36.6	38.0	41.0	50.4	68.8	73.8	76.0	78.8	65.1	57.9	49.9	37.2	56.1
RECORD MEAN	31.9	34.3	43.0	53.9	63.7	72.6	76.2	74.9	68.1	57.3	44.5	34.7	54.6
MAX	39.9	42.6	52.4	64.1	74.3	83.0	86.7	85.6	78.6	68.1	52.8	42.0	64.2
MIN	23.8	26.0	33.6	43.6	53.1	62.1	65.7	64.2	57.5	46.5	36.1	27.4	45.0

# Indicates a station move or relocation of instruments.

Precipitation

Year	Jan	Feb	Mar	Apr	May	June	July	Aug	Sept	Oct	Nov	Dec	Annual
1936	1.28	2.04	2.55	3.11	1.04	0.80	0.84	4.32	3.71	4.45	3.95	2.60	30.69
1937	13.68	1.33	1.06	2.93	2.93	3.66	3.94	3.30	2.08	3.03	1.64	3.65	43.23
1938	1.68	2.25	6.54	2.07	6.57	2.29	6.98	4.02	3.80	0.31	4.03	1.41	41.95
1939	3.77	4.27	6.93	7.35	2.41	6.29	2.76	2.16	0.71	2.18	0.85	1.41	41.09
1940	1.27	3.71	3.32	7.31	3.97	3.87	0.33	2.40	1.23	0.92	4.02	2.38	34.73
1941	2.06	0.64	1.13	1.37	0.85	5.81	3.47	2.19	1.88	4.38	1.53	2.70	28.01
1942	2.02	2.71	2.64	3.20	3.92	5.38	4.77	5.56	2.63	1.68	4.85	4.44	43.80
1943	1.23	1.76	6.46	2.66	5.08	3.50	4.58	1.65	1.65	1.36	0.72	1.39	32.04
1944	0.99	4.26	5.40	4.55	3.13	0.59	2.27	5.79	1.21	0.70	2.71	3.76	35.36
1945	1.58	5.42	10.94	5.10	3.14	7.26	1.67	1.25	4.43	1.98	4.14	2.05	48.96
1946	1.18	4.56	4.19	2.30	6.55	5.78	2.68	2.60	1.45	2.76	4.70	3.10	41.85
1947	4.90	0.48	1.38	8.62	5.99	3.76	3.62	1.99	2.75	1.96	2.61	1.21	39.27
1948	2.42	3.97	6.68	5.72	2.93	3.70	3.73	3.07	0.79	2.08	6.05	3.66	44.80
1949	9.22	2.99	3.94	1.84	1.33	6.10	4.40	2.75	1.94	2.71	0.68	3.11	41.01
1950	10.38	5.34	1.95	3.37	4.25	4.96	3.92	3.07	4.89	2.07	5.53	2.78	52.51
1951	5.99	2.79	3.98	2.46	2.91	3.15	2.03	0.59	2.68	2.61	4.42	6.03	39.64
1952	4.29	3.15	4.95	3.53	4.01	4.05	3.53	2.81	2.80	1.87	2.28	3.93	41.20
1953	4.58	1.09	2.70	2.95	4.61	1.66	3.78	1.20	0.72	1.17	1.30	1.70	27.46
1954	2.34	1.96	2.41	3.03	1.62	5.93	2.30	6.54	2.02	4.88	1.56	2.71	37.30
1955	2.63	6.24	5.01	2.92	3.97	1.73	5.74	4.14	5.86	4.70	4.22	0.56	47.72
1956	2.44	5.57	3.91	3.69	5.71	3.62	3.97	2.73	1.92	1.53	1.71	2.98	39.78
1957	3.21	2.97	1.13	7.74	5.53	6.31	4.91	5.03	3.67	2.01	5.83	5.60	53.94
1958	2.46	0.47	1.66	3.92	4.30	5.29	7.74	4.08	3.53	1.33	2.53	0.78	38.09
1959	8.32	2.71	2.54	2.12	3.76	4.16	2.01	2.12	1.40	2.62	3.98	3.06	38.80
1960	2.85	3.51	1.32	1.36	3.42	5.89	4.97	5.61	1.42	2.94	2.27	2.32	37.88
1961	1.80	4.07	5.57	3.48	6.46	3.58	6.06	1.92	2.06	1.61	3.87	3.39	43.87
1962	3.90	5.68	4.10	0.91	5.02	2.00	7.06	1.92	2.20	3.69	2.13	1.56	40.17
1963	2.03	0.91	9.83	2.35	4.79	1.22	3.99	2.44	0.54	0.10	0.80	0.95	29.95
1964	2.95	1.56	11.49	6.96	1.06	6.58	1.67	1.99	2.35	0.71	2.61	4.39	44.31
1965	4.19	5.33	3.16	5.96	0.74	1.63	3.60	2.94	7.48	3.87	1.85	1.16	41.91
1966	3.57	3.17	1.31	5.70	2.23	1.54	1.94	2.85	4.66	0.63	4.27	3.31	35.18
1967	0.64	1.75	3.72	3.20	6.27	1.84	2.84	0.65	1.67	2.41	3.68	3.81	32.48
1968	1.72	0.45	4.24	3.67	10.22	1.50	8.37	4.22	3.00	1.39	3.71	3.73	46.22
1969	4.70	1.25	1.54	3.95	2.59	3.77	3.82	2.62	3.47	1.75	3.91	2.47	35.84
1970	1.42	1.66	4.66	6.85	2.38	5.18	3.21	4.39	3.55	2.54	2.00	3.55	41.39
1971	2.27	5.75	2.34	1.57	3.58	2.58	2.85	3.15	8.68	1.66	1.63	3.45	39.51
1972	2.02	1.72	3.61	6.36	6.53	2.50	1.70	2.16	4.19	2.78	5.73	4.12	43.42
1973	1.85	1.33	6.11	6.26	3.23	8.12	8.47	1.14	1.33	3.79	4.46	2.57	48.66
1974	3.13	1.57	3.20	3.90	4.83	2.69	0.74	6.22	5.12	1.20	3.61	2.38	38.59
1975	3.02	3.15	5.78	2.79	1.68	3.40	1.54	3.67	3.73	4.57	2.49	3.24	39.06
RECORD MEAN	3.35	2.56	4.03	3.77	3.81	3.83	3.73	3.26	3.05	2.37	2.98	2.88	39.62

Record mean values above are means through the current year for the period beginning in 1915 for temperature and precipitation, 1916 for snowfall.

(Continued)

Floods: - Due to the narrow Flood Plain, only a small percent of the City is subject to flooding. However, this small percent is highly commercialized, resulting in considerable loss during major flooding. The greatest flood on record occurred in January 1937, when the river was above flood stage (52 feet) 19 consecutive days, cresting at 80 feet on the 26th. Even then only 15 percent of the City was inundated. Since 1858 crests at flood or above have been recorded 78 times in 59 of the years of record, 33 of these being of major proportion (5 feet above flood stage). This gives an average major flood about once each three years.

Normals, Means, and Extremes

Month	Normal Degree days Base 65 °F: Heating	Normal Degree days Base 65 °F: Cooling	Precipitation in inches, Water equivalent: Normal	Maximum monthly	Year	Minimum monthly	Year	Maximum in 24 hrs.	Year	Snow, Ice pellets $: Maximum monthly	Year	Maximum in 24 hrs.	Year	Relative humidity pct.: Hour (Local time)	Hour	Hour	Hour
(a)				59		59		59		57		57					
J	1020	0	3.40	13.68	1937	0.64	1967	4.53	1959	20.2	1918	9.6	1951				
F	857	0	2.95	6.24	1955	0.45	1968	2.43	1971	14.6	1971	7.6	1971				
M	692	7	4.13	11.49	1964	1.06	1937	4.63	1964	13.0	1937	9.3	1968				
A	307	10	3.85	8.62	1947	0.84	1915	3.43	1939	5.2	1920	4.2	1916				
M	118	100	3.96	10.22	1968	0.74	1965	4.77	1933	T	1966	T	1966				
J	7	250	3.92	9.07	1928	0.59	1944	3.46	1924	0.0		0.0					
J	0	347	3.96	10.02	1926	0.33	1940	4.07	1926	0.0		0.0					
A	0	313	3.02	6.54	1954	0.59	1951	3.48	1960	0.0		0.0					
S	37	139	2.69	8.68	1971	0.54	1963	3.74	1965	0.0		0.0					
O	245	22	2.20	9.51	1919	0.10	1963	2.15	1955	4.7	1925	2.5	1925				
N	612	0	3.08	6.46	1927	0.31	1917	2.99	1948	10.2	1966	8.9	1936				
D	949	0	2.87	6.94	1923	0.56	1955	3.34	1921	16.3	1917	11.0	1917				
YR	4844	1188	40.03	13.68	JAN 1937	0.10	OCT 1963	4.77	MAY 1933	20.2	JAN 1918	11.0	DEC 1917				

(To better understand these tables, see full explanation of terms beginning on page 322)

Month	Wind Ø: Mean speed m.p.h.	Prevailing direction	Fastest mile: Speed m.p.h.	Direction	Year	Pct. of possible sunshine	Mean sky cover, tenths, sunrise to sunset	Mean number of days, Sunrise to sunset: Clear	Partly cloudy	Cloudy	Precipitation .01 inch or more	Snow, Ice pellets 1.0 inch or more	Thunderstorms	Heavy fog, visibility ¼ mile or less	Temperatures °F (b) Max.: 90° and above	Max.: 32° and below	Min.: 32° and below	Min.: 0° and below	Average station pressure mb. Elev. feet m.s.l.
(a)	43	40	53	53		59					59	58	49		59	59	59	59	
J	8.3	SW	49	SW	1959	41					12	2	1		0	9	23	1	
F	8.4	SW	49	SW	1918	45					11	2	1		0	6	21	*	
M	9.0	SW	49	SW	1922	51					13	1	3		0	2	16	0	
A	8.4	SW	47	SW	1920	55					13	*	4		*	*	3	0	
M	6.7	SW	36	W	1945	61					12	0	7		1	0	*	0	
J	6.4	SW	40	W	1934	67					13	0	9		5	0	0	0	
J	5.2	SW	43	SW	1928	68					10	0	10		10	0	0	0	
A	5.1	SW	38	W	1944	67					9	0	7		8	0	0	0	
S	5.4	SW	38	SW	1941	66					9	0	4		4	0	*	0	
O	6.1	SW	35	SW	1937	59					9	*	2		*	0	2	0	
N	7.7	SW	47	SW	1919	44					10	1	1		0	1	11	0	
D	7.9	SW	41	SW	1920	38					11	1	*		0	6	22	*	
YR	7.1	SW	49	SW	JAN 1959	57					132	6	50		28	23	98	2	

Ø Wind observation record at Abbe Observatory began April 1, 1915;
transferred to Lunken Airport January 2, 1946; transferred to Federal Building March 6, 1947;
transferred back to Abbe Observatory April 18, 1951.
Wind record for 6 years through 1951 not used due to poor instrumental exposure.

Station: CLEVELAND, OHIO
CLEVELAND HOPKINS INTL AP
Elevation (ground): 777 feet

TEMPERATURES °F

Month	Normal			Extremes			
	Daily maximum	Daily minimum	Monthly	Record highest	Year	Record lowest	Year
(a)				15		15	
J	33.4	20.3	26.9	68	1967	-19	1963
F	35.0	20.8	27.9	69	1961	-15	1963
M	44.1	28.1	36.1	80	1967	4	1974
A	58.0	38.5	48.3	85	1962	10	1964
M	68.4	48.1	58.3	91	1962	25	1966
J	78.2	57.5	67.9	95	1971	31	1972
J	81.6	61.2	71.4	98	1965	41	1968
A	80.4	59.6	70.0	95	1975	41	1965
S	74.2	53.5	63.9	93	1973	34	1961
O	63.6	43.9	53.8	86	1963	22	1969
N	48.8	34.4	41.6	79	1961	13	1970
D	36.4	24.1	30.3	69	1971	-4	1963
YR	58.5	40.8	49.7	98	JUL 1965	-19	JAN 1963

IMPORTANT:
The time-period covered by this record is limited: See footnotes on next page for explanation and for additional history of EXTREME HIGHS AND LOWS recorded in the general area.

Cleveland is on the south shore of Lake Erie which has an average level of 572 feet above mean sea level. Metropolitan Cleveland has a lake frontage of 31 miles and it reaches inland about 16 miles with a total area of about 250 square miles, or a little more than half of Cuyahoga County. The surrounding terrain is mostly level except for a ridge on the southeastern edge of the City rising some 500 feet above the shore terrain. A rather deep but narrow North-South valley, in which flows the Cuyahoga River, approximately bisects the city of Cleveland. The climate is mainly continental in character, but with strong modifying influences by Lake Erie. Otherwise, local topography is of minor importance as a determining factor.

The National Weather Service Office is located at Cleveland Hopkins International Airport, 10 miles southwest of the downtown business area and about 5 miles south of the lake shoreline where the official weather records have been maintained since 1941. Records since 1871 were previously made in downtown Cleveland as designated on the last page of this publication. Comparative records show that daytime temperatures average from 2° to 4° higher at the Airport except during the winter months and that nighttime temperatures average from 2° to 4° lower at the Airport during all seasons. Differences as much as 12° have occurred on some individual days. Precipitation differences between the two locations are slight.

In the winter, Cleveland lies in the path of many cold airmasses advancing south and east from Canada, but the accompanying low temperatures are usually mitigated by such air having to cross the relatively warm waters of the lake. Such a combination, however, despite the ameliorating temperature effects of the lake, results in an excessive amount of winter cloudiness and quite frequent snows. The persistence of snow cover is seldom great, though, since the temperature rarely remains freezing for any considerable length of time.

Spring is generally a brief and rather sporadic transition season, the noticeable change being rather from wintry to summerlike conditions in a relatively short period. The possibility of a temperature of 32° or below remains until early June, although the average latest date is April 21.

In summer, Lake Erie plays its winter role in reverse; when sections further inland are experiencing heat waves, the "lake breeze" frequently sets in locally and sections near the shore enjoy its cooling effect which is noticeable for a considerable distance inland.

Autumn is usually the most pleasant season of the year, with mild, sunny weather often being prolonged into November and even December. The average date of the first temperature of 32° or below is November 2, and the average growing season is 195 days, considerably longer than for most locations in this latitude, or in Ohio.

Precipitation is moderate in amount and evenly distributed throughout the year, while humidity is moderately high. During excessively heavy rains in summer thunderstorms maximum falls have reached 1.20 inches in 10 minutes; 2.21 inches in one hour; 3.02 inches in two hours; and 4.97 inches in 24 hours. Much heavier falls have occurred in the elevated sections of the eastern suburbs. Although tornadoes are fairly common in Ohio, only five have occurred within Cleveland city limits since records began in 1870. Several additional tornadoes have occurred in the Cleveland suburbs during this period. Most damaging winds occur during summer thundersqualls.

CLEVELAND, OHIO

Normals, Means, and Extremes

(To better understand these tables, see full explanation of terms beginning on page 322)

Month	Normal Degree days Base 65 °F: Heating	Normal Degree days: Cooling	Precipitation in inches, Water equivalent: Normal	Maximum monthly	Year	Minimum monthly	Year	Maximum in 24 hrs.	Year	Snow, Ice pellets: Maximum monthly	Year	Maximum in 24 hrs.	Year	Relative humidity pct. Hour 01 (Local time)	Hour 07	Hour 13	Hour 19	Wind: Mean speed m.p.h.	Prevailing direction	Fastest mile: Speed m.p.h.	Direction	Year	Pct. of possible sunshine	Mean sky cover, tenths, sunrise to sunset	Mean number of days, Sunrise to sunset: Clear	Partly cloudy	Cloudy	Precipitation .01 inch or more	Snow, Ice pellets 1.0 inch or more	Thunderstorms	Heavy fog, visibility ¼ mile or less	Temperatures °F Max. (b) 90° and above	Max. 32° and below	Min. 32° and below	Min. 0° and below	Average station pressure mb. Elev. 805 feet m.s.l.
(a)				34		34		34		34		34		15	15	15	15	34	14	34	34		34	34	34	34	34	34	34	34	34	15	15	15	15	3
J	1181	0	2.56	7.01	1950	0.36	1961	2.33	1959	18.7	1945	9.3	1952	73	76	69	71	12.5	SW	68	SW	1959	32	8.1	3	5	23	16	4	*	2	0	15	27	3	988.9
F	1039	0	2.18	4.64	1950	0.73	1963	2.33	1959	20.7	1942	10.6	1973	74	77	68	71	12.3	S	65	W	1956	37	7.9	3	5	20	15	4	1	2	0	13	25	2	987.9
M	896	0	3.05	6.07	1954	0.78	1958	2.76	1948	26.3	1954	14.9	1954	74	77	65	70	12.5	W	74	W	1948	44	7.5	4	7	20	16	3	2	2	0	6	22	0	985.9
A	501	0	3.49	6.61	1961	1.18	1946	2.24	1961	14.5	1943	7.6	1957	71	75	57	61	11.9	S	65	W	1951	53	7.0	5	8	17	14	1	4	1	0	*	10	0	986.4
M	244	37	3.49	6.04	1947	1.00	1963	3.73	1955	2.1	1974	2.1	1974	75	77	58	59	10.4	S	68	SW	1957	59	6.6	6	10	15	13	*	5	1	*	0	1	0	984.4
J	40	127	3.28	9.06	1972	1.17	1967	4.00	1972	0.0		0.0		80	79	59	62	9.5	S	57	SW	1958	65	6.0	7	11	12	11	0	7	1	2	0	*	0	985.9
J	9	208	3.45	6.47	1969	1.23	1952	2.87	1969	0.0		0.0		81	82	57	61	8.7	S	65	W	1956	68	5.5	9	12	10	10	0	6	1	3	0	0	0	987.4
A	17	172	3.00	8.96	1975	0.53	1969	3.07	1947	0.0		0.0		83	85	60	66	8.4	S	61	W	1956	64	5.4	9	12	10	9	0	5	1	2	0	0	0	989.1
S	95	62	2.80	6.37	1945	0.74	1964	2.26	1969	T	1970	T	1970	81	84	61	69	9.1	S	45	S	1953	60	5.8	9	9	12	10	0	3	1	1	0	0	0	989.6
O	354	7	2.57	9.50	1954	0.61	1952	3.44	1954	8.0	1962	6.7	1962	77	80	59	68	10.0	S	43	W	1946	55	5.9	9	8	14	10	*	2	1	0	0	3	0	991.0
N	702	0	2.76	6.44	1950	0.92	1964	2.23	1958	22.3	1950	15.0	1950	76	78	67	72	12.1	S	59	W	1948	31	7.9	3	6	21	15	2	1	1	0	1	11	0	988.3
D	1076	0	2.36	5.60	1951	0.71	1958	2.06	1974	30.3	1962	12.2	1974	75	76	71	73	12.3	S	49	SW	1971	26	8.3	2	6	23	16	4	*	1	0	11	24	*	988.6
YR	6154	613	34.99	9.50	OCT 1954	0.36	JAN 1961	4.00	JUN 1972	30.3	DEC 1962	15.0	NOV 1950	77	79	63	67	10.8	S	74	W	MAR 1948	52	6.8	69	99	197	156	18	36	13	8	45	124	5	987.8

FOOTNOTES

Means and extremes above are from existing and comparable exposures. Annual extremes have been exceeded at other sites in the locality as follows: Highest temperature 103 in July 1941; maximum monthly precipitation 9.77 in June 1902; minimum monthly precipitation 0.17 in August 1881; maximum precipitation in 24 hours 4.97 in September 1901; maximum monthly snowfall 30.5 in February 1908; maximum snowfall in 24 hours 17.4 in November 1913; fastest mile of wind 78 from Southwest in May 1940.

Snowfall

Season	July	Aug	Sept	Oct	Nov	Dec	Jan
1936-37	0.0	0.0	0.0	T	14.3	4.3	5.3
1937-38	0.0	0.0	0.0	1.0	6.0	4.1	8.9
1938-39	0.0	0.0	0.0	0.0	6.7	7.8	12.7
1939-40	0.0	0.0	0.0	T	0.4	3.9	17.1
#1940-41	0.0	0.0	0.0	T	3.9	6.0	15.2
1941-42	0.0	0.0	0.0	0.0	0.5	3.1	5.6
1942-43	0.0	0.0	T	T	3.5	9.4	11.8
1943-44	0.0	0.0	0.0	T	5.8	6.9	4.8
1944-45	0.0	0.0	0.0	0.0	3.9	28.9	18.7
1945-46	0.0	0.0	0.0	T	1.3	18.2	6.1
1946-47	0.0	0.0	0.0	0.0	T	8.8	10.7
1947-48	0.0	0.0	0.0	0.0	4.2	3.4	12.0
1948-49	0.0	0.0	0.0	T	T	5.7	7.1
1949-50	0.0	0.0	0.0	0.0	16.0	7.6	3.7
1950-51	0.0	0.0	0.0	0.0	22.3	11.7	17.5
1951-52	0.0	0.0	0.0	T	18.8	22.1	9.3
1952-53	0.0	0.0	0.0	0.8	0.5	8.4	12.5
1953-54	0.0	0.0	0.0	T	8.4	6.0	13.2
1954-55	0.0	0.0	0.0	6.4	0.2	11.6	9.4
#1955-56	0.0	0.0	0.0	T	8.7	9.8	14.1
1956-57	0.0	0.0	0.0	0.0	7.4	11.4	12.8
1957-58	0.0	0.0	0.0	2.5	2.5	7.5	4.4
1958-59	0.0	0.0	0.0	T	7.4	9.7	14.0
1959-60	0.0	0.0	0.0	T	7.2	5.3	2.8
1960-61	0.0	0.0	0.0	T	4.7	14.1	6.0
1961-62	0.0	0.0	0.0	T	0.9	4.3	6.0
1962-63	0.0	0.0	0.0	8.0	T	30.3	12.4
1963-64	0.0	0.0	0.0	0.0	0.1	14.1	16.9
1964-65	0.0	0.0	0.0	T	1.0	8.7	13.6
1965-66	0.0	0.0	0.0	T	1.2	1.2	15.3
1966-67	0.0	0.0	0.0	0.0	8.8	10.9	2.0
1967-68	0.0	0.0	0.0	0.1	9.1	2.8	14.5
1968-69	0.0	0.0	0.0	T	6.8	8.3	5.8
1969-70	0.0	0.0	0.0	0.6	6.6	17.4	10.5
1970-71	0.0	0.0	T	T	5.2	6.0	8.6
1971-72	0.0	0.0	0.0	0.0	5.3	1.9	15.0
1972-73	0.0	0.0	0.0	5.5	7.8	15.2	9.8
1973-74	0.0	0.0	0.0	T	3.3	13.8	8.9
1974-75	0.0	0.0	0.0	1.6	5.3	24.1	9.7
1975-76	0.0	0.0	0.0	0.0	5.6	13.1	
RECORD MEAN	0.0	0.0	T	0.8	5.6	11.1	10.2

Heating Degree Days

Season	July	Aug	Sept	Oct	Nov	Dec	Jan
#1955-56	0	1	52	320	785	1127	1151
1956-57	4	13	159	198	665	828	1295
1957-58	0	6	97	403	656	891	1137
1958-59	0	21	86	316	608	1288	1261
#1959-60	0	0	78	348	769	894	1039
1960-61	38	7	67	427	671	1299	1336
1961-62	19	3	74	258	668	1085	1264
1962-63	10	17	151	331	674	1206	1452
1963-64	30	32	152	191	627	1326	1084
1964-65	3	46	117	483	617	1009	1165
1965-66	24	49	67	418	671	852	1328
1966-67	6	15	162	452	655	1063	1000
1967-68	21	19	137	351	784	934	1295
1968-69	26	34	93	414	672	1080	1220
1969-70	1	7	121	406	736	1166	1425
1970-71	9	12	86	332	696	1009	1344
1971-72	9	13	63	168	704	828	1160
1972-73	32	27	95	485	752	937	1067
1973-74	3	9	73	234	605	946	1015
1974-75	2	5	176	423	660	1026	1021
1975-76	5	4	187	345	532	1015	

Cooling Degree Days

Year	Jan	Feb	Mar	Apr	May	June	July
1969	0	0	0	10	41	120	237
1970	0	0	0	22	89	189	230
1971	0	0	0	0	22	198	158
1972	0	0	0	1	5	63	239
1973	0	0	0	13	7	168	244
1974	0	0	0	14	18	91	231
1975	0	0	0	0	75	187	206

Feb	Mar	Apr	May	June	Total
6.5	9.7	0.1	0.0	0.0	40.2
2.0	0.6	8.4	0.0	0.0	31.0
10.2	3.0	2.2	0.0	0.0	42.6
14.9	13.4	5.3	0.0	0.0	55.0
14.2	7.0	0.0	0.0	0.0	46.3
20.7	8.8	0.4	0.0	0.0	39.1
11.7	10.1	14.5	T	0.0	61.0
14.2	11.2	2.3	0.0	0.0	45.2
8.6	3.9	T	0.0	0.0	64.0
9.1	1.8	T	0.0	0.0	36.5
11.4	20.9	T	T	0.0	51.8
4.0	7.1	0.3	0.0	0.0	31.0
3.6	13.2	0.9	0.0	0.0	30.5
13.8	10.1	3.0	0.0	0.0	54.2
10.6	14.5	0.6	0.0	0.0	77.2
8.6	9.0	7.8	0.0	0.0	75.6
4.2	5.0	4.3	0.0	0.0	35.7
14.7	26.3	T	T	0.0	68.6
7.8	13.9	T	0.0	0.0	49.3
8.9	10.7	2.0	T	0.0	54.2
3.1	8.4	13.2	T	0.0	56.3
9.4	4.6	0.2	0.0	0.0	31.1
5.8	14.6	T	T	0.0	51.5
14.6	19.5	0.5	T	0.0	49.9
6.8	1.4	5.1	T	0.0	38.1
16.2	8.9	1.0	0.0	0.0	37.3
13.4	10.4	0.3	0.1	0.0	74.9
15.7	8.5	0.5	0.0	0.0	55.8
15.6	12.9	0.4	0.0	0.0	52.2
10.1	7.0	2.5	T	0.0	37.3
18.5	7.3	0.1	0.0	0.0	47.6
8.9	7.7	0.2	T	0.0	43.3
5.6	9.0	1.5	T	0.0	37.0
6.6	11.5	0.2	T	0.0	53.4
14.3	16.6	0.7	0.0	0.0	51.4
14.8	6.3	2.3	0.0	0.0	45.6
20.4	8.3	0.9	0.6	0.0	68.5
16.9	7.1	6.4	2.1	0.0	58.5
9.9	15.2	1.2	0.0	0.0	67.0
11.2	10.3	2.2	0.1	0.0	51.5

Average Temperature

Year	Jan	Feb	Mar	Apr	May	June	July	Aug	Sept	Oct	Nov	Dec	Annual
1936	23.8	21.0	39.5	44.3	62.6	66.2	74.6	73.8	68.0	54.2	39.0	36.4	50.3
1937	35.8	30.9	31.7	47.1	59.4	67.5	73.2	74.4	63.3	50.8	40.6	30.1	50.4
1938	29.0	33.8	43.6	50.3	59.4	68.0	73.6	75.0	63.4	56.4	46.6	33.5	52.7
1939	32.5	32.0	37.5	45.5	61.6	71.2	73.2	73.2	67.4	56.2	41.8	35.9	52.3
1940	19.6	28.5	31.0	43.2	56.0	69.0	73.8	71.6	63.0	54.0	41.8	36.7	49.0
#1941	29.6	26.6	30.5	52.0	62.2	70.6	75.2	70.7	67.8	56.4	43.2	36.9	51.8
1942	27.3	24.2	39.2	52.6	62.0	70.6	73.8	71.0	64.1	54.7	42.6	26.8	50.7
1943	26.8	29.0	36.1	43.2	58.1	73.7	74.0	71.8	62.6	51.8	39.3	28.4	49.6
1944	32.0	29.5	33.8	44.9	65.6	72.4	74.0	74.1	65.0	53.0	43.2	25.6	51.1
1945	18.8	29.4	48.6	52.0	54.1	66.6	71.7	72.0	66.9	51.8	43.2	25.2	50.0
1946	29.4	30.6	49.5	48.4	57.7	68.2	72.3	68.0	66.8	58.6	46.0	34.0	52.5
1947	32.7	22.6	31.8	46.8	56.2	67.0	70.0	77.8	66.6	61.4	38.2	31.5	50.2
1948	20.0	28.6	38.9	52.6	56.6	68.3	74.4	71.8	66.4	50.1	47.0	33.8	50.7
1949	34.8	34.2	37.1	47.4	61.8	73.9	77.6	73.4	60.0	59.2	41.3	34.2	52.9
1950	36.8	29.2	33.0	42.9	60.7	68.1	70.9	70.6	64.5	57.6	37.4	25.1	49.7
1951	29.9	29.9	38.1	46.8	60.9	69.1	73.6	70.3	62.9	57.8	35.7	30.4	50.5
1952	32.2	32.1	36.7	50.1	58.0	73.3	76.5	72.0	65.6	49.2	44.0	34.9	52.1
1953	33.6	33.7	40.0	45.5	61.9	71.5	74.4	73.5	65.6	57.4	45.2	34.1	53.0
1954	28.5	36.3	35.1	54.6	57.4	72.1	73.1	71.3	67.8	56.2	42.6	32.1	52.3
1955	26.9	30.8	38.6	55.9	62.7	67.9	79.1	76.1	67.2	54.8	38.7	28.4	52.3
#1956	27.6	31.3	36.0	45.9	57.8	68.7	71.7	71.7	61.2	58.7	42.7	38.0	50.9
1957	23.0	33.0	38.1	50.7	59.1	70.3	72.1	70.2	64.9	51.8	42.8	36.1	51.0
1958	28.2	23.2	35.5	51.4	58.7	64.4	73.5	70.4	64.9	55.1	44.5	23.3	49.4
1959	24.0	29.1	36.5	49.8	64.3	70.0	73.3	76.1	68.9	54.3	39.1	36.0	51.8
#1960	31.3	29.5	24.0	51.0	56.8	65.8	67.6	69.8	65.0	51.0	42.4	22.9	48.1
1961	21.6	31.6	40.0	43.4	54.3	65.0	71.3	70.9	68.5	56.8	42.5	29.7	49.7
1962	23.9	26.0	33.8	47.4	65.0	67.9	69.4	70.2	62.0	54.6	42.4	25.9	49.0
1963	18.0	17.5	39.1	48.4	54.7	67.8	71.3	66.7	60.3	59.4	43.9	21.9	47.4
1964	29.8	25.5	37.1	48.8	60.7	67.5	72.2	67.5	63.5	49.2	44.2	32.2	49.8
1965	27.2	28.0	31.7	45.6	63.2	66.9	69.0	68.7	67.4	51.3	42.5	37.4	49.9
1966	21.9	26.7	37.8	46.2	54.2	68.9	72.7	68.8	60.9	50.3	42.8	30.5	48.5
1967	32.4	25.9	37.2	49.7	52.3	71.7	69.7	68.8	61.7	54.0	38.6	34.7	49.7
1968	23.0	22.6	37.6	49.4	54.4	66.5	70.0	71.7	63.9	52.1	42.4	30.0	48.6
1969	25.4	27.9	34.3	49.4	58.6	65.5	72.4	71.8	63.6	51.9	40.2	27.2	49.0
1970	18.9	27.2	33.8	50.2	62.7	69.8	71.9	69.9	66.0	54.4	41.6	32.2	49.9
1971	21.4	27.9	31.6	43.2	56.5	71.0	69.5	68.9	67.7	59.9	41.4	38.1	49.8
1972	27.3	25.7	34.8	46.0	58.6	62.7	71.4	68.9	63.8	49.1	39.6	34.5	48.5
1973	30.4	27.9	46.5	50.2	56.7	70.4	72.6	73.2	66.3	57.7	44.6	34.3	52.6
1974	32.0	27.8	39.6	51.3	56.4	66.2	72.2	70.4	59.9	51.2	42.9	31.7	50.1
1975	31.9	30.4	34.6	41.8	62.3	69.8	71.3	72.3	58.6	53.8	47.0	32.0	50.5
RECORD MEAN	27.5	27.8	35.9	47.0	58.3	67.9	72.2	70.6	64.6	53.8	41.6	31.3	49.9
MAX	34.3	35.0	43.5	55.5	67.0	76.5	80.5	78.8	73.1	62.0	48.3	37.4	57.7
MIN	20.6	20.5	28.2	38.5	49.5	59.3	63.8	62.3	56.1	45.6	34.8	25.2	42.0

# Indicates a station move or relocation of instruments.

CLEVELAND, OH

Feb	Mar	Apr	May	June	Total
967	891	566	265	69	6194
891	825	471	221	29	5599
1164	907	413	218	73	5965
998	877	451	133	43	6082
1023	1262	430	265	58	6166
930	771	640	341	95	6622
1085	958	547	124	43	6128
1327	793	500	328	52	6841
1139	859	481	179	80	6180
1032	1025	576	130	64	6267
1067	837	562	346	53	6274
1087	858	461	393	17	6169
1224	845	459	328	59	6456
1032	946	471	234	100	6322
1052	960	462	154	39	6529
1032	1031	650	277	16	6494
1133	930	564	196	124	5892
1033	569	450	254	3	5704
1035	777	419	280	49	5445
962	934	691	154	38	6092

Aug	Sept	Oct	Nov	Dec	Total
223	84	10	0	0	725
171	121	10	0	0	832
143	152	19	0	0	692
157	64	0	0	0	529
273	119	17	0	0	841
180	30	3	2	0	569
241	6	5	0	0	720

Precipitation

Year	Jan	Feb	Mar	Apr	May	June	July	Aug	Sept	Oct	Nov	Dec	Annual
1936	1.41	2.19	3.28	2.18	2.05	2.32	2.23	2.92	2.75	1.78	3.32	1.64	28.07
1937	6.58	1.74	2.00	3.33	2.27	6.64	4.87	2.10	0.99	3.36	1.47	2.52	37.87
1938	1.07	3.01	3.52	2.70	2.69	2.45	3.28	0.81	6.17	0.70	3.31	1.72	31.43
1939	2.43	2.99	2.77	2.80	1.48	3.25	1.53	0.72	2.93	1.84	1.24	1.17	25.15
1940	1.35	3.24	2.59	3.95	3.60	3.68	0.96	3.82	1.83	1.39	2.19	4.07	32.67
#1941	1.85	1.35	1.28	1.13	2.41	2.79	3.34	3.23	1.49	3.22	1.11	1.76	24.96
1942	1.79	3.98	3.47	2.80	3.70	4.09	4.09	3.50	3.08	2.81	3.30	2.94	39.55
1943	1.88	2.50	2.95	3.43	4.64	4.02	5.37	2.50	3.53	3.40	1.21	1.02	36.45
1944	1.30	1.66	3.12	3.86	3.26	3.04	1.29	3.68	3.50	0.94	1.85	2.43	29.93
1945	1.21	1.67	4.13	3.66	3.61	4.41	3.11	1.61	6.37	4.20	1.86	1.36	37.20
1946	0.79	1.81	1.70	1.18	5.06	5.14	1.26	1.71	1.88	3.51	2.08	1.85	27.97
1947	4.44	0.75	4.15	4.38	6.04	6.07	4.69	5.19	2.51	1.92	2.01	1.84	43.99
1948	1.66	2.19	5.81	3.24	4.39	3.95	3.73	4.47	2.49	2.86	3.46	2.71	40.96
1949	3.61	2.39	2.66	2.78	4.18	1.63	4.21	3.59	2.87	1.04	2.73	3.30	34.99
1950	7.01	4.64	4.27	5.90	3.22	3.77	5.15	1.81	3.84	1.73	6.44	2.60	50.38
1951	3.72	3.79	4.80	2.69	2.60	3.25	3.47	2.43	4.49	1.53	5.85	5.60	44.22
1952	5.02	2.19	3.29	3.81	2.74	1.48	1.23	1.98	3.02	0.61	2.49	2.70	30.56
1953	4.04	1.21	2.05	2.82	4.00	3.30	3.08	3.87	1.57	1.28	2.32	2.62	32.16
1954	3.12	2.88	6.07	5.36	1.04	1.38	1.49	3.16	1.98	9.50	1.34	2.33	39.65
1955	2.22	2.69	5.59	3.72	5.00	2.68	2.50	3.82	1.61	5.88	2.87	0.96	39.54
#1956	2.75	3.23	4.60	3.61	5.49	4.14	3.74	5.14	1.56	0.85	1.14	2.70	38.95
1957	2.03	1.40	1.50	5.78	4.60	5.85	3.25	2.30	2.62	2.64	2.27	3.38	37.62
1958	1.49	0.96	0.78	3.31	2.14	4.67	4.82	3.98	3.62	1.63	4.76	0.71	32.87
1959	4.61	4.24	2.14	4.70	4.71	1.82	4.32	1.85	3.07	3.57	2.96	2.39	40.38
1960	2.33	1.87	2.06	2.78	3.56	3.01	3.33	6.95	1.84	1.02	2.07	1.09	31.91
1961	0.36	3.23	3.20	6.61	1.31	2.95	4.30	4.28	2.35	2.15	2.78	1.84	35.36
1962	2.83	1.85	1.73	1.78	1.91	2.95	3.42	1.30	4.39	3.60	2.77	3.05	31.58
1963	1.06	0.73	2.83	2.41	1.00	1.93	1.88	1.70	2.00	0.71	1.33	1.05	18.63
1964	1.45	1.49	5.21	4.87	3.02	2.06	3.37	3.82	0.74	1.78	0.92	2.67	31.40
1965	4.45	3.00	1.66	1.83	2.29	3.05	3.01	3.58	2.53	2.55	1.89	2.07	31.91
1966	1.53	2.31	2.26	3.61	2.21	1.83	3.89	3.48	1.66	1.18	5.16	2.84	31.96
1967	0.97	2.35	2.08	3.12	3.82	1.17	1.90	1.85	2.08	2.11	2.88	2.46	26.79
1968	3.27	0.79	2.07	2.25	4.08	2.32	3.58	1.82	3.36	2.90	4.35	3.94	34.73
1969	2.84	0.75	1.82	4.49	5.73	4.61	6.47	0.53	4.92	1.90	2.86	2.46	39.38
1970	1.28	1.35	2.37	2.64	2.95	4.98	4.14	0.92	3.16	3.98	3.69	2.25	33.66
1971	1.35	3.69	2.01	1.24	3.29	3.79	3.72	0.91	4.27	1.61	2.02	3.90	31.80
1972	1.95	2.01	2.97	3.40	3.74	9.06	4.44	6.38	4.91	1.64	4.58	3.26	48.34
1973	1.62	2.40	3.48	3.40	4.79	6.72	2.94	3.11	2.69	3.95	2.62	3.53	41.25
1974	2.56	2.43	3.88	3.64	4.78	3.57	1.90	3.29	3.06	1.19	4.72	4.86	39.88
1975	3.06	3.20	3.47	1.31	3.23	4.10	2.54	8.96	3.35	1.73	2.09	3.77	40.81
RECORD MEAN	2.53	2.35	2.86	2.79	3.16	3.32	3.39	2.97	3.10	2.59	2.64	2.45	34.15

Record mean values above are means through the current year for the period beginning in 1871 for temperature and precipitation, 1942 for snowfall. Data are from City Office locations through May 1941 and from Airport locations thereafter.

COLUMBUS, OHIO

Station: COLUMBUS, OHIO
PORT COLUMBUS INTL AIRPORT
Elevation (ground): 812 feet

TEMPERATURES °F

Month	Normal			Extremes			
	Daily maximum	Daily minimum	Monthly	Record highest	Year	Record lowest	Year
(a)				16		16	
J	36.4	20.4	28.4	68	1967	-15	1963
F	39.2	21.4	30.3	72	1961	-11	1963
M	49.3	29.1	39.2	80	1974	-2	1967
A	62.8	39.5	51.2	88	1960	18	1972
M	72.9	49.3	61.1	93	1975	25	1966
J	81.9	58.9	70.4	96	1966	35	1972
J	84.8	62.4	73.6	97	1966	43	1972
A	83.7	60.1	71.9	98	1964	39	1965
S	77.6	52.7	65.2	96	1964	31	1963
O	66.4	42.0	54.2	86	1963	20	1962
N	50.9	32.4	41.7	79	1961	11	1964
D	38.7	22.7	30.7	72	1971	-10	1963
YR	62.1	40.9	51.5	98	AUG 1964	-15	JAN 1963

IMPORTANT:
The time-period covered by this record is limited: See footnotes following table of NORMALS, MEANS AND EXTREMES for explanation and for additional history of EXTREME HIGHS AND LOWS recorded in the general area.

Columbus is located in the center of the state and in the drainage area of the Ohio River. The airport is located at the eastern boundary of the City approximately 7 miles from the center of the business district. The ground elevation of the airport is 812 feet above m.s.l.

Four nearly parallel streams run through or adjacent to the City. The Scioto River is the principal stream and flows from the northwest into the center of the City and then flows straight south toward the Ohio River. The Olentangy River runs almost due south and empties into the Scioto just west of the business district. Two minor streams run through portions of Columbus or skirt the eastern and southern fringes of the area. They are Alum Creek and Big Walnut Creek. Alum Creek empties into the Big Walnut southeast of the City and the Big Walnut empties into the Scioto a few miles downstream. The Scioto and Olentangy are gorge-like in character with very little flood plain and the two creeks have only a little more flood plain or bottomland.

The narrow valleys associated with the streams flowing through the City supply the only variation in the micro-climate of the area. The City proper shows the typical metropolitan effect with shrubs and flowers blossoming earlier than in the immediate surroundings and in retarding light frost on clear quiet nights. Many small areas to the southeast and to the north and northeast show marked effects of air drainage as evidenced by the frequent formation of shallow ground fog at daybreak during the summer and fall months and the higher frequency of frost in the spring and fall.

(Continued page 586)

Snowfall

Season	July	Aug	Sept	Oct	Nov	Dec	Jan
1936-37	0.0	0.0	0.0	0.0	3.6	3.8	4.2
1937-38	0.0	0.0	0.0	T	2.4	1.9	2.9
1938-39	0.0	0.0	0.0	0.0	1.7	0.3	6.9
1939-40	0.0	0.0	0.0	T	T	3.1	8.5
1940-41	0.0	0.0	0.0	0.0	0.3	0.1	6.4
1941-42	0.0	0.0	0.0	0.0	0.3	T	2.8
1942-43	0.0	0.0	0.0	T	2.0	8.0	5.5
1943-44	0.0	0.0	0.0	T	1.2	0.3	T
1944-45	0.0	0.0	0.0	0.0	T	4.2	6.0
1945-46	0.0	0.0	0.0	0.0	0.4	7.7	1.1
1946-47	0.0	0.0	0.0	0.0	0.0	2.4	1.7
#1947-48	0.0	0.0	0.0	0.0	0.4	6.2	13.5
1948-49	0.0	0.0	0.0	0.0	T	4.3	9.0
1949-50	0.0	0.0	0.0	0.0	T	0.7	0.2
1950-51	0.0	0.0	0.0	0.0	15.2	10.5	6.2
1951-52	0.0	0.0	0.0	T	1.9	13.7	2.7
1952-53	0.0	0.0	0.0	T	2.3	3.6	6.7
1953-54	0.0	0.0	0.0	0.0	3.0	5.3	4.5
1954-55	0.0	0.0	0.0	0.2	1.9	1.5	7.1
1955-56	0.0	0.0	0.0	T	5.1	2.9	11.4
1956-57	0.0	0.0	0.0	0.0	2.6	5.0	10.2
1957-58	0.0	0.0	0.0	T	T	8.5	2.3
1958-59	0.0	0.0	0.0	0.0	6.2	7.5	6.5
1959-60	0.0	0.0	0.0	0.0	3.5	5.5	0.5
1960-61	0.0	0.0	0.0	0.0	0.8	17.3	7.6
1961-62	0.0	0.0	0.0	0.0	1.3	8.8	3.9
1962-63	0.0	0.0	0.0	1.3	T	9.5	10.1
1963-64	0.0	0.0	0.0	0.0	1.2	7.3	12.3
1964-65	0.0	0.0	0.0	0.0	1.0	3.2	10.2
1965-66	0.0	0.0	0.0	0.0	0.2	1.1	7.6
1966-67	0.0	0.0	0.0	T	10.4	6.4	2.8
1967-68	0.0	0.0	T	T	6.5	5.2	11.6
1968-69	0.0	0.0	0.0	0.0	1.0	6.8	2.5
1969-70	0.0	0.0	0.0	0.0	1.8	9.7	18.4
1970-71	0.0	0.0	0.0	0.0	0.9	1.4	6.5
1971-72	0.0	0.0	0.0	0.0	5.0	0.6	5.8
1972-73	0.0	0.0	0.0	T	6.3	2.8	4.4
1973-74	0.0	0.0	0.0	0.0	T	6.4	2.3
1974-75	0.0	0.0	0.0	T	0.3	7.4	8.1
1975-76	0.0	0.0	0.0	0.0	1.1	2.9	
RECORD MEAN	0.0	0.0	T	0.1	2.8	5.9	7.0

Heating Degree Days

Season	July	Aug	Sept	Oct	Nov	Dec	Jan
1955-56	0	0	29	302	748	1075	1152
1956-57	0	8	114	173	651	745	1211
1957-58	0	0	73	413	640	867	1131
1958-59	1	7	68	326	632	1284	1201
#1959-60	0	0	62	336	758	878	950
1960-61	1	0	33	306	612	1229	1282
1961-62	2	2	60	297	689	1087	1249
1962-63	8	3	165	342	721	1236	1334
1963-64	6	14	93	174	603	1336	1076
1964-65	0	28	90	424	589	957	1132
1965-66	4	28	53	330	645	873	1325
1966-67	1	5	106	440	671	999	929
1967-68	7	23	164	406	843	942	1276
1968-69	6	20	57	362	624	1043	1173
1969-70	0	2	107	359	763	1175	1369
1970-71	10	0	58	297	674	944	1256
1971-72	3	5	52	181	733	815	1133
1972-73	22	18	77	473	727	889	1041
1973-74	0	3	35	219	589	963	977
1974-75	0	0	130	374	609	954	999
1975-76	0	0	110	321	520	973	

Cooling Degree Days

Year	Jan	Feb	Mar	Apr	May	June	July
1969	0	0	0	3	45	165	290
1970	0	0	0	22	125	166	281
1971	0	0	0	0	21	266	181
1972	0	0	0	1	24	67	245
1973	0	0	3	14	17	236	295
1974	0	0	4	20	58	117	296
1975	0	0	0	1	130	248	320

Feb	Mar	Apr	May	June	Total
1.3	2.3	T	0.0	0.0	15.2
3.4	2.1	T	0.0	0.0	12.7
9.2	T	0.2	0.0	0.0	18.3
10.4	4.3	0.4	T	0.0	26.7
3.2	0.6	0.0	0.0	0.0	10.6
0.6	1.2	T	0.0	0.0	4.9
1.1	4.4	0.8	0.0	0.0	21.8
8.8	3.2	0.1	0.0	0.0	13.6
0.6	T	T	0.0	0.0	10.8
0.5	T	0.2	0.0	0.0	9.9
5.4	3.3	0.0	T	0.0	12.8
10.1	0.8	0.0	0.0	0.0	31.0
0.2	3.9	T	0.0	0.0	17.4
2.4	2.0	1.0	T	0.0	6.3
5.6	4.9	T	0.0	0.0	42.4
4.1	1.3	T	0.0	0.0	23.7
0.8	3.9	4.5	0.0	0.0	21.8
5.7	5.5	0.9	T	0.0	24.9
7.7	3.9	T	0.0	0.0	22.3
0.8	7.6	0.6	0.0	0.0	28.4
3.0	3.4	0.8	T	0.0	25.0
4.8	5.9	T	0.0	0.0	21.5
1.8	5.1	0.1	0.0	0.0	27.2
9.7	10.8	T	0.0	0.0	30.0
13.1	0.7	2.7	0.0	0.0	42.2
8.8	13.5	1.1	0.0	0.0	37.4
8.7	2.4	T	0.0	0.0	32.0
11.3	2.9	T	0.0	0.0	35.0
7.6	8.6	T	0.0	0.0	30.6
6.7	1.2	0.7	T	0.0	17.5
15.6	11.4	0.0	0.0	0.0	46.6
2.8	6.1	T	0.0	0.0	32.2
2.5	1.9	0.5	0.0	0.0	15.2
3.2	10.3	0.9	0.0	0.0	44.3
12.3	12.3	T	0.0	0.0	33.4
6.6	5.0	0.6	0.0	0.0	23.6
1.8	2.1	7.1	0.0	0.0	24.5
5.0	4.5	0.3	0.0	0.0	18.5
3.7	2.6	T	0.0	0.0	22.1
5.9	5.2	0.8	T	0.0	27.7

Average Temperature

Year	Jan	Feb	Mar	Apr	May	June	July	Aug	Sept	Oct	Nov	Dec	Annual
1936	23.8	24.4	43.8	47.2	65.5	72.0	79.6	77.8	70.8	55.5	38.3	37.0	53.0
1937	37.8	32.3	36.6	51.1	62.5	71.6	75.1	76.6	65.0	52.6	40.2	31.0	52.7
1938	31.2	38.1	47.0	54.4	63.2	70.3	76.5	76.8	67.4	57.1	45.4	34.8	55.2
#1939	35.3	33.9	42.4	48.4	66.2	74.4	74.6	74.9	72.4	57.2	42.1	35.8	54.8
1940	15.6	30.0	36.1	46.6	57.8	71.0	74.5	74.0	62.7	55.1	40.2	36.8	50.0
1941	29.7	27.1	33.0	56.1	63.0	71.7	75.9	72.2	69.1	58.2	44.1	36.9	53.1
1942	27.8	27.1	42.3	54.0	62.7	71.7	75.3	71.9	65.1	55.6	43.7	27.2	52.0
1943	30.6	31.5	36.7	45.2	62.3	75.5	75.1	72.6	63.1	52.5	38.4	28.9	51.0
1944	32.2	33.2	36.6	49.5	68.1	73.7	75.7	75.0	65.5	53.5	42.3	25.5	52.6
1945	22.2	31.4	50.1	53.5	56.6	68.5	72.4	72.3	69.4	52.7	43.2	25.1	51.5
1946	30.9	33.6	51.7	51.2	59.6	69.8	73.6	67.6	66.5	58.1	46.5	35.9	53.8
1947	34.8	23.2	33.3	51.3	58.2	69.3	69.6	78.0	66.7	62.4	39.3	31.5	51.5
1948	20.5	30.3	43.3	55.2	60.0	71.0	75.6	72.5	67.3	50.7	47.1	35.2	52.4
1949	37.0	36.6	40.9	49.3	62.9	74.4	78.3	74.0	61.0	59.5	42.6	35.5	54.3
1950	39.9	33.6	36.3	45.8	62.8	68.4	72.2	69.8	64.2	58.1	37.0	24.8	51.1
1951	31.4	30.9	39.9	49.2	63.1	72.5	74.2	71.8	64.4	56.8	36.7	31.8	51.9
1952	35.1	34.5	39.9	51.9	60.8	74.5	76.9	73.2	65.7	48.6	43.3	35.3	53.3
1953	35.3	35.7	42.5	48.2	64.9	73.7	75.5	73.3	66.2	57.2	43.6	34.0	54.2
1954	31.8	39.0	37.8	57.4	57.7	72.9	74.4	72.3	69.0	56.1	42.5	32.3	53.6
#1955	28.5	32.1	41.4	56.8	63.8	66.9	79.0	77.2	69.2	55.2	39.9	30.1	53.3
1956	27.7	35.6	39.5	48.5	61.3	71.1	73.8	73.3	63.4	59.4	43.1	40.8	53.1
1957	25.8	36.5	40.7	54.1	62.7	72.3	75.1	73.3	66.3	51.5	43.4	36.8	53.2
1958	28.4	24.9	37.7	52.4	61.4	67.2	74.4	72.6	66.1	54.4	43.9	23.4	50.6
#1959	26.0	32.7	38.8	52.6	66.8	71.5	75.4	77.3	69.6	55.1	39.5	36.4	53.5
1960	34.1	28.8	28.4	55.3	59.4	69.7	71.8	74.9	68.3	55.1	44.4	25.1	51.3
1961	23.5	36.9	45.3	47.1	56.5	67.2	73.7	73.1	71.0	55.3	41.8	29.7	51.8
1962	24.6	28.8	36.9	48.7	67.2	72.3	71.3	71.6	61.5	54.4	40.8	24.9	50.2
1963	21.7	22.4	42.8	51.1	58.8	70.8	73.9	69.9	63.7	59.9	44.6	21.6	50.1
1964	30.1	27.7	41.1	53.6	63.4	70.3	74.4	71.2	65.0	51.1	45.1	33.9	52.3
1965	28.3	29.1	34.8	51.4	68.1	69.4	72.0	71.0	68.3	54.4	43.3	36.6	52.2
1966	22.2	29.4	41.8	49.4	56.1	71.4	75.6	71.3	63.2	50.7	42.4	32.6	50.5
1967	34.8	25.8	40.4	52.6	55.4	71.8	71.7	68.3	60.4	51.9	36.7	34.3	50.3
1968	23.6	25.7	43.3	53.1	58.5	71.5	74.1	73.0	65.5	54.1	44.0	31.1	51.5
1969	27.0	31.4	35.3	51.5	61.7	68.5	74.1	71.2	63.8	53.9	39.3	26.8	50.4
1970	20.6	28.5	36.9	53.4	64.9	69.8	73.5	72.4	68.9	55.6	42.4	34.3	51.8
1971	24.3	30.8	36.6	49.0	58.0	73.5	70.5	68.9	67.8	59.8	40.4	38.4	51.5
1972	28.2	27.7	37.0	48.8	60.8	63.6	71.9	70.1	64.6	49.6	40.5	36.1	49.9
1973	31.2	31.4	50.4	51.1	59.5	72.6	74.3	74.2	68.9	58.6	45.1	33.7	54.3
1974	33.2	31.2	44.6	54.3	60.8	67.7	74.4	74.0	62.2	52.8	44.5	34.0	52.8
1975	32.5	33.4	37.3	46.7	66.6	72.4	75.1	77.3	62.7	54.7	47.5	33.5	53.3
RECORD MEAN	29.4	30.8	40.0	51.1	61.9	70.9	74.8	72.9	66.6	55.0	42.3	32.4	52.3
MAX	36.9	38.8	48.9	61.2	72.4	81.3	85.3	83.3	77.2	65.3	50.4	39.5	61.7
MIN	21.8	22.8	31.0	41.0	51.4	60.5	64.3	62.5	55.9	44.7	34.1	25.3	42.9

# Indicates a station move or relocation of instruments.

COLUMBUS, OH

Feb	Mar	Apr	May	June	Total
845	786	495	186	42	5660
792	745	379	138	9	4965
1115	841	383	141	28	5632
898	809	366	98	34	5724
1043	1128	315	205	7	5682
782	601	536	267	53	5702
1005	866	496	76	2	5831
1186	683	424	208	18	6330
1075	735	340	113	40	5605
999	932	403	39	26	5619
989	710	465	286	29	5737
1093	756	374	300	9	5683
1133	667	351	205	6	6023
933	916	402	143	54	5733
1017	861	365	119	13	6150
950	871	475	230	4	5769
1077	860	482	146	101	5588
934	444	427	184	0	5236
940	628	332	178	31	4895
878	850	542	73	18	5427

Aug	Sept	Oct	Nov	Dec	Total
203	76	18	0	0	800
237	179	13	0	0	1023
135	144	24	0	0	771
183	71	0	0	0	591
292	160	25	0	0	1042
286	52	3	0	0	836
389	48	10	1	0	1147

Precipitation

Year	Jan	Feb	Mar	Apr	May	June	July	Aug	Sept	Oct	Nov	Dec	Annual
1936	1.26	2.87	3.10	3.17	2.34	2.23	1.80	4.94	3.29	3.41	2.95	1.79	33.15
1937	10.71	0.87	1.56	3.16	3.28	6.71	3.91	2.89	2.45	2.41	1.02	3.00	41.97
1938	1.11	2.73	4.32	3.07	4.82	1.98	5.22	3.32	5.40	0.70	1.94	1.04	35.65
#1939	3.17	3.92	2.41	4.62	0.33	6.06	2.55	0.49	1.39	3.17	1.06	1.20	30.37
1940	1.55	3.14	3.37	6.09	4.05	3.36	0.48	2.43	1.55	1.52	3.66	2.63	33.83
1941	2.19	0.80	0.61	1.78	2.71	6.51	4.82	3.08	1.38	5.09	1.77	1.89	32.63
1942	1.51	2.40	2.46	2.24	4.02	6.11	2.73	2.44	3.08	1.17	3.68	3.18	35.02
1943	1.89	1.82	4.64	2.03	5.26	3.72	4.23	2.01	1.27	1.04	1.54	0.99	30.44
1944	0.53	2.02	5.09	3.87	5.35	3.42	2.58	4.41	3.29	0.33	1.47	3.03	35.39
1945	0.90	3.19	8.39	5.67	4.92	5.08	3.68	0.87	3.74	2.70	3.52	1.80	44.46
1946	0.81	3.63	3.47	1.70	4.82	7.29	2.91	2.75	0.95	2.67	3.13	2.25	36.38
1947	4.62	0.51	1.29	6.03	7.43	4.12	5.52	5.16	3.48	2.24	2.22	1.23	43.85
1948	2.07	3.07	5.03	5.32	4.47	4.81	5.69	2.44	2.59	2.28	5.06	2.86	45.69
1949	7.23	3.17	3.83	3.03	2.58	7.51	5.23	3.78	3.31	1.52	1.55	2.86	45.60
1950	8.29	3.22	2.65	4.97	2.90	2.28	4.74	3.16	2.09	2.06	5.40	3.14	44.90
#1951	4.50	2.82	4.86	3.00	3.18	4.43	0.99	0.58	3.00	1.36	4.42	5.07	38.21
1952	5.99	2.31	3.95	4.07	4.33	2.75	3.01	1.87	2.49	0.81	1.09	2.58	35.25
1953	4.83	1.41	1.49	2.32	3.05	1.79	4.89	2.62	2.12	0.59	1.43	1.88	28.42
1954	2.92	1.78	2.82	3.77	2.56	3.27	3.26	5.18	0.74	5.24	1.08	1.69	34.31
1955	1.44	3.73	3.63	2.09	3.56	2.63	4.77	2.38	2.69	1.95	3.38	0.46	32.71
1956	2.13	4.33	3.49	4.06	4.05	3.22	4.92	2.23	1.37	1.15	0.97	3.21	35.93
1957	1.94	1.87	1.61	5.70	5.41	5.20	2.98	0.89	2.99	1.27	3.23	4.68	37.77
1958	1.87	0.82	1.50	4.09	3.54	9.75	9.46	2.81	3.01	1.27	1.56	0.69	40.37
1959	7.44	3.08	1.45	3.60	4.15	1.55	3.23	1.55	1.55	3.33	3.71	2.27	36.91
1960	2.31	2.57	1.11	1.60	5.82	2.47	4.54	2.48	0.83	2.55	1.60	1.62	29.50
1961	0.65	2.90	4.83	4.58	2.90	3.49	4.61	2.73	1.05	1.18	3.49	2.42	34.83
1962	3.17	3.46	2.43	1.33	2.31	2.26	3.59	2.31	3.62	2.06	2.94	1.76	31.24
1963	1.39	1.01	7.14	3.27	1.61	1.25	2.90	3.67	0.51	0.11	0.80	0.85	24.51
1964	1.82	1.68	9.59	6.36	1.95	5.71	2.97	3.19	1.66	0.38	1.81	4.09	41.21
1965	2.70	3.76	2.90	5.90	4.00	2.42	3.76	4.62	6.18	3.98	1.19	1.24	42.65
1966	2.87	2.59	1.04	4.89	3.13	1.28	5.91	4.90	3.56	0.79	4.05	3.33	38.34
1967	0.78	2.46	4.40	3.29	4.59	2.92	4.22	1.51	2.63	1.39	3.22	2.55	33.96
1968	2.22	0.38	3.01	2.20	9.11	2.96	2.80	3.08	1.77	2.59	4.26	3.40	37.78
1969	3.40	1.17	1.32	3.10	3.04	8.19	7.65	3.25	1.40	1.52	3.87	2.30	40.21
1970	1.60	1.68	3.04	5.52	5.37	5.65	3.73	3.94	3.95	2.07	2.88	2.50	41.93
1971	1.57	3.16	2.70	0.67	3.66	4.16	4.22	2.81	3.08	1.32	1.73	4.61	33.69
1972	1.40	1.74	2.86	3.74	6.56	3.98	2.60	7.96	5.13	1.74	4.40	3.49	45.60
1973	2.46	1.29	3.43	3.72	3.36	8.77	4.07	4.97	2.82	3.29	5.37	2.70	46.25
1974	2.40	2.30	4.38	2.66	3.29	5.04	1.14	4.88	3.32	1.51	3.39	2.68	36.99
1975	3.21	3.47	4.10	2.71	3.17	3.53	2.04	4.51	5.46	2.29	1.54	3.01	39.04
RECORD MEAN	2.93	2.50	4.09	3.17	3.68	3.69	3.68	3.18	2.59	2.21	2.69	2.57	36.98

Record mean values above are means through the current year for the period beginning in 1879 for temperature and precipitation, 1948 for snowfall. Data are from City Office locations through 1939 except that snowfall data continue from City Office locations through 1947. Data for later years are from Airport locations.

(Continued)

The average date of the last freezing temperatures in the spring, within the City proper is April 16, and the average date of the first freeze in the fall is October 31, but in the immediate surroundings there is much variation; for example, at Valley Crossing located at the southeastern outskirts of the City, the average date of the last 32° temperature in the spring is May 2, while the average date of the first 32° temperature in the fall is October 12.

The records show a high frequency of calm or very low wind speeds during the late evening and early morning hours, from June through September. The rolling landscape is conducive to air drainage and from the Weather Bureau location at the airport the air drainage is toward the northwest with the wind direction indicated as southeast. Air drainage takes place at speeds generally 4 m.p.h. or less and frequently provides the only perceptible breeze during the night.

Columbus is located in the area of changeable weather. Airmasses from central and northwest Canada frequently invade this region. The tropical Gulf masses often reach central Ohio during the summer and to a much lesser extent in the fall and winter. There are also occasional weather changes brought about by cool outbreaks from the Hudson Bay region of Canada, especially during the spring months. At infrequent intervals the general circulation will bring showers or snow to Columbus from the Atlantic. Although Columbus does not have a "wet" or "dry" season as such, the month of October has a higher frequency of light rainfall than any other month and comes closest to providing a normal dry period.

Normals, Means, and Extremes

Month	Normal Degree days Base 65 °F		Precipitation in inches												Relative humidity pct.			
			Water equivalent							Snow, Ice pellets					Hour 01	Hour 07	Hour 13	Hour 19
	Heating	Cooling	Normal	Maximum monthly	Year	Minimum monthly	Year	Maximum in 24 hrs.	Year	Maximum monthly	Year	Maximum in 24 hrs.	Year	(Local time)			
(a)				36		36		28		28		28		16	16	16	16
J	1135	0	2.87	8.29	1950	0.53	1944	4.81	1959	18.4	1970	7.2	1965	74	76	67	69
F	972	0	2.32	4.33	1956	0.38	1968	2.15	1975	15.6	1967	8.9	1971	73	76	64	67
M	800	0	3.44	9.59	1964	0.61	1941	3.40	1964	13.5	1962	8.6	1962	71	75	59	62
A	418	0	3.71	6.36	1964	0.67	1971	2.37	1957	7.1	1973	6.3	1973	70	75	53	56
M	176	55	4.10	9.11	1968	1.61	1963	2.72	1968	T	1966	T	1966	77	79	55	58
J	13	175	4.13	9.75	1958	1.25	1963	2.93	1958	0.0		0.0		81	82	55	59
J	0	267	4.21	9.46	1958	0.48	1940	3.82	1969	0.0		0.0		82	84	55	59
A	8	222	2.86	7.96	1972	0.58	1951	3.79	1972	0.0		0.0		85	88	57	63
S	76	82	2.41	6.18	1965	0.51	1963	2.02	1965	T	1967	T	1967	84	88	58	66
O	342	8	1.89	5.24	1954	0.11	1963	1.87	1965	1.3	1962	1.3	1962	78	82	55	64
N	699	0	2.68	5.40	1950	0.80	1963	2.05	1973	15.2	1950	8.2	1950	78	82	65	71
D	1063	0	2.39	5.07	1951	0.46	1955	1.63	1950	17.3	1960	8.7	1960	77	79	70	73
YR	5702	809	37.01	9.75	JUN 1958	0.11	OCT 1963	4.81	JAN 1959	18.4	JAN 1970	8.9	FEB 1971	78	80	60	64

(To better understand these tables, see full explanation of terms beginning on page 322)

Month	Wind					Pct. of possible sunshine	Mean sky cover, tenths, sunrise to sunset	Mean number of days											Average station pressure mb.
			Fastest mile					Sunrise to sunset							Temperatures °F Max.		Min.		
	Mean speed m.p.h.	Prevailing direction	Speed m.p.h.	Direction	Year			Clear	Partly cloudy	Cloudy	Precipitation .01 inch or more	Snow, Ice pellets 1.0 inch or more	Thunderstorms	Heavy fog, visibility ¼ mile or less	(b) 90° and above	32° and below	32° and below	0° and below	Elev. 833 feet m.s.l.
(a)	26	14	24	24		24	26	26	26	26	36	27	36	26	16	16	16	16	3
J	10.3	SSW	56	W	1959	37	7.7	4	7	20	13	2	*	2	0	13	26	2	989.2
F	10.5	NW	57	W	1956	41	7.6	4	6	18	12	2	1	1	0	9	25	1	987.4
M	10.8	SSW	63	NW	1955	44	7.5	5	6	20	14	2	2	1	0	3	19	*	985.1
A	10.2	WNW	56	W	1970	52	7.1	5	8	17	13	*	4	1	0	*	7	0	986.0
M	8.6	S	54	NW	1964	58	6.6	6	10	15	13	0	7	1	1	0	1	0	983.9
J	7.5	SSW	47	NW	1966	62	6.1	6	12	12	11	0	8	1	4	0	0	0	985.6
J	6.7	SSW	49	NW	1956	64	6.0	7	13	11	11	0	8	1	5	0	0	0	986.9
A	6.4	NNW	43	NW	1965	63	5.7	8	13	10	9	0	6	2	3	0	0	0	988.5
S	6.8	S	38	N	1963	62	5.7	10	9	11	9	0	3	2	2	0	*	0	989.2
O	7.6	S	39	SW	1965	58	5.4	11	8	12	8	*	1	2	0	0	4	0	990.6
N	9.5	S	61	N	1952	38	7.4	5	7	18	11	1	1	2	0	1	14	0	988.7
D	9.8	W	47	SW	1971	30	7.8	4	6	21	13	2	*	1	0	9	24	1	988.3
YR	8.7	SSW	63	NW	MAR 1955	53	6.7	75	105	185	136	9	42	18	15	36	121	5	987.5

FOOTNOTES

Means and extremes above are from existing and comparable exposures. Annual extremes have been exceeded at other sites in the locality as follows: Highest temperature 106 in July 1936; lowest temperature -20 in February 1899+; maximum monthly precipitation 10.71 in January 1937; minimum monthly precipitation .10 in October 1924; maximum monthly snowfall 29.2 in February 1910; fastest mile wind 84 NW in July 1916.

Station: TOLEDO, OHIO
TOLEDO EXPRESS AIRPORT
Elevation (ground): 669 feet

TEMPERATURES °F

Month	Normal			Extremes			
	Daily maximum	Daily minimum	Monthly	Record highest	Year	Record lowest	Year
(a)				20		20	
J	32.4	17.2	24.8	62	1967	-17	1972
F	35.2	18.9	27.1	68	1957	-14	1967
M	45.0	26.6	35.8	80	1963	-4	1974
A	59.5	37.2	48.4	87	1960	11	1964
M	70.5	47.1	58.8	95	1962	25	1974
J	80.5	57.2	68.9	99	1971	32	1972
J	83.8	60.8	72.3	99	1974	43	1972
A	82.4	59.1	70.8	98	1964	37	1965
S	75.7	51.8	63.8	95	1960	26	1974
O	64.8	41.2	53.0	91	1963	16	1974
N	48.0	31.1	39.6	78	1968	2	1958
D	35.4	20.5	28.0	67	1971	-11	1960
YR	59.4	39.1	49.3	99	JUL 1974	-17	JAN 1972

IMPORTANT:
The time-period covered by this record is limited: See footnotes on next page for explanation and for additional history of EXTREME HIGHS AND LOWS recorded in the general area.

Toledo is located on the western end of Lake Erie at the mouth of the Maumee River. Except for a bank up from the river about 30 feet, the terrain is generally level with only a slight slope toward the river and Lake Erie. The City has quite a diversified industrial section and excellent harbor facilities, making it a large transportation center for rail, water, and motor freight. Generally rich agricultural land is found in the surrounding area, expecially up the Maumee Valley towards the Indiana State Line.

Rainfall is usually sufficient for general agriculture. The terrain being level, drainage is rather poor; therefore, a little less than the normal precipitation during the growing season is better than excessive amounts. In 1894 the total precipitation was only 21.34 inches, making it the driest year on record, and 1950, with almost two and one-half time as much, was the wettest. Snowfall is generally light in this area, distributed throughout the winter from November to March with frequent thaws. The greatest total snowfall for any winter was 63.7 inches in 1895-96, and the least 6.0 inches in 1889-90. The average number of days per winter with a tenth of an inch or more of snowfall is twenty-seven. The earliest record of snow in the fall occurred on September 27, 1942, and the latest in the spring on May 24, 1925.

The nearness of Lake Erie and the other Great Lakes has a moderating effect on the temperature, and extremes are seldom recorded. On the average, there are only fifteen days a year when the temperature reaches 90 degrees or higher, and only eight days when it drops to zero or lower. The absolute maximum ever recorded here was 105 degrees in July 1936, and the minimum was -17 degrees in January 1963. The growing season averages 160 days; the longest was 224 days in 1910 and the shortest was 125 days in 1961. The average date of the last freezing temperature in the spring is April 27. The date of the last killing frost averages near May 2 and the last light frost about May 15. On the average, the first frost in the fall occurs on September 24, the first killing frost on October 12, and the first freezing temperature on October 15.

Humidity is rather high throughout the year in this area, and there is an excessive amount of cloudiness. In the winter months the sun shines during only about 30 percent of the daylight hours; December and January, the cloudiest months, sometimes have as little as 16 percent of the possible hours of sunshine.

Severe windstorms, causing more than minor damage, occur infrequently. There are on the average twenty-three days per year having a sustained wind velocity of 32 mph or more.

Flooding in the Toledo area is produced by several factors. Heavy rains of an inch or more will cause a sudden rise in creeks and drainage ditches to the point of overflow. The western shores of Lake Erie are subject to flooding when the Lake level is high and prolonged periods of east to northeast winds prevail.

TOLEDO, OHIO

Normals, Means, and Extremes

(To better understand these tables, see full explanation of terms beginning on page 322)

Month	Normal Degree days Base 65 °F: Heating	Normal Degree days Base 65 °F: Cooling	Precipitation, Water equivalent: Normal	Maximum monthly	Year	Minimum monthly	Year	Maximum in 24 hrs.	Year	Snow, Ice pellets: Maximum monthly	Year	Maximum in 24 hrs.	Year
(a)				20		20		20		20		20	
J	1246	0	2.08	4.61	1965	0.27	1961	1.78	1959	14.2	1970	6.6	1957
F	1061	0	1.75	3.13	1960	0.27	1969	1.35	1959	14.4	1967	7.4	1967
M	905	0	2.52	4.88	1964	0.58	1958	1.56	1964	11.6	1964	7.5	1962
A	498	0	2.95	4.94	1961	0.88	1962	2.39	1956	12.0	1957	9.8	1957
M	229	37	3.33	5.13	1968	0.96	1964	1.96	1970	T	1974	T	1974
J	32	149	3.38	6.51	1973	1.89	1964	2.50	1956	0.0		0.0	
J	5	231	3.23	6.75	1969	0.68	1974	4.39	1969	0.0		0.0	
A	18	198	3.07	8.47	1965	0.81	1967	2.42	1972	0.0		0.0	
S	99	63	2.40	8.10	1972	0.58	1963	3.97	1972	T	1967	T	1967
O	379	7	2.24	3.72	1959	0.28	1964	1.71	1957	0.2	1972	0.2	1972
N	762	0	2.32	4.63	1966	0.77	1964	2.06	1969	17.9	1966	8.3	1966
D	1147	0	2.24	6.81	1967	0.54	1958	3.53	1967	23.9	1974	13.9	1974
YR	6381	685	31.51	8.47	AUG 1965	0.27	FEB 1969	4.39	JUL 1969	23.9	DEC 1974	13.9	DFC 1974

Month	Relative humidity pct. Hour 01 (Local time)	Hour 07	Hour 13	Hour 19	Wind: Mean speed m.p.h.	Prevailing direction	Fastest mile: Speed m.p.h.	Direction	Year	Pct. of possible sunshine	Mean sky cover, tenths, sunrise to sunset
(a)	20	20	20	20	20	8	20	20		20	20
J	73	78	68	73	10.9	WSW	47	W	1972	43	7.5
F	72	78	65	70	10.9	WSW	56	SW	1967	47	7.4
M	73	80	61	66	11.0	WSW	56	W	1957	48	7.5
A	76	79	55	59	11.0	E	72	SW	1956	52	6.9
M	77	79	52	56	9.9	WSW	45	W	1957	60	6.4
J	82	82	55	59	8.4	SW	50	W	1969	63	6.1
J	84	85	54	61	7.5	WSW	54	NW	1970	68	5.7
A	86	90	58	66	7.3	SW	47	W	1965	66	5.5
S	86	90	57	70	7.8	SSW	47	NW	1969	60	5.9
O	81	84	55	68	8.7	WSW	40	SW	1956	59	5.8
N	81	83	66	74	10.2	WSW	65	SW	1957	39	7.7
D	82	83	74	78	10.4	SW	45	SW	1971	34	7.9
YR	79	83	60	67	9.5	WSW	72	SW	APR 1956	55	6.7

Month	Mean number of days: Sunrise to sunset: Clear	Partly cloudy	Cloudy	Precipitation .01 inch or more	Snow, Ice pellets 1.0 inch or more	Thunderstorms	Heavy fog, visibility ¼ mile or less	Temperatures °F Max. (b) 90° and above	Max. 32° and below	Min. 32° and below	Min. 0° and below	Average station pressure mb. Elev. 692 feet m.s.l.
(a)	20	20	20	20	20	20	20	20	20	20	20	3
J	5	6	20	13	3	*	2	0	16	29	4	992.7
F	4	7	17	11	2	*	2	0	12	27	2	992.1
M	4	7	20	14	2	2	2	0	4	24	*	989.8
A	6	7	17	13	1	4	1	0	*	11	0	990.2
M	6	11	14	12	0	6	1	1	0	2	0	987.8
J	7	11	12	11	0	8	1	4	0	*	0	989.1
J	7	14	10	10	0	8	1	4	0	0	0	990.8
A	9	12	10	9	0	6	2	4	0	0	0	992.6
S	8	10	12	10	0	4	2	1	0	*	0	993.2
O	9	9	13	8	0	1	2	*	0	7	0	994.7
N	4	7	19	11	1	1	2	0	2	18	0	991.7
D	3	7	21	14	3	*	2	0	12	27	2	992.6
YR	72	108	185	136	12	40	19	13	48	145	8	991.4

FOOTNOTES Means and extremes above are from existing and comparable exposures. Annual extremes have been exceeded at other sites in the locality as follows: Highest temperature 105 in July 1936; maximum monthly precipitation 8.49 in October 1881; minimum monthly precipitation 0.04 in November 1904; maximum precipitation in 24 hours 5.98 in September 1918; maximum monthly snowfall 26.2 in January 1918; maximum snowfall in 24 hours 18.0 in February 1900; fastest mile wind 87 in March 1948.

Snowfall

Season	July	Aug	Sept	Oct	Nov	Dec	Jan
1936-37	0.0	0.0	0.0	T	1.1	5.0	4.8
1937-38	0.0	0.0	0.0	T	0.9	1.2	4.3
1938-39	0.0	0.0	0.0	0.0	5.2	2.7	16.4
1939-40	0.0	0.0	0.0	T	T	2.5	7.2
1940-41	0.0	0.0	0.0	0.0	10.2	6.7	6.1
1941-42	0.0	0.0	0.0	0.0	1.1	2.1	1.1
#1942-43	0.0	0.0	T	0.0	4.5	8.5	13.2
1943-44	0.0	0.0	0.0	T	2.0	1.4	0.7
1944-45	0.0	0.0	0.0	0.0	T	16.7	9.7
1945-46	0.0	0.0	0.0	0.0	0.2	5.5	3.4
1946-47	0.0	0.0	0.0	0.0	T	6.3	3.1
1947-48	0.0	0.0	0.0	0.0	4.5	10.0	7.7
1948-49	0.0	0.0	0.0	0.0	T	2.8	3.2
1949-50	0.0	0.0	0.0	0.0	1.1	4.1	9.0
1950-51	0.0	0.0	0.0	0.0	9.1	9.2	12.2
1951-52	0.0	0.0	0.0	0.0	7.0	25.5	5.8
1952-53	0.0	0.0	0.0	T	0.1	4.4	7.9
1953-54	0.0	0.0	0.0	0.0	2.9	6.7	4.9
1954-55	0.0	0.0	0.0	0.1	1.9	2.4	4.0
1955-56	0.0	0.0	0.0	T	3.1	3.8	13.3
1956-57	0.0	0.0	0.0	0.0	3.5	7.7	13.2
1957-58	0.0	0.0	0.0	T	T	4.2	8.1
1958-59	0.0	0.0	0.0	0.0	3.1	6.2	10.2
1959-60	0.0	0.0	0.0	0.0	8.3	4.6	3.0
1960-61	0.0	0.0	0.0	0.0	0.5	5.9	3.4
1961-62	0.0	0.0	0.0	0.0	0.9	8.9	6.9
1962-63	0.0	0.0	0.0	0.2	T	13.2	12.4
1963-64	0.0	0.0	0.0	0.0	T	8.1	8.6
1964-65	0.0	0.0	0.0	0.0	3.6	7.4	9.0
1965-66	0.0	0.0	0.0	0.0	0.1	0.9	5.3
1966-67	0.0	0.0	0.0	0.0	17.9	13.6	4.1
1967-68	0.0	0.0	T	T	1.9	5.1	10.4
1968-69	0.0	0.0	0.0	0.0	1.8	8.2	9.2
1969-70	0.0	0.0	0.0	T	5.7	19.0	14.2
1970-71	0.0	0.0	0.0	0.0	3.6	8.1	8.5
1971-72	0.0	0.0	0.0	0.0	5.7	1.4	10.1
1972-73	0.0	0.0	0.0	0.2	5.0	7.7	3.0
1973-74	0.0	0.0	0.0	0.0	0.2	13.8	7.5
1974-75	0.0	0.0	0.0	T	2.8	23.9	5.4
1975-76	0.0	0.0	0.0	0.0	5.7	12.2	
RECORD MEAN	0.0	0.0	T	T	3.5	9.0	8.3

Heating Degree Days

Season	July	Aug	Sept	Oct	Nov	Dec	Jan
#1955-56	0	3	92	347	843	1189	1266
1956-57	1	13	190	256	745	923	1385
1957-58	0	9	145	471	741	944	1210
1958-59	4	19	117	367	681	1354	1359
#1959-60	0	0	98	470	899	983	1113
1960-61	7	0	64	393	716	1327	1313
1961-62	27	12	87	344	775	1188	1333
1962-63	1	2	169	348	795	1305	1549
1963-64	9	33	120	199	646	1399	1121
1964-65	1	55	150	536	676	1149	1242
1965-66	27	57	129	486	759	953	1381
1966-67	1	15	147	451	729	1150	1105
1967-68	27	57	206	437	900	1031	1324
1968-69	8	17	71	424	726	1184	1340
1969-70	3	7	126	446	818	1213	1507
1970-71	14	11	118	345	749	1111	1379
1971-72	18	12	78	197	813	966	1283
1972-73	28	36	134	543	810	1073	1135
1973-74	3	16	114	289	686	1157	1197
1974-75	2	0	190	478	730	1108	1104
1975-76	7	6	227	406	585	1110	

Cooling Degree Days

Year	Jan	Feb	Mar	Apr	May	June	July
1969	0	0	0	7	43	101	220
1970	0	0	0	19	62	142	210
1971	0	0	0	1	13	219	148
1972	0	0	0	0	22	67	236
1973	0	0	0	5	3	163	237
1974	0	0	0	4	25	91	243
1975	0	0	0	0	79	172	197

Feb	Mar	Apr	May	June	Total
2.0	4.5	T	0.0	0.0	17.4
12.8	0.5	6.7	0.0	0.0	26.4
9.6	2.6	0.5	0.0	0.0	37.0
9.6	9.4	3.1	T	0.0	31.8
4.6	1.5	0.0	0.0	0.0	29.1
9.0	2.5	0.8	0.0	0.0	16.6
1.4	3.1	T	0.0	0.0	30.7
7.0	6.2	T	0.0	0.0	17.3
6.4	4.3	T	0.0	0.0	37.1
6.9	T	0.0	0.0	0.0	16.0
5.1	7.6	1.5	T	0.0	23.6
4.2	4.8	T	0.0	0.0	31.2
0.6	6.2	0.8	0.0	0.0	13.6
9.3	8.4	0.7	0.0	0.0	32.6
6.7	8.8	0.0	0.0	0.0	46.0
6.3	4.8	2.4	0.0	0.0	51.8
3.8	0.8	0.1	0.0	0.0	17.1
8.6	14.6	T	T	0.0	37.7
5.9	5.1	T	0.0	0.0	19.4
6.2	7.9	1.6	0.0	0.0	35.9
2.2	2.6	12.0	0.0	0.0	41.2
7.1	3.5	T	0.0	0.0	22.9
1.1	3.5	T	0.0	0.0	24.1
14.2	11.2	T	T	0.0	41.3
3.3	0.6	7.6	T	0.0	21.3
14.2	9.6	T	0.0	0.0	40.5
9.4	5.6	0.3	0.0	0.0	41.1
12.4	11.6	0.1	0.0	0.0	40.8
12.6	10.2	1.4	0.0	0.0	44.2
4.5	7.9	1.1	T	0.0	19.8
14.4	9.8	0.8	0.0	0.0	60.6
5.6	11.2	0.2	0.0	0.0	34.4
2.5	4.9	1.5	0.0	0.0	28.1
7.7	8.3	4.5	0.0	0.0	59.4
8.0	5.2	T	0.0	0.0	33.4
7.6	3.3	1.8	0.0	0.0	29.9
11.6	4.0	T	0.0	0.0	31.5
11.6	2.9	1.1	T	0.0	37.1
5.5	5.3	1.8	0.0	0.0	44.7
8.1	6.5	1.8	T	0.0	37.2

Average Temperature

Year	Jan	Feb	Mar	Apr	May	June	July	Aug	Sept	Oct	Nov	Dec	Annual
1936	20.9	17.8	39.3	43.9	63.6	68.1	76.0	75.0	67.8	52.8	36.8	33.6	49.6
1937	31.2	28.8	32.0	46.4	60.0	68.7	74.0	74.8	62.8	50.1	38.9	27.8	49.6
1938	26.8	33.0	43.7	49.8	59.8	68.6	74.6	75.8	63.8	56.3	43.8	31.0	52.2
1939	30.2	29.0	35.6	45.0	63.0	72.0	73.5	72.4	68.0	54.8	40.5	34.0	51.5
1940	17.4	27.8	30.2	44.0	57.0	70.2	74.2	71.3	63.6	54.4	38.8	34.0	48.6
1941	27.4	25.8	31.4	53.4	64.0	70.6	74.5	72.0	68.8	56.8	42.8	36.2	52.0
1942	26.5	23.4	38.6	53.8	61.4	69.8	74.5	70.4	63.4	54.0	42.2	25.5	50.3
#1943	23.4	28.5	33.6	42.6	57.7	73.2	73.2	71.1	60.0	50.9	37.6	26.2	48.2
1944	30.6	28.2	31.6	43.2	63.6	71.6	73.4	72.6	64.4	51.8	41.0	22.6	49.6
1945	16.7	27.4	47.7	50.2	52.6	65.6	70.2	70.7	65.4	50.4	41.6	23.0	48.5
1946	27.9	28.7	46.5	47.8	56.6	67.5	72.6	67.2	65.1	57.2	43.5	32.0	51.0
1947	30.4	22.0	31.2	45.8	55.3	66.2	69.8	77.2	65.0	60.4	36.8	28.2	49.0
1948	18.8	25.6	36.0	52.0	56.4	68.0	73.6	71.2	66.6	49.0	44.8	31.8	49.5
1949	32.8	32.4	36.6	47.0	60.8	74.1	77.6	73.1	59.0	58.0	40.0	33.2	52.1
1950	33.9	27.4	31.5	42.3	59.4	68.2	70.6	69.6	62.8	56.1	35.9	23.1	48.4
1951	27.8	27.6	36.5	46.1	60.0	68.4	72.6	69.6	62.0	55.8	34.7	27.7	49.1
1952	30.8	30.4	35.9	49.0	57.8	73.8	76.6	71.8	65.0	48.0	42.5	33.0	51.2
1953	31.4	31.9	39.3	44.6	60.9	71.9	74.1	73.3	64.6	56.1	43.2	33.1	52.1
1954	27.0	35.4	34.1	51.9	55.4	72.3	72.1	70.1	66.7	54.3	40.9	30.2	50.9
#1955	25.6	29.0	36.7	55.3	61.9	67.3	78.3	74.8	64.9	53.9	36.7	26.5	50.9
1956	23.9	28.8	33.7	45.6	57.8	69.8	72.1	71.0	59.8	56.8	40.0	35.1	49.5
1957	20.1	31.4	36.8	48.7	57.9	68.6	72.6	70.4	62.9	49.6	40.0	34.3	49.5
1958	25.8	22.2	35.9	49.5	58.2	63.9	72.2	69.6	63.2	53.4	42.0	21.1	48.1
#1959	21.0	26.8	35.3	48.7	63.7	70.0	73.2	76.1	66.7	49.6	34.8	33.1	49.9
1960	28.7	27.5	25.7	50.3	57.3	65.3	69.8	71.6	66.4	52.2	40.9	21.9	48.2
1961	22.4	31.2	39.1	41.6	54.6	65.2	70.1	69.8	67.6	53.9	38.9	26.5	48.4
1962	21.8	24.8	35.0	48.3	65.6	69.6	69.6	70.6	61.2	54.2	38.3	22.7	48.5
1963	14.9	18.1	37.0	47.5	55.3	67.9	72.7	67.4	61.7	59.1	43.1	19.6	47.0
1964	28.5	25.9	35.0	48.6	62.6	68.8	73.8	67.8	62.5	47.5	42.3	27.8	49.2
1965	24.7	25.8	29.8	46.8	63.5	66.9	68.5	67.2	63.7	49.1	39.5	34.1	48.3
1966	20.2	27.0	38.1	45.6	53.8	70.8	74.1	69.1	61.7	50.4	40.4	27.7	48.2
1967	29.1	23.0	34.8	49.0	52.4	71.1	69.1	65.4	58.4	51.2	34.8	31.6	47.5
1968	22.1	24.5	38.6	49.5	55.9	69.6	71.9	74.0	65.2	52.0	40.6	26.6	49.2
1969	21.6	27.4	33.2	49.3	58.4	64.6	71.8	71.4	62.9	50.5	37.6	25.7	47.9
1970	16.2	24.3	31.8	48.9	61.1	67.2	71.1	69.6	64.4	54.0	39.8	28.9	48.1
1971	20.3	27.9	32.9	46.1	56.4	71.3	69.0	69.0	66.8	59.0	37.6	33.6	49.1
1972	23.4	24.4	34.1	46.1	60.4	63.9	71.4	68.4	62.2	47.2	37.7	30.3	47.5
1973	28.2	25.2	44.1	48.3	55.7	70.1	72.3	71.3	64.4	55.7	41.9	27.5	50.4
1974	26.1	23.2	36.2	48.8	56.0	65.4	72.5	71.5	59.6	49.5	40.4	28.9	48.2
1975	29.2	28.3	33.3	42.7	62.5	69.0	70.8	72.0	57.4	51.9	45.3	28.9	49.3
RECORD MEAN	26.0	27.1	35.8	47.5	59.0	68.8	73.2	71.1	64.5	53.2	40.4	29.7	49.7
MAX	33.1	34.5	44.0	56.8	68.8	78.5	83.1	80.8	74.2	62.5	47.8	36.3	58.4
MIN	18.8	19.6	27.6	38.2	49.2	59.1	63.3	61.4	54.7	43.8	33.0	23.1	41.0

# Indicates a station move or relocation of instruments.

TOLEDO, OH

Feb	Mar	Apr	May	June	Total
1040	961	575	271	55	[illegible]
934	868	509	236	45	6105
1193	897	465	233	70	6378
1064	914	485	136	31	6531
1078	1211	451	244	62	6609
938	795	698	322	92	6665
1120	924	510	125	17	6462
1310	859	520	317	55	7230
1128	920	493	146	58	6272
1088	1084	538	123	51	6693
1058	828	579	348	30	6635
1170	929	479	390	16	6582
1168	814	458	284	27	6733
1047	976	470	239	107	6609
1130	1022	495	176	70	7013
1035	987	561	272	22	6604
1169	952	560	158	95	6301
1106	639	499	285	3	6291
1166	885	483	295	71	6362
1021	974	664	148	45	6464

Aug	Sept	Oct	Nov	Dec	Total
215	69	1	0	0	656
159	107	10	0	0	709
143	138	18	0	0	680
148	55	0	0	0	528
222	103	9	0	0	742
206	34	5	0	0	608
230	7	7	0	0	692

Precipitation

Year	Jan	Feb	Mar	Apr	May	June	July	Aug	Sept	Oct	Nov	Dec	Annual
1936	1.40	2.76	1.90	1.75	2.00	2.31	3.26	1.62	6.70	2.17	1.28	2.82	29.97
1937	5.36	1.59	1.22	4.77	2.23	6.67	4.55	2.78	2.23	2.34	0.73	1.52	35.99
1938	0.55	3.39	5.22	3.00	3.03	4.28	2.97	0.86	2.44	1.22	1.75	1.57	30.28
1939	2.53	4.21	3.17	4.77	1.43	4.91	2.16	1.08	1.32	2.54	0.82	0.98	29.92
1940	1.26	1.73	2.23	3.17	3.73	3.41	3.29	3.60	1.17	1.65	2.37	3.55	31.16
1941	1.42	0.66	1.05	1.38	4.42	3.08	1.42	1.79	1.77	4.32	1.63	1.59	24.53
1942	1.75	2.70	3.02	2.40	2.51	3.47	3.47	3.81	2.40	2.21	3.25	2.06	33.05
#1943	1.90	0.96	1.98	2.88	8.04	2.18	6.05	1.99	1.85	2.06	1.50	0.61	32.00
1944	0.69	1.22	2.68	4.80	3.17	6.12	1.94	3.30	0.69	0.91	1.82	1.64	28.98
1945	0.51	1.29	4.40	2.43	3.57	4.36	2.59	1.64	3.46	4.54	1.24	1.75	31.78
1946	0.79	1.28	2.49	0.84	3.45	5.54	1.56	1.44	0.37	2.02	1.81	1.98	23.57
1947	3.61	0.43	1.78	4.24	4.77	5.37	1.99	4.13	2.65	2.56	1.63	1.87	35.03
1948	2.22	2.41	3.94	2.59	4.03	4.42	2.72	2.85	2.16	1.75	3.74	2.35	35.18
1949	3.37	2.56	1.82	2.52	4.28	1.39	1.63	6.13	2.83	3.77	1.06	2.73	34.09
1950	6.30	4.32	2.78	5.97	1.64	4.80	3.53	2.06	6.44	4.02	3.73	2.25	47.84
1951	2.16	3.05	2.93	3.01	2.71	5.09	2.11	1.50	2.07	3.83	3.49	4.23	36.18
1952	3.61	1.40	3.36	2.90	3.62	0.12	3.09	1.51	1.83	0.37	1.92	2.03	25.76
1953	2.54	1.11	2.13	2.44	3.18	2.57	1.52	2.38	1.81	0.78	0.63	1.86	22.95
1954	2.21	2.89	4.04	3.06	1.66	3.65	2.18	3.80	1.00	5.04	1.37	1.29	32.19
#1955	1.65	2.60	2.13	2.22	1.38	2.75	2.16	3.53	1.69	4.24	3.61	0.73	28.69
1956	1.49	2.18	3.39	3.77	4.73	3.65	2.98	5.81	0.76	0.37	2.11	2.52	33.76
1957	1.66	1.47	1.11	4.24	2.19	3.61	2.03	3.66	2.17	3.34	1.94	3.61	31.03
1958	1.23	0.82	0.58	2.00	2.29	3.04	6.71	5.08	2.06	0.73	3.20	0.54	28.28
1959	3.89	2.74	3.15	3.67	3.95	2.37	3.13	3.12	2.04	3.72	3.09	2.37	37.24
1960	2.94	3.13	1.01	1.62	3.11	4.86	3.62	2.12	2.27	0.99	1.02	0.55	27.24
1961	0.27	2.64	3.09	4.94	2.15	2.70	2.78	2.02	2.86	0.86	2.04	1.29	27.64
1962	2.46	2.17	1.74	0.88	2.83	2.22	4.28	1.38	3.39	2.08	1.70	1.23	26.36
1963	0.93	0.81	3.14	2.17	2.63	4.31	1.98	2.22	0.58	0.67	1.78	0.83	22.05
1964	1.87	0.95	4.88	3.49	0.96	1.89	1.58	3.80	1.61	0.28	0.77	2.20	24.28
1965	4.61	1.96	1.77	2.07	3.80	2.57	2.03	8.47	4.93	3.28	1.75	3.61	40.85
1966	0.46	1.46	1.82	2.81	1.88	3.42	3.73	4.60	1.17	0.97	4.63	5.12	32.07
1967	1.29	2.12	1.72	2.77	2.28	1.92	3.95	0.81	2.14	3.07	2.85	6.81	31.73
1968	1.91	1.29	2.26	3.01	5.13	3.40	4.50	1.45	1.52	1.11	3.52	3.97	33.07
1969	3.70	0.27	1.54	3.64	3.74	4.82	6.75	1.15	2.70	1.58	3.81	2.10	35.80
1970	1.09	0.89	2.61	4.26	4.05	4.59	5.99	3.00	5.78	2.00	2.09	1.49	37.84
1971	0.82	2.59	1.34	1.08	2.33	2.64	2.77	1.10	1.84	1.77	1.17	3.73	23.18
1972	1.42	0.77	2.33	3.74	2.63	4.09	2.77	4.47	8.10	1.46	3.55	3.08	38.41
1973	1.63	1.05	4.20	1.79	2.85	6.51	3.17	1.18	1.09	2.76	3.27	3.17	32.67
1974	2.27	2.00	2.93	2.55	4.18	3.31	0.68	1.61	1.41	0.70	3.57	3.41	28.62
1975	2.57	2.57	1.90	2.34	3.83	4.21	4.99	5.52	2.70	2.42	2.17	3.35	38.57
RECORD MEAN	2.18	1.92	2.56	2.79	3.20	3.42	2.99	2.85	2.63	2.28	2.35	2.36	31.53

Record mean values above are means through the current year for the period beginning in 1874 for temperature, 1871 for precipitation and 1956 for snowfall. Data are from City Office locations through January 1943 and from Airport locations thereafter.

Station: OKLAHOMA CITY, OKLAHOMA
WILL ROGERS WORLD AIRPORT
Elevation (ground): 1285 feet

TEMPERATURES °F

Month	Normal: Daily maximum	Normal: Daily minimum	Normal: Monthly	Extremes: Record highest	Extremes: Year	Extremes: Record lowest	Extremes: Year
(a)				10		10	
J	47.6	26.0	36.8	79	1967	-1	1973
F	52.6	30.0	41.3	81	1972	3	1971
M	59.8	36.5	48.2	93	1967	9	1967
A	71.6	49.1	60.4	100	1972	21	1975
M	78.7	57.9	68.3	96	1973	39	1971
J	87.0	66.6	76.8	102	1972	51	1974
J	92.6	70.4	81.5	108	1966	53	1971
A	92.5	69.6	81.1	106	1970	54	1967
S	84.7	61.3	73.0	101	1971	37	1972
O	74.2	50.6	62.4	96	1972	31	1973
N	60.9	37.4	49.2	84	1965	13	1975
D	50.7	29.2	40.0	80	1966	1	1968
YR	71.1	48.7	59.9	108	JUL 1966	-1	JAN 1973

IMPORTANT:
The time-period covered by this record is limited: See footnotes following table of NORMALS, MEANS AND EXTREMES for explanation and for additional history of EXTREME HIGHS AND LOWS recorded in the general area.

Oklahoma City is located along the North Canadian River, a frequently near-dry stream, at the geographic center of the State. It is not quite 1,000 miles south of the Canadian Border and a little less than 500 miles north of the Gulf of Mexico. Surrounding country is gently rolling with nearest hills or low mountains, the Arbuckles, 80 miles south. Elevation ranges around 1,250 feet above mean sea level.

Although some influence is exerted at times by warm, moist air currents from the Gulf of Mexico, the climate of Oklahoma City falls mainly under continental controls characteristic of the Great Plains Region. The continental effect produces pronounced daily and seasonal temperature changes and considerable variation in seasonal and annual precipitation. Summers are long and usually hot. Winters are comparatively mild and short.

Normal annual temperature is approximately 60°. During an average year there will be 67 days with maximum temperature of 90° or higher, 11 days of which will reach 100° or higher. The record year with 100° or higher was 1934 when 45 days reached at least 100°. While summers are usually hot, the discomforting effect of extreme heat is considerably mitigated by low humidity and the prevalence of a moderate southerly breeze. During the cooler season, an average of 80 days will have temperatures of 32° or lower, but only one winter in three has temperatures of zero or lower. The record winter with the most days with zero degrees or lower was that of 1894-95 with seven. Periods of exceptionally low temperatures are short.

The length of the growing season varies from 180 to 251 days, with an average of 220 days. Average date of last freeze (32°) in spring is April 1, but

(Continued page 592)

Snowfall

Season	July	Aug	Sept	Oct	Nov	Dec	Jan
1936-37	0.0	0.0	0.0	0.0	0.0	T	3.0
1937-38	0.0	0.0	0.0	0.0	T	T	T
1938-39	0.0	0.0	0.0	0.0	1.9	0.9	3.1
1939-40	0.0	0.0	0.0	0.0	0.0	3.0	6.4
1940-41	0.0	0.0	0.0	0.0	T	T	T
1941-42	0.0	0.0	0.0	T	T	0.1	2.2
1942-43	0.0	0.0	0.0	0.0	T	4.8	0.3
1943-44	0.0	0.0	0.0	0.0	T	1.3	9.0
1944-45	0.0	0.0	0.0	0.0	0.0	T	1.6
1945-46	0.0	0.0	0.0	0.0	0.0	T	0.2
1946-47	0.0	0.0	0.0	0.0	0.2	0.5	4.3
1947-48	0.0	0.0	0.0	0.0	0.0	3.5	6.1
1948-49	0.0	0.0	0.0	0.0	0.6	T	15.9
1949-50	0.0	0.0	0.0	0.0	0.0	0.9	1.4
1950-51	0.0	0.0	0.0	0.0	T	0.3	2.3
1951-52	0.0	0.0	0.0	0.0	1.6	T	2.4
1952-53	0.0	0.0	0.0	0.0	0.1	0.1	2.9
#1953-54	0.0	0.0	0.0	0.0	T	T	5.0
1954-55	0.0	0.0	0.0	T	0.0	5.6	3.2
1955-56	0.0	0.0	0.0	0.0	0.3	T	T
1956-57	0.0	0.0	0.0	0.0	0.0	1.6	T
1957-58	0.0	0.0	0.0	T	T	0.0	1.4
1958-59	0.0	0.0	0.0	0.0	2.6	7.0	3.3
1959-60	0.0	0.0	0.0	0.0	0.3	T	8.2
1960-61	0.0	0.0	0.0	0.0	0.0	8.2	1.9
1961-62	0.0	0.0	0.0	0.0	0.0	0.8	8.5
1962-63	0.0	0.0	0.0	0.0	T	1.2	0.5
1963-64	0.0	0.0	0.0	0.0	0.0	2.5	T
1964-65	0.0	0.0	0.0	0.0	0.0	T	2.0
1965-66	0.0	0.0	0.0	0.0	0.0	T	5.8
1966-67	0.0	0.0	0.0	0.0	T	0.6	T
1967-68	0.0	0.0	0.0	T	1.2	1.2	0.4
1968-69	0.0	0.0	0.0	0.0	1.4	1.3	T
1969-70	0.0	0.0	0.0	0.0	0.0	4.2	0.4
1970-71	0.0	0.0	0.0	0.0	T	T	T
1971-72	0.0	0.0	0.0	0.0	0.5	5.2	0.8
1972-73	0.0	0.0	0.0	0.0	7.5	1.4	8.3
1973-74	0.0	0.0	0.0	0.0	0.0	0.6	0.7
1974-75	0.0	0.0	0.0	0.0	1.0	2.0	0.6
1975-76	0.0	0.0	0.0	0.0	0.7	3.9	
RECORD MEAN	0.0	0.0	0.0	T	0.5	1.7	2.9

Heating Degree Days

Season	July	Aug	Sept	Oct	Nov	Dec	Jan
1955-56	0	0	5	151	595	849	888
1956-57	0	0	0	72	531	713	978
1957-58	0	0	17	263	572	633	789
1958-59	0	0	17	158	410	876	983
1959-60	0	0	24	206	640	644	880
1960-61	0	0	2	96	407	852	885
1961-62	0	0	40	106	547	868	1006
1962-63	0	0	19	129	458	750	1131
1963-64	0	0	7	23	381	988	761
1964-65	0	0	24	150	454	831	808
#1965-66	0	0	28	129	262	496	961
1966-67	0	0	6	166	338	837	713
1967-68	0	0	27	155	464	773	872
1968-69	0	0	0	152	561	829	808
1969-70	0	0	0	274	481	752	1022
1970-71	0	0	18	254	559	651	866
1971-72	0	0	59	88	475	702	923
1972-73	0	0	23	225	640	940	975
1973-74	0	0	37	99	362	787	922
1974-75	0	0	56	89	463	784	763
1975-76	0	0	64	126	430	713	

Cooling Degree Days

Year	Jan	Feb	Mar	Apr	May	June	July
1969	0	0	0	29	128	310	593
1970	0	0	1	47	169	357	536
1971	0	0	4	31	117	416	493
1972	0	2	11	97	133	429	470
1973	0	0	0	19	119	312	465
1974	0	0	22	26	217	280	553
1975	0	0	1	53	108	310	410

Feb	Mar	Apr	May	June	Total
0.6	3.4	0.0	0.0	0.0	7.0
2.2	0.0	4.1	0.0	0.0	6.3
0.1	0.0	T	0.0	0.0	6.0
5.2	0.0	0.0	0.0	0.0	14.6
2.8	0.2	0.0	0.0	0.0	3.0
2.7	0.8	T	0.0	0.0	5.8
T	3.9	0.0	0.0	0.0	9.0
T	2.2	0.0	0.0	0.0	12.5
7.1	0.0	0.0	0.0	0.0	8.7
2.4	0.0	0.0	0.0	0.0	2.6
T	1.7	0.0	0.0	0.0	6.7
3.1	12.5	0.0	0.0	0.0	25.2
0.2	T	T	0.0	0.0	16.7
T	0.2	T	0.0	0.0	2.5
8.8	T	T	0.0	0.0	11.4
4.7	T	0.0	0.0	0.0	8.7
0.8	T	0.0	0.0	0.0	3.9
T	1.7	0.0	0.0	0.0	6.7
0.1	3.2	0.0	0.0	0.0	12.1
6.0	0.2	0.0	0.0	0.0	6.5
T	0.1	0.7	0.0	0.0	2.4
0.5	6.8	0.0	0.0	0.0	8.7
0.5	1.2	0.0	0.0	0.0	14.6
5.4	3.2	0.0	0.0	0.0	17.1
7.2	0.7	T	0.0	0.0	18.0
0.8	0.0	0.0	0.0	0.0	10.1
1.6	0.0	0.0	0.0	0.0	3.3
0.6	1.5	0.0	0.0	0.0	4.6
0.9	0.1	0.0	0.0	0.0	3.0
2.3	0.0	0.0	0.0	0.0	8.1
0.1	0.4	0.0	0.0	0.0	1.1
7.7	13.9	0.0	0.0	0.0	24.4
1.3	8.2	0.0	0.0	0.0	12.2
T	2.3	T	0.0	0.0	6.9
5.1	0.7	0.0	0.0	0.0	5.8
4.9	0.0	0.0	0.0	0.0	11.4
0.2	T	T	0.0	0.0	17.4
1.0	0.5	0.0	0.0	0.0	2.8
0.9	0.1	0.0	0.0	0.0	4.6
2.3	1.8	T	0.0	0.0	9.2

Average Temperature

Year	Jan	Feb	Mar	Apr	May	June	July	Aug	Sept	Oct	Nov	Dec	Annual
1936	35.0	33.5	56.2	61.7	71.2	80.8	86.7	88.7	76.2	58.6	47.6	44.3	61.7
1937	30.4	40.4	46.4	60.6	71.2	78.8	84.4	85.8	75.0	62.1	45.9	37.7	59.9
1938	41.0	45.6	57.4	59.2	68.8	76.8	82.1	85.4	76.6	69.8	48.6	42.0	62.8
1939	45.0	37.4	54.2	60.2	72.1	78.4	84.7	82.1	80.2	67.2	49.6	46.3	63.1
1940	24.9	40.5	52.2	59.8	69.0	75.6	80.4	79.3	73.6	68.0	45.6	43.0	59.3
1941	41.4	40.4	46.2	61.2	71.6	75.6	82.5	82.2	75.2	63.9	50.2	44.3	61.2
1942	37.8	40.8	51.0	62.8	68.0	77.1	82.0	80.0	70.4	62.0	52.2	40.8	60.4
1943	37.3	46.6	45.2	64.8	65.8	80.4	85.0	87.2	74.2	61.4	50.2	36.8	61.2
1944	39.4	44.7	47.3	58.0	69.8	79.8	82.6	83.6	73.6	64.6	52.0	37.4	61.1
1945	39.5	41.0	55.6	58.0	67.2	74.7	79.3	80.4	73.1	62.0	53.7	35.9	60.0
1946	39.2	47.7	56.8	65.3	66.0	76.6	84.0	83.2	73.0	65.4	50.1	45.6	62.7
1947	38.5	37.8	46.0	58.7	66.7	78.0	80.3	85.6	78.2	70.5	46.6	42.1	60.8
1948	32.5	38.3	44.6	67.8	69.4	78.6	81.6	81.4	76.2	63.0	48.8	43.8	60.5
1949	30.6	40.6	50.0	59.9	71.4	78.7	83.0	79.0	69.8	62.1	55.0	42.2	60.2
1950	38.0	45.9	49.2	59.3	68.8	77.0	76.2	76.8	70.9	68.1	47.2	39.8	59.8
1951	39.7	42.9	48.6	58.1	68.4	76.0	82.5	84.8	73.0	62.4	43.9	41.6	60.2
1952	44.7	46.0	47.6	57.4	69.0	82.5	82.2	85.4	76.2	60.6	48.6	39.1	61.6
#1953	43.1	44.8	55.3	56.2	68.7	85.4	79.8	79.4	76.8	64.0	50.0	40.0	62.0
1954	38.0	51.3	47.5	65.6	63.0	77.9	87.4	85.9	79.0	63.8	51.7	41.4	62.7
1955	38.7	39.8	49.5	64.1	70.6	73.1	83.1	80.8	75.0	61.0	44.9	37.5	59.9
1956	36.1	40.6	50.5	57.9	72.6	78.1	83.0	84.4	76.6	66.3	47.1	41.7	61.3
1957	33.2	45.4	46.7	55.9	65.7	74.2	83.5	80.7	69.3	57.3	45.6	44.3	58.5
1958	39.4	35.5	41.0	56.1	69.4	76.8	80.1	79.9	73.2	61.9	51.4	36.5	58.4
1959	33.0	40.0	49.6	58.5	70.4	75.7	77.4	80.1	72.6	58.3	43.5	44.2	58.6
1960	36.3	34.5	39.7	61.7	66.5	77.3	78.2	79.3	74.5	64.4	51.4	37.4	58.4
1961	36.3	42.7	52.2	59.2	67.7	74.1	79.1	78.4	70.6	63.0	46.5	36.7	58.9
1962	32.3	45.1	48.1	58.3	74.3	75.3	82.2	82.5	71.4	64.7	49.4	40.6	60.4
1963	28.3	40.0	53.8	64.8	70.3	78.7	83.1	82.0	75.1	71.1	52.3	33.0	61.1
1964	40.1	38.5	47.1	64.1	70.0	77.4	85.3	80.8	72.3	60.3	49.9	37.9	60.3
#1965	38.8	39.5	40.7	65.5	71.3	78.0	84.6	80.6	73.9	62.8	56.3	48.8	61.8
1966	33.8	38.6	52.8	57.8	68.7	77.9	86.4	78.8	70.5	60.9	54.3	37.8	59.9
1967	41.8	41.7	56.4	65.4	66.9	77.4	79.7	79.3	70.9	62.6	49.4	39.8	60.9
1968	36.6	36.4	50.7	58.1	64.7	74.8	79.8	80.0	70.5	62.1	46.2	38.1	58.1
1969	38.8	42.3	42.0	60.4	67.7	75.0	83.9	80.2	73.3	57.6	48.7	40.4	59.2
1970	31.8	42.7	45.0	60.2	69.2	76.3	82.1	83.6	75.1	57.9	46.0	43.9	59.5
1971	36.9	39.1	49.1	60.4	67.3	78.6	80.7	77.2	73.3	63.4	49.0	42.2	59.8
1972	34.9	42.1	53.4	63.2	67.6	79.0	79.8	80.4	75.8	61.1	43.4	34.4	59.6
1973	33.3	39.8	52.5	56.0	66.8	75.2	79.8	79.7	70.6	64.3	53.1	39.3	59.2
1974	35.0	44.4	54.8	60.0	71.5	74.1	82.7	78.5	65.5	63.5	49.3	39.6	59.9
1975	40.3	36.5	46.1	58.7	67.4	75.1	78.0	80.1	68.3	63.4	50.7	41.8	58.8
RECORD MEAN	37.2	40.8	49.8	60.2	68.2	77.0	81.4	81.1	73.7	62.7	49.4	39.9	60.1
MAX	47.2	51.5	61.2	71.2	78.3	87.2	92.1	92.2	84.6	73.8	60.0	49.5	70.7
MIN	27.2	30.0	38.3	49.2	58.1	66.8	70.7	70.0	62.7	51.5	38.8	30.2	49.5

# Indicates a station move or relocation of instruments.

OKLAHOMA CITY, OK

Feb	Mar	Apr	May	June	Total
700	464	257	14	0	3923
542	560	284	72	9	3761
818	737	268	24	3	4124
692	481	248	27	0	3892
877	777	134	73	0	4255
618	395	247	49	0	3551
560	524	230	5	0	3886
692	372	101	50	0	3702
762	547	116	27	6	3618
706	745	71	2	0	3791
734	388	223	62	0	3283
647	307	71	77	0	3162
826	444	215	71	0	3847
629	708	158	38	2	3885
620	615	187	31	12	3994
718	492	163	36	0	3757
660	365	144	46	0	3462
701	380	283	55	0	4222
573	330	168	8	0	3286
792	583	235	29	0	3793

Aug	Sept	Oct	Nov	Dec	Total
477	255	52	0	0	1844
582	328	38	0	0	2058
388	313	45	3	0	1810
483	351	109	0	0	2085
462	216	83	11	0	1687
426	80	47	0	0	1651
476	170	83	4	0	1615

Precipitation

Year	Jan	Feb	Mar	Apr	May	June	July	Aug	Sept	Oct	Nov	Dec	Annual
1936	0.09	0.76	0.21	0.03	5.56	0.23	0.06	0.17	8.49	1.93	0.06	1.31	18.90
1937	1.21	0.12	1.15	2.66	1.82	4.65	0.74	2.44	2.90	2.25	2.47	1.12	23.53
1938	0.92	3.66	5.51	3.06	5.92	5.45	2.75	0.84	1.23	0.21	1.94	0.38	31.87
1939	3.76	0.43	1.16	1.08	2.88	7.83	0.62	5.52	0.06	2.39	0.84	0.93	27.50
1940	0.70	3.35	0.02	4.46	3.89	3.05	5.21	3.14	2.71	1.72	4.66	1.89	34.80
1941	1.12	1.83	0.58	5.90	5.22	5.99	1.08	3.08	4.57	10.35	1.49	1.07	42.28
1942	0.37	1.40	0.53	8.58	0.43	6.97	0.60	4.87	6.73	2.50	0.73	2.07	35.78
1943	0.03	0.89	1.45	2.79	9.76	2.07	0.31	0.77	2.87	1.28	0.37	2.92	25.51
1944	2.30	2.03	3.82	4.87	2.72	6.14	1.79	1.97	2.20	3.19	2.39	2.30	35.72
1945	1.21	2.91	4.16	7.00	2.59	10.05	4.42	3.43	7.42	0.37	0.27	0.08	43.91
1946	3.31	1.92	2.64	2.07	6.92	3.80	0.18	2.39	1.70	1.22	4.30	1.71	32.16
1947	0.53	0.02	0.48	11.91	7.92	2.07	5.13	1.19	2.43	0.79	1.68	2.35	36.50
1948	0.56	3.11	6.18	2.06	4.97	9.42	3.54	1.63	0.17	0.54	1.78	0.30	34.26
1949	5.64	0.56	1.43	1.65	6.91	4.35	1.36	1.70	3.35	2.97	T	1.07	30.99
1950	1.76	1.32	0.12	0.85	10.34	2.60	9.35	2.92	1.55	1.99	0.65	0.07	33.52
1951	1.88	2.15	1.26	3.85	7.16	4.94	2.97	2.14	4.46	1.54	1.42	0.05	33.82
1952	1.07	1.89	2.95	1.92	5.87	0.76	3.09	2.72	0.25	T	1.97	0.80	23.29
#1953	0.79	1.01	4.30	4.31	1.63	1.33	4.56	3.98	1.39	6.17	0.74	1.20	31.41
1954	0.43	0.69	0.67	3.04	6.21	0.93	0.79	1.24	0.63	1.77	0.10	1.34	17.84
1955	1.03	1.35	1.50	0.78	9.40	6.68	0.36	3.18	4.73	8.34	0.04	0.03	37.42
1956	0.26	1.31	0.56	2.43	5.07	2.46	2.19	0.86	0.20	3.76	1.49	1.97	22.56
1957	1.49	0.86	2.19	7.32	8.67	8.60	0.63	1.08	5.58	2.65	2.25	0.72	42.04
1958	1.29	0.83	3.39	2.22	3.10	7.17	2.02	3.56	3.87	T	0.60	1.11	29.16
1959	0.31	0.69	1.40	2.81	7.60	2.93	8.44	4.10	7.90	6.08	0.94	3.26	46.46
1960	1.47	2.12	0.85	3.01	6.79	5.68	7.69	2.89	1.62	4.66	0.24	2.48	39.50
1961	0.15	1.98	3.35	0.73	1.92	3.86	4.82	2.91	7.37	2.86	3.81	1.04	34.80
1962	1.45	1.02	0.80	2.16	2.64	7.84	1.71	2.26	3.08	2.43	1.34	0.76	27.49
1963	0.21	0.22	3.21	2.77	1.91	2.35	6.19	1.61	1.91	2.05	2.45	0.89	25.77
1964	0.83	2.17	1.30	2.06	5.21	0.77	2.01	4.91	2.96	0.84	5.46	0.62	29.14
1965	0.98	0.85	0.86	3.24	2.14	3.65	1.57	3.37	3.94	1.00	0.06	2.51	24.17
1966	1.05	2.39	1.30	3.68	0.88	2.63	2.38	6.77	2.82	0.37	0.84	0.45	25.56
1967	0.77	0.20	2.49	5.71	4.25	2.27	1.21	1.40	3.15	2.92	0.40	1.04	25.81
1968	2.19	1.02	2.84	3.03	8.40	2.39	1.41	3.75	2.64	2.40	4.11	1.33	35.51
1969	0.20	1.93	3.01	1.66	3.99	4.92	1.42	2.38	6.51	1.58	0.06	1.44	29.10
1970	0.32	0.29	2.09	5.33	6.53	2.45	1.30	0.80	9.64	3.29	1.03	0.26	33.33
1971	0.75	1.95	0.07	0.62	2.68	5.15	4.13	2.13	4.25	2.62	0.29	2.79	27.43
1972	0.21	0.43	1.13	3.10	4.03	1.36	3.22	1.82	2.04	7.17	2.28	0.84	27.63
1973	3.39	0.31	6.76	2.32	3.61	6.31	3.38	1.36	8.00	3.05	2.81	0.47	41.77
1974	0.10	2.68	3.12	4.66	5.01	3.36	0.48	4.42	6.24	5.57	2.34	1.47	39.45
1975	1.99	1.90	1.72	1.92	8.76	4.82	7.71	0.60	1.92	0.84	1.77	1.30	35.25
RECORD MEAN	1.26	1.22	2.13	3.26	5.01	3.92	2.76	2.71	3.29	2.81	1.89	1.45	31.71

Record mean values above are means through the current year for the period beginning in 1891 for temperature and precipitation, 1940 for snowfall. Data are from City Office locations through 1953.

(Continued)

the latest date on record was May 3 in 1954. Average date of first freeze in fall is November 7, but the earliest date on record was October 7 in 1952.

There are almost three clear days for every two cloudy days, with sunniest skies occurring during summer and the least percentage of possible sunshine occurring in winter. The City is almost smoke-free as a result of favorable atmospheric conditions and the almost exclusive use of natural gas for heating. Flying conditions are generally very good, with "contact" flight possible about 93 percent of the time.

Summer rainfall comes mainly from showers and thunderstorms. Winter precipitation is generally associated with airmass movements and changes. An average year has 82 days with .01 inch or more, and 9 days with 1.00 inch or more. As many as 122 days and as few as 55 days with .01 inch or more have occurred in a year. Seasonal distribution of precipitation is normally as follows: 12 percent in winter, 34 percent in spring, 30 percent in summer, and 24 percent in fall. The month with the fewest rainy days is November and the month with the most rainy days is May. Thunderstorms occur an average of about 51 days per year, most often in late spring and early summer. Large hail or destructive winds on occasion accompany the thunderstorms. Snowfall averages less than 10 inches per year and seldom remains on the ground very long. Occasional brief periods of freezing rain and sleet storms occur.

Heavy fogs are infrequent. Prevailing winds are southerly except in January and February when northerly breezes predominate. The average wind speed is 12 m.p.h. in summer and 15 m.p.h. in spring.

Normals, Means, and Extremes

	Normal Degree days Base 65 °F		Precipitation in inches												Relative humidity pct.			
			Water equivalent							Snow, Ice pellets								
Month	Heating	Cooling	Normal	Maximum monthly	Year	Minimum monthly	Year	Maximum in 24 hrs.	Year	Maximum monthly	Year	Maximum in 24 hrs.	Year	Hour 00 (Local time)	Hour 06 (Local time)	Hour 12 (Local time)	Hour 18 (Local time)
(a)				36		36		36		36		36		10	10	10	10
J	874	0	1.11	5.68	1949	0.02	1943	1.52	1946	17.3	1949	8.0	1944	76	81	63	63
F	664	0	1.32	2.94	1940	T	1947	1.75	1940	8.8	1951	5.3	1945	74	79	57	54
M	532	11	2.05	7.16	1948	T	1940	3.44	1944	13.9	1968	8.4	1948	69	76	53	49
A	180	42	3.47	10.78	1947	0.62	1971	3.80	1970	0.7	1957	0.7	1957	70	78	52	50
M	36	138	5.20	9.53	1950	0.33	1942	5.63	1970	0.0		0.0		76	82	56	53
J	0	354	4.22	8.60	1957	0.63	1952	4.39	1946	0.0		0.0		77	84	56	53
J	0	512	2.66	8.44	1959	0.08	1946	3.52	1960	0.0		0.0		72	81	50	47
A	0	499	2.56	6.77	1966	0.35	1947	3.34	1966	0.0		0.0		73	82	51	47
S	12	252	3.55	9.64	1970	T	1948	7.68	1970	0.0		0.0		80	86	58	57
O	148	68	2.57	9.22	1941	T	1958	4.82	1955	T	1967	T	1967	75	81	53	57
N	474	0	1.40	5.46	1964	T	1949	2.01	1961	7.5	1972	5.5	1972	73	78	55	60
D	775	0	1.26	3.26	1959	0.03	1955	2.24	1965	8.2	1960	4.9	1971	75	80	60	64
YR	3695	1876	31.37	10.78	APR 1947	T	OCT 1958	7.68	SEP 1970	17.3	JAN 1949	8.4	MAR 1948	74	81	55	54

(To better understand these tables, see full explanation of terms beginning on page 322)

	Wind							Mean number of days											Average station pressure mb.
			Fastest mile					Sunrise to sunset							Temperatures °F Max.		Min.		
Month	Mean speed m.p.h.	Prevailing direction	Speed m.p.h.	Direction	Year	Pct. of possible sunshine	Mean sky cover, tenths, sunrise to sunset	Clear	Partly cloudy	Cloudy	Precipitation .01 inch or more	Snow, Ice pellets 1.0 inch or more	Thunderstorms	Heavy fog, visibility ¼ mile or less	(b) 90° and above	32° and below	32° and below	0° and below	Elev. 1304 feet m.s.l.
(a)	27	15	25	25		23	27	27	27	27	36	36	36	27	10	10	10	10	3
J	13.3	N	63	W	1960	59	5.9	10	6	15	5	1	1	4	0	6	22	*	971.7
F	13.7	N	61	W	1960	61	5.7	9	7	12	7	1	2	3	0	2	19	0	971.0
M	15.1	SSE	61	S	1954	63	5.8	10	8	13	7	*	3	2	*	0	9	0	965.7
A	15.1	SSE	75	NW	1960	63	5.8	9	8	13	8	0	6	1	*	0	2	0	967.3
M	13.3	SSE	72	SE	1960	65	5.7	9	10	12	10	0	9	1	2	0	0	0	965.4
J	12.7	SSE	87	NNW	1951	73	4.9	11	11	8	9	0	9	*	13	0	0	0	967.1
J	11.3	SSE	73	NW	1960	75	4.7	13	10	8	7	0	7	*	22	0	0	0	969.4
A	10.8	SSE	56	S	1953	77	4.2	15	10	6	7	0	6	*	21	0	0	0	969.6
S	11.5	SSE	54	NW	1961	69	4.6	14	8	8	7	0	5	1	6	0	0	0	970.8
O	12.2	SSE	65	S	1951	68	4.4	15	7	9	6	0	3	2	*	0	*	0	971.8
N	12.7	S	66	S	1958	60	4.9	13	6	11	5	*	1	2	0	0	8	0	970.6
D	12.8	S	56	NW	1961	59	5.5	12	6	13	6	1	1	3	0	2	20	0	970.9
YR	12.9	SSE	87	NNW	JUN 1951	67	5.2	140	97	128	82	3	51	20	64	9	80	*	969.3

FOOTNOTES

Means and extremes above are from existing and comparable exposures. Annual extremes have been exceeded at other sites in the locality as follows: Highest temperature 113 in August 1936; lowest temperature -17 in February 1899; maximum monthly precipitation 14.12 in June 1932; maximum precipitation in 24 hours 7.87 in October 1927; maximum monthly snowfall 20.7 in March 1924; maximum snowfall in 24 hours 11.3 in March 1924.

Station: TULSA, OKLAHOMA
INTERNATIONAL AIRPORT
Elevation (ground): 650 feet

TEMPERATURES °F

Month	Normal			Extremes			
	Daily maximum	Daily minimum	Monthly	Record highest	Year	Record lowest	Year
(a)				16		16	
J	47.0	26.1	36.6	77	1965	-2	1963
F	52.2	30.2	41.2	86	1962	2	1971
M	59.7	36.9	48.3	96	1974	4	1960
A	71.8	49.7	60.8	102	1972	23	1975
M	79.2	58.4	68.8	93	1973	35	1961
J	87.3	67.3	77.3	100	1966	51	1964
J	92.8	71.4	82.1	109	1974	51	1971
A	92.7	70.0	81.4	110	1970	52	1967
S	84.8	61.7	73.3	103	1965	39	1967
O	75.0	50.8	62.9	97	1963	31	1961
N	60.8	38.0	49.4	84	1965	13	1964
D	50.1	29.5	39.8	80	1966	-3	1963
YR	71.1	49.2	60.2	110	AUG 1970	-3	DEC 1963

IMPORTANT:
The time-period covered by this record is limited: See footnotes on next page for explanation and for additional history of EXTREME HIGHS AND LOWS recorded in the general area.

The city of Tulsa lies along the Arkansas River at an elevation of 700 feet above sea level. The surrounding terrain is gently rolling hills and there are no factors such as mountains or large water surfaces that influence its climatic conditions.

At a latitude of 36°, Tulsa is far enough north to escape the long periods of heat in summer, yet far enough south to miss the extreme cold of winter. The influence of warm moist air from the Gulf of Mexico is often noted due to the high humidity, but the climate is essentially continental, characterized by rapid temperature changes. Generally the winter months are mild. Low temperatures occasionally fall below zero but only last a very short time. Temperatures of 100° or higher are frequently experienced from the latter part of July to early September, but are usually accompanied by low relative humidity and a good southerly breeze. The fall season is long with a great number of pleasant, sunny days and cool, bracing nights.

Rainfall is ample for most agricultural pursuits and is distributed favorably throughout the year for the development of all vegetation. Spring is the wettest season having an abundance of rain in the form of showers and thundershowers that by the time the drier period of summer arrive, gardens are mature and grains continue to ripen in maximum sunshine. The steady rains of fall are a contrast to the spring and summer showers and provide a good supply of moisture and more ideal conditions for the growth of winter grains and pastures. The average annual snowfall is less than 10 inches and little or none occurs in the fall or early winter. The greatest amounts are received in January and the first half of March. The snow is usually light and only remains on the ground for brief periods - even the heavy falls in March melt rapidly due to the warmer temperatures at the end of the winter season.

The average date for the last occurrence in the spring of temperatures as low as 32° is March 30, with the latest occurrence on record May 2, 1909. The average date of the first occurrence in the fall is November 1, while the earliest occurrence on record has been October 8, 1952. The longest growing season, 252 days, occurred in 1918, the shortest season, 164 days, in 1909. The average growing season is 216 days. (Period of record 1906 - 1970, inclusive).

The Tulsa area is subject to violent windstorms and tornadoes which occur mostly during spring and early summer, although occurrences have been noted throughout the year.

Prevailing surface winds are southerly during most of the year. Heavy fogs are infrequent. Sunshine is abundant. The prevalence of good flying weather throughout the year has contributed to Tulsa's development as an aviation center.

TULSA, OKLAHOMA

Normals, Means, and Extremes

(To better understand these tables, see full explanation of terms beginning on page 322)

Month	Normal Degree days Base 65 °F: Heating	Cooling	Precipitation in inches — Water equivalent: Normal	Maximum monthly	Year	Minimum monthly	Year	Maximum in 24 hrs.	Year	Snow, Ice pellets: Maximum monthly	Year	Maximum in 24 hrs.	Year	Relative humidity pct. Hour 00 (Local time)	Hour 06	Hour 12	Hour 18	Wind: Mean speed m.p.h.	Prevailing direction	Fastest mile: Speed m.p.h.	Direction	Year	Pct. of possible sunshine	Mean sky cover, tenths, sunrise to sunset	Mean number of days — Sunrise to sunset: Clear	Partly cloudy	Cloudy	Precipitation .01 inch or more	Snow, Ice pellets 1.0 inch or more	Thunderstorms	Heavy fog, visibility ¼ mile or less	Temperatures °F Max. 90° and above (b)	Max. 32° and below	Min. 32° and below	Min. 0° and below	Average station pressure mb. Elev. 676 feet m.s.l.
(a)				37		37		37		37		37		15	15	15	15	27	15	33	33		33	33	37	37	37	37	37	37	37	15	15	15	15	3
J	880	0	1.43	6.65	1949	T	1943	2.25	1946	10.8	1949	9.0	1944	73	79	60	60	10.8	N	55	SW	1947	52	6.1	9	7	15	6	1	1	2	0	6	24	1	994.8
F	666	0	1.72	4.18	1971	0.40	1947	2.27	1971	10.1	1960	6.3	1944	70	77	55	53	11.3	N	50	N	1948	55	5.8	9	6	13	7	1	1	2	0	2	19	0	994.0
M	528	10	2.52	11.94	1973	0.08	1971	2.67	1969	11.8	1968	9.8	1968	68	76	53	49	12.6	SSE	51	SW	1950	56	6.0	9	8	14	8	*	3	1	1	*	11	0	988.5
A	176	50	4.17	9.23	1947	0.51	1950	4.58	1964	1.7	1957	1.7	1957	70	78	52	49	12.5	S	70	NW	1943	57	6.0	8	9	13	9	*	6	*	1	0	1	0	989.4
M	28	145	5.11	18.00	1943	1.33	1945	7.30	1943	0.0		0.0		78	85	57	55	11.0	S	75	SW	1949	60	6.0	8	10	13	10	0	9	*	2	0	0	0	987.5
J	0	369	4.69	11.17	1948	0.53	1963	5.01	1941	0.0		0.0		79	87	59	57	10.3	S	65	NW	1948	67	5.4	9	11	10	9	0	9	*	13	0	0	0	989.1
J	0	530	3.51	10.88	1961	0.03	1954	7.54	1963	0.0		0.0		73	83	54	50	9.3	S	56	N	1945	71	5.0	11	12	8	7	0	6	*	23	0	0	0	991.1
A	0	508	2.95	7.47	1942	0.21	1945	4.16	1942	0.0		0.0		75	85	54	50	9.0	SSE	56	N	1954	73	4.5	13	11	7	7	0	6	*	21	0	0	0	991.5
S	10	259	4.07	18.81	1971	T	1948	6.39	1940	0.0		0.0		83	89	61	61	9.4	SSE	48	E	1956	65	4.9	13	8	9	7	0	5	1	8	0	0	0	993.0
O	143	78	3.22	16.51	1941	T	1952	5.50	1971	T	1967	T	1967	77	84	53	56	10.0	SSE	45	NW	1948	65	4.6	14	7	10	7	0	3	1	2	0	*	0	994.4
N	468	0	1.87	7.57	1946	0.01	1949	5.14	1974	5.6	1972	4.0	1972	75	81	57	59	10.6	S	56	SW	1944	59	5.2	12	7	11	6	*	1	1	0	*	8	0	993.3
D	781	0	1.64	6.34	1971	0.16	1950	3.19	1965	9.9	1958	8.8	1954	76	80	62	64	10.5	S	56	SW	1948	53	5.9	10	7	14	7	1	1	2	0	3	21	*	993.8
YR	3680	1949	36.90	18.81	SEP 1971	T	OCT 1952	7.54	JUL 1963	11.8	MAR 1968	9.8	MAR 1968	75	82	56	55	10.6	S	75	SW	MAY 1949	62	5.4	125	103	137	90	4	53	10	70	11	84	1	991.7

FOOTNOTES Means and extremes above are from existing and comparable exposures. Annual extremes have been exceeded at other sites in the locality as follows: Highest temperature 115 in August 1936; lowest temperature -16 in January 1930; minimum monthly precipitation 0.00 in December 1896 and earlier; maximum monthly snowfall 19.2 in March 1924; maximum snowfall in 24 hours 11.5 in March 1924.

Snowfall

Season	July	Aug	Sept	Oct	Nov	Dec	Jan
1936-37	0.0	0.0	0.0	0.0	0.0	0.0	10.0
1937-38	0.0	0.0	0.0	0.0	3.4	0.3	0.0
#1938-39	0.0	0.0	0.0	0.0	0.9		4.0
1939-40	0.0	0.0	0.0	0.0	0.2	T	6.5
1940-41	0.0	0.0	0.0	0.0	T	0.0	3.4
1941-42	0.0	0.0	0.0	0.0	T	2.2	1.6
1942-43	0.0	0.0	0.0	0.0	0.0	2.6	T
1943-44	0.0	0.0	0.0	0.0	T	1.0	9.0
1944-45	0.0	0.0	0.0	0.0	0.0	T	1.1
1945-46	0.0	0.0	0.0	0.0	0.0	1.1	T
1946-47	0.0	0.0	0.0	0.0	0.0	T	8.6
1947-48	0.0	0.0	0.0	0.0	T	T	5.7
1948-49	0.0	0.0	0.0	0.0	T	T	10.8
1949-50	0.0	0.0	0.0	0.0	0.0	T	3.1
1950-51	0.0	0.0	0.0	0.0	0.0	1.5	1.0
1951-52	0.0	0.0	0.0	0.0	4.0	1.4	1.6
1952-53	0.0	0.0	0.0	0.0	1.7	T	6.1
1953-54	0.0	0.0	0.0	0.0	T	0.2	6.0
1954-55	0.0	0.0	0.0	0.0	0.0	8.8	3.0
1955-56	0.0	0.0	0.0	0.0	0.3	0.3	2.8
1956-57	0.0	0.0	0.0	0.0	0.0	0.4	1.3
1957-58	0.0	0.0	0.0	T	T	T	4.6
1958-59	0.0	0.0	0.0	0.0	2.0	9.9	4.6
1959-60	0.0	0.0	0.0	0.0	0.2	0.0	6.1
1960-61	0.0	0.0	0.0	0.0	0.0	1.0	T
1961-62	0.0	0.0	0.0	0.0	T	2.0	2.7
1962-63	0.0	0.0	0.0	0.0	T	1.0	0.6
1963-64	0.0	0.0	0.0	0.0	0.0	4.0	1.1
1964-65	0.0	0.0	0.0	0.0	0.0	T	0.3
1965-66	0.0	0.0	0.0	0.0	0.0	T	4.3
1966-67	0.0	0.0	0.0	0.0	T	3.1	0.7
1967-68	0.0	0.0	0.0	T	0.9	1.6	0.6
1968-69	0.0	0.0	0.0	0.0	T	1.4	T
1969-70	0.0	0.0	0.0	0.0	0.0	5.8	4.7
1970-71	0.0	0.0	0.0	0.0	T	0.0	T
1971-72	0.0	0.0	0.0	0.0	2.0	1.0	0.8
1972-73	0.0	0.0	0.0	0.0	5.6	1.7	4.3
1973-74	0.0	0.0	0.0	0.0	T	1.8	T
1974-75	0.0	0.0	0.0	0.0	1.7	T	T
1975-76	0.0	0.0	0.0	0.0	0.8	1.3	
RECORD MEAN	0.0	0.0	0.0	T	0.5	1.5	3.0

Heating Degree Days

Season	July	Aug	Sept	Oct	Nov	Dec	Jan
1955-56	0	0	0	129	560	816	905
1956-57	0	0	0	41	509	689	957
1957-58	0	0	5	225	515	582	814
1958-59	0	0	18	146	345	853	969
#1959-60	0	0	14	170	614	618	858
1960-61	0	0	0	88	393	814	943
1961-62	0	0	37	129	563	918	1072
1962-63	0	0	21	117	450	771	1119
1963-64	0	0	5	20	376	1038	739
1964-65	0	0	18	162	385	797	775
1965-66	0	0	15	122	283	556	992
1966-67	0	0	13	202	376	859	776
1967-68	0	0	37	184	498	781	892
1968-69	0	0	1	160	543	864	863
1969-70	0	0	0	241	498	789	1088
1970-71	0	0	18	217	577	692	878
1971-72	0	0	53	60	446	653	932
1972-73	0	0	19	183	634	964	954
1973-74	0	0	24	95	343	824	951
1974-75	0	0	74	94	473	777	773
1975-76	0	0	57	146	429	762	

Cooling Degree Days

Year	Jan	Feb	Mar	Apr	May	June	July
1969	0	0	0	29	185	312	656
1970	0	0	0	50	209	382	555
1971	0	0	3	40	97	442	471
1972	0	6	11	99	144	446	487
1973	0	0	0	35	124	357	508
1974	0	0	47	48	232	270	641
1975	0	0	9	77	156	335	509

Feb	Mar	Apr	May	June	Total
0.2	0.1	0.0	0.0	0.0	10.3
1.5	0.0	T	0.0	0.0	5.2
0.7	0.0	0.0	0.0	0.0	
T	0.0	0.0	0.0	0.0	6.7
3.1	0.5	0.0	0.0	0.0	7.0
3.1	0.0	0.0	0.0	0.0	6.9
0.0	2.8	T	0.0	0.0	5.4
6.3	T	0.0	0.0	0.0	16.3
4.5	T	0.0	0.0	0.0	5.6
2.0	T	0.0	0.0	0.0	3.1
2.0	0.1	0.0	0.0	0.0	10.7
2.5	9.7	0.0	0.0	0.0	17.9
2.4	1.3	T	0.0	0.0	14.5
0.1	T	0.0	0.0	0.0	3.2
5.5	T	T	0.0	0.0	8.0
3.2	T	0.0	0.0	0.0	10.2
0.5	T	T	0.0	0.0	8.3
T	0.3	0.0	0.0	0.0	6.5
T	3.5	0.0	0.0	0.0	15.3
1.0	T	T	0.0	0.0	4.4
T	0.1	1.7	0.0	0.0	3.5
1.0	11.6	0.0	0.0	0.0	17.2
2.5	T	T	0.0	0.0	19.0
10.1	3.0	0.0	0.0	0.0	19.4
5.2	T	0.0	0.0	0.0	6.2
1.8	0.0	0.0	0.0	0.0	6.5
1.5	0.0	0.0	0.0	0.0	3.1
T	8.8	0.0	0.0	0.0	13.9
1.5	0.6	0.0	0.0	0.0	2.4
5.1	T	0.0	0.0	0.0	9.4
0.9	1.1	0.0	0.0	0.0	5.8
2.1	11.8	0.0	0.0	0.0	17.0
5.3	1.3	0.0	0.0	0.0	8.0
T	9.9	T	0.0	0.0	20.4
6.5	T	0.0	0.0	0.0	6.5
4.9	T	0.0	0.0	0.0	8.7
2.2	0.0	0.3	0.0	0.0	14.1
T	T	T	0.0	0.0	1.8
3.0	1.8	T	0.0	0.0	6.5
2.4	1.8	0.1	0.0	0.0	9.3

Feb	Mar	Apr	May	June	Total
653	429	245	29	0	3766
505	513	235	36	3	3488
834	696	194	23	0	3888
652	416	196	21	0	3616
864	818	161	88	0	4205
619	394	281	70	0	3602
628	586	250	3	0	4186
736	343	90	46	0	3693
734	553	87	19	1	3572
711	752	73	1	0	3674
722	395	227	67	0	3379
724	362	100	101	0	3513
803	479	184	67	0	3925
652	680	127	24	2	3916
642	625	174	26	18	4101
721	463	176	37	0	3779
670	373	161	47	0	3395
700	321	233	42	0	4050
591	341	137	5	0	3311
780	610	205	19	0	3805

Aug	Sept	Oct	Nov	Dec	Total
496	307	77	0	0	2062
619	307	39	0	0	2161
444	298	65	7	0	1867
524	339	64	0	0	2120
452	249	101	5	0	1831
419	71	40	2	0	1770
542	192	97	12	0	1929

TULSA, OKLAHOMA

Average Temperature

Year	Jan	Feb	Mar	Apr	May	June	July	Aug	Sept	Oct	Nov	Dec	Annual
1936	35.2	33.8	59.0	62.6	73.0	81.8	89.2	91.0	79.0	60.8	49.2	45.2	63.3
1937	32.4	41.4	47.9	62.6	71.2	79.4	83.9	85.0	73.1	60.5	46.0	39.1	60.2
#1938	41.7	47.0	59.2	61.0	69.2	76.6	82.0	81.7	73.4	68.9	50.3	43.4	62.9
1939	44.4	36.2	53.8	59.0	70.0	76.8	83.6	82.2	80.6	66.6	47.4	45.2	62.2
1940	22.6	39.5	50.6	58.4	67.2	75.1	79.3	78.0	71.0	66.1	45.6	42.0	58.0
1941	40.4	39.3	45.4	61.8	71.6	75.4	82.0	80.8	73.8	64.8	49.2	43.6	60.7
1942	36.7	39.0	50.2	62.5	66.2	75.8	80.4	78.8	70.3	61.7	51.8	40.3	59.5
1943	36.1	44.9	43.8	63.0	66.9	78.8	84.5	85.9	70.4	59.0	48.6	35.9	59.8
1944	38.6	43.4	47.4	57.2	69.2	78.7	80.9	81.8	72.0	64.2	51.8	35.6	60.1
1945	38.1	39.6	55.0	58.4	65.8	73.8	78.6	80.4	72.8	60.6	52.2	33.3	59.0
1946	39.0	47.6	57.1	64.7	64.7	75.7	83.4	82.2	72.2	65.4	49.8	45.2	62.2
1947	38.3	36.5	44.2	58.8	65.4	76.6	78.8	85.8	76.9	69.5	46.4	41.6	59.9
1948	31.3	37.6	44.9	65.8	69.0	77.2	80.2	78.6	73.9	61.2	48.6	42.5	59.2
1949	32.0	39.6	48.8	59.6	70.7	78.3	81.5	78.0	67.8	62.0	53.6	41.7	59.5
1950	38.6	44.4	47.4	57.9	68.0	76.5	76.0	75.5	70.5	67.2	46.1	37.5	58.8
1951	38.7	42.2	47.7	56.9	68.9	74.7	81.7	83.6	71.2	61.7	43.4	39.8	59.2
1952	42.8	45.3	46.9	56.5	68.6	82.2	82.4	84.3	74.1	58.8	47.8	39.5	60.8
1953	41.2	45.3	54.4	55.5	69.2	84.1	80.4	79.9	76.1	64.9	50.4	41.0	61.9
1954	37.0	50.9	48.2	66.4	64.4	79.6	90.2	87.3	79.9	65.3	52.6	42.5	63.7
1955	39.8	40.9	50.7	65.5	71.1	74.9	85.7	82.2	76.1	62.4	46.1	38.4	61.2
1956	35.6	42.2	51.7	58.0	72.9	78.8	85.2	86.8	78.0	68.0	47.9	42.5	62.3
1957	34.0	46.7	48.2	58.0	68.0	76.3	85.9	82.0	70.9	58.6	47.7	46.0	60.2
1958	38.6	35.1	42.3	59.0	71.0	78.7	81.4	80.7	74.6	62.3	53.5	37.3	59.5
1959	33.6	41.4	51.5	60.5	71.5	77.1	78.3	81.7	74.0	59.7	44.5	44.9	59.9
#1960	37.1	35.0	38.4	60.7	65.8	76.5	79.1	79.7	75.4	65.6	51.9	38.5	58.6
1961	34.3	42.7	52.0	57.6	65.9	73.8	78.6	77.3	70.7	62.6	46.2	35.1	58.1
1962	30.2	42.5	46.1	57.6	75.3	75.2	81.5	81.4	70.7	64.9	49.8	39.9	59.6
1963	28.6	38.5	54.8	65.6	70.9	81.7	85.0	82.7	76.0	72.2	52.3	31.3	61.6
1964	40.9	39.4	46.9	65.7	71.7	78.2	84.9	80.7	73.0	60.1	52.7	39.1	61.1
1965	39.8	39.4	40.5	66.2	72.6	78.1	83.2	81.7	75.3	63.3	55.7	46.8	61.9
1966	32.8	39.0	52.7	57.9	67.6	77.3	87.3	78.5	70.3	59.5	53.4	37.2	59.5
1967	39.6	38.9	55.1	64.3	65.2	76.5	77.5	76.0	69.2	61.2	48.2	39.7	59.3
1968	36.0	37.0	49.8	59.3	65.5	76.8	80.6	80.9	71.9	62.2	46.7	36.8	58.6
1969	36.9	41.4	42.7	61.6	69.9	75.0	85.9	80.8	74.9	59.5	48.1	39.3	59.7
1970	29.7	41.9	44.6	60.7	70.7	76.9	82.8	84.8	74.5	58.9	45.6	42.5	59.4
1971	36.5	39.0	49.9	60.2	66.7	79.4	80.0	79.0	73.0	65.0	50.1	43.7	60.2
1972	34.8	41.8	53.0	62.8	68.0	79.5	80.4	81.7	75.5	60.9	43.6	33.7	59.6
1973	34.0	39.8	54.3	58.2	67.5	76.7	81.2	79.3	72.3	65.0	53.4	38.1	60.0
1974	34.1	43.7	55.2	61.8	72.1	73.8	85.4	78.3	64.7	63.0	49.1	39.7	60.1
1975	39.9	36.9	45.3	60.4	69.1	76.0	81.2	82.2	69.2	63.2	50.8	40.1	59.5
RECORD MEAN	37.2	41.5	50.1	60.7	68.8	77.6	82.5	81.8	74.0	63.0	49.8	40.2	60.6
MAX	47.5	52.6	61.8	72.1	79.5	88.2	93.8	93.6	85.8	75.2	61.1	50.3	71.8
MIN	26.8	30.4	38.4	49.3	58.0	67.0	71.1	69.9	62.2	50.7	38.5	30.1	49.4

# Indicates a station move or relocation of instruments.

Precipitation

Year	Jan	Feb	Mar	Apr	May	June	July	Aug	Sept	Oct	Nov	Dec	Annual
1936	0.14	0.87	0.29	1.41	3.91	4.44	0.33	0.20	12.04	7.11	0.60	2.30	33.64
1937	4.47	0.25	3.14	2.50	2.30	3.91	2.47	5.76	7.06	2.38	2.84	0.98	38.06
#1938	1.82	4.93	5.90	3.88	5.03	4.94	3.42	7.39	1.22	0.70	1.47	0.50	41.20
1939	2.56	1.00	0.91	0.83	7.37	4.90	1.97	1.13	0.01	1.60	1.75	1.09	25.12
1940	0.55	2.60	0.25	8.06	3.67	6.08	2.43	5.57	6.71	1.65	6.00	1.42	44.99
1941	1.63	1.86	0.66	6.98	3.72	7.42	1.72	4.14	10.14	16.51	1.90	1.53	58.21
1942	0.21	1.03	0.48	7.33	2.26	11.09	2.41	7.47	4.82	2.86	1.62	1.71	43.29
1943	T	0.70	2.09	0.97	18.00	4.54	0.26	1.84	6.80	4.72	0.02	3.92	43.86
1944	1.44	3.31	3.77	2.62	5.50	6.29	1.89	4.94	3.96	2.70	2.84	1.43	40.74
1945	0.64	2.87	4.67	8.41	1.33	6.25	2.65	0.21	9.17	0.65	0.10	0.26	37.21
1946	3.43	2.09	2.90	3.72	5.08	2.58	0.16	2.60	1.77	1.59	7.57	2.46	35.95
1947	0.88	0.40	1.71	9.23	6.26	5.01	0.80	0.43	3.90	1.69	2.06	1.03	33.40
1948	0.38	1.59	3.70	1.40	2.94	11.17	3.61	5.43	T	0.66	1.00	1.35	33.23
1949	6.65	2.46	1.50	3.83	8.34	3.78	2.26	3.54	4.53	2.27	0.01	1.44	40.61
1950	1.86	2.48	1.02	0.51	9.32	2.78	9.01	2.87	1.51	0.86	0.27	0.16	32.65
1951	2.07	3.95	1.75	2.57	1.76	9.30	2.14	2.53	5.83	8.72	1.98	0.38	42.98
1952	0.91	2.00	2.52	4.35	3.45	3.46	1.81	1.47	0.36	T	3.81	0.74	24.88
1953	2.02	1.27	5.58	8.51	2.87	2.38	5.20	0.42	1.85	3.46	1.73	1.17	36.46
1954	0.93	0.87	1.54	4.60	5.17	1.65	0.03	2.55	1.23	2.52	0.26	3.13	24.48
1955	0.77	2.55	2.15	2.13	4.20	1.56	4.39	4.98	1.51	4.34	0.10	0.29	28.97
1956	0.98	1.15	1.23	2.31	5.13	2.03	1.36	0.30	0.87	2.72	2.78	2.38	23.24
1957	1.60	1.46	3.01	8.74	9.80	7.25	0.50	3.79	5.33	1.58	2.09	1.44	46.59
1958	1.78	0.86	6.14	4.39	3.69	3.08	3.33	3.58	3.61	0.21	1.39	0.82	32.88
1959	0.77	1.69	3.02	1.46	6.66	3.30	9.85	2.13	7.42	9.08	1.48	2.53	49.39
1960	1.22	2.65	1.06	3.63	8.91	1.65	9.01	1.87	0.89	3.53	0.63	3.01	38.06
1961	0.66	2.86	3.30	1.49	9.09	6.36	10.88	3.16	7.37	0.86	3.18	2.18	51.39
1962	1.33	1.44	3.24	3.40	1.69	5.52	4.83	3.10	10.50	3.92	2.13	0.36	41.46
1963	0.98	0.42	2.84	2.21	2.49	0.53	10.60	3.28	2.01	0.18	2.28	0.98	28.80
1964	0.63	2.17	3.96	5.87	4.77	5.79	1.80	6.14	3.33	1.24	6.90	1.67	44.27
1965	1.56	1.45	0.73	3.00	3.91	3.76	3.39	3.72	4.59	0.26	0.03	4.29	30.69
1966	0.69	2.35	0.86	4.84	1.86	2.56	2.00	4.59	2.68	1.39	0.51	2.53	26.86
1967	1.51	0.65	1.42	5.09	5.34	4.60	6.88	0.57	4.89	3.75	1.09	1.12	36.91
1968	3.26	1.08	3.49	4.40	3.56	4.08	1.37	1.90	2.80	2.64	5.19	2.01	35.78
1969	1.63	1.34	3.25	1.56	1.98	6.40	1.08	3.24	1.67	5.86	0.32	1.62	29.95
1970	0.41	0.57	2.05	5.66	4.20	4.60	0.13	1.85	6.73	5.83	0.84	1.15	34.02
1971	1.37	4.18	0.08	1.37	6.59	3.27	3.34	1.86	18.81	7.99	1.21	6.34	56.41
1972	0.17	0.49	0.91	4.45	2.43	2.69	2.68	5.16	2.95	7.58	5.00	1.03	35.54
1973	3.39	0.74	11.94	7.22	5.30	7.69	6.47	4.70	6.56	6.16	6.32	3.39	69.88
1974	0.79	3.17	2.62	3.65	6.94	7.88	0.55	5.30	11.78	6.40	7.30	2.88	59.26
1975	2.61	3.44	5.45	2.20	7.22	6.75	2.14	3.52	3.34	1.47	3.53	3.04	44.71
RECORD MEAN	1.67	1.62	2.80	4.07	5.14	4.66	3.20	3.23	3.88	3.43	2.42	1.92	38.04

Record mean values above are means through the current year for the period beginning in 1906 for temperature, 1888 for precipitation and 1939 for snowfall. Data are from cooperative locations through November 1931 and June 1934 through December 1938; otherwise from airport locations.

PENDLETON, OREGON

Pendleton is located in the southeastern part of the Columbia Basin; that low country of northern Oregon and central and eastern Washington which is almost entirely surrounded by mountains. This Basin is bounded on the south by the high country of central Oregon; on the north by the mountains of western Canada; on the west by the Cascade Range and on the east by the Blue Mountains and the north Idaho plateau. The gorge in the Cascades through which the Columbia River reaches the Pacific is the most important break in the barriers surrounding this basin. These physical features have important influences on the general climate of Pendleton and the surrounding territory.

The Weather Bureau station at Pendleton Airport is located in rolling country which slopes generally upward toward the Blue Mountains about 15 miles to the east and southeast. The Columbia River approaches the area from the northwest to its junction with the Walla Walla River at an elevation of 351 feet and some 25 miles north of Pendleton, then turns southwestward to be joined a few miles below by the Umatilla River. Both the Walla Walla and Umatilla Rivers have their sources in the Blue Mountains and flow westward to the Columbia. The observation station is at an elevation of 1,492 feet, about 3 miles northwest of downtown Pendleton. The city of Pendleton lies in the shallow east-west valley of the Umatilla River, approximately 400 feet lower than the airport.

Precipitation in the Pendleton area is definitely seasonal in occurrence with an average of only 10 percent of the annual total occurring in the 3-month period, July-September. Most precipitation reaching this area accompanies cyclonic storms moving in from the Pacific Ocean. These storms reach their greatest intensity and frequency from October through April. The Cascade Range west of the Columbia Basin reduces the amount of precipitation received from the Pacific cyclonic storms. This influence is felt, particularly, in the desert area of the central part of the Basin. A gradual rise in elevation from the Columbia River to the foothills of the Blue Mountains again results in increased precipitation. This increase supplies sufficient moisture for productive wheat, pea, and stock raising activity in the area surrounding Pendleton. The lighter summertime precipitation usually accompanies thunderstorms which often move into the area from the south or southwest. On occasion, these storms are quite intense, causing flash flooding with resultant heavy property damage and even loss of life.

Although seasonal temperature extremes are usually quite moderate for the latitude, at the downtown weather station where temperature records have been kept since 1890, the extremes range from an August high of 119° to a December and January low of 28° below zero. The average date for the last occurrence in the spring of temperatures as low as 32° F. is April 17, and the average date of the first occurrence in the fall of 32° is October 24. At the downtown station, where cool air settles in the valley on still nights, temperatures of 32° have been recorded later in the spring and earlier in the fall, as a rule, with the average date since 1890 being May 8 and October 1.

Under usual atmospheric conditions, air from the Pacific, with moderate temperature characteristics, moves across the Cascades or through the Columbia Gorge to result in mild temperatures in the Pendleton area. When this flow of air from the west is impeded by slow-moving high

Station: PENDLETON, OREGON
MUNICIPAL AIRPORT
Elevation (ground): 1482 feet

TEMPERATURES °F

	Normal			Extremes			
Month	Daily maximum	Daily minimum	Monthly	Record highest	Year	Record lowest	Year
(a)				40		40	
J	38.6	25.3	32.0	68	1974	-22	1957
F	46.5	31.3	38.9	68	1972	-18	1950
M	53.2	34.3	43.8	79	1964	10	1955
A	61.9	39.8	50.9	89	1946	18	1936
M	70.4	46.5	58.5	99	1936	25	1954
J	78.3	52.8	65.6	108	1961	36	1966
J	88.2	58.8	73.5	110	1939	42	1971
A	85.5	57.5	71.5	113	1961	41	1964
S	76.9	51.1	64.0	102	1955	30	1970
O	63.4	41.8	52.6	90	1975	11	1935
N	48.9	33.8	41.4	77	1975	-6	1955
D	41.8	29.6	35.7	67	1975	-13	1972
YR	62.8	41.9	52.4	113	AUG 1961	-22	JAN 1957

IMPORTANT:
The time-period covered by this record is limited: See footnotes following table of **NORMALS, MEANS AND EXTREMES** for explanation and for additional history of **EXTREME HIGHS AND LOWS** recorded in the general area.

(Continued)

pressure systems over the interior of the continent, temperature conditions sometimes become rather severe; hot in summer and cold in winter. During the summer or early fall, if a stagnant high predominates to the north or east of Pendleton, the hot, dry conditions may prove detrimental to crops during late May and June, and cause fire danger to rise in forest and grassland areas during late summer and early fall. During winter, coldest temperatures occur when air from a cold high pressure system in central Canada moves southwestward across the Rockies and flows down into the Columbia Basin. Under this condition the heavy cold air sometimes remains at low levels in the Basin for several days while warmer air from the Pacific flows above it, to give comparatively mild temperatures at higher elevation.

Extreme winter temperatures are not particularly common in the Pendleton area. Below zero readings have been recorded in approximately 6 winters out of 10 since temperature records began in 1890. Maximum temperatures usually reach 100° or slightly higher on a few days during July and August. June has 100° weather in about one year out of 5, while May and September have 100° readings in less than one year out of 10.

PENDLETON, OREGON

Normals, Means, and Extremes

(To better understand these tables, see full explanation of terms beginning on page 322)

Month	Normal Degree days Base 65 °F: Heating	Normal Degree days Base 65 °F: Cooling	Precipitation in inches, Water equivalent: Normal	Maximum monthly	Year	Minimum monthly	Year	Maximum in 24 hrs.	Year	Snow, Ice pellets: Maximum monthly	Year	Maximum in 24 hrs.	Year
(a)				40		40		40		40		40	
J	1023	0	1.60	3.92	1970	0.21	1949	1.29	1956	41.6	1950	13.3	1950
F	731	0	1.07	3.03	1940	0.07	1964	1.09	1959	15.8	1936	9.7	1949
M	657	0	1.00	2.31	1957	0.24	1941	1.01	1972	4.9	1971	4.0	1970
A	423	0	1.01	2.45	1958	0.01	1956	0.98	1969	2.2	1975	2.2	1975
M	220	18	1.24	3.02	1962	0.03	1964	1.52	1972	T	1975	T	1975
J	70	88	1.01	2.70	1947	0.12	1940	1.49	1947	0.0		0.0	
J	6	269	0.26	1.26	1948	T	1967	1.19	1948	0.0		0.0	
A	13	214	0.34	1.60	1941	0.00	1969	0.63	1941	0.0		0.0	
S	97	67	0.64	2.34	1941	T	1974	0.95	1955	0.0		0.0	
O	384	0	1.11	2.79	1947	0.04	1936	1.09	1957	3.2	1973	3.2	1973
N	708	0	1.50	3.76	1973	0.04	1939	1.35	1971	9.2	1961	6.6	1961
D	908	0	1.53	4.68	1973	0.27	1965	1.23	1958	12.6	1972	9.9	1948
YR	5240	656	12.31	4.68	DEC 1973	0.00	AUG 1969	1.52	MAY 1972	41.6	JAN 1950	13.3	JAN 1950

Month	Relative humidity pct. Hour 04 (Local time)	Hour 10	Hour 16	Hour 22	Wind: Mean speed m.p.h.	Prevailing direction	Fastest mile: Speed m.p.h.	Direction	Year	Pct. of possible sunshine	Mean sky cover, tenths, sunrise to sunset	Mean number of days, Sunrise to sunset: Clear	Partly cloudy	Cloudy	Precipitation .01 inch or more	Snow, Ice pellets 1.0 inch or more	Thunderstorms	Heavy fog, visibility ¼ mile or less	Temperatures °F Max. (b) 90° and above	Max. 32° and below	Min. 32° and below	Min. 0° and below	Average station pressure mb. Elev. 1495 feet m.s.l.
(a)	36	36	36	36	27	14	22	22			30	40	40	40	40	40	40	40	40	40	40	40	3
J	80	76	74	80	8.5	SE	49	27	1962		8.3	3	5	23	13	3	0	7	0	9	21	2	964.3
F	78	70	65	77	8.9	SE	54	25	1955		8.0	3	5	20	11	1	*	5	0	2	16	1	963.9
M	73	57	48	69	10.0	W	63	29	1956		7.2	5	7	19	10	*	*	2	0	*	10	0	959.6
A	71	51	41	62	10.7	W	77	27	1960		6.7	6	9	15	9	*	1	*	0	0	3	0	963.3
M	69	46	36	57	10.2	W	48	27	1959		5.9	8	11	12	8	0	2	*	1	0	*	0	962.4
J	65	42	32	52	10.5	W	62	29	1956		5.3	10	10	10	7	0	2	*	5	0	0	0	961.1
J	53	33	22	37	9.6	WNW	46	28	1968		2.7	21	7	3	2	0	2	0	15	0	0	0	961.5
A	54	36	25	41	9.2	SE	40	27	1961		3.2	19	8	4	3	0	2	*	11	0	0	0	961.4
S	61	42	32	51	9.0	SE	47	27	1954		4.0	15	8	7	4	0	1	*	3	0	*	0	964.1
O	73	56	48	67	6.1	SE	49	25	1959		5.8	10	8	13	8	*	*	1	*	0	2	0	963.9
N	80	72	70	78	8.0	SE	62	27	1959		7.8	4	6	20	11	*	*	6	0	2	12	*	962.3
D	81	77	77	80	8.5	SE	63	29	1959		8.3	3	4	24	13	1	*	8	0	6	18	*	965.6
YR	70	55	48	63	9.3	SE	77	27	APR 1960		6.1	107	88	170	100	6	10	29	35	20	82	3	962.8

FOOTNOTES

Means and extremes above are from existing and comparable exposures. Annual extremes have been exceeded at other sites in the locality as follows: Highest temperature 119 in August 1898; lowest temperature -28 in December 1919.

Snowfall

Season	July	Aug	Sept	Oct	Nov	Dec	Jan
1936-37	0.0	0.0	0.0	0.0	T	T	27.8
1937-38	0.0	0.0	0.0	0.0	0.0	2.0	4.0
1938-39	0.0	0.0	0.0	0.0	0.3	3.0	3.0
1939-40	0.0	0.0	0.0	0.0	0.0	0.8	14.4
1940-41	0.0	0.0	0.0	0.0	4.9	T	4.5
1941-42	0.0	0.0	0.0	0.0	0.0	3.0	8.2
#1942-43	0.0	0.0	0.0	0.0	4.4	5.0	11.5
1943-44	0.0	0.0	0.0	0.0	0.0	T	T
1944-45	0.0	0.0	0.0	0.0	T	T	3.0
1945-46	0.0	0.0	0.0	0.0	2.8	4.8	T
1946-47	0.0	0.0	0.0	T	3.9	3.0	6.1
1947-48	0.0	0.0	0.0	0.0	T	1.2	1.0
1948-49	0.0	0.0	0.0	0.0	T	11.0	5.1
1949-50	0.0	0.0	0.0	T	0.0	6.4	41.6
1950-51	0.0	0.0	0.0	0.0	3.2	2.0	3.3
1951-52	0.0	0.0	0.0	0.0	0.4	7.3	11.9
1952-53	0.0	0.0	0.0	0.0	T	5.3	0.1
1953-54	0.0	0.0	0.0	0.0	0.0	T	6.7
1954-55	0.0	0.0	0.0	0.0	0.0	T	5.4
1955-56	0.0	0.0	0.0	T	8.8	9.5	9.6
1956-57	0.0	0.0	0.0	T	T	1.2	22.8
1957-58	0.0	0.0	0.0	0.0	0.0	T	1.2
1958-59	0.0	0.0	0.0	0.0	1.1	1.1	5.3
1959-60	0.0	0.0	0.0	0.0	0.9	1.6	10.9
1960-61	0.0	0.0	0.0	0.0	0.0	0.4	T
1961-62	0.0	0.0	0.0	T	9.2	5.6	8.2
1962-63	0.0	0.0	0.0	0.0	T	T	12.1
1963-64	0.0	0.0	0.0	0.0	T	2.0	T
1964-65	0.0	0.0	0.0	0.0	0.2	4.9	7.0
1965-66	0.0	0.0	0.0	0.0	T	0.1	11.5
1966-67	0.0	0.0	0.0	T	0.4	2.9	2.3
1967-68	0.0	0.0	0.0	0.0	0.8	2.5	1.3
1968-69	0.0	0.0	0.0	0.0	T	11.9	27.4
1969-70	0.0	0.0	0.0	0.0	T	3.5	9.9
1970-71	0.0	0.0	0.0	0.0	1.6	2.3	4.0
1971-72	0.0	0.0	0.0	1.9	T	11.8	3.6
1972-73	0.0	0.0	0.0	T	T	12.6	2.2
1973-74	0.0	0.0	0.0	3.2	9.1	5.3	2.6
1974-75	0.0	0.0	0.0	0.0	T	T	16.6
1975-76	0.0	0.0	0.0	0.0	5.2	3.0	
RECORD MEAN	0.0	0.0	0.0	0.1	1.4	3.4	8.0

Heating Degree Days

Season	July	Aug	Sept	Oct	Nov	Dec	Jan
1955-56	41	1	158	372	895	976	953
1956-57	1	22	63	429	824	872	1424
1957-58	0	4	61	483	712	729	832
1958-59	1	0	100	326	686	814	891
1959-60	11	13	149	351	816	966	1221
#1960-61	0	43	72	347	670	1061	860
1961-62	0	0	167	458	855	863	1006
1962-63	15	16	67	375	585	789	1170
1963-64	8	9	57	308	611	993	760
1964-65	6	30	92	397	742	990	912
1965-66	15	19	153	226	602	865	820
1966-67	19	10	48	333	590	736	691
1967-68	0	0	24	306	711	866	850
1968-69	0	15	73	434	664	977	1327
1969-70	0	11	79	480	646	926	1007
1970-71	0	1	260	540	731	903	767
1971-72	11	9	182	428	633	868	955
1972-73	5	4	165	422	663	1170	1036
1973-74	1	16	97	372	666	721	1064
1974-75	8	0	39	313	600	750	857
1975-76	0	12	43	332	673	751	

Cooling Degree Days

Year	Jan	Feb	Mar	Apr	May	June	July
1969	0	0	0	0	45	183	238
1970	0	0	0	0	11	201	313
1971	0	0	0	0	36	50	363
1972	0	0	0	0	50	134	314
1973	0	0	0	0	63	137	327
1974	0	0	0	0	9	219	272
1975	0	0	0	0	27	88	423

Feb	Mar	Apr	May	June	Total
6.0	T	0.0	0.0	0.0	33.8
8.7	T	0.0	0.0	0.0	14.7
8.3	T	0.0	0.0	0.0	14.6
1.0	T	0.0	0.0	0.0	16.2
0.9	0.0	0.0	0.0	0.0	10.3
1.5	T	T	0.0	0.0	12.7
0.9	T	0.0	T	0.0	21.8
5.6	1.0	T	0.0	0.0	6.6
6.6	0.6	T	0.0	0.0	10.2
2.0	T	T	0.0	0.0	9.6
T	T	T	0.0	0.0	13.0
7.1	T	T	0.0	0.0	9.3
12.0	T	0.0	0.0	0.0	28.1
3.3	0.7	1.9	0.0	0.0	53.9
1.7	4.5	0.0	0.0	0.0	14.7
5.5	1.0	0.0	0.0	0.0	26.1
3.6	0.8	T	0.0	0.0	9.8
T	2.0	T	0.0	0.0	8.7
4.8	2.8	T	0.0	0.0	13.0
7.6	0.5	T	0.0	0.0	36.0
6.9	0.7	0.0	0.0	0.0	31.6
T	3.1	0.0	0.0	0.0	4.3
13.4	T	T	0.0	0.0	20.9
0.4	4.3	T	0.0	0.0	18.1
T	0.1	T	0.0	0.0	0.5
1.3	0.7	T	0.0	0.0	25.0
0.3	T	1.0	0.0	0.0	13.4
0.3	0.5	T	0.0	0.0	2.8
0.5	2.5	0.0	0.0	0.0	15.1
1.6	0.2	T	0.0	0.0	13.4
0.4	3.3	T	0.0	0.0	9.3
T	T	T	0.0	0.0	4.6
2.7	T	0.0	0.0	0.0	42.0
3.8	1.3	T	T	0.0	18.5
0.6	4.9	T	T	0.0	13.4
6.2	0.1	1.1	0.0	0.0	24.7
5.9	T	0.1	0.0	0.0	20.8
0.5	T	T	0.0	0.0	20.7
3.3	T	2.2	T	0.0	22.1
3.8	0.9	0.2	T	0.0	17.8

PENDELTON, OR

Feb	Mar	Apr	May	June	Total
1054	660	330	181	97	5718
804	651	372	132	28	5622
502	682	444	91	20	4560
757	609	393	295	53	4925
748	643	392	284	40	5634
540	573	434	237	25	4862
699	660	333	334	86	5461
613	598	504	205	61	4998
688	662	487	257	70	4910
664	750	357	223	44	5207
702	597	382	194	75	4650
621	659	571	218	21	4517
638	505	462	174	46	4582
820	623	450	140	32	5555
707	660	568	228	83	5395
698	755	460	169	95	5379
793	528	515	171	29	5122
738	588	434	169	73	5467
589	573	391	241	29	4760
721	609	517	194	57	4665

Aug	Sept	Oct	Nov	Dec	Total
177	76	0	0	0	719
243	4	0	0	0	772
379	12	13	0	0	853
358	55	0	0	0	911
232	72	0	0	0	831
332	122	4	0	0	958
179	109	8	0	0	834

Average Temperature

Year	Jan	Feb	Mar	Apr	May	June	July	Aug	Sept	Oct	Nov	Dec	Annual
1936	35.8	19.4	43.0	55.1	62.8	67.1	73.4	72.8	63.0	56.2	36.4	39.6	52.0
1937	14.1	34.3	46.4	49.2	58.8	65.3	74.8	69.4	65.0	56.5	44.4	37.6	51.3
1938	35.5	36.2	44.8	52.0	58.8	66.8	76.4	70.6	69.0	53.9	38.6	37.0	53.3
1939	40.0	35.6	46.6	53.9	61.2	63.7	74.6	74.2	65.2	53.8	43.1	41.2	54.4
1940	31.1	41.8	49.8	53.2	62.6	69.8	72.8	72.9	66.0	56.5	35.4	36.2	54.0
1941	34.0	41.0	49.2	53.7	58.2	64.4	77.0	71.4	59.6	50.7	44.4	38.6	53.5
1942	21.8	37.6	45.0	53.4	56.6	63.0	74.4	74.8	66.0	55.5	40.2	38.6	52.2
#1943	25.2	37.0	42.4	53.8	55.5	61.7	73.4	69.0	67.3	53.8	39.9	32.3	50.9
1944	32.6	37.1	42.6	51.2	58.8	64.0	73.4	70.3	66.5	57.8	40.1	31.4	52.2
1945	36.3	39.8	43.0	49.2	59.6	64.2	75.1	73.4	61.8	55.4	42.2	33.6	52.8
1946	38.2	41.1	44.6	52.2	59.8	63.3	72.8	72.2	61.6	48.8	38.2	37.4	52.5
1947	30.6	40.0	48.2	53.2	64.0	63.4	71.4	69.4	64.4	54.0	41.6	38.0	53.2
1948	33.5	35.2	41.3	48.2	55.3	68.4	69.2	68.6	61.6	50.2	41.9	30.4	50.3
1949	16.8	33.8	43.3	54.6	62.5	65.2	71.2	70.4	64.6	48.4	45.4	36.8	51.1
1950	16.6	32.9	42.1	48.7	56.2	63.8	73.3	73.2	65.1	52.3	42.0	39.3	50.4
1951	33.7	37.5	40.7	52.1	58.5	65.8	73.7	70.7	64.8	51.0	40.6	30.5	51.6
1952	29.0	38.9	42.9	53.8	59.4	63.6	74.1	71.5	66.8	57.5	34.0	36.2	52.3
1953	45.8	41.0	45.3	49.4	55.0	59.8	72.5	70.5	66.2	53.8	45.7	39.9	53.8
1954	34.5	39.0	40.3	49.6	59.1	61.7	71.2	67.3	62.0	50.2	46.4	34.7	51.4
1955	33.8	36.1	38.8	46.2	54.7	66.7	69.7	72.0	63.0	52.8	34.9	33.3	50.2
1956	34.0	28.4	43.5	54.0	61.2	63.2	75.9	71.5	65.3	50.9	37.4	36.7	51.8
1957	19.0	36.1	43.7	52.7	61.5	67.9	71.1	69.0	66.3	49.1	41.0	41.3	51.5
1958	37.9	46.8	42.8	49.9	64.9	69.8	77.6	76.9	63.5	54.7	41.9	38.4	55.4
1959	36.0	37.7	45.1	51.7	55.4	66.2	74.6	69.7	61.0	53.5	37.6	33.6	51.9
#1960	25.4	39.0	44.0	51.7	55.9	67.4	78.3	69.1	64.3	53.8	42.5	30.6	51.8
1961	37.1	45.5	46.3	50.2	57.4	71.6	75.8	76.9	59.5	50.0	36.3	36.9	53.7
1962	32.3	39.8	43.5	53.8	54.0	65.1	72.9	69.8	65.0	52.7	45.2	39.3	52.8
1963	27.0	42.8	45.4	48.0	58.9	65.8	68.6	71.7	67.6	55.5	44.4	32.7	52.4
1964	40.3	41.1	43.5	48.5	56.8	64.9	72.2	68.4	62.7	51.9	40.1	32.9	51.9
1965	35.4	41.1	40.6	52.9	58.0	66.0	73.8	71.5	60.1	57.5	44.7	36.9	53.2
1966	38.3	39.7	45.4	52.0	59.9	64.6	71.0	72.4	66.6	54.0	45.1	41.1	54.2
1967	42.4	42.5	43.5	45.8	58.5	69.7	76.4	79.7	69.9	54.9	41.1	36.8	55.1
1968	37.3	42.8	48.5	49.6	59.7	67.5	77.2	70.9	65.9	50.8	42.6	33.3	53.8
1969	22.0	35.5	44.6	49.8	61.7	69.8	72.5	70.1	64.7	49.3	43.2	34.9	51.5
1970	32.3	39.5	43.5	45.8	57.8	68.7	74.8	72.5	56.3	47.4	40.4	35.7	51.2
1971	40.0	39.8	40.5	49.4	60.5	63.3	76.1	76.8	59.1	51.4	43.7	36.9	53.1
1972	34.0	37.4	47.8	47.6	60.9	68.3	74.7	76.2	61.1	51.1	42.6	27.1	52.4
1973	31.3	38.4	45.8	50.3	61.3	66.9	75.3	71.7	64.0	52.8	42.6	41.5	53.5
1974	30.4	43.8	46.4	51.7	57.3	71.1	73.3	75.5	67.5	54.8	44.8	40.6	54.8
1975	37.1	39.0	45.2	47.5	59.3	65.8	78.4	70.1	67.0	54.3	42.3	40.5	53.9
RECORD MEAN	32.5	37.9	45.0	51.4	58.7	65.7	73.4	71.5	63.1	52.6	41.5	35.7	52.4
MAX	39.7	46.1	55.3	63.8	72.1	80.0	90.2	87.9	77.8	65.0	50.0	42.4	64.2
MIN	25.3	29.6	34.6	38.9	45.2	51.4	56.6	55.1	48.4	40.1	33.0	29.0	40.6

# Indicates a station move or relocation of instruments.

Precipitation

Year	Jan	Feb	Mar	Apr	May	June	July	Aug	Sept	Oct	Nov	Dec	Annual
1936	2.26	1.97	0.31	0.40	0.41	1.87	0.06	T	0.78	0.04	0.09	0.88	9.03
1937	1.61	0.92	1.46	2.39	0.32	2.41	0.02	0.12	0.03	0.72	1.85	1.82	13.67
1938	1.03	1.38	1.02	1.46	0.52	1.05	0.02	0.04	0.26	1.41	1.00	0.94	10.13
1939	1.02	1.58	1.55	0.53	0.38	0.25	0.29	0.07	0.25	1.01	0.04	1.97	8.94
1940	2.04	3.03	2.17	1.23	0.18	0.12	0.69	0.00	1.41	1.66	1.83	1.37	15.73
1941	1.20	0.73	0.24	0.79	2.38	2.24	0.16	1.60	2.34	1.34	1.73	1.48	16.23
1942	1.22	1.10	0.53	1.15	2.87	2.54	0.93	0.15	0.01	2.04	2.47	2.72	17.73
#1943	1.38	0.58	1.04	2.04	0.54	1.67	0.14	0.64	T	1.70	0.43	1.11	11.27
1944	0.43	1.59	0.44	1.90	0.38	0.70	T	0.02	1.01	0.31	1.32	0.64	8.74
1945	1.80	1.64	1.93	0.91	2.22	0.29	T	0.06	1.25	0.37	2.75	1.99	15.21
1946	1.05	0.62	1.00	0.47	1.70	1.40	0.18	0.10	1.03	1.65	1.38	1.12	11.70
1947	0.82	0.33	1.16	1.68	0.32	2.70	0.38	0.24	0.55	2.79	2.13	1.66	14.76
1948	1.40	1.23	0.37	1.85	1.97	1.99	1.26	0.08	0.34	0.64	1.17	2.21	14.51
1949	0.21	1.83	1.59	0.16	2.03	0.19	T	0.01	0.56	0.54	1.64	0.89	9.65
1950	2.16	1.08	1.30	0.82	0.88	1.64	0.07	0.20	0.13	2.52	1.81	2.10	14.71
1951	1.99	0.96	1.46	1.02	0.44	0.76	0.24	T	0.44	2.59	1.14	0.82	11.86
1952	0.84	1.37	0.52	0.68	1.02	2.02	T	0.17	0.90	0.10	0.60	1.86	10.08
1953	2.88	1.48	1.38	1.62	1.91	0.76	T	0.97	0.16	0.71	1.58	2.00	15.45
1954	1.30	0.48	0.65	0.52	0.67	1.42	0.13	0.88	0.75	0.83	1.21	1.00	9.84
1955	0.83	0.44	0.62	1.20	1.26	0.41	0.88	0.00	1.36	2.08	2.69	1.99	13.76
1956	2.97	0.81	0.54	0.01	2.82	0.56	0.27	1.00	T	1.39	0.34	1.27	11.98
1957	1.81	0.88	2.31	0.90	2.21	0.67	0.11	0.01	0.71	1.79	1.10	1.85	14.35
1958	2.26	1.58	1.41	2.45	1.09	0.59	0.02	0.02	0.35	0.05	1.88	2.53	14.23
1959	2.45	1.90	0.92	0.51	0.79	1.19	0.41	0.42	2.03	0.65	0.31	0.62	12.20
1960	1.10	0.99	1.95	0.80	1.57	0.52	0.02	0.72	0.49	1.22	1.70	0.63	11.71
1961	0.47	2.46	2.25	1.30	0.94	0.28	0.08	0.09	0.17	0.70	1.46	1.27	11.47
1962	0.70	0.72	1.14	0.76	3.02	0.15	T	0.43	0.79	1.62	1.38	1.46	12.17
1963	1.40	1.67	0.37	1.86	0.65	0.21	0.32	0.30	0.70	0.44	2.03	1.29	11.24
1964	1.07	0.07	0.66	0.34	0.03	1.01	0.64	0.21	0.15	0.80	1.93	3.23	10.14
1965	3.08	0.37	0.29	0.65	0.57	1.10	0.51	1.21	0.23	0.19	1.95	0.27	10.42
1966	2.19	0.83	0.96	0.08	0.07	0.55	0.79	0.17	0.43	0.75	2.09	2.65	11.56
1967	1.59	0.15	0.89	1.05	0.56	0.41	T	T	0.40	0.64	0.63	0.45	6.77
1968	0.59	1.82	0.47	0.17	0.66	0.89	0.17	0.61	0.57	1.03	2.06	2.19	11.23
1969	2.88	0.88	0.57	2.05	1.40	0.86	0.02	0.00	0.42	1.13	0.36	1.88	12.45
1970	3.92	1.48	0.99	0.63	0.32	0.57	0.08	0.03	0.78	0.81	1.78	0.80	12.19
1971	0.84	0.69	1.11	1.15	1.41	1.73	0.32	0.14	1.03	0.70	2.73	2.59	14.44
1972	0.96	1.08	1.47	0.68	1.97	0.80	0.58	0.36	0.16	0.58	0.70	2.31	11.65
1973	0.50	1.09	0.43	0.27	0.67	0.15	0.01	0.08	1.34	1.71	3.76	4.68	14.69
1974	0.79	1.57	0.81	2.13	0.26	0.19	0.90	T	T	0.29	1.00	1.59	9.53
1975	3.53	1.30	0.65	0.97	0.30	0.28	0.73	0.67	0.00	1.80	0.84	1.98	13.05
RECORD MEAN	1.60	1.32	1.18	1.04	1.12	0.99	0.32	0.38	0.71	1.11	1.53	1.64	12.94

Record mean values above are means through the current year for the period beginning in 1900 for temperature and precipitation, 1936 fo- snowfall. Partial years' data of temperature, 1902, 1903, 1904, 1911, 1912, and 1926, are not considered in computing Record Mean temperatures. Data are from Cooperative locations through April 1935 and from Airport locations thereafter.

PORTLAND, OREGON

Station: PORTLAND, OREGON INTERNATIONAL AIRPORT
Elevation (ground): 21 feet

TEMPERATURES °F

Month	Normal: Daily maximum	Normal: Daily minimum	Normal: Monthly	Extremes: Record highest	Extremes: Year	Extremes: Record lowest	Extremes: Year
(a)				35		35	
J	43.6	32.5	38.1	62	1974	-2	1950
F	50.1	35.5	42.8	70	1968	-3	1950
M	54.3	37.0	45.7	80	1947	19	1955
A	60.3	40.8	50.6	87	1957	29	1955
M	67.0	46.3	56.7	92	1973	29	1954
J	72.1	51.8	62.0	100	1942	39	1966
J	79.0	55.2	67.1	107	1965	43	1955
A	78.1	55.0	66.6	104	1972	44	1951
S	73.9	50.5	62.2	101	1944	34	1965
O	62.9	44.7	53.8	90	1970	26	1971
N	52.1	38.5	45.3	73	1975	13	1955
D	46.0	35.3	40.7	64	1950	6	1964
YR	61.6	43.6	52.6	107	JUL 1965	-3	FEB 1950

IMPORTANT:
The time-period covered by this record is limited: See footnotes following table of NORMALS, MEANS AND EXTREMES for explanation and for additional history of EXTREME HIGHS AND LOWS recorded in the general area.

The Portland Weather Service Office is located six miles north-northeast of downtown Portland. Portland is situated about 65 miles inland from the Pacific Coast and midway between the northerly oriented low coast range on the west and the higher Cascade range on the east, each about 30 miles distant. The airport lies on the south bank of the Columbia River. The coast range provides limited shielding from the Pacific Ocean. The Cascade range provides a steep slope for orographic lift of moisture-laden westerly winds and consequent moderate rainfall and also froms a barrier from continental airmasses originating over the interior Columbia Basin. Airflow is usually northwesterly in Portland in spring and summer and southeasterly in fall and winter, interrupted infrequently by outbreaks of dry continental air moving westward through the Cascade passes.

Portland has a very definite winter rainfall climate. Approximately 88 percent of the annual total occurs in the months of October through May, 9 percent in June and September, while only 3 percent comes in July and August. Precipitation is mostly rain, as on the average there are only 5 days each year with measurable snow. Seldom is snowfall measured for more than a couple of inches, and it generally lasts only a few days. The greatest measured snowfall in period of record is 15 inches.

The winter season is marked by relatively mild temperatures, cloudy skies and rain with southeasterly surface winds predominating. Summer produces pleasantly mild temperatures, northwesterly winds and very little precipitation. Fall and spring are transitional in nature. Fall and early winter are times with most frequent fog. At all times, incurisons of marine air are a frequent moderating influence. Outbreaks of continental high

(Continued page 602)

Snowfall

Season	July	Aug	Sept	Oct	Nov	Dec	Jan
1939-40							T
1940-41	0.0	0.0	0.0	0.0	0.0	0.0	
1941-42	0.0	0.0	0.0	0.0		T	T
1942-43	0.0	0.0	0.0	0.0	0.0	2.0	17.3
1943-44	0.0	0.0	0.0	0.0	0.0	0.0	0.2
1944-45	0.0	0.0	0.0	0.0	0.0	0.0	0.0
1945-46	0.0	0.0	0.0	0.0	0.0	0.0	T
1946-47	0.0	0.0	0.0	0.0	0.5	0.0	2.0
1947-48	0.0	0.0	0.0	0.0	0.0	0.0	0.9
1948-49	0.0	0.0	0.0	0.0	0.0	T	9.8
1949-50	0.0	0.0	T	0.0	0.0	0.2	41.4
1950-51	0.0	0.0	0.0	0.7	0.0	0.0	0.2
1951-52	0.0	0.0	0.0	0.0	0.0	0.7	8.9
1952-53	0.0	0.0	0.0	0.0	T	T	T
1953-54	0.0	0.0	0.0	0.0	T	T	10.6
1954-55	0.0	0.0	0.0	0.0	0.0	1.2	1.1
1955-56	0.0	0.0	0.0	T	8.2	2.0	9.3
1956-57	0.0	0.0	0.0	0.0	0.0	2.6	4.2
1957-58	0.0	0.0	0.0	0.0	0.0	T	0.0
1958-59	0.0	0.0	0.0	0.0	T	0.0	0.9
1959-60	0.0	0.0	0.0	0.0	0.0	T	10.3
1960-61	0.0	0.0	0.0	0.0	0.0	0.0	0.0
1961-62	0.0	0.0	0.0	0.0	0.0	1.0	0.7
1962-63	0.0	0.0	0.0	0.0	0.0	0.0	5.0
1963-64	0.0	0.0	0.0	0.0	T	0.0	T
1964-65	0.0	0.0	0.0	0.0	T	11.0	T
1965-66	0.0	0.0	0.0	0.0	0.0	T	T
1966-67	0.0	0.0	0.0	0.0	0.0	0.0	T
1967-68	0.0	0.0	0.0	0.0	0.0	5.7	5.2
1968-69	0.0	0.0	0.0	0.0	0.0	15.7	18.3
1969-70	0.0	0.0	0.0	0.0	0.0	0.0	T
1970-71	0.0	0.0	0.0	0.0	T	1.4	6.9
1971-72	0.0	0.0	0.0	T	0.0	4.6	0.4
1972-73	0.0	0.0	0.0	0.0	0.0	6.1	0.4
1973-74	0.0	0.0	0.0	0.0	T	0.0	T
1974-75	0.0	0.0	0.0	0.0	0.0	T	T
1975-76	0.0	0.0	0.0	0.0	T	T	
RECORD MEAN	0.0	0.0	T	T	0.2	1.5	4.4

Heating Degree Days

Season	July	Aug	Sept	Oct	Nov	Dec	Jan
1955-56	80	33	173	346	701	793	770
1956-57	22	47	120	407	662	746	1041
1957-58	25	35	45	370	624	644	656
1958-59	3	5	105	295	579	657	755
1959-60	26	32	142	326	659	781	910
1960-61	18	52	114	316	548	807	654
1961-62	11	4	169	359	656	740	811
1962-63	49	19	71	299	515	687	925
1963-64	72	24	41	329	561	830	739
1964-65	67	81	191	358	711	860	761
1965-66	22	16	139	227	451	786	759
1966-67	27	16	56	345	531	635	655
1967-68	3	0	29	306	558	758	789
1968-69	17	43	123	395	544	852	1022
1969-70	17	22	85	357	526	678	751
1970-71	14	14	130	369	530	771	757
1971-72	33	5	123	388	578	756	793
1972-73	10	6	153	363	497	848	799
1973-74	6	47	59	326	618	624	832
1974-75	32	16	29	301	500	640	722
1975-76	24	41	48	354	565	686	

Cooling Degree Days

Year	Jan	Feb	Mar	Apr	May	June	July
1969	0	0	0	0	13	102	74
1970	0	0	0	0	8	106	150
1971	0	0	0	0	5	14	170
1972	0	0	0	0	27	39	200
1973	0	0	0	0	34	65	178
1974	0	0	0	0	1	60	102
1975	0	0	0	0	12	39	157

Feb	Mar	Apr	May	June	Total
0.0	0.0	0.0	0.0	0.0	
	0.0	0.0	0.0	0.0	
T	T	0.0	0.0	0.0	T
T	T	0.0	0.0	0.0	19.3
0.0	0.0	0.0	0.0	0.0	0.2
0.0	T	0.0	0.0	0.0	T
0.0	0.6	0.0	0.0	0.0	0.6
0.0	0.0	0.0	0.0	0.0	2.5
0.3	T	T	0.0	0.0	1.2
13.2	0.0	0.0	0.0	0.0	23.0
2.1	0.8	0.0	T	0.0	44.5
T	12.9	0.0	0.0	0.0	13.3
T	T	T	0.0	0.0	9.6
T	T	0.0	0.6	0.0	0.6
0.0	T	T	0.0	0.0	10.6
1.3	0.8	T	T	0.0	4.4
1.1	1.8	0.0	0.0	0.0	22.4
1.4	T	0.0	0.0	0.0	8.2
0.0	0.0	0.0	0.0	0.0	T
2.0	T	0.0	0.0	0.0	2.9
T	2.6	0.0	T	0.0	12.9
T	T	T	0.0	0.0	T
3.8	0.1	0.0	0.0	0.0	5.6
0.0	0.0	T	0.0	0.0	5.0
0.0	T	0.0	0.0	0.0	T
0.0	0.3	0.0	T	0.0	11.3
T	0.6	0.0	0.0	0.0	0.6
T	T	T	0.0	0.0	T
0.0	0.0	T	0.0	0.0	10.9
T	0.0	0.0	0.0	0.0	34.0
T	T	T	0.0	0.0	T
1.7	T	T	0.0	0.0	10.0
T	T	T	0.0	0.0	5.0
T	T	T	0.0	0.0	6.5
T	T	0.0	T	0.0	T
0.1	T	T	T	0.0	0.1
0.8	0.6	T	T	0.0	7.5

Average Temperature

Year	Jan	Feb	Mar	Apr	May	June	July	Aug	Sept	Oct	Nov	Dec	Annual
1940											42.5	42.2	
1941	41.3	46.1	52.0	54.4	57.6	62.1	71.4	67.8	60.4	54.6	48.0	42.9	54.9
1942	35.4	42.8	46.4	52.8	56.4	61.0	69.4	69.0	63.2	55.6	44.9	43.0	53.3
1943	33.2	43.4	45.5	54.3	55.6	60.3	67.2	66.8	65.8	54.8	46.1	40.0	52.8
1944	39.2	42.2	45.4	50.8	57.5	61.6	67.9	66.8	65.2	58.5	45.2	39.4	53.3
1945	42.4	44.4	45.2	50.4	58.8	61.8	69.0	67.9	60.8	54.2	45.1	39.8	53.3
1946	40.9	42.7	46.6	51.4	59.7	61.2	67.6	67.8	62.0	50.6	43.2	41.8	53.0
1947	37.2	45.2	49.8	53.9	61.3	62.0	66.8	65.8	63.6	55.4	47.0	42.9	54.2
1948	39.5	40.8	44.8	48.9	56.0				61.8	53.5	43.7	38.1	
1949	27.6	39.1	45.7	52.4	59.2	61.7	65.9	66.5	63.2	48.6	49.9	41.4	51.7
1950	27.0	38.8	45.1	48.6	54.5	61.8	66.9	68.8	61.8	52.4	46.4	46.4	51.5
1951	39.8	42.9	42.0	53.5	56.8	64.5	67.1	65.7	63.1	53.7	45.7	37.5	52.7
1952	35.6	41.7	45.4	52.4	57.5	60.3	68.0	67.9	64.8	58.7	40.7	41.6	52.8
1953	47.3	43.8	45.9	49.9	54.4	58.6	66.2	65.6	62.5	54.3	48.6	43.7	53.4
1954	39.0	42.6	43.8	49.6	56.7	58.0	63.1	63.3	60.2	53.1	49.7	40.9	51.7
1955	39.7	40.4	41.5	46.5	52.9	60.7	63.5	65.5	60.4	53.6	41.4	39.2	50.4
1956	39.9	35.9	44.2	52.7	59.1	59.0	68.0	65.4	60.8	51.7	42.6	40.7	51.7
1957	31.2	41.7	46.2	51.8	58.9	62.1	65.6	64.5	65.3	52.8	44.0	43.9	52.3
1958	43.6	48.6	45.5	50.9	61.8	65.2	70.6	70.3	62.3	55.2	45.5	43.6	55.2
1959	40.4	42.7	46.8	52.3	55.7	62.8	68.7	65.5	60.3	54.2	42.8	39.6	52.7
1960	35.4	42.3	45.0	50.6	54.0	63.0	69.1	65.4	61.5	54.5	46.5	38.7	52.2
1961	43.6	47.2	47.7	50.1	56.6	65.3	69.4	70.3	59.5	53.3	42.9	40.9	53.9
1962	38.6	43.0	45.3	52.6	53.9	61.6	66.4	66.0	63.3	55.1	47.6	42.6	53.0
1963	35.0	47.8	45.2	48.6	56.6	60.0	63.1	66.1	65.1	54.2	46.0	38.0	52.1
1964	40.9	40.1	43.8	46.7	52.6	58.7	64.5	63.7	58.4	53.2	41.0	37.0	50.1
1965	40.2	43.4	47.6	51.8	54.3	61.8	69.7	68.6	60.4	57.5	49.7	39.5	53.7
1966	40.3	42.8	47.2	50.6	57.0	62.4	66.4	67.5	64.4	53.7	47.1	44.2	53.7
1967	43.6	43.7	44.0	46.9	57.1	65.9	69.3	72.9	66.4	54.8	46.2	40.4	54.3
1968	39.3	48.2	48.2	48.0	56.3	62.2	68.6	65.8	61.5	52.1	46.5	37.3	52.8
1969	31.9	39.7	46.5	50.1	59.5	66.5	66.6	66.1	63.4	53.3	47.2	42.9	52.8
1970	40.6	46.0	46.9	48.4	57.0	65.9	69.2	68.2	60.7	53.0	47.1	40.0	53.6
1971	40.4	42.8	43.7	49.6	56.8	60.2	69.2	71.6	60.8	52.4	45.5	40.4	52.8
1972	39.2	43.8	49.8	48.0	60.2	64.0	70.9	71.7	61.2	53.0	48.2	37.4	53.9
1973	39.0	44.9	47.9	52.3	59.4	63.9	70.3	65.9	64.4	54.3	44.2	44.7	54.2
1974	38.0	43.0	47.2	51.3	55.7	64.4	67.1	68.9	67.3	55.2	48.1	44.1	54.2
1975	41.5	41.2	45.0	47.3	57.5	61.9	69.0	65.3	65.7	53.5	46.0	42.7	53.1
RECORD MEAN	38.5	43.0	45.9	50.6	57.0	60.2	65.8	65.3	62.7	54.0	45.7	41.1	52.5
MAX	44.1	50.3	54.4	60.3	67.3	70.2	77.3	76.5	74.4	63.1	52.4	46.4	61.4
MIN	32.9	35.7	37.4	40.9	46.7	50.2	54.2	54.1	51.0	44.8	39.0	35.7	43.6

# Indicates a station move or relocation of instruments.

PORTLAND, OR

Feb	Mar	Apr	May	June	Total
838	639	364	201	174	5112
648	578	390	190	95	4946
451	599	420	128	62	4059
618	559	375	280	89	4320
653	612	424	337	78	4980
494	530	442	261	66	4302
613	605	364	339	118	4789
477	606	486	272	168	4574
716	650	539	380	182	5065
599	533	388	325	113	4987
620	545	425	249	99	4338
591	647	535	246	50	4334
482	515	500	261	110	4311
703	570	442	178	51	4940
526	553	493	246	71	4325
615	653	454	253	149	4709
607	466	501	174	61	4485
560	525	378	202	89	4430
610	545	403	282	72	4424
660	615	523	240	127	4405

Aug	Sept	Oct	Nov	Dec	Total
65	43	0	0	0	297
120	8	2	0	0	394
217	7	3	0	0	416
221	44	0	0	0	531
81	45	0	0	0	403
144	102	0	0	0	409
57	75	2	0	0	342

Precipitation

Year	Jan	Feb	Mar	Apr	May	June	July	Aug	Sept	Oct	Nov	Dec	Annual
1940											4.53	4.85	
1941	5.27	1.59	1.74	1.66	4.27	0.81	0.03	1.45	3.58	2.18	5.04	9.11	36.73
1942	3.63	3.64	1.63	2.38	2.84	1.94	1.40	0.17	0.06	3.49	11.57	9.37	42.12
1943	5.50	3.27	5.54	2.21	1.42	2.80	0.32	1.39	0.06	5.59	2.20	2.70	33.00
1944	2.81	3.11	1.93	2.28	1.07	0.81	0.06	0.03	2.73	1.64	5.00	1.90	23.37
1945	4.10	4.36	5.30	2.42	4.57	0.07	0.51	0.37	3.96	2.11	8.58	5.61	41.96
1946	5.12	4.99	4.23	0.78	1.24	1.91	1.08	0.18	1.15	4.81	7.57	5.47	38.53
1947	3.72	2.77	4.11	1.81	0.66	2.93	0.94	0.29	1.06	8.04	4.08	4.64	35.05
1948	5.87	5.02	4.24	3.41	3.76				3.28	2.39	6.89	8.06	
1949	1.02	9.46	2.78	0.72	2.12	0.68	0.91	0.24	1.66	2.35	5.56	4.86	32.36
1950	10.10	5.77	4.76	2.74	0.57	2.50	0.50	0.72	1.45	7.00	8.67	6.31	51.09
1951	7.71	5.02	3.86	1.14	1.75	0.03	0.28	0.02	2.55	6.81	5.31	5.06	39.54
1952	4.40	3.59	3.82	1.45	0.78	2.23	T	0.18	0.33	0.72	1.44	6.76	25.70
1953	12.83	3.71	3.82	1.89	3.45	2.04	0.03	1.79	1.16	3.56	6.16	7.85	48.29
1954	8.95	4.57	2.55	2.54	1.83	3.58	1.24	1.92	0.85	3.40	5.09	5.01	41.53
1955	2.30	3.37	3.06	4.72	1.24	1.83	0.89	T	2.86	6.69	7.34	10.14	44.44
1956	11.66	3.03	4.30	0.53	2.50	2.03	0.01	2.56	1.12	5.10	1.47	3.64	37.95
1957	2.23	4.14	7.52	1.84	1.97	0.73	0.19	0.69	0.49	3.53	3.07	6.15	32.55
1958	6.56	5.13	2.20	3.33	1.35	3.04	T	0.02	1.05	1.49	6.39	5.06	35.62
1959	7.57	4.18	3.22	0.92	2.89	2.38	0.56	0.09	2.81	3.51	3.30	3.08	34.51
1960	3.93	4.00	4.77	3.33	3.37	0.52	T	1.00	1.37	2.39	8.63	2.61	35.92
1961	4.50	8.92	6.04	3.59	2.80	0.47	0.42	1.07	0.64	2.89	4.67	5.94	41.95
1962	1.58	3.43	4.25	3.15	2.56	0.78	0.06	1.49	1.66	3.31	9.32	2.59	34.18
1963	2.27	3.48	4.69	3.78	2.74	1.71	1.17	0.87	0.75	3.04	5.64	3.60	33.74
1964	9.51	0.78	2.30	1.56	1.04	1.96	0.68	0.90	1.61	0.84	6.78	9.92	37.88
1965	7.44	2.22	1.10	2.20	1.31	0.83	0.44	0.73	0.01	2.03	5.64	7.34	31.29
1966	5.74	1.70	4.71	0.85	0.91	1.02	1.19	0.59	1.70	3.06	5.50	6.89	33.86
1967	6.21	2.02	4.31	2.17	1.02	1.01	0.00	T	0.76	4.72	2.27	4.75	29.24
1968	4.58	6.64	2.68	1.91	3.63	2.20	0.14	4.53	2.20	5.03	6.23	11.12	50.89
1969	7.60	3.14	1.13	2.28	1.61	2.99	0.14	0.04	3.86	3.02	3.18	8.12	37.11
1970	11.81	4.77	2.58	2.94	1.55	0.49	0.05	T	1.10	2.85	5.72	7.49	41.35
1971	7.09	3.36	4.87	2.72	1.00	1.76	0.26	0.95	3.53	2.37	5.76	8.05	41.72
1972	5.71	4.08	5.41	2.98	2.23	0.68	0.56	0.67	3.06	0.87	3.78	8.79	38.82
1973	3.69	1.94	2.45	1.33	1.43	1.45	0.06	1.41	3.29	3.14	11.55	9.93	41.67
1974	8.51	4.61	5.65	1.76	1.74	0.80	2.01	0.07	0.21	2.14	6.73	6.05	40.28
1975	8.43	4.75	3.45	1.88	1.35	1.13	0.43	2.10	T	4.76	4.10	6.68	39.06
RECORD MEAN	6.00	4.02	3.74	2.21	2.02	1.53	0.49	0.84	1.66	3.45	5.72	6.30	37.98

Record mean values above are means through the current year for the period beginning in 1941.

PORTLAND, OREGON

(Continued)

pressure from east of the Cascade Mountains produce strong easterly flow through the Columbia Gorge into the Portland area. In winter this brings the coldest weather with the extremes of low temperature registered in the cold airmass. Freezing rain and ice glaze are sometimes transitional effects. In summer hot, dry continental air brings the highest temperatures. Temperatures below zero are very infrequent. The lowest recorded is 3 degrees F. below zero. Temperatures above 100 degrees F. are also infrequent. The highest recorded temperature is 107 degrees F. Temperatures 90 degrees F. or higher are reached every year, but seldom persist for more than 2 or 3 days.

Destructive storms are infrequent in the Portland area. Surface winds seldom exceed gale force and only twice in the period of record have winds reached higher than 75 m.p.h. Thunderstorms occur about once a month through the spring and summer months. Heavy downpours are infrequent but gentle rains occur almost daily during winter months.

Most rural areas around Portland are farmed for berries, green beans, and vegetables for fresh market and processing. The long growing season with mild temperatures and ample moisture favor local nursery and seed industries. Tourist visitation is very heavy in Portland in summer owing to immediate accessibility of choice recreational areas of diversified nature ranging from marine to mountain.

Normals, Means, and Extremes

Month	Normal Degree days Base 65 °F		Precipitation in inches: Water equivalent							Precipitation in inches: Snow, Ice pellets				Relative humidity pct.			
	Heating	Cooling	Normal	Maximum monthly	Year	Minimum monthly	Year	Maximum in 24 hrs.	Year	Maximum monthly	Year	Maximum in 24 hrs.	Year	Hour 04 (Local time)	Hour 10	Hour 16	Hour 22
(a)				35		35		35		35		35		35	35	35	35
J	834	0	5.88	12.83	1953	1.02	1949	2.61	1974	41.4	1950	10.6	1950	86	82	76	83
F	622	0	4.06	9.46	1949	0.78	1964	2.00	1968	13.2	1949	3.2	1962	86	79	68	81
M	598	0	3.64	7.52	1957	1.10	1965	1.83	1943	12.9	1951	7.7	1951	85	72	60	78
A	432	0	2.22	4.72	1955	0.53	1956	1.47	1962	T	1975	T	1975	86	68	55	75
M	264	7	2.09	4.57	1945	0.57	1950	1.47	1968	0.6	1953	0.5	1953	85	66	53	74
J	128	38	1.59	3.58	1954	0.03	1951	1.82	1958	0.0		0.0		84	65	49	72
J	48	114	0.47	2.01	1974	0.00	1967	0.91	1966	0.0		0.0		82	61	45	68
A	56	106	0.82	4.53	1968	T	1970	1.38	1968	0.0		0.0		84	64	46	71
S	119	35	1.60	3.96	1945	T	1975	2.23	1969	T	1949	T	1949	86	66	49	75
O	347	0	3.59	8.04	1947	0.72	1952	2.18	1941	0.2	1950	0.2	1950	90	79	64	84
N	591	0	5.61	11.57	1942	1.44	1952	2.62	1973	8.2	1955	4.5	1955	88	82	74	85
D	753	0	6.04	11.12	1968	1.90	1944	2.17	1942	15.7	1968	8.0	1964	87	84	79	85
YR	4792	300	37.61	12.83	JAN 1953	0.00	JUL 1967	2.62	NOV 1973	41.4	JAN 1950	10.6	JAN 1950	86	72	60	78

(To better understand these tables, see full explanation of terms beginning on page 322)

Month	Wind		Wind: Fastest mile			Pct. of possible sunshine	Mean sky cover, tenths, sunrise to sunset	Mean number of days: Sunrise to sunset							Temperatures °F: Max.		Min.		Average station pressure mb.
	Mean speed m.p.h.	Prevailing direction	Speed m.p.h.	Direction	Year			Clear	Partly cloudy	Cloudy	Precipitation .01 inch or more	Snow, Ice pellets 1.0 inch or more	Thunderstorms	Heavy fog, visibility ¼ mile or less	90° and above (b)	32° and below	32° and below	0° and below	Elev. 39 feet m.s.l.
(a)	27	15	27	27		26	27	27	27	27	35	35	35	33	35	35	35	35	3
J	10.1	ESE	54	S	1951	24	8.6	2	3	26	19	1	*	4	0	3	13	*	1017.4
F	8.8	ESE	61	SW	1958	35	8.3	3	3	22	16	*	*	4	0	*	9	*	1016.4
M	8.3	ESE	57	S	1963	42	8.1	3	4	24	17	*	1	2	0	*	6	0	1013.6
A	7.2	NW	60	S	1957	48	7.7	4	5	21	14	0	1	1	0	0	1	0	1018.5
M	6.9	NW	42	SW	1960	54	7.1	5	7	19	11	*	1	*	*	0	*	0	1017.1
J	6.9	NW	40	SW	1958	51	6.8	6	7	17	9	0	1	*	1	0	0	0	1016.3
J	7.4	NW	31	S	1956	69	4.5	14	8	9	3	0	1	*	4	0	0	0	1015.7
A	7.0	NW	29	SW	1961	64	5.1	11	10	10	5	0	1	*	3	0	0	0	1016.0
S	6.4	NW	61	S	1963	60	5.4	11	7	12	7	0	1	3	2	0	0	0	1015.8
O	6.4	ESE	88	S	1962	40	7.2	5	7	19	13	0	*	8	*	0	1	0	1016.7
N	8.4	ESE	56	SW	1961	27	8.3	3	4	23	18	*	*	6	0	*	5	0	1014.7
D	9.6	ESE	57	S	1951	20	8.9	2	2	27	19	1	*	5	0	1	9	0	1018.5
YR	7.8	NW	88	S	OCT 1962	47	7.2	69	67	229	153	2	7	33	10	4	43	*	1016.4

FOOTNOTES

Means and extremes above are from existing and comparable exposures. Annual extremes have been exceeded at other sites in the locality as follows: Maximum monthly precipitation 20.14 in December 1882; maximum precipitation in 24 hours 7.66 in December 1882; maximum snowfall in 24 hours 16.0 in January 1937.

Station: HARRISBURG, PENNSYLVANIA
CAPITAL CITY AIRPORT
Elevation (ground): 338 feet

TEMPERATURES °F

Month	Normal Daily maximum	Normal Daily minimum	Normal Monthly	Extremes Record highest	Extremes Year	Extremes Record lowest	Extremes Year
(a)				37		37	
J	37.7	22.5	30.1	73	1950	-5	1968
F	40.5	24.0	32.3	75	1954	-2	1967
M	50.7	31.2	41.0	86	1945	8	1943
A	64.1	41.5	52.8	92	1957	21	1969
M	74.5	51.6	63.1	97	1942	31	1966
J	83.0	61.0	72.0	100	1966	41	1961
J	86.8	65.4	76.1	107	1966	49	1945
A	84.6	63.2	73.9	101	1944	46	1944
S	78.0	56.0	67.0	102	1953	30	1963
O	66.9	44.6	55.8	97	1941	23	1969
N	52.9	34.7	43.8	84	1950	13	1955
D	40.1	25.0	32.6	71	1946	-8	1960
YR	63.3	43.4	53.4	107	JUL 1966	-8	DEC 1960

IMPORTANT:
The time-period covered by this record is limited: See footnotes on next page for explanation and for additional history of EXTREME HIGHS AND LOWS recorded in the general area.

Harrisburg, the capital of Pennsylvania and the county seat of Dauphin County, is situated on the left bank of the Susquehanna River. It is in the Great Valley formed by the eastern foothills of the Appalachian Chain, and about 60 miles outheast of the Commonwealth's geographic center. It is nestled in a saucer-like bowl. 8 to 10 miles south of Blue Mountain, which serves as a barrier to provide a modifying influence upon the severe winter climate experienced 50 to 100 miles to the north and west. Although the severity of the winter climate is lessened, the City lies a little too far inland (150 miles) from the coast to derive the full benefits of the coastal climate.

Cool air is frequently trapped in the saucer, and this favors fog formation and heavy accumulations of industrial smoke, which are removed only by a vigorous change in airmass. Fortunately, the airmasses change with some regularity, and any one condition does not persist for many days in succession. The mountain barrier occasionally prevents cold waves from reaching the Great Valley. The City is favorably located to receive precipitation produced when warm, maritime air from the Atlantic Ocean is forced upslope to cross the Blue Ridge Mountains.

The growing season is favorably affected by geographic influences. The average growing season runs from April 10 to October 28, 201 days. The normal annual temperature is 2.4 degrees higher than at Pittsburgh and 2.7 degrees lower than at Philadelphia. The longest period with maximum temperature 90 degrees or above was 17 days in July and August 1941. A daily minimum temperature of 32 degrees or less was recorded consecutively for 60 days during the winter of 1944-45. The longest spell of minima zero degrees or below was 4 days in January 1936.

Excessive precipitaition is relatively infrequent, with the heaviest amounts usually during the summer months. The heaviest downpour occurred on August 8, 1925, when 1.04 inches fell in 5 minutes; 1.30 inches in 10 minutes; 1.50 inches in 15 minutes; and 2.20 inches in 20 minutes. During June 1972, Hurricane Agnes produced 15.11 inches from the 20th to the 23rd. Prolonged dry spells occur occasionally. During August and September 1947 there were 35 consecutive days with less than .01 of precipitation.

Tropical hurricanes rarely reach Harrisburg with destructive winds. However, 1955 saw two such storms within one week (August 13 and August 19) which was an unprecedented anomaly, but damage was relatively slight. The worst recorded brush with a hurricane occurred October 15, 1954, when the center of Hurricane Hazel passed a short distance west of Harrisburg with gale winds reaching a peak gust of 80 m.p.h. Although tornadoes are fairly common in Pennsylvania, the only tornadic winds observed in Harrisburg have been in connection with severe thunderstorms. rather than the true funnel-type vortices. On November 17, 1918, such a storm swept over the "Riverside" section north of the City about 11:30 p.m. A double house was lifted from its foundation and dropped back into the cellar. Some 30 other buildings were damaged heavily. On May 22, 1949, another severe thunderstorm with tornadic winds uprooted many trees in the River Park area, and did considerable property damage in the metropolitan area.

Flood stage on the Susquehanna River occurs on the average of about every four years in Harrisburg, but serious flooding is much less frequent. About one-third of all floods have occurred during March. The Flood of 1972 was the highest on record, cresting at 32.57 feet at 10:00 a.m. on Saturday June 24th. This was 15.57 feet above flood stage and 3.34 feet above the March 19, 1936, crest. Rain from Hurricane Agnes was associated with this flood.

HARRISBURG, PENNSYLVANIA

Normals, Means, and Extremes

(To better understand these tables, see full explanation of terms beginning on page 322)

Month	Normal Degree days Base 65 °F: Heating	Cooling	Precipitation in inches — Water equivalent: Normal	Maximum monthly	Year	Minimum monthly	Year	Maximum in 24 hrs.	Year	Snow, Ice pellets: Maximum monthly	Year	Maximum in 24 hrs.	Year	Relative humidity pct. Hour 01 (Local time)	Hour 07	Hour 13	Hour 19
(a)				37		37		37		37		37		36	37	36	37
J	1082	0	2.57	4.78	1964	0.70	1955	1.94	1944	34.0	1961	21.0	1945	69	71	58	64
F	916	0	2.42	5.62	1971	0.53	1968	1.93	1965	30.2	1964	19.6	1964	67	70	56	61
M	744	0	3.22	5.47	1944	1.20	1949	2.11	1952	22.6	1960	10.7	1960	67	71	52	57
A	370	0	2.98	6.23	1973	0.57	1946	2.18	1940	3.1	1959	3.1	1959	67	70	49	55
M	128	69	3.76	8.06	1953	0.51	1964	3.11	1944	T	1966	T	1966	73	73	51	57
J	0	214	3.11	18.55	1972	0.07	1966	12.55	1972	0.0		0.0		78	76	53	60
J	0	344	3.70	9.72	1969	0.78	1955	5.36	1969	0.0		0.0		78	78	51	60
A	0	279	3.22	9.07	1955	0.93	1957	3.35	1955	0.0		0.0		81	82	54	65
S	51	111	2.66	14.97	1975	0.72	1941	7.22	1975	0.0		0.0		82	84	55	68
O	293	8	2.57	6.82	1943	0.04	1963	2.61	1943	1.2	1972	1.2	1972	79	82	54	67
N	636	0	3.19	7.20	1972	0.53	1939	2.93	1943	15.4	1953	15.4	1953	74	77	56	65
D	1004	0	3.07	6.52	1973	0.23	1955	2.01	1950	28.3	1969	12.9	1969	71	73	59	64
YR	5224	1025	36.47	18.55	JUN 1972	0.04	OCT 1963	12.55	JUN 1972	34.0	JAN 1961	21.0	JAN 1945	74	76	54	62

Month	Wind: Mean speed m.p.h.	Prevailing direction	Fastest mile: Speed m.p.h.	Direction	Year	Pct. of possible sunshine	Mean sky cover, tenths, sunrise to sunset	Mean number of days — Sunrise to sunset: Clear	Partly cloudy	Cloudy	Precipitation .01 inch or more	Snow, Ice pellets 1.0 inch or more	Thunderstorms	Heavy fog, visibility ¼ mile or less	Temperatures °F Max.: (b) 90° and above	32° and below	Min.: 32° and below	0° and below	Average station pressure mb. Elev. 351 feet m.s.l.
(a)	37	14	37	37		37	25	37	37	37	37	37	37	37	37	37	37	37	3
J	8.3	WNW	47	W	1956	47	6.7	7	7	17	11	2	*	3	0	9	26	1	1007.0
F	9.2	WNW	60		1939	53	6.7	6	8	14	10	2	*	2	0	6	23	*	1005.3
M	9.7	WNW	68	W	1955	56	6.8	7	8	16	12	2	1	2	0	1	18	0	1003.4
A	9.4	WNW	56	SW	1952	57	6.7	6	8	16	12	*	2	1	*	0	4	0	1002.4
M	7.7	W	46		1940	59	6.5	6	10	15	12	0	6	1	1	0	*	0	1001.7
J	6.8	W	48	W	1963	63	6.2	6	11	13	11	0	6	1	5	0	0	0	1003.5
J	6.3	W	47	NW	1954	68	6.0	7	11	13	10	0	7	1	9	0	0	0	1003.7
A	6.0	W	45		1939	67	5.8	8	11	12	10	0	5	1	6	0	0	0	1005.5
S	6.1	WNW	40	W	1967	62	5.7	9	9	12	9	0	3	2	2	0	*	0	1006.6
O	6.6	W	50	E	1954	58	5.6	10	8	13	8	*	1	3	*	0	2	0	1008.2
N	7.9	WNW	58	SE	1950	46	6.8	6	9	15	10	1	*	2	0	*	11	0	1005.9
D	8.1	WNW	61	NW	1953	43	7.0	6	8	17	10	2	*	3	0	5	23	*	1006.6
YR	7.7	WNW	68	W	MAR 1955	58	6.4	84	108	173	125	9	33	21	25	21	107	1	1005.0

FOOTNOTES Means and extremes above are from existing and comparable exposures. Annual extremes have been exceeded at other sites in the locality as follows: Lowest temperature -14 in January 1912; minimum monthly precipitation 0.02 in October 1924.

Snowfall

Season	July	Aug	Sept	Oct	Nov	Dec	Jan
1936-37	0.0	0.0	0.0	T	1.5	5.2	3.7
1937-38	0.0	0.0	0.0	T	T	2.3	2.5
#1938-39	0.0	0.0	0.0	0.0	10.2	3.2	15.1
1939-40	0.0	0.0	0.0	T	T	5.3	5.0
1940-41	0.0	0.0	0.0	1.2	2.5	1.5	10.3
1941-42	0.0	0.0	0.0	0.0	T	0.4	7.7
1942-43	0.0	0.0	0.0	0.0	T	7.8	17.8
1943-44	0.0	0.0	0.0	0.0	T	0.1	5.7
1944-45	0.0	0.0	0.0	0.0	0.3	10.2	31.4
1945-46	0.0	0.0	0.0	0.0	T	14.6	2.1
1946-47	0.0	0.0	0.0	0.0	0.0	2.7	3.8
1947-48	0.0	0.0	0.0	0.0	2.9	6.0	17.0
1948-49	0.0	0.0	0.0	0.0	2.2	9.9	6.9
1949-50	0.0	0.0	0.0	0.0	T	2.5	0.3
1950-51	0.0	0.0	0.0	0.0	2.7	8.0	4.4
1951-52	0.0	0.0	0.0	0.0	0.7	19.5	4.3
1952-53	0.0	0.0	0.0	T	3.0	7.3	6.9
1953-54	0.0	0.0	0.0	0.0	15.4	T	12.0
1954-55	0.0	0.0	0.0	0.0	1.8	0.4	5.9
1955-56	0.0	0.0	0.0	0.0	4.6	3.4	5.4
1956-57	0.0	0.0	0.0	0.0	1.0	0.7	10.8
1957-58	0.0	0.0	0.0	T	T	7.0	4.8
1958-59	0.0	0.0	0.0	0.0	1.7	2.4	6.6
1959-60	0.0	0.0	0.0	0.0	T	8.0	0.7
1960-61	0.0	0.0	0.0	T	0.0	22.1	34.0
1961-62	0.0	0.0	0.0	0.0	3.7	18.8	2.3
1962-63	0.0	0.0	0.0	T	4.5	16.6	9.1
1963-64	0.0	0.0	0.0	0.0	T	15.8	19.4
1964-65	0.0	0.0	0.0	0.0	T	1.4	13.4
1965-66	0.0	0.0	0.0	T	T	T	24.8
1966-67	0.0	0.0	0.0	0.0	0.2	19.9	1.6
1967-68	0.0	0.0	0.0	0.0	9.7	13.0	3.0
1968-69	0.0	0.0	0.0	0.0	3.0	0.2	1.2
1969-70	0.0	0.0	0.0	T	2.1	28.3	9.8
1970-71	0.0	0.0	0.0	0.0	0.0	10.9	11.6
1971-72	0.0	0.0	0.0	0.0	8.8	T	2.6
1972-73	0.0	0.0	0.0	1.2	5.9	0.5	T
1973-74	0.0	0.0	0.0	0.0	T	15.3	7.0
1974-75	0.0	0.0	0.0	0.0	T	0.5	11.3
1975-76	0.0	0.0	0.0	0.0	T	2.2	
RECORD MEAN	0.0	0.0	0.0	0.1	2.1	7.7	9.1

Heating Degree Days

Season	July	Aug	Sept	Oct	Nov	Dec	Jan
1955-56	0	0	67	257	718	1124	1015
1956-57	7	0	146	295	613	762	1139
1957-58	0	0	76	376	594	855	1070
1958-59	0	0	62	336	596	1177	1095
1959-60	0	0	59	280	683	895	961
1960-61	0	0	23	307	593	1216	1232
1961-62	0	2	41	244	569	1042	1139
1962-63	0	3	126	297	712	1132	1198
1963-64	1	7	149	242	570	1173	1072
1964-65	0	4	71	399	570	958	1192
1965-66	0	7	44	357	677	900	1191
1966-67	0	0	69	312	592	1024	966
1967-68	0	5	85	369	750	931	1266
1968-69	0	3	18	277	593	1038	1083
1969-70	0	3	89	352	662	1036	1299
1970-71	0	0	39	213	564	931	1192
1971-72	0	0	40	146	643	759	940
1972-73	0	1	25	395	686	865	964
1973-74	0	1	34	238	534	887	931
1974-75	0	0	94	414	600	911	977
1975-76	0	0	87	232	445	951	

Cooling Degree Days

Year	Jan	Feb	Mar	Apr	May	June	July
1969	0	0	0	3	71	235	327
1970	0	0	0	7	102	191	353
1971	0	0	0	0	17	241	331
1972	0	0	0	0	33	133	357
1973	0	0	0	8	13	266	334
1974	0	0	0	34	79	176	401
1975	0	0	0	0	97	192	325

Feb	Mar	Apr	May	June	Total
4.5	9.5	T	0.0	0.0	24.4
1.7	2.3	T	0.0	0.0	8.8
1.1	2.2	T	0.0	0.0	31.8
13.7	2.9	T	0.0	0.0	26.9
2.2	16.6	0.0	0.0	0.0	34.3
4.9	10.2	T	0.0	0.0	23.2
4.6	4.5	0.6	0.0	0.0	35.3
6.5	13.2	0.4	0.0	0.0	25.9
9.7	T	0.0	0.0	0.0	51.6
11.4	T	0.0	0.0	0.0	28.1
18.2	3.6	0.0	0.0	0.0	28.3
15.0	0.9	T	0.0	0.0	41.8
7.9	6.2	T	0.0	0.0	33.1
6.0	1.0	T	0.0	0.0	9.8
1.8	2.7	T	0.0	0.0	19.6
2.0	9.1	0.0	0.0	0.0	35.6
2.1	4.4	0.5	0.0	0.0	24.2
1.3	0.2	T	0.0	0.0	28.9
8.6	2.6	0.0	0.0	0.0	19.3
4.6	20.2	T	T	0.0	38.2
16.4	2.4	0.7	0.0	0.0	32.0
13.0	16.8	T	0.0	0.0	41.6
2.8	8.8	3.1	0.0	0.0	25.4
9.5	22.6	0.1	0.0	0.0	40.9
18.7	4.0	2.5	0.0	0.0	81.3
15.9	10.9	T	0.0	0.0	51.6
14.2	6.1	T	T	0.0	50.5
30.2	9.0	0.3	0.0	0.0	74.7
1.7	15.1	0.2	0.0	0.0	31.8
16.8	1.0	T	T	0.0	42.6
16.5	10.2	T	0.0	0.0	48.4
1.8	3.5	0.0	0.0	0.0	31.0
16.8	3.8	0.0	0.0	0.0	25.0
7.5	12.9	T	0.0	0.0	60.6
5.1	5.3	T	0.0	0.0	32.9
21.6	0.5	1.1	0.0	0.0	34.6
5.7	T	T	0.0	0.0	13.3
5.5	T	T	0.0	0.0	27.8
13.1	6.1	T	0.0	0.0	31.0
9.6	6.5	0.3	T	0.0	35.4

Average Temperature

Year	Jan	Feb	Mar	Apr	May	June	July	Aug	Sept	Oct	Nov	Dec	Annual
1936	25.6	24.1	45.2	48.6	65.5	70.4	76.3	75.0	67.9	55.9	40.6	36.1	52.6
1937	37.7	33.0	37.6	49.6	63.4	72.2	74.8	75.0	63.8	52.8	43.6	32.8	53.0
#1938	31.0	35.0	44.6	53.4	61.0	70.2	75.7	77.2	64.1	56.8	44.8	34.1	54.0
1939	31.8	36.3	40.7	48.6	66.4	72.5	75.2	77.2	68.0	55.7	42.8	35.8	54.2
1940	21.8	32.3	35.4	47.6	62.0	70.5	76.5	70.4	64.0	51.6	43.6	37.6	51.1
1941	29.7	29.4	36.0	58.2	65.4	71.6	76.1	72.8	69.2	59.8	46.5	37.4	54.3
1942	29.1	29.8	42.8	56.0	66.2	71.4	76.0	72.1	66.6	57.0	43.8	30.5	53.4
1943	30.8	33.5	40.6	46.0	63.6	76.8	76.2	75.2	64.8	53.5	41.7	32.5	52.9
1944	32.8	33.0	37.0	48.9	68.8	72.0	77.1	75.3	67.0	53.7	44.3	27.6	53.3
1945	23.9	32.3	52.0	54.7	59.7	71.4	74.2	72.0	68.3	53.9	44.6	28.9	53.0
1946	32.4	32.0	48.8	51.7	62.1	68.8	74.6	69.4	67.0	58.4	47.2	36.4	54.1
1947	36.0	27.6	36.6	52.1	61.1	69.0	73.4	76.4	66.8	61.3	41.5	32.6	52.9
1948	23.6	30.1	43.0	52.2	61.4	70.4	75.3	73.1	66.4	52.8	48.2	34.2	52.6
1949	36.8	37.2	42.3	51.2	62.4	73.4	78.1	74.6	62.6	60.0	43.4	35.6	54.8
1950	39.8	32.0	36.0	47.6	60.8	69.7	72.6	72.2	62.8	56.3	43.6	30.1	52.0
1951	33.5	33.4	40.9	51.6	62.1	70.1	75.1	72.8	66.3	56.9	38.7	33.9	53.0
1952	34.6	36.4	39.2	53.9	60.2	73.5	77.7	73.4	66.5	51.1	44.5	36.1	53.9
1953	36.1	37.9	42.8	51.0	64.8	72.0	75.6	73.2	67.1	57.2	44.3	37.6	54.9
1954	29.5	39.4	40.4	55.4	59.6	71.6	74.9	71.4	67.7	57.9	42.4	33.4	53.6
1955	30.4	32.1	42.1	55.3	64.6	68.7	80.4	77.1	65.8	56.9	40.8	28.5	53.5
1956	32.0	35.4	38.2	49.1	59.7	71.0	72.0	72.4	62.5	55.2	43.7	40.2	52.6
1957	28.0	35.9	41.3	54.3	62.7	73.6	75.0	72.3	67.8	52.7	44.9	37.3	53.8
1958	30.3	26.8	38.5	53.9	61.1	66.6	76.0	72.9	65.8	54.2	45.0	26.8	51.5
1959	29.5	32.5	39.8	54.8	66.0	72.2	76.0	76.0	69.8	58.2	42.0	36.0	54.4
1960	33.8	34.1	32.0	56.7	59.9	70.5	72.9	75.0	67.4	55.1	45.1	25.6	52.3
1961	25.1	33.6	41.5	48.1	59.1	69.9	75.1	73.5	72.3	57.2	46.0	31.1	52.7
1962	28.0	28.2	39.3	52.0	64.9	72.1	74.9	73.0	62.8	55.7	41.1	28.2	51.7
1963	26.2	25.2	43.2	54.4	61.6	72.3	76.4	70.1	61.5	57.1	45.8	26.9	51.7
1964	30.2	28.9	40.5	49.6	64.3	71.4	76.1	71.5	66.2	52.0	45.7	33.9	52.5
1965	26.4	32.5	37.5	50.1	66.5	71.7	75.6	74.6	69.8	53.4	42.2	35.7	53.0
1966	26.3	31.5	43.8	49.0	61.4	74.6	79.9	78.3	66.7	54.7	45.1	31.7	53.6
1967	33.6	26.9	38.8	53.0	55.2	73.9	74.2	71.8	65.3	53.3	39.8	34.8	51.7
1968	24.0	29.2	43.7	53.7	58.0	70.3	77.3	76.7	67.6	56.1	44.9	31.3	52.7
1969	29.9	33.3	38.6	53.4	63.2	72.4	75.3	73.4	65.6	53.8	42.7	31.4	52.8
1970	22.9	30.4	36.7	51.4	65.1	70.7	76.2	75.6	71.6	58.7	46.0	34.8	53.4
1971	26.4	33.2	38.6	50.4	60.0	72.5	75.5	72.2	69.9	60.6	43.5	40.3	53.6
1972	34.5	30.2	40.0	49.6	62.3	67.7	76.2	74.0	68.4	52.1	41.8	36.8	52.8
1973	33.7	31.7	45.2	50.9	57.8	73.4	75.5	76.1	68.6	57.4	46.9	36.2	54.5
1974	34.8	32.3	42.8	56.2	63.0	70.5	77.6	77.1	64.5	51.6	44.9	35.4	54.2
1975	33.3	32.4	38.3	47.4	64.8	70.7	75.3	76.2	63.3	57.7	50.0	34.2	53.7
RECORD MEAN	30.5	31.0	40.2	50.5	62.2	70.9	75.3	73.2	66.6	55.2	43.5	33.1	52.7
MAX	37.3	38.3	48.4	59.1	72.1	80.6	84.8	82.6	76.0	64.5	51.3	39.9	61.2
MIN	23.6	23.7	31.9	41.8	52.2	61.1	65.7	63.8	57.1	45.9	35.6	26.3	44.1

# Indicates a station move or relocation of instruments.

HARRISBURG, PA

Feb	Mar	Apr	May	June	Total
850	824	484	202	19	5560
809	730	358	137	13	5009
1065	815	339	148	42	5380
904	773	307	103	23	5376
885	1017	292	171	3	5246
871	720	509	204	22	5697
1025	791	415	120	2	5390
1107	666	325	146	4	5716
1041	753	460	93	34	5595
902	847	441	66	27	5477
932	648	472	166	12	5406
1061	806	364	306	3	5503
1032	654	331	216	12	5651
882	809	345	123	8	5179
962	872	407	93	13	5785
884	812	432	165	12	5244
1001	766	457	108	44	4907
926	607	422	227	7	5125
910	683	289	133	2	4642
903	818	520	97	13	5347

Aug	Sept	Oct	Nov	Dec	Total
267	113	11	0	0	1027
333	246	24	0	0	1256
236	195	17	6	0	1043
287	137	3	0	0	950
352	148	9	0	0	1130
381	88	1	3	0	1163
354	44	12	2	0	1026

Precipitation

Year	Jan	Feb	Mar	Apr	May	June	July	Aug	Sept	Oct	Nov	Dec	Annual
1936	5.58	3.32	6.61	3.61	1.60	4.61	5.02	2.97	2.45	2.00	1.35	6.06	45.18
1937	5.34	3.16	1.45	4.58	3.19	7.14	4.83	6.24	1.02	6.76	4.50	1.52	49.73
#1938	2.07	2.03	2.83	2.19	3.45	2.92	2.65	4.28	4.41	2.42	3.83	3.65	36.73
1939	3.06	4.00	2.55	2.79	0.54	2.44	1.63	4.09	3.43	3.88	0.53	1.90	30.84
1940	1.21	3.09	4.99	4.70	3.56	2.93	3.17	6.22	3.46	2.63	4.22	2.86	43.04
1941	2.38	0.83	2.10	1.76	1.93	3.47	2.80	2.63	0.72	1.49	1.92	3.49	25.52
1942	2.37	2.93	3.14	1.54	6.39	3.63	5.53	4.60	2.58	4.40	2.19	5.04	44.34
1943	2.33	1.42	2.69	3.28	6.24	2.32	2.05	1.68	0.85	6.82	3.72	1.06	34.46
1944	2.97	1.25	5.47	3.94	5.03	5.49	0.88	1.51	3.94	3.04	3.39	3.61	40.52
1945	3.34	2.02	1.95	4.09	5.26	3.95	8.52	4.76	5.41	1.07	5.54	3.32	49.23
1946	1.07	1.73	3.18	0.57	7.54	5.61	3.36	2.97	1.55	3.33	0.68	1.99	33.58
1947	3.33	1.77	1.37	3.13	5.27	3.67	5.46	3.24	1.35	0.72	5.59	1.15	36.05
1948	2.75	1.28	3.34	3.97	5.64	3.26	2.02	3.70	0.77	3.45	4.57	3.53	38.28
1949	4.18	2.41	1.20	3.20	2.12	1.09	8.28	2.49	1.61	2.67	0.94	2.77	32.96
1950	2.48	3.15	3.78	1.66	5.60	1.68	3.19	1.28	1.82	2.30	3.04	3.75	33.73
1951	3.65	2.89	3.42	1.35	1.88	4.79	1.16	1.25	2.40	1.40	4.61	4.75	33.55
1952	3.43	1.80	4.89	5.97	5.80	0.86	4.09	2.92	4.69	0.74	5.17	3.17	43.53
1953	4.41	2.29	3.86	3.28	8.06	3.04	3.58	1.20	2.32	1.64	2.92	3.20	39.80
1954	1.47	2.18	3.52	3.58	3.28	0.58	2.33	5.79	1.51	3.75	2.53	2.94	33.46
1955	0.70	2.48	3.97	2.02	0.96	4.09	0.78	9.07	3.36	5.01	1.78	0.23	34.45
1956	1.45	3.47	4.41	2.66	2.43	2.66	4.57	3.48	3.24	3.52	1.97	4.26	38.12
1957	1.64	2.64	1.97	3.89	0.84	3.38	1.68	0.93	2.19	1.78	2.81	5.23	28.98
1958	4.61	3.61	3.67	3.21	3.29	3.08	2.76	2.46	4.20	1.30	3.85	0.66	36.70
1959	2.66	1.92	2.57	3.18	1.51	4.81	3.20	5.54	0.91	4.17	2.14	3.01	35.62
1960	2.10	3.30	2.52	2.59	7.41	4.17	4.73	1.85	5.34	1.34	1.39	2.41	39.15
1961	3.46	3.07	4.19	4.56	2.03	1.93	6.60	5.49	1.24	0.92	3.56	3.42	40.47
1962	2.15	4.33	2.70	2.81	2.96	4.03	1.20	4.18	3.59	4.21	4.10	3.32	39.58
1963	2.19	1.83	3.86	1.52	2.66	2.36	1.97	2.55	2.82	0.04	5.93	2.36	30.09
1964	4.78	3.12	2.94	4.91	0.51	4.20	2.25	3.07	1.77	1.92	1.87	3.11	34.45
1965	2.70	3.29	3.61	1.25	2.38	2.60	3.10	3.99	2.12	3.65	1.63	0.87	31.19
1966	3.57	4.44	1.88	3.44	0.98	0.07	0.81	1.53	6.12	2.12	3.56	3.08	31.60
1967	1.81	1.54	5.26	2.58	4.32	1.90	5.96	5.61	1.80	3.15	2.89	4.27	41.09
1968	1.32	0.53	3.40	2.43	6.55	2.25	1.94	1.77	5.18	2.34	3.38	2.12	33.21
1969	1.06	1.70	2.20	2.13	1.56	2.54	9.72	2.07	2.32	1.63	3.29	6.46	36.68
1970	0.88	3.25	3.64	5.03	2.39	5.80	6.34	2.97	2.12	3.20	4.59	3.50	43.71
1971	2.70	5.62	2.67	1.04	5.30	1.80	2.84	7.77	1.94	2.85	4.96	1.93	41.42
1972	2.65	5.00	2.68	4.10	5.56	18.55	2.26	2.52	1.41	2.03	7.20	5.31	59.27
1973	3.24	2.50	2.00	6.23	6.37	3.34	2.18	2.19	5.73	2.47	1.04	6.52	43.81
1974	3.82	1.36	4.64	3.21	4.38	3.69	2.79	4.13	6.79	1.25	2.30	4.59	42.95
1975	4.12	3.10	3.78	2.80	5.25	6.51	3.13	1.83	14.97	2.62	2.92	3.19	54.22
RECORD MEAN	2.83	2.70	3.19	3.02	3.61	3.61	3.61	3.76	3.21	2.82	2.66	2.94	37.96

Record mean values above are means through the current year for the period beginning in 1889 for temperature and precipitation, 1939 for snowfall. Data are from City Office locations through 1938 and from Airport locations thereafter.

Station: PHILADELPHIA, PENNSYLVANIA INTERNATIONAL AIRPORT
Elevation (ground): 5 feet

TEMPERATURES °F

Month	Normal			Extremes			
	Daily maximum	Daily minimum	Monthly	Record highest	Year	Record lowest	Year
(a)				16		16	
J	40.1	24.4	32.3	69	1967	-5	1963
F	42.2	25.5	33.9	69	1972	-4	1961
M	51.2	32.5	41.9	80	1960	9	1960
A	63.5	42.3	52.9	92	1960	24	1969
M	74.1	52.3	63.2	96	1962	28	1966
J	83.0	61.6	72.3	100	1964	44	1972
J	86.8	66.7	76.8	104	1966	51	1966
A	84.8	64.7	74.8	99	1975	45	1965
S	78.4	57.8	68.1	97	1973	35	1963
O	67.9	46.9	57.4	88	1975	25	1969
N	55.5	36.9	46.2	81	1974	17	1964
D	43.2	27.2	35.2	71	1966	3	1962
YR	64.2	44.9	54.6	104	JUL 1966	-5	JAN 1963

IMPORTANT:
The time-period covered by this record is limited: See footnotes following table of NORMALS, MEANS AND EXTREMES for explanation and for additional history of EXTREME HIGHS AND LOWS recorded in the general area.

Snowfall

Season	July	Aug	Sept	Oct	Nov	Dec	Jan
1936-37	0.0	0.0	0.0	0.0	T	0.3	0.4
1937-38	0.0	0.0	0.0	0.0	T	T	2.3
1938-39	0.0	0.0	0.0	0.0	11.5	0.2	11.0
1939-40	0.0	0.0	0.0	0.0	0.4	2.9	2.9
1940-41	0.0	0.0	0.0	2.2	T	2.9	6.2
1941-42	0.0	0.0	0.0	0.0	0.0	0.5	5.3
#1942-43	0.0	0.0	0.0	0.0	0.0	5.2	2.3
1943-44	0.0	0.0	0.0	0.0	T	T	3.2
1944-45	0.0	0.0	0.0	0.0	T	1.5	11.7
1945-46	0.0	0.0	0.0	0.0	0.2	13.4	1.8
1946-47	0.0	0.0	0.0	0.0	0.0	T	3.2
1947-48	0.0	0.0	0.0	0.0	T	7.6	9.9
1948-49	0.0	0.0	0.0	0.0	0.0	7.6	3.4
1949-50	0.0	0.0	0.0	0.0	T	T	0.7
1950-51	0.0	0.0	0.0	0.0	1.8	0.2	2.4
1951-52	0.0	0.0	0.0	0.0	T	5.7	4.0
1952-53	0.0	0.0	0.0	T	0.6	2.0	5.1
1953-54	0.0	0.0	0.0	0.0	8.8	T	13.3
1954-55	0.0	0.0	0.0	0.0	0.0	T	2.7
1955-56	0.0	0.0	0.0	0.0	2.9	1.1	7.0
1956-57	0.0	0.0	0.0	0.0	T	0.2	4.7
1957-58	0.0	0.0	0.0	T	T	7.8	3.7
1958-59	0.0	0.0	0.0	0.0	T	0.3	3.3
1959-60	0.0	0.0	0.0	0.0	T	5.7	0.8
1960-61	0.0	0.0	0.0	0.0	0.0	17.5	19.7
1961-62	0.0	0.0	0.0	0.0	3.2	5.2	1.1
1962-63	0.0	0.0	0.0	T	T	9.5	6.1
1963-64	0.0	0.0	0.0	0.0	T	8.0	7.4
1964-65	0.0	0.0	0.0	0.0	T	2.6	11.9
1965-66	0.0	0.0	0.0	T	0.0	T	16.0
1966-67	0.0	0.0	0.0	0.0	T	18.8	0.6
1967-68	0.0	0.0	0.0	0.0	4.9	5.6	1.5
1968-69	0.0	0.0	0.0	0.0	0.4	3.1	1.9
1969-70	0.0	0.0	0.0	0.0	0.2	7.5	7.5
1970-71	0.0	0.0	0.0	T	0.0	1.1	7.7
1971-72	0.0	0.0	0.0	0.0	T	0.1	3.2
1972-73	0.0	0.0	0.0	T	T	T	T
1973-74	0.0	0.0	0.0	0.0	T	4.6	4.1
1974-75	0.0	0.0	0.0	0.0	T	0.8	3.9
1975-76	0.0	0.0	0.0	0.0	0.0	1.1	
RECORD MEAN	0.0	0.0	0.0	T	0.7	4.2	5.3

Heating Degree Days

Season	July	Aug	Sept	Oct	Nov	Dec	Jan
1955-56	0	0	32	200	626	1061	1011
1956-57	2	2	107	222	556	718	1103
1957-58	0	0	64	335	510	786	1023
1958-59	0	0	64	296	547	1096	1030
#1959-60	0	0	46	246	589	823	947
1960-61	0	0	25	312	577	1150	1232
1961-62	0	0	45	283	593	1049	1078
1962-63	0	4	109	272	681	1048	1159
1963-64	0	7	118	242	502	1144	985
1964-65	0	2	51	377	532	847	1107
1965-66	0	18	41	342	614	862	1110
1966-67	0	0	83	362	538	908	893
1967-68	0	0	55	271	660	814	1112
1968-69	0	0	14	234	576	1008	1084
1969-70	0	0	54	316	611	970	1247
1970-71	0	0	29	191	499	899	1145
1971-72	0	0	17	79	576	719	920
1972-73	0	0	22	378	635	775	940
1973-74	0	0	18	196	507	810	897
1974-75	0	0	46	313	500	786	852
1975-76	0	0	45	152	372	866	

Cooling Degree Days

Year	Jan	Feb	Mar	Apr	May	June	July
1969	0	0	0	9	77	259	319
1970	0	0	0	3	100	204	376
1971	0	0	0	0	19	292	394
1972	0	0	3	0	47	143	381
1973	0	0	0	16	35	294	404
1974	0	0	0	24	55	179	373
1975	0	0	0	0	121	224	366

The Appalachian Mountains to the west and the Atlantic Ocean to the east have a moderating effect on climate. Sustained periods of very high or very low temperatures seldom last for more than 3 or 4 days as conditions change fairly rapidly. Below zero and above 100 degree readings are relatively rare. On those occasions when the area becomes engulfed with maritime air during the summer months, high humidity can add to the discomfort of seasonably warm temperatures.

Precipitation is fairly evenly distributed throughout the year with maximum amounts during the late summer months. Much of the summer rainfall is in connection with local thunderstorms and is variable in amount in different parts of the City, due in part to the higher elevations in the western and northern sections. Snowfall amounts often are considerably larger in the northern suburbs than in the central and southern parts of the City. In many cases, the precipitation will change from snow to rain within the City. Single storms of 10 inches or more occur about every five years. The maximum amount of 21.0 inches fell on December 25-26, 1909.

The prevailing wind direction for the summer months is from the southwest, while northwesterly winds prevail during the winter. The annual prevailing direction is from the west-southwest. Destructive velocities are comparatively rare and occur mostly in gustiness during summer thunder-

(Continued page 608)

Feb	Mar	Apr	May	June	Total
4.1	7.8	T	0.0	0.0	12.6
4.1	1.9	T	0.0	0.0	8.3
0.5	4.0	T	0.0	0.0	27.2
11.7	3.2	1.2	0.0	0.0	22.3
8.9	11.3	0.0	0.0	0.0	31.5
2.0	2.5	T	0.0	0.0	10.3
1.0	7.8	T	0.0	0.0	16.3
4.7	7.8	T	0.0	0.0	15.7
7.9	0.0	0.0	0.0	0.0	21.1
3.3	0.0	0.0	0.0	0.0	18.7
17.8	2.7	0.0	0.0	0.0	23.7
12.8	1.4	0.0	0.0	0.0	31.7
7.4	0.9	T	0.0	0.0	19.3
1.2	T	T	0.0	0.0	1.9
0.2	T	0.0	0.0	0.0	4.6
T	6.5	0.0	0.0	0.0	16.2
2.0	7.1	T	0.0	0.0	16.8
0.2	0.3	T	0.0	0.0	22.6
6.8	2.6	0.0	0.0	0.0	12.1
1.1	10.9	T	0.0	0.0	23.0
1.8	1.2	T	0.0	0.0	7.9
16.9	13.4	T	0.0	0.0	41.8
T	1.5	T	0.0	0.0	5.1
3.1	12.2	T	0.0	0.0	21.8
11.8	0.1	T	0.0	0.0	49.1
12.5	7.2	T	0.0	0.0	29.2
4.7	0.2	0.0	T	0.0	20.5
12.4	5.1	T	0.0	0.0	32.9
2.2	6.5	3.0	0.0	0.0	26.2
11.4	T	T	0.0	0.0	27.4
18.4	6.4	0.1	0.0	0.0	44.3
1.7	2.2	0.0	0.0	0.0	15.9
9.5	8.8	0.0	0.0	0.0	23.7
2.7	2.4	T	0.0	0.0	20.3
0.8	4.4	4.3	0.0	0.0	18.3
8.2	0.3	0.4	0.0	0.0	12.2
T	T	T	0.0	0.0	T
12.1	T	T	0.0	0.0	20.8
6.6	2.3	T	0.0	0.0	13.6
6.2	3.7	0.2	T	0.0	20.3

PHILADELPHIA, PA

Feb	Mar	Apr	May	June	Total
790	808	456	170	11	5165
765	695	346	126	15	4657
1024	770	328	136	27	5003
884	721	311	91	24	5064
850	997	274	129	5	4906
862	672	452	214	15	5511
963	748	408	133	7	5307
1072	680	375	175	12	5587
955	685	424	76	13	5151
883	839	475	66	26	5205
931	693	509	207	21	5348
1001	817	396	280	6	5284
995	633	305	170	7	5022
918	782	290	84	2	4992
890	821	399	92	0	5400
802	746	394	140	3	4848
941	748	450	86	26	4562
874	547	359	176	1	4707
926	667	292	128	11	4452
812	732	483	66	4	4594

Aug	Sept	Oct	Nov	Dec	Total
323	126	15	0	0	1128
367	247	46	0	0	1343
326	223	37	14	0	1305
344	153	3	0	0	1074
435	193	23	0	0	1400
372	145	5	12	0	1165
380	98	42	12	0	1243

Average Temperature

Year	Jan	Feb	Mar	Apr	May	June	July	Aug	Sept	Oct	Nov	Dec	Annual
1936	29.9	27.6	48.3	50.2	65.8	71.8	77.3	76.0	69.5	58.6	43.5	39.6	54.8
1937	41.4	35.8	38.7	51.2	65.3	72.6	77.1	77.2	66.4	55.0	46.2	36.0	55.2
1938	33.6	37.4	45.8	55.2	61.5	71.3	77.2	78.4	66.3	59.3	48.6	37.6	56.0
1939	34.4	39.4	41.7	50.4	66.4	73.2	76.2	77.8	69.2	57.6	44.9	38.1	55.8
#1940	25.3	34.8	37.5	48.2	62.4	71.4	77.2	72.0	67.4	54.3	46.4	40.4	53.1
1941	30.7	30.7	36.2	57.9	65.0	71.6	76.1	73.1	69.7	61.0	47.4	38.3	54.8
1942	30.5	30.8	43.8	54.9	67.1	72.5	77.2	73.1	68.3	57.2	45.4	30.9	54.3
1943	31.8	34.1	41.3	46.8	63.3	76.8	76.4	76.4	66.4	54.0	43.9	32.8	53.7
1944	34.0	33.8	38.5	49.4	67.4	72.2	78.4	75.4	68.6	54.7	45.6	32.2	54.2
#1945	24.8	33.8	51.2	56.4	60.2	71.5	76.0	74.1	70.9	57.2	48.6	29.8	54.5
1946	33.8	34.5	49.8	51.8	63.3	69.2	75.2	70.7	69.4	60.2	49.1	38.0	55.4
1947	38.3	28.4	37.8	52.7	62.0	69.7	75.4	75.8	68.2	62.8	43.6	34.2	54.1
1948	26.0	31.8	43.8	52.0	62.0	71.2	76.4	74.6	67.7	55.2	50.9	37.4	54.1
1949	39.8	39.2	43.9	53.4	64.4	74.6	80.0	76.2	65.6	61.8	45.8	39.0	57.0
1950	43.2	33.8	38.6	49.2	61.0	71.1	75.4	73.7	64.5	59.5	47.3	34.2	54.3
1951	36.0	36.4	43.1	53.6	63.6	71.3	77.0	74.9	68.3	60.2	42.5	38.7	55.4
1952	37.3	38.2	41.2	55.5	61.7	74.7	80.1	75.2	68.5	53.8	46.7	38.5	55.9
1953	38.0	38.9	45.1	53.1	65.3	73.2	77.9	75.3	69.4	59.6	46.7	39.4	56.8
1954	31.7	41.2	42.3	56.3	61.2	72.9	77.9	73.5	69.1	61.2	45.4	36.0	55.7
1955	32.6	36.1	44.4	55.9	66.1	69.2	81.4	78.1	68.0	59.1	44.0	30.5	55.5
1956	32.1	37.6	38.8	49.9	60.9	72.3	73.6	74.1	65.2	57.7	46.3	41.7	54.2
1957	29.2	37.4	42.3	54.2	63.5	74.9	76.6	73.2	69.2	54.1	47.8	39.4	55.1
1958	31.8	28.2	39.9	54.2	61.2	67.8	77.4	73.4	65.9	55.7	46.6	29.4	52.6
#1959	31.6	33.3	41.5	54.8	66.4	72.2	75.9	76.5	70.8	60.1	45.2	38.2	55.5
1960	34.2	35.4	32.7	56.7	61.2	70.6	73.3	74.5	67.3	54.8	45.5	27.6	52.8
1961	25.0	34.0	43.1	49.8	58.6	69.9	75.6	73.5	71.5	55.7	45.2	31.0	52.7
1962	30.0	30.4	40.5	52.0	64.1	71.7	72.0	72.0	63.1	56.3	42.1	31.0	52.1
1963	27.5	26.5	42.9	52.5	60.2	70.4	76.0	71.2	62.8	57.1	48.0	27.9	51.9
1964	33.0	31.8	42.7	50.8	65.1	72.4	76.6	72.2	67.2	52.6	47.1	37.5	54.1
1965	29.2	33.3	37.6	49.0	65.5	70.0	74.1	73.1	69.2	53.7	44.2	37.0	53.0
1966	29.1	31.5	42.5	47.8	59.5	72.1	77.9	74.8	65.2	53.1	46.8	35.5	53.0
1967	36.0	29.0	38.5	51.7	55.9	72.1	76.6	75.1	67.0	56.8	42.8	38.5	53.3
1968	28.9	30.4	44.4	54.6	59.7	71.2	77.1	77.8	69.4	58.1	45.6	32.3	54.1
1969	29.8	32.0	39.7	55.3	64.6	73.4	75.1	75.2	67.2	55.0	44.4	33.5	53.8
1970	24.5	33.1	38.3	51.5	64.9	71.6	76.9	76.7	72.0	60.1	48.2	35.8	54.5
1971	27.8	36.1	40.7	51.6	60.9	74.3	77.4	75.3	71.6	63.5	46.1	41.6	55.6
1972	35.1	32.4	40.7	49.7	63.6	68.7	77.1	76.0	69.2	52.7	43.6	39.9	54.1
1973	34.4	33.6	47.2	53.4	60.3	74.6	77.9	78.8	70.7	59.2	48.0	38.6	56.4
1974	35.9	31.7	43.3	55.8	62.4	70.3	76.9	76.8	68.1	54.8	48.5	39.4	55.3
1975	37.3	35.8	41.2	48.7	66.6	72.2	76.6	77.1	66.6	61.2	52.7	36.9	56.1
RECORD MEAN	33.1	33.8	41.6	52.2	63.0	71.8	76.6	74.7	68.4	57.5	46.2	36.2	54.6
MAX	40.1	41.2	49.8	61.4	72.5	81.0	85.3	83.1	76.9	66.1	53.8	43.0	62.9
MIN	26.0	26.3	33.4	42.9	53.4	62.6	67.9	66.3	59.9	48.8	38.6	29.3	46.3

# Indicates a station move or relocation of instruments.

Precipitation

Year	Jan	Feb	Mar	Apr	May	June	July	Aug	Sept	Oct	Nov	Dec	Annual
1936	6.44	3.46	4.02	2.25	1.67	3.96	2.60	3.30	3.72	1.76	0.69	4.83	38.70
1937	5.71	1.66	2.98	4.38	2.62	3.51	1.16	4.10	1.55	5.24	3.44	1.05	37.40
1938	2.32	2.54	1.83	1.92	2.86	10.06	6.52	4.10	7.35	2.09	3.11	2.22	46.92
1939	4.46	6.12	4.32	6.40	1.91	4.45	2.19	6.90	1.91	4.30	1.26	1.18	45.40
#1940	0.96	2.90	4.10	6.06	4.89	2.52	1.82	7.87	4.58	2.38	4.24	2.53	44.85
1941	2.88	1.76	2.56	2.62	1.01	4.51	7.16	3.95	0.88	1.64	2.27	3.91	35.15
1942	2.49	2.84	5.27	1.14	1.87	1.74	5.19	8.93	2.52	3.26	3.44	4.36	43.05
1943	3.25	1.89	2.92	2.61	5.63	4.03	3.94	0.65	1.69	5.21	3.72	1.23	36.77
1944	2.99	1.93	5.46	4.69	2.25	3.23	1.05	2.78	5.82	1.81	4.71	2.80	39.52
#1945	2.86	3.35	1.72	2.89	3.85	3.77	8.86	3.75	3.96	1.90	5.69	4.02	46.62
1946	1.39	1.77	2.94	1.43	6.09	6.69	6.37	3.26	2.83	1.24	2.01	2.33	38.35
1947	3.63	2.02	2.22	6.58	7.22	5.15	2.12	3.65	2.71	2.13	5.23	1.80	44.46
1948	4.68	2.84	3.76	3.92	7.41	4.94	1.89	5.95	2.09	1.53	4.79	5.26	49.06
1949	6.06	3.55	2.77	2.35	5.91	0.11	4.25	4.53	4.10	2.74	1.08	3.03	40.48
1950	1.85	3.41	4.68	2.10	3.89	2.36	5.80	4.29	2.59	2.16	5.22	2.12	40.47
1951	3.83	3.24	4.52	2.49	4.00	4.17	2.24	0.89	1.73	3.33	5.83	5.48	41.75
1952	4.75	1.98	5.37	5.22	4.85	2.59	3.04	6.32	3.05	0.49	4.91	3.27	45.84
1953	5.01	2.44	6.27	4.81	5.85	4.97	3.98	2.47	1.74	4.38	1.93	4.28	48.13
1954	1.93	1.37	3.71	3.75	2.40	2.59	1.24	4.86	3.26	2.40	3.87	2.66	34.04
1955	0.45	2.49	4.80	1.93	0.91	4.06	1.04	9.70	1.71	4.53	1.16	0.25	33.03
1956	2.30	4.64	4.65	2.68	3.84	3.86	4.61	2.79	3.75	3.47	5.71	3.70	46.00
1957	1.67	2.81	3.24	4.22	1.21	2.41	0.64	3.38	3.10	2.05	2.98	4.49	32.20
1958	3.53	4.64	4.97	4.19	3.65	5.13	5.98	6.20	2.55	3.85	2.05	1.13	47.87
1959	2.03	1.60	3.55	2.25	0.80	5.28	7.48	3.73	1.33	3.41	3.29	3.62	38.37
1960	3.11	3.44	1.96	2.92	3.65	0.71	5.52	3.19	8.78	2.79	1.92	3.16	41.15
1961	3.16	3.13	5.17	4.82	3.38	2.95	5.96	3.42	2.41	1.83	2.04	2.78	41.05
1962	2.95	3.51	3.91	3.69	1.85	7.40	2.30	6.58	2.77	0.95	4.60	2.11	42.62
1963	2.31	2.19	3.94	1.13	1.06	2.88	3.13	3.35	6.44	0.09	6.67	1.76	34.95
1964	3.92	2.83	1.94	5.27	0.47	0.21	3.83	0.49	2.42	1.73	1.64	5.13	29.88
1965	2.35	2.18	3.19	2.33	1.23	2.85	3.22	4.05	3.02	2.02	1.05	1.85	29.34
1966	2.82	4.30	0.68	4.35	2.95	0.41	2.35	1.63	8.70	5.12	2.36	4.33	40.00
1967	1.67	1.82	4.53	2.17	3.49	4.12	7.11	7.08	2.96	2.00	1.99	5.88	44.82
1968	2.90	1.40	4.98	1.57	5.17	5.89	2.00	1.24	0.44	3.15	4.17	2.54	35.45
1969	1.57	1.88	1.92	1.68	3.30	7.31	8.33	2.66	4.38	1.13	1.97	7.23	43.36
1970	0.74	2.08	3.83	6.12	2.57	4.60	2.75	3.99	0.82	3.66	4.71	3.27	39.14
1971	2.13	5.43	2.58	1.84	4.10	1.01	4.84	9.61	5.83	3.84	5.37	1.21	47.79
1972	2.34	5.09	2.69	4.08	4.11	5.79	2.62	3.76	1.12	3.77	9.06	5.20	49.63
1973	3.93	2.96	3.52	6.68	4.14	7.88	2.39	2.03	3.39	2.16	0.64	6.34	46.06
1974	2.95	2.14	4.91	2.77	3.21	4.43	2.08	3.83	4.68	1.93	0.81	4.04	37.78
1975	4.00	2.91	4.68	2.97	4.99	7.57	6.32	2.21	7.21	3.24	3.14	2.89	52.13
RECORD MEAN	3.16	3.11	3.52	3.29	3.34	3.65	4.10	4.50	3.41	2.79	3.10	3.21	41.18

Record mean values above are means through the current year for the period beginning in 1874 for temperature, 1872 for precipitation, and 1943 for snowfall. Temperature, degree days, and precipitation: Data are from City Office locations through December 1949 (except through June 1940 for degree days); from Southwest Airport (later named International Airport) through June 1945; from 2nd and Chestnut Streets (Bourse Building for precipitation) through November 1945; and from International Airport locations thereafter.
Precipitation totals for 1941 and 1942 are based on an observational day ending at 1:30 a.m.
Snowfall: Data are from City Office locations through 1942 and from International Airport locations thereafter except that data for November 1945 are from 2nd and Chestnut Streets.

(Continued)

storms. High winds occurring in the winter months, as a rule, come with the advance of cold air after the passage of a deep low pressure system. Only rarely have hurricanes in the vicinity caused widespread damage, then primarily through flooding.

Flood stages in the Schuylkill River normally occur about twice a year. Flood stages seldom last over 12 hours and ususally occur after excessive thunderstorms. Flooding rarely occurs on the Delaware River.

Normals, Means, and Extremes

Month	Normal Degree days Base 65 °F		Precipitation in inches												Relative humidity pct.			
			Water equivalent							Snow, Ice pellets					Hour 01	Hour 07	Hour 13	Hour 19
	Heating	Cooling	Normal	Maximum monthly	Year	Minimum monthly	Year	Maximum in 24 hrs.	Year	Maximum monthly	Year	Maximum in 24 hrs.	Year	(Local time)				
(a)				33		33		29		33		33		16	16	16	16
J	1014	0	2.81	6.06	1949	0.45	1955	2.27	1968	19.7	1961	13.2	1961	71	74	60	66
F	871	0	2.62	5.43	1971	1.37	1954	1.96	1966	18.4	1967	13.0	1958	68	71	57	61
M	716	0	3.69	6.27	1953	0.68	1966	2.39	1968	13.4	1958	10.0	1958	68	71	53	58
A	367	0	3.29	6.68	1973	1.13	1963	2.76	1970	4.3	1971	4.3	1971	68	69	49	54
M	122	67	3.35	7.41	1948	0.47	1964	2.09	1956	T	1963	T	1963	76	75	53	58
J	0	223	3.70	7.88	1973	0.11	1949	4.62	1973	0.0		0.0		81	78	55	62
J	0	366	4.09	8.33	1969	0.64	1957	4.26	1969	0.0		0.0		82	79	54	63
A	0	304	4.11	9.70	1955	0.49	1964	5.68	1971	0.0		0.0		82	81	54	65
S	38	131	3.03	8.78	1960	0.44	1968	5.45	1960	0.0		0.0		82	83	56	70
O	249	13	2.53	5.21	1943	0.09	1963	3.78	1966	T	1972	T	1972	80	82	53	69
N	564	0	3.39	9.06	1972	0.64	1973	3.46	1950	8.8	1953	8.7	1953	74	77	55	66
D	924	0	3.32	7.23	1969	0.25	1955	1.77	1951	18.8	1966	14.6	1960	73	74	61	68
YR	4865	1104	39.93	9.70	AUG 1955	0.09	OCT 1963	5.68	AUG 1971	19.7	JAN 1961	14.6	DEC 1960	75	76	55	63

(To better understand these tables, see full explanation of terms beginning on page 322)

Month	Wind					Pct. of possible sunshine	Mean sky cover, tenths, sunrise to sunset	Mean number of days											Average station pressure mb.
			Fastest mile					Sunrise to sunset							Temperatures °F				
															Max. (b)		Min.		Elev. 28 feet m.s.l.
	Mean speed m.p.h.	Prevailing direction	Speed m.p.h.	Direction	Year			Clear	Partly cloudy	Cloudy	Precipitation .01 inch or more	Snow, Ice pellets 1.0 inch or more	Thunderstorms	Heavy fog, visibility ¼ mile or less	90° and above	32° and below	32° and below	0° and below	
(a)	35	23	35	35		33	35	35	35	35	35	35	35	35	16	16	16	16	3
J	10.3	WNW	61	NE	1958	50	6.7	7	8	16	11	2	*	3	0	8	25	*	1018.9
F	11.1	NW	59	NW	1956	53	6.4	7	7	14	9	2	*	3	0	5	23	*	1016.9
M	11.5	N	56	NW	1955	56	6.4	7	9	15	11	1	1	2	0	1	16	0	1014.7
A	11.1	SW	59	SW	1958	56	6.5	7	9	14	11	*	2	1	*	0	3	0	1013.7
M	9.7	WSW	56	SW	1957	57	6.5	6	11	14	11	0	4	1	1	0	*	0	1013.1
J	8.8	WSW	73	NW	1958	63	6.2	7	11	12	10	0	5	1	4	0	0	0	1014.9
J	8.1	WSW	47	W	1959	63	6.1	7	12	12	9	0	6	1	7	0	0	0	1014.8
A	7.9	SW	67	E	1955	63	5.9	8	11	12	9	0	5	1	5	0	0	0	1016.6
S	8.3	SW	49	NE	1960	60	5.7	10	9	11	8	0	2	2	2	0	0	0	1017.6
O	8.9	WSW	66	SW	1954	60	5.5	11	8	12	7	*	1	4	0	0	2	0	1019.6
N	9.7	WSW	60	SW	1958	53	6.3	7	10	13	9	*	1	3	0	0	10	0	1017.3
D	10.1	WNW	47	NW	1958	49	6.5	7	9	15	10	1	*	3	0	4	22	0	1017.8
YR	9.6	WSW	73	NW	JUN 1958	58	6.2	91	114	160	116	6	27	25	19	19	101	*	1016.3

FOOTNOTES

Means and extremes above are from existing and comparable exposures. Annual extremes have been exceeded at other sites in the locality as follows: Highest temperature 106 in August 1918: lowest temperature -11 in February 1934; maximum monthly precipitation 12.10 in August 1911; maximum precipitation in 24 hours 5.89 in August 1898; maximum monthly snowfall 31.5 in February 1899; maximum snowfall in 24 hours 21.0 in December 1909; fastest mile of wind 88 from North in July 1931.

Station: PITTSBURGH, PENNSYLVANIA
FEDERAL BUILDING
Elevation (ground): 747

TEMPERATURES °F

Month	Normal			Extremes			
	Daily maximum	Daily minimum	Monthly	Record highest	Year	Record lowest	Year
(a)				41		41	
J	37.4	23.7	30.6	77	1950	-13	1963
F	39.5	24.4	32.0	74	1937	-5	1958
M	48.9	31.8	40.4	83	1950	4	1943
A	62.5	42.4	52.5	90	1970	18	1950
M	72.3	52.0	62.2	92	1962	29	1966
J	81.0	61.5	71.3	99	1952	39	1972
J	84.0	65.2	74.6	103	1936	50	1972
A	82.6	63.3	73.0	100	1948	45	1965
S	76.7	56.2	66.5	100	1953	35	1974
O	66.1	45.4	55.8	91	1951	24	1972
N	51.6	36.5	44.1	83	1961	5	1958
D	39.8	26.8	33.3	73	1971	-7	1951
YR	61.9	44.1	53.0	103	JUL 1936	-13	JAN 1963

IMPORTANT:
The time-period covered by this record is limited: See footnotes on next page for explanation and for additional history of EXTREME HIGHS AND LOWS recorded in the general area.

Pittsburgh lies at the foothills of the Allegheny Mountains at the confluence of the Allegheny and Monongahela Rivers which form the Ohio. The city is a little over a hundred miles southeast of Lake Erie. It has a humid continental type of climate modified only slightly by its nearness to the Atlantic Seaboard and the Great Lakes.

The predominant type of air which influences the climate of Pittsburgh has a polar continental source in Canada and moves in upon the region by way of tracks which vary from almost due north from the Hudson Bay region to a long westerly trajectory resulting from polar outbreaks into the Rockies which progress eastward. There are frequent invasions of air from the Gulf of Mexico during the summer season with resulting spells of warm humid weather. During the winter season air from the Gulf occasionally reaches as far north as Pittsburgh and causes the normal alternate periods of freezing and thawing. The last killing frost in spring will usually occur about April 21 and the first in autumn near October 20, to give an average growing season of about 180 days. There is a wide varitation in the time of the first and last frosts over a radius of 25 miles from the center of Pittsburgh due to terrain differences.

Precipitation is distributed well throughout the year. During the winter months about a fourth of the precipitation occurs as snow and there is about a 50% chance of measurable precipitation on any day. Thunderstorms occur normally during all months except the midwinter ones, and have a maximum frequency in midsummer. The first appreciable snowfall is generally late in November and usually the last occurs early in April. Snow lies on the ground in the suburbs an average of about 33 days during the year.

Seven months of the year, April through October, have sunshine more than 50% of the possible time. During the remaining five months cloudiness is heavier because the track of migratory storms from west to east is closer to the area and because of the frequent periods of cloudy, showery weather a sociated with northwest winds from across the Great Lakes. Cold air drainage induced by the many hills leads to the frequent formation of early morning fog which may be quite persistent in the river valleys during the colder months.

Rises from the tributary streams cause occasional flooding at Pittsburgh. Serious inconvenience is occasioned by the Ohio River reaching the flood stage of 25 feet about once each year. Significant flooding, or a 30 foot stage, occurs about once each three years.

PITTSBURGH, PENNSYLVANIA

Normals, Means, and Extremes

(To better understand these tables, see full explanation of terms beginning on page 322)

Month	Normal Degree days Base 65 °F: Heating	Cooling	Precipitation in inches — Water equivalent: Normal	Maximum monthly	Year	Minimum monthly	Year	Maximum in 24 hrs.	Year	Snow, Ice pellets: Maximum monthly	Year	Maximum in 24 hrs.	Year
(a)				41		41		41		41		41	
J	1066	0	2.61	8.20	1937	0.73	1940	1.84	1952	22.7	1964	17.8	1964
F	924	0	2.29	5.97	1956	0.37	1941	2.04	1975	23.9	1940	17.0	1940
M	763	0	3.58	6.38	1967	0.94	1969	2.52	1945	17.8	1967	17.0	1942
A	382	7	3.44	6.26	1948	0.44	1971	2.25	1948	6.0	1953	4.9	1953
M	161	74	3.59	6.33	1968	1.12	1936	2.84	1971	1.0	1966	1.0	1966
J	10	199	3.74	7.44	1951	0.95	1966	2.71	1947	0.0		0.0	
J	0	298	3.78	7.96	1943	1.26	1938	3.44	1967	0.0		0.0	
A	6	254	3.18	8.17	1955	0.29	1957	3.34	1956	0.0		0.0	
S	58	103	2.53	8.84	1945	0.63	1963	3.13	1962	0.0		0.0	
O	298	13	2.47	7.79	1954	0.16	1963	3.57	1954	1.3	1972	1.3	1972
N	627	0	2.49	7.40	1950	0.26	1939	2.37	1950	27.7	1950	20.1	1950
D	983	0	2.52	5.09	1944	0.17	1955	1.75	1944	24.2	1944	17.5	1944
YR	5278	948	36.22	8.84	SEP 1945	0.16	OCT 1963	3.57	OCT 1954	27.7	NOV 1950	20.1	NOV 1950

Month	Relative humidity pct.: Hour	Hour	Hour	Hour (Local time)	Wind: Mean speed m.p.h.	Prevailing direction	Fastest mile: Speed m.p.h.	Direction	Year	Pct. of possible sunshine	Mean sky cover, tenths, sunrise to sunset	Mean number of days — Sunrise to sunset: Clear	Partly cloudy	Cloudy	Precipitation .01 inch or more	Snow, Ice pellets 1.0 inch or more	Thunderstorms	Heavy fog, visibility ¼ mile or less	Temperatures °F Max.: 90° and above (b)	32° and below	Min.: 32° and below	0° and below	Average station pressure mb. Elev. feet m.s.l.
(a)										41					41	41			41	41	41	41	
J										27					15	2			0	10	23	1	
F										31					14	2			0	7	21	*	
M										39					15	2			0	3	17	0	
A										45					14	*			*	*	4	0	
M										50					13	*			1	0	*	0	
J										53					12	0			4	0	0	0	
J										53					11	0			6	0	0	0	
A										50					9	0			4	0	0	0	
S										52					8	0			2	0	0	0	
O										45					10	*			*	0	1	0	
N										31					12	1			0	1	9	0	
D										23					14	2			0	7	21	*	
YR										42					147	9			16	27	97	1	

FOOTNOTES Means and extremes above are from existing and comparable exposures. Annual extremes have been exceeded at other sites in the locality as follows: Lowest temperature -20 in February 1899; maximum monthly precipitation 9.51 in July 1887; minimum monthly precipitation 0.06 in October 1874; maximum precipitation in 24 hours 4.08 in September 1876; maximum monthly snowfall 36.3 in December 1890.

Snowfall

Season	July	Aug	Sept	Oct	Nov	Dec	Jan
1936-37	0.0	0.0	0.0	0.0	0.6	10.1	2.8
1937-38	0.0	0.0	0.0	T	2.0	3.9	7.2
1938-39	0.0	0.0	0.0	0.0	7.5	1.3	13.5
1939-40	0.0	0.0	0.0	T	T	5.1	4.5
1940-41	0.0	0.0	0.0	T	1.2	0.6	10.3
1941-42	0.0	0.0	0.0	0.0	T	0.1	6.2
1942-43	0.0	0.0	0.0	T	1.7	12.8	14.5
1943-44	0.0	0.0	0.0	T	0.5	0.6	T
1944-45	0.0	0.0	0.0	0.0	1.7	24.2	16.0
1945-46	0.0	0.0	0.0	0.0	0.3	12.5	3.7
1946-47	0.0	0.0	0.0	0.0	0.0	3.1	3.5
1947-48	0.0	0.0	0.0	0.0	0.4	1.6	11.0
1948-49	0.0	0.0	0.0	0.0	1.0	3.9	4.0
1949-50	0.0	0.0	0.0	0.0	0.8	0.7	0.4
1950-51	0.0	0.0	0.0	0.0	27.7	12.0	7.3
1951-52	0.0	0.0	0.0	T	3.8	10.6	3.0
1952-53	0.0	0.0	0.0	0.3	1.6	11.0	4.0
1953-54	0.0	0.0	0.0	0.0	1.4	1.8	6.4
1954-55	0.0	0.0	0.0	0.2	0.4	3.1	4.3
1955-56	0.0	0.0	0.0	0.0	4.6	1.0	5.3
1956-57	0.0	0.0	0.0	0.0	1.2	7.5	5.5
1957-58	0.0	0.0	0.0	0.4	0.6	3.5	7.8
1958-59	0.0	0.0	0.0	0.0	6.1	5.0	8.8
1959-60	0.0	0.0	0.0	0.0	2.2	9.9	1.7
1960-61	0.0	0.0	0.0	T	0.6	16.3	16.8
1961-62	0.0	0.0	0.0	0.0	2.8	5.5	3.8
1962-63	0.0	0.0	0.0	T	T	11.8	6.2
1963-64	0.0	0.0	0.0	0.0	5.3	11.8	22.7
1964-65	0.0	0.0	0.0	T	0.5	2.6	7.5
1965-66	0.0	0.0	0.0	T	0.1	0.3	18.5
1966-67	0.0	0.0	0.0	0.0	2.9	3.0	1.6
1967-68	0.0	0.0	0.0	0.0	5.5	6.6	9.2
1968-69	0.0	0.0	0.0	T	3.0	4.6	3.4
1969-70	0.0	0.0	0.0	0.6	4.2	11.0	9.7
1970-71	0.0	0.0	0.0	0.0	0.2	5.6	5.3
1971-72	0.0	0.0	0.0	0.0	6.1	0.7	4.2
1972-73	0.0	0.0	0.0	1.3	3.2	2.4	1.2
1973-74	0.0	0.0	0.0	0.0	0.3	2.0	4.1
1974-75	0.0	0.0	0.0	T	0.7	17.2	11.0
1975-76	0.0	0.0	0.0	0.0	0.2	1.1	
RECORD MEAN	0.0	0.0	0.0	0.1	2.5	6.4	7.4

Heating Degree Days

Season	July	Aug	Sept	Oct	Nov	Dec	Jan
1955-56	0	0	30	275	693	1013	1050
1956-57	0	6	127	183	595	682	1124
1957-58	0	0	64	394	568	808	1074
1958-59	0	2	64	312	540	1179	1116
1959-60	0	0	55	285	661	807	910
1960-61	0	0	18	284	540	1133	1176
1961-62	6	0	45	226	587	949	1100
1962-63	0	0	142	274	630	1123	1185
1963-64	7	4	86	135	524	1201	953
1964-65	0	15	67	361	491	858	1068
1965-66	1	15	50	393	593	780	1230
1966-67	0	2	125	386	593	975	895
1967-68	9	10	123	345	782	862	1176
1968-69	1	9	25	308	591	1034	1117
1969-70	0	0	84	327	709	1109	1290
1970-71	3	0	45	242	585	919	1200
1971-72	0	3	35	140	668	747	990
1972-73	13	4	38	433	707	787	995
1973-74	2	3	39	243	573	916	879
1974-75	0	0	142	416	591	925	929
1975-76	0	0	121	288	467	937	

Cooling Degree Days

Year	Jan	Feb	Mar	Apr	May	June	July
1969	0	0	0	7	81	197	303
1970	0	0	0	33	138	181	281
1971	0	0	0	0	22	261	226
1972	0	0	0	2	54	94	269
1973	0	0	0	26	14	247	300
1974	0	0	3	18	55	102	267
1975	0	0	0	0	109	205	285

Feb	Mar	Apr	May	June	Total
5.5	6.8	0.1	0.0	0.0	25.9
3.1	0.5	1.2	0.0	0.0	17.9
7.5	0.3	0.4	0.0	0.0	30.5
23.9	4.7	0.9	0.0	0.0	39.1
3.3	11.9	0.0	0.0	0.0	27.3
4.8	17.4	0.0	0.0	0.0	28.5
5.3	6.1	0.9	T	0.0	41.3
2.4	10.1	1.3	0.0	0.0	14.9
3.1	1.5	T	0.0	0.0	46.5
5.2	0.3	0.0	0.0	0.0	22.0
13.9	4.8	0.0	0.0	0.0	25.3
6.9	1.0	T	0.0	0.0	20.9
0.5	3.7	0.5	0.0	0.0	13.6
2.6	5.2	0.6	0.0	0.0	10.3
2.2	6.5	0.6	0.0	0.0	56.3
1.8	8.3	1.9	0.0	0.0	29.4
1.1	6.2	6.0	T	0.0	30.2
2.8	4.7	0.1	T	0.0	17.2
7.6	3.6	T	0.0	0.0	19.2
0.3	9.5	1.0	0.0	0.0	21.7
2.8	4.9	0.3	0.0	0.0	22.2
5.0	4.8	0.2	0.0	0.0	22.3
1.0	10.0	3.7	0.0	0.0	34.6
16.1	16.4	0.4	0.0	0.0	46.7
19.6	0.9	2.8	0.0	0.0	57.0
8.8	11.4	0.1	0.0	0.0	32.4
11.4	2.5	T	0.8	0.0	32.7
9.1	4.7	0.2	0.0	0.0	53.8
5.9	8.9	0.8	0.0	0.0	26.2
7.4	3.2	1.3	1.0	0.0	31.8
13.7	17.8	T	0.0	0.0	39.0
4.3	4.7	T	0.0	0.0	30.3
4.5	3.6	0.0	0.0	0.0	19.1
6.7	11.8	T	0.0	0.0	44.0
9.1	10.5	T	0.0	0.0	30.7
9.8	5.6	0.8	0.0	0.0	27.2
1.8	1.5	0.5	T	0.0	11.9
1.1	0.2	0.4	T	0.0	8.1
10.7	5.6	0.8	0.0	0.0	46.0
6.7	6.1	0.8	T	0.0	30.0

PITTSBURGH, PA
FEDERAL OFFICE BUILDING

Feb	Mar	Apr	May	June	Total
808	759	466	184	44	5322
757	694	355	118	13	4654
1082	818	351	138	45	5342
835	779	338	95	30	5290
934	1065	287	173	6	5183
784	638	551	244	23	5391
887	791	442	63	2	5098
1110	611	385	162	17	5639
993	692	342	87	38	5062
936	890	428	48	37	5199
914	705	482	261	29	5453
1013	710	371	296	5	5371
1150	668	325	245	30	5725
926	882	330	129	29	5381
963	870	357	107	12	5823
893	881	510	213	1	5492
1033	819	441	96	87	5059
937	453	431	207	0	5005
926	691	364	199	24	4859
860	830	564	74	27	5358

Aug	Sept	Oct	Nov	Dec	Total
248	95	23	0	0	954
284	209	26	0	0	1152
200	188	30	0	0	927
238	108	0	0	0	765
319	129	16	0	0	1051
243	44	7	1	0	740
299	33	17	4	0	952

Average Temperature

Year	Jan	Feb	Mar	Apr	May	June	July	Aug	Sept	Oct	Nov	Dec	Annual
1936	26.1	25.6	44.1	48.0	65.1	71.2	77.1	76.4	69.8	56.4	40.6	38.6	53.3
1937	40.2	33.2	36.7	49.8	62.6	72.0	74.8	76.7	64.0	52.2	42.0	32.6	51.0
1938	32.2	38.1	47.0	53.6	61.8	69.3	76.8	76.7	65.4	58.4	45.9	35.4	55.1
1939	35.6	36.5	41.9	49.0	65.7	73.2	73.2	75.2	69.4	57.0	42.7	36.5	54.7
1940	20.4	32.2	35.7	48.2	61.1	72.0	75.1	72.8	64.1	54.6	43.5	40.3	51.7
1941	31.3	28.2	33.7	58.2	63.4	72.6	76.2	72.9	69.1	59.7	46.3	39.4	54.3
1942	31.7	28.2	43.1	56.0	65.0	72.8	75.7	72.6	66.6	57.7	45.0	31.0	53.8
1943	33.2	33.9	40.0	46.4	63.0	76.6	75.3	73.4	64.4	52.4	41.8	32.0	52.7
1944	35.0	34.2	38.2	50.0	70.6	73.8	76.0	74.8	66.4	55.0	45.0	29.8	54.1
1945	24.5	34.1	52.2	55.8	58.2	70.4	75.0	73.6	69.4	54.1	45.5	29.2	53.5
1946	34.2	34.8	52.6	51.4	61.5	70.3	74.4	69.2	68.0	59.2	48.6	38.5	55.2
1947	38.8	25.2	35.0	53.5	60.6	70.4	72.0	78.7	68.3	63.2	41.8	35.1	53.6
1948	24.4	34.7	45.2	56.0	61.9	71.8	75.6	73.2	68.1	52.0	49.6	37.1	54.1
1949	40.0	39.8	42.4	50.8	64.0	74.6	78.4	74.8	62.5	60.6	44.3	37.9	55.8
1950	42.7	34.2	36.6	47.3	63.3	70.3	72.6	72.2	65.4	58.6	40.7	29.8	52.8
1951	35.4	35.2	41.9	50.9	63.5	72.0	75.5	73.4	65.8	59.2	39.4	36.4	54.1
1952	37.0	36.9	40.6	54.0	60.4	74.3	78.1	74.0	67.6	51.7	47.0	37.3	54.9
1953	38.7	37.9	43.6	50.4	66.6	73.6	76.1	74.5	67.6	57.9	46.9	38.1	56.0
1954	33.0	40.4	39.6	58.7	59.4	72.2	74.8	72.4	69.4	57.9	44.3	34.1	54.7
1955	30.8	35.2	43.6	58.5	64.7	67.6	79.5	76.7	68.5	56.3	41.7	32.1	54.6
1956	30.9	36.9	40.4	49.7	61.0	70.6	73.1	72.9	63.1	58.9	44.9	42.8	53.8
1957	28.5	37.8	42.4	55.1	63.9	73.2	74.9	72.6	67.5	52.2	45.8	38.7	54.4
1958	30.2	26.1	38.4	53.5	61.7	66.8	75.4	72.1	66.0	55.1	46.9	26.7	51.6
1959	28.8	35.0	39.5	53.7	66.5	71.3	75.7	77.6	70.7	57.3	42.9	38.7	54.8
1960	35.4	32.5	30.4	57.7	60.9	70.2	72.1	74.9	69.3	55.8	46.8	28.2	52.8
1961	26.9	36.7	44.2	46.6	57.8	68.9	74.2	74.6	71.5	58.0	45.4	34.2	53.3
1962	29.3	33.1	39.3	51.5	67.9	72.4	72.9	73.9	62.7	56.6	43.8	28.5	52.6
1963	26.6	25.1	45.1	52.5	60.8	70.5	73.9	70.6	64.2	61.1	47.3	26.0	52.0
1964	34.0	30.5	42.5	53.6	64.8	71.1	75.8	70.4	66.3	53.3	48.4	37.1	54.0
1965	30.3	31.3	36.0	50.5	67.2	69.1	72.6	71.8	69.0	52.2	45.1	39.6	52.9
1966	25.1	32.1	42.1	48.9	57.7	71.3	76.0	72.7	62.5	52.5	45.1	33.4	51.6
1967	35.9	28.6	42.0	53.1	55.4	73.7	72.2	70.0	62.4	54.3	38.7	37.0	52.0
1968	26.8	25.0	43.3	53.9	57.2	69.7	74.9	74.6	67.8	55.7	45.1	31.5	52.1
1969	28.8	31.7	36.3	54.0	63.2	70.4	74.6	72.7	65.2	55.2	41.1	29.0	51.9
1970	23.2	30.4	36.7	53.9	65.7	70.3	73.8	74.0	70.2	57.8	45.3	35.1	53.0
1971	26.0	32.8	36.4	47.8	58.6	73.4	72.1	71.2	69.8	61.2	42.5	40.7	52.7
1972	32.9	29.1	38.3	50.2	63.4	65.1	73.1	72.3	67.1	50.8	41.2	39.4	51.9
1973	32.7	31.3	50.2	51.3	58.5	73.0	74.4	75.0	67.8	57.6	45.7	35.2	54.4
1974	36.4	31.7	42.7	53.2	60.2	67.4	73.4	72.6	61.4	51.6	45.0	34.9	52.6
1975	34.8	34.0	38.0	46.0	66.0	70.7	74.0	74.4	61.9	56.1	49.3	34.6	53.3
RECORD MEAN	31.7	32.8	41.1	52.1	62.4	71.2	74.9	73.6	66.6	56.1	44.5	34.6	53.5
MAX	38.9	40.5	49.9	62.0	72.8	81.2	84.6	83.2	76.4	65.7	52.1	41.2	62.4
MIN	24.5	25.0	32.3	42.1	52.0	61.2	65.1	64.0	56.8	46.4	36.9	28.0	44.5

# Indicates a station move or relocation of instruments.

Precipitation

Year	Jan	Feb	Mar	Apr	May	June	July	Aug	Sept	Oct	Nov	Dec	Annual
1936	2.87	1.99	6.03	2.02	1.12	2.32	1.99	3.45	3.66	4.82	2.76	3.01	36.04
1937	8.20	1.47	1.93	6.19	3.22	2.49	4.14	3.10	0.88	4.40	1.32	2.96	40.30
1938	2.01	2.37	3.26	3.43	4.23	4.81	1.26	2.02	3.34	1.11	2.75	1.11	31.70
1939	2.48	4.41	2.74	3.26	1.65	6.44	3.22	1.14	1.55	3.21	0.26	1.91	32.27
1940	0.73	3.96	3.93	5.63	4.72	4.37	3.81	3.16	4.24	1.06	3.61	2.97	42.19
1941	2.97	0.37	1.69	1.46	3.39	4.74	4.76	6.30	1.48	4.21	1.84	1.91	35.12
1942	1.88	2.19	5.21	2.76	4.68	2.64	2.93	2.41	3.43	4.16	2.95	5.03	40.27
1943	2.51	1.68	3.06	2.81	4.73	1.62	7.96	2.19	0.73	3.93	0.99	1.15	33.36
1944	1.59	2.08	5.81	3.84	3.39	5.24	2.30	5.19	1.91	2.99	2.22	5.09	41.65
1945	1.73	3.25	6.04	3.63	5.76	2.87	2.56	1.75	8.84	2.39	3.74	2.12	44.68
1946	0.92	2.67	2.46	0.94	4.38	6.89	2.23	2.21	1.57	3.47	1.27	2.41	31.42
1947	4.02	1.30	1.59	2.43	4.41	4.75	6.19	2.37	1.43	0.78	3.41	1.43	34.11
1948	2.02	2.10	3.76	6.26	2.82	5.26	3.49	3.30	1.65	3.60	3.43	3.35	41.04
1949	3.84	2.98	3.27	2.55	2.02	3.64	6.75	1.36	2.57	1.38	1.33	2.80	34.49
1950	6.23	3.03	3.53	2.61	3.64	4.65	5.01	3.84	3.71	1.30	7.40	2.50	47.45
1951	4.32	3.01	4.99	4.87	2.89	7.44	3.90	0.49	3.08	1.07	3.32	3.65	43.03
1952	4.99	2.17	4.33	3.17	4.83	4.63	2.90	3.87	1.23	1.18	2.29	3.01	38.60
1953	2.93	1.37	3.17	3.71	5.39	2.36	3.41	3.54	2.50	1.23	1.25	1.84	32.70
1954	1.95	1.74	4.32	3.91	2.65	4.37	1.57	5.33	2.31	7.79	0.96	2.74	39.64
1955	1.02	3.32	4.49	4.13	1.71	3.94	2.23	8.17	1.84	3.27	2.90	0.17	37.19
1956	1.75	5.97	5.03	4.18	6.08	4.13	4.15	5.28	2.91	1.63	0.76	3.43	45.30
1957	1.50	1.74	2.56	4.94	2.72	4.75	2.83	0.29	3.19	1.42	1.80	4.60	32.34
1958	2.72	0.93	1.56	3.12	4.92	2.63	5.57	5.64	3.21	0.85	2.18	0.94	34.27
1959	3.79	2.17	2.08	4.57	2.46	2.34	4.14	3.02	1.80	4.52	2.68	2.55	36.12
1960	2.85	2.67	2.02	1.43	4.88	3.82	2.90	2.92	2.54	2.07	1.40	1.58	31.08
1961	2.04	3.35	3.68	5.50	2.67	4.22	4.64	2.62	1.78	2.55	3.33	1.66	38.04
1962	2.62	3.71	3.90	3.39	2.28	2.25	3.13	3.16	6.29	1.64	1.25	2.24	35.86
1963	1.35	2.07	5.63	2.04	1.70	3.41	2.47	1.83	0.63	0.16	2.96	1.59	25.84
1964	2.45	1.92	5.10	5.34	2.47	5.62	3.95	2.51	0.87	1.94	2.76	3.75	38.68
1965	3.67	2.41	3.15	2.19	1.28	1.69	1.47	2.63	3.88	2.48	2.38	0.50	27.73
1966	4.21	3.47	1.43	4.16	2.82	0.95	2.30	3.77	1.99	1.26	3.99	1.66	32.01
1967	0.87	1.94	6.38	4.62	5.25	1.08	5.90	3.05	1.59	2.09	2.65	2.03	37.45
1968	2.30	0.72	3.60	2.34	6.33	2.18	1.62	1.99	3.40	2.09	2.11	2.69	31.37
1969	2.01	0.68	0.94	3.09	1.93	4.00	4.53	2.48	0.92	2.11	2.29	3.81	28.79
1970	1.36	1.55	2.65	3.29	3.10	4.12	5.49	1.88	2.51	4.62	2.71	3.44	36.72
1971	2.06	3.61	2.36	0.44	4.37	3.32	5.25	2.58	2.71	0.87	1.88	3.26	32.71
1972	1.87	2.52	3.50	4.20	2.09	7.04	3.29	1.71	6.30	2.44	3.64	2.56	41.16
1973	1.86	1.46	3.12	4.63	3.98	4.05	2.10	1.27	3.99	3.94	3.05	1.99	35.44
1974	3.18	1.83	3.01	2.40	4.73	4.55	2.30	3.67	5.62	1.03	2.30	4.44	39.06
1975	3.15	4.21	4.14	2.37	3.04	2.97	4.19	7.24	4.80	3.42	1.70	2.96	44.19
RECORD MEAN	2.66	2.42	3.52	3.41	3.53	3.85	3.58	3.15	2.81	2.50	2.44	2.58	36.45

Record mean values above are means through the current year for the period beginning in 1935.

Station: AVOCA, PENNSYLVANIA
WILKES-BARRE SCRANTON AIRPORT
Elevation (ground): 930 feet

TEMPERATURES °F

Month	Normal			Extremes			
	Daily maximum	Daily minimum	Monthly	Record highest	Year	Record lowest	Year
(a)				20		20	
J	33.5	18.4	26.0	67	1967	-10	1968
F	35.3	19.3	27.3	62	1974	-11	1961
M	44.7	27.2	36.0	78	1968	-4	1967
A	58.9	38.0	48.5	89	1962	15	1964
M	70.0	47.8	58.9	93	1962	27	1974
J	79.0	56.8	67.9	97	1964	34	1972
J	83.0	61.3	72.2	101	1966	45	1957
A	80.7	59.2	70.0	94	1975	43	1957
S	73.6	52.1	62.9	95	1959	30	1974
O	63.0	42.2	52.6	84	1959	19	1972
N	48.8	32.8	40.8	77	1974	10	1958
D	36.1	22.0	29.1	65	1966	-7	1969
YR	58.9	39.8	49.4	101	JUL 1966	-11	FEB 1961

IMPORTANT:
The time-period covered by this record is limited: See footnotes following table of NORMALS, MEANS AND EXTREMES for explanation and for additional history of EXTREME HIGHS AND LOWS recorded in the general area.

The Wilkes-Barre Scranton National Weather Service Office is located about midway between the two cities, at the southwest end of the crescent-shaped Lackawanna River Valley. The river flows through this valley and empties into the Susquehanna River and the Wyoming Valley a few miles west of the airport. The surrounding mountains protect both cities and the airport from high winds, and influence the temperature and precipitation during both summer and winter, causing wide departures in both within a few miles of the station. Because of the proximity of the mountains, the climate is relatively cool in summer with frequent shower and thundershower type precipitation, usually of brief duration. The winters in the valley are not severe; sub-zero temperatures are not frequent, neither are severe snowstorms. A high percentage of the winter precipitation occurs as rain.

For the period of record, the temperature extremes were recorded when the office was located in Scranton; 103 degrees on July 9, 1936, and -19 degrees on February 9, 1934. Maximum temperatures of 100 degrees or higher have been recorded on 7 days. There have been 2 days when the maximum temperature was zero degrees.

The greatest 24-hour rainfall occurred on September 29-30, 1924, 5.09 inches. Other 24-hour amounts associated with historically important storms were 4.58 inches with Hurricane Diane on August 18-19, 1955, and 3.10 inches with Hurricane Agnes on June 21-22, 1972.

The greatest 24-hour snowfall, 20.5 inches, occurred with the Thanksgiving Day storm of November 24-25, 1971, but the greatest snowfall of record was

(Continued page 614)

Snowfall

Season	July	Aug	Sept	Oct	Nov	Dec	Jan
1936-37	0.0	0.0	0.0	T	3.8	3.4	4.0
1937-38	0.0	0.0	0.0	T	2.2	3.8	8.4
1938-39	0.0	0.0	0.0	0.0	12.2	4.2	11.5
1939-40	0.0	0.0	0.0	T	0.6	9.4	2.8
1940-41	0.0	0.0	0.0	T	7.0	1.5	16.1
1941-42	0.0	0.0	0.0	0.0	T	0.2	7.5
1942-43	0.0	0.0	0.0	T	T	8.3	13.3
1943-44	0.0	0.0	0.0	T	1.7	1.0	1.1
1944-45	0.0	0.0	0.0	T	2.1	12.0	28.2
1945-46	0.0	0.0	0.0	0.0	1.6	13.5	1.8
1946-47	0.0	0.0	0.0	T	T	3.7	8.7
1947-48	0.0	0.0	0.0	0.0	1.3	8.2	23.1
1948-49	0.0	0.0	0.0	0.2	T	11.9	5.9
1949-50	0.0	0.0	0.0	0.0	1.8	4.6	1.9
1950-51	0.0	0.0	0.0	0.0	5.1	11.0	8.2
1951-52	0.0	0.0	0.0	0.0	3.8	13.8	4.1
1952-53	0.0	0.0	0.0	1.0	0.1	2.6	3.7
1953-54	0.0	0.0	0.0	0.0	9.6	0.1	11.1
#1954-55	0.0	0.0	0.0	T	4.4	3.1	2.4
1955-56	0.0	0.0	0.0	0.3	4.5	7.8	4.7
1956-57	0.0	0.0	T	0.0	2.7	5.6	11.1
1957-58	0.0	0.0	0.0	T	0.3	6.0	8.1
1958-59	0.0	0.0	0.0	T	2.4	3.8	7.2
1959-60	0.0	0.0	0.0	T	0.5	9.2	6.2
1960-61	0.0	0.0	0.0	0.4	0.7	19.0	19.0
1961-62	0.0	0.0	0.0	0.0	2.4	12.8	2.7
1962-63	0.0	0.0	0.0	4.4	4.6	12.9	15.2
1963-64	0.0	0.0	0.0	T	1.4	13.1	27.9
1964-65	0.0	0.0	0.0	0.2	0.1	4.1	11.5
1965-66	0.0	0.0	0.0	0.6	0.5	1.3	20.7
1966-67	0.0	0.0	0.0	T	T	17.7	8.3
1967-68	0.0	0.0	0.0	T	7.2	13.8	6.0
1968-69	0.0	0.0	0.0	T	10.9	5.8	2.7
1969-70	0.0	0.0	0.0	T	2.7	33.9	9.5
1970-71	0.0	0.0	0.0	0.3	T	12.3	15.2
1971-72	0.0	0.0	0.0	0.0	22.5	4.1	5.9
1972-73	0.0	0.0	0.0	0.8	7.9	3.9	5.0
1973-74	0.0	0.0	0.0	T	0.4	16.0	12.8
1974-75	0.0	0.0	0.0	0.2	2.2	5.2	13.7
1975-76	0.0	0.0	0.0	0.0	1.3	3.7	
RECORD MEAN	0.0	0.0	T	0.3	3.5	10.2	10.7

Heating Degree Days

Season	July	Aug	Sept	Oct	Nov	Dec	Jan
1955-56	0	0	133	340	813	1277	1222
1956-57	28	29	241	394	736	943	1337
1957-58	11	37	139	479	685	966	1222
1958-59	0	15	157	463	711	1316	1243
#1959-60	0	4	94	372	810	1012	1109
1960-61	8	4	92	446	700	1331	1422
1961-62	3	7	80	370	743	1092	1236
1962-63	3	10	199	414	848	1260	1289
1963-64	11	20	175	253	588	1254	1140
1964-65	0	31	110	475	621	1028	1293
1965-66	7	35	99	471	731	971	1270
1966-67	1	0	170	451	642	1063	998
1967-68	5	17	139	427	844	1023	1388
1968-69	0	28	55	359	725	1165	1204
1969-70	6	15	134	440	765	1212	1459
1970-71	2	5	109	371	695	1162	1404
1971-72	5	22	90	263	783	951	1152
1972-73	21	20	125	603	860	988	1124
1973-74	2	11	140	368	699	1036	1145
1974-75	5	2	155	503	655	941	1024
1975-76	0	8	158	291	509	1043	

Cooling Degree Days

Year	Jan	Feb	Mar	Apr	May	June	July
1969	0	0	0	7	34	141	193
1970	0	0	0	10	40	81	189
1971	0	0	0	0	16	145	160
1972	0	0	0	0	20	53	232
1973	0	0	0	4	0	132	212
1974	0	0	0	10	28	52	194
1975	0	0	0	0	91	146	278

Feb	Mar	Apr	May	June	Total
4.6	9.1	0.1	0.0	0.0	25.0
3.3	2.0	11.3	0.0	0.0	31.0
5.9	6.4	0.5	0.0	0.0	40.7
21.4	10.5	1.5	0.0	0.0	46.2
4.1	20.7	T	0.0	0.0	49.4
4.8	10.1	8.3	0.0	0.0	30.9
5.0	5.0	3.9	T	0.0	35.5
7.0	5.7	2.0	0.0	0.0	18.5
10.9	T	T	T	T	53.2
13.7	T	1.0	0.0	0.0	31.6
16.9	11.7	T	T	0.0	41.0
5.4	7.8	T	0.0	0.0	45.8
5.0	5.4	T	0.0	0.0	28.4
12.9	19.3	1.8	0.0	0.0	42.3
2.5	5.1	T	0.0	0.0	31.9
4.6	9.2	0.1	0.0	0.0	35.6
2.1	2.9	1.5	0.0	0.0	13.9
1.2	0.6	0.3	T	0.0	22.9
7.6	2.9	0.4	0.0	0.0	20.8
8.6	14.5	12.0	0.0	0.0	52.4
3.3	6.7	8.0	0.0	0.0	37.4
19.5	18.6	1.1	0.0	0.0	53.6
3.9	11.5	0.4	0.0	0.0	29.2
15.4	22.3	3.6	0.0	0.0	57.2
16.9	9.3	8.4	0.0	0.0	73.7
11.2	2.8	3.0	T	0.0	34.9
18.0	8.3	0.5	0.2	0.0	64.1
22.0	9.7	0.6	0.0	0.0	74.7
2.3	9.9	3.8	0.0	0.0	31.9
17.5	3.8	0.7	0.6	0.0	45.7
14.4	29.7	4.8	0.4	0.0	75.3
2.9	2.7	0.0	0.0	0.0	32.6
14.8	2.5	0.0	0.0	0.0	36.7
9.5	20.6	0.6	T	0.0	76.8
12.1	15.6	1.6	0.0	0.0	57.1
19.7	6.6	3.8	0.0	0.0	62.6
3.1	1.9	0.2	0.4	0.0	23.2
4.5	15.7	2.8	0.0	0.0	52.2
15.2	5.5	1.2	0.0	0.0	43.2
11.7	10.9	2.9	0.1	0.0	50.3

Average Temp.

Year	Jan	Feb	Mar	Apr	May	June	July	Aug	Sept	Oct	Nov	Dec	Annual
1936	24.0	21.5	43.4	45.9	61.8	68.0	73.7	72.4	65.4	52.6	37.6	34.4	50.1
1937	35.4	30.4	31.4	46.8	60.7	69.2	73.0	74.0	61.2	50.4	41.4	30.2	50.3
1938	27.9	31.0	41.8	50.5	58.1	67.4	73.3	73.6	60.6	54.3	42.8	32.0	51.1
1939	27.9	32.4	35.4	45.8	62.8	69.2	72.8	74.0	64.2	51.7	38.4	31.6	50.5
1940	20.2	28.2	30.8	44.0	59.0	66.8	72.4	68.2	60.6	48.2	40.4	33.7	47.7
1941	25.4	25.6	30.4	55.0	60.6	68.6	73.8	68.3	65.3	56.4	44.8	34.4	50.7
1942	26.4	24.1	40.1	52.6	63.0	68.6	72.7	69.3	63.6	54.2	41.4	26.6	50.2
1943	25.9	28.4	36.2	41.4	60.2	73.2	73.8	71.2	61.4	50.4	38.6	27.2	49.0
1944	30.6	28.6	33.4	45.0	66.0	68.8	73.7	72.8	64.2	50.6	41.0	27.2	50.2
1945	18.9	28.5	47.8	52.5	56.4	66.6	71.4	69.6	66.0	51.0	42.4	26.4	49.8
1946	29.6	27.6	47.2	47.4	58.8	65.6	72.0	66.4	65.4	56.7	45.6	33.2	51.3
1947	33.0	23.7	33.0	47.6	58.6	66.5	70.8	74.0	64.5	59.0	38.9	29.4	49.9
1948	19.9	26.4	39.0	49.6	58.4	66.7	72.1	70.8	64.6	51.2	47.7	32.2	49.9
1949	34.0	34.1	38.6	49.2	60.0	72.8	76.8	72.8	60.4	57.7	40.4	33.4	52.5
1950	37.7	28.1	32.6	44.8	59.4	66.6	70.3	70.3	60.3	55.4	42.6	28.5	49.7
1951	31.3	31.7	37.8	49.5	60.6	67.4	72.7	70.0	62.4	54.6	36.8	32.5	50.6
1952	30.7	32.1	36.4	51.6	56.9	70.5	75.4	70.4	63.8	49.3	43.3	34.2	51.2
1953	33.5	34.0	39.6	47.5	61.7	69.4	73.1	70.2	64.2	54.6	43.3	36.4	52.3
1954	25.8	36.5	36.8	52.3	57.4	69.4	71.2	68.4	63.9	55.7	41.4	30.7	50.8
#1955	25.3	29.6	37.6	52.6	61.0	66.0	77.4	73.6	61.9	53.9	37.7	23.5	50.0
1956	25.4	30.0	31.5	44.9	54.7	67.1	67.5	67.9	58.0	52.1	40.4	34.2	47.8
1957	21.6	31.1	36.2	49.1	57.3	69.3	69.6	66.2	62.6	49.2	41.9	33.6	49.0
1958	25.3	21.0	34.2	49.0	56.5	62.2	72.3	69.6	61.1	49.8	41.1	22.4	47.1
#1959	24.7	25.7	35.4	50.4	62.8	68.6	72.7	73.4	67.4	54.0	37.8	32.1	50.4
1960	28.9	29.5	25.3	52.4	57.7	67.2	68.8	70.5	62.8	50.5	41.4	21.9	48.1
1961	18.9	28.9	35.1	42.0	56.1	67.1	72.6	71.0	68.4	52.9	40.1	29.6	48.6
1962	24.9	24.6	36.6	49.0	62.6	68.5	70.3	70.4	59.5	51.6	36.6	24.0	48.2
1963	23.2	19.3	38.2	49.1	57.8	67.4	71.5	68.3	60.0	56.7	45.1	24.3	48.4
1964	27.9	23.5	36.9	46.6	62.0	67.4	74.1	68.2	63.8	49.4	44.1	31.6	49.6
1965	23.0	28.1	34.2	45.3	63.7	68.0	71.0	69.5	64.5	49.6	40.4	33.5	49.2
1966	23.8	27.2	39.0	46.0	55.7	70.1	75.0	72.4	60.2	50.2	43.4	30.5	49.4
1967	32.6	23.5	34.9	49.1	52.7	71.1	71.7	68.9	61.6	51.2	36.6	31.7	48.8
1968	20.0	24.1	40.4	52.9	56.3	67.5	73.7	71.0	64.4	53.4	40.7	27.2	49.3
1969	26.0	26.6	34.4	50.5	59.9	68.2	70.8	69.9	62.7	50.6	39.2	25.7	48.7
1970	17.7	25.7	31.8	48.4	60.4	64.9	70.8	69.6	64.2	52.8	41.5	27.3	47.9
1971	19.5	27.2	33.0	45.0	55.9	68.6	69.9	68.3	65.5	56.4	38.8	34.1	48.5
1972	27.6	24.3	32.8	43.5	60.0	62.9	71.5	69.6	61.9	45.3	36.0	32.9	47.4
1973	28.5	24.5	41.9	47.5	53.4	68.3	71.5	71.6	62.4	53.2	41.5	31.3	49.7
1974	27.8	24.2	34.7	49.1	56.2	64.4	70.8	68.5	61.2	48.5	43.0	34.4	48.6
1975	31.8	32.1	35.8	43.9	64.9	68.8	73.7	71.2	59.9	55.8	47.8	31.1	51.4
RECORD MEAN	27.2	27.3	36.7	47.9	59.1	67.6	72.2	69.9	63.2	52.4	41.1	30.3	49.6
MAX	34.5	35.1	45.1	57.7	69.7	78.1	82.7	80.2	73.4	62.2	48.6	37.0	58.7
MIN	19.8	19.4	28.2	38.0	48.4	57.0	61.6	59.6	52.9	42.5	33.5	23.6	40.4

# Indicates a station move or relocation of instruments.

AVOCA, PA

Feb	Mar	Apr	May	June	Total
1007	1033	602	338	47	6812
946	886	485	264	41	6330
1225	946	478	268	118	6574
1095	911	429	167	55	6562
1024	1225	393	221	29	6293
1005	922	684	293	44	6951
1125	874	508	155	16	6209
1272	820	475	236	45	6871
1198	866	544	139	69	6257
1027	951	582	100	55	6273
1053	799	565	300	41	6342
1154	923	475	379	12	6268
1181	754	357	261	42	6438
1068	943	434	188	38	6207
1094	1022	500	176	76	6899
1051	985	593	292	32	6701
1175	992	634	168	109	6344
1131	704	521	354	25	6476
1135	934	480	291	65	6306
913	902	627	88	25	5840

Aug	Sept	Oct	Nov	Dec	Total
178	73	1	0	0	627
159	92	2	0	0	573
132	113	4	3	0	573
167	42	0	0	0	514
223	72	7	0	0	650
117	46	0	0	0	447
207	13	14	0	0	749

Precipitation

Year	Jan	Feb	Mar	Apr	May	June	July	Aug	Sept	Oct	Nov	Dec	Annual
1936	4.47	1.31	5.25	2.85	2.18	6.75	0.73	4.58	1.70	2.11	2.59	2.75	37.27
1937	4.18	2.47	2.18	3.51	2.66	5.89	2.67	6.43	1.42	6.02	1.53	1.95	40.91
1938	2.41	2.82	1.50	2.94	3.23	4.64	4.97	1.62	5.42	1.61	3.24	3.51	37.91
1939	2.65	3.72	2.58	3.30	2.17	1.29	0.58	3.87	2.92	3.11	0.46	2.58	29.23
1940	0.47	2.48	6.52	3.76	2.98	3.71	2.66	5.13	2.72	3.14	3.05	2.11	38.73
1941	1.49	1.12	1.64	1.52	1.95	4.61	3.45	4.93	1.00	2.18	1.92	1.47	27.28
1942	1.36	1.25	2.98	1.52	6.73	3.71	5.08	1.66	4.60	4.56	3.41	4.73	41.59
1943	2.11	0.88	3.21	2.15	4.25	3.11	3.04	2.83	0.52	6.49	3.14	0.79	32.52
1944	0.81	1.31	2.67	3.27	2.56	5.66	2.60	3.28	3.41	1.75	2.22	2.33	31.87
1945	3.07	2.55	2.15	3.71	5.78	4.30	11.75	5.37	4.52	3.29	5.97	1.26	53.72
1946	0.62	1.97	2.96	1.02	7.62	3.80	9.41	2.97	1.92	2.14	0.83	1.46	36.72
1947	2.54	1.25	2.75	6.64	6.99	1.86	9.70	1.39	1.82	1.70	3.60	1.22	41.46
1948	2.57	1.10	3.54	4.60	4.10	7.68	7.17	2.14	0.90	1.92	4.59	4.72	45.03
1949	3.22	1.68	1.50	3.85	3.68	1.64	4.68	4.98	3.19	1.94	1.61	3.86	35.83
1950	2.84	2.85	4.08	3.03	3.70	3.73	4.48	1.73	2.48	1.61	5.80	3.90	40.23
1951	2.77	3.41	3.20	2.43	1.60	5.64	5.18	1.62	1.80	3.81	5.27	2.48	39.21
1952	2.59	1.45	3.01	5.22	5.79	1.92	5.71	4.43	3.11	1.13	2.36	3.19	39.91
1953	3.32	1.96	3.67	4.77	3.67	2.03	2.61	0.78	2.70	3.11	2.79	3.85	35.26
1954	1.57	2.11	2.62	4.02	3.93	2.11	1.75	4.41	2.21	1.98	4.70	2.81	34.22
#1955	0.57	2.66	2.92	2.19	2.04	0.99	1.13	11.76	2.83	6.95	2.63	0.37	37.04
1956	1.01	3.64	2.48	3.16	2.25	4.68	3.18	3.03	2.54	1.35	1.31	3.24	31.87
1957	1.49	0.89	1.66	5.81	1.44	4.01	2.05	1.38	2.18	2.54	2.42	4.04	29.91
1958	2.42	3.12	2.18	3.59	3.40	3.41	3.57	4.30	7.11	3.37	2.78	0.35	39.60
1959	3.11	2.23	1.77	3.76	0.77	3.23	4.46	3.00	1.09	4.25	3.77	2.71	34.15
1960	2.94	2.64	1.49	3.40	4.32	3.33	5.55	3.54	7.78	1.22	1.77	1.01	38.99
1961	1.82	1.92	2.87	2.48	3.30	3.80	5.96	3.98	0.99	1.58	3.57	2.52	34.79
1962	2.67	3.04	1.98	2.59	0.84	1.71	1.48	4.05	3.14	5.46	2.80	2.20	31.96
1963	2.06	1.95	2.19	1.30	2.44	1.93	4.03	2.04	1.69	0.03	4.62	1.94	26.22
1964	3.40	2.03	3.54	3.82	0.98	5.00	1.23	2.85	0.82	1.13	1.86	3.67	30.33
1965	2.07	1.90	1.83	2.63	2.51	1.22	1.30	5.23	3.13	1.80	1.43	1.30	26.35
1966	1.66	2.31	1.60	2.91	3.32	0.27	1.89	4.76	2.70	2.04	2.97	2.00	28.43
1967	1.11	0.89	3.91	2.09	4.41	4.48	3.61	5.20	2.13	2.58	2.31	2.45	35.17
1968	2.03	0.30	2.73	2.37	4.64	4.82	1.23	1.43	4.20	1.65	3.40	1.95	30.75
1969	0.64	0.96	1.45	3.04	2.42	4.58	6.81	4.47	1.92	2.20	3.77	3.42	35.68
1970	0.52	2.41	2.33	3.07	2.75	2.56	5.19	2.72	3.03	2.24	2.87	1.85	31.54
1971	1.54	3.92	1.93	1.29	3.38	2.44	5.73	4.88	1.93	3.00	3.55	2.08	35.67
1972	2.05	2.42	4.00	3.31	7.33	7.04	1.23	1.64	1.57	3.30	7.69	3.61	45.19
1973	2.13	1.28	1.79	4.38	3.80	5.99	3.87	2.61	3.62	1.97	1.50	6.07	39.01
1974	2.66	1.48	4.75	2.71	1.89	3.85	2.80	3.50	6.85	1.07	2.26	3.40	37.22
1975	2.78	3.26	2.52	1.17	4.01	5.64	3.85	2.78	6.10	3.29	3.00	1.84	40.24
RECORD MEAN	2.34	2.28	2.87	3.04	3.20	3.73	4.06	3.69	3.11	2.82	2.76	2.65	36.55

Record mean values above are means through the current year for the period beginning in 1901 for temperature and precipitation, 1956 for snowfall.

(Continued)

21.1 inches over a 29 hour period on January 12-13, 1964.

From a meteorological viewpoint, severe storms are most interesting. In going back to the period before the National Weather Service was established in Scranton, the blizzard of 1888 is the only severe storm worthy of note. This storm began March 11 as rain, with wind velocities estimated at 65 miles an hour. The rain changed to snow the night of March 11, and continued as snow for two more days. Snow depth was 15 inches, and drifts 15 to 20 feet were reported. The "Billy Sunday Storm" of March 1, 1914, so-called as it coincided with an appearance of the famed evangelist, had a snowfall of 17 inches, and high winds which caused huge drifts. There were 4 deaths, and some 3,000 people were marooned in the tabernacle overnight.

While the incidence of tornadoes is very low, Wilkes-Barre has been hit with 2 of these storms. 19 people died in a tornado on August 19, 1890, and there were 7 deaths with another on August 21, 1914.

The area has felt the effects of tropical storms. Hurricane Hazel, on October 15, 1954, resulted in considerable wind damage. Back to back hurricanes in August 1955, Connie and Diane, resulted in the flood of record on the Lackawanna River from Scranton, south. A stage of 20.05 feet was recorded at the Old Forge gage, about 5 miles southwest of Scranton, on August 19. Hurricane Agnes, in June 1972, resulted in the worst natural disaster to hit the region with record flooding along the Susquehanna River. In Wilkes-Barre, the river crested on June 24 at a height of 40.91 feet, almost 8 feet above the previous record. There were 5 deaths attributed to the storm, and property damage in the Wilkes-Barre area was set at nearly 1 billion dollars.

Fortunately, severe weather is uncommon in this area, and the averages of the meteorological data are comparable to this latitude, and to the state in general.

Normals, Means, and Extremes

Month	Normal Degree days Base 65 °F		Precipitation in inches												Relative humidity pct.			
			Water equivalent							Snow, Ice pellets					Hour 01	Hour 07	Hour 13	Hour 19
	Heating	Cooling	Normal	Maximum monthly	Year	Minimum monthly	Year	Maximum in 24 hrs.	Year	Maximum monthly	Year	Maximum in 24 hrs.	Year		(Local time)			
(a)				20		20		20		20		20			20	20	20	20
J	1209	0	2.04	3.40	1964	0.52	1970	1.52	1959	27.9	1964	20.1	1964		72	76	65	67
F	1056	0	1.96	3.92	1971	0.30	1968	1.60	1962	22.0	1964	13.3	1961		72	75	63	65
M	899	0	2.50	4.75	1974	1.45	1969	2.20	1964	29.7	1967	15.5	1960		71	75	59	62
A	495	0	3.06	5.81	1957	1.17	1975	1.59	1970	12.0	1956	8.4	1956		68	72	51	55
M	219	30	3.50	7.33	1972	0.77	1959	2.58	1972	0.6	1966	0.6	1966		73	75	52	56
J	28	115	3.40	7.04	1972	0.27	1966	3.61	1973	0.0		0.0			80	82	56	61
J	7	230	4.09	6.81	1969	1.23	1972	2.33	1969	0.0		0.0			81	84	55	62
A	18	173	3.21	5.23	1965	1.38	1957	3.18	1966	0.0		0.0			83	87	57	66
S	116	53	2.82	7.78	1960	0.82	1964	3.09	1960	T	1956	T	1956		84	88	60	71
O	391	7	2.71	5.46	1962	0.03	1963	2.61	1962	4.4	1962	4.4	1962		79	84	58	67
N	726	0	3.01	7.69	1972	1.31	1956	2.91	1972	22.5	1971	20.5	1971		76	79	64	69
D	1113	0	2.51	6.07	1973	0.35	1958	2.30	1973	33.9	1969	12.4	1969		76	78	68	71
YR	6277	608	34.81	7.78	SEP 1960	0.03	OCT 1963	3.61	JUN 1973	33.9	DEC 1969	20.5	NOV 1971		76	80	59	64

(To better understand these tables, see full explanation of terms beginning on page 322)

Month	Wind					Pct. of possible sunshine	Mean sky cover, tenths, sunrise to sunset	Mean number of days												Average station pressure mb.
			Fastest mile					Sunrise to sunset							Temperatures °F					
															Max.		Min.			
	Mean speed m.p.h.	Prevailing direction	Speed m.p.h.	Direction	Year			Clear	Partly cloudy	Cloudy	Precipitation .01 inch or more	Snow, Ice pellets 1.0 inch or more	Thunderstorms	Heavy fog, visibility ¼ mile or less	(b) 90° and above	32° and below	32° and below	0° and below		Elev. 948 feet m.s.l.
(a)	20	8	20	20		20	20	20	20	20	20	20	20	20	20	20	20	20		3
J	8.9	SW	43	SE	1964	44	7.4	4	8	19	12	3	*	2	0	15	28	2		983.7
F	9.3	SW	60	W	1956	47	7.3	4	7	17	12	3	*	2	0	12	26	2		982.3
M	9.4	NW	49	S	1970	48	7.2	5	7	19	13	3	1	3	0	4	23	*		980.8
A	9.7	SW	47	NW	1957	53	6.9	6	8	16	12	1	2	2	0	*	10	0		979.9
M	8.8	WSW	40	NW	1956	56	6.7	6	10	15	13	0	4	1	*	0	1	0		979.8
J	7.9	SW	43	W	1956	60	6.3	7	11	12	12	0	6	1	2	0	0	0		981.9
J	7.4	WSW	42	NW	1960	61	6.2	6	13	12	12	0	8	2	3	0	0	0		982.3
A	7.2	SW	50	NE	1956	61	6.0	7	13	11	11	0	5	2	2	0	0	0		984.3
S	7.4	SW	38	SW	1957	55	6.1	7	10	13	10	0	3	3	*	0	*	0		985.0
O	7.9	WSW	38	E	1973	54	6.0	9	8	14	9	*	1	2	0	0	4	0		986.1
N	8.6	WSW	45	S	1957	36	7.6	4	6	20	12	1	*	2	0	1	15	0		982.9
D	8.8	SW	47	SW	1957	34	7.8	4	6	21	14	3	*	3	0	12	26	1		983.4
YR	8.4	SW	60	W	FEB 1956	52	6.8	69	107	189	140	13	31	25	8	45	133	4		982.7

FOOTNOTES

Means and extremes above are from existing and comparable exposures. Annual extremes have been exceeded at other sites in the locality as follows: Highest temperature 103 in July 1936; lowest temperature -19 in February 1934; maximum monthly precipitation 11.76 in August 1955; maximum precipitation in 24 hours 5.09 in September 1924; maximum monthly snowfall 38.0 in March 1916.

Station: BLOCK ISLAND, RHODE ISLAND
STATE AIRPORT
Elevation (ground): 110 feet

TEMPERATURES °F

Month	Normal			Extremes			
	Daily maximum	Daily minimum	Monthly	Record highest	Year	Record lowest	Year
(a)				24		24	
J	37.4	25.4	31.4	57	1962	-2	1968
F	37.2	25.3	31.3	55	1974	-2	1961
M	42.7	31.0	36.9	60	1960	8	1967
A	51.7	38.8	45.3	73	1973	21	1954
M	60.4	47.2	53.8	82	1969	34	1972
J	69.7	56.5	63.1	90	1952	41	1967
J	75.6	63.3	69.5	91	1972	51	1962
A	75.3	63.1	69.2	91	1973	48	1971
S	69.8	57.7	63.8	87	1953	42	1973
O	61.4	49.2	55.3	77	1967	30	1969
N	51.8	40.1	46.0	70	1956	20	1957
D	41.2	29.1	35.2	64	1953	-4	1962
YR	56.2	43.9	50.1	91	AUG 1973	-4	DEC 1962

IMPORTANT:
The time-period covered by this record is limited: See footnotes on next page for explanation and for additional history of EXTREME HIGHS AND LOWS recorded in the general area.

Block Island, R. I. consists of nearly 7,000 acres of terminal moraine material lying in the Atlantic Ocean twelve miles east-northeast of Long Island and the same distance south of Charleston, R. I. Hence, the climate is typically maritime, but under conditions of extreme cold or heat the effect is felt on the island as well as on the mainland. For instance the temperature went to -10° in February 1934, and to -6° in 1917. In 1948 the temperature reached 95°.

Summers are usually dry, but the highest rainfall in any one month, 12.93 inches, fell in June, 1881. The record low amount was in June also, 1949 and 1957, when only a trace fell. In July and August maximum temperatures average 74°. The island is too small to build up cumulonimbus clouds, and local thunderstorms do not occur. Fog occurs on one out of four days in the early summer, when the ocean is relatively cold.

Winters are distinguished for their comparative mildness with maxima averaging 4 to 10° above freezing and minima averaging 25° in February. Since the surface winds are usually from easterly when snow begins it soon changes to rain or melts rapidly even if it does pile up. The Ocean temperatures are of course always somewhat above freezing and not too far off shore are relatively high.

The Ocean has a dampening effect on hot winds in summer and an accelerating effect on cold winds from the mainland in the winter. Katabaric winds from Narrangansett Bay and Long Island reach as high as 40 M.P.H. when anticyclonic conditions prevail on the mainland in winter. The wind velocity averages 17 M.P.H. for the year, but in the winter months the mean is 20 M.P.H., when gales are frequent. In the early fall the island is affected to some extent, at least, by most of the tropical storms moving up the coast.

BLOCK ISLAND, RHODE ISLAND

Normals, Means, and Extremes

(To better understand these tables, see full explanation of terms beginning on page 322)

Month	Normal Degree days Base 65 °F: Heating	Normal Degree days Base 65 °F: Cooling	Precipitation in inches, Water equivalent: Normal	Maximum monthly	Year	Minimum monthly	Year	Maximum in 24 hrs.	Year	Snow, Ice pellets: Maximum monthly	Year	Maximum in 24 hrs.	Year
(a)				24		24		24		25		25	
J	1042	0	3.41	6.74	1958	0.27	1970	4.06	1962	21.5	1965	9.0	1965
F	944	0	3.32	6.88	1971	1.20	1968	2.86	1972	16.9	1961	16.9	1961
M	871	0	3.88	8.52	1959	1.16	1966	3.63	1968	24.1	1956	11.5	1960
A	591	0	3.51	7.78	1973	1.15	1963	2.67	1973	2.0	1973	2.0	1973
M	347	0	3.25	5.98	1967	0.72	1955	2.35	1961	0.0		0.0	
J	82	25	2.20	6.81	1962	T	1957	2.39	1972	0.0		0.0	
J	9	149	2.74	6.15	1959	0.39	1952	3.16	1973	0.0		0.0	
A	11	142	3.86	9.73	1954	0.26	1964	4.86	1953	0.0		0.0	
S	79	43	3.00	11.51	1961	0.33	1971	8.52	1960	0.0		0.0	
O	301	0	2.88	8.74	1955	0.81	1952	6.63	1955	T	1970	T	1970
N	570	0	4.35	8.06	1969	1.23	1973	3.96	1969	2.5	1955	2.5	1955
D	924	0	4.11	8.12	1967	0.83	1955	4.39	1967	10.4	1963	6.3	1960
YR	5771	359	40.51	11.51	SEP 1961	T	JUN 1957	8.52	SEP 1960	24.1	MAR 1956	16.9	FEB 1961

Month	Relative $ humidity pct. Hour 01	Hour 07	Hour 13	Hour 19 (Local time)	Wind: Mean speed m.p.h.	Prevailing direction	Fastest mile: Speed m.p.h.	Direction	Year	Pct. of possible sunshine	Mean sky cover, tenths, sunrise to sunset ¢	Mean number of days, Sunrise to sunset ¢: Clear	Partly cloudy	Cloudy	Precipitation .01 inch or more	Snow, Ice pellets 1.0 inch or more	Thunderstorms %	Heavy fog, visibility ¼ mile or less %	Temperatures °F Max.: 90° and above (b)	32° and below	Min.: 32° and below	0° and below	Average station pressure mb. (Elev. 118 feet m.s.l.)
(a)		14	14								19	19	19	19	24	24	14	14	24	24	24	24	
J		73	65								6.5	8	9	14	11	2	*	4	0	8	24	*	
F		73	65								6.0	8	8	12	10	2	*	4	0	7	22	*	
M		75	65								5.8	9	9	13	10	2	*	5	0	1	17	0	
A		79	65								6.3	8	9	13	10	*	2	9	0	0	3	0	
M		80	67								6.2	7	11	13	10	0	2	11	0	0	0	0	
J		84	69								6.3	8	10	12	8	0	2	11	*	0	0	0	
J		87	72								6.8	7	11	13	7	0	4	12	*	0	0	0	
A		86	71								6.6	7	11	13	8	0	4	11	*	0	0	0	
S		84	70								5.9	10	9	11	7	0	1	5	0	0	0	0	
O		80	66								5.4	11	8	12	7	0	1	4	0	0	*	0	
N		76	65								6.6	7	9	14	10	*	*	3	0	*	5	0	
D		72	65								6.2	7	10	14	11	1	*	3	0	4	18	*	
YR		79	67								6.2	97	114	154	111	6	17	82	*	20	89	*	

FOOTNOTES

% Through 1964. The station did not operate 24 hours daily. Fog and thunderstorm data may be incomplete.

$ Through 1964.

¢ Through 1968. plus January - July 1974.

Snowfall

Season	July	Aug	Sept	Oct	Nov	Dec	Jan
1936-37	0.0	0.0	0.0	0.0	0.7	T	3.1
1937-38	0.0	0.0	0.0	0.0	T	T	5.3
1938-39	0.0	0.0	0.0	0.0	1.7	0.5	4.9
1939-40	0.0	0.0	0.0	0.0	T	3.0	2.2
1940-41	0.0	0.0	0.0	0.0	2.5	T	2.1
1941-42	0.0	0.0	0.0	0.0	0.0	T	7.9
1942-43	0.0	0.0	0.0	0.0	T	10.8	5.8
1943-44	0.0	0.0	0.0	0.0	T	0.3	1.1
1944-45	0.0	0.0	0.0	0.0	T	7.0	6.8
1945-46	0.0	0.0	0.0	0.0	0.5	9.7	0.2
1946-47	0.0	0.0	0.0	T	0.0	T	5.7
1947-48	0.0	0.0	0.0	0.0	0.0	5.4	8.4
1948-49	0.0	0.0	0.0	0.0	0.0	2.2	4.2
1949-50	0.0	0.0	0.0	0.0	1.6	0.9	0.9
#1950-51	0.0	0.0	0.0	0.0	T	4.3	4.4
1951-52	0.0	0.0	0.0	0.0	T	2.2	4.0
1952-53	0.0	0.0	0.0	0.0	1.0	1.0	2.0
1953-54	0.0	0.0	0.0	0.0	T	T	9.6
1954-55	0.0	0.0	0.0	0.0	T	7.7	0.5
1955-56	0.0	0.0	0.0	0.0	2.5	4.9	10.2
1956-57	0.0	0.0	0.0	0.0	T	2.2	2.2
1957-58	0.0	0.0	0.0	0.0	T	1.5	T
1958-59	0.0	0.0	0.0	0.0	T	4.4	0.6
1959-60	0.0	0.0	0.0	0.0	T	4.2	7.9
1960-61	0.0	0.0	0.0	0.0	0.0	7.0	9.0
1961-62	0.0	0.0	0.0	0.0	0.0	4.2	3.8
1962-63	0.0	0.0	0.0	T	0.3	7.2	5.2
1963-64	0.0	0.0	0.0	0.0	0.1	10.4	5.9
1964-65	0.0	0.0	0.0	0.0	0.0	1.1	21.5
1965-66	0.0	0.0	0.0	0.0	T	T	8.5
1966-67	0.0	0.0	0.0	0.0	0.0	3.2	0.5
1967-68	0.0	0.0	0.0	0.0	0.4	3.7	8.8
1968-69	0.0	0.0	0.0	0.0	0.0	0.1	T
1969-70	0.0	0.0	0.0	0.0	T	1.5	1.4
1970-71	0.0	0.0	0.0	T	0.0	4.2	3.5
1971-72	0.0	0.0	0.0	0.0	T	1.0	2.2
1972-73	0.0	0.0	0.0	0.0	T	0.9	0.3
1973-74	0.0	0.0	0.0	0.0	0.0	T	8.8
1974-75	0.0	0.0	0.0	0.0	T	T	2.5
1975-76	0.0	0.0	0.0	0.0	0.0	1.8	
RECORD MEAN	0.0	0.0	0.0	T	0.2	2.9	4.9

Heating Degree Days

Season	July	Aug	Sept	Oct	Nov	Dec	Jan
1955-56	0	2	74	261	629	1115	1015
1956-57	15	11	130	306	571	772	1131
1957-58	3	14	67	316	491	714	974
1958-59	6	3	86	374	535	1070	1050
1959-60	2	10	73	282	585	825	984
1960-61	2	5	79	309	504	1021	1182
1961-62	7	4	39	257	577	932	1052
1962-63	11	11	106	344	645	1047	1073
1963-64	7	9	162	266	478	1076	988
1964-65	9	14	99	359	555	884	1136
1965-66	1	20	96	405	657	877	1099
1966-67	0	0	101	371	523	883	898
1967-68	2	9	115	294	695	865	1166
1968-69	7	10	40	239	583	992	1060
1969-70	5	3	74	319	568	943	1255
1970-71	0	0	70	288	524	963	1180
1971-72	0	12	31	162	619	805	962
1972-73	4	4	53	409	636	808	984
1973-74	0	2	97	272	577	782	943
1974-75	6	0	73	417	546	797	874
1975-76	0	6	76		427	944	

Cooling Degree Days

Year	Jan	Feb	Mar	Apr	May	June	July
1969	0	0	0	0	8	52	136
1970	0	0	0	0	0	12	186
1971	0	0	0	0	0	38	185
1972	0	0	0	0	0	8	208
1973	0	0	0	0	2	48	184
1974	0	0	0	0	0	32	157
1975	0	0	0	0	4	40	217

Feb	Mar	Apr	May	June	Total
1.8	6.4	T	0.0	0.0	12.0
0.7	T	4.3	0.0	0.0	10.3
1.5	4.3	T	0.0	0.0	12.9
2.6	1.3	T	0.0	0.0	9.1
2.3	6.9	0.0	T	0.0	13.8
2.2	T	2.0	0.0	0.0	12.1
1.1	3.5	T	0.0	0.0	21.2
6.3	2.8	T	0.0	0.0	10.5
12.6	0.3	0.0	0.0	0.0	26.7
3.6	T	0.4	0.0	0.0	14.4
13.3	T	T	0.0	0.0	19.0
10.9	3.1	T	0.0	0.0	27.8
10.5	8.2	0.0	0.0	0.0	25.1
5.5	3.4	3.9	0.0	0.0	16.2
6.6	4.2	0.0	0.0	0.0	19.5
15.5	5.2	0.0	0.0	0.0	26.9
3.0	T	1.0	0.0	0.0	8.0
0.1	0.1	1.1	0.0	0.0	10.9
4.8	1.9	T	0.0	0.0	14.9
0.7	24.1	T	0.0	0.0	42.4
2.8	4.2	1.1	0.0	0.0	12.5
15.4	18.1	T	0.0	0.0	35.0
1.8	7.8	0.3	0.0	0.0	14.9
1.9	13.7	T	0.0	0.0	27.7
16.9	5.4	T	0.0	0.0	38.3
12.0	0.8	0.0	0.0	0.0	20.8
2.5	3.0	0.5	0.0	0.0	18.7
12.1	1.9	0.0	0.0	0.0	30.4
2.2	2.6	1.3	0.0	0.0	28.7
4.6	2.0	0.0	0.0	0.0	15.1
15.6	19.3	T	0.0	0.0	38.6
2.8	4.4	0.0	0.0	0.0	20.1
8.3	8.5	0.0	0.0	0.0	16.9
2.2	11.7	T	0.0	0.0	16.8
0.5	T	0.0	0.0	0.0	8.2
5.0	0.2	0.5	0.0	0.0	8.9
2.1	1.4	2.0	0.0	0.0	6.7
8.5	T	0.6	0.0	0.0	17.9
10.3	7.8	T	0.0	0.0	20.6
6.3	5.9	0.3	0.0	0.0	20.5

Average Temperature

Year	Jan	Feb	Mar	Apr	May	June	July	Aug	Sept	Oct	Nov	Dec	Annual
1936	30.4	25.2	40.2	43.1	54.3	63.1	68.0	69.0	63.4	55.2	43.1	39.0	49.5
1937	39.5	34.6	35.2	44.4	55.6	63.4	69.7	72.4	62.9	53.4	45.8	35.3	51.0
1938	32.2	33.5	39.2	45.8	53.1	62.4	69.6	71.2	62.5	56.4	48.2	37.7	51.0
1939	31.9	35.2	35.6	43.8	53.7	62.9	68.8	72.8	63.6	54.8	42.3	35.8	50.1
1940	25.2	31.9	32.8	42.1	53.2	60.8	69.4	66.4	63.3	51.0	45.0	38.5	48.3
1941	29.0	30.3	33.5	47.0	55.5	62.0	67.9	68.6	64.2	56.5	48.8	38.0	50.1
1942	30.4	28.3	39.8	45.4	55.8	63.9	69.2	68.6	63.3	56.0	45.8	31.7	49.8
1943	29.4	31.6	36.0	41.4	53.6	65.4	69.8	69.3	63.5	55.2	45.2	32.7	49.4
1944	32.7	31.2	35.0	43.3	57.4	63.6	71.2	71.4	65.4	54.8	44.9	34.2	50.4
1945	26.8	31.8	42.6	48.8	53.2	64.0	69.3	68.6	66.0	54.7	47.0	32.0	50.4
1946	32.8	30.9	42.9	44.8	53.8	61.6	67.8	66.6	64.8	58.4	49.8	38.8	51.1
1947	36.0	30.4	36.8	44.5	52.6	60.6	71.1	70.8	65.0	59.6	44.2	34.2	50.5
1948	27.3	29.2	37.0	44.2	52.4	61.2	69.5	70.8	65.0	54.9	50.6	39.2	50.1
1949	37.6	36.6	37.8	47.5	54.5	66.4	73.0	71.4	63.8	60.0	46.2	39.4	52.8
#1950	40.1	31.5	34.5	43.7	51.2	62.5	69.1	68.8	61.8	56.6	48.7	37.0	50.5
1951	35.7	35.2	38.5	48.0	56.2	62.7	70.7	69.5	65.3	56.4	44.3	39.0	51.8
1952	35.8	33.7	37.5	47.9	54.6	65.6	73.8	71.2	64.6	53.4	46.0	37.8	51.8
1953	36.5	36.4	39.5	47.0	55.6	64.4	69.5	68.8	65.7	56.3	48.5	41.5	52.5
1954	31.0	36.9	38.5	46.3	53.6	63.6	68.4	67.3	62.7	58.0	45.7	36.1	50.7
1955	30.4	32.5	37.5	45.9	55.7	62.3	72.2	72.0	63.5	56.5	43.8	28.8	50.1
1956	32.1	33.5	34.2	42.5	49.8	62.9	67.1	69.0	61.9	54.8	45.8	39.9	49.5
1957	28.2	34.3	38.6	46.5	54.8	66.1	69.3	67.7	65.1	54.6	48.4	41.8	51.3
1958	33.3	27.0	38.0	46.9	52.1	59.8	68.7	69.1	62.7	52.7	47.0	30.1	48.9
1959	30.9	29.5	36.8	46.1	56.0	62.1	68.9	69.8	66.2	56.1	45.3	38.1	50.5
1960	33.0	35.6	32.4	46.3	55.1	64.8	68.5	68.4	63.2	54.7	48.0	31.7	50.1
1961	26.6	31.9	36.4	43.6	51.4	61.6	69.1	69.3	67.7	56.6	45.6	34.6	49.6
1962	30.9	28.5	36.4	45.1	54.7	64.3	67.2	68.5	62.3	53.8	43.3	31.0	48.8
1963	30.1	26.6	37.0	45.3	52.3	63.5	69.4	67.9	59.7	56.2	48.8	30.0	48.9
1964	32.9	29.5	37.0	43.3	54.9	62.8	68.4	66.7	63.0	53.2	46.3	36.2	49.5
1965	28.1	29.7	35.0	42.5	54.6	61.0	68.5	69.6	62.9	51.7	42.9	36.4	48.6
1966	29.3	31.5	37.3	42.2	51.0	62.3	70.1	69.8	62.4	52.8	47.3	36.3	49.3
1967	35.8	28.7	33.2	42.2	48.5	61.6	69.9	68.8	61.5	55.5	41.6	36.8	48.7
1968	27.2	26.5	37.6	46.6	53.0	62.2	70.2	69.7	65.3	57.4	45.3	32.8	49.5
1969	30.7	30.6	34.7	45.7	54.8	64.9	69.0	71.4	64.3	54.6	45.8	34.4	50.1
1970	24.3	30.6	35.3	44.6	54.9	62.1	70.8	71.4	64.3	55.7	47.4	33.7	49.6
1971	26.8	31.8	36.3	42.9	53.3	63.6	70.8	70.1	67.4	59.7	44.1	38.8	50.4
1972	33.7	30.9	36.0	42.5	53.5	61.6	71.4	70.3	64.3	51.6	43.7	38.7	49.9
1973	33.0	31.6	41.6	46.7	54.4	65.2	70.6	72.0	63.9	56.1	45.6	39.6	51.7
1974	34.4	30.4	38.5	47.1	52.7	62.9	69.6	72.0	64.5	51.3	46.6	39.1	50.8
1975	36.5	33.1	36.7	42.9	55.9	64.0	71.7	71.3	62.9		50.5	34.3	
RECORD MEAN	31.7	30.8	36.5	44.5	53.4	62.5	69.0	68.9	64.4	55.5	45.9	36.2	50.0
MAX	37.7	36.6	42.0	50.3	59.5	68.5	74.8	74.4	69.9	61.0	51.3	42.0	55.7
MIN	25.7	24.9	31.0	38.6	47.3	56.5	63.1	63.4	58.9	50.0	40.5	30.4	44.2

BLOCK ISLAND, RI

Feb	Mar	Apr	May	June	Total
904	948	671	464	104	6187
853	812	548	307	60	5516
1058	830	537	394	158	5556
988	868	561	276	112	5929
844	1001	556	298	37	5497
920	880	634	415	100	6051
1015	881	591	313	65	5733
1071	860	585	384	92	6229
1024	860	644	309	96	5919
982	923	669	320	132	6082
931	854	675	429	105	6149
1012	977	676	507	105	6053
1109	846	543	365	103	6112
959	931	572	318	45	5756
957	915	601	307	95	6042
927	883	659	357	73	5924
982	895	669	350	105	5592
926	716	542	325	37	5444
961	816	532	377	86	5445
887	870	657	280	66	5473

Aug	Sept	Oct	Nov	Dec	Total
209	60	3	0	0	468
208	55	5	0	0	466
177	111	2	0	0	513
174	38	0	0	0	428
225	73	4	0	0	536
227	64	0	0	0	480
208	18		0	0	

Precipitation

\# Indicates a station move or relocation of instruments.

Year	Jan	Feb	Mar	Apr	May	June	July	Aug	Sept	Oct	Nov	Dec	Annual
1936	5.49	3.43	6.50	2.53	1.18	3.50	1.34	1.11	5.07	2.08	1.44	4.42	38.09
1937	4.51	1.81	3.55	4.59	3.26	3.82	1.22	5.85	3.54	3.42	4.44	2.22	42.23
1938	2.73	1.93	2.61	3.64	4.24	6.53	3.08	5.27	6.31	2.94	3.03	3.44	45.75
1939	3.32	5.45	4.70	3.99	0.90	2.66	0.47	5.22	0.92	4.27	0.92	1.60	34.42
1940	2.01	2.92	2.92	5.01	3.31	1.88	2.21	1.16	2.85	2.52	6.37	3.10	36.26
1941	3.93	1.44	2.25	1.81	0.92	5.90	4.55	2.61	0.08	2.56	2.38	2.38	30.81
1942	4.03	2.52	6.20	2.85	1.73	1.64	2.73	5.70	1.85	3.60	4.46	5.36	42.67
1943	2.90	1.95	3.38	3.33	2.36	1.50	4.01	2.42	1.65	2.53	2.92	2.07	31.02
1944	3.04	1.64	5.19	5.05	1.26	2.94	0.42	2.06	3.66	1.89	9.73	3.14	40.02
1945	3.46	5.16	1.61	2.43	4.39	1.88	2.30	2.00	0.84	2.31	6.84	6.29	39.51
1946	4.50	2.44	1.88	2.38	4.19	2.80	1.54	8.08	1.90	0.22	0.86	3.23	34.02
1947	3.54	1.66	3.37	5.86	3.71	3.32	4.73	0.69	2.80	3.28	3.67	3.04	39.67
1948	5.56	3.19	4.75	4.67	8.37	2.50	2.27	0.98	1.01	3.88	4.33	2.59	44.10
1949	4.94	6.32	3.55	3.42	2.93	T	0.96	3.71	1.53	0.92	3.18	3.54	35.00
#1950	3.14	3.94	2.91	2.67	3.57	2.13	2.83	2.62	0.40	1.14	3.91	2.99	32.25
1951	3.71	3.31	3.95	2.27	3.28	2.00	0.79	3.14	1.28	3.03	6.54	5.35	38.65
1952	5.51	4.25	5.01	3.36	3.64	1.32	0.39	9.26	1.29	0.81	1.50	2.71	39.05
1953	6.33	4.09	6.52	5.21	2.45	0.51	4.24	5.31	3.01	4.64	6.21	6.18	54.70
1954	3.17	2.65	2.69	4.38	4.63	1.19	3.73	9.73	7.42	1.68	4.30	5.57	51.14
1955	0.73	2.80	4.17	3.19	0.72	0.81	1.61	6.34	3.07	8.74	4.48	0.83	37.49
1956	3.59	4.62	5.47	1.99	2.72	1.50	4.35	1.63	1.86	2.30	3.06	3.49	36.58
1957	1.79	1.27	3.18	3.70	2.40	T	1.84	5.62	1.58	2.42	2.84	5.62	32.26
1958	6.74	4.44	5.09	5.54	5.25	2.12	4.85	5.53	5.50	3.75	3.01	2.20	54.02
1959	1.61	3.97	8.52	3.64	2.62	4.24	6.15	3.55	0.38	5.21	4.49	5.37	49.75
1960	4.28	5.67	1.91	4.07	4.37	2.47	4.14	1.05	11.36	2.65	3.84	6.37	52.18
1961	2.35	3.68	2.92	6.24	5.38	0.94	2.33	4.06	11.51	3.17	5.51	4.15	52.24
1962	5.07	6.44	2.52	6.11	1.59	6.81	1.97	6.74	4.24	7.31	7.49	3.30	59.59
1963	3.39	3.52	3.45	1.15	3.56	0.94	3.13	4.96	1.62	1.49	5.77	3.24	36.22
1964	3.37	3.54	2.99	5.82	1.41	1.32	1.89	0.26	3.73	2.73	1.29	6.61	34.96
1965	2.92	2.00	1.57	2.70	1.76	1.82	1.75	4.09	1.70	1.14	1.27	1.36	24.08
1966	3.23	2.29	1.16	1.32	5.62	1.55	1.18	1.41	4.74	2.40	2.89	2.49	30.28
1967	1.90	2.18	5.28	3.46	5.98	2.48	4.09	2.75	2.67	1.32	4.15	8.12	44.38
1968	2.37	1.20	6.69	1.26	2.78	4.50	0.78	1.28	0.65	2.74	5.41	5.38	35.04
1969	0.88	3.89	3.44	2.46	2.34	1.72	4.02	2.94	3.87	2.60	8.06	7.31	43.53
1970	0.27	3.63	4.74	2.99	1.69	3.09	2.63	5.35	2.79	3.83	6.20	2.97	40.18
1971	2.48	6.88	3.07	3.33	4.57	0.60	3.11	1.24	0.33	2.44	5.15	1.97	35.17
1972	2.18	5.85	4.95	3.98	4.73	6.20	1.87	0.99	6.53	2.16	7.88	5.86	53.18
1973	2.30	2.21	3.37	7.78	4.15	3.21	5.29	3.81	3.08	3.33	1.23	6.66	46.42
1974	3.85	2.12	3.58	3.17	3.17	2.88	2.10	2.90	2.73	1.91	1.36	4.71	34.48
1975	6.02	4.26	4.01	3.24	4.42	5.05	1.34	4.39	5.06		4.69	3.40	
RECORD MEAN	3.59	3.53	3.85	3.57	3.32	2.61	2.81	3.52	3.11	3.25	3.78	3.81	40.75

Record mean values above are means through the current year for the period beginning in 1881 for temperature and precipitation, 1951 for snowfall.

TEMPERATURES °F

Station: PROVIDENCE, RHODE IS THEO FRANCIS GREEN ST A.P
Elevation (ground): 51 feet

Month	Normal: Daily maximum	Normal: Daily minimum	Normal: Monthly	Extremes: Record highest	Extremes: Year	Extremes: Record lowest	Extremes: Year
(a)				12		12	
J	36.2	20.6	28.4	66	1974	-5	1971
F	37.6	21.2	29.4	59	1974	-5	1967
M	44.7	29.0	36.9	73	1964	1	1967
A	56.7	37.8	47.3	90	1974	19	1969
M	66.8	46.9	56.9	94	1964	32	1970
J	76.3	56.5	66.4	95	1973	41	1967
J	81.1	63.0	72.1	97	1964	49	1965
A	79.8	61.0	70.4	104	1975	40	1965
S	73.1	53.6	63.4	93	1969	34	1974
O	63.9	43.4	53.7	85	1968	21	1969
N	52.0	34.6	43.3	78	1974	14	1972
D	39.6	23.4	31.5	69	1965	-4	1975
YR	59.0	40.9	50.0	104	AUG 1975	-5	JAN 1971

IMPORTANT:
The time-period covered by this record is limited: See footnotes following table of **NORMALS, MEANS AND EXTREMES** for explanation and for additional history of **EXTREME HIGHS AND LOWS** recorded in the general area.

The proximity to Narragansett Bay and the Atlantic Ocean plays an important part in determining the climate for Providence and vicinity. In winter, the temperatures are modified considerably, and a good many of the major storms drop their precipitation in the form of rain, rather than snow. In summer, many days that would otherwise be uncomfortably warm are cooled by refreshing seabreezes. At other times of the year, sea fog may be advected in over land by onshore winds. In fact, most cases of dense fog are produced in this way; but the number of such days is few, averaging 2 or 3 days per month. In early fall, severe coastal storms of tropical origin sometimes bring destructive winds to this area. Even at other times of the year, it is usually coastal storms which produce the most severe kind of weather.

The temperature for the entire year averages around 50 degrees, ranging from a low of 47 degrees in 1917 to a high of 54 degrees in 1949. January and February are the coldest months, with a mean temperature near 29 degrees, while July is the hottest with a mean close to 73 degrees. The average temperature for the first 2 months has ranged from as low as 17 degrees in February of 1934 to as high as 39 degrees in January of 1932; while the range for July has been from 68 degrees in 1914 to 78 degrees in 1952. August is nearly as warm as July, with an average temperature around 71 degrees.

Freezing temperatures occur on the average about 125 days per year. They become of common daily occurrence the latter part of November, and cease to be common near the end of March. The average date for the last killing freeze in spring is April 14, while the average date for the first in fall is October 26, thus making the growing season about 195 days in length. Subzero weather in winter seldom occurs, averaging less than 1 day for December and 1 or 2 days for each of the months of January and February. The lowest temperature ever recorded in Providence has been 17 degrees below zero (February 9, 1934).

Seventy-degree temperatures become of common daily occurrence near the end of May, and cease to be common the latter part of September. During this period, there may be several days with 90 degrees

(Continued page 620)

Snowfall

Season	July	Aug	Sept	Oct	Nov	Dec	Jan
1936-37	0.0	0.0	0.0	0.0	3.7	T	3.5
1937-38	0.0	0.0	0.0	0.0	T	2.9	19.7
1938-39	0.0	0.0	0.0	0.0	8.4	2.7	7.3
#1939-40	0.0	0.0	0.0	0.0	T	6.5	4.2
1940-41	0.0	0.0	0.0	0.0	6.5	2.9	14.9
#1941-42	0.0	0.0	0.0	0.0	T	T	13.6
1942-43	0.0	0.0	0.0	0.0	T	9.1	24.5
1943-44	0.0	0.0	0.0	0.0	T	T	0.3
1944-45	0.0	0.0	0.0	0.0	0.6	10.7	20.1
1945-46	0.0	0.0	0.0	0.0	10.2	26.7	4.5
1946-47	0.0	0.0	0.0	0.0	0.0	3.4	5.1
1947-48	0.0	0.0	0.0	0.0	0.2	22.4	31.9
1948-49	0.0	0.0	0.0	0.0	T	13.4	10.3
1949-50	0.0	0.0	0.0	0.0	2.0	1.3	2.2
1950-51	0.0	0.0	0.0	0.0	T	2.9	5.9
1951-52	0.0	0.0	0.0	0.0	T	5.1	6.3
#1952-53	0.0	0.0	0.0	T	T	4.6	8.7
1953-54	0.0	0.0	0.0	0.0	T	0.2	17.0
1954-55	0.0	0.0	0.0	0.0	0.0	9.2	1.1
1955-56	0.0	0.0	0.0	0.0	3.6	2.2	10.0
1956-57	0.0	0.0	0.0	0.0	T	6.1	14.8
1957-58	0.0	0.0	0.0	T	0.2	0.3	7.5
1958-59	0.0	0.0	0.0	0.0	T	7.5	2.2
1959-60	0.0	0.0	0.0	0.0	T	5.1	9.9
1960-61	0.0	0.0	0.0	T	T	14.1	17.4
1961-62	0.0	0.0	0.0	T	1.7	9.2	4.9
1962-63	0.0	0.0	0.0	1.6	1.7	6.6	5.3
1963-64	0.0	0.0	0.0	T	T	19.8	12.5
1964-65	0.0	0.0	0.0	0.0	T	6.9	28.7
1965-66	0.0	0.0	0.0	0.0	T	1.9	16.1
1966-67	0.0	0.0	0.0	0.0	T	7.2	1.3
1967-68	0.0	0.0	0.0	0.0	0.8	19.0	13.5
1968-69	0.0	0.0	0.0	0.0	0.1	2.7	0.5
1969-70	0.0	0.0	0.0	0.0	T	15.4	6.5
1970-71	0.0	0.0	0.0	T	0.0	17.8	11.0
1971-72	0.0	0.0	0.0	0.0	T	4.7	2.2
1972-73	0.0	0.0	0.0	0.7	0.3	4.1	2.0
1973-74	0.0	0.0	0.0	0.0	T	T	15.1
1974-75	0.0	0.0	0.0	0.0	0.3	2.1	2.0
1975-76	0.0	0.0	0.0	T	1.2	7.5	
RECORD MEAN	0.0	0.0	0.0	0.1	0.5	7.7	9.2

Heating Degree Days

Season	July	Aug	Sept	Oct	Nov	Dec	Jan
1955-56	0	11	116	326	711	1219	1066
1956-57	13	13	194	394	630	885	1304
1957-58	0	22	93	369	576	817	1056
1958-59	2	6	108	415	595	1225	1134
1959-60	0	6	101	354	644	942	1106
1960-61	0	8	117	382	573	1159	1274
1961-62	0	6	49	284	633	1013	1123
1962-63	12	14	152	389	717	1125	1115
#1963-64	6	8	173	259	536	1242	1059
1964-65	9	24	125	377	605	981	1231
1965-66	3	29	99	395	711	907	1115
1966-67	1	1	135	417	577	994	963
1967-68	0	7	103	356	761	937	1246
1968-69	2	16	59	295	672	1072	1117
1969-70	2	4	119	365	673	1065	1399
1970-71	0	0	102	342	602	1124	1298
1971-72	0	7	42	181	736	922	1054
1972-73	8	10	64	473	717	945	1044
1973-74	2	3	125	331	632	819	1028
1974-75	0	0	114	512	634	899	951
1975-76	0	13	132	298	506	1013	

Cooling Degree Days

Year	Jan	Feb	Mar	Apr	May	June	July
1969	0	0	0	0	23	125	211
1970	0	0	0	0	13	86	289
1971	0	0	0	0	3	157	296
1972	0	0	0	1	7	60	248
1973	0	0	0	8	17	181	272
1974	0	0	0	7	27	79	242
1975	0	0	0	0	55	100	300

Feb	Mar	Apr	May	June	Total
0.5	4.1	T	0.0	0.0	11.8
11.6	0.8	1.1	0.0	0.0	36.1
5.0	16.5	T	0.0	0.0	39.9
17.1	3.0	0.2	0.0	0.0	31.0
1.2	19.5	0.0	0.0	0.0	45.0
8.1	1.6	1.0	0.0	0.0	24.3
3.2	10.1	0.4	0.0	0.0	47.3
7.2	8.9	T	0.0	0.0	16.4
23.9	1.4	0.0	0.0	0.0	56.7
11.5	0.6	0.1	0.0	0.0	53.6
12.3	1.5	0.4	0.0	0.0	22.7
12.4	8.7	T	0.0	0.0	75.6
11.4	11.4	0.0	0.0	0.0	46.5
12.9	3.7	T	0.0	0.0	22.1
9.4	4.1	0.0	0.0	0.0	22.3
13.1	3.0	0.0	0.0	0.0	27.5
8.9	T	2.5	0.0	0.0	24.7
0.2	T	0.6	0.0	0.0	18.0
7.0	4.6	T	0.0	0.0	21.9
7.3	31.6	1.4	0.0	0.0	56.1
3.5	10.5	2.1	0.0	0.0	37.0
11.0	14.4	3.7	0.0	0.0	37.1
5.2	11.0	T	0.0	0.0	25.9
1.6	21.6	T	0.0	0.0	38.2
18.7	12.2	0.3	0.0	0.0	62.7
30.9	T	0.3	0.0	0.0	47.0
5.2	9.4	T	0.0	0.0	29.8
14.8	2.5	T	0.0	0.0	49.6
2.7	6.6	T	0.0	0.0	44.9
9.1	8.1	T	0.0	0.0	35.2
23.1	24.9	1.6	0.0	0.0	58.1
4.6	5.1	0.0	0.0	0.0	43.0
26.7	6.0	0.0	0.0	0.0	36.0
6.8	15.7	1.1	0.0	0.0	45.5
5.0	6.1	1.9	0.0	0.0	41.8
13.7	8.7	0.7	0.0	0.0	30.0
3.2	0.6	0.4	0.0	0.0	11.3
11.1	0.4	1.3	0.0	0.0	27.9
18.2	2.2	0.2	0.0	0.0	25.0
10.4	9.2	0.7	0.0	0.0	37.8

Average Temperature

Year	Jan	Feb	Mar	Apr	May	June	July	Aug	Sept	Oct	Nov	Dec	Annual
1936	28.3	23.4	43.8	45.4	60.0	67.0	71.6	71.6	63.4	54.0	39.4	35.6	50.3
1937	37.6	34.2	34.6	46.4	60.0	67.8	73.5	75.0	62.9	51.6	43.8	31.8	51.6
1938	28.4	31.8	40.2	49.7	57.0	67.0	73.2	74.6	62.6	56.6	46.0	34.2	51.8
1939	28.2	33.2	34.6	45.4	58.8	66.6	72.8	75.0	64.2	53.7	40.2	34.0	50.6
#1940	22.8	30.0	33.3	44.5	56.6	66.0	73.4	69.2	63.9	50.4	42.9	35.4	49.0
#1941	26.5	30.2	34.0	52.6	60.6	68.8	72.8	71.2	66.1	56.4	46.5	34.4	51.7
1942	29.0	28.1	41.8	50.5	62.0	68.7	72.8	71.5	65.8	55.8	43.7	28.7	51.5
1943	26.9	31.4	37.2	44.0	59.4	72.2	74.7	72.2	63.3	54.1	43.7	30.4	50.8
1944	31.7	30.4	35.6	46.1	64.2	68.6	76.0	75.6	66.8	54.6	43.6	31.2	52.0
1945	24.4	31.4	48.0	54.5	57.2	68.7	74.6	71.9	68.4	53.8	45.7	28.8	52.3
1946	30.0	29.0	48.4	47.6	59.0	68.7	72.8	68.6	66.6	58.4	48.2	35.6	52.7
1947	33.2	30.0	38.4	48.0	58.1	66.0	75.5	74.0	65.4	61.4	41.6	31.4	51.9
1948	24.4	27.3	39.4	49.6	57.4	66.0	76.0	74.3	66.3	54.0	49.8	36.6	51.8
1949	36.3	36.3	40.4	52.1	60.6	72.0	77.2	74.4	63.6	58.6	43.6	37.6	54.4
1950	37.4	28.4	34.2	46.9	56.6	68.7	73.8	71.2	61.2	56.4	47.9	35.3	51.5
1951	34.8	36.0	40.3	51.9	59.6	66.4	74.2	71.3	65.8	55.9	42.0	36.2	52.9
1952	34.1	33.3	38.0	51.1	58.0	70.6	78.2	72.8	66.0	53.2	45.7	36.2	53.1
#1953	35.7	36.2	40.7	49.5	58.2	68.9	71.2	70.2	64.3	53.8	45.8	38.3	52.7
1954	25.9	35.4	38.1	49.6	55.6	66.5	70.3	67.8	62.2	57.5	42.9	33.4	50.4
1955	28.0	31.5	37.1	48.7	59.7	65.2	75.5	73.0	62.2	54.4	41.1	25.5	50.2
1956	30.4	32.3	33.0	43.9	53.4	67.1	70.5	70.5	60.1	52.1	43.9	36.2	49.4
1957	22.7	33.9	38.9	49.5	58.8	70.5	72.4	67.8	64.8	52.9	45.5	38.4	51.3
1958	30.7	24.7	38.4	47.8	54.9	62.5	71.5	70.7	63.0	51.5	44.9	25.3	48.8
1959	28.2	26.8	36.4	49.0	60.9	64.6	72.5	73.7	66.8	54.1	43.3	34.5	50.9
1960	29.1	35.1	31.5	48.7	58.5	67.5	71.0	70.8	62.5	52.6	45.7	27.4	50.0
1961	23.7	30.6	37.0	45.4	55.2	67.5	72.2	71.0	69.0	55.8	43.6	32.1	50.3
1962	28.5	26.6	37.7	48.6	56.6	66.6	68.5	69.0	60.8	52.2	40.9	28.6	48.7
#1963	28.9	26.3	38.9	48.3	57.1	67.5	72.8	69.4	59.6	56.8	46.9	24.7	49.8
1964	30.6	27.9	37.8	46.1	60.3	66.3	71.7	66.6	62.5	52.6	44.6	33.2	50.0
1965	25.0	28.4	36.1	45.4	60.0	67.0	71.6	71.6	64.1	52.1	41.1	35.4	49.8
1966	28.8	29.9	38.8	43.8	54.4	67.4	72.7	70.7	61.3	51.4	45.5	32.8	49.8
1967	33.7	25.7	33.3	44.8	51.2	66.8	72.8	70.6	62.7	53.7	39.5	34.5	49.1
1968	24.5	24.6	38.1	49.9	55.7	65.0	73.1	70.6	64.8	55.9	42.4	30.2	49.6
1969	28.8	28.7	35.0	49.7	57.7	68.2	71.5	74.3	64.0	53.3	42.4	30.5	50.4
1970	19.6	29.3	35.0	47.8	58.2	65.6	74.1	72.3	64.4	54.2	44.7	28.5	49.5
1971	22.9	30.9	36.7	45.9	58.1	69.0	74.3	73.0	68.7	59.2	40.4	35.0	51.2
1972	30.8	28.0	36.4	44.3	57.7	64.9	72.6	70.6	65.1	49.6	40.9	34.3	49.6
1973	31.1	29.6	43.7	50.0	56.7	70.3	73.6	75.0	63.4	54.2	43.8	38.3	52.5
1974	31.6	29.0	38.7	50.6	55.6	65.3	72.6	72.6	63.2	48.2	43.7	35.7	50.5
1975	34.1	30.4	35.5	44.5	61.4	66.0	74.3	71.4	61.0	55.3	48.0	32.1	51.2
RECORD MEAN	29.4	29.3	37.6	47.5	57.8	66.9	72.7	71.0	63.9	54.0	43.4	32.6	50.5
MAX	37.1	37.3	45.7	56.6	67.5	76.5	81.8	80.1	73.1	63.3	51.3	40.1	59.2
MIN	21.6	21.2	29.4	38.3	48.1	57.3	63.5	61.8	54.6	44.6	35.4	25.1	41.7

# Indicates a station move or relocation of instruments.

PROVIDENCE, RI

Feb	Mar	Apr	May	June	Total
941	986	625	365	52	6418
866	804	463	222	35	5823
1124	816	509	309	114	5804
1063	879	473	180	88	6168
861	1034	480	196	30	5754
955	864	581	302	26	6241
1068	840	489	274	40	5819
1076	805	493	252	46	6196
1066	835	560	188	52	5984
1018	891	581	182	67	6091
975	806	630	326	57	6053
1093	976	598	424	48	6227
1166	827	447	281	74	6205
1010	923	452	241	22	5881
996	924	509	214	60	6330
949	868	566	212	34	6097
1064	879	616	226	55	5782
984	653	451	268	16	5633
1003	808	433	313	62	5559
962	907	606	160	64	5809

Aug	Sept	Oct	Nov	Dec	Total
299	94	9	0	0	761
237	91	14	0	0	730
263	158	8	5	0	890
190	76	1	0	0	583
318	84	3	0	0	883
244	66	0	1	0	666
218	16	4	1	0	694

Precipitation

Year	Jan	Feb	Mar	Apr	May	June	July	Aug	Sept	Oct	Nov	Dec	Annual
1936	6.84	3.77	6.78	3.79	1.68	2.92	2.34	3.00	5.29	2.49	1.05	9.44	49.39
1937	4.61	1.75	3.82	5.27	2.54	3.14	1.16	4.13	3.01	4.06	5.42	3.22	42.13
1938	4.37	2.34	2.39	2.22	4.49	7.21	6.92	2.21	5.16	3.01	3.40	3.31	47.03
1939	2.30	4.09	4.62	4.33	0.57	2.70	1.07	4.08	2.39	4.31	0.76	3.12	34.34
#1940	2.50	3.13	3.69	5.30	5.01	2.22	3.24	0.99	2.57	1.86	6.38	2.15	39.04
#1941	3.57	2.34	3.54	1.53	3.10	4.01	5.68	2.45	1.03	1.07	2.79	3.37	34.48
#1942	3.98	3.84	7.98	0.72	1.77	3.44	4.56	4.54	1.68	3.09	5.03	6.39	47.02
1943	4.07	1.61	3.74	3.72	3.34	1.88	1.97	0.82	1.24	4.39	2.32	1.15	30.25
1944	2.58	2.52	5.00	3.82	0.86	4.16	0.96	1.34	9.74	3.33	7.52	3.42	45.25
1945	4.08	4.26	2.21	2.57	4.25	3.97	1.98	2.63	1.87	2.29	8.50	7.82	46.43
1946	3.63	3.55	1.49	2.25	3.99	2.91	1.25	12.24	1.70	0.16	0.67	3.64	37.68
1947	2.85	1.83	3.36	4.91	3.73	3.93	4.71	2.01	2.96	2.27	5.42	3.73	41.71
1948	6.15	2.34	3.73	3.71	9.25	3.50	5.13	2.15	2.36	4.85	5.00	2.30	50.47
1949	4.23	3.66	2.32	5.17	3.47	0.04	0.96	3.23	3.42	1.98	3.27	1.86	33.61
1950	3.73	4.44	3.84	2.88	2.15	1.97	0.98	5.66	1.88	2.77	6.89	4.27	41.46
1951	4.63	3.90	5.58	3.93	4.60	1.52	2.38	3.66	1.70	3.52	8.10	5.50	49.02
1952	4.41	4.57	4.41	4.15	3.73	2.70	0.24	7.06	1.68	2.75	2.73	3.40	41.83
#1953	7.12	4.51	8.31	6.70	3.25	0.55	4.43	3.99	2.99	4.71	6.59	5.42	58.57
1954	2.84	2.68	3.53	4.91	5.92	1.31	2.56	8.30	6.04	2.79	4.92	5.73	51.53
1955	0.78	4.97	5.35	3.61	2.37	3.72	3.34	11.12	3.27	7.00	5.60	0.58	51.71
1956	4.92	4.60	5.51	3.08	1.43	1.57	4.92	0.91	3.10	3.74	3.62	5.27	42.67
1957	2.17	1.68	3.29	4.46	0.93	0.39	1.41	2.51	0.87	2.52	3.99	5.86	30.08
1958	7.12	2.95	3.45	7.21	4.05	3.15	6.29	5.15	5.02	3.08	2.58	1.49	51.54
1959	2.27	3.67	6.04	3.83	1.46	4.83	4.01	3.53	0.77	4.71	3.85	4.17	43.14
1960	3.02	5.63	2.48	2.94	3.79	1.26	4.61	1.06	5.98	2.24	2.77	4.30	40.08
1961	3.52	4.68	4.16	7.32	5.21	1.48	2.76	3.86	7.92	2.39	3.10	3.16	49.56
1962	4.70	5.16	1.93	3.85	2.14	5.52	1.62	2.73	3.67	11.89	4.49	2.63	50.33
1963	3.40	3.15	3.78	1.62	4.69	3.54	3.35	1.56	4.10	1.63	6.53	2.15	39.50
1964	5.65	3.15	2.26	5.34	0.71	2.34	2.63	2.38	3.95	2.11	2.43	5.46	38.41
1965	3.46	3.77	1.72	2.43	1.08	1.91	1.28	1.90	1.64	2.75	2.08	1.42	25.44
1966	3.40	4.30	2.40	1.48	3.85	2.31	2.77	3.37	5.23	2.60	3.93	3.04	38.68
1967	1.60	2.51	5.49	4.19	7.27	2.72	3.95	3.24	3.17	2.25	2.75	7.36	46.50
1968	3.50	1.31	7.83	1.49	3.54	4.74	1.49	1.61	1.14	1.79	6.22	6.70	41.36
1969	2.23	4.30	3.10	3.95	2.41	1.23	2.98	2.58	3.09	1.62	6.35	10.75	44.59
1970	0.50	5.34	4.75	3.91	3.03	4.25	1.00	6.59	1.79	4.41	5.31	4.54	45.42
1971	2.01	5.36	3.81	2.31	3.83	1.64	3.48	3.03	2.54	2.88	5.16	2.37	38.42
1972	1.85	5.19	6.70	3.71	5.73	6.83	4.25	2.98	7.31	4.36	8.45	7.70	65.06
1973	3.06	3.55	2.78	7.16	3.99	3.48	2.92	5.17	3.04	3.17	2.29	7.63	48.24
1974	4.45	3.04	4.51	2.86	2.74	3.28	1.64	3.10	6.15	2.79	1.56	4.54	40.66
1975	6.78	3.29	3.07	2.99	2.06	4.73	3.51	2.19	6.15	4.66	6.29	5.11	50.83
RECORD MEAN	3.59	3.29	3.70	3.57	3.14	2.99	3.06	3.56	3.37	3.04	3.73	3.66	40.90

Record mean values above are means through the current year for the period beginning in 1905 for temperature and precipitation, 1954 for snowfall. Data are from City Office locations through 5-20-53 except that temperatures are from the Airport 11-10-41 through 12-31-41 and precipitation is from the Airport 11-10-41 through 2-28-42.

PROVIDENCE, RHODE ISLAND

(Continued)

and over, averaging near 8 days per year. However, 90 degree temperatures have been recorded as early as March 29 (1945), and as late as October 10 (1949). Readings of 100 degrees and over do not occur very often, and have been confined to the months of June, July and August. Some of the hottest days of summer come in August, with the all-time high of 102 degrees being recorded August 26, 1948.

Measurable precipitation occurs about 1 day out of every 3, and is fairly evenly distributed throughout the year. The annual average is a little more than 40 inches, but this has varied from as little as 25.44 inches in 1965 to as much as 65.06 inches in 1972. The driest month of record has been June 1949, with only 0.04 inches, while the wettest was August 1946, with 12.24 inches. There is usually no definite "dry season" but occasionally rather serious droughts are experienced, as for example, during the summer of 1949, when only 1 inch of rain fell during the months of June and July.

Thunderstorms are responsible for much of the rainfall from May through August. They usually produce heavy, and sometimes even excessive, amounts of rainfall; but since the duration is relatively short, damage therefrom is ordinarily light. The thunderstorms of summer are frequently accompanied by extremely gusty winds, which may result in some damage to property, especially to small pleasure and fishing craft.

The first measurable snowfall of winter usually comes toward the end of November, whereas the last in spring is about the middle of March. The average snowfall for a winter season is close to 40 inches, ranging from as low as 11.3 inches in 1972-73 to as high as 75.6 inches in 1947-48. Only 9 winters have had over 50 inches of snow, while 19 have had less than 25 inches. The month of greatest snowfall is usually February, but January and March are close seconds, with the record snowfall for any month being 31.9 inches in January 1948. It is unusual for the ground to remain well covered with snow for any long period of time. However, during the winter of 1947-48, there was a consistent snow cover from December 23 to March 18.

Normals, Means, and Extremes

Month	Normal Degree days Base 65 °F		Precipitation in inches												Relative humidity pct.			
			Water equivalent							Snow, Ice pellets				Hour 01	Hour 07	Hour 13	Hour 19
	Heating	Cooling	Normal	Maximum monthly	Year	Minimum monthly	Year	Maximum in 24 hrs.	Year	Maximum monthly	Year	Maximum in 24 hrs.	Year	(Local time)			
(a)				22		22		22		22		22		12	12	12	12
J	1135	0	3.52	7.12	1958	0.50	1970	3.34	1962	28.7	1965	10.6	1964	69	71	56	63
F	997	0	3.45	5.63	1960	1.31	1968	2.72	1970	30.9	1962	18.3	1961	67	70	55	61
M	871	0	3.99	7.83	1968	1.72	1965	4.53	1968	31.6	1956	16.9	1960	68	69	54	60
A	531	0	3.72	7.32	1961	1.48	1966	2.82	1970	3.7	1958	3.7	1958	70	69	48	59
M	259	8	3.49	7.27	1967	0.71	1964	3.76	1967	0.0		0.0		77	72	52	63
J	36	78	2.65	6.83	1972	0.39	1957	2.09	1972	0.0		0.0		83	76	57	67
J	0	224	2.85	6.29	1958	1.00	1970	2.80	1958	0.0		0.0		82	78	57	68
A	10	177	3.90	11.12	1955	0.91	1956	5.47	1955	0.0		0.0		82	78	54	68
S	93	45	3.26	7.92	1961	0.77	1959	4.89	1961	0.0		0.0		84	82	57	74
O	350	0	3.27	11.89	1962	1.62	1969	6.63	1962	1.6	1962	1.6	1962	80	79	53	70
N	651	0	4.52	8.45	1972	1.56	1974	3.13	1975	3.6	1955	3.6	1955	76	77	59	70
D	1039	0	4.13	10.75	1969	0.58	1955	3.85	1969	19.8	1963	11.2	1960	74	76	61	70
YR	5972	532	42.75	11.89	OCT 1962	0.39	JUN 1957	6.63	OCT 1962	31.6	MAR 1956	18.3	FEB 1961	76	75	55	66

(To better understand these tables, see full explanation of terms beginning on page 322)

Month	Wind					Pct. of possible sunshine	Mean sky cover, tenths, sunrise to sunset	Mean number of days												Average station pressure mb.
	Mean speed m.p.h.	Prevailing direction	Fastest mile					Sunrise to sunset			Precipitation .01 inch or more	Snow, Ice pellets 1.0 inch or more	Thunderstorms	Heavy fog, visibility ¼ mile or less	Temperatures °F					
			Speed m.p.h.	Direction	Year			Clear	Partly cloudy	Cloudy					Max. (b) 90° and above	Max. 32° and below	Min. 32° and below	Min. 0° and below	Elev. 62 feet m.s.l.
(a)	22	10	22	22		22	22	22	22	22	22	22	22	22	12	12	12	12	3
J	11.5	NW	46	18	1957	57	6.2	10	7	14	11	3	*	2	0	11	27	2	1015.7
F	11.9	NNW	46	16	1972	56	6.5	8	7	13	11	3	*	2	0	8	26	1	1014.2
M	12.4	WNW	60	18	1959	55	6.7	9	7	15	11	2	1	2	0	1	21	0	1012.4
A	12.5	SW	51	20	1956	55	6.5	8	8	14	11	*	1	2	*	0	8	0	1010.6
M	11.1	S	42	20	1956	57	6.6	7	10	14	11	0	3	2	1	0	*	0	1012.0
J	10.1	SW	40	20	1957	57	6.4	7	10	13	11	0	4	3	2	0	0	0	1013.9
J	9.5	SW	35	34	1964	59	6.4	7	11	13	9	0	5	2	3	0	0	0	1012.8
A	9.5	SSW	90	11	1954	59	6.1	9	11	11	10	0	3	2	2	0	0	0	1014.9
S	9.6	SW	58	18	1960	58	5.8	10	8	12	9	0	2	2	1	0	0	0	1016.0
O	9.7	NW	41	14	1954	60	5.4	11	8	12	8	*	1	3	0	0	4	0	1017.5
N	10.6	SW	52	18	1957	49	6.4	8	7	15	11	*	1	2	0	*	13	0	1014.1
D	11.0	WNW	48	14	1957	51	6.2	8	8	15	12	2	*	2	0	6	24	*	1015.7
YR	10.8	SW	90	11	AUG 1954	56	6.3	102	102	161	125	10	20	26	8	26	123	2	1014.2

FOOTNOTES

Means and extremes above are from existing and comparable exposures.
Annual extremes have been exceeded at other sites in the locality as follows:
Lowest temperature -17 in February 1934; maximum monthly precipitation 12.24 in August 1946; minimum monthly precipitation .04 in June 1949;
maximum monthly snowfall 31.9 in January 1948; fastest mile wind 95 SW in September 1938.

The northern aurora is produced by interactions of solar energetic particles, the ionosphere, and the earth's magnetic field.

CHARLESTON, SOUTH CAROLINA

The city of Charleston, prior to expansion that began in 1960, was limited to the peninsula bounded on the west and south by the Ashley River, on the east by the Cooper River, and on the southeast by a spacious harbor. Weather records for the City are from observation sites on the lower portion of the peninsula, while airport records are from sites some 10 miles inland. The terrain is generally level, ranging in elevation from sea level to 20 feet on the peninsula, with gradual increases in elevation toward inland areas. The soil is sandy to sandy loam with lesser amounts of loam. The drainage varies from good to poor. Because of the very low elevation, a considerable portion of this community and the nearby coastal islands are vulnerable to tidal flooding, though only a few tides have exceeded 8 feet above mean low water.

The climate is temperate, modified considerably by the nearness to the ocean. The marine influence is noticeable during winter when the minimum temperatures are sometimes 10° to 15° higher on the peninsula than at the airport. By the same token, maximum temperatures are dampened 3° lower on the peninsula. The wind direction is vital to life and work along the coast. The prevailing winds are northerly in the fall and winter, southerly in the spring and summer.

Summer is warm and humid. Temperatures of 100° or higher are infrequent. Maximum temperatures are generally several degrees lower along the coast than inland due to the cooling effect of the sea breeze. Summer is the rainiest season with 41 percent of the annual fall. The rain, aside from occasional tropical storms, is generally of a shower or thundershower nature, producing variable amounts over scattered areas.

The fall season passes through the warm "Indian Summer" period to the prewinter cold spells which begin late in November. From late September to early November the weather is mostly sunny and extremes of temperature are rare. Late summer and early fall, however, is the period of maximum threat to the South Carolina coast from hurricanes. Some memorable hurricanes that have affected the Charleston area occurred in August 1885, August 1893, August 1911, July 1916, September 1928, August 1940, August 1952, and September 1959. The highest storm tide of record for which accurate heights were obtained was 11.2 feet above mean low water in the August 1893 storm.

The winter months, December through February, are mild with rainfall averaging 18 percent of the annual total. The winter rainfall is generally of a more uniform type, although a few thundershowers do occur. There is some chance of a snow flurry, with the best probability of its occurrence in January, but a significant amount is rarely measured. An average winter would experience less than one cold wave and severe freeze. Temperatures of 20° or less on the peninsula and along the coast are very unusual.

Station: CHARLESTON, SOUTH CAROLINA
MUNICIPAL AIRPORT
Elevation (ground): 40 feet

TEMPERATURES °F

Month	Normal			Extremes			
	Daily maximum	Daily minimum	Monthly	Record highest	Year	Record lowest	Year
(a)				33		33	
J	59.8	37.3	48.6	83	1950	11	1970
F	61.9	39.0	50.5	86	1962	12	1973
M	67.8	45.1	56.5	90	1974	21	1960
A	76.2	53.0	64.6	93	1968	29	1944
M	83.1	61.1	72.1	98	1953	36	1963
J	87.7	68.1	77.9	103	1944	50	1972
J	89.1	71.2	80.2	101	1949	58	1952
A	88.6	70.6	79.6	102	1954	58	1944
S	84.5	65.9	75.2	99	1944	42	1967
O	77.1	55.1	66.1	94	1954	27	1952
N	68.4	44.1	56.3	88	1961	15	1950
D	60.8	37.7	49.3	83	1972	8	1962
YR	75.4	54.0	64.7	103	JUN 1944	8	DEC 1962

IMPORTANT:
The time-period covered by this record is limited: See footnotes following table of NORMALS, MEANS AND EXTREMES for explanation and for additional history of EXTREME HIGHS AND LOWS recorded in the general area.

(Continued)

The most spectacular time of the year, weather-wise, is spring with its rapid changes from windy and cold in March to warm and pleasant in May. The spring rainfall represents about 20 percent of the total annual rain. Severe local storms are more likely to occur in the spring than in other seasons; however, some of the most destructive local storms of the 20th century were a series of severe tornadoes on September 29, 1938, and a single small tornado accompanying a hurricane on September 11, 1960.

The average date of the first freeze in the fall is December 10, and the average date of the last freeze before spring is February 19, giving an average growing season of 294 days. Freeze has been reported in the immediate inland areas as late as April 16 (1962) and as early as October 24 (1937).

Normals, Means, and Extremes

(To better understand these tables, see full explanation of terms beginning on page 322)

Month	Normal Degree days Base 65 °F: Heating	Cooling	Precipitation in inches, Water equivalent: Normal	Maximum monthly	Year	Minimum monthly	Year	Maximum in 24 hrs.	Year	Snow, Ice pellets: Maximum monthly	Year	Maximum in 24 hrs.	Year
(a)				33		33		33		33		33	
J	521	12	2.90	6.68	1966	0.63	1950	2.26	1946	0.8	1966	0.8	1966
F	419	14	3.27	6.32	1964	0.33	1947	3.28	1944	7.1	1973	5.9	1973
M	300	35	4.75	11.11	1959	0.99	1963	6.63	1959	2.0	1969	2.0	1969
A	69	57	2.95	9.50	1958	0.01	1972	4.10	1958	0.0		0.0	
M	5	225	3.81	9.28	1957	0.68	1944	6.23	1967	0.0		0.0	
J	0	387	6.30	27.24	1973	0.96	1970	10.10	1973	0.0		0.0	
J	0	471	8.21	18.46	1964	1.76	1972	5.81	1960	0.0		0.0	
A	0	453	6.44	16.99	1974	2.28	1955	5.77	1964	0.0		0.0	
S	0	306	5.17	17.31	1945	0.53	1971	8.84	1945	0.0		0.0	
O	74	108	3.05	9.12	1959	0.08	1943	5.77	1944	0.0		0.0	
N	271	10	2.13	7.35	1972	0.48	1966	5.24	1969	T	1950	T	1950
D	487	0	3.14	7.09	1953	0.82	1944	2.38	1958	2.1	1943	2.1	1943
YR	2146	2078	52.12	27.24	JUN 1973	0.01	APR 1972	10.10	JUN 1973	7.1	FEB 1973	5.9	FEB 1973

Month	Relative humidity pct. Hour 01 (Local time)	Hour 07	Hour 13	Hour 19	Wind: Mean speed m.p.h.	Prevailing direction	Fastest mile: Speed m.p.h.	Direction	Year	Pct. of possible sunshine	Mean sky cover, tenths, sunrise to sunset	Mean number of days, Sunrise to sunset: Clear	Partly cloudy	Cloudy	Precipitation .01 inch or more	Snow, Ice pellets 1.0 inch or more	Thunderstorms	Heavy fog, visibility ½ mile or less	Temperatures °F Max. (b) 90° and above	Max. 32° and below	Min. 32° and below	Min. 0° and below	Average station pressure mb. Elev. 48 feet m.s.l.
(a)	33	33	33	33	26	14	15	15		17	26	27	27	27	33	33	33	26	33	33	33	33	3
J	82	84	56	73	9.2	SW	54	W	1964	56	6.3	8	7	16	10	0	1	5	0	*	10	0	1019.3
F	79	82	52	68	10.2	NNE	62	SW	1963	59	6.0	9	6	13	9	*	1	2	0	*	8	0	1016.8
M	81	83	50	67	10.4	SSW	51	SW	1973	65	5.9	9	9	13	11	*	2	2	*	0	3	0	1015.2
A	83	84	50	67	10.0	SSW	71	NW	1971	69	5.4	11	8	11	8	0	3	2	1	0	*	0	1016.4
M	38	84	54	72	8.9	S	60	N	1967	70	6.0	8	11	12	9	0	7	2	4	0	0	0	1013.2
J	90	86	59	75	8.5	S	65	NW	1968	65	6.3	6	11	13	11	0	10	2	11	0	0	0	1014.2
J	91	88	64	79	8.0	SW	58	N	1971	65	6.6	4	13	14	14	0	14	1	14	0	0	0	1015.2
A	92	90	63	80	7.4	SW	69	N	1968	63	6.3	6	13	12	13	0	12	2	13	0	0	0	1016.7
S	91	91	63	82	8.0	NNE	46	SE	1964	61	6.2	7	11	12	9	0	5	2	5	0	0	0	1015.6
O	88	89	56	80	8.1	NNE	54	W	1967	66	5.1	12	8	11	6	0	1	3	*	0	*	0	1018.5
N	85	86	51	77	8.2	N	55	SW	1962	65	5.0	13	7	10	7	0	1	4	0	0	4	0	1019.3
D	82	84	55	74	8.7	NNE	54	S	1968	60	5.9	9	8	14	8	*	*	4	0	*	10	0	1018.6
YR	86	86	56	74	8.8	NNE	71	NW	APR 1971	64	5.9	102	112	151	115	*	57	29	48	*	35	0	1016.6

FOOTNOTES Means and extremes above are from existing and comparable exposures. Annual extremes have been exceeded at other sites in the locality (East Bay Street) as follows: Highest temperature 104 in June 1944; lowest temperature 7° in February 1899; maximum precipitation in 24 hours 10.57 in September 1933.

Snowfall

Season	July	Aug	Sept	Oct	Nov	Dec	Jan
1970-71	0.0	0.0	0.0	0.0	0.0	0.0	T
1971-72	0.0	0.0	0.0	0.0	0.0	0.0	0.0
1972-73	0.0	0.0	0.0	0.0	0.0	0.0	T
1973-74	0.0	0.0	0.0	0.0	0.0	T	0.0
1974-75	0.0	0.0	0.0	0.0	0.0	0.0	0.0
1975-76	0.0	0.0	0.0	0.0	0.0	0.0	
RECORD MEAN	0.0	0.0	0.0	0.0	T	0.1	T

Heating Degree Days

Season	July	Aug	Sept	Oct	Nov	Dec	Jan
1955-56	0	0	0	104	323	549	610
1956-57	0	0	12	38	347	260	465
1957-58	0	0	5	130	224	453	674
1958-59	0	0	0	113	183	568	574
#1959-60	0	0	0	38	279	465	483
1960-61	0	0	0	62	216	651	635
1961-62	0	0	3	92	251	443	553
1962-63	0	0	8	95	339	597	604
1963-64	0	0	2	33	233	650	504
1964-65	0	0	0	135	153	385	507
1965-66	0	0	0	95	225	481	644
1966-67	0	0	0	51	280	498	442
1967-68	0	0	15	112	334	367	657
1968-69	0	0	0	80	334	564	624
1969-70	0	0	1	50	349	567	735
1970-71	0	0	11	42	324	392	465
1971-72	0	0	0	13	261	220	317
1972-73	0	0	0	33	268	302	520
1973-74	0	0	0	34	158	428	131
1974-75	0	0	5	136	299	432	350
1975-76	0	0	0	40	221	466	

Cooling Degree Days

Year	Jan	Feb	Mar	Apr	May	June	July
1969	0	0	1	46	165	465	555
1970	0	0	9	126	253	410	552
1971	2	5	5	65	215	469	480
1972	7	3	5	93	163	275	475
1973	1	0	50	42	233	412	554
1974	41	7	63	80	288	319	417
1975	8	13	26	74	318	414	449

CHARLESTON, SOUTH CAROLINA

Feb	Mar	Apr	May	June	Total
T	T	0.0	0.0	0.0	T
0.0	0.0	0.0	0.0	0.0	0.0
7.1	0.0	0.0	0.0	0.0	7.1
0.0	0.0	0.0	0.0	0.0	T
0.0	0.0	0.0	0.0	0.0	0.0
0.3	0.1	0.0	0.0	0.0	0.5

CHARLESTON (APT), SC

Feb	Mar	Apr	May	June	Total
245	275	117	6	0	2229
245	307	90	29	0	1793
609	387	91	15	0	2588
330	314	100	3	0	2185
474	582	65	12	0	2398
347	155	181	11	2	2260
263	363	160	0	0	2128
545	172	69	29	0	2458
500	240	61	4	0	2227
392	340	95	0	0	2007
427	338	119	15	2	2346
460	194	50	29	4	2008
667	307	67	4	0	2530
551	444	90	6	0	2693
454	249	82	9	0	2496
424	404	127	16	0	2205
463	249	113	8	0	1644
524	167	141	18	0	1973
378	150	114	2	0	1395
294	273	152	0	0	1941

Aug	Sept	Oct	Nov	Dec	Total
394	268	158	6	0	2058
487	384	130	3	1	2355
457	369	199	31	32	2329
488	351	110	30	22	2022
501	445	184	56	10	2488
450	312	46	18	3	2044
516	361	171	58	0	2408

Average Temperature

Year	Jan	Feb	Mar	Apr	May	June	July	Aug	Sept	Oct	Nov	Dec	Annual
1936	47.1	48.4	59.9	64.5	73.0	78.8	82.9	81.6	78.8	70.4	57.2	52.2	66.2
1937	61.7	51.0	57.0	64.6	72.6	80.8	81.0	81.0	75.5	65.2	55.2	48.4	66.2
1938	50.3	55.3	63.2	66.3	76.1	77.6	80.0	83.0	77.6	65.8	60.9	50.9	67.2
1939	52.8	57.8	61.5	66.0	72.3	81.8	81.8	80.2	79.2	69.4	55.0	51.4	67.4
1940	40.0	48.8	55.0	62.6	70.2	80.8	81.4	80.7	74.9	66.6	59.0	55.0	64.6
1941	49.6	45.5	51.4	66.0	73.0	78.7	81.6	82.4	78.4	73.8	60.2	54.4	66.2
#1942	49.6	45.2	58.1	65.9	73.2	80.0	84.1	80.8	78.0	69.4	61.1	50.4	66.3
1943	49.8	50.4	55.4	62.6	72.7	81.3	80.6	80.4	72.8	63.8	53.4	48.3	64.3
1944	49.2	55.0	58.0	62.6	73.2	80.6	78.6	78.3	77.8	64.8	54.3	44.5	64.7
1945	47.6	53.8	65.4	68.6	69.2	79.2	79.6	79.1	79.0	65.3	58.0	44.6	65.8
1946	50.8	52.8	62.2	65.0	71.7	77.0	79.5	78.8	75.0	67.2	62.2	52.8	66.2
1947	55.8	44.0	49.3	67.6	72.4	76.8	77.6	79.4	76.1	70.0	54.4	49.8	64.4
1948	43.2	50.4	59.6	66.6	72.4	79.0	80.7	78.2	74.0	61.5	62.9	54.2	65.2
#1949	58.4	58.4	57.8	64.1	71.6	77.4	80.6	80.2	74.1	70.2	54.2	52.4	66.6
1950	60.6	55.5	55.0	62.5	72.9	79.5	79.2	78.5	74.4	68.2	53.0	44.7	65.3
1951	49.2	50.4	57.3	62.5	69.9	78.0	80.3	79.7	75.0	69.2	53.4	54.3	64.9
1952	55.2	51.9	57.6	62.7	73.7	82.0	81.1	80.5	74.6	61.8	56.4	48.0	65.5
1953	52.5	52.7	60.3	63.5	77.1	77.6	80.0	78.6	75.1	66.1	54.6	50.6	65.7
1954	51.5	54.3	56.2	67.3	67.9	79.1	81.2	82.3	77.5	66.4	54.6	48.2	65.5
1955	47.6	52.1	60.3	66.8	73.8	75.0	80.1	79.8	75.0	64.2	54.7	47.1	64.7
1956	45.1	56.8	56.9	63.3	73.0	76.9	79.9	79.3	71.9	65.8	53.8	57.0	65.0
1957	50.1	56.6	55.3	64.2	71.6	77.4	78.9	78.9	75.9	61.8	58.2	50.2	64.9
1958	42.9	43.0	52.3	64.3	70.9	76.7	81.2	79.9	76.1	62.5	59.8	46.4	64.5
1959	46.3	53.4	54.8	64.3	73.1	75.9	77.9	78.3	73.8	69.0	56.5	49.8	64.4
#1960	49.2	48.4	46.3	65.8	72.2	77.5	80.1	80.1	75.9	67.8	57.9	43.7	63.7
1961	44.3	52.6	61.3	59.7	69.5	76.7	80.6	79.0	76.8	63.7	59.2	51.0	64.5
1962	47.1	56.2	53.2	62.1	75.9	76.3	80.8	79.0	73.9	66.5	53.5	45.6	64.2
1963	45.3	45.3	60.9	65.8	71.6	79.2	79.9	80.9	73.8	67.2	57.3	43.8	64.3
1964	48.5	47.5	57.6	66.0	73.1	80.0	[illegible]	79.6	75.4	62.5	60.5	52.9	65.1
1965	48.4	51.2	54.5	64.5	75.3	76.1	[illegible]	79.6	75.9	65.2	57.6	49.3	64.7
1966	43.9	49.6	53.9	63.2	70.6	73.7	79.6	80.0	75.8	67.4	56.3	48.9	63.6
1967	50.6	48.5	60.0	67.1	71.3	75.6	79.9	79.5	69.9	62.6	53.8	53.4	64.4
1968	43.5	41.8	55.7	65.7	71.7	77.8	81.5	81.5	75.1	67.1	53.7	46.5	63.5
1969	44.6	45.2	50.6	63.3	69.9	80.3	82.7	77.5	73.7	68.2	53.4	46.5	63.0
1970	41.0	48.5	57.1	66.3	72.7	78.4	82.5	80.6	77.3	67.5	54.1	52.1	64.8
1971	49.9	49.8	51.9	62.7	71.1	80.4	80.3	79.6	77.1	70.8	57.1	58.8	65.8
1972	54.8	48.9	56.9	64.0	69.8	74.0	80.1	80.4	76.4	67.3	56.8	55.7	65.5
1973	48.0	46.1	61.0	61.5	71.7	78.4	82.6	81.0	79.6	69.6	61.4	51.3	66.0
1974	61.8	51.5	62.0	63.6	74.0	75.4	78.2	79.3	75.0	61.8	55.5	51.0	65.8
1975	53.8	54.7	56.9	62.3	75.1	78.5	79.2	81.5	76.8	69.0	59.3	49.7	66.4
RECORD MEAN	50.2	51.6	57.5	64.6	72.6	78.6	81.1	80.5	76.5	67.3	57.7	51.1	65.8
MAX	58.9	60.4	66.3	73.4	80.8	86.2	88.3	87.6	83.6	75.6	66.8	59.9	74.0
MIN	41.5	42.8	48.6	55.7	64.4	71.0	73.8	73.4	69.4	59.0	48.6	42.3	57.5

# Indicates a station move or relocation of instruments.

Precipitation

Year	Jan	Feb	Mar	Apr	May	June	July	Aug	Sept	Oct	Nov	Dec	Annual
1936	2.54	3.45	5.51	2.20	1.79	3.08	3.42	6.37	2.47	5.55	0.83	2.99	40.20
1937	3.91	4.68	1.84	6.55	1.60	3.11	9.62	4.09	4.34	2.68	4.86	1.48	48.76
1938	1.12	0.76	0.33	2.65	3.94	3.10	5.99	3.60	5.24	2.63	0.60	1.14	31.10
1939	2.09	8.96	1.87	2.05	2.54	6.63	10.77	8.78	1.16	0.89	1.91	1.39	49.04
1940	3.31	3.73	2.62	1.77	2.01	2.07	7.15	16.71	2.16	0.06	1.54	2.36	45.49
1941	1.63	2.56	3.55	1.38	0.07	11.03	13.39	12.77	0.78	2.55	2.36	10.56	62.63
#1942	2.88	2.94	4.92	0.85	2.70	5.30	7.37	4.65	5.23	0.01	1.56	2.96	41.37
1943	3.93	0.56	6.84	3.19	1.61	5.37	6.15	14.53	0.73	0.08	1.81	4.03	48.83
1944	3.24	5.27	10.23	4.39	0.68	5.54	2.87	2.89	2.80	5.93	2.91	0.82	47.57
1945	1.66	5.00	1.52	3.72	2.56	7.12	11.42	6.07	17.31	2.14	1.14	4.52	64.18
1946	4.29	2.94	3.00	2.96	7.57	5.20	8.54	4.47	1.28	3.75	4.91	1.06	49.97
1947	1.16	0.33	8.16	4.76	3.64	6.82	6.98	3.53	9.93	4.72	5.17	5.40	60.60
1948	3.50	3.98	8.13	5.39	8.30	1.43	8.03	5.74	9.40	2.64	3.90	3.43	63.87
#1949	0.77	3.07	2.48	2.26	4.30	6.35	5.21	12.98	6.56	1.99	2.11	0.83	48.91
1950	0.63	0.37	4.43	1.65	3.74	3.47	14.32	6.48	5.93	2.88	1.17	3.61	48.68
1951	0.76	1.07	3.81	1.92	0.70	4.70	6.26	4.56	4.28	1.11	2.46	2.43	34.06
1952	1.06	5.99	4.08	2.30	4.75	3.59	5.86	7.36	7.24	1.29	1.90	1.88	47.30
1953	1.86	5.11	4.59	0.92	2.43	3.98	4.36	7.90	6.94	0.75	1.60	7.09	47.53
1954	0.89	0.56	1.38	2.25	3.18	0.96	5.90	2.41	1.55	5.81	1.12	4.30	30.31
1955	3.29	1.69	1.06	3.24	1.84	3.47	7.06	2.28	8.93	1.22	1.20	0.83	36.11
1956	2.56	2.91	2.45	2.39	4.62	7.69	10.60	5.97	4.81	3.89	0.88	0.95	49.72
1957	1.43	3.35	5.53	1.70	9.28	6.83	8.32	5.86	8.44	1.83	4.71	3.57	60.85
1958	7.20	4.04	5.78	9.50	4.43	12.09	7.74	7.87	5.54	3.31	0.52	4.15	72.17
1959	4.20	5.99	11.11	2.39	4.91	1.36	8.47	5.45	9.60	9.12	2.07	2.49	67.16
1960	5.81	4.06	2.72	2.05	2.26	6.76	14.10	3.15	7.60	0.98	0.79	2.13	52.41
1961	1.77	4.15	5.83	5.78	5.23	6.84	6.67	6.07	2.97	1.71	1.59	1.43	50.04
1962	3.59	1.28	7.88	2.52	1.81	16.07	5.93	11.54	3.81	3.25	2.01	1.46	61.15
1963	3.14	4.90	0.99	2.68	1.70	14.34	7.94	6.34	2.75	2.27	4.74	3.18	54.97
1964	6.53	6.32	4.40	2.72	4.77	6.95	18.46	7.67	4.11	7.53	0.52	3.01	72.99
1965	1.69	5.49	7.99	3.10	1.32	6.68	8.90	5.90	4.66	6.23	0.87	1.20	54.03
1966	6.68	4.61	2.65	2.83	7.71	6.03	11.48	3.45	2.20	1.70	0.48	3.76	53.58
1967	4.93	3.12	2.81	0.84	8.91	4.06	9.19	3.74	1.39	0.52	1.35	2.79	43.65
1968	2.25	1.27	1.35	1.99	2.54	9.41	7.77	4.42	1.66	6.86	2.67	3.65	45.84
1969	1.19	2.05	5.14	3.46	2.34	4.88	5.34	11.84	5.37	1.50	5.49	3.52	52.12
1970	2.51	2.86	7.72	1.34	3.78	0.96	5.93	10.64	2.53	4.08	0.67	2.90	45.92
1971	5.45	4.71	4.05	4.11	4.15	4.07	6.04	16.32	0.53	7.22	1.61	2.28	60.54
1972	4.13	5.18	2.52	0.01	5.67	5.29	1.76	4.52	1.82	0.25	7.35	4.36	42.86
1973	4.59	5.57	6.15	2.55	1.83	27.24	3.60	6.66	7.93	0.63	0.84	4.58	72.17
1974	1.42	2.96	3.04	0.86	4.82	9.45	3.09	16.99	4.80	0.40	3.78	3.00	54.61
1975	4.92	3.54	4.54	3.74	5.06	5.96	9.34	7.18	5.16	1.97	1.43	3.35	56.19
RECORD MEAN	3.01	3.33	3.65	2.76	3.47	5.30	7.24	6.80	5.00	3.16	2.25	2.84	48.81

Record mean values above are means through the current year for the period beginning in 1874 for temperature, 1871 for precipitation and 1943 for snowfall. Data are from City Office locations through 1942 and from Airport locations thereafter.

Station: RAPID CITY, SOUTH DAKOTA
REGIONAL AIRPORT
Elevation (ground) : 3162 feet

TEMPERATURES °F

Month	Normal			Extremes			
	Daily maximum	Daily minimum	Monthly	Record highest	Year	Record lowest	Year
(a)				33		33	
J	34.2	9.6	21.9	74	1953	-27	1950
F	37.6	13.9	25.8	74	1954	-22	1971
M	42.7	19.7	31.2	82	1946	-17	1962
A	57.2	32.0	44.6	89	1962	1	1975
M	67.4	42.9	55.2	98	1969	18	1950
J	76.3	52.0	64.2	106	1961	31	1951
J	86.3	58.8	72.6	110	1973	39	1959
A	85.9	57.2	71.6	106	1947	38	1966
S	74.7	46.3	60.5	104	1960	22	1972
O	63.6	36.4	50.0	94	1963	10	1972
N	47.5	23.2	35.4	77	1965	-19	1959
D	38.0	14.9	26.5	75	1965	-23	1972
YR	59.3	33.9	46.6	110	JUL 1973	-27	JAN 1950

IMPORTANT:
The time-period covered by this record is limited: See footnotes following table of NORMALS, MEANS AND EXTREMES for explanation and for additional history of EXTREME HIGHS AND LOWS recorded in the general area.

Rapid City, which is not far from the geographical center of North America, experiences the large temperature ranges, both daily and seasonal, that are typical of semi-arid continental climates.

The city is surrounded by contrasting landforms, with the forested Black Hills rising immediately west of the city, and rolling prairie extending out in the other three directions. From 40 to 70 miles southeast lie the eroded "Badlands." The Black Hills, many of which are more than 5,000 feet above sea level, with a number of peaks above 7,000 feet, exert a pronounced influence on the climate of this area. The rolling land to the east of the city is cut by the valleys of the Box Elder and Rapid Creeks, which flow generally east-southeastward. The station is located on the north slope of the irrigated Rapid Valley. An eastwest ridge 200-300 feet higher than the airport separates the station from the Box Elder Creek Valley.

The growing season ranges from an annual average of about 150 days near Rapid City to a very short season in the higher hills where there is the possibility of freezing temperatures every month of the year. The principal agricultural products in the area are cattle and wheat, and ranchers and farmers are dependent on the current weather forecasts, which are at times of vital interest in the protection of livestock.

Although the annual precipitation averages less than 15 inches per year in the lower elevations, the distribution is beneficial to agriculture with the greatest amounts occurring during the growing season. The heaviest snows are expected in the spring, which helps to furnish moisture for the early maturing crops such as wheat, while heavy winter snows at the higher elevations provide irrigation water for the fertile valleys.

Summer days are normally warm with cool, comfortable nights. Nearly all of the summer precipitation occurs as thunderstorms. Hail is often associated with the more severe thunderstorms, with resultant damage to vegetation as well as other fragile material in the path of the storms. Autumn, which begins soon after the first of September, is characterized by mild, balmy days and cool, invigorating mornings and evenings. Autumn weather usually extends into November and often into December.

The mean monthly temperatures for the winter months of December, January, and February are among the warmest in South Dakota due to the protection of the Black Hills, the frequent occurrence of Chinook winds, and the fact that the winter tracks of Arctic air masses usually pass east of Rapid City. Rapid City has become the retirement home for many farmers and ranchers from the western half of the State because of the cool summer nights and the relatively mild winters.

Snowfall is normally light with the greatest monthly average of about 8 inches occurring in March. Cold waves can be expected occasionally, and one or more blizzards may occur each winter. On the average a rather severe blizzard in which the visibility is held to near zero for 24 hours or more can be expected once out of every three or four years.

Spring is characterized by unsettled conditions. Wide variations usually occur in temperatures, and snows may fall as late as May.

RAPID CITY, SOUTH DAKOTA

Normals, Means, And Extremes

(To better understand these tables, see full explanation of terms beginning on page 322)

Month	Normal Degree days Base 65 °F: Heating	Cooling	Precipitation in inches, Water equivalent: Normal	Maximum monthly	Year	Minimum monthly	Year	Maximum in 24 hrs.	Year	Snow, Ice pellets: Maximum monthly	Year	Maximum in 24 hrs.	Year	Relative humidity pct. (Local time): Hour 05	Hour 11	Hour 17	Hour 23	Wind: Mean speed m.p.h.	Prevailing direction	Fastest mile: Speed m.p.h.	Direction	Year	Pct. of possible sunshine	Mean sky cover, tenths, sunrise to sunset	Mean number of days, Sunrise to sunset: Clear	Partly cloudy	Cloudy	Precipitation .01 inch or more	Snow, Ice pellets 1.0 inch or more	Thunderstorms	Heavy fog, visibility ¼ mile or less	Temperatures °F Max.: 90° and above (b)	32° and below	Min.: 32° and below	0° and below	Average station pressure mb. Elev. 3168 feet m.s.l.
(a)				33		33		33		33		33		25	25	25	25	25	13	25	25		33	33	33	33	33	33	25	33	33	33	33	33	33	3
J	1336	0	0.47	1.77	1944	0.01	1952	1.26	1944	24.0	1949	16.3	1944	68	59	63	68	10.6	NNW	65	SW	1967	54	6.6	7	8	16	7	1	0	2	0	13	30	8	902.6
F	1098	0	0.57	2.46	1953	0.06	1950	1.00	1953	23.7	1953	10.0	1953	72	60	63	72	10.9	NNW	59	NW	1970	59	6.5	6	8	14	7	3	0	2	0	10	27	4	904.2
M	1048	0	0.99	3.02	1945	0.14	1948	2.19	1945	30.7	1950	14.9	1973	74	56	55	72	12.6	NNW	65	W	1953	61	6.8	6	9	16	9	3	*	2	0	8	28	2	900.3
A	612	0	2.09	5.16	1967	0.27	1954	3.01	1946	30.6	1970	16.0	1970	73	48	46	68	13.3	NNW	61	NW	1967	59	6.7	6	9	15	10	2	1	2	0	1	15	0	901.4
M	319	15	2.81	7.35	1946	0.33	1966	3.40	1965	11.6	1950	13.4	1967	74	49	46	70	12.4	NNW	56	NW	1967	57	6.4	7	10	14	12	*	6	1	1	*	3	0	902.0
J	134	110	3.67	7.00	1968	0.64	1973	4.01	1963	3.6	1951	3.6	1951	76	51	49	73	10.8	NNW	57	NW	1975	60	5.7	9	11	10	13	*	11	1	3	0	*	0	902.2
J	13	249	2.10	6.13	1969	0.60	1965	2.51	1944	0.0		0.0		72	45	40	64	9.9	NNW	66	SW	1959	71	4.3	13	13	5	9	0	12	1	11	0	0	0	905.4
A	17	222	1.47	4.40	1945	0.10	1943	1.65	1972	0.0		0.0		68	41	35	58	10.2	NNW	65	NW	1951	73	4.2	14	12	5	7	0	9	1	12	0	0	0	904.7
S	191	56	1.22	3.94	1946	0.03	1975	2.13	1966	2.0	1970	2.0	1970	67	41	38	59	11.0	NNW	61	NW	1964	67	4.6	13	9	8	6	*	3	*	3	0	1	0	907.8
O	474	9	0.86	2.25	1946	T	1960	1.45	1962	10.2	1971	7.6	1971	64	40	44	60	11.1	NNW	59	NW	1971	65	4.9	13	8	10	4	*	*	*	*	*	10	0	905.3
N	888	0	0.48	2.09	1944	0.03	1945	1.09	1944	12.6	1959	8.2	1944	68	51	58	66	10.9	NNW	59	NW	1966	56	6.2	8	8	14	6	1	*	2	0	5	25	1	904.3
D	1194	0	0.39	1.65	1975	0.04	1957	1.04	1975	17.9	1975	9.8	1975	68	59	64	68	10.4	NNW	60	W	1955	54	6.3	8	8	15	6	2	*	2	0	11	30	4	903.5
YR	7324	661	17.12	7.35	MAY 1946	T	OCT 1960	4.01	JUN 1963	30.7	MAR 1950	16.3	JAN 1944	70	50	50	66	11.2	NNW	66	SW	JUL 1959	62	5.7	110	113	142	95	12	42	16	31	48	169	20	903.6

FOOTNOTES Means and extremes above are from existing and comparable exposures. Annual extremes have been exceeded at other sites in the locality as follows: Lowest temperature -33 in February 1936; maximum monthly precipitation 9.66 in July 1905; maximum precipitation in 24 hours 5.57 in May 1926; maximum monthly snowfall 38.5 in April 1927; maximum snowfall in 24 hours 18.3 in March 1927; fastest mile of wind 75 from Northwest in February 1947.

Snowfall

Season	July	Aug	Sept	Oct	Nov	Dec	Jan
1936-37	0.0	0.0	0.0	4.9	8.3	0.6	6.4
1937-38	0.0	0.0	0.0	0.1	2.4	4.5	4.2
1938-39	0.0	0.0	0.0	0.0	6.1	0.8	3.9
1939-40	0.0	0.0	T	1.2	0.0	2.7	2.2
1940-41	0.0	0.0	0.0	0.0	0.4	4.3	1.2
#1941-42	0.0	0.0	T	1.0	0.6	5.8	0.5
1942-43	0.0	0.0	0.5	1.0	1.8	3.0	4.6
1943-44	0.0	0.0	0.0	2.6	1.7	2.7	22.5
1944-45	0.0	0.0	T	1.0	9.7	7.0	4.9
1945-46	0.0	0.0	T	T	0.1	1.6	2.1
1946-47	0.0	0.0	T	5.1	3.1	2.9	5.3
1947-48	0.0	0.0	0.0	1.5	8.1	1.6	4.2
1948-49	0.0	0.0	0.0	T	1.6	5.9	24.0
1949-50	0.0	0.0	T	0.7	T	5.0	2.7
#1950-51	0.0	0.0	T	3.8	3.0	0.9	1.2
1951-52	0.0	0.0	0.0	1.2	2.4	5.5	0.1
1952-53	0.0	0.0	0.0	T	0.3	0.7	6.5
1953-54	0.0	0.0	0.0	0.0	5.8	0.8	2.3
1954-55	0.0	0.0	0.0	9.3	7.3	1.2	4.1
1955-56	0.0	0.0	0.0	0.8	4.2	8.7	3.6
1956-57	0.0	0.0	0.0	0.2	12.1	5.3	4.1
1957-58	0.0	0.0	T	T	2.1	0.2	4.2
1958-59	0.0	0.0	0.0	T	2.8	4.1	3.7
1959-60	0.0	0.0	T	T	12.6	3.0	2.0
1960-61	0.0	0.0	T	T	1.8	7.1	1.0
1961-62	0.0	0.0	0.2	3.7	2.7	5.5	4.9
1962-63	0.0	0.0	T	T	0.4	1.6	10.8
1963-64	0.0	0.0	0.0	T	0.3	3.0	3.5
1964-65	0.0	0.0	0.0	0.0	2.6	7.8	4.3
1965-66	0.0	0.0	1.5	0.0	0.8	0.7	2.4
1966-67	0.0	0.0	T	2.1	6.4	8.5	4.0
1967-68	0.0	0.0	0.0	0.0	2.2	9.1	4.0
1968-69	0.0	0.0	0.0	0.0	2.7	7.5	1.2
1969-70	0.0	0.0	0.0	4.1	2.9	5.7	5.5
1970-71	0.0	0.0	2.0	5.7	4.5	7.8	13.2
1971-72	0.0	0.0	0.0	10.2	6.9	2.0	2.6
1972-73	0.0	0.0	0.0	0.7	3.6	6.0	2.0
1973-74	0.0	0.0	0.0	1.4	9.7	5.6	2.0
1974-75	0.0	0.0	0.0	T	1.5	1.4	13.7
1975-76	0.0	0.0	0.0	4.6	8.4	17.9	
RECORD MEAN	0.0	0.0	0.1	1.8	4.1	4.7	5.4

Heating Degree Days

Season	July	Aug	Sept	Oct	Nov	Dec	Jan
1955-56	0	0	184	415	1203	1331	1294
1956-57	1	37	119	364	950	1083	1678
1957-58	0	22	189	553	876	924	1019
1958-59	30	7	127	412	826	1168	1374
1959-60	8	1	260	630	1107	949	1266
1960-61	1	12	154	407	837	1234	1158
1961-62	2	0	327	469	898	1295	1414
1962-63	4	36	165	372	721	1073	1634
1963-64	4	4	59	205	755	1305	1129
1964-65	0	64	198	410	931	1419	1218
#1965-66	3	27	461	312	797	978	1573
1966-67	0	83	158	504	905	1180	1143
1967-68	31	19	129	464	902	1311	1285
1968-69	26	46	176	428	881	1438	1516
1969-70	0	0	62	750	781	1135	1461
1970-71	2	0	245	644	918	1330	1463
1971-72	43	2	267	578	909	1284	1473
1972-73	74	43	193	649	1010	1436	1181
1973-74	16	0	246	416	972	1223	1329
1974-75	1	42	242	407	849	1112	1274
1975-76	3	16	206	493	929	1096	

Cooling Degree Days

Year	Jan	Feb	Mar	Apr	May	June	July
1969	0	0	0	0	35	29	193
1970	0	0	0	0	7	96	248
1971	0	0	0	0	0	81	142
1972	0	0	0	0	21	70	98
1973	0	0	0	0	7	80	202
1974	0	0	0	1	3	143	390
1975	0	0	0	0	9	41	314

Feb	Mar	Apr	May	June	Total
2.6	16.4	0.4	0.0	0.0	39.6
2.2	1.4	9.8	1.2	0.0	25.8
5.5	9.0	4.2	0.0	0.0	29.5
2.8	6.0	8.6	0.0	0.0	23.5
0.8	2.9	0.5	T	0.0	10.1
5.2	4.2	T	8.0	0.0	25.3
3.1	11.9	T	T	T	25.9
6.5	12.7	T	T	0.0	48.7
7.0	4.6	2.8	0.6	0.0	37.6
0.4	12.0	6.8	T	0.0	23.0
5.8	2.2	5.6	T	0.0	30.0
5.7	1.9	0.1	1.5	0.0	24.6
1.3	2.9	T	0.0	0.0	35.7
0.7	30.7	15.2	11.6	0.0	66.6
1.1	6.8	1.2	0.0	3.6	21.6
6.7	7.1	0.3	0.0	0.0	23.3
23.7	8.4	8.6	0.7	0.0	48.9
1.3	21.0	0.1	2.2	0.0	33.5
12.2	6.4	3.3	0.0	0.0	43.8
5.7	7.5	11.1	T	0.0	41.6
3.9	7.0	16.2	0.0	0.0	48.8
8.4	7.1	8.8	0.0	0.0	30.8
6.8	1.2	13.9	T	0.0	32.5
8.7	7.4	4.3	0.0	0.0	38.0
2.2	3.8	5.2	T	0.0	21.1
6.9	7.9	0.1	0.0	0.0	31.9
12.0	17.3	7.4	0.0	0.0	49.5
8.9	5.7	4.2	0.0	0.0	25.6
1.9	4.6	5.5	8.8	0.0	35.5
10.0	16.5	10.0	0.4	0.0	42.3
7.4	7.6	14.0	3.1	0.0	53.1
3.4	1.3	13.7	T	0.0	33.7
7.9	6.3	5.2	T	0.5	31.3
6.0	14.8	30.6	T	0.0	69.6
15.7	13.8	5.3	0.0	0.0	68.0
8.0	1.2	1.0	T	0.0	31.9
3.1	16.9	1.9	0.0	0.0	34.2
4.0	1.7	4.7	0.0	0.0	29.1
6.1	27.4	1.3	0.0	0.0	51.4
6.4	9.3	6.3	0.9	0.1	39.1

RAPID CITY, SD

Feb	Mar	Apr	May	June	Total
1180	953	774	270	0	7604
1042	966	714	336	106	7396
1201	1057	622	129	121	6713
1206	833	643	352	47	7025
1325	1140	520	262	58	7526
884	787	690	314	25	6503
1139	1121	483	213	60	7421
968	776	607	253	28	6637
1064	1081	555	237	85	6483
1098	1351	534	327	55	7605
1273	923	784	285	103	7519
1042	917	622	473	162	7189
1083	755	669	432	107	7187
1102	1145	458	264	176	7656
950	1157	767	293	74	7430
1182	996	563	344	35	7722
1182	877	634	322	74	7645
1008	847	659	350	83	7533
905	840	530	343	87	6907
1318	1151	728	343	119	7586

Aug	Sept	Oct	Nov	Dec	Total
280	63	0	0	0	600
279	78	5	0	0	713
284	43	0	0	0	550
178	34	0	0	0	401
295	15	0	0	0	599
132	28	0	0	0	697
188	19	12	0	0	583

Average Temperature

Year	Jan	Feb	Mar	Apr	May	June	July	Aug	Sept	Oct	Nov	Dec	Annual
1936	16.8	1.4	35.0	41.1	62.4	70.7	82.4	75.0	64.8	48.8	37.6	27.2	46.9
1937	6.0	23.6	30.9	44.1	58.0	63.8	74.6	76.7	64.2	51.2	34.4	26.5	46.2
1938	29.0	26.5	39.3	46.0	54.2	67.0	73.6	74.5	65.9	55.4	33.6	29.6	49.6
1939	32.4	17.0	36.0	46.5	62.5	64.0	77.2	71.6	65.3	49.2	43.8	36.6	50.2
1940	16.2	27.6	34.0	41.3	57.9	67.8	77.0	71.8	66.6	56.0	32.0	32.4	48.4
1941	27.2	27.8	31.9	45.0	61.0	65.0	73.7	71.8	58.8	48.0	40.1	31.3	48.5
#1942	28.2	23.0	35.8	50.1	51.0	61.8	72.0	70.4	57.4	49.7	36.1	27.9	47.0
1943	13.8	32.6	25.4	50.2	51.8	62.7	73.4	74.4	60.4	51.8	35.9	29.7	46.8
1944	28.1	21.3	22.2	42.5	57.8	60.8	69.0	69.8	60.8	52.6	33.0	25.7	45.3
1945	26.5	24.6	36.6	40.6	51.2	55.6	71.2	70.9	58.0	51.6	35.6	22.4	45.4
1946	28.7	32.5	41.6	52.3	50.0	63.7	72.6	67.0	59.4	42.6	33.7	28.4	47.7
1947	27.6	20.4	26.4	43.3	52.8	59.2	72.7	75.3	62.1	55.6	28.3	30.4	46.2
1948	24.2	21.2	29.3	48.8	54.8	62.7	70.8	71.6	66.6	50.6	34.1	23.1	46.5
1949	8.8	17.6	30.7	49.8	57.4	64.4	75.0	74.2	59.7	47.2	46.0	22.2	46.1
#1950	9.0	29.9	25.1	38.0	50.5	63.9	66.9	67.7	59.0	53.8	32.1	28.5	43.7
1951	20.8	27.7	24.6	40.6	56.3	57.7	70.8	69.5	55.8	46.6	33.2	17.4	43.4
1952	22.5	26.8	25.8	50.2	56.1	69.0	71.6	72.4	67.2	50.2	34.3	30.1	48.0
1953	31.3	25.8	36.7	38.4	52.5	66.8	72.5	72.5	63.2	55.9	41.7	30.4	49.0
1954	20.1	41.2	27.7	45.9	54.2	63.7	77.7	72.5	63.2	46.8	42.6	32.4	49.0
1955	24.0	19.3	28.6	49.8	59.2	62.2	76.9	76.2	62.2	51.8	24.7	21.8	46.4
1956	23.1	24.1	34.1	39.1	56.8	72.8	72.0	69.5	63.0	53.4	33.2	29.9	47.6
1957	10.8	27.6	33.7	41.0	54.0	62.7	75.3	71.6	59.2	47.5	35.4	34.9	46.1
1958	31.9	22.0	30.7	44.0	61.8	62.4	67.1	74.7	63.8	52.3	37.2	27.0	47.9
1959	20.6	21.8	37.9	43.3	53.7	70.1	73.8	75.7	58.8	44.5	27.9	34.2	46.8
1960	24.0	19.1	28.0	47.5	56.9	65.7	76.8	72.4	63.6	51.8	36.9	25.0	47.3
1961	27.3	33.2	39.4	41.8	55.8	71.3	73.1	77.2	55.6	49.9	34.9	23.0	48.6
1962	19.3	24.2	28.6	49.1	58.3	65.3	69.2	71.2	60.3	52.9	40.6	30.1	47.4
1963	12.3	30.2	39.7	44.5	57.0	68.1	74.4	73.8	66.5	59.4	39.6	22.7	49.0
1964	28.4	28.1	29.9	46.3	58.5	64.9	76.7	69.5	59.0	51.7	33.7	18.9	47.1
#1965	25.4	25.6	21.2	47.0	54.7	64.5	72.1	70.7	49.7	54.8	38.2	33.3	46.4
1966	14.2	19.3	35.0	38.7	56.0	65.3	76.6	65.9	61.3	48.6	34.6	26.7	45.2
1967	27.9	27.5	35.2	44.1	49.8	60.0	70.6	70.6	63.4	50.1	34.6	22.5	46.3
1968	23.4	27.4	40.4	42.6	50.8	63.0	69.2	67.0	59.8	51.0	35.5	18.5	45.7
1969	16.0	25.4	27.8	49.6	57.5	59.8	71.0	73.8	64.8	40.6	38.7	28.2	46.1
1970	17.8	30.8	27.5	39.2	55.6	65.6	72.7	73.8	59.1	44.1	34.2	21.9	45.2
1971	17.5	22.6	32.6	46.0	53.6	66.4	68.0	73.9	57.4	46.1	34.5	23.3	45.2
1972	17.3	24.0	36.5	43.6	55.2	64.7	65.6	69.1	59.4	43.8	31.0	18.6	44.1
1973	26.8	28.9	37.5	42.9	53.7	64.7	70.7	74.3	57.1	51.3	32.3	25.4	47.1
1974	21.9	32.5	37.6	47.2	53.8	66.6	77.3	67.7	57.6	51.7	36.4	28.9	48.3
1975	23.7	17.6	27.6	40.5	54.0	62.2	74.7	70.3	58.5	49.2	33.8	29.4	45.1
RECORD MEAN	22.9	25.1	32.8	44.8	54.9	64.5	72.3	70.9	60.6	49.5	36.1	26.7	46.8
MAX	34.5	36.4	44.1	56.4	66.4	76.1	85.3	84.3	73.9	62.2	47.7	37.8	58.8
MIN	11.2	13.7	21.5	33.1	43.3	52.8	59.2	57.5	47.3	36.7	24.5	15.6	34.7

Precipitation

Year	Jan	Feb	Mar	Apr	May	June	July	Aug	Sept	Oct	Nov	Dec	Annual
1936	0.51	0.59	0.82	1.21	0.09	1.21	0.27	0.70	0.56	0.81	0.69	0.05	7.51
1937	0.35	0.24	1.63	0.50	2.80	2.77	3.45	0.43	0.67	0.14	0.22	0.79	13.99
1938	0.35	0.20	0.83	3.07	3.24	3.57	1.56	0.66	1.29	0.24	0.62	0.08	15.71
1939	0.38	0.35	0.84	0.74	1.04	2.16	1.78	1.28	0.80	1.34	T	0.31	11.02
1940	0.19	0.23	1.03	3.06	0.42	1.91	0.69	1.18	1.27	0.74	0.21	0.34	11.27
1941	0.12	0.08	0.45	6.47	1.34	5.10	1.11	2.17	1.09	2.06	0.08	0.48	20.55
#1942	0.04	0.44	0.55	4.21	4.78	3.23	1.79	0.24	1.74	1.68	0.38	0.36	19.44
1943	0.75	0.34	0.84	1.10	1.89	4.93	2.51	0.10	0.32	1.12	0.16	0.18	14.24
1944	1.77	0.52	1.13	1.54	3.53	4.97	4.54	0.45	0.40	0.92	2.09	0.37	22.23
1945	0.53	0.45	3.02	0.50	2.52	4.26	1.44	4.40	2.12	0.20	0.03	0.17	19.64
1946	0.13	0.20	1.54	2.31	7.35	5.37	2.93	1.18	3.94	2.25	0.29	0.21	27.70
1947	0.49	0.36	0.39	1.47	1.14	5.68	0.82	0.46	0.31	1.17	0.76	0.15	13.20
1948	0.37	0.53	0.14	1.62	1.67	4.86	2.65	3.06	0.59	1.70	0.29	0.48	17.96
1949	1.68	0.12	0.25	2.06	1.63	3.24	0.82	1.16	1.05	0.88	0.15	0.47	13.51
#1950	0.25	0.06	2.66	1.63	2.43	0.90	1.62	2.74	2.79	0.40	0.35	0.04	15.87
1951	0.12	0.10	0.79	0.51	1.87	3.75	1.63	2.92	1.46	0.88	0.21	0.53	14.77
1952	0.01	0.65	0.81	0.32	3.75	3.04	1.51	0.70	0.21	0.01	0.15	0.08	11.24
1953	0.75	2.46	0.66	2.77	1.68	4.05	1.32	0.94	0.37	0.23	0.84	0.18	16.25
1954	0.18	0.34	2.28	0.27	2.68	3.18	1.24	2.11	0.20	1.92	0.64	0.25	15.29
1955	0.46	0.88	0.63	1.55	1.70	2.14	2.14	1.65	3.08	0.26	0.36	0.68	15.53
1956	0.47	0.52	0.75	1.69	2.09	1.32	2.27	3.15	0.30	0.10	1.48	0.36	14.50
1957	0.40	0.29	0.66	2.06	7.05	3.43	2.01	1.03	0.69	1.29	0.39	0.04	19.34
1958	0.43	0.84	1.08	3.03	1.04	3.86	4.49	0.26	0.03	0.22	0.42	0.37	16.07
1959	0.39	0.63	0.60	1.89	3.25	2.79	0.67	0.36	2.37	0.22	1.18	0.26	14.61
1960	0.16	0.85	0.78	1.21	2.23	2.19	0.70	1.24	0.68	T	0.39	0.80	11.23
1961	0.10	0.22	0.75	1.53	1.29	0.76	2.11	0.43	0.98	0.94	0.36	0.51	9.98
1962	0.51	0.98	1.28	0.69	6.90	4.01	4.53	1.03	0.67	1.63	0.08	0.19	22.50
1963	1.03	0.92	1.60	3.80	1.18	5.47	2.03	1.32	1.21	0.77	0.12	0.32	19.77
1964	0.35	0.83	0.63	1.24	2.52	4.69	0.77	1.87	0.69	0.50	0.30	0.78	15.17
1965	0.61	0.22	0.46	1.50	6.97	3.56	0.60	1.46	1.46	0.57	0.15	0.12	17.68
1966	0.24	1.00	1.78	2.50	0.33	1.31	3.93	3.24	2.84	1.50	0.95	0.79	20.41
1967	0.47	0.59	0.82	5.16	3.20	6.78	1.07	0.95	2.10	0.28	0.28	0.89	22.59
1968	0.43	0.35	0.21	1.82	1.68	7.00	2.44	2.46	0.89	0.14	0.46	0.58	18.46
1969	0.11	0.73	0.66	1.60	2.20	2.04	6.13	0.31	0.35	0.85	0.35	0.57	15.90
1970	0.73	0.54	1.48	4.63	2.41	2.16	1.04	0.67	1.57	1.23	0.80	0.61	17.87
1971	1.18	1.00	1.25	2.86	3.70	1.92	1.46	0.52	2.32	2.02	0.79	0.15	19.17
1972	0.22	0.44	0.47	2.78	3.28	4.11	1.67	2.49	0.24	0.77	0.38	0.34	17.19
1973	0.11	0.31	2.71	2.69	2.37	0.64	1.46	0.74	1.44	1.38	0.73	0.54	15.12
1974	0.16	0.30	0.34	1.55	1.32	1.10	0.68	1.37	0.88	1.18	0.12	0.12	9.12
1975	1.05	0.35	2.45	1.37	1.23	5.63	1.57	0.87	0.03	0.69	0.57	1.65	17.46
RECORD MEAN	0.44	0.47	1.01	2.00	3.14	3.32	2.29	1.57	1.26	0.98	0.59	0.53	17.60

# Indicates a station move or relocation of instruments.

Record mean values above are means through the current year for the period beginning in 1900 for temperature and precipitation, 1943 for snowfall. Data are from City Office locations through July 29, 1942 and from Airport locations thereafter.

Sioux Falls is located in the Big Sioux River Valley in the southeastern portion of South Dakota. The City is about 15 miles west of the Minnesota line and 7 miles west-northwest of the Iowa line. It is at latitude 43 degrees and 34 minutes north and at longitude 96 degrees and 44 minutes west. The elevation of the observation point at the airport is 1418 feet above sea level. The surrounding terrain is gently rolling. Within a 100-mile radius of Sioux Falls, it slopes upward 300 to 400 feet to the north and northwest and slopes downward 200 to 300 feet to the southeast. There is little change in elevation in the remaining directions.

The climate is of the invigorating continental type and features wide variations in temperature with normally ample spring and summer rainfall and lighter winter precipitation. There are frequent changes in weather from day to day or week to week as the locality is visited by differing airmasses. These can be cold airmasses from the interior of Canada; warm, moist air from the Gulf of Mexico; cool, rather dry air that moves eastward from the northern Pacific; or hot, drier air from the southwest.

Temperatures fluctuate frequently in this area. Cold airmasses often move in very rapidly, causing strong gusty winds for several hours. During the late fall and winter, these cold fronts sometimes bring temperature drops of 20 degrees or 30 degrees in a 24-hour period. There are usually a few occasions each year when the temperature lowers to 20 degrees or 25 degrees below zero during nighttime hours after winds have subsided. Severe cold spells ordinarily last only a few days but, in 1936, from January 18 to February 22, daily minimum temperatures were all well below zero and maximum temperatures did not exceed 17 degrees above zero. That winter of 1935-1936 was the coldest on record, with temperatures December through February averaging 12.7 degrees below normal. During a cold winter, frost will penetrate the ground to a depth of around 3-1/2 to 4 feet, unless there is a heavy snow cover to protect the ground. The warmest winter, in 1930-1931, averaged 10.3 degrees above normal.

Temperatures of 100 degrees and above are quite rare. There are normally only 2 or 3 such occurrences each year and these are most likely to occur in July. There is usually enough cooling to make the summer nights comfortable. The coolest summer (June through August) was in 1915 when the temperature averaged 7.1 degrees below normal. Warmest summer was in 1936 with an average temperature 6.9 degrees above normal.

The average date of the last freeze (32 degrees and below) in the spring is May 5. Average date of the frist freeze in the fall is October 3, making the average growing season 152 days. The latest date on which 32 degrees or lower has ever occurred in the

Station: SIOUX FALLS, SOUTH DAKOTA
FOSS FIELD
Elevation (ground): 1418 feet

TEMPERATURES °F

Month	Normal			Extremes			
	Daily maximum	Daily minimum	Monthly	Record highest	Year	Record lowest	Year
(a)				12		12	
J	24.6	3.7	14.2	57	1964	-36	1970
F	29.7	9.0	19.4	59	1964	-30	1965
M	39.7	20.2	30.0	87	1968	-14	1975
A	57.8	34.4	46.1	92	1964	5	1975
M	69.7	45.7	57.7	100	1967	17	1967
J	78.9	56.3	67.6	101	1974	33	1969
J	85.1	61.5	73.3	106	1966	38	1971
A	83.8	59.8	71.8	108	1973	37	1964
S	73.0	48.7	60.9	101	1970	22	1974
O	62.7	37.6	50.2	94	1963	9	1972
N	43.5	22.7	33.1	76	1975	-17	1964
D	29.6	10.4	20.0	60	1970	-26	1973
YR	56.5	34.2	45.4	108	AUG 1973	-36	JAN 1970

IMPORTANT:
The time-period covered by this record is limited: See footnotes on next page for explanation and for additional history of EXTREME HIGHS AND LOWS recorded in the general area.

spring was on June 7, 1897, and 1901. The earliest date in the fall when the temperature dropped to 32 degrees lower was September 7, 1895. The longest growing season on record was 196 days in 1938 and the shortest was 131 days in 1897.

Rainfall is normally ample for agriculture, which is the main industry of the area. Approximately 64 percent of the normal yearly precipitation falls during the growing season (April through August). This southeastern protion of South Dakota receives more precipitation annually than do the other sections of the State. Moist airmasses, spreading northward from the Gulf of Mexico, are more likely to reach the southeastern portion.

Sioux Falls usually has 1 or 2 very heavy snows during each winter season. Eight to 12 inches of snow may fall in 24 hours, and there have been a few instances of falls in excess of 15 inches. The only 24-hour snowfall to reach the 20-inch class was 26.0 inches on February 17-18, 1962. The snowfall is at times accompanied by much drifting. During such storms, highways are usually blocked for a day or part of a day and country roads may be blocked much longer. There is much runoff over the frozen or partially frozen ground as the snow melts in the spring. Consequently, the moisture in the snow is of limited value to agriculture.

Southerly winds prevail at Sioux Falls in summer and early fall, but during the late fall and winter northwesterly winds often prevail. Incomplete records of wind velocity show the strongest winds as 70 m.p.h. with gust to 90 m.p.h. on June 23, 1952. Strong winds and blowing snow normally bring blizzard conditions a few times each year.

Thunderstorms are quite frequent during the late spring and summer with the greatest number usually occurring in June and July. They are most likely to occur during the late afternoon and evening, but there is also a period between 2 and 5 o'clock in the morning when many thunderstorms have been noted. Some of the most severe thunderstorms, with unusually strong winds and chances of tornadoes, occur as cold fronts, or squall lines ahead of the fronts, move eastward or southeastward across the locality. Hail falls in this general area on an average of 2 or 3 times per year. Tornadoes are observed occasionally, but they are not as frequent here as in the Southern Plains States. Hail and tornadoes are most likely to occur in June.

There is occasional flooding in the lower areas of Sioux Falls near the Big Sioux River and at the mouth of Skunk Creek during the spring months. The most recent damaging floods occurred in the spring of 1951, 1952 and 1969, when there had been a heavy snow cover north of Sioux Falls, and in June 1957, due to abnormally heavy rains in the basin.

Normals, Means, and Extremes

(To better understand these tables, see full explanation of terms beginning on page 322)

Month	Normal Degree days Base 65 °F: Heating	Cooling	Precipitation in inches, Water equivalent: Normal	Maximum monthly	Year	Minimum monthly	Year	Maximum in 24 hrs.	Year	Snow, Ice pellets: Maximum monthly	Year	Maximum in 24 hrs.	Year	Relative humidity pct. Hour 00 (Local time)	Hour 06	Hour 12	Hour 18	Wind: Mean speed m.p.h.	Prevailing direction	Fastest mile: Speed m.p.h.	Direction	Year	Pct. of possible sunshine	Mean sky cover, tenths, sunrise to sunset	Mean number of days, Sunrise to sunset: Clear	Partly cloudy	Cloudy	Precipitation .01 inch or more	Snow, Ice pellets 1.0 inch or more	Thunderstorms	Heavy fog, visibility ¼ mile or less	Temperatures °F Max. (b) 90° and above	Max. 32° and below	Min. 32° and below	Min. 0° and below	Average station pressure mb. Elev. 1427 feet m.s.l.
(a)				30		30		30		30		30		12	12	12	12	27	15	27	27			30	30	30	30	30	30	30	30	12	12	12	12	3
J	1575	0	0.57	1.71	1969	0.05	1958	1.61	1960	19.6	1969	11.8	1960	75	76	67	72	11.0	NW	45	31	1975		6.5	8	7	16	6	2	0	3	0	21	31	14	964.7
F	1277	0	1.04	4.05	1962	0.05	1949	2.00	1962	48.4	1962	26.0	1962	77	78	66	70	11.2	NW	44	30	1972		6.6	7	7	14	6	2	*	3	0	16	28	9	966.1
M	1085	0	1.40	3.52	1973	0.14	1967	1.96	1956	31.5	1951	18.9	1956	78	81	62	63	12.6	NW	60	02	1950		7.0	6	8	17	8	3	1	3	0	9	27	2	962.1
A	567	0	2.30	5.23	1953	0.17	1969	2.64	1953	10.7	1957	9.0	1957	75	81	56	53	13.6	NW	48	25	1955		6.6	7	8	15	8	*	3	1	*	*	13	0	961.9
M	259	32	3.37	7.29	1965	0.72	1967	3.92	1972	0.2	1954	0.2	1954	72	81	53	49	12.1	S	46	11	1950		6.3	7	10	14	10	0	6	1	1	0	3	0	960.6
J	65	143	4.32	7.94	1951	1.48	1958	4.32	1957	0.0		0.0		76	83	57	53	10.7	S	70	23	1952		5.7	8	11	11	11	0	9	1	4	0	0	0	961.1
J	10	267	2.94	7.79	1948	0.25	1947	2.83	1948	0.0		0.0		75	82	52	49	9.7	S	60	27	1955		4.8	12	12	7	9	0	9	1	12	0	0	0	964.1
A	18	229	2.84	9.09	1975	0.53	1970	4.59	1975	0.0		0.0		77	84	52	50	9.8	S	52	29	1956		4.8	13	10	8	9	0	8	1	9	0	0	0	964.3
S	165	42	2.85	6.34	1966	0.29	1956	4.02	1966	T	1961	T	1961	80	87	58	58	10.3	S	50	16	1953		5.1	11	9	10	8	0	5	1	1	0	2	0	966.4
O	465	6	1.50	5.73	1973	T	1952	4.54	1973	5.1	1970	5.0	1970	75	81	56	58	10.8	S	60	27	1949		5.3	12	7	12	6	*	2	2	0	0	11	0	965.1
N	957	0	0.85	2.45	1971	0.03	1967	1.62	1972	17.0	1959	9.2	1975	80	84	65	71	11.6	NW	52	36	1975		6.6	7	8	15	6	1	*	3	0	6	26	1	964.7
D	1395	0	0.74	2.62	1968	0.09	1954	1.44	1955	41.1	1968	16.6	1968	79	80	71	75	10.7	NW	46	29	1956		6.7	7	7	17	6	2	*	4	0	20	31	7	965.4
YR	7838	719	24.72	9.09	AUG 1975	T	OCT 1952	4.59	AUG 1975	48.4	FEB 1962	26.0	FEB 1962	77	81	60	60	11.2	S	70	23	JUN 1952		6.0	105	104	156	94	11	44	22	26	72	170	33	963.9

FOOTNOTES Means and extremes above are from existing and comparable exposures. Annual extremes have been exceeded at other sites in the locality as follows: Highest temperature 110 in July 1936; lowest temperature -42 in February 1899; maximum monthly precipitation 9.42 in May 1898; minimum monthly precipitation 0.00 in November 1914.

Snowfall

Season	July	Aug	Sept	Oct	Nov	Dec	Jan
1936-37	0.0	0.0	0.0	T	4.3	13.2	20.5
1937-38	0.0	0.0	0.0	2.0	4.6	5.1	7.5
1938-39	0.0	0.0	0.0	T	T	3.5	5.6
1939-40	0.0	0.0	0.0	0.0	0.5	3.1	0.7
1940-41	0.0	0.0	0.0	0.0	13.0	10.0	5.5
#1941-42	0.0	0.0	0.0	T	T	6.7	1.2
#1942-43	0.0	0.0	0.0	0.0	0.0		
1943-44	0.0	0.0	0.0		4.0	1.0	T
1944-45	0.0	0.0	0.0	0.0	T	T	6.9
#1945-46	0.0	0.0	0.1	0.0	T	20.6	0.5
1946-47	0.0	0.0	0.0	0.2	8.6	2.5	16.1
#1947-48	0.0	0.0	0.0	0.0	12.3	4.7	2.3
1948-49	0.0	0.0	0.0	0.0	12.2	1.8	7.6
1949-50	0.0	0.0	0.0	T	0.1	4.4	12.4
1950-51	0.0	0.0	0.0	T	0.3	5.1	4.6
1951-52	0.0	0.0	0.0	2.9	3.2	17.3	5.7
1952-53	0.0	0.0	0.0	0.0	4.7	3.7	6.6
1953-54	0.0	0.0	0.0	0.0	2.7	13.4	1.9
1954-55	0.0	0.0	0.0	T	7.9	1.0	4.7
1955-56	0.0	0.0	0.0	0.1	3.8	17.2	9.2
1956-57	0.0	0.0	0.0	T	4.1	3.8	2.2
1957-58	0.0	0.0	0.0	T	1.6	0.1	0.5
1958-59	0.0	0.0	0.0	0.0	2.8	4.5	2.4
1959-60	0.0	0.0	0.0	0.6	17.0	3.7	12.3
1960-61	0.0	0.0	0.0	T	0.1	6.4	3.4
1961-62	0.0	0.0	T	0.0	1.0	7.7	3.8
1962-63	0.0	0.0	0.0	0.7	T	1.7	11.0
1963-64	0.0	0.0	0.0	0.0	0.0	11.6	3.5
1964-65	0.0	0.0	0.0	0.0	3.9	6.5	3.3
1965-66	0.0	0.0	0.0	0.0	1.6	0.1	6.2
1966-67	0.0	0.0	0.0	0.4	2.3	9.3	6.0
1967-68	0.0	0.0	0.0	0.5	0.4	2.5	4.6
1968-69	0.0	0.0	0.0	0.7	1.9	41.1	19.6
1969-70	0.0	0.0	0.0	T	2.9	15.2	5.9
1970-71	0.0	0.0	0.0	5.1	0.5	8.5	1.9
1971-72	0.0	0.0	0.0	T	4.4	10.6	1.8
1972-73	0.0	0.0	0.0	0.2	2.5	6.2	5.5
1973-74	0.0	0.0	0.0	T	0.1	11.6	1.9
1974-75	0.0	0.0	0.0	0.0	2.5	1.1	18.3
1975-76	0.0	0.0	0.0	T	13.2	2.5	
RECORD MEAN	0.0	0.0	T	0.4	4.0	7.5	6.2

Heating Degree Days

Season	July	Aug	Sept	Oct	Nov	Dec	Jan
1955-56	0	3	164	418	1212	1639	1663
1956-57	0	27	165	284	957	1243	1729
1957-58	0	13	189	509	943	1099	1271
1958-59	7	17	104	397	901	1465	1646
1959-60	3	0	192	623	1194	1100	1572
1960-61	3	2	173	439	867	1357	1566
1961-62	0	5	236	427	943	1512	1616
1962-63	18	5	191	391	786	1305	1609
#1963-64	0	24	92	222	767	1603	1299
1964-65	0	55	210	499	965	1528	1639
1965-66	2	37	405	408	964	1129	1856
1966-67	0	41	188	508	1016	1406	1462
1967-68	36	32	141	549	963	1328	1490
1968-69	14	14	152	489	938	1511	1742
1969-70	2	2	117	668	941	1404	1867
1970-71	16	3	195	577	986	1526	1754
1971-72	29	12	177	409	945	1470	1737
1972-73	29	43	194	631	984	1555	1440
1973-74	1	0	178	373	902	1481	1616
1974-75	2	39	240	419	927	1279	1476
1975-76	3	5	271	407	937	1377	

Cooling Degree Days

Year	Jan	Feb	Mar	Apr	May	June	July
1969	0	0	0	0	58	43	270
1970	0	0	0	6	54	172	280
1971	0	0	0	4	1	211	167
1972	0	0	0	0	60	108	197
1973	0	0	0	0	13	143	300
1974	0	0	0	2	23	118	450
1975	0	0	0	0	44	134	428

Feb	Mar	Apr	May	June	Total
0.7	4.1	8.5	0.0	0.0	51.3
16.7	5.5	8.0	T	0.0	49.4
13.5	4.7	T	0.0	0.0	27.3
17.2	20.3	T	0.0	0.0	41.8
4.2	7.3	T	0.0	0.0	40.0
4.9	4.1		T	0.0	
		T	2.0	0.0	
11.0	10.8	T	3.0	0.0	
18.1	2.5	6.0	T	0.0	33.5
5.8	8.0	T	T	0.0	35.0
3.2	0.8	3.2	T	0.0	34.6
8.0	4.2	T	0.0	0.0	31.5
1.2	15.3	0.6	0.0	0.0	38.7
10.1	16.2	7.2	T	0.0	50.4
13.5	31.5	0.9	0.0	0.0	55.9
18.6	14.9	0.9	0.0	0.0	63.5
15.1	12.1	2.9	0.0	0.0	45.1
9.2	11.7	T	0.2	0.0	39.1
12.6	5.3	T	0.0	0.0	31.5
3.9	21.6	4.7	0.0	0.0	60.5
4.5	19.0	10.7	0.0	0.0	44.3
2.9	8.2	T	0.0	0.0	13.3
15.4	3.6	1.0	0.0	0.0	29.7
3.0	20.4	4.6	0.0	0.0	61.6
11.6	12.0	T	0.0	0.0	33.5
48.4	14.7	4.2	0.0	0.0	79.8
6.8	2.8	2.3	0.0	0.0	25.3
0.7	9.1	T	0.0	0.0	24.9
21.1	13.3	0.4	0.0	0.0	48.5
1.8	4.6	0.9	T	0.0	15.2
11.8	1.0	T	0.1	0.0	30.9
0.9	T	0.1	0.1	0.0	9.1
28.5	2.9	0.0	0.0	0.0	94.7
1.5	19.3	3.0	T	0.0	47.8
1.7	4.7	0.3	0.0	0.0	22.7
10.6	5.0	0.8	0.0	0.0	33.2
7.4	0.3	T	0.0	0.0	22.1
2.9	5.1	3.3	0.0	0.0	24.9
3.1	17.9	T	0.0	0.0	42.9
9.5	10.2	1.7	T	0.0	39.5

Average Temperature

Year	Jan	Feb	Mar	Apr	May	June	July	Aug	Sept	Oct	Nov	Dec	Annual
1936	5.0	0.5	36.0	44.8	66.0	70.4	84.6	78.5	67.8	49.6	33.7	25.4	46.9
1937	5.4	17.1	32.4	46.2	63.0	68.0	77.1	78.0	65.6	49.4	33.6	20.4	46.4
1938	19.1	23.4	41.2	51.6	59.3	71.0	76.6	76.0	65.9	58.8	33.7	26.2	50.2
1939	26.6	13.4	34.4	47.9	67.4	71.3	77.0	69.9	66.4	50.0	38.4	31.3	49.5
1940	7.0	21.5	29.5	44.5	59.2	69.8	77.0	68.7	65.3	56.6	28.8	25.7	46.1
#1941	20.2	18.0	31.0	51.5	65.2	69.0	74.6	75.2	64.7	50.6	35.6	26.9	48.5
#1942	20.8	21.8	34.8	51.0	54.3	66.5	72.6	71.6	57.3	50.4	34.7	18.0	46.2
1943	9.3	25.2	26.8	48.7	56.4	68.7	74.2	70.8	58.3	49.9	32.2	25.1	45.5
1944	27.8	22.1	26.0	42.6	63.0	68.0	69.8	68.1	60.0	50.8	36.4	21.8	46.4
#1945	20.0	24.2	40.5	45.3	53.6	61.5	71.0	70.0	60.2	51.2	32.2	13.8	45.3
1946	17.3	22.0	42.0	52.0	54.3	67.3	74.0	68.1	59.9	49.2	30.3	22.8	46.6
#1947	22.4	14.7	29.4	43.0	53.6	63.8	72.6	78.8	64.0	57.2	28.6	17.5	45.5
1948	13.0	16.8	28.6	51.6	57.8	65.5	74.0	73.0	67.0	49.5	32.4	19.0	45.8
1949	10.4	13.5	30.2	47.8	61.9	70.4	75.6	73.6	57.6	49.7	40.0	21.4	46.0
1950	5.9	19.8	25.1	37.8	54.7	66.3	68.0	67.5	62.1	52.7	29.0	17.1	42.2
1951	13.1	24.2	20.3	42.3	58.7	62.2	70.8	69.2	56.1	47.6	27.6	14.0	42.2
1952	12.4	24.9	25.5	48.9	57.5	71.2	73.1	70.0	64.5	45.5	33.9	22.4	45.8
1953	18.2	22.3	32.8	40.5	57.0	70.9	73.1	73.2	61.6	55.3	38.3	20.5	47.0
1954	10.2	33.4	27.7	48.3	52.7	69.4	76.4	71.5	62.5	47.1	39.9	22.9	46.8
1955	19.1	13.0	29.4	54.6	63.4	66.1	79.5	77.9	63.4	51.5	24.3	12.0	46.2
1956	11.2	13.6	27.6	40.9	60.1	75.1	70.8	71.0	61.2	56.1	32.8	24.7	45.4
1957	9.2	23.4	31.4	45.2	56.0	66.7	78.6	71.1	59.1	48.3	33.3	29.4	46.0
1958	23.9	16.9	31.3	46.3	61.8	64.4	70.3	74.6	63.9	52.8	34.8	17.6	46.6
1959	11.8	13.8	35.2	46.8	58.7	72.4	74.3	76.0	61.2	44.7	25.0	29.3	45.8
1960	14.1	14.2	17.7	45.9	58.0	65.6	73.9	72.8	62.8	50.7	35.9	21.0	44.4
1961	14.2	23.6	35.6	41.9	55.0	68.8	72.2	74.0	59.3	51.3	33.4	16.0	45.5
1962	12.8	17.2	24.6	45.7	63.0	67.6	70.7	71.3	59.4	52.7	38.6	22.7	45.6
#1963	6.7	19.8	38.9	49.4	59.4	73.5	75.8	70.8	64.3	58.1	39.2	13.2	47.4
1964	23.0	26.9	26.6	48.1	61.6	70.1	77.3	68.3	59.3	48.7	32.7	15.5	46.5
1965	12.0	13.0	21.7	45.9	59.0	65.5	70.8	69.4	51.5	51.7	32.8	28.4	43.5
1966	5.1	17.3	37.7	41.1	54.3	68.5	78.7	68.8	59.9	48.3	31.0	19.4	44.2
1967	17.6	15.3	37.1	46.0	53.1	66.3	71.7	69.9	61.3	47.2	32.7	21.9	45.0
1968	16.8	18.9	39.8	47.8	52.6	69.6	71.8	72.7	61.0	49.4	33.5	16.2	45.9
1969	8.8	19.0	20.5	48.4	59.6	61.4	73.5	73.3	62.3	43.4	33.4	19.5	43.6
1970	4.7	19.4	26.4	44.8	59.9	69.0	73.3	72.5	61.9	46.2	32.0	15.6	43.8
1971	8.3	18.8	31.2	47.8	55.3	71.3	69.3	73.0	61.5	51.7	33.3	17.4	44.9
1972	8.9	11.5	31.5	43.8	59.1	66.7	70.2	70.5	59.5	44.4	31.9	14.8	42.7
1973	18.5	23.1	39.7	46.4	56.9	68.9	74.4	76.7	60.1	52.9	34.7	17.1	47.5
1974	12.8	24.3	34.5	48.9	55.7	65.9	79.2	67.6	57.7	51.4	33.9	23.6	46.3
1975	17.1	16.5	25.5	41.4	61.1	67.6	78.5	72.7	57.0	52.1	33.5	20.4	45.3
RECORD MEAN	15.2	20.4	31.8	46.9	58.8	68.4	74.3	71.9	61.8	50.5	33.5	20.8	46.2
MAX	25.1	30.5	41.7	58.6	71.1	80.1	86.4	83.8	73.6	62.4	43.3	30.0	57.2
MIN	5.2	10.3	21.9	35.2	46.5	56.6	62.1	59.9	49.9	38.6	23.7	11.6	35.1

# Indicates a station move or relocation of instruments.

SIOUX FALLS, SD

Feb	Mar	Apr	May	June	Total
1486	1155	719	221	11	8691
1157	1039	591	292	37	7521
1341	1036	554	148	97	7200
1430	918	540	236	27	7688
1469	1462	576	233	38	8462
1153	906	689	321	43	7519
1333	1245	593	117	42	8064
1261	803	467	203	7	7246
1101	1181	509	174	47	7019
1452	1340	568	195	41	8492
1331	838	709	343	49	8071
1385	858	563	399	37	7863
1331	776	511	380	53	7590
1283	1373	493	217	143	8369
1274	1192	603	206	46	8322
1288	1041	511	297	17	8211
1551	1031	628	236	50	8275
1166	775	549	256	19	7641
1133	939	477	303	85	7488
1351	1217	701	157	51	7859

Aug	Sept	Oct	Nov	Dec	Total
265	41	4	0	0	681
241	108	2	0	0	863
268	79	2	0	0	732
219	35	0	0	0	619
370	38	8	0	0	872
126	26	6	0	0	751
252	36	16	0	0	910

Precipitation

Year	Jan	Feb	Mar	Apr	May	June	July	Aug	Sept	Oct	Nov	Dec	Annual
1936	1.34	1.18	1.99	2.18	9.03	2.18	0.80	2.85	1.05	0.14	0.73	1.81	25.28
1937	1.76	0.01	1.36	5.19	3.96	3.20	2.63	5.06	1.48	1.75	0.53	0.72	27.65
1938	0.56	1.65	1.88	3.04	4.75	3.40	2.79	2.58	5.89	0.13	2.17	0.59	29.43
1939	1.00	1.48	0.51	1.67	4.19	6.44	3.00	4.04	1.12	1.46	0.04	0.38	25.33
1940	0.08	1.33	3.44	3.39	0.39	5.25	2.49	4.17	1.27	1.98	1.84	1.01	26.64
#1941	1.25	0.58	0.93	5.45	1.71	3.81	1.64	0.77	1.70	2.16	0.44	0.24	20.68
#1942	0.04	0.33	2.53	1.54	7.18	3.82	4.45	4.51	3.04	0.17	0.19	0.14	27.94
1943	0.23	0.50	0.45	0.86	3.63	7.28	3.08	3.90	0.55	2.41	0.52	0.04	23.45
1944	1.51	1.60	0.95	2.96	4.35	4.82	4.58	7.36	1.85	0.37	1.86	T	32.21
#1945	0.60	2.18	1.07	1.64	4.85	4.45	3.00	1.49	2.17	0.08	0.87	2.97	25.37
1946	0.05	0.73	1.58	0.73	2.29	4.39	2.97	2.45	5.21	3.99	1.58	0.29	26.26
#1947	1.34	0.19	0.58	2.93	1.42	7.27	0.25	2.32	2.82	3.55	2.22	0.72	25.61
1948	0.12	1.28	0.44	2.61	2.56	5.68	7.79	0.83	2.97	1.64	1.54	0.12	27.58
1949	1.07	0.05	3.33	0.32	2.42	1.88	3.37	2.69	3.90	1.06	0.06	0.61	20.76
1950	0.48	0.55	1.71	1.23	4.33	3.65	2.24	0.93	3.75	1.80	0.33	0.24	21.24
1951	0.20	1.60	2.70	2.33	4.37	7.94	2.73	2.16	3.40	1.51	0.26	1.59	30.79
1952	0.94	2.09	1.70	1.53	1.93	4.39	1.59	3.39	0.47	T	0.55	0.28	18.86
1953	0.55	1.91	1.86	5.23	2.71	5.35	2.31	4.26	2.51	0.50	1.16	1.70	30.05
1954	0.16	1.88	2.68	1.32	1.84	4.12	3.74	2.27	4.33	1.54	0.72	0.09	24.69
1955	0.32	0.92	0.34	2.12	2.16	4.24	3.25	1.22	0.72	0.82	0.30	1.75	18.16
1956	0.58	0.38	2.19	1.29	1.31	6.86	4.02	4.09	0.29	0.62	0.87	0.24	22.74
1957	0.12	0.26	1.84	3.15	4.89	5.41	2.80	3.76	2.66	1.24	1.66	0.40	28.19
1958	0.05	1.77	0.95	2.55	0.81	1.48	3.52	0.61	2.11	0.08	1.15	0.25	15.33
1959	0.16	0.92	0.53	0.36	7.28	2.02	0.39	7.47	4.62	3.29	1.89	0.88	29.81
1960	1.65	0.22	1.90	3.64	5.08	3.97	0.72	5.17	2.21	0.67	1.51	0.77	27.51
1961	0.25	0.92	1.14	1.04	4.67	3.86	2.16	1.79	2.36	2.66	1.40	0.80	23.05
1962	0.29	4.05	1.72	1.70	6.07	3.98	5.50	2.77	3.58	0.46	0.16	0.19	30.47
1963	0.90	0.53	1.16	1.25	2.00	2.51	6.45	0.94	2.40	1.65	0.36	0.85	21.00
1964	0.34	0.08	2.12	4.03	1.29	1.68	4.03	3.87	4.06	0.09	0.38	0.59	22.56
1965	0.24	1.46	1.09	3.35	7.29	4.91	1.49	1.29	4.91	1.05	0.26	0.60	27.94
1966	0.54	0.99	0.70	1.71	1.94	2.68	1.54	2.12	6.34	1.43	0.20	0.65	20.84
1967	0.75	0.44	0.14	3.90	0.72	4.26	0.53	3.46	0.87	0.39	0.03	0.91	16.40
1968	0.33	0.09	0.61	4.34	2.69	4.10	2.37	1.70	4.01	4.57	0.39	2.62	27.82
1969	1.71	2.55	1.09	0.17	2.43	4.85	2.73	5.07	2.41	2.05	0.34	1.18	26.58
1970	0.37	0.10	2.03	3.75	4.83	3.81	2.98	0.53	3.14	3.13	2.17	0.54	27.38
1971	0.13	0.90	0.85	1.59	1.06	6.10	2.92	0.71	3.23	3.06	2.45	0.64	23.64
1972	0.18	0.40	0.97	2.73	7.25	2.09	3.49	2.65	1.75	1.78	1.89	1.25	26.43
1973	0.43	0.43	3.52	2.12	1.93	2.38	3.50	1.05	5.61	5.73	1.01	0.48	28.19
1974	0.13	0.30	1.65	1.33	3.11	2.79	1.27	5.16	0.58	0.34	0.27	0.10	17.03
1975	1.35	0.22	1.95	2.45	1.66	4.48	0.62	9.09	1.35	0.49	2.25	0.19	26.10
RECORD MEAN	0.62	0.82	1.36	2.47	3.59	4.27	3.01	3.11	2.70	1.56	1.01	0.74	25.26

Record mean values above are means through the current year for the period beginning in 1921 for temperature, 1891 for precipitation and 1946 for snowfall.

Station: KNOXVILLE, TENNESSEE
MC GHEE TYSON AIRPORT
Elevation (ground): 980 feet

TEMPERATURES °F

Month	Normal Daily maximum	Normal Daily minimum	Normal Monthly	Extremes Record highest	Year	Record lowest	Year
(a)				15		15	
J	48.9	32.2	40.6	72	1972	-9	1966
F	52.0	33.5	42.8	75	1972	0	1970
M	60.4	39.4	49.9	86	1963	18	1975
A	72.0	48.6	60.3	89	1965	27	1964
M	79.8	56.9	68.4	94	1962	34	1963
J	86.1	64.8	75.5	96	1964	44	1972
J	88.0	68.3	78.2	98	1966	51	1961
A	87.3	67.2	77.3	99	1968	53	1968
S	82.0	61.2	71.6	96	1975	36	1967
O	71.8	50.0	60.9	85	1971	25	1962
N	58.9	39.4	49.2	83	1961	13	1970
D	49.8	33.1	41.5	75	1970	-2	1962
YR	69.8	49.5	59.7	99	AUG 1968	-9	JAN 1966

IMPORTANT:
The time-period covered by this record is limited: See footnotes following table of NORMALS, MEANS AND EXTREMES for explanation and for additional history of EXTREME HIGHS AND LOWS recorded in the general area.

Knoxville is located in a broad valley between the Cumberland Mountains, which lie northwest of the City and the Great Smoky Mountains, which lie southeast of the City. These two mountain ranges exercise a marked influence upon the climate of the valley. The Cumberland Mountains, to the northwest, serve to retard and weaken the force of the cold winter air which frequently penetrates far south of the latitude of Knoxville over the plains areas to the west of the mountains.

The mountains also serve to modify the hot summer winds which are common to the plains to the west. In addition, they serve as a fixed incline plane which lifts the warm, moist air flowing northward from the Gulf of Mexico and thereby increases the frequency of afternoon thunderstorms. These thunderstorms usually come on those days when the warmest air, with the highest moisture charge, is moving northward. The relief from extremely high temperatures which such thunderstorms afford serves to reduce the number of extremely warm days in the valley.

July is usually the warmest month of the year. July 1954 is the hottest month of record, with an average temperature of 81.8°. The highest temperature ever recorded at this station is 104°. This occurred on July 12, 1930. The coldest weather usually occurs during the month of January. The coldest month of record occurred in January 1940, with an average temperature of 26.7°. The lowest temperature of record is 16° below zero, and this occurred on January 6, 1884. Sudden great temperature changes occur infre-

(Continued page 636)

Snowfall

Season	July	Aug	Sept	Oct	Nov	Dec	Jan
1936-37	0.0	0.0	0.0	0.0	0.6	0.6	0.0
1937-38	0.0	0.0	0.0	T	T	1.3	2.8
1938-39	0.0	0.0	0.0	0.0	1.3	0.3	0.3
1939-40	0.0	0.0	0.0	0.0	T	T	13.6
1940-41	0.0	0.0	0.0	0.0	T	0.0	T
#1941-42	0.0	0.0	0.0	0.0	T	0.0	1.9
1942-43	0.0	0.0	0.0	0.0	0.0	6.1	0.1
1943-44	0.0	0.0	0.0	0.0	0.0	T	1.8
1944-45	0.0	0.0	0.0	0.0	T	3.9	T
1945-46	0.0	0.0	0.0	0.0	T	5.1	T
1946-47	0.0	0.0	0.0	0.0	0.0	T	0.0
1947-48	0.0	0.0	0.0	0.0	0.0	T	9.1
1948-49	0.0	0.0	0.0	0.0	0.0	T	2.0
1949-50	0.0	0.0	0.0	0.0	T	T	0.0
1950-51	0.0	0.0	0.0	0.0	5.5	2.4	T
1951-52	0.0	0.0	0.0	0.0	T	T	T
1952-53	0.0	0.0	0.0	0.0	18.2	T	2.0
1953-54	0.0	0.0	0.0	0.0	T	T	2.1
1954-55	0.0	0.0	0.0	0.0	T	T	3.4
1955-56	0.0	0.0	0.0	0.0	T	T	7.0
1956-57	0.0	0.0	0.0	0.0	0.6	0.4	T
1957-58	0.0	0.0	0.0	0.0	T	0.6	0.3
1958-59	0.0	0.0	0.0	0.0	T	4.3	2.5
1959-60	0.0	0.0	0.0	0.0	0.6	3.7	8.9
1960-61	0.0	0.0	0.0	0.0	0.0	2.0	5.4
1961-62	0.0	0.0	0.0	0.0	T	4.5	15.1
1962-63	0.0	0.0	0.0	T	T	6.9	4.2
1963-64	0.0	0.0	0.0	0.0	5.9	12.2	8.5
1964-65	0.0	0.0	0.0	0.0	T	T	6.3
1965-66	0.0	0.0	0.0	0.0	T	T	14.2
1966-67	0.0	0.0	0.0	0.0	T	3.1	2.2
1967-68	0.0	0.0	0.0	0.0	0.0	T	5.9
1968-69	0.0	0.0	0.0	0.0	0.3	T	0.5
1969-70	0.0	0.0	0.0	0.0	T	8.9	12.9
1970-71	0.0	0.0	0.0	0.0	T	6.3	1.3
1971-72	0.0	0.0	0.0	0.0	T	T	0.4
1972-73	0.0	0.0	0.0	0.0	T	T	9.0
1973-74	0.0	0.0	0.0	0.0	0.0	2.0	T
1974-75	0.0	0.0	0.0	0.0	T	1.6	1.3
1975-76	0.0	0.0	0.0	0.0	T	T	
RECORD MEAN	0.0	0.0	0.0	T	0.9	2.1	3.8

Heating Degree Days

Season	July	Aug	Sept	Oct	Nov	Dec	Jan
1955-56	0	0	0	226	567	806	890
1956-57	0	0	31	75	524	415	728
1957-58	0	0	23	264	430	648	902
1958-59	0	0	5	169	412	847	854
1959-60	0	0	0	157	547	686	744
#1960-61	0	0	3	142	481	917	947
1961-62	0	0	15	222	405	771	862
1962-63	0	0	32	156	548	861	973
1963-64	0	0	18	101	525	1072	884
1964-65	0	8	9	308	374	657	765
1965-66	0	0	13	200	393	674	956
1966-67	0	0	9	232	472	767	709
1967-68	1	0	63	229	617	626	860
1968-69	0	0	5	215	501	859	879
1969-70	0	0	11	200	579	840	1063
1970-71	0	0	13	109	497	640	813
1971-72	0	0	0	53	496	450	692
1972-73	0	0	9	251	522	622	828
1973-74	0	0	10	135	373	734	481
1974-75	0	0	23	215	439	713	666
1975-76	0	0	42	172	437	733	

Cooling Degree Days

Year	Jan	Feb	Mar	Apr	May	June	July
1969	0	0	0	15	125	294	438
1970	0	0	0	33	162	258	427
1971	0	0	0	20	50	333	328
1972	0	0	0	53	51	193	332
1973	0	0	4	19	56	298	369
1974	0	0	9	39	142	179	399
1975	0	0	0	39	173	293	397

KNOXVILLE, TENNESSEE

Feb	Mar	Apr	May	June	Total
6.6	0.9	0.0	0.0	0.0	8.7
T	0.0	T	0.0	0.0	4.1
T	0.5	0.0	0.0	0.0	2.4
T	6.1	T	T	0.0	19.7
0.8	T	0.0	0.0	0.0	0.8
8.7	13.0	0.0	0.0	0.0	23.6
T	5.9	T	0.0	0.0	12.1
0.9	T	T	0.0	0.0	2.7
T	0.0	0.0	T	0.0	3.9
T	0.0	0.0	0.0	0.0	5.1
4.3	1.2	0.0	0.0	0.0	5.5
2.8	T	0.0	0.0	0.0	11.9
T	T	T	0.0	0.0	2.0
T	T	T	0.0	0.0	T
1.8	1.2	T	0.0	0.0	10.9
T	T	T	0.0	0.0	T
8.1	T	T	0.0	0.0	28.3
4.9	2.7	0.0	0.0	0.0	9.7
2.8	T	0.0	0.0	0.0	6.2
0.0	T	0.0	0.0	0.0	7.0
0.0	3.1	T	0.0	0.0	4.1
10.3	T	0.0	0.0	0.0	11.2
T	0.3	0.0	0.0	0.0	7.1
23.3	20.2	T	0.0	0.0	56.7
3.4	0.1	T	0.0	0.0	10.9
T	1.9	T	0.0	0.0	21.5
7.2	T	0.0	0.0	0.0	18.3
5.2	T	0.0	0.0	0.0	31.8
6.9	4.4	0.0	0.0	0.0	17.6
T	0.5	0.0	0.0	0.0	14.7
5.7	0.0	0.0	0.0	0.0	11.0
4.7	1.9	0.0	0.0	0.0	12.5
7.7	5.2	0.0	0.0	0.0	13.7
4.6	T	0.0	0.0	0.0	26.4
6.4	3.6	7.0	0.0	0.0	24.6
4.2	6.7	0.0	0.0	0.0	11.3
T	1.9	T	0.0	0.0	10.9
T	1.8	0.0	0.0	0.0	3.8
T	2.5	0.0	0.0	0.0	5.4
3.5	2.0	0.2	T	0.0	12.5

Average Temperature

Year	Jan	Feb	Mar	Apr	May	June	July	Aug	Sept	Oct	Nov	Dec	Annual
1936	34.8	37.8	52.7	57.2	72.0	79.7	80.4	80.2	76.1	62.0	47.0	44.9	60.4
1937	51.4	40.4	47.4	58.4	68.0	77.2	78.0	79.2	71.0	57.0	45.2	39.6	59.4
1938	40.3	49.2	57.0	61.1	68.2	73.2	78.4	79.5	71.9	62.0	50.4	39.8	60.9
1939	42.6	47.0	51.9	57.2	68.6	78.2	78.8	77.6	75.9	63.6	47.0	42.4	60.9
1940	26.7	40.2	47.2	57.8	65.4	75.6	77.0	77.4	69.6	61.3	48.6	46.2	57.8
#1941	40.7	36.6	44.0	62.8	70.5	76.2	79.2	79.0	75.8	67.1	48.0	45.2	60.4
1942	37.5	36.1	50.2	61.6	67.8	76.7	78.5	75.0	69.2	60.0	51.2	38.9	58.6
1943	42.4	42.1	46.2	57.0	69.8	79.9	78.0	79.0	67.9	56.8	46.8	39.8	58.8
1944	40.9	46.6	49.4	57.3	71.8	79.0	78.4	77.5	71.6	59.4	47.0	37.2	59.7
1945	38.0	43.5	59.0	60.4	64.1	74.2	77.8	77.2	74.5	58.3	50.6	35.0	59.4
1946	40.2	43.9	57.8	61.6	66.5	74.0	78.8	74.4	70.2	60.4	53.6	44.2	60.5
1947	43.4	33.2	41.2	61.9	65.4	74.3	74.6	79.2	73.0	66.0	47.8	41.0	58.4
1948	32.2	44.5	54.2	63.5	67.4	76.1	79.2	76.6	71.5	57.0	52.0	42.4	59.7
1949	48.4	47.8	49.4	56.8	68.8	76.5	80.6	77.0	67.5	65.2	47.0	43.1	60.6
1950	52.0	45.9	47.4	55.8	70.5	74.8	75.5	74.1	69.4	63.9	43.4	35.4	59.0
1951	41.9	44.1	49.6	56.8	67.0	75.5	79.3	78.9	71.9	61.9	42.7	43.5	59.4
1952	46.5	45.4	49.1	59.3	68.5	81.4	81.1	77.2	70.4	55.9	46.5	40.8	60.2
1953	44.7	44.8	52.3	56.2	71.6	78.0	78.2	78.4	71.5	63.1	47.9	39.4	60.5
1954	39.8	47.0	48.3	64.6	62.3	76.5	81.8	79.9	76.0	61.5	46.1	38.5	60.2
1955	38.8	43.4	52.3	62.9	70.4	70.5	79.9	80.5	75.5	58.8	45.9	38.8	59.8
1956	36.1	47.3	50.0	56.6	69.9	74.6	77.5	78.4	69.1	63.6	47.2	51.4	60.1
1957	41.4	49.6	48.8	62.8	69.9	76.7	79.6	77.7	72.7	56.6	50.6	43.9	60.9
1958	35.6	31.9	45.9	59.0	68.2	75.7	78.5	77.2	72.1	59.8	51.4	37.4	57.8
1959	37.3	43.7	47.1	60.0	71.5	75.0	78.5	79.3	73.2	62.4	46.7	42.6	59.8
1960	40.8	38.6	36.8	61.3	65.9	74.8	78.4	78.2	73.1	61.8	48.8	35.2	57.8
#1961	34.2	46.7	51.6	52.7	62.1	70.7	74.4	74.2	72.4	57.9	51.7	39.9	57.4
1962	37.0	47.2	46.8	54.7	74.0	74.4	78.3	78.2	70.9	62.5	46.4	37.0	59.0
1963	33.4	35.0	55.1	60.8	65.9	72.4	73.6	75.5	69.4	62.0	47.3	30.2	56.7
1964	36.3	36.1	47.7	60.5	66.9	75.1	75.7	73.7	70.0	55.5	52.3	43.5	57.8
1965	40.1	39.7	46.8	62.4	72.3	73.9	78.0	77.5	73.5	59.0	51.7	43.0	59.9
1966	34.0	41.6	50.4	58.9	66.1	74.3	79.3	75.0	68.9	57.5	49.1	40.0	57.9
1967	41.9	38.1	54.7	62.7	63.5	73.2	71.8	73.2	65.6	58.2	44.2	44.6	57.6
1968	37.1	33.3	49.9	59.0	65.3	73.6	77.2	78.4	69.1	58.8	48.1	37.0	57.3
1969	36.5	39.4	42.1	59.5	67.3	74.5	78.9	74.5	69.3	59.1	45.5	37.7	57.0
1970	30.6	39.3	48.7	61.2	68.6	73.4	78.5	77.1	75.3	62.8	48.1	44.1	59.0
1971	38.5	39.4	45.6	58.5	63.9	75.9	75.4	76.0	73.3	65.3	48.7	50.4	59.2
1972	42.5	39.4	48.2	59.5	64.9	70.8	75.5	75.9	71.9	56.8	47.5	44.8	58.1
1973	38.0	39.9	55.8	56.4	63.5	74.8	76.7	76.2	73.8	62.4	52.4	41.1	59.2
1974	49.3	43.1	55.2	59.8	68.1	70.5	77.7	76.5	69.8	58.6	50.8	41.9	60.1
1975	43.3	45.5	46.6	57.5	70.1	74.6	77.6	78.8	68.9	60.1	50.2	41.1	59.5
RECORD MEAN	39.4	41.8	49.3	58.8	67.4	74.8	77.7	76.7	71.4	59.9	48.2	40.6	58.9
MAX	47.9	51.0	59.4	69.5	78.2	85.0	87.5	86.5	81.8	71.1	58.1	49.0	68.8
MIN	30.9	32.6	39.1	48.0	56.5	64.6	67.9	66.8	60.9	48.7	38.2	32.2	48.9

# Indicates a station move or relocation of instruments.

KNOXVILLE, TN

Feb	Mar	Apr	May	June	Total
506	466	279	14	23	3777
425	496	168	33	0	2895
920	586	188	53	0	4014
589	550	182	30	0	3638
758	869	158	108	0	4027
507	400	377	112	6	3892
492	556	324	5	0	3652
835	312	176	64	0	3957
834	532	160	44	1	4171
701	559	125	0	0	3506
650	452	217	59	9	3623
748	330	112	121	8	3508
912	467	191	66	0	4032
710	704	175	50	4	4102
712	496	139	45	0	4085
710	596	209	76	0	3663
735	516	211	47	11	3211
697	283	272	97	0	3581
606	304	190	41	10	2884
542	563	257	9	0	3427

Precipitation

Year	Jan	Feb	Mar	Apr	May	June	July	Aug	Sept	Oct	Nov	Dec	Annual
1936	7.84	4.36	7.96	4.76	0.76	1.39	7.94	1.97	2.13	2.06	1.20	6.21	48.58
1937	11.63	4.51	1.61	3.04	4.38	2.52	6.33	5.70	2.11	4.08	1.06	3.29	50.26
1938	4.30	2.55	5.78	6.52	8.81	4.99	4.83	2.19	3.13	0.50	4.68	2.71	50.99
1939	3.82	10.69	5.04	5.00	1.03	4.83	8.37	2.12	0.94	0.38	2.21	3.18	47.61
1940	2.31	3.47	5.09	4.28	5.13	4.48	2.46	5.25	1.17	2.12	1.76	2.90	40.42
#1941	2.28	0.87	4.13	4.01	0.71	3.95	8.37	3.34	0.97	2.54	2.55	2.45	36.17
1942	4.25	3.72	5.02	0.84	5.20	2.04	9.19	8.88	2.82	3.12	0.97	8.30	54.35
1943	2.09	4.83	5.17	3.48	2.88	3.55	9.29	1.48	3.51	3.70	2.02	2.33	44.33
1944	2.05	9.38	6.08	3.78	1.55	0.20	1.40	2.87	8.61	1.66	2.87	4.71	45.16
1945	2.18	7.03	3.29	4.56	4.75	4.34	5.46	2.14	2.88	3.57	4.02	5.48	49.70
1946	8.84	5.01	3.65	4.10	6.40	3.94	3.10	0.97	2.04	4.03	3.45	4.41	49.94
1947	9.64	2.67	2.91	2.42	3.36	2.68	3.33	2.11	1.37	1.61	3.33	2.13	37.56
1948	3.57	6.38	5.19	2.67	3.28	3.47	5.91	1.71	1.52	1.27	10.36	5.81	51.14
1949	6.81	2.86	5.06	4.04	2.57	3.22	5.52	5.07	2.38	6.67	1.51	3.03	48.74
1950	9.39	5.72	5.17	1.06	5.42	3.10	7.43	4.37	1.75	1.55	2.48	3.07	50.51
1951	5.02	4.80	7.46	5.33	1.29	5.81	4.06	1.30	4.37	2.90	4.96	5.43	52.73
1952	4.56	2.11	3.87	1.12	3.32	1.98	2.64	4.57	1.94	0.63	5.27	3.99	36.00
1953	4.12	6.22	4.22	4.23	4.50	3.02	3.74	0.88	2.93	0.68	1.65	3.36	39.55
1954	11.74	3.14	4.67	2.24	3.55	2.32	3.34	0.77	1.30	0.64	3.40	5.97	43.08
1955	1.63	5.62	5.38	3.70	3.51	3.65	3.97	1.93	2.48	3.20	3.30	2.73	41.10
1956	3.18	8.29	4.58	5.07	3.27	2.69	4.54	1.45	1.66	2.59	1.98	8.06	47.36
1957	9.63	7.86	2.26	4.56	3.53	5.86	0.70	4.07	6.98	3.43	7.45	5.16	61.49
1958	2.13	2.81	4.29	5.41	4.78	2.01	5.57	2.83	1.49	0.68	3.06	2.19	37.25
1959	4.09	4.06	4.12	4.17	3.53	2.78	2.97	4.91	0.93	5.00	4.68	4.03	45.27
1960	3.39	3.00	4.78	1.83	1.12	4.89	2.36	3.72	4.58	4.34	2.55	3.61	40.17
1961	2.55	7.82	7.80	2.50	4.18	4.54	3.49	3.04	0.50	3.41	3.04	11.64	54.51
1962	6.22	7.96	4.13	3.84	1.88	5.05	7.82	2.08	5.13	2.20	4.60	3.67	54.58
1963	4.20	3.54	9.92	3.63	4.51	3.32	4.92	3.64	2.37	T	5.23	2.86	48.14
1964	4.71	4.09	5.75	6.98	3.96	0.97	3.70	5.75	1.10	2.10	2.80	4.02	45.93
1965	3.94	3.25	9.31	4.16	3.13	4.84	3.49	2.18	2.48	1.08	2.50	0.45	40.81
1966	3.88	4.68	2.72	2.88	2.92	2.27	5.44	4.09	4.41	4.80	5.12	2.66	45.87
1967	2.67	4.58	4.08	2.00	4.10	6.53	10.09	4.06	2.70	2.33	5.57	6.95	55.66
1968	4.13	0.74	4.78	4.12	3.01	3.97	2.57	1.29	2.53	3.40	2.00	3.22	35.76
1969	4.11	5.54	2.89	2.41	1.33	7.58	3.51	6.72	3.03	1.56	2.56	7.74	48.98
1970	3.04	2.86	3.18	7.20	0.74	4.26	3.11	4.89	2.75	5.33	1.40	4.67	43.43
1971	5.03	4.93	4.21	3.87	3.78	3.73	8.76	3.05	3.41	1.98	2.21	5.48	50.44
1972	7.35	4.19	4.98	2.54	4.49	5.02	6.76	1.61	4.70	5.99	3.36	7.02	58.01
1973	3.24	2.59	10.24	5.15	5.71	5.26	4.38	2.31	3.28	3.48	5.01	7.38	58.03
1974	7.05	5.24	6.15	5.77	10.98	2.70	2.92	3.14	3.33	2.35	5.18	4.52	59.33
1975	4.66	4.68	10.42	2.43	2.98	2.43	2.25	1.61	3.28	4.02	2.92	3.59	45.27
RECORD MEAN	4.66	4.66	5.21	4.16	3.75	4.05	4.52	3.71	2.82	2.64	3.34	4.43	47.95

Aug	Sept	Oct	Nov	Dec	Total
304	147	23	0	0	1346
384	326	46	0	0	1636
350	252	69	13	3	1418
347	223	4	2	0	1205
355	282	60	2	0	1445
365	171	19	17	0	1340
434	168	26	0	0	1530

Record mean values above are means through the current year for the period beginning in 1871 for temperature and precipitation, 1943 for snowfall. Data are from City Office locations through 1941 and Airport thereafter.

(Continued)

quently. This again is due mainly to the retarding effect of the mountains. The diurnal variation between night and daytime temperature averages about 20°. As a result, summer nights are nearly always comfortable.

Rainfall is ample for agricultural purposes and is favorably distributed during the year for most crops. Precipitation is greatest in the wintertime. Another peak period occurs during the late spring and summer months. The period of lowest rainfall occurs during the fall. A cumulative total of approximately 12 inches of snow falls annually. However, this usually comes in amounts of less than 4 inches at one time. It is unusual for snow to remain on the ground in measurable amounts longer than one week.

The topography also has a pronounced effect upon the prevailing wind direction. Daytime winds usually have a southwesterly component, while nighttime winds usually move from the northeast. The winds are relatively light and tornadoes are extremely rare.

Normals, Means, and Extremes

Month	Normal Degree days Base 65 °F		Precipitation in inches												Relative humidity pct.			
			Water equivalent							Snow, Ice pellets					Hour 01	Hour 07	Hour 13	Hour 19
	Heating	Cooling	Normal	Maximum monthly	Year	Minimum monthly	Year	Maximum in 24 hrs.	Year	Maximum monthly	Year	Maximum in 24 hrs.	Year		(Local time)			
(a)				34		34		34		34		34			15	15	15	15
J	756	0	4.67	11.74	1954	1.63	1955	3.89	1946	15.1	1962	12.0	1962		76	80	64	65
F	630	8	4.71	9.38	1944	0.74	1968	2.89	1956	23.3	1960	17.5	1960		72	77	60	59
M	484	16	4.86	10.42	1975	2.26	1957	4.85	1973	20.2	1960	12.1	1942		70	78	55	55
A	173	32	3.61	7.20	1970	0.84	1942	2.92	1974	7.0	1971	7.0	1971		70	78	51	51
M	47	152	3.28	10.98	1974	0.74	1970	3.36	1974	T	1945	T	1945		78	84	55	57
J	0	315	3.63	7.58	1969	0.20	1944	3.57	1972	0.0		0.0			84	88	59	62
J	0	409	4.70	10.09	1967	0.70	1957	4.69	1942	0.0		0.0			86	90	62	65
A	0	381	3.24	8.88	1942	0.77	1954	3.25	1959	0.0		0.0			87	92	61	66
S	10	208	2.78	8.61	1944	0.50	1961	5.08	1944	0.0		0.0			86	91	59	66
O	175	48	2.67	6.67	1949	T	1963	2.44	1961	T	1962	T	1962		83	88	55	62
N	474	0	3.56	10.36	1948	0.97	1942	4.06	1948	18.2	1952	18.2	1952		78	83	59	65
D	729	0	4.47	11.63	1961	0.45	1965	4.89	1969	12.2	1963	8.9	1969		77	81	64	68
YR	3478	1569	46.18	11.74	JAN 1954	T	OCT 1963	5.08	SEP 1944	23.3	FEB 1960	18.2	NOV 1952		79	84	59	62

(To better understand these tables, see full explanation of terms beginning on page 322)

Month	Wind					Pct. of possible sunshine	Mean sky cover, tenths, sunrise to sunset	Mean number of days												Average station pressure mb.
	Mean speed m.p.h.	Prevailing direction	Fastest mile					Sunrise to sunset			Precipitation .01 inch or more	Snow, Ice pellets 1.0 inch or more	Thunderstorms	Heavy fog, visibility ¼ mile or less	Temperatures °F					Elev. 980 feet m.s.l.
			Speed m.p.h.	Direction	Year			Clear	Partly cloudy	Cloudy					Max. (b) 90° and above	Max. 32° and below	Min. 32° and below	Min. 0° and below		
(a)	33	14	31	31		33	33	33	33	33	33	33	33	33	15	15	15	15		3
J	8.2	NE	60	SW	1959	38	7.1	6	7	18	13	1	1	3	0	3	19	*		984.9
F	8.6	NE	61	SW	1958	45	6.7	6	6	16	12	1	1	2	0	1	17	*		982.8
M	9.2	NE	61	SW	1947	51	6.7	7	7	17	13	1	3	2	0	*	8	0		980.7
A	9.2	WSW	71	SW	1944	59	6.1	8	9	13	11	*	5	1	0	0	1	0		982.1
M	7.3	SW	59	SW	1952	61	6.1	8	10	13	11	0	7	2	1	0	0	0		979.9
J	6.7	SW	65	W	1948	61	5.9	7	13	10	11	0	8	2	4	0	0	0		981.7
J	6.3	WSW	73	SW	1961	60	6.1	6	13	12	12	0	10	2	7	0	0	0		982.3
A	5.7	NE	56	S	1962	60	5.7	8	13	10	10	0	7	3	6	0	0	0		983.9
S	5.9	NE	56	W	1943	59	5.6	9	10	11	9	0	3	4	2	0	0	0		983.5
O	5.8	NE	42	SW	1947	61	4.9	13	8	10	8	0	1	5	0	0	1	0		986.2
N	7.2	NE	43	SW	1960	48	6.1	9	7	14	10	*	1	3	0	*	8	0		985.4
D	7.5	NE	52	SW	1954	37	6.9	7	6	18	11	1	1	3	0	1	17	*		984.1
YR	7.3	NE	73	SW	JUL 1961	56	6.2	94	109	162	128	4	48	32	19	6	71	1		983.1

FOOTNOTES

Means and extremes above are from existing and comparable exposures. Annual extremes have been exceeded at other sites in the locality as follows: Highest temperature 104 in July 1930; lowest temperature -16 in January 1884; maximum monthly precipitation 17.32 in April 1874; maximum precipitation in 24 hours 6.30 in July 1917; maximum monthly snowfall 25.7 in February 1895.

Station: MEMPHIS, TENNESSEE INTERNATIONAL AIRPORT
Elevation (ground): 258 feet

TEMPERATURES °F

Month	Normal			Extremes			
	Daily maximum	Daily minimum	Monthly	Record highest	Year	Record lowest	Year
(a)				34		34	
J	49.4	31.6	40.5	78	1972	-4	1962
F	53.1	34.4	43.8	81	1962	-11	1951
M	60.8	41.1	51.0	85	1963	12	1943
A	72.7	52.3	62.5	91	1952	29	1944
M	81.2	60.6	70.9	97	1951	38	1944
J	88.7	68.5	78.6	104	1954	48	1966
J	91.6	71.5	81.6	106	1952	52	1947
A	90.6	70.1	80.4	105	1943	48	1946
S	84.3	62.8	73.6	103	1954	36	1949
O	74.9	51.1	63.0	95	1954	25	1952
N	61.5	40.3	50.9	85	1955	9	1950
D	51.7	33.7	42.7	79	1951	-13	1963
YR	71.7	51.5	61.6	106	JUL 1952	-13	DEC 1963

IMPORTANT:
The time-period covered by this record is limited: See footnotes on next page for explanation and for additional history of EXTREME HIGHS AND LOWS recorded in the general area.

Topography varies from the level alluvial area in east-central Arkansas to the slightly rolling area in northwestern Mississippi and southwestern Tennessee.

Agricultural interests are varied, with major crops being cotton, corn, hay, soybeans, peaches, apples and a considerable number of vegetables. The climate is quite favorable for dairy interests, and for the raising of cattle and hogs.

The average annual temperature is in the low sixties, and varies from the low forties in January to the low eighties in July. The growing season is about 230 days in length. The average last killing frost in spring is about March 20, and the average first in autumn is early in November.

Precipitation of near 50 inches per year is fairly well distributed.
Crops and pastures receive, on the average, an adequate supply of moisture during the growing season, with lesser amounts during the fall harvesting period.

Sunshine averages slightly over 70 percent of the possible amount during the growing season. Relative humidity averages about 70 percent for the year.

Memphis, although not in the normal paths of storms coming from the Gulf or from western Canada, is affected by both, and thereby has comparatively frequent changes in weather. Extremely high or low temperatures, however, are relatively rare, as there are only about 70 days per year with maximum temperatures over 90°, and only about 55 days with minimum temperatures under 32°.

MEMPHIS, TENNESSEE

Normals, Means, and Extremes

(To better understand these tables, see full explanation of terms beginning on page 322)

Month	Normal Degree days Base 65 °F: Heating	Cooling	Precipitation in inches, Water equivalent: Normal	Maximum monthly	Year	Minimum monthly	Year	Maximum in 24 hrs.	Year	Snow, Ice pellets: Maximum monthly	Year	Maximum in 24 hrs.	Year
(a)				25		25		25		25		25	
J	760	0	4.93	12.21	1951	0.84	1961	3.89	1974	12.2	1966	6.5	1960
F	594	0	4.73	9.39	1956	1.98	1968	3.63	1966	7.6	1960	5.8	1960
M	457	23	5.10	12.08	1975	1.50	1966	5.95	1975	17.3	1968	16.1	1968
A	131	56	5.42	12.29	1955	2.05	1965	3.50	1955	T	1971	T	1971
M	22	205	4.39	11.58	1953	0.84	1962	4.94	1958	0.0		0.0	
J	0	408	3.46	6.88	1951	0.04	1953	2.91	1968	0.0		0.0	
J	0	515	3.53	8.84	1959	0.43	1954	3.31	1953	0.0		0.0	
A	0	477	3.33	7.84	1960	0.43	1953	3.35	1969	0.0		0.0	
S	7	265	3.01	7.61	1958	0.19	1953	4.63	1957	0.0		0.0	
O	142	80	2.58	6.20	1970	T	1963	2.47	1968	0.0		0.0	
N	423	0	3.92	8.56	1957	0.75	1965	3.64	1972	0.8	1971	0.8	1971
D	691	0	4.70	9.37	1972	1.05	1955	4.15	1964	14.3	1963	14.3	1963
YR	3227	2029	49.10	12.29	APR 1955	T	OCT 1963	5.95	MAR 1975	17.3	MAR 1968	16.1	MAR 1968

Month	Relative humidity pct. Hour 00 (Local time)	Hour 06	Hour 12	Hour 18	Wind: Mean speed m.p.h.	Prevailing direction	Fastest mile #: Speed m.p.h.	Direction	Year	Pct. of possible sunshine	Mean sky cover, tenths, sunrise to sunset	Mean number of days, Sunrise to sunset: Clear	Partly cloudy	Cloudy	Precipitation .01 inch or more	Snow, Ice pellets 1.0 inch or more	Thunderstorms	Heavy fog, visibility ¼ mile or less	Temperatures °F Max.: (b) 90° and above	32° and below	Min.: 32° and below	0° and below	Average station pressure mb. Elev. 284 feet m.s.l.
(a)	36	36	36	36	27	15	21	21		25	27	25	25	25	25	25	25	25	34	34	34	34	3
J	76	80	64	69	10.6	S	43	NW	1956	48	6.9	7	6	18	10	1	2	2	0	3	18	*	1010.2
F	74	79	60	63	10.6	S	49	SW	1951	54	6.4	8	5	15	10	*	2	1	0	1	12	*	1008.8
M	71	77	57	58	11.3	S	54	S	1952	57	6.4	8	7	16	11	*	5	1	0	*	6	0	1004.5
A	72	79	54	55	10.8	S	57	W	1970	63	6.1	9	7	14	10	0	7	*	*	0	*	0	1006.2
M	77	82	55	56	9.0	S	50	NW	1953	59	5.8	9	10	12	9	0	6	*	3	0	0	0	1003.2
J	79	83	56	57	8.1	S	50	NW	1951	73	5.4	10	11	9	8	0	7	*	15	0	0	0	1004.7
J	80	85	57	59	7.6	S	56	NW	1964	72	5.6	9	13	9	9	0	8	*	21	0	0	0	1005.5
A	81	86	56	60	7.1	S	42	NE	1967	75	5.0	12	11	8	8	0	6	*	18	0	0	0	1007.0
S	81	86	56	62	7.6	E	47	SE	1968	69	5.1	12	8	10	7	0	4	1	7	0	0	0	1007.3
O	78	84	51	61	7.8	S	47	W	1955	71	4.5	15	7	9	6	0	2	1	1	0	*	0	1010.2
N	75	80	55	64	9.4	S	43	S	1952	58	5.6	10	7	13	8	0	2	1	0	*	7	0	1009.7
D	76	79	62	69	10.1	S	43	N	1954	49	6.4	9	5	17	10	*	2	2	0	1	15	*	1009.5
YR	77	82	57	61	9.2	S	57	W	APR 1970	64	5.8	118	97	150	107	2	53	11	65	6	59	*	1007.2

FOOTNOTES

Means and extremes above are from existing and comparable exposures. Annual extremes have been exceeded at other sites in the locality as follows: Maximum monthly precipitation 18.16 in June 1877; minimum monthly precipitation 0.00 in September 1897; maximum precipitation in 24 hours 10.48 in November 1934; maximum monthly snowfall 18.5 in March 1892; maximum snowfall in 24 hours 18.0 in March 1892.

Data through 1970.

Snowfall

Season	July	Aug	Sept	Oct	Nov	Dec	Jan
1936-37	0.0	0.0	0.0	0.0	0.2	0.2	0.0
1937-38	0.0	0.0	0.0	0.0	0.2	1.2	0.0
1938-39	0.0	0.0	0.0	0.0	0.6	0.0	0.0
1939-40	0.0	0.0	0.0	0.0	0.0	T	4.6
1940-41	0.0	0.0	0.0	0.0	0.0	0.0	T
1941-42	0.0	0.0	0.0	0.0	0.0	0.0	1.4
1942-43	0.0	0.0	0.0	0.0	0.0	T	T
1943-44	0.0	0.0	0.0	0.0	0.0	T	3.9
1944-45	0.0	0.0	0.0	0.0	T	T	T
1945-46	0.0	0.0	0.0	0.0	0.0	6.8	2.9
1946-47	0.0	0.0	0.0	0.0	0.0	0.0	T
1947-48	0.0	0.0	0.0	0.0	0.0	0.0	15.1
1948-49	0.0	0.0	0.0	0.0	T	T	4.0
1949-50	0.0	0.0	0.0	0.0	0.0	T	T
#1950-51	0.0	0.0	0.0	0.0	1.0	0.8	4.1
1951-52	0.0	0.0	0.0	0.0	0.2	T	T
1952-53	0.0	0.0	0.0	0.0	T	T	T
1953-54	0.0	0.0	0.0	0.0	0.0	T	3.8
1954-55	0.0	0.0	0.0	0.0	0.0	T	0.3
1955-56	0.0	0.0	0.0	0.0	T	T	5.2
1956-57	0.0	0.0	0.0	0.0	T	0.0	T
1957-58	0.0	0.0	0.0	0.0	T	T	1.0
1958-59	0.0	0.0	0.0	0.0	T	4.0	T
1959-60	0.0	0.0	0.0	0.0	T	0.0	6.5
1960-61	0.0	0.0	0.0	0.0	0.0	1.2	T
1961-62	0.0	0.0	0.0	0.0	T	T	5.0
1962-63	0.0	0.0	0.0	0.0	0.0	3.0	1.2
1963-64	0.0	0.0	0.0	0.0	0.0	14.3	0.5
1964-65	0.0	0.0	0.0	0.0	T	T	T
1965-66	0.0	0.0	0.0	0.0	0.0	0.0	12.2
1966-67	0.0	0.0	0.0	0.0	T	0.7	0.6
1967-68	0.0	0.0	0.0	0.0	0.0	T	2.0
1968-69	0.0	0.0	0.0	0.0	0.0	0.0	T
1969-70	0.0	0.0	0.0	0.0	T	0.1	3.3
1970-71	0.0	0.0	0.0	0.0	T	1.0	T
1971-72	0.0	0.0	0.0	0.0	0.8	0.0	0.3
1972-73	0.0	0.0	0.0	0.0	T	T	1.4
1973-74	0.0	0.0	0.0	0.0	0.0	0.2	0.9
1974-75	0.0	0.0	0.0	0.0	T	0.2	3.9
1975-76	0.0	0.0	0.0	0.0	0.0	0.1	
RECORD MEAN	0.0	0.0	0.0	0.0	T	1.0	2.1

Heating Degree Days

Season	July	Aug	Sept	Oct	Nov	Dec	Jan
1955-56	0	0	0	158	487	695	806
1956-57	0	0	0	48	439	482	788
1957-58	0	0	6	191	407	526	844
1958-59	0	0	11	138	344	795	781
1959-60	0	0	0	111	547	602	713
#1960-61	0	0	0	104	425	853	892
1961-62	0	0	8	148	467	690	887
1962-63	0	0	14	107	436	772	944
1963-64	0	0	10	33	352	1034	739
1964-65	0	0	13	202	335	634	666
1965-66	0	0	22	162	275	590	947
1966-67	0	0	9	227	344	732	707
1967-68	0	0	34	144	469	613	803
1968-69	0	0	1	149	423	716	733
1969-70	0	0	0	151	473	768	917
1970-71	0	0	7	150	455	571	781
1971-72	0	0	9	13	432	435	698
1972-73	0	0	12	172	583	766	809
1973-74	0	0	8	67	244	665	599
1974-75	0	0	28	121	367	607	591
1975-76	0	0	40	90	352	643	

Cooling Degree Days

Year	Jan	Feb	Mar	Apr	May	June	July
1969	0	0	0	48	240	422	627
1970	3	0	0	104	251	375	463
1971	0	0	3	46	107	474	489
1972	0	0	3	95	179	383	449
1973	0	0	4	48	143	486	571
1974	6	0	46	59	228	299	550
1975	8	0	3	93	272	421	507

Feb	Mar	Apr	May	June	Total
T	T	0.0	0.0	0.0	0.4
T	0.0	0.0	0.0	0.0	1.4
T	0.0	0.0	0.0	0.0	0.6
3.9	T	0.0	0.0	0.0	8.5
4.9	0.0	0.0	0.0	0.0	4.9
0.5	T	0.0	0.0	0.0	1.9
T	T	0.0	0.0	0.0	T
T	T	0.0	0.0	0.0	3.9
T	0.0	0.0	0.0	0.0	T
3.4	0.0	0.0	0.0	0.0	13.1
1.5	1.6	0.0	0.0	0.0	3.1
1.5	T	0.0	0.0	0.0	16.6
0.0	T	0.0	0.0	0.0	4.0
T	T	0.0	0.0	0.0	T
1.6	0.4	0.0	0.0	0.0	7.9
T	T	0.0	0.0	0.0	0.2
0.0	0.0	0.0	0.0	0.0	T
0.0	0.0	0.0	0.0	0.0	3.8
T	T	0.0	0.0	0.0	0.3
0.0	T	0.0	0.0	0.0	5.2
T	T	0.0	0.0	0.0	T
4.8	0.0	0.0	0.0	0.0	5.8
0.6	0.0	0.0	0.0	0.0	4.6
7.6	6.4	0.0	0.0	0.0	20.5
0.2	0.0	0.0	0.0	0.0	1.4
T	T	0.0	0.0	0.0	5.0
0.8	0.0	0.0	0.0	0.0	5.0
T	T	0.0	0.0	0.0	14.8
3.3	4.6	0.0	0.0	0.0	7.9
T	T	0.0	0.0	0.0	12.2
T	0.3	0.0	0.0	0.0	1.6
4.5	17.3	0.0	0.0	0.0	23.8
T	T	0.0	0.0	0.0	T
0.2	T	0.0	0.0	0.0	3.6
6.7	1.6	T	0.0	0.0	9.3
0.1	T	0.0	0.0	0.0	1.2
T	0.0	0.0	0.0	0.0	1.4
0.5	T	0.0	0.0	0.0	1.6
0.5	1.4	0.0	0.0	0.0	6.0
1.3	1.3	T	0.0	0.0	5.7

MEMPHIS, TN

Feb	Mar	Apr	May	June	Total
492	425	185	7	1	3256
414	447	145	25	0	2788
862	592	154	36	0	3618
570	410	155	15	0	3219
691	763	91	69	0	3587
490	309	249	70	2	3394
410	543	229	5	0	3387
760	291	119	34	0	3477
713	406	91	13	0	3391
614	645	72	0	0	3181
634	382	175	47	5	3239
715	301	60	35	0	3130
795	444	114	21	0	3437
601	608	103	12	0	3346
648	500	97	20	0	3574
593	509	171	50	0	3287
582	391	146	27	0	2733
679	237	200	32	0	3490
535	235	150	1	0	2504
521	463	180	2	0	2880

Aug	Sept	Oct	Nov	Dec	Total
449	243	91	0	0	2120
509	400	51	6	2	2164
426	349	154	14	0	2062
464	346	66	6	0	1991
458	350	156	19	0	2235
445	138	46	23	0	1840
510	224	121	23	2	2184

Average Temperature

Year	Jan	Feb	Mar	Apr	May	June	July	Aug	Sept	Oct	Nov	Dec	Annual
1936	36.4	36.6	57.4	58.6	73.2	80.6	82.0	83.7	77.8	62.6	48.7	46.2	62.0
1937	44.4	42.8	47.8	62.6	72.7	79.2	79.8	82.2	72.8	60.8	49.4	42.5	61.4
1938	41.8	51.6	60.6	63.2	72.2	76.6	83.0	84.2	76.1	68.0	52.9	43.8	64.5
1939	46.9	45.2	56.0	59.2	70.8	79.2	81.8	80.2	80.1	66.6	49.8	46.6	63.5
1940	27.2	41.2	51.6	60.6	68.0	77.1	79.0	80.0	73.8	67.6	51.6	48.4	60.5
#1941	43.3	40.0	47.4	64.8	73.0	78.8	82.5	81.8	76.9	69.0	49.0	45.2	62.6
1942	36.9	40.0	53.6	63.4	69.3	78.8	82.8	78.6	71.8	63.2	55.6	42.4	61.4
1943	41.6	46.4	46.8	62.0	73.0	81.6	83.8	84.0	70.5	60.8	48.8	40.7	61.7
1944	42.0	48.5	52.0	60.1	72.0	81.0	81.0	80.6	74.6	62.8	52.0	37.8	62.0
1945	39.2	44.2	60.1	63.4	66.6	76.6	79.7	79.9	75.2	60.8	53.0	37.2	61.3
1946	41.0	46.8	59.4	65.7	67.4	77.2	80.6	78.4	73.3	63.8	55.8	48.6	63.2
1947	43.6	36.4	45.0	62.8	68.1	78.2	78.5	84.8	75.8	70.0	48.6	44.4	61.4
1948	32.2	42.2	52.4	65.8	70.0	78.8	82.0	78.9	73.0	60.0	52.6	45.9	61.2
1949	45.6	47.7	51.3	60.3	72.6	78.6	82.4	79.5	69.6	65.2	51.2	46.4	62.5
1950	50.3	47.3	49.0	58.3	72.4	77.9	79.0	76.1	71.3	66.7	46.5	37.6	61.0
1951	42.7	44.5	52.1	58.3	70.5	77.3	81.8	82.2	72.7	63.7	45.6	45.9	61.4
1952	47.5	48.4	50.4	58.9	71.1	84.6	83.8	81.7	71.8	54.8	49.7	44.0	62.2
1953	45.8	46.6	56.5	58.7	71.8	85.6	82.7	81.0	74.6	64.3	50.5	41.8	63.3
1954	42.8	50.8	51.7	67.2	66.0	81.2	86.5	85.0	78.0	64.5	50.4	43.1	63.9
1955	41.5	44.2	53.0	65.6	73.3	74.2	82.6	81.5	76.7	62.2	49.7	42.5	62.3
1956	38.7	47.8	51.5	60.4	73.2	77.3	82.6	82.5	72.9	65.7	50.6	49.4	62.7
1957	39.3	50.1	50.4	64.4	71.7	78.3	80.4	79.0	72.0	59.6	51.3	47.8	62.0
1958	37.6	34.0	45.6	60.4	71.1	78.0	81.4	79.9	73.5	62.1	54.0	39.1	59.8
1959	39.5	44.4	51.7	61.5	74.4	77.4	79.3	81.1	75.7	64.5	46.6	45.4	61.8
#1960	41.9	40.8	40.2	64.8	68.5	77.8	81.8	81.6	76.1	63.8	50.8	37.2	60.4
1961	36.1	47.2	55.1	58.2	66.7	75.1	80.2	77.8	74.6	62.5	49.6	42.4	60.4
1962	36.2	50.3	47.3	58.8	76.8	77.1	81.3	80.8	73.4	65.9	50.2	39.9	61.5
1963	34.4	37.6	56.7	64.2	71.1	78.6	80.1	80.2	73.4	68.6	53.4	31.5	60.8
1964	41.1	40.2	51.7	64.0	71.9	79.3	80.6	78.6	72.9	58.9	54.4	44.3	61.5
1965	43.4	42.9	44.0	66.4	74.7	78.1	81.8	80.2	73.7	60.8	55.8	45.8	62.3
1966	34.2	42.2	52.8	60.6	67.9	76.6	84.7	76.9	70.8	58.1	53.7	41.4	60.0
1967	42.2	39.2	56.7	66.5	68.8	78.3	77.7	76.0	70.3	62.4	49.1	45.0	61.0
1968	38.9	37.3	50.9	62.7	69.7	79.5	80.8	82.0	71.3	62.2	50.9	41.7	60.7
1969	41.2	43.3	45.0	62.9	72.1	78.8	84.9	79.3	72.9	62.9	49.0	40.1	61.1
1970	35.3	41.7	48.7	65.0	72.3	77.3	79.7	81.2	77.9	61.7	49.8	46.4	61.4
1971	39.6	43.5	48.4	60.5	66.6	80.6	80.6	78.6	76.1	69.3	50.9	50.7	62.1
1972	42.3	44.7	52.2	63.1	69.7	77.5	79.4	79.7	75.9	61.4	45.5	40.0	60.9
1973	38.6	40.5	57.3	59.8	68.3	81.0	83.2	79.6	76.1	67.6	57.3	43.3	62.7
1974	45.7	45.6	58.7	61.8	72.1	74.7	82.5	79.2	68.5	62.4	53.3	45.2	62.5
1975	45.9	46.2	49.9	61.9	73.5	78.8	81.1	81.2	70.9	65.8	53.8	44.1	62.8
RECORD MEAN	41.3	44.1	52.2	62.1	70.5	78.2	81.2	80.0	74.1	63.5	51.6	43.6	61.9
MAX	49.2	52.4	61.1	71.3	79.6	87.2	89.9	88.8	83.3	73.5	60.6	51.4	70.7
MIN	33.3	35.7	43.3	52.9	61.3	69.2	72.4	71.1	64.8	53.4	42.6	35.7	53.0

# Indicates a station move or relocation of instruments.

Precipitation

Year	Jan	Feb	Mar	Apr	May	June	July	Aug	Sept	Oct	Nov	Dec	Annual
1936	2.19	1.82	4.12	1.21	1.91	1.22	6.49	0.40	6.04	3.39	3.64	6.84	39.27
1937	17.56	1.95	1.96	3.59	4.04	4.07	4.32	1.72	2.50	5.49	4.18	3.92	55.30
1938	5.61	5.88	6.90	5.90	2.86	3.03	1.78	0.97	1.38	0.38	2.72	2.36	39.77
1939	9.72	10.07	5.14	7.34	4.51	4.05	3.46	2.23	2.31	0.94	2.18	2.90	54.85
1940	1.83	4.71	2.51	4.88	1.74	2.78	4.11	2.40	1.88	1.69	3.27	3.17	34.97
1941	2.82	1.68	1.39	3.72	0.99	1.20	3.51	3.45	0.46	5.62	1.69	4.01	30.54
1942	4.35	4.22	5.56	5.14	2.33	2.39	1.78	4.90	0.67	3.54	3.16	5.04	43.08
1943	1.23	0.72	7.45	2.89	6.02	2.02	0.01	0.60	5.56	0.45	3.42	3.72	34.09
1944	2.04	9.24	5.20	6.50	3.14	2.44	1.69	3.21	3.43	2.73	4.17	11.97	55.76
1945	2.95	5.48	7.05	5.99	2.36	5.89	3.32	0.52	6.04	1.31	10.26	4.24	55.41
1946	8.86	4.73	5.49	4.90	4.75	4.12	1.69	1.22	1.61	2.66	5.46	3.91	49.40
1947	5.94	0.71	1.96	4.56	4.68	5.49	0.63	2.42	0.62	5.67	5.07	3.36	41.11
1948	2.67	9.21	8.21	3.59	2.28	5.06	2.39	2.62	2.22	2.21	9.16	2.84	52.46
1949	8.87	1.90	5.42	6.77	3.93	10.30	3.73	2.36	1.42	8.16	0.69	7.06	60.61
#1950	15.45	8.25	5.35	2.53	6.13	2.85	5.66	5.75	3.52	3.02	4.59	2.38	65.48
1951	12.21	2.23	3.92	2.78	1.88	6.88	5.15	2.72	4.02	3.02	2.89	6.86	54.56
1952	5.55	6.39	5.75	2.55	3.62	0.76	2.41	2.97	2.56	0.70	3.93	3.07	40.26
1953	3.86	4.48	8.91	7.41	11.58	0.04	5.53	0.43	0.19	2.28	4.00	4.67	53.38
1954	10.79	4.97	1.99	4.34	4.31	2.41	0.43	2.66	1.43	0.62	1.06	3.46	38.47
1955	2.02	6.14	7.55	12.29	5.96	4.02	5.96	4.07	1.31	2.47	3.52	1.05	56.36
1956	4.14	9.39	2.54	6.74	3.41	3.71	3.05	2.48	0.57	2.36	2.58	3.79	44.76
1957	11.39	4.65	4.37	9.31	7.10	6.64	4.95	4.31	7.48	3.64	8.56	4.45	76.85
1958	2.75	3.11	4.04	6.77	8.88	4.00	5.55	4.05	7.61	1.03	3.81	2.33	53.93
1959	4.34	5.21	3.56	3.73	1.85	4.82	8.84	4.56	2.73	1.57	2.66	5.33	49.20
1960	3.74	3.08	4.20	3.65	4.20	5.34	1.30	7.84	4.05	4.11	3.62	4.30	49.43
1961	0.84	6.89	7.13	4.65	4.40	1.49	3.97	1.71	0.66	1.28	8.06	8.56	49.64
1962	4.19	4.22	4.80	3.62	0.84	5.71	3.94	4.18	5.28	2.57	2.31	1.35	43.01
1963	1.28	2.91	6.17	5.60	3.77	4.33	4.38	2.15	2.06	T	2.72	3.31	38.68
1964	3.73	3.50	7.34	11.03	3.28	1.39	6.14	5.76	2.74	2.21	2.59	7.97	57.68
1965	4.79	6.78	5.35	2.05	7.42	0.98	1.60	3.98	7.38	0.54	0.75	1.17	42.79
1966	2.84	6.88	1.50	5.42	5.69	0.52	2.18	4.28	3.23	1.92	1.57	5.21	41.24
1967	2.23	2.33	4.65	4.46	6.38	1.70	6.01	5.17	1.86	2.38	1.90	7.37	46.44
1968	5.57	1.98	6.52	5.15	5.21	3.76	2.69	1.61	5.58	2.87	4.89	6.04	51.87
1969	3.14	3.20	2.63	8.29	1.34	1.60	1.92	6.62	0.90	1.24	4.19	7.05	42.12
1970	1.16	3.87	5.32	7.08	3.70	5.76	4.99	1.78	3.80	6.20	2.62	3.71	49.99
1971	2.15	7.21	3.64	2.89	3.90	3.82	2.90	6.00	3.42	0.06	1.49	6.71	44.19
1972	4.73	2.23	4.80	3.51	4.55	5.50	4.89	1.94	5.46	3.92	8.05	9.37	58.95
1973	4.62	3.62	7.63	9.44	6.23	1.00	4.49	4.88	5.06	3.37	8.49	5.35	64.18
1974	8.90	4.65	3.40	6.34	7.76	6.30	6.33	4.78	3.45	2.67	4.96	5.03	64.57
1975	4.65	5.53	12.08	4.98	8.72	2.42	2.26	2.03	2.62	2.69	7.77	2.93	58.68
RECORD MEAN	5.03	4.40	5.22	5.06	4.27	3.62	3.39	3.24	2.94	2.75	4.21	4.61	48.74

Record mean values above are means through the current year for the period beginning in 1875 for temperature, 1872 for precipitation, and 1951 for snowfall. Temperature and Degree Day data are from City Office locations through March 1941 and from Airport locations thereafter. Precipitation and Snowfall data are from City Office locations through 1950 and from Airport locations thereafter.

Station: NASHVILLE, TENNESSEE METROPOLITAN AIRPORT

Elevation (ground): 590 feet

TEMPERATURES °F

Month	Normal Daily maximum	Normal Daily minimum	Normal Monthly	Extremes Record highest	Extremes Year	Extremes Record lowest	Extremes Year
(a)				10		10	
J	47.6	29.0	38.3	78	1972	-6	1966
F	50.9	31.0	41.0	79	1972	-5	1971
M	59.2	38.1	48.7	86	1967	14	1968
A	71.3	48.8	60.1	88	1965	24	1973
M	79.8	57.3	68.5	91	1974	35	1971
J	87.5	65.7	76.6	98	1971	42	1966
J	90.2	69.0	79.6	103	1966	54	1972
A	89.2	67.7	78.5	99	1968	51	1967
S	83.5	60.5	72.0	95	1973	37	1967
O	73.2	48.6	60.9	90	1971	27	1968
N	59.0	37.7	48.4	84	1971	12	1970
D	49.6	31.1	40.4	74	1971	6	1966
YR	70.1	48.7	59.4	103	JUL 1966	-6	JAN 1966

IMPORTANT:
The time-period covered by this record is limited: See footnotes following table of **NORMALS, MEANS AND EXTREMES** for explanation and for additional history of **EXTREME HIGHS AND LOWS** recorded in the general area.

The city of Nashville is located on the Cumberland River, in the northwestern corner of the Central Basin of middle Tennessee near the escarpment of the "Highland Rim." The Rim, as it is called, rises to the height of 300 to 400 feet above the mean elevation of the basin, forming an amphitheater about the City from the southwest to the southeast, and south being more or less open, but undulating.

Temperatures are moderate, with great extremes of either heat or cold rarely occurring; yet there are changes of sufficient amplitude and frequency to give variety. Temperature extremes during the month of June and July occurred in 1952 with a high of 106 degrees in June and 107 degrees in July. The record low temperature, 15 degrees below zero, occurred in January 1940 and 1963.

The average growing season in the Nashville area for the 20-year period 1953-1973 is 211 days. The mean date of earliest freezes in fall for the period is October 31, and latest in the spring, April 3. The earliest freeze in fall on record is October 7, 1935, and the latest in spring, April 24, 1893.

Precipitation averages 46 inches a year with the highest monthly amounts in the winter and early spring. The maximum monthly amount, 14.75 inches, fell in January 1937, while the least amount, a trace, was recorded October 1963.

(Continued page 642)

Snowfall

Season	July	Aug	Sept	Oct	Nov	Dec	Jan
1936-37	0.0	0.0	0.0	0.0	1.3	T	0.0
1937-38	0.0	0.0	0.0	0.0	0.1	0.2	0.1
1938-39	0.0	0.0	0.0	0.0	1.5	T	0.1
1939-40	0.0	0.0	0.0	0.0	T	T	6.1
#1940-41	0.0	0.0	0.0	0.0	0.0	0.0	T
1941-42	0.0	0.0	0.0	0.0	T	0.0	5.3
1942-43	0.0	0.0	0.0	0.0	0.0	2.4	0.8
1943-44	0.0	0.0	0.0	0.0	T	T	3.0
1944-45	0.0	0.0	0.0	0.0	T	3.4	1.0
1945-46	0.0	0.0	0.0	0.0	T	9.4	4.2
1946-47	0.0	0.0	0.0	0.0	0.0	2.5	T
1947-48	0.0	0.0	0.0	0.0	0.0	T	18.8
#1948-49	0.0	0.0	0.0	0.0	T	T	3.5
1949-50	0.0	0.0	0.0	0.0	T	T	T
1950-51	0.0	0.0	0.0	0.0	9.2	1.6	7.7
1951-52	0.0	0.0	0.0	0.0	2.4	0.5	0.3
1952-53	0.0	0.0	0.0	T	0.4	0.1	0.4
1953-54	0.0	0.0	0.0	0.0	T	3.0	0.2
1954-55	0.0	0.0	0.0	T	1.0	0.3	4.3
1955-56	0.0	0.0	0.0	0.0	T	T	5.1
1956-57	0.0	0.0	0.0	0.0	T	T	T
1957-58	0.0	0.0	0.0	0.0	1.2	0.3	2.0
1958-59	0.0	0.0	0.0	0.0	T	T	1.0
1959-60	0.0	0.0	0.0	0.0	T	T	7.4
1960-61	0.0	0.0	0.0	0.0	0.0	0.2	3.0
1961-62	0.0	0.0	0.0	0.0	T	2.0	2.2
1962-63	0.0	0.0	0.0	0.0	T	8.2	6.8
1963-64	0.0	0.0	0.0	0.0	T	13.2	5.0
1964-65	0.0	0.0	0.0	0.0	T	0.0	1.2
1965-66	0.0	0.0	0.0	0.0	T	0.0	11.4
1966-67	0.0	0.0	0.0	0.0	7.2	4.3	1.2
1967-68	0.0	0.0	0.0	0.0	0.0	8.4	7.2
1968-69	0.0	0.0	0.0	0.0	T	T	5.2
1969-70	0.0	0.0	0.0	0.0	0.3	3.8	5.6
1970-71	0.0	0.0	0.0	0.0	T	1.2	1.2
1971-72	0.0	0.0	0.0	0.0	0.1	T	0.4
1972-73	0.0	0.0	0.0	0.0	0.1	0.6	4.8
1973-74	0.0	0.0	0.0	0.0	0.0	2.4	T
1974-75	0.0	0.0	0.0	0.0	T	2.1	4.2
1975-76	0.0	0.0	0.0	0.0	T	T	
RECORD MEAN	0.0	0.0	0.0	0.0	0.6	2.1	3.7

Heating Degree Days

Season	July	Aug	Sept	Oct	Nov	Dec	Jan
1955-56	0	0	0	214	574	785	895
1956-57	0	0	10	73	512	450	845
1957-58	0	0	10	270	488	619	911
1958-59	0	0	16	187	420	886	861
1959-60	0	0	0	170	587	674	769
1960-61	0	0	0	148	509	931	977
1961-62	0	0	23	186	471	734	916
1962-63	0	0	43	152	508	924	1050
1963-64	0	0	28	48	465	1062	803
#1964-65	0	3	18	265	398	685	768
1965-66	0	0	26	198	386	618	1007
1966-67	0	0	13	255	423	763	697
1967-68	0	3	58	216	615	688	952
1968-69	0	0	4	220	484	825	855
1969-70	0	0	10	201	551	854	1005
1970-71	0	0	13	159	522	671	902
1971-72	0	0	0	39	462	483	713
1972-73	0	0	10	168	533	682	830
1973-74	0	0	8	84	316	753	601
1974-75	0	0	48	196	464	685	665
1975-76	0	0	68	138	398	683	

Cooling Degree Days

Year	Jan	Feb	Mar	Apr	May	June	July
1969	0	0	0	33	165	378	554
1970	0	0	0	56	163	265	386
1971	0	0	0	23	55	380	374
1972	0	0	1	62	117	250	385
1973	0	0	14	25	61	339	432
1974	0	0	16	39	191	203	410
1975	3	0	3	55	183	341	424

Feb	Mar	Apr	May	June	Total
1.2	0.3	0.0	0.0	0.0	2.8
T	0.0	T	0.0	0.0	0.4
T	T	0.0	0.0	0.0	1.6
0.6	4.5	T	0.0	0.0	11.2
2.7	0.8	0.0	0.0	0.0	3.5
0.9	0.9	0.0	0.0	0.0	7.1
0.5	3.1	T	0.0	0.0	6.8
T	T	0.0	0.0	0.0	3.0
T	0.0	0.0	0.0	0.0	4.4
2.2	0.0	0.0	0.0	0.0	15.8
13.3	5.9	0.0	0.0	0.0	21.7
1.0	T	0.0	0.0	0.0	19.8
0.0	T	0.0	0.0	0.0	3.5
T	T	T	0.0	0.0	T
5.2	8.8	1.0	0.0	0.0	33.5
0.3	T	T	0.0	0.0	3.5
T	T	0.0	0.0	0.0	0.9
T	0.2	0.0	0.0	0.0	3.4
2.0	0.4	0.0	0.0	0.0	8.0
T	T	0.0	0.0	0.0	5.1
T	3.1	T	0.0	0.0	3.1
6.6	0.1	0.0	0.0	0.0	10.2
2.0	T	0.0	0.0	0.0	3.0
15.0	16.1	T	0.0	0.0	38.5
1.6	0.2	0.0	0.0	0.0	5.0
1.1	1.4	T	0.0	0.0	6.7
8.7	0.0	0.0	0.0	0.0	23.7
4.2	T	0.0	0.0	0.0	22.4
2.9	3.4	0.0	0.0	0.0	7.5
T	T	0.0	0.0	0.0	11.4
T	T	0.0	0.0	0.0	12.7
2.9	8.5	0.0	0.0	0.0	27.0
6.9	4.8	0.0	0.0	0.0	16.9
3.0	T	0.0	0.0	0.0	12.7
6.5	3.0	1.1	0.0	0.0	13.0
0.5	0.9	T	0.0	0.0	1.9
T	0.2	0.1	0.0	0.0	5.8
0.3	T	0.0	0.0	0.0	2.7
T	T	T	0.0	0.0	6.3
2.6	1.8	0.1	0.0	0.0	10.9

Average Temperature

Year	Jan	Feb	Mar	Apr	May	June	July	Aug	Sept	Oct	Nov	Dec	Annual
1936	33.0	35.7	53.8	56.2	71.3	79.8	81.2	81.8	76.0	61.0	46.0	43.8	60.0
1937	47.0	40.2	45.8	59.0	68.6	78.1	78.2	81.0	70.0	58.0	46.1	39.4	59.3
1938	38.9	49.7	57.2	61.6	68.6	73.8	79.2	80.4	71.8	63.3	50.0	41.6	61.3
1939	44.5	44.2	53.2	57.0	67.8	76.7	79.8	77.8	77.3	64.6	47.0	43.6	61.1
1940	24.8	39.7	47.4	57.7	64.8	75.9	77.6	79.1	71.0	63.9	48.3	46.0	58.0
#1941	40.4	36.6	44.2	64.0	71.2	77.7	80.6	79.6	76.2	67.8	47.9	44.6	60.9
1942	35.0	37.2	50.5	61.2	68.4	77.8	81.3	77.0	70.1	61.4	52.8	39.6	59.4
1943	40.6	43.2	45.4	57.8	70.8	81.0	81.8	82.2	68.8	58.8	46.8	38.6	59.6
1944	40.2	46.6	48.8	57.8	72.2	80.8	80.0	78.7	72.3	59.7	48.7	36.1	60.2
1945	36.0	41.8	59.1	61.3	64.4	74.6	77.8	78.6	75.3	58.7	50.1	34.4	59.4
1946	39.4	43.9	58.7	62.6	65.8	76.6	79.4	74.2	71.4	62.1	54.4	45.7	61.2
1947	42.9	32.3	41.3	61.0	64.9	75.8	75.2	82.4	73.6	67.9	47.4	41.4	58.8
#1948	29.4	42.0	52.8	63.7	67.7	78.8	80.8	78.4	71.9	58.0	50.8	43.8	59.8
1949	46.6	45.0	49.5	56.9	69.7	76.7	81.2	77.2	68.2	64.2	48.1	43.4	60.6
1950	48.7	44.0	47.0	55.2	70.9	75.9	76.1	73.7	69.5	64.9	42.5	34.4	58.6
1951	40.2	41.7	49.3	55.6	67.8	76.3	79.7	80.4	71.6	62.0	42.7	43.8	59.3
1952	44.3	45.3	48.4	57.7	69.5	84.7	83.1	80.7	70.2	52.9	48.4	42.2	60.6
1953	45.2	44.0	52.9	56.5	71.6	81.0	79.7	79.1	72.8	63.3	48.1	39.1	61.0
1954	40.1	47.3	48.4	65.3	62.9	78.1	84.1	82.3	76.8	61.4	48.2	40.0	61.2
1955	37.9	41.6	50.7	64.1	71.2	71.4	82.4	80.9	76.4	59.9	46.2	39.5	60.2
1956	35.9	46.9	49.5	57.7	70.2	76.1	81.3	79.8	71.4	64.0	47.7	50.3	60.9
1957	37.5	47.4	48.3	63.1	69.6	77.3	79.1	77.5	72.5	56.6	48.6	44.8	60.2
1958	35.4	31.0	44.0	58.4	68.2	75.0	80.1	77.7	71.8	59.6	51.7	36.2	57.4
1959	37.0	42.1	47.8	59.7	71.3	74.9	79.1	79.8	74.0	61.8	45.1	43.1	59.7
1960	40.0	35.6	36.3	61.0	65.7	75.0	78.3	79.5	73.6	61.6	47.9	34.7	57.4
1961	33.2	46.9	52.2	54.5	63.6	72.4	77.4	76.4	73.5	59.8	49.6	41.1	58.4
1962	35.3	46.2	45.3	56.0	75.2	75.0	79.1	79.7	69.3	62.9	47.9	35.0	58.9
1963	30.9	34.2	53.8	61.6	67.3	75.9	77.6	76.8	70.0	65.5	49.3	30.5	57.8
1964	38.9	37.2	49.0	62.6	69.7	77.7	78.7	77.2	71.3	56.7	51.7	42.7	59.4
#1965	40.0	39.8	41.9	60.9	71.7	75.1	78.6	79.0	74.1	59.3	51.9	44.8	59.7
1966	32.3	41.3	50.5	58.8	65.3	75.1	82.3	76.5	69.5	57.0	50.7	40.2	58.3
1967	42.3	37.5	57.0	63.9	66.3	76.3	75.7	72.6	66.8	59.3	44.3	42.6	58.7
1968	34.0	32.4	47.8	58.7	66.3	74.9	77.8	79.5	69.9	59.5	48.7	38.1	57.3
1969	37.2	39.8	42.6	60.9	68.9	77.2	82.7	78.1	70.8	60.6	46.5	37.3	58.6
1970	32.4	38.4	46.8	61.3	68.4	73.6	77.2	79.2	76.9	61.0	47.5	43.2	58.8
1971	35.6	38.7	44.6	57.9	63.3	77.5	76.8	76.4	74.4	66.7	49.9	49.2	59.3
1972	41.8	41.8	50.2	60.5	67.4	73.0	77.3	77.2	75.7	60.2	47.3	42.8	59.6
1973	38.0	39.7	56.8	56.4	64.2	76.1	78.7	78.1	76.2	66.2	54.7	40.5	60.5
1974	45.4	41.8	54.9	58.6	70.0	71.4	78.0	77.6	67.5	59.4	50.0	42.6	59.8
1975	43.4	44.6	47.3	58.5	70.4	76.0	78.5	79.1	67.9	62.4	52.1	42.8	60.2
RECORD MEAN	39.1	41.0	49.5	59.5	68.2	76.3	79.4	78.3	72.2	61.1	48.9	41.1	59.6
MAX	47.6	50.0	59.2	69.7	78.5	86.2	89.1	88.1	82.6	72.1	58.5	49.5	69.3
MIN	30.5	32.0	39.7	49.2	57.9	66.3	69.6	68.4	61.7	50.0	39.3	32.7	49.8

# Indicates a station move or relocation of instruments.

NASHVILLE, TN

Feb	Mar	Apr	May	June	Total
518	479	249	21	18	3753
487	511	175	45	0	3108
950	643	204	56	1	4152
634	526	191	35	0	3756
845	886	171	121	0	4223
501	393	336	98	4	3897
523	605	303	5	0	3766
855	358	170	63	0	4123
797	490	139	23	0	3855
698	711	168	3	0	3717
657	452	234	78	7	3663
763	300	106	69	1	3390
941	531	205	64	1	4274
700	692	149	38	3	3970
737	556	156	51	0	4121
733	624	227	101	0	3952
667	454	193	36	6	3053
702	261	275	83	0	3544
641	320	227	28	3	2981
567	547	241	6	0	3419

Aug	Sept	Oct	Nov	Dec	Total
416	191	74	0	0	1811
446	374	40	1	1	1732
360	293	101	16	1	1603
387	341	24	6	0	1573
412	351	128	8	0	1770
399	130	30	22	0	1440
444	164	62	19	0	1698

Precipitation

Year	Jan	Feb	Mar	Apr	May	June	July	Aug	Sept	Oct	Nov	Dec	Annual
1936	3.52	1.52	8.40	3.70	1.41	0.21	8.33	0.59	1.86	3.38	3.52	4.72	41.16
1937	14.75	1.90	1.57	3.73	5.33	2.65	2.49	2.17	2.05	4.31	2.06	3.12	46.13
1938	5.81	1.82	4.78	2.23	4.35	4.98	5.93	2.38	3.40	0.47	3.06	2.00	41.21
1939	6.80	8.87	4.83	3.96	1.98	4.85	3.11	1.87	0.95	1.13	1.48	2.68	42.51
1940	1.13	5.06	7.63	5.24	3.32	2.84	2.17	1.33	0.87	1.30	3.71	2.44	37.04
#1941	1.81	0.64	1.71	2.40	0.87	2.61	7.12	3.64	0.62	2.12	2.81	3.89	30.24
1942	2.81	3.50	3.82	3.96	2.39	1.87	2.77	8.31	1.82	3.05	2.27	6.06	42.63
1943	1.44	1.88	8.43	2.97	5.29	1.61	2.51	1.55	5.98	0.81	1.61	3.44	37.52
1944	2.74	7.14	5.81	3.85	4.33	1.33	0.87	6.26	4.40	0.68	2.40	7.10	46.91
1945	3.47	7.50	1.72	5.51	5.70	2.73	5.15	1.83	3.40	2.09	9.04	3.91	52.05
1946	8.97	4.28	5.48	3.45	3.73	1.30	4.86	2.22	4.13	1.80	5.11	4.04	49.37
1947	7.62	1.07	2.69	3.56	6.47	2.44	4.56	3.05	0.47	2.10	3.21	2.48	39.72
#1948	5.59	7.83	6.49	1.15	1.65	1.64	1.65	2.07	3.31	1.59	7.85	5.58	46.40
1949	7.12	2.94	5.46	5.27	5.65	7.16	4.25	2.87	0.76	4.38	0.54	5.68	52.08
1950	13.92	7.78	3.77	1.58	4.10	4.69	7.75	6.66	3.59	1.65	6.60	2.17	64.26
1951	10.54	2.94	5.16	4.75	0.83	7.40	3.79	0.95	2.92	4.35	4.16	10.60	58.39
1952	5.10	4.10	9.87	2.01	2.81	0.78	1.30	4.12	3.65	1.36	2.33	2.38	39.81
1953	7.09	3.31	5.52	4.53	5.57	1.90	6.62	1.20	1.00	0.42	0.70	3.45	41.31
1954	7.65	4.00	4.22	4.42	3.80	2.42	0.71	1.61	4.28	2.93	1.12	5.57	42.73
1955	1.25	6.76	9.87	4.62	2.92	2.94	1.76	4.02	4.26	2.04	3.78	1.21	45.43
1956	5.67	10.31	4.08	4.23	2.87	2.42	1.94	1.89	0.28	1.99	1.73	6.53	43.94
1957	9.39	5.24	2.85	2.79	8.23	7.06	1.83	2.55	4.09	3.89	6.31	5.84	60.07
1958	2.60	1.61	3.92	6.35	2.72	3.30	6.15	5.10	3.04	1.24	3.38	1.49	40.90
1959	3.26	4.60	3.71	2.49	5.20	2.41	3.90	2.54	3.73	6.13	4.96	5.04	47.97
1960	3.22	5.40	4.37	2.04	3.16	9.37	1.46	1.72	3.96	1.38	2.72	3.62	42.42
1961	1.44	5.33	6.52	4.50	4.36	2.96	5.34	2.62	0.35	1.12	3.87	6.44	44.85
1962	6.51	9.07	5.89	6.91	1.87	7.29	1.97	2.45	8.03	2.29	3.37	1.92	57.57
1963	1.60	2.83	10.03	3.37	2.47	3.09	5.33	7.63	3.43	T	2.43	2.15	44.36
1964	3.70	3.26	5.92	5.86	5.04	1.21	2.16	4.56	2.65	1.83	3.67	5.15	45.01
1965	2.98	4.71	6.13	5.72	3.12	2.74	3.32	2.53	5.02	0.57	1.82	1.01	39.67
1966	3.93	3.63	1.39	5.08	3.99	1.09	2.70	5.29	3.87	2.50	2.76	5.69	41.92
1967	1.62	1.78	4.44	3.40	6.98	4.23	7.46	2.06	1.93	1.57	3.87	5.88	45.22
1968	3.50	0.64	4.47	3.57	6.28	2.26	6.87	0.69	2.76	3.92	5.39	3.58	43.93
1969	4.96	4.48	2.12	6.03	4.81	3.34	5.33	2.27	2.06	2.01	1.83	8.03	47.27
1970	1.16	4.36	3.87	6.81	5.90	6.73	3.61	2.99	2.76	2.94	2.20	3.60	46.93
1971	2.66	4.70	2.95	3.34	2.93	3.47	5.00	5.87	2.11	1.27	1.18	5.17	40.65
1972	5.15	3.45	4.34	3.58	3.52	2.54	6.40	4.30	3.71	4.06	5.22	8.14	54.41
1973	3.40	3.63	9.88	7.00	5.72	4.80	7.67	1.79	1.56	3.32	7.78	3.23	59.78
1974	9.45	3.01	5.25	3.97	5.04	6.80	2.10	4.13	10.44	1.47	6.23	2.81	60.70
1975	4.67	5.22	12.35	3.55	6.52	2.22	2.96	4.69	5.42	5.86	3.00	4.12	60.58
RECORD MEAN	4.77	4.21	5.21	4.21	3.90	3.82	4.00	3.39	3.27	2.44	3.47	3.92	46.61

Record mean values above are means through the current year for the period beginning in 1871 for temperature and precipitation, 1942 for snowfall. Data are from City Office locations through June 1941 and from Airport locations thereafter.

(Continued)

The average annual snowfall, about 10.7 inches, at Nashville is seldom sufficient to interfere with outdoor occupations more than a few days in a season.

Humidity is an important phase of climate in relation to bodily health and comfort. The Nashville records show that the average relative humidity is moderate as compared with the general conditions east of the Mississippi River and south of the Ohio.

Nashville is not in the most frequented path of general storms that cross the country; however, it is in the zone of moderate frequency of thunderstorms. The thunderstorm season usually begins in the latter part of March and continues thorough Septmeber.

Normals, Means, and Extremes

Month	Normal Degree days Base 65 °F: Heating	Cooling	Precipitation in inches — Water equivalent: Normal	Maximum monthly	Year	Minimum monthly	Year	Maximum in 24 hrs.	Year	Snow, Ice pellets: Maximum monthly	Year	Maximum in 24 hrs.	Year	Relative humidity pct. Hour 00 (Local time)	Hour 06	Hour 12	Hour 18
(a)				36		36		36		36		36		10	10	10	10
J	828	0	4.75	13.92	1950	1.16	1970	4.40	1946	18.8	1948	7.5	1966	75	81	66	67
F	672	0	4.43	10.31	1956	0.64	1968	4.04	1948	15.0	1960	7.4	1960	74	80	60	61
M	524	19	5.00	12.35	1975	1.39	1966	4.66	1975	16.1	1960	8.8	1951	72	79	54	55
A	176	29	4.11	7.00	1973	1.15	1948	3.25	1962	1.1	1971	1.1	1971	73	81	53	54
M	45	153	4.10	8.23	1957	0.69	1941	3.57	1944	0.0		0.0		83	87	56	59
J	0	348	3.38	9.37	1960	0.78	1952	4.91	1960	0.0		0.0		84	88	55	59
J	0	453	3.83	7.75	1950	0.71	1954	3.56	1950	0.0		0.0		87	91	59	64
A	0	419	3.24	8.31	1942	0.69	1968	5.34	1963	0.0		0.0		88	92	61	66
S	10	220	3.09	10.44	1974	0.28	1956	5.09	1962	0.0		0.0		86	91	61	67
O	180	53	2.16	6.13	1959	T	1963	3.75	1975	T	1954	T	1954	82	87	55	62
N	498	0	3.46	9.04	1945	0.54	1949	3.74	1973	9.2	1950	9.2	1950	77	81	60	64
D	763	0	4.45	10.66	1951	1.01	1965	3.88	1951	13.2	1963	10.2	1963	77	81	66	68
YR	3696	1694	46.00	13.92	JAN 1950	T	OCT 1963	5.34	AUG 1963	18.8	JAN 1948	10.2	DEC 1963	80	85	59	62

(To better understand these tables, see full explanation of terms beginning on page 322)

Month	Wind: Mean speed m.p.h.	Prevailing direction	Fastest mile: Speed m.p.h.	Direction	Year	Pct. of possible sunshine	Mean sky cover, tenths, sunrise to sunset	Mean number of days — Sunrise to sunset: Clear	Partly cloudy	Cloudy	Precipitation .01 inch or more	Snow, Ice pellets 1.0 inch or more	Thunderstorms	Heavy fog, visibility ¼ mile or less	Temperatures °F Max. (b) 90° and above	32° and below	Min. 32° and below	0° and below	Average station pressure mb. Elev. 605 feet m.s.l.
(a)	34	22	36	36		33	35	34	34	34	34	34	34	34	10	10	10	10	3
J	9.2	S	56	SW	1949	40	7.2	6	6	19	11	1	2	3	0	5	21	1	998.2
F	9.4	S	52	NW	1962	47	6.7	7	6	15	11	1	2	1	0	2	17	*	996.5
M	10.0	S	70	NW	1953	52	6.6	7	8	16	12	1	5	1	0	0	10	0	993.1
A	9.6	S	61	W	1958	59	6.1	8	9	13	11	*	6	1	0	0	2	0	994.7
M	7.6	S	43	SW	1961	62	5.9	9	10	12	10	0	8	1	1	0	0	0	992.1
J	7.0	S	73	NW	1953	67	5.6	8	13	9	9	0	8	1	9	0	0	0	993.8
J	6.4	S	52	NW	1963	64	5.7	8	13	10	10	0	10	1	15	0	0	0	994.5
A	6.1	S	45	NW	1956	66	5.3	10	12	9	9	0	8	2	10	0	0	0	996.0
S	6.4	S	42	NW	1952	63	5.2	11	8	11	8	0	4	2	4	0	0	0	996.2
O	6.5	S	38	NW	1955	64	4.8	13	9	9	7	0	2	2	*	0	1	0	999.0
N	8.4	S	43	SE	1947	50	6.0	9	7	14	9	*	2	2	0	*	8	0	998.0
D	8.8	S	47	W	1946	40	6.8	7	7	17	11	1	1	2	0	1	16	0	997.3
YR	7.9	S	73	NW	JUN 1953	57	6.0	103	108	154	119	4	56	17	38	8	74	1	995.8

FOOTNOTES

Means and extremes above are from existing and comparable exposures. Annual extremes have been exceeded at other sites in the locality as follows: Highest temperature 107 in July 1952; lowest temperature -15 in January 1963 and earlier; maximum monthly precipitation 14.75 in January 1937; maximum precipitation in 24 hours 6.05 in November 1900; maximum monthly snowfall 21.5 in March 1892; maximum snowfall in 24 hours 17.0 in March 1892.

Station: AMARILLO, TEXAS
AMARILLO AIR TERMINAL
Elevation (ground): 3604 feet

TEMPERATURES °F

Month	Normal			Extremes			
	Daily maximum	Daily minimum	Monthly	Record highest	Year	Record lowest	Year
(a)				15		15	
J	49.4	22.5	36.0	79	1970	-9	1963
F	53.0	26.4	39.7	88	1963	0	1971
M	60.0	31.2	45.6	94	1971	7	1967
A	70.9	42.1	56.5	98	1965	18	1973
M	79.2	51.9	65.6	99	1974	30	1970
J	88.0	61.2	74.6	104	1970	43	1970
J	91.4	65.9	78.7	104	1970	54	1972
A	90.4	64.7	77.6	104	1964	52	1972
S	82.9	56.7	69.8	100	1970	36	1970
O	72.9	46.1	59.5	94	1973	25	1970
N	60.0	32.5	46.3	85	1975	12	1975
D	51.5	25.5	38.5	76	1965	-3	1961
YR	70.8	43.9	57.4	104	JUL 1970	-9	JAN 1963

IMPORTANT:
The time-period covered by this record is limited: See footnotes on next page for explanation and for additional history of EXTREME HIGHS AND LOWS recorded in the general area.

The station is located 7 statute miles ENE of the downtown post office in a region of rather flat topography. The Canadian River flows eastward 18 miles north of the station, with its bed about 800 feet below the plains. The Prairie Dog Town Fork of the Red River flows southeastward about 15 miles south of the station where it enters the Palo Duro Canyon, which is about 1,000 feet deep. There are numerous shallow lakes, often dry, over the area and the nearly treeless grasslands slope gradually downward to the east. The terrain gradually rises to the west and northwest. To the east, south, and west most of the land is under cultivation with considerable irrigation; while to the northwest, north, and northeast grazing land predominates. Soil of the area is chestnut loam interspersed with gray and red loams.

Departures from normal precipitation are wide, with yearly totals ranging from 9.56 inches in 1970 to 39.75 inches in 1923. A period of 5 consecutive years, 1952-56, with significantly below normal rainfall resulted in the most severe drought of record. Three-fourths of the total annual precipitation falls between April and September, occurring from thunderstorm activity. The average frequency of precipitation amounts include annually: 53 days with a trace, 11 days .50 or more, 4 days 1.00 inch or more, and 1 day 2.00 inches or more. An even snow cover is very unusual because of high winds, but winter snowfall averages near 14 inches ranging from 0.1 inch in 1949-50 up to 48.7 in 1918-19. Snow usually melts within a few days after it falls. Heavier snowfalls of 10 inches or more, usually with near blizzard conditions, have occurred 20 times in 80 years, mostly over a 2-3-day period. The heaviest, 20.6 inches, occurred March 25-26, 1934, in 23 hours, but much of it melted as it fell, and the greatest depth on the ground reached only 4.5 inches. The record greatest snow depth on ground was 16.5 inches February 26, 1903, when 17.5 inches fell in 49 hours. The most damaging blizzard occurred March 23-25, 1957, when 11.1 inches of snow fell, reached a depth of 10 inches, and northerly winds averaging 40 m.p.h. for 24 hours, with gusts over 50 m.p.h., produced severe drifting.

The Amarillo area is subject to rapid and large temperature changes, especially during the winter months, when cold fronts from the northern Rocky Mountain and Plains states sweep across the level plains at speeds up to 40 m.p.h. Temperature drops of from 50 to 60 degrees within a 12-hour period are not uncommon in association with these fronts, and 40-degree drops have occurred within a few minutes. Normally, the coldest period occurs in mid-January, however, the record minimum temperature, -16 degrees, occurred February 12, 1899. Long-term records of 0 degrees, or lower, average less than 2 days per year. Normally the warmest period occurs in July, but the record maximum temperature of 108 degrees occurred June 24, 1953. Temperatures 100 degrees, or higher, average 6 days per year, slightly

(Continued page 646)

Normals, Means, and Extremes

(To better understand these tables, see full explanation of terms beginning on page 322)

Month	Normal Degree days Base 65 °F: Heating	Normal Degree days Base 65 °F: Cooling	Precipitation in inches, Water equivalent: Normal	Maximum monthly	Year	Minimum monthly	Year	Maximum in 24 hrs.	Year	Snow, Ice pellets: Maximum monthly	Year	Maximum in 24 hrs.	Year	Relative humidity pct.: Hour 00 (Local time)	Hour 06	Hour 12	Hour 18	Wind: Mean speed m.p.h.	Prevailing direction	Fastest mile Ø: Speed m.p.h.	Direction	Year	Pct. of possible sunshine	Mean sky cover, tenths, sunrise to sunset	Mean number of days, Sunrise to sunset: Clear	Partly cloudy	Cloudy	Precipitation .01 inch or more	Snow, Ice pellets 1.0 inch or more	Thunderstorms	Heavy fog, visibility ¼ mile or less	Temperatures °F Max. (b): 90° and above	Max.: 32° and below	Min.: 32° and below	Min.: 0° and below	Average station pressure mb. Elev. 3604 feet m.s.l.
(a)				35		35		35		35		35		14	14	14	14	34	15	34	34		34	34	34	34	34	34	34	34	34	14	14	14	14	3
J	899	0	0.54	2.33	1968	T	1967	1.74	1968	12.9	1960	6.7	1960	63	70	49	44	13.1	SW	62	NE	1953	69	5.1	13	7	11	4	1	*	3	0	4	27	2	890.4
F	708	0	0.56	1.83	1948	T	1943	1.28	1971	17.3	1971	13.5	1971	63	71	48	40	14.2	SW	70	NW	1956	68	5.1	11	7	10	4	1	1	4	0	2	22	*	890.6
M	601	0	0.77	3.99	1973	T	1950	2.27	1973	14.7	1961	9.8	1957	56	67	42	33	15.6	SW	72	W	1950	71	5.2	12	8	11	4	1	1	3	*	1	15	0	886.0
A	275	20	1.23	3.74	1942	T	1964	1.57	1942	6.4	1947	5.1	1947	53	65	36	29	15.5	SW	74	SW	1942	73	4.9	12	8	10	5	*	3	2	1	*	3	0	887.7
M	81	99	2.83	9.81	1951	0.19	1966	6.75	1951	T	1953	T	1953	57	70	38	33	14.8	S	84	SW	1949	73	5.0	11	11	9	8	0	8	2	6	0	*	0	887.9
J	10	298	3.45	10.73	1965	0.01	1953	6.15	1960	0.0		0.0		63	76	44	38	14.4	S	75	NW	1974	77	4.3	13	12	5	8	0	9	1	12	0	0	0	889.5
J	0	425	2.95	7.59	1960	0.12	1946	4.09	1943	0.0		0.0		61	73	43	38	12.4	S	66	SW	1948	77	4.6	13	12	6	9	0	10	1	21	0	0	0	892.7
A	0	391	2.93	7.55	1974	0.39	1947	4.26	1945	0.0		0.0		65	76	45	42	12.0	S	65	E	1946	78	4.2	15	10	6	8	0	9	1	16	0	0	0	892.7
S	20	164	1.93	5.02	1950	0.24	1947	3.42	1941	T	1945	T	1945	71	80	50	46	13.0	S	68	NE	1942	74	3.9	16	7	7	6	0	4	2	6	0	0	0	893.1
O	206	36	1.83	7.64	1941	0.00	1952	3.45	1948	3.9	1970	2.9	1970	62	71	42	40	13.0	SW	68	S	1949	75	3.8	17	7	7	5	*	2	2	2	*	1	0	892.9
N	561	0	0.53	2.26	1961	T	1960	1.29	1971	13.6	1952	12.2	1952	65	72	47	48	13.2	SW	59	NW	1970	73	4.3	15	7	8	3	*	1	2	0	1	13	0	891.0
D	822	0	0.73	4.52	1959	T	1970	3.11	1943	8.5	1943	7.4	1971	64	69	48	49	13.0	SW	62	NE	1953	67	4.8	13	8	10	4	1	*	3	0	3	26	*	890.6
YR	4183	1433	20.28	10.73	JUN 1965	0.00	OCT 1952	6.75	MAY 1951	17.3	FEB 1971	13.5	FEB 1971	62	72	44	40	13.7	SW	84	SW	MAY 1949	73	4.6	161	104	100	68	4	48	25	64	12	106	2	890.4

FOOTNOTES

Means and extremes above are from existing and comparable exposures. Annual extremes have been exceeded at other sites in the locality as follows: Highest temperature 108 in June 1953; lowest temperature -16 in February 1899; maximum monthly snowfall 28.7 in February 1903; maximum snowfall in 24 hours 20.6 in March 1934.

Ø Through 1974

Snowfall

Season	July	Aug	Sept	Oct	Nov	Dec	Jan
1936-37	0.0	0.0	0.0	2.3	0.0	0.5	3.1
1937-38	0.0	0.0	0.0	0.0	1.1	2.3	0.7
1938-39	0.0	0.0	0.0	0.0	T	1.0	6.9
1939-40	0.0	0.0	0.0	0.0	0.0	10.4	4.3
#1940-41	0.0	0.0	0.0	0.0	T	0.8	0.9
1941-42	0.0	0.0	0.0	0.7	3.1	1.8	4.0
1942-43	0.0	0.0	0.0	0.0	0.0	6.0	1.2
1943-44	0.0	0.0	0.0	0.0	2.0	8.5	6.1
1944-45	0.0	0.0	0.0	0.0	1.0	2.4	3.1
1945-46	0.0	0.0	T	T	0.0	T	6.9
1946-47	0.0	0.0	0.0	0.0	1.5	0.9	4.7
1947-48	0.0	0.0	0.0	0.0	T	4.1	7.3
1948-49	0.0	0.0	0.0	0.0	0.7	0.2	8.6
1949-50	0.0	0.0	0.0	T	0.0	0.1	T
1950-51	0.0	0.0	0.0	0.0	T	0.5	4.3
1951-52	0.0	0.0	0.0	0.0	0.9	4.5	4.0
1952-53	0.0	0.0	0.0	0.0	13.6	4.7	6.4
1953-54	0.0	0.0	0.0	0.0	0.0	1.5	3.1
1954-55	0.0	0.0	0.0	0.0	0.0	1.6	0.2
1955-56	0.0	0.0	0.0	0.0	0.2	1.8	0.7
1956-57	0.0	0.0	0.0	0.0	T	T	1.6
1957-58	0.0	0.0	0.0	T	2.9	0.0	5.2
1958-59	0.0	0.0	0.0	0.0	2.1	2.7	1.7
1959-60	0.0	0.0	0.0	0.0	0.9	T	12.9
1960-61	0.0	0.0	0.0	0.0	T	3.6	1.8
1961-62	0.0	0.0	0.0	0.0	4.9	0.5	2.3
1962-63	0.0	0.0	0.0	0.0	7.6	0.8	0.5
1963-64	0.0	0.0	0.0	0.0	0.0	3.6	T
1964-65	0.0	0.0	0.0	0.0	T	0.5	5.6
1965-66	0.0	0.0	0.0	0.0	0.0	1.4	7.2
1966-67	0.0	0.0	0.0	T	T	1.8	T
1967-68	0.0	0.0	0.0	T	2.1	6.1	0.6
1968-69	0.0	0.0	0.0	0.0	0.3	1.8	0.2
1969-70	0.0	0.0	0.0	0.0	T	7.1	0.1
1970-71	0.0	0.0	0.0	3.9	2.6	T	0.8
1971-72	0.0	0.0	0.0	0.0	T	7.9	1.6
1972-73	0.0	0.0	0.0	0.4	9.9	2.8	7.0
1973-74	0.0	0.0	0.0	0.0	0.4	1.5	3.6
1974-75	0.0	0.0	0.0	0.0	T	1.5	3.8
1975-76	0.0	0.0	0.0	0.0	0.4	1.8	
RECORD MEAN	0.0	0.0	T	0.1	1.6	2.4	3.4

Heating Degree Days

Season	July	Aug	Sept	Oct	Nov	Dec	Jan
1955-56	0	0	32	180	641	731	844
1956-57	0	9	7	127	634	702	871
1957-58	0	0	45	303	721	683	867
1958-59	0	0	37	233	546	852	1008
1959-60	0	0	46	311	671	758	1033
#1960-61	3	0	27	210	530	929	935
1961-62	0	0	63	189	702	879	1026
1962-63	0	0	23	159	508	741	1114
1963-64	0	0	11	42	458	1000	855
1964-65	0	0	48	149	517	795	740
1965-66	0	0	73	191	376	676	1145
1966-67	0	23	22	250	395	908	743
1967-68	0	1	23	185	544	911	820
1968-69	0	0	6	159	583	865	726
1969-70	0	0	1	374	543	817	981
1970-71	0	0	47	359	544	661	837
1971-72	1	0	120	245	575	843	900
1972-73	13	2	48	274	833	987	972
1973-74	0	0	56	154	420	813	922
1974-75	0	0	119	199	571	890	853
1975-76	0	0	104	158	569	757	

Cooling Degree Days

Year	Jan	Feb	Mar	Apr	May	June	July
1969	0	0	0	30	147	264	550
1970	0	0	0	14	176	327	495
1971	0	0	13	18	94	334	381
1972	0	0	4	44	59	265	313
1973	0	0	0	3	53	310	414
1974	0	0	6	52	228	306	449
1975	0	0	0	24	61	273	330

Feb	Mar	Apr	May	June	Total
1.1	4.2	1.1	0.0	0.0	12.3
15.7	0.1	5.1	0.0	0.0	25.0
2.4	1.2	3.3	0.0	0.0	14.8
6.8	0.2	6.9	0.0	0.0	28.6
6.2	4.5	0.0	0.0	0.0	12.4
2.5	7.5	T	0.0	0.0	19.6
0.0	0.2	0.0	0.0	0.0	7.4
1.3	T	0.0	0.0	0.0	17.9
1.3	0.5	1.7	0.0	0.0	10.0
0.8	T	0.0	0.0	0.0	7.7
1.0	5.4	6.4	0.0	0.0	19.9
8.6	4.1	0.0	0.0	0.0	24.1
0.3	T	2.4	0.0	0.0	12.2
T	T	T	0.0	0.0	0.1
1.3	0.3	T	0.0	0.0	6.4
0.4	0.2	T	0.0	0.0	10.0
1.2	T	0.0	T	0.0	25.9
0.2	1.5	0.0	0.0	0.0	6.3
0.2	0.1	0.2	0.0	0.0	2.3
14.7	0.3	T	0.0	0.0	17.7
1.6	11.1	T	0.0	0.0	14.3
5.2	8.6	T	0.0	0.0	21.9
0.9	1.4	T	0.0	0.0	8.8
5.9	0.5	0.0	0.0	0.0	20.2
3.1	14.7	0.3	0.0	0.0	23.5
0.1	T	0.0	0.0	0.0	7.8
4.8	T	0.0	0.0	0.0	13.7
17.3	T	T	0.0	0.0	20.9
3.8	2.3	0.0	0.0	0.0	12.2
0.4	0.1	0.0	0.0	0.0	9.1
1.1	0.4	0.0	0.0	0.0	3.3
8.0	2.9	0.0	0.0	0.0	19.7
2.9	10.3	0.0	0.0	0.0	15.5
T	14.1	1.8	0.0	0.0	23.1
17.3	1.0	T	0.0	0.0	25.6
2.0	0.6	0.0	0.0	0.0	12.1
4.2	0.5	5.7	0.0	0.0	30.5
1.2	T	0.0	0.0	0.0	6.7
11.7	1.2	T	0.0	0.0	18.2
3.7	2.6	0.5	T	0.0	14.3

Average Temperature

Year	Jan	Feb	Mar	Apr	May	June	July	Aug	Sept	Oct	Nov	Dec	Annual
1936	35.6	33.5	52.2	58.0	67.0	77.5	80.6	81.9	69.2	56.5	46.5	42.9	58.4
1937	30.8	40.4	44.2	57.5	67.4	74.4	81.0	82.1	73.1	61.8	47.6	40.0	58.4
1938	40.8	42.9	52.8	56.6	65.9	75.0	79.2	81.6	73.6	64.8	45.6	41.9	60.1
1939	41.9	35.4	51.4	58.2	67.6	76.6	80.6	77.7	75.8	63.0	48.3	44.0	60.0
1940	29.3	41.2	50.7	57.0	66.8	73.4	82.0	76.8	72.2	64.8	44.1	42.5	58.4
#1941	39.4	40.8	43.2	55.3	64.1	70.4	75.3	75.8	69.2	58.2	47.6	39.6	56.6
1942	34.8	36.9	44.0	56.2	63.5	74.4	78.6	75.4	66.5	56.8	49.2	38.0	56.2
1943	37.4	44.0	43.8	60.8	62.2	76.2	78.2	81.8	69.0	57.6	44.4	32.3	57.3
1944	35.2	39.6	44.2	52.7	65.2	75.5	77.1	79.0	69.0	58.8	47.2	35.0	56.3
1945	37.8	40.6	50.6	51.2	66.0	72.6	77.2	77.4	69.8	58.6	49.0	36.4	57.3
1946	34.7	42.6	50.9	63.0	62.4	74.8	80.5	78.0	68.5	59.2	45.0	43.2	58.6
1947	35.6	35.2	42.2	52.8	62.8	73.2	78.2	79.0	74.0	64.4	40.8	38.1	56.4
1948	31.0	34.0	40.2	61.4	65.8	75.0	78.9	76.2	70.6	58.5	42.4	40.6	56.2
1949	26.7	39.2	46.7	53.8	64.8	73.6	78.2	75.0	68.2	57.8	52.8	38.4	56.3
1950	39.4	45.9	46.9	56.0	65.9	75.8	74.3	73.7	67.0	64.7	46.0	39.8	57.9
1951	34.8	41.0	44.8	53.7	64.9	72.2	81.1	79.7	70.0	59.0	42.9	38.4	56.9
1952	41.5	42.6	45.0	54.4	65.0	80.2	78.4	81.7	69.9	57.9	42.5	37.0	58.0
1953	44.7	40.3	52.9	54.6	65.4	83.3	80.2	77.1	72.8	60.5	47.9	36.4	59.7
1954	39.8	48.6	45.6	61.4	61.1	76.6	83.1	79.9	75.3	61.1	50.5	42.3	60.5
1955	37.7	37.6	47.7	59.4	65.7	71.7	77.4	76.7	70.4	59.8	43.4	41.2	57.4
1956	37.5	35.3	47.5	53.8	70.1	78.0	77.6	77.2	73.0	62.7	43.7	42.1	58.2
1957	36.6	46.4	45.0	52.4	60.7	72.3	81.2	77.1	66.4	56.0	40.7	42.7	56.4
1958	36.8	37.7	37.0	51.1	66.7	76.0	78.0	78.2	70.5	58.1	46.7	37.3	56.2
1959	32.3	39.2	45.9	55.0	66.0	74.6	75.5	78.4	70.2	54.8	42.4	40.3	56.2
1960	31.4	31.4	42.3	58.3	65.1	74.3	75.5	76.2	69.5	58.6	47.1	34.9	55.4
#1961	34.6	39.3	48.5	56.2	67.3	73.9	76.4	77.2	67.6	59.5	41.3	36.5	56.5
1962	31.7	45.5	46.7	57.2	71.7	72.4	78.0	78.3	70.4	61.5	47.8	40.9	58.5
1963	28.9	41.7	50.4	61.8	69.0	74.1	81.3	77.8	72.3	66.2	49.5	32.5	58.8
1964	37.2	32.1	44.8	57.9	68.9	76.5	81.9	78.1	69.6	60.6	47.5	39.1	57.9
1965	41.0	37.6	38.4	59.4	66.9	72.1	78.6	76.9	68.5	59.5	52.5	42.9	57.8
1966	27.8	34.1	50.0	54.5	66.0	74.2	82.9	73.5	68.5	57.7	51.6	35.5	56.3
1967	40.7	40.6	53.4	60.6	63.4	73.7	77.2	75.0	68.3	60.9	46.6	35.4	58.0
1968	38.3	38.0	48.7	55.3	63.4	74.9	77.0	77.0	69.1	62.1	45.4	36.9	57.2
1969	41.4	40.4	38.8	59.9	67.2	72.8	82.6	80.2	71.1	54.5	46.7	38.4	57.8
1970	33.2	43.2	41.7	56.0	68.8	74.5	80.7	79.1	70.9	54.0	46.6	43.4	57.7
1971	37.8	38.8	48.3	55.7	64.9	75.9	76.9	72.2	67.1	57.2	45.6	37.6	56.5
1972	35.7	40.9	51.7	59.5	63.2	73.6	74.5	73.9	69.2	57.9	36.9	32.9	55.8
1973	33.4	39.5	47.1	50.3	62.9	75.1	78.1	78.8	68.7	62.0	50.8	38.6	57.1
1974	35.0	42.2	53.1	60.2	71.5	75.0	79.3	73.6	62.9	59.0	45.7	36.1	57.8
1975	37.1	35.3	45.0	54.9	64.5	73.3	75.5	76.7	65.8	61.1	45.8	40.4	56.3
RECORD MEAN	36.6	39.2	47.0	56.3	64.9	74.1	77.9	76.8	69.7	59.0	46.5	38.0	57.2
MAX	49.3	52.3	60.8	70.1	77.9	86.9	90.1	89.0	82.2	71.9	59.4	50.2	70.0
MIN	23.8	26.1	33.1	42.4	51.9	61.2	65.7	64.6	57.2	46.1	33.5	25.8	44.3

# Indicates a station move or relocation of instruments.

AMARILLO, TX

Feb	Mar	Apr	May	June	Total
851	540	339	24	0	4182
515	616	381	140	26	4028
758	861	412	66	5	4721
716	584	321	74	3	4374
965	696	214	80	0	4774
714	507	303	54	7	4219
540	563	254	23	15	4254
648	450	139	61	7	3850
949	618	235	53	7	4228
762	820	194	56	7	4088
857	456	312	99	1	4186
675	356	159	135	9	3675
777	504	290	109	0	4164
681	808	176	69	24	4097
602	713	280	50	33	4394
726	524	290	89	0	4077
692	409	203	106	0	4094
706	548	438	113	0	4934
633	368	190	17	0	3573
826	612	323	67	16	4476

Aug	Sept	Oct	Nov	Dec	Total
478	190	54	0	0	1713
446	231	24	0	0	1713
232	189	10	0	0	1271
285	182	60	0	0	1212
435	173	67	1	0	1456
274	61	20	0	0	1396
367	134	46	0	0	1235

Precipitation

Year	Jan	Feb	Mar	Apr	May	June	July	Aug	Sept	Oct	Nov	Dec	Annual
1936	1.02	0.25	T	0.25	9.02	0.84	0.51	1.39	4.74	0.82	T	0.88	19.72
1937	0.29	0.18	1.10	0.39	6.83	2.83	1.49	0.64	2.61	0.31	0.14	0.29	17.10
1938	0.18	2.87	1.24	1.07	4.03	2.49	1.88	0.15	1.62	3.06	0.43	0.08	19.10
1939	2.51	0.17	0.25	2.30	1.75	7.59	0.57	3.28	0.45	1.10	0.06	0.98	21.01
1940	0.52	0.88	0.24	1.10	2.68	1.64	0.88	0.71	0.54	0.29	3.87	0.27	13.62
#1941	0.40	0.94	2.55	1.29	7.47	5.07	3.36	3.18	4.30	7.64	0.33	0.68	37.21
1942	0.06	0.63	0.42	3.74	0.91	2.29	0.80	3.95	1.45	6.18	T	1.19	21.62
1943	0.08	T	0.01	1.06	1.82	1.01	6.64	2.09	0.79	0.72	0.39	3.77	18.38
1944	1.67	0.72	T	1.83	3.72	4.33	5.06	1.40	2.08	0.84	0.75	1.20	23.60
1945	0.77	0.28	0.41	1.58	0.42	1.61	1.62	5.17	4.02	1.31	T	T	17.19
1946	1.05	0.33	0.66	0.55	0.82	2.37	0.12	3.96	3.25	5.73	0.78	1.18	20.80
1947	0.32	0.07	0.77	2.07	4.59	3.19	1.54	0.39	0.24	0.12	0.92	1.26	15.48
1948	0.63	1.83	0.72	0.73	2.82	4.92	1.52	5.16	1.27	2.58	2.11	0.09	24.38
1949	2.04	0.59	0.57	1.99	6.43	2.82	3.90	3.78	1.69	1.03	0.01	0.30	25.15
1950	T	0.20	T	0.64	1.83	3.25	7.32	4.54	5.02	T	0.03	0.35	23.18
1951	0.38	1.17	0.55	0.43	9.81	4.34	2.01	1.52	2.01	2.37	0.25	0.45	25.29
1952	0.53	0.24	0.56	2.46	2.05	1.75	1.36	0.88	0.38	0.00	1.44	0.50	12.15
1953	0.64	0.53	0.38	0.62	0.70	0.01	1.81	2.00	0.26	4.56	0.56	0.98	13.05
1954	0.25	0.09	0.17	2.31	4.44	1.95	0.55	2.91	0.30	0.73	T	0.19	13.89
1955	0.53	0.06	0.33	0.38	2.70	1.49	3.35	1.49	3.13	0.13	0.02	0.10	13.71
1956	0.09	1.10	0.03	0.23	1.99	2.03	2.82	0.79	0.48	0.38	T	T	9.94
1957	0.33	1.11	2.82	2.69	4.36	0.53	0.13	4.85	0.88	2.57	0.94	0.03	21.24
1958	1.05	0.58	2.36	1.74	2.45	4.22	6.16	2.08	1.60	0.15	0.60	0.30	23.29
1959	0.16	0.06	0.26	1.18	4.82	2.19	2.85	2.24	2.29	2.10	0.14	4.52	22.81
1960	1.30	0.95	1.66	1.66	0.82	9.85	7.59	3.15	4.22	4.82	T	0.65	36.67
1961	0.12	0.27	2.55	0.24	3.40	3.42	4.10	3.14	1.87	0.91	2.26	0.16	22.44
1962	0.47	0.39	0.02	1.48	1.76	10.16	7.51	3.29	2.66	0.85	0.53	0.64	29.76
1963	0.06	0.67	0.28	0.47	3.66	3.60	2.04	3.93	0.43	1.54	0.33	0.29	17.30
1964	T	1.37	0.03	T	1.69	1.90	0.94	5.69	3.95	0.08	1.53	0.79	17.97
1965	0.55	0.47	0.72	0.23	1.88	10.73	1.54	1.71	0.79	1.02	0.07	0.38	20.09
1966	0.43	0.69	0.01	0.87	0.19	4.62	1.37	3.77	2.40	0.29	0.08	0.19	14.91
1967	T	0.15	0.42	1.95	1.40	2.55	3.70	1.81	2.47	1.61	0.28	0.51	16.85
1968	2.33	0.73	0.45	0.93	2.84	1.68	2.96	3.35	0.62	0.90	0.92	0.26	17.97
1969	0.02	0.50	1.15	0.30	2.93	4.09	2.55	4.51	2.77	2.56	0.34	0.83	22.55
1970	0.02	0.02	2.10	1.33	0.23	1.54	1.39	1.27	0.34	1.06	0.26	T	9.56
1971	0.10	1.65	0.10	0.77	0.91	4.17	1.75	3.33	4.70	2.59	2.08	0.89	23.04
1972	0.21	0.11	0.11	0.03	2.81	3.87	2.59	1.73	0.71	1.66	1.19	0.32	15.34
1973	0.56	0.42	3.99	1.88	1.43	0.84	4.08	2.31	1.22	1.05	0.10	0.17	18.05
1974	0.33	0.24	0.60	0.04	4.06	3.33	1.31	7.55	1.65	3.44	0.12	0.42	23.09
1975	0.28	1.33	0.51	1.02	2.47	4.15	5.19	3.97	0.76	0.33	0.92	0.15	21.08
RECORD MEAN	0.53	0.69	0.84	1.41	2.89	3.06	2.72	3.02	2.11	1.66	0.85	0.71	20.49

Record mean values above are means through the current year for the period beginning in 1892 for temperature and precipitation, 1942 for snowfall. Data are from City Office locations through March 1941.

(Continued)

more frequent in July than June or August.

The nearness to the paths of moving pressure systems tend to cause strong winds, with March and April having the strongest winds. Light winter precipitation makes the spring season favorable for wind erosion and resultant duststorms that occasionally reduce visibility to less than 1 mile. Duststorms have been infrequent in recent years. The fastest winds recorded have been in connection with thunderstorms, 84 m.p.h. was recorded May 15, 1949, when a tornado moving northeastward passed about a mile west of the station. The wind is below 15 m.p.h. 63 percent of the time.

Humidity averages rather low, frequently dropping below 20 percent and occasionally below 4 percent in the spring. Low humidity moderates the effect of high summer afternoon temperatures, permits evaporative cooling systems to be very effective, and makes for pleasant evenings and nights.

Abundant sunshine and adequate growing season permit a broad variety of agriculture and gardening. The average freeze-free period (above 32 degrees) is 198 days, but has ranged from 164 days, 1909 and 1917, to 243 days in 1963. The latest spring freeze has ranged from March 14, 1963, to May 7, 1915, and 1917, with April 16 as the average (median) date. The earliest autumn freeze has ranged from September 25, 1926, to November 21, 1934, with October 31 the average (median) date.

Severe local storms are infrequent, though a few thunderstorms, with damaging hail, lightning, and wind in a very localized area, occur most years, usually in spring and summer. These storms are often accompanied by very heavy rain, which produces local flooding, particularly of roads and streets. Tornadoes are rare, one of record moving through the city of Amarillo late Sunday afternoon, May 15, 1949, causing 6 deaths and 87 injuries, with damage estimated at $4,800,000.

Station: DALLAS-FORT WORTH, TEXAS REGIONAL AIRPORT
Elevation (ground): 551 feet

TEMPERATURES °F

Month	Normal			Extremes			
	Daily maximum	Daily minimum	Monthly	Record highest	Year	Record lowest	Year
(a)				12		12	
J	55.7	33.9	44.8	88	1969	4	1964
F	59.8	37.6	48.7	87	1969	12	1971
M	66.6	43.3	55.0	96	1974	19	1965
A	76.3	54.1	65.2	95	1972	30	1973
M	82.8	62.1	72.5	96	1967	42	1971
J	90.8	70.3	80.6	105	1972	51	1964
J	95.5	74.0	84.8	106	1974	59	1972
A	96.1	73.7	84.9	108	1964	56	1967
S	88.5	66.8	77.7	102	1963	46	1971
O	79.2	56.0	67.6	96	1963	37	1966
N	67.5	44.1	55.8	88	1965	22	1975
D	58.7	37.0	47.9	84	1966	10	1963
YR	76.5	54.4	65.5	108	AUG 1964	4	JAN 1964

IMPORTANT:
The time-period covered by this record is limited: See footnotes on next page for explanation and for additional history of EXTREME HIGHS AND LOWS recorded in the general area.

The Dallas-Fort Worth Metroplex is located in North Central Texas, approximately 250 miles north of the Gulf of Mexico. It is near the headwaters of the Trinity River, which lie in the upper margins of the Coastal Plain. The rolling hills in the area range from 500-800 feet in elevation.

The Dallas-Fort Worth climate is humid, subtropical with hot summers. It is also continental, characterized by a wide range in annual temperature extremes. Precipitation averages near 32 inches annually, but varies considerably from year to year ranging from less than 20 to more than 50 inches.

Winters are mild, but "northers" occur about three times each month, and often are accompanied by sudden drops in temperature. Periods of extreme cold that occasionally occur are short-lived, so that even in January, mild weather occurs frequently. In an average year, temperature minima of 20 degrees or below occur on only six days.

The highest temperatures of summer are associated with fair skies, westerly winds and low humidities. Characteristically, hot spells in summer are broken into three-to-five day periods by thunderstorm activity. There are only a few nights each summer when the minimum temperature exceeds 80 degrees, but a year when the temperature does not exceed 100 degrees is rare. Refrigerated-type air conditioners are recommended for maximum comfort indoors, and travelling via automobile.

Throughout the year, rainfall occurs more frequently during the night. Usually, periods of rainy weather last for only a day or two, and are followed by several days with fair skies. A large part of the annual precipitation results from thunderstorm activity, with occasional heavy rainfall over brief periods of time. Greatest amounts of rain occur during the months of April and May. July and August are relatively dry months. Thunderstorms occur throughout the year, but are most frequent in the Spring. Hail falls on about two or three days a year, ordinarily with only slight and scattered damage. Windstorms occuring during thunderstorm activity are sometimes destructive. Snowfall is rare with a measurable fall occurring only once in an average year.

The average length of the warm season (freeze-free period) in the Dallas-Fort Worth Metroplex is 249 days. Since 1940, the longest was 292 days in 1973; the shortest was 196 days in 1957. The average date of the last occurrence of 32 degrees or below is March 16. During the period 1940-1970, the earliest occurrence was February 14, 1946; the latest was April 13, 1957. The average date of the first occurrence of 32 degrees or below in the Fall is November 21. The earliest occurrence during the period 1940-1970, was October 27, 1957; the latest was January 4, 1972.

Normals, Means, and Extremes

(To better understand these tables, see full explanation of terms beginning on page 322)

Month	Normal Degree days Base 65 °F: Heating	Normal Degree days: Cooling	Precipitation in inches, Water equivalent: Normal	Maximum monthly	Year	Minimum monthly	Year	Maximum in 24 hrs.	Year	Snow, Ice pellets: Maximum monthly	Year	Maximum in 24 hrs.	Year
(a)				22		22		22		22		22	
J	626	0	1.80	3.60	1968	0.19	1971	2.39	1975	12.1	1964	12.1	1964
F	456	0	2.36	6.20	1965	0.15	1963	4.06	1965	3.7	1975	3.7	1975
M	335	25	2.54	6.39	1968	0.10	1972	2.99	1958	2.5	1962	2.5	1962
A	88	94	4.30	12.19	1957	0.92	1959	4.55	1957	0.0		0.0	
M	0	236	4.47	12.64	1957	1.06	1961	4.86	1965	0.0		0.0	
J	0	468	3.05	6.94	1962	0.40	1964	3.11	1966	0.0		0.0	
J	0	614	1.84	11.13	1973	0.09	1965	3.76	1975	0.0		0.0	
A	0	617	2.26	6.85	1970	0.01	1973	3.30	1970	0.0		0.0	
S	0	381	3.15	9.52	1964	0.23	1956	4.76	1965	0.0		0.0	
O	60	141	2.68	9.22	1959	T	1975	5.91	1959	0.0		0.0	
N	287	11	2.03	6.23	1964	0.20	1970	2.83	1964	T	1974	T	1974
D	530	0	1.82	6.99	1971	0.21	1955	3.10	1971	2.6	1963	2.5	1963
YR	2382	2587	32.30	12.64	MAY 1957	T	OCT 1975	5.91	OCT 1959	12.1	JAN 1964	12.1	JAN 1964

Month	Relative humidity pct. Hour 00 (Local time)	Hour 06	Hour 12	Hour 18	Wind: Mean speed m.p.h.	Prevailing direction	Fastest mile: Speed m.p.h.	Direction	Year	Pct. of possible sunshine	Mean sky cover, tenths, sunrise to sunset	Mean number of days, Sunrise to sunset: Clear	Partly cloudy	Cloudy	Precipitation .01 inch or more	Snow, Ice pellets 1.0 inch or more	Thunderstorms	Heavy fog, visibility ¼ mile or less	Temperatures °F Max. (b) 90° and above	Max. 32° and below	Min. 32° and below	Min. 0° and below	Average station pressure mb. Elev 596 feet m.s.l.
(a)	12	12	12	12	22	10	22	22			22	22	22	22	22	22	22	22	12	12	12	12	3
J	75	82	61	59	11.5	S	46	36	1957		6.1	10	6	15	7	1	1	3	0	1	14	0	998.4
F	71	80	57	52	12.3	S	51	36	1962		5.6	10	6	12	7	*	2	2	0	*	10	0	997.9
M	72	80	57	51	13.3	S	55	29	1954		5.8	10	7	14	7	*	4	1	*	0	4	0	992.2
A	75	85	59	54	13.1	S	55	32	1970		6.1	9	7	14	8	0	7	1	1	0	*	0	993.9
M	80	88	62	59	11.4	S	55	14	1955		5.8	8	11	12	8	0	7	*	3	0	0	0	991.5
J	74	86	57	52	11.0	S	52	32	1955		4.8	11	11	8	6	0	6	*	19	0	0	0	992.8
J	68	81	50	45	9.7	S	65	36	1961		4.3	15	9	7	5	0	5	0	27	0	0	0	994.6
A	70	83	53	48	9.3	S	73	36	1959		4.3	15	10	6	5	0	5	*	25	0	0	0	994.8
S	79	88	60	58	9.7	S	53	11	1961		4.8	13	8	9	7	0	4	*	11	0	0	0	995.3
O	76	85	56	57	9.9	S	44	27	1957		4.5	14	7	10	5	0	3	1	2	0	0	0	997.6
N	75	82	56	58	10.9	S	50	34	1957		5.0	13	5	12	6	0	2	1	0	0	3	0	997.4
D	76	81	60	60	11.2	S	53	32	1968		5.6	12	6	13	7	*	1	3	0	*	9	0	997.8
YR	74	83	57	55	11.1	S	73	36	AUG 1959		5.2	140	93	132	79	1	45	11	88	2	39	0	995.4

FOOTNOTES Means and extremes above are from existing and comparable exposures. Annual extremes have been exceeded at other sites in the locality as follows: Highest temperature 112 in August 1936; lowest temperature -8 in February 1899; maximum monthly precipitation 17.64 in April 1922; minimum monthly precipitation 0.00 in November 1903; maximum precipitation in 24 hours 9.57 in September 1932.

Snowfall

Season	July	Aug	Sept	Oct	Nov	Dec	Jan
1936-37	0.0	0.0	0.0	0.0	0.0	0.0	4.2
1937-38	0.0	0.0	0.0	0.0	5.0	0.0	0.0
1938-39	0.0	0.0	0.0	0.0	0.0	0.0	0.0
#1939-40	0.0	0.0	0.0	0.0	0.0	0.0	4.0
1940-41	0.0	0.0	0.0	0.0	T	0.0	0.0
1941-42	0.0	0.0	0.0	0.0	0.0	0.0	1.3
1942-43	0.0	0.0	0.0	0.0	0.0	T	T
1943-44	0.0	0.0	0.0	0.0	0.0	T	T
1944-45	0.0	0.0	0.0	0.0	0.0	T	0.0
1945-46	0.0	0.0	0.0	0.0	0.0	T	0.1
1946-47	0.0	0.0	0.0	0.0	0.0	2.6	T
1947-48	0.0	0.0	0.0	0.0	0.0	T	7.9
1948-49	0.0	0.0	0.0	0.0	T	T	3.5
1949-50	0.0	0.0	0.0	0.0	0.0	T	1.0
1950-51	0.0	0.0	0.0	0.0	0.0	T	1.8
1951-52	0.0	0.0	0.0	0.0	0.6	0.0	0.0
#1952-53	0.0	0.0	0.0	0.0	T	0.0	1.0
1953-54	0.0	0.0	0.0	0.0	T	0.0	1.3
1954-55	0.0	0.0	0.0	0.0	0.0	T	T
1955-56	0.0	0.0	0.0	0.0	T	0.0	3.8
1956-57	0.0	0.0	0.0	0.0	0.0	0.0	T
1957-58	0.0	0.0	0.0	0.0	T	0.0	T
1958-59	0.0	0.0	0.0	0.0	0.0	0.3	0.2
1959-60	0.0	0.0	0.0	0.0	0.0	T	0.9
1960-61	0.0	0.0	0.0	0.0	0.0	T	3.5
1961-62	0.0	0.0	0.0	0.0	0.0	0.0	2.6
1962-63	0.0	0.0	0.0	0.0	0.0	T	T
1963-64	0.0	0.0	0.0	0.0	0.0	2.6	12.1
1964-65	0.0	0.0	0.0	0.0	0.0	T	0.0
1965-66	0.0	0.0	0.0	0.0	0.0	0.0	4.4
1966-67	0.0	0.0	0.0	0.0	0.0	0.0	0.0
1967-68	0.0	0.0	0.0	0.0	0.0	0.0	0.4
1968-69	0.0	0.0	0.0	0.0	T	0.0	0.0
1969-70	0.0	0.0	0.0	0.0	0.0	T	T
1970-71	0.0	0.0	0.0	0.0	0.0	0.0	0.0
1971-72	0.0	0.0	0.0	0.0	T	0.0	T
1972-73	0.0	0.0	0.0	0.0	T	1.4	2.3
1973-74	0.0	0.0	0.0	0.0	0.0	0.0	T
1974-75	0.0	0.0	0.0	0.0	T	T	T
1975-76	0.0	0.0	0.0	0.0	0.0	0.4	
RECORD MEAN	0.0	0.0	0.0	0.0	T	0.2	1.4

Heating Degree Days

Season	July	Aug	Sept	Oct	Nov	Dec	Jan
1955-56	0	0	0	55	356	553	625
1956-57	0	0	0	21	374	468	656
1957-58	0	0	0	144	402	410	615
1958-59	0	0	0	82	247	659	690
1959-60	0	0	0	68	470	450	643
1960-61	0	0	0	45	253	658	740
1961-62	0	0	0	50	381	590	781
#1962-63	0	0	0	46	280	545	839
1963-64	0	0	0	4	227	760	651
1964-65	0	0	6	81	260	550	550
1965-66	0	0	2	60	103	376	760
1966-67	0	0	0	79	182	627	514
1967-68	0	0	13	80	282	548	631
1968-69	0	0	0	47	348	540	492
1969-70	0	0	0	116	306	463	756
1970-71	0	0	7	105	316	369	564
1971-72	0	0	12	7	270	389	615
1972-73	0	0	3	96	446	644	690
1973-74	0	0	1	36	182	509	656
1974-75	0	0	20	16	296	546	489
1975-76	0	0	4	33	266	500	

Cooling Degree Days

Year	Jan	Feb	Mar	Apr	May	June	July
1969	3	3	3	67	228	453	715
1970	5	0	7	108	236	433	595
1971	0	6	21	71	195	546	606
1972	2	14	57	185	249	498	569
1973	1	0	6	60	230	435	593
1974	0	2	115	101	341	419	660
1975	0	0	15	107	236	483	580

Feb	Mar	Apr	May	June	Total
0.1	2.0	0.0	0.0	0.0	6.3
3.1	0.0	T	0.0	0.0	8.1
T	0.0	0.0	0.0	0.0	T
T	0.0	0.0	0.0	0.0	4.0
0.0	T	0.0	0.0	0.0	T
T	6.0	0.0	0.0	0.0	7.3
0.0	T	0.0	0.0	0.0	T
0.0	0.0	0.0	0.0	0.0	T
T	0.0	0.0	0.0	0.0	T
T	0.0	0.0	0.0	0.0	0.1
T	3.9	0.0	0.0	0.0	6.5
0.9	T	0.0	0.0	0.0	8.8
T	T	0.0	0.0	0.0	3.5
T	T	0.0	0.0	0.0	1.0
4.2	T	0.0	0.0	0.0	6.0
T	0.0	0.0	0.0	0.0	0.6
T	T	0.0	0.0	0.0	1.0
0.0	1.7	0.0	0.0	0.0	3.0
T	T	0.0	0.0	0.0	T
0.7	T	0.0	0.0	0.0	4.5
0.0	0.0	0.0	0.0	0.0	T
0.9	T	0.0	0.0	0.0	0.9
2.0	0.0	0.0	0.0	0.0	2.5
1.0	T	0.0	0.0	0.0	1.9
2.9	0.0	0.0	0.0	0.0	6.4
T	2.5	0.0	0.0	0.0	5.1
T	0.1	0.0	0.0	0.0	0.1
0.2	0.4	0.0	0.0	0.0	15.3
T	T	0.0	0.0	0.0	T
2.9	0.0	0.0	0.0	0.0	7.3
T	T	0.0	0.0	0.0	T
2.6	T	0.0	0.0	0.0	3.0
T	0.0	0.0	0.0	0.0	T
0.0	0.8	0.0	0.0	0.0	0.8
T	1.6	0.0	0.0	0.0	1.6
T	0.0	0.0	0.0	0.0	T
T	0.0	0.0	0.0	0.0	3.7
0.0	0.0	0.0	0.0	0.0	T
3.7	T	0.0	0.0	0.0	3.7
0.8	0.3	0.0	0.0	0.0	2.7

DALLAS - FORT WORTH, TX

Feb	Mar	Apr	May	June	Total
445	260	97	0	0	2391
311	381	142	21	0	2374
592	496	138	9	0	2806
452	276	143	4	0	2553
639	499	54	32	0	2855
409	209	132	9	2	2457
328	345	107	2	0	2584
517	185	34	13	0	2459
608	285	65	1	0	2601
530	551	36	0	0	2564
542	274	84	26	0	2227
503	146	15	21	0	2087
598	330	100	2	0	2584
416	468	49	6	4	2370
455	404	63	21	1	2585
440	307	97	19	0	2224
398	143	26	1	0	1861
475	155	182	12	0	2703
352	173	70	1	0	1980
508	355	112	0	0	2342

Aug	Sept	Oct	Nov	Dec	Total
602	372	133	17	0	2596
653	409	115	12	22	2595
456	382	171	36	1	2491
618	480	183	4	0	2859
559	342	146	33	0	2405
563	202	153	20	2	2578
620	331	189	39	9	2609

Average Temperature

Year	Jan	Feb	Mar	Apr	May	June	July	Aug	Sept	Oct	Nov	Dec	Annual
1936	44.0	42.2	62.7	64.8	74.0	84.0	84.4	87.6	79.8	62.6	52.4	50.4	65.7
1937	41.0	48.8	51.6	66.2	75.0	81.8	85.0	86.6	79.8	67.4	52.4	46.1	65.1
1938	49.2	54.3	64.2	63.2	72.9	81.3	83.6	85.9	80.3	73.0	54.5	48.9	67.6
#1939	50.8	45.4	60.1	65.0	75.8	81.6	86.6	85.4	83.7	71.4	54.4	52.6	67.7
1940	34.9	47.8	60.0	64.2	71.6	76.8	81.6	81.7	76.6	70.4	53.1	48.9	64.0
1941	48.2	46.7	51.9	65.4	75.6	78.1	84.4	84.9	79.8	71.2	55.2	50.0	66.0
1942	43.1	48.3	56.2	65.6	72.6	81.4	84.8	84.4	74.3	65.4	60.0	47.5	65.3
1943	45.0	53.2	51.4	69.2	73.4	82.4	86.1	89.3	76.2	66.3	55.4	44.5	66.0
1944	46.5	51.8	54.9	64.6	72.2	83.1	85.5	85.5	77.2	68.9	58.0	44.2	66.0
1945	45.8	49.6	61.6	63.0	71.8	79.6	81.7	83.2	78.2	65.4	59.8	43.4	65.2
1946	45.0	52.4	60.8	68.4	69.7	78.4	85.4	85.0	75.2	68.8	56.4	52.2	66.5
1947	45.2	43.9	49.8	65.0	71.2	81.0	84.2	86.2	79.2	73.2	51.6	48.0	64.9
1948	38.4	46.3	52.8	71.0	73.2	82.8	84.8	85.8	77.6	66.8	55.6	51.4	65.5
1949	39.1	48.6	57.0	63.6	75.7	82.2	86.0	83.0	75.4	65.5	58.8	49.8	65.4
1950	47.9	53.0	56.0	63.6	73.7	80.2	81.3	82.2	75.2	71.8	54.6	46.5	65.5
1951	46.0	49.5	56.8	64.7	72.6	80.6	87.1	90.3	79.4	69.8	52.3	50.1	66.6
1952	54.0	54.4	55.5	62.5	72.6	85.3	86.3	91.1	79.8	65.1	55.1	46.6	67.4
#1953	51.9	50.7	61.6	62.4	72.8	87.5	85.1	84.0	79.1	68.8	53.7	44.9	66.9
1954	45.6	56.3	55.9	70.7	68.8	83.9	90.5	88.8	81.9	69.9	55.6	49.7	68.1
1955	46.3	48.6	57.9	69.6	76.5	78.0	85.4	84.2	80.8	68.3	55.4	47.1	66.5
1956	44.9	50.1	58.4	64.8	77.7	83.3	89.0	88.0	80.9	71.0	52.7	50.0	67.6
1957	43.7	54.1	52.6	61.6	71.5	80.2	87.4	85.1	75.1	62.3	51.6	51.7	64.8
1958	44.9	43.6	48.7	61.5	73.1	82.3	85.7	85.0	78.4	65.8	57.4	43.6	64.2
1959	42.5	48.9	56.6	63.4	75.1	80.7	83.1	84.5	79.7	66.1	49.5	50.2	65.0
1960	44.1	43.0	49.1	67.3	72.0	82.9	84.6	84.0	79.6	70.0	57.5	43.7	64.8
1961	40.9	50.3	59.3	64.0	73.1	77.9	82.3	82.7	76.9	67.3	52.7	45.8	64.5
1962	39.6	53.3	54.0	64.3	77.6	79.9	85.5	85.6	77.1	70.4	55.5	47.2	65.8
#1963	37.8	46.4	61.2	70.4	75.0	83.1	87.4	87.3	79.2	73.5	58.4	40.3	66.7
1964	43.8	43.8	55.6	66.8	73.2	81.0	87.1	85.3	76.9	63.6	57.6	47.1	65.2
1965	47.1	45.8	47.0	68.4	72.9	79.9	86.3	84.1	79.4	66.6	62.9	52.8	66.1
1966	40.3	45.4	56.3	63.8	70.8	79.6	86.3	82.7	75.8	65.0	60.7	45.3	64.4
1967	48.3	46.8	63.3	71.1	71.4	81.4	82.9	83.1	74.1	65.4	55.6	47.0	65.9
1968	44.4	44.2	54.6	63.4	72.4	79.5	81.0	83.5	74.6	67.8	53.9	47.4	63.9
1969	49.0	50.0	49.8	65.4	71.9	79.8	87.9	84.2	77.1	65.3	55.1	49.9	65.5
1970	40.6	48.6	52.1	66.2	71.7	79.1	84.0	85.8	78.2	65.1	54.7	53.6	65.0
1971	46.7	49.2	55.6	64.0	70.5	82.9	84.4	79.5	77.1	70.1	57.0	52.2	65.8
1972	45.0	51.5	62.1	70.1	72.7	81.4	83.1	84.7	80.8	67.5	50.1	44.0	66.1
1973	42.5	47.9	60.0	60.7	71.7	79.3	83.9	82.9	76.1	68.3	59.8	48.4	65.1
1974	43.6	52.3	62.9	65.8	75.7	78.7	86.1	82.9	70.9	69.2	55.5	47.2	65.9
1975	49.0	46.6	53.8	64.7	72.4	80.9	83.6	84.8	75.6	69.8	57.3	49.0	65.6
RECORD MEAN	45.6	48.8	56.9	65.2	72.7	80.9	84.5	84.6	77.8	67.8	56.1	47.7	65.7
MAX	55.9	59.5	68.0	75.8	82.6	91.0	94.7	95.1	88.1	78.6	66.6	57.7	76.1
MIN	35.3	38.1	45.7	54.5	62.7	70.7	74.2	74.1	67.4	56.9	45.6	37.6	55.2

# Indicates a station move or relocation of instruments.

Precipitation

Year	Jan	Feb	Mar	Apr	May	June	July	Aug	Sept	Oct	Nov	Dec	Annual
1936	0.67	0.45	0.63	0.99	9.48	0.03	2.35	0.23	7.30	3.72	0.46	1.84	28.15
1937	1.71	0.30	3.88	0.58	1.00	5.74	1.93	1.02	0.32	3.55	4.39	5.31	29.73
1938	2.74	4.57	3.89	3.03	2.80	1.61	2.16	0.11	0.78	0.11	1.17	1.26	24.23
#1939	2.66	2.42	1.64	1.48	2.54	4.04	2.02	1.44	0.12	0.55	2.72	0.68	22.31
1940	0.59	2.00	0.40	5.97	7.15	7.30	2.86	2.16	0.68	1.47	6.35	4.72	41.65
1941	1.45	3.42	1.52	3.52	2.02	7.12	1.49	2.71	1.28	3.68	1.08	1.88	31.17
1942	0.39	0.64	1.37	16.97	2.85	3.23	0.62	4.69	3.82	6.18	0.92	1.59	43.27
1943	0.20	0.51	4.05	1.63	7.83	3.93	0.73	T	7.31	0.73	0.51	3.32	30.75
1944	2.58	4.81	1.30	2.70	6.42	0.76	2.52	2.65	0.80	2.53	3.82	3.60	34.49
1945	1.92	6.96	6.19	2.87	1.81	4.12	3.07	0.62	2.17	2.31	1.13	0.55	33.72
1946	2.79	2.93	2.80	2.49	12.09	0.65	0.90	6.84	2.69	1.31	6.50	3.40	45.39
1947	1.21	0.55	2.92	2.98	2.50	4.08	0.10	4.18	2.81	2.14	2.23	4.50	30.20
1948	0.96	4.12	1.07	1.11	4.34	2.46	1.93	0.90	0.19	2.09	0.50	0.44	20.11
1949	5.45	4.75	3.69	2.47	10.64	3.52	0.10	2.27	3.13	6.50	0.09	1.04	43.65
1950	5.01	2.47	1.58	4.73	6.16	3.16	4.53	3.05	3.21	0.30	0.02	T	34.22
1951	1.39	2.42	1.33	2.27	4.60	4.12	2.22	0.47	1.84	1.62	1.00	0.09	23.37
1952	0.58	1.12	1.39	6.51	3.21	T	0.56	0.44	0.54	0.01	5.84	2.49	22.69
#1953	0.54	1.34	2.52	4.82	3.55	0.55	0.97	1.09	1.68	4.27	2.09	1.32	24.74
1954	2.08	0.73	0.66	3.62	4.38	1.20	0.24	0.81	1.46	2.35	1.24	0.78	19.55
1955	1.17	2.01	2.15	1.94	6.58	4.99	0.64	1.00	3.68	0.20	0.59	0.21	25.16
1956	1.34	2.54	0.11	3.12	3.83	0.88	0.38	0.23	0.23	1.20	2.61	2.08	18.55
1957	1.72	1.77	4.18	12.19	12.64	3.96	0.65	0.12	3.23	3.53	4.72	1.78	50.49
1958	1.70	0.84	5.49	8.63	1.50	0.67	3.69	3.64	5.10	1.07	2.26	1.09	35.68
1959	0.36	1.61	2.31	0.92	3.27	5.27	3.27	0.93	2.40	9.22	1.74	2.84	34.14
1960	2.29	2.16	0.74	1.67	1.89	1.72	3.96	2.76	1.25	1.82	0.49	4.22	24.97
1961	3.29	2.20	2.95	2.23	1.06	5.93	2.32	0.02	2.92	2.82	2.72	2.12	30.58
1962	1.00	2.01	1.80	5.66	1.58	6.94	6.36	3.22	3.79	4.15	3.93	0.99	41.43
1963	0.86	0.15	0.48	6.20	2.52	0.57	2.28	2.73	1.70	0.23	1.29	1.45	20.46
1964	3.53	1.17	3.35	2.71	2.85	0.40	0.25	2.43	9.52	0.62	6.23	1.25	34.31
1965	2.77	6.20	1.45	2.15	8.97	1.50	0.09	2.26	5.04	1.97	2.43	1.73	36.56
1966	1.68	2.84	1.38	10.74	3.13	5.47	3.26	3.38	4.23	1.48	0.53	1.17	39.29
1967	0.28	0.32	2.09	3.84	4.02	0.72	2.20	0.48	5.94	4.19	0.92	2.30	27.30
1968	3.60	1.48	6.39	2.41	6.02	3.50	1.88	2.71	2.53	2.18	4.58	1.20	38.48
1969	1.26	1.99	3.62	3.40	7.12	0.63	0.77	2.56	4.55	5.82	1.22	2.75	35.69
1970	0.72	4.78	3.49	4.68	3.62	0.61	0.94	6.85	6.25	2.95	0.20	1.01	36.10
1971	0.19	1.32	0.34	2.76	1.88	0.83	3.60	5.70	3.24	7.64	1.77	6.99	36.26
1972	1.09	0.26	0.10	3.25	2.35	1.50	0.59	0.81	2.42	6.89	2.36	0.61	22.23
1973	3.26	1.92	2.28	6.06	3.18	5.88	11.13	0.01	7.16	6.85	2.06	0.83	50.62
1974	1.79	1.01	0.80	2.51	6.00	5.44	0.67	4.19	6.04	5.93	3.32	1.93	39.63
1975	3.34	3.72	1.67	3.40	6.88	1.95	5.06	0.30	0.87	T	0.42	1.49	29.10
RECORD MEAN	1.81	2.01	2.24	3.94	4.59	2.96	2.26	2.23	2.94	2.90	2.26	1.97	32.11

Record mean values above are means through the current year for the period beginning in 1899 for temperature and precipitation, 1954 for snowfall. Data are from City Office locations through 1939.

The city of El Paso is located in the extreme west point of Texas at an elevation of about 3,700 feet in the business district, with the Weather Bureau station located on a mesa at about 200 feet higher elevation. The climate of the region is characterized by the abundance of sunshine throughout the year, high but no extreme daytime summer temperatures, with very low humidity, scanty rainfall, and a relatively cool winter season typical of arid areas.

Rainfall throughout the year is light, insufficient for any growth except desert vegetation, and irrigation is necessary for crops, gardens, and lawns. Dry periods of several months' duration without appreciable rainfall are not unusual. Almost half of the precipitation occurs in the three-month period, July - September, from brief, but at times heavy, thunderstorms. Small amounts of snow fall nearly every winter, but snow cover rarely amounts to more than an inch and seldom remains on the ground for more than a few hours.

Daytime summer temperatures are high, frequently above 90° and occasionally above 100°, but summer nights are usually comfortable, with minimum temperatures usually in the sixties. The average number of days with temperatures 90° or higher is 102 per year. The highest temperature on record is 109° on June 21, 1960, and July 3, 1960. It should be noted that when temperatures are high the relative humidity is generally quite low. A 20-year tabulation of observations with temperatures above 90° shows that in April, May, and June the humidity averaged from 10 to 14 percent, while in July, August, and September it averaged 22 to 24 percent. This low humidity aids the efficiency of evaporative air coolers, which are widely used in homes and public buildings and are quite effective in cooling the air to comfortable temperatures.

Winter daytime temperatures are mild, rising to 55° to 60° on the average. At night they drop below freezing about half the time in December and January, and the average number of days with temperatures 32° or lower is 51 per year. Temperatures below 10° are rare, having occurred on only 28 days in over 80 years of record, although an extreme of 8° below zero has been recorded. The flat, irrigated land of the Rio Grande Valley in the vicinity of El Paso is noticeably cooler, particularly at night, than the airport or the City proper, both in summer and winter. This results in more comfortable temperatures in summer, but increases the severity of frosts in winter. The cooler air in the Valley also causes marked short-period fluctuations of temperature and dewpoint at the airport with changes in wind direction, especially during the early morning hours.

The Franklin Mountains begin within the City limits and extend northward for about 16 miles; peaks of these mountains range from 4,687 to

Station: EL PASO, TEXAS
INTERNATIONAL AIRPORT
Elevation (ground): 3918 feet

TEMPERATURES °F

Month	Normal Daily maximum	Normal Daily minimum	Normal Monthly	Extremes Record highest	Year	Record lowest	Year
(a)				16		16	
J	57.0	30.2	43.6	80	1970	-8	1962
F	62.5	34.3	48.4	83	1972	11	1974
M	68.9	40.3	54.6	88	1971	14	1971
A	78.5	49.3	63.9	98	1965	24	1973
M	87.2	57.2	72.2	101	1974	31	1967
J	94.9	65.7	80.3	108	1973	51	1968
J	94.6	69.9	82.3	106	1963	59	1973
A	92.8	68.2	80.5	105	1969	56	1973
S	87.4	61.0	74.2	100	1973	42	1975
O	78.5	49.5	64.0	96	1973	25	1970
N	66.1	37.0	51.6	84	1973	18	1973
D	57.8	30.9	44.4	80	1973	10	1973
YR	77.2	49.5	63.4	108	JUN 1973	-8	JAN 1962

IMPORTANT:
The time-period covered by this record is limited: See footnotes following table of **NORMALS, MEANS AND EXTREMES** for explanation and for additional history of **EXTREME HIGHS AND LOWS** recorded in the general area.

(Continued)

7,152 feet above sea level. They add noticeably to the gustiness of the winds during high velocities, and cause changes in direction during periods of light winds.

Dust and sandstorms are the most unpleasant features of the weather in El Paso. While wind velocities are not excessively high, the soil surface is dry and loose and natural vegetation is sparse, so moderately strong winds raise considerable dust and sand. A tabulation of duststorms, for a period of 20 years, shows definitely that they are most frequent in March and April, and comparatively rare in the fall months, although they do occur at all times of the year. The highest monthly average is in March, nearly 40 hours a month with visibility reduced to 6 miles or less by dust.

Prevailing winds are from the north in winter and south in summer, with the prevailing direction for the year north by a small margin.

EL PASO, TEXAS

Normals, Means, and Extremes

(To better understand these tables, see full explanation of terms beginning on page 322)

Month	Normal Degree days Base 65 °F: Heating	Normal Degree days Base 65 °F: Cooling	Precipitation in inches, Water equivalent: Normal	Maximum monthly	Year	Minimum monthly	Year	Maximum in 24 hrs.	Year	Snow, Ice pellets: Maximum monthly	Year	Maximum in 24 hrs.	Year	Relative humidity pct. Hour 05 (Local time)	Hour 11	Hour 17	Hour 23	Wind: Mean speed m.p.h.	Prevailing direction	Fastest mile: Speed m.p.h.	Direction	Year	Pct. of possible sunshine	Mean sky cover, tenths, sunrise to sunset	Mean number of days, Sunrise to sunset: Clear	Partly cloudy	Cloudy	Precipitation .01 inch or more	Snow, Ice pellets 1.0 inch or more	Thunderstorms	Heavy fog, visibility ¼ mile or less	Temperatures °F Max. (b) 90° and above	Max. 32° and below	Min. 32° and below	Min. 0° and below	Average station pressure mb. Elev. 3916 feet m.s.l.
(a)				36		36		36		36		36		15	15	15	15	33	15	36	36		33	33	33	33	33	36	36	36	36	15	15	15	15	3
J	663	0	0.39	1.84	1949	0.00	1967	0.61	1960	8.3	1949	4.6	1973	61	43	33	52	9.2	N	61	SW	1943	78	4.5	14	8	9	4	1	*	1	0	1	19	*	883.1
F	465	0	0.42	1.69	1973	0.00	1943	0.87	1956	8.9	1956	7.2	1956	51	35	25	41	10.0	N	69	W	1960	82	4.1	14	7	7	3	*	*	*	0	*	12	0	883.1
M	328	6	0.39	2.26	1958	T	1972	1.72	1941	7.3	1958	7.3	1958	44	29	21	33	11.9	WSW	70	SW	1950	85	4.3	15	8	8	2	*	*	*	0	0	5	0	878.9
A	89	56	0.24	1.23	1942	0.00	1973	1.08	1966	T	1971	T	1971	34	21	15	24	12.0	WSW	66	W	1958	87	3.6	16	9	5	2	0	1	*	2	0	*	0	879.4
M	0	223	0.32	1.92	1941	0.00	1962	1.23	1941	0.0		0.0		37	21	14	26	11.0	WSW	70	NW	1950	89	3.2	18	9	4	2	0	2	*	14	0	*	0	879.6
J	0	459	0.60	2.67	1966	T	1975	1.45	1966	0.0		0.0		42	24	17	30	10.1	S	68	N	1947	89	2.8	20	7	3	3	0	5	0	26	0	0	0	880.1
J	0	536	1.53	5.53	1968	0.17	1965	2.63	1968	0.0		0.0		61	39	30	46	8.9	SSE	68	NE	1966	79	4.6	12	13	6	8	0	10	0	27	0	0	0	882.6
A	0	481	1.12	4.11	1957	T	1962	2.00	1957	0.0		0.0		62	41	32	49	8.4	S	63	N	1948	80	4.2	14	12	5	7	0	10	0	23	0	0	0	883.0
S	0	276	1.16	6.68	1974	T	1959	2.52	1958	0.0		0.0		66	45	34	53	8.4	S	52	SW	1970	82	3.2	19	6	5	5	0	4	*	10	0	0	0	882.9
O	92	61	0.78	4.31	1945	0.00	1952	1.77	1945	0.0		0.0		59	35	27	48	8.2	N	49	W	1956	84	3.0	20	6	5	4	0	2	*	1	0	*	0	883.9
N	402	0	0.32	1.63	1961	0.00	1964	1.19	1943	7.8	1961	7.8	1961	58	37	31	50	8.6	N	57	W	1944	83	3.5	18	6	6	2	*	*	*	0	0	7	0	883.5
D	639	0	0.50	1.73	1960	0.00	1955	1.05	1946	10.1	1960	7.1	1951	61	43	36	53	8.6	N	66	W	1970	78	4.2	16	7	8	4	*	*	*	0	*	18	0	883.7
YR	2678	2098	7.77	6.68	SEP 1974	0.00	APR 1973	2.63	JUL 1968	10.1	DEC 1960	7.8	NOV 1961	53	34	26	42	9.6	N	70	NW	MAY 1950	83	3.8	196	98	71	45	2	36	2	103	1	63	*	882.0

FOOTNOTES

Means and extremes above are from existing and comparable exposures. Annual extremes have been exceeded at other sites in the locality as follows: Highest temperature 109 in June and July 1960; maximum monthly precipitation 8.18 in July 1881; maximum precipitation in 24 hours 6.50 in July 1881; maximum snowfall in 24 hours 8.4 in November 1906.

Snowfall

Season	July	Aug	Sept	Oct	Nov	Dec	Jan
1936-37	0.0	0.0	0.0	0.0	T	0.0	0.0
1937-38	0.0	0.0	0.0	0.0	0.0	1.2	0.0
1938-39	0.0	0.0	0.0	0.0	0.0	0.0	T
1939-40	0.0	0.0	0.0	0.0	0.0	T	3.6
1940-41	0.0	0.0	0.0	0.0	0.0	0.0	0.0
1941-42	0.0	0.0	0.0	0.0	0.0	T	0.0
#1942-43	0.0	0.0	0.0	0.0	0.0	0.0	1.5
1943-44	0.0	0.0	0.0	0.0	4.2	T	T
1944-45	0.0	0.0	0.0	0.0	T	0.0	T
1945-46	0.0	0.0	0.0	0.0	0.0	T	6.0
1946-47	0.0	0.0	0.0	0.0	T	0.8	5.3
1947-48	0.0	0.0	0.0	0.0	0.0	0.6	2.4
1948-49	0.0	0.0	0.0	0.0	0.0	T	8.3
1949-50	0.0	0.0	0.0	0.0	0.0	T	T
1950-51	0.0	0.0	0.0	0.0	0.0	0.0	3.8
1951-52	0.0	0.0	0.0	0.0	0.0	7.1	T
1952-53	0.0	0.0	0.0	0.0	T	T	0.0
1953-54	0.0	0.0	0.0	0.0	T	2.2	T
1954-55	0.0	0.0	0.0	0.0	0.0	0.6	T
1955-56	0.0	0.0	0.0	0.0	0.0	0.0	0.0
1956-57	0.0	0.0	0.0	0.0	0.0	2.3	T
1957-58	0.0	0.0	0.0	0.0	4.1	0.0	2.0
1958-59	0.0	0.0	0.0	0.0	0.8	0.0	0.0
1959-60	0.0	0.0	0.0	0.0	0.0	T	T
1960-61	0.0	0.0	0.0	0.0	0.0	10.1	T
1961-62	0.0	0.0	0.0	0.0	7.8	T	1.6
1962-63	0.0	0.0	0.0	0.0	0.0	0.0	0.8
1963-64	0.0	0.0	0.0	0.0	0.0	T	0.0
1964-65	0.0	0.0	0.0	0.0	0.0	T	0.0
1965-66	0.0	0.0	0.0	0.0	0.0	T	0.4
1966-67	0.0	0.0	0.0	0.0	0.0	T	0.0
1967-68	0.0	0.0	0.0	0.0	0.0	5.6	2.1
1968-69	0.0	0.0	0.0	0.0	7.0	T	0.0
1969-70	0.0	0.0	0.0	0.0	6.0	1.9	0.3
1970-71	0.0	0.0	0.0	0.0	0.0	0.0	3.8
1971-72	0.0	0.0	0.0	0.0	0.0	1.0	2.5
1972-73	0.0	0.0	0.0	0.0	0.0	T	5.3
1973-74	0.0	0.0	0.0	0.0	T	0.0	T
1974-75	0.0	0.0	0.0	0.0	0.0	5.3	2.2
1975-76	0.0	0.0	0.0	0.0	0.0	T	
RECORD MEAN	0.0	0.0	0.0	0.0	0.8	1.0	1.4

Heating Degree Days

Season	July	Aug	Sept	Oct	Nov	Dec	Jan
1955-56	0	0	0	34	317	477	468
1956-57	0	0	0	65	494	624	478
1957-58	0	0	4	127	476	570	677
1958-59	0	0	16	120	343	549	523
1959-60	0	0	0	33	439	573	691
#1960-61	0	0	0	86	357	806	735
1961-62	0	0	0	82	513	575	754
1962-63	0	0	0	65	333	608	753
1963-64	0	0	0	17	341	683	789
1964-65	0	0	0	76	391	643	521
1965-66	0	0	4	107	240	592	769
1966-67	0	0	2	126	307	695	718
1967-68	0	0	2	106	352	720	691
1968-69	0	0	0	61	414	728	503
1969-70	0	0	0	62	371	504	556
1970-71	0	0	39	180	388	519	625
1971-72	0	0	31	112	381	624	607
1972-73	0	0	3	87	480	563	679
1973-74	0	0	7	90	336	592	636
1974-75	0	0	41	107	445	728	672
1975-76	0	0	20	64	399	640	

Cooling Degree Days

Year	Jan	Feb	Mar	Apr	May	June	July
1969	0	0	1	71	250	501	627
1970	0	0	2	57	263	448	559
1971	0	0	45	45	235	492	543
1972	0	4	15	70	159	404	543
1973	0	0	0	7	152	355	459
1974	0	0	19	84	338	540	459
1975	0	0	9	35	170	482	469

Feb	Mar	Apr	May	June	Total
0.6	0.0	0.0	0.0	0.0	0.6
0.0	0.0	0.0	0.0	0.0	1.2
0.5	T	T	0.0	0.0	0.5
T	0.0	0.0	0.0	0.0	3.6
T	T	0.0	0.0	0.0	T
T	0.1	0.0	0.0	0.0	0.1
0.0	0.0	0.0	0.0	0.0	1.5
T	T	0.0	0.0	0.0	4.2
T	T	T	0.0	0.0	T
T	T	0.0	0.0	0.0	6.0
0.0	3.8	0.0	0.0	0.0	9.9
0.6	T	0.0	0.0	0.0	3.6
T	T	T	0.0	0.0	8.3
T	T	0.0	0.0	0.0	T
1.8	T	T	0.0	0.0	5.6
1.0	T	T	0.0	0.0	8.1
T	0.0	0.0	0.0	0.0	T
0.0	0.0	0.0	0.0	0.0	2.2
T	0.8	0.0	0.0	0.0	1.4
8.9	0.0	T	0.0	0.0	8.9
0.0	T	0.0	0.0	0.0	2.3
0.0	7.3	T	0.0	0.0	13.4
T	T	0.0	0.0	0.0	0.8
2.1	T	T	0.0	0.0	2.1
0.0	T	0.0	0.0	0.0	10.1
0.0	T	0.0	0.0	0.0	9.4
5.3	0.0	0.0	0.0	0.0	6.1
T	T	0.0	0.0	0.0	T
0.3	T	0.0	0.0	0.0	0.3
T	T	0.0	0.0	0.0	0.4
T	0.0	T	0.0	0.0	T
2.3	0.8	0.0	0.0	0.0	10.8
0.0	T	0.0	0.0	0.0	7.0
1.7	T	0.0	0.0	0.0	9.9
T	0.0	T	0.0	0.0	3.8
0.0	0.0	0.0	0.0	0.0	3.5
4.6	T	0.0	0.0	0.0	9.9
T	0.0	0.0	0.0	0.0	T
0.2	2.0	0.0	0.0	0.0	9.7
0.8	0.4	T	0.0	0.0	4.4

EL PASO, TX

Feb	Mar	Apr	May	June	Total
578	238	132	0	0	2244
205	242	102	19	0	2229
370	422	116	3	0	2765
434	335	86	3	0	2409
534	176	58	10	0	2514
473	266	97	1	0	2821
318	433	36	3	0	2714
438	279	41	0	0	2517
695	354	99	3	0	2981
504	397	54	7	2	2595
612	264	59	4	0	2651
469	173	56	25	0	2571
415	377	128	0	0	2791
464	477	43	24	0	2714
348	286	94	33	0	2254
457	254	110	6	0	2578
364	126	56	3	0	2304
499	384	218	31	0	2944
558	178	79	5	0	2481
445	309	188	13	0	2948

Aug	Sept	Oct	Nov	Dec	Total
647	372	155	2	0	2626
514	321	19	0	0	2183
375	293	43	0	0	2071
401	247	120	0	0	1963
448	340	44	7	0	1812
378	181	54	0	0	2053
502	241	41	1	0	1950

Average Temperature

Year	Jan	Feb	Mar	Apr	May	June	July	Aug	Sept	Oct	Nov	Dec	Annual
#1936	45.5	51.2	58.0	65.8	74.2	82.4	82.6	80.8	73.7	63.4	50.6	46.8	64.6
1937	42.4	49.3	52.8	64.4	74.4	82.4	84.4	84.3	76.9	66.8	55.2	47.4	65.1
1938	47.2	53.8	57.4	63.8	73.1	81.2	80.6	81.0	73.8	68.6	49.8	48.4	64.9
1939	45.8	43.6	58.2	65.6	75.0	83.6	83.1	80.7	77.2	64.4	51.5	49.4	64.8
1940	42.6	50.4	58.4	63.6	73.8	79.2	83.4	79.6	77.2	66.0	50.8	50.4	64.6
1941	46.7	53.0	53.8	60.2	73.7	78.6	80.9	79.8	74.4	65.2	53.3	48.2	64.0
#1942	47.7	48.2	54.1	63.6	73.5	83.6	83.6	79.4	73.5	64.8	58.1	47.7	64.8
1943	44.4	51.2	55.8	67.2	72.6	79.6	80.7	84.0	73.8	63.8	51.2	43.6	64.0
1944	40.8	49.4	54.0	61.6	71.7	79.4	82.3	80.0	72.6	65.6	51.4	44.7	62.8
1945	45.8	51.5	54.2	61.8	73.2	79.0	81.7	81.5	75.8	63.8	54.9	45.4	64.0
1946	41.0	48.5	55.8	67.8	71.6	82.6	82.0	81.8	76.8	66.2	49.8	47.0	64.2
1947	40.0	49.7	55.4	61.4	73.5	79.4	83.6	80.0	76.4	68.0	49.4	43.0	63.3
1948	40.6	48.8	50.8	67.4	74.6	82.2	83.2	82.2	76.0	64.4	47.9	47.8	63.8
1949	36.1	48.2	57.0	62.1	72.5	80.6	81.6	80.1	74.7	62.7	55.7	44.0	62.9
1950	49.2	53.4	58.0	65.9	72.1	82.5	79.6	80.6	74.4	70.7	54.0	49.5	65.8
1951	44.2	47.6	54.5	61.3	73.1	80.8	85.6	82.5	77.9	67.8	51.0	46.4	64.4
1952	49.2	47.5	50.7	63.0	72.0	82.7	81.3	83.6	76.2	65.4	49.5	44.1	63.8
1953	50.3	48.1	58.7	64.4	68.8	84.1	83.5	82.1	76.3	64.2	53.8	39.5	64.5
1954	47.0	52.6	54.9	68.6	73.2	81.2	83.2	79.3	78.5	67.9	54.5	46.0	65.6
1955	42.3	45.4	55.8	64.8	71.6	79.8	79.7	80.1	76.8	66.3	54.4	49.4	63.9
1956	49.7	44.9	57.5	61.8	75.7	83.9	82.0	79.9	77.4	67.5	48.4	44.6	64.4
1957	49.3	57.6	57.0	62.4	69.5	81.9	83.9	80.5	74.5	62.4	49.0	46.4	64.5
1958	42.9	51.6	51.2	63.3	74.2	83.5	84.5	82.6	74.0	62.5	53.3	47.0	64.2
1959	47.9	49.3	54.0	65.0	73.9	83.0	82.9	81.0	77.9	66.1	50.3	46.3	64.8
#1960	42.4	46.3	59.7	66.3	73.7	85.0	81.9	82.5	75.6	63.5	52.9	38.8	64.0
1961	41.0	47.9	56.3	64.1	74.1	80.8	82.8	80.5	74.5	63.5	47.8	46.3	63.3
1962	40.5	53.5	50.9	67.3	74.1	80.0	81.3	84.0	73.9	64.9	53.7	45.2	64.1
1963	40.9	49.2	56.4	66.5	74.9	81.1	84.9	80.3	76.2	66.4	53.5	42.7	64.4
1964	39.3	40.8	53.6	63.2	73.9	81.5	84.5	82.6	75.2	63.4	51.8	44.0	62.8
1965	48.0	46.7	52.1	65.3	71.8	78.2	84.2	81.1	74.0	63.0	56.8	45.7	63.9
1966	40.1	42.9	56.4	65.1	74.5	79.5	83.6	78.7	73.4	62.1	54.5	42.4	62.8
1967	41.6	48.0	59.6	65.1	70.9	79.1	83.0	78.6	73.3	63.7	53.1	41.5	63.1
1968	42.4	50.4	53.0	61.4	73.0	81.0	79.1	76.5	72.4	65.0	51.0	41.3	62.2
1969	48.6	48.4	49.4	65.8	72.1	81.5	84.9	85.7	77.1	67.7	52.5	48.6	65.2
1970	46.9	52.3	55.6	63.5	72.2	79.7	82.8	81.4	74.2	59.5	51.9	48.0	64.0
1971	44.6	48.4	58.1	62.6	72.1	81.1	82.3	77.0	73.5	62.5	52.1	44.7	63.2
1972	45.2	52.3	61.2	65.2	69.8	78.3	82.2	77.7	72.9	65.7	48.8	46.6	63.8
1973	42.9	47.0	52.4	57.7	68.7	76.6	79.7	79.2	75.9	63.3	53.8	45.7	61.9
1974	44.3	44.8	59.6	65.0	75.6	82.8	79.6	77.0	69.4	63.0	49.9	41.3	62.7
1975	43.1	48.9	55.1	59.7	69.8	80.9	79.8	80.9	72.2	64.0	51.5	44.2	62.5
RECORD													
MEAN	44.7	49.3	55.6	63.8	72.2	80.8	81.9	80.2	74.8	64.7	52.5	45.2	63.8
MAX	57.3	62.3	69.1	77.5	86.0	94.3	93.8	91.9	86.8	77.8	65.7	57.4	76.7
MIN	32.1	36.2	42.1	50.0	58.4	67.2	70.0	68.5	62.8	51.5	39.2	32.9	50.9

# Indicates a station move or relocation of instruments.

Precipitation

Year	Jan	Feb	Mar	Apr	May	June	July	Aug	Sept	Oct	Nov	Dec	Annual
#1936	0.57	0.06	T	0.11	0.56	0.34	0.68	1.94	3.52	0.32	1.32	0.51	9.93
1937	0.12	0.32	0.48	T	0.19	1.05	0.39	0.36	0.48	1.71	0.22	0.91	6.23
1938	1.22	0.17	0.49	T	0.02	2.82	0.60	0.20	2.31	0.19	T	0.28	8.30
#1939	0.65	0.08	0.44	0.45	0.01	T	0.60	0.91	0.90	0.93	0.75	0.19	5.91
1940	0.47	0.53	0.01	0.01	1.21	0.84	0.67	0.35	0.26	0.69	1.17	0.32	6.53
1941	0.59	0.55	1.97	1.18	1.92	0.18	0.77	1.42	5.19	1.55	0.49	0.48	16.29
1942	0.06	0.65	0.01	1.23	T	0.05	1.08	1.86	0.64	1.61	T	1.26	8.45
1943	0.25	0.00	0.07	T	T	1.63	0.92	0.44	1.36	T	1.53	0.82	7.02
1944	0.45	1.42	0.15	T	0.39	1.67	1.52	1.04	0.25	1.30	0.41	0.48	9.08
1945	0.11	0.17	0.64	T	T	0.03	0.47	0.84	0.12	4.31	0.00	0.05	6.74
1946	1.23	T	0.04	0.36	1.23	0.20	0.71	1.19	1.51	0.41	0.03	1.31	8.22
1947	0.87	T	0.66	0.06	0.68	0.53	0.97	1.63	0.02	0.35	0.53	0.82	7.12
1948	0.25	0.63	0.04	0.11	T	0.96	0.82	1.82	0.03	0.18	T	0.86	5.70
1949	1.84	0.22	0.04	0.05	0.39	0.51	1.18	0.43	1.74	1.50	T	0.86	8.76
1950	0.29	0.26	T	T	0.10	0.11	3.57	0.16	1.32	0.94	0.00	0.00	6.75
1951	0.33	0.63	0.59	0.45	T	T	2.48	0.72	0.04	0.43	0.12	0.68	6.47
1952	0.02	0.96	0.92	1.08	0.46	1.14	1.88	1.06	0.07	0.00	0.23	0.15	7.97
1953	0.00	0.34	0.12	0.71	0.27	0.53	0.99	0.42	T	0.65	T	0.39	4.42
1954	0.10	T	0.09	0.19	1.26	0.23	0.88	2.37	0.95	0.30	0.00	0.02	6.39
1955	0.59	0.05	0.18	0.00	0.26	0.18	3.70	0.70	0.16	0.73	0.15	0.00	6.70
1956	0.35	1.06	T	0.05	T	1.19	1.10	0.61	0.43	0.01	T	0.64	5.44
1957	0.24	0.46	0.33	0.09	0.10	0.02	2.64	4.11	0.11	2.34	0.74	0.02	11.20
1958	0.74	1.11	2.26	0.05	0.40	1.66	1.36	1.14	6.29	1.98	0.20	T	17.19
1959	0.21	T	0.07	0.15	0.30	0.46	0.40	2.39	T	0.58	0.14	0.29	4.99
1960	0.72	0.37	0.21	0.02	0.04	0.76	3.61	0.77	0.01	0.77	0.11	1.73	9.12
1961	0.41	T	0.29	0.01	T	0.27	2.18	1.40	0.69	0.18	1.63	0.63	7.69
1962	0.94	0.58	0.24	0.10	0.00	T	1.82	T	3.54	0.55	0.21	0.30	8.28
1963	0.13	0.53	T	T	0.71	0.05	0.52	1.03	0.64	0.55	0.76	T	4.92
1964	T	T	0.99	0.08	0.02	T	0.18	0.76	2.40	0.40	0.00	0.52	5.35
1965	0.19	0.59	0.03	0.01	0.11	0.66	0.17	0.49	2.12	0.18	0.12	0.74	5.41
1966	0.38	0.20	T	1.08	0.04	2.67	1.17	1.85	1.79	0.01	0.01	0.04	9.24
1967	0.00	0.04	0.17	0.03	0.05	1.41	0.84	0.54	1.54	0.09	0.23	0.78	5.72
1968	0.47	1.11	0.85	0.10	T	0.03	5.53	1.71	0.53	0.11	1.35	0.23	12.02
1969	0.05	0.08	0.17	T	0.28	T	1.14	0.28	0.43	0.59	0.63	0.69	4.34
1970	0.03	0.55	0.47	T	0.71	0.73	1.41	0.41	1.01	0.68	T	0.06	6.06
1971	0.17	0.04	0.00	0.42	T	0.01	2.34	1.59	0.96	1.07	0.14	0.50	7.24
1972	0.44	T	T	0.00	0.04	1.62	0.71	2.59	1.60	1.25	0.33	0.42	9.00
1973	1.23	1.69	0.60	0.00	0.29	0.71	2.12	0.73	0.01	0.07	0.08	T	7.53
1974	0.27	T	0.36	0.12	0.05	0.36	2.21	0.63	6.68	1.90	0.50	0.87	13.95
1975	0.70	0.59	0.19	T	0.03	T	1.11	0.45	2.18	0.25	T	0.71	6.21
RECORD MEAN	0.43	0.41	0.34	0.25	0.34	0.60	1.70	1.42	1.26	0.79	0.43	0.50	8.47

Record mean values above are means through the current year for the period beginning in 1887 for temperature, 1879 for precipitation and 1940 for snowfall. Temperature, degree days, and snowfall data are from City Office locations through November 1942, precipitation through 1939.

HOUSTON, TEXAS

Station: HOUSTON, TEXAS INTERCONTINENTAL AIRPORT
Elevation (ground): 96 feet

TEMPERATURES °F

Month	Normal Daily maximum	Normal Daily minimum	Normal Monthly	Extremes Record highest	Year	Extremes Record lowest	Year
(a)				6		6	
J	62.6	41.5	52.1	84	1975	19	1973
F	66.0	44.6	55.3	82	1974	22	1973
M	71.8	49.8	60.8	90	1974	25	1971
A	79.4	59.3	69.4	89	1973	31	1973
M	85.9	65.6	75.8	93	1974	46	1970
J	91.3	70.9	81.1	99	1969	52	1970
J	93.8	72.8	83.3	101	1969	62	1972
A	94.3	72.4	83.4	101	1969	62	1970
S	90.1	68.2	79.2	97	1971	48	1975
O	83.5	58.3	70.9	93	1975	39	1970
N	73.0	49.1	61.1	88	1969	24	1975
D	65.8	43.4	54.6	83	1974	21	1973
YR	79.8	58.0	68.9	101	AUG 1969	19	JAN 1973

IMPORTANT:
The time-period covered by this record is limited: See footnotes following table of NORMALS, MEANS AND EXTREMES for explanation and for additional history of EXTREME HIGHS AND LOWS recorded in the general area.

Houston, the largest city in Texas, is located in the flat Coastal Plains, about 50 miles from the Gulf of Mexico and about 25 miles from Galveston Bay. The climate is predominantly marine. The terrain includes numerous small streams and bayous which, together with the nearness to Galveston Bay, favor the development of both ground and advective fogs. Prevailing winds are from the southeast and south, except in January, when frequent passages of high pressure areas bring invasions of polar air and prevailing northerly winds.

Temperatures are moderated by the influence of winds from the Gulf, which results in mild winters and, on the whole, relatively cool summer nights. Another effect of the nearness of the Gulf is abundant rainfall, except for rare extended dry periods. Polar air penetrates the area frequently enough to provide stimulating variability in the weather.

The average number of days with minimum temperatures of 32 degrees or lower is only 7 per year at the City Office, about 15 at William P. Hobby Airport located in southeast Houston, and about 23 at Intercontinental Airport located in north Houston. Most freezing temperatures last only a few hours since they are usually accompanied by clear skies. The extreme persistence of freezing temperatures was in January-February 1951, when the temperature remained 32 degrees or below for 123 consecutive hours.

Monthly rainfall is evenly distributed throughout the year. Annual downtown rainfall has varied from 72.86 inches in 1900 to 17.66 in 1917; 72.86 inches was also recorded at William P. Hobby Airport in 1946. About 75 percent of the years have total precipitation between 30 and 60 inches. Monthly precipitation

(Continued page 656)

Snowfall

Season	July	Aug	Sept	Oct	Nov	Dec	Jan
1970-71	0.0	0.0	0.0	0.0	0.0	0.0	T
1971-72	0.0	0.0	0.0	0.0	0.0	0.0	T
1972-73	0.0	0.0	0.0	0.0	0.0	0.0	2.0
1973-74	0.0	0.0	0.0	0.0	0.0	0.0	0.0
1974-75	0.0	0.0	0.0	0.0	0.0	0.0	T
1975-76	0.0	0.0	0.0	0.0	0.0	0.0	
RECORD MEAN	0.0	0.0	0.0	0.0	0.0	T	0.2

Heating Degree Days

Season	July	Aug	Sept	Oct	Nov	Dec	Jan
1955-56	0	0	0	21	196	290	342
1956-57	0	0	0	0	204	220	256
1957-58	0	0	0	71	185	245	449
1958-59	0	0	0	48	145	375	452
1959-60	0	0	0	7	309	306	416
#1960-61	0	0	0	17	104	390	473
1961-62	0	0	0	16	184	287	480
1962-63	0	0	0	8	157	313	515
1963-64	0	0	0	0	108	551	413
1964-65	0	0	0	31	114	315	300
1965-66	0	0	2	20	23	212	516
1966-67	0	0	0	27	99	359	342
1967-68	0	0	3	18	99	312	390
#1968-69	0	0	0	5	199	297	284
1969-70	0	0	0	29	238	304	579
1970-71	0	0	0	72	274	209	298
1971-72	0	0	2	6	195	194	315
1972-73	0	0	2	50	320	410	540
1973-74	0	0	0	8	74	364	330
1974-75	0	0	0	15	196	336	290
1975-76	0	0	0	26	217	399	

Cooling Degree Days

Year	Jan	Feb	Mar	Apr	May	June	July
#1969	35	13	11	167	328	456	608
1970	18	3	7	188	238	409	513
1971	48	18	55	126	292	466	594
1972	58	20	71	208	275	480	480
1973	1	4	41	111	253	434	564
1974	24	33	158	132	374	454	558
1975	47	8	61	155	342	455	514

Feb	Mar	Apr	May	June	Total
0.0	0.0	0.0	0.0	0.0	T
0.0	0.0	0.0	0.0	0.0	T
2.8	0.0	0.0	0.0	0.0	4.8
0.0	0.0	0.0	0.0	0.0	0.0
0.0	0.0	0.0	0.0	0.0	T
0.2	T	0.0	0.0	0.0	0.4

Average Temperature

Year	Jan	Feb	Mar	Apr	May	June	July	Aug	Sept	Oct	Nov	Dec	Annual
1936	50.8	51.1	64.9	65.7	74.0	81.4	80.8	82.0	79.4	67.3	57.2	55.1	67.5
1937	56.6	56.4	56.6	65.5	74.0	81.4	82.6	83.2	78.0	68.4	56.3	54.1	67.8
1938	54.4	59.8	66.6	65.4	73.8	79.8	82.2	81.9	77.4	72.1	57.9	55.7	68.9
1939	55.8	55.9	63.4	67.6	75.6	80.6	82.4	82.1	79.5	71.2	57.6	56.6	69.0
#1940	42.1	52.9	61.4	66.3	72.8	78.6	81.7	81.8	76.0	70.0	60.6	57.4	66.8
1941	56.1	52.4	56.7	69.0	74.9	80.8	83.3	83.4	79.7	75.2	58.4	56.1	68.8
1942	50.1	53.0	59.6	67.1	74.9	81.2	81.4	82.4	76.2	71.2	63.5	55.8	68.0
1943	52.4	58.3	58.6	70.2	77.0	81.6	83.0	83.6	76.0	68.6	57.8	53.2	68.4
1944	52.3	61.4	61.7	69.5	73.3	82.0	84.4	83.8	79.4	69.9	61.8	52.2	69.3
1945	52.4	58.6	67.8	68.8	73.1	80.9	83.0	83.0	79.9	68.5	65.5	51.4	69.4
1946	51.6	56.4	64.0	70.6	75.4	79.2	82.2	82.8	78.4	72.1	62.2	57.8	69.4
1947	52.2	48.8	56.0	69.4	75.4	81.6	82.5	82.6	80.0	75.0	59.0	55.0	68.1
1948	46.2	54.8	61.7	71.4	76.7	82.4	84.3	84.5	77.3	69.6	60.5	59.0	69.0
1949	52.5	59.0	62.5	66.1	78.0	82.6	83.2	82.0	80.0	71.9	62.8	58.2	69.9
1950	63.1	61.3	60.5	67.0	78.0	80.3	82.3	82.4	79.3	73.0	60.7	55.1	70.2
1951	53.8	55.2	62.9	67.0	75.0	82.1	84.3	85.8	79.6	72.4	58.2	58.1	69.5
1952	62.0	58.8	60.1	64.9	73.3	81.3	82.7	84.6	78.5	65.9	59.0	53.7	68.7
1953	56.6	55.8	68.5	68.7	76.7	83.9	84.1	82.1	79.4	71.5	60.0	51.4	69.9
1954	56.4	60.6	60.9	71.5	72.4	81.3	84.8	84.5	81.4	73.0	60.0	57.4	70.3
1955	54.1	56.1	64.7	71.2	77.0	79.4	83.1	82.8	80.3	70.7	61.5	56.2	69.8
1956	54.3	59.2	62.6	67.7	77.3	80.8	84.3	83.8	80.2	73.3	59.9	59.0	70.2
1957	57.9	62.9	61.2	68.6	76.5	80.5	85.4	83.8	76.9	67.9	61.3	57.3	70.0
1958	50.3	49.9	57.8	69.2	77.2	83.4	84.8	84.2	79.7	69.6	62.5	52.6	68.4
1959	50.3	56.3	60.3	66.7	76.9	82.3	82.3	82.3	80.1	72.2	55.8	55.0	68.4
#1960	51.8	49.7	57.4	69.8	73.9	82.4	84.7	82.4	79.5	73.2	64.3	52.8	68.5
1961	49.5	57.9	66.8	68.0	77.0	80.4	82.6	82.2	79.7	70.5	59.8	56.3	69.2
1962	49.3	63.9	58.9	68.1	75.7	79.8	84.1	85.9	81.3	74.6	60.1	54.8	69.7
1963	48.3	52.6	64.9	74.5	77.5	82.0	84.3	84.3	80.4	75.0	64.1	47.1	69.6
1964	51.6	49.4	60.4	70.2	75.8	30.4	83.7	84.4	79.3	67.8	65.0	55.9	68.7
1965	56.0	55.1	58.7	73.5	77.1	83.0	85.1	83.5	81.2	69.4	69.1	58.9	70.9
1966	48.4	52.8	61.5	70.6	75.9	80.0	84.3	82.4	79.6	69.7	64.7	54.2	68.7
1967	54.9	54.5	67.6	75.7	75.9	82.6	82.1	81.1	77.6	70.5	64.1	55.4	70.2
1968	52.7	50.4	59.0	71.1	76.3	80.5	82.5	84.0	78.6	73.5	59.7	55.7	68.7
#1969	56.7	56.9	56.1	70.3	75.4	80.0	84.4	83.2	78.2	71.0	58.5	55.2	68.8
1970	46.7	53.9	56.9	69.3	72.1	78.4	81.4	83.1	78.9	66.7	56.9	60.5	67.1
1971	56.7	55.7	59.4	66.6	74.1	80.3	83.9	80.4	78.3	72.0	60.0	59.9	68.9
1972	56.5	55.2	64.3	71.2	73.7	80.8	80.3	80.3	79.6	69.8	54.7	52.0	68.2
1973	47.4	51.4	63.7	64.6	72.8	79.2	83.0	79.5	78.1	71.8	67.3	53.5	67.7
1974	55.0	56.2	66.8	67.2	76.9	79.9	82.8	81.6	74.6	70.6	60.2	54.6	68.9
1975	56.9	55.4	61.1	68.3	75.9	80.0	81.5	81.1	74.9	69.5	59.7	52.7	68.1
RECORD MEAN	53.2	54.6	62.0	67.9	74.3	79.8	82.4	81.3	77.5	70.2	59.6	55.5	68.2
MAX	63.5	66.9	73.0	78.2	84.2	90.0	93.3	91.5	87.1	81.6	71.7	66.9	79.0
MIN	42.9	42.3	51.0	57.5	64.3	69.5	71.5	71.1	67.9	58.7	47.5	44.0	57.4

# Indicates a station move or relocation of instruments.

HOUSTON, TX

Feb	Mar	Apr	May	June	Total
219	141	27	0	0	1236
129	138	45	3	0	995
417	234	30	0	0	1631
254	163	58	0	0	1495
441	260	8	1	0	1748
227	56	61	0	0	1328
99	209	32	0	0	1307
351	88	7	0	0	1439
446	158	19	0	0	1695
284	250	0	0	0	1294
334	144	12	0	0	1263
298	68	0	0	0	1193
415	229	17	0	0	1483
234	281	1	0	2	1303
309	252	51	12	0	1774
273	219	72	3	0	1420
295	85	17	0	0	1109
379	75	117	5	0	1898
273	95	60	0	0	1204
270	179	48	0	0	1334

Aug	Sept	Oct	Nov	Dec	Total
569	402	222	48	9	2868
567	423	131	38	76	2611
485	409	229	52	44	2818
482	447	206	17	12	2756
458	401	225	151	12	2655
519	295	196	60	18	2821
505	303	174	68	24	2656

Precipitation

Year	Jan	Feb	Mar	Apr	May	June	July	Aug	Sept	Oct	Nov	Dec	Annual
1936	2.77	2.06	0.85	1.72	12.19	0.13	6.86	3.23	3.68	1.85	2.57	6.05	43.96
1937	2.92	1.82	4.41	0.36	T	4.91	2.82	3.64	4.81	4.73	2.22	5.73	38.37
1938	5.88	1.83	1.03	3.88	7.77	4.12	2.05	3.09	4.42	1.55	2.17	2.08	39.87
1939	3.16	1.98	1.21	1.10	5.86	2.55	8.27	2.39	1.42	3.36	1.98	2.04	35.32
#1940	0.92	2.25	1.89	1.12	1.20	5.80	3.11	0.76	3.67	4.20	9.53	4.58	39.03
1941	1.97	2.57	6.45	6.56	4.51	9.25	5.70	3.24	11.17	11.48	2.41	2.35	67.66
1942	1.29	2.41	2.03	4.94	1.77	3.31	12.38	5.56	2.72	1.57	3.99	3.72	45.69
1943	3.69	1.31	3.98	1.76	3.91	2.43	9.14	1.92	3.19	1.04	12.14	4.79	49.30
1944	10.51	2.15	6.64	1.14	12.44	2.17	0.24	2.61	9.15	0.65	3.71	6.38	57.79
1945	1.97	2.58	2.18	4.33	7.35	5.69	2.29	18.51	3.44	4.44	0.51	7.15	60.44
1946	6.56	2.82	2.48	3.87	9.60	9.77	5.35	4.32	8.84	2.01	14.36	2.88	72.86
1947	4.39	1.09	2.79	2.02	8.54	1.74	2.17	8.86	1.29	1.91	4.58	3.82	43.20
1948	4.44	4.11	1.94	2.19	5.35	3.59	2.74	2.80	2.74	0.92	7.23	1.37	39.42
1949	4.76	5.24	4.43	6.17	1.18	2.55	9.39	3.87	1.31	22.31	0.18	9.80	71.19
1950	4.62	5.00	1.22	4.96	2.49	7.10	3.29	0.72	1.50	0.69	1.17	1.12	33.88
1951	5.37	1.42	4.84	1.28	3.32	3.32	1.06	2.01	5.40	1.18	1.55	2.53	33.28
1952	0.86	7.12	2.16	6.12	3.51	3.74	4.33	1.09	2.62	T	6.58	5.53	43.66
1953	1.57	3.40	0.07	1.27	7.86	3.49	2.06	8.38	0.14	2.62	5.27	7.24	43.37
1954	1.65	0.09	0.89	2.81	2.70	1.24	4.86	3.89	0.49	6.98	1.74	1.42	28.76
1955	5.57	6.03	0.93	3.51	3.54	1.56	2.01	10.10	5.34	0.63	1.06	1.60	41.88
1956	3.96	2.42	0.78	1.84	3.32	4.07	0.38	0.38	1.88	2.66	1.52	5.11	28.32
1957	0.91	2.46	11.42	8.07	1.87	3.96	0.84	3.23	8.29	11.53	6.70	1.83	61.11
1958	4.69	3.59	1.47	2.58	2.40	0.47	6.04	3.16	15.40	2.03	1.32	0.78	43.93
1959	2.70	11.33	1.58	7.76	6.20	2.78	9.67	8.45	4.76	5.76	1.90	5.34	68.23
1960	2.05	3.93	0.38	1.42	0.90	14.66	2.34	7.42	0.61	7.32	3.69	8.97	53.69
1961	4.44	3.88	1.84	2.42	3.59	11.11	10.07	4.17	7.89	0.05	10.20	3.31	62.97
1962	1.73	0.71	0.94	4.81	1.15	7.40	0.07	2.77	3.97	3.12	5.68	4.78	37.13
1963	3.09	2.60	0.55	0.92	0.62	7.79	2.08	1.85	1.94	0.30	5.72	4.83	32.29
1964	2.89	4.97	2.24	1.63	2.25	1.89	1.68	2.61	6.76	2.35	4.28	5.57	39.12
1965	1.87	3.27	0.81	0.95	6.53	3.06	1.57	2.29	3.56	3.09	4.82	6.15	37.97
1966	4.46	7.75	2.20	7.98	11.21	4.42	1.45	7.11	4.01	5.45	1.56	1.53	59.13
1967	2.41	2.17	1.83	4.42	2.54	0.17	7.77	1.60	4.84	3.18	0.50	5.02	36.45
1968	8.02	1.99	2.92	3.02	13.24	11.18	6.49	2.90	3.87	3.91	2.71	1.19	61.44
#1969	2.74	5.31	3.18	3.34	4.73	1.51	3.89	2.67	6.08	3.30	2.13	4.33	43.26
1970	1.93	2.52	5.08	2.21	14.39	0.26	2.28	2.03	6.22	9.09	1.54	0.64	48.19
1971	0.36	2.11	1.21	2.14	3.41	2.42	1.42	6.95	5.17	3.49	1.82	7.33	37.83
1972	3.30	1.20	8.52	2.85	6.99	3.02	2.76	3.90	6.23	3.34	6.49	2.20	50.80
1973	5.00	3.40	3.68	7.15	4.22	13.46	6.77	3.73	9.38	9.31	1.59	2.47	70.16
1974	7.68	0.55	4.20	1.68	5.61	0.59	1.75	6.94	4.51	4.53	7.90	3.35	49.29
1975	1.97	2.63	3.19	4.80	7.57	7.50	5.48	5.72	0.80	5.62	2.08	3.61	50.97
RECORD MEAN	3.69	3.11	2.69	3.36	4.79	4.44	4.18	4.22	4.56	3.82	4.01	4.20	47.07

Record mean values above are means through the current year for the period beginning in June 1969 for temperature, January 1933 for precipitation, and 1935 for snowfall. Data are from airport locations.

(Continued)

at the city office has ranged from 17.64 inches to only a trace. Since thundershowers are the main source of rainfall, precipitation may vary substantially in different sections of the City on a day-to-day basis.

Records of sky cover for daylight hours indicate about one-fourth of the days per year as clear, with a maximum of clear days in October and November. Cloudy days are relatively frequent from December to May and partly cloudy days are the more frequent for June through September.Sunshine averaged near 60 percent of the possible amount for the year at the Federal Building for 1938-1960, ranging from 46 percent for the winter months to 69 percent for the summer. Data from the airport locations since 1961 indicate slightly higher percentages of sunshine. Snow rarely occurs; however, on February 14-15, 1895, 20.0 inches of unmelted snow was measured, but 24-hour amounts were not reported. In only one winter season, 1972-73, were as many as three measurable snows recorded.

Heavy fog occurs on an average of 16 days a year and light fog occurs about 62 days a year in the City, but the frequency of heavy fog is considerably higher at William P. Hobby Airport and at Intercontinental Airport.

Destructive windstorms are fairly infrequent, but both thundersqualls and tropical storms occasionally pass through the area.

At the city office, the average date of the last temperature 32 degrees or lower in spring is February 5. The average date of the first 32 degree temperature in fall is December 11. The average period from the last 32 degree temperature in spring to the first in fall is 309 days. The latest date of 32 degree temperature in spring is March 27, 1955, and the earliest date in fall is October 25, 1892.

Normals, Means, and Extremes

Month	Normal Degree days Base 65 °F		Precipitation in inches Ø												Relative humidity pct.			
			Water equivalent							Snow, Ice pellets				Hour 00	Hour 06	Hour 12	Hour 18
	Heating	Cooling	Normal	Maximum monthly	Year	Minimum monthly	Year	Maximum in 24 hrs.	Year	Maximum monthly	Year	Maximum in 24 hrs.	Year	(Local time)			
(a)				6		6		6		6		6		6	6	6	6
J	416	16	3.57	7.68	1974	0.36	1971	2.00	1974	2.0	1973	2.0	1973	87	89	67	73
F	294	23	3.54	3.40	1973	0.55	1974	1.55	1973	2.8	1973	1.4	1973	84	87	57	59
M	189	58	2.68	8.52	1972	1.21	1971	7.47	1972	0.0		0.0		85	89	61	62
A	23	155	3.54	7.15	1973	1.68	1974	2.54	1973	0.0		0.0		88	90	60	64
M	0	335	5.10	14.39	1970	3.41	1971	4.69	1970	0.0		0.0		90	93	61	65
J	0	483	4.52	13.46	1973	0.26	1970	6.61	1973	0.0		0.0		89	92	59	62
J	0	567	4.12	6.77	1973	1.42	1971	3.99	1973	0.0		0.0		89	93	58	63
A	0	570	4.35	6.95	1971	2.03	1970	3.21	1974	0.0		0.0		93	95	62	70
S	0	426	4.65	9.38	1973	0.80	1975	2.87	1973	0.0		0.0		93	95	66	74
O	24	207	4.05	9.31	1973	3.30	1969	4.06	1970	0.0		0.0		93	95	60	76
N	155	38	4.03	7.90	1974	1.54	1970	3.55	1974	0.0		0.0		87	90	59	74
D	333	11	4.04	7.33	1971	0.64	1973	3.43	1971	0.0		0.0		86	88	62	74
YR	1434	2889	48.19	14.39	MAY 1970	0.26	JUN 1970	7.47	MAR 1972	2.8	FEB 1973	2.0	JAN 1973	89	91	61	68

(To better understand these tables, see full explanation of terms beginning on page 322)

Month	Wind Ø					Pct. of possible sunshine	Mean sky cover, tenths, sunrise to sunset	Mean number of days											Average station pressure mb.
			Fastest mile					Sunrise to sunset							Temperatures °F Max.		Min.		
	Mean speed m.p.h.	Prevailing direction	Speed m.p.h.	Direction	Year			Clear	Partly cloudy	Cloudy	Precipitation .01 inch or more	Snow, Ice pellets 1.0 inch or more	Thunderstorms	Heavy fog, visibility ¼ mile or less	(b) 90° and above	32° and below	32° and below	0° and below	Elev. 108 feet m.s.l.
(a)	6	15	6	6		6	6	6	6	6	6	6	6	6	6	6	6	6	3
J	8.1	NNW	30	34	1975	41	7.0	7	6	18	11	*	2	7	0	1	8	0	1015.8
F	8.6	SSE	35	29	1974	54	6.2	8	6	14	7	*	2	5	0	0	6	0	1015.7
M	9.4	SSE	32	24	1972	48	6.6	8	6	17	10	0	4	5	*	0	1	0	1010.1
A	9.5	SSE	33	30	1973	51	6.7	7	6	17	7	0	4	3	0	0	*	0	1011.6
M	7.8	SSE	36	13	1973	57	6.2	7	10	14	10	0	8	2	4	0	0	0	1008.9
J	7.3	SSE	45	30	1973	63	6.0	7	12	11	8	0	8	2	18	0	0	0	1010.6
J	6.3	S	46	10	1969	68	6.0	6	15	10	10	0	13	0	26	0	0	0	1012.3
A	5.1	SSE	32	18	1973	61	6.1	6	14	11	11	0	14	1	22	0	0	0	1012.5
S	6.7	SSE	35	10	1973	57	6.3	6	10	14	10	0	8	2	11	0	0	0	1011.3
O	6.3	ESE	35	32	1973	61	5.2	11	9	11	8	0	4	5	2	0	0	0	1015.0
N	7.9	SSE	37	33	1972	58	5.2	11	8	11	8	0	2	4	0	0	2	0	1015.3
D	7.7	SSE	35	31	1973	69	6.5	9	4	18	9	0	2	6	0	0	5	0	1016.1
YR	7.6	SSE	46	10	JUL 1969	56	6.2	93	106	166	108	1	72	41	83	1	23	0	1012.9

FOOTNOTES

Ø Extremes for period June 1969 to date.

Means and extremes above are from existing and comparable exposures. Annual extremes have been exceeded at other sites in the locality as follows: Highest temperature 108 in August 1909; lowest temperature 5 in January 1940 and earlier; maximum monthly precipitation 22.31 in October 1949; minimum monthly precipitation Trace in October 1952 and May 1937; maximum precipitation in 24 hours 15.65 in August 1945; maximum monthly snowfall 4.4 in February 1960; maximum snowfall in 24 hours 4.4 in February 1960; fastest mile of wind 84 from NW in March 1926.

Station: SAN ANTONIO, TEXAS INTERNATIONAL AIRPORT
Elevation (ground): 788 feet

TEMPERATURES °F

Month	Normal			Extremes			
	Daily maximum	Daily minimum	Monthly	Record highest	Year	Record lowest	Year
(a)				34		34	
J	61.6	39.8	50.7	89	1971	0	1949
F	65.6	43.4	54.5	92	1959	6	1951
M	72.5	49.1	60.8	100	1971	21	1948
A	80.3	58.8	69.6	99	1963	33	1975
M	86.2	65.7	76.0	101	1967	44	1954
J	92.4	72.0	82.2	103	1960	53	1964
J	95.6	73.8	84.7	106	1954	62	1967
A	95.9	73.4	84.7	106	1962	61	1966
S	89.8	68.8	79.3	102	1951	41	1942
O	81.8	59.2	70.5	95	1962	33	1970
N	71.1	48.2	59.7	91	1962	23	1959
D	64.6	41.8	53.2	90	1955	14	1950
YR	79.8	57.8	68.8	106	AUG 1962	0	JAN 1949

IMPORTANT:
The time-period covered by this record is limited: See footnotes on next page for explanation and for additional history of EXTREME HIGHS AND LOWS recorded in the general area.

The City of San Antonio is located in the south-central portion of Texas. Northwest of the city the terrain slopes upward to the Edwards Plateau and to the southeast it slopes downward to the Gulf Coastal Plains. Soils are blackland clay and silty loam on the Plains and thin limestone soils on the Edwards Plateau.

The location of San Antonio on the edge of the Gulf Coastal Plains results in a modified sub-tropical climate, predominantly continental during the winter months and marine during the summer months. Normal mean temperatures range from 50.7 degrees in January to a high of 84.7 degrees in July. While the summer is hot, with daily maximum temperatures above 90 degrees over 80% of the time, extremely high temperatures are rare, the highest on record being 107 degrees. Mild weather prevails during much of the winter months, with below-freezing temperatures occurring on an average of about 20 days each year.

San Antonio is situated between a semiarid area to the west and the coastal area of heavy precipitation to the southeast. The normal annual rainfall of 27.54 inches is sufficient for the normal production of most crops. Precipitation is fairly well distributed throughout the year with heaviest amounts during May in the spring and September in the fall. Precipitation from April through September usually occurs with thunderstorms, with fairly large amounts falling in short periods of time, while most of the winter precipitation occurs as light rain or drizzle. Thunderstorms and heavy rains have occurred in all months of the year. Hail of damaging intensity seldom occurs but light hail is frequent in connection with the springtime thunderstorms. Measurable snow occurs only once in 3 or 4 years with the greatest annual amount 7.4 inches in 1926.

Northerly winds prevail during most of the winter, while south-easterly winds from the Gulf of Mexico prevail during the summertime and may be experienced for long periods during the winter. Rather strong northerly winds occasionally occur during the winter months in connection with "northers". No tornadoes have been experienced in the immediate area.

Being located only 140 miles from the Gulf of Mexico, tropical storms occasionally affect the city with strong winds and heavy rains. The fastest mile of wind recorded, 74 m.p.h., occurred as a tropical storm moved inland east of the city in August 1942.

Relative humidity averages above 80% during the early morning hours most of the year, dropping to near 50% in the late afternoon.

San Antonio, popularly known as the place "where the sunshine spends the winter", has about 50% of the possible amount of sunshine during the winter months and more than 70% during the summer months. Skies are clear more than 35% of the time and cloudy about 30%. Air carried over San Antonio by south-easterly winds is lifted orographically, causing low stratus clouds to develop frequently during the later part of the night. These clouds usually dissipate before noon with clear skies prevailing a high percentage of the time during the afternoon.

SAN ANTONIO, TEXAS

Normals, Means, and Extremes

(To better understand these tables, see full explanation of terms beginning on page 322)

Month	Normal Degree days Base 65 °F: Heating	Cooling	Precipitation in inches — Water equivalent: Normal	Maximum monthly	Year	Minimum monthly	Year	Maximum in 24 hrs.	Year	Snow, Ice pellets: Maximum monthly	Year	Maximum in 24 hrs.	Year	Relative humidity pct. Hour 00 (Local time)	Hour 06	Hour 12	Hour 18	Wind: Mean speed m.p.h.	Prevailing direction	Fastest mile: Speed m.p.h.	Direction	Year	Pct. of possible sunshine	Mean sky cover, tenths, sunrise to sunset	Mean number of days — Sunrise to sunset: Clear	Partly cloudy	Cloudy	Precipitation .01 inch or more	Snow, Ice pellets 1.0 inch or more	Thunderstorms	Heavy fog, visibility ¼ mile or less	Temperatures °F Max. (b) 90° and above	Max. 32° and below	Min. 32° and below	Min. 0° and below	Average station pressure mb. Elev. 794 feet m.s.l.
(a)				33		33		33		33		33		33	33	33	33	33	15	33	33		33	33	33	33	33	33	33	33	33	33	33	33	33	3
J	451	8	1.66	8.52	1968	0.04	1971	3.18	1968	4.7	1949	4.7	1949	76	81	60	58	9.1	N	56	NW	1953	49	6.2	9	6	16	8	*	1	5	0	*	8	*	990.4
F	310	17	2.06	6.43	1965	0.03	1954	2.34	1965	3.5	1966	3.5	1966	75	80	57	53	9.8	NE	56	N	1954	52	6.1	8	6	14	8	*	1	3	*	*	4	0	990.4
M	194	63	1.54	4.19	1957	0.03	1961	2.36	1945	T	1965	T	1965	72	79	53	47	10.5	SE	57	NE	1955	58	6.1	9	7	15	7	0	2	3	1	0	2	0	984.5
A	31	169	2.54	9.32	1957	0.14	1955	2.77	1946	0.0		0.0		76	83	56	52	10.6	SE	57	W	1953	56	6.4	7	8	15	7	0	4	1	3	0	0	0	985.9
M	0	341	3.07	11.24	1972	0.17	1961	6.53	1972	0.0		0.0		81	88	58	54	10.1	SE	73	NW	1946	57	6.3	7	11	13	8	0	6	1	9	0	0	0	984.0
J	0	516	2.79	10.44	1973	0.01	1967	6.18	1951	0.0		0.0		80	88	55	51	10.1	SE	59	E	1953	68	5.5	7	16	7	6	0	4	*	22	0	0	0	985.4
J	0	611	1.69	8.19	1942	T	1944	6.97	1958	0.0		0.0		75	87	50	44	9.1	SSE	52	NE	1943	76	5.0	9	16	6	4	0	3	*	29	0	0	0	987.5
A	0	611	2.41	11.14	1974	0.00	1952	5.57	1950	0.0		0.0		74	86	50	46	8.5	SE	74	NE	1942	74	4.9	11	14	6	5	0	4	*	28	0	0	0	987.8
S	0	429	3.71	15.78	1946	0.06	1947	7.28	1973	0.0		0.0		78	86	55	52	8.4	SE	49	NE	1952	68	5.2	10	12	8	7	0	4	*	17	0	0	0	987.2
O	32	202	2.84	9.56	1942	T	1952	5.29	1942	0.0		0.0		77	84	53	53	8.4	N	43	NW	1945	66	4.8	12	10	9	6	0	2	2	4	0	0	0	990.1
N	179	20	1.77	5.39	1974	T	1966	4.33	1974	0.3	1957	0.3	1957	76	80	55	56	8.9	N	43	N	1950	57	5.4	11	7	12	6	0	2	3	*	0	2	0	990.0
D	373	7	1.46	4.51	1965	0.03	1950	2.89	1944	0.2	1964	0.2	1964	76	81	57	57	8.6	N	48	NW	1947	52	5.9	10	6	15	7	0	1	5	*	0	6	0	990.6
YR	1570	2994	27.54	15.78	SEP 1946	0.00	AUG 1952	7.28	SEP 1973	4.7	JAN 1949	4.7	JAN 1949	76	84	55	52	9.3	SE	74	NE	AUG 1942	62	5.6	110	119	136	80	*	36	23	113	*	22	*	987.8

FOOTNOTES

Means and extremes above are from existing and comparable exposures. Annual extremes have been exceeded at other sites in the locality as follows: Highest temperature 107 in August 1909; maximum monthly snowfall 6.4 in January 1926; maximum snowfall in 24 hours 5.0 in January 1940.

Snowfall

Season	July	Aug	Sept	Oct	Nov	Dec	Jan
1936-37	0.0	0.0	0.0	0.0	0.0	0.0	0.0
1937-38	0.0	0.0	0.0	0.0	0.0	0.0	0.0
1938-39	0.0	0.0	0.0	0.0	0.0	0.0	0.0
1939-40	0.0	0.0	0.0	0.0	0.0	0.0	3.2
#1940-41	0.0	0.0	0.0	0.0	0.0	0.0	0.0
1941-42	0.0	0.0	0.0	0.0	0.0	0.0	0.0
1942-43	0.0	0.0	0.0	0.0	0.0	0.0	T
1943-44	0.0	0.0	0.0	0.0	0.0	0.0	1.1
1944-45	0.0	0.0	0.0	0.0	0.0	0.0	0.0
1945-46	0.0	0.0	0.0	0.0	0.0	0.0	T
1946-47	0.0	0.0	0.0	0.0	0.0	0.0	0.0
1947-48	0.0	0.0	0.0	0.0	0.0	T	T
1948-49	0.0	0.0	0.0	0.0	T	0.0	4.7
1949-50	0.0	0.0	0.0	0.0	0.0	0.0	T
1950-51	0.0	0.0	0.0	0.0	0.0	0.0	0.9
1951-52	0.0	0.0	0.0	0.0	0.0	0.0	0.0
1952-53	0.0	0.0	0.0	0.0	0.0	0.0	T
1953-54	0.0	0.0	0.0	0.0	0.0	0.0	T
1954-55	0.0	0.0	0.0	0.0	0.0	0.0	0.0
1955-56	0.0	0.0	0.0	0.0	T	0.0	0.0
1956-57	0.0	0.0	0.0	0.0	0.0	0.0	T
1957-58	0.0	0.0	0.0	0.0	0.3	0.0	0.0
1958-59	0.0	0.0	0.0	0.0	0.0	0.0	0.0
1959-60	0.0	0.0	0.0	0.0	T	0.0	0.0
1960-61	0.0	0.0	0.0	0.0	0.0	T	T
1961-62	0.0	0.0	0.0	0.0	0.0	0.0	0.0
1962-63	0.0	0.0	0.0	0.0	0.0	0.0	0.0
1963-64	0.0	0.0	0.0	0.0	0.0	T	T
1964-65	0.0	0.0	0.0	0.0	0.0	0.2	0.0
1965-66	0.0	0.0	0.0	0.0	0.0	0.0	T
1966-67	0.0	0.0	0.0	0.0	0.0	0.0	T
1967-68	0.0	0.0	0.0	0.0	0.0	0.0	0.0
1968-69	0.0	0.0	0.0	0.0	0.0	0.0	0.0
1969-70	0.0	0.0	0.0	0.0	0.0	T	T
1970-71	0.0	0.0	0.0	0.0	0.0	0.0	0.0
1971-72	0.0	0.0	0.0	0.0	0.0	0.0	T
1972-73	0.0	0.0	0.0	0.0	0.0	T	0.8
1973-74	0.0	0.0	0.0	0.0	0.0	0.0	0.0
1974-75	0.0	0.0	0.0	0.0	0.0	T	T
1975-76	0.0	0.0	0.0	0.0	0.0	0.0	
RECORD MEAN	0.0	0.0	0.0	0.0	T	T	0.2

Heating Degree Days

Season	July	Aug	Sept	Oct	Nov	Dec	Jan
1955-56	0	0	0	28	224	359	413
1956-57	0	0	0	3	229	271	370
1957-58	0	0	0	71	270	292	453
1958-59	0	0	0	75	171	451	497
1959-60	0	0	0	27	374	336	467
1960-61	0	0	0	17	138	457	523
1961-62	0	0	0	19	223	351	586
1962-63	0	0	0	9	164	393	575
1963-64	0	0	0	0	141	592	428
1964-65	0	0	0	41	155	414	346
1965-66	0	0	2	62	64	301	607
1966-67	0	0	0	57	131	456	470
1967-68	0	0	8	48	164	429	477
1968-69	0	0	0	9	278	437	394
1969-70	0	0	0	52	253	299	599
1970-71	0	0	1	72	247	201	282
1971-72	0	0	1	0	129	266	382
1972-73	0	0	0	29	334	457	551
1973-74	0	0	0	4	85	391	437
1974-75	0	0	2	19	260	433	389
1975-76	0	0	1	21	214	394	

Cooling Degree Days

Year	Jan	Feb	Mar	Apr	May	June	July
1969	11	5	8	133	273	494	683
1970	3	3	20	208	259	478	592
1971	14	36	130	189	414	564	658
1972	11	31	105	276	252	465	542
1973	8	0	69	129	310	431	570
1974	11	22	171	188	387	439	568
1975	29	1	51	151	273	457	502

Feb	Mar	Apr	May	June	Total
0.0	0.0	0.0	0.0	0.0	0.0
0.0	0.0	0.0	0.0	0.0	0.0
0.0	0.0	0.0	0.0	0.0	0.0
T	0.0	0.0	0.0	0.0	3.2
0.1	0.0	0.0	0.0	0.0	0.1
0.0	0.0	0.0	0.0	0.0	0.0
0.0	0.0	0.0	0.0	0.0	T
0.0	0.0	0.0	0.0	0.0	1.1
0.0	0.0	0.0	0.0	0.0	0.0
0.0	0.0	0.0	0.0	0.0	T
0.0	T	0.0	0.0	0.0	T
0.0	T	0.0	0.0	0.0	T
0.0	0.0	0.0	0.0	0.0	4.7
0.0	0.0	0.0	0.0	0.0	T
0.4	0.0	0.0	0.0	0.0	1.3
0.0	0.0	0.0	0.0	0.0	0.0
0.0	0.0	0.0	0.0	0.0	T
0.0	0.0	0.0	0.0	0.0	T
T	0.0	0.0	0.0	0.0	T
0.0	0.0	0.0	0.0	0.0	T
0.0	0.0	0.0	0.0	0.0	T
1.2	T	0.0	0.0	0.0	1.5
0.0	T	0.0	0.0	0.0	T
T	0.0	0.0	0.0	0.0	T
T	0.0	0.0	0.0	0.0	T
0.0	0.0	0.0	0.0	0.0	0.0
T	0.0	0.0	0.0	0.0	T
2.0	0.0	0.0	0.0	0.0	2.0
T	T	0.0	0.0	0.0	0.2
3.5	0.0	0.0	0.0	0.0	3.5
T	0.0	0.0	0.0	0.0	T
T	0.0	0.0	0.0	0.0	T
0.0	0.0	0.0	0.0	0.0	0.0
T	0.0	0.0	0.0	0.0	T
0.0	0.0	0.0	0.0	0.0	0.0
0.0	0.0	0.0	0.0	0.0	T
2.1	0.0	0.0	0.0	0.0	2.9
0.0	0.0	0.0	0.0	0.0	0.0
0.0	0.0	0.0	0.0	0.0	T
0.3	T	0.0	0.0	0.0	0.5

Average Temperature

Year	Jan	Feb	Mar	Apr	May	June	July	Aug	Sept	Oct	Nov	Dec	Annual
1936	52.0	51.0	66.3	68.0	74.0	82.4	81.6	83.8	79.2	66.3	57.8	56.4	68.2
#1937	50.4	56.2	58.0	70.0	76.9	82.5	83.6	86.0	82.0	72.6	58.5	52.8	69.1
1938	54.5	61.3	68.3	66.9	75.2	82.4	85.0	84.6	79.6	73.1	58.5	55.8	70.4
1939	54.6	54.1	65.4	70.8	79.2	83.1	85.2	83.4	81.2	73.4	58.4	58.8	70.6
#1940	43.8	56.0	64.0	68.8	75.6	79.6	83.7	85.1	79.0	72.3	59.4	56.8	68.7
1941	55.7	52.8	56.1	68.6	76.3	81.0	84.4	84.8	81.6	75.8	59.1	54.9	69.3
#1942	50.2	53.8	61.4	69.6	76.0	83.4	81.2	82.7	75.6	69.6	63.0	55.0	68.5
1943	50.2	58.4	58.3	71.8	77.2	81.2	83.4	85.8	76.4	67.6	57.1	50.5	68.2
1944	50.3	57.0	60.4	68.0	71.8	81.3	84.4	84.0	78.0	69.7	60.2	49.0	67.8
1945	51.4	55.6	67.2	67.2	75.2	82.4	84.2	84.6	80.2	68.4	63.8	50.8	69.2
1946	49.2	55.6	63.0	71.1	75.4	80.0	84.4	83.8	78.2	72.4	60.4	55.8	69.1
1947	48.4	48.6	56.0	68.2	75.2	83.9	84.2	83.3	80.4	76.3	57.4	53.4	67.9
1948	45.4	52.6	60.4	72.8	78.2	84.4	85.4	85.2	77.7	70.4	57.7	55.8	68.8
1949	46.5	57.4	62.2	64.6	78.4	81.0	83.6	82.5	80.8	70.6	62.6	55.8	68.8
1950	58.4	56.7	60.6	67.1	76.9	80.7	84.2	82.5	79.5	73.3	59.4	52.8	69.4
1951	50.5	54.3	62.6	68.9	75.4	81.9	86.7	87.1	80.5	72.9	58.1	55.2	69.5
1952	59.5	58.6	60.7	65.7	73.3	81.9	83.6	86.2	77.5	65.6	58.4	51.6	68.6
1953	55.9	54.8	67.9	69.2	76.0	85.0	86.1	84.6	78.3	71.2	59.0	49.4	69.8
1954	54.9	60.4	62.3	73.7	74.9	83.5	85.8	86.7	82.6	73.1	60.6	58.3	71.4
1955	53.1	56.4	63.4	73.8	78.9	81.4	84.5	84.6	81.9	70.5	59.8	53.5	70.2
1956	52.1	57.1	63.3	69.7	78.9	84.7	85.5	84.8	80.0	73.0	57.8	56.9	70.3
1957	53.3	62.9	61.9	66.3	73.4	81.0	85.7	86.0	77.8	66.9	57.1	55.5	69.0
1958	50.1	50.0	55.8	67.7	75.1	82.8	84.6	84.8	79.2	67.7	60.8	50.1	67.4
1959	48.9	54.0	60.0	65.9	77.1	82.9	84.0	84.4	81.4	70.4	53.3	54.0	68.0
1960	50.1	49.9	56.1	69.7	74.1	83.3	84.2	83.6	78.6	73.3	62.2	50.1	67.9
1961	47.9	55.9	65.7	68.5	78.5	81.3	82.6	82.5	80.5	71.1	58.0	54.2	68.9
1962	45.9	62.8	59.1	69.7	77.9	82.3	86.9	87.5	80.9	75.5	60.4	52.2	70.1
1963	46.2	52.6	65.6	74.6	77.7	83.4	85.4	85.7	81.1	74.1	62.4	45.7	69.6
1964	51.0	49.8	61.5	70.5	77.6	82.4	86.3	86.2	80.0	66.4	62.6	52.3	68.9
1965	54.4	49.8	54.9	71.6	75.0	81.6	84.9	84.0	80.7	66.8	64.5	55.5	68.6
1966	45.4	49.8	60.0	68.6	73.5	78.8	84.2	81.9	77.5	67.0	63.0	50.7	66.7
1967	50.2	51.8	66.9	76.6	76.6	84.5	85.3	82.7	75.5	66.9	60.5	51.0	69.0
1968	49.8	48.3	58.0	68.1	75.3	80.5	82.7	84.2	76.0	72.2	56.4	50.7	66.8
1969	52.5	53.6	54.9	69.0	73.5	81.2	86.8	85.7	79.6	69.8	58.1	55.1	68.3
1970	45.6	54.8	56.8	70.2	72.9	80.7	84.0	85.7	81.1	67.7	58.0	60.1	68.1
1971	56.0	57.4	64.6	69.4	78.1	83.6	85.9	81.2	80.1	73.9	63.2	57.2	70.9
1972	52.8	56.7	66.3	73.7	72.8	80.3	82.2	82.1	82.0	71.9	54.0	50.3	68.8
1973	47.2	51.9	66.1	66.0	74.7	79.2	83.2	82.1	79.3	72.5	65.8	52.2	68.4
1974	51.0	56.5	67.9	69.7	77.3	79.4	83.0	81.2	72.3	68.2	57.3	50.9	67.9
1975	53.2	53.5	61.4	68.4	73.5	80.0	80.9	81.7	76.0	71.1	60.3	53.1	67.8
RECORD MEAN	52.1	55.4	62.2	69.4	75.5	81.6	83.9	84.1	79.3	70.9	60.5	53.8	69.1
MAX	62.5	66.2	73.4	80.0	85.5	91.6	94.4	94.8	89.4	81.8	71.0	64.1	79.6
MIN	41.6	44.5	51.0	58.8	65.4	71.5	73.4	73.3	69.1	60.0	50.0	43.4	58.5

# Indicates a station move or relocation of instruments.

SAN ANTONIO, TX

Feb	Mar	Apr	May	June	Total
275	140	22	0	0	1461
126	132	71	7	0	1209
419	289	22	0	0	1816
311	179	90	0	0	1774
433	291	14	7	0	1949
272	82	63	0	0	1552
108	206	27	0	0	1520
349	87	17	3	0	1597
434	143	23	0	0	1761
419	327	13	0	0	1715
426	182	39	5	0	1688
366	80	0	0	0	1560
478	254	39	0	0	1897
319	315	5	3	0	1760
282	266	45	7	0	1803
239	134	52	1	0	1229
263	61	7	0	0	1109
362	29	94	1	0	1857
257	74	39	0	0	1287
316	152	41	0	0	1612

Aug	Sept	Oct	Nov	Dec	Total
652	448	207	53	2	2969
651	493	163	40	57	2967
509	459	281	81	31	3366
539	515	249	12	6	3003
536	437	242	114	0	2846
506	229	124	34	5	2684
524	337	217	80	30	2652

Precipitation

Year	Jan	Feb	Mar	Apr	May	June	July	Aug	Sept	Oct	Nov	Dec	Annual
1936	0.43	0.40	2.66	2.77	6.13	6.43	2.68	2.73	4.07	1.89	2.17	1.75	34.11
#1937	0.96	0.13	2.10	0.84	7.68	2.19	1.82	0.14	0.04	3.09	0.86	6.22	26.07
1938	3.35	0.33	3.82	6.06	3.88	0.65	0.91	0.44	1.82	0.13	0.63	1.24	23.26
1939	2.08	0.95	0.65	0.78	3.22	0.10	2.12	5.08	1.90	0.07	0.99	0.89	18.83
#1940	0.64	1.86	0.94	2.50	4.19	7.47	0.64	1.22	1.42	4.66	2.40	2.85	30.79
1941	2.14	1.86	2.95	4.56	2.50	2.03	0.62	0.23	4.88	3.13	0.47	0.97	26.34
#1942	0.13	2.01	0.29	3.48	2.19	1.95	8.19	1.88	7.67	9.56	0.47	0.64	38.46
1943	0.73	0.09	1.58	1.48	2.56	1.91	3.72	0.78	4.34	0.17	1.95	1.20	20.51
1944	3.49	1.68	3.72	0.94	6.76	1.64	T	4.32	1.30	1.52	3.66	4.16	33.19
1945	2.97	3.90	2.73	2.91	1.24	5.31	1.19	1.19	3.00	3.49	1.35	1.18	30.46
1946	3.64	2.24	1.75	5.54	3.47	2.92	0.20	4.03	15.78	1.31	1.86	2.43	45.17
1947	2.14	0.29	1.46	0.30	3.32	0.31	1.00	5.34	0.06	0.19	1.01	1.90	17.32
1948	0.61	1.86	0.59	1.40	1.59	2.96	2.35	5.83	1.98	3.24	1.00	0.23	23.64
1949	2.91	2.98	2.27	8.99	0.85	8.26	2.24	1.03	0.78	7.58	0.13	2.79	40.81
1950	0.32	1.43	0.24	3.42	2.41	1.03	1.60	6.15	3.02	0.08	0.13	0.03	19.86
1951	0.25	2.43	2.76	0.93	4.44	7.07	0.51	0.06	3.75	1.44	0.67	0.13	24.44
1952	0.81	2.01	2.34	3.40	1.91	1.86	2.75	0.00	3.02	T	4.47	3.67	26.24
1953	0.41	0.90	0.53	2.08	1.00	2.19	0.01	3.12	2.48	3.06	0.34	1.44	17.56
1954	0.51	0.03	0.03	1.94	1.46	2.71	1.25	1.05	0.52	1.98	2.02	0.20	13.70
1955	1.45	2.33	1.40	0.14	4.44	2.88	1.32	0.81	0.79	0.39	1.57	0.66	18.18
1956	0.81	0.85	0.27	0.49	3.07	0.27	0.53	3.94	0.62	1.23	1.13	1.10	14.31
1957	0.51	2.53	4.19	9.32	8.22	3.49	0.73	0.21	11.10	4.71	2.90	0.92	48.83
1958	4.57	3.88	1.08	1.32	1.98	3.39	7.39	0.45	8.36	5.43	0.77	1.07	39.69
1959	0.52	2.50	0.13	2.55	2.43	1.32	1.48	3.05	1.72	5.11	2.17	1.52	24.50
1960	0.76	1.22	1.65	2.08	1.21	2.70	1.31	5.96	0.76	7.84	1.30	2.97	29.76
1961	0.68	1.79	0.03	0.32	0.17	7.87	7.04	0.15	2.24	3.39	2.09	0.70	26.47
1962	0.48	0.90	0.91	4.02	1.31	2.44	0.13	1.57	2.69	2.19	4.97	2.29	23.90
1963	0.27	3.59	0.21	1.88	3.03	2.28	0.03	0.63	1.11	2.75	1.93	0.94	18.65
1964	3.40	1.89	1.73	1.16	1.79	4.88	0.02	5.19	4.15	1.64	4.81	1.22	31.88
1965	2.40	6.43	2.30	1.97	8.18	2.42	0.08	1.65	3.13	2.69	0.89	4.51	36.65
1966	1.47	2.30	1.14	3.20	3.53	1.78	0.06	4.28	2.13	1.11	T	0.44	21.44
1967	0.18	0.48	2.18	0.94	2.22	0.01	2.12	3.17	11.16	2.00	3.42	1.38	29.26
1968	8.52	1.85	1.27	1.92	2.82	2.63	1.53	0.94	2.99	0.69	4.58	0.66	30.40
1969	1.76	2.90	2.35	2.46	4.61	2.32	0.36	4.19	1.32	5.85	1.02	2.28	31.42
1970	1.10	2.66	1.98	1.13	7.30	0.89	0.91	0.95	4.35	1.31	0.01	0.15	22.74
1971	0.04	0.81	0.04	1.39	1.52	2.74	1.05	9.42	4.57	4.62	2.74	2.86	31.80
1972	1.35	0.40	0.13	1.94	11.24	2.86	3.13	4.24	1.40	1.99	2.37	0.44	31.49
1973	2.77	2.76	1.58	5.41	2.73	10.44	6.91	1.29	13.09	4.85	0.29	0.16	52.28
1974	1.36	0.04	0.94	2.18	4.28	1.02	1.28	11.14	3.85	4.09	5.39	1.43	37.00
1975	1.04	3.30	0.52	2.69	6.91	4.60	1.06	1.28	0.51	2.25	0.03	1.48	25.67
RECORD MEAN	1.59	1.70	1.63	2.89	3.39	2.84	2.00	2.43	3.21	2.41	1.81	1.66	27.56

Record mean values above are means through the current year for the period beginning in 1885 for temperature and precipitation, 1943 for snow. Data are from City Office locations through 1940 and Airport thereafter.

SALT LAKE CITY, UTAH

Station: SALT LAKE CITY, UTAH INTERNATIONAL AIRPORT
Elevation (ground): 4220 feet

TEMPERATURES °F

Month	Normal			Extremes			
	Daily maximum	Daily minimum	Monthly	Record highest	Year	Record lowest	Year
(a)				16		16	
J	37.4	18.5	28.0	61	1971	-18	1963
F	43.4	23.3	33.4	69	1972	-4	1960
M	50.8	28.3	39.6	78	1960	2	1966
A	61.8	36.6	49.2	85	1962	22	1971
M	72.4	44.2	58.3	92	1961	25	1965
J	81.3	51.1	66.2	104	1961	35	1962
J	92.8	60.5	76.7	107	1960	40	1968
A	90.2	58.7	74.5	103	1960	37	1965
S	80.3	49.3	64.8	96	1967	27	1965
O	66.4	38.4	52.4	89	1963	16	1971
N	50.0	28.1	39.1	75	1967	11	1959
D	39.0	21.5	30.3	67	1969	-15	1972
YR	63.8	38.2	51.0	107	JUL 1960	-18	JAN 1963

IMPORTANT:
The time-period covered by this record is limited: See footnotes following table of NORMALS, MEANS AND EXTREMES for explanation and for additional history of EXTREME HIGHS AND LOWS recorded in the general area.

Salt Lake City is located in northern Utah on the western slope of the Wasatch Mountains, a range rising to heights of 8,500 to nearly 12,000 feet above sea level. Due to the proximity of this mountain range, about three to five inches more precipitation per year can be expected along the eastern edge of the city than over the valley a few miles to the west.

Aside from the altitude (approximately 4,200 feet above sea level) and the Wasatch Mountains, the most influential natural condition affecting the climate of Salt Lake City is the Great Salt Lake. This large inland body of water, which never freezes over due to its high salt content, tends to moderate the temperature of cold winter winds blowing from the west and northwest. Of lesser importance are the Oquirrh Mountains located twenty miles to the southwest. This range, with several peaks to above 10,000 feet, shelters the Salt Lake Valley somewhat from storms associated with southwesterly winds.

Salt Lake City has a semi-arid continental climate, with four well-defined seasons. Summers are characterized by hot, dry weather; but the high temperatures during this season are usually not oppressive, since the relative humidity is generally low and the nights usually cool. July is the hottest month with average maximum readings in the nineties.

The average daily temperature range is about thirty degrees in the summer and eighteen degrees during the winter. Temperatures above 102° in the summer or colder than 10° below zero in the winter are likely to occur one season out of four.

Winters are cold, but usually not severe. Mountains to the north and east act as a barrier to

(Continued page 662)

Snowfall

Season	July	Aug	Sept	Oct	Nov	Dec	Jan
1936-37	0.0	0.0	0.0	0.0	6.5	17.7	32.3
1937-38	0.0	0.0	0.0	0.0	T	1.0	2.4
1938-39	0.0	0.0	0.0	T	1.5	2.8	11.8
1939-40	0.0	0.0	0.0	0.0	0.0	3.5	9.0
1940-41	0.0	0.0	0.0	0.0	8.8	4.7	8.2
1941-42	0.0	0.0	0.0	T	11.1	15.2	12.6
1942-43	0.0	0.0	0.0	T	1.8	2.1	6.7
1943-44	0.0	0.0	0.0	T	T	9.3	24.7
1944-45	0.0	0.0	0.0	0.0	6.2	4.0	5.3
1945-46	0.0	0.0	0.0	T	14.3	5.2	13.3
1946-47	0.0	0.0	T	T	9.5	10.1	14.9
1947-48	0.0	0.0	0.0	T	11.4	9.1	3.7
1948-49	0.0	0.0	0.0	T	11.2	34.3	30.1
1949-50	0.0	0.0	0.0	1.1	T	19.0	22.8
1950-51	0.0	0.0	T	0.0	2.5	3.8	15.7
1951-52	0.0	0.0	0.0	T	11.5	26.0	25.2
1952-53	0.0	0.0	0.0	0.0	5.6	14.1	11.4
#1953-54	0.0	0.0	0.0	T	0.4	12.7	10.6
1954-55	0.0	0.0	0.0	T	1.6	4.2	22.5
1955-56	0.0	0.0	0.0	T	15.8	10.1	6.5
1956-57	0.0	0.0	0.0	10.4	7.0	11.8	18.4
1957-58	0.0	0.0	0.0	0.0	6.3	11.1	7.6
1958-59	0.0	0.0	0.0	T	10.4	2.9	11.8
1959-60	0.0	0.0	0.0	T	0.6	10.6	13.5
1960-61	0.0	0.0	0.0	T	5.0	4.5	0.1
1961-62	0.0	0.0	0.0	8.3	11.1	8.5	15.6
1962-63	0.0	0.0	0.0	T	2.4	0.9	7.4
1963-64	0.0	0.0	0.0	T	7.6	12.9	18.2
1964-65	0.0	0.0	0.0	0.0	6.7	6.2	15.7
1965-66	0.0	0.0	2.2	0.0	2.6	12.8	5.9
1966-67	0.0	0.0	0.0	3.6	3.2	8.7	30.4
1967-68	0.0	0.0	0.0	0.0	4.2	27.1	6.8
1968-69	0.0	0.0	0.0	T	8.7	33.3	13.7
1969-70	0.0	0.0	0.0	0.1	5.6	16.0	2.8
1970-71	0.0	0.0	0.0	0.3	0.7	25.8	13.6
1971-72	0.0	0.0	4.0	16.6	5.4	17.7	10.5
1972-73	0.0	0.0	0.0	6.0	1.1	35.2	20.9
1973-74	0.0	0.0	0.0	1.3	19.5	19.6	20.1
1974-75	0.0	0.0	0.0	T	T	8.8	12.5
1975-76	0.0	0.0	0.0	0.1	18.0	11.8	
RECORD MEAN	0.0	0.0	0.1	1.1	6.3	12.4	13.4

Heating Degree Days

Season	July	Aug	Sept	Oct	Nov	Dec	Jan
1955-56	2	0	120	374	873	858	908
1956-57	0	12	58	398	915	1077	1203
1957-58	0	1	101	401	909	971	1053
1958-59	0	0	116	300	778	887	956
#1959-60	1	0	170	423	814	1142	1212
1960-61	0	19	16	419	730	1088	1116
1961-62	0	0	207	461	881	1132	1373
1962-63	3	17	59	322	695	1128	1403
1963-64	0	1	18	243	777	1252	1331
1964-65	0	44	134	365	808	975	1046
1965-66	0	20	239	317	564	1069	1058
1966-67	0	4	57	460	649	1101	1097
1967-68	0	0	57	387	653	1228	1246
1968-69	3	49	166	407	786	1174	1009
1969-70	1	0	17	530	759	1003	935
1970-71	0	0	218	550	667	1103	1002
1971-72	0	0	201	535	817	1176	1085
1972-73	0	0	110	347	761	1307	1400
1973-74	1	0	140	333	732	975	1181
1974-75	0	5	54	316	638	1025	1157
1975-76	0	1	62	365	825	989	

Cooling Degree Days

Year	Jan	Feb	Mar	Apr	May	June	July
1969	0	0	0	1	53	68	366
1970	0	0	0	0	32	152	365
1971	0	0	0	0	5	136	361
1972	0	0	0	0	34	213	386
1973	0	0	0	0	38	226	370
1974	0	0	0	0	31	303	446
1975	0	0	0	0	9	89	439

Feb	Mar	Apr	May	June	Total
8.8	5.5	2.2	0.0	0.0	73.0
12.5	13.9	T	0.3	0.0	30.1
20.1	7.4	0.0	0.0	0.0	43.6
6.0	T	0.0	0.0	0.0	18.5
0.5	1.8	6.1	0.0	0.0	30.1
8.4	11.4	T	T	0.0	58.7
13.6	7.2	T	T	T	31.4
20.1	30.8	6.4	0.0	0.0	91.3
2.2	13.4	6.8	T	0.0	37.9
1.5	1.6	0.9	0.0	0.0	36.8
6.5	2.8	3.9	0.0	0.0	47.7
7.7	20.5	1.9	T	0.0	54.3
10.3	2.3	0.0	0.0	T	88.2
2.3	4.0	1.8	2.2	0.0	53.2
3.4	8.9	1.7	T	0.0	36.0
19.0	35.6	T	0.0	0.0	117.3
T	10.1	5.3	0.1	0.0	46.6
5.6	10.7	0.0	T	T	40.0
16.5	0.6	21.8	2.9	0.0	70.1
18.6	2.2	2.7	T	0.0	55.9
0.3	4.2	5.1	T	0.0	57.2
9.5	15.7	15.5	0.0	0.0	65.7
15.2	0.4	1.3	0.0	0.0	42.0
18.2	11.4	0.7	1.0	0.0	56.0
16.0	4.9	0.8	T	0.0	31.3
10.1	25.3	1.6	0.0	0.0	80.5
0.5	16.0	14.3	0.0	0.0	41.5
8.0	33.5	1.9	5.3	0.0	87.4
9.5	1.1	2.4	5.3	0.0	46.9
18.1	17.4	2.8	0.0	0.0	61.8
4.5	11.8	11.4	1.0	0.0	74.6
13.6	8.4	14.2	T	T	74.3
27.9	5.4	0.2	0.0	0.0	89.2
3.9	5.2	23.6	0.0	0.0	57.2
8.7	8.9	1.7	1.4	0.0	61.1
7.6	1.4	15.0	0.0	0.0	78.2
3.6	17.8	2.6	0.0	0.0	87.2
17.2	6.7	26.4	T	T	110.8
7.9	22.8	13.1	7.5	0.0	72.6
9.7	9.5	5.0	0.6	T	58.1

Average Temperature

Year	Jan	Feb	Mar	Apr	May	June	July	Aug	Sept	Oct	Nov	Dec	Annual
1936	29.0	32.4	40.4	53.2	61.8	70.4	78.2	75.5	61.9	52.4	36.2	33.6	52.1
1937	13.2	30.7	41.0	46.4	61.6	66.8	77.6	76.4	67.4	54.4	43.6	36.3	51.2
1938	35.7	36.9	40.0	50.0	55.2	67.8	73.8	74.0	68.7	54.0	32.4	34.1	51.9
1939	30.5	22.6	41.6	52.6	60.5	64.8	75.6	74.4	64.2	52.2	43.0	36.3	51.5
1940	30.2	37.8	45.0	51.2	63.7	71.8	79.4	77.2	65.4	55.6	35.6	32.6	53.8
1941	30.6	38.6	43.0	46.9	60.2	65.6	75.6	73.8	59.7	49.2	40.0	34.4	51.4
1942	20.4	27.0	35.8	50.6	53.2	64.8	78.2	74.4	64.2	52.7	40.6	33.2	49.6
1943	31.0	33.6	40.2	55.6	56.0	63.8	76.0	75.7	67.6	54.8	39.9	31.2	52.1
1944	19.2	29.4	36.4	46.2	58.9	63.0	76.0	73.8	63.8	56.2	38.4	30.9	49.4
1945	32.1	36.4	38.9	44.8	58.6	60.2	75.9	73.5	60.6	55.1	39.2	30.0	50.4
1946	27.1	34.3	44.0	54.6	57.1	69.0	77.3	75.4	63.4	46.6	38.4	35.8	51.9
1947	22.0	38.4	44.6	48.6	62.8	63.6	77.6	74.1	65.0	56.4	35.5	29.8	51.5
1948	30.1	33.2	35.6	49.7	59.0	68.0	75.7	75.6	66.0	53.1	35.4	25.2	50.6
1949	11.6	22.8	42.4	53.6	60.1	67.0	76.8	76.0	67.1	48.3	44.3	30.1	50.0
1950	26.6	36.2	40.8	48.5	54.3	66.0	74.3	73.8	63.4	57.9	41.6	35.4	51.6
1951	29.6	36.3	37.1	50.3	59.0	63.7	75.8	73.5	64.6	50.5	37.1	26.1	50.3
1952	27.0	28.6	33.3	51.8	60.6	67.8	74.6	76.3	68.1	57.5	34.3	32.0	51.0
1953	39.5	37.0	43.2	46.4	52.9	66.7	78.5	75.7	68.2	54.1	46.1	29.9	53.2
#1954	34.0	36.4	38.5	53.7	61.5	65.3	78.3	73.2	64.8	52.3	44.0	30.3	52.7
1955	21.1	24.0	36.7	45.7	56.8	66.3	75.5	76.3	65.0	52.8	35.7	37.1	49.4
1956	35.5	26.4	42.4	49.9	60.4	69.6	76.4	72.7	67.0	52.1	34.3	30.0	51.4
1957	26.0	40.3	43.1	48.4	57.2	66.8	77.0	76.5	64.6	52.2	34.5	33.4	51.7
1958	30.7	41.7	39.2	47.2	65.1	70.6	74.9	77.8	65.4	55.3	38.8	36.2	53.6
#1959	33.9	36.1	41.4	51.6	55.7	71.5	77.2	74.1	62.0	51.0	37.7	27.8	51.7
1960	25.6	28.7	42.5	50.8	58.7	71.0	81.2	74.2	68.2	51.6	40.4	29.6	51.9
1961	28.7	38.1	42.9	50.1	60.8	74.7	79.9	77.8	60.0	50.0	35.3	28.2	52.2
1962	20.5	31.4	35.1	52.8	58.7	68.2	75.9	73.1	65.8	55.3	41.6	28.4	50.6
1963	19.5	38.6	39.4	44.3	60.7	63.3	77.8	77.9	67.8	57.8	38.9	24.4	50.9
1964	21.9	25.8	32.0	45.6	55.8	63.2	77.5	71.9	61.5	53.0	37.8	33.3	48.3
1965	31.0	33.0	36.8	51.0	54.7	64.8	75.0	70.9	57.5	54.5	46.1	30.2	50.5
1966	30.6	29.4	41.6	49.6	62.7	69.2	80.1	74.1	67.5	49.9	43.1	29.2	52.3
1967	29.4	37.5	44.2	46.1	56.3	64.6	78.4	78.6	66.7	52.4	43.0	25.1	51.8
1968	24.5	38.2	44.7	45.4	56.4	67.5	78.3	69.4	61.4	51.7	38.5	26.8	50.2
1969	32.2	28.7	38.4	50.4	64.0	64.8	76.6	77.6	69.7	47.7	39.5	32.4	51.9
1970	34.6	40.4	40.6	44.2	58.8	67.6	76.6	77.7	59.0	47.1	42.6	29.2	51.5
1971	32.4	34.9	40.4	48.2	56.6	67.5	76.4	76.9	59.8	47.5	37.6	26.9	50.4
1972	29.8	37.8	46.9	48.1	60.5	71.9	77.2	75.8	63.9	53.6	39.4	22.7	52.3
1973	19.6	32.3	41.8	47.6	61.6	70.2	76.6	76.6	61.5	54.1	40.5	33.4	51.3
1974	26.7	31.4	45.2	48.1	58.8	73.4	79.2	74.2	66.5	54.7	43.4	31.7	52.8
1975	27.4	35.5	41.1	44.3	54.3	64.8	78.8	73.4	65.4	53.4	37.3	32.9	50.7
RECORD													
MEAN	28.0	33.2	40.7	49.0	58.3	68.1	77.2	75.4	65.1	53.1	40.5	31.4	51.7
MAX	36.2	41.4	50.2	59.8	70.3	81.4	91.1	88.9	78.4	64.9	50.1	39.2	62.7
MIN	19.8	24.9	31.1	38.2	46.2	54.7	63.3	61.9	51.7	41.3	30.9	23.6	40.6

# Indicates a station move or relocation of instruments.

SALT LAKE CITY, UT

Feb	Mar	Apr	May	June	Total
1114	694	446	172	35	5596
685	667	489	238	70	5812
649	794	527	106	13	5525
804	722	404	296	34	5297
1049	692	419	227	14	6163
743	678	440	183	14	5446
936	921	369	220	75	6575
731	787	614	135	98	5992
1130	1016	576	303	125	6772
889	869	414	316	61	5921
989	717	456	140	40	5609
763	638	564	287	76	5696
772	622	583	276	57	5881
1010	818	433	75	67	5997
681	754	619	218	69	5586
836	754	499	258	55	5942
783	556	499	168	2	5822
909	711	515	135	67	6262
935	603	502	214	41	5657
819	734	613	334	92	5787

Precipitation

Year	Jan	Feb	Mar	Apr	May	June	July	Aug	Sept	Oct	Nov	Dec	Annual
1936	2.02	3.22	1.21	0.85	0.35	1.81	1.44	0.67	0.16	1.69	0.99	1.88	16.29
1937	1.76	1.12	1.18	1.09	1.05	0.14	1.21	0.48	0.83	2.24	0.69	1.27	13.06
1938	0.55	0.89	3.11	1.13	2.04	0.12	0.51	0.23	0.09	1.49	1.48	1.41	13.05
1939	1.23	1.78	0.78	0.92	0.51	1.08	0.30	0.14	0.88	1.14	0.01	0.59	9.36
1940	3.14	1.66	1.07	1.61	0.01	0.22	0.14	0.23	1.52	1.72	2.25	1.35	14.92
1941	0.98	1.30	2.11	2.87	1.56	1.35	1.05	1.12	0.51	2.30	1.81	1.83	18.79
1942	1.18	1.17	1.54	1.33	3.16	0.47	0.37	0.20	0.13	0.57	1.68	1.48	13.28
1943	0.95	1.70	1.23	1.14	0.68	2.09	0.15	0.47	T	1.61	0.05	0.83	10.90
1944	1.67	1.11	3.67	4.90	1.67	2.78	0.04	T	0.52	0.18	1.44	0.51	18.49
1945	0.39	1.19	1.49	1.37	0.90	2.73	1.92	3.28	0.64	0.58	2.30	0.92	17.71
1946	1.01	0.12	1.43	1.59	2.59	0.01	0.55	0.95	0.30	3.61	1.44	1.91	15.51
1947	0.95	0.81	0.58	2.32	1.88	2.93	0.01	1.38	1.01	2.43	1.88	0.79	16.97
1948	0.34	0.86	2.30	1.56	0.26	2.47	0.39	0.49	0.59	0.87	1.71	2.63	14.47
1949	2.31	0.64	2.95	1.25	2.66	0.17	0.30	0.70	0.64	2.79	0.88	1.41	16.70
1950	1.80	1.19	0.98	1.29	2.18	0.16	1.06	0.03	1.73	0.58	2.00	0.49	13.49
1951	1.69	0.64	1.26	2.60	0.87	0.09	2.17	1.79	T	1.90	1.59	2.90	17.50
1952	2.20	1.84	3.56	1.86	1.07	1.07	1.09	0.19	0.02	0.00	1.08	1.16	15.14
1953	2.73	0.39	0.86	2.77	1.05	0.51	0.81	0.88	0.13	0.32	0.96	0.91	12.32
#1954	0.90	0.81	1.50	0.65	0.63	1.83	0.91	1.77	0.59	0.54	1.61	0.69	12.43
1955	1.34	1.31	0.20	2.04	1.35	0.95	0.80	0.44	0.97	0.90	2.24	1.09	13.63
1956	2.39	1.10	0.10	1.50	2.33	0.63	0.08	0.03	0.14	1.86	0.56	1.67	12.39
1957	1.37	0.72	2.18	3.24	3.37	1.47	0.31	1.69	0.33	0.78	1.37	1.61	18.44
1958	0.87	2.20	2.19	2.92	0.30	0.04	0.05	0.23	0.25	T	1.13	0.54	10.72
1959	1.50	1.41	0.79	1.61	2.05	1.38	0.19	1.76	1.66	0.22	0.10	1.05	13.82
1960	0.96	1.58	2.45	1.11	0.73	0.39	0.02	1.33	0.49	1.19	1.73	0.39	12.37
1961	0.09	2.06	1.85	0.95	0.24	0.09	0.54	1.20	1.10	1.60	1.15	0.88	11.75
1962	0.84	1.43	2.34	2.98	2.12	0.49	2.52	0.26	0.27	0.93	0.44	0.28	14.90
1963	0.53	0.67	2.11	3.86	0.23	1.67	T	0.54	1.08	1.05	1.56	0.79	14.09
1964	0.94	0.35	2.26	2.69	2.77	2.61	0.26	0.17	0.13	0.45	1.42	3.82	17.87
1965	2.13	1.13	0.14	2.30	2.02	1.87	1.50	2.08	1.93	0.39	1.13	1.81	18.43
1966	0.41	1.19	1.21	1.43	0.51	0.07	0.33	0.22	0.83	1.18	0.75	0.86	8.99
1967	2.05	0.67	1.94	2.08	2.15	2.73	1.14	0.07	0.73	0.66	0.66	1.64	16.52
1968	0.46	2.32	2.21	2.82	2.18	1.58	0.09	3.66	0.56	1.64	1.32	2.27	21.11
1969	1.69	2.84	0.57	1.38	0.18	2.83	1.51	0.34	0.18	1.96	0.92	1.69	16.09
1970	1.24	0.94	1.01	3.25	0.89	1.63	0.86	0.57	2.80	1.61	2.27	2.80	19.87
1971	1.06	2.13	1.01	2.16	1.34	0.64	0.94	2.15	1.75	3.23	1.03	1.35	18.79
1972	1.22	0.48	1.18	3.62	0.14	0.15	0.06	0.21	1.36	2.74	1.36	3.22	15.74
1973	1.49	0.91	2.67	1.64	1.74	0.19	1.07	1.16	4.07	0.67	2.52	2.26	20.39
1974	1.80	1.65	0.97	4.57	0.39	0.28	0.18	0.32	0.03	2.03	0.90	1.34	14.46
1975	1.28	1.24	3.44	2.46	2.58	1.81	0.28	0.10	0.08	1.91	1.71	1.03	17.92
RECORD													
MEAN	1.29	1.35	1.82	2.02	1.72	0.91	0.60	0.87	0.88	1.41	1.37	1.39	15.63

Aug	Sept	Oct	Nov	Dec	Total
398	164	0	0	0	1050
398	46	0	0	0	993
374	50	0	0	0	926
340	85	0	0	0	1058
367	44	3	0	0	1048
298	108	3	0	0	1189
269	80	14	0	0	900

Record mean values above are means through the current year for the period beginning in May 1874 for temperature and precipitation, 1929 for snowfall. Data are from the Dooley Block through June 1909, from the Boston Building through 1928, and from Airport locations thereafter.

(Continued)

frequent invasions of cold continental air. The average annual snowfall ranges from 52 inches at the Airport to over 70 inches in the foothill area of the eastern portion of the city. Similarly, the average maximum depth of snow during the winter varies from 9 to about 13 inches. The average duration of continuous snow cover is 29 days. Precipitation, generally light during the summer and early fall, reaches a maximum in spring when storms from the Pacific Ocean are moving through the area more frequently than at any other season of the year. Winds are usually light, although occasional high winds have occurred in every month of the year, particularly in March.

The growing season, or freeze-free period, is quite long, averaging over five months in length. Yard and garden foliage generally are making good growth by the end of March or the first week in April, even though the last freezing temperature in the spring usually occurs in late April.

Normals, Means, and Extremes

Month	Normal Degree days Base 65 °F		Precipitation in inches												Relative humidity pct.			
			Water equivalent							Snow, Ice pellets					Hour 05	Hour 11	Hour 17	Hour 23
	Heating	Cooling	Normal	Maximum monthly	Year	Minimum monthly	Year	Maximum in 24 hrs.	Year	Maximum monthly	Year	Maximum in 24 hrs.	Year		(Local time)			
(a)				47		47		47		47		47			16	16	16	16
J	1147	0	1.27	3.14	1940	0.09	1961	1.36	1953	32.3	1937	9.7	1962		77	69	67	76
F	885	0	1.19	3.22	1936	0.12	1946	1.05	1958	27.9	1969	8.7	1944		76	63	58	75
M	787	0	1.63	3.67	1944	0.10	1956	1.83	1944	35.6	1952	15.4	1944		69	51	44	67
A	474	0	2.12	4.90	1944	0.45	1934	2.41	1957	26.4	1974	16.2	1974		67	45	39	62
M	237	30	1.49	3.37	1957	T	1934	2.03	1942	7.5	1975	6.4	1975		63	36	31	55
J	88	124	1.30	2.93	1947	0.01	1946	1.88	1948	T	1974	T	1974		61	32	27	51
J	0	363	0.70	2.52	1962	T	1963	2.35	1962	0.0		0.0			51	26	20	41
A	5	300	0.93	3.66	1968	T	1944	1.96	1932	0.0		0.0			54	28	22	44
S	105	99	0.68	4.07	1973	T	1951	2.19	1970	4.0	1971	4.0	1971		61	34	27	54
O	402	11	1.16	3.61	1946	0.00	1952	1.47	1947	16.6	1971	8.5	1971		67	43	40	65
N	777	0	1.31	2.57	1934	0.01	1939	1.13	1954	19.5	1973	11.0	1930		74	58	59	73
D	1076	0	1.39	3.82	1964	0.28	1962	1.82	1972	35.2	1972	18.1	1972		78	71	72	78
YR	5983	927	15.17	4.90	APR 1944	0.00	OCT 1952	2.41	APR 1957	35.6	MAR 1952	18.1	DEC 1972		67	46	42	62

(To better understand these tables, see full explanation of terms beginning on page 322)

Month	Wind					Pct. of possible sunshine	Mean sky cover, tenths, sunrise to sunset	Mean number of days												Average station pressure mb.
	Mean speed m.p.h.	Prevailing direction	Fastest mile					Sunrise to sunset			Precipitation .01 inch or more	Snow, Ice pellets 1.0 inch or more	Thunderstorms	Heavy fog, visibility ¼ mile or less	Temperatures °F					Elev. 4227 feet m.s.l.
			Speed m.p.h.	Direction	Year			Clear	Partly cloudy	Cloudy					Max. (b) 90° and above	Max. 32° and below	Min. 32° and below	Min. 0° and below		
(a)	46	32	40	40		38	40	47	47	47	47	47	47	47	16	16	16	16		3
J	7.7	SSE	52	SE	1950	47	7.1	6	7	18	10	4	*	4	0	11	27	2		873.6
F	8.2	SE	56	SE	1954	55	7.0	5	7	16	9	3	1	2	0	4	24	*		873.7
M	9.2	SSE	71	NW	1954	64	6.6	7	9	15	9	3	1	*	0	1	19	0		867.7
A	9.5	SE	57	NW	1964	66	6.3	7	10	13	10	1	2	*	0	0	9	0		869.2
M	9.3	SE	57	NW	1953	73	5.6	10	10	11	8	*	5	*	1	0	1	0		869.4
J	9.3	SSE	63	W	1963	78	4.4	14	10	6	6	0	6	0	9	0	0	0		870.2
J	9.4	SSE	49	W	1936	84	3.5	17	10	4	4	0	7	0	26	0	0	0		871.7
A	9.5	SSE	58	SW	1946	83	3.6	16	11	4	5	0	8	0	20	0	0	0		871.3
S	9.0	SE	61	W	1952	84	3.5	17	8	5	5	*	4	0	3	0	1	0		873.5
O	8.5	SE	67	NW	1950	73	4.6	14	8	9	6	*	2	*	0	*	7	0		873.5
N	7.8	SSE	63	NW	1937	54	6.1	9	8	13	7	2	*	1	0	*	18	0		873.1
D	7.5	SSE	54	S	1955	44	7.1	6	7	18	9	4	*	3	0	10	28	1		875.5
YR	8.7	SSE	71	NW	MAR 1954	70	5.4	128	105	132	88	18	35	11	59	26	133	4		871.9

FOOTNOTES

Means and extremes above are from existing and comparable exposures. Annual extremes have been exceeded at other sites in the locality as follows: Lowest temperature -30 in February 1933; maximum monthly precipitation 5.81 in November 1875; maximum precipitation in 24 hours 2.72 in May 1901;maximum monthly snowfall 39.1 in December 1948.

Station: BURLINGTON, VERMONT INTERNATIONAL AIRPORT
Elevation (ground): 332 feet

TEMPERATURES °F

Month	Normal			Extremes			
	Daily maximum	Daily minimum	Monthly	Record highest	Year	Record lowest	Year
(a)				11		11	
J	25.9	7.6	16.8	56	1966	-27	1968
F	28.2	8.9	18.6	51	1966	-25	1971
M	38.0	20.1	29.1	67	1968	-13	1968
A	53.3	32.6	43.0	84	1968	2	1972
M	66.1	43.5	54.8	91	1975	24	1966
J	76.5	53.9	65.2	93	1975	33	1965
J	81.0	58.5	69.8	98	1966	40	1969
A	78.3	56.4	67.4	99	1975	35	1965
S	70.0	48.6	59.3	90	1973	29	1974
O	58.7	38.8	48.8	80	1968	15	1972
N	44.3	29.7	37.0	71	1975	2	1972
D	30.3	14.8	22.6	62	1964	-23	1968
YR	54.2	34.5	44.4	99	AUG 1975	-27	JAN 1968

IMPORTANT:
The time-period covered by this record is limited: See footnotes on next page for explanation and for additional history of EXTREME HIGHS AND LOWS recorded in the general area.

Burlington is located on the eastern shore of Lake Champlain at the widest part of the lake. About 35 miles to the west lie the highest peaks of the Adirondacks, while the foothills of the Green Mountains begin 10 miles to the east and southeast.

Its northerly latitude assures the variety and vigor of a true New England climate, while thanks to the modifying influence of the Lake, the many rapid and marked weather changes are tempered in severity. Due to its location in the path of the St. Lawrence Valley storm track and the Lake effects, the city is one of the cloudiest in the United States.

Lake Champlain exercises a tempering influence on the local temperature, during the winter months temperatures along the lake shore often run from 5 to 10 degrees warmer than at the airport 3-1/2 miles inland. At the airport the average date of the last freeze in spring is May 10 and that of the first in fall is October 3, giving a mean growing season from freeze to freeze of 145 days. This section is justly proud of its delightful summer weather. On an average there are only four days a year with maxima of 90 degrees or higher. This moderate summer heat gives way to a cooler but none the less pleasant fall period, usually extending well into October. High pressure systems moving down rapidly from Central Canada or Hudson Bay produce the coldest temperatures during the winter months, but extended periods of very cold weather are rare.

Precipitation, although generally plentiful and well distributed throughout the year, is less in the Champlain Valley than in other areas of Vermont due to the shielding effect of the mountain barriers to the east and west. The heaviest rainfall usually occurs during summer thunderstorms but excessively heavy rainfall is quite uncommon. The rainfall during the historic flood of November 1927 was the heaviest on record. Droughts are of infrequent occurrence.

Because of the trend of the Champlain Valley between the Adirondack and Green Mountain ranges, most winds have a northerly or southerly component. The prevailing direction most of the year is from the south. Winds of damaging force are very uncommon, the most destructive occurring during the hurricane of October 1954 and the whole gales of November 1950.

Smoke pollution is nearly non-existent since there is no concentration of heavy industry here; however, haze has been on the increase during the last decade due to the large increase in industry to the north and south. During the spring and fall months, fog occasionally forms along the Winooski River to the north and east and may drift over the airport with favorable winds. In spite of the high percentage of cloudiness, periods of low aircraft ceilings and visibilities are usually of short duration, allowing this area to have one of the highest percentages of flying weather in New England.

BURLINGTON, VERMONT

Normals, Means, and Extremes

(To better understand these tables, see full explanation of terms beginning on page 322)

Month	Normal Degree days Base 65 °F: Heating	Normal Degree days Base 65 °F: Cooling	Precipitation, Water equivalent: Normal	Water equivalent: Maximum monthly	Year	Water equivalent: Minimum monthly	Year	Water equivalent: Maximum in 24 hrs.	Year	Snow, Ice pellets: Maximum monthly	Year	Snow, Ice pellets: Maximum in 24 hrs.	Year	Relative humidity pct. Hour 01 (Local time)	Hour 07	Hour 13	Hour 19	Wind: Mean speed m.p.h.	Wind: Prevailing direction	Fastest mile: Speed m.p.h.	Fastest mile: Direction	Fastest mile: Year	Pct. of possible sunshine	Mean sky cover, tenths, sunrise to sunset	Mean number of days, Sunrise to sunset: Clear	Partly cloudy	Cloudy	Precipitation .01 inch or more	Snow, Ice pellets 1.0 inch or more	Thunderstorms	Heavy fog, visibility ¼ mile or less	Temperatures °F Max. (b) 90° and above	Max. 32° and below	Min. 32° and below	Min. 0° and below	Average station pressure mb. Elev. 340 feet m.s.l.
(a)				32		32		32		32		32		10	10	10	10	32	20	32	32		32	32	32	32	32	32	32	32	32	11	11	11	11	3
J	1494	0	1.74	3.74	1958	0.56	1955	1.46	1945	41.3	1966	14.5	1961	69	69	63	65	9.7	S	57	S	1950	42	7.5	4	7	20	14	5	*	1	0	21	30	11	1005.1
F	1299	0	1.68	3.98	1954	0.63	1964	1.64	1954	34.3	1958	16.5	1966	69	71	61	64	9.4	S	50	SE	1965	48	7.3	4	7	17	12	5	0	1	0	19	27	10	1004.7
M	1113	0	1.93	3.58	1972	0.38	1965	1.62	1971	33.1	1971	15.6	1971	71	72	58	62	9.3	N	56	S	1951	52	7.2	6	6	19	13	4	*	1	0	11	28	2	1002.5
A	660	0	2.62	4.27	1954	0.93	1966	2.16	1968	16.8	1974	13.0	1974	75	75	53	58	9.3	S	52	S	1948	50	7.1	5	8	17	12	1	1	1	0	1	19	0	1000.7
M	331	15	3.01	5.90	1945	1.05	1965	2.26	1955	3.9	1966	3.5	1966	78	75	52	58	8.8	S	45	NW	1974	56	7.0	5	9	17	13	*	3	1	*	0	4	0	1000.9
J	63	69	3.46	7.69	1973	1.09	1949	2.83	1972	0.0		0.0		83	79	58	64	8.2	S	42	SW	1957	60	6.7	5	11	14	12	0	6	1	1	0	0	0	1002.7
J	20	169	3.54	6.12	1972	1.29	1953	2.43	1945	0.0		0.0		84	80	54	63	7.8	S	46	NW	1974	65	6.4	5	14	12	12	0	7	1	3	0	0	0	1002.0
A	49	123	3.72	11.54	1955	0.72	1957	3.59	1955	0.0		0.0		86	84	58	68	7.4	S	54	N	1955	62	6.3	6	12	13	12	0	6	1	1	0	0	0	1004.7
S	191	20	3.05	8.18	1945	0.87	1948	2.48	1960	T	1963	T	1963	88	88	64	77	8.0	S	45	S	1947	55	6.4	6	10	14	12	0	2	3	*	0	1	0	1005.6
O	502	0	2.74	6.22	1959	0.50	1963	1.69	1951	5.1	1969	5.1	1969	80	82	62	72	8.6	S	70	SE	1954	50	6.7	6	9	16	11	*	1	2	0	*	8	0	1007.1
N	840	0	2.86	5.17	1948	0.63	1952	1.80	1959	19.2	1971	10.1	1958	81	82	71	77	9.5	S	72	SE	1950	30	8.3	3	5	22	14	2	*	1	0	5	19	0	1003.5
D	1314	0	2.19	5.95	1973	0.62	1960	2.60	1950	56.7	1970	15.0	1969	78	78	72	74	9.7	S	47	S	1950	33	8.1	3	6	22	15	5	*	2	0	18	28	4	1006.0
YR	7876	396	32.54	11.54	AUG 1955	0.38	MAR 1965	3.59	AUG 1955	56.7	DEC 1970	16.5	FEB 1966	79	78	60	67	8.8	S	72	SE	NOV 1950	51	7.1	58	104	203	152	22	25	16	5	76	164	28	1003.8

FOOTNOTES Means and extremes above are from existing and comparable exposures. Annual extremes have been exceeded at other sites in the locality as follows: Minimum monthly precipitation 0.15 in October 1924; maximum precipitation in 24 hours 4.49 in November 1927; maximum snowfall in 24 hours 24.2 in January 1934; highest temperature 101 in August 1944; lowest temperature -30 in January 1957.

Snowfall

Season	July	Aug	Sept	Oct	Nov	Dec	Jan
1936-37	0.0	0.0	0.0	0.1	11.8	15.3	4.4
1937-38	0.0	0.0	0.0	T	T	15.6	8.5
1938-39	0.0	0.0	0.0	0.0	7.3	7.6	14.5
1939-40	0.0	0.0	T	T	1.4	6.6	9.9
1940-41	0.0	0.0	0.0	T	5.2	8.2	13.2
1941-42	0.0	0.0	0.0	T	0.5	11.7	9.3
#1942-43	0.0	0.0	0.0	T	4.4	9.8	10.7
1943-44	0.0	0.0	0.0	T	11.6	2.5	16.6
1944-45	0.0	0.0	0.0	T	9.3	13.0	18.7
1945-46	0.0	0.0	0.0	0.0	9.3	4.8	17.2
1946-47	0.0	0.0	0.0	T	0.5	23.3	23.9
1947-48	0.0	0.0	T	0.0	5.9	14.2	18.3
1948-49	0.0	0.0	0.0	T	T	3.9	17.5
#1949-50	0.0	0.0	0.0	0.0	8.1	7.1	20.0
1950-51	0.0	0.0	T	T	4.8	10.9	12.6
1951-52	0.0	0.0	0.0	T	14.4	24.7	8.7
1952-53	0.0	0.0	0.0	0.8	4.3	20.2	12.3
1953-54	0.0	0.0	0.0	0.0	0.4	4.1	33.0
1954-55	0.0	0.0	0.0	T	4.0	26.1	7.6
1955-56	0.0	0.0	0.0	T	5.5	13.2	16.7
1956-57	0.0	0.0	T	T	10.3	22.0	12.2
1957-58	0.0	0.0	T	T	1.8	12.0	33.7
1958-59	0.0	0.0	0.0	T	11.2	9.3	29.2
1959-60	0.0	0.0	0.0	T	6.8	22.4	16.0
1960-61	0.0	0.0	0.0	T	0.7	9.1	15.9
1961-62	0.0	0.0	0.0	T	5.9	21.1	6.9
1962-63	0.0	0.0	0.0	0.1	4.3	16.8	12.8
1963-64	0.0	0.0	0.0	T	4.4	14.8	7.5
1964-65	0.0	0.0	0.0	0.1	1.2	23.0	11.8
1965-66	0.0	0.0	0.0	0.4	12.4	11.9	41.3
1966-67	0.0	0.0	0.0	T	2.4	36.2	20.5
1967-68	0.0	0.0	0.0	T	10.3	17.1	18.4
1968-69	0.0	0.0	0.0	T	18.8	28.6	15.8
1969-70	0.0	0.0	0.0	5.1	10.5	50.8	11.1
1970-71	0.0	0.0	0.0	0.1	2.7	56.7	17.1
1971-72	0.0	0.0	0.0	0.0	19.2	19.3	14.3
1972-73	0.0	0.0	0.0	T	12.2	39.0	11.4
1973-74	0.0	0.0	0.0	0.1	2.6	24.1	21.5
1974-75	0.0	0.0	0.0	0.1	11.5	16.8	14.8
1975-76	0.0	0.0	0.0	T	5.3	16.0	
RECORD MEAN	0.0	0.0	T	0.2	6.9	19.8	17.4

Heating Degree Days

Season	July	Aug	Sept	Oct	Nov	Dec	Jan
1955-56	3	29	234	435	878	1496	1400
1956-57	41	46	298	480	807	1196	1649
1957-58	17	82	167	503	764	1092	1404
1958-59	20	21	191	543	810	1603	1478
#1959-60	5	16	177	525	889	1200	1497
1960-61	28	55	195	600	767	1399	1728
1961-62	34	47	104	468	849	1266	1529
1962-63	71	54	296	571	997	1386	1491
1963-64	30	118	343	411	735	1609	1327
#1964-65	12	102	280	601	872	1238	1585
1965-66	43	80	236	558	956	1125	1531
1966-67	17	26	280	551	725	1285	1269
1967-68	11	35	223	495	957	1216	1751
1968-69	32	104	127	472	979	1451	1496
1969-70	41	41	244	589	856	1434	1906
1970-71	10	36	174	444	773	1567	1710
1971-72	12	49	131	344	938	1254	1357
1972-73	26	69	212	694	982	1310	1344
1973-74	10	17	256	480	825	1160	1431
1974-75	2	6	224	665	858	1128	1276
1975-76	0	45	208	448	681	1385	

Cooling Degree Days

Year	Jan	Feb	Mar	Apr	May	June	July
1969	0	0	0	0	2	96	134
1970	0	0	0	0	11	75	189
1971	0	0	0	0	17	87	138
1972	0	0	0	0	14	64	169
1973	0	0	0	3	0	149	187
1974	0	0	0	5	9	89	171
1975	0	0	0	0	75	131	306

Feb	Mar	Apr	May	June	Total
3.9	26.3	1.7	0.0	0.0	63.5
5.6	10.7	4.7	0.0	0.0	45.1
17.0	11.9	16.2	0.0	0.0	74.5
14.1	17.1	6.6	0.0	0.0	55.7
4.2	27.7	0.0	T	0.0	58.5
18.2	13.0	5.0	0.0	0.0	57.7
9.7	7.9	6.5	T	0.0	49.0
25.9	3.7	3.1	0.0	0.0	63.4
6.5	0.1	T	T	0.0	47.6
19.1	T	3.9	0.0	0.0	54.3
31.4	15.1	3.3	T	0.0	97.5
9.8	12.4	T	0.0	0.0	60.6
11.6	7.5	0.2	0.0	0.0	40.7
19.7	11.0	0.9	0.0	0.0	66.8
12.2	7.0	3.0	0.0	0.0	50.5
23.2	11.6	T	T	0.0	82.6
14.7	0.3	4.6	T	0.0	57.2
29.9	15.3	0.9	0.0	0.0	83.6
21.0	21.8	1.9	T	0.0	82.4
18.8	28.0	0.2	0.3	0.0	82.7
1.3	8.6	1.0	T	0.0	55.4
34.3	12.3	0.8	T	0.0	94.9
24.4	13.1	0.1	T	0.0	87.3
19.3	8.0	0.9	0.0	0.0	73.4
2.4	16.5	7.0	T	0.0	51.6
24.3	15.0	3.6	0.0	0.0	76.8
15.8	21.5	1.3	T	0.0	72.6
8.8	14.4	6.5	0.0	0.0	56.4
4.3	7.9	1.1	0.0	0.0	49.4
28.5	8.3	4.9	3.9	0.0	111.6
12.6	6.1	4.7	2.6	0.0	85.1
24.8	14.5	T	0.0	0.0	85.1
17.0	12.4	3.7	0.0	0.0	96.3
13.8	10.5	2.4	0.4	0.0	104.6
23.1	33.1	12.6	0.0	0.0	145.4
25.1	21.8	9.2	0.0	0.0	108.9
18.5	2.3	6.3	0.0	0.0	89.7
9.9	20.9	16.8	0.0	0.0	95.9
22.0	12.4	13.3	0.0	0.0	90.9
17.9	12.3	3.7	0.2	0.0	78.4

Average Temperature

Year	Jan	Feb	Mar	Apr	May	June	July	Aug	Sept	Oct	Nov	Dec	Annual
1936	15.2	13.6	36.6	41.2	57.4	64.6	67.6	65.8	58.8	48.0	31.2	25.6	43.8
1937	27.6	25.6	23.8	41.7	57.0	64.4	71.0	72.0	59.4	47.6	37.8	21.8	45.8
1938	17.2	22.1	31.3	44.6	54.0	66.8	69.8	70.0	55.3	49.6	38.2	26.0	45.4
1939	16.8	20.0	24.0	38.0	54.8	63.4	69.6	70.8	59.2	47.6	32.1	23.4	43.3
1940	11.6	17.2	24.8	39.2	56.0	62.5	68.4	66.2	58.2	44.7	35.5	23.5	42.3
1941	13.4	20.6	23.6	48.1	55.3	66.7	70.5	64.2	60.1	47.0	39.3	26.0	44.6
1942	17.8	16.5	35.4	45.4	59.2	65.1	68.4	66.6	59.2	49.3	36.2	19.1	44.8
#1943	13.2	20.6	27.5	36.3	54.2	67.2	70.3	67.5	58.4	47.9	35.0	19.0	43.1
1944	20.6	16.6	25.4	38.7	62.1	65.0	72.1	72.1	60.8	46.4	37.4	19.6	44.7
1945	10.0	20.2	39.6	49.6	52.2	65.6	70.0	69.4	62.6	46.8	37.6	19.2	45.2
1946	19.2	16.0	39.8	42.0	53.7	64.8	68.6	65.0	62.4	52.2	39.6	25.9	45.8
1947	20.8	16.4	30.4	40.6	54.1	63.6	72.6	73.1	61.8	56.4	34.2	19.1	45.3
1948	12.4	14.9	27.7	44.0	54.0	63.8	71.1	70.0	61.8	46.2	44.4	28.6	44.9
1949	25.0	23.9	31.0	45.1	56.5	71.9	73.8	70.8	59.2	53.2	33.2	28.4	47.7
#1950	26.4	17.0	23.5	40.2	56.5	67.1	70.0	66.5	55.1	50.5	40.2	24.6	44.8
1951	22.3	22.5	32.5	44.8	56.0	64.1	70.0	65.2	59.9	50.1	32.7	25.0	45.4
1952	20.8	24.3	29.9	45.9	51.8	65.6	73.2	69.0	61.7	45.7	39.6	26.9	46.2
1953	24.7	25.5	34.0	43.9	57.9	67.2	71.2	67.3	60.3	49.3	42.3	31.5	47.9
1954	12.8	27.1	29.7	43.4	54.6	65.4	67.3	65.1	57.8	51.8	38.1	23.2	44.7
1955	16.2	20.2	28.3	46.2	60.4	66.7	73.8	71.3	57.9	50.7	35.5	16.7	45.3
1956	19.6	23.0	23.7	40.8	50.0	64.9	66.5	66.7	55.9	49.4	37.9	26.3	43.7
1957	11.7	25.1	31.4	45.4	54.0	68.2	68.4	64.1	60.9	48.6	39.4	29.6	45.6
1958	19.5	12.9	32.7	45.4	51.9	59.8	68.0	68.0	59.1	47.3	37.8	13.1	43.0
#1959	17.2	13.8	27.8	45.0	58.3	65.5	72.5	71.3	63.3	48.0	35.1	26.0	45.3
1960	16.5	24.5	23.9	43.9	60.9	64.7	66.9	66.0	59.5	45.4	39.2	19.7	44.3
1961	9.2	18.6	26.5	38.5	51.1	63.5	68.2	66.8	65.4	49.6	36.5	23.9	43.2
1962	15.5	13.7	29.0	41.9	55.7	64.6	64.0	65.5	55.7	46.3	31.6	20.1	42.0
1963	16.6	10.7	26.0	40.3	52.4	65.5	70.3	62.5	53.5	51.7	40.3	12.9	41.9
#1964	21.9	17.2	31.1	43.3	58.6	63.0	69.6	62.9	55.8	45.3	35.7	24.8	44.1
1965	13.7	20.0	27.4	39.3	57.2	62.9	65.1	66.0	58.7	46.8	32.9	28.6	43.2
1966	15.5	17.9	30.3	41.3	51.2	65.3	69.6	67.4	55.7	47.0	40.6	23.4	43.7
1967	23.9	11.7	25.3	40.7	47.6	67.6	70.1	67.0	58.1	48.8	32.9	25.5	43.3
1968	8.4	11.0	29.6	46.2	51.7	60.8	68.7	63.7	61.0	49.8	32.2	17.9	41.8
1969	16.5	18.5	24.3	41.4	51.3	64.1	67.8	68.6	57.9	45.8	36.3	18.6	42.6
1970	3.6	16.9	25.8	42.6	54.1	63.7	70.6	68.4	60.1	50.5	39.0	14.3	42.5
1971	9.7	20.0	24.1	37.3	54.5	64.9	68.9	67.1	63.5	53.8	33.5	24.3	43.5
1972	21.1	17.0	24.8	35.6	56.2	63.1	69.5	65.3	58.7	42.4	32.1	22.5	42.4
1973	21.5	14.6	37.1	44.6	53.6	66.9	70.6	72.1	58.5	49.3	37.2	27.4	46.1
1974	18.7	15.6	29.2	44.4	51.3	66.5	70.2	69.1	58.2	43.4	36.2	28.5	44.3
1975	23.6	20.7	28.0	37.1	62.3	66.4	74.6	69.1	58.0	50.4	42.1	20.1	46.1
RECORD MEAN	18.0	18.4	29.3	42.6	55.2	64.8	69.7	67.3	59.6	48.8	36.6	23.3	44.5
MAX	26.5	27.2	37.5	51.7	65.3	74.8	79.6	77.0	69.0	57.5	43.3	30.5	53.3
MIN	9.4	9.6	21.0	33.4	45.1	54.8	59.8	57.6	50.2	40.1	29.9	16.0	35.6

# Indicates a station move or relocation of instruments.

BURLINGTON, VT

Feb	Mar	Apr	May	June	Total
1209	1273	719	470	66	8212
1113	1035	582	350	72	7669
1456	994	580	405	169	7633
1430	1145	594	260	97	8192
1169	1267	624	147	81	7597
1297	1187	788	454	91	8589
1433	1109	690	324	73	7926
1514	1204	731	385	84	8784
1380	1046	677	229	124	8029
1256	1159	766	257	136	8264
1313	1069	707	432	91	8141
1490	1225	722	533	29	8152
1561	1089	562	407	140	8447
1298	1256	700	422	107	8444
1342	1208	663	341	105	8770
1257	1263	821	336	83	8474
1387	1239	872	281	113	7977
1410	855	608	345	86	7941
1378	1101	618	430	37	7743
1236	1141	831	152	82	7601

Aug	Sept	Oct	Nov	Dec	Total
160	38	0	0	0	420
150	36	1	0	0	462
118	90	4	0	0	454
81	30	0	0	0	358
243	68	0	0	0	650
140	27	1	0	0	442
181	5	1	0	0	699

Precipitation

Year	Jan	Feb	Mar	Apr	May	June	July	Aug	Sept	Oct	Nov	Dec	Annual
1936	3.46	1.48	3.80	3.48	2.88	1.51	3.67	3.94	2.77	4.75	2.30	2.20	36.24
1937	1.63	1.59	2.69	1.33	4.27	3.97	2.97	4.18	1.82	2.89	2.42	2.29	32.05
1938	1.99	1.64	2.09	2.31	2.13	2.04	4.69	3.66	6.87	1.37	1.71	3.64	34.14
1939	1.29	3.08	2.24	4.21	3.38	5.35	2.83	2.78	3.77	2.19	0.92	1.75	33.79
1940	0.77	1.48	3.22	1.88	4.78	3.32	6.11	2.11	2.54	2.70	2.67	2.50	34.08
1941	1.45	0.88	2.13	0.70	2.14	1.52	6.35	2.11	0.93	1.99	1.35	1.43	22.98
1942	1.43	1.45	2.89	3.08	2.13	6.36	2.21	4.19	4.97	3.21	1.65	2.99	36.56
#1943	0.92	1.11	1.25	2.24	4.35	4.12	4.48	4.84	1.71	3.82	3.29	0.51	32.64
1944	1.77	2.53	1.37	3.22	1.75	4.06	3.63	2.76	3.85	2.56	1.96	1.36	30.82
1945	2.97	0.82	1.91	3.84	5.90	2.93	4.57	1.84	8.18	4.55	3.45	1.17	42.13
1946	1.53	1.84	1.39	2.31	4.03	1.57	3.89	4.32	3.45	4.35	3.76	2.13	34.57
1947	3.51	1.42	1.70	1.39	5.05	4.84	4.90	1.83	2.50	0.88	3.20	1.12	32.34
1948	1.41	1.01	1.99	2.94	3.03	2.88	4.54	3.41	0.87	2.51	5.17	2.53	32.29
1949	2.09	2.08	1.40	2.34	1.58	1.09	4.70	4.42	2.64	1.46	2.62	1.80	28.22
#1950	2.42	1.31	2.79	1.52	1.58	2.38	2.41	3.90	2.45	1.61	4.36	4.10	30.83
1951	1.72	3.69	2.57	3.55	1.63	3.17	4.46	2.06	4.10	2.25	4.48	2.19	35.87
1952	1.64	2.10	1.73	2.63	3.14	4.02	2.14	3.30	2.26	2.28	0.63	4.12	29.99
1953	1.87	1.38	3.03	3.51	3.31	2.67	1.29	5.81	1.52	2.26	1.38	1.94	29.97
1954	2.12	3.98	2.41	4.27	3.30	3.89	2.18	3.60	4.22	2.83	3.08	3.49	39.37
1955	0.56	2.79	3.27	2.16	4.25	4.05	3.10	11.54	3.15	4.31	2.78	0.71	42.67
1956	1.92	1.78	2.37	2.47	4.74	2.92	4.06	2.00	3.91	1.58	1.67	1.80	31.22
1957	1.20	0.90	0.95	2.11	2.95	7.35	5.34	0.72	3.27	1.55	3.07	3.93	33.34
1958	3.74	2.21	1.06	2.84	2.93	3.77	3.89	3.06	3.88	4.66	1.89	0.82	34.75
1959	2.72	1.98	1.31	1.57	1.49	3.41	1.81	4.38	2.03	6.22	5.07	2.55	34.54
1960	1.24	1.98	1.42	2.64	3.64	3.51	3.37	1.53	4.90	4.04	1.96	0.62	30.85
1961	0.93	1.65	1.56	3.96	2.63	3.71	4.98	3.24	2.69	2.50	2.31	1.75	31.91
1962	1.07	1.36	1.86	2.59	2.24	2.66	5.93	3.46	3.56	3.28	2.75	1.73	32.49
1963	1.14	1.22	2.35	2.52	2.37	1.90	2.79	5.11	1.42	0.50	3.95	0.96	26.23
1964	2.27	0.63	2.64	2.11	4.67	3.00	2.87	4.10	1.49	2.20	2.10	1.63	29.71
1965	0.60	0.93	0.38	2.16	1.05	4.08	2.91	6.27	3.19	3.32	2.65	1.47	29.01
1966	2.02	2.49	2.63	0.93	2.49	2.63	1.92	4.46	3.33	1.41	1.41	2.82	28.54
1967	1.65	0.77	0.51	3.77	3.19	3.12	4.60	3.79	3.06	3.03	2.12	2.61	32.22
1968	1.26	1.28	3.23	3.54	2.43	3.66	2.70	2.36	2.06	2.73	4.37	3.12	32.74
1969	2.43	0.94	1.93	2.93	3.10	4.01	2.40	3.71	1.88	1.62	4.98	4.59	34.52
1970	0.65	1.95	2.01	2.78	3.14	4.38	1.92	3.44	3.93	2.66	2.35	3.77	32.98
1971	1.24	2.98	2.71	2.65	2.97	2.29	4.29	4.85	1.63	2.16	2.29	1.93	31.99
1972	0.93	1.69	3.58	2.26	2.83	6.52	6.12	2.35	1.69	2.60	4.10	3.43	38.10
1973	2.13	1.55	2.09	3.80	5.38	7.69	3.02	5.41	5.02	1.93	2.31	5.95	46.28
1974	1.90	1.54	2.73	3.47	4.61	4.45	3.70	2.60	3.23	0.78	3.60	2.08	34.69
1975	2.20	2.01	2.86	1.71	1.17	2.47	3.77	2.85	4.12	3.85	3.14	2.36	32.51
RECORD MEAN	1.76	1.66	2.15	2.46	3.00	3.54	3.61	3.42	3.29	2.85	2.71	2.09	32.54

Record mean values above are means through the current year for the period beginning in 1893 for temperature, 1884 for precipitation, and 1944 for snowfall. Data are from City Office locations through May 1943 and from Airport locations thereafter.

NORFOLK, VIRGINIA

Station: NORFOLK, VIRGINIA
NORFOLK REGIONAL AIRPORT
Elevation (ground): 24 feet

TEMPERATURES °F

Month	Normal			Extremes			
	Daily maximum	Daily minimum	Monthly	Record highest	Year	Record lowest	Year
(a)				27		27	
J	48.8	32.2	40.5	78	1970	8	1972
F	50.0	32.7	41.4	79	1975	8	1965
M	57.3	38.9	48.1	85	1968	20	1950
A	67.7	47.9	57.8	97	1960	28	1964
M	76.2	57.2	66.7	97	1956	36	1966
J	83.5	65.5	74.5	101	1964	45	1967
J	86.6	69.9	78.3	103	1952	56	1972
A	84.9	68.9	76.9	99	1968	52	1965
S	79.6	63.9	71.8	98	1954	45	1967
O	70.1	53.3	61.7	95	1954	29	1965
N	60.5	42.6	51.6	86	1974	20	1950
D	50.6	34.0	42.3	79	1971	14	1962
YR	68.0	50.6	59.3	103	JUL 1952	8	JAN 1972

IMPORTANT:
The time-period covered by this record is limited: See footnotes following table of **NORMALS, MEANS AND EXTREMES** for explanation and for additional history of **EXTREME HIGHS AND LOWS** recorded in the general area.

Snowfall

Season	July	Aug	Sept	Oct	Nov	Dec	Jan
1936-37	0.0	0.0	0.0	0.0	T	T	0.0
1937-38	0.0	0.0	0.0	0.0	0.0	0.1	0.7
1938-39	0.0	0.0	0.0	0.0	0.4	0.0	9.4
1939-40	0.0	0.0	0.0	0.0	0.0	3.3	12.7
1940-41	0.0	0.0	0.0	0.0	T	0.0	3.3
1941-42	0.0	0.0	0.0	0.0	0.0	0.0	2.4
1942-43	0.0	0.0	0.0	0.0	0.0	7.7	2.0
1943-44	0.0	0.0	0.0	0.0	T	1.1	4.7
1944-45	0.0	0.0	0.0	0.0	0.0	0.7	T
1945-46	0.0	0.0	0.0	0.0	T	3.2	4.4
1946-47	0.0	0.0	0.0	0.0	0.0	0.0	0.0
1947-48	0.0	0.0	0.0	0.0	T	2.3	8.7
1948-49	0.0	0.0	0.0	0.0	0.0	1.2	0.4
1949-50	0.0	0.0	0.0	0.0	0.0	T	0.0
1950-51	0.0	0.0	0.0	0.0	0.4	T	0.8
1951-52	0.0	0.0	0.0	0.0	T	T	T
#1952-53	0.0	0.0	0.0	0.0	T	T	T
1953-54	0.0	0.0	0.0	0.0	T	T	1.6
1954-55	0.0	0.0	0.0	0.0	0.0	3.6	13.8
1955-56	0.0	0.0	0.0	0.0	0.0	0.9	0.4
1956-57	0.0	0.0	0.0	0.0	T	T	4.1
1957-58	0.0	0.0	0.0	0.0	0.0	1.1	3.0
1958-59	0.0	0.0	0.0	0.0	0.0	14.7	1.1
1959-60	0.0	0.0	0.0	0.0	T	T	T
1960-61	0.0	0.0	0.0	0.0	0.0	0.7	3.1
1961-62	0.0	0.0	0.0	0.0	T	T	11.9
1962-63	0.0	0.0	0.0	0.0	0.0	4.5	1.9
1963-64	0.0	0.0	0.0	0.0	0.0	T	T
1964-65	0.0	0.0	0.0	0.0	T	0.0	10.6
1965-66	0.0	0.0	0.0	0.0	0.0	T	14.2
1966-67	0.0	0.0	0.0	0.0	T	1.0	4.2
1967-68	0.0	0.0	0.0	0.0	T	2.0	1.5
1968-69	0.0	0.0	0.0	0.0	T	3.8	T
1969-70	0.0	0.0	0.0	0.0	0.0	T	3.0
1970-71	0.0	0.0	0.0	0.0	T	T	T
1971-72	0.0	0.0	0.0	0.0	T	T	0.0
1972-73	0.0	0.0	0.0	0.0	T	0.0	9.1
1973-74	0.0	0.0	0.0	0.0	0.0	1.4	T
1974-75	0.0	0.0	0.0	0.0	0.0	T	0.3
1975-76	0.0	0.0	0.0	0.0	0.0	T	
RECORD MEAN	0.0	0.0	0.0	0.0	T	1.2	3.1

Heating Degree Days

Season	July	Aug	Sept	Oct	Nov	Dec	Jan
1955-56	0	0	0	122	433	837	854
1956-57	0	0	21	69	422	390	778
1957-58	0	0	9	214	329	558	852
#1958-59	0	0	7	132	282	855	778
1959-60	0	0	10	137	424	621	714
1960-61	0	0	0	139	368	877	921
1961-62	0	0	7	155	368	722	800
1962-63	0	0	37	148	449	854	859
1963-64	0	0	44	156	384	920	697
1964-65	0	0	4	232	312	575	780
1965-66	0	6	1	195	398	657	897
1966-67	0	0	22	191	437	725	588
1967-68	0	0	36	211	566	644	928
1968-69	0	0	0	124	361	726	814
1969-70	0	0	8	131	469	741	960
1970-71	0	0	16	93	393	552	812
1971-72	0	0	3	27	391	390	572
1972-73	0	0	4	197	406	486	752
1973-74	0	0	0	83	353	575	504
1974-75	0	0	16	217	371	584	584
1975-76	0	0	6	98	290	671	

Cooling Degree Days

Year	Jan	Feb	Mar	Apr	May	June	July
1969	0	0	0	42	125	369	446
1970	1	0	0	19	140	303	374
1971	0	3	0	3	76	336	383
1972	0	0	8	20	40	183	398
1973	0	0	16	27	112	363	420
1974	3	0	16	64	124	244	419
1975	2	3	0	22	157	366	429

The city of Norfolk, Virginia, is located at Latitude 36° 51' North and Longitude 76° 17' West. It is almost surrounded by water, with Chesapeake Bay immediately to the north, Hampton Roads to the west, and the Atlantic Ocean only 18 miles to the east. It is traversed by numerous rivers and waterways and its average elevation above mean sea level is 13 feet. There are no nearby hilly areas and the land is low and level throughout the City. The climate, therefore, is necessarily a modification of the more desirable marine variety. The City's geographic position with respect to the principal storm tracks is especially favorable, being south of the average path of storms originating in the higher latitudes and north of the usual track of hurricanes and other tropical storms. These features combine to place Norfolk in one of the favored climatic regions of the world.

The winters are mild, while the autumn and spring seasons usually are delightful. Summers, though warm and long, frequently are tempered by cool periods, often associated with northeasterly winds off the Atlantic. Temperatures of 100° or higher are of very infrequent occurrence. Cold waves seldom penetrate to this area and during the period of continuous official record now available, a temperature of zero has never been recorded in Norfolk. Occasional winters pass without a measurable amount of snowfall. Most of Norfolk's snow generally occurs in light falls, which usually melts and disappears within 24 hours. Thus, from a climatological standpoint, Norfolk's weather is

(Continued page 668)

Feb	Mar	Apr	May	June	Total
9.8	T	0.0	0.0	0.0	9.8
T	0.0	0.0	0.0	0.0	0.8
0.0	3.2	0.0	0.0	0.0	13.0
1.0	4.6	1.3	0.0	0.0	22.9
5.7	0.3	0.0	0.0	0.0	9.3
T	0.0	0.0	0.0	0.0	2.4
0.2	0.1	0.0	0.0	0.0	10.0
T	T	T	0.0	0.0	5.8
T	0.0	0.0	0.0	0.0	0.7
T	0.0	0.0	0.0	0.0	7.6
3.0	10.0	0.0	0.0	0.0	13.0
11.8	T	0.0	0.0	0.0	22.8
0.0	T	0.0	0.0	0.0	1.6
0.7	0.8	0.0	0.0	0.0	1.5
2.7	T	0.0	T	T	3.9
1.8	T	0.0	0.0	0.0	1.8
T	0.5	T	0.0	0.0	0.5
0.0	0.0	T	0.0	0.0	1.6
T	T	0.0	0.0	0.0	17.4
0.0	T	T	0.0	0.0	1.3
T	T	T	0.0	0.0	4.1
0.4	T	0.0	0.0	0.0	4.5
0.0	T	0.0	0.0	0.0	15.8
3.9	7.9	0.0	0.0	0.0	11.8
1.2	0.0	0.0	0.0	0.0	5.0
0.8	1.2	T	0.0	0.0	13.9
7.5	T	0.0	0.0	0.0	13.9
5.8	1.0	1.2	0.0	0.0	8.0
3.9	T	0.0	0.0	0.0	14.5
0.5	0.0	0.0	0.0	0.0	14.7
5.1	T	0.0	0.0	0.0	10.3
2.9	0.9	0.0	0.0	0.0	7.3
0.8	1.9	0.0	0.0	0.0	6.5
2.8	T	0.0	0.0	0.0	5.8
2.4	4.2	T	0.0	0.0	6.6
1.8	T	T	0.0	0.0	1.8
4.7	T	0.0	0.0	0.0	13.8
0.9	7.5	0.0	0.0	0.0	9.8
T	0.8	T	0.0	0.0	1.1
1.9	1.0	T	0.0	0.0	7.2

Average Temperature

Year	Jan	Feb	Mar	Apr	May	June	July	Aug	Sept	Oct	Nov	Dec	Annual
1936	37.4	37.0	53.8	55.9	67.9	74.0	79.1	79.6	73.6	65.0	50.4	46.2	60.0
1937	51.8	41.8	46.5	57.0	67.6	76.8	79.4	79.6	69.9	59.6	51.2	42.1	60.3
1938	41.2	46.8	54.6	60.8	67.2	74.5	79.0	80.4	71.8	61.2	55.6	45.2	61.5
1939	45.2	49.8	52.4	58.8	67.8	77.2	77.3	79.2	74.8	64.3	50.0	44.4	61.8
1940	31.0	42.4	46.8	55.2	66.4	77.0	78.6	76.8	70.4	59.8	52.8	48.4	58.8
1941	40.4	38.0	44.0	60.6	69.6	74.8	79.1	78.2	75.0	68.8	55.9	47.4	61.0
1942	41.1	38.8	51.1	60.2	70.9	77.3	82.0	77.6	74.6	64.6	54.8	42.4	61.3
1943	43.3	44.6	49.0	55.5	70.3	80.0	79.1	78.6	70.8	60.2	51.5	42.8	60.4
1944	41.7	43.4	47.9	57.8	72.4	77.4	79.2	77.4	74.0	62.4	51.1	39.8	60.4
1945	37.8	44.0	59.5	62.1	66.4	77.1	78.4	77.1	76.2	62.9	54.2	38.6	61.2
1946	43.0	44.9	56.4	58.1	68.4	73.7	76.8	75.4	72.7	64.8	57.5	48.4	61.7
1947	49.0	37.0	42.6	59.0	68.8	73.7	77.0	78.8	74.5	67.4	51.4	43.3	60.2
1948	36.0	43.1	52.9	58.8	68.1	75.7	79.8	78.0	72.2	60.1	58.2	47.2	60.8
1949	49.8	50.0	50.9	58.8	67.2	75.8	81.7	78.8	71.9	66.7	52.8	47.5	62.7
1950	53.9	45.4	47.8	56.3	65.7	75.3	78.1	76.5	71.8	65.6	52.1	40.4	60.7
1951	45.5	44.7	48.8	58.8	66.6	75.4	79.6	78.3	73.2	65.3	49.7	48.2	61.2
#1952	46.8	45.3	49.1	60.6	68.2	79.8	82.0	79.2	73.5	60.1	53.5	44.7	61.9
1953	46.1	46.2	51.2	58.7	71.4	73.9	79.7	77.1	71.8	63.0	51.4	45.6	61.4
1954	41.7	46.7	48.7	60.8	64.0	75.6	78.0	77.9	73.8	64.6	50.0	41.3	60.3
1955	38.4	41.2	52.4	60.5	67.7	71.9	81.4	79.9	72.2	62.5	50.6	37.8	59.7
1956	37.2	45.9	48.1	56.6	64.3	75.3	78.7	77.3	70.8	63.5	51.1	52.2	60.1
1957	39.7	44.6	48.4	62.3	68.1	77.7	78.6	75.7	74.8	58.2	53.9	46.7	60.7
1958	37.3	36.4	43.6	57.8	66.7	71.8	81.7	77.8	70.7	61.4	55.6	37.2	58.2
#1959	39.7	43.7	49.4	60.2	69.7	76.4	78.7	79.4	73.6	64.7	51.1	44.8	60.9
1960	41.7	41.4	39.2	63.7	68.3	75.5	77.8	80.0	72.8	61.8	52.7	36.5	59.3
1961	35.0	43.6	53.1	55.5	63.6	72.4	80.6	77.7	75.3	60.6	53.2	41.5	59.4
1962	38.9	41.0	43.7	56.4	68.0	73.4	75.2	76.0	69.1	61.8	49.8	37.2	57.6
1963	37.1	35.7	53.4	60.3	64.6	73.2	77.0	76.7	66.7	60.1	52.0	35.2	57.7
1964	42.3	39.9	49.5	55.2	66.4	74.5	77.3	74.4	70.8	57.7	54.6	46.5	59.1
1965	39.7	41.0	44.4	54.5	69.7	72.8	76.7	77.1	73.6	59.0	51.6	43.5	58.6
1966	35.8	38.6	47.9	54.5	63.6	71.6	78.0	74.9	69.9	59.3	50.5	41.4	57.1
1967	45.7	39.9	47.7	58.0	61.2	71.2	76.3	75.2	66.5	58.7	45.9	44.0	57.5
1968	34.8	34.0	50.0	55.1	64.6	74.9	78.0	80.5	71.5	63.1	52.9	41.4	58.4
1969	38.5	39.8	44.7	59.8	67.4	77.1	79.2	76.2	71.1	62.2	49.1	40.9	58.9
1970	33.9	39.3	44.7	56.7	67.5	74.9	76.9	78.0	74.7	63.7	51.7	47.0	59.1
1971	38.6	44.7	46.9	55.9	65.0	76.0	77.2	75.7	73.2	66.7	52.4	52.3	60.4
1972	46.4	43.2	49.0	56.4	63.5	70.5	77.6	75.8	71.9	59.2	51.6	49.2	59.5
1973	40.5	39.7	52.3	58.5	66.9	76.9	78.3	78.5	75.0	64.2	53.5	46.2	60.9
1974	48.6	43.4	53.1	60.8	66.8	72.8	78.3	77.4	71.4	58.7	53.5	46.0	60.9
1975	46.0	45.4	47.4	52.7	68.3	77.0	78.6	79.6	72.3	63.4	55.7	43.2	60.8
RECORD MEAN	41.6	42.3	48.8	57.4	66.7	74.7	78.6	77.5	72.4	62.2	52.1	43.6	59.8
MAX	49.4	50.5	57.6	66.6	75.7	83.2	86.7	84.9	79.6	69.8	60.0	51.2	67.9
MIN	33.8	34.0	40.0	48.1	57.6	66.1	70.5	70.0	65.2	54.6	44.1	36.0	51.7

# Indicates a station move or relocation of instruments.

NORFOLK, VA

Feb	Mar	Apr	May	June	Total
546	527	280	121	2	3722
564	508	173	59	1	2985
795	655	242	44	7	3705
591	478	180	37	4	3344
679	796	152	37	1	3566
595	385	318	110	16	3729
668	655	288	50	0	3713
815	357	202	108	0	3829
719	482	303	108	4	3817
667	635	320	29	15	3569
734	527	330	121	21	3887
699	533	244	157	21	3617
895	471	294	88	0	4133
697	624	192	44	0	3582
714	622	263	57	0	3965
567	555	269	69	0	3326
628	494	272	81	11	2869
703	403	217	47	0	3215
599	377	183	63	0	2737
547	541	382	47	0	3285

Aug	Sept	Oct	Nov	Dec	Total
357	199	49	0	0	1587
412	311	60	0	0	1620
343	259	87	23	5	1518
343	217	22	10	2	1243
424	307	64	17	1	1751
390	213	26	32	0	1531
460	233	55	17	0	1744

Precipitation

Year	Jan	Feb	Mar	Apr	May	June	July	Aug	Sept	Oct	Nov	Dec	Annual
1936	6.60	4.16	3.83	4.71	0.98	3.95	9.30	1.77	4.95	5.31	1.87	4.88	52.31
1937	8.46	2.53	3.08	6.44	3.35	7.49	5.69	6.77	4.47	3.98	5.57	1.87	59.70
1938	2.80	1.10	3.73	5.78	5.06	7.25	5.28	2.78	7.76	2.09	3.19	2.45	49.27
1939	3.93	5.52	2.40	4.26	1.53	6.51	12.40	9.20	0.56	5.04	3.14	1.15	55.64
1940	2.35	2.38	2.05	3.37	3.64	2.31	3.44	10.14	4.10	1.10	4.45	1.16	40.49
1941	2.12	2.58	2.50	3.24	0.94	4.31	4.52	4.99	2.80	2.37	1.57	2.87	34.81
1942	2.76	2.63	5.52	0.73	2.70	1.23	1.61	15.61	2.83	5.87	0.96	5.15	47.60
1943	2.80	1.81	4.18	2.77	3.83	4.26	10.27	1.00	6.08	3.90	1.36	2.01	44.27
1944	4.47	5.90	6.97	2.57	0.85	1.24	1.43	6.25	9.61	3.45	4.08	2.43	49.25
1945	1.72	5.16	1.30	2.12	2.64	7.72	12.92	3.32	5.74	1.32	4.02	5.87	53.85
1946	3.27	3.70	1.60	3.42	6.50	4.56	7.24	3.51	5.94	1.26	3.55	1.31	45.86
1947	4.18	1.26	3.54	2.92	1.86	3.89	8.28	2.17	4.01	1.47	6.25	2.35	42.18
1948	4.36	3.65	2.82	4.86	6.98	4.66	4.86	5.15	2.24	2.41	5.51	4.09	51.59
1949	1.62	4.27	2.85	1.71	5.42	2.57	6.35	14.51	2.06	2.29	3.51	2.10	49.26
1950	2.11	1.09	2.79	3.55	2.27	3.07	10.79	2.35	2.05	1.95	1.53	2.84	36.39
1951	1.61	1.59	2.99	2.29	3.68	4.86	2.78	8.68	0.53	3.63	6.34	2.67	41.65
#1952	4.31	5.52	4.41	2.16	1.97	2.29	4.14	4.73	2.36	2.75	4.83	3.23	42.70
1953	1.72	3.48	2.67	5.80	3.16	2.92	3.56	9.14	4.17	1.05	2.74	2.69	43.10
1954	6.40	1.59	4.14	2.46	5.78	0.37	4.96	7.27	2.77	1.70	2.13	3.62	43.19
1955	2.41	2.71	3.96	1.73	1.58	2.47	2.34	8.16	9.26	1.48	2.05	2.14	40.29
1956	2.49	5.72	3.09	3.81	2.57	2.07	6.63	5.04	3.70	8.06	1.51	2.76	47.45
1957	4.11	4.74	4.06	1.86	1.94	3.56	2.18	5.96	7.18	3.44	4.81	4.53	48.37
1958	4.16	3.55	6.41	3.28	6.23	4.99	6.27	10.48	0.36	4.88	3.07	4.10	57.78
1959	1.52	1.84	3.96	5.03	1.98	2.49	7.49	2.81	10.73	8.78	1.85	2.65	51.13
1960	3.85	3.57	2.54	1.40	4.43	2.57	4.78	6.49	5.88	2.76	1.10	2.37	41.74
1961	3.52	4.56	3.59	2.74	7.77	6.70	1.69	7.42	1.62	4.12	1.20	3.74	48.67
1962	5.56	2.50	4.32	4.49	3.68	3.03	9.05	4.09	3.07	4.48	4.06	3.80	52.13
1963	3.36	3.75	2.98	1.29	1.55	9.72	2.01	2.40	6.84	1.21	5.31	2.85	43.27
1964	4.56	4.56	2.26	2.38	1.56	2.58	7.33	10.58	12.26	5.55	1.14	2.95	57.71
1965	2.73	2.53	2.83	2.24	1.48	4.69	3.46	3.08	0.77	1.29	0.49	1.06	26.67
1966	4.86	3.83	1.50	1.68	5.95	1.82	4.26	5.24	3.39	1.25	1.05	3.13	37.96
1967	5.44	3.56	1.34	1.31	3.25	1.37	7.21	11.19	3.02	0.93	1.75	4.84	45.21
1968	3.62	2.01	4.76	3.17	2.16	3.07	4.23	2.04	1.51	4.44	3.56	3.14	37.71
1969	2.26	2.16	4.88	2.07	2.05	4.13	12.70	5.28	2.72	3.18	2.97	3.93	48.33
1970	2.27	3.97	3.37	3.19	2.58	4.10	5.33	2.04	1.72	1.30	2.34	3.01	35.22
1971	4.03	3.59	3.88	2.18	4.46	2.16	4.81	4.63	5.46	10.12	0.97	1.44	47.73
1972	2.94	3.50	2.55	2.15	3.35	4.93	4.65	1.60	6.91	4.09	5.44	4.12	46.23
1973	2.54	3.21	4.69	3.44	3.62	5.93	4.19	7.92	0.86	1.37	1.90	5.83	45.50
1974	3.52	2.98	5.16	3.34	3.74	4.76	5.47	8.33	4.40	1.23	1.22	3.81	47.96
1975	4.18	4.18	5.72	4.19	3.37	1.16	13.73	0.74	4.82	3.19	1.63	3.62	50.53
RECORD MEAN	3.26	3.36	3.73	3.20	3.64	4.05	5.79	5.43	3.86	3.12	2.56	3.22	45.22

Record mean values above are means through the current year for the period beginning in 1875 for temperature, 1871 for precipitation, and 1949 for snowfall. Data are from City Office locations through 1952.

(Continued)

well suited for most outdoor activities at all seasons of the year.

From an agricultural standpoint, the Norfolk area, with its long frost-free period and prolonged growing season, averaging 244 days, is exceptionally well favored. The average date of the last freezing temperature in the spring is March 22, while the average date of the first in autumn is November 21. The average annual amount of rainfall is about 45 inches and considerably more than one-half of it falls in well distributed amounts during the crop growing season, April to October, inclusive, a fact of great importance to agricultural interests, which together with the light, warm, sandy soil of this section, makes it an area of unusual productive capacity, yielding bountiful supplies of various truck crops.

Normals, Means, and Extremes

Month	Normal Degree days Base 65 °F		Precipitation in inches												Relative humidity pct.			
			Water equivalent							Snow, Ice pellets					Hour 01	Hour 07	Hour 13	Hour 19
	Heating	Cooling	Normal	Maximum monthly	Year	Minimum monthly	Year	Maximum in 24 hrs.	Year	Maximum monthly	Year	Maximum in 24 hrs.	Year		(Local time)			
(a)				27		27		27		27		27			27	27	27	27
J	760	0	3.35	6.40	1954	1.60	1949	3.80	1967	14.2	1966	9.1	1973		74	76	60	68
F	661	0	3.31	5.72	1956	0.86	1950	1.87	1970	7.5	1963	6.3	1963		73	75	57	66
M	532	8	3.42	6.41	1958	1.34	1967	3.18	1958	7.9	1960	7.5	1974		71	73	54	62
A	226	10	2.71	5.80	1953	1.29	1963	2.70	1975	1.2	1964	1.2	1964		73	74	51	62
M	53	106	3.34	7.77	1961	1.48	1965	2.94	1961	0.0		0.0			81	78	56	68
J	0	285	3.62	9.72	1963	0.37	1954	6.85	1963	0.0		0.0			83	80	58	68
J	0	412	5.70	13.73	1975	1.69	1961	5.64	1969	0.0		0.0			85	82	60	72
A	0	369	5.92	11.19	1967	0.74	1975	11.40	1964	0.0		0.0			87	85	62	75
S	9	213	4.20	12.26	1964	0.36	1958	6.79	1959	0.0		0.0			85	84	62	76
O	141	38	3.06	10.12	1971	0.93	1967	4.38	1971	0.0		0.0			83	83	61	76
N	402	0	2.94	7.01	1951	0.49	1965	3.35	1952	0.6	1950	0.6	1950		76	78	55	69
D	704	0	3.11	5.83	1973	1.08	1965	2.12	1958	14.7	1958	11.4	1958		73	76	59	68
YR	3488	1441	44.68	13.73	JUL 1975	0.36	SEP 1958	11.40	AUG 1964	14.7	DEC 1958	11.4	DEC 1958		79	79	58	69

(To better understand these tables, see full explanation of terms beginning on page 322)

Month	Wind					Pct. of possible sunshine	Mean sky cover, tenths, sunrise to sunset	Mean number of days											Average station pressure mb.
			Fastest mile					Sunrise to sunset							Temperatures °F				
															Max.		Min.		Elev. 30
	Mean speed m.p.h.	Prevailing direction	Speed m.p.h.	Direction	Year			Clear	Partly cloudy	Cloudy	Precipitation .01 inch or more	Snow, Ice pellets 1.0 inch or more	Thunderstorms	Heavy fog, visibility ¼ mile or less	(b) 90° and above	32° and below	32° and below	0° and below	feet m.s.l.
(a)	27	15	19	19		19	27	27	27	27	27	27	27	27	27	27	27	27	3
J	11.7	SW	56	SW	1959	57	6.3	9	6	16	10	1	*	2	0	2	16	0	1019.5
F	12.1	NNE	66	SW	1965	58	6.2	8	6	14	10	1	1	3	0	1	14	0	1017.2
M	12.5	SW	57	W	1963	63	6.1	9	7	15	11	*	2	2	0	*	6	0	1015.1
A	11.9	SW	62	N	1956	66	5.9	9	9	12	10	*	3	2	*	0	*	0	1015.2
M	10.3	SW	53	SW	1965	67	6.1	8	10	13	10	0	5	2	1	0	0	0	1013.8
J	9.6	SW	52	W	1970	68	5.8	8	11	11	9	0	6	1	7	0	0	0	1015.1
J	8.8	SW	63	SW	1956	65	6.0	8	11	12	11	0	8	1	11	0	0	0	1015.6
A	8.7	SW	57	NE	1957	65	5.8	8	12	11	11	0	7	2	8	0	0	0	1016.9
S	9.6	NE	73	W	1960	64	5.7	9	9	12	8	0	3	2	3	0	0	0	1017.3
O	10.4	NE	78	S	1954	60	5.3	12	7	12	8	0	1	3	*	0	*	0	1019.7
N	10.7	SW	52	SE	1962	60	5.3	11	8	11	8	0	1	2	0	0	3	0	1018.6
D	11.1	SW	48	NW	1960	57	6.0	10	7	14	9	*	*	2	0	1	14	0	1018.2
YR	10.6	SW	78	S	OCT 1954	63	5.9	109	103	153	116	2	37	23	30	5	53	0	1016.9

FOOTNOTES

Means and extremes above are from existing and comparable exposures. Annual extremes have been exceeded at other sites in the locality as follows: Highest temperature 105 in August 1918; lowest temperature 2 in February 1895; maximum monthly precipitation 15.61 in August 1942; minimum monthly precipitation 0.04 in October 1874; maximum monthly snowfall 18.6 in December 1892; maximum snowfall in 24 hours 17.7 in December 1892; fastest mile wind 80 W in June 1925.

Station: RICHMOND, VIRGINIA
BYRD FIELD
Elevation (ground): 164 feet

TEMPERATURES °F

Month	Normal: Daily maximum	Normal: Daily minimum	Normal: Monthly	Extremes: Record highest	Year	Record lowest	Year
(a)				46		46	
J	47.4	27.6	37.5	80	1950	-12	1940
F	49.9	28.8	39.4	83	1932	-10	1936
M	58.2	35.5	46.9	93	1938	11	1960
A	70.3	45.2	57.8	96	1960	26	1964
M	78.4	54.5	66.5	100	1941	31	1956
J	85.4	62.9	74.2	104	1952	40	1967
J	88.2	67.5	77.9	104	1936	51	1965
A	86.6	65.9	76.3	102	1953	46	1934
S	80.9	59.0	70.0	103	1954	35	1974
O	71.2	47.4	59.3	99	1941	21	1962
N	60.6	37.3	49.0	86	1974	10	1933
D	49.1	28.8	39.0	80	1971	-1	1942
YR	68.8	46.7	57.8	104	JUN 1952	-12	JAN 1940

IMPORTANT:
The time-period covered by this record is limited: See footnotes on next page for explanation and for additional history of EXTREME HIGHS AND LOWS recorded in the general area.

Richmond is located in east-central Virginia at the head of navigation on the James River and along a line separating the Coastal Plains (Tidewater Virginia) from the Piedmont. The Blue Ridge Mountains lie about 90 miles to the west and the Chesapeake Bay 60 miles to the east. Elevations range from a few feet above sea level along the river to a little over 300 feet in parts of the west section of the City.

The climate might be classified as modified continental. Summers are warm and humid and winters generally mild. The mountains to the west act as a partial barrier to outbreaks of cold, continental air in winter, the coldest air being delayed long enough to be modified, then further warmed as it subsides in its approach to Richmond. The open waters of the Chesapeake Bay and Atlantic Ocean contribute to the humid summers and mild winters. The coldest weather normally occurs in late December and in January, when low temperatures usually average in the upper twenties and the high temperatures in the upper forties. Temperatures seldom lower to zero. The record lowest temperature of minus 12 degrees was recorded at the Airport in January 1940. The record high temperature of 107 degrees occurred in August 1918 at Chimborazo Park.

Precipitation is rather uniformly distributed throughout the year. However, dry periods lasting several weeks do occur, especially in autumn when long periods of pleasant, mild weather are most common. There is considerable variability in total monthly amounts from year to year so that no one month can be depended upon to be normal. Snow has been recorded during seven of the twelve months. Falls of 4 inches or more occur on an average of once a year. Snow usually remains on the ground only 1 or 2 days at a time, but on one occasion it remained 21 days (January 23 to February 13, 1948). Ice storms (freezing rain or glaze) are not uncommon in winter, but they are seldom severe enough to do any considerable damage. A notable exception was the spectacular glaze storm of January 27-28, 1943, when heavy damage was done to trees and overhead transmission lines of all kinds.

The James River reaches tidewater at Richmond where flooding has occurred in every month of the year, most frequently in March and least in July. Hurricanes and less severe storms of tropical origin have been responsible for most of the flooding during the summer and early fall months. The flood of record at Richmond was Agnes in June, 1972 which produced on the 23rd crests 6 and one half feet above old high water marks dating back 200 years. Agnes was followed closely by serious flooding on October 7, 1972 and preceded by Camille on August 22, 1969 which is now the fourth greatest flood of record. In 1955 three hurricanes brought record rainfall to Richmond within a 6-week period. The most noteworthy of these were Hurricanes Connie and Diane that brought heavy rains five days apart.

Damaging storms occur mainly from snow and freezing rain in winter and from hurricanes, tornadoes, and severe thunderstorms at other seasons. Damage may be from wind, flooding, or rain, or from any combination of these. Tornadoes are infrequent but some notable occurrences have been observed within the Richmond area. The highest wind recorded has been 68 m.p.h. with a peak gust of 79 m.p.h. at the time of Hurricane Hazel, October 15, 1954.

The dates of the last freeze in spring and of the first in autumn mark the limits of the growing season for most crops. The average growing season is 216 days. May 11, 1966, has been the latest date in spring when a temperature of 32 degrees or lower was recorded; October 5, 1965, has been the earliest date in autumn.

RICHMOND, VIRGINIA

Normals, Means, and Extremes

Month	Normal Degree days Base 65 °F: Heating	Cooling	Precipitation in inches, Water equivalent: Normal	Maximum monthly	Year	Minimum monthly	Year	Maximum in 24 hrs.	Year	Snow, Ice pellets: Maximum monthly	Year	Maximum in 24 hrs.	Year	Relative humidity pct.: Hour 01 (Local time)	Hour 07	Hour 13	Hour 19
(a)				38		38		38		38		38		41	41	41	41
J	853	0	2.86	5.95	1962	1.08	1951	3.31	1962	28.5	1940	21.6	1940	77	81	57	69
F	717	0	3.01	5.61	1944	0.98	1968	1.91	1973	17.1	1967	9.2	1947	74	79	52	63
M	569	8	3.38	8.04	1975	0.94	1966	2.04	1942	19.7	1960	12.1	1962	73	78	48	59
A	226	10	2.77	5.32	1952	0.64	1963	2.07	1952	2.0	1940	2.0	1940	74	75	45	56
M	64	111	3.42	8.87	1972	0.87	1965	2.53	1972	0.0		0.0		83	79	50	65
J	0	276	3.52	9.24	1938	0.91	1960	4.61	1963	0.0		0.0		87	82	53	68
J	0	400	5.63	18.87	1945	0.52	1963	5.73	1969	0.0		0.0		89	85	57	72
A	0	350	5.06	14.10	1955	0.52	1943	8.79	1955	0.0		0.0		90	88	57	76
S	21	171	3.58	10.98	1975	0.69	1954	3.82	1955	0.0		0.0		90	89	56	79
O	203	27	2.94	9.39	1971	0.30	1963	6.50	1961	T	1972	T	1972	87	89	52	77
N	480	0	3.20	7.64	1959	0.36	1965	4.07	1956	7.3	1953	7.3	1953	80	84	50	70
D	806	0	3.22	7.07	1973	0.72	1965	3.16	1958	12.5	1958	7.5	1966	78	81	55	70
YR	3939	1353	42.59	18.87	JUL 1945	0.30	OCT 1963	8.79	AUG 1955	28.5	JAN 1940	21.6	JAN 1940	82	83	53	69

Month	Wind: Mean speed m.p.h.	Prevailing direction	Fastest mile: Speed m.p.h.	Direction	Year	Pct. of possible sunshine	Mean sky cover, tenths, sunrise to sunset	Mean number of days, Sunrise to sunset: Clear	Partly cloudy	Cloudy	Precipitation .01 inch or more	Snow, Ice pellets 1.0 inch or more	Thunderstorms	Heavy fog, visibility ¼ mile or less	Temperatures °F Max.: 90° and above (b)	32° and below	Min.: 32° and below	0° and below	Average station pressure mb. Elev. 177 feet m.s.l.
(a)	27	15	25	25		25	30	30	30	30	38	38	38	46	46	46	46	46	3
J	7.9	S	43	NW	1971	51	6.5	8	7	16	10	1	*	3	0	3	21	*	1013.8
F	8.6	NNE	45	SW	1951	54	6.2	9	6	13	9	1	*	2	0	1	19	*	1011.9
M	9.0	W	42	SE	1952	59	6.2	8	9	14	11	1	2	2	*	*	10	0	1009.7
A	8.9	S	40	NW	1972	62	6.1	8	9	13	9	*	2	2	1	0	2	0	1009.6
M	7.8	SSW	45	N	1962	64	6.3	7	11	13	11	0	6	2	3	0	*	0	1008.1
J	7.2	S	52	NW	1952	67	6.0	7	12	11	10	0	7	2	9	0	0	0	1009.7
J	6.7	SSW	56	NW	1955	65	6.2	7	12	12	11	0	9	2	13	0	0	0	1010.3
A	6.3	S	54	W	1964	64	6.0	7	12	12	10	0	7	3	10	0	0	0	1011.6
S	6.6	S	45	SE	1952	63	5.7	10	8	12	8	0	3	3	4	0	0	0	1012.2
O	6.8	NNE	68	SE	1954	59	5.3	12	7	12	7	0	1	4	*	0	2	0	1014.3
N	7.4	S	35	SE	1972	56	5.6	10	8	12	8	*	1	2	0	*	10	0	1013.2
D	7.5	SW	40	SW	1968	51	6.2	10	6	15	9	1	*	3	0	2	21	*	1012.7
YR	7.6	S	68	SE	OCT 1954	60	6.0	103	107	155	114	4	37	29	41	6	85	1	1011.4

FOOTNOTES Means and extremes above are from existing and comparable exposures. Annual extremes have been exceeded at other sites in the locality as follows: Highest temperature 107 in August 1918; minimum monthly precipitation 0.11 in November 1890 and earlier.

Snowfall

Season	July	Aug	Sept	Oct	Nov	Dec	Jan
1937-38	0.0	0.0	0.0	0.0	T	0.6	1.5
1938-39	0.0	0.0	0.0	0.0	4.4	0.0	0.6
1939-40	0.0	0.0	0.0	0.0	0.0	2.9	28.5
1940-41	0.0	0.0	0.0	0.0	0.0	0.0	0.4
1941-42	0.0	0.0	0.0	0.0	0.0	0.0	5.5
#1942-43	0.0	0.0	0.0	0.0	0.0	6.0	T
1943-44	0.0	0.0	0.0	0.0	0.5	1.4	2.5
1944-45	0.0	0.0	0.0	0.0	0.0	0.0	0.5
#1945-46	0.0	0.0	0.0	0.0	0.0	8.2	6.0
1946-47	0.0	0.0	0.0	0.0	0.0	0.3	T
1947-48	0.0	0.0	0.0	0.0	T	T	16.1
1948-49	0.0	0.0	0.0	0.0	0.0	0.6	1.5
#1949-50	0.0	0.0	0.0	0.0	0.0	0.0	0.0
1950-51	0.0	0.0	0.0	0.0	T	0.7	T
1951-52	0.0	0.0	0.0	0.0	T	T	2.4
1952-53	0.0	0.0	0.0	0.0	1.0	T	T
1953-54	0.0	0.0	0.0	0.0	7.3	0.0	7.5
1954-55	0.0	0.0	0.0	T	0.0	2.2	9.3
1955-56	0.0	0.0	0.0	0.0	T	T	1.1
1956-57	0.0	0.0	0.0	0.0	T	T	5.8
1957-58	0.0	0.0	0.0	0.0	T	2.9	3.7
1958-59	0.0	0.0	0.0	0.0	0.0	12.5	2.4
1959-60	0.0	0.0	0.0	0.0	T	1.2	2.5
1960-61	0.0	0.0	0.0	0.0	0.0	1.7	7.2
1961-62	0.0	0.0	0.0	0.0	T	0.9	20.6
1962-63	0.0	0.0	0.0	0.0	0.9	8.1	1.6
1963-64	0.0	0.0	0.0	0.0	T	0.4	5.7
1964-65	0.0	0.0	0.0	0.0	0.4	0.0	12.4
1965-66	0.0	0.0	0.0	0.0	0.0	T	26.2
1966-67	0.0	0.0	0.0	0.0	0.2	12.2	6.3
1967-68	0.0	0.0	0.0	0.0	T	5.6	2.3
1968-69	0.0	0.0	0.0	0.0	1.2	2.8	T
1969-70	0.0	0.0	0.0	0.0	0.0	1.8	5.4
1970-71	0.0	0.0	0.0	0.0	0.0	0.9	3.3
1971-72	0.0	0.0	0.0	0.0	T	0.0	T
1972-73	0.0	0.0	0.0	T	0.6	0.0	4.3
1973-74	0.0	0.0	0.0	0.0	0.0	9.9	T
1974-75	0.0	0.0	0.0	0.0	0.0	T	2.7
1975-76	0.0	0.0	0.0	0.0	0.0	T	
RECORD MEAN	0.0	0.0	0.0	T	0.4	2.2	5.2

Heating Degree Days

Season	July	Aug	Sept	Oct	Nov	Dec	Jan
1955-56	0	0	9	186	555	928	896
1956-57	0	3	75	146	519	493	915
1957-58	0	0	50	317	434	674	936
1958-59	0	0	24	212	409	973	847
1959-60	0	0	36	217	530	717	807
1960-61	0	0	24	257	439	936	971
1961-62	0	0	27	218	459	860	875
1962-63	0	0	73	175	526	891	897
1963-64	0	0	71	197	439	1004	826
1964-65	0	0	32	357	402	676	909
1965-66	0	6	25	275	498	726	1043
1966-67	0	0	47	293	466	833	738
1967-68	0	0	64	256	623	708	956
1968-69	0	0	0	161	403	864	957
1969-70	0	0	45	221	541	907	1076
1970-71	0	0	12	124	445	756	960
1971-72	0	0	11	69	512	526	748
1972-73	0	0	17	285	513	588	843
1973-74	0	0	5	163	414	744	589
1974-75	0	0	62	310	513	715	746
1975-76	0	0	27	121	356	770	

Cooling Degree Days

Year	Jan	Feb	Mar	Apr	May	June	July
1969	0	0	0	21	90	328	417
1970	0	0	0	35	185	328	418
1971	0	0	0	0	56	297	367
1972	0	0	7	30	52	180	381
1973	0	0	13	42	91	338	391
1974	0	0	10	58	106	180	377
1975	0	0	0	16	135	267	348

Feb	Mar	Apr	May	June	Total
0.0	0.0	0.0	0.0	0.0	2.1
0.0	T	0.0	0.0	0.0	5.0
0.3	0.5	2.0	0.0	0.0	34.2
3.6	5.2	0.0	0.0	0.0	9.2
0.0	0.0	0.0	0.0	0.0	5.5
0.0	4.6	0.0	0.0	0.0	10.6
1.6	0.0	0.0	0.0	0.0	6.0
0.0	0.0	0.0	0.0	0.0	0.5
0.0	0.0	0.0	0.0	0.0	14.2
9.3	13.5	0.0	0.0	0.0	23.1
10.1	0.0	0.0	0.0	0.0	26.2
T	T	0.0	0.0	0.0	2.1
2.9	5.9	0.0	0.0	0.0	8.8
T	T	T	0.0	0.0	0.7
11.0	T	0.0	0.0	0.0	13.4
T	5.6	0.2	0.0	0.0	6.8
0.0	0.0	T	0.0	0.0	14.8
1.4	0.0	0.0	0.0	0.0	12.9
T	T	T	0.0	0.0	1.1
0.7	T	1.2	0.0	0.0	7.7
7.7	6.3	0.0	0.0	0.0	20.6
0.0	0.0	0.0	0.0	0.0	14.9
8.9	19.7	0.0	0.0	0.0	32.3
5.0	T	0.0	0.0	0.0	13.9
1.2	16.2	0.0	0.0	0.0	38.9
6.3	T	0.0	0.0	0.0	16.9
10.2	7.0	1.2	0.0	0.0	24.5
6.6	1.0	0.0	0.0	0.0	20.4
3.0	0.0	0.0	0.0	0.0	29.2
17.1	T	0.0	0.0	0.0	35.8
2.4	2.8	0.0	0.0	0.0	13.1
T	11.9	0.0	0.0	0.0	15.9
0.4	0.0	0.0	0.0	0.0	7.6
2.0	8.4	0.6	0.0	0.0	15.2
13.7	0.0	T	0.0	0.0	13.7
0.4	1.4	0.0	0.0	0.0	6.7
5.0	T	0.0	0.0	0.0	14.9
2.9	0.4	0.0	0.0	0.0	6.0
3.5	2.9	0.1	0.0	0.0	14.3

Average Temperature

Year	Jan	Feb	Mar	Apr	May	June	July	Aug	Sept	Oct	Nov	Dec	Annual
1936	31.4	33.7	51.2	53.1	66.5	73.7	79.7	76.5	71.6	59.8	46.3	40.1	57.0
1937	46.0	38.3	43.3	55.3	65.8	76.0	76.8	77.2	66.0	55.0	46.2	38.4	57.0
1938	37.2	43.1	53.6	59.9	64.9	71.6	76.8	78.3	68.4	57.7	49.9	40.3	58.5
1939	41.6	44.8	48.8	56.0	66.9	76.4	75.7	77.1	71.8	59.0	44.8	39.8	58.6
1940	24.2	38.2	43.3	52.4	65.0	74.7	76.0	73.6	66.2	55.8	47.4	42.5	54.9
1941	35.2	34.2	40.8	59.8	66.8	73.0	78.3	75.8	72.2	64.7	48.7	41.9	57.6
#1942	34.2	35.2	48.0	58.8	69.5	75.2	79.4	75.2	71.3	60.8	50.0	37.1	57.9
1943	40.0	41.5	47.0	53.9	69.0	79.2	78.5	78.4	68.4	57.3	47.5	38.6	58.3
1944	38.6	40.4	45.2	56.2	71.6	76.4	77.7	75.4	71.2	57.9	48.2	36.1	57.9
1945	34.2	40.8	58.6	61.4	63.9	75.7	76.2	75.2	73.6	57.8	49.6	33.4	58.4
#1946	38.0	41.7	53.8	57.2	65.8	72.8	75.4	72.6	70.0	60.9	52.9	43.4	58.8
1947	44.6	33.5	40.0	57.5	67.0	72.2	74.8	78.5	70.1	63.7	46.4	38.4	57.2
1948	31.1	39.8	50.8	57.7	66.3	74.4	78.2	75.7	68.6	56.2	52.9	42.0	57.8
1949	45.2	46.5	48.6	55.7	66.0	75.2	80.1	76.6	67.4	62.5	49.0	42.4	59.6
#1950	49.7	40.7	44.4	54.7	65.0	74.2	76.8	75.5	68.2	61.2	47.3	36.1	57.8
1951	40.8	41.3	46.8	56.6	64.6	74.3	78.6	76.0	70.0	61.6	44.7	42.0	58.1
1952	42.4	42.2	46.3	58.1	65.4	77.6	80.4	76.4	69.2	55.2	49.4	39.2	58.5
1953	42.9	43.4	48.3	58.0	71.5	75.2	79.9	77.3	70.0	60.7	48.5	42.5	59.9
1954	38.0	44.9	47.0	61.2	63.0	74.6	78.6	76.8	74.4	62.3	46.1	38.2	58.8
1955	35.8	40.1	50.2	60.8	67.2	70.1	81.3	78.7	70.6	59.5	46.4	34.8	58.0
1956	36.0	43.0	46.3	55.5	65.0	74.7	77.8	76.5	67.9	60.9	47.6	48.9	58.3
1957	35.2	43.3	47.2	61.5	67.8	76.2	78.4	74.6	71.9	54.6	50.3	43.0	58.7
1958	34.6	33.8	42.3	57.5	65.7	71.3	80.2	76.4	69.1	58.7	51.2	33.4	56.2
1959	37.5	41.6	47.3	59.3	69.4	74.8	77.9	79.0	70.8	61.4	47.3	41.6	59.0
1960	38.8	39.3	35.9	61.8	64.9	73.7	76.3	77.5	69.3	57.1	50.1	34.6	56.6
1961	33.5	42.2	50.8	53.0	63.6	72.8	78.5	77.1	73.5	58.1	50.1	37.1	57.5
1962	36.6	39.7	45.0	57.5	70.6	74.0	74.8	74.6	66.2	60.5	47.2	36.1	56.9
1963	35.9	33.3	50.8	59.2	64.0	72.0	76.1	75.7	65.5	58.6	50.1	32.4	56.1
1964	38.1	37.2	47.6	55.4	66.4	73.1	75.8	73.1	67.1	53.4	51.5	42.9	56.8
1965	35.6	38.8	43.0	53.9	69.6	70.7	74.9	75.9	70.7	56.1	48.2	41.3	56.6
1966	31.1	37.7	47.5	52.8	63.1	71.4	76.4	74.6	67.2	55.5	49.5	38.0	55.4
1967	40.9	34.8	46.6	58.8	60.7	72.1	76.6	75.5	65.7	57.2	44.0	41.9	56.2
1968	33.9	34.2	52.0	58.8	64.7	74.7	78.9	78.9	70.9	61.9	51.3	37.0	58.1
1969	33.9	36.8	42.3	57.6	65.5	75.7	78.3	75.1	68.1	58.5	46.8	35.5	56.2
1970	30.1	37.1	42.9	58.2	69.1	75.7	78.3	78.0	74.8	62.9	49.9	40.4	58.1
1971	33.8	39.5	44.5	55.0	63.3	74.7	76.6	75.3	71.4	64.6	48.5	48.0	57.9
1972	40.7	37.6	47.2	56.2	64.6	70.1	77.1	75.2	70.1	55.8	47.9	45.9	57.4
1973	37.6	38.5	52.6	57.9	65.1	76.0	77.4	77.5	72.3	60.6	51.3	40.8	59.0
1974	45.8	40.1	50.4	59.9	65.8	70.6	76.9	75.7	67.4	55.4	48.5	41.7	58.2
1975	40.7	41.4	45.3	52.9	67.7	73.6	76.0	78.8	69.3	62.5	53.6	40.0	58.5
RECORD MEAN	38.0	39.4	46.9	56.9	66.1	74.0	77.6	76.1	69.9	58.9	48.7	39.7	57.7
MAX	47.9	50.0	58.2	69.3	78.0	85.1	87.9	86.2	80.7	70.8	60.2	49.8	68.7
MIN	28.1	28.7	35.5	44.4	54.2	62.8	67.2	66.0	59.1	46.9	37.1	29.5	46.6

# Indicates a station move or relocation of instruments.

Feb	Mar	Apr	May	June	Total
631	578	323	107	10	4223
600	546	201	63	5	3566
871	696	254	70	6	4308
650	542	212	44	10	3923
737	894	184	88	2	4212
632	461	390	106	7	4223
702	623	276	32	0	4072
882	434	218	102	1	4199
801	537	306	74	12	4267
726	674	339	17	34	4161
759	538	371	133	27	4401
841	560	230	171	17	4196
887	416	191	86	0	4187
783	695	237	66	0	4166
778	677	231	51	0	4527
709	627	295	104	3	4035
788	554	286	58	21	3573
735	394	247	79	0	3701
691	455	204	75	5	3345
654	604	368	44	1	4017

Aug	Sept	Oct	Nov	Dec	Total
321	147	26	0	0	1350
410	313	67	0	0	1756
327	209	62	22	5	1345
326	178	9	8	0	1171
395	231	32	9	2	1544
340	141	21	26	0	1259
433	165	51	18	0	1433

Precipitation

Year	Jan	Feb	Mar	Apr	May	June	July	Aug	Sept	Oct	Nov	Dec	Annual
1938	3.28	1.82	3.72	3.24	4.92	9.24	11.89	0.95	4.41	1.57	2.74	2.74	50.52
1939	3.40	3.98	5.33	3.04	1.39	5.41	5.23	8.34	1.70	4.84	2.18	1.51	46.35
1940	4.16	2.99	2.31	4.22	4.26	4.02	4.45	9.33	1.77	2.27	4.59	1.83	46.20
1941	2.19	1.17	1.97	3.44	1.31	1.83	2.82	3.05	1.23	0.35	0.66	2.89	22.91
#1942	3.59	1.03	5.31	0.78	1.11	5.30	3.52	6.61	3.71	6.74	1.31	3.04	42.05
1943	2.87	2.27	3.01	2.11	4.04	3.15	3.87	0.52	5.13	2.90	1.44	1.98	33.29
1944	2.83	5.61	5.85	3.59	1.41	1.42	7.76	6.44	5.50	1.79	3.94	2.26	48.40
1945	2.25	3.57	1.33	3.50	5.09	1.71	18.87	2.92	8.49	0.91	3.09	5.28	57.01
#1946	2.16	2.69	2.23	2.59	7.73	6.01	6.64	3.87	4.39	2.36	1.90	2.71	45.28
1947	4.31	1.43	2.22	2.53	4.69	4.48	3.33	1.87	6.38	2.37	7.03	1.56	42.20
1948	4.11	2.66	5.54	4.59	6.42	2.73	4.05	7.75	3.05	3.21	5.74	4.14	53.99
1949	3.26	2.55	2.12	2.22	5.11	3.53	6.34	8.99	2.64	3.87	1.88	1.94	44.45
#1950	2.17	1.71	3.20	0.74	4.27	0.99	6.69	3.32	4.04	1.77	1.74	2.73	33.37
1951	1.08	1.90	2.85	2.26	2.51	5.85	2.63	5.23	0.98	2.71	4.52	3.63	36.15
1952	5.71	2.76	5.05	5.32	3.72	4.50	2.71	6.41	2.35	2.04	6.42	3.37	50.36
1953	4.47	3.36	3.95	3.16	2.35	3.06	2.04	0.99	6.84	2.16	1.85	2.94	37.17
1954	3.70	1.56	2.44	3.08	4.36	1.09	1.30	3.95	0.69	4.99	1.86	2.43	31.45
1955	1.09	3.18	2.66	3.14	1.79	3.06	7.93	14.10	5.79	2.57	1.76	0.86	47.93
1956	1.65	3.57	3.06	2.75	4.35	3.28	10.32	2.28	2.96	4.92	6.11	3.98	49.23
1957	3.36	5.29	2.82	2.25	2.75	3.92	1.80	7.46	3.43	5.35	5.30	6.88	50.61
1958	2.96	4.38	3.81	4.35	5.79	6.09	3.27	9.77	1.90	5.35	1.43	4.43	53.53
1959	1.31	1.87	2.92	4.32	2.44	3.45	12.85	5.75	3.30	3.25	7.64	2.24	51.34
1960	2.13	4.56	3.29	3.57	3.59	0.91	7.34	7.20	6.21	3.31	0.85	3.04	46.00
1961	2.57	5.39	4.02	1.73	4.83	6.49	2.85	3.90	1.64	8.78	1.81	5.05	49.06
1962	5.95	3.00	4.87	3.80	4.08	5.57	5.65	2.37	3.46	0.50	6.73	2.64	48.62
1963	1.55	2.98	5.62	0.64	2.39	7.01	0.52	3.75	3.20	0.30	6.70	2.80	37.46
1964	4.16	4.46	2.61	2.71	1.14	2.40	6.46	9.88	2.56	3.62	1.98	3.05	45.03
1965	2.51	2.77	3.68	2.13	0.87	3.39	6.33	0.81	4.81	1.38	0.36	0.72	29.76
1966	4.58	3.80	0.94	2.18	2.58	2.54	4.07	1.31	5.06	4.81	1.31	3.07	36.25
1967	1.50	3.35	2.34	1.32	3.71	3.58	5.00	6.65	0.95	1.00	1.76	6.48	37.64
1968	2.53	0.98	4.00	2.93	3.13	2.89	3.41	3.71	1.78	1.59	3.87	2.28	33.10
1969	2.04	3.95	3.95	2.60	3.32	4.36	13.90	9.31	3.89	1.88	1.87	5.26	56.33
1970	1.32	2.37	3.70	2.84	1.84	1.12	4.74	1.69	1.02	1.55	3.10	3.00	28.29
1971	1.84	4.37	2.68	1.76	6.82	4.10	4.40	3.73	2.35	9.39	2.76	0.75	44.95
1972	1.43	5.15	2.11	3.35	8.87	8.82	5.80	3.84	3.35	7.89	5.82	2.91	59.34
1973	2.66	3.11	3.44	4.58	3.56	2.45	3.64	4.34	1.82	2.56	1.27	7.07	40.50
1974	3.21	2.54	3.79	1.58	3.02	1.80	2.25	6.84	4.83	0.39	1.23	4.22	35.70
1975	5.71	2.96	8.04	2.78	2.59	4.00	12.29	2.31	10.98	3.10	2.04	4.51	61.31
RECORD MEAN	2.94	3.08	3.49	2.83	3.64	3.83	5.76	5.04	3.65	3.17	3.12	3.22	43.77

Record mean values above are means through the current year for the period beginning in 1930 for temperature, 1938 for precipitation and snowfall. Data are from airport locations.

TEMPERATURES °F

Month	Normal: Daily maximum	Normal: Daily minimum	Normal: Monthly	Extremes: Record highest	Extremes: Year	Extremes: Record lowest	Extremes: Year
(a)				11		11	
J	45.6	27.2	36.4	75	1975	-4	1972
F	47.9	28.3	38.1	78	1972	1	1970
M	56.3	34.3	45.3	86	1968	14	1965
A	67.9	43.9	55.9	88	1974	22	1972
M	76.1	52.7	64.4	93	1969	31	1966
J	83.0	60.4	71.7	97	1968	40	1966
J	85.9	64.4	75.2	100	1966	48	1972
A	84.9	63.3	74.1	96	1973	43	1965
S	79.5	56.5	68.0	95	1973	36	1974
O	69.9	45.6	57.8	85	1975	22	1972
N	57.6	35.8	46.7	82	1974	11	1970
D	46.6	28.1	37.4	75	1971	7	1968
YR	66.8	45.0	55.9	100	JUL 1966	-4	JAN 1972

IMPORTANT:
The time-period covered by this record is limited: See footnotes following table of **NORMALS, MEANS AND EXTREMES** for explanation and for additional history of **EXTREME HIGHS AND LOWS** recorded in the general area.

Station: ROANOKE, VIRGINIA WOODRUM AIRPORT
Elevation (ground): 1149 feet

The climate of Roanoke, Virginia, may well be termed "mild," since the extremes often found in summer and winter are lacking. Roanoke is apparently surrounded by mountains, but is actually in a part of the Great Valley that runs from the northernmost partof the statesouthwestward to Scott County. As the valley curves, the Blue Ridges seem to meet the Alleghenies. This location offers a natural barrier to the winter cold as it moves southward, often slowing it down and allowing time for it to moderate as well as lose force. The location is also inland far enough to cause tropical hurricanes to lose their destructive force before reaching Roanoke. The elevation in vicinity usually produces cool summer nights that make a light cover almost always necessary. Thus the natural influences that temper the weather are easily seen in a study of past records. Although extremes in temperature run to over 100 degrees for the high in summer and below zero for the low in winter, many years pass without seeing either extreme.

Roanoke is located near the headwaters of the Roanoke River, which flows in a general southeasterly direction. Numerous creeks and small streams from nearby mountainous areas empty into the Roanoke River. The usual low water stage is 1 to 1.5 feet, and flood stage is 10 feet. Some low lying streets in Roanoke and Salem have to be blocked off with 7 to 8 foot stages, but damage is minor until the river overflows its banks. The highest stage on record was 19.61 feet recorded at 9PM EDT June 21, 1972. Damage was widespread and amounted to

(Continued page 674)

Snowfall

Season	July	Aug	Sept	Oct	Nov	Dec	Jan
1938-39							1.0
1939-40	0.0	0.0	0.0	0.0	8.0	9.0	14.0
1940-41	0.0	0.0	0.0	0.0	T	T	2.2
1941-42	0.0	0.0	0.0	0.0	0.0	T	2.5
1942-43	0.0	0.0	0.0	0.0	0.0	7.7	T
1943-44	0.0	0.0	0.0	0.0	0.3	3.0	1.1
1944-45	0.0	0.0	0.0	0.0	T	9.0	1.0
1945-46	0.0	0.0	0.0	0.0	T	11.0	4.3
1946-47	0.0	0.0	0.0	0.0	0.0	4.0	0.7
1947-48	0.0	0.0	0.0	0.0	T	1.0	20.7
1948-49	0.0	0.0	0.0	0.0	T	4.5	5.5
1949-50	0.0	0.0	0.0	0.0	T	2.0	T
1950-51	0.0	0.0	0.0	0.0	8.2	1.1	0.4
#1951-52	0.0	0.0	0.0	0.0	T	5.2	2.3
1952-53	0.0	0.0	0.0	T	1.7	1.3	T
1953-54	0.0	0.0	T	0.0	1.0	T	8.4
1954-55	0.0	0.0	0.0	0.0	1.4	1.1	11.0
1955-56	0.0	0.0	0.0	0.0	1.0	2.3	2.5
1956-57	0.0	0.0	0.0	0.0	0.1	T	1.6
1957-58	0.0	0.0	0.0	1.0	2.2	T	4.1
1958-59	0.0	0.0	0.0	0.0	T	2.3	4.9
1959-60	0.0	0.0	0.0	0.0	T	T	4.8
1960-61	0.0	0.0	0.0	0.0	T	9.8	10.0
1961-62	0.0	0.0	0.0	0.0	2.9	4.5	8.3
1962-63	0.0	0.0	0.0	T	2.4	14.4	T
1963-64	0.0	0.0	0.0	0.0	T	10.1	15.7
1964-65	0.0	0.0	0.0	0.0	0.5	T	12.1
1965-66	0.0	0.0	0.0	0.0	T	0.3	41.2
1966-67	0.0	0.0	0.0	0.0	T	22.6	2.7
1967-68	0.0	0.0	0.0	0.0	T	14.8	15.4
1968-69	0.0	0.0	0.0	T	13.8	T	0.1
1969-70	0.0	0.0	0.0	0.0	T	16.8	4.4
1970-71	0.0	0.0	0.0	0.0	2.0	10.8	1.1
1971-72	0.0	0.0	0.0	0.0	10.2	0.2	T
1972-73	0.0	0.0	0.0	0.0	T	T	2.4
1973-74	0.0	0.0	0.0	T	T	7.9	T
1974-75	0.0	0.0	0.0	T	3.3	6.6	4.6
1975-76	0.0	0.0	0.0	0.0	T	0.1	
RECORD MEAN	0.0	0.0	T	T	2.0	4.8	6.6

Heating Degree Days

Season	July	Aug	Sept	Oct	Nov	Dec	Jan
1955-56	0	0	21	228	606	947	910
1956-57	0	6	86	202	573	526	901
1957-58	0	3	67	349	498	735	974
1958-59	0	0	30	256	436	948	893
1959-60	0	0	28	238	602	734	829
1960-61	0	0	19	209	511	1001	981
1961-62	0	0	36	211	485	856	904
1962-63	0	0	100	221	594	975	989
1963-64	0	1	64	150	485	1063	852
#1964-65	0	9	41	338	409	770	892
1965-66	0	9	38	287	520	722	1058
1966-67	0	0	51	317	527	837	740
1967-68	0	0	105	321	643	728	984
1968-69	0	12	11	244	502	963	1005
1969-70	0	0	53	274	607	967	1087
1970-71	1	1	24	194	553	769	959
1971-72	0	0	12	117	595	603	780
1972-73	10	1	33	391	582	628	852
1973-74	0	0	12	196	461	826	607
1974-75	0	0	84	308	539	801	783
1975-76	0	0	59	173	415	809	

Cooling Degree Days

Year	Jan	Feb	Mar	Apr	May	June	July
1969	0	0	0	2	86	256	347
1970	0	0	0	22	128	246	351
1971	0	0	0	4	40	239	270
1972	0	0	0	26	13	118	305
1973	0	0	3	15	29	269	331
1974	0	0	7	27	82	117	303
1975	0	0	0	5	108	213	301

ROANOKE, VIRGINIA

Feb	Mar	Apr	May	June	Total
0.0	0.4	0.0	0.0	0.0	
T	0.5	T	0.0	0.0	31.5
0.4	7.0	0.0	0.0	0.0	9.6
T	7.0	T	0.0	0.0	9.5
1.8	6.5	T	0.0	0.0	16.0
4.0	1.0	T	0.0	0.0	9.4
0.5	0.0	0.0	0.0	0.0	10.5
2.5	0.0	0.0	0.0	0.0	17.8
17.8	21.5	0.0	0.0	0.0	44.0
11.4	1.4	0.0	0.0	0.0	34.5
3.7	T	T	0.0	0.0	13.7
T	5.4	T	0.0	0.0	7.4
1.3	4.3	0.0	0.0	0.0	15.3
0.0	0.2	0.0	0.0	0.0	7.7
2.0	5.2	T	0.0	0.0	10.2
1.3	T	T	0.0	0.0	10.7
2.1	1.0	T	0.0	0.0	16.6
2.4	T	0.6	0.0	0.0	8.8
1.4	T	0.6	0.0	0.0	3.7
6.2	14.8	T	0.0	0.0	28.3
T	T	0.7	0.0	0.0	7.9
27.6	30.3	T	0.0	0.0	62.7
20.7	0.3	T	0.0	0.0	40.8
3.3	11.3	T	0.0	0.0	30.3
12.2	0.7	0.0	T	0.0	29.7
20.2	4.3	0.0	0.0	0.0	50.3
4.0	4.1	0.0	0.0	0.0	20.7
8.4	T	0.0	0.0	0.0	49.9
15.6	0.8	0.0	0.0	0.0	41.7
3.8	T	0.0	0.0	0.0	34.0
11.4	13.8	0.0	0.0	0.0	39.1
5.4	T	0.2	0.0	0.0	26.8
3.6	7.3	7.3	0.0	0.0	32.1
12.8	T	T	0.0	0.0	23.2
1.4	5.5	0.2	0.0	0.0	9.5
9.7	T	0.0	0.0	0.0	17.6
6.3	6.2	T	0.0	0.0	27.0
7.1	4.2	0.3	T	0.0	25.0

ROANOKE, VA

Feb	Mar	Apr	May	June	Total
662	588	365	87	36	4450
599	600	246	52	10	3801
920	727	282	82	3	4640
668	597	218	49	8	4103
819	955	206	142	0	4553
663	465	433	127	15	4424
688	658	354	34	1	4227
917	470	228	89	5	4588
848	566	265	62	15	4371
794	710	305	21	19	4308
831	565	409	118	25	4582
838	505	202	206	28	4251
902	423	255	111	3	4475
772	746	227	77	9	4568
783	691	269	66	2	4799
719	658	285	143	3	4309
837	594	305	99	31	3973
812	428	344	144	1	4226
722	440	255	96	14	3629
683	699	361	60	12	4330

Aug	Sept	Oct	Nov	Dec	Total
272	107	21	0	0	1091
291	261	35	0	0	1334
245	163	35	13	1	1010
262	118	0	2	0	844
346	192	23	0	0	1208
267	83	3	12	0	901
379	114	27	5	0	1152

Average Temperature

Year	Jan	Feb	Mar	Apr	May	June	July	Aug	Sept	Oct	Nov	Dec	Annual
1939	40.3	47.1	48.6	54.7	66.4	76.7	74.5	74.3	70.9	58.4	45.1	40.6	58.1
1940	25.7	38.6	42.7	53.2	63.6	72.6	74.2	72.1	65.3	57.2	42.0	42.0	54.5
1941	35.7	33.8	40.9	60.4	66.9	71.6	76.5	75.8	71.4	63.4	48.2	42.6	57.3
1942	35.6	34.2	47.4	59.2	66.9	73.6	77.4	73.2	67.9	58.6	47.6	35.0	56.4
1943	40.0	39.6	44.6	52.8	66.7	71.9	75.8	76.4	65.9	57.0	46.4	38.4	56.3
1944	38.6	40.4	43.6	53.0	68.9	73.8	74.0	74.0	68.0	55.6	45.0	33.0	55.7
1945	34.3	39.2	55.1	57.8	60.6	71.2	75.5	73.7	70.6	56.2	47.7	32.1	56.2
1946	37.1	40.4	52.2	56.8	61.9	70.8	73.7	70.0	67.3	58.6	50.5	41.3	56.6
1947	41.2	30.2	37.6	57.5	64.1	70.4	71.9	76.4	67.6	60.6	43.4	38.2	54.8
1948	31.0	38.8	48.5	58.3	63.9	71.4	75.3	72.8	66.4	54.0	49.2	40.5	55.8
1949	44.8	44.2	46.4	53.6	65.0	73.8	77.2	73.2	64.8	61.5	47.1	40.4	58.1
1950	47.6	40.3	42.6	53.7	65.5	71.4	73.2	72.2	65.8	60.9	43.2	34.6	55.9
1951	38.5	39.8	45.4	54.5	64.3	72.8	76.0	75.7	68.1	60.3	41.2	38.4	56.2
#1952	42.1	42.0	45.1	56.3	65.2	77.8	78.3	73.4	66.8	54.4	47.5	39.5	57.4
1953	41.5	42.6	47.6	55.2	70.9	74.6	78.4	76.8	68.8	60.9	47.7	39.1	58.7
1954	37.4	43.8	45.5	60.5	60.7	73.5	77.5	75.7	71.9	59.3	43.1	37.0	57.1
1955	35.3	39.0	48.3	60.1	67.7	68.0	79.8	77.2	68.8	58.1	44.5	34.2	56.7
1956	35.4	42.0	45.9	53.6	65.7	72.3	76.3	75.7	66.8	58.9	45.6	47.9	57.2
1957	35.7	43.4	45.4	59.8	67.6	73.7	76.5	73.7	68.5	53.5	48.1	41.1	57.2
1958	33.4	31.8	41.3	55.9	64.6	71.8	78.1	75.0	68.2	57.0	50.4	34.2	55.2
1959	36.0	40.9	45.5	58.5	68.8	73.8	77.1	79.1	70.3	59.6	44.8	41.1	58.0
1960	38.0	36.6	34.0	60.2	63.2	73.1	75.9	77.7	69.7	58.8	47.7	32.4	55.6
1961	33.2	41.1	50.1	51.0	61.5	71.3	76.6	75.6	71.9	58.3	49.3	37.2	56.4
1962	35.7	40.2	43.5	53.8	69.9	72.4	74.2	74.4	64.8	59.4	45.0	33.3	55.6
1963	32.9	32.0	49.7	58.6	64.4	72.9	75.0	73.9	66.0	60.5	48.6	30.5	55.4
#1964	37.3	35.6	46.6	56.9	67.4	74.6	75.9	74.0	66.8	54.0	51.1	40.0	56.7
1965	36.0	36.4	41.9	54.9	69.2	69.7	73.9	74.2	69.7	56.0	47.5	41.5	55.9
1966	30.6	35.1	46.7	51.5	63.3	71.1	77.9	73.0	66.1	54.6	47.2	37.8	54.6
1967	40.8	34.8	48.5	59.0	59.0	70.3	73.4	72.6	63.2	54.7	43.4	41.3	55.1
1968	33.0	33.8	51.3	56.5	62.4	71.3	75.6	75.2	66.7	57.4	48.1	33.7	55.4
1969	32.3	37.2	40.7	57.3	65.0	73.1	76.0	73.5	66.7	56.6	44.5	33.6	54.7
1970	29.8	36.9	42.5	56.5	66.8	72.9	76.1	74.1	72.6	59.7	46.3	40.0	56.2
1971	33.9	39.1	43.6	55.5	61.5	72.6	73.5	72.6	69.8	62.1	45.4	45.3	56.3
1972	39.6	36.0	45.6	55.5	62.0	67.7	74.3	73.2	67.6	52.2	45.4	44.5	55.3
1973	37.3	35.8	51.1	53.8	61.1	73.8	75.5	76.0	70.8	59.2	49.3	38.2	56.8
1974	45.3	39.0	50.8	57.2	64.3	68.1	74.5	73.5	64.8	55.0	47.3	38.9	56.6
1975	39.6	40.4	42.2	52.9	66.5	71.5	74.5	77.0	66.6	60.0	51.1	38.8	56.8
RECORD MEAN	36.9	38.5	45.6	57.0	64.9	72.2	76.0	74.7	67.8	57.8	46.8	38.4	56.4
MAX	46.1	48.3	56.1	67.7	76.4	83.7	86.9	85.4	78.8	69.2	57.1	47.4	66.9
MIN	27.7	28.7	35.0	46.2	53.4	60.6	65.0	63.9	56.7	46.3	36.4	29.4	45.8

# Indicates a station move or relocation of instruments.

Precipitation

Year	Jan	Feb	Mar	Apr	May	June	July	Aug	Sept	Oct	Nov	Dec	Annual
1939	2.83	4.05	2.23	2.41	1.38	2.37	7.69	8.15	1.90	0.78	1.67	1.36	36.82
1940	1.77	2.23	2.08	3.18	8.27	3.41	3.92	12.91	0.59	1.04	3.25	3.03	45.68
1941	1.57	0.60	2.06	3.01	2.45	4.12	6.63	1.01	1.57	0.92	0.84	4.00	28.78
1942	1.50	1.22	2.38	0.37	6.43	5.40	3.00	9.11	5.08	3.85	2.01	3.46	43.81
1943	2.55	1.56	3.74	4.39	4.43	5.28	5.19	1.54	1.42	1.89	1.27	2.99	36.25
1944	2.29	5.43	4.51	1.46	4.17	1.37	3.79	1.94	9.16	3.61	1.96	2.47	42.16
1945	2.39	3.66	4.08	2.16	3.41	3.43	3.65	0.71	10.01	0.96	3.35	3.97	41.78
1946	3.15	2.91	2.94	2.76	5.42	2.11	4.79	1.69	2.23	3.73	1.93	2.67	36.33
1947	5.63	1.33	2.25	2.92	2.35	5.93	4.48	8.83	4.04	7.25	4.70	0.87	50.58
1948	3.64	2.49	4.75	3.53	5.70	5.64	3.84	8.59	4.60	2.55	6.36	7.10	58.79
1949	4.35	1.93	2.91	5.15	3.37	6.67	7.85	9.12	1.46	3.29	1.68	1.80	49.58
1950	2.40	2.61	2.17	1.71	8.42	2.73	5.21	2.74	6.10	2.43	1.26	3.89	41.67
1951	1.03	2.19	4.06	4.47	1.27	5.37	2.33	1.63	1.84	1.12	3.41	3.83	32.55
#1952	4.44	2.58	3.67	4.76	3.53	2.12	1.86	7.79	0.89	1.17	3.16	3.14	39.11
1953	2.78	3.08	5.13	2.69	4.12	5.34	1.47	2.08	1.47	0.42	1.03	3.81	33.42
1954	4.77	3.83	2.76	1.08	3.42	2.82	3.27	3.18	1.13	6.76	2.91	3.95	39.88
1955	1.19	3.87	4.84	3.84	3.12	3.70	2.73	4.70	1.64	1.61	1.88	0.84	33.96
1956	0.60	4.87	2.22	3.12	1.58	1.72	2.85	2.58	5.74	6.80	1.84	1.91	35.83
1957	3.74	5.31	1.48	4.55	2.23	5.35	1.13	1.20	7.06	2.37	3.39	2.46	40.27
1958	3.66	3.40	4.76	2.83	5.00	1.88	6.21	3.28	1.56	1.12	1.66	4.15	39.51
1959	2.37	1.04	3.38	4.27	3.17	2.82	2.81	4.49	4.95	3.97	1.94	2.18	37.39
1960	1.92	7.17	3.96	2.19	5.91	1.46	2.06	4.69	3.30	3.62	0.44	2.23	38.95
1961	1.61	4.50	4.17	3.86	2.05	3.79	1.59	5.14	1.79	3.35	3.62	5.07	40.54
1962	2.54	3.22	4.76	1.69	2.70	3.08	5.34	3.55	3.66	2.22	5.11	3.35	41.22
1963	1.10	1.97	3.89	0.87	1.94	2.61	2.68	1.81	2.87	0.27	3.80	1.86	25.67
1964	5.20	5.33	1.81	3.54	1.79	1.97	3.37	3.54	2.70	2.80	3.09	2.73	37.87
1965	3.72	3.53	3.93	1.70	3.83	1.83	5.50	1.16	1.97	3.42	0.95	0.18	31.72
1966	4.26	4.78	0.43	2.59	3.49	1.54	3.00	4.73	7.25	4.04	1.73	3.25	41.09
1967	1.25	2.51	4.51	1.67	3.95	3.19	4.05	6.36	1.78	2.42	1.30	4.84	37.83
1968	3.33	0.56	3.03	2.73	1.89	2.11	2.95	5.36	0.44	8.06	2.82	1.80	35.08
1969	1.86	2.74	3.35	1.40	1.58	4.95	5.35	5.41	2.79	2.22	1.40	5.54	38.59
1970	1.31	2.36	1.95	2.80	1.51	4.87	3.28	6.40	1.99	7.51	3.67	2.81	40.46
1971	1.21	5.13	2.28	2.55	7.50	4.84	5.23	4.46	3.87	6.75	2.18	0.83	46.83
1972	2.49	4.80	1.76	3.31	6.00	7.55	4.89	2.62	4.79	3.18	5.63	4.62	51.64
1973	2.60	2.95	5.92	5.39	5.58	3.65	5.10	3.34	1.84	4.28	1.79	5.60	48.04
1974	3.33	2.13	3.12	1.86	3.76	2.93	3.71	4.93	3.04	0.77	1.28	3.16	34.02
1975	3.59	3.05	7.80	2.04	6.65	1.54	5.15	5.68	6.46	3.01	1.77	3.67	50.41
RECORD MEAN	2.72	3.35	3.53	2.94	3.75	3.50	3.74	4.31	3.18	3.27	2.54	3.24	40.07

Record mean values above are means through the current year for the period beginning in 1948. Data are from airport locations.

(Continued)

several million dollars in the City of Roanoke alone. Flood stage has been equalled or exceeded 22 times and the 14 foot stage exceeded 4 times since 1896 — in 1901, 1928, 1940, and 1972.

The growing season averages 190 days, with the average date of the latest freezing temperature in spring April 15, and the average date of the first freezing temperature in fall October 22.

Rainfall is well apportioned throughout the year with about 23 inches in the average warm season (April — September, inclusive). Droughts are so infrequent that quoting actual records would be difficult. Snow usually falls each winter with extremes ranging from only a trace to more than 60 inches. The average is between 19 and 22 inches.

Normals, Means, and Extremes

Month	Normal Degree days Base 65 °F: Heating	Cooling	Precipitation in inches — Water equivalent: Normal	Maximum monthly	Year	Minimum monthly	Year	Maximum in 24 hrs.	Year	Snow, Ice pellets: Maximum monthly	Year	Maximum in 24 hrs.	Year	Relative humidity pct. Hour 01	Hour 07	Hour 13	Hour 19 (Local time)
(a)				28		28		28		28		28		11	11	11	11
J	887	0	2.74	5.20	1964	0.60	1956	2.71	1968	41.2	1966	13.7	1966	67	69	52	57
F	753	0	3.09	7.17	1960	0.56	1968	2.54	1954	27.6	1960	15.7	1960	61	65	48	52
M	611	0	3.37	7.80	1975	0.43	1966	2.77	1975	30.3	1960	17.4	1960	62	67	46	49
A	283	10	2.80	5.39	1973	0.87	1963	1.83	1971	7.3	1971	7.3	1971	63	69	46	48
M	101	83	3.47	8.42	1950	1.27	1951	3.99	1973	T	1963	T	1963	76	77	52	57
J	0	205	3.51	7.55	1972	1.46	1960	3.98	1972	0.0		0.0		83	81	54	63
J	0	316	3.74	7.85	1949	1.13	1957	2.72	1966	0.0		0.0		85	83	56	65
A	0	282	4.15	9.12	1949	1.16	1965	3.35	1970	0.0		0.0		87	86	58	69
S	32	122	3.42	7.25	1966	0.44	1968	3.45	1959	T	1953	T	1953	86	87	56	69
O	235	12	3.19	8.06	1968	0.27	1963	6.41	1968	1.0	1957	1.0	1957	79	82	51	63
N	549	0	2.48	6.36	1948	0.44	1960	3.00	1962	13.8	1968	10.0	1968	69	73	49	57
D	856	0	3.11	7.10	1948	0.18	1965	3.40	1948	22.6	1966	16.4	1969	68	71	53	60
YR	4307	1030	39.03	9.12	AUG 1949	0.18	DEC 1965	6.41	OCT 1968	41.2	JAN 1966	17.4	MAR 1960	74	76	52	59

(To better understand these tables, see full explanation of terms beginning on page 322)

Month	Wind: Mean speed m.p.h.	Prevailing direction	Fastest mile: Speed m.p.h.	Direction	Year	Pct. of possible sunshine	Mean sky cover, tenths, sunrise to sunset	Mean number of days — Sunrise to sunset: Clear	Partly cloudy	Cloudy	Precipitation .01 inch or more	Snow, Ice pellets 1.0 inch or more	Thunderstorms	Heavy fog, visibility ¼ mile or less	Temperatures °F Max. (b) 90° and above	Max. 32° and below	Min. 32° and below	Min. 0° and below	Average station pressure mb. Elev. 1176 feet m.s.l.
(a)	27	15	14	14			27	28	28	28	28	28	28	28	11	11	11	11	3
J	9.7	WNW	53	30	1964		6.3	8	8	15	11	2	*	3	0	4	22	*	977.4
F	10.3	SE	40	31	1972		6.2	8	7	13	10	2	*	3	0	3	21	0	975.2
M	10.6	WNW	52	32	1967		6.2	8	9	14	11	1	1	2	0	0	13	0	973.8
A	10.2	SE	58	32	1963		6.1	8	9	13	10	*	3	1	0	0	3	0	974.1
M	8.2	SE	46	36	1962		6.2	7	11	13	12	0	6	2	1	0	*	0	972.9
J	7.0	SE	46	28	1966		5.9	7	12	11	10	0	7	1	4	0	0	0	975.2
J	6.6	W	37	35	1974		6.0	6	14	11	12	0	9	2	8	0	0	0	975.9
A	6.3	SE	44	30	1975		5.8	8	13	10	11	0	7	2	5	0	0	0	977.4
S	6.2	SE	29	31	1971		5.5	10	9	11	9	0	3	3	2	0	0	0	977.5
O	7.0	SE	35	34	1963		4.9	14	6	11	7	*	1	2	0	0	3	0	979.0
N	8.7	NW	52	34	1963		5.7	9	9	12	9	1	*	2	0	*	10	0	977.5
D	9.1	NW	40	30	1970		6.2	9	8	14	9	1	*	3	0	2	19	0	976.5
YR	8.3	SE	58	32	APR 1963		5.9	102	115	148	121	7	38	26	20	9	90	*	976.0

FOOTNOTES

Means and extremes above are from existing and comparable exposures. Annual extremes have been exceeded at other sites in the locality as follows: Highest temperature 105 in July 1936; lowest temperature -12 in December 1917; maximum monthly precipitation 12.91 in August 1940; minimum monthly precipitation .16 in November 1931.

SEATTLE, WASHINGTON

Station: SEATTLE, WASHINGTON
SEATTLE-TACOMA AIRPORT
Elevation (ground): 400 feet

TEMPERATURES °F

Month	Normal: Daily maximum	Normal: Daily minimum	Normal: Monthly	Extremes: Record highest	Extremes: Year	Extremes: Record lowest	Extremes: Year
(a)				16		16	
J	43.4	33.0	38.2	61	1960	12	1972
F	48.5	36.0	42.3	70	1968	18	1962
M	51.5	36.6	44.1	71	1964	23	1971
A	57.0	40.3	48.7	77	1972	29	1975
M	64.1	45.6	54.9	93	1963	33	1962
J	69.0	50.6	59.8	94	1970	41	1962
J	75.1	53.8	64.5	97	1961	45	1973
A	73.8	53.7	63.8	99	1960	45	1960
S	68.7	50.4	59.6	93	1967	35	1972
O	59.4	44.9	52.2	81	1975	30	1971
N	50.4	38.8	44.6	72	1970	22	1975
D	45.4	35.5	40.5	60	1965	6	1968
YR	58.8	43.3	51.1	99	AUG 1960	6	DEC 1968

IMPORTANT:
The time-period covered by this record is limited: See footnotes on next page for explanation and for additional history of EXTREME HIGHS AND LOWS recorded in the general area.

The Seattle-Tacoma International Airport is located 6 miles south of the Seattle city limits and 14 miles north-northeast of the city of Tacoma. It is situated atop a low north-south ridge lying between Puget Sound on the west and the Green River-White River Valley on the east. The terrain slopes moderately to the shores of Puget Sound 2.2 miles west of the field. The Olympic Mountain Range rises sharply from the west shores of Puget Sound and is about 50 miles distant from the airport. To the east about 2.5 miles rather steep bluffs border the Green River Valley. The foothills of the Cascades begin 10-15 miles east of the field and the Cascade Range is some 40-50 miles east.

The middle-latitude west coast climate of the Seattle-Tacoma area is modified by the imposing barrier of the Cascade Range on the east and to a lesser extent by the comparatively short Olympic Range to the west and northwest. It is characterized by equable temperatures, a pronounced though not sharply defined rainy season and considerable cloudiness, particularly during the winter months.

The Cascades are very effective in excluding continental influences from the Seattle-Tacoma areas, particularly in keeping cold air from draining westward during the winter. Occasionally the pressure distribution will result in a southward flow of cold air from Canada west of the Cascades and it is only under these conditions that extremely cold weather strikes the southern Puget Sound area. The prevailing southwesterly circulation keeps the average winter daytime temperatures in the forties and the nighttime readings in the thirties. Summertime temperatures are predominately modified by the relative proximity of the ocean. During the summer months the nighttime readings are very consistently in the lower or middle fifties. On what may be called a typical summer afternoon the readings hover in the seventies or possibly lower eighties.

Occasionally during the warm season,even as early as April and as late as September, a weak elongated area of low barometric pressure develops along the immediate coast and rather dry hot continental air moves toward the lower pressure, spreading over the sections west of the Cascades. It is under these conditions that Seattle-Tacoma and vicinity gets its few hot days. These hot spells are only of a few days duration and almost invariably "break" or end with a sharp drop to temperatures of 70 degrees or so, as it only takes a small change in the general pressure pattern to bring cool maritime air back in over the coastal lowlands.

The agreeable temperatures along with the light precipitation characteristic of the warm season give the Seattle-Tacoma area a very pleasant summer climate. The dry season is centered around July and early August. July is the driest month of the year normally and December the wettest. However, the precipitation is rather evenly distributed through the winter and early spring months. Better than 75

(Continued page 678)

SEATTLE, WASHINGTON

Normals, Means, and Extremes

(To better understand these tables, see full explanation of terms beginning on page 322)

Month	Normal Degree days Base 65 °F: Heating	Cooling	Precipitation in inches — Water equivalent: Normal	Maximum monthly	Year	Minimum monthly	Year	Maximum in 24 hrs.	Year	Snow, Ice pellets: Maximum monthly	Year	Maximum in 24 hrs.	Year	Relative humidity pct. Hour 04 (Local time)	Hour 10	Hour 16	Hour 22	Wind: Mean speed m.p.h.	Prevailing direction	Fastest mile: Speed m.p.h.	Direction	Year	Pct. of possible sunshine	Mean sky cover, tenths, sunrise to sunset	Mean number of days — Sunrise to sunset: Clear	Partly cloudy	Cloudy	Precipitation .01 inch or more	Snow, Ice pellets 1.0 inch or more	Thunderstorms	Heavy fog, visibility ¼ mile or less	Temperatures °F Max. (b) 90° and above	Max. 32° and below	Min. 32° and below	Min. 0° and below	Average station pressure mb. Elev. 450 feet m.s.l.
(a)				31		31		31		31		31		16	16	16	16	27	15	8	8		10	31	31	31	31	31	31	31	31	16	16	16	16	3
J	831	0	5.79	12.92	1953	0.86	1949	2.41	1967	57.2	1950	21.4	1950	80	79	75	78	10.4	SSW	45	SW	1971	21	8.5	2	4	25	20	2	*	5	0	2	11	0	1000.0
F	636	0	4.19	9.11	1961	1.66	1964	3.41	1951	13.1	1949	7.2	1962	80	76	66	76	9.9	SW	36	SW	1972	42	8.2	3	4	21	16	1	*	3	0	0	5	0	1000.0
M	648	0	3.61	8.40	1950	0.57	1965	2.86	1972	18.2	1951	5.6	1951	81	74	62	75	10.2	SSW	41	SW	1971	49	8.0	3	6	22	18	1	1	3	0	0	4	0	997.2
A	489	0	2.46	4.12	1972	0.33	1956	1.85	1965	2.3	1972	2.3	1972	83	72	59	75	9.8	SW	38	SW	1972	51	7.8	3	7	20	14	*	1	1	0	0	*	0	1002.5
M	313	0	1.70	4.76	1948	0.35	1947	1.83	1969	T	1974	T	1974	83	68	54	71	9.2	SW	32	SW	1968	58	7.1	4	10	17	10	0	1	1	*	0	0	0	1001.7
J	167	11	1.53	3.90	1946	0.13	1951	1.75	1968	0.0		0.0		82	67	54	70	9.0	SW	29	SW	1974	54	7.1	5	7	18	10	0	1	1	*	0	0	0	1001.1
J	80	65	0.71	2.10	1955	T	1960	0.84	1974	0.0		0.0		83	66	49	67	8.4	SW	24	SW	1973	67	5.2	11	10	10	5	0	1	2	1	0	0	0	1001.4
A	82	45	1.08	4.59	1975	0.01	1974	1.75	1968	0.0		0.0		84	70	52	72	8.1	SW	25	N	1972	65	5.7	9	9	13	7	0	1	3	1	0	0	0	1001.3
S	170	8	1.99	5.57	1969	T	1975	1.77	1953	T	1972	T	1972	86	74	58	76	8.3	N	29	SW	1970	61	6.1	8	9	13	9	0	1	7	*	0	0	0	1001.7
O	397	0	3.91	8.95	1947	0.72	1972	2.27	1947	2.0	1971	2.0	1971	87	80	69	82	8.9	S	30	SW	1973	42	7.6	4	7	20	14	*	*	8	0	0	*	0	1000.9
N	612	0	5.88	9.69	1963	1.11	1952	3.41	1959	13.7	1946	9.4	1946	84	81	75	81	9.4	S	34	SW	1975	27	8.4	2	5	23	18	*	1	6	0	0	3	0	997.7
D	760	0	5.94	9.50	1955	3.75	1960	2.53	1959	22.1	1968	13.0	1968	82	81	78	81	10.0	SSW	42	S	1969	17	8.8	2	3	26	21	1	*	6	0	1	9	0	1001.4
YR	5185	129	38.79	12.92	JAN 1953	T	SEP 1975	3.41	NOV 1959	57.2	JAN 1950	21.4	JAN 1950	83	74	62	75	9.3	SSW	45	SW	JAN 1971	49	7.4	56	81	228	161	5	8	47	3	3	32	0	1000.6

FOOTNOTES Means and extremes above are from existing and comparable exposures. Annual extremes have been exceeded at other sites in the locality as follows: Highest temperature 100 in June 1955 and earlier; lowest temperature zero in January 1950; maximum monthly precipitation 15.33 in December 1933; minimum monthly precipitation 0.00 in July 1922 and earlier. Maximum precipitation in 24 hours 3.52 in December 1921; maximum snowfall in 24 hours 21.5 in February 1916; highest wind (fastest observed 1-minute speed) 55 from 20 degrees in February 1958.

Snowfall

Season	July	Aug	Sept	Oct	Nov	Dec	Jan
1944-45							0.0
1945-46	0.0	0.0	0.0	T	T	T	T
1946-47	0.0	0.0	0.0	0.0	13.7	T	8.0
1947-48	0.0	0.0	0.0	0.0	0.0	T	1.3
1948-49	0.0	0.0	0.0	0.0	T	2.2	6.1
1949-50	0.0	0.0	0.0	0.0	0.0	6.0	57.2
1950-51	0.0	0.0	0.0	T	1.0	2.0	5.7
1951-52	0.0	0.0	0.0	0.0	0.0	3.3	6.7
1952-53	0.0	0.0	0.0	0.0	0.0	T	T
1953-54	0.0	0.0	0.0	0.0	T	T	20.0
1954-55	0.0	0.0	0.0	0.0	0.0	T	T
1955-56	0.0	0.0	0.0	0.0	6.0	6.1	0.4
1956-57	0.0	0.0	0.0	T	0.0	3.0	7.5
1957-58	0.0	0.0	0.0	0.0	0.0	T	0.0
1958-59	0.0	0.0	0.0	0.0	0.2	0.0	3.2
1959-60	0.0	0.0	0.0	0.0	T	T	2.2
1960-61	0.0	0.0	0.0	0.0	5.2	0.0	0.0
1961-62	0.0	0.0	0.0	0.0	T	0.9	1.0
1962-63	0.0	0.0	0.0	0.0	0.0	T	3.1
1963-64	0.0	0.0	0.0	0.0	1.0	T	0.5
1964-65	0.0	0.0	0.0	0.0	3.3	7.6	7.3
1965-66	0.0	0.0	0.0	0.0	0.0	15.3	2.1
1966-67	0.0	0.0	0.0	0.0	0.0	2.0	5.9
1967-68	0.0	0.0	0.0	0.0	0.0	3.6	7.5
1968-69	0.0	0.0	0.0	0.0	0.0	22.1	45.4
1969-70	0.0	0.0	0.0	0.0	T	0.0	T
1970-71	0.0	0.0	0.0	0.0	T	2.9	9.1
1971-72	0.0	0.0	0.0	2.0	T	10.6	14.0
1972-73	0.0	0.0	T	0.0	T	5.6	2.7
1973-74	0.0	0.0	0.0	0.0	0.2	0.3	3.7
1974-75	0.0	0.0	0.0	0.0	0.0	9.8	1.3
1975-76	0.0	0.0	0.0	0.0	1.6	2.6	
RECORD MEAN	0.0	0.0	T	0.1	1.0	3.4	7.2

Heating Degree Days

Season	July	Aug	Sept	Oct	Nov	Dec	Jan
1955-56	152	125	243	446	776	818	800
1956-57	70	89	208	474	663	760	995
1957-58	97	95	72	434	638	656	656
1958-59	15	19	165	338	640	617	742
#1959-60	59	87	217	396	628	758	804
1960-61	41	126	210	374	607	783	657
1961-62	23	8	197	437	689	789	821
1962-63	95	100	158	377	550	698	959
1963-64	78	37	71	320	612	743	771
1964-65	76	91	189	349	679	882	761
1965-66	24	44	194	261	462	754	732
1966-67	95	54	106	414	585	658	695
1967-68	16	0	44	310	524	718	737
1968-69	33	70	179	415	538	871	983
1969-70	49	49	144	381	547	607	731
1970-71	53	44	190	435	548	801	778
1971-72	82	17	214	429	570	843	863
1972-73	48	32	295	455	544	825	807
1973-74	70	114	111	388	633	632	809
1974-75	60	66	74	380	591	690	804
1975-76	23	73	93	413	594	723	

Cooling Degree Days

Year	Jan	Feb	Mar	Apr	May	June	July
1969	0	0	0	0	19	55	44
1970	0	0	0	0	1	60	58
1971	0	0	0	0	4	2	106
1972	0	0	0	0	22	3	85
1973	0	0	0	0	16	19	67
1974	0	0	0	0	0	36	38
1975	0	0	0	0	0	21	108

Feb	Mar	Apr	May	June	Total
T	T	T	0.0	0.0	
T	2.6	0.0	0.0	0.0	2.6
T	0.0	0.0	0.0	0.0	21.7
2.2	0.1	T	0.0	0.0	3.6
13.1	0.0	0.0	0.0	0.0	21.4
0.4	T	T	0.0	0.0	63.6
0.5	18.2	T	0.0	0.0	27.4
T	T	0.0	0.0	0.0	10.0
T	T	T	0.0	0.0	T
T	3.3	T	0.0	0.0	23.3
3.2	10.2	0.0	0.0	0.0	13.4
9.4	2.3	0.0	0.0	0.0	24.2
7.2	0.0	T	0.0	0.0	17.7
0.0	T	0.0	0.0	0.0	T
6.5	T	0.0	0.0	0.0	9.9
0.0	5.1	0.0	0.0	0.0	7.3
T	1.8	0.0	0.0	0.0	7.0
7.0	1.7	0.0	0.0	0.0	10.6
0.5	T	0.0	0.0	0.0	3.6
T	T	T	0.0	0.0	1.5
T	T	0.0	T	0.0	18.2
T	5.5	T	0.0	0.0	22.9
T	T	T	0.0	0.0	7.9
0.0	0.0	0.5	0.0	0.0	11.6
T	0.0	0.0	0.0	0.0	67.5
0.0	T	T	0.0	0.0	T
2.2	1.9	T	0.0	0.0	16.1
0.3	T	2.3	0.0	0.0	29.2
T	0.8	T	0.0	0.0	9.1
T	T	0.0	T	0.0	4.2
T	T	0.2	0.0	0.0	11.3
1.7	1.7	0.1	T	0.0	15.2

Average Temperature

Year	Jan	Feb	Mar	Apr	May	June	July	Aug	Sept	Oct	Nov	Dec	Annual
1945	41.9	42.2	43.2	46.7	57.0	58.8	65.4	63.6	56.7	52.4	43.2	39.0	50.8
1946	39.4	41.2	43.2	47.8	57.2	58.1	64.4	63.6	58.6	47.8	40.6	38.9	50.1
1947	35.0	44.0	47.6	51.1	57.8	59.8	63.6	62.8	59.2	51.8	43.0	42.0	51.5
1948	38.0	38.9	42.9	45.4	52.9	61.7	62.4	61.2	57.2	50.4	42.0	36.0	49.1
1949	30.0	37.3	45.6	50.1	57.3	59.0	62.6	63.6	60.8	48.6	49.4	38.4	50.2
1950	24.9	40.0	42.1	46.4	51.6	60.2	63.6	63.8	57.8	49.2	43.6	44.8	49.0
1951	37.0	40.6	39.4	49.6	54.2	61.1	64.4	61.7	59.1	50.8	44.5	36.4	49.9
1952	36.4	40.7	42.3	48.5	54.0	56.5	63.5	63.0	59.2	54.3	41.0	41.7	50.1
1953	44.3	40.2	43.0	46.8	52.6	55.5	61.9	62.7	59.7	53.2	46.7	42.3	50.7
1954	36.1	42.2	40.7	45.6	53.9	56.3	60.1	60.6	58.7	50.6	49.0	40.8	49.5
1955	39.1	38.2	39.2	44.6	50.7	58.0	60.1	60.9	57.0	50.4	38.9	38.4	47.9
1956	39.0	35.7	40.8	49.6	56.8	56.9	64.6	63.0	57.9	49.5	42.6	40.2	49.7
1957	32.6	39.5	44.4	50.1	57.9	60.4	61.8	61.6	62.7	50.7	43.5	43.7	50.7
1958	43.6	47.5	44.0	49.2	60.4	64.0	68.8	66.6	59.8	53.9	43.4	44.9	53.8
#1959	40.8	41.0	44.2	49.6	53.5	59.6	66.1	62.3	57.4	52.0	43.9	40.3	50.9
1960	38.9	41.2	43.5	49.3	52.7	59.5	66.7	62.2	58.0	52.7	44.5	39.5	50.8
1961	43.6	44.4	45.3	47.0	53.8	63.5	67.1	68.4	58.7	50.8	41.9	39.3	52.0
1962	38.4	43.1	43.3	50.0	50.6	59.9	63.5	62.0	59.6	52.6	46.5	42.3	51.0
1963	33.9	48.2	43.8	48.3	57.7	59.9	62.4	64.6	63.5	54.5	44.4	40.8	51.8
1964	40.0	41.3	44.1	46.8	53.2	57.9	63.5	62.6	58.5	53.5	42.1	36.4	50.0
1965	40.2	43.0	47.0	49.5	51.9	60.8	67.8	65.7	58.4	56.4	49.4	40.4	52.6
1966	41.1	43.9	45.1	50.0	54.5	58.7	62.1	64.5	61.5	51.4	45.4	43.5	51.8
1967	42.4	42.8	42.2	46.6	55.4	62.7	66.5	71.1	65.7	54.8	47.3	41.6	53.2
1968	40.9	48.5	48.6	48.7	57.3	60.7	67.0	63.7	59.1	51.5	46.8	36.6	52.5
1969	33.1	42.3	46.9	48.9	58.0	64.3	64.7	64.0	61.0	52.4	46.6	45.2	52.3
1970	41.2	47.0	46.0	46.1	54.7	62.7	64.9	64.5	58.6	50.8	46.5	39.0	51.8
1971	39.7	42.3	41.3	48.9	54.5	55.9	65.5	67.7	57.6	51.0	45.7	37.5	50.6
1972	37.0	41.4	46.9	47.0	58.3	60.1	66.0	66.7	55.4	50.1	46.7	38.1	51.1
1973	38.7	43.9	44.1	48.6	56.5	59.3	64.7	61.6	61.9	52.2	43.7	44.4	51.6
1974	38.7	43.2	46.3	50.3	54.9	62.6	64.0	64.6	64.4	52.5	45.1	42.4	52.4
1975	38.8	40.8	42.9	45.8	54.6	60.7	67.5	63.2	63.0	51.4	44.9	41.5	51.3
RECORD MEAN	38.2	42.2	43.9	48.1	55.0	59.9	64.4	63.8	59.6	51.8	44.6	40.5	51.0
MAX	43.2	48.2	50.9	56.3	64.3	69.0	75.0	73.9	68.7	58.9	50.2	45.3	58.7
MIN	33.2	36.1	36.8	39.9	45.7	50.7	53.8	53.7	50.4	44.6	39.0	35.7	43.3

# Indicates a station move or relocation of instruments.

SEATTLE, WA
SEATTLE - TACOMA AIRPORT

Feb	Mar	Apr	May	June	Total
844	741	455	260	238	5898
706	629	441	213	135	5383
482	645	468	163	81	4487
667	637	456	355	166	4817
684	660	465	373	164	5295
569	607	531	345	93	4943
610	668	443	438	167	5290
465	651	496	255	171	4975
682	640	535	370	204	5063
611	553	459	400	136	5186
584	610	442	321	190	4618
614	700	548	292	92	4853
472	503	485	232	139	4180
627	554	478	230	71	5049
499	586	563	314	122	4592
628	728	472	321	267	5265
678	557	531	222	144	5150
586	639	484	272	183	5170
606	573	433	306	99	4774
671	678	570	317	144	5045

Aug	Sept	Oct	Nov	Dec	Total
25	28	0	0	0	171
36	6	0	0	0	161
107	0	0	0	0	219
91	11	0	0	0	212
17	21	0	0	0	140
62	60	0	0	0	196
29	39	0	0	0	197

Precipitation

Year	Jan	Feb	Mar	Apr	May	June	July	Aug	Sept	Oct	Nov	Dec	Annual
1945	4.62	6.14	4.33	3.34	2.62	0.62	0.11	0.31	3.62	2.86	6.31	6.31	41.19
1946	5.29	5.83	3.71	2.45	0.41	3.90	0.56	0.33	2.61	3.22	5.53	6.47	40.31
1947	4.20	4.02	2.40	2.17	0.35	2.15	1.04	0.49	1.84	8.95	3.62	6.02	37.25
1948	4.49	5.26	3.68	3.75	4.76	2.09	1.53	1.87	3.85	2.33	6.06	6.13	45.80
1949	0.86	5.89	3.54	1.18	1.30	0.93	1.04	0.45	1.43	3.85	6.78	5.30	32.55
1950	8.91	5.74	8.40	2.92	0.78	0.59	1.00	2.17	2.30	7.21	7.98	7.14	55.14
1951	6.80	8.76	3.76	0.65	1.61	0.13	0.31	1.02	2.03	5.87	5.44	3.92	40.30
1952	4.89	2.46	3.52	2.03	0.99	1.04	0.41	0.70	0.32	1.29	1.11	5.02	23.78
1953	12.92	3.70	3.72	2.10	2.51	1.85	0.66	1.11	3.28	4.43	7.22	5.92	49.42
1954	8.36	4.38	2.07	2.64	1.89	2.44	1.46	1.57	1.68	1.91	7.67	5.20	41.27
1955	3.35	4.30	3.25	3.64	1.95	1.27	2.10	0.17	1.52	6.60	8.96	9.50	46.61
1956	8.67	2.17	4.95	0.33	0.83	2.47	0.33	0.76	2.42	6.71	1.59	5.62	36.85
1957	2.41	5.57	6.26	2.23	1.17	1.18	1.10	1.64	0.76	3.79	3.00	5.52	34.63
1958	8.72	5.36	2.26	3.51	0.94	0.90	T	0.31	1.42	3.99	8.07	7.15	42.63
1959	7.98	3.64	4.12	3.59	1.60	1.82	0.93	0.60	4.60	2.67	8.14	6.83	46.52
1960	5.48	4.01	4.08	2.88	3.04	0.70	T	1.92	1.17	4.22	8.03	3.75	39.28
1961	7.71	9.11	4.46	2.35	3.07	0.54	0.75	0.82	0.46	3.27	4.67	5.32	42.53
1962	2.43	2.29	2.86	2.03	1.82	0.68	0.69	1.96	2.31	4.16	9.34	5.22	35.79
1963	2.25	4.36	3.43	3.06	0.90	1.68	1.18	0.73	0.59	5.06	9.69	5.79	38.72
1964	9.76	1.66	2.96	1.56	0.91	3.82	0.99	1.23	2.27	1.00	9.65	5.53	41.34
1965	5.27	3.88	0.57	3.73	1.63	0.59	0.38	2.18	0.49	2.76	4.98	7.10	33.56
1966	5.43	2.31	4.38	1.99	1.35	1.15	1.35	0.42	1.77	2.92	6.85	8.31	38.23
1967	9.32	2.72	3.71	2.50	0.38	2.04	0.01	0.02	0.94	6.66	2.56	4.72	35.58
1968	6.90	6.08	5.08	1.33	1.67	3.02	0.83	4.58	1.93	4.32	5.86	8.55	50.15
1969	5.71	3.16	2.20	3.45	2.93	0.91	0.27	0.45	5.57	1.19	2.21	5.68	33.73
1970	8.22	2.26	3.16	3.31	1.17	0.43	0.48	0.32	2.23	2.52	5.03	8.28	37.41
1971	5.32	4.36	7.12	2.39	1.43	2.28	0.68	0.57	3.51	3.57	5.31	6.67	43.21
1972	7.24	8.11	6.74	4.12	0.69	1.81	1.34	1.13	4.10	0.72	3.38	8.98	48.36
1973	4.29	1.89	1.62	1.35	1.60	2.50	0.08	0.27	1.81	3.31	7.99	8.33	35.04
1974	7.78	4.01	5.84	2.39	1.37	1.25	1.51	0.01	0.21	1.99	5.06	6.45	37.87
1975	6.01	5.80	2.87	2.49	1.13	0.84	0.27	4.59	T	7.75	5.07	7.66	44.48
RECORD MEAN	6.18	4.49	3.90	2.50	1.57	1.54	0.75	1.12	2.03	3.91	5.91	6.40	40.30

Record mean values above are means through the current year for the period beginning in 1945. Data are from airport locations.

(Continued)

percent of the yearly average falls from October 1 through March. The rainfall of Seattle-Tacoma and vicinity comes almost entirely from the moving storms or areas of low barometric pressure common to the middle latitudes. These disturbances are most vigorous during the winter and through this season follow paths that bring them close to western Washington; whereas in the summer the storm tracks shift northward and the weaker individual storms are not the wind and rain producers that they are during the winter months. Local summer afternoon showers and a few thundershowers do occur in the Seattle-Tacoma area, but they are not sufficiently common to contribute materially to the average precipitation.

The occurrence of snow in the Seattle-Tacoma area is extremely variable and very often when it does fall it melts before accumulating measurable depth. There are winters on record with only a trace of snow and on the other extreme as much as 21.4 inches have fallen in a 24-hour period (January 1950). This is understandable in view of the fact that the air brought in over the area by the winter storms usually has had a long trajectory over the ocean. In fact, it is only when a storm is so oriented as to enable it to bring cold air out of Canada directly or over only a short water trajectory that deep snowfalls occur in the southern Puget Sound area.

Since the southern end of the Puget Sound trough is open to the southwest winds generated by the storms moving in off the ocean, the prevalent wind for the eight months encompassing the storm season is southwest. The Puget Sound trough also is open to the north. Hence, the occasionally severe winter storm that develops to the south or moves inland to the south of the Seattle-Tacoma area will result in strong winds from the northerly quarter.

Winds are relatively light during the summer months. During the course of a typical summer day the winds will be light and variable at night, becoming northerly and picking up to 8 to 15 m.p.h. during the afternoon, the proximity of the Sound resulting in a form of land-and-sea breeze.

Fog or stratus that forms over the Sound due to radiation and advection very seldom closes the field for more than a few hours in the morning. This also is true of fall, winter, and spring stratus with northeast winds from Lake Washington which is 6 miles eastnortheast of the field. The steep bluffs along the Green River Valley tend to contain the fog until after sunrise when circulation increases and the fog drifts in, decreasing visibilities for a short time. Fall ground fogs frequently are deep enough to close the field during mornings; otherwise ground fogs are generally unimportant. Most of the summer stratus moves into the area from the southwest quadrant.

The most important smoke source is the extensive Seattle industrial area 6-10 miles north to northwest. Visibility is occasionally 1 mile in stable air and light northerly winds, otherwise seldom less than 3 miles because of smoke.

Station: SPOKANE, WASHINGTON INTERNATIONAL AIRPORT
Elevation (ground): 2356 feet

TEMPERATURES °F

Month	Normal			Extremes			
	Daily maximum	Daily minimum	Monthly	Record highest	Year	Record lowest	Year
(a)				16		16	
J	31.1	19.6	25.4	59	1971	-19	1969
F	39.0	25.3	32.2	60	1968	-12	1972
M	46.2	28.8	37.5	71	1960	1	1971
A	57.0	35.2	46.1	80	1968	17	1966
M	66.5	42.8	54.7	92	1966	26	1965
J	73.6	49.4	61.5	100	1973	34	1962
J	84.3	55.1	69.7	103	1967	38	1971
A	81.9	54.0	68.0	108	1961	35	1965
S	72.5	46.7	59.6	93	1973	25	1965
O	58.1	37.5	47.8	85	1963	13	1971
N	41.8	29.2	35.5	67	1975	-2	1959
D	33.9	24.0	29.0	53	1968	-25	1968
YR	57.2	37.3	47.3	108	AUG 1961	-25	DEC 1968

IMPORTANT:
The time-period covered by this record is limited: See footnotes on next page for explanation and for additional history of EXTREME HIGHS AND LOWS recorded in the general area.

Spokane lies on the eastern edge of the broad Columbia Basin area of Washington which is bounded by the Cascade Range on the west and the Rocky Mountains on the east. The elevations in eastern Washington vary from less than 400 feet above sea level near Pasco where the Columbia River flows out of Washington to over 5,000 feet in the mountain areas of the extreme eastern edge of the State. Spokane is located on the upper plateau area where the long gradual slope from the Columbia River meets the sharp rise of the Rocky Mountain Ranges.

Much of the urban area of Spokane lies along both sides of the Spokane River at an elevation of approximately 2,000 feet, but the residential areas have spread to the crests of the plateaus on either side of the river with elevations up to 2,500 feet above sea level. Spokane International Airport is situated on the plateau area six miles west-southwest and some 400 feet higher than the downtown business district.

Spokane's climate combines some of the characteristics of damp coastal type weather and arid interior conditions. Most of the air masses which reach Spokane are brought in by the prevailing westerly and southwesterly circulations. Frequently much of the moisture in the storms that move eastward and southeastward from the Gulf of Alaska and the eastern Pacific Ocean is precipitated out as the storms are lifted across the Coast and Cascade Ranges. Annual precipitation totals in the Spokane area are generally less than twenty inches and less than 50 percent of the amounts received west of the Cascades. However, the precipitation and total cloudiness in the Spokane vicinity is greater than that of the desert areas of south-central Washington. The lifting action on the air masses as they move up the east slope of the Columbia Basin frequently produces the cooling and condensation necessary for formation of clouds and precipitation.

Infrequently the Spokane area comes under the influence of dry continental air masses from the north or east. On occasions when these air masses penetrate into eastern Washington the result is high temperatures and very low humidity in the summer and sub-zero temperatures in the winter. In the winter most of the severe arctic outbursts of cold air move southward on the east side of the Continental Divide and do not affect Spokane.

In general, Spokane weather has the characteristics of a mild, arid climate during the summer months and a cold, coastal type in the winter. Approximately 70 percent of the total annual precipitation falls between the first of October and the end of March and about half of that falls as snow. The growing season usually extends over nearly six months from mid-April to mid-October. Irrigation is required for all crops except dryland type grains. The summer weather is ideal for full enjoyment of the many mountain and lake recreational areas in the immediate vicinity. Winter weather includes many cloudy or foggy days and below freezing temperatures with occasional snowfall of several inches in depth. Sub-zero temperatures and traffic-stopping snowfalls are infrequent. The nearby winter sports areas have a season of four to five months with plenty of facilities for skiing and other winter outdoor activities.

SPOKANE, WASHINGTON

Normals, Means, and Extremes

(To better understand these tables, see full explanation of terms beginning on page 322)

Month	Normal Degree days Base 65 °F: Heating	Normal Degree days: Cooling	Precipitation in inches, Water equivalent: Normal	Water equivalent: Maximum monthly	Year	Water equivalent: Minimum monthly	Year	Water equivalent: Maximum in 24 hrs.	Year	Snow, Ice pellets: Maximum monthly	Year	Snow, Ice pellets: Maximum in 24 hrs.	Year	Relative humidity pct. Hour 04 (Local time)	Hour 10	Hour 16	Hour 22	Wind: Mean speed m.p.h.	Wind: Prevailing direction	Fastest mile: Speed m.p.h.	Fastest mile: Direction	Fastest mile: Year	Pct. of possible sunshine	Mean sky cover, tenths, sunrise to sunset	Mean number of days, Sunrise to sunset: Clear	Partly cloudy	Cloudy	Precipitation .01 inch or more	Snow, Ice pellets 1.0 inch or more	Thunderstorms	Heavy fog, visibility ¼ mile or less	Temperatures °F Max.: 90° and above (b)	Max.: 32° and below	Min.: 32° and below	Min.: 0° and below	Average station pressure mb. Elev. 2365 feet m.s.l.
(a)				28		28		28		28		28		16	16	16	16	28	15	28	28		27	28	28	28	28	28	28	28	28	16	16	16	16	3
J	1228	0	2.47	4.96	1959	0.50	1949	1.48	1954	56.9	1950	13.0	1950	82	81	76	80	9.0	NE	59	SW	1972	26	8.2	3	5	23	15	6	*	8	0	15	27	3	931.6
F	918	0	1.68	3.94	1961	0.40	1967	1.11	1963	28.5	1975	8.9	1975	83	78	68	79	9.1	SSW	54	SW	1949	41	7.8	4	5	19	12	3	*	8	0	4	23	*	932.0
M	853	0	1.53	3.75	1950	0.31	1965	0.91	1950	15.3	1962	5.3	1970	78	67	54	72	9.5	SSW	54	SW	1971	53	7.3	4	8	19	11	2	*	3	0	1	22	0	927.6
A	567	0	1.12	3.08	1948	0.08	1956	0.89	1962	6.6	1964	4.9	1964	75	56	44	65	9.7	SW	50	SW	1962	60	7.1	5	8	17	9	*	1	1	0	0	12	0	931.1
M	327	8	1.46	5.71	1948	0.45	1964	1.67	1948	3.5	1967	3.5	1967	74	51	40	61	8.8	SSW	49	W	1957	63	6.5	6	10	15	9	*	1	1	*	0	2	0	930.9
J	144	39	1.36	3.06	1964	0.16	1960	2.07	1964	T	1954	T	1954	72	48	35	56	8.8	SSW	39	SW	1949	65	6.0	7	11	12	8	0	3	1	3	0	0	0	930.0
J	21	167	0.40	1.60	1975	T	1973	0.86	1975	0.0		0.0		60	38	24	41	8.2	SW	43	SW	1970	81	3.5	18	8	5	4	0	2	*	10	0	0	0	931.4
A	47	140	0.58	1.73	1965	T	1969	1.09	1959	0.0		0.0		59	42	27	44	8.0	SW	38	SW	1950	78	4.0	16	8	7	5	0	2	*	8	0	0	0	930.8
S	196	34	0.83	2.05	1959	0.03	1975	1.12	1973	0.0		0.0		68	49	33	53	8.1	NE	38	SW	1961	71	4.7	13	8	9	6	0	1	1	1	0	1	0	934.0
O	533	0	1.42	4.05	1950	0.05	1965	0.98	1955	6.1	1957	6.1	1957	79	66	50	71	8.2	SSW	56	SW	1950	51	6.5	8	7	16	8	*	*	5	0	*	9	0	932.6
N	885	0	2.20	5.10	1973	0.34	1956	1.41	1960	24.7	1955	9.0	1973	86	82	75	84	8.3	NE	54	SW	1949	28	8.0	3	5	22	13	2	*	9	0	3	20	0	930.5
D	1116	0	2.37	5.13	1964	1.21	1959	1.60	1951	42.0	1964	12.1	1951	86	84	81	85	8.8	NE	51	SW	1956	20	8.5	3	3	25	16	5	0	12	0	12	26	1	933.2
YR	6835	388	17.42	5.71	MAY 1948	T	JUL 1973	2.07	JUN 1964	56.9	JAN 1950	13.0	JAN 1950	75	62	50	66	8.7	SSW	59	SW	JAN 1972	57	6.5	90	86	189	115	18	11	48	21	35	141	5	931.3

FOOTNOTES Means and extremes above are from existing and comparable exposures. Annual extremes have been exceeded at other sites in the locality as follows: Lowest temperature -30 in January 1888; maximum monthly precipitation 5.85 in November 1897; minimum monthly precipitation 0.00 in July 1883; maximum precipitation in 24 hours 2.22 in June 1888.

Snowfall

Season	July	Aug	Sept	Oct	Nov	Dec	Jan
1936-37	0.0	0.0	0.0	T	T	9.5	36.0
1937-38	0.0	0.0	0.0	0.0	2.8	13.5	6.2
1938-39	0.0	0.0	0.0	0.0	1.2	9.2	6.0
1939-40	0.0	0.0	0.0	1.0	0.0	3.9	6.2
#1940-41	0.0	0.0	0.0	0.0	7.9	1.0	8.1
1941-42	0.0	0.0	0.0	0.0	1.8	6.8	4.9
1942-43	0.0	0.0	0.0	0.0	7.2	10.6	17.7
1943-44	0.0	0.0	0.0	T	T	0.8	2.4
1944-45	0.0	0.0	0.0	0.0	3.9	4.4	1.7
1945-46	0.0	0.0	0.0	T	6.2	8.8	6.3
1946-47	0.0	0.0	0.0	T	16.1	5.0	6.3
#1947-48	0.0	0.0	0.0	0.0	5.8	11.9	8.5
1948-49	0.0	0.0	0.0	T	8.0	33.2	6.4
1949-50	0.0	0.0	0.0	0.4	3.2	13.8	56.9
1950-51	0.0	0.0	0.0	0.0	11.5	8.0	29.2
1951-52	0.0	0.0	0.0	1.2	0.7	39.4	24.2
1952-53	0.0	0.0	0.0	0.0	T	25.6	10.5
1953-54	0.0	0.0	0.0	0.0	1.1	4.8	46.5
1954-55	0.0	0.0	0.0	0.0	T	7.8	15.6
1955-56	0.0	0.0	0.0	T	24.7	18.5	18.9
1956-57	0.0	0.0	0.0	0.7	1.5	7.3	20.8
1957-58	0.0	0.0	0.0	6.1	2.0	10.8	7.4
1958-59	0.0	0.0	0.0	0.0	8.6	8.4	22.4
1959-60	0.0	0.0	0.0	0.0	10.7	6.5	8.3
1960-61	0.0	0.0	0.0	0.0	2.5	8.6	7.8
1961-62	0.0	0.0	0.0	T	8.9	26.2	12.2
1962-63	0.0	0.0	0.0	0.0	4.4	0.5	8.7
1963-64	0.0	0.0	0.0	0.0	0.4	19.6	26.3
1964-65	0.0	0.0	0.0	T	15.2	42.0	20.1
1965-66	0.0	0.0	0.0	T	6.3	15.4	13.9
1966-67	0.0	0.0	0.0	T	0.9	9.0	6.5
1967-68	0.0	0.0	0.0	T	4.8	12.7	11.8
1968-69	0.0	0.0	0.0	0.0	1.2	19.8	48.7
1969-70	0.0	0.0	0.0	0.0	T	10.4	19.4
1970-71	0.0	0.0	0.0	T	6.8	12.0	6.1
1971-72	0.0	0.0	0.0	3.1	4.0	34.2	17.2
1972-73	0.0	0.0	0.0	0.8	T	4.7	6.5
1973-74	0.0	0.0	0.0	0.8	23.6	9.1	15.0
1974-75	0.0	0.0	0.0	0.0	0.3	16.6	30.9
1975-76	0.0	0.0	0.0	3.9	11.4	6.9	
RECORD MEAN	0.0	0.0	0.0	0.6	5.8	15.4	18.8

Heating Degree Days

Season	July	Aug	Sept	Oct	Nov	Dec	Jan
1955-56	92	14	238	549	1101	1179	1114
1956-57	17	66	149	572	963	1055	1547
1957-58	30	39	105	612	877	922	1015
1958-59	5	10	226	452	868	1005	1111
#1959-60	55	84	311	581	997	1113	1374
1960-61	3	97	153	503	886	1186	1067
1961-62	1	0	268	604	1025	1180	1309
1962-63	60	65	159	531	804	981	1411
1963-64	35	28	77	426	802	1186	1098
1964-65	31	118	290	524	976	1268	1121
1965-66	31	62	330	377	804	1078	1088
1966-67	30	42	67	544	838	975	956
1967-68	8	2	71	508	882	1146	1149
1968-69	19	89	199	607	897	1245	1504
1969-70	40	44	192	655	855	1097	1208
1970-71	13	5	321	614	864	1146	1022
1971-72	64	19	297	641	882	1208	1308
1972-73	36	18	292	545	795	1219	1171
1973-74	17	47	193	546	933	978	1265
1974-75	41	22	134	519	852	1062	1276
1975-76	22	75	136	554	933	1048	

Cooling Degree Days

Year	Jan	Feb	Mar	Apr	May	June	July
1969	0	0	0	0	7	99	121
1970	0	0	0	0	3	143	253
1971	0	0	0	0	10	17	216
1972	0	0	0	0	28	41	138
1973	0	0	0	0	31	67	216
1974	0	0	0	0	0	137	134
1975	0	0	0	0	0	7	256

Feb	Mar	Apr	May	June	Total
16.2	0.6	T	0.0	0.0	62.3
21.1	3.6	0.0	T	0.0	47.2
26.3	14.3	T	0.0	0.0	57.0
10.9	T	T	0.0	0.0	22.0
2.0	0.0	0.0	0.0	0.0	19.0
7.9	1.3	T	T	0.0	22.7
9.0	1.5	0.0	T	0.0	46.0
10.1	2.0	T	T	T	15.3
0.9	4.4	1.0	0.0	0.0	16.3
5.2	4.2	0.1	0.0	0.0	30.8
0.2	1.0	T	0.0	0.0	28.6
12.0	1.0	0.3	T	0.0	39.5
18.7	4.0	T	0.0	0.0	70.3
11.2	7.7	0.1	0.2	0.0	93.5
10.6	12.4	0.0	0.0	0.0	71.7
8.0	6.1	0.0	0.0	0.0	79.6
4.9	3.5	T	T	0.0	44.5
3.9	0.1	T	0.0	T	56.4
16.0	5.1	0.6	T	0.0	45.1
13.5	7.6	T	0.0	0.0	83.2
10.5	6.4	1.4	0.0	0.0	48.6
0.7	1.9	T	0.0	0.0	28.9
20.6	3.1	T	T	0.0	63.1
3.5	9.0	0.6	T	0.0	38.6
7.8	6.7	0.1	0.0	0.0	33.5
4.5	15.3	T	0.0	0.0	67.1
2.7	1.2	0.5	T	0.0	18.0
5.2	5.2	6.6	0.0	0.0	63.3
2.3	2.0	0.1	0.0	0.0	81.7
1.6	7.2	T	T	0.0	44.4
3.1	6.4	0.8	3.5	0.0	30.2
0.4	T	T	T	0.0	29.7
5.4	2.0	0.4	0.0	0.0	77.5
2.8	6.9	0.3	0.1	0.0	39.9
5.5	1.5	T	0.0	0.0	31.9
5.9	2.5	0.2	0.0	0.0	67.1
3.5	0.5	T	0.0	0.0	16.0
4.4	2.5	0.4	0.4	0.0	56.2
28.5	7.6	5.1	T	0.0	89.0
7.8	4.8	0.6	0.2	T	54.0

SPOKANE, WA

Feb	Mar	Apr	May	June	Total
1223	890	448	252	191	7291
1011	841	506	186	129	7042
697	804	596	143	76	5916
960	794	517	441	131	6520
990	823	567	420	118	7433
775	771	592	367	70	6470
905	932	450	430	149	7253
768	748	593	318	145	6583
1030	897	609	369	149	6706
915	942	528	387	129	7229
896	808	561	291	190	6516
799	859	677	370	96	6253
783	702	654	343	138	6386
1080	905	559	236	88	7428
797	859	696	305	101	6849
873	918	584	270	215	6845
991	726	684	274	127	7221
838	734	558	286	152	6644
824	814	554	455	97	6723
1122	953	694	375	173	7223

Aug	Sept	Oct	Nov	Dec	Total
112	40	0	0	0	379
175	2	0	0	0	576
306	9	0	0	0	558
213	10	0	0	0	430
177	39	0	0	0	530
127	7	0	0	0	405
57	20	0	0	0	340

Average Temperature

Year	Jan	Feb	Mar	Apr	May	June	July	Aug	Sept	Oct	Nov	Dec	Annual
1936	31.8	17.4	38.7	52.2	62.0	65.5	72.8	71.0	59.1	52.2	32.3	33.0	49.0
1937	9.9	28.6	42.2	46.6	57.3	63.3	72.4	66.2	62.6	52.6	40.4	34.2	48.0
1938	31.5	33.6	41.1	49.8	56.8	66.8	75.0	67.8	67.8	51.2	35.1	32.8	50.8
1939	34.6	28.1	41.2	51.6	58.9	60.8	72.4	72.6	62.1	49.5	39.6	37.0	50.7
#1940	30.0	35.9	45.3	50.6	60.5	68.3	72.8	70.6	64.6	53.0	32.2	33.9	51.5
1941	32.0	38.4	45.6	51.8	55.7	62.6	73.8	68.5	55.6	47.5	40.2	33.7	50.5
1942	22.6	31.0	39.6	49.8	53.0	59.6	71.2	70.4	61.8	50.4	35.0	32.4	48.1
1943	21.8	33.2	35.8	50.4	52.4	58.6	69.3	66.8	62.6	50.2	37.6	29.2	47.3
1944	30.2	32.5	37.0	47.9	56.8	62.6	69.7	66.8	61.6	54.2	36.8	28.4	48.7
1945	32.6	35.1	37.8	44.7	56.9	60.5	70.9	69.4	56.6	50.8	36.8	29.8	48.5
1946	30.9	35.2	41.1	48.0	57.0	60.5	69.4	68.6	58.8	44.2	34.6	32.6	48.4
#1947	24.4	36.1	42.6	48.2	59.6	61.5	70.1	66.7	59.0	50.8	34.8	31.2	48.8
1948	27.5	29.0	36.2	43.5	52.8	65.4	65.1	65.2	58.1	47.3	34.8	21.5	45.5
1949	8.5	26.4	38.0	49.2	59.1	61.8	68.6	68.6	61.6	44.2	41.2	27.8	46.2
1950	9.0	29.8	35.7	43.9	52.2	61.0	69.1	70.2	62.0	46.7	36.2	33.6	45.8
1951	27.1	32.2	34.3	48.3	54.5	61.3	71.0	68.3	60.2	45.7	35.7	22.2	46.8
1952	23.5	30.2	36.7	49.8	56.5	61.0	70.1	68.4	63.8	54.5	32.7	30.3	48.1
1953	37.9	35.1	40.0	45.6	52.4	57.2	69.3	68.0	61.7	51.6	40.3	33.2	49.4
1954	26.9	33.1	36.3	43.5	55.4	57.2	67.5	64.5	57.5	46.2	41.5	30.2	46.6
1955	26.9	27.9	31.2	40.6	49.4	62.7	66.4	68.4	59.4	47.1	28.1	26.8	44.6
1956	28.9	22.6	36.1	49.9	58.1	58.9	71.6	67.6	60.7	46.3	32.7	30.7	47.0
1957	15.0	28.7	37.6	48.0	59.3	62.1	67.5	65.6	62.8	45.0	35.6	35.1	46.9
1958	32.0	39.8	38.9	44.9	62.7	65.6	73.0	73.7	58.7	50.2	35.7	32.4	50.7
#1959	29.0	30.5	39.2	47.4	50.6	61.7	70.6	64.4	55.1	46.1	31.5	28.8	46.3
1960	20.5	30.6	38.2	45.9	51.2	62.2	75.1	65.1	60.3	48.6	35.2	26.6	46.6
1961	30.3	37.0	39.9	45.1	53.0	66.6	71.9	74.0	55.9	45.2	30.7	26.6	48.0
1962	22.6	32.4	34.6	49.8	50.9	61.1	68.2	65.4	60.7	47.6	37.9	33.1	47.0
1963	19.3	37.4	40.6	45.0	54.8	61.7	66.7	69.1	66.0	51.1	38.1	26.5	48.0
1964	29.3	29.2	35.7	44.5	52.9	60.4	68.3	62.8	55.2	47.9	32.2	24.0	45.2
1965	28.6	32.1	34.4	47.2	52.4	61.3	70.1	67.9	53.8	52.7	38.0	30.0	47.4
1966	29.7	32.8	38.7	46.0	55.9	58.8	68.2	68.2	64.6	47.3	36.9	33.4	48.4
1967	33.9	36.2	37.1	42.3	52.8	63.5	70.6	74.5	65.3	48.4	35.4	27.8	49.0
1968	27.8	37.8	42.1	43.0	53.8	61.2	71.1	65.1	58.9	45.2	34.9	24.6	47.1
1969	16.3	26.1	35.6	46.2	57.4	65.2	67.4	67.1	59.8	43.7	36.3	29.4	45.9
1970	25.9	36.3	37.0	41.6	54.9	66.2	72.5	70.2	54.2	44.9	36.0	27.7	47.3
1971	31.8	33.6	35.2	45.3	56.3	58.2	69.7	74.1	55.2	44.2	35.4	25.8	47.0
1972	22.6	30.7	41.4	42.0	56.9	62.0	68.1	71.1	55.4	47.2	38.3	25.4	46.8
1973	27.0	34.9	41.1	45.2	56.5	62.0	71.2	69.1	59.7	47.2	33.7	33.3	48.5
1974	24.1	35.4	38.5	46.4	50.2	66.0	67.8	68.2	60.5	48.0	36.4	30.5	47.7
1975	23.6	24.7	34.0	41.7	52.7	59.2	72.4	64.1	61.0	46.9	33.8	30.9	45.4
RECORD MEAN	26.8	31.7	39.4	47.6	55.8	62.5	70.2	68.7	59.5	48.7	37.0	30.4	48.2
MAX	32.7	38.8	48.3	58.5	67.5	74.5	84.3	82.8	72.3	59.2	43.5	35.5	58.2
MIN	20.9	24.5	30.5	36.7	44.1	50.5	56.0	54.5	46.6	38.1	30.4	25.2	38.2

# Indicates a station move or relocation of instruments.

Precipitation

Year	Jan	Feb	Mar	Apr	May	June	July	Aug	Sept	Oct	Nov	Dec	Annual
1936	2.78	1.57	0.58	0.18	0.57	2.33	0.07	0.23	1.64	0.28	0.08	2.39	12.70
1937	1.94	1.49	1.11	2.53	0.23	3.13	0.56	0.61	0.62	0.87	3.05	2.76	18.90
1938	1.44	1.90	2.09	0.35	0.47	0.83	0.26	0.29	0.09	0.83	0.89	1.63	11.07
1939	1.55	2.37	1.20	0.61	0.30	0.71	0.40	0.04	0.23	0.95	0.28	2.83	11.47
#1940	1.09	5.62	2.91	1.86	0.64	0.36	1.46	0.01	2.12	2.47	2.37	2.59	23.50
1941	1.61	0.83	0.69	0.32	3.18	2.55	0.09	1.85	1.36	0.85	1.63	2.78	17.74
1942	1.24	1.30	0.48	0.98	3.19	0.93	0.34	0.08	0.22	1.12	2.69	1.70	14.27
1943	1.25	1.15	1.60	1.33	1.19	1.42	0.35	0.98	0.12	3.13	0.60	0.54	13.66
1944	0.53	1.08	0.57	1.40	0.94	1.11	0.21	1.02	0.56	0.45	1.64	1.14	10.65
1945	1.27	0.95	2.46	1.12	2.20	1.37	T	0.55	2.24	0.79	2.41	2.00	17.36
1946	1.51	1.43	1.69	0.98	1.43	1.08	0.03	0.07	1.76	1.38	3.16	0.90	15.42
#1947	1.24	0.26	1.60	1.17	0.31	1.98	0.72	0.83	1.57	5.41	1.67	1.80	18.56
1948	2.72	2.75	0.45	3.08	5.71	2.17	1.29	0.27	1.46	0.66	2.38	3.13	26.07
1949	0.50	3.08	2.17	0.42	0.90	0.22	0.07	0.19	1.06	1.52	2.28	1.50	13.91
1950	4.13	1.93	3.75	0.43	0.72	2.84	0.56	0.41	0.06	4.05	1.96	2.16	23.00
1951	3.16	1.61	1.72	0.38	0.66	1.04	0.37	0.40	0.47	3.26	1.88	4.35	19.30
1952	2.41	1.33	1.14	0.28	0.63	2.44	0.06	0.18	0.52	0.11	0.80	3.10	13.00
1953	4.56	1.07	1.77	1.48	1.59	0.81	T	1.36	0.50	0.19	2.00	1.90	17.23
1954	4.90	1.19	0.83	0.53	0.78	0.75	0.85	1.25	1.55	0.77	1.42	1.44	16.26
1955	1.38	1.32	0.79	1.83	0.67	0.80	1.28	T	1.13	2.84	3.92	3.82	19.78
1956	2.87	1.44	1.29	0.08	0.59	1.18	0.50	1.41	0.09	1.87	0.34	1.22	12.88
1957	1.34	1.54	1.82	0.81	3.74	2.74	0.04	0.30	0.68	2.33	0.82	1.93	18.09
1958	3.55	3.27	0.84	1.72	0.71	1.63	1.15	0.13	0.47	0.79	3.72	2.93	20.91
1959	4.96	2.01	1.21	0.57	2.26	0.39	0.05	1.24	2.05	1.32	2.30	1.21	19.57
1960	1.05	1.64	2.36	1.51	2.73	0.16	T	0.56	0.72	0.95	4.64	1.37	17.69
1961	1.61	3.94	1.75	0.96	1.77	1.64	0.37	0.30	0.17	1.05	1.83	3.91	19.30
1962	1.39	1.72	2.56	1.02	1.65	0.78	0.29	0.63	0.90	1.62	3.02	1.44	17.02
1963	0.89	2.21	1.65	1.32	0.98	0.96	0.41	0.50	0.36	1.11	2.58	2.29	15.26
1964	3.15	0.98	1.53	0.98	0.45	3.06	0.39	1.46	1.03	0.46	2.89	5.13	21.51
1965	2.82	1.13	0.31	2.35	1.02	0.74	0.69	1.73	0.28	0.05	1.71	1.63	14.46
1966	1.94	0.50	2.43	0.13	0.49	0.70	0.95	0.15	0.51	0.36	3.01	2.96	14.13
1967	2.44	0.40	1.72	1.71	1.31	1.99	0.06	T	0.24	1.18	0.82	2.02	13.89
1968	1.57	2.12	0.71	0.10	1.16	0.87	0.23	1.35	0.63	2.24	2.35	2.93	16.26
1969	4.08	1.21	0.53	2.16	0.54	1.17	0.03	T	0.71	0.45	0.37	2.45	13.70
1970	4.15	1.83	1.30	0.93	0.94	1.60	0.59	0.10	0.48	2.13	2.04	1.43	17.52
1971	2.11	0.88	2.11	1.85	1.39	2.46	0.50	0.59	1.37	0.82	1.51	2.89	18.48
1972	1.74	1.13	1.05	1.09	1.99	1.56	0.25	0.87	0.86	0.19	0.88	1.92	13.53
1973	2.05	0.48	0.77	0.42	1.34	0.57	T	0.19	1.44	0.97	5.10	3.78	17.11
1974	3.79	1.79	2.22	0.80	1.03	0.23	0.71	0.04	0.18	0.12	2.59	2.54	16.04
1975	2.53	3.12	1.83	1.78	1.41	1.45	1.60	0.93	0.03	2.23	1.94	2.42	21.27
RECORD MEAN	2.14	1.60	1.34	1.07	1.32	1.29	0.50	0.58	0.83	1.25	2.04	2.23	16.19

Record mean values above are means through the current year for the period beginning in 1882 for temperature and precipitation, 1948 for snowfall.

San Juan is located on the northeast coast of the island of Puerto Rico at Latitude 18° 28' N, and Longitude 66° 7' W. It is surrounded by the waters of the Atlantic Ocean and San Juan Bay. Santurce, directly to the east of the Bay, is the urbanized section of San Juan. The surrounding terrain is level with a gradual upslope inland. Mountain ranges, with peak elevations of 4,000 feet, extend east and west through the central portion of Puerto Rico, and are located 15 to 20 miles east and south of the capital City. This mountain range has a decided influence on the rainfall in the San Juan area, especially summertime thunderstorms.

The climate is tropical marine, slightly modified by insular influences when land breezes blow. Radiational cooling frequently causes land winds at night, consequently, somewhat lower nighttime temperatures occur than would normally be experienced with sea breezes. This air drainage from the higher altitudes in the interior of the island to the coastal areas gives delightfully invigorating night temperatures, especially during December to March, inclusive. Minimum temperatures during this period are frequently 2° to 3° higher within the City than at Isla Verde Airport, which is located 6.5 miles east and slightly inland. By the same token, maximum temperatures are 1° to 2° lower in the City.

San Juan has a small annual temperature range, which is characteristic of all tropical marine climates. The difference between the average temperatures of the warmest and coolest months is about 5.7° F. in San Juan, 6.5° F. at Isla Verde Airport, and is representative of most of the coastal localities in the island. This is also true concerning the absolute range of temperature. For the San Juan-Isla Verde Airport area, the highest temperature of record is 96° F. and lowest, 60° F. at the airport. These conditions are in significant contrast to those prevailing in the mountain and valley regions of the interior, where much greater daily and annual ranges of temperature occur. The highest temperature that has been recorded in Puerto Rico is 103° F. at San Lorenzo, while the lowest is 40° F. at Aibonite.

San Juan's average annual rainfall is near 60.00 inches, with fairly even distribution throughout the year. The geographical distribution of the rainfall over the island shows that the heaviest is centered over El Yunque in the Luquillo Mountains in the northeastern section. The annual rainfall there is approximately 150 inches greater than at San Juan, about 23 miles distant. At Isla Verde Airport, about 12 miles west of this mountain range, the annual rainfall is 64.00 inches. The heavier monthly amounts normally occur during the period from May to December, inclusive. Rainfall is generally of the showery type except for the continuous rains which occur in connection with the passage of tropical storms, or when the trailing edge of a cold front which has swept to have a definite effect upon Puerto Rico rainfall. This infrequently occurs from about November to April. Sunshine is plentiful, with only an average of 5 days a year entirely without sunshine, although there is an average of 209 days a year with measurable precipitation. The average duration of the showers is not

Station: SAN JUAN, PUERTO RICO
ISLA VERDE INTL AIRPORT
Elevation (ground): 13 feet

TEMPERATURES °F

Month	Normal			Extremes			
	Daily maximum	Daily minimum	Monthly	Record highest	Year	Record lowest	Year
(a)				21		21	
J	81.9	68.8	75.4	90	1958	61	1962
F	82.1	68.4	75.3	92	1968	62	1968
M	83.6	68.9	76.3	93	1958	60	1957
A	84.4	70.6	77.5	93	1973	64	1968
M	85.6	72.8	79.2	94	1974	66	1962
J	87.0	74.0	80.5	96	1975	69	1957
J	87.0	74.8	80.9	93	1974	69	1959
A	87.5	75.1	81.3	96	1974	70	1956
S	87.6	74.6	81.1	94	1974	69	1960
O	87.4	73.7	80.6	95	1970	67	1959
N	85.0	72.3	78.7	92	1973	66	1969
D	83.1	70.5	76.8	90	1965	63	1964
YR	85.2	72.0	78.6	96	JUN 1975	60	MAR 1957

IMPORTANT:
The time-period covered by this record is limited: See footnotes following table of NORMALS, MEANS AND EXTREMES for explanation and for additional history of EXTREME HIGHS AND LOWS recorded in the general area.

(Continued)

more than 10 to 15 minutes, although on many occasions, especially in the summer a series of intermittent showers will extend over a period of an hour or two. Being marine, the climate is naturally humid. Relative humidity averages about 85 percent in the nighttime and 65 percent near midday. Dense fogs never occur in the San Juan area.

The easterly trade winds, aided by the daily reccurrence of the land and sea breeze constitute the most characteristic feature of the climate for San Juan throughout the year. The wind is almost constantly from the ocean during daylight hours. Usually, after sunset the wind shifts to the south or southeast, off the land. This daily variation in the circulation pattern of surface winds is a contributing factor to the delightful climate of the island. The sea water temperature about San Juan range from a minimum of 78 $^{\circ}$ F. in March to a maximum of about 83 $^{\circ}$ F. in September.

Puerto Rico is in the tropical hurricane region of the eastern Caribbean where the season for these storms begins June 1 and ends November 30. Several hurricanes affect this area every season, but weather records show that only 6 of these storms have caused winds of hurricane intensity in the San Juan area during the past 60 years. The last hurricane which caused considerable loss of life and great property damage in San Juan occurred in September 26, 1932; however, on August 12, 1956, Hurricane Betsy passed over Puerto Rico. Hurricane winds were felt at San Juan, but there was no loss of life reported, and property damage was not great.

Mild temperatures, refreshing sea breezes in the daytime, plenty of sunshine, and adequate rainfall make the climate of San Juan enjoyable and exceptionally favorable for tourists and visitors.

Normals, Means, and Extremes

(To better understand these tables, see full explanation of terms beginning on page 322)

Month	Normal Degree days Base 65 °F: Heating	Cooling	Precipitation in inches: Water equivalent: Normal	Maximum monthly	Year	Minimum monthly	Year	Maximum in 24 hrs.	Year	Snow, Ice pellets: Maximum monthly	Year	Maximum in 24 hrs.	Year
(a)				21		21		21		21		21	
J	0	322	3.73	7.49	1969	0.94	1960	5.08	1969	0.0		0.0	
F	0	299	2.50	6.44	1956	0.71	1975	2.73	1969	0.0		0.0	
M	0	339	2.04	5.41	1958	0.72	1970	3.91	1969	0.0		0.0	
A	0	375	3.40	8.48	1973	0.50	1968	6.37	1973	0.0		0.0	
M	0	440	6.54	14.99	1965	0.44	1972	3.08	1965	0.0		0.0	
J	0	465	5.64	10.96	1965	1.24	1971	3.55	1965	0.0		0.0	
J	0	493	6.41	9.35	1961	1.12	1974	2.28	1969	0.0		0.0	
A	0	505	6.98	11.76	1955	3.06	1972	5.08	1955	0.0		0.0	
S	0	483	6.07	10.85	1963	1.93	1961	3.44	1975	0.0		0.0	
O	0	484	5.64	15.06	1970	1.63	1963	5.00	1970	0.0		0.0	
N	0	411	5.49	11.11	1968	2.31	1971	3.72	1968	0.0		0.0	
D	0	366	4.71	10.00	1961	0.68	1963	3.54	1961	0.0		0.0	
YR	0	4982	59.15	15.06	OCT 1970	0.44	MAY 1972	6.37	APR 1973	0.0		0.0	

Month	Relative humidity pct. Hour 02 (Local time)	Hour 08	Hour 14	Hour 20	Wind: Mean speed m.p.h.	Prevailing direction	Fastest mile: Speed m.p.h.	Direction	Year	Pct. of possible sunshine	Mean sky cover, tenths, sunrise to sunset	Mean number of days: Sunrise to sunset: Clear	Partly cloudy	Cloudy	Precipitation .01 inch or more	Snow, Ice pellets 1.0 inch or more	Thunderstorms	Heavy fog, visibility ¼ mile or less	Temperatures °F Max. (b) 90° and above	Max. 32° and below	Min. 32° and below	Min. 0° and below	Average station pressure mb. Elev. 62 feet m.s.l.
(a)	20	20	20	20	20	8	20	20		20	20	20	20	20	20	20	20	20	20	20	20	20	3
J	81	81	64	75	9.3	ENE	34	SE	1974	65	5.2	8	18	5	18	0	*	0	*	0	0	0	1015.8
F	80	80	62	73	9.3	ENE	40	E	1965	69	5.0	7	17	4	13	0	*	0	*	0	0	0	1014.9
M	80	78	60	73	9.7	ENE	37	NE	1969	74	5.0	8	19	4	12	0	*	0	1	0	0	0	1014.6
A	80	75	62	73	9.4	ENE	35	E	1970	69	5.4	7	17	6	13	0	1	0	2	0	0	0	1014.1
M	83	77	65	75	8.7	ENE	34	E	1975	61	6.5	3	17	11	17	0	4	0	4	0	0	0	1014.0
J	84	78	66	76	9.0	ENE	38	NE	1970	57	6.5	3	16	11	17	0	5	0	6	0	0	0	1014.2
J	83	79	66	77	9.9	ENE	44	E	1975	64	6.1	4	18	9	20	0	5	0	4	0	0	0	1014.6
A	83	79	66	77	9.2	ENE	80	NE	1956	65	6.2	4	18	9	19	0	6	0	5	0	0	0	1013.6
S	84	80	67	78	7.6	ENE	47	SE	1973	59	6.4	2	18	10	18	0	8	0	6	0	0	0	1012.3
O	84	81	66	78	6.9	ENE	44	NE	1972	59	6.3	3	17	11	17	0	7	0	6	0	0	0	1011.5
N	83	81	66	77	7.7	ENE	35	NE	1961	57	5.8	4	18	8	18	0	3	0	1	0	0	0	1012.1
D	82	80	65	76	8.9	ENE	46	NE	1970	56	5.8	5	19	7	19	0	*	0	*	0	0	0	1013.8
YR	82	79	64	76	8.8	ENE	80	NE	AUG 1956	63	5.9	58	212	95	200	0	40	0	37	0	0	0	1013.8

FOOTNOTES

Means and extremes above are from existing and comparable exposures.
Annual extremes at City locations (1890-1964) were: Highest temperature 96 in October 1963 and earlier; lowest temperature 62 in December 1917 and earlier; maximum monthly precipitation 16.88 in May 1936; minimum monthly precipitation 0.05 in February 1941; maximum precipitation in 24 hours 10.55 in December 1910; fastest mile of wind 149 from East in September 1928.

Snowfall

Season	July	Aug	Sept	Oct	Nov	Dec	Jan

Heating Degree Days

Season	July	Aug	Sept	Oct	Nov	Dec	Jan

Cooling Degree Days

Year	Jan	Feb	Mar	Apr	May	June	July
1969	328	287	401	447	496	517	501
1970	362	321	409	460	490	506	548
1971	398	353	438	445	511	545	562
1972	400	376	431	458	525	569	592
1973	438	379	428	458	562	553	578
1974	390	368	424	442	511	558	586
1975	375	346	420	446	501	543	565

Feb	Mar	Apr	May	June	Total

Average Temperature

Year	Jan	Feb	Mar	Apr	May	June	July	Aug	Sept	Oct	Nov	Dec	Annual
1951	74.6	73.3	73.9	77.7	80.8	80.7	80.7	82.1	81.3	80.9	79.1	76.9	78.5
1952	75.5	75.1	76.9	78.3	80.2	81.2	79.8	81.7	80.7	80.9	78.3	75.3	78.7
1953	74.9	75.2	75.9	78.0	79.1	80.6	81.3	81.3	81.6	80.6	79.6	77.7	78.8
1954	75.5	75.5	76.9	76.9	79.4	80.3	81.0	81.6	80.4	78.9	78.3	76.7	78.5
#1955	75.6	75.2	74.9	76.5	79.4	80.0	80.3	81.2	80.5	80.2	79.0	75.6	78.2
1956	73.9	74.3	75.7	77.1	78.6	79.1	80.3	80.6	80.3	79.4	77.7	75.6	77.7
1957	74.8	74.8	75.6	76.3	78.0	79.0	80.9	81.2	80.9	80.1	78.6	75.7	78.1
1958	75.7	75.8	77.6	79.2	80.2	81.4	80.5	81.6	81.4	80.0	78.0	76.1	79.0
1959	75.1	75.5	76.7	77.9	77.9	80.7	81.0	81.3	81.6	80.7	79.2	77.8	78.8
1960	75.9	76.3	77.3	78.4	80.0	81.2	81.1	81.1	80.3	80.6	79.4	76.5	79.0
1961	76.0	75.6	76.6	78.4	79.7	79.9	80.5	81.6	81.2	79.8	77.5	77.2	78.7
1962	75.2	74.2	75.7	77.2	78.5	80.5	81.7	81.3	81.0	80.4	78.9	77.3	78.5
1963	75.7	76.2	76.3	77.6	78.2	80.8	81.3	81.8	81.3	81.5	78.7	78.9	79.1
1964	76.6	77.5	78.8	78.5	80.9	81.6	81.8	82.2	82.2	80.6	79.0	75.7	79.6
1965	74.7	75.9	77.7	77.7	78.9	80.3	81.7	81.5	82.2	81.5	79.8	77.4	79.1
1966	77.4	76.7	78.1	78.5	79.5	81.0	82.1	82.6	81.1	80.0	77.5	77.1	79.3
1967	76.7	76.3	75.9	78.0	79.7	81.8	82.1	82.2	81.8	81.4	80.4	77.5	79.5
1968	76.4	76.5	76.2	77.0	79.9	80.4	81.2	82.0	81.8	81.6	79.5	77.5	79.2
1969	75.4	75.0	77.8	79.6	80.7	82.0	80.9	81.1	81.2	80.9	78.7	77.1	79.2
1970	76.5	76.2	77.9	80.0	80.6	81.6	82.4	82.3	82.2	81.9	80.2	78.2	80.0
1971	77.6	77.4	78.9	79.7	81.3	83.0	82.9	83.2	83.9	81.9	80.6	78.8	80.8
1972	77.7	77.8	78.7	80.1	81.7	83.8	83.9	83.4	82.9	82.6	81.1	79.2	81.1
1973	78.9	78.3	78.6	80.0	82.9	83.2	83.4	83.2	82.7	83.5	80.7	77.9	81.1
1974	77.3	78.0	78.5	79.6	81.4	83.4	83.7	83.2	82.9	82.5	80.0	78.3	80.7
1975	76.9	77.2	78.4	79.6	81.0	82.9	83.0	82.7	82.1	81.6	79.8	77.5	80.2
RECORD													
MEAN	76.0	76.0	77.0	78.3	80.0	81.3	81.6	81.9	81.6	81.0	79.1	77.2	79.3
MAX	82.1	82.5	83.6	84.7	86.3	87.6	87.5	88.0	87.9	87.5	85.3	83.0	85.5
MIN	69.8	69.5	70.3	71.9	73.6	74.9	75.7	75.8	75.2	74.4	72.9	71.4	73.0

# Indicates a station move or relocation of instruments.

SAN JUAN, PR

Feb	Mar	Apr	May	June	Total

Precipitation

Year	Jan	Feb	Mar	Apr	May	June	July	Aug	Sept	Oct	Nov	Dec	Annual
1951	3.29	0.75	0.45	4.35	6.33	7.03	8.51	6.11	9.19	6.30	6.88	10.80	69.99
1952	4.61	4.13	0.56	7.05	8.25	6.22	10.97	6.97	7.82	6.96	10.58	2.48	76.60
1953	1.97	1.31	2.18	3.49	5.49	5.84	4.20	5.46	5.17	6.23	6.49	4.15	51.98
1954	3.96	7.34	1.15	2.40	4.76	6.57	5.32	9.64	9.82	4.22	1.48	2.86	59.52
#1955	1.80	1.64	2.39	1.75	11.81	2.19	3.93	11.76	7.14	3.88	4.61	7.03	59.93
1956	3.48	6.44	4.83	4.54	9.66	9.30	3.51	6.78	5.74	7.97	3.18	4.18	69.61
1957	3.78	1.29	1.51	1.14	2.25	6.51	7.16	7.68	4.53	6.40	4.13	6.63	53.01
1958	4.39	1.51	5.41	2.98	13.59	9.33	7.39	6.65	5.52	7.67	4.57	5.04	74.05
1959	5.79	1.61	1.34	6.18	7.01	3.02	2.80	4.67	4.29	6.59	4.85	3.50	51.65
1960	0.94	3.33	2.39	5.76	7.09	5.84	5.02	8.49	8.34	4.63	4.56	8.01	64.40
1961	3.51	1.31	2.64	2.82	1.77	5.26	9.35	5.19	1.93	8.47	9.26	10.00	61.51
1962	4.24	2.67	0.97	3.70	7.53	6.70	6.46	6.98	4.85	2.80	3.84	4.11	54.85
1963	3.13	1.39	4.68	5.21	6.85	2.74	5.02	3.43	10.85	1.63	3.00	0.68	48.61
1964	2.02	1.70	1.27	6.38	3.96	4.50	7.03	6.71	5.10	3.13	3.39	2.35	47.54
1965	2.62	0.79	0.86	2.19	14.99	10.96	5.88	8.66	4.80	5.08	3.93	5.05	65.81
1966	1.34	1.64	4.63	5.62	5.69	3.26	4.21	3.41	7.20	8.99	7.99	6.21	60.19
1967	3.07	2.93	1.46	0.85	4.15	3.38	4.79	4.20	5.12	4.47	5.00	3.13	42.55
1968	2.15	1.60	1.79	0.50	6.31	5.98	5.25	7.36	5.26	2.33	11.11	3.56	53.20
1969	7.49	3.97	2.89	2.42	5.79	4.04	7.49	6.89	4.86	6.99	6.70	2.28	61.81
1970	2.94	1.33	0.72	1.15	7.98	9.26	3.58	4.66	5.66	15.06	8.00	5.98	66.32
1971	2.18	3.67	1.78	2.93	3.87	1.24	1.69	5.18	2.19	4.61	2.31	3.93	35.58
1972	2.76	2.00	3.40	2.79	0.44	1.58	2.24	3.06	3.68	5.46	2.78	7.53	37.72
1973	2.27	0.92	4.66	8.48	0.48	4.71	2.44	7.00	3.13	3.29	3.01	4.16	44.55
1974	2.92	0.82	1.92	1.20	2.42	2.34	1.12	6.57	3.67	8.23	6.55	3.92	41.68
1975	2.69	0.71	1.13	1.01	1.04	2.64	3.35	4.08	9.29	6.60	10.90	7.82	51.26
RECORD													
MEAN	3.17	2.27	2.28	3.48	5.98	5.22	5.15	6.30	5.81	5.92	5.56	5.02	56.16

Aug	Sept	Oct	Nov	Dec	Total
506	493	500	417	382	5275
540	523	528	461	416	5564
573	577	531	473	438	5844
578	543	554	490	446	5962
570	539	579	475	406	5965
575	544	549	455	418	5820
556	521	519	450	395	5637

Record mean values above are means through the current year for the period beginning in 1951 for temperature and precipitation, 1956 for snowfall. Data are from airport locations.

CHARLESTON, WEST VIRGINIA

Station: CHARLESTON, WEST VIRGINIA
KANAWHA AIRPORT

Elevation (ground): 939 feet

TEMPERATURES °F

Month	Normal Daily maximum	Normal Daily minimum	Normal Monthly	Extremes Record highest	Year	Record lowest	Year
(a)				28		28	
J	43.6	25.3	34.5	79	1950	-12	1963
F	46.2	26.8	36.5	77	1950	-6	1968
M	55.2	33.8	44.5	87	1954	7	1950
A	67.9	43.8	55.9	91	1974	19	1972
M	76.6	52.3	64.5	93	1969	26	1966
J	83.4	60.6	72.0	98	1953	33	1972
J	85.6	64.3	75.0	102	1954	46	1963
A	84.4	62.8	73.6	100	1953	41	1965
S	79.0	55.9	67.5	102	1953	34	1974
O	69.1	44.8	57.0	92	1951	17	1962
N	55.8	35.0	45.4	85	1948	6	1950
D	45.2	27.2	36.2	80	1971	-2	1963
YR	66.0	44.4	55.2	102	JUL 1954	-12	JAN 1963

IMPORTANT:
The time-period covered by this record is limited: See footnotes following table of **NORMALS, MEANS AND EXTREMES** for explanation and for additional history of **EXTREME HIGHS AND LOWS** recorded in the general area.

Located in the western foothills of the Appalachians at the junction of the Kanawha and Elk Rivers, Charleston has a climate characterized by sharp temperature contrasts, both seasonal and day to day. The months of May through September are generally warm; those of November through March moderately cold, with April and October months of fairly rapid transition. Cold waves occur on an average of 2 or 3 times during the winter, but severe cold spells are seldom of more than 2 to 3 days duration. Below zero temperatures have been recorded in December, January, and February, as well as temperatures in the neighborhood of 80°. Record summer highs of 105° in June and 108° in July and August contrast with lows of 46° and 48° during these same months.

Ample precipitation which averages near 44 inches annually for a long-term period is well distributed throughout the year, with a normal maximum of 5.67 inches in July, and a normal minimum of 2.58 inches in October. Summer rainfall occurs mostly during thunderstorms or showery precipitation, while the heaviest winter precipitation usually is associated with storms originating to the southwest, moving northeastward over the Ohio Valley. The maximum recorded monthly amount of 13.54 inches occurred in July 1961, and the least, none, in October 1897. Snowfall occurs chiefly from November through March, and occasionally in April. Maximum amounts for the month are above 18 inches for the months of November through March, yet there have been instances when each of these months produced less than 1 inch of snow. Seasonal totals have varied greatly at Kanawha Airport, ranging from less than 5 inches to over 50 inches.

Kanawha Airport is located on a manmade plateau about 2 miles northeast of the junction of the Kana-

(Continued page 688)

Snowfall

Season	July	Aug	Sept	Oct	Nov	Dec	Jan
1936-37	0.0	0.0	0.0	0.0	1.0	2.5	0.0
1937-38	0.0	0.0	0.0	T	T	6.7	1.4
1938-39	0.0	0.0	0.0	0.0	11.0	1.0	2.0
1939-40	0.0	0.0	0.0	0.0	T	3.5	12.7
1940-41	0.0	0.0	0.0	0.0	2.0	0.0	1.6
1941-42	0.0	0.0	0.0	0.0	T	T	6.5
#1942-43							
1943-44	0.0	0.0	0.0	0.0	T	2.0	5.0
#1944-45						13.7	5.0
1945-46	0.0	0.0	0.0	0.0	0.2	13.2	3.3
1946-47	0.0	0.0	0.0	0.0	0.0	T	8.0
#1947-48	0.0	0.0	0.0	0.0	T	T	19.5
1948-49	0.0	0.0	0.0	0.0	T	T	0.7
1949-50	0.0	0.0	0.0	0.0	T	T	T
1950-51	0.0	0.0	0.0	0.0	25.8	1.7	2.5
1951-52	0.0	0.0	0.0	0.0	3.7	1.9	2.2
1952-53	0.0	0.0	0.0	T	2.8	1.3	8.2
1953-54	0.0	0.0	0.0	0.0	2.5	3.9	15.6
1954-55	0.0	0.0	0.0	T	0.7	4.3	8.4
1955-56	0.0	0.0	0.0	0.0	0.4	5.0	8.4
1956-57	0.0	0.0	0.0	0.0	1.4	2.2	5.7
1957-58	0.0	0.0	0.0	0.8	0.8	2.7	6.8
1958-59	0.0	0.0	0.0	0.0	1.1	3.7	5.6
1959-60	0.0	0.0	0.0	0.0	6.5	3.4	3.7
1960-61	0.0	0.0	0.0	0.0	0.8	4.1	15.1
1961-62	0.0	0.0	0.0	2.8	0.6	5.6	3.9
1962-63	0.0	0.0	0.0	0.6	0.2	18.6	10.7
1963-64	0.0	0.0	0.0	T	3.6	12.6	11.3
1964-65	0.0	0.0	0.0	0.0	1.3	0.9	13.7
1965-66	0.0	0.0	0.0	T	T	2.7	19.8
1966-67	0.0	0.0	0.0	T	3.8	6.0	3.6
1967-68	0.0	0.0	0.0	0.0	0.2	16.6	13.3
1968-69	0.0	0.0	0.0	T	4.3	4.7	2.0
1969-70	0.0	0.0	0.0	0.0	4.3	9.5	12.6
1970-71	0.0	0.0	0.0	0.0	0.2	10.9	11.6
1971-72	0.0	0.0	0.0	0.0	4.2	0.8	4.0
1972-73	0.0	0.0	0.0	0.9	6.9	1.4	3.4
1973-74	0.0	0.0	0.0	0.0	T	6.5	0.3
1974-75	0.0	0.0	0.0	0.6	2.7	8.3	18.1
1975-76	0.0	0.0	0.0	0.0	T	4.0	
RECORD MEAN	0.0	0.0	0.0	0.2	2.8	5.1	8.2

Heating Degree Days

Season	July	Aug	Sept	Oct	Nov	Dec	Jan
1955-56	0	0	6	261	661	963	1049
1956-57	0	7	115	156	583	558	1002
1957-58	0	0	43	385	534	756	1038
1958-59	0	1	54	289	511	1032	988
1959-60	0	0	32	253	634	769	845
#1960-61	0	0	16	215	523	1074	1154
1961-62	3	0	57	275	559	853	965
1962-63	3	0	114	273	661	1052	1144
1963-64	10	6	81	177	558	1200	899
1964-65	0	13	40	364	474	791	974
1965-66	0	15	58	382	561	776	1166
1966-67	0	1	44	315	507	910	815
1967-68	4	6	124	297	704	802	1104
1968-69	2	11	35	298	541	946	994
1969-70	0	0	95	352	703	1007	1125
1970-71	3	0	40	246	563	817	1097
1971-72	0	1	13	78	578	543	809
1972-73	16	2	14	378	642	701	945
1973-74	0	1	19	202	541	833	659
1974-75	0	0	110	388	590	869	899
1975-76	0	0	106	227	441	813	

Cooling Degree Days

Year	Jan	Feb	Mar	Apr	May	June	July
1969	0	0	0	7	79	277	368
1970	0	0	0	40	147	251	310
1971	0	0	0	0	32	265	237
1972	0	0	0	24	56	85	283
1973	0	0	4	22	34	256	304
1974	0	0	14	43	99	118	292
1975	0	0	0	7	99	212	291

Feb	Mar	Apr	May	June	Total
6.5	T	T	0.0	0.0	10.0
T	T	T	0.0	0.0	8.1
3.0	0.5	0.5	0.0	0.0	18.0
5.7	0.5	0.5	0.0	0.0	22.9
4.5	14.0	0.0	0.0	0.0	22.1
1.8	11.2	T			
			0.0	0.0	
1.3	T	1.2	0.0		
1.6	0.0	T	0.0	0.0	
9.0	0.0	T	0.0	0.0	25.7
10.5	4.9	0.0	0.0	0.0	23.4
6.4	T	0.0	0.0	0.0	25.9
T	2.5	T	0.0	0.0	3.2
2.0	2.8	T	0.0	0.0	4.8
2.2	7.6	T	0.0	0.0	39.8
0.9	0.6	T	0.0	0.0	9.3
2.3	4.5	0.9	0.0	0.0	20.0
2.1	10.5	T	0.0	0.0	34.6
5.3	0.2	T	0.0	0.0	18.9
1.3	2.8	0.8	0.0	0.0	18.7
3.5	1.4	T	0.0	0.0	14.2
16.7	9.4	T	0.0	0.0	37.2
1.4	0.4	5.9	0.0	0.0	18.1
21.5	18.3	T	0.0	0.0	53.4
6.5	0.6	0.5	0.0	0.0	27.6
4.8	8.5	T	0.0	0.0	26.2
19.0	T	T	0.2	0.0	49.3
21.8	2.2	T	0.0	0.0	51.5
6.7	8.5	T	0.0	0.0	31.1
8.0	1.7	T	0.0	0.0	32.2
20.6	2.2	0.0	0.0	0.0	36.2
9.2	2.0	0.0	0.0	0.0	41.3
1.3	4.8	0.0	0.0	0.0	17.1
14.2	2.9	T	0.0	0.0	43.5
10.5	11.7	T	0.0	0.0	44.9
9.8	3.5	T	0.0	0.0	22.3
2.9	4.8	0.9	0.0	0.0	21.2
13.0	0.9	1.2	0.0	0.0	21.9
2.4	8.1	0.1	0.0	0.0	40.3
7.7	4.4	0.4	T	0.0	28.8

Feb	Mar	Apr	May	June	Total
665	647	415	112	45	4824
657	645	268	89	3	4083
1042	784	328	93	15	5018
710	674	282	73	19	4633
892	994	214	177	4	4814
696	522	471	201	33	4905
687	656	424	37	0	4516
1002	476	302	148	26	5201
917	563	226	54	20	4711
820	780	299	24	15	4594
793	538	354	147	25	4815
932	517	275	217	17	4550
1095	539	263	141	15	5094
828	807	264	98	9	4833
801	666	239	82	1	5071
828	778	387	184	2	4945
856	649	333	90	81	4031
832	394	351	157	4	4436
775	500	277	115	25	3947
749	772	445	59	4	4885

Aug	Sept	Oct	Nov	Dec	Total
227	75	15	0	0	1048
273	197	18	0	0	1236
219	190	49	11	5	1008
247	132	0	0	0	827
305	181	22	2	0	1130
275	62	6	1	0	910
372	82	7	4	0	1074

Average Temperature

Year	Jan	Feb	Mar	Apr	May	June	July	Aug	Sept	Oct	Nov	Dec	Annual
1936	32.6	34.6	50.9	55.5	68.6	74.7	79.4	78.6	72.8	58.8	43.4	39.9	57.5
1937	46.4	37.2	41.8	55.8	62.6	70.2	71.7	73.6	64.0	53.4	41.8	35.4	54.5
1938	37.0	43.8	50.7	59.6	65.0	71.6	76.2	77.2	69.7	57.6	47.9	38.1	57.9
1939	39.2	41.4	46.4	52.8	66.7	77.4	76.0	76.2	72.0	59.8	44.0	39.0	57.6
1940	24.4	37.2	42.4	52.5	62.4	73.5	75.4	74.8	65.6	56.6	45.4	41.9	54.3
1941	35.4	32.8	37.9	60.0	67.6	74.4	77.4	75.3					
1942													
#1943					68.0	78.7	78.0	78.0	68.6	57.4	45.6	38.1	
#1944	38.8	43.5	45.6	56.2	71.9							30.4	
1945	30.6	37.0	54.6	58.8	61.5	71.8	75.6	74.5	71.8	56.8	47.6	31.1	56.0
1946	36.4	38.8	54.0	58.0	64.0	72.4	76.1	71.0	70.0	60.2	51.4	40.8	57.8
#1947	41.6	27.8	37.4	61.0	63.7	72.2	72.7	80.8	72.4	64.2	44.6	36.6	56.2
1948	25.4	38.9	49.4	59.6	61.8	71.6	74.9	72.8	67.2	52.1	49.4	39.1	55.2
1949	44.0	42.7	44.7	52.2	64.8	74.4	78.0	74.3	63.4	61.6	45.1	40.0	57.1
#1950	46.4	38.6	40.8	51.2	65.0	70.4	72.6	71.7	65.7	61.5	41.6	33.5	54.9
1951	38.8	38.9	45.8	53.9	64.3	72.5	75.8	73.3	66.7	59.7	41.1	40.6	56.0
1952	41.6	40.7	44.5	55.3	63.3	75.7	77.1	74.1	66.9	51.8	46.6	39.8	56.5
1953	42.0	40.7	47.3	53.0	68.9	74.1	76.5	74.7	67.9	60.1	45.6	37.7	57.4
#1954	38.0	43.5	43.6	62.4	59.7	72.4	75.0	73.1	70.5	57.8	43.6	35.6	56.3
1955	32.9	37.7	47.0	59.2	65.6	65.8	78.1	77.1	70.9	57.1	42.8	33.7	55.7
1956	30.9	41.8	44.2	52.0	64.4	70.0	73.5	73.1	64.1	60.0	45.3	46.9	55.5
1957	32.5	41.4	44.1	58.5	65.3	74.3	75.3	73.4	69.9	52.5	47.0	40.4	56.2
1958	31.2	27.5	39.3	54.3	63.4	68.5	76.0	72.3	66.8	55.6	48.2	31.5	52.9
1959	32.9	39.4	43.1	55.9	68.3	70.7	75.7	77.4	70.4	58.3	43.9	40.0	56.3
#1960	37.6	34.0	32.7	59.5	61.0	70.5	73.0	75.9	69.8	58.1	47.3	30.1	54.1
1961	27.5	40.0	48.0	49.7	59.4	67.9	72.4	73.7	71.1	56.1	46.3	37.2	54.1
1962	33.6	40.2	43.6	51.6	69.8	73.0	73.0	74.4	65.0	57.3	42.9	30.8	54.6
1963	27.9	29.0	49.5	56.1	61.3	69.1	72.0	70.2	64.5	59.2	46.2	26.1	52.6
1964	35.8	33.2	46.7	58.5	67.0	72.9	75.0	73.1	67.5	53.2	49.0	39.2	55.9
1965	33.3	35.6	39.6	55.1	69.2	70.0	73.2	72.5	69.3	52.6	46.1	39.8	54.7
1966	27.1	36.6	47.7	54.1	62.1	72.0	77.3	73.5	66.5	55.0	48.2	35.5	54.6
1967	38.5	31.6	48.5	56.3	58.3	71.6	71.1	70.2	62.1	55.9	41.3	38.9	53.7
1968	29.1	27.1	47.5	56.4	61.0	70.6	74.2	74.1	66.3	56.0	46.8	34.2	53.6
1969	32.7	35.2	38.7	56.2	64.1	73.7	76.6	72.1	64.1	53.9	41.3	32.3	53.4
1970	28.5	36.2	43.3	58.2	66.9	73.1	74.6	73.6	70.0	57.4	46.0	38.4	55.5
1971	29.4	35.2	39.7	51.9	59.9	73.5	72.4	71.9	70.7	63.8	45.9	47.3	55.2
1972	38.7	35.2	43.8	54.5	63.7	64.9	73.4	72.7	68.7	52.5	43.4	42.1	54.5
1973	34.3	35.1	52.2	53.8	60.8	73.3	74.5	74.6	70.1	58.9	46.8	38.0	56.0
1974	43.5	37.1	49.1	56.9	64.2	67.8	74.2	73.6	63.2	52.4	45.2	36.8	55.3
1975	35.7	38.0	39.8	50.2	66.1	71.7	74.2	76.7	63.9	57.6	50.2	38.6	55.2
RECORD MEAN	36.6	38.0	46.0	56.0	64.8	72.3	76.0	74.8	69.3	58.0	46.7	38.2	56.4
MAX	46.8	48.9	57.8	69.0	77.7	84.4	87.5	86.3	81.7	70.8	58.1	48.1	68.1
MIN	26.3	27.0	34.1	43.0	51.9	60.1	64.4	63.3	56.9	45.1	35.2	28.3	44.6

# Indicates a station move or relocation of instruments.

Precipitation

Year	Jan	Feb	Mar	Apr	May	June	July	Aug	Sept	Oct	Nov	Dec	Annual
1936	3.88	1.91	4.77	3.34	1.19	1.26	3.51	3.30	0.93	4.36	2.96	4.40	35.81
1937	8.46	3.35	1.85	2.49	2.96	4.90	4.30	6.38	0.85	6.34	2.08	1.90	45.86
1938	2.38	3.08	4.46	4.90	6.29	3.20	11.32	4.10	4.86	0.64	5.20	1.46	51.89
1939	3.69	7.00	5.86	5.50	1.45	4.35	5.28	2.44	0.68	2.11	0.63	2.74	41.73
1940	1.33	4.72	4.27	6.52	1.95	5.81	2.79	4.34	3.77	1.61	2.67	1.31	41.09
1941	2.20	0.88	2.81	1.33	2.52	5.33	6.73	4.23	4.18	2.32	3.04	2.48	38.05
1942	2.65	2.06	4.98	2.06								2.63	
#1943					3.38	3.40	3.49	2.98	1.04	2.14	2.08	4.12	
1944	2.70	3.05	4.95	3.51	4.66								
1945	4.56	5.33	3.53	2.92	5.13	4.28	4.77	2.03	4.11	2.33	5.96	2.37	47.32
1946	2.28	3.10	3.02	1.96	5.61	2.50	4.08	3.84	2.78	2.94	1.93	2.16	36.20
#1947	4.66	1.14	1.65	1.65	2.92	4.63	3.59	5.84	5.83	1.22	1.86	1.02	36.01
1948	2.83	2.81	3.51	6.46	3.39	3.89	6.91	3.51	2.76	2.31	4.32	4.57	47.27
1949	5.43	3.87	2.69	3.43	3.03	4.54	5.46	3.06	2.14	2.82	1.73	4.11	42.31
#1950	9.11	2.73	4.12	1.89	4.65	6.43	7.30	5.89	7.38	3.16	5.81	2.17	60.64
1951	5.18	3.57	6.19	2.97	4.64	5.12	3.19	3.65	4.66	1.47	4.72	5.73	51.09
1952	5.68	2.12	4.01	4.41	5.85	3.36	3.38	1.98	2.01	0.93	2.09	3.42	39.24
1953	5.58	2.40	4.95	2.96	3.63	2.73	3.50	1.33	1.55	0.39	1.00	2.45	32.47
#1954	3.63	2.17	3.25	2.55	2.67	3.87	5.11	7.96	2.92	4.99	1.43	3.18	43.73
1955	2.05	5.64	6.52	2.51	4.51	2.07	5.90	2.09	1.53	2.59	1.50	1.23	38.14
1956	2.72	6.89	6.59	4.16	4.36	2.70	4.80	3.45	4.39	1.63	1.48	5.73	48.90
1957	5.78	4.69	2.52	2.60	2.83	1.69	4.27	0.66	3.51	3.14	1.99	3.80	37.48
1958	3.49	3.09	3.09	5.78	5.88	3.32	9.36	10.45	2.53	1.58	2.64	1.24	52.45
1959	3.27	2.90	2.28	4.77	2.40	1.90	6.74	2.02	0.65	3.64	3.81	2.02	36.40
1960	3.29	4.08	2.05	3.23	2.74	4.26	5.57	3.84	1.82	2.21	2.11	2.17	37.37
1961	3.79	3.63	4.86	3.22	4.23	5.22	13.54	1.19	1.50	6.11	2.89	4.74	54.92
1962	2.81	5.37	3.91	4.12	2.22	4.94	8.03	1.94	3.67	2.53	6.27	3.46	49.27
1963	1.85	2.70	6.37	1.21	3.48	2.67	3.06	2.85	1.34	0.09	3.19	1.44	30.25
1964	2.58	3.58	3.65	3.20	0.95	3.82	2.76	3.23	2.53	0.59	2.95	3.14	32.98
1965	4.65	2.02	4.52	6.46	1.90	2.18	2.46	4.38	3.21	2.09	0.64	0.45	34.96
1966	3.57	2.78	1.51	5.06	1.52	0.70	2.94	3.31	3.74	1.72	3.05	2.53	32.43
1967	1.21	2.95	6.80	3.21	6.45	1.83	4.59	1.85	1.68	2.09	4.30	4.72	41.68
1968	2.01	0.64	4.79	2.58	6.59	2.83	4.02	5.42	3.32	3.16	2.47	2.38	40.21
1969	1.50	1.27	1.43	2.35	1.95	2.43	6.13	8.20	3.27	1.52	2.22	4.85	37.12
1970	1.15	3.51	4.23	3.19	1.13	2.35	3.53	4.84	3.55	5.19	2.34	3.81	38.82
1971	2.35	3.40	1.97	1.19	5.17	2.58	6.59	2.12	7.61	1.30	2.83	1.71	38.82
1972	5.47	5.51	2.17	5.16	2.55	4.33	4.13	4.13	3.61	2.48	5.26	6.35	51.15
1973	1.52	2.41	3.40	5.44	5.36	4.48	6.88	2.07	3.91	4.75	5.42	3.68	49.32
1974	4.67	2.50	4.54	3.05	6.06	5.07	2.16	4.22	2.64	1.64	3.72	3.19	43.46
1975	4.84	3.10	6.01	4.03	6.44	4.25	2.71	5.14	4.99	3.08	2.66	3.74	50.99
RECORD MEAN	3.77	3.33	4.12	3.71	3.76	3.88	4.91	4.09	3.01	2.71	3.06	3.31	43.66

Record mean values above are means through the current year for the period beginning in 1902 for temperature, 1901 for precipitation, and 1948 for snowfall. Data are from Cooperative locations through November 1947 and from Airport locations thereafter.

(Continued)

wha and Elk Rivers and the city of Charleston. The airport site is approximately 350 feet above the Kanawha and Elk Valley floors, and is within 250 feet of the summits of most nearby hills. One of the important results of this location in the foothills of the Appalachians and the valley of the Kanawha River, which flows southeast to northwest through Charleston to its junction with the Ohio about 50 miles northwest, is that only air reaching Charleston and the airport from the northwest quadrant has had a trajectory which is primarily upslope.

When a northwesterly circulation persists following the passage of a cold front through Charleston, especially during the winter months, the clearing of post frontal cloudiness is materially delayed. Windflows from the northwest quadrant are nearly always associated with the formation of heavy fogs at Kanawha Airport during the night and early morning hours of the period, May through October. Conversely, air reaching Charleston from any other direction has followed a primarily downslope path. Consequently, low ceilings at Kanawha Airport are not likely to persist for more than a few hours when the wind is from a quadrant other than northwest, and weather conditions at Kanawha Airport are often considerably better than would otherwise be expected due to this downslope effect. However, due to the increased stability of the lower atmosphere, concentrations of smoke over the city of Charleston and the Kanawha Valley are greater with a light downslope windflow, and visibility to the southwest of the airport under these conditions is often much less than in any other direction.

Normals, Means, and Extremes

Month	Normal Degree days Base 65 °F		Precipitation in inches												Relative humidity pct.			
			Water equivalent							Snow, Ice pellets					Hour 01	Hour 07	Hour 13	Hour 19
	Heating	Cooling	Normal	Maximum monthly	Year	Minimum monthly	Year	Maximum in 24 hrs.	Year	Maximum monthly	Year	Maximum in 24 hrs.	Year		(Local time)			
(a)				28		28		28		28		28			28	28	28	28
J	946	0	3.39	9.11	1950	1.15	1970	1.91	1961	19.8	1966	13.0	1966		74	77	62	65
F	798	0	3.11	6.89	1956	0.64	1968	2.45	1951	21.8	1964	8.3	1960		72	77	59	61
M	642	7	4.03	6.80	1967	1.43	1969	2.86	1967	18.3	1960	9.9	1954		69	75	54	56
A	287	14	3.33	6.46	1965	1.19	1971	2.72	1948	5.9	1959	5.5	1959		68	75	48	50
M	113	97	3.48	6.59	1968	0.95	1964	2.48	1974	0.2	1963	0.2	1963		80	82	50	56
J	10	220	3.31	6.43	1950	0.70	1966	2.24	1962	0.0		0.0			87	86	54	61
J	0	310	5.04	13.54	1961	2.16	1974	5.60	1961	0.0		0.0			90	90	61	67
A	0	267	3.68	10.45	1958	0.66	1957	4.17	1958	0.0		0.0			92	92	58	69
S	46	121	2.94	7.61	1971	0.65	1959	2.40	1956	0.0		0.0			89	91	55	71
O	267	19	2.45	6.11	1961	0.09	1963	2.48	1961	2.8	1961	2.8	1961		84	88	53	66
N	588	0	2.81	6.27	1962	0.64	1965	2.35	1973	25.8	1950	15.1	1950		75	80	56	63
D	893	0	3.18	6.35	1972	0.45	1965	2.10	1948	18.6	1962	11.2	1967		75	78	62	66
YR	4590	1055	40.75	13.54	JUL 1961	0.09	OCT 1963	5.60	JUL 1961	25.8	NOV 1950	15.1	NOV 1950		80	83	56	63

(To better understand these tables, see full explanation of terms beginning on page 322)

Month	Wind					Pct. of possible sunshine	Mean sky cover, tenths, sunrise to sunset	Mean number of days											Average station pressure mb.
			Fastest mile					Sunrise to sunset							Temperatures °F Max.		Min.		
	Mean speed m.p.h.	Prevailing direction	Speed m.p.h.	Direction	Year			Clear	Partly cloudy	Cloudy	Precipitation .01 inch or more	Snow, Ice pellets 1.0 inch or more	Thunderstorms	Heavy fog, visibility ¼ mile or less	(b) 90° and above	32° and below	32° and below	0° and below	Elev. 951 feet m.s.l.
(a)	28	16	26	26			28	28	28	28	28	28	28	28	28	28	28	28	3
J	7.6	WSW	45	25	1951		7.7	4	6	21	15	3	1	5	0	7	22	1	985.3
F	7.9	WSW	40	29	1952		7.5	4	6	18	14	2	1	4	0	4	20	*	983.4
M	8.6	WSW	46	32	1955		7.5	4	8	19	15	1	2	3	0	1	15	0	981.0
A	7.9	SW	45	27	1953		7.1	5	8	17	14	*	4	3	*	0	5	0	982.0
M	6.3	SW	55	25	1953		6.7	5	11	15	13	0	7	9	1	0	*	0	980.3
J	5.6	SW	50	32	1951		6.5	4	14	12	11	0	7	13	5	0	0	0	982.2
J	5.0	S	46	29	1957		6.7	4	13	14	13	0	10	17	7	0	0	0	983.2
A	4.5	S	50	29	1952		6.5	4	15	12	10	0	6	20	5	0	0	0	984.9
S	4.8	S	35	20	1956		6.3	6	12	12	9	0	3	17	2	0	0	0	985.0
O	5.3	S	45	25	1950		5.9	9	10	12	9	*	1	12	*	0	3	0	986.9
N	6.9	SW	40	29	1954		7.2	5	7	18	12	1	1	5	0	1	13	0	985.3
D	7.2	SW	55	25	1953		7.6	4	7	20	14	2	*	5	0	4	21	*	984.3
YR	6.5	SW	55	25	DEC 1953		6.9	58	117	190	149	9	43	112	21	17	100	1	983.7

FOOTNOTES

Means and extremes above are from existing and comparable exposures. Annual extremes have been exceeded at other sites in the locality as follows: Highest temperature 108 in July 1931; lowest temperature -17 in December 1917 (early records which were maintained irregularly show -24 in January 1857); minimum monthly precipitation 0.00 in October 1897.

Station: MADISON, WISCONSIN
TRUAX FIELD
Elevation (ground): 858 feet

TEMPERATURES °F

Month	Normal			Extremes			
	Daily maximum	Daily minimum	Monthly	Record highest	Year	Record lowest	Year
(a)				16		16	
J	25.4	8.2	16.8	54	1967	-30	1963
F	29.5	11.1	20.3	56	1962	-23	1965
M	39.2	21.2	30.2	78	1967	-29	1962
A	56.0	34.6	45.3	87	1962	9	1972
M	67.3	44.6	56.0	93	1975	20	1966
J	76.9	54.6	65.8	95	1971	31	1972
J	81.4	58.8	70.1	98	1965	36	1965
A	80.0	57.3	68.7	95	1964	35	1968
S	70.9	48.5	59.7	90	1973	25	1974
O	60.9	38.9	49.9	90	1975	15	1972
N	43.0	26.4	34.7	76	1964	1	1964
D	29.8	14.0	21.9	62	1970	-22	1962
YR	55.0	34.8	44.9	98	JUL 1965	-30	JAN 1963

IMPORTANT:
The time-period covered by this record is limited: See footnotes on next page for explanation and for additional history of EXTREME HIGHS AND LOWS recorded in the general area.

Madison is set on a narrow isthmus of land between Lakes Mendota and Monona. Lake Mendota (15 sq. mi.) lies northwest of Lake Monona (5 sq. mi.) and the lakes are only two-thirds of a mile apart at one point. Drainage at Madison is southeast through two other lakes into the Rock River, which flows south into Illinois, and then west to the Mississippi. The westward flowing Wisconsin River is only 20 miles northwest of Madison. Madison lakes are normally frozen from December 17 to April 5.

Madison has the typical continental climate of interior North America with a large annual temperature range and with frequent short period temperature changes. The absolute temperature range is from 107 degrees (City Office) to -37 degrees (Truax Field). Winter temperatures (December-February) average 20 degrees and the summer average (June-August) is 68 degrees. Daily mean temperatures average below 32 degrees for 118 days and above 42 degrees for 206 days of the year.
Madison lies in the path of the frequent cyclones and anticyclones which move eastward over this area during fall, winter and spring. In summer, the cyclones have diminished intensity and tend to pass farther north. The most frequent airmasses are of polar origin. Occasional outbreaks of arctic air affect this area during the winter months. Although northward moving tropical airmasses contribute considerable cloudiness and precipitation, the true gulf airmass does not reach this area in winter, and only occasionally at other seasons. Summers are pleasant, with only occasional periods of extreme heat or high humidity.

There are no dry and wet seasons, but 59 percent of the annual precipitation falls in the 5 months of May through September. Cold season precipitation is lighter, but lasts longer. Soil moisture is usually adequate in the first part of the growing season. During July, August and September, the crops depend on current rainfall, which is mostly from thunderstorms and tends to be erratic and variable. Average occurrence of thunderstorms is just under 7 days per month during this period.

March and November are the windiest months. Tornadoes are infrequent. The average occurrence for Dane County is about one tornado in every three to five years.

The ground is covered with an inch or more of snow about 60 percent of the time from December 10 to February 25 in an average winter. The soil is usually frozen from the first of December through most of March with an average frost penetration of 25 to 30 inches. The growing season averages 175 days. The most probable period (50 percent of the years) for the last crop damaging freeze in spring is April 17 to May 2. The first frost/freeze in autumn is most probable from October 6 to 25. The latest recorded killing freeze was on June 10, 1972 and the earliest in fall was on September 12, 1955.

Farming is diversified with the main emphasis on dairying. Field crops are mainly corn, oats, clover and alfalfa, but barley, wheat, rye, and tobacco are also raised. Canning factories pack peas, sweet corn and lima beans. Fruits are mainly apples, strawberries and raspberries.

MADISON, WISCONSIN

Normals, Means, and Extremes

Month	Normal Degree days Base 65 °F: Heating	Cooling	Precipitation in inches, Water equivalent: Normal	Maximum monthly	Year	Minimum monthly	Year	Maximum in 24 hrs.	Year	Snow, Ice pellets: Maximum monthly	Year	Maximum in 24 hrs.	Year
(a)				36		36		27		27		27	
J	1494	0	1.25	2.45	1974	0.19	1961	1.27	1960	21.9	1971	11.6	1971
F	1252	0	0.95	2.77	1953	0.08	1958	1.55	1953	20.9	1975	10.3	1950
M	1079	0	1.93	5.04	1973	0.38	1958	2.52	1973	25.4	1959	13.6	1971
A	591	0	2.66	7.11	1973	0.96	1946	2.83	1975	17.4	1973	12.9	1973
M	297	18	3.41	6.26	1960	0.98	1971	3.64	1966	0.7	1966	0.7	1966
J	72	96	4.33	8.15	1963	0.81	1973	3.67	1963	0.0		0.0	
J	14	172	3.81	10.93	1950	1.38	1946	5.25	1950	0.0		0.0	
A	39	154	3.05	7.47	1972	0.70	1948	2.90	1965	0.0		0.0	
S	173	14	3.36	9.51	1941	0.49	1952	3.57	1961	T	1965	T	1965
O	474	6	2.16	5.55	1959	0.06	1952	2.01	1960	0.9	1967	0.9	1967
N	909	0	1.87	3.94	1961	0.34	1962	2.32	1971	8.9	1954	6.8	1954
D	1336	0	1.47	3.64	1971	0.25	1960	1.66	1971	20.8	1970	16.0	1970
YR	7730	460	30.25	10.93	JUL 1950	0.06	OCT 1952	5.25	JUL 1950	25.4	MAR 1959	16.0	DFC 1970

Month	Relative humidity pct. Hour 00 (Local time)	Hour 06	Hour 12	Hour 18	Wind: Mean speed m.p.h.	Prevailing direction	Fastest mile: Speed m.p.h.	Direction	Year	Pct. of possible sunshine	Mean sky cover, tenths, sunrise to sunset
(a)	16	16	16	16	29	14	29	29		29	27
J	77	78	69	73	10.5	WNW	68	E	1947	48	6.8
F	77	79	66	69	10.6	WNW	57	W	1948	52	6.5
M	78	81	64	67	11.3	NW	70	SW	1954	54	6.9
A	76	81	56	57	11.6	NW	73	SW	1947	52	6.8
M	77	80	55	56	10.4	S	77	SW	1950	58	6.5
J	81	83	57	57	9.2	S	59	W	1947	64	6.1
J	85	86	57	58	8.2	S	72	NW	1951	69	5.6
A	87	90	59	62	8.1	S	47	W	1955	68	5.6
S	88	92	61	69	8.8	S	52	W	1948	62	5.7
O	81	86	59	67	9.6	S	73	SW	1951	57	5.7
N	83	86	68	76	10.8	S	56	SE	1947	40	7.2
D	82	83	73	78	10.2	W	65	SW	1949	39	7.2
YR	81	84	62	66	9.9	S	77	SW	MAY 1950	57	6.4

Month	Mean number of days: Sunrise to sunset: Clear	Partly cloudy	Cloudy	Precipitation .01 inch or more	Snow, Ice pellets 1.0 inch or more	Thunderstorms	Heavy fog, visibility ¼ mile or less	Temperatures °F Max. (b) 90° and above	Max. 32° and below	Min. 32° and below	Min. 0° and below	Average station pressure mb. Elev. 866 feet m.s.l.
(a)	29	29	29	27	27	27	29	16	16	16	16	3
J	8	6	17	10	2	*	3	0	20	30	11	984.9
F	7	6	15	8	2	*	2	0	16	28	7	985.7
M	6	8	17	11	3	2	3	0	7	27	2	983.0
A	6	8	16	11	1	4	1	0	*	15	0	983.1
M	7	9	15	12	0	6	1	*	0	4	0	980.7
J	7	10	13	11	0	7	1	3	0	*	0	981.3
J	9	12	10	9	0	7	1	4	0	0	0	984.1
A	10	11	10	9	0	6	2	3	0	0	0	985.4
S	10	8	12	9	0	4	1	1	0	1	0	986.7
O	10	8	13	9	0	2	2	*	*	9	0	986.8
N	6	6	18	9	1	1	2	0	3	21	0	984.3
D	6	6	19	10	3	*	3	0	18	29	6	985.5
YR	92	98	175	117	12	41	22	11	65	163	25	984.3

FOOTNOTES

Means and extremes above are from existing and comparable exposures. Annual extremes have been exceeded at other sites in the locality as follows: Highest temperature 107 in July 1936; lowest temperature -37 in January 1951; minimum monthly precipitation T in October 1889 and earlier; maximum precipitation in 24 hours 5.31 in September 1941; maximum monthly snowfall 31.8 in January 1929.

Snowfall

Season	July	Aug	Sept	Oct	Nov	Dec	Jan
1936-37	0.0	0.0	0.0	0.0	1.4	6.2	6.6
1937-38	0.0	0.0	0.0	T	4.1	3.6	11.8
1938-39	0.0	0.0	0.0	T	1.9	5.6	7.0
1939-40	0.0	0.0	0.0	T	T	T	12.7
1940-41	0.0	0.0	0.0	0.0	14.9	3.5	7.5
1941-42	0.0	0.0	0.0	0.0	0.5	10.8	10.4
1942-43	0.0	0.0	T	T	4.4	7.5	25.8
1943-44	0.0	0.0	0.0	T	2.4	T	3.1
1944-45	0.0	0.0	0.0	0.0	2.9	16.1	7.8
1945-46	0.0	0.0	0.0	0.0	10.3	10.8	7.5
1946-47	0.0	0.0	0.0	0.0	0.6	7.1	19.4
#1947-48	0.0	0.0	0.0	0.0	13.4	5.3	7.9
1948-49	0.0	0.0	0.0	0.0	0.9	4.3	12.7
1949-50	0.0	0.0	0.0	0.0	2.7	6.9	2.3
1950-51	0.0	0.0	0.0	0.0	3.7	18.7	19.7
1951-52	0.0	0.0	0.0	0.7	8.6	15.1	12.2
1952-53	0.0	0.0	0.0	0.8	1.4	9.5	7.6
1953-54	0.0	0.0	0.0	0.0	2.2	4.7	8.0
1954-55	0.0	0.0	0.0	T	8.9	13.1	2.6
1955-56	0.0	0.0	0.0	T	3.1	2.8	3.9
1956-57	0.0	0.0	0.0	0.0	2.0	9.4	6.6
1957-58	0.0	0.0	0.0	T	2.3	6.8	6.1
1958-59	0.0	0.0	0.0	0.0	3.2	4.8	18.9
1959-60	0.0	0.0	0.0	T	8.7	12.4	9.0
1960-61	0.0	0.0	0.0	0.0	2.7	0.6	2.1
1961-62	0.0	0.0	0.0	0.1	1.4	12.0	10.0
1962-63	0.0	0.0	0.0	0.2	1.0	6.4	12.0
1963-64	0.0	0.0	0.0	0.0	0.1	8.2	1.4
1964-65	0.0	0.0	0.0	0.5	3.7	3.5	18.3
1965-66	0.0	0.0	T	0.0	T	5.7	9.6
1966-67	0.0	0.0	0.0	T	0.1	10.1	9.4
1967-68	0.0	0.0	0.0	0.9	0.7	2.4	3.9
1968-69	0.0	0.0	0.0	0.0	0.5	11.4	9.7
1969-70	0.0	0.0	0.0	0.0	1.0	19.5	6.4
1970-71	0.0	0.0	0.0	0.0	0.2	20.8	21.9
1971-72	0.0	0.0	0.0	0.0	8.8	8.9	3.6
1972-73	0.0	0.0	0.0	T	1.3	16.3	1.9
1973-74	0.0	0.0	0.0	0.0	0.4	10.9	10.5
1974-75	0.0	0.0	0.0	0.0	3.0	15.4	5.2
1975-76	0.0	0.0	0.0	0.0	5.5	2.8	
RECORD MEAN	0.0	0.0	T	0.1	2.9	9.6	8.7

Heating Degree Days

Season	July	Aug	Sept	Oct	Nov	Dec	Jan
1955-56	0	4	133	412	998	1398	1357
1956-57	10	20	169	285	870	1216	1605
1957-58	1	17	197	535	883	1142	1360
1958-59	12	26	137	371	814	1499	1684
#1959-60	6	0	137	566	1129	1046	1355
1960-61	23	23	134	484	816	1361	1484
1961-62	11	18	188	444	876	1426	1630
1962-63	23	11	252	414	884	1376	1850
1963-64	2	47	174	228	769	1660	1237
1964-65	13	68	216	556	789	1427	1517
1965-66	27	69	231	486	878	1086	1702
1966-67	11	40	252	533	862	1290	1321
1967-68	61	120	239	535	955	1229	1401
1968-69	34	66	159	460	873	1305	1548
1969-70	13	9	202	579	951	1346	1705
1970-71	28	18	196	431	853	1310	1718
1971-72	28	21	131	293	885	1179	1616
1972-73	44	42	188	587	905	1475	1279
1973-74	4	25	180	349	847	1342	1416
1974-75	1	37	253	443	829	1179	1329
1975-76	18	11	236	412	687	1217	

Cooling Degree Days

Year	Jan	Feb	Mar	Apr	May	June	July
1969	0	0	0	0	25	39	161
1970	0	0	0	12	47	125	210
1971	0	0	0	0	13	229	144
1972	0	0	0	0	41	61	156
1973	0	0	0	0	2	112	215
1974	0	0	0	9	17	68	228
1975	0	0	0	0	81	176	256

Feb	Mar	Apr	May	June	Total
4.4	9.9	T	0.0	0.0	28.5
4.3	2.9	1.3	0.0	0.0	28.0
7.3	12.3	0.2	0.0	0.0	34.3
12.3	8.0	2.1	0.8	0.0	35.9
2.6	12.6	T	0.0	0.0	41.1
5.0	0.9	T	T	0.0	27.6
3.1	12.7	T	0.0	0.0	53.5
6.0	11.4	0.1	0.0	0.0	23.0
9.4	0.4	T	2.7	0.0	39.3
7.5	9.6	0.0	T	0.0	45.7
1.2	6.8	2.0	T	0.0	37.1
6.5	18.2	T	0.0	0.0	51.3
9.3	1.8	3.2	0.0	0.0	32.2
12.4	11.5	0.7	0.0	0.0	36.5
8.7	7.1	1.2	0.0	0.0	59.1
7.6	12.6	0.4	0.0	0.0	57.2
2.2	6.2	0.3	0.0	0.0	28.0
2.1	3.6	T	T	0.0	20.6
7.5	7.1	0.0	0.0	0.0	39.2
5.4	14.3	0.4	0.0	0.0	29.9
1.1	9.0	2.6	0.0	0.0	30.7
1.1	5.2	0.4	0.0	0.0	21.9
14.6	25.4	0.4	0.0	0.0	67.3
12.3	8.0	1.8	T	0.0	52.2
0.4	13.1	3.2	0.0	0.0	22.1
16.1	7.0	2.7	0.0	0.0	49.3
4.1	12.8	0.7	T	0.0	37.2
3.7	17.4	0.3	0.0	0.0	31.1
4.7	19.4	0.8	0.0	0.0	50.9
3.8	5.5	0.1	0.7	0.0	25.4
13.9	4.5	T	T	0.0	38.0
3.9	0.5	0.4	0.0	0.0	12.7
1.7	10.1	T	T	0.0	33.4
1.7	7.0	1.9	0.0	0.0	37.5
3.7	20.1	0.7	0.0	0.0	67.4
6.3	18.8	3.9	0.0	0.0	50.3
6.0	1.1	17.4	T	0.0	44.0
14.1	6.6	0.4	T	0.0	42.9
20.9	10.0	5.9	0.0	0.0	60.4
7.0	9.8	1.8	T	0.0	39.9

Average Temperature

Year	Jan	Feb	Mar	Apr	May	June	July	Aug	Sept	Oct	Nov	Dec	Annual
1940	11.0	22.6	27.4	43.4	54.6	68.1	74.0	69.4	61.7	53.2	33.4	25.8	45.4
1941	22.0	19.4	28.0	51.4	61.9	68.0	73.0	71.5	64.1	52.1	39.2	30.2	48.4
1942	19.0	20.4	37.0	51.7	56.3	67.0	71.0	69.6	59.3	50.9	36.6	17.6	46.4
1943	16.1	21.6	27.0	44.2	55.2	69.8	74.4	72.0	57.6	49.5	32.0	24.4	45.3
1944	27.0	24.4	28.6	42.6	62.6	70.0	71.2	71.6	63.5	49.8	39.8	17.4	47.4
1945	14.6	22.1	44.6	46.8	52.2	62.2	69.6	69.8	60.4	47.9	35.5	17.4	45.3
1946	21.7	23.3	42.3	49.9	55.5	66.8	72.2	68.6	61.5	54.4	37.6	25.7	48.3
1947	23.1	17.0	30.4	44.4	52.6	63.8	70.4	77.8	64.3	59.8	30.6	24.2	46.5
1948	13.2	19.5	30.3	50.9	55.2	66.8	73.8	72.4	65.6	48.2	39.5	24.8	46.7
1949	20.8	19.9	32.8	46.4	59.3	70.9	75.2	72.0	56.8	53.6	36.9	25.4	47.5
1950	20.7	21.0	27.7	39.5	57.9	66.7	69.7	66.2	60.9	54.7	30.8	15.8	44.3
1951	13.7	19.8	28.7	43.9	60.9	64.2	70.8	67.0	58.8	50.0	28.2	20.3	43.9
1952	20.5	27.2	29.5	49.4	57.4	69.7	74.1	68.8	61.8	44.2	39.1	27.4	47.4
1953	22.8	25.0	33.8	43.0	58.2	70.5	73.1	72.5	62.4	55.3	40.5	27.8	48.7
1954	19.8	32.9	31.5	49.4	53.2	71.0	73.1	69.2	62.9	50.5	37.9	23.9	47.9
1955	18.9	20.7	30.6	53.1	60.2	65.5	78.1	75.7	63.0	51.5	31.5	19.6	47.4
1956	21.0	22.4	30.0	43.6	57.0	71.8	70.0	70.7	59.8	55.8	35.7	25.7	47.0
1957	13.1	27.4	33.2	47.9	55.3	67.5	73.1	69.8	59.2	47.4	35.3	27.9	46.4
1958	20.9	17.0	34.0	46.8	58.4	62.7	69.4	71.1	61.5	52.8	37.6	16.4	45.7
#1959	10.6	16.3	29.3	46.3	62.9	69.0	71.0	74.5	63.7	46.5	27.1	31.1	45.7
1960	21.1	19.7	18.4	48.1	55.2	63.8	67.8	69.3	64.3	49.2	37.5	20.8	44.6
1961	16.9	28.3	33.8	40.6	54.0	66.4	69.9	69.4	61.7	50.5	35.6	18.8	45.5
1962	12.4	17.0	29.5	45.0	61.4	66.7	67.3	69.8	57.1	51.9	35.4	20.4	44.5
1963	5.4	14.1	34.0	47.8	55.4	69.6	73.1	67.6	60.2	58.1	39.2	11.3	44.6
1964	24.9	24.9	30.8	47.5	62.6	68.5	73.1	66.9	59.6	46.9	38.6	18.8	46.9
1965	15.9	18.7	25.0	43.7	59.6	64.2	68.3	66.7	58.3	49.2	35.6	29.8	44.6
1966	10.0	21.3	35.4	42.0	50.3	66.6	71.1	66.2	57.1	47.7	36.0	23.2	43.9
1967	22.2	14.7	33.3	45.6	50.2	66.2	67.1	62.0	57.6	48.0	33.0	25.1	43.7
1968	19.6	19.0	39.2	47.8	54.3	66.2	68.9	68.8	60.1	50.7	35.6	22.6	46.1
1969	14.8	23.6	27.9	47.0	56.4	59.5	69.6	70.3	59.5	46.4	33.1	21.3	44.1
1970	9.9	20.1	31.1	47.9	58.5	66.5	70.6	68.5	60.0	51.0	36.3	22.4	45.2
1971	9.6	19.9	28.6	45.4	55.1	71.7	68.5	68.3	65.1	55.9	35.2	26.8	45.9
1972	12.7	16.5	28.7	41.3	59.2	62.8	68.3	69.2	59.4	45.8	34.6	17.3	43.0
1973	23.4	24.0	41.6	44.9	54.4	67.9	71.6	70.6	60.7	54.1	36.6	21.5	47.6
1974	19.2	18.4	33.1	48.7	54.1	64.0	72.1	66.8	57.4	50.5	37.1	26.8	45.7
1975	21.9	21.3	26.1	41.0	62.5	69.2	72.4	70.6	57.5	52.2	41.9	25.5	46.8
RECORD MEAN	17.5	21.1	31.5	46.1	57.0	67.0	71.3	69.8	60.7	51.0	35.7	22.8	46.0
MAX	26.3	30.4	40.8	57.4	69.1	79.0	83.6	81.9	72.6	62.6	44.2	30.9	56.6
MIN	8.6	11.8	22.1	34.7	44.8	54.9	59.0	57.6	48.7	39.4	27.2	14.7	35.3

# Indicates a station move or relocation of instruments.

MADISON, WI

Feb	Mar	Apr	May	June	Total
1229	1076	637	281	30	7555
1047	977	512	302	47	7060
1339	955	545	221	104	7299
1357	1098	557	152	32	7739
1305	1440	513	296	77	7870
1018	959	726	352	62	7442
1337	1093	601	185	54	7863
1420	957	508	299	48	8042
1156	1052	519	133	76	7053
1294	1234	631	208	79	8032
1220	911	684	454	83	7831
1407	978	574	462	46	7776
1327	792	510	330	76	7575
1152	1143	535	282	197	7754
1252	1044	521	244	73	7939
1258	1124	582	312	22	7852
1401	1119	705	212	117	7707
1143	720	596	325	15	7319
1298	979	494	347	90	7371
1220	1198	714	150	43	7396

Aug	Sept	Oct	Nov	Dec	Total
179	45	11	0	0	460
133	53	4	0	0	584
131	140	20	0	0	677
180	27	0	0	0	465
207	58	19	0	0	613
102	31	2	0	0	457
190	18	21	0	0	742

Precipitation

Year	Jan	Feb	Mar	Apr	May	June	July	Aug	Sept	Oct	Nov	Dec	Annual
1940	0.94	0.76	1.03	2.40	2.70	5.04	2.88	6.76	0.81	2.39	2.49	1.21	29.41
1941	2.33	0.40	1.92	1.16	6.21	4.88	3.02	2.79	9.51	4.09	0.51	1.74	38.56
1942	1.35	0.39	0.95	1.14	4.34	3.40	3.52	1.15	6.87	1.64	2.71	1.82	29.28
1943	2.07	0.51	2.70	1.99	2.51	3.70	2.71	2.69	2.04	1.70	0.95	0.98	24.55
1944	1.24	1.69	2.34	2.60	2.22	5.05	2.23	2.48	2.59	0.25	3.29	1.03	27.01
1945	0.42	1.07	1.27	3.02	4.47	3.55	1.61	4.36	4.06	0.52	3.12	1.07	28.54
1946	1.89	0.47	2.09	0.96	2.12	4.00	1.38	2.29	4.46	1.78	1.89	1.48	24.81
1947	1.97	0.12	1.33	4.86	4.20	6.45	2.81	2.58	3.92	1.36	2.53	1.37	33.50
1948	0.49	2.13	2.86	2.97	2.90	2.55	2.55	0.70	1.87	1.29	3.56	1.75	25.62
1949	1.97	1.26	2.35	1.10	2.22	6.43	5.76	2.20	1.12	1.86	1.04	1.70	29.01
1950	2.43	1.65	2.34	2.67	3.43	6.24	10.93	2.69	2.09	1.23	1.04	1.97	38.71
1951	1.44	1.70	2.13	4.42	3.00	2.55	3.08	3.08	2.56	5.38	2.17	1.47	32.98
1952	2.21	0.60	2.92	1.21	3.18	4.08	7.60	4.73	0.49	0.06	2.94	1.67	31.69
1953	0.64	2.77	2.58	3.12	1.02	5.15	4.28	3.49	2.11	1.81	0.52	2.17	29.66
1954	0.76	0.63	1.19	4.09	2.98	7.36	5.73	2.78	3.82	3.72	0.81	1.20	35.07
1955	0.65	1.67	0.96	3.65	2.10	2.78	3.93	1.55	0.80	3.24	0.57	0.59	22.49
1956	0.43	1.00	2.53	3.54	5.11	3.24	4.50	5.64	1.42	0.31	2.78	1.01	31.51
1957	0.41	0.38	1.19	2.40	5.80	6.41	4.00	4.86	0.95	2.14	2.91	1.41	32.86
1958	0.52	0.08	0.38	2.73	3.93	2.16	1.69	2.06	2.44	2.50	2.29	0.31	21.09
1959	1.40	1.58	2.90	4.01	3.06	3.86	4.12	5.68	3.44	5.55	2.29	2.45	40.34
1960	2.19	1.14	1.93	4.02	6.26	2.09	6.04	6.18	3.90	3.32	1.47	0.25	38.79
1961	0.19	1.01	3.42	1.33	1.17	1.84	3.67	1.78	7.92	3.75	3.94	1.02	31.04
1962	1.12	1.39	1.73	1.43	3.01	2.09	4.39	2.04	1.31	1.68	0.34	0.90	21.43
1963	0.76	0.39	2.33	1.67	1.82	8.15	2.29	3.23	2.30	0.64	1.96	0.65	26.19
1964	0.93	0.26	2.12	3.15	3.87	2.28	4.28	2.52	1.85	0.08	1.94	0.34	23.62
1965	1.80	0.74	2.51	2.94	1.86	2.31	3.30	6.77	9.22	1.69	1.96	2.50	37.60
1966	1.07	1.36	2.11	1.54	4.31	2.91	3.24	3.83	0.51	1.65	1.28	2.62	26.43
1967	1.63	1.17	1.49	2.57	3.53	6.46	2.51	2.71	2.68	5.52	1.83	1.89	33.99
1968	0.56	0.49	0.59	4.18	2.02	7.82	2.54	2.58	4.45	0.85	1.74	2.89	30.71
1969	2.26	0.18	1.47	2.72	3.45	7.96	4.28	0.96	1.35	2.65	0.70	1.66	29.64
1970	0.44	0.16	1.17	2.53	6.09	2.26	2.42	0.97	8.82	2.65	1.06	2.12	30.69
1971	1.48	2.59	1.52	2.42	0.98	2.27	1.65	3.96	1.87	1.30	3.48	3.64	27.16
1972	0.40	0.42	2.23	2.02	2.83	1.65	3.49	7.47	5.26	2.42	0.86	1.91	30.96
1973	1.54	1.20	5.04	7.11	5.27	0.81	2.68	2.53	3.59	2.30	1.48	1.98	35.53
1974	2.45	1.17	3.43	4.24	5.77	3.86	2.69	4.60	1.08	3.18	1.79	1.80	36.06
1975	0.98	1.54	3.09	4.19	4.57	4.30	6.05	5.25	0.84	0.64	2.79	0.29	34.53
RECORD MEAN	1.26	1.00	2.06	2.84	3.45	4.11	3.72	3.39	3.18	2.14	1.92	1.52	30.59

Record mean values above are means through the current year for the period beginning in 1940 for temperature and precipitation, 1949 for snowfall. Temperature and precipitation are from the Airport location. Heating degree days and snowfall are from the City Office through June 1948 and from the Airport location thereafter.

MILWAUKEE, WISCONSIN

The climate of Milwaukee is influenced by the general storms which move eastward across the upper Ohio River valley and the Great Lakes region. Large high pressure systems moving southeastward out of Canada also have a pronounced effect on the Milwaukee climate and it is seldom that a period of more than 2 or 3 days will pass without a distinct change in the weather, particularly during the winter and spring months. Some of the most severe snowstorms, which produce in excess of 10 inches, develop near the Oklahoma Panhandle and pass across northern Indiana about 140 miles south of Milwaukee. Winds shifting to the northwest at upper levels behind one of the Panhandle storms will frequently set the stage for a secondary storm to move rapidly southeastward from Alberta, Canada, to the vicinity of southern Wisconsin. These storms can produce in excess of 6 inches of snow in Milwaukee, however their low water content make them relatively easy to plow by comparison to the Panhandle storms which derive much of their moisture from the Gulf of Mexico source region.

Milwaukee's climate is influenced to a considerable extent by Lake Michigan. This is especially true in the spring, summer, and fall months when the temperature of Lake water differs considerably from the air temperature. During the spring and early summer, a shift of wind from a westerly to an easterly direction frequently causes a sudden 10° to 15° drop in temperatures. In the autumn, the relatively warm water of the Lake prevents nighttime temperatures from falling as low as they do a few miles inland from the shoreline.

The following averages and extremes are based upon the combined weather records made at the former city office in downtown Milwaukee and those made at General Mitchell Field, covering a period from 1871 through 1970.

Milwaukee's annual average temperature for the period of record, 1871 through 1970, was 46.4°. Monthly temperatures average from 20.9° in January to 70.7° in July. The highest temperature ever recorded in the City was 105° on July 24, 1934, and the lowest was -25° on January 9, 1875. The City has an average of 13 days per year when the temperature reaches zero or lower and 132 days when it reaches 32° or lower. Minima of 0° have been recorded as late as March 25, and 32° as late as May 27 in the spring. In the autumn, a low of 32° has been recorded as early as September 20, and 0° as early as November 21. The average number of days per year with the temperature reaching 90° or higher is 8. Consecutive days with readings of 90° or higher seldom exceed 3, although there have been as many as 10.

The average annual precipitation is about 30 inches. About two-thirds of the annual amount occurs during the growing season. Since 1841, the wettest year was 1876 with 50.36 inches, and the driest year was 1901

Station: MILWAUKEE, WISCONSIN
GENERAL MITCHELL FIELD
Elevation (ground): 672 feet

TEMPERATURES °F

	Normal			Extremes			
Month	Daily maximum	Daily minimum	Monthly	Record highest	Year	Record lowest	Year
(a)				16		16	
J	27.3	11.4	19.4	57	1967	-24	1963
F	30.3	14.6	22.5	51	1961	-15	1971
M	39.4	23.4	31.4	77	1967	-10	1962
A	54.6	34.7	44.7	85	1962	13	1971
M	65.0	43.3	54.2	92	1975	21	1966
J	75.3	53.6	64.5	95	1965	36	1969
J	80.4	59.3	69.9	98	1963	40	1965
A	79.7	58.7	69.2	99	1973	44	1965
S	71.5	50.7	61.1	94	1973	28	1974
O	61.4	40.6	51.0	89	1963	21	1960
N	44.4	28.5	36.5	74	1964	6	1964
D	31.5	16.8	24.2	63	1970	-15	1963
YR	55.1	36.3	45.7	99	AUG 1973	-24	JAN 1963

IMPORTANT:
The time-period covered by this record is limited: See footnotes following table of NORMALS, MEANS AND EXTREMES for explanation and for additional history of EXTREME HIGHS AND LOWS recorded in the general area.

(Continued)

with 18.69 inches. The long- term average annual snowfall is about 46 inches, but it varies considerably from season to season. During the winter of 1884-85 the snowfall totaled only 11 inches. The 1967-68 season produced 12 inches.

Thunderstorms occur less frequently and with less severity in the Milwaukee area than in areas to the south and west. Hail size is generally ½ inch or less, although it has been noted as large as 2 inches in diameter with unusually severe storms. The maximum rainfall which has occurred in a 24 - hour period is 5.76 inches in June 1917. As much as 0.79 inch has fallen in 5 minutes, 1.11 inches in 10 minutes, 1.34 inches in 15 minutes, 1.86 inches in 30 minutes, and 2.25 inches in 1 hour.

There are about twice as many cloudy days during the winter as there are during the summer. The average percentage of possible sunshine ranges from 40 percent in December to 70 percent in July.

The city office of the Weather Bureau was located in the Federal Building from April 22, 1899 to May 1, 1954, ½ mile from the Lake Michigan shore and ¼ mile from the Milwaukee River. Thermometers and precipitation gages were located on the roof of the building, more than 100 feet above ground.

The airport office is presently located on the second floor of the FAA/National Weather Service Office Building about 600 feet northwest of the Airport Terminal Building at General Mitchell Field. Hygrothermometers and wind equipment are located at the runway intersection. Precipitation gages are located on a ground- level instrument plot in close proximity to the Weather Service Office. The present location is the 4th one at General Mitchell Field and is approximately 3 miles west of the Lake Michigan shore. Lake breeze fronts reach the station much less frequently than at the downtown location, perhaps 2 or 3 times a month in the spring, summer and fall seasons.

MILWAUKEE, WISCONSIN

Normals, Means, and Extremes

(To better understand these tables, see full explanation of terms beginning on page 322)

Month	Normal Degree days Base 65 °F: Heating	Normal Degree days: Cooling	Precipitation in inches, Water equivalent: Normal	Maximum monthly	Year	Minimum monthly	Year	Maximum in 24 hrs.	Year	Snow, Ice pellets: Maximum monthly	Year	Maximum in 24 hrs.	Year
(a)				35		35		35		35		35	
J	1414	0	1.63	4.04	1960	0.31	1961	1.71	1960	28.4	1943	12.8	1962
F	1190	0	1.13	3.10	1974	0.05	1969	1.67	1960	42.0	1974	16.7	1960
M	1042	0	2.24	4.29	1974	0.31	1968	2.57	1960	26.7	1965	11.2	1961
A	609	0	2.76	7.31	1973	0.81	1942	3.04	1973	15.8	1973	11.6	1973
M	348	13	2.88	5.27	1945	0.90	1971	2.06	1948	0.4	1960	0.4	1960
J	90	75	3.58	8.28	1954	0.85	1965	3.13	1950	0.0		0.0	
J	15	167	3.41	7.66	1964	0.95	1946	4.35	1959	0.0		0.0	
A	36	166	2.68	7.07	1960	0.46	1948	4.05	1953	0.0		0.0	
S	140	23	3.02	9.87	1941	0.30	1956	5.28	1941	T	1960	T	1960
O	440	6	1.98	6.42	1959	0.15	1956	2.60	1959	0.8	1967	0.8	1967
N	855	0	2.01	3.37	1958	0.62	1949	2.18	1943	9.6	1951	6.3	1954
D	1265	0	1.75	4.34	1971	0.34	1958	1.93	1942	26.5	1951	11.1	1959
YR	7444	450	29.07	9.87	SEP 1941	0.05	FEB 1969	5.28	SEP 1941	42.0	FEB 1974	16.7	FEB 1960

Month	Relative humidity pct.: Hour 00	Hour 06	Hour 12	Hour 18 (Local time)	Wind: Mean speed m.p.h.	Prevailing direction	Fastest mile: Speed m.p.h.	Direction	Year	Pct. of possible sunshine	Mean sky cover, tenths, sunrise to sunset	Mean number of days, Sunrise to sunset: Clear	Partly cloudy	Cloudy	Precipitation .01 inch or more	Snow, Ice pellets 1.0 inch or more	Thunderstorms	Heavy fog, visibility ¼ mile or less	Temperatures °F Max.: 90° and above (b)	Max.: 32° and below	Min.: 32° and below	Min.: 0° and below	Average station pressure mb. Elev. 693 feet m.s.l.
(a)	15	15	15	15	35	14	35	35		35	35	35	35	35	35	35	35	35	15	15	15	15	3
J	74	75	68	72	12.9	WNW	62	W	1950	44	6.8	7	6	18	11	3	*	2	0	20	30	9	991.4
F	74	75	67	70	12.8	WNW	58	NE	1960	47	6.7	7	6	15	9	3	*	2	0	16	27	4	992.0
M	77	80	67	71	13.2	WNW	73	SW	1954	51	6.9	6	8	17	12	3	1	3	0	7	24	*	989.5
A	76	79	63	65	13.2	NNE	66	SW	1947	54	6.6	7	8	15	12	*	4	3	0	*	12	0	989.7
M	76	79	61	62	12.0	NNE	72	SW	1950	59	6.3	7	10	14	12	0	5	3	*	0	2	0	987.4
J	79	82	62	63	10.5	NNE	62	W	1971	63	5.9	8	10	12	11	0	7	3	2	0	0	0	987.6
J	80	82	60	63	9.7	SW	59	W	1952	70	5.2	11	11	9	9	0	6	1	3	0	0	0	990.2
A	84	87	62	67	9.6	SW	50	W	1974	67	5.2	11	11	9	9	0	5	2	3	0	0	0	991.7
S	84	87	63	71	10.7	SSW	62	S	1941	60	5.5	10	9	11	9	0	4	1	1	0	*	0	993.0
O	77	81	63	69	11.5	SSW	60	S	1949	57	5.6	10	9	12	8	0	2	2	0	0	4	0	993.5
N	78	80	67	74	12.8	WNW	72	W	1955	41	7.1	6	6	18	10	1	1	2	0	2	18	0	990.9
D	78	80	73	76	12.5	WNW	62	SW	1948	38	7.2	6	6	19	11	3	*	2	0	16	28	3	992.2
YR	78	81	65	69	11.8	WNW	73	SW	MAR 1954	56	6.3	96	100	169	123	13	36	27	9	62	146	15	990.8

FOOTNOTES

Means and extremes above are from existing and comparable exposures. Annual extremes have been exceeded at other sites in the locality as follows: Highest temperature 105 in July 1934; lowest temperature -25 in January 1875; maximum monthly precipitation 10.03 in June 1917; maximum precipitation in 24 hours 5.76 in June 1917; maximum monthly snowfall 52.6 in January 1918; maximum snowfall in 24 hours 20.3 in February 1924.

Snowfall

Season	July	Aug	Sept	Oct	Nov	Dec	Jan
1936-37	0.0	0.0	0.0	T	0.9	3.5	0.7
1937-38	0.0	0.0	0.0	T	2.0	4.5	7.8
1938-39	0.0	0.0	0.0	T	0.9	4.2	15.7
1939-40	0.0	0.0	0.0	T	T	0.4	9.5
#1940-41	0.0	0.0	0.0	0.0	18.0	1.3	7.4
1941-42	0.0	0.0	0.0	0.0	3.1	8.5	8.1
1942-43	0.0	0.0	T	T	5.1	8.1	28.4
1943-44	0.0	0.0	0.0	0.0	1.6	T	3.0
1944-45	0.0	0.0	0.0	0.0	0.8	12.5	6.4
1945-46	0.0	0.0	0.0	0.0	1.5	11.9	3.5
1946-47	0.0	0.0	0.0	T	0.1	6.8	26.3
1947-48	0.0	0.0	0.0	0.0	9.0	5.2	16.2
1948-49	0.0	0.0	0.0	0.0	0.0	2.8	13.7
#1949-50	0.0	0.0	0.0	0.0	3.1	6.2	3.8
1950-51	0.0	0.0	0.0	0.0	5.8	20.1	27.3
1951-52	0.0	0.0	0.0	0.0	12.4	30.7	15.7
1952-53	0.0	0.0	0.0	T	T	6.3	10.5
#1953-54	0.0	0.0	0.0	0.0	1.3	1.6	6.7
1954-55	0.0	0.0	0.0	T	7.6	17.6	2.8
1955-56	0.0	0.0	0.0	0.0	2.4	5.2	4.4
1956-57	0.0	0.0	0.0	0.0	0.3	10.6	11.2
1957-58	0.0	0.0	0.0	T	0.8	8.0	16.7
1958-59	0.0	0.0	0.0	0.0	2.1	6.9	27.5
1959-60	0.0	0.0	0.0	T	9.3	14.3	19.4
1960-61	0.0	0.0	T	0.2	2.8	2.3	3.9
1961-62	0.0	0.0	0.0	T	2.4	7.7	22.1
1962-63	0.0	0.0	0.0	0.1	0.9	6.5	8.1
1963-64	0.0	0.0	0.0	0.0	T	12.8	3.8
1964-65	0.0	0.0	0.0	T	1.4	8.1	23.6
1965-66	0.0	0.0	0.0	T	T	14.5	24.6
1966-67	0.0	0.0	0.0	0.0	2.0	9.9	13.1
1967-68	0.0	0.0	0.0	0.8	0.4	1.2	4.6
1968-69	0.0	0.0	0.0	0.0	0.3	11.6	11.1
1969-70	0.0	0.0	0.0	T	0.7	14.9	6.0
1970-71	0.0	0.0	0.0	0.0	0.6	19.6	15.8
1971-72	0.0	0.0	0.0	0.0	6.1	2.7	6.8
1972-73	0.0	0.0	0.0	T	3.4	13.7	0.2
1973-74	0.0	0.0	0.0	0.0	T	19.6	14.2
1974-75	0.0	0.0	0.0	T	2.0	9.1	3.5
1975-76	0.0	0.0	0.0	0.0	8.4	12.2	
RECORD MEAN	0.0	0.0	T	T	2.7	10.0	12.0

Heating Degree Days

Season	July	Aug	Sept	Oct	Nov	Dec	Jan
#1955-56	0	3	104	373	939	1308	1234
1956-57	27	18	188	287	840	1139	1544
1957-58	8	8	193	503	848	1087	1330
1958-59	13	16	133	348	768	1429	1594
1959-60	13	0	117	529	1059	999	1259
#1960-61	40	20	142	494	766	1312	1407
1961-62	18	9	134	422	815	1303	1561
1962-63	24	22	227	395	804	1342	1749
1963-64	20	38	135	217	692	1601	1199
1964-65	7	47	177	515	730	1290	1404
1965-66	25	51	149	438	793	987	1579
1966-67	4	41	198	496	804	1249	1249
1967-68	46	53	164	460	888	1112	1333
1968-69	31	23	82	403	799	1214	1434
1969-70	34	5	143	539	913	1228	1600
1970-71	7	7	145	383	823	1259	1615
1971-72	20	37	119	308	824	1097	1518
1972-73	40	32	133	534	859	1381	1242
1973-74	10	5	111	324	788	1218	1340
1974-75	0	20	237	461	786	1103	1260
1975-76	17	4	203	353	610	1144	

Cooling Degree Days

Year	Jan	Feb	Mar	Apr	May	June	July
1969	0	0	0	0	24	38	126
1970	0	0	0	4	29	119	270
1971	0	0	0	0	0	148	120
1972	0	0	0	0	3	42	180
1973	0	0	0	0	0	140	216
1974	0	0	0	3	6	36	210
1975	0	0	0	0	30	98	230

	Feb	Mar	Apr	May	June	Total
	1.9	13.2	T	0.0	0.0	20.2
	2.9	3.8	0.3	0.0	0.0	21.3
	5.8	10.1	0.6	0.0	0.0	37.3
	14.8	15.1	2.5	T	0.0	42.3
	2.7	4.3	T	0.0	0.0	33.7
	6.4	1.8	T	0.0	0.0	27.9
	3.5	9.4	T	0.0	0.0	54.5
	9.3	7.1	T	0.0	0.0	21.0
	6.7	T	T	T	0.0	26.4
	7.8	5.4	0.0	0.0	0.0	30.1
	5.2	9.4	0.9	T	0.0	48.7
	6.1	12.6	T	0.0	0.0	49.1
	9.5	3.7	0.3	0.0	0.0	30.0
	8.6	14.9	5.1	0.0	0.0	41.7
	10.3	15.0	0.8	T	0.0	79.3
	8.2	22.1	1.7	0.0	0.0	90.8
	1.7	6.5	T	0.0	0.0	25.0
	4.9	3.3	T	T	0.0	17.8
	6.7	4.4	0.0	0.0	0.0	39.1
	9.9	11.7	0.1	0.0	0.0	33.7
	3.0	9.0	0.3	0.0	0.0	34.4
	1.6	4.8	T	0.0	0.0	31.9
	10.8	14.5	1.5	0.0	0.0	63.3
	34.0	14.3	1.6	0.4	0.0	93.3
	2.4	14.3	7.0	0.0	0.0	32.9
	22.2	11.4	4.0	0.0	0.0	69.8
	6.4	7.1	T	T	0.0	29.1
	5.7	19.8	T	0.0	0.0	42.1
	10.1	26.7	4.1	0.0	0.0	74.0
	7.7	2.8	1.3	0.1	0.0	51.0
	27.1	7.4	T	T	0.0	59.5
	3.5	1.2	0.4	0.0	0.0	12.1
	0.7	6.2	0.0	T	0.0	29.9
	2.0	10.7	5.2	0.0	0.0	39.5
	2.5	18.1	0.7	T	0.0	57.3
	10.2	14.9	1.2	0.0	0.0	41.9
	9.9	1.8	15.8	T	0.0	44.8
	42.0	7.4	T	0.0	0.0	83.2
	12.2	15.1	10.4	0.0	0.0	52.3
						-
	9.1	9.6	1.8	T	0.0	45.2

Average Temperature

Year	Jan	Feb	Mar	Apr	May	June	July	Aug	Sept	Oct	Nov	Dec	Annual
1936	16.2	10.8	36.5	40.8	60.7	62.0	74.8	72.8	66.0	49.8	35.5	31.1	46.4
1937	23.1	24.0	31.2	42.7	55.6	63.8	73.5	74.8	63.8	48.8	35.8	25.0	46.8
1938	21.8	31.1	41.3	47.2	54.6	65.4	71.9	73.4	62.8	56.6	40.9	27.4	49.5
1939	28.6	23.2	34.8	43.7	57.9	68.0	73.2	72.0	67.5	53.2	41.2	33.8	49.8
1940	15.7	27.4	28.8	41.4	52.2	64.9	72.8	68.4	63.2	55.3	36.3	29.5	46.3
#1941	25.6	23.0	29.3	49.3	58.6	66.6	71.0	70.8	64.6	52.5	40.0	32.3	48.6
1942	20.0	22.2	36.4	49.5	55.0	64.0	71.4	69.2	59.6	50.3	39.0	20.1	46.4
1943	18.6	23.1	29.0	42.6	52.8	67.0	71.8	71.4	58.0	50.3	34.0	25.1	45.3
1944	27.6	25.5	29.4	40.4	57.8	67.8	70.4	71.2	63.6	51.2	41.4	19.8	47.2
1945	17.4	24.7	44.4	46.4	50.1	60.6	67.8	69.4	61.8	48.8	37.4	20.5	45.8
1946	22.8	24.1	41.6	47.2	52.6	64.1	70.7	67.8	61.7	55.1	39.0	27.9	47.9
1947	25.6	17.6	30.0	42.8	49.9	60.8	68.8	75.8	63.9	59.4	32.6	26.9	46.2
1948	15.0	23.2	31.9	48.8	52.3	64.4	72.4	72.0	66.4	50.2	41.4	28.0	47.2
1949	25.6	23.5	33.4	44.8	57.0	69.5	74.4	72.0	58.6	53.8	38.2	28.6	48.3
#1950	24.8	24.0	29.0	39.1	53.8	65.8	68.7	65.7	60.5	55.6	32.7	18.4	44.9
1951	20.4	24.3	31.5	43.0	57.3	61.0	70.4	67.2	60.9	52.0	31.5	24.7	45.4
1952	24.6	29.7	31.0	48.2	54.7	67.3	73.3	69.6	64.2	47.9	41.0	31.6	48.6
#1953	27.0	28.3	35.6	43.1	55.3	67.9	72.6	73.8	64.7	57.3	43.6	29.8	49.9
1954	23.0	33.1	31.6	47.6	51.7	69.0	71.0	69.7	64.3	52.2	40.2	28.0	48.4
#1955	21.7	24.7	31.9	50.7	58.2	65.2	76.7	76.4	63.9	52.9	33.5	22.6	48.2
#1956	24.9	25.0	31.4	43.0	53.7	68.7	67.9	70.1	59.3	55.8	36.7	28.1	47.0
1957	14.9	27.8	32.4	45.0	52.7	65.0	70.9	69.2	59.5	48.6	36.5	29.7	46.0
1958	21.9	16.8	33.3	45.7	55.9	60.2	69.2	70.8	62.2	53.6	39.2	18.7	45.6
1959	13.4	19.3	30.9	45.0	59.5	67.3	70.2	73.8	64.7	47.7	29.5	32.5	46.2
1960	24.1	23.4	21.5	48.0	51.8	61.4	67.1	67.8	63.4	48.8	39.2	22.5	44.9
#1961	19.4	29.8	35.2	41.2	50.8	65.3	69.9	70.3	64.8	51.2	37.6	22.8	46.5
1962	14.5	21.1	30.3	44.5	59.2	63.9	66.7	68.9	58.0	52.6	37.9	21.5	44.9
1963	8.7	15.9	35.2	45.8	52.3	65.6	70.8	67.1	61.2	58.6	41.7	13.2	44.7
1964	26.1	25.3	31.7	44.8	60.3	66.5	72.3	67.7	61.2	48.2	40.4	23.2	47.3
1965	19.5	21.2	25.3	42.7	58.6	63.1	68.9	66.8	61.7	50.8	38.5	32.9	45.8
1966	13.9	22.3	35.4	42.3	49.6	67.0	73.5	66.8	59.1	48.9	38.0	24.5	45.1
1967	24.5	17.5	33.2	44.9	50.2	66.5	68.6	66.0	60.8	50.4	35.2	28.9	45.6
1968	21.8	20.7	40.3	47.6	53.2	66.3	69.5	71.4	63.5	52.7	38.1	25.6	47.5
1969	18.6	27.3	29.8	44.9	55.3	58.9	67.8	70.9	62.0	47.5	34.3	25.1	45.2
1970	13.3	22.6	30.5	46.2	56.0	65.3	73.3	71.8	62.0	52.5	37.3	24.3	46.2
1971	12.7	21.6	28.6	40.9	51.1	67.5	68.0	67.0	64.9	55.5	37.3	29.5	45.4
1972	15.9	19.8	27.7	39.4	55.0	61.6	69.3	69.1	61.3	47.5	36.2	20.2	43.6
1973	24.7	25.4	39.9	42.7	51.0	69.2	71.4	72.5	63.9	54.6	38.5	25.5	48.3
1974	21.6	22.9	33.8	46.1	50.6	62.4	71.5	67.3	58.0	49.9	38.6	29.1	46.0
1975	24.0	23.5	28.6	37.7	57.1	65.7	71.7	71.2	58.5	54.1	44.5	27.9	47.0
RECORD MEAN	20.9	23.2	32.6	44.3	54.3	64.5	70.7	69.7	62.5	51.5	37.7	26.1	46.5
MAX	28.1	30.3	39.5	52.2	63.3	73.6	79.2	77.8	70.6	59.3	44.5	32.6	54.3
MIN	13.6	16.0	25.6	36.3	45.3	55.4	62.2	61.6	54.4	43.6	30.8	19.5	38.7

# Indicates a station move or relocation of instruments.

MILWAUKEE, WI

Feb	Mar	Apr	May	June	Total
1153	1036	652	370	67	7239
1036	1006	598	381	88	7152
1346	977	575	291	165	7331
1273	1049	592	215	73	7503
1200	1342	515	402	132	7567
978	918	708	434	86	7305
1224	1067	623	254	119	7549
1372	915	570	388	82	7890
1141	1026	598	192	105	6964
1222	1226	664	232	123	7637
1189	915	674	473	88	7361
1325	978	596	458	47	7445
1277	758	521	363	74	7049
1053	1087	596	317	215	7254
1180	1062	561	301	104	7670
1211	1122	716	421	65	7774
1305	1149	758	305	139	7579
1101	769	659	426	6	7182
1173	959	560	448	106	7042
1157	1122	814	267	69	7296

Aug	Sept	Oct	Nov	Dec	Total
197	59	5	0	0	449
227	60	4	0	0	713
105	123	20	0	0	516
166	26	0	0	0	417
247	84	6	0	0	693
98	32	1	0	0	386
203	16	21	0	0	598

Precipitation

Year	Jan	Feb	Mar	Apr	May	June	July	Aug	Sept	Oct	Nov	Dec	Annual
1936	2.54	2.32	0.67	2.30	2.55	1.93	0.28	5.92	5.59	3.77	0.34	2.14	30.35
1937	3.12	1.72	1.74	4.80	2.70	2.64	3.06	0.80	1.14	1.83	0.85	1.42	25.82
1938	4.60	3.33	3.29	0.97	3.73	6.93	2.70	6.47	6.12	0.76	1.86	1.10	41.86
1939	1.60	2.24	1.54	2.81	1.40	3.50	0.51	5.03	1.53	2.43	0.33	0.46	23.38
1940	1.57	1.33	2.07	2.96	3.80	7.54	0.91	6.68	0.55	1.48	2.80	0.95	32.64
#1941	2.50	0.63	1.82	1.93	3.03	3.42	2.93	1.29	9.87	2.86	0.93	1.29	32.50
1942	1.16	0.50	1.46	0.81	4.49	4.26	3.58	4.14	3.43	2.44	3.27	2.55	32.09
1943	2.15	0.76	2.48	0.99	2.88	2.33	1.54	2.31	0.37	0.83	3.15	0.99	20.78
1944	1.40	1.69	2.46	3.74	2.33	3.42	2.77	1.54	3.05	0.29	1.54	1.14	25.37
1945	0.31	1.40	1.40	2.89	5.27	2.81	2.65	4.07	6.27	0.78	2.34	1.47	31.66
1946	1.97	0.88	2.88	0.94	2.14	2.81	0.95	1.63	1.28	1.79	2.08	1.54	20.89
1947	2.26	0.29	1.73	3.68	4.35	3.98	2.17	1.58	6.03	1.85	2.82	1.72	32.46
1948	1.07	1.68	3.59	1.91	4.05	3.19	2.16	0.46	1.24	0.33	2.44	2.50	24.62
1949	2.59	1.74	2.57	1.38	1.72	3.79	3.46	1.08	1.88	1.62	0.62	2.27	24.72
#1950	2.17	1.39	2.50	3.58	2.04	5.11	6.07	3.29	1.75	0.55	1.60	2.59	32.64
1951	2.38	1.87	3.33	4.91	3.87	2.97	3.12	2.56	2.75	4.42	1.99	2.26	36.43
1952	2.08	0.82	3.67	2.95	2.86	4.03	6.69	3.59	0.36	0.17	3.37	2.10	32.69
#1953	1.16	1.62	1.18	2.81	1.77	2.65	2.78	4.34	1.65	0.46	0.58	1.67	22.87
1954	0.92	1.31	1.65	3.27	1.83	8.28	5.13	3.86	2.78	3.18	1.06	2.64	35.91
#1955	0.62	1.32	1.05	2.43	4.29	4.58	2.10	3.62	2.36	3.57	0.87	1.09	27.90
1956	0.57	1.43	2.36	4.14	4.55	3.87	5.37	2.96	0.30	0.15	1.62	1.03	28.35
1957	0.88	0.96	1.59	2.70	3.82	4.01	1.50	2.03	0.88	1.34	2.88	2.36	24.95
1958	1.41	0.15	0.46	1.84	2.07	1.71	1.02	1.71	2.85	3.24	3.37	0.34	20.17
1959	2.48	1.98	3.03	3.29	1.28	1.67	6.82	3.47	2.31	6.42	2.08	2.85	37.68
1960	4.04	3.05	3.80	2.92	4.27	3.28	3.50	7.07	3.25	3.06	2.12	0.35	40.71
1961	0.31	1.22	3.80	3.89	1.25	1.53	2.91	2.35	9.41	2.75	2.37	1.02	32.81
1962	2.48	2.04	1.69	1.49	2.17	1.33	3.74	1.98	1.49	2.14	0.81	0.55	21.91
1963	0.66	0.42	2.20	2.54	1.95	1.50	2.36	2.48	1.78	0.34	2.17	0.70	19.10
1964	1.18	0.41	3.05	3.81	2.57	1.70	7.66	2.62	1.74	0.17	2.29	0.98	28.18
1965	3.33	1.04	3.61	3.47	2.12	0.85	2.64	6.15	6.85	2.68	2.02	3.73	38.49
1966	2.06	1.27	3.61	2.67	2.00	1.68	3.32	3.27	0.48	1.76	2.70	2.31	27.13
1967	1.49	1.31	1.35	2.70	1.80	7.38	1.35	1.23	1.69	2.70	1.52	1.33	25.85
1968	0.98	0.56	0.31	2.90	3.28	7.79	3.59	2.59	3.36	0.94	2.56	2.65	31.51
1969	1.83	0.05	1.05	3.42	3.05	7.53	6.61	0.53	2.18	4.48	1.14	1.18	33.05
1970	0.41	0.13	1.62	2.71	3.41	3.92	1.93	0.64	6.94	2.09	2.03	3.02	28.85
1971	1.37	2.50	2.83	1.31	0.90	2.67	2.60	2.28	1.30	1.90	2.45	4.34	26.45
1972	0.75	0.86	2.57	2.76	2.33	3.33	4.60	4.82	7.57	3.28	1.34	2.47	36.68
1973	1.12	1.51	2.86	7.31	3.39	1.96	1.55	0.95	4.50	2.97	1.83	3.80	33.75
1974	3.61	3.10	4.29	3.83	4.10	3.48	3.51	2.54	0.50	1.96	1.86	2.10	34.88
1975	2.25	2.53	3.01	4.08	2.01	3.99	1.14	3.89	1.00	0.72	2.83	1.70	29.15
RECORD MEAN	1.83	1.57	2.44	2.78	3.19	3.52	2.89	2.80	3.13	2.27	1.99	1.77	30.18

Record mean values above are means through the current year for the period beginning in 1875 for temperature, 1871 for precipitation and 1941 for snowfall. Data are from City Office locations through February 1941 and for the period July 1950 through December 1953; otherwise from Airport locations.

CHEYENNE, WYOMING

The city of Cheyenne is located in the extreme southeastern corner of Wyoming at an elevation of approximately 6,100 feet. The surrounding country is mostly rolling prairie which is used primarily for grazing. The ground level rises rapidly to a ridge approximately 9,000 feet elevation about 30 miles west of the City. This ridge is known as the Laramie Mountains, one of the ranges of the Rockies, and extends in a north-south direction. As a result of this ridge, winds from the northwest through west to southwest are downslope and produce a marked chinook effect in Cheyenne which is especially noticeable during the winter months. The air is heated by compression 5.5° for every 1,000-feet decrease in elevation and this is known as downslope winds. Since Cheyenne is located on a broad ridge between the North Platte and South Platte Rivers, winds from either the north or south, as well as any easterly direction, are upslope. With the proper amount of moisture present upslope winds may cause fog or low stratus clouds in the Cheyenne area. Because of this terrain variation the wind direction plays an important part in controlling the local temperature and weather.

Cheyenne experiences large diurnal and annual temperature ranges. This is due to the advent of both warm and cold airmasses and the relative high elevation of the City. The higher elevation permits rapid incoming and outgoing radiation. The daily range averages about 30° in the summer and 23° in the winter. The annual mean temperature ranges from 26.6° in **January** to 69.1° in **July**. Since the beginning of record in 1870 the temperature here has never reached 101°, and only 8 percent of the summer days in an average year shows temperatures rising into the nineties.

Many of the outbreaks of cold air from the north during the winter months miss Cheyenne due to the downslope of the land to the east and the prevailing westerlies. Other times only the edge of the very cold air will invade the area and move out again within 24 to 48 hours. Of course, some of the arctic airmasses do move over the City, but only 13 percent of the days in an average January, the coldest month of the year, show temperatures dropping to zero or below. It is also interesting to note that temperatures here during the winter months average a few degrees higher than over the Mississippi and Missouri Valleys at the same latitude.

Windy days are quite frequent during the winter and spring months. Since the wind is usually strongest during the daytime it is a very noticeable weather element and leads one to believe that the wind is higher than average velocities indicate. Another important consideration is that the strong winds are almost invariably from a westerly direction and this tends to raise the temperature because the air is moving downslope.

Most of the airmasses reaching this area move in from the Pacific and since the mountains to the west are quite effective moisture barriers the climate is semiarid. Precipitation is least in December, rising to a maximum in late May and early June. Moisture then decreases rapidly the latter part of June, remaining at a medium level until fall when it decreases again to a December minimum. Fortunately, about 70 percent of the 15 inches of normal annual precipitation occurs during the growing season.

Station: CHEYENNE, WYOMING
MUNICIPAL AIRPORT
.levation (ground): 6126 feet

TEMPERATURES °F

Month	Normal			Extremes			
	Daily maximum	Daily minimum	Monthly	Record highest	Year	Record lowest	Year
(a)				16		16	
J	38.2	14.9	26.6	62	1974	-27	1963
F	40.7	17.3	29.0	71	1962	-24	1962
M	43.5	19.6	31.6	73	1967	-11	1960
A	55.4	30.0	42.7	82	1960	-8	1975
M	65.1	39.7	52.4	90	1969	21	1967
J	74.4	48.1	61.3	94	1963	34	1969
J	83.7	54.5	69.1	98	1973	39	1968
A	81.9	53.2	67.6	96	1969	36	1975
S	72.8	43.5	58.2	93	1960	22	1962
O	61.8	33.9	47.9	83	1967	7	1969
N	47.5	23.5	35.5	70	1971	-8	1959
D	40.3	18.1	29.2	66	1962	-24	1972
YR	58.8	33.0	45.9	98	JUL 1973	-27	JAN 1963

IMPORTANT:
The time-period covered by this record is limited: See footnotes following table of **NORMALS, MEANS AND EXTREMES** for explanation and for additional history of **EXTREME HIGHS AND LOWS** recorded in the general area.

(Continued)

In the summer months precipitation is mostly of the shower type and occurs mainly in connection with thunderstorms. As a result of these showers, amounts of precipitation may vary widely in different parts of the City. Also in connection with the thunderstorms, hail is frequent and occasionally destructive. Most of the snow falls during the late winter and early spring months. It is not uncommon to have heavy snow in May and on rarer occasions during the first few days of June.

The growing season in Cheyenne averages 132 days a year and extends from May 18 to September 27. One year in five the temperature is expected to drop to 32° or lower after May 30; also, one year in five the temperature is expected to drop to 32° or lower before September 15. Freezing temperatures have occurred as late in the spring as June 16, and as early in the fall as August 25.

Relative humidity averages just better than 50 percent on an annual basis with major daily variations. Very seldom is the relative humidity above 30 percent with the temperature above 80°.

Sunshine averages 64 percent on an annual basis, with a great daily but small monthly variation.

Normals, Means, and Extremes

(To better understand these tables, see full explanation of terms beginning on page 322)

Month	Normal Degree days Base 65 °F: Heating	Cooling	Precipitation in inches, Water equivalent: Normal	Maximum monthly	Year	Minimum monthly	Year	Maximum in 24 hrs.	Year	Snow, Ice pellets: Maximum monthly	Year	Maximum in 24 hrs.	Year	Relative humidity pct. Hour 05 (Local time)	Hour 11	Hour 17	Hour 23
(a)				40		40		40		40		40		16	16	16	16
J	1190	0	0.46	2.78	1949	T	1952	1.41	1949	18.5	1940	10.0	1962	53	44	48	55
F	1008	0	0.46	2.16	1953	0.02	1972	1.60	1953	19.9	1953	14.0	1953	59	44	46	59
M	1035	0	1.05	2.54	1954	0.12	1966	1.88	1946	27.0	1973	15.6	1973	62	45	46	62
A	669	0	1.57	5.04	1942	0.35	1946	1.81	1942	26.2	1945	16.5	1955	65	41	39	62
M	394	0	2.52	5.35	1957	0.11	1974	2.00	1942	30.4	1943	15.0	1942	67	39	40	63
J	156	45	2.41	5.32	1955	0.37	1940	2.68	1955	8.7	1947	8.7	1947	69	40	41	63
J	22	149	1.82	5.01	1973	0.58	1969	3.42	1973	0.0		0.0		68	34	37	62
A	31	112	1.45	3.12	1961	0.03	1944	1.96	1961	0.0		0.0		65	33	34	58
S	225	21	1.03	4.52	1973	0.10	1953	2.75	1973	7.4	1971	5.3	1971	64	37	38	61
O	530	0	0.95	3.57	1942	0.03	1964	1.70	1947	21.3	1969	6.1	1971	58	37	39	57
N	885	0	0.58	1.91	1942	T	1965	0.88	1944	18.2	1942	11.6	1973	58	41	47	57
D	1110	0	0.35	1.68	1937	0.03	1959	0.57	1951	21.3	1958	9.9	1958	56	44	50	56
YR	7255	327	14.65	5.35	MAY 1957	T	NOV 1965	3.42	JUL 1973	30.4	MAY 1943	16.5	APR 1955	62	40	42	60

Month	Wind: Mean speed m.p.h.	Prevailing direction	Fastest mile: Speed m.p.h.	Direction	Year	Pct. of possible sunshine	Mean sky cover, tenths, sunrise to sunset	Mean number of days, Sunrise to sunset: Clear	Partly cloudy	Cloudy	Precipitation .01 inch or more	Snow, Ice pellets 1.0 inch or more	Thunderstorms	Heavy fog, visibility ¼ mile or less	Temperatures °F Max.: (b) 90° and above	32° and below	Min.: 32° and below	0° and below	Average station pressure mb. Elev. 6141 feet m.s.l.
(a)	18	15	40	40		40	40	40	40	40	40	40	40	40	16	16	16	16	3
J	15.8	WNW	66	NW	1975	61	5.8	9	9	13	6	2	0	1	0	10	28	5	807.3
F	15.3	W	65	W	1955	65	6.2	7	9	12	6	2	*	2	0	7	27	2	808.9
M	14.9	WNW	75	NW	1972	64	6.2	7	10	14	10	4	*	3	0	7	27	2	805.3
A	15.0	WNW	68	NW	1967	61	6.5	6	10	14	10	3	2	3	0	1	19	*	807.3
M	13.1	WNW	69	NW	1967	59	6.6	5	12	14	12	1	8	3	*	0	3	0	809.8
J	11.8	WNW	56	W	1969	65	5.5	8	13	9	11	*	11	2	1	0	0	0	811.9
J	10.5	WNW	52	E	1955	68	5.0	10	15	6	11	0	13	1	6	0	0	0	815.6
A	10.8	W	49	NW	1964	68	5.1	10	13	8	9	0	10	1	3	0	0	0	814.9
S	11.5	W	54	W	1955	69	4.6	13	9	8	7	*	4	2	*	*	2	0	815.3
O	12.5	W	61	W	1958	68	4.7	13	9	9	5	1	1	2	0	1	12	0	813.2
N	13.8	WNW	66	W	1967	60	5.5	10	9	11	6	2	*	2	0	3	24	*	809.7
D	15.0	WNW	65	W	1968	59	5.8	9	9	13	5	2	0	1	0	9	29	3	808.9
YR	13.3	WNW	75	NW	MAR 1972	64	5.6	107	127	131	97	17	50	24	10	37	172	12	810.7

FOOTNOTES

Means and extremes above are from existing and comparable exposures. Annual extremes have been exceeded at other sites in the locality as follows: Highest temperature 100 in June 1954 and earlier; lowest temperature -38 in January 1875; maximum monthly precipitation 7.66 in April 1900; minimum monthly precipitation .00 in September 1879; maximum precipitation in 24 hours 4.70 in July 1896; maximum monthly snowfall 46.5 in April 1905.

Snowfall

Season	July	Aug	Sept	Oct	Nov	Dec	Jan
1936-37	0.0	0.0	0.7	5.8	2.3	4.2	5.6
1937-38	0.0	0.0	0.1	2.8	7.6	16.2	4.3
1938-39	0.0	0.0	0.0	2.2	7.7	11.7	5.1
1939-40	0.0	0.0	T	2.9	1.2	3.6	18.5
1940-41	0.0	0.0	0.0	1.5	7.6	4.5	4.0
1941-42	0.0	0.0	2.0	1.0	7.3	8.0	11.5
1942-43	0.0	0.0	4.8	6.3	18.2	4.3	6.6
1943-44	0.0	0.0	0.0	0.5	4.5	2.0	6.2
1944-45	0.0	0.0	0.0	0.0	6.7	7.3	10.2
1945-46	0.0	0.0	3.1	4.6	5.9	2.8	3.6
1946-47	0.0	0.0	0.4	6.6	14.0	2.1	7.7
1947-48	0.0	0.0	0.0	3.2	10.0	8.3	4.7
1948-49	0.0	0.0	0.0	3.6	3.5	12.4	15.1
1949-50	0.0	0.0	0.0	7.2	T	2.3	2.5
1950-51	0.0	0.0	T	0.8	6.4	1.7	9.6
1951-52	0.0	0.0	T	12.2	9.4	8.3	T
1952-53	0.0	0.0	0.0	4.2	10.4	2.0	3.0
1953-54	0.0	0.0	0.0	1.3	5.4	3.9	2.9
#1954-55	0.0	0.0	2.2	0.5	2.9	3.1	7.1
1955-56	0.0	0.0	0.0	0.5	13.7	3.8	8.6
1956-57	0.0	0.0	0.0	T	13.9	4.0	7.6
1957-58	0.0	0.0	T	0.5	8.0	1.0	0.6
1958-59	0.0	0.0	T	T	5.3	21.3	7.3
1959-60	0.0	0.0	3.7	9.1	3.8	0.4	2.8
1960-61	0.0	0.0	T	T	5.8	5.2	1.2
1961-62	0.0	0.0	0.8	3.6	3.5	1.5	13.0
1962-63	0.0	0.0	T	T	3.8	3.5	8.9
1963-64	0.0	0.0	0.0	T	0.1	6.0	1.0
1964-65	0.0	0.0	0.0	0.0	2.0	1.6	8.5
1965-66	0.0	0.0	2.0	T	T	2.4	1.3
1966-67	0.0	0.0	T	4.5	2.3	0.8	5.4
1967-68	0.0	0.0	0.0	0.4	3.6	4.8	0.2
1968-69	0.0	0.0	0.0	0.5	6.0	5.5	3.0
1969-70	0.0	0.0	0.0	21.3	1.8	2.4	1.2
1970-71	0.0	0.0	T	11.0	4.7	4.9	8.6
1971-72	0.0	0.0	7.4	8.1	0.9	1.4	7.4
1972-73	0.0	0.0	T	5.0	8.8	7.6	4.6
1973-74	0.0	0.0	T	0.5	17.4	13.9	5.0
1974-75	0.0	0.0	1.9	1.4	2.4	1.5	5.8
1975-76	0.0	0.0	0.6	5.5	4.7	8.4	
RECORD MEAN	0.0	0.0	0.7	3.5	6.1	5.3	5.9

Heating Degree Days

Season	July	Aug	Sept	Oct	Nov	Dec	Jan
1955-56	1	12	221	470	1035	1041	1113
1956-57	19	69	136	445	989	994	1365
1957-58	8	23	284	553	1049	923	1081
1958-59	61	23	203	467	854	1052	1195
#1959-60	15	15	309	675	949	978	1214
1960-61	17	45	176	496	877	1176	1109
1961-62	17	8	405	622	977	1285	1419
1962-63	40	57	187	425	751	1031	1492
1963-64	3	10	76	323	742	1174	1203
1964-65	2	95	239	500	883	1095	1012
1965-66	11	47	454	397	702	1016	1208
1966-67	0	51	166	526	781	1049	1036
1967-68	12	45	202	481	891	1308	1117
1968-69	40	82	221	481	924	1137	1034
1969-70	3	3	113	859	854	1038	1115
1970-71	3	5	302	732	874	1108	1087
1971-72	56	6	364	633	863	1108	1226
1972-73	85	75	248	599	1056	1358	1275
1973-74	80	4	323	482	883	1098	1264
1974-75	4	55	302	509	873	1180	1215
1975-76	11	39	274	515	920	998	

Cooling Degree Days

Year	Jan	Feb	Mar	Apr	May	June	July
1969	0	0	0	0	14	12	211
1970	0	0	0	0	2	52	149
1971	0	0	0	0	0	58	77
1972	0	0	0	0	0	11	69
1973	0	0	0	0	0	65	112
1974	0	0	0	0	4	88	173
1975	0	0	0	0	0	7	90

Feb	Mar	Apr	May	June	Total
2.7	22.0	15.1	0.2	3.0	61.6
3.3	12.9	10.0	3.6	0.0	60.8
12.3	19.0	20.4	T	0.0	78.4
6.9	9.7	9.5	T	0.0	52.3
3.1	12.3	21.9	0.0	0.0	54.9
7.4	10.9	22.0	21.5	0.5	92.1
7.0	10.7	4.0	30.4	0.0	92.3
9.2	22.0	8.0	1.8	0.0	54.2
10.1	11.4	26.2	T	T	71.9
5.0	17.2	1.6	8.6	T	52.4
8.2	6.2	6.7	6.6	8.7	67.2
7.3	4.1	1.6	T	0.0	39.2
0.5	20.2	4.6	T	0.0	59.9
1.1	9.3	12.6	12.4	1.4	48.8
3.9	5.3	5.3	T	T	33.0
9.5	14.5	3.3	T	0.0	57.2
19.9	5.8	12.9	3.5	0.0	61.7
1.0	22.6	4.9	2.0	0.0	44.0
6.0	8.8	16.6	0.1	0.0	47.3
8.1	4.0	0.7	0.6	0.0	40.0
1.0	10.6	21.8	7.7	T	66.6
6.2	17.8	6.2	0.0	T	40.3
4.3	14.3	14.0	1.3	0.0	67.8
8.8	3.7	5.6	T	0.0	37.9
3.8	23.2	7.8	11.5	0.0	58.5
10.8	5.5	2.5	T	0.0	41.2
3.1	11.8	3.2	T	0.0	34.3
3.3	6.9	7.1	0.5	0.0	24.9
5.5	10.0	2.5	1.4	0.0	31.5
2.7	1.1	3.6	T	0.0	13.1
8.0	3.4	15.9	11.0	0.0	51.3
2.5	2.8	15.4	2.2	0.0	31.9
4.7	2.9	3.0	0.0	T	25.6
1.5	19.4	8.3	T	T	55.9
9.3	15.2	13.0	1.2	0.0	67.9
0.4	10.6	8.5	0.3	0.0	45.0
0.6	27.0	12.8	1.2	0.0	67.6
0.8	16.3	8.0	0.0	0.0	61.9
4.3	14.0	5.4	0.8	0.0	37.5
5.5	12.0	9.4	3.3	0.3	52.0

CHEYENNE, WY

Feb	Mar	Apr	May	June	Total
1222	986	758	310	21	7190
838	976	839	519	155	7344
891	1218	774	255	100	7159
1086	1045	767	441	71	7265
1301	975	542	288	89	7350
923	1028	722	377	90	7036
1056	1106	576	303	167	7941
890	1023	633	277	89	6895
1229	1160	720	340	166	7146
1088	1320	569	435	169	7407
1061	841	758	291	143	6929
945	800	622	490	221	6687
932	833	777	487	107	7192
919	1118	498	297	248	6999
846	1113	811	326	168	7249
1093	1007	713	481	99	7504
916	791	668	419	61	7111
980	1017	824	414	122	8053
922	862	643	304	110	6975
1115	1070	819	506	212	7860

Aug	Sept	Oct	Nov	Dec	Total
185	9	0	0	0	431
189	11	0	0	0	403
128	13	0	0	0	276
69	2	0	0	0	151
116	0	0	0	0	293
67	17	0	0	0	349
86	10	0	0	0	193

Average Temperature

Year	Jan	Feb	Mar	Apr	May	June	July	Aug	Sept	Oct	Nov	Dec	Annual
1936	25.4	20.2	33.2	43.0	55.8	65.2	72.4	68.5	58.3	44.4	35.4	30.5	46.0
1937	12.7	26.5	30.4	41.0	52.8	59.6	69.4	71.1	60.4	48.7	34.0	26.6	44.4
1938	27.4	30.2	36.6	42.5	49.9	61.8	68.0	68.6	60.0	49.7	31.4	27.4	46.1
1939	28.2	19.2	34.4	42.6	54.4	61.2	71.8	66.2	60.2	48.8	37.9	35.0	46.7
1940	18.8	29.0	38.0	42.0	53.9	64.8	70.1	67.2	60.1	50.2	32.2	31.4	46.5
1941	30.2	32.1	31.6	40.6	54.3	59.3	67.8	66.6	54.6	44.8	38.2	29.8	45.8
1942	24.6	21.4	37.0	45.0	48.7	58.6	69.0	65.6	55.3	46.3	36.0	31.6	44.5
1943	27.7	33.6	28.4	48.2	47.2	60.2	69.8	69.2	57.5	47.2	36.8	29.7	46.3
1944	27.4	27.0	28.0	37.8	52.4	59.5	66.4	68.1	57.3	49.6	35.8	27.3	44.7
#1945	28.4	27.7	34.6	34.8	50.4	55.2	68.2	66.8	54.3	49.3	38.0	25.8	44.5
1946	28.0	30.0	38.2	49.0	46.0	61.6	68.8	65.8	56.7	43.0	32.6	34.5	46.2
1947	26.9	23.9	30.9	40.0	49.8	56.4	68.6	68.6	60.6	51.5	28.8	29.7	44.6
1948	24.6	23.9	27.7	44.8	52.8	60.6	67.8	67.4	61.7	46.3	31.2	26.4	44.6
1949	14.1	25.4	32.2	44.6	51.8	59.7	68.0	67.0	57.8	43.6	45.2	27.5	44.7
1950	24.0	33.8	31.3	40.3	46.2	60.2	63.5	64.1	54.9	52.7	35.1	33.5	45.0
1951	22.6	30.8	29.2	37.3	51.2	54.6	66.8	65.1	54.6	43.8	33.5	24.4	42.9
1952	28.5	28.7	27.9	42.7	51.7	65.7	66.8	67.4	60.8	48.4	28.6	30.0	45.6
1953	35.6	27.6	37.1	36.6	47.7	63.3	69.0	66.6	60.8	49.4	38.9	27.7	46.7
#1954	32.3	38.9	27.7	46.4	50.7	62.2	71.9	68.2	61.4	47.5	40.2	32.5	48.3
1955	24.9	23.2	28.7	42.8	53.2	58.1	70.6	69.1	58.7	49.5	30.3	31.2	45.0
1956	28.9	22.6	33.0	39.5	54.8	67.2	67.5	64.7	61.1	50.4	31.9	32.7	46.2
1957	20.7	34.9	33.2	36.9	48.1	60.4	69.0	67.4	55.4	46.9	29.8	35.0	44.8
1958	29.9	33.0	25.5	39.0	56.9	62.8	64.5	68.7	58.6	49.6	36.2	30.8	46.3
#1959	26.3	26.0	31.1	39.3	50.6	65.4	68.2	69.1	55.7	43.0	33.1	33.1	45.1
1960	25.6	19.9	33.4	46.8	55.7	64.4	70.8	68.7	61.2	48.8	35.6	26.8	46.5
1961	29.0	31.8	31.6	40.7	52.8	64.8	69.1	68.1	51.4	44.8	32.3	23.4	45.0
1962	19.0	27.2	29.0	45.6	55.1	59.9	65.6	67.3	58.9	51.0	39.8	31.5	45.8
1963	16.7	33.0	31.8	43.7	55.8	64.0	72.7	68.3	63.1	54.4	40.0	26.9	47.5
1964	26.1	22.3	27.4	40.8	54.6	60.5	70.9	64.3	56.9	48.7	35.4	29.5	44.8
1965	32.1	26.0	27.2	45.7	50.8	59.3	68.2	64.7	49.6	52.0	41.4	32.1	45.4
1966	25.8	26.8	37.7	39.6	55.6	61.5	74.5	66.2	59.9	47.8	38.8	31.0	47.1
1967	31.4	31.1	39.0	44.1	49.1	57.7	67.3	66.0	58.4	49.3	35.1	22.5	45.9
1968	28.7	32.6	38.0	38.9	49.2	62.6	68.2	64.5	57.6	49.2	34.0	28.0	46.0
1969	31.4	32.0	28.7	48.1	55.7	57.0	71.5	70.7	61.2	37.1	36.4	31.3	46.8
1970	28.7	34.6	28.9	37.8	54.3	60.9	69.5	70.7	55.0	41.2	35.7	29.1	45.5
1971	29.7	25.8	32.4	41.0	49.2	63.4	65.5	68.7	53.1	44.3	36.0	29.1	44.8
1972	25.3	33.2	39.3	42.5	51.2	63.2	64.3	64.6	56.6	45.5	29.5	21.0	44.7
1973	23.7	29.7	31.9	37.3	51.4	62.9	65.8	68.4	54.1	49.3	35.3	29.4	44.9
1974	24.1	31.9	37.1	43.3	55.0	64.1	70.1	65.2	55.3	48.3	35.6	26.6	46.4
1975	25.5	25.0	30.2	37.5	48.4	57.9	67.3	66.3	56.0	48.1	34.2	32.6	44.1
RECORD MEAN	26.1	27.7	32.4	41.4	51.0	61.0	67.7	66.4	57.3	46.4	35.2	28.6	45.1
MAX	37.2	38.9	43.7	53.3	63.4	74.5	81.7	80.3	71.3	59.4	46.8	39.5	57.5
MIN	15.0	16.4	21.0	29.4	38.6	47.5	53.7	52.4	43.2	33.4	23.6	17.7	32.7

# Indicates a station move or relocation of instruments.

Precipitation

Year	Jan	Feb	Mar	Apr	May	June	July	Aug	Sept	Oct	Nov	Dec	Annual
1936	0.30	0.59	1.17	1.26	2.90	2.64	1.76	1.10	1.14	0.68	0.24	0.41	14.19
1937	0.47	0.27	2.09	1.57	1.19	1.28	1.97	1.34	0.49	1.23	0.90	1.68	14.48
1938	0.37	0.28	1.33	2.11	2.31	2.02	1.32	2.26	3.33	0.54	0.63	0.97	17.47
#1939	0.71	0.75	1.73	1.82	1.69	0.83	0.70	0.43	0.49	0.37	0.06	0.26	9.84
1940	1.54	0.56	1.21	1.36	1.29	0.37	2.87	0.82	3.75	0.24	0.73	0.28	15.02
1941	0.33	0.32	1.37	3.70	0.68	4.66	2.08	1.86	1.10	1.43	0.71	0.72	18.96
1942	0.77	0.58	1.02	5.04	3.27	2.48	1.07	2.06	1.70	3.57	1.91	0.22	23.69
1943	0.56	0.53	0.95	1.34	4.21	2.34	1.25	1.11	0.53	0.54	0.41	0.18	13.95
1944	0.42	0.63	1.98	2.85	2.00	1.97	4.00	0.03	0.18	0.06	0.90	0.55	15.57
1945	0.97	1.03	1.02	3.08	1.31	3.47	1.57	1.35	1.43	0.53	0.46	0.29	16.51
1946	0.31	0.49	2.29	0.35	4.15	1.25	1.42	3.04	0.81	2.54	1.34	0.19	18.18
1947	0.54	0.69	0.81	1.55	2.19	3.75	1.87	1.37	0.78	2.12	0.78	0.52	16.97
1948	0.41	0.74	0.41	0.73	0.92	3.08	2.34	0.86	0.54	0.53	0.32	1.03	11.91
1949	2.78	0.04	2.44	1.61	4.27	3.26	2.17	2.04	0.25	1.36	0.02	0.26	20.50
1950	0.23	0.15	0.89	1.81	2.48	1.51	2.79	0.39	2.67	0.25	1.09	0.14	14.40
1951	0.69	0.17	0.51	1.94	2.77	1.76	2.74	1.85	0.75	2.26	0.79	0.93	17.16
1952	T	0.80	1.84	0.86	2.67	1.48	1.19	1.86	0.29	0.34	1.06	0.21	12.60
1953	0.34	2.16	0.89	1.45	1.47	3.58	2.51	1.89	0.10	0.13	0.46	0.26	15.24
#1954	0.21	0.08	2.54	0.40	1.45	1.37	1.20	1.38	1.08	0.15	0.28	0.20	10.34
1955	0.29	0.58	0.57	1.16	2.27	5.32	0.93	1.21	1.40	0.18	1.23	0.32	15.46
1956	0.70	0.46	0.24	1.31	2.56	0.99	1.43	1.73	0.14	0.16	1.27	0.41	11.40
1957	0.67	0.08	0.99	2.82	5.35	2.01	2.42	2.92	0.56	1.35	0.57	0.10	19.84
1958	0.06	0.50	2.08	1.13	2.98	1.79	3.85	1.35	0.91	0.20	0.45	1.27	16.57
#1959	0.52	0.30	1.09	1.54	4.16	0.71	0.80	0.77	1.61	1.38	0.16	0.03	13.07
1960	0.17	0.49	0.31	0.82	0.96	1.36	0.94	0.69	0.66	1.11	0.43	0.28	8.22
1961	0.06	0.37	2.08	0.83	2.92	2.91	1.53	3.12	2.17	0.56	0.35	0.09	16.99
1962	0.67	0.56	0.39	0.54	2.72	2.82	4.02	0.40	1.30	0.62	0.33	0.25	14.62
1963	0.51	0.17	0.74	1.66	1.14	2.84	0.77	2.28	3.28	1.06	0.02	0.42	14.89
1964	0.03	0.24	0.58	1.30	0.84	1.01	1.00	0.28	0.33	0.03	0.14	0.16	5.94
1965	0.57	0.26	0.76	0.57	3.11	4.03	0.89	1.54	1.32	0.75	T	0.22	14.02
1966	0.11	0.22	0.12	0.48	0.21	1.95	3.38	2.78	2.12	0.68	0.29	0.08	12.42
1967	0.45	0.54	0.76	2.15	4.04	2.63	1.71	0.99	0.88	0.46	0.32	0.46	15.39
1968	0.04	0.30	0.31	2.34	3.54	0.87	1.25	1.21	0.20	0.86	0.71	0.28	11.91
1969	0.23	0.25	0.27	0.82	1.77	2.70	0.58	0.99	0.84	2.04	0.23	0.21	10.93
1970	0.10	0.04	1.32	0.85	3.13	2.42	0.82	0.14	1.10	1.30	0.30	0.31	11.83
1971	0.51	0.62	1.08	2.81	2.38	0.97	1.08	1.41	1.76	1.16	0.05	0.07	13.90
1972	0.36	0.02	0.79	0.80	2.76	1.71	1.35	1.83	1.01	0.42	0.59	0.40	12.04
1973	0.23	0.07	1.85	1.75	0.31	1.20	5.01	0.27	4.52	0.06	1.25	1.06	17.58
1974	0.48	0.03	1.24	0.50	0.11	2.81	1.41	1.29	0.50	0.91	0.49	0.10	9.87
1975	0.40	0.17	1.17	0.47	2.27	1.49	2.62	0.39	0.52	0.49	0.20	0.52	10.71
RECORD MEAN	0.42	0.55	1.03	1.77	2.39	1.80	1.96	1.49	1.19	0.90	0.53	0.45	14.48

Record mean values above are means through the current year for the period beginning in 1871 for temperature and precipitation, 1936 for snowfall.
Data are from city locations through August 1935.

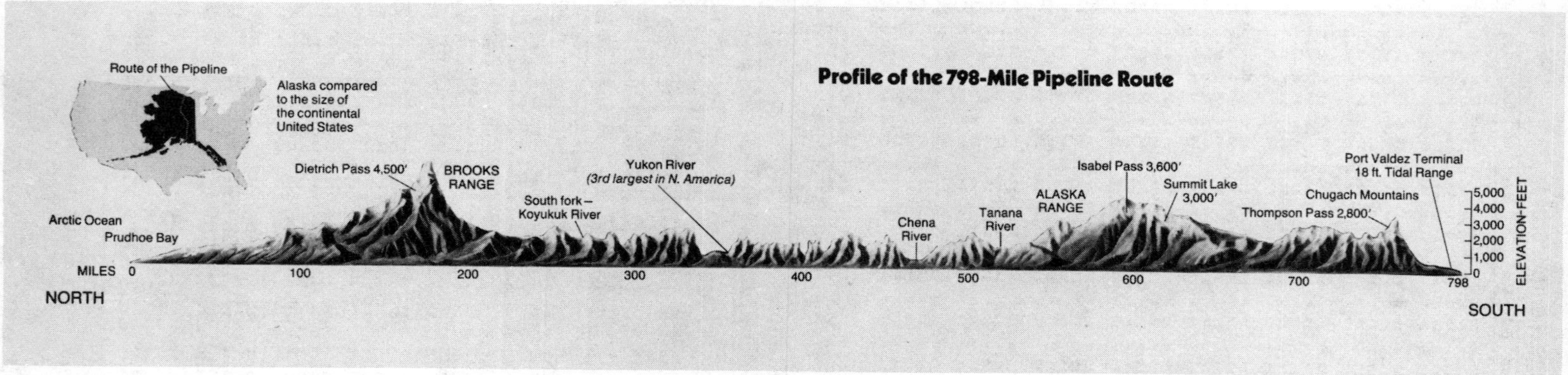

Altitude and terrain features are vital in determining the climate and weather for a specific location no matter what the general geographic disposition of the region in which it lies. This profile of the 798-mile Alaska pipeline route should, therefore, be of material aid in understanding why so many varieties of weather are encountered along that oil transportation route. Exxon Corporation is the developer of this pictorial representation, and it is available here through their courtesy.

ALASKA PIPELINE CLIMATE

CLIMATE ALONG THE ALASKA PIPELINE

Harold W. Searby, Regional Climatologist
Anchorage, Alaska

Editors note: The U.S. Weather Bureau, in December, 1968, developed a special report to aid in the planning of the Alaska Pipeline. The full report provided a summary of climatic conditions along two proposed routes which were still under consideration then. The following is that part of the report which dealt with the route which was ultimately choosen. It is still current.

This report is supplemented by a series of tables which provide detail of climate conditions at various camps and stations along the route.

Introduction

This report concerns itself with the climate along a possible pipeline route from the Arctic to the Gulf of Alaska.

A pipeline built southward will first traverse the marshes and muskeg to the foothills of the Brooks Mountain Range, then up the northern slopes of the Range itself. The most logical place to cross the mountains appears to be through Anaktuvuk Pass. From this point the route would be generally toward Bettles. Moving on southward the first major river crossing arises at the Yukon. The crossing would probably be made between Rampart and Stevens Village, with the pipeline then headed in the general direction of Fairbanks. Two possible routes* exist from this point to the Gulf of Alaska. One route would take it southward along the railroad, ending in Cook Inlet, Whittier or Seward. The other would follow the highway to Valdez.

Permafrost, lakes and marshy ground are problems that will exist over most of the route. The permafrost does become discontinuous and variable in thickness south of Bettles, and the lakes and marshes are fewer in number south of the Brooks Range.

A much shorter route to water would be to head for Kotzebue Sound or Norton Sound, but at present neither of these have adequate ports and are not open for year round operation.

Now that a proposed route for the pipeline has been outlined, let us talk about the climatic factors along the route.

Climatic Conditions, Arctic Coast to the Brooks Mountains

Surface winds predominate from the east with an annual average of about 12 mph along the coast and slightly lighter inland. Speeds of 35 to 50 mph are common in association with winter storms.

Conditions of temperature and wind north of the Brooks Range are undoubtedly the least desirable to be found anywhere in the state. It is not only the coldest area, it is the coldest area to also be accompanied by relatively strong winds. Minimum wintertime temperatures average between a minus 15 and a minus 30 degrees. If we give the average wind a range of 10 to 15 mph, and use it together with the temperature, the result is an "equivalent chill temperature" ranging from a minus 40 to a minus 80 degrees. During times of extreme cold the temperature will drop to 40 or 50 below zero. Usually winds are much lighter under conditions of extreme cold. However, a man walking is enough to

* The highway route was chosen.

create a lower equivalent chill temperature and anyone riding in an open vehicle and exposed to the free air is creating the same conditions that results from the wind. In summer daily temperatures usually warm to readings in the 40's and occasionally the 50's. Inland near the foothills temperatures in the upper 50's and 60's are common in summer. Extremes of 85 and a minus 63 have been recorded at Umiat.

Precipitation for the year amounts to 4 to 6 inches which includes the 30 to 50 inches of snowfall in winter. Drifting snow is common because of strong winds and dryness of the snow.

Climatic Conditions, Brooks Mountain Range

The village of Anaktuvuk Pass is located on the south side of the pass, near the highest point. The Weather Bureau established a climatological weather station there in July of 1953. The sudden interest in a pipeline gives the data new importance.

A contractor working in this area can expect an average annual snowfall of 63 inches, which makes up a large portion of the annual precipitation figire of 10.65 inches.

Wintertime temperatures have been as cold as minus 56 degrees and will have a daily range from a minus 8 to a minus 25 degrees. In summer the daily range is from near 40 to the low 60's, and will occasionally go into the 70's. The highest on record is 91 degrees.

Climatic Conditions, Brooks Range to Fairbanks

Continuing to the Fairbanks area, although temperature extremes are greater than for Anaktuvuk Pass, the climate is slightly milder. There are fewer occasions of strong winds and the maximum speeds are less. Some drifting of snow occurs, but not nearly as much as over the Arctic slope. Wind data for Bettles and Fairbanks are found in Table 1.

Warmest temperatures in summer are mostly in the upper 60's and the 70's. Extremes go into the 90's. The range of average wintertime lows is from about a minus 5 to minus 25 with extremes in the minus 40's and 50's. The all time recorded low is minus 76 at Tanana.

Annual precipitation amounts are 10 to 13 inches. Summer months receive the heaviest amounts because of thunderstorm activity. Winter snow amounts to 50 to 70 inches.

A problem along this route resulting from climatic conditions are the spring floods caused by ice jams on the various streams. For example the Yukon river usually has several spring ice jams along its hundreds of miles of length with some of them resulting in floods, which could cause trouble for a pipeline.

Climate Conditions, Alaska Mountain Range

Strong surface winds in the mountains are usually localized and are found in passes and near the mouths of valleys. The weather reporting station at Summit, which is in a location where strong winds frequently occur in winter, verifies this many times each winter season. The reports of strong winds are always accompanied by reduced visibility in blowing snow which causes drifts.

Temperatures here are not as warm in summer or as cold in winter as are found to be north of the range. Recorded extremes are 89 in summer and minus 54 in winter. Summer maximums are usually in the 60's and winter minimums between zero and minus 10.

Total precipitation varies from 15 to 30 inches each year which includes the water equivalent of the wintertime snowfall of 75 to 150 inches. Numerous thunderstorms each summer make the months of July and August the heaviest for precipitation.

Climate Conditions, Fairbanks to Southern Slopes of Chugach Mountains

This portion of the route along the highway covers a rather long distance, including considerable variation in altitude and terrain. Yet with a few exceptions average values of wind, temperature and precipitation show only small variations from one place to another. The Alaska Range crosses this portion of the highway route roughly at mid point. On either side of the mountains surface winds average 5 to mph annually with monthly variations of 3 to 10 mph with the strongest during spring and summer months. Near and in the mountains there are isolated areas of strong winds, primarily in winter. These areas are through mountain passes and narrow valleys. Drifting of snow in winter in these areas creates a serious problem for the highway department in keeping the roads open during strong wind periods. Isabell Pass is an excellent example of this problem. Trims Camp near the top of the pass reports speeds of 20 to 40 mph in summer and 30 to 55 mph in winter with occasional occurrences to 75 mph.

Daytime temperatures in summer usually range between 60 and 75 degrees dropping into the low 50's and upper 40's at night. Extreme maximum values are in the 80's and occasionally near 90. Winter daytime temperatures vary between 5 and 15 degrees with a few days in the 20's, dropping to minus 10 to 25 degrees during midwinter. Extreme winter lows will range as low as minus 45 to 60. A prolonged period of cold weather usually occurs each winter. During these times there is little fluctuation of temperature from day to night with readings in the minus 40's or colder. Fortunately wind speeds are quite light during these periods, but as on the Arctic Slope, the equivalent chill temperature is a concern to those exposed to the free air.

Precipitation annually is 10 to 12 inches. As usual this includes the annual snowfall amounts of 35 to 70 inches. This much variation in snowfall amounts might be expected to cause a considerable variation in the water equivalent of the snow as well. There is variation, but since the snow is necessarily "dry snow" because of the cold temperatures at which it usually occurs, the variation is not large enough to be reflected to any great extent in the total annual precipitation amount.

Spring floods caused by ice jams also create problems along this route because of the necessity of crossing numerous streams. It should not be as serious however as for the route along the railroad.

Climatic Conditions, through the Chugach Mountains to Valdez

The last leg of this route again passes through mountains, and also through the area that holds the record for total snowfall in Alaska during a winter season (September through April). A total of 974.5 inches of snow was recorded for the winter season of 1952-53 by the Cooperative Weather Station in Thompson Pass. In February of 1964 a record monthly amount of 346.1 inches was measured. The average seasonal snowfall is 558.6 inches. Like other passes that have been mentioned, surface winds cause considerable trouble for the highway crews. Snow drifted by winds of 30 to 70 mph occurs several times each month during the snow season. A figure for the total annual precipitation is not available because the observing station operated by the Highway Department is open only during the winter. The water equivalent for just the snow amounts to 61 inches annually.

Because of the proximity of the pass to the warmer air of the Gulf of Alaska, wintertime temperatures are much warmer than the area immediately to the north. During the coldest part of the winter readings are usually between zero and 15 degrees and the coldest temperature recorded at this station is minus 39 degrees, occurring in February of 1964.

Climatic conditions coming down the southern slopes of the Chugach mountains reflects a gradual moderation of temperatures and a decrease in precipitation amounts. At

Valdez surface winds although still strong on numerous occasions are not as strong as through Thompson Pass.

Temperatures show considerable change from that in the interior. The extremes range from 87 to a minus 28. Summertime days warm into the 50's and low 60's and in winter the nights during the coldest months have temperatures dropping to between 5 and 25 degrees. Equivalent chill temperatures are still a consideration, but not nearly as important as for the areas where subzero readings are common.

Precipitation is heavy compared to other areas described. Annual snowfall ranges 250 to 400 inches and is usually a wet snow, making a substantial contribution to the total annual precipitation of 60 to 90 inches. Heaviest precipitation amounts occur from August through November.

FACILITIES LOCATION MAP
PIPELINES AND ROADS

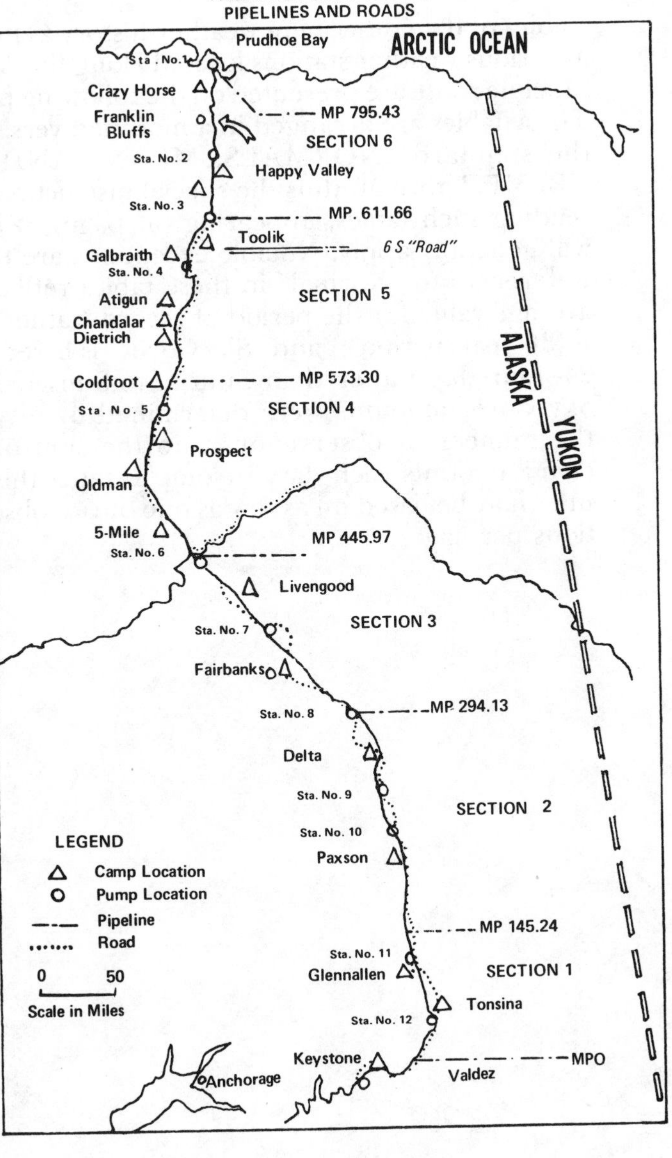

About the tables that follow:

Tables of data describing weather history as logged at various weather stations located along the Alaska pipeline route are presented on the following pages. These tables are arranged in a modified version of the standard "NORMALS, MEANS AND EXTREMES" format, thus the special instructions for reading such tables, appearing on pages 321-327 will generally apply. Notable exceptions are these: References to "Normal" in these tables reflect the average value for the period of record (rather than a 30-year period); and "Sky Cover" is based on a 24-hour day rather than Sunrise-to-Sunset. Daily Sky Cover amounts were determined by dividing the number of observations into the sum of the cloud amounts each day. In some instance this figure may be based on as few as one or two observations per day.

501492 Chandalar Lake Alaska

Month	Temperature: Normal: Daily maximum	Daily minimum	Monthly	Extremes: Record highest	Year	Record lowest	Year	Precipitation: Normal total	Maximum monthly	Year	Minimum monthly	Year	Maximum in 24 hrs.	Year	Snow, Ice pellets: Mean total	Maximum monthly	Year	Maximum in 24 hrs.	Year	Wind &: Mean speed	Prevailing direction	Fastest mile: Speed	Direction	Year	Pct. of possible sunshine	Mean sky cover sunrise to sunset
(a)	(b)	(b)	(b)	4		4		(b)	4		4		4		2	2		2								
J	-16.6	-34.6	-25.6	30	1973	-60	1973+	0.41	1.01	1973	T	1969	0.47	1973	1.0	1.9	1972	1.0	1972							
F	-1.9	-24.4	-13.2	28	1969	-64	1972	0.53	1.53	1964	T	1972	0.48	1964	2.0	4.0	1969	2.0	1969							
M	12.0	-17.5	-2.8	39	1969	-47	1972	0.15	0.29	1970	0.04	1972	0.09	1970	4.2	10.0	1970	3.0	1970							
A	28.6	-.3	14.2	46	1969	-38	1972	0.06	0.06	1969	0.06	1969	0.04	1969	2.5	2.5	1969	1.5	1969							
M	50.7	25.5	38.1	70	1969	12	1972	0.06	0.13	1969	T	1972	0.13	1969	0.5	1.0	1969	1.0	1969							
J	69.1	41.5	55.3	87	1969	23	1969	0.61	0.61	1969	0.61	1969	0.31	1969	0.0	0.0	1972+	0.0	1972+							
J	67.6	40.6	54.1	84	1972	25	1969	1.17	1.39	1972	0.94	1969	0.80	1972	0.1	T	1969	T	1969							
A	58.3	35.0	46.7	71	1972	17	1969	2.05	2.11	1969	1.98	1972	0.81	1969	0.0	0.0	1972+	0.0	1972+							
S	47.0	24.1	35.6	71	1963	4	1969	0.36	0.64	1969	0.00	1963	0.45	1969	0.5	1.0	1972	1.0	1972							
O	26.8	11.0	18.9	48	1969	-27	1972	0.65	1.09	1969	T	1963	0.60	1969	1.5	1.5	1969	1.5	1969							
N	2.4	-15.5	-6.6	27	1969	-47	1971	0.50	1.35	1971	0.01	1963	0.50	1971	7.4	8.0	1971	4.0	1968							
D	1.5	-20.0	-9.3	29	1972	-51	1971+	0.52	0.60	1971+	0.43	1972	0.24	1968	7.8	9.5	1971	3.0	1968							
YR	28.8	5.5	17.1	87	JUN. 1969	-64	FEB. 1972	7.07	2.11	AUG. 1969	0.00	SEP. 1963	0.81	AUG. 1969	27.5	10.0	MAR. 1970	4.0	NOV. 1968							

521030 Coldfoot Camp Alaska

Month	Temperature: Normal: Daily maximum	Daily minimum	Monthly	Extremes: Record highest	Year	Record lowest	Year	Precipitation: Normal total	Maximum monthly	Year	Minimum monthly	Year	Maximum in 24 hrs.	Year	Snow, Ice pellets: Mean total	Maximum monthly	Year	Maximum in 24 hrs.	Year	Wind &: Mean speed	Prevailing direction	Fastest mile: Speed	Direction	Year	Pct. of possible sunshine	Mean sky cover sunrise to sunset
(a)	(b)	(b)	(b)	3		3		(b)	0		0		0		2	2		2		3		3	3			3
J	-20.3	-38.1	-29.2	30	1973	-74	1971		0.00		0.00		0.00		31.5	55.0	1973	14.5	1973	4.3		29	SSE	1973		3.2
F	-6.4	-30.6	-18.5	26	1971	-56	1971	0.05	0.05	1972	0.05	1972	0.05	1972	11.5	22.5	1971	6.0	1971	6.1		81	N	1973		3.5
M	5.0	-25.3	-10.2	32	1971	-58	1971		0.00		0.00		0.00		7.3	8.0	1971	3.5	1972	6.8		31	NE	1971		3.8
A	27.8	1.6	14.7	47	1971	-32	1971	0.23	0.45	1972	T	1971	0.25	1972	2.3	4.5	1972	2.5	1972	3.5		17	N	1971+		3.2
M	48.7	31.7	40.2	68	1972	14	1971	0.89	1.50	1972	0.27	1971	1.00	1972	2.6	5.0	1972	2.0	1972	4.6		23	NW	1971		5.0
J	67.7	43.3	55.5	88	1972	28	1971	1.29	1.39	1971	1.19	1972	0.34	1972	0.0	0.0	1972+	0.0	1972+	5.9		29	S	1972		5.0
J	69.7	44.2	57.0	88	1972	32	1972	3.04	3.44	1971	2.64	1972	0.83	1971	0.0	0.0	1972+	0.0	1972+	4.4		17	S	1972		5.2
A	61.8	39.1	50.5	73	1972	25	1972	1.80	2.85	1972	0.75	1971	1.30	1972	0.0	0.0	1972+	0.0	1972+	3.7		29	N	1971		6.1
S	46.5	25.1	35.8	61	1972	9	1972	2.23	2.23	1972	2.22	1971	0.60	1972	5.4	10.0	1972	6.0	1972	4.7		22	N	1971		6.9
O	13.9	3.4	8.7	40	1970	-35	1970	2.82	3.54	1970	2.10	1971	0.80	1970	32.3	45.0	1972	7.5	1972	3.5		17	N	1970+		6.1
N	4.5	-13.1	-4.3	35	1970	-52	1970	1.85	2.06	1970	1.64	1971	0.60	1970+	18.1	27.0	1970	8.0	1970	5.2		41	SW	1971		3.9
D	-2.6	-21.6	-12.1	28	1972+	-56	1971+	0.00	0.00	1972	0.00	1972	0.00	1972	33.8	43.5	1970	11.5	1972	5.9		29	N	1972		4.5
YR	26.4	5.0	15.7	88	JUL. 1972+	-74	JAN. 1971	14.20	3.54	OCT. 1970	0.00	DEC. 1972+	1.30	AUG. 1972	144.8	55.0	JAN. 1973	14.5	JAN. 1973	4.9		81	N	FEB. 1973		4.6

502107 College Magnetic Observatory Alaska

Month	Temperature: Normal: Daily maximum	Temperature: Normal: Daily minimum	Temperature: Normal: Monthly	Temperature: Extremes: Record highest	Year	Record lowest	Year	Precipitation: Normal total	Maximum monthly	Year	Minimum monthly	Year	Maximum in 24 hrs.	Year	Snow, Ice pellets: Mean total	Maximum monthly	Year	Maximum in 24 hrs.	Year	Wind: Mean speed	Prevailing direction	Fastest mile: Speed	Direction	Year	Pct. of possible sunshine	Mean sky cover sunrise to sunset
(a)	(b)	(b)	(b)	24		24		(b)	24		24		24		24	24		24								
J	-1.8	-16.1	-9.0	45	1965	-60	1969	0.74	2.35	1950	0.06	1966	0.38	1950	11.1	34.5	1950	8.4	1968							
F	7.0	-10.0	-1.5	43	1963	-46	1969	0.55	1.54	1966	0.11	1958+	0.66	1966	8.9	24.3	1966	13.2	1966							
M	21.7	.0	10.9	51	1970+	-40	1956	0.52	2.74	1963	T	1968	1.07	1963	6.8	26.7	1963	8.0	1963							
A	39.1	19.3	29.2	70	1953	-15	1960	0.29	1.35	1967	T	1953	0.29	1965	2.9	11.0	1970	3.5	1970							
M	57.2	35.5	46.4	88	1960	3	1964	0.58	1.55	1955	0.04	1971	0.76	1959	0.5	4.0	1964	4.0	1964							
J	69.5	46.5	58.0	94	1969	29	1970+	1.45	3.44	1955	0.23	1971	1.23	1962	T	T	1962	T	1962							
J	70.2	48.8	59.5	90	1955+	32	1957	2.15	4.30	1962	0.58	1957	1.89	1962	0.0	0.0	1972+	0.0	1972+							
A	65.4	45.1	55.3	85	1962+	26	1969	2.45	7.36	1967	0.57	1966	2.51	1967	0.0	T	1955+	T	1955+							
S	53.6	34.7	44.2	82	1957	10	1956	1.26	3.21	1960	0.11	1968	1.00	1962	1.0	8.6	1972	6.0	1972							
O	32.4	17.8	25.1	64	1969	-17	1956	0.77	2.05	1970	0.14	1954	0.72	1970	8.6	21.6	1970	8.9	1970							
N	13.0	-.8	6.1	49	1954	-37	1956	0.80	3.89	1970	0.01	1953	1.04	1970	11.7	40.6	1970	11.0	1950							
D	.4	-12.9	-6.3	42	1969+	-66	1961	0.91	2.74	1970	0.06	1952	1.30	1968	12.4	29.3	1970	13.8	1968							
YR	35.6	17.3	26.5	94	JUN. 1969	-66	DEC. 1961	12.47	7.36	AUG. 1967	T	MAR. 1968+	2.51	AUG. 1967	63.9	40.6	NOV. 1970	13.8	DEC. 1968							

502161 Copper Center Alaska

Month	Temperature: Normal: Daily maximum	Temperature: Normal: Daily minimum	Temperature: Normal: Monthly	Temperature: Extremes: Record highest	Year	Record lowest	Year	Precipitation: Normal total	Maximum monthly	Year	Minimum monthly	Year	Maximum in 24 hrs.	Year	Snow, Ice pellets: Mean total	Maximum monthly	Year	Maximum in 24 hrs.	Year	Wind: Mean speed	Prevailing direction	Fastest mile: Speed	Direction	Year	Pct. of possible sunshine	Mean sky cover sunrise to sunset
(a)	(b)	(b)	(b)	6		6		(b)	6		6		6		6	6		6								
J	-2.9	-28.2	-15.6	47	1965	-61	1965	0.74	1.96	1962	0.19	1969	0.67	1962	7.6	20.0	1962	7.0	1962							
F	15.0	-11.2	1.9	49	1968	-54	1969	0.95	2.21	1968	0.16	1969	0.51	1968	7.5	12.2	1968	3.5	1968							
M	32.5	-2.2	15.2	53	1967	-53	1964	0.19	0.34	1964	0.06	1970	0.22	1967	2.6	5.8	1967	5.1	1964							
A	45.9	18.6	32.3	62	1967	-16	1964	0.16	0.50	1970	0.00	1969	0.23	1970	1.8	3.0	1970	2.0	1970							
M	58.0	30.6	44.3	79	1964	16	1967	0.65	1.03	1966	0.23	1964	0.35	1966	0.1	0.3	1967	0.3	1967							
J	71.0	40.9	56.0	92	1969	27	1968+	1.36	2.17	1966	0.57	1969	0.87	1968	0.0	0.0	1970+	0.0	1970+							
J	70.8	43.6	57.2	86	1966	30	1966+	1.86	3.55	1969	0.52	1967	0.72	1969	0.0	0.0	1969+	0.0	1969+							
A	65.2	38.9	52.1	78	1965	18	1967	0.92	1.47	1961	0.47	1969	0.45	1966	0.0	0.0	1969+	0.0	1969+							
S	58.4	31.0	44.7	72	1964+	9	1968	1.08	2.91	1961	0.01	1969	0.68	1961	0.0	0.0	1969+	0.0	1969+							
O	37.5	14.3	25.9	59	1967+	-23	1965	1.00	1.71	1964	0.47	1961	0.73	1964	8.2	13.4	1965	5.9	1967							
N	16.0	-6.3	4.9	63	1964	-42	1965	0.92	1.97	1961	0.04	1964	1.01	1961	7.3	14.0	1966	6.4	1965							
D	-1.9	-27.0	-14.5	42	1967	-62	1964	0.84	2.22	1961	0.14	1965	0.57	1961	6.1	12.5	1961	5.0	1961							
YR	38.8	11.9	25.4	92	JUN. 1969	-62	DEC. 1964	10.67	3.55	JUL. 1969	0.00	APR. 1969	1.01	NOV. 1961	41.2	20.0	JAN. 1962	7.0	JAN. 1962							

524250 Dietrich Camp Alaska

Month	Temperature – Normal – Daily maximum	Temperature – Normal – Daily minimum	Temperature – Normal – Monthly	Temperature – Extremes – Record highest	Year	Temperature – Extremes – Record lowest	Year	Precipitation – Normal total	Maximum monthly	Year	Minimum monthly	Year	Maximum in 24 hrs.	Year	Snow, Ice pellets – Mean total	Maximum monthly	Year	Maximum in 24 hrs.	Year	Wind & – Mean speed	Prevailing direction	Fastest mile – Speed	Direction	Year	Pct. of possible sunshine	Mean sky cover sunrise to sunset
(a)	(b)	(b)	(b)	2		2		(b)	1		1		1		1	1		1				2	2			2
J	-24.4	-42.6	-33.5	24	1972+	-70	1971	0.26	0.26	1971	0.26	1971	0.18	1971	4.0	4.0	1971	3.0	1971			0	C	1971+		2.3
F	-9.3	-37.6	-23.5	23	1971	-64	1971	0.39	0.77	1971	0.00	1972	0.24	1971	6.5	13.0	1971	4.0	1971	.0		0	C	1971+		3.1
M	6.3	-28.9	-11.3	32	1971	-61	1971		0.00		0.00		0.00			0.0		0.0		1.7		14	N	1971		2.9
A	29.5	-7.8	10.9	45	1971	-39	1972	0.12	0.25	1971	T	1972	0.20	1971	1.2	2.5	1971	2.0	1971	4.8		41	NE	1972		2.7
M	45.5	28.5	38.5	63	1971	5	1971	0.76	0.76	1971	0.76	1971	0.20	1971	1.8	1.8	1971	1.0	1971	3.7		41	NNW	1971		3.9
J	67.9	42.3	55.1	85	1971	31	1971	0.63	0.63	1971	0.63	1971	0.12	1971	0.0	0.0	1971	0.0	1971	4.5		32	S	1971		4.2
J	66.4	42.9	54.7	78	1971	32	1971	1.87	1.87	1971	1.87	1971	0.30	1971	0.0	0.0	1971	0.0	1971	3.3		14	NE	1972		3.8
A	61.0	34.7	47.9	67	1971	26	1971	0.49	0.49	1971	0.49	1971	0.16	1971	0.0	0.0	1971	0.0	1971	2.8		12	N	1971+		6.3
S	45.6	23.7	34.7	60	1971	10	1971	0.95	0.95	1971	0.95	1971	0.30	1971	0.1	T	1971	T	1971	3.3		20	N	1972		6.0
O	18.0	-8.3	4.9	37	1971	-37	1970	1.04	1.39	1970	0.69	1971	0.52	1970	10.3	12.0	1970	3.7	1970	1.5		16	N	1971		6.1
N	-2.1	-24.6	-13.4	34	1970	-51	1970	1.70	2.07	1970	1.32	1971	0.45	1970	15.9	18.1	1970	5.8	1970	.5		17	N	1972		4.1
D	-7.0	-29.0	-18.0	27	1970	-54	1971	0.36	0.73	1970	T	1971	0.26	1970	6.3	12.7	1970	3.0	1970			0	C	1971		5.0
YR	25.0	-.6	12.3	85	JUN. 1971	-70	JAN. 1971	8.57	2.07	NOV. 1970	0.00	FEB. 1972+	0.52	OCT. 1970		18.1	NOV. 1970	5.8	NOV. 1970	2.9		41	NE	APR. 1972+		4.1

502835 Ernestine Alaska

Month	Temperature – Normal – Daily maximum	Temperature – Normal – Daily minimum	Temperature – Normal – Monthly	Temperature – Extremes – Record highest	Year	Temperature – Extremes – Record lowest	Year	Precipitation – Normal total	Maximum monthly	Year	Minimum monthly	Year	Maximum in 24 hrs.	Year	Snow, Ice pellets – Mean total	Maximum monthly	Year	Maximum in 24 hrs.	Year	Wind & – Mean speed	Prevailing direction	Fastest mile – Speed	Direction	Year	Pct. of possible sunshine	Mean sky cover sunrise to sunset
(a)	(b)	(b)	(b)	2		2		(b)	2		2		2		2	2		2								
J	.9	-19.5	-9.3	40	1968	-48	1972	0.34	0.46	1972	0.21	1968	0.21	1972	6.0	7.0	1968	4.0	1968							
F	24.5	5.1	14.8	58	1968	-45	1968	1.46	3.87	1968	0.22	1972	2.80	1968	16.0	35.6	1968	24.0	1968							
M	31.8	3.2	17.5	50	1968	-39	1972	1.48	2.80	1968	T	1969	2.80	1968	13.7	24.0	1968	24.0	1968							
A	41.6	19.7	30.7	55	1969	-24	1972	0.22	0.70	1968	0.00	1969	0.50	1968	2.5	6.0	1968	4.0	1968							
M	55.5	29.8	42.7	72	1970	4	1972	0.39	0.49	1972	0.28	1968	0.29	1972	0.1	T	1968	T	1968							
J	64.2	37.4	50.8	80	1968	22	1972	1.67	3.24	1970	0.10	1968	1.30	1970	T	T	1972	T	1972							
J	69.1	41.6	55.4	85	1969	20	1970	0.37	0.60	1965	T	1969	0.47	1965	0.0	0.0	1972+	0.0	1972+							
A	62.0	39.3	50.7	85	1968	25	1971+	1.40	2.80	1968	T	1969	1.00	1968	0.0	0.0	1971+	0.0	1971+							
S	52.8	30.8	41.8	72	1967	14	1971	0.86	1.92	1967	0.10	1969	1.00	1967	0.0	0.0	1971+	0.0	1971+							
O	35.4	19.9	27.7	55	1967	-12	1971	1.89	4.73	1971	0.72	1968	1.56	1971	15.8	34.0	1971	14.0	1971							
N	18.1	.3	9.2	44	1967	-28	1971	2.15	3.70	1968	0.51	1972	2.80	1968	23.7	30.0	1972	14.0	1968							
D	1.7	-15.2	-6.8	42	1967	-40	1971+	0.68	1.38	1971	0.16	1968	0.30	1971	16.2	29.7	1971	9.0	1971							
YR	38.1	16.0	27.1	85	JUL. 1969+	-48	JAN. 1972	12.91	4.73	OCT. 1971	0.00	APR. 1969	2.80	NOV. 1968+	94.0	35.6	FEB. 1968	24.0	MAR. 1968+							

530820 Five Mile Camp Alaska

Month	Temperature: Normal: Daily maximum	Temperature: Normal: Daily minimum	Temperature: Normal: Monthly	Temperature: Extremes: Record highest	Year	Record lowest	Year	Precipitation: Normal total	Maximum monthly	Year	Minimum monthly	Year	Maximum in 24 hrs.	Year	Snow, Ice pellets: Mean total	Maximum monthly	Year	Maximum in 24 hrs.	Year	Wind &: Mean speed	Prevailing direction	Fastest mile: Speed	Direction	Year	Pct. of possible sunshine	Mean sky cover sunrise to sunset
(a)	(b)	(b)	(b)	1		1		(b)	1		1		1		1	1		1		3		3	3			3
J	-22.3	-35.1	-28.7	20	1972	-61	1972	0.01	T	1972	T	1972		1972	0.1	T	1972	T	1972	.0		6	S	1972		2.8
F	-1.6	-27.1	-14.4	29	1972	-50	1972	0.00	0.00	1972	0.00	1972	0.00	1972	0.0	0.0	1972	0.0	1972	1.6		29	NE	1972+		3.4
M		-30.2				-42	1972		0.00		0.00		0.00		12.5	12.5	1972	5.1	1972	3.1		29	E	1973		3.3
A	34.0	6.2	20.1	55	1971	-28	1971	0.53	0.53	1971	0.53	1971	0.28	1971	5.3	5.3	1971	2.8	1971	3.9		67	NW	1971		3.4
M	56.0	29.7	42.9	69	1971	7	1971	1.12	1.12	1971	1.12	1971	1.12	1971	0.0	0.0	1971	0.0	1971	2.8		29	NE	1971		3.9
J	75.8	44.1	60.0	90	1971	30	1971	2.60	2.60	1971	2.60	1971	0.90	1971	0.0	0.0	1971	0.0	1971	3.7		17	SSE	1971+		3.3
J	73.0	43.4	58.2	83	1971	34	1971	3.56	3.56	1971	3.56	1971	1.08	1971	0.0	0.0	1971	0.0	1971	1.7		12	W	1971+		5.0
A									0.00		0.00		0.00			0.0		0.0		1.8		17	N	1971		5.8
S	47.5	24.6	36.1	63	1971	-8	1970	0.80	1.09	1971	0.50	1970	0.28	1971	0.2	0.4	1971	0.4	1971	2.1		23	NNE	1971		6.1
O	22.5	4.5	13.5	40	1971+	-27	1970	0.60	1.00	1971	0.20	1970	0.25	1971	6.3	10.5	1971	3.0	1971	.9		12	NE	1971		7.3
N	2.5	-15.1	-6.3	20	1971	-40	1971	1.50	1.50	1971	1.50	1971	0.60	1971	15.0	15.0	1971	6.0	1971	.8		12	NE	1972		6.3
D	-7.2	-23.4	-15.3	19	1970	-59	1970		0.00		0.00		0.00		8.2	8.2	1971	1.5	1971	1.2		23	N	1972		4.6
YR	28.0	2.0	16.6		1972		1972	10.72		00000	0.00	FEB. 1972+		00000		15.0	NOV. 1971	6.0	NOV. 1971	1.8		67	NW	APR. 1971		4.6

532100 Galbraith Camp Alaska

Month	Temperature: Normal: Daily maximum	Temperature: Normal: Daily minimum	Temperature: Normal: Monthly	Temperature: Extremes: Record highest	Year	Record lowest	Year	Precipitation: Normal total	Maximum monthly	Year	Minimum monthly	Year	Maximum in 24 hrs.	Year	Snow, Ice pellets: Mean total	Maximum monthly	Year	Maximum in 24 hrs.	Year	Wind &: Mean speed	Prevailing direction	Fastest mile: Speed	Direction	Year	Pct. of possible sunshine	Mean sky cover sunrise to sunset
(a)	(b)	(b)	(b)	1		1		(b)	1		1		1		1	1		1		1		1	1			1
J	-9.1	-28.6	-18.9	25	1971	-49	1971	0.24	0.24	1971	0.24	1971	0.14	1971	2.7	2.7	1971	1.8	1971	3.1		17	NW	1971		2.8
F	-11.3	-33.7	-22.5	32	1971	-49	1971	0.23	0.23	1971	0.23	1971	0.23	1971	1.0	1.0	1971	1.0	1971	1.2		12	WNW	1971		2.9
M	-3.0	-26.0	-14.5	31	1971	-49	1971	0.01	T	1971	T	1971		1971	0.1	T	1971	T	1971	3.4		29	E	1971		3.3
A	14.2	-10.7	1.8	38	1971	-38	1971	0.02	0.04	1971	0.00	1972	0.04	1971	0.3	0.5	1971	0.5	1971	3.0		29	S	1972		3.0
M	36.2	16.0	26.1	52	1971	-13	1971	0.01	T	1971	T	1971		1971	0.1	T	1971	T	1971	4.5		23	ESE	1971		5.0
J	57.5	38.1	47.8	78	1971	16	1971	0.44	0.44	1971	0.44	1971	0.38	1971	3.0	3.0	1971	3.0	1971	8.3		17	ESE	1971		4.8
J	59.8	42.5	51.2	69	1971	30	1971	0.01	T	1971	T	1971		1971	0.1	T	1971	T	1971	4.7		17	S	1971		6.8
A	46.4	32.1	40.3	62	1971	20	1971	0.01	0.01	1971	0.01	1971	0.01	1971	0.1	0.1	1971	0.1	1971	5.7		14	NNW	1971		8.4
S	35.1	20.2	27.7	45	1971	2	1971		0.00		0.00		0.00		12.5	12.5	1971	5.0	1971	2.9		29	SSE	1971		6.7
O	9.7	-12.1	-1.2	42	1970	-32	1970	0.36	0.36	1970	0.36	1970	0.13	1970	3.0	3.0	1970	1.0	1970	5.2		35	S	1970+		4.5
N	15.5	-6.4	4.6	40	1970	-28	1970	0.33	0.33	1970	0.33	1970	0.18	1970	3.6	3.6	1970	1.0	1970	1.6		32	SSE	1971		4.4
D	-3.3	-20.9	-12.1	32	1970	-44	1970	0.20	0.20	1970	0.20	1970	0.13	1970	0.7	0.7	1970	0.5	1970			0	C	1971		7.0
YR	20.8	.9	10.9	78	JUN. 1971	-49	MAR. 1971+	1.86	0.44	JUN. 1971	0.00	APR. 1972+		1971	27.2	12.5	SEP. 1971	5.0	SEP. 1971	3.9		35	S	OCT. 1970+		4.9

503304 Glennallen Alaska

Month	Temperature: Normal: Daily maximum	Temperature: Normal: Daily minimum	Temperature: Normal: Monthly	Temperature: Extremes: Record highest	Year	Record lowest	Year	Precipitation: Normal total	Maximum monthly	Year	Minimum monthly	Year	Maximum in 24 hrs.	Year	Snow, Ice pellets: Mean total	Maximum monthly	Year	Maximum in 24 hrs.	Year	Wind &: Mean speed	Prevailing direction	Fastest mile: Speed	Direction	Year	Pct. of possible sunshine	Mean sky cover sunrise to sunset
(a)	(b)	(b)	(b)	8		8		(b)	8		8		8		8	8		8								
J	-2.6	-28.6	-15.6	42	1971	-60	1971	0.36	0.90	1972	0.08	1971	0.25	1967	6.1	10.1	1972	5.0	1973							
F	17.0	-10.3	3.4	47	1970+	-60	1968	0.59	1.71	1968	0.14	1972	0.72	1968	5.9	12.2	1967	4.8	1968							
M	27.2	-4.1	11.6	54	1971	-50	1972	0.21	0.33	1970	0.02	1971	0.24	1967	4.5	16.2	1972	7.0	1972							
A	41.5	13.7	27.6	60	1967	-23	1972	0.10	0.29	1970	0.03	1969	0.19	1970	1.6	4.0	1970	2.0	1970							
M	55.3	27.9	41.6	77	1969	10	1972	0.55	1.00	1967	0.07	1971	0.52	1967	0.5	1.6	1967	1.0	1972+							
J	67.0	39.0	53.0	90	1969	24	1971	1.33	2.24	1970	0.24	1969	0.91	1968	0.0	0.0	1972+	0.0	1972+							
J	69.6	41.9	55.8	88	1967	27	1970	1.54	2.89	1969	0.96	1968	0.67	1966	0.0	0.0	1972+	0.0	1972+							
A	65.0	37.1	51.1	83	1968	17	1969	1.39	3.21	1971	0.55	1966	1.87	1971	0.0	0.0	1972+	0.0	1972+							
S	53.9	25.8	39.9	68	1967	0	1970	0.95	1.71	1970	T	1969	0.76	1967	1.3	7.7	1970	3.0	1970							
O	35.3	12.1	23.7	65	1969	-25	1970	0.98	2.52	1971	0.11	1969	0.50	1971	11.5	26.7	1971	8.0	1971							
N	15.7	-5.4	5.2	45	1970+	-44	1969	0.58	0.90	1966	0.18	1969	0.35	1967	10.2	16.7	1971	3.5	1971							
D	2.9	-20.4	-8.8	42	1967	-56	1970	0.56	1.96	1967	0.06	1969+	0.54	1967	6.6	21.8	1971	5.3	1971							
YR	37.3	10.7	24.0	90	JUN. 1969	-60	JAN. 1971+	9.14	3.21	AUG. 1971	T	SEP. 1969	1.87	AUG. 1971	48.2	26.7	OCT. 1971	8.0	OCT. 1971							

535580 Happy Valley Alaska

Month	Temperature: Normal: Daily maximum	Temperature: Normal: Daily minimum	Temperature: Normal: Monthly	Temperature: Extremes: Record highest	Year	Record lowest	Year	Precipitation: Normal total	Maximum monthly	Year	Minimum monthly	Year	Maximum in 24 hrs.	Year	Snow, Ice pellets: Mean total	Maximum monthly	Year	Maximum in 24 hrs.	Year	Wind &: Mean speed	Prevailing direction	Fastest mile: Speed	Direction	Year	Pct. of possible sunshine	Mean sky cover sunrise to sunset
(a)	(b)	(b)	(b)	2		2		(b)	2		2		2		1	1		1		2		2	2			2
J	-9.0	-27.0	-18.0	31	1972	-52	1972	0.07	0.14	1972	0.00	1971	0.10	1972	0.0	0.0	1971	0.0	1971	9.3		35	SW	1971		4.1
F	-13.7	-35.2	-24.5	26	1972	-57	1972	1.00	1.00	1972	1.00	1972	0.50	1972	10.0	10.0	1972	5.0	1972	9.0		46	SSE	1971		3.6
M	-7.7	-28.1	-17.9	30	1971	-52	1971	0.00	0.00	1972	0.00	1972	0.00	1972	0.0	0.0	1972	0.0	1972	9.5		23	N	1971+		3.6
A	8.0	-17.7	-4.9	34	1971	-46	1971	0.01	T	1972	T	1972		1972	0.1	T	1972	T	1972	7.2		26	SW	1972		3.0
M	35.8	14.2	25.0	54	1972	-9	1972	0.00	0.00	1972	0.00	1972	0.00	1972	0.0	0.0	1972	0.0	1972	7.5		25	WSW	1972		5.3
J	60.1	34.5	47.3	81	1972	22	1971	0.75	1.30	1972	0.20	1971	0.45	1972	1.0	2.0	1971	2.0	1971	9.1		23	SW	1971		6.0
J	67.2	40.4	53.8	79	1972	29	1971	1.52	2.00	1971	1.04	1972	0.49	1971	0.1	T	1971	T	1971	8.4		23	SW	1971		5.6
A	55.7	34.2	45.0	70	1972+	20	1971	0.95	1.10	1972	0.79	1971	0.42	1971	0.1	T	1971	T	1971	7.6		18	NNE	1971		7.0
S	37.9	19.6	28.8	72	1972	3	1972	0.29	0.29	1972	0.29	1972	0.29	1972		0.0		0.0		8.7		21	E	1972		7.7
O	18.2	-.3	9.0	34	1971	-21	1971	1.27	1.27	1971	1.27	1971	0.40	1971	12.7	12.7	1971	4.0	1971	7.2		23	S	1972		4.5
N	7.7	-13.4	-2.9	35	1970	-37	1971	0.10	0.10	1971	0.10	1971	0.05	1971		0.0		0.0		6.9		37	SW	1971		4.8
D	-3.2	-23.7	-13.5	48	1971	-51	1971	0.00	0.00	1970	0.00	1970	0.00	1970	0.0	0.0	1970	0.0	1970	8.6		35	SW	1971		3.6
YR	21.4	-.2	10.6	81	JUN. 1972	-57	FEB. 1972	5.96	2.00	JUL. 1971	0.00	MAY 1972+		1972		12.7	OCT. 1971	5.0	FEB. 1972	8.2		46	SSE	FEB. 1971		4.9

564280 Livengood Alaska

Month	Temperature – Normal – Daily maximum	Temperature – Normal – Daily minimum	Temperature – Normal – Monthly	Temperature – Extremes – Record highest	Temperature – Extremes – Year	Temperature – Extremes – Record lowest	Temperature – Extremes – Year	Precipitation – Normal total	Precipitation – Maximum monthly	Precipitation – Year	Precipitation – Minimum monthly	Precipitation – Year	Precipitation – Maximum in 24 hrs.	Precipitation – Year	Snow, Ice pellets – Mean total	Snow, Ice pellets – Maximum monthly	Snow, Ice pellets – Year	Snow, Ice pellets – Maximum in 24 hrs.	Snow, Ice pellets – Year	Wind & – Mean speed	Wind & – Prevailing direction	Wind & – Fastest mile – Speed	Wind & – Fastest mile – Direction	Wind & – Fastest mile – Year	Pct. of possible sunshine	Mean sky cover sunrise to sunset
(a)	(b)	(b)	(b)	3		3		(b)	3		3		3		3	3		3								
J	-8.9	-19.0	-14.0	38	1963	-54	1963	0.36	0.69	1963	0.03	1966	0.17	1963	6.3	10.7	1963	3.0	1963							
F	-4.1	-15.8	-10.0	26	1963	-44	1963	0.28	0.44	1966	0.09	1963	0.17	1966	5.3	7.9	1966	2.6	1966							
M	15.8	-2.8	6.5	49	1965	-41	1964	0.66	1.30	1963	0.29	1964	0.35	1963	8.8	18.6	1963	4.0	1963							
A	33.8	11.6	22.7	91	1965	-17	1964	0.61	0.85	1963	0.49	1965	0.46	1963	5.9	11.3	1963	5.3	1963							
M	51.4	30.1	40.8	77	1964	-5	1964	0.91	1.64	1966	0.44	1964	0.68	1963+	0.0	T	1966+	T	1966+							
J	67.3	42.9	55.1	80	1966	29	1963	1.98	4.11	1965	0.62	1966	1.12	1965	0.0	0.0	1966+	0.0	1966+							
J	68.8	45.4	57.1	85	1963	31	1964	2.65	4.10	1964	1.71	1965	1.45	1964	0.0	0.0	1965+	0.0	1965+							
A	61.5	42.6	52.1	81	1963	28	1965	3.14	3.56	1963	2.75	1964	1.01	1964	0.0	0.0	1965+	0.0	1965+							
S	50.5	31.8	41.2	77	1965	13	1964	1.76	4.12	1965	0.30	1964	0.96	1965	T	T	1962	T	1962							
O	26.1	14.2	20.2	46	1963+	-16	1965	0.85	1.24	1963	0.63	1962	0.58	1963	7.7	12.0	1965	4.3	1965							
N	5.1	-5.2	-.1	33	1965	-47	1963	0.40	0.87	1965	T	1963	0.21	1965	6.2	14.8	1965	4.1	1965							
D	-1.1	-14.9	-8.0	39	1962	-50	1964	0.77	1.08	1965	0.50	1963	0.63	1962	13.3	18.3	1965	8.0	1962							
YR	30.5	13.4	22.0	91	APR. 1965	-54	JAN. 1963	14.37	4.12	SEP. 1965	T	NOV. 1963	1.45	JUL. 1964	53.5	18.6	MAR. 1963	8.0	DEC. 1962							

561440 Murphy Lake Alaska

Month	Temperature – Normal – Daily maximum	Temperature – Normal – Daily minimum	Temperature – Normal – Monthly	Temperature – Extremes – Record highest	Temperature – Extremes – Year	Temperature – Extremes – Record lowest	Temperature – Extremes – Year	Precipitation – Normal total	Precipitation – Maximum monthly	Precipitation – Year	Precipitation – Minimum monthly	Precipitation – Year	Precipitation – Maximum in 24 hrs.	Precipitation – Year	Snow, Ice pellets – Mean total	Snow, Ice pellets – Maximum monthly	Snow, Ice pellets – Year	Snow, Ice pellets – Maximum in 24 hrs.	Snow, Ice pellets – Year	Wind & – Mean speed	Wind & – Prevailing direction	Wind & – Fastest mile – Speed	Wind & – Fastest mile – Direction	Wind & – Fastest mile – Year	Pct. of possible sunshine	Mean sky cover sunrise to sunset
(a)	(b)	(b)	(b)	1		1		(b)	1		1		1		1	1		1		1		1	1			1
J	-11.4	-32.0	-21.7	15	1971	-51	1971	0.58	0.58	1971	0.58	1971	0.25	1971	4.5	4.5	1971	2.0	1971	4.1		23	W	1971		4.2
F	-15.5	-36.1	-25.8	21	1971	-50	1971	0.37	0.37	1971	0.37	1971	0.19	1971	2.3	2.3	1971	1.0	1971	4.8		17	WSW	1971		3.7
M									0.00		0.00		0.00			0.0		0.0		5.6		23	NE	1971		1.6
A	-8.5	-35.7	-22.1	-2	1971	-45	1971	0.00	0.00	1971	0.00	1971	0.00	1971	0.0	0.0	1971	0.0	1971	.6		6	N	1971		2.5
M																						0	C	1971		.0
J																										
J																										
A																										
S																										
O	8.7	-10.8	-1.1	41	1970	-31	1970	1.18	1.18	1970	1.18	1970	0.50	1970		0.0		0.0		5.3		17	S	1970		1.7
N	15.6	-8.0	3.8	39	1970	-31	1970	1.53	1.53	1970	1.53	1970	0.54	1970	19.1	19.1	1970	6.0	1970	5.4		23	SE	1970		3.4
D																										
YR	-2.2	-24.5	-13.4		1971		1971	3.66		1971		1971+		1971												

570950 Paxson Alaska

Month	Temperature							Precipitation													Wind &						
	Normal			Extremes											Snow, Ice pellets							Fastest mile				
Month	Daily maximum	Daily minimum	Monthly	Record highest	Year	Record lowest	Year	Normal total	Maximum monthly	Year	Minimum monthly	Year	Maximum in 24 hrs.	Year	Mean total	Maximum monthly	Year	Maximum in 24 hrs.	Year	Mean speed	Prevailing direction	Speed	Direction	Year	Pct. of possible sunshine	Mean sky cover sunrise to sunset
(a)	(b)	(b)	(b)	12		12		(b)	10		10		10		11	11		11								
J	2.0	-19.8	-8.9	38	1965	-59	1971	1.09	3.78	1963	0.05	1969	0.80	1963	14.9	42.0	1963	9.0	1963							
F	15.8	-6.8	4.5	42	1970	-44	1971+	0.85	2.41	1962	0.10	1969	1.03	1962	14.0	31.0	1962	15.0	1962							
M	22.1	-4.3	8.9	49	1965	-45	1971	0.98	2.54	1967	0.24	1962	1.10	1967	11.8	17.7	1972	6.5	1971							
A	34.9	10.2	22.6	52	1967	-26	1972	0.87	2.34	1961	0.02	1967	0.78	1961	10.7	17.0	1971+	8.0	1961							
M	48.0	25.6	36.8	69	1969	-9	1964	1.21	2.98	1961	0.16	1967	0.96	1961	2.0	7.0	1972	4.0	1972							
J	61.6	36.3	49.0	85	1969	23	1971	2.51	3.34	1967	1.60	1971	0.95	1966	0.3	2.3	1971	2.3	1971							
J	63.3	41.0	52.2	80	1972+	28	1964	3.22	5.74	1969	1.01	1966	1.92	1964	0.0	0.0	1972+	0.0	1972+							
A	59.5	38.0	48.8	78	1960	13	1966	2.64	4.68	1960	0.92	1964	1.12	1963	0.0	0.0	1972+	0.0	1972+							
S	49.3	29.4	39.4	71	1963	6	1972	2.94	8.72	1960	0.25	1969	1.25	1960	5.3	15.0	1960	13.0	1972							
O	33.1	15.2	24.2	58	1969	-20	1970+	1.80	3.78	1972	0.41	1966	1.15	1961	17.9	37.0	1971	14.0	1971							
N	15.7	-4.5	5.6	42	1970	-39	1969	0.97	2.15	1967	0.21	1963	1.24	1960	14.4	25.9	1970	16.0	1960							
D	6.6	-13.5	-3.5	39	1967+	-55	1964	1.23	2.98	1961	0.27	1969	0.76	1971	18.4	61.5	1971	17.0	1971							
YR	34.3	12.2	23.3	85	JUN. 1969	-59	JAN. 1971	20.31	8.72	SEP. 1960	0.02	APR. 1967	1.92	JUL. 1964	109.7	61.5	DEC. 1971	17.0	DEC. 1971							

577780 Prospect Creek Camp Alaska

Month	Temperature							Precipitation													Wind &						
	Normal			Extremes											Snow, Ice pellets							Fastest mile				
Month	Daily maximum	Daily minimum	Monthly	Record highest	Year	Record lowest	Year	Normal total	Maximum monthly	Year	Minimum monthly	Year	Maximum in 24 hrs.	Year	Mean total	Maximum monthly	Year	Maximum in 24 hrs.	Year	Mean speed	Prevailing direction	Speed	Direction	Year	Pct. of possible sunshine	Mean sky cover sunrise to sunset
(a)	(b)	(b)	(b)	2		2		(b)	2		2		2		3	3		3		2		3	3			3
J	-29.8	-44.9	-37.4	30	1972	-80	1971	0.38	0.75	1971	0.00	1972	0.75	1971	12.0	19.0	1973	10.0	1972	.6		17	N	1972		3.6
F	-6.3	-34.8	-20.6	29	1971	-64	1971	0.67	1.35	1971	T	1972	0.50	1971	6.7	13.5	1971	5.0	1971	2.1		29	NE	1972		3.4
M	5.1	-33.9	-14.4	26	1971	-62	1971	0.60	0.60	1972	0.60	1972	0.20	1972	6.0	6.0	1972	2.0	1972	7.3		35	NE	1971		3.2
A	28.6	-6.2	11.2	50	1971	-43	1971	0.26	0.31	1971	0.20	1972	0.31	1971	2.8	3.5	1971	3.5	1971	6.3		23	NE	1972		3.9
M	51.4	26.8	39.1	62	1971	7	1971	0.95	0.95	1971	0.95	1971	0.47	1971	0.1	T	1971	T	1971	6.4		17	ENE	1971+		5.0
J	68.4	43.0	55.7	87	1971	20	1971	1.07	1.70	1972	0.44	1971	0.50	1972	0.0	0.0	1972+	0.0	1972+	6.3		17	ENE	1971+		4.8
J	68.0	43.1	55.6	87	1972	33	1972	1.27	1.40	1972	1.13	1971	0.73	1971	0.0	0.0	1972	0.0	1972	5.0		18	NE	1971		6.2
A	65.9	36.7	51.3	77	1972	24	1971	1.98	2.16	1972	1.80	1971	0.74	1972	0.0	0.0	1972+	0.0	1972+	4.6		16	E	1971		6.3
S	47.3	25.8	36.6	65	1972	4	1971	1.89	2.06	1971	1.71	1972	0.45	1971	5.0	5.0	1972+	5.0	1971	4.5		13	S	1971		7.2
O	23.4	1.9	12.7	44	1972	-35	1970	0.96	1.59	1972	T	1971	1.12	1970	5.8	15.9	1972	3.0	1972	2.0		14	ENE	1971		6.4
N	.8	-12.4	-5.8	26	1971	-62	1970		0.00		0.00		0.00			0.0		0.0		1.9		14	N	1972		5.6
D	-6.9	-26.1	-16.5	30	1970	-68	1970		0.00		0.00		0.00		18.3	20.0	1970	5.5	1970	1.3		23	SE	1971		4.6
YR	26.3	1.6	14.0	87	JUL. 1972+	-80	JAN. 1971	10.03	2.16	AUG. 1972	0.00	JAN. 1972+	1.12	OCT. 1970		20.0	DEC. 1970	10.0	JAN. 1972	4.0		35	NE	MAR. 1971		4.9

599990 Prudhoe Bay Alaska

Month	Temperature: Normal: Daily maximum	Normal: Daily minimum	Normal: Monthly	Extremes: Record highest	Year	Record lowest	Year	Precipitation: Normal total	Maximum monthly	Year	Minimum monthly	Year	Maximum in 24 hrs.	Year	Snow, Ice pellets: Mean total	Maximum monthly	Year	Maximum in 24 hrs.	Year	Wind: Mean speed	Prevailing direction	Fastest mile: Speed	Direction	Year	Pct. of possible sunshine	Mean sky cover sunrise to sunset
(a)	(b)	(b)	(b)	3		3		(b)	0		0		0													
J	-13.2	-27.7	-20.5	32	1973	-48	1971		0.00		0.00		0.00			0.0		0.0								
F	-18.9	-33.0	-26.0	24	1973	-58	1972		0.00		0.00		0.00			0.0		0.0								
M	-16.2	-31.7	-24.0	8	1973+	-52	1973+		0.00		0.00		0.00			0.0		0.0								
A	2.5	-15.7	-6.6	20	1971	-34	1971		0.00		0.00		0.00			0.0		0.0								
M	26.5	14.1	20.3	47	1971	-18	1971		0.00		0.00		0.00			0.0		0.0								
J	43.6	32.9	38.3	58	1971	24	1972		0.00		0.00		0.00			0.0		0.0								
J	52.8	38.2	45.5	75	1971	30	1971		0.00		0.00		0.00			0.0		0.0								
A	46.6	35.7	41.2	68	1971	27	1971		0.00		0.00		0.00			0.0		0.0								
S	36.0	27.8	31.9	53	1972	15	1972		0.00		0.00		0.00			0.0		0.0								
O	16.5	3.0	9.8	37	1972	-23	1970		0.00		0.00		0.00			0.0		0.0								
N	4.5	-8.5	-2.0	26	1970	-36	1971		0.00		0.00		0.00			0.0		0.0								
D	-7.2	-20.0	-13.6	34	1972	-49	1971		0.00		0.00		0.00			0.0		0.0								
YR	14.5	1.3	7.9	75	JUL. 1971	-58	FEB. 1972	0.00	0.00	0000+	0.00	DEC. +	0.00	0000+		0.0		0.0								

507977 Richardson Alaska

Month	Temperature: Normal: Daily maximum	Normal: Daily minimum	Normal: Monthly	Extremes: Record highest	Year	Record lowest	Year	Precipitation: Normal total	Maximum monthly	Year	Minimum monthly	Year	Maximum in 24 hrs.	Year	Snow, Ice pellets: Mean total	Maximum monthly	Year	Maximum in 24 hrs.	Year	Wind: Mean speed	Prevailing direction	Fastest mile: Speed	Direction	Year	Pct. of possible sunshine	Mean sky cover sunrise to sunset
(a)	(b)	(b)	(b)	5		5		(b)	5		5		5		5	5		5								
J	-5.4	-24.9	-15.2	37	1970+	-63	1971	0.84	1.96	1968	0.28	1970	0.80	1968	15.7	33.0	1968	14.0	1968							
F	15.6	-7.2	4.2	50	1968	-55	1968	0.21	0.30	1967	0.04	1969	0.16	1968	6.2	9.5	1968	4.0	1968							
M	30.3	2.7	16.5	57	1970	-47	1971	0.38	1.88	1967	T	1970+	0.34	1967	7.3	35.0	1967	7.0	1967							
A	44.4	20.9	32.7	63	1967	-10	1971	0.30	0.79	1967	T	1969	0.27	1967	6.3	14.0	1967	4.0	1970+							
M	60.5	33.3	46.9	76	1970+	18	1967	0.98	2.33	1968	0.42	1971	0.88	1968	0.6	3.0	1968	3.0	1968							
J	72.9	44.0	58.5	98	1969	29	1971+	1.41	2.64	1968	0.19	1969	0.75	1968	0.0	0.0	1971+	0.0	1971+							
J	73.1	46.0	59.6	90	1970	30	1971	2.58	7.40	1967	T	1966	1.65	1967	0.0	0.0	1971+	0.0	1971+							
A	67.3	41.5	54.4	84	1968+	22	1969	1.68	2.87	1967	0.93	1968	1.07	1967	T	T	1969	T	1969							
S	57.1	32.6	44.9	73	1966	8	1970	0.73	2.17	1970	0.06	1969	0.50	1970	0.0	T	1968+	T	1968+							
O	35.2	16.0	25.6	67	1969	-18	1970	0.60	1.00	1966	0.15	1969	0.60	1967	9.0	14.0	1968	10.0	1968							
N	19.0	1.7	10.4	52	1970	-41	1969	1.43	2.66	1966	0.24	1968	1.05	1969	23.9	48.5	1970	16.0	1970							
D	6.3	-12.5	-3.1	44	1969	-54	1966	0.63	1.39	1967	T	1969	0.85	1968	10.8	21.0	1967	10.0	1968							
YR	39.7	16.2	28.0	98	JUN. 1969	-63	JAN. 1971	11.77	7.40	JUL. 1967	T	MAR. 1970+	1.65	JUL. 1967	79.8	48.5	NOV. 1970	16.0	NOV. 1970							

588130 Summit Lake Alaska

Month	Temperature: Normal: Daily maximum	Temperature: Normal: Daily minimum	Temperature: Normal: Monthly	Temperature: Extremes: Record highest	Year	Record lowest	Year	Precipitation: Normal total	Maximum monthly	Year	Minimum monthly	Year	Maximum in 24 hrs.	Year	Snow, Ice pellets: Mean total	Maximum monthly	Year	Maximum in 24 hrs.	Year	Wind: Mean speed	Prevailing direction	Fastest mile: Speed	Direction	Year	Pct. of possible sunshine	Mean sky cover sunrise to sunset
(a)	(b)	(b)	(b)	5		5		(b)	5		5		5		5	5		5								
J	-2.0	-22.3	-12.2	34	1968	-53	1971	0.59	0.84	1970	0.26	1969	0.51	1971	12.1	25.3	1970	11.0	1972							
F	14.7	-7.2	3.8	39	1970	-50	1968	1.85	4.50	1968	0.27	1969	1.18	1968	26.5	44.4	1968	17.3	1972							
M	22.0	-4.5	8.8	41	1969	-47	1971	0.50	0.95	1969	T	1968	0.28	1969	10.9	21.3	1970	7.9	1971							
A	31.8	6.0	18.9	47	1968	-27	1972	0.35	0.64	1968	0.03	1969	0.34	1970	10.4	19.2	1971	8.5	1970							
M	44.7	25.6	35.2	62	1969	2	1972	0.54	1.02	1968	0.17	1972	0.85	1968	4.4	8.3	1971	5.1	1971							
J	57.2	36.3	46.8	79	1969	24	1971+	1.81	2.90	1972	0.67	1969	0.89	1971	1.3	5.0	1970	5.0	1970							
J	61.0	42.1	51.6	76	1972	27	1971	3.29	6.59	1969	1.72	1972	0.99	1969	0.0	0.0	1972+	0.0	1972+							
A	55.7	39.3	47.5	69	1972	25	1969	2.51	4.60	1970	0.83	1969	1.59	1970	T	T	1969	T	1969							
S	47.2	30.1	38.7	58	1972	12	1972+	2.30	4.87	1972	0.10	1969	0.95	1972	4.1	9.7	1972	6.2	1970							
O	32.0	15.3	23.7	52	1969	-16	1970	1.90	3.82	1972	0.34	1968	0.99	1972	16.0	34.1	1971	16.8	1971							
N	18.5	-4.4	7.1	40	1969	-33	1971	0.69	1.09	1970	0.29	1969	0.42	1970	13.2	21.7	1971	7.9	1971							
D	8.8	-13.5	-2.4	38	1967	-44	1971	1.22	2.17	1967	0.34	1969	0.60	1967	26.8	70.5	1971	14.2	1971							
YR	32.6	11.9	22.3	79	JUN. 1969	-53	JAN. 1971	17.55	6.59	JUL. 1969	T	MAR. 1968	1.59	AUG. 1970	125.7	70.5	DEC. 1971	17.3	FEB. 1972							

509146 Thompson Pass Alaska

Month	Temperature: Normal: Daily maximum	Temperature: Normal: Daily minimum	Temperature: Normal: Monthly	Temperature: Extremes: Record highest	Year	Record lowest	Year	Precipitation: Normal total	Maximum monthly	Year	Minimum monthly	Year	Maximum in 24 hrs.	Year	Snow, Ice pellets: Mean total	Maximum monthly	Year	Maximum in 24 hrs.	Year	Wind: Mean speed	Prevailing direction	Fastest mile: Speed	Direction	Year	Pct. of possible sunshine	Mean sky cover sunrise to sunset
(a)	(b)	(b)	(b)	19		19		(b)	20		20		20		21	21		21								
J	10.5	-.4	5.1	44	1961	-33	1972	5.88	17.31	1958	0.14	1971	4.26	1958	61.9	170.2	1958	42.4	1958							
F	18.1	8.5	13.3	43	1970	-28	1968	8.55	31.72	1953	2.00	1972	5.42	1953	93.5	346.1	1964	49.3	1953							
M	24.5	12.6	18.6	49	1953	-28	1964	7.21	15.35	1965	2.48	1957	4.32	1963	68.2	133.8	1963	42.5	1962							
A	36.6	22.4	29.5	60	1963	-10	1964	6.39	16.49	1971	0.68	1969	4.20	1959	57.4	133.4	1959	42.0	1959							
M	41.8	29.5	35.7	62	1953	0	1964	3.77	15.50	1960	0.15	1959	1.20	1952	17.1	62.3	1964	14.2	1964							
J	49.1	35.4	42.3	68	1952	29	1952	1.71	2.64	1952	0.77	1955	1.15	1952	T	T	1955	T	1955							
J	59.8	44.7	52.3	75	1952	37	1952	4.66	5.92	1952	3.40	1953	1.71	1952	0.0	0.0	1953+	0.0	1953+							
A	54.6	41.6	48.1	68	1952	31	1952	4.63	6.15	1953	3.10	1952	1.40	1953	0.0	0.0	1953+	0.0	1953+							
S	42.1	33.6	37.9	58	1953	20	1956	4.61	7.44	1952	0.84	1955	2.50	1956	8.1	33.8	1956	26.3	1956							
O	32.7	23.9	28.3	60	1969	-3	1958	10.77	27.52	1952	4.24	1966	4.80	1965	67.7	126.2	1965	46.0	1956							
N	21.2	11.4	16.3	44	1970	-23	1963	10.22	37.46	1952	0.87	1963	6.50	1961	83.2	204.2	1952	36.0	1967							
D	14.0	3.8	8.9	58	1965	-39	1964	9.89	21.75	1955	2.25	1972	6.62	1967	94.7	225.8	1955	62.0	1955							
YR	33.8	22.3	28.0	75	JUL. 1952	-39	DEC. 1964	78.29	37.46	NOV. 1952	0.14	JAN. 1971	6.62	DEC. 1967	551.8	346.1	FEB. 1964	62.0	DEC. 1955							

509385 Tonsina Lodge Alaska

Month	Temperature: Normal: Daily maximum	Temperature: Normal: Daily minimum	Temperature: Normal: Monthly	Temperature: Extremes: Record highest	Year	Record lowest	Year	Precipitation: Normal total	Maximum monthly	Year	Minimum monthly	Year	Maximum in 24 hrs.	Year	Snow, Ice pellets: Mean total	Maximum monthly	Year	Maximum in 24 hrs.	Year	Wind: Mean speed	Prevailing direction	Fastest mile: Speed	Direction	Year	Pct. of possible sunshine	Mean sky cover sunrise to sunset
(a)	(b)	(b)	(b)	10		10		(b)	9		9		9		9	9		9								
J	-.6	-24.0	-12.3	45	1971+	-58	1972	0.39	0.84	1972	0.06	1971	0.44	1972	5.7	14.1	1967	4.0	1972+							
F	19.1	-7.3	5.9	48	1968	-53	1968	1.21	3.79	1968	0.11	1972	1.10	1968	7.8	18.5	1964	5.3	1970							
M	30.1	-.5	14.8	54	1965	-46	1964	0.60	1.34	1964	0.14	1971	1.00	1964	6.1	12.4	1972	7.0	1972							
A	42.6	16.8	29.7	60	1967+	-17	1972+	0.48	1.22	1971	0.02	1969	0.85	1971	4.2	12.9	1971	7.0	1971							
M	53.6	29.1	41.4	78	1969	6	1964	0.55	1.29	1970	0.06	1971	0.40	1968	1.9	8.2	1964	6.0	1964							
J	66.1	39.7	52.9	80	1969	21	1972+	1.33	2.93	1966	0.27	1967	1.00	1965	0.0	0.0	1972+	0.0	1972+							
J	69.8	43.3	56.6	87	1966	30	1970	1.65	4.21	1965	0.75	1968	1.40	1965	0.0	0.0	1972+	0.0	1972+							
A	65.4	39.3	52.4	85	1968	22	1969	0.95	1.88	1965	0.20	1966	0.55	1965	0.0	0.0	1972+	0.0	1972+							
S	56.6	30.8	43.7	77	1966	4	1970	1.06	1.98	1967	0.36	1964	0.81	1966	1.1	10.5	1970	10.0	1970							
O	38.5	17.0	27.8	62	1969	-15	1964	1.41	4.72	1965	0.00	1963	2.30	1965	10.0	28.5	1965	9.5	1965							
N	16.7	-4.6	6.1	51	1964	-41	1969	1.45	5.67	1966	0.30	1964	2.50	1966	12.2	36.1	1966	11.0	1966							
D	4.2	-16.3	-6.1	49	1963	-61	1964	1.21	3.07	1964	T	1972	1.27	1964	9.2	20.6	1971	7.5	1964							
YR	38.5	13.6	26.1	90	JUN. 1969	-61	DEC. 1964	12.29	5.67	NOV. 1966	0.00	OCT. 1963	2.50	NOV. 1966	58.2	36.1	NOV. 1966	11.0	NOV. 1966							

509410 Trims Camp Alaska

Month	Temperature: Normal: Daily maximum	Temperature: Normal: Daily minimum	Temperature: Normal: Monthly	Temperature: Extremes: Record highest	Year	Record lowest	Year	Precipitation: Normal total	Maximum monthly	Year	Minimum monthly	Year	Maximum in 24 hrs.	Year	Snow, Ice pellets: Mean total	Maximum monthly	Year	Maximum in 24 hrs.	Year	Wind: Mean speed	Prevailing direction	Fastest mile: Speed	Direction	Year	Pct. of possible sunshine	Mean sky cover sunrise to sunset
(a)	(b)	(b)	(b)	18		18		(b)	18		18		18		18	18		18								
J	8.6	-9.8	-.6	45	1961	-57	1973+	2.16	4.90	1963	0.10	1959	1.96	1967	28.7	73.0	1962	36.0	1962							
F	14.7	-3.9	5.4	46	1970	-47	1968	3.49	10.58	1964	0.35	1958	4.30	1956	47.1	133.9	1964	43.0	1956							
M	19.4	.1	9.8	46	1965	-49	1971	2.96	10.36	1963	0.14	1968	2.40	1960	37.3	107.5	1963	33.0	1960							
A	33.3	13.0	23.2	54	1958	-18	1964	2.32	8.39	1964	0.19	1958	1.47	1964	33.3	96.0	1964	19.4	1963							
M	48.1	28.4	38.3	77	1960	-4	1964	1.62	6.03	1966	0.00	1954	2.80	1962	9.4	37.5	1971	7.0	1971+							
J	62.0	39.1	50.6	86	1969	9	1965	2.76	9.45	1962	0.00	1954	2.02	1961	0.7	4.5	1971	4.0	1971							
J	63.1	42.4	52.8	83	1958	24	1971	4.84	8.10	1967	1.86	1966	2.41	1967	T	0.1	1959	0.1	1959							
A	59.6	39.7	49.7	80	1962+	21	1969	5.03	9.16	1967	1.91	1969	2.56	1962	0.4	6.0	1969	3.0	1969							
S	48.6	30.4	39.5	76	1963	3	1956	4.87	11.66	1960	0.53	1969	4.75	1960	8.0	29.0	1970	14.0	1967							
O	31.3	15.3	23.3	57	1969	-18	1970	3.86	7.75	1972	1.14	1968	2.27	1972	34.4	87.0	1965	24.0	1961							
N	18.7	2.0	10.4	48	1970	-48	1960	2.89	9.64	1967	0.01	1953	2.28	1959	33.6	109.0	1967	36.0	1959							
D	11.3	-7.0	2.2	42	1963+	-55	1961	3.41	9.01	1955	0.65	1968	3.97	1955	40.6	100.5	1965	39.7	1955							
YR	34.9	15.8	25.4	86	JUN. 1969	-57	JAN. 1973+	40.21	11.66	SEP. 1960	0.00	JUN. 1954+	4.75	SEP. 1960	273.5	133.9	FEB. 1964	43.0	FEB. 1956							

265080 Umiat Alaska

Month	Temperature							Precipitation												Wind &					Pct. of possible sunshine	Mean sky cover sunrise to sunset
	Normal			Extremes											Snow, Ice pellets							Fastest mile				
	Daily maximum	Daily minimum	Monthly	Record highest	Year	Record lowest	Year	Normal total	Maximum monthly	Year	Minimum monthly	Year	Maximum in 24 hrs.	Year	Mean total	Maximum monthly	Year	Maximum in 24 hrs.	Year	Mean speed	Prevailing direction	Speed	Direction	Year		
(a)	(b)	(b)	(b)	8		8		(b)	7		7		7		7	7		7								
J	-12.8	-30.9	-21.9	30	1950	-62	1951	0.31	0.88	1950	0.06	1948	0.24	1952	3.2	9.2	1950	2.4	1952							
F	-21.7	-37.5	-29.6	28	1948	-76	1955	0.19	0.49	1953	T	1947	0.30	1953	1.9	4.0	1953+	3.0	1953							
M	-7.2	-25.3	-16.3	35	1949	-52	1947	0.17	0.38	1954	T	1947	0.22	1954	2.0	3.8	1954	2.2	1954							
A	10.1	-11.4	-.7	40	1954+	-46	1952	0.32	1.50	1948	T	1953	0.34	1954	3.2	14.5	1948	4.2	1948							
M	27.1	13.2	20.2	55	1951	-22	1952	0.11	0.29	1954	T	1953+	0.19	1954	1.1	3.5	1949	1.9	1954							
J	50.8	34.7	42.8	74	1954	20	1949	0.54	1.25	1953	T	1947	0.39	1953	0.6	4.4	1948	2.1	1948							
J	63.2	42.7	53.0	85	1953+	30	1954	0.79	1.68	1951	0.14	1950	0.52	1951	T	T	1954+	T	1954+							
A	57.1	38.7	47.9	77	1951+	24	1952+	1.51	4.00	1947	0.05	1954	1.03	1947	0.5	2.0	1940	1.9	1953							
S	38.7	26.3	32.5	63	1950	-6	1948	0.52	0.86	1951	0.24	1947	0.35	1952	2.3	5.8	1952	3.3	1952							
O	19.6	4.8	12.2	45	1952	-27	1953	0.47	0.78	1947	0.14	1949	0.37	1947	5.8	7.9	1952	3.7	1947							
N	7.9	-8.4	-.3	43	1952	-53	1948	0.42	1.07	1950	0.15	1953+	0.27	1950	5.5	10.7	1950	2.7	1950							
D	-12.8	-27.6	-20.2	31	1951	-56	1948	0.38	0.66	1951	0.08	1948	0.24	1951	4.5	6.6	1951	2.4	1951							
YR	18.3	1.6	10.0	85	JUL. 1953+	-76	FEB. 1955	5.73	4.00	AUG. 1947	T	MAY 1953+	1.03	AUG. 1947	30.6	14.5	APR. 1948	4.2	APR. 1948							

INDEX

INDEX

** Asterisk indicates city is the subject of a multi-page climate analysis.*

Indicates this reference is to a special, multi-page climate analysis of the named city.

**** Indicates this reference is to a special, multi-page climate analysis of the named city.***

***** Indicates this reference is to a special, multi-page climate analysis of the named city.**

**** Indicates this reference is to a special, multi-page climate analysis of the named city.***

**** Indicates this reference is to a special, multi-page climate analysis of the named city.***